Handbook of Stem Cells

Volume 1

Embryonic

Handbook of Stem Cells

Volume 1

Embryonic

EDITORS

Robert Lanza

John Gearhart
Brigid Hogan
Douglas Melton
Roger Pedersen
James Thomson
Michael West

ELSEVIER
ACADEMIC
PRESS

AMSTERDAM • BOSTON • HEIDELBERG • LONDON
NEW YORK • OXFORD • PARIS • SAN DIEGO
SAN FRANCISCO • SINGAPORE • SYDNEY • TOKYO

Elsevier Academic Press
200 Wheeler Road, 6th Floor, Burlington, MA 01803, USA
525 B Street, Suite 1900, San Diego, California 92101-4495, USA
84 Theobald's Road, London WC1X 8RR, UK

This book is printed on acid-free paper.

Library of Congress Cataloging-in-Publication Data
Application submitted

British Library Cataloguing in Publication Data
A catalogue record for this book is available from the British Library

ISBN: 0-12-436643-0 (set)
ISBN: 0-12-436642-2 (volume 1)
ISBN: 0-12-436641-4 (volume 2)
ISBN: 0-12-436644-9 (CD-Rom)

For all information on all Academic Press publications
visit our Web site at www.books.elsevier.com

Printed in the United States of America

04   05   06   07   08   09   9   8   7   6   5   4   3   2   1

Contents

Introduction to embryonic stem cells

PART ONE
Basic biology/mechanisms

Contents

PART SEVEN
Applications

Contents

PART EIGHT
Regulation and ethics

PART NINE
The patient's perspective

Contributors

Numbers in parentheses indicate the chapter to which the author contributed.

Russell C. Addis (43)
Johns Hopkins University School of Medicine, Institute for Cellular Engineering, Baltimore, MD

Bruce Alberts, PhD (Foreword)
President, National Academy of Sciences, Washington, DC

Michal Amit, PhD (40)
Bruce Rappaport Faculty of Medicine, Technion - Israel Institute of Technology, Haifa, Israel

Peter W. Andrews (9, 56)
Arthur Jackson Professor of Biomedical Science, Department of Biomedical Science, The University of Sheffield, Western Bank, United Kingdom

Hitomi Aoki (20)
Department of Tissue and Organ Development, Regeneration and Advanced Medical Science, Gifu University Graduate School of Medicine, Japan

Makoto Asashima, PhD (46)
Dean and Professor, Department of Life Sciences, University of Tokyo, Meguro-ku, Tokyo, Japan

Joyce Axelman (43)
Johns Hopkins University School of Medicine, Institute for Cellular Engineering, Baltimore, MD

Daniel Becker, MD (69)
Department of Neurology, Vanderbilt University Medical Center, Nashville, TN

Nissim Benvenisty, MD, PhD (53, 66)
Professor of Genetics, Department of Genetics, Institute of Life Sciences, The Hebrew University of Jerusalem, Jerusalem, Israel

Mickie Bhatia, PhD (38, 50)
Director and Scientist, Stem Cell Biology and Regenerative Medicine, Robarts Research Institute, The Krembil Centre for Stem Cell Biology, Associate Professor, Faculty of Medicine, University of Western Ontario, London, Ontario, Canada

C. Clare Blackburn, PhD (37)
Leukaemia Research Fund Senior Fellow, Institute for Stem Cell Research, University of Edinburgh, Edinburgh, United Kingdom

Michele Boiani, PhD (64)
Department of Animal Biology, University of Pennsylvania (New Bolton Center), Kennett Square, PA

Susan Bonner-Weir, PhD (71)
Associate Professor/Senior Investigator, Diabetes Center, Harvard University, Boston, MA

Josephine Bowles, PhD (33)
Institute for Molecular Bioscience, The University of Queensland, Brisbane, Queensland, Australia

Richard L. Boyd, PhD (67)
Associate Professor, Department of Pathology and Immunology, Monash University, Melbourne, Victoria, Australia

Marianne Bronner-Fraser, PhD (19)
California Institute of Technology, Division of Biology, Beckman Institute, Pasadena, CA

Eric W. Brunskill, PhD (58)
Professor, Division of Cardiology, University of Cincinnati College of Medicine, Cincinnati, OH

Scott Bultman, PhD (6)
Department of Genetics, University of North Carolina, Chapel Hill, NC

Frederick Charles Campbell, MD (35)
Professor, Department of Surgery, Cancer Centre, Queen's University of Belfast, Belfast, Antrim, Northern Ireland

Anne Camus, PhD (11)
Department of Developmental Biology, Institut Jacques Monod, Paris, France

Melissa K. Carpenter, PhD (38, 52)
Stem Cell Biology and Regenerative Medicine, Robarts Research Institute, Associate Professor, Faculty of Medicine, University of Western Ontario, London, Ontario, Canada

Fatima Cavaleri (3)
Max Planck Institute for Molecular Biomedicine, Department of Cell and Developmental Biology, Münster, Germany

Constance Cepko, PhD (22)
Professor, Department of Genetics, Investigator, Howard Hughes Medical Institute, Harvard Medical School, Boston, MA

Yijing Chen, PhD (60)
Department of Genetics, University of North Carolina, Chapel Hill, NC

Susana M. Chuva de Sousa Lopes, PhD (12)
Professor, Hubrecht Laboratory, University of Utrecht, Utrecht, The Netherlands

Gregory O. Clark, MD (43)
Johns Hopkins University School of Medicine, Institute for Cellular Engineering, Baltimore, MD

Jérôme Collignon, PhD (11)
Department of Developmental Biology, Institut Jacques Monod, Paris, France

Paul Collodi, PhD (47)
Professor, Department of Animal Sciences, Purdue University, West Lafayette, IN

Chad Cowan, PhD (Foreward)
Department of Molecular and Cellular Biology, Harvard University, Cambridge, MA

George Q. Daley, MD, PhD (25)
Division of Hematology/Oncology, Children's Hospital, Boston, MA

Christian Dani, PhD (31)
Director of Research INSERM, Centre de Biochimie CNRS UMR6543, Institute of Signaling, Developmental Biology and Cancer, University of Nice-Sophia Antipolis, Nice, France

Joshua D. Dowell, MD, PhD (70)
Department of Medicine, Indiana University School of Medicine, Indianapolis, IN

Jonathan S. Draper, PhD (56)
Department of Biomedical Science, University of Sheffield, Sheffield, United Kingdom

Gregory R. Dressler, PhD (32)
Associate Professor, Department of Pathology, University of Michigan, Ann Arbor, MI

Micha Drukker (66)
Department of Genetics, Silberman Institute of Life Sciences, The Hebrew University, Jerusalem, Israel

Gabriela Durcova-Hills, PhD (42)
Professor, The Wellcome Trust/Cancer Research UK Gurdon Institute, University of Cambridge, Cambridge, Cambridgeshire, United Kingdom

Robert G. Edwards (1)
Chief Editor, Reproductive BioMedicine Online, Duck End Farm, Dry Drayton, Cambridge, United Kingdom

Rebecca S. Eisenberg, JD (79)
Robert and Barbara Luciano Professor of Law, University of Michigan Law School, Ann Arbor, MI

Ravindhra Elluru (36)
Divisions of Neonatology and Pulmonary Biology, Cincinnati Children's Hospital Medical Center, Cincinnati, OH

Sir Martin Evans, PhD (39)
Director and Professor, Cardiff School of Biosciences,
Cardiff University, Wales, United Kingdom

Lianchun Fan, PhD (47)
Research Associate, Department of Animal Sciences, Purdue
University, West Lafayette, IN

Margaret A. Farley, PhD (76)
Gilbert Stark Professor of Christian Ethics, Divinity School
and Department of Religious Studies, Yale University,
New Haven, CT

Donna M. Fekete, PhD (22)
Department of Neurobiology, Harvard Medical School,
Boston, MA

Loren J. Field, PhD (70)
Professor of Medicine, Department of Medicine, Indiana
University School of Medicine, Indianapolis, IN

Donald W. Fink Jr., PhD (77)
Biologist, Division of Cell and Gene Therapy, Center for
Biologics Evaluation and Research/US Food and Drug
Administration, Rockville, MD

Lesley M. Forrester, PhD (34)
John Hughes Bennett Laboratories, Department of
Oncology, University of Edinburgh, Western General
Hospital, Edinburgh, United Kingdom

Margaret T. Fuller, PhD (14)
Professor, Departments of Developmental Biology and
Genetics, Stanford University School of Medicine,
Stanford, CA

Miho Furue, DDS, PhD (46)
Department of Biochemistry and Molecular Biology,
Kanagawa Dental College, Yokosuka, Kanagawa, Japan

David L. Garbers, PhD (15)
Director of The Cecil H. and Ida Green Center for
Reproductive Biology Sciences, Investigator, Howard
Hughes Medical Institute, Professor of Pharmacology, The
University of Texas Southwestern Medical Center at Dallas,
Dallas, TX

Richard L. Gardner (2)
E P Abraham Research Professor of the Royal Society in the
University of Oxford, Departement of Zoology, University of
Oxford, Oxford, United Kingdom

John D. Gearhart, PhD (43)
Johns Hopkins University School of Medicine, Institute for
Cellular Engineering, Baltimore, MD

Sharon Gerecht-Nir, PhD (30)
Bruce Rappaport Faculty of Medicine, Technion-Israel
Institute of Technology, Haifa, Israel

Jason W. Gill, PhD (67)
Department of Pathology and Immunology, Monash
University, Melbourne, Victoria, Australia

Rodolfo Gonzalez, MS (68)
Joint Program in Molecular Pathology, The Burnham
Institute and the University of California, San Diego, La
Jolla, CA

Daniel H.D. Gray, PhD (67)
Department of Pathology and Immunology, Monash
University, Melbourne, Victoria, Australia

Ronald M. Green, PhD (75)
Director, Ethics Institute, Eunice and Julian Cohen Professor
for the Study of Ethics and Human Values, Chair,
Department of Religion, Dartmouth College, Hanover, NH

Michal Gropp, PhD (55)
The Hadassah Embryonic Stem Cell Research Center, The
Goldyne Savad Institute of Gene Therapy, Hadassah
University Hospital, Jerusalem, Israel

Alexandra Haagensen (71)
Section on Islet Transplantation and Cell Biology, Joslin
Diabetes Center, Harvard Medical School, Boston, MA

F. Kent Hamra, PhD (15)
Department of Pharmacology and The Cecil H. and Ida
Green Center for Reproductive Biology Sciences, The
University of Texas Southwestern Medical Center at Dallas,
Dallas, TX

Richard P. Harvey, PhD (28)
Sir Peter Finley Professor of Cardiac Research, Head,
Developmental Biology Program, Victor Chang Cardiac
Research Institute, Darlinghurst, New South Wales, Australia

Susan M. Hawes, PhD (48)
Research Fellow, Institute for Reproduction and
Development, Monash University, Melbourne, Victoria,
Australia

Shin-Ichi Hayashi, MD, PhD (27)
Professor, Division of Immunology, Department of
Molecular and Cellular Biology, School of Life Science,
Faculty of Medicine, Tottori University, Tottori, Japan

Anne L. Hazlehurst (78)
Center for Biomedical Engineering, Brown University,
Providence, RI

Hiroaki Hemmi, PhD (27)
Ralph Steinman Laboratory, Cellular Physiology and
Immunology, Rockefeller University, New York, NY

Hiroshi Hisatsune (29)
Department of Molecular Genetics, Graduate School of
Medicine, Kyoto University, Kyoto, Japan

James Huettner, PhD (69)
Center for the Study of Nervous System Injury and the
Restorative Treatment and Research Program, Department of
Cell Biology and Physiology, Washington University School
of Medicine, St. Louis, MO

Bradley Huntsman, BS (58)
Division of Developmental Biology, Cincinnati Children's
Hospital Medical Center, University of Cincinnati,
Cincinnati, OH

Catherine Iéhlé, PhD (31)
Senior Scientist, Unité de Virologie, Institut Pasteur de
Madagascar, Antananarivo, Madagascar

Jamie Imitola, MD (68)
Department of Neurology, Brigham and Women's Hospital,
Boston, MA

Joseph Itskovitz-Eldor, MD, DSc (30, 40)
Professor and Director, Department of Obstetrics and
Gynecology, Rambam Medical Center and Bruce Rappaport
Faculty of Medicine, Technion-Israel Institute of
Technology, Haifa, Israel

Rudolf Jaenisch, MD (10)
Professor of Biology, Whitehead Institute for Biomedical
Research, Department of Biology, Massachusetts Institute of
Technology, Cambridge, MA

Penny A. Johnson, PhD (9)
Senior Research Scientist, Intercytex Ltd., Manchester,
United Kingdom

D. Leanne Jones, PhD (14)
Department of Developmental Biology,
Stanford University School of Medicine,
Stanford, CA

Elizabeth A. Jones, MA, MB, BChir, MRCP, PhD (34)
Institute of Human Genetics, University of Newcastle upon
Tyne, Newcastle upon Tyne, United Kingdom

Gerard Karsenty, MD, PhD (26)
Professor of Molecular and Human Genetics, Baylor College
of Medicine, Houston, TX

Gil Katz, PhD (66)
The Lautenberg Center for General and Tumor Immunology,
Hadassah Medical School, The Hebrew University,
Jerusalem, Israel

Pritinder Kaur, PhD (72)
Head, Epithelial Stem Cell Biology Laboratory, Stem Cell
Program, Peter MacCallum Cancer Centre, Melbourne,
Victoria, Australia

Robert G. Kelly (28)
Department of Genetics and Development, Columbia
University, New York, NY

Kathleen C. Kent (43)
Johns Hopkins University School of Medicine, Institute for
Cellular Engineering, Baltimore, MD

Candace L. Kerr, PhD (43)
Johns Hopkins University School of Medicine, Institute for
Cellular Engineering, Baltimore, MD

Ali Khademhosseini, MASc (73)
Division of Biological Engineering, Massachusetts Institute
of Technology, Cambridge, MA

Hanita Khaner, PhD (49)
Research Associate, The Hadassah Embryonic Stem Cell
Research Center, Goldyne Savad Institute of Gene Therapy,
Hadassah University Hospital, Jerusalem, Israel

Chris Kintner, PhD (18)
Professor, Molecular Neurobiology Laboratory, The Salk
Institute for Biological Studies, La Jolla, CA

Irina Klimanskaya, PhD (41)
Senior Scientist, Advanced Cell Technology, Worcester, MA

Nobuyuki Kondoh (29)
Satomi Nishikawa, Riken Center for Developmental
Biology, Kobe, Japan

Peter Koopman, PhD (33)
Professor of Developmental Biology, Institute for Molecular
Bioscience, The University of Queensland, Brisbane,
Queensland, Australia

Naoko Koyano-Nakagawa, PhD (18)
Assistant Professor, Department of Neuroscience, University
of Minnesota, Minneapolis, MN

Jennifer N. Kraszewski (43)
Johns Hopkins University School of Medicine, Institute for
Cellular Engineering, Baltimore, MD

Robb Krumlauf, PhD (19)
Scientific Director, Stowers Institute for Medical Research,
Kansas City, MO

Tilo Kunath, PhD (17, 45)
Institute for Stem Cell Research, University of Edinburgh,
Edinburgh, United Kingdom

Takahiro Kunisada, PhD (20)
Professor, Department of Tissue and Organ Development, Regeneration and Advanced Medical Science, Gifu University Graduate School of Medicine, Gifu, Japan

Robert Langer, ScD (73)
Professor, Department of Chemical Engineering, Massachusetts Institute of Technology, Cambridge, MA

Robert Lanza, MD (Preface)
Vice President, Medical and Scientific Development, Advanced Cell Technology, Adjunct Professor of Surgical Sciences, Institute of Regenerative Medicine, Wake Forest University School of Medicine, Winston-Salem, NC

Jean Pyo Lee, PhD (68)
Department of Neurology, Beth Israel Deaconess Medical Center, Boston, Massachusetts

Shulamit Levenberg, PhD (73)
Research Associate, Langer Laboratory, Department of Chemical Engineering, Massachusetts Institute of Technology, Cambridge, MA

Haifan Lin, PhD (13)
Associate Professor, Department of Cell Biology, Duke University Medical School, Durham, NC

John W. Littlefield, MD (43)
Johns Hopkins University School of Medicine, Institute for Cellular Engineering, Baltimore, MD

Michael J. Lysaght, PhD (78)
Professor and Director, Center for Biomedical Engineering, Brown University, Providence, RI

Fiona A. Mack (7)
Cell Growth and Cancer Graduate Group, University of Pennsylvania, Philadelphia, PA

Terry Magnuson, PhD (6, 60)
Professor, Department of Genetics, University of North Carolina, Chapel Hill, NC

Anna Malashicheva, PhD (5)
Laboratory of Molecular Basis of Cell Differentiation, Institute of Cytology, St. Petersburg, Russia

Ofer Mandelboim (66)
The Lautenberg Center for General and Tumor Immunology, Hadassah Medical School, The Hebrew University, Jerusalem, Israel

Nancy R. Manley, PhD (37)
Associate Professor, Department of Genetics, University of Georgia, Athens, GA

Klaus I. Matthaei, PhD (59)
Senior Fellow and Head, Gene Targeting Laboratory, The John Curtin School of Medical Research, The Australian National University, Canberra, ACT, Australia

Yoav Mayshar, (53)
Department of Genetics, The Silberman Institute for Life Sciences, The Hebrew University, Jerusalem, Israel

John W. McDonald, MD, PhD (69)
Associate Professor of Neurology, Neurological Surgery and Anatomy and Neurobiology, Director of the Spinal Cord Injury Program, Restorative Treatment and Research Center, Washington University School of Medicine, St. Louis, MO

Dame Anne McLaren, PhD (16, 42)
Professor, The Wellcome Trust/Cancer Research UK Gurdon Institute, University of Cambridge, Cambridge, Cambridgeshire, United Kingdom

Jill McMahon, MSc (41)
Molecular and Cellular Biology Department, Harvard University, Cambridge, MA

Alexander Meissner, Dipl Ing (10)
Whitehead Institute for Biomedical Research, Massachusetts Institute of Technology, Cambridge, MA

Harald von Melchner, MD, PhD (61)
Professor of Cell Biology and Molecular Genetics, Department of Molecular Hematology, University of Frankfurt Medical School, Frankfurt am Main, Germany

Douglas A. Melton, PhD (Foreword)
Thomas Dudley Cabot Professor in the Natural Sciences, Department of Molecular and Cellular Biology, Harvard University, Investigator, Howard Hughes Medical Institute, Cambridge, MA

Nathan Montgomery (6)
Department of Genetics, University of North Carolina, Chapel Hill, NC

Mary Tyler Moore (80)
International Chairman, Juvenile Diabetes Research Foundation, New York, NY

Tsutomu Motohashi, PhD (20)
Department of Tissue and Organ Development, Regeneration and Advanced Medical Science, Gifu University Graduate School of Medicine, Gifu, Japan

Franz-Josef Mueller, MD (68)
Program in Developmental and Regenerative Cell Biology, The Burnham Institute, La Jolla, CA

Christine Mummery, PhD (12)
Professor, Hubrecht Laboratory, University of Utrecht, Utrecht, The Netherlands

Satomi Nishikawa (29)
Riken Center for Developmental Biology Kobe, Japan

Shin-Ichi Nishikawa, MD, PhD (29)
Group Director, Stem Cell Research Group, Riken Center for Developmental Biology, Kobe, Japan

Andras Nagy, PhD (57)
Senior Scientist, Mount Sinai Hospital, Samuel Lunenfeld Research Institute, Professor, Department of Medical Genetics and Microbiology, University of Toronto, Toronto, Ontario, Canada

Hitoshi Niwa, MD, PhD (4)
Laboratory for Pluripotent Cell Studies, Riken Center for Developmental Biology (CDB), Kobe, Hyogo, Japan

Hiromi Okuyama (21)
Center for Cells and Gene Theraphy, Takara Bio Inc., Ostu, Shiga, Japan

Jitka Ourednik, PhD (68)
Associate Professor, Department of Biomedical Sciences, Iowa State University, Ames, IA

Vaclav Ourednik, PhD (68)
Associate Professor, Department of Biomedical Sciences, Iowa State University, Ames, IA

Masahito Oyamada, MD, PhD (8)
Associate Professor, Department of Pathology and Cell Regulation, Kyoto Prefectural University of Medicine, Kyoto, Japan

Yumiko Oyamada, MD, PhD (8)
Department of Pathology and Cell Regulation, Kyoto Prefectural University of Medicine, Kyoto, Japan

Virginia E. Papaioannou, PhD (24)
Professor of Genetics and Development, Department of Genetics and Development, College of Physicians and Surgeons of Columbia University, New York, NY

Kook I. Park, MD (68)
Professor, Department of Pediatrics and Pharmacology, Yonsei University College of Medicine, Seoul, Korea

Ethan S. Patterson (43)
Johns Hopkins University School of Medicine, Institute for Cellular Engineering, Baltimore, MD

Larry T. Patterson, MD (58)
Professor, Division of Nephrology and Hypertension, Cincinnati Children's Hospital Medical Center, University of Cincinnati, Cincinnati, OH

Alice Pébay, PhD (51)
Monash Institute of Reproduction and Development, Monash University, Clayton, Victoria, Australia

Martin F. Pera, BA, PhD (48, 51)
Associate Professor, Monash Institute of Reproduction and Development, Monash University, Clayton, Victoria, Australia

Aitana Perea-Gomez, PhD (11)
Department of Developmental Biology, Institut Jacques Monod, Paris, France

Anthony C.F. Perry, PhD (62)
Head of Laboratory, Laboratory of Mammalian Molecular Embryology, Riken Center for Developmental Biology, Kobe, Japan

James N. Petitte, PhD (44)
Professor, Department of Poultry Science, College of Agriculture and Life Sciences, North Carolina State University, Raleigh, NC

Blaine W. Phillips, PhD (31)
Research Scientist, ES Cell International, Singapore

S. Steven Potter, PhD (58)
Professor, Division of Developmental Biology, Cincinnati Children's Hospital Medical Center, University of Cincinnati, Cincinnati, OH

Arti K. Rai (79)
Professor of Law, Duke Law School, Duke University, Durham, NC

Christopher Reeve (81)
Chairman, Christopher Reeve Paralysis Foundation, Springfield, NJ

Benjamin Reubinoff, MD, PhD (49, 55)
Associate Professor in Obstetrics and Gynecology, Director, The Hadassah Embryonic Stem Cell Research Center, The Goldyne Savad Institute of Gene Therapy, Department of Obstetrics and Gynecology, Hadassah University Hospital, Jerusalem, Israel

Janet Rossant, PhD (17, 45, Foreword)
Senior Investigator, Samuel Lunenfeld Research Institute, Mount Sinai Hospital, Toronto, Ontario, Canada

Michael Rubart, MD (70)
Department of Medicine, Indiana University School of Medicine, Indianapolis, IN

Pierre Savatier, PhD (5)
Director of Research, U371 "Cerveau et Vision", Institut National de la Santé et de la Recherche Médicale, Bron, France

Hans Schöler (3, 64)
Max Planck Institute for Molecular Biomedicine, Department of Cell and Developmental Biology, Münster, Germany

Cordula Schulz, PhD (14)
Research Investigator, Cold Spring Harbor Laboratory, Cold Spring Harbor, NY

Nikolaus Schultz, PhD (15)
The Cecil H. and Ida Green Center for Reproductive Biology Sciences, The University of Texas Southwestern Medical Center at Dallas, Dallas, TX, Freie Universität Berlin, Institut für Biochemie, Thielallee 63, Berlin, Germany

Michael J. Shamblott, PhD (43)
Johns Hopkins University School of Medicine, Institute for Cellular Engineering, Baltimore, MD

Richard L. Sidman, MD (68)
Bullard Professor of Neuropathology, Emeritus, Harvard Medical School, Boston, MA

M. Celeste Simon, PhD (7)
Associate Investigator, Howard Hughes Medical Institute, Associate Professor, Abramson Family Cancer Research Institute and Department of Cell and Developmental Biology, University of Pennsylvania School of Medicine, Philadelphia, PA

Evan Y. Snyder, MD, PhD (68)
Professor and Director, Program in Developmental and Regenerative Cell Biology, The Burnham Institute, La Jolla, CA

A. Francis Stewart, PhD (61)
Professor, Department of Genomics, BioInnovationZentrum, Dresden University of Technology, Dresden, Germany

Lorenz Studer, MD (21, 62)
Developmental Biology and Neurosurgery, Memorial Sloan Kettering Cancer Center, New York, NY

Azim Surani, PhD (65)
Wellcome Trust/Cancer Research UK Gurdon Institute, University of Cambridge, Cambridge, United Kingdom

Tetsuro Takamatsu, MD, PhD (8)
Professor, Department of Pathology and Cell Regulation, Kyoto Prefectural University of Medicine, Kyoto, Japan

Yang D. Teng, MD, PhD (68)
Assistant Professor, Department of Neurosurgery, Harvard Medical School/Children's Hospital, Boston/Brigham and Women's Hospital, Boston, and SCI Laboratory, VA Boston Healthcare System, Boston, MA

Irma Thesleff, DDS (23)
Professor, Research Director, Institute of Biotechnology, University of Helsinki, Helsinki, Finland

James A. Thomson, VMD, PhD, Dipl. ACVP (54)
John D. MacArthur Professor, Department of Anatomy, University of Wisconsin–Madison Medical School, The Wisconsin National Primate Research Center, Madison, WI

David Tosh, PhD (34)
Biology and Biochemistry, University of Bath, Bath, United Kingdom

Paul Trainor, PhD (19)
Stowers Institute for Medical Research, Kansas City, MO

Alan O. Trounson, PhD (67)
Professor of Stem Cell Sciences, Monash Immunology and Stem Cell Laboratories, Monash University, Clayton, Victoria, Australia

Motokazu Tsuneto (27)
Division of Immunology, Department of Molecular and Cellular Biology, School of Life Science, Tottori University, Tottori, Japan

Mark Tummers, MSc (23)
Developmental Biology Programme, Institute of Biotechnology, University of Helsinki, Finland

Edward Upjohn, MD (72)
Department of Dermatology, Royal Children's Hospital, Melbourne, Victoria, Australia

George Varigos, MB, BS, PhD, FACD (72)
Department of Dermatology, Royal Melbourne and Childrens' Hospitals, Parkville, Victoria, Australia

Cécile Vernochet, PhD (31)
Centre de Biochimie CNRS UMR6543, Institute of Signaling, Developmental Biology and Cancer, University of Nice-Sophia Antipolis, Nice, France

Jay L. Vivian, PhD (60)
Department of Genetics, University of North Carolina, Chapel Hill, NC

Zhongde Wang, PhD (10)
Whitehead Institute for Biomedical Research, Massachusetts Institute of Technology, Cambridge, MA

Gordon C. Weir, MD (71)
Professor of Medicine, Harvard Medical School, Head, Section on Islet Transplantation and Cell Biology, Diabetes Research and Wellness Foundation, Chair, Joslin Diabetes Center, Boston, MA

Susan E. Wert (36)
Divisions of Neonatology and Pulmonary Biology, Cincinnati Children's Hospital Medical Center, Cincinnati, OH

Jeffrey A. Whitsett, MD (36)
Professor of Pediatrics, Chief, Section of Neonatology, Pulmonary, and Perinatal Biology, Cincinnati Children's Hospital Medical Center, University of Cincinnati College of Medicine, Cincinnati, OH

J. David Wininger, PhD (63)
Wake Forest University Baptist Medical Center, Program for Assisted Reproduction, Department of Obstetrics and Gynecology, Winston-Salem, NC

Zhuoru Wu, PhD (15)
Department of Pharmacology, The University of Texas Southwestern Medical Center at Dallas, Dallas, TX

Chunhui Xu, PhD (52)
Senior Scientist, Geron Corporation, Menlo Park, CA

Toshiyuki Yamane, PhD (20, 27)
Irving Weissman Laboratory, Department of Pathology, Stanford University School of Medicine, Stanford, CA

Jun Yamashita (29)
Department of Molecular Genetics, Graduate School of Medicine, Kyoto University, Kyoto, Japan

Yukiko M. Yamashita, PhD (14)
Department of Developmental Biology, Stanford University School of Medicine, Stanford, CA

Hidetoshi Yamazaki, DDS, PhD (27)
Associate Professor, Division of Regenerative Medicine and Therapeutics, Department of Genetic Medicine and Regenerative Therapeutics, Institute of Regenerative Medicine and Biofunction, Tottori University Graduate School of Medical Science, Division of Immunology, Department of Molecular and Cellular Biology, School of Life Science, Faculty of Medicine, Tottori University, Tottori, Japan

Laurie Zoloth, PhD (74)
Professor of Medical Humanities and of Religion, Medical Humanities and Bioethics, Feinberg School of Medicine, Northwestern University, Chicago, IL

Thomas P. Zwaka, MD (54)
The Wisconsin National Primate Research Center, Madison, WI

Robert Zweigerdt, PhD (70)
Department of Medicine, Heinrich Heine University, Duesseldorf, Germany

Preface

New discoveries in the field of stem cells increasingly dominate the news and scientific literature. Wave upon wave of papers has led to an avalanche of new knowledge and research tools that may soon lead to new therapies for cancer, heart disease, diabetes, and a wide variety of other diseases that afflict humanity. The *Handbook of Stem Cells* integrates this exciting area of biology, combining in two volumes the prerequisites for a general understanding of adult and embryonic stem cells; the tools, methods, and experimental protocols needed to study and characterize stem cells and progenitor populations; as well as a presentation by the world's experts of what is currently known about each specific organ system. No topic in the field of stem cells is left uncovered, including basic biology/mechanisms, early development, ectoderm, mesoderm, endoderm, methods (such as detailed descriptions of how to derive and maintain animal and human embryonic stem cells), application of stem cells to specific human diseases, regulation and ethics, and patient perspectives from Mary Tyler Moore (diabetes) and Christopher Reeve (spinal cord injury). The result is a comprehensive two-volume reference that will be useful for students and experts alike. It represents the combined effort of 12 editors and more than 300 scholars and scientists whose pioneering work has defined our understanding of stem cells.

Robert Lanza, MD
Boston, Massachusetts

Foreword

What can usefully be said about stem cells in a foreword to a collection of definitive articles by the world's experts, inasmuch as this volume already covers every conceivable aspect of the subject? In response to this question, I shall attempt to place the work described here in the broader context of science—and of modern cell and developmental biology specifically.

My view of the science in this book comes from the perspective of someone who spent 30 years in universities probing the molecular details of basic cell processes. Over this time, our understanding of cells increased at a rate that startled even those most closely involved in the wave upon wave of new discoveries. This increase in knowledge was catalytic: As our understanding of cells advanced, it allowed new research tools to be developed that directly sped further advances in understanding, which in turn led to new tools, and so on. Consider, for example, the DNA chip technology described in Chapter 58 of Volume one and Chapter three of Volume two, which allows an investigator to examine the expression of tens of thousands of genes simultaneously. Because hundreds of small steps were needed to move from the striking initial discovery of DNA hybridization in 1961[1] to this new technology, its development was unpredictable in advance.

It is the same for the advance of science itself, as emphasized repeatedly in the "Beyond Discovery" series of brief articles from the National Academy of Sciences.[2] Designed to explain science to the general public, each of these eight-page documents traces the path leading to a breakthrough of great human benefit—such as the global positioning system (GPS) or the cure for childhood leukemia. In every case, the final discovery depended on knowledge developed over decades through the efforts of a large number of independent scientists and engineers. Each piece of knowledge, often seemingly useless on its own, was combined in unexpected ways with other knowledge to produce a final result whose power seems almost magical.

The great enterprise of science, sparked simply by human curiosity about how the world works—for example, an attempt to account for the motions of the planets in the night sky—has transformed our world. And because new knowledge builds on old knowledge, the pace continually accelerates as the amount of old knowledge increases. Thus, we should expect the inventions that benefit humans in this new century to be even more dramatic than those of the last century. But we can be equally sure of the futility of attempting to predict what they will be in advance.

What does all this have to do with stem cells? Personally, I become uncomfortable whenever I hear claims that describe the precise benefits to be derived from this research—especially when they are associated with a timeline. Nevertheless, the history of science makes it certain that the knowledge derived from research on stem cells will eventually lead to enormous benefits for human health, even if they are unpredictable. Eventually, we will be able to use our profound understanding of biology to grow new organs that can be safely transplanted into human patients, and the work with stem cells will no doubt make important contributions to this breakthrough. But the research outlined in this volume is equally certain to contribute to cures for cancer and for a large number of other less famous diseases—many of mysterious origin—that are terrible afflictions for humanity.

Bert Vogelstein, the chairman of the National Academies committee that produced the report "Stem Cells and the Future of Regenerative Medicine" reminds us that "The stem cell debate has led scientists and nonscientists alike to contemplate profound issues, such as who we are and what makes us human."[3] The debate has also made it clear that the success of modern societies will depend on education systems that place a much higher value on conveying an understanding of the nature of science to everyone.

Accomplishing such a goal will require new recognition by scientists of their teaching responsibilities at the college level as well as of their different but critical roles in the support of inquiry-based science education for students from 5 to 18 years old.[4] We must all face the realization that, even under the best of circumstances, the transitions to the science-centered education systems that our nations need will require decades. In the end, the life of a scientist must change—incorporating a much broader view of what it means to be a scientist and changing the way that most of us apportion our time. In a sense, therefore, we scientists should view the controversy over stem cell research as a healthy wake-up call—a call to action in a new century in which our startling discoveries will increasingly dominate the news.

Bruce Alberts, PhD

REFERENCES

1. Marmur, J., and Doty, P. (1961). Thermal renaturation of DNA. *J. Mol. Biol.* **3,** 585–594.
2. National Academy of Sciences. "Beyond Discovery" series. *Available at:* http://www.BeyondDiscovery.org.
3. National Research Council. (2002). "Stem Cells and the Future of Regenerative Medicine." National Academies Press, Washington, DC. *Available for purchase at:* http://www.nap.edu/catalog/10195.html.
4. National Research Council. (1996). "National Science Education Standards." National Academies Press, Washington, DC. *Available for purchase or download at:* http://www.nap.edu/catalog/4962.html.

Embryonic Stem Cells in Perspective

Biologists have explored the development of embryos of all sorts, from worms to humans, in search of the answer to the question of how a complex organism derives from a single cell, the fertilized egg. We now know many of the genes involved in regulating development in different species and find remarkable conservation of genetic pathways across evolution. We also have a good understanding of the logic of development—how the embryo repeatedly uses the same kinds of strategies to achieve cellular specialization, tissue patterning, and organogenesis. One common strategy of development is the use of the stem cell to help generate and maintain a given tissue or organ. A stem cell is a cell that, when it divides, can produce a copy of itself as well as a differentiated cell progeny. This self-renewal capacity underlies the ability of adult stem cells, such as hematopoietic stem cells and spermatogonial stem cells, to constantly renew tissues that turn over rapidly in the adult. The concept of the stem cell arose from the pioneering studies of Till and McCullogh on the hematopoietic stem cell and those of Leblond on spermatogenesis and the intestinal crypt. Even in tissues like the brain, where cells do not turn over so rapidly in the adult, there are long-lived quiescent stem cells that may be reactivated to repair damage.

Much current research is focused on the identification, characterization, and isolation of stem cells from the adult, with the hope that such cells may be useful for therapeutic repair of adult tissues either by exogenous cell therapy or by reactivation of endogenous stem cells. However, to date, most adult stem cells have restricted potential, and achieving indefinite proliferation and expansion of the stem cells in culture is still not routine. During embryogenesis, cells are initially proliferative and pluripotent; they only gradually become restricted to different cell fates. The question of whether pluripotent stem cells exist in the embryo has been of interest for years. In mammals, it was known in the 1960s and 1970s that early mouse embryos, up to late gastrulation stages, could produce tumors known as teratocarcinomas when transplanted to ectopic sites, such as the kidney capsule. These tumors contain a variety of differentiated cells types, including muscle, nerve, and skin, as well as an undifferentiated cell type, the embryonal carcinoma (EC) cell. EC cells could be propagated in the undifferentiated state *in vitro*. Importantly, Pierce in 1964 showed that a single EC cell could regenerate a tumor containing both EC cells and differentiated progeny,[1] demonstrating that EC cells are the stem cells of the tumor.

What was the relevance of these tumor cells to normal development? Many studies were carried out in the 1970s showing that EC cells could reveal their pluripotency when injected back into early embryos. The best, most karyotypically normal EC cells could contribute to many different cell types in the resulting chimeras, including, in rare instances, the germ line. This led to excitement that these cells might be used to introduce new genetic alterations into the mouse and that normalization of tumorigenicity could be achieved by promoting differentiation of tumor cells. However, chimerism was often weak, and EC-derived tumors were a common feature of the chimeras.[2] Thus, although EC cells had remarkable properties of differentiation, they were still clearly tumor cells. In 1981, Martin[3] and Evans and Kaufman[4] discovered that permanent pluripotent cell lines, known as embryonic stem (ES) cells, could be derived directly from the blastocyst in culture. This changed the whole perspective of the field. The differentiation of these cells, although they make teratomatous tumors in ectopic sites, is easier to control than that of EC cells. Dramatically, ES cells grown for many passages in culture can make an entire mouse when supported by tetraploid extraembryonic tissues.[5] When such mice are made from robust hybrid cell lines, they show no enhanced tumor susceptibility and appear normal in all respects.[6] All of these properties have made mouse ES cells an incredibly powerful tool for introducing alterations into the mouse genome and analyzing their effects.[7]

Are ES cells true stem cells? The *in vivo* equivalent of the ES cell is unclear. ES cells resemble the cells of the primitive ectoderm or epiblast in their gene expression patterns and their pattern of tissue contribution in chimeras. Transcription factors, such as Oct4 and Nanog, that are required for formation and survival of the pluripotent cells in the embryo are also needed for ES survival.[8–10] However, *in vivo,* the epiblast only has a limited period of possible stem cell expansion before all cells differentiate into the tissues of the three germ layers at gastrulation. Germ cells, which are set aside at gastrulation, go on to provide the gametes that will impart pluripotency to the zygotes of the next generation. However, there is no evidence that germ cells are a special stem cell pool in the epiblast, which could be the ES equivalent. Rather, it appears that all epiblast cells have the capacity to form germ cells in the right environment.[11] Thus, the germ cell is just one of the differentiation options of epiblast.

In vitro, it is clear that ES cells can be expanded indefinitely in the undifferentiated state and still retain the capacity for differentiation. In this regard, they certainly have stem cell properties. However, there has not been a clear demonstration that a single cell can both self-renew and differentiate, as has been shown for EC cells. It is known that single cells are fully pluripotent, since chimeras made by injecting single ES cells into blastocysts show ES contributions to all fetal cell types analyzed.[12] However, in some ways ES cells seem more like progenitor cells, where the population can be expanded by the right growth factor environment but all cells will differentiate when the supportive environment for self-renewal is removed. Practically, the difference is probably not important, but if true, it may be misleading to extrapolate from what we know about how ES cells maintain the proliferative state to other stem cells. The search for "stemness" genes and proteins may not be a useful undertaking until we agree on how to define different stem cell populations.

So much of the excitement about mouse ES cells has focused on their use as a tool for germ line transmission of genetic alterations, that the remarkable differentiation properties of these cells in culture have been underexplored. The derivation of cell lines from early human embryos that seem to share many of the properties of mouse ES cells[13,14] has refocused attention on the *in vitro* properties of ES cells. Many questions remain before ES cells can be transformed from an interesting biological system to a robust therapeutic modality for degenerative diseases. How similar are mouse and human ES cells, and how valid is it to use data from one

to drive research in the other? How can ES cells be maintained through many passages in a truly stable state, where all cells are stem (or progenitor) cells, epigenetic programming is stable, and genetic abnormalities are minimal? How can ES cells be directed to differentiate reproducibly into given cell types, and how can differentiated progenitors be isolated and maintained? How can we ensure that ES cells will not be tumorigenic *in vivo?*

All this research on ES cells, both mouse and human, will provide new insights into embryonic development and new clues as to how to isolate and characterize new stem cells from different embryonic or adult tissues. Conversely, research on how normal embryonic development is regulated will provide new clues as to how to maintain and differentiate stem–progenitor cells in culture. The interplay between developmental biologists and stem cell biologists will be key to a fundamental understanding of stem cell development and its translation into therapeutic outcomes.

Janet Rossant, PhD

REFERENCES

1. Kleinsmith, L.J., and Pierce, G.B. (1964). Multipotentiality of single embryonal carcinoma cells. *Cancer Res.* **24,** 1544–1551.

2. Papaioannou, V.E., and Rossant, J. (1984). Effects of the embryonic environment on proliferation and differentiation of embryonal carcinoma cells. *Cancer Surv.* **2,** 165–183.

3. Martin, G.R. (1981). Isolation of a pluripotent cell line from early mouse embryos cultured in medium conditioned by teratocarcinoma stem cells. *Proc. Nat. Acad. Sci. USA* **78,** 7634–7638.

4. Evans, M., and Kaufman, M.H. (1981). Establishment in culture of pluripotential cells from mouse embryos. *Nature* **292,** 154–155.

5. Nagy, A., Rossant, J., Nagy, R., Abramow-Newerly, W., and Roder, J.C. (1993). Derivation of completely cell culture-derived mice from early-passage embryonic stem cells. *Proc. Nat. Acad. Sci. USA* **90,** 8424–8428.

6. Eggan, K., Akutsu, H., Loring, J., Jackson-Grusby, L., Klemm, M., Rideout, W.M., III, Yanagimachi, R., and Jaenisch, R. (2001). Hybrid vigor, fetal overgrowth, and viability of mice derived by nuclear cloning and tetraploid embryo complementation. *Proc. Nat. Acad. Sci. USA* **98,** 6209–6214.

7. Rossant, J., and Nagy, A. (1995). Genome engineering: the new mouse genetics. *Nat. Med.* **1,** 592–594.

8. Chambers, I., Colby, D., Robertson, M., Nichols, J., Lee, S., Tweedie, S., and Smith, A. (2003). Functional expression cloning of Nanog, a pluripotency sustaining factor in embryonic stem cells. *Cell* **113,** 643–655.

9. Mitsui, K., Tokuzawa, Y., Itoh, H., Segawa, K., Murakami, M., Takahashi, K., Maruyama, M., Maeda, M., and Yamanaka, S. (2003). The homeoprotein Nanog is required for maintenance of pluripotency in mouse epiblast and ES cells. *Cell* **113,** 631–642.

10. Nichols, J., Zevnik, B., Anastassiadis, K., Niwa, H., Klewe-Nebenius, D., Chambers, I., Scholer, H., and Smith, A. (1998). Formation of pluripotent stem cells in the mammalian embryo depends on the POU transcription factor Oct4. *Cell* **95,** 379–391.

11. Tam, P.P., and Zhou, S.X. (1996). The allocation of epiblast cells to ectodermal and germ line lineages is influenced by the position

of the cells in the gastrulating mouse embryo. *Dev. Biol.* **178,** 124–132.

12. Beddington, R.S.P., and Robertson, E.J. (1989). An assessment of the developmental potential of embryonic stem cells in the midgestation mouse embryo. *Development* **105,** 733–737.

13. Shamblott, M.J., Axelman, J., Wang, S., Bugg, E.M., Littlefield, J.W., Donovan, P.J., Blumenthal, P.D., Huggins, G.R., and Gearhart, J.D. (1998). Derivation of pluripotent stem cells from cultured human primordial germ cells. *Proc. Nat. Acad. Sci. USA* **95,** 13,726–13,731.

14. Thomson, J.A., Itskovitz-Eldor, J., Shapiro, S.S., Waknitz, M.A., Swiergiel, J.J., Marshall, V.S., and Jones, J.M. (1998). Embryonic stem cell lines derived from human blastocysts. *Science* **282,** 1145–1147.

"Stemness": Definitions, Criteria, and Standards

Introduction

Stem cells have recently generated more public and professional interest than almost any other topic in biology. One reason stem cells capture the imagination of so many is the promise that understanding their unique properties may provide deep insights into the biology of cells as well as a path toward treatments for a variety of degenerative illnesses. And although the field of stem cell biology has grown rapidly, there exists considerable confusion and disagreement as to the nature of stem cells. This confusion can be partly attributed to the sometimes idiosyncratic terms and definitions used to describe stem cells. Although definitions can be restrictive, they are useful when they provide a basis for mutual understanding and experimental standardization. With this intention, I present explanations of definitions, criteria, and standards for stem cells. Moreover, I highlight a central question in stem cell biology, namely the origin of these cells. I also suggest criteria or standards for identifying, isolating, and characterizing stem cells. Finally, I summarize the notion of "stemness" and describe its possible application in understanding stem cells and their biology.

What Is a Stem Cell?

Stem cells are defined functionally as cells that have the capacity to self-renew as well as the ability to generate differentiated cells.[1,2] More explicitly, stem cells can generate daughter cells identical to their mother (self-renewal) as well as produce progeny with more restricted potential (differentiated cells). This simple and broad definition may be satisfactory for embryonic or fetal stem cells that do not perdure for the lifetime of an organism. But this definition breaks down in trying to discriminate between transient adult progenitor cells that have a reduced capacity for self-renewal and adult stem cells. It is therefore important when describing adult stem cells to further restrict this definition to cells that self-renew throughout the life span of the animal.[3] Another parameter that should be considered is potency: Does the stem cell generate to multiple differentiated cell types (multipotent), or is it only capable of producing one type of differentiated cell (unipotent)? Thus, a more complete description of a stem cell includes a consideration of replication capacity, clonality, and potency. Some theoretical as well as practical considerations surrounding these concepts are considered in this chapter.

SELF-RENEWAL

Stem cell literature is replete with terms such as "immortal," "unlimited," "continuous," and "capable of extensive proliferation," all used to describe the cell's replicative capacity. These rather extreme and vague terms are not very helpful, as it can be noted that experiments designed to test the "immortality" of a stem cell would by necessity outlast authors and readers alike. Most somatic cells cultured *in vitro* display a finite number of (less than 80) population doublings prior to replicative arrest or senescence, and this can be contrasted with the seemingly unlimited proliferative capacity of stem cells in culture.[4–8] Therefore, it is reasonable to say that a cell that can undergo more than twice this number of population doublings (160) without oncogenic transformation can be termed "capable of extensive proliferation." In a few cases, this criteria has been met, most notably with embryonic stem (ES) cells derived from either humans or mice as well as with adult neural stem cells (NSCs).[2,9] An incomplete understanding of the factors required for self-renewal *ex vivo* for many adult stem cells precludes establishing similar proliferative limits *in vitro*. In some cases, a rigorous assessment of the capacity for self-renewal of certain adult stem cells can be obtained by single-cell or serial transfer into acceptable hosts, an excellent example of which is adult hematopoietic stem cells (HSCs).[10,11] Adult stem cells are probably still best defined *in vivo*, where they must display sufficient proliferative capacity to last the lifetime of the animal. Terms such as "immortal" and "unlimited" are probably best used sparingly if at all.

CLONALITY

A second parameter, perhaps the most important, is the idea that stem cells are clonogenic entities: single cells with the capacity to create more stem cells. This issue has been exhaustively dealt with elsewhere and is essential for any definitive characterization of self-renewal, potential, and lineage.[1] Methods for tracing the lineage of stem cells are described in subsequent chapters. Although the clonal "gold standard" is well understood, there remain several confusing practical issues. For instance, what constitutes a cell line? The lowest standard would include any population of cells that can be grown in culture, frozen, thawed, and subsequently repassaged *in vitro*. A higher standard would be a clonal or apparently homogenous population of cells with these characteristics, but it must be recognized that cellular preparations that do not derive from a single cell may be a mixed population containing stem cells and a separate population of "supportive" cells required for the propagation of the purported stem cells. Hence, any reference to a stem cell line should be made with an explanation of their derivation. For example, it can be misleading to report on stem cells or "stem cell lines" from a tissue if they are cellular preparations containing of a mixed population, possibly contaminated by stem cells from another tissue.

POTENCY

The issue of potency maybe the most contentious part of a widely accepted definition for stem cells. A multipotent stem cell sits atop a lineage hierarchy and can generate multiple types of differentiated cells, the latter being cells with distinct morphologies and gene expression patterns. At the same time, many would argue that a self-renewing cell that can only produce one type of differentiated descendant is nonetheless a stem cell.[12] A case can be made, for clarity, that a unipotent cell is probably best described as a progenitor. Progenitors are typically the descendants of stem cells, only they more constrained in their differentiation potential or capacity for self-renewal and are often more limited in both senses.

DEFINITION

In conclusion, a working definition of a stem cell is a clonal, self-renewing entity that is multipotent and thus can generate several differentiated cell types. Admittedly, this definition is not applicable in all instances and is best used as a guide to help describe cellular attributes.

Where Do Stem Cells Come From?

The origin or lineage of stem cells is well understood for ES cells; their origin in adults is less clear and in some cases controversial. It may be significant that ES cells originate before germ layer commitment, raising the intriguing possibility that this may be a mechanism for the development of multipotent stem cells, including some adult stem cells. The paucity of information on the developmental origins of adult stems cells leaves open the possibility that they too escape lineage restriction in the early embryo and subsequently colonize specialized niches, which function to both maintain their potency as well as restrict their lineage potential. Alternatively, the more widely believed, though still unsubstantiated, model for the origin of adult stem cells assumes that they are derived after somatic lineage specification, whereupon multipotent stem cells–progenitors arise and colonize their respective cellular niches. In this section, I briefly summarize the origin of stem cells from the early embryo and explain what is known about the ontogeny of adult stem cells focusing attention on HSCs and NSCs.

STEM CELLS OF THE EARLY EMBRYO

Mouse and human ES cells are derived directly from the inner cell mass of preimplantation embryos after the formation of a cystic blastocyst.[13] This population of cells would normally produce the epiblast and eventually all adult tissues, which may help to explain the developmental plasticity exhibited by ES cells. In fact, ES cells appear to be the *in vitro* equivalent of the epiblast, as they have the capacity to contribute to all somatic lineages and in mice to produce germ line chimeras.

By the time the zygote has reached the blastocyst stage, the developmental potential of certain cells has been restricted. The outer cells of the embryo have begun to differentiate to form trophectoderm, from which a population of embryonic trophoblast stem cells has also been derived in mice.[14] These specialized cells can generate all cell types of the trophectoderm lineage, including differentiated giant trophoblast cells.

At the egg cylinder stage of embryonic development (embryonic day (E) 6.5 in mice), a population of cells near the epiblast (Figure 1) can be identified as primordial germ cells (PGCs), which are subsequently excluded from somatic specification or restriction.[15] PGCs migrate to and colonize the genital ridges, where they produce mature germ cells and generate functional adult gametes. PGCs can be isolated either prior or subsequent to their arrival in the genital ridges and, when cultured with appropriate factors *in vitro*, can generate embryonic germ (EG) cells.[16,17] EG cells have many of the characteristics of ES cells with respect to their differentiation potential and their contribution to the germ line of chimeric mice.[18,19] The most notable difference between ES and EG cells is that the latter may display (depending upon the developmental stage of their derivation) considerable imprinting of specific genes.[20–22] Consequently, certain EG cell lines are incapable of producing normal chimeric mice.

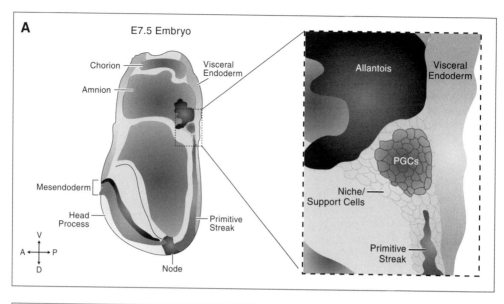

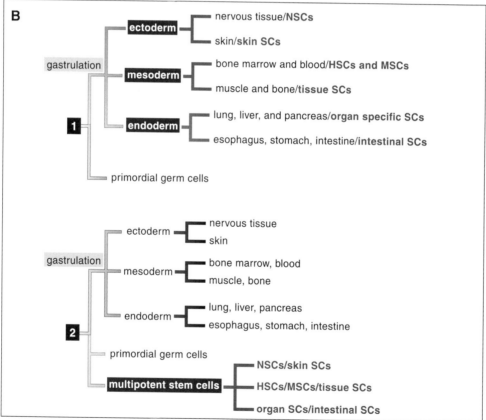

Figure 1. (A) Development of primordial germ cells. A schematic of an embryonic day 7.5 mouse embryo highlights the position of the developing primordial germ cells (PGCs) proximal to the epiblast. The expanded view on the right serves to illustrate the point that PGCs escape lineage commitment/restriction by avoiding the morphogenetic effects of migrating through the primitive streak during gastrulation. (B) Putative developmental ontogeny of stem cells. In lineage tree 1, the development of stem cells occurs after the formation of germ layers. These stem cells are thus restricted by germ layer commitment to their respective lineage (e.g., mesoderm is formed, giving rise to hematopoietic progenitors that become hematopoietic stem cells). Lineage tree 2 illustrates the idea that stem cells might develop similarly to PGCs, in that they avoid the lineage commitments during gastrulation and subsequently migrate to specifc tissue and organ niches.

Importantly, no totipotent stem cell has been isolated from the early embryo. ES and EG cells generate all somatic lineages as well as germ cells but rarely if ever contribute to the trophectoderm, extraembryonic endoderm, or extraembryonic mesoderm. Trophectoderm stem (TS) cells have been isolated, and these only generate cells of the trophectoderm lineage. It remains to be seen whether cells can be derived and maintained from totipotent embryonic stages.

Although our understanding of cell fates in the early embryo is incomplete, it appears that the only pluripotent stem cells found after gastrulation are PGCs (with the possible exceptions of multipotential adult progenitor cells[23] and teratocarcinomas). It may be that PGCs escape germ layer commitment during gastrulation by developing near the epiblast and subsequently migrate to positions inside the embryo proper. This developmental strategy may not be unique to PGCs, and it raises the interesting possibility that other stem cells might have similar developmental origins. Alternatively, it may be the case that adult stem cells are derived from PGCs. Although intriguing, it is important to stress that this idea lacks experimental evidence.

ONTOGENY OF ADULT STEM CELLS

The origin of most adult stem cells is poorly understood. With the issue of adult stem cell plasticity at the forefront, as described in this section, studies designed to elucidate the ontogeny of adult stem cells may help to reveal their specific lineage relationships and shed light on their plasticity and potential. Information on the origins of adult stem cells would also help to define the molecular programs involved in lineage determination, which may in turn provide insights into methods for manipulating their differentiation. To this end, I summarize what is known about the development of adult stem cells within the context of the hematopoietic and neural systems.

The development of hematopoietic cells in mice occurs soon after gastrulation (E7.5), although HSCs with the same activities as those in the adult have only been observed and isolated at midgestational stages (E10.5).[24-26] These observations suggest that the embryo has a unique hematopoietic lineage hierarchy, which may not be founded by an adult-type HSC. Thus, hematopoiesis appears to occur at multiple times or in successive waves within the embryo, and the emergence of an HSC may not precede or be concomitant with the appearance of differentiated hematopoietic cells.

The first site of hematopoiesis in the mouse is the extraembryonic yolk sac, soon followed by the intraembryonic aorta–gonad–mesonephros (AGM) region. Which of these sites leads to the generation of the adult hematopoietic system and, importantly, HSCs is still unclear. Results from nonmammalian embryo-grafting experiments, with various findings in the mouse, suggest that the mammalian embryo, specifically the AGM, generates the adult hematopoietic system and HSCs.[27-29] Interestingly, the midgestational AGM is also the region that harbors migrating PGCs and is thought to produce populations of mesenchymal stem cells, vascular progenitors, and perhaps hemangioblasts.[30-34] In the absence

of studies designed to clonally evaluate the lineage potential of cells from the AGM, and without similarly accurate fate mapping of this region, it remains possible that all of the adult stem cell types thought to emerge within the AGM arise from a common unrestricted precursor. This hypothetical precursor could help to explain reports of nonfusion-based adult stem cell plasticity. The observed lineage specificity of most adult stem cells could likewise be attributed to the high-fidelity lineage restriction imposed on them by the specific niche they colonize or are derived from. Simple ideas such as these have not been ruled out by experimental evidence, underscoring both the opportunity and the necessity for further study of the developmental origins of adult stem cells.

A key lesson from studies of the developing hematopoietic system is that the appearance of differentiated cells does not tell us where or when the corresponding adult stem cells originate. Definitive lineage tracing, with assays of clonogenic potential, remains the method of choice for identifying the origin of stem cells. Another potential pitfall revealed by these studies is that the definition of the stem cell can make all the difference in its identification.

The development of NSCs begins with the formation of nervous tissue from embryonic ectoderm following gastrulation. Induction of the neural plate is thought to coincide with the appearance of NSCs as well as restricted progenitor types.[35] The exact frequency and location of stem cells within the developing neuroepithelium remains unknown; specific markers must be discovered to fully unravel this question. An emerging view in the field is that embryonic neuroepithelia generate radial glial that subsequently develop into periventricular astrocytes and that these cells are the embryonic and adult NSCs within the central nervous system.[36-39] Developing and adult NSCs also appear to acquire positional and temporal information. For example, stem cells isolated from different neural regions generate region-appropriate progeny.[40-42] In addition, several studies suggest that temporal information is encoded within NSCs, that earlier stem cells give rise more frequently to neurons, and that more mature stem cells preferentially differentiate into glia.[35,43,44] Moreover, more mature NSCs appear incapable of making cells appropriate for younger stages when transplanted into the early cerebral cortex.[45] Thus, the nervous system appears to follow a classical lineage hierarchy, with a common progenitor cell generating most if not all differentiated cell types in a regional- and temporal-specific manner. There may also be rare stem cells in the nervous system, perhaps not of neural origin, that have greater plasticity in terms of producing diverse somatic cell types and lacking temporal and spatial constraints.[26,35]

There are several caveats that must be considered when describing the developmental origins of NSCs. First, disrupting the neuroepithelia to purify NSCs may have the undesirable effect of dysregulating spatial patterning acquired by these cells. Second, growth of purified NSCs in culture may reprogram the stem cells through exposure to nonphysiological *in vitro* culture conditions. Both of these problems can be addressed either by *in vivo* lineage tracing or by prospectively isolating NSCs and transplanting them into acceptable hosts without intervening culture. Carefully designed experiments promise to answer questions important not only for stem cell biology but also for neuroembryology and development. These include which features of the developmental program are intrinsic to individual cells, which differentiation or patterning signals act exclusively to instruct specific cell fates, and how developmental changes in cell-intrinsic programs restrict the responses of progenitors to cell-extrinsic signals.

How Are Stem Cells Identified, Isolated, and Characterized?

How stem cells are identified, isolated, and characterized are the key methodological questions in stem cell biology, so much so that subsequent chapters are devoted to addressing these problems in detail. Here, I briefly outline standards and criteria that may be employed when approaching the challenge of identifying, isolating, and characterizing a stem cell.

EMBRYONIC STEM CELLS

The basic characteristics of an ES cell include self-renewal, multilineage differentiation *in vitro* and *in vivo,* clonogenicity, a normal karyotype, extensive proliferation *in vitro* under well-defined culture conditions, and the ability to be frozen and thawed. In animal species, *in vivo* differentiation can be assessed rigorously by the ability of ES cells to contribute to all somatic lineages and produce germ line chimerism. These criteria are not appropriate for human ES cells; consequently, these cells must generate embryoid bodies and teratomas containing differentiated cells of all three germ layers. Moreover, as a stringent *in vivo* assessment of pluripotency is impossible, human ES cells must be shown to be positive for well-known molecular markers of pluripotent cells. These markers are defined as factors expressed consistently, and enriched, in human ES cells.[46] As a substitute for whole-animal chimerism, human ES cells could be tested for their contributions to specific tissues when transplanted in discrete regions of nonhuman adults or embryos. A complementary analysis might include transplanting human ES cells into nonhuman blastocysts and evaluating their contribution to various organs and tissues, though this experiment has raised ethical concerns in some quarters. Finally, a practical consideration is the passage number of ES cells. Although it is important to establish the capacity of ES cells to proliferate extensively, it is equally important that low-passage cells are evaluated experimentally to guard against any artifacts introduced through *in vitro* manipulation.

ADULT STEM CELLS

The basic characteristics of an adult stem cell are a single cell (clonal) that self-renews and generates differentiated cells. The most rigorous assessment of these characteristics is to prospectively purify a population of cells (usually by cell surface markers), transplant a single cell into an acceptable host without any intervening *in vitro* culture, and observe self-renewal and tissue, organ, or lineage reconstitution. Admittedly, this type of *in vivo* reconstitution assay is not well defined for many types of adult stem cells. Thus, it is important to arrive at

an accurate functional definition for cells whose developmental potential is assessed *in vitro* only. Above all, clonal assays should be the standard by which fetal and adult stem cells are evaluated because this assay removes doubts about contamination with other cell types.

Two concepts about the fate or potential of stem cells have moved to the forefront of adult stem cell research. The first is plasticity, the idea that restrictions in cell fates are not permanent but are flexible and reversible. The most obvious and extreme example of reversing a committed cell fate comes from experiments in which a terminally differentiated somatic cell generates to another animal following nuclear transfer or cloning.[47,48] Nuclear transfer experiments show that differentiated cells, given the appropriate conditions, can be returned to their most primal state. Thus, it may not be surprising if conditions are found for more committed or specified cells to dedifferentiate and gain a broader potential. A related concept is that of transdifferentiation. Transdifferentiation is the generation of functional cells of a tissue, organ, or lineage that is distinct from that of the founding stem cell.[49,50] Important issues here are whether the cells proposed to transdifferentiate are clonal and whether the mechanism by which they form the functional cell requires fusion.[51–54] Experiments designed to carefully evaluate these possibilities will yield insight into the nature of stem cells.

Stemness: Progress Toward a Molecular Definition of Stem Cells

Stemness refers to the common molecular processes underlying the core stem cell properties of self-renewal and the generation of differentiated progeny. Although stems cells in different cellular microenvironments or niches will by necessity have different physiological demands and therefore distinct molecular programs, there are likely certain genetic characteristics specific to and shared by all stem cells. Through transcriptional profiling, many of the genes enriched in ES cell, TS cell, HSC, and NSC populations have been identified.[55–60] By extending this approach to other stem cells and more organisms, it may be possible to develop a molecular fingerprint for stem cells. This fingerprint could be used as the basis for a molecular definition of stem cells that, when combined with their functional definition, would provide a more comprehensive set of criteria for understanding their unique biology. Perhaps more importantly, these types of studies could be used to help identify and isolate new stem cells. This goal is far from being accomplished, but the preliminary findings for specific stem cells have been described.

The transcriptional profiling of stem cells has suggested that they share several distinct molecular characteristics. Stem cells appear to have the capacity to sense a broad range of growth factors and signaling molecules and to express many of the downstream signaling components involved in the transduction of these signals. Signal transduction pathways present and perhaps active in stem cells include TGFβ, Notch, Wnt, and Jak/Stat family members. Stem cells also express many components involved in establishing their specialized cell cycles, either related to maintaining cell cycle arrest in G_1

(for most quiescent adult stem cells) or connected to progression through cell cycle checkpoints promoting rapid cycling (as is the case for ES cells and mobilized adult stem cells).[61,62] Most stem cells also express molecules involved in telomere maintenance and display elevated levels of telomerase activity. There is also considerable evidence that stem cells have significantly remodeled chromatin acted upon by DNA methylases or transcriptional repressors of histone deacetylase and Groucho family members. Another common molecular feature is the expression of specialized posttranscriptional regulatory machinery regulated by RNA helicases of the Vasa type. Finally, a shared molecular and functional characteristic of stem cells appears to be their resistance to stress, mediated by multidrug resistance transporters, protein-folding machinery, ubiquitin, and detoxifier systems.

Although in its infancy, the search for a molecular signature to define stem cells continues. We have begun to understand in general terms what molecular components are most often associated with stem cells. In the future, it may be possible to precisely define stem cells as a whole and individually by their telltale molecular identities. Until that time, stemness remains a concept of limited utility with tremendous potential.

ACKNOWLEDGMENTS

I would like to thank Jayaraj Rajagopal and Kevin Eggan for helpful discussion and suggestions. I apologize to those authors whose work was inadvertently overlooked or omitted because of space limitations.

Douglas A. Melton, PhD
Chad Cowan, PhD

REFERENCES

1. Weissman, I.L., Anderson, D.J., and Gage, F. (2001). Stem and progenitor cells: origins, phenotypes, lineage commitments, and transdifferentiations. *Annu. Rev. Cell Dev. Biol.* **17**, 387–403.
2. Smith, A.G. (2001). Embryo-derived stem cells: of mice and men. *Annu. Rev. Cell Dev. Biol.* **17**, 435–462.
3. van der Kooy, D., and Weiss, S. (2000). Why stem cells? *Science* **287**, 1439–1441.
4. Houck, J.C., Sharma, V.K., and Hayflick, L. (1971). Functional failures of cultured human diploid fibroblasts after continued population doublings. *Proc. Soc. Exp. Biol. Med.* **137**, 331–333.
5. Hayflick, L. (1973). The biology of human aging. *Am. J. Med. Sci.* **265**, 432–445.
6. Hayflick, L. (1974). The longevity of cultured human cells. *J. Am. Geriatr. Soc.* **22**, 1–12.
7. Sherr, C.J., and DePinho, R.A. (2000). Cellular senescence: mitotic clock or culture shock? *Cell* **102**, 407–410.
8. Shay, J.W., and Wright, W.E. (2000). Hayflick, his limit, and cellular ageing. *Nat. Rev. Mol. Cell Biol.* **1**, 72–76.
9. Morrison, S.J., Shah, N.M., and Anderson, D.J. (1997). Regulatory mechanisms in stem cell biology. *Cell* **88**, 287–298.
10. Allsopp, R.C., and Weissman, I.L. (2002). Replicative senescence of hematopoietic stem cells during serial transplantation: does telomere shortening play a role? *Oncogene* **21**, 3270–3273.
11. Iscove, N.N., and Nawa, K. (1997). Hematopoietic stem cells expand during serial transplantation *in vivo* without apparent exhaustion. *Curr. Biol.* **7**, 805–808.
12. Slack, J.M. (2000). Stem cells in epithelial tissues. *Science* **287**, 1431–1433.
13. Papaioannou, V. (2001). Stem cells and differentiation. *Differentiation* **68**, 153–154.
14. Tanaka, S., *et al.* (1998). Promotion of trophoblast stem cell proliferation by FGF4. *Science* **282**, 2072–2075.
15. Saitou, M., Barton, S.C., and Surani, M.A. (2002). A molecular program for the specification of germ cell fate in mice. *Nature* **418**, 293–300.
16. Matsui, Y., Zsebo, K., and Hogan, B.L. (1992). Derivation of pluripotential embryonic stem cells from murine primordial germ cells in culture. *Cell* **70**, 841–847.
17. Resnick, J.L., *et al.* (1992). Long-term proliferation of mouse primordial germ cells in culture. *Nature* **359**, 550–551.
18. Labosky, P.A., Barlow, D.P., and Hogan, B.L. (1994). Mouse embryonic germ (EG) cell lines: transmission through the germ line, and differences in the methylation imprint of insulin-like growth factor 2 receptor *(Igf2r)* gene compared with embryonic stem (ES) cell lines. *Development* **120**, 3197–3204.
19. Stewart, C.L., Gadi, I., and Bhatt, H. (1994). Stem cells from primordial germ cells can reenter the germ line. *Dev. Biol.* **161**, 626–628.
20. Surani, M.A. (1998). Imprinting and the initiation of gene silencing in the germ line. *Cell* **93**, 309–312.
21. Surani, M.A. (2001). Reprogramming of genome function through epigenetic inheritance. *Nature* **414**, 122–128.
22. Howell, C.Y., *et al.* (2001). Genomic imprinting disrupted by a maternal effect mutation in the *Dnmt1* gene. *Cell* **104**, 829–838.
23. Jiang, Y., *et al.* (2002). Pluripotency of mesenchymal stem cells derived from adult marrow. *Nature* **418**, 41–49.
24. Orkin, S.H. (1996). Development of the hematopoietic system. *Curr. Opin. Genet. Dev.* **6**, 597–602.
25. Dzierzak, E. (2002). Hematopoietic stem cells and their precursors: Developmental diversity and lineage relationships. *Immunol. Rev.* **187**, 126–138.
26. Weissman, I.L. (2000). Stem cells: units of development, units of regeneration, and units in evolution. *Cell* **100**, 157–168.
27. Kau, C.L., and Turpen, J.B. (1983). Dual contribution of embryonic ventral blood island and dorsal lateral plate mesoderm during ontogeny of hemopoietic cells in *Xenopus laevis*. *J. Immunol.* **131**, 2262–2266.
28. Medvinsky, A.L., *et al.* (1993). An early preliver intraembryonic source of CFU-S in the developing mouse. *Nature* **364**, 64–67.
29. Medvinsky, A., and Dzierzak, E. (1996). Definitive hematopoiesis is autonomously initiated by the AGM region. *Cell* **86**, 897–906.
30. Molyneaux, K.A., *et al.* (2001). Time-lapse analysis of living mouse germ cell migration. *Dev. Biol.* **240**, 488–498.
31. Minasi, M.G., *et al.* (2002). The mesoangioblast: A multipotent, self-renewing cell that originates from the dorsal aorta and differentiates into most mesodermal tissues. *Development* **129**, 2773–2783.
32. Alessandri, G., *et al.* (2001). Human vasculogenesis *ex vivo*: embryonal aorta as a tool for isolation of endothelial cell progenitors. *Lab. Invest.* **81**, 875–885.
33. Hara, T., *et al.* (1999). Identification of podocalyxin-like protein 1 as a novel cell surface marker for hemangioblasts in the murine aorta–gonad–mesonephros region. *Immunity* **11**, 567–578.
34. Munoz-Chapuli, R., *et al.* (1999). Differentiation of hemangioblasts from embryonic mesothelial cells? A model on the origin of the vertebrate cardiovascular system. *Differentiation* **64**, 133–141.

35. Temple, S. (2001). The development of neural stem cells. *Nature* **414**, 112–117.

36. Alvarez-Buylla, A., Garcia-Verdugo, J.M., and Tramontin, A.D. (2001). A unified hypothesis on the lineage of neural stem cells. *Nat. Rev. Neurosci.* **2**, 287–293.

37. Tramontin, A.D., *et al.* (2003). Postnatal development of radial glia and the ventricular zone (VZ): a continuum of the neural stem cell compartment. *Cereb. Cortex* **13**, 580–587.

38. Doetsch, F., *et al.* (1999). Subventricular zone astrocytes are neural stem cells in the adult mammalian brain. *Cell* **97**, 703–716.

39. Gaiano, N., and Fishell, G. (2002). The role of notch in promoting glial and neural stem cell fates. *Annu. Rev. Neurosci.* **25**, 471–490.

40. Kalyani, A.J., *et al.* (1998). Spinal cord neuronal precursors generate multiple neuronal phenotypes in culture. *J. Neurosci.* **18**, 7856–7868.

41. He, W., *et al.* (2001). Multipotent stem cells from the mouse basal forebrain contribute GABAergic neurons and oligodendrocytes to the cerebral cortex during embryogenesis. *J. Neurosci.* **21**, 8854–8862.

42. Anderson, D.J., *et al.* (1997). Cell lineage determination and the control of neuronal identity in the neural crest. *Cold Spring Harb. Symp. Quant. Biol.* **62**, 493–504.

43. Qian, X., *et al.* (2000). Timing of CNS cell generation: a programmed sequence of neuron and glial cell production from isolated murine cortical stem cells. *Neuron* **28**, 69–80.

44. White, P.M., *et al.* (2001). Neural crest stem cells undergo cell-intrinsic developmental changes in sensitivity to instructive differentiation signals. *Neuron* **29**, 57–71.

45. Desai, A.R., and McConnell, S.K. (2000). Progressive restriction in fate potential by neural progenitors during cerebral cortical development. *Development* **127**, 2863–2872.

46. Brivanlou, A.H., *et al.* (2003). Stem cells: setting standards for human embryonic stem cells. *Science* **300**, 913–916.

47. Solter, D. (2000). Mammalian cloning: advances and limitations. *Nat. Rev. Genet.* **1**, 199–207.

48. Rideout, W.M., 3rd, Eggan, K., and Jaenisch, R. (2001). Nuclear cloning and epigenetic reprogramming of the genome. *Science* **293**, 1093–1098.

49. Liu, Y., and Rao, M.S. (2003). Transdifferentiation: Fact or artifact. *J. Cell Biochem.* **88**, 29–40.

50. Blau, H.M., Brazelton, T.R., and Weimann, J.M. (2001). The evolving concept of a stem cell: entity or function? *Cell* **105**, 829–841.

51. Medvinsky, A., and Smith, A. (2003). Stem cells: fusion brings down barriers. *Nature* **422**, 823–835.

52. Terada, N., *et al.* (2002). Bone marrow cells adopt the phenotype of other cells by spontaneous cell fusion. *Nature* **416**, 542–545.

53. Wang, X., *et al.* (2003). Cell fusion is the principal source of bone marrow-derived hepatocytes. *Nature* **422**, 897–901.

54. Ying, Q.L., *et al.* (2002). Changing potency by spontaneous fusion. *Nature* **416**, 545–548.

55. Ivanova, N.B., *et al.* (2002). A stem cell molecular signature. *Science* **298**, 601–604.

56. Ramalho-Santos, M., *et al.* (2002). "Stemness": Transcriptional profiling of embryonic and adult stem cells. *Science* **298**, 597–600.

57. Tanaka, T.S., *et al.* (2002). Gene expression profiling of embryo-derived stem cells reveals candidate genes associated with pluripotency and lineage specificity. *Genome Res.* **12**, 1921–1928.

58. Anisimov, S.V., *et al.* (2002). SAGE identification of gene transcripts with profiles unique to pluripotent mouse R1 embryonic stem cells. *Genomics* **79**, 169–176.

59. Luo, Y., *et al.* (2002). Microarray analysis of selected genes in neural stem and progenitor cells. *J. Neurochem.* **83**, 1481–1497.

60. Park, I.K., *et al.* (2002). Differential gene expression profiling of adult murine hematopoietic stem cells. *Blood* **99**, 488–498.

61. Burdon, T., *et al.* (1999). Signaling mechanisms regulating self-renewal and differentiation of pluripotent embryonic stem cells. *Cells Tiss. Organs* **165**, 131–143.

62. Savatier, P., *et al.* (2002). Analysis of the cell cycle in mouse embryonic stem cells. *Methods Mol. Biol.* **185**, 27–33.

History of Embryo Stem Cells

Robert G. Edwards

Introduction

The systematic analysis of embryo stem cells began in the early 1960s at Glasgow University. At this time, I resumed studies on the maturation of human oocytes 30 years after original work by Pincus and Saunders in 1939.[1] These two events led to human *in vitro* fertilisation (IVF), preimplantation genetic diagnosis, and growth of human stem cells for therapeutic purposes. Successive publications covering these topics were summarised in 2001 and 2002 by Edwards,[2,3] providing the basis for this chapter. Coincidentally, preimplantation growth in mammals were increasing in number following initial work in 1890 by Heape,[4] who obtained rabbit offspring after transferring marked blastocysts into recipient does. In the early 20th century, Lewis and Gregory[5] and Lewis and Wright[6] cultured rabbit and mouse embryos through one or several cleavages. Pincus and Enzmann[7] released rabbit ovarian oocytes from their follicles into culture media and recorded their spontaneous maturation to metaphase 2 and the extrusion of the first polar body. Experimental studies in 1940 by Nicholas and Hall[8] and in 1952 by Seidel[9] assessed the developmental capacity of each two-cell blastomere in rabbit embryos after the other was destroyed; at the same time, Beatty and Fischberg[10] inactivated the second metaphase spindle by warming ovulated mouse oocytes *in vivo* to produce triploid embryos after fertilization. As Alan Beatty's Ph.D. student, I modified his treatments to produce androgenetic and gynogenetic haploid embryos, triploids, tetraploids, and various heteroploids.[11]

Work among a team of dedicated researchers led to numerous studies on preimplantation mammalian embryos, providing a secure foundation for later work on human embryos. Uptake and turnover of radiolabelled precursors of DNA, RNA, and proteins in mouse oocytes and embryos were measured by autoradiography in 1956.[12] Axial gradients in RNA and proteins, typical of amphibian oocytes, were not identified in mouse eggs, although RNAs distributed unevenly in ooplasm. Stimulating adult mice with gonadotrophins resulted in closely timed multifolliculation, oestrus and ovulation in adult mice by Fowler and Edwards.[13] The final meiotic stages in oocytes, fertilization, cleavage, and blastulation succeeded each other in an astonishingly precise timing.[14] These strict timetables

awoke my interest in human studies, since mature human ovarian oocytes *in vitro* would provide a source of oocytes for *in vitro* fertilization. Between 1962 and 1965, my accumulating data on timing human maturation, a long and tedious task, did not confirm data of Pincus and Saunders,[1] since these oocytes needed 37 and not 12 hours for full maturation.[15,16] During these years, Tarkowski[17,18] and Mintz[19] were disaggregating and fusing intact individual blastomeres of 2-, 4-, 8-, and 16-cell mouse embryos to produce chimaeric offspring, revealing mammalian blastomeres to be highly multipotent. My proposed approach to studying totipotency and differentiation differed, since I wished to disaggregate cleaving mouse and rabbit embryos and then transfer these cells singly into blastocoelic cavities of recipient blastocysts to assess their developmental potential in resulting chimaeric embryos. Cleavage-stage rabbit blastomeres divided briefly *in vitro* as separate cells, hinting at new approaches to establishing stem cell lines.[20]

First Studies on Stem Cells *In Vitro*

John Paul in Glasgow sent me a surprising note in 1962. A brilliant teacher, biochemist, and cell biologist, he asked me to join him and Robin Cole for a year of collaborative studies on embryo stem cells. Far ahead of those in most laboratories, his techniques and ideas included maintaining cell strains in continuous culture, cryopreservation, modern biochemical methods, and strict methods of tissue culture using CO_2 incubators, droplets of medium held beneath paraffin overlays, and analyses on embryonic inducers. These methods are standard practice in IVF and stem cell laboratories today. We decided in 1963 to prepare disaggregates of single or grouped cells from rabbit preimplantation embryos in droplets of NCTC109, 199, F10, Eagle's, and Waymouth's media held under paraffin oil.[21,22] Added supplements included sera from fetal calves, rabbits, and humans, with irradiated HeLa feeder cells and a gas phase of 5% CO_2 in air.[21,22] Novel approaches included coating glass or plastic culture vessels with collagen prepared from rat tails[23] and adding mesodermalising inducers to some colonies.[24]

CULTURING INTACT RABBIT BLASTOCYSTS

Disaggregates from zona-denuded four- to eight-cell rabbit embryos grouped in culture droplets produced occasional migratory cell types. Improved growth was gained with 8- to 16-cell stages and was better still with 32-cell stages and morulae. A migratory cell appearing in these cultures frequently attached to and flattened on surfaces of culture dishes. A few rounded, perhaps embryonic-like cells did not persist in our cultures.[21,22] Retaining embryo structure in culture led to some four-cell colonies producing small or misshapen blastocysts after 5 days, their trophoblast attaching to culture dishes to form flat, epithelial cell outgrowths.

Intact 6-day rabbit blastocysts denuded of their zona pellucida were cultured on collagen or with mesodermalising inducer. Their trophectoderm attached to culture dishes, and the embryos collapsed then partially reexpanded several times.[21,22] Attached trophoblast cells migrated rapidly and transformed to thin cell multicellular sheets and a central cell bundle. Small round cells, presumably from the inner cell mass, migrated over trophectodermal pavement to form clumps later termed embryoid bodies. Structures and vesicles formed then regressed as most colonies became static[22] (Fig. 1–1). Younger, smaller blastocysts produced only trophoblast, mostly diploid and rarely tetraploid.

Stained preparation of cell colonies derived from intact blastocyst preparations contained numerous tissues.[21,22,25] These included blood islands after 12 days postattachment (Fig. 1–1), structures typical of yolk sac, sheets of muscle-like cells with minor if any contractions, neurones, macrophages with apparently ingested material, and connective and other tissues stained with Alcian blue or Mallory's triple stain. Perhaps the inducer had stressed growth towards mesoderm.

The full totipotency of the inner cell mass had been revealed in these complex mixtures of cells from all body tissues. The first thoughts on human stem cells and their therapeutic use began to emerge in mid-1963 (Fig. 1–2). Much of our work on culturing intact embryos was repeated in mice, but without immediate intentions of assessing stem cell growth and differentiation.[26]

RABBIT STEM CELL LINES FROM ISOLATED OR DISAGGREGATED INNER CELL MASS

An alternative approach to making embryo stem cells was tested in Glasgow. It involved culturing the intact rabbit inner cell mass of 6-day blastocysts trimmed of its trophectoderm or disaggregating the inner cell mass and culturing its component cells.[21,22] This approach produced results different from those obtained from cultures of intact embryos. Isolated masses placed in media droplets on collagen attached within 10–15 hours, forming sheets of cells. When the few trophoblast cells became dominant, the cell masses were sliced into pieces and recultured. Cell monolayers migrating out 4–5 days after attachment formed epithelial and fibroblastic cells. Central cell masses degenerated as surrounding cells formed monolayers, which were isolated for onward culture by passaging them as fibroblasts on collagen-free surfaces.

Colonies of disaggregated single cells from embryonic discs of individual day 6 embryos were also cultured on collagen

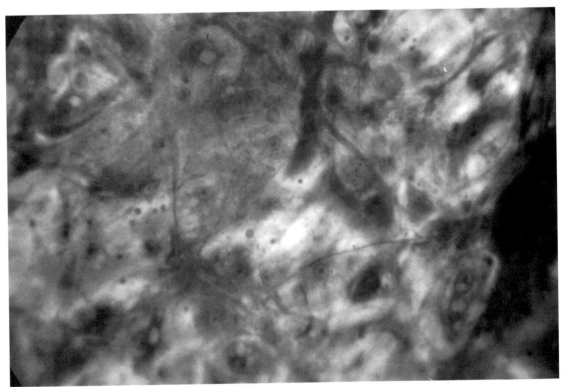

Figure 1–1A. Examples of structures identified in outgrowths from intact rabbit blastocysts grown in culture. One shows muscle fibres, and the other shows a blood island. These illustrations are taken from the first studies on embryo stem cells in Glasgow University carried out in 1963–1964.

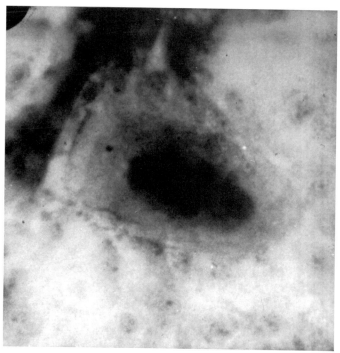

Figure 1–1B. Examples of structures identified in outgrowths from intact rabbit blastocysts grown in culture. One shows muscle fibres, and the other shows a blood island. These illustrations are taken from the first studies on embryo stem cells in Glasgow University carried out in 1963–1964.

under 5% CO_2 in air. Many attached to collagen, spreading in 24 hours although not yet attaching directly to glass or plastic. Small epithelial and fibroblastic colonies identified between 5–7 days helped establish up to 20 epithelial and fibroblastic cell lines from a single inner cell mass, which grew on glass (Table 1–1). Many colonies soon died. Colonies could not be established from younger embryos.

Established stem cell lines were typified by unusual growth characteristics. Many multiplied strongly, seemingly held at specific stages of differentiation. Most cell lines were diploid; two were tetraploid. They were characterised by high activities of alkaline phosphatase or arginase, characteristics persisting over many generations. Two of our primary cultures proliferating on glass at approximately 6 weeks after

PURPOSES OF INTRODUCING HUMAN IVF

Infertility
Origin of chromosome disorders
Diagnosis of genetic disease in embryos
Contraception and fundamental knowledge
    on human conception
Stem cells from embryos
ETHICS OF EARLY HUMAN LIFE

Figure 1–2. A slide outlining the purposes of introducing human IVF. Notice that ethics were stressed. This slide, made on an electric typewriter in the early 1980s, was a copy of an earlier slide used as an opener in many conferences from the early 1970s.

explantation included a fibroblastic line RB/1 and an epithelioid line RB3/3.[21,22] Each had a varying morphology with large nuclei and many nucleoli (Tables 1–1 and 1–2). These two immortal lines cleaved endlessly over months and even years. Cryopreserved samples immediately resumed division when thawed, some after years in cryostore.[22,27] Culture methods clearly suited embryos, as shown when 50 two-cell mouse embryos grown to blastocysts *in vitro* all hatched on one night.[28]

With hindsight, collagen substrates must have been significant in sustaining blastocyst cell outgrowths and rabbit stem cell lines. Today, various substrates are used to commit stem cells to various pathways by modifying their gene expression. Collagen-1 was later found to stimulate the formation of epithelial pavements[29]; in our work, it may have helped trophectoderm to form a platform supporting cells migrating from the rabbit inner cell mass. Many investigators now routinely apply similar methods, using cultures of intact embryos to produce either highly differentiated tissues or culturing disaggregated cells to prepare embryonic stem (ES) cell lines seemingly suspended in an early phase of differentiation.

Once embryo stem cell lines could be made *in vitro*, new experimental approaches were needed to assess developmental capacities of single, marked ES cells. The mouse was the ideal species, with many well-characterised marker genes enabling cells to be traced as they migrated through recipient tissues. Tarkowski[18] assessed such forms of growth in mouse fusion chimaeras derived from cleaving embryos. My approach

TABLE 1–1
Establishing Rabbit Embryonic Stem Cell Lines *In Vitro*[21,22]

Embryonic discs excised from blastocysts

Some cultured intact between slightly compressed glass surfaces

Others disaggregated into separate cells

Cells encouraged to attach with the provision of collagen-coated surfaces

Piles of cells and outgrowths

20 stem cell cultures possible from a single embryonic disc

40 subcultures initially, some passing through an estimated 200 generations

Properties of Long-Lasting Rabbit Embryo Stem Cell Lines *In Vitro*

Name	Origin	Established at	Characteristics[a]	Enzymes	Persistence
RB/1	Day 6, outgrowths of embryonic disc	6 weeks	Fibroblastic, spindle shaped	High arginase	>11 months or 200 generations
RB2	Day 6, outgrowths of embryonic disc	6 weeks	Fibroblastic diffuse		
RB3/3	Day 6		Epithelial	High AP[b]	>9.5 months[c]
RB3/4	Day 6		Fibroblastic, like RB1		

[a]RB1 and RB3/3 remained largely diploid.
[b]Alkaline phosphatase.
[c]Cell lines cryopreserved and thawed without loss of characteristics.

TABLE 1–2
Colonisation, Haematopoietic Expression, and Survival of 129-*W*ʰ*W*ʰ Recipients After Donations of C57Bl/10 Blastocyst Cells[55]

Numbers of Colonised Recipients

Degree of Donor Markers in Recipients[a]

Days postgraft	1–10%		11–50%		51–100%	
	Hb	GPI	Hb	GPI	Hb	GPI
1–2	10		8			
4	7	18	10		1	
8	3	9	3	8	12	1
16	0	1	2	10	16	7
32	0	0	0	0	18	18
300	0	0	0	0	18	18

Expression of Donor Markers and Period of Recipient Survival

Recipients with Donor Markers

Nucleated cells injected (×10⁴)	Donor cells in culture (days)	Haemoglobin	GPI	Recipient survival (days)
4.9–5.7	3	4/5	4/5	317–355
6.1–7.8	3	5/5	5/5	306–360
6.8–8.9	4	5/5	5/5	309–351
9.5–10.5	4	4/5	4/5	312–341

[a]Levels assessed by densitometry.

was to develop microsurgical methods for injecting single embryo stem cells into blastocoelic cavities of recipient blastocysts (Fig. 1–3). Human embryo stem cells were still in my mind, but they would have to await the growth of human blastocysts *in vitro* and the birth of IVF children as proof of high quality in embryos.[15] By curious coincidence, the first human oocyte matured *in vitro* to metaphase-2 and extruded its first polar body during my final days in Glasgow. This large step to human IVF offered distant promises of human blastocysts and their stem cells. Cambridge was calling, ending our first work on embryo stem cells.

Developmental Potential of Single Mouse Embryo Stem Cells Placed in Recipient Blastocysts

In Cambridge, I was fortunate to supervise many Ph.D. students over 25 years. Making injection chimaeras seemed to be an ideal Ph.D. project, demanding delicate experimental methods and a deep understanding of developmental biology.

Richard Gardner accepted this exciting project for his Ph.D., among the first of many attracted to preimplantation embryology.

An opening study by Gardner and me used micromanipulation to operate on rabbit blastocysts, their large size offering initial experience with this approach. Deciding that identifying male and female embryos would be a feasible project, a few trophectoderm cells were excised and typed for sex chromatin. Female (+) and male (−) embryos were classified simply and transferred to hosts. Sex ratios at full term were correctly identified. This and other studies introduced the preimplantation genetic diagnosis of inherited disease in humans and animals.[30,31] Later, attempts to identify sex chromatin in human blastocysts were unsuccessful, thwarting a similar form of control over human sex ratios.

To prepare chimaeras, Gardner isolated entire inner cell masses of mouse blastocysts or their disaggregated single cells and then injected them singly into blastocoelic cavities of recipient blastocysts to measure their capacity for colonisation and differentiation in the resulting chimaeras[32] (Fig. 1–3). Chimaerism was distinct in some offspring, weak in others, and most organs except trophectoderm were colonised in 14% of

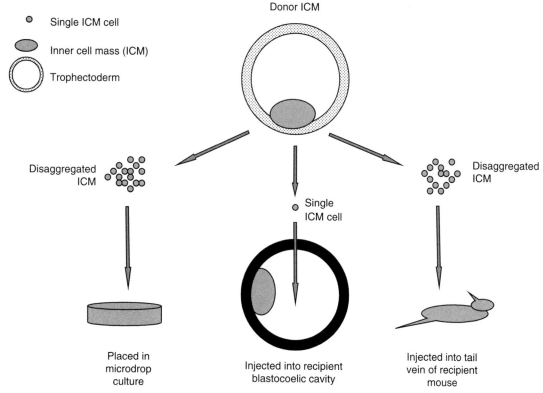

Figure 1-3. Initial studies on rabbit embryo stem cells led to a plan of research in 1965 to clarify the properties of embryo stem cells and their therapeutic application. Three lines of research were needed. (A) The first, long-range ambition was to make human stem cells in culture. (B) Their embryological and developmental capacities had to be assessed by injecting them singly into recipient blastocysts to make chimaeras. (C) Studies had to be devised in animals for grafting embryo stem cells into sick recipients to measure their therapeutic capacities. It was also essential to produce methods of checking blastocyst quality; this was done in rabbits by excising small pieces of trophectoderm from rabbit blastocysts and sexing them by using the sex chromatin body as a genetic marker (this study is not shown in the figure). Full details of these successive studies are given in the text.

recipients (Table 1–3). Germ line colonisation was measured in back- and intercrosses between chimaeras and donor strains. Donor cells could be synchronous or asynchronous, could be injected singly or in groups, could come from a different species,[33] and could be derived from teratocarcinomas[34–36] and from parthenogenetic embryos.[37] Fate maps were prepared for different types of donor embryonic cells.[38] At least 2 of 23 primitive ectoderm cells were found to contribute to soma and germ line.[39] Embryo stem cells clearly were highly multipotent in injection chimaeras, confirming their potential found with cultures of whole blastocysts in Glasgow.

Single-cell injections became even more powerful when gene insertion using homologous recombination in single donor cells led to gene knockout and knockin mice.[40,41] Mouse teratocarcinoma cells displayed an inherited potential in injection chimaeras[36] and produced clonal stem cell lines.[42] Multipotent embryo stem cell lines derived from mouse blastocysts[43,44] had characteristics similar to rabbit stem cells studied in Glasgow

10 years earlier.[21,22] Mouse embryo stem cells *in vitro* differentiated into blood, nerves, muscle, and connective tissue, as they did in rabbits.[45]

Prospects of human embryo stem cells were edging closer as our work on human IVF developed slowly, delayed by endless ethical issues. Successive developmental stages were mastered *in vitro*, including fertilising human eggs and cleaving embryos in culture. Human blastocysts grew to day 5 and day 9, their splendid inner cell masses and embryonic discs packed with stem cells.[46–48] The first IVF baby was delivered in 1978—after considerable effort—signalling the imminence of alleviating infertility, introducing preimplantation genetic diagnosis, and using human stem cells for therapeutic purposes. This period was nearly euphoric for me as these clinical opportunities emerged. Two lines of research developed in our laboratories: attempts to produce human embryo stem cells and use of mouse blastocyst and postimplantation foetuses as sources of stem cells for therapeutic grafting into sick recipients.

TABLE 1–3
Colonisation, Haematopoietic Expression, and Survival of Balb/C Recipients After Donations of C57Bl/10 Blastocyst Cells[55]

Cells Injected, Period of Blastocyst Culture, and Donor Markers and Survival in Recipients				
		Recipients with Donor Markers		
Nucleated cells injected (×10⁴)	Donor cells in culture (days)	Haemoglobin	GPI	Survival of positive recipients (days)
4.8–7.1	3	7/10	7/10	13,17,301,315,322,323,339,341
7.8–10.6	4	7/10	7/10	13,18,311,326,326,335,343
0 (saline)ᵃ				12–14

Haematological Parameters in Recipients				
	Haemoglobin (g 100 ml⁻¹)*			
Days postgraft	recipients	controls	Mean no. erythrocytes in recipients	Mean no. leucocytes in recipients
1	13.3 ± 0.1	13.0 ± 0.1	7.0	3.8
7	14.7 ± 0.1	12.3 ± 0.1	7.8	4.0
31	15.3 ± 0.1	11.3 ± 0.1	8.7	4.3
62	15.2 ± 0.1	10.0 ± 0.1	8.0	4.0
200	15.0 ± 0.1	4.8 ± 0.1	8.2	4.1

Haematological Parameters in Controls		
Days postgraft	Mean no. erythrocytes	Mean no. leucocytes
1	7.7	2.6
2	7.0	2.0
4	7.0	0.9
8	6.5	0.1
12	1.1	0.03

ᵃTen recipients were injected with saline.

Preliminary Studies with Human Stem Cells

The opening of Bourn Hall, Cambridge, in early 1980s as the world's largest IVF clinic attracted a crescendo of ethical debates. Arguments centred on the use of human embryos for research, risks of cloning, and dangers of embryo cryopreservation among other items. Pressures compelled me to issue eight libel actions in the High Court of London against some pillars of British society. As IVF expanded, some "spare" human blastocysts seemed to have little or no chances of implantation in their mothers. Gaining parental permission, we decided to use them to make human embryo stem cell lines *in vitro*. This step followed my proposals to mend diseased organs in animals and humans using specific embryo stem cells as suggested from the early 1970s.[25,49] It was now apposite to begin work on stem cells, since Bourn Hall had conceived more than 100 IVF children, and high-quality blastocysts were growing *in vitro*.

Six fertilised human eggs were cultured in Earle's medium reinforced with pyruvate and 15% V/V maternal serum in our initial attempts to prepare stem cells.[50] They cleaved well, but four soon arrested. The other two embryos revealed good trophoblast activity as assessed by HCGβ assays at 120 and 170 hours after insemination. Denuded of their zona pellucida, they expanded and attached to plastic culture dishes at 189 and 216 hours after insemination, respectively. Their trophectoderm formed colonies extending over the plastic dish. Rounded and fibroblastic cells then migrated from the inner cell mass, associated with trophoblast outgrowths. Cells derived from one embryo regressed at 197 hours. The other displayed a period of healthy cell growth before regressing at 317 hours.

This encouraging beginning[50] was terminated soon after it began, as ethical problems emerged about the ownership of blastocysts. Parents' consent to use their blastocysts for such an unlikely purpose had become more constrained when many IVF babies were being conceived, and problems arose over identifying which embryos could establish pregnancies. Bourn Hall staff and the Ethical Committee jointly decided in 1984 to cryopreserve all embryos for 10 years for parents' later use. Embryos unwanted by their parents would then become available for research. Ten years later, I was no longer in Bourn Hall, the parents of many frozen embryos were no longer traceable, and the new Human Fertilization and Embryology Authority sanctioned the destruction of embryos whose parents could not be traced. Thousands of cryopreserved embryos were destroyed across the United Kingdom. Laboratory facilities were not available from 1989, and my human stem cell project folded.

Mouse Embryo Stem Cells: Colonisation of Deficient Organs

Even though human studies had been interrupted, research continued on animal embryo stem cells. All previous evidence indicated they would develop well in chimaeric animals. This was the basis of experiments testing their therapeutic potential in the 1980s, which proved decisive in fulfilling the widest scope of stem cell therapy. Earlier, fetal tissues had been used in grafting, especially haemopoietic cells,[51–53] and fetal liver cells from 13-day mouse foetuses injected via placental vessels repaired macrocytic anaemia in 11- to 12-day-old fetal recipients.[54] No one had contemplated therapeutic trials using cell extracts from preimplantation embryos. Testing the value of mouse embryo stem cells to restore haemopoietic functions in lethally X-irradiated adult recipients offered a challenging Ph.D. project. Peter Hollands accepted it.

STEM CELLS FROM CULTURED BLASTOCYSTS

Repairing Deficient Organs in Irradiated Recipients

Mouse blastocysts at day 3.5 post coitum flushed from uteri of C57Bl/10 mice were cultured by Hollands either as singletons or in groups.[55] The former died within 24 hours. Groups of 50 in 0.1 ml droplets of CMRL 1066 medium were supplemented with pyruvate, glutamine, and fetal calf serum or blood from human umbilical cords. Haemoglobin and glucose phosphate isomerase-deficiency (GPI) variants marked donor and recipient cells. Many blastocysts lost their morphology as they expanded and attached to plastic within 24 hours. Outgrowths of their cells formed cystic embryoid bodies and occasional blood islands, sometimes characterised by aggregates of pigmented cells.[55] Approximately 90% of surviving embryos were used to prepare stem cells for injection into recipients. Harvested after 3–4 days in culture (i.e., the equivalent of gestation days 6–7), each droplet of 50 embryos yielded an average of $1.1–2.6 \times 10^4$ cells for injection into tail veins of lethally irradiated or anaemic mice recipients. Subsequently, 90 •1 blood collected from recipient tail veins a few days after grafting and at weekly and longer intervals was assessed for markers of haemoglobin and GPI. Controls included cell lines from blastocysts cultured *in vitro* for <3 days[55] and standard ES cells as described by other investigators.[44]

Two-thirds of irradiated adult recipient 129-$W^v W^v$ and Balb/C mice given stem cell injections from outgrowths of C57Bl/10 blastocysts displayed both donor haemoglobin markers within 1–2 days and donor GPI within 3–4 days[55] (Tables 1–2 and 1–3). Hollands obtained similar results using varying numbers of donor cells between $4.8–10.6 \times 10^4$, where the embryos had been cultured for 3 or 4 days. Rates of colonisation were slightly lower than with preparations of cells from implanted embryos of equivalent postcoital age (see later sections of this chapter). Of the recipients, 90% with successful grafts survived; the rest died within several days, perhaps from irradiation-induced diarrhoea and not because of graft failure. Each recipient had received 10^4 haemopoietic cells, assuming their precursors formed 10% of injected cells. Cell cycles must have been very short in donor cells to accomplish such rapid proliferation.

Most recipients survived to old ages, their bone marrow populated with cells expressing donor erythropoietic and lymphopoietic markers. In contrast, levels of innate haemoglobin and GPI declined steadily in irradiated, nongrafted mice until they died within 12–14 days. Donor cells from blastocysts cultured for <3 days and from standard ES cell lines displayed no capacities for colonisation. Donor strain C57Bl/10 skin grafts were rejected 12–14 days after grafting into recipients expressing donor markers and into controls. Each of these studies on grafting illustrated the unique ability of stem cells from blastocysts briefly cultured *in vitro* to repair bone marrow and confer a full life span in irradiated recipients.[55]

Repairing Nonirradiated Anaemic Recipients

Hollands used similar experimental approaches to reveal how blastocyst stem cells could colonise nonirradiated recipients of strain 129-W^vW^v mice.[55] This strain is homozygous for an inherited macrocytic anaemia. Donor cells were injected into their tail veins 1–2 days after weaning when they were 21–22 days old, because 90% die naturally a day or so later. Grafted samples containing 4.9–10.5×10^4 cells colonised equally effectively. Donor haemoglobin appeared in 90% of recipients by 24–48 hours after injection and donor GPI appeared a day later (Table 1–2). Initially reaching 10% of recipients' haematopoietic output, they were almost totally colonised by day 16. Similar results with donor GPI revealed 90% of recipients with initial colonisation by days 3–4 and near-total colonisation by day 16. After slight variations in postgrafting, donor haemoglobin and GPI almost reached 100% of levels in recipients by 6 days after grafting.[55]

Macrocytosis disappeared as haemoglobin levels and erythrocyte counts returned to normal. Haematological assays revealed a reversal of anaemia. Leukocyte counts did not change after grafting. The remaining 10% of recipients died within 2–3 days, as in controls, without displaying donor markers. All mice given cultured blastocyst stem cells and displaying donor markers lived >600 days.[55]

Among other controls, cells from blastocysts <3 days old and ES or embryonal carcinoma cells prepared according to Solter and Damjanov,[56] Evans and Kaufman,[44] and Martin[57] failed to colonise recipients and died at similar times as irradiated controls. Marker genes were not identified in any of these recipients. Likewise, infusions of stem cells from day 5 embryos or from donor bone marrow also failed to colonise

W^vW^v mice. These data again showed how embryo stem cells seem to have properties of colonisation not shared by other stem cell forms. Even though colonisation was weak, Hollands had shown for the first time how embryo donor stem cells colonised intact histoincompatible recipients.[58,59]

STEM CELLS FROM NEWLY IMPLANTED EMBRYOS

Repairing Bone Marrow in Irradiated Adult Recipients

Comparative studies on colonisation of irradiated adult recipients, carried out using donor cells from recently implanted donor embryos, were also performed by Hollands.[55,60] This work was intended to test the properties of embryo stem cells developing *in vivo* at ages comparable to those prepared from blastocyst tissues grown in culture. It involved injecting stem cells from early postimplantation embryos into several donor strains, including CBA, MF1, and C57L. Donors also included CBA mice carrying the T6 chromosome marker (CBA-T6T6) to distinguish host and donor mitoses and gain direct measures of the degree of colonisation. Recipient adult Balb/C and strain-129 mice were exposed to lethal doses of X-irradiation before grafting. Blood samples for assays were collected at specific intervals soon after grafting, and haemoglobin and GPI variants marked haemopoietic and lymphoid cells, respectively, as described earlier. HLA types differed between some donor and some recipient strains.[55,60]

Haemopoietic stem cells were identified in mouse embryos at day 6, slightly earlier than expected.[55] Disaggregates of entire recently implanted embryos produced a mean of 4.5×10^4 cells, approximating 10^4 haematopoietic cells, for injection into recipients' tail veins (Tables 1–4A and 1–4B). Just as with blastocyst stem cells, the recipients' liver and bone marrow was colonised extremely rapidly (Tables 1–4A, 1–4B, and 1–5). Markers for donor haemoglobin emerged in recipients within 2–3 days, reaching 20% of the total within days. The donor cells secreted adult and not fetal haemoglobin. Donor GPI markers appeared in recipients from 3–4 days postgraft, reaching 20% of the total in 3–4 days.[60] Recipient markers faded within 30 days.

TABLE 1–4A

Survival of Irradiated 129 and Balb/C Mice Injected with Cells from Newly Implanted Embryos or Adult Bone Marrow from Various Mouse Strains[a,60]

Series	Strain combinations	Embryo Cells		Adult Bone Marrow	
		No recipients	No. surviving >350 days[b]	No. recipients	No. surviving >350 days
1–3	MF1 ≥ 129	40	32	30	2–3
4–7	C57Bl/10 ≥ Balb/c	80	62	40	7
8	CBA ≥ Balb/C	12	10	12	2
9–11	C57Bl/10 ≥ Balb/C	50	40	25	10
		172	136 (80%)	102	22 (21%)

[a]Of Balb/C recipients of embryo cells, 80% had donor Hb and GPI markers.
[b]Survivors in Series 1–3 lived 600± days, and Series 4–10 were alive and well at 450 days.

Four-fifths of recipients survived to old ages, all expressing donor markers. Successful grafting required at least 8×10^5 nucleated donor cells, equivalent to one embryo. Histocompatibility differences were breached without obvious effects.[60] Recipient tissues were not colonised using donor cells from embryos <6 days, standard donor bone marrow preparations, or decidual cells used as control for methods of isolating foetuses from the uterus. Controls died by 14 days after irradiation without expressing donor markers.

Rapid liver colonisation was confirmed using CBA-T6T6 donor cells injected into adult irradiated Balb/C mice. Marker mitoses revealed massive donor colonisation of recipients' liver within 24–48 hours—persisting until day 8 postgraft, when stem cells increasingly entered bone marrow (Table 1–5). By 64 days postgraft, up to 10% of all mitoses in spleen involved marked donor cells. It seemed either that donated cell preparations contained hepatic, splenetic, and haemopoietic precursor cells or that haemopoietic precursors migrated through recipients' liver to spleen and bone marrow to comprise 50–100% of mitoses.[59] If so, they migrated along fetal pathways.

Repairing Bone Marrow in Nonirradiated Adult Recipients

Applying models similar to those used with blastocyst stem cells, Hollands'[58] intact, nonirradiated recipients were grafted with 0.1–0.2 ml of donor cells from disaggregated day 7 mouse embryos. Recipients failing to engraft were reinjected. Some recipients also received donor skin grafts from donors 12–14 days after grafting.

Again, liver, spleen, and bone marrow in intact W^vW^v recipients were weakly colonised by donor T6T6 cells (Tables 1–6 and 1–7). Donor cells persisted >64 days in bone marrow[58] (Table 1–6). Overall, donor haemoglobin and GPI markers emerged weakly in 16–40 Balb/C recipients (40%) by 3–6 weeks after grafting, as recipient markers remained predominant.[58] Varying graft size did not overcome weaker colonisation as compared with irradiated recipients.[60] Three successive monthly regrafts to numerous recipients failing the original graft also failed. Recipients may have been sensitised by initial grafts, may have had differing types of sensitisation, or may have lacked organ space for donor cells. Some recipients rejected matching skin grafts, and grafting allogeneic bone

TABLE 1–4B
Donor Haemoglobin and GPI Expressed in Irradiated Recipient Strain-129 Mice Given Day 6–7 Embryo Cells from MFI Donors[a,60]

Erythrocytic (Marked by Haemoglobin)

Days postinjection	Colonisation of Recipients (%)			
	0	1–10	11–50	51–100
1	4	12	4	0
2	4	11	5	0
4	4	9	7	0
8	4	7	9	0
16	4	4	9	3
32	0	0	0	16
450	0	0	0	16

Lymphocytic (Marked by GPI)

Days postinjection	Colonisation of Recipients (%)			
	0	1–10	11–50	51–100
1	20			
2	20			
4	4	14	2	
8	4	12	4	
16	4	8	7	1
32				16
450				16

[a]Measured by densitometry.

TABLE 1–5
Chromosome Markers Identifying Colonisation of Liver and Bone Marrow by Donor Cells from Newly Implanted CBA-T6T6 Embryos Injected into Irradiated Balb/C Recipients[60]

	Colonisation of Recipients (%)							
	Liver				Bone Marrow			
Days Postinjection	0	1–10	11–50	51–100	0	1–10	11–50	51–100
1	16	4			20			
2	9	7	4		20			
4	2	4	14		14	6		
8	0	9	11		3	9	8	
16	20					4	12	4
32	20					2	14	4
64	20						3	17

TABLE 1–6
Donations to W^vW^v Recipients and Rates of Survival[58,59]

Data on Grafting W^vW^v Recipients				
No. recipients	No. nucleated cells ×10^6	Age of donor embryos (days)	Donor Hb/GPI	Survival (days)
15	1.6–6.0	6	+/+	>600
15	1.5–6.1	7	+/+	>600
10	0 (saline)		–/–	2–3
Minimal Number of Effective Cells				
No. recipients	No. injected cells ×10^6	Donor Hb/GPI	Survival (days)	
50	0.8–2.5	+/+	>150	
20	0.2–0.25	–/–	2–3	
20	0.8–0.9	+/+	>200	
15	0 (saline)	–/–	2–3	

marrow failed to colonise recipients.[58] This study again revealed the capacity of embryo stem cells to weakly graft intact incompatible recipients.

Similar studies with intact recipients carrying other forms of anaemia included 129-W^vW^v with macrocytic anaemia; W^{sh}, a less severe anaemia with normal life durations; $Sl^{/+}$ (Steel anaemia); Sl^p (Steel–Peru anaemia); and athymic *nude* mice.[58,59] Injections were given 1–2 days after weaning to W^v mice and 5–6 weeks or slightly later to W^{sh} and other recipients. Donors included MF1 outbred mice and strain C57Bl/10 inbred mice. Injections into strains carrying W^{sh}, $Sl^{/+}$, and Sl^p, which do not succumb to anaemia, colonised approximately 30% of recipients.

All this work on grafting embryo stem cells from disaggregated outgrowths of blastocysts or from newly implanted mouse foetuses revealed their properties to be similar. Clinical implications of these studies are apparent. Similar human grafts may be equally effective, overcoming tissue rejection in humans to establish lifelong grafts without inflammation or tumour formation. In a sense, the demonstrable colonising properties of these embryo stem cells seemed to resemble those of mouse stem cells injected singly into recipient blastocysts. Such evidence also implies that human cell outgrowths

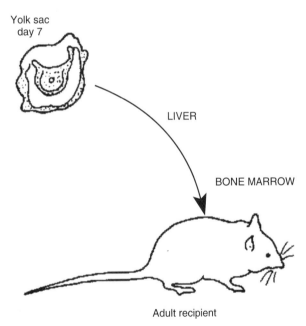

Yolk sac
day 7

LIVER

BONE MARROW

Adult recipient

Donation of yolk sac haemopoietic stem cells

Figure 1–4. A cartoon from the late 1980s on the migration of donor mouse or rat embryo stem cells extracted from a day 7 yolk sac. They are illustrated as derived from a single stem cell population that migrated through liver and into bone marrow in lethally irradiated adult mice and those with various forms of anaemia. An alternative explanation is that three types of embryo stem cell (e.g., haemopoietic, splenetic, and hepatic) were in the aggregates of newly implanted embryos. This cartoon was used in many conferences debating the ethics of human conception *in vitro* (Hollands, 1987).

TABLE 1–7
Migration of CBA-T6T6 Donor Stem Cells Through Liver to Bone Marrow in Recipient CBA Mice[58]

	Numbers of colonised recipients	
Days postgraft	Donor mitoses–liver[a]	Donor mitoses–bone marrow
1	3 (3)	
2	1 (3)	2
4	0 (3)	3
8	1 (1)	2 (2)
16		3 (3)
32		3 (3)
64		3 (3)

[a]Parentheses indicate the number of recipients.

from blastocysts may retain their multipotency during their period in culture. The clear results from these varied groups of donors and grafted recipients signified that the original work begun in Glasgow had achieved its primary target.

New Outlooks on Stem Cells and Their Value in Grafting

From their onset, this succession of stem cell studies challenged or extended concepts in medicine, cell, and tissue biology. Novel approaches to the study of differentiation emerged from initial studies on rabbit embryo stem cells in 1963. They were the first to demonstrate marked differences between the nature of differentiation among stem cell outgrowths from intact rabbit blastocysts and the nature of those from disaggregated inner cell masses. The former differentiated into numerous differentiated cell types, whereas the latter led to long-lived stem cell lines apparently in an early noncommitted stage of growth. This finding on rabbit embryo stem cells has been repeated over and over, including work on human blastocyst stem cells. Earlier assumptions of somatic cells being restricted to circa 50 generations were disproved by 1964,[61] when rabbit embryo stem cell lines grew *in vitro* for months or years. Introducing injection chimaeras in mice revealed how single cells isolated from the inner cell mass colonised all somatic and germinal tissues in recipient blastocysts–including germ line but not trophectoderm. Stem cells for trophectoderm but not germ line had presumably differentiated in blastocyst stem cells before their use for donation. Success obtained with injection chimaeras also opened pathways to knockout mice and gene insertion into stem cell lines using homologous recombination.[41]

Haemopoietic tissues including blood islands differentiate early in the growth of mouse and human foetuses. The initial stages of this process probably began while day 3.5 mouse blastocysts were being cultured intact 2–3 days. Blood islands among stem cells in blastocyst cell colonies, plus hints of other stem cells, in blastocyst preparations and tissues of early postimplantation foetuses implied that each of them contained committed haemopoietic tissue when grafted. This observation matches observations on culturing intact rabbit blastocysts, where blood islands were observed in outgrowths within a few days *in vitro*. They may have approximated the human equivalent of Carnegie stage 5 at 12 or more days of gestation. These haemopoietic stem cells may have colonised liver, spleen, and bone marrow in sequence, as they did in foetuses. Alternatively, some early stem cells may have been specific for haemopoietic, splenetic, and hepatic stem cells and rapidly colonised liver then spleen and bone marrow. Such stem cells seemed to be absent from freshly collected blastocysts in earlier stages of differentiation or to await a differentiation stimulus. Haemopoietic differentiation in cultured blastocysts apparently postdated or differed from that in ES and bone marrow cells, which failed to colonise bone marrow in recipients.[55,58,59] Stem cells in many tissues may share a common origin from the inner cell mass, and mesenchyme could be a close descendant retaining many of

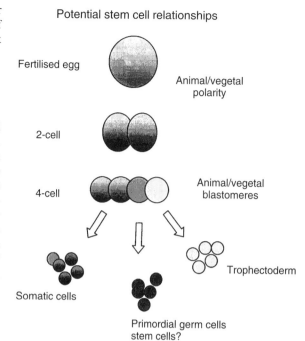

Potential stem cell relationships

Fertilised egg

Animal/vegetal polarity

2-cell

4-cell

Animal/vegetal blastomeres

Trophectoderm

Somatic cells

Primordial germ cells stem cells?

Figure 1–5. Where do different forms of stem cells come from? Notice the parallels with primordial germ cells, which may arise from one blastomere in 4-cell embryos.[86,87] Could a group of multipotent cells distribute to numerous tissues, including gonads? Stem cells derived from cultures of intact blastocysts or disaggregated inner cell mass might fail to produce trophectoderm because this tissue differentiated in cleavage stages.

its properties, including the establishment of wide organ chimaerism.

It is far from clear how stem cells in cultured blastocysts acquired their astonishing capacities for differentiation and colonisation. Initial steps of this process must represent a very early stage in stem cell development. Early commitment, short cell cycles, and high mitotic rates would explain their rapid entry into liver beginning within 24–48 hours and completed within a few weeks. Stem cells also displayed a lack of species specificity. Rat stem cells displayed competences and longevities equal to mouse donor cells when colonising target tissues in mice. The absence of either neoplasia or inflammation in recipient mice receiving mouse or rat stem cells implied that colonisation was cooperative and not aggressive. Their considerable powers of colonisation meant only a few embryo stem cells were needed for full colonisation, further evidence suggestive of short cell cycles. Other investigators drew similar conclusions at the time, using as few as 50 stem cells to colonise thymus glands in adults and haematopoietic systems in lethally X-irradiated recipient adult mice.[62–64] Finally, Hollands' work showing how embryo stem cells had an astonishing ability to cross histocompatibility barriers[58,59] was confirmed by Fandrich *et al.* in 2002.[65] Should human embryo stem cells share this property, there may be no need for cord blood from "designer babies" to provide tolerant bone marrow precursors for children inheriting Fanconi's anaemia and other conditions.[66]

Novelty in scientific and clinical studies with embryo stem cells was matched by new and perhaps inevitable ethical dilemmas over preparing and using embryo stem cells therapeutically. I first raised these issues 30 years ago[67] and mentioned them briefly in an address to the Vatican Academy of Science: "This fanciful use of ES cells for grafting into adults is perhaps the ultimate application of *in vitro* fertilization."[68] Numerous publications and endless lectures (e.g., see Edwards[67]) stressed how embryo stem cells had "a unique advantage, because graft rejection could be completely avoided...by experimental methods to tailor embryos to suit a particular recipient. Replica tissues without any histoincompatibility for a woman could be formed by inducing parthenogenesis in her oocytes... and androgenesis would offer similar benefits for men. Tissues compatible with an adult host might also be obtained through cloning."[67]

Summaries on ethical and technical aspects of fetal stem cell transplantation were covered in a book published in 1992.[69] Ethical chapters described procuring embryonic and fetal tissues and relationships among moral values related to embryonic and fetal tissue transplantation.[70,71] Technical chapters covered using fetal tissue to colonise several organ systems and the immense potential of embryo stem cells. At the time, the fetal liver seemed to offer a source of haemopoietic donor tissues without incurring rejection,[72] and grafts of fetal brain,[73] fetal pancreas,[74] cornea, and gonadal tissue were coming into vogue. The use of coelocentesis as an alternative and early form of grafting for donating tissue to first-trimester human foetuses was raised 3 years later.[75] Ethical dilemmas that arose in Bourn Hall have not been satisfactorily resolved. The U.S. president and government, and now the German and other governments,[76] opposed making stem cells from human blastocysts, preferring to buy them from private clinics or from abroad. This seriously flawed ethical standard was basically an attempt to shift ethical responsibility from those knowingly using human stem cells to those making them. Commissioning them is surely far less honourable than making them. In contrast, in the United Kingdom, open Parliamentary debate sanctioned "therapeutic" cloning of human embryos to prepare stem cells tolerant to recipients. Ironically, as this legislation was passed, its need was questioned when a long succession of studies on the ability of donor embryo stem cells to avoid graft rejection in fetal and adult recipients was confirmed.[58,65,72,77,78]

During the late 1980s and early 1990s, other investigators joined the search for animal and human embryo stem cells. Among them, Gearing *et al.*[79] identified the role of leukaemia inhibitory factor (LIF) in maintaining stem cell functions; this approach was applied by Williams *et al.*,[80] who used it to maintain stem cell properties in cultures of mouse embryos. Cytokines were found by several investigators to have major roles in initiating and stimulating the formation of haemopoietic cells, including interleukins and especially *IL-1, -3,* and *-6*[81]; stem cell factor[82]; and granulocyte–macrophage colony-stimulating factor.[83] Direct studies on human stem cells were renewed when Bongso *et al.*[84] isolated inner cell masses from hatched human blastocysts and showed how they attached to a monolayer of tubal epithelial cells *in vitro*. Two fibroblastic stem cell cultures and several resembling diploid–epithelioid stem cells positive for alkaline phosphatase were maintained by adding HLIF to cultures. This study extended the original human work of Fishel *et al.*[50] and offered a replica of the studies in rabbits 30 years previously.[21,22] Numerous follow-up studies can be found within the chapters of this book.

Summary

Introducing IVF, preimplantation genetic diagnosis, and embryo stem cell lines has offered an exhilarating series of scientific and clinical experiences. These three stunning approaches to averting or mending human disorders were invented through collaboration with many teachers, colleagues, and students. I am still thrilled when in today's world of molecular biology and reconstructive surgery, tissues are switched to desired pathways on three-dimensional biodegradable meshes coated with specific substrates. Meshes shaped like human organs such as ears or thumbs promise immense human benefits, even more so when allied with stem cells.

This paper has given a factual account of work on embryo stem cells since its inception in the early 1960s. It does not truly cover the sheer wonder and even astonishment of some of its findings. IVF and preimplantation genetic diagnosis have opened new aspects of the worldwide clinical scene. Stem cells are on the verge of clinical application. Their astonishing properties for proliferation, colonisation, and differentiation enabling them to colonise virtually all organs, whether placed in blastocoelic cavities or injected into tail veins, were clear to us by the late 1980s. Their enormous potential, with IVF and preimplantation genetic diagnosis (PGD), nearly led me to euphoria in the 1980s about incredible clinical prospects, appreciated at that time by few other investigators. It is a pleasure to observe the same delighted responses today as new investigators appreciate the astonishing properties of embryo and tissue stem cells.

REFERENCES

1. Pincus, G., and Saunders, B. (1939). The comparative behaviour of mammalian eggs *in vitro* and *in vivo*: VI. The maturation of human ovarian ova. *Anat. Rec.* **75,** 357.
2. Edwards, R.G. (2001). IVF and the history of stem cells. *Nature* **413,** 349–351.
3. Edwards, R.G. (2002). Personal pathways to embryonic stem cells. *Reprod. BioMed. Online* **4,** 263–278.
4. Heape, W. (1890). Preliminary note on the transplantation and growth of mammalian ova within a foster mother. *Proc. R. Soc. Lond. B.* **48,** 457–458.
5. Lewis, W.H., and Gregory, P.W. (1933). Cinematographs of living developing rabbit eggs. *Science* **69,** 226–229.
6. Lewis, W.H., and Wright, E.S. (1935). On the early development of the mouse egg. *Contrib. Embryol. Carnegie Institute Washington* **25,** 113–143.
7. Pincus, G., and Enzmann, E.V. (1935). The comparative behaviour of mammalian eggs *in vitro* and *in vivo*. *J. Exp. Med.* **62,** 665–675.

8. Nicholas, J.S., and Hall, B.V. (1940). Experiments on developing rats: II. The development of isolated blastomeres and fused eggs. *J. Exp. Zool.* **90**, 441–457.

9. Seidel, F. (1952). Die Entwicklungspotenzen einen isolierten Blastomere des Zweicellstadiums in Säugetiere. *Naturwissenschaften* **39**, 355–356.

10. Beatty, R.A., and Fischberg, M. (1951). Heteroploidy in mammals:1. Spontaneous heteroploidy in preimplantation mouse eggs. *J. Genet.* **50**, 345–359.

11. Edwards, R.G. (1957). The experimental induction of gynogenesis in the mouse: I. Irradiation of the sperm by X-rays. *Proc. R. Soc Lond. B.* **146**, 469–487.

12. Edwards, R.G., and Sirlin, J.L. (1956). Studies in gametogenesis, fertilization, and early development in the mouse using radioactive tracers. *Proc. 2nd World Cong. Fertil. Steril. Naples* (International Federation of Fertility Societies) 376–386.

13. Fowler, R.E., and Edwards, R.G. (1957). Induction of superovulation and pregnancy in mature mice by gonadotrophins. *J. Endocrin.* **15**, 374–384.

14. Edwards, R.G., and Gates, A.H. (1959). Timing of the stages of the maturation divisions, ovulation, fertilization, and the first cleavage of eggs of adult mice treated with gonadotrophins. *J. Endocrin.* **18**, 292–304.

15. Edwards, R.G. (1962). Meiosis in ovarian oocytes of adult mammals. *Nature* **196**, 446–450.

16. Edwards, R.G. (1965). Maturation *in vitro* of human ovarian oocytes. *Lancet* **2**, 926–929.

17. Tarkowski, A.K. (1959). Experimental studies on regulation in the development of isolated blastomeres of mouse eggs. *Acta. Theriol.* **3**, 191–267.

18. Tarkowski, A.K. (1961). Mouse chimaeras developed from fused eggs. *Nature* **190**, 857–860.

19. Mintz, B. (1964). Formation of genetically mosaic mouse embryos and early development of "lethal (t^{12}t^{12}) normal" mosaics. *J. Exp. Zool.* **157**, 273–285.

20. Edwards, R.G. (1964). Cleavage of one- and two-celled rabbit eggs *in vitro* after removal of the zona pellucida. *J. Reprod. Fertil.* **7**, 413–415.

21. Cole, R.J., Edwards, R.G., and Paul, J. (1965). Cytodifferentiation in cell colonies and cell strains derived from cleaving ova and blastocysts of the rabbit. *Exp. Cell Res.* **37**, 501–504.

22. Cole R.J., Edwards, R.G., and Paul, J. (1966). Cytodifferentiation and embryogenesis in cell colonies and tissue cultures derived from ova and blastocysts of the rabbit. *Dev. Biol.* **13**, 385–407.

23. Ehrmann, R.L., and Gey, G.O. (1956). The growth of cells on a transparent gel of reconstituted rat-tail collagen. *J. US Nat. Cancer Inst.* **26**, 1375–1403.

24. Tiedemann, H., and Tiedemann, H. (1959). Versuche zur Gewinnung eines mesodermalen Induktionstoffe aus Hühnerembryonen. *Hoppe-Seyler's Z. Physiol. Chem.* **314**, 156–176.

25. Edwards, R.G. (1980). "Conception in the Human Female," Academic Press, London.

26. Chen, L.T., and Hsu, Y.C. (1979). Hemopoiesis of the cultured whole mouse embryo. *Exp. Haematol.* **7**, 231–244.

27. Paul, J. (1975). (Personal communication).

28. Cole, R.J., and Paul, J. (1965). Properties of cultured preimplantation mouse and rabbit embryos, and cell strains derived from them. *In* "Preimplantation Stages of Pregnancy," (G. Wolstenholme *et al.,* Eds.), pp. 82–112. Ciba Foundation Symposium.

29. Delabarre, S., Claudon, C., and Laurent, F. (1997). Influence of several extracellular matrix compartments in primary cultures of bovine mammary epithelial cells. *Tissue Cell Res.* **29**, 99–106.

30. Edwards, R.G., and Gardner, R.L. (1967). Sexing of live rabbit blastocysts. *Nature* **214**, 576–577.

31. Gardner, R.L., and Edwards, R.G. (1968). Control of the sex ratio at full term in the rabbit. *Nature* **218**, 346–348.

32. Gardner, R.L. (1968). Mouse chimaeras obtained by the injection of cells into the blastocyst. *Nature* **220**, 596–597.

33. Gardner, R.L., and Johnson, M.H. (1973). Investigation of early mammalian development using interspecific chimaeras between rat and mouse. *Nature New Biol.* **246**, 86–89.

34. Pierce, G.B. (1967). Teratocarcinoma model for a developmental concept of cancer. *Curr. Top. Dev. Biol.* **2**, 223–246.

35. Stevens, L.C., and Little, C.C. (1954). Spontaneous testicular tumours in an inbred strain of mice. *Proc. Natl. Acad. Sci. USA* **40**, 1080–1087.

36. Brinster, R.L. (1973). The effect of cells transferred into the mouse blastocyst on subsequent development. *J. Exp. Med.* **140**, 1049–1056.

37. Surani, M.A.H., Barton, S.C., and Kaufman, M.H. (1977). Development to term of chimaeras between diploid parthenogenetic and fertilised embryos. *Nature* **270**, 601–603.

38. Gardner, R.L., and Papaioannou, V.E. (1975). Differentiation of the trophectoderm and inner cell mass. *In* "The Early Development of Mammals," (M. Balls, *et al.,* Eds.), pp. 107–132. Cambridge University Press, London.

39. Weissman, X., Papaioannou, V., and Gardner, R.L. (1978). Fetal haemopoietic origin of the haematolymphoid system. *In* "Differentiation of Normal and Neoplastic Haemopoietic Cells," (B. Clarkson *et al.,* Eds.), pp. 33–47. Coldspring Harbor, New York.

40. Smithies, O., Gregg, R.G., Boggs, S.S., *et al.* (1985). Insertion of DNA sequences into the human chromosomal beta-globulin locus by homologous recombination. *Nature* **317**, 230–234.

41. Capecchi, M.R. (1980). Altering the genome by homologous recombination. *Science* **244**, 1288.

42. Martin, G.R., and Evans, M.J. (1975). Differentiation of clonal lines of teratocarcinoma cells: formation of embryoid bodies. *Proc. Natl. Acad. Sci. USA* **72**, 1441–1445.

43. Sherman, M.I. (1975). The culture of cells derived from mouse blastocysts. *Cell* **5**, 343–349.

44. Evans, M.J., and Kaufman, M.H. (1981). Establishment in culture of mouse pluripotential cells from mouse embryos. *Nature* **292**, 154–156.

45. Doetschman, T.C., Eistetter, H., Katz, M., *et al.* (1985). The *in vitro* development of blastocyst-derived embryonic stem cell lines: formation of visceral yolk sac, blood islands, and myocardium. *J. Exp. Embryol. Morphol.* **87**, 27–45.

46. Edwards, R.G., Bavister, B.D., and Steptoe, P.C. (1969). Early stages of fertilization *in vitro* of human oocytes matured *in vitro*. *Nature* **221**, 632–635.

47. Steptoe, P.C., Edwards, R.G., and Purdy, J.M. (1971). Human blastocysts grown in culture. *Nature* **229**, 132–133.

48. Edwards, R.G., and Surani, M.A.H. (1978). The primate blastocyst and its environment. *Uppsala J. Med. Sci.* **22 (Suppl.),** 39–50.

49. Edwards, R.G. (1982). First stages of the development of the human ovum. *In* "Pfizer Colloquium, Maformations Congènitales des Mammifères," (H. Tuchmann-Duplessis, Ed.). Massson et Cie, Paris.

50. Fishel, S.B, Edwards, R.G., and Evans, C.J. (1984). Human chorionic gonadotrophin secreted by preimplantation embryos. *Science* **223**, 816–818.

51. Uphoff, D. (1958). Preclusion of secondary phase of irradiation syndrome by inoculation of foetal haemopoietic tissue following lethal total body X irradiation. *J. Natl. Cancer Inst.* **20**, 625–632.

52. Till, J.E., and McCulloch, E.A. (1961). A direct measurement of the radiation sensitivity of normal bone marrow cells. *Radiation Res.* **14,** 213–222.

53. Harrison, D.E., Astle, C.M., and Lerner, C. (1988). Number and continuous proliferation pattern of transplanted primitive haematopoietic stem cells. *Proc. Natl. Acad. Sci. USA* **85,** 222–226.

54. Fleischman, R.A., and Mintz, B. (1979). Prevention of genetic anaemias by microinjection of normal haemopoietic stem cells into the fetal placenta. *Proc. Natl. Acad. Sci. USA,* **76,** 5736–5740.

55. Hollands, P. (1988). Differentiation of embryo haemopoietic stem cells from mouse blastocysts grown *in vitro. Development* **102,** 135–141.

56. Solter, D., and Damjanov, I. (1979). Teratocarcinoma the expression of oncodevelopmental genes. *Methods in Cancer Res.* **18,** 277–332.

57. Martin, G.R. (1981). Isolation of a pluripotent cell line from early mouse embryos cultured in medium conditioned by teratocarcinoma stem cells. *Proc. Natl. Acad. Sci. USA,* **78,** 7634–7638.

58. Hollands, P. (1988). Transplantation of embryonic haemopoietic stem cells without prior X irradiation. *Brit. J. Haematol.* **69,** 437–440.

59. Hollands, P. (1988). Embryonic haemopoietic stem cell grafts in the treatment of murine genetic anaemia. *Brit. J. Haematol.* **70,** 157–163.

60. Hollands, P. (1987). Differentiation and grafting of haemopoietic cells from early postimplantation embryos. *Development* **99,** 69–76.

61. Hayflick, L., and Moorhead, P.S. (1961). The serial cultivation of human diploid cell strains. *Exp. Cell Res.* **25,** 581.

62. Williams, D.A., Lemischka, I.R., Nathan, D.G., and Mulligan, R.C. (1984). Introduction of new genetic material into pluripotent haematopoietic stem cells of the mouse. *Nature* **310,** 476–480.

63. Spangrude, G.J., Heimfeld, S., and Weissman I.L. (1988). Identification and characterisation of mouse haemopoietic stem cells. *Science* **241,** 58–62.

64. Jones, R.J., Caleno, P., Sharkis, S.J., and Sensenbrenener, L.L. (1989). The phases of engraftment established by serial bone marrow transplantation in mice. *Blood* **73,** 397–401.

65. Fandrich, F., Lin, G.X., Chai, M., *et al.* Preimplantation-stage stem cells induce long-term allogeneic graft acceptance. *Nat. Med.* **8,** 171–178.

66. Verlinsky, Y., Rechitsky, S., Schoolcraft, W., *et al.* (2000). Case report: simultaneous preimplantation genetic diagnosis for Fanconi anaemia and HLA typing for cord blood transplantation. *Reprod. BioMed. Online* **1,** 31.

67. Edwards, R.G. (1982). The case for studying human embryos and their constituent tissues *in vitro. In* "Human Conception *In Vitro,*" (R.G. Edwards *et al.,* Eds.), pp. 371–387. Academic Press, London.

68. Edwards, R.G. (1984). The ethical, scientific, and medical implications of human conception *in vitro. Pontifical Acad. Sci.* **51,** 193–249.

69. Edwards, R.G. (Ed.) (1992). "Fetal Tissue Transplants in Medicine," Cambridge University Press, Cambridge.

70. Poikinghorne, J.C. (1992). Law and ethics of transplanting fetal tissue. *In* "Fetal Tissue Transplants in Medicine," (R.G. Edwards, Ed.), pp. 331–334. Cambridge University Press, Cambridge.

71. Wong, L. (1992). The procurement of human fetal tissues for clinical transplantation: Practice and problems. *In* "Fetal Tissue Transplants in Medicine," (R.G. Edwards, Ed.), pp. 129–154. Cambridge University Press, Cambridge.

72. Touraine, J.L. (1992). Transplantation of fetal haemopoietic and lymphopoietic cells in humans, with special reference to *in utero* transplantation. *In* "Fetal Tissue Transplants in Medicine," (R.G. Edwards, Ed.), pp. 155–176. Cambridge University Press, Cambridge.

73. Sauer, H., Dunnett, S.B., and Brundin, P. (1992). The biology of fetal brain grafts: from mouse to man. *In* "Fetal Tissue Transplants in Medicine," (R.G. Edwards, Ed.), pp. 177–214. Cambridge University Press, Cambridge.

74. Tuch, B.E. (1992). Clinical results of transplanting fetal pancreas. *In* " Fetal Tissue Transplants in Medicine," (R.G. Edwards, Ed.), pp. 215–238. Cambridge University Press, Cambridge.

75. Edwards, R.G., Jauniaux, E., Binns, R.M., *et al.* (1995). Induced tolerance and chimaerism in human foetuses using coelocentesis: a medical opportunity to avert genetic disease? *Hum. Reprod. Update* **1,** 419–427.

76. Ludwig, M. (2002). Germany votes to import embryo stem cells. *Reprod. BioMed. Online* **4,** 311.

77. Touraine, J.L. (1983). Bone marrow and fetal liver transplantation in immunodeficiencies and inborn error of metabolism: lack of significant restriction of T-cell function in long-term chimaeras despite HLA-mismatch. *Immuno. Rev.* **71,** 103–121.

78. Hollands, P. (1991). Embryo stem cell grafting: the therapy of the future? *Hum. Reprod.* **6,** 79–84.

79. Gearing, D.P., Gouch, N.M., King, J.A., *et al.* (1987). Molecular cloning and expression of cDNA encoding a murine leukaemia inhibitory factor (LIF). *EMBO J.* **6,** 3995–4002.

80. Williams, R.L., Hilton, D.J., Pease, S., *et al.* (1988). Myeloid leukaemia inhibitory factor maintains the developmental potential of embryonic stem cells. *Nature* **336,** 684–692.

81. Ogawa, M. (1993). Differentiation and proliferation of haemopoietic stem cells. *Blood* **81,** 2844–2853.

82. Zsebo, K.M., Wppych, J., McNeice, I.K, *et al.* (1990). Identification, purification, and biological characterization of haemopoietic stem cell factor from buffalo rat liver-condition medium. *Cell* **63,** 196–201.

83. Haylock, D.N., To, L.B., Dowse, T.L., *et al.* (1992). *Ex vivo* expansion and maturation of peripheral CD34+ cells into the myeloid lineage. *Blood* **80,** 1405–1412.

84. Bongso, A., Fong, C.Y., Ng, S.C., and Ratnam, S. (1994). Isolation and culture of inner cell mass cells from human blastocysts. *Hum. Reprod.* **9,** 2110–2117.

85. Aldhous, P. (2001). Can they rebuild us? *Nature* **410,** 622–625.

86. Edwards, R.G., and Beard, H. (1997). Oocyte polarity and cell determination in early mammalian embryos. *Mol. Hum. Reprod.* **3,** 863–905.

87. Hansis, C., and Edwards, R.G. (2003). Cell differentiation in the preimplantation human embryo. *Reprod. BioMed. Online,* **6,** 215–220.

Pluripotential Stem Cells from Vertebrate Embryos: Present Perspective and Future Challenges

Richard L. Gardner

Introduction

Many have contributed to the various developments that brought recognition of the enormous potential of cells of early embryonic origin for genetic modification of organisms, regenerative medicine, and investigation of facets of development that are difficult to explore *in vivo*. However, historically, this field is firmly rooted in the pioneering work of Roy Stevens and Barry Pierce on mouse teratomas and teratocarcinomas, tumours that continued well after these workers had embarked on their studies to be regarded with disdain by many mainstream pathologists and oncologists (see Pierce[1]). Stevens developed and exploited mouse strains with high incidences of such tumours to determine their cellular origins.[2,3] Pierce focused his attention on the nature of the cell that endowed teratocarcinomas with the potential for indefinite growth, which the more common teratomas lacked. Conversion of solid teratocarcinomas to an ascites form proved to be a significant advance in enabling dramatic enrichment of the morphologically undifferentiated cells in such tumours, among which their stem cells were expected to be included.[4] Then, an impressive experiment by Pierce and a colleague[5] showed unequivocally that, on transplantation to histocompatible adult hosts, individual morphologically undifferentiated cells could form self-sustaining teratocarcinomas that contained as rich a variety of differentiated tissues as their parent tumour. Hence, the embryonal carcinoma (EC) cell, as the stem cell of teratocarcinomas has come to be known, was the first self-perpetuating pluripotential cell to be characterised. Although teratocarcinomas were obtained initially as a result of genetically determined aberrations in the differentiation of male or female germ cells, it was found later that they could also be established in certain genotypes of mice by grafting early embryos ectopically in adults.[6,7] Adaptation of culture conditions soon followed to enable EC cells to be perpetuated in an undifferentiated state or induced to differentiate *in vitro*. Although the range of differentiation detected in these circumstances was more limited than *in vivo*,

it could nevertheless be impressive (e.g., see Evans and Martin[8]). Research on murine EC cells, in turn, provided the impetus for obtaining and harnessing the human counterpart of these cells from testicular tumours for *in vitro* study.[9]

One outstanding question regarding the use of murine EC cells as a model system for studying aspects of development remained, namely, the basis of their malignancy. Was this a consequence of genetic change or simply because such "embryonic" cells failed to relate to the ectopic sites into which they were transplanted? The obvious way of addressing this was to ask how EC cells behave when placed in an embryonic rather than an adult environment. This was done independently in three laboratories by injecting the cells into blastocysts. The results from each laboratory led to the same rather striking conclusion: EC cells—which, if injected into an adult, would grow progressively and kill it—were able to participate in normal development following their introduction into the blastocyst.[10–12] Using genetic differences between donor and host as cell markers, EC cells were found to be able to contribute to most if not all organs and tissue of the resulting offspring. Most intriguingly, according to reports from one laboratory, this could very exceptionally include the germ line.[11,13] The potential significance of this finding was considerable in its implications for possible controlled genetic manipulation of the mammalian genome. It raised the prospect of being able to select for extremely rare events, thus bringing the scope for genetic manipulation in mammals closer to that in microorganisms.

There were problems, however. One was that the EC contribution in chimaeric offspring was typically both more modest and more patchy than that of cells transplanted directly between blastocysts. Also, the chimaeras frequently formed tumours; those that proved to be teratocarcinomas were often evident already at birth,[12] suggesting that growth regulation of at least some transplanted EC cells failed altogether. Other chimaeras developed more specific tumours such as rhabdomyosarcomas as they aged that were also clearly of donor origin,[14] thereby revealing that the transplanted EC cells had progressed further along various lineages before their differentiation went awry. In extreme cases, the transplanted EC cells disrupted development altogether, so that fetuses did not survive to birth (reviewed by Gardner[15] and by Papaioannou and Rossant[16]). Although the best

Handbook of Stem Cells
Volume 1
Copyright © 2004 by Academic Press
All rights of reproduction in any form reserved.

EC lines could contribute to all or most tissues of the body of chimaeras, they did so exceptionally. Finally, the frequency with which colonization of the germ line could be obtained with EC cells was too low to enable them to be harnessed for genetic modification. It seemed likely, therefore, that the protracted process of generating teratocarcinomas *in vivo* and then adapting them to culture militated against the retention of a normal genetic constitution by their stem cells. If this was indeed the case, the obvious way forward was to see if such stem cells could be obtained in a less circuitous manner. This prompted investigation of what happens when murine blastocysts are explanted directly on growth-inactivated feeder cells in an enriched culture medium. The result was the derivation of lines of cells indistinguishable from EC cells in both their morphology and the expression of various antigenic and other markers, as well as in the appearance of the colonies they formed during growth.[17,18] Moreover, like EC cells, these self-perpetuating blastocyst-derived stem cells could form aggressive teratocarcinomas in both syngeneic[17] and immunologically compromised nonsyngeneic adult hosts.[18,19] They differed from EC cells principally by giving much more frequent and widespread somatic chimaerism following reintroduction into the preimplantation conceptus and, if tended carefully, by also routinely colonising the germ line.[20] Moreover, when combined with host conceptuses whose development was compromised by tetraploidy, they could sometimes form offspring in which no host-derived cells were discernible.[21,22] Thus, these cells, which exhibited all the desirable characteristics of EC cells and few of their shortcomings, came to be called embryonic stem (ES) cells. Once it had been shown that ES cells could retain their ability to colonise the germ line after *in vitro* transfection and selection, their future was assured. Surprisingly, however, despite the wealth of studies demonstrating their capacity for differentiation *in vitro,* particularly in the mouse, it was a long time before the idea of harnessing ES cells for therapeutic purposes took root. Thus, although Edwards explicitly argued more than 20 years ago that human ES cells might be used thus,[23] it is only within the past few years that this notion has gained momentum, encouraged particularly by derivation of the first cell lines from human blastocysts.[24]

Terminology

There is some confusion in the literature about terminology in discussing the range of different types of cells that ES cells are able to form, an attribute that, in embryological parlance, is termed their potency. Some refer to these cells as being totipotent because, at least in the mouse, they have been shown to be able to generate all types of fetal cells and, under certain conditions, entire offspring.[21,22] This is inappropriate on two counts. First, totipotency is reserved by embryologists for cells that retain the capacity to form an entire conceptus and thus produce a new individual unaided. The only cells that have so far been shown to be able to do this are blastomeres from early cleavage stages. Second, murine ES cells seem unable to form all the different types of cell of which the

conceptus is composed. Following injection into blastocysts, they normally generate only cells types that are products of the epiblast lineage. Although they can also form derivatives of the primitive endoderm lineage[25]—which, for some obscure reason, they do much more readily *in vitro* than *in vivo*—they have never been shown to contribute to the trophectodermal lineage.[26] Hence, a widely adopted convention is to describe ES cells as pluripotent stem cells to distinguish them from stem cells like those of the haematopoietic system, which have a narrower but nevertheless impressive range of differentiative potential. Another source of confusion is the surprisingly common practice of referring to cells, particularly putative ES cells from mammals other than the mouse, as totipotent because their nuclei have been shown to be able to support development to term when used for reproductive cloning.

Another facet of terminology relates to the definition of an ES cell, which again is not employed in a consistent manner. One view, to which the author subscribes, is that use of this term should be restricted to pluripotent cells derived from pre- or peri-implantation conceptuses that can form functional gametes as well as the full range of somatic cells of offspring. Although there are considerable differences among strains of mice in the facility with which morphologically undifferentiated cell lines can be obtained from their early conceptuses, competence to colonise the germ line as well as somatic tissues seems nevertheless to be common to lines from all strains that have yielded them. This is true, for example, even for the nonobese diabetic (NOD) strain, whose lines have so far been found to grow too poorly to enable their genetic modification.[27,28]

ES-like Cells in Other Species

As shown in Table 2–1, cell lines that can be maintained for variable periods *in vitro* in a morphologically undifferentiated state have been obtained from morulae or blastocysts in a variety of species of mammals in addition to the mouse. They have also been obtained from the stage X blastoderm in the chick and from blastulae in three species of teleost fish. The criteria employed to support claims that such lines are counterparts of murine ES cells are quite varied and often far from unequivocal. They range from maintenance of an undifferentiated morphology during propagation or expression of at least some ES cell markers, through differentiation into a variety of cell types *in vitro,* to production of histologically diverse teratomas or chimaerism *in vivo.*

What such ES-like (ESL) cells lines have in common with murine ES cells, in addition to a morphologically undifferentiated appearance, is a high nuclear–cytoplasmic ratio. Among the complications in assessing cell lines in different species is the variability in the morphology of the growing colonies. Although colonies of ESL cells in the hamster and rabbit are very similar to colonies of murine ES cells, those of most other mammals are not. This is particularly true in the human, whose undifferentiated ESL cell colonies closely resemble those formed by human EC cells of testicular origin,[9] as do ESL cell colonies from other primates.[29,30] In the marmoset,

TABLE 2–1
Vertebrates from Which ES-like Cells Have Been Obtained

Species	Basis of Validation[a]	Reference
Rat	CP but mouse ES contamination	Iannaccone et al.[109]
	M&M	Ouhibi et al.[110]
	CP	Stranzinger[111]
	M&M	Brenin et al.[112]
	M&M	Vassilieva et al.[113]
Golden hamster	IVD	Doetschman et al.[114]
Rabbit	M&M, IVD	Graves and Moreadith[115]
	CP	Schoonjans et al.[116]
Mink	T (but limited range of cell types),	Sukoyan et al.[117]
	T (wide range of cell types)	Sukoyan et al.[118]
	IVD	Polejaeva et al.[119]
	M&M	Polejaeva et al.[120]
Pig	IVD	Evans et al.[121]
	M&M	Strojek et al.[42]
	CP	Wheeler et al.[35]
	CP	Chen et al.[36]
Sheep	M&M	Notarianni et al.[122]
	?[b]	Campbell et al.[31]
	?[b]	Wells et al.[32]
Cow	M&M	Saito et al.[123]
	IVD	Sims and First[124]
	IVD	Polejaeva et al.[119]
		Van Stekelenberg-Hamers et al.[125]
	?	Stranzinger[111]
	CP	Cibelli et al.[126]
	CP	Iwasaki et al.[78]
	IVD	Mitalpova et al.[73]
Horse	IVD	Saito et al.[127]
Marmoset	IVD	Thomson et al.[30]
Rhesus monkey	T	Thomson et al.[29]
Human	T	Thomson et al.[24]
Chicken	IVD (& CP including germ line but only with passage 1–3 cells)	Pain et al.[40]
Medaka	IVD	Wakamatsu et al.[128]
	CP	Hong et al.[43,44,92]
Zebra fish	IVD (limited) & CP (with short-term cultured cells)	Sun et al.[90]
Gilthead sea bream	IVD & (CP with short-term cultured cells)	Bejar et al.[45,89]

[a]M&M: morphology and ES cell markers, IVD: differentiation *in vitro*, T: teratoma production *in vivo*, CP: chimaera production by morula aggregation or blastocyst injection.
[b]Exhibited an ES-like morphology initially but rapidly acquired a more epithelial one thereafter.

rhesus monkey, and human, ESL cells not only form relatively flattened colonies but also exhibit several differences from mouse ES cells in the markers they express.[4] Because they closely resemble human EC cells in all these respects,[9] the differences seem to relate to species rather than to cell type.

In two studies in the sheep, colonies are reported to look like those formed by murine ES cells initially, but to adopt a more epithelial-like appearance rapidly thereafter.[31,32] This change in morphology bears an intriguing similarity to the transition in conditioned medium of murine ES cells to so-called epiblast-like cells,[33,34] which is accompanied by loss of their ability to colonise the blastocyst. Given that this transition is reversible, whether a comparable one is occurring spontaneously in sheep clearly warrants further investigation.

In no species has the production of chimaeras with ESL cells rivalled that obtained with murine ES cells. Where it has been attempted, both the rates and the levels of chimerism are typically much lower than found with murine ES cells. An apparent exception is one report for the pig, in which 72% of offspring were judged to be chimaeric.[35] However, this figure is presented in an overview of work that remains unpublished, and no details are provided regarding the number of times the donor cells were passaged before they were injected into blastocysts. In a subsequent study in this species using ESL cells that had been through 11 passages, one chimaera was recorded among 34 offspring.[36] However, as the authors of this latter study point out, rates of chimerism of only 10–12% have been obtained following direct transfer of inner cell mass cells to blastocysts in the pig (e.g., see Kasiwazaki et al.,[37] Anderson et al.,[38] and Onishi et al.[39]). Hence, technical limitations may have contributed to the low success with ESL cells in this species.

The only species listed in Table 2–1 in which colonisation of the germ line has been demonstrated is the chicken, but this was with cells that had been passaged only 1–3 times before being injected into host embryos.[40] Hence, they do not really qualify as stem cells that can be propagated indefinitely *in vitro*. Consequently, in conformity with the terminology discussed earlier, morphologically undifferentiated cell lines in all species listed in Table 2–1 should be assigned the status of ESL cells rather than ES cells.

Generally, the strategy for attempting to derive ES cell lines in other species has been initially to follow the conditions that proved successful in the mouse, namely the use of enriched medium in conjunction with growth-inactivated feeder cells and either leukaemia inhibitory factor (LIF) or a related cytokine. Various modifications introduced subsequently include same-species rather than murine feeder cells (e.g., see Amit et al.[41]) and, in several species including the human, dispensing with LIF. Optimal conditions for deriving cell lines may differ from those for maintaining them. Thus, in one study in the pig, the use of same-species feeder cells was found to be necessary to obtain cell lines, though murine STO cells were adequate for securing their propagation thereafter.[42] Feeder-free conditions were found to work best in both the medaka and the gilthead sea bream.[43–45] Moreover, the cloning efficiency of human ESL lines was improved in serum-free culture conditions.[46]

Unexpectedly, despite being closely related to the mouse, the rat has proved particularly refractory to derivation of ES cell lines (see Table 2–1). So far, the only cell lines that have proved to be sustainable long-term in this species seem to lack all properties of mouse ES cells, including differentiation potential, apart from colony morphology.[47] Indeed, except for the 129 strain of mouse, establishing cells lines that can be propagated *in vitro* in a morphologically undifferentiated state seems almost more difficult in rodents than in most of the other vertebrates in which it has been attempted.

Overall, one is struck by species variability in the growth factors, status of conceptus or embryo, and other requirements for obtaining pluripotential cell lines in species other than the mouse. So far, one can discern no clear recipe for success.

Of course, obtaining cells that retain the capacity to colonise the germ line following long-term culture is essential only for genetically modifying animals in a controlled manner. Having cells that fall short of this but are nevertheless able to differentiate into a range of distinct types of cells *in vitro* may suffice for many other purposes.

Embryonic Germ Cells

The preimplantation conceptus is not the only source of pluripotential stem cells in the mouse. Sustainable cultures of undifferentiated cells that strikingly resemble ES cells in their colony morphology have also been obtained from primordial germ cells and very early gonocytes in this species.[48,49] These cells, termed embryonic germ (EG) cells, have also been shown to be capable of yielding high rates of both somatic and germ line chimerism following injection into blastocysts.[49–51]

These findings have prompted those struggling to derive ES cell lines in other species to explore primordial germ cells as an alternative for achieving controlled genetic modification of the germ line. As shown in Table 2–2, EG-like (EGL) cells have been obtained in several mammals as well as the chick, but as with ESL cells, their ability to participate in chimaera formation has, with one exception,[52] only been demonstrated at low passage. Moreover, although donor cells have been detected in the gonad of a chimaera obtained from low-passage EGL cells in the pig (e.g., see Piedrahita et al.[53]), no case of germ line colonisation has been reported except with cells from chick genital ridges that were cultured for only 5 days.[54] Even here, the proportion of offspring of the donor type was very low.

It is, however, noteworthy that even in the mouse rates of malformation and perinatal mortality appear to be higher in

TABLE 2–2
Vertebrates from Which Embryonic Germ Cells
Have Been Obtained

Species	Basis of Validation[a]	Reference
Mouse	M&M	Resnick et al.[48]
	CP	Matsui et al.[49]
	CP (including germ line)	Laborski et al.[50]
	CP (including germ line)	Stewart et al.[51]
	IVD	Rohwedel et al.[129]
Pig	CP	Shim et al.[52]
	CP (with transfected cells)	Piedrahita et al.[53]
Cow	IVD (& short-term CP)	Cherny et al.[130]
Human	IVD	Shamblott et al.[131]
Chicken	CP (including germ line, but cells cultured for only five days)	Chang et al.[54]
	CP	Park and Han[132]

[a]Abbreviations as listed in the footnote to Table 2–1.

EG than in ES cell chimaeras.[49] This may relate to erasure of imprinting in the germ line, which seems to have begun by the time primordial germ cells have colonised the genital ridges[55] or, for certain genes, even earlier.[50,56] It is perhaps because of such concerns that the potential of EG cells for transgenesis in strains of mice that have failed to yield ES cells has not been explored. Interestingly, unlike in the mouse, EGL cell lines derived from genital ridges and the associated mesentery of 5- to 11-week human foetuses seem not to have embarked on erasure of imprinting.[56] Obviously, it is important to confirm that this is the case before contemplating the use of such cells as grafts for repairing tissue damage in humans.

Future Challenges

The value of ES and ESL cells as resources for both basic and applied research is now acknowledged almost universally. Present barriers to exploitation of their full potential in both areas are considered in the next sections of this chapter, together with possible ways of addressing these. Fundamental to progress is gaining a better understanding of both the nature and the basic biology of these cells.

BIOLOGY OF ES AND ESL CELLS

Germ Line Competence

Although murine ES cells have been used extensively for modifying the genome, there are still several problems that limit their usefulness in this respect. Among these is the loss of competence to colonise the germ line, a common and frustrating problem whose basis remains elusive. It is not attributable simply to the occurrence of sufficient chromosomal change to disrupt gametogenesis because it can occur in lines and clones found to be karyotypically normal.[57] At present, it is not known whether it is because of the failure of the cells to be included in the pool of primordial germ cells or their inability to undergo appropriate differentiation thereafter, possibly as a consequence of perturbation of the establishment of genomic imprinting or its erasure (e.g., see Surani[58]). Even within cloned ES lines, cells have been found to be heterogeneous in expression of imprinted genes.[59] Given that many ES cell lines are likely to have originated polyclonally from several epiblast founder cells, there is the further possibility that they might, *ab initio,* consist of a mixture of germ line-competent and -noncompetent subpopulations.[60] Recent studies on the involvement of bone morphogenetic protein signalling in the induction of primordial germ cells have been interpreted as evidence against a specific germ cell lineage in mammals.[61,62] Particular significance has been attached to experiments in which distal epiblast, which does not usually produce primordial germ cells, was found to do so when grafted to the proximal site whence these cells normally originate.[63,64] However, because of the extraordinary degree of cell mixing that occurs in the epiblast before gastrulation,[65] descendants of all epiblast founder cells are likely to be present throughout the tissue by the time of primordial germ cell induction. Hence the possibility remains that competence for

induction is lineage dependent, and thereby segregates to only some epiblast founder cells. Because ES cell lines are typically produced by pooling all colonies derived from a single blastocyst,[66] they might originate from of a mixture of germ line–competent and –noncompetent founder cells.

Male ES cell lines have almost invariably been used in gene-targeting studies, even though this complicates work on X-linked genes whose inactivation may lead to cell-autonomous early lethality or compromise viability in the hemizygous state.[67] Here, female (XX) lines would, in principle, offer a simpler alternative except that they are generally held to suffer partial deletion or complete loss of one X-chromosome after relatively few passages. However, the security of this conclusion is not clear because few references to their use have appeared in literature since the early reports, in which consistent loss of all or part of one X was first documented.[68,69] More recently, one of only two female lines tested was found to be germ line competent, but the entirely donor-derived litters were unusually small,[70] raising the possibility, not entertained by the authors, that the line in question was XO. Interestingly, female human ESL cell lines seem not to show a similar propensity for X-chromosome loss.[46]

Origin and Properties of ES and ESL Cells

It is evident from the earlier overview that there is considerable diversity even among eutherian mammals in the characteristics of cells from early conceptuses that can be perpetuated *in vitro* in a morphologically undifferentiated state. The reason for this is far from clear, particularly because most such cell lines have been derived at a corresponding stage—namely, the preimplantation blastocyst—often using inner cell mass tissue isolated therefrom. In the mouse, in contrast to their EC counterparts, ES cells have not been obtained from postimplantation stages, arguing that there is a rather narrow window during which their derivation is possible.[60] What this relates to in developmental terms remains obscure, although the finding that ES cells can shift reversibly to a condition that shows altered colony morphology and gene expression, together with loss of ability to generate chimaeras following blastocyst injection,[33,34] offers a possible approach for addressing this problem. Whether the late blastocyst stage sets the limit for obtaining ESL cell lines in other mammals has not yet been addressed critically.

Just as ES cell lines have been obtained from preblastocyst stages in the mouse,[71,72] ESL cell lines have been obtained from such stages in other mammals (e.g., see Mitalpova *et al.*[73]). However, neither in the mouse nor in other species have the properties of cell lines derived from morulae been compared with those from blastocysts to see if they show consistent differences. Indeed, it remains to be ascertained whether the lines from morulae originate at an earlier stage in development rather than progressing to blastocyst or, more specifically, epiblast formation before doing so. Although it has been claimed that lines isolated from morulae have an advantage over those from blastocysts in being able to produce trophoblast,[73] this has not actually been shown to be the case. However, species-, as opposed to stage-related differences in the ability of cell lines to produce trophoblast tissue have been encountered. Early claims that mouse ES cells can form trophoblastic giant cells are almost certainly attributable to the short-term persistence of contaminating polar trophectoderm tissue. Thus, the production of such cells seems to be limited to the early passage of ES lines derived from entire blastocysts.[25] It has never been observed with lines established from microsurgically isolated epiblasts.[26,60] Although the situation is not clear in many species, in primates, differentiation of trophoblast has been observed routinely in ESL cell lines established from immunosurgically isolated inner cell masses.[24,29,30] Moreover, differentiation of human cell lines to the stage of syncytiotrophoblast formation has been induced efficiently by exposing them to BMP4.[74]

Pluripotency

A seminal characteristic of ES or ESL cells is their pluripotency. The most critical test of this—not practicable in some species, particularly the human—is the ability to form the entire complement of cells of normal offspring. This assay, originally developed in the mouse, entails introducing clusters of ES cells into conceptuses whose development has been compromised by making them tetraploid, either by suppressing cytokinesis or by fusing sister blastomeres electrically at the two-cell stage. ES cells are then either aggregated with the tetraploid cleavage stages[22] or injected into tetraploid blastocysts.[75] Some resulting offspring contain no discernible host cells. It seems likely that host epiblast cells are present initially and play an essential role in "entraining" the donor ES cells before being outcompeted, because groups of ES cells on their own cannot substitute for the epiblast or inner cell mass.[76] Selection against tetraploid cells is already evident by the late blastocyst stage in chimaeras made between diploid and tetraploid morulae.[77] Aggregating ESL cells between pairs of tetraploid morulae has been tried in cattle, but resulted in their contributing only very modestly to fetuses and neonates.[78]

The second most critical test is whether the cells yield widespread if not ubiquitous chimaerism in offspring following introduction into the early conceptus, either by injection into blastocysts or by aggregation with morulae. The third is the formation teratomas in ectopic grafts to histocompatible or immunosuppressed adult hosts, since it is clear from earlier experience with murine and human EC cells that a wider range of differentiation can be obtained in these circumstances than in vitro. For such an assay to be incisive, it is necessary to use clonal cell lines and thus ensure that the diversity of differentiation obtained originates from one type of stem cell rather than from a medley of cells with more limited developmental potential. Although teratoma formation has been demonstrated with clonal ESL cells in the human,[46] this is not true for corresponding cell lines in other species. A note of caution regarding the use of teratomas for assessing pluripotency comes from the work of Choi et al.[79] These workers found that hepatocyte differentiation depended not only on the site of inoculation of mouse ES cells but also on the status of the host. Thus, positive results were obtained

with spleen rather than hind-limb grafts and only when using nude rather than syngeneic mice as hosts.

Conditions of Culture

ES and ESL cells are usually propagated in complex culture conditions that are poorly defined because they include both growth-inactivated feeder cells and serum. This complicates the task of determining the growth factor and other requirements necessary for their maintenance as well as for inducing them to form specific types of differentiated cells. Although differentiation of murine ES cells in a chemically defined medium has been achieved,[80] their maintenance under such conditions has not. Murine ES cells can be both derived and maintained independently of feeder cells, provided that a cytokine that signals via the gp 130 receptor is present in the medium.[81–88] However, whether the relatively high incidence of early aneuploidy recorded in the two studies in which LIF was used throughout in place of feeders is significant or coincidental is not clear.[83,84] It is important to resolve this so as to learn whether feeder cells serve any function other than acting as a source of LIF or a related cytokine. Production of extracellular matrix is one possibility. However, species variability is also a factor here since LIF is not required for maintaining human ESL lines, whose cloning efficiency is actually improved by omission of serum,[46] though feeder cells are required. The norm has been to use murine feeder cells both for obtaining and for perpetuating ESL cell lines in other mammals, including the human. Recently, however, there has been a move to use feeders of human origin for human ESL cells.[41] This is a notable development because it would not be acceptable to employ xenogeneic cells for growing human ESL cell lines destined for therapeutic rather than laboratory use. The situation is somewhat confusing in the case of the pig; in one study, but not in others, porcine feeders were found to be necessary for deriving ESL cell lines that could then be perpetuated on murine STO cells.[42] Moreover, among teleost fish, feeder-free conditions seem to be optimal for maintaining ESL cells in both the medaka and the sea bream[43–45,89] but possibly not in the zebra fish.[90]

Susceptibility versus Resistance to Derivation

An area whose further investigation could be informative in facilitating the establishment of pluripotent stem cell lines in other species is the basis of susceptibility versus resistance to ES cell derivation in the mouse. Thus, although ES cell lines can be obtained easily in 129 mice and relatively so in C57BL/6 and a few additional strains (Table 2–3), other genotypes have proved more resistant. Notable among the latter is the NOD strain from which, despite considerable effort, genetically manipulable lines have not yet been obtained. This is not simply related to the susceptibility of this strain to insulin-dependent diabetes, because the ICR strain from which NOD was developed has proved to be equally refractory. However, refractoriness seems to be a recessive trait because excellent lines with high competence to colonise the germ line have been obtained from [NOD×129]F1 epiblasts.[28] Moreover, this is not the only example in which

TABLE 2–3
Genotypes of ES Cells Other Than 129 for Which Germ Line Transmission Has Been Demonstrated

Genotype	Reference
C57BL/6	Ledermann et al.,[133] Kawase et al.,[134] Auerbach et al.[135]
C57BL/6N	Schoonjans et al.[136]
C57BL/6JOla	Schoonjans et al.[136]
[C57BL/6× CBA]F1	Tokunaga and Tsunoda,[137] Yagi et al.[138]
CBA/CaOla	Brook and Gardner,[60] Schoonjans et al.[136]
BALB/c	Noben-Trauth et al.,[139] Dinkel et al.,[140] Schoonjans et al.[136]
DBA/1lacJ	Roach et al.[141]
DBA/1Ola	Schoonjans et al.[136]
DBA/2N	Schoonjans et al.[136]
C3H/He	Kitani et al.[142]
C3H/Hen	Schoonjans et al.[136]
FVB/N	Schoonjans et al.[136]
CD1[a]	Suda et al.[143]
NOD	Nagafuchi et al.[27]
[NOD×129/Ola]F1	Brook et al.[28]
129×[129 × DDK]F1	Kress et al.[91]
PO[a]	Brook and Gardner[60]

[a]Outbred strains.

refractoriness has been overcome by intercrossing.[91] Interestingly, marked differences in the permissiveness for ESL cell derivation have also been found among inbred strains of the medaka.[92]

Human ESL Cell

Mouse EC and ES cells have been used extensively to study aspects of development that, for various reasons, are difficult to investigate in the intact conceptus. Exploiting corresponding cells for this purpose is even more pressing for gaining a better understanding of early development in our own species, given the relative scarcity of material, ethical concerns about experimenting on conceptuses, and statutory or technical limitations on the period for which they can be maintained *in vitro.* Obviously, in view of their provenance, human ESL cells are likely to provide a more apposite model system than human EC cells, which have mainly been used until recently. One concern here is that so-called spare conceptuses (i.e., those surplus to the needs of infertility treatment) are the sole source of material for producing human ESL cell lines. Because the conceptuses produced *in vitro* by IVF or related techniques that are judged to be of the highest quality are selected for treating infertility treatment, those used for deriving ESL lines tend to be of lower quality. Does this

matter so far as the properties of the resulting cell lines are concerned, particularly if their use therapeutically is contemplated? Is the ability to form a blastocyst that looks satisfactory morphologically adequate, or will it prove acceptable to produce conceptuses specifically for generating ESL cell lines, so that quality is less of a concern?

ES Cell Transgenesis

One important use of ES cell transgenesis is to obtain animal models of human genetic diseases. Because few would claim that the mouse is the ideal species for this purpose, the incentive for being able to undertake such studies in more appropriate or experimentally tractable mammals must remain a high priority. For example, given its widespread use for studying respiratory physiology, the sheep would be a more relevant species than the mouse as a model system for studying cystic fibrosis. However, unless pluripotential cells able to colonise the germ line can be obtained in other species, this approach to transgenesis will continue to be limited to the mouse. Although the feasibility of an alternative strategy— namely, genetically modifying and selecting cells that are not germ line competent, such as fetal fibroblasts, then exploiting transfer of their nuclei to oocytes—has been demonstrated, it is extremely demanding technically and entails considerable fetal attrition.[93]

STEM CELL THERAPY

Potential Hurdles

One major interest in ESL cells is the prospect of exploiting them therapeutically to repair damage to tissues or organs resulting from disease or injury. This poses a host of new challenges, not all of which have received the attention they deserve. Perhaps the most obvious one is whether it will be possible to obtain efficient directed differentiation of stem cells to yield pure cultures of the desired type of more differentiated cells as opposed to a mixed population. If the latter proves to be the case, the rigorous purging of cultures of residual undifferentiated or inappropriately differentiated cells will be necessary. How this is approached will depend on whether any contamination of grafts is acceptable and, if so, how much. One way in which this particular problem has been circumvented in murine model systems for *in vitro* differentiation of ES cells is to transfect them with the coding region of a gene for an antibiotic resistance or fluorescent protein coupled to a promoter that is expressed only in the desired type of differentiated cell.[94–97] Recent advances have made it possible to carry out similar genetic modification of human ESL cells.[98] Although effective selection of the desired type of differentiated cell may be achieved with this approach, it remains to be seen whether use of genetically modified cells will be acceptable in a clinical as opposed to a laboratory context.

Another important issue in contemplating stem cell therapy is the cycle status of the desired type of cell. In certain cases, including cells that are not postmitotic in grafts may be highly undesirable or even hazardous. In others, the presence of such cells may be essential to meet the demands of tissue growth or turnover. The latter would depend on obtaining the differentiation of ESL cells to stem cells rather than to fully differentiated cells of the desired type. Given the growing evidence that tissue stem cells require a specific niche for their maintenance (e.g., see Watt et al.[99]), this could prove difficult to achieve. Establishing and maintaining an appropriate niche *in vitro* to be able to enrich for tissue-specific stem cells is likely to pose a considerable challenge and will unquestionably depend on better knowledge of the normal biology of individual tissues.

Yet another important issue is whether engrafted cells will survive and function properly when placed in a damaged tissue or organ. When the donor cells are to provide a hormone, neural transmitter, or soluble growth factor, it may be possible to place them at some distance from the site of damage. However, when this is not practicable, there remains the question of whether transplanted cells will fare better than native ones in a tissue or organ seriously damaged by disease or injury. If they do not, how can one circumvent this difficulty, bearing in mind that achieving organogenesis *in vitro* is still a rather remote prospect? Regarding neurodegenerative disease, some progress has been made in "cleaning up" sites of tissue damage. For example, antibody-mediated clearance of plaques from the brain in transgenic mice overexpressing amyloid precursor protein has been demonstrated.[100,101] However, such intervention may not be necessary in all cases. Transplanting differentiated murine ES cells enriched for putative cardiomyocytes to a damaged region of the left ventricle in rats led concomitantly to a reduction in size of this region and an improvement in the performance of the heart.[102]

Therapeutic Cloning

Establishing ESL cell lines from blastocysts derived by nuclear replacement, so-called therapeutic cloning, has been widely advocated as a way of tailoring grafts to individual patients, thereby circumventing the problem of graft rejection. Although the feasibility of producing ES cells in this way has been demonstrated in the mouse, there is sharp division of opinion within the biomedical research community about whether such cells would be safe to use therapeutically (reviewed by Gardner[103]). Particular concern centres on the normality of the donor genome regarding the epigenetic status of imprinted genes. Moreover, recent observations on chromosome segregation during mitosis in early cloned primate embryos has raised doubts about whether cloning by nuclear replacement will work in the human.[104]

Embryonic versus Adult Stem Cells

Concern about the use of early human conceptuses as a source of stem cells focused much attention on recent studies that suggest so-called adult stem cells are more versatile in their range of differentiation than has generally been supposed. There is a continuing lively debate about the interpretation of many findings, which do not at present justify the common assertion that adult cells render the use of ESL cells for therapeutic purposes unnecessary. Of particular concern is a growing body of evidence that adult cells may be changing their differentiated state not as independent entities but through fusing with cells of the type to which they are claimed to have converted.[105–108]

There is a more general point that, with few exceptions—among which the haematopoietic system is the clearest example—evidence is lacking that cells from adult organs and tissue that can be propagated in culture actually functioned as stem cells *in situ*. Hence, the adoption of the term "stem cell" for cells from many adult sources is questionable. It is possible, if not likely, that cells that are strictly postmitotic in their normal environment can be induced to resume cycling when removed from it and placed in an enriched culture medium, which may contain growth factors to which they would not otherwise be exposed. Such cells might lack features of true stem cells, such as accurate proofing of DNA replication, conservation of turnover through transit amplification of differentiating progeny, and maintenance of telomere length. They might therefore be severely compromised in their ability to function in grafts.

Summary

Since the pioneering studies of Steven and Pierce pointed the way in the 1950s and 1960s, impressive progress has been made in harnessing stem cells of embryonic as opposed to fetal or adult origin for basic research and for exploring new approaches to regenerative medicine. There is, however, still a great deal to be learnt about the origin and properties of such cells, as well as the control of their self-renewal versus differentiation, if we are to take full advantage of what they have to offer. The effort of acquiring the necessary knowledge will undoubtedly provide us with the further reward of gaining deeper insight into the biology of stem cells in general.

REFERENCES

1. Pierce, G.B. (1975). Teratocarcinoma: Introduction and perspectives. *In* "Teratomas and Differentiation" (M.I. Sherman *et al.*, eds.), pp. 3–12. Academic Press, New York.
2. Stevens, L.C. (1967). Origin of testicular teratomas from primordial germ cells in mice. *J. Natl. Cancer Inst.* **38**, 549–552.
3. Stevens, L.C., and Varnum, D.S. (1974). The development of teratomas from parthenogenetically activated ovarian mouse eggs. *Dev. Biol.* **37**, 369–380.
4. Pierce, G.B., and Dixon, F.J. (1959). Testicular teratomas: II. Teratocarcinoma as an ascites tumour. *Cancer* **12**, 584–589.
5. Kleinsmith, L.J., and Pierce, G.B. (1964). Multipotentiality of single embryonal carcinoma cells. *Cancer Res.* **24**, 1544–1552.
6. Stevens, L.C. (1970). The development of transplantable teratocarcinomas from intratesticular grafts of pre- and postimplantation mouse embryos. *Dev. Biol.* **21**, 364–382.
7. Solter, D., Skreb, N., and Damjanov, I. (1970). Extrauterine growth of mouse egg cylinders results in malignant teratoma. *Nature* **227**, 503–504.

8. Evans, M.J., and Martin, G.R. (1975). The differentiation of clonal teratocarcinoma cell cultures *in vitro*. *In* "Teratomas and Differentiation" (M.I. Sherman *et al.*, eds.), pp. 237–250. Academic Press, New York.

9. Andrews, P.W., Przyborski, S.A., and Thomson, J.A. (2001). Embryonal carcinoma cells as embryonic stem cells. *In* "Stem Cell Biology" (D.R. Marshak *et al.*, eds.), pp. 231–265. Cold Spring Harbor Laboratory Press, New York.

10. Brinster, R.L. (1974) The effect of cells transferred into the mouse blastocyst on subsequent development. *J. Exp. Med.* **140**, 1049–1056.

11. Mintz, B., and Illmensee, K. (1975). Normal genetically mosaic mice produced from malignant teratocarcinoma cells. *Proc. Natl. Acad. Sci. USA* **72**, 3585–3589.

12. Papaioannou, V.E., McBurney, M.W., Gardner, R.L., and Evans, M.J. (1975). Fate of teratocarcinoma cells injected into early mouse embryos. *Nature* **258**, 70–73.

13. Stewart, T.A., and Mintz, B. (1981). Successive generations of mice produced from and established culture line of euploid teratocarcinoma cells. *Proc. Natl. Acad. Sci. USA* **78**, 6314–6318.

14. Papaioannou, V.E., Gardner, R.L., McBurney, M.W., Babinet, C., and Evans, M.J. (1978). Participation of cultured teratocarcinoma cells in mouse embryogenesis. *J. Embryol. Exp. Morph.* **44**, 93–104.

15. Gardner, R.L. (1983). Teratomas in perspective. *Cancer Surv.* **2**, 1–19.

16. Papaioannou, V.E., and Rossant, J. (1983). Effects of the embryonic environment on proliferation and differentiation of embryonal carcinoma cells. *Cancer Surv.* **2**, 165–183.

17. Evans, M.J., and Kaufman, M.H. (1981). Establishment in culture of pluripotential cell line from mouse embryos cells from mouse embryos. *Nature* **292**, 154–156.

18. Martin, G.R. (1981). Isolation of a pluripotential cell line from early mouse embryos cultured *in vitro* in medium conditioned by teratocarcinoma stem cells. *Proc. Natl. Acad. Sci. USA* **78**, 7634–7638.

19. Martin, G.R., and Lock, L.F. (1983). Pluripotent cell lines derived from early mouse embryos cultured in medium conditioned by teratocarcinoma stem cells. *In* "Teratocarcinoma Stem Cells" (L.M. Silver *et al.*, eds.) pp. 635–646. Cold Spring Harbor Laboratory Press, New York.

20. Bradley, A., Evans, M.J., Kaufman, M.H., and Robertson, E.J. (1984). Formation of germ line chimaeras from embryo-derived teratocarcinoma cells. *Nature* **309**, 255–256.

21. Nagy, A., Gozca, E., Diaz, E.M., Prideaux, V.R., Ivanyi, E., Markkula, M., and Rossant, J. (1990). Embryonic stem cells alone are able to support fetal development in the mouse. *Development* **110**, 815–821.

22. Nagy, A., Rossant, J., Abramow-Newerly, W., and Roder, J.C. (1993). Derivation of completely cell culture-derived mice from early passage embryonic stem cells. *Proc. Natl. Acad. Sci. USA* **90**, 8424–8428.

23. Edwards, R.G. (1982). The case for studying human embryos and their constituent tissues *in vitro*. *In* "Human Conception *In Vitro*" (R.G. Edwards *et al.*, eds.), pp. 371–388. Academic Press, London.

24. Thomson, J.A., Itskovitz-Eldor, J., Shapiro, S.S., Waknitz, M.A., Swiergiel, J.J., Marshall, V.S.J., and Jones, J.M. (1998). Embryonic stem cell lines derived from human blastocysts. *Science* **282**, 1145–1147.

25. Beddington, R.S.P., and Robertson, E.J. (1989). An assessment of the developmental potential of embryonic stem cells in the midgestation mouse embryo. *Development* **105**, 733–737.

26. Gardner, R.L., and Brook, F.A. (1997). Reflections on the biology of embryonic stem (ES) cells. *Int. J. Dev. Biol.* **41**, 235–243.

27. Nagafuchi, S., Katsuta, H., Kogawa, K., Akashi, T., Kondo, S., Sakai, Y., Tsukiyama, T., Kitamura, D., Niho, Y., and Watanabe, T. (1999). Establishment of an embryonic stem (ES) cell line derived from a nonobese diabetic (NOD) mouse: *In vivo* differentiation into lymphocytes and potential for germ line transmission. *FEBS Lett.* **455**, 101–104.

28. Brook, F.A., Evans, E.P., Lord, C.J., Lyons, P.A., Rainbow, D.B., Howlett, S.K., Wicker, L.S., Todd, J.A., and Gardner, R.L. (2003). The derivation of highly germ line-competent embryonic stem cells containing NOD-derived genome. *Diabetes* **52**, 205–208.

29. Thomson, J.A., Kalishman J., Golos, T.G., Durning, M., Harris, C.P., Becker, R.A., and Hearn, J.P. (1995). Isolation of a primate embryonic stem cell line. *Proc. Natl. Acad. Sci. USA* **92**, 7844–7848.

30. Thomson, J.A., Kalishman J., Golos, T.G., Durning, M., Harris, C.P., and Hearn, J.P. (1996). Pluripotent cell lines derived from common marmoset *(Callithrix jacchus)*. *Biol. Reprod.* **55**, 254–259.

31. Campbell, K.H.S., McWhir, J., Ritchie, W.A., and Wilmut, I. (1996). Sheep cloned by nuclear transfer from a cultured cell line. *Nature* **380**, 64–66.

32. Wells, D.N., Misica, P.M., Day, T.A.M., and Tervit, H.R. (1997). Production of cloned lambs from an established embryonic cell line: a comparison between *in vivo*- and *in vitro*-matured cytoplasts. *Biol. Reprod.* **57**, 385–393.

33. Rathjen, J., Lake, J.A., Bettess, M.D., Washington, J.M., Chapman, G., and Rathjen, P.D. (1999). Formation of a primitive ectoderm-like cell population, EPL cells, from ES cells in response to biologically derived factors. *J. Cell Sci.* **112**, 601–612.

34. Lake, J.A., Rathjen, J., Remiszewski, J., and Rathjen, P.D. (2000). Reversible programming of pluripotent cell differentiation. *J. Cell Sci.* **113**, 555–566.

35. Wheeler, M.B. (1994). Development and validation of swine embryonic stem cells: a review. *Reprod. Fertil. Dev.* **6**, 563–568.

36. Chen, L.R., Shiue, Y.L., Bertolini, L., Medrano, J.F., BonDurant, R.H., and Anderson, G.B. (1999). Establishment of pluripotent cell lines from porcine preimplantation embryos. *Theriogenology* **52**, 195–212.

37. Kasiwazaki, N., Nakao, H., Ohtani, S., and Nakatsuji, N. (1992). Production of chimerical piglets by the blastocyst injection method. *Vet. Rec.* **130**, 186–187.

38. Anderson, G.B., Choi, S.J., and BonDurant, R.H. (1994). Survival of porcine inner cell masses in culture and after injection into blastocysts. *Theriogenology* **42**, 204–212.

39. Onishi, A., Takeda, K., Komatsu, M., Akita, T., and Kojima, T. (1994). Production of chimerical pigs and the analysis of chimerism using mitochondrial deoxyribosenucleic acid as a cell marker. *Biol. Reprod.* **51**, 1069–1075.

40. Pain, B., Clark, M.E., Shen, M., Naakaazawa, H., Sakurai, M., Samaarut, J., and Etches, R.J. (1996). Long-term *in vitro* culture and characterisation of avian embryonic stem cells with multiple morphogenetic potentialities. *Development* **122**, 2339–2348.

41. Amit, M., Margulets, V., Segev, H., Shariki, K., Laevsky, I., Coleman, R., and Itskovitz-Eldor, J. (2003). Human feeder layers for human embryonic stem cells. *Biol. Reprod.* **68**, 2150–2156.

42. Strojeck, M., Reed, M.A., Hoover, J.L., and Wagner, T.E. (1990). A method for cultivating morphologically undifferentiated embryonic stem cells from porcine blastocysts. *Theriogenology* **33**, 901–913.

23

43. Hong, Y., Winkler, C., and Schartl, M. (1996). Pluripotency and differentiation of embryonic stem cell lines from the medaka fish (*Oryzias latipes*). *Mech. Dev.* **60**, 33–44.

44. Hong, Y., Winkler, C., and Schartl, M. (1998). Production of medaka fish chimaeras from a stable embryonic stem cell line. *Proc. Natl. Acad. Sci. USA* **95**, 3679–3684.

45. Bejar, J., Hong, Y., and Alvarez, M.C. (1999). Towards obtaining ES cells in the marine fish species *Sparus aurata*: multipassage maintenance, characterisation, and transfection. *Genet. Anal.* **15**, 125–129.

46. Amit, M., Carpenter, M.K., Inokuma, M.S., Chiu, C.P., Harris, C.P., Waknitz, M.A., Itskovitz-Eldor, J., and Thomson, J.A. (2000). Clonally derived human embryonic stem cell lines maintain pluripotency and proliferative potential for prolonged periods. *Dev. Biol.* **227**, 271–278.

47. Buehr, M., Nichols, J., Stenhouse, F., Mountford, P., Greenhalgh, C.J., Kantachuvesin, S., Brooker, G., Mullins, J., and Smith, A.G. (2003). Rapid loss of *Oct-4* and pluripotency in cultured rodent blastocysts and derivative cell lines. *Biol. Reprod.* **68**, 222–229.

48. Resnick, J.L., Bixler, L.S., Cheng, L., and Donovan, P.J. (1992). Long-term proliferation of mouse primordial germ cells in culture. *Nature* **359**, 550–551.

49. Matsui, Y., Zsebo, K., and Hogan, B.L. (1992). Derivation of pluripotential embryonic stem cells from murine primordial germ cells in culture. *Cell* **70**, 841–847.

50. Laborsky, P.A., Barlow, D.P., and Hogan B.L.M. (1994). Mouse embryonic germ (EG) cell lines: transmission through the germ line and differences in the methylation imprint of insulin-like growth factor 2 receptor *(Igf2r)* gene compared with embryonic stem (ES) cell lines. *Development* **120**, 3197–3204.

51. Stewart, C.L., Gadi, I., and Bhatt, H. (1994). Stem cells from primordial germ cells can reenter the germ line. *Dev. Biol.* **161**, 626–628.

52. Shim, H., Gutierrez-Adan, A., Chen, L.R., BonDurant, R.H., Behboodi, E., and Anderson, G.B. (1997). Isolation of pluripotent stem cells from cultured porcine primordial germ cells. *Biol. Reprod.* **57**, 1089–1095.

53. Piedrahita, J.A., Moore, K., Oetama, B., Lee, C.K., Scales, N., Ramsoondar, J., Bazar, F.W., and Ott, T. (1998). Generation of transgenic porcine chimeras using primordial germ cell-derived colonies. *Biol. Reprod.* **58**, 1321–1329.

54. Chang, I.K., Jeong, D.L., Hong, Y.H., Park, T.S., Moon, Y.K., Ohno, T., and Han, J.Y. (1997). Production of germ line chimerical chickens by transfer of cultured primordial germ cells. *Cell Biol. Int.* **21**, 495–499.

55. Lee, J., Inoue, K., Ono, R., Ogonuki, N., Kohda, T., Kaneko-Ishino, T., Ogura, A., and Ishino, F. (2002). Erasing genomic imprinting memory in mouse clone embryos produced from day 11.5 primordial germ cells. *Development* **129**, 1807–1817.

56. Onyango, P., Jiang, S., Uejima, H., Shamblott, M.J., Gearhart, J.D., Cui, H., and Feinberg, A.P. (2003). Monoallelic expression and methylation of imprinted genes in human and mouse embryonic germ cell lineages. *Proc. Natl. Acad. Sci. USA* **99**, 10,599–10,604.

57. Evans, E.P. (Personal communication).

58. Surani, M.A. (2001). Reprogramming of genome function through epigenetic inheritance. *Nature* **414**, 122–128.

59. Humpherys, D., Eggan, K., Akutsu, H., Hochedlinger, K., Rideout, W.M., 3rd, Biniszkiewicz, D., Yanagimachi, R., and Jaenisch, R. (2001). Epigenetic instability in ES cells and cloned mice. *Science* **293**, 95–97.

60. Brook, F.A., and Gardner, R.L. (1997). The origin and efficient derivation of embryonic stem cells in the mouse. *Proc. Natl. Acad. Sci. USA* **94**, 5709–5712.

61. Lawson, K.A., Dunn, N.R., Roelen, B.A., Zeinstra, L.M., Davis, A.M., Wright, C.V., Korving, J.P., and Hogan, B.L. (1999). Bmp4 is required for the generation of primordial germ cells in the mouse embryo. *Genes Dev.* **13**, 424–436.

62. Ying, Y., Liu, X.M., Marble, A., Lawson, K.A., and Zhao, G.Q. (2000). Requirement of Bmp8b for generation of primordial germ cells in the mouse. *Mol. Endocrinol.* **14**, 1053–1063.

63. Tam, P.P., and Zhou, S.X. (1996). The allocation of epiblast cells to ectodermal and germ line lineages is influenced by the position of the cells in the gastrulating mouse embryo. *Dev. Biol.* **178**, 124–132.

64. Tsang, T.E., Khoo, P.L., Jamieson, R.V., Zhou, S.X., Ang, S.L., Behringer, R., and Tam, P.P. (2001). The allocation and differentiation of mouse primordial germ cells. *Int. J. Dev. Biol.* **45**, 549–555.

65. Gardner, R.L., and Cockroft, D.L. (1998). Complete dissipation of coherent clonal growth occurs before gastrulation in mouse epiblast. *Development* **125**, 2397–2402.

66. Robertson, E.J. (1987). Embryo-derived stem cell lines. *In* "Teratocarcinomas and Embryonic Stem Cells: A Practical Approach" (E.J. Robertson, ed.), pp. 71–112. IRL Press, Oxford.

67. Shafi, R., Iyer, S.P., Ellies, L.G., O'Donnell, N., Marek, K.W., Chui, D., Hart, G.W., and Marth, J.D. (2000). The *O-GlcNAc* transferase gene resides on the X-chromosome and is essential for embryonic stem cell viability and mouse ontogeny. *Proc. Natl. Acad. Sci. USA* **97**, 5735–5739.

68. Robertson, E.J., Kaufman, M.H., Bradley, A., and Evans, M.J. (1983). Isolation, properties and karyotype analysis of pluripotential (EK) cell lines from normal and parthenogenetic embryos. *In* "Teratocarcinoma Stem Cells" (L.M. Silver *et al.*, eds.), pp. 647–663. Cold Spring Harbor Laboratory, New York.

69. Rastan, S., and Roberston, E.J. (1985). X-chromosome deletions in embryo-derived (EK) cell lines associated with lack of X-chromosome inactivation. *J. Embryol. Exp. Morph.* **90**, 379–388.

70. Voss, A.K., Thomas, T., and Gruss, P. (1997). Germ line chimeras from female ES cells. *Exp. Cell Res.* **230**, 45–49.

71. Eistetter, H.R. (1989). Pluripotent embryonal stem cell lines can be established from disaggregated mouse morulae. *Dev. Growth Diff.* **31**, 275–282.

72. Delhaise, F., Bralion, V., Schuurbiers, N., and Dessy, F. (1996). Establishment of an embryonic stem cell line from 8-cell mouse embryos. *Eur. J. Morphol.* **34**, 237–243.

73. Mitalpova, M., Beyhan, Z., and First, N.L. (2001). Pluripotency of bovine embryonic cell line derived from precompacting embryos. *Cloning* **3**, 59–67.

74. Xu, R.H., Chen, X., Li, R., Addicks, G.C., Glennon, C., Zwakaa, T.P., and Thomson, J.A. (2002). BMP4 initiates human embryonic stem cell differentiation to trophoblast. *Nat. Biotechnol.* **20**, 1261–1264.

75. Wang, Z.Q., Kiefer, F., Urbanek, P., and Wagner, E.F. (1997). Generation of completely embryonic stem cell-derived mutant mice using tetraploid blastocyst injection. *Mech. Dev.* **62**, 137–145.

76. Gardner, R.L. (Unpublished observations).

77. Everett, C.A., and West, J.D. (1998). Evidence for selection against tetraploid cells in tetraploid–diploid mouse chimaeras before the late blastocyst stage. *Genet. Res.* **72**, 225–228.

78. Iwasaki, S., Campbell, K.H., Galli, C., and Akiyama, K. (2000). Production of live calves from embryonic stem-like cells aggregated with tetraploid embryos. *Biol. Reprod.* **62**, 470–475.

24

79. Choi, D., Oh, H.J., Chang, U.J., Koo, S.K., Jiang, J.X., Hwang, S.Y., Lee, J.D., Yeoh, G.C., Shin, H.S., Lee, J.S., and Oh, B. (2002). *In vivo* differentiation of mouse embryonic stem cells into hepatocytes. *Cell Transplant.* **11**, 359–368.

80. Wiles, M.V., and Johansson, B.M. (1999). Embryonic stem cell development in a chemically defined medium. *Exp. Cell Res.* **247**, 241–248.

81. Smith, A.G., Heath, J.K., Donaldson, D.D., Wong, G.G., Moreau, J., Stahl, M., and Rogers, D. (1988). Inhibition of pluripotential embryonic stem cell differentiation by purified polypeptide. *Nature* **336**, 688–690.

82. Williams, R.L., Hilton, D.J., Pease, S., Willson, T.A., Stewart, C.L., Gearing, D.P., Wagner, E.F., Metcalf, D., Nicola, N.A., and Gough, N.M. (1988). Myeloid leukaemia inhibitory factor maintains the developmental potential of embryonic stem cells. *Nature* **336**, 684–687.

83. Nichols, J., Evans, E.P., and Smith, A.G. (1990). Establishment of germ line-competent embryonic stem (ES) cells using differentiation inhibiting activity. *Development* **110**, 1341–1348.

84. Pease, S., Braghetta, P., Gearing, D., Grail, D., and Williams, R.L. (1990). Isolation of embryonic stem (ES) cells in media supplemented with leukaemia inhibitory factor. *Dev. Biol.* **141**, 344–352.

85. Conover, J.C., Ip, N.Y., Poueymirou, W.T., Bates, B., Goldfarb, M.P., DeChiara, T.M., and Yancopoulos, G.D. (1993). Ciliary neurotrophic factor maintains the pluripotentiality of embryonic stem cells. *Development* **119**, 559–565.

86. Nichols, J., Chambers, I., and Smith, A. (1994). Derivation of germ line competent embryonic stem cells with a combination of interleukin 6 and soluble interleukin 6 receptor. *Exp. Cell Res.* **215**, 237–239.

87. Piquet-Pellorce, C., Grey, L., Mereau, A., and Heath, J.K. (1994). Are LIF and related cytokines functionally equivalent? *Exp. Cell Res.* **213**, 340–347.

88. Yoshida, K., Chambers, I., Nichols, J., Smith, A., Saito, M., Yasukawa, K., Shoyab, M., Taga, T., and Kishimoto, T. (1994). Maintenance of the pluripotent phenotype of embryonic stem cells through direct activation of gp 103 signalling pathways. *Mech. Dev.* **45**, 163–171.

89. Bejar, J., Hong, Y., and Alvarez, M.C. (2002). An ES-like cell line from the marine fish *Sparus aurata*: characterisation and chimaeras production. *Transgenic Res.* **11**, 279–289.

90. Sun, L., Bradford, C.S., Ghosh, C., Collodi, P., and Barnes, D.W. (1995). ES-like cell cultures derived from early zebra fish embryos. *Mol. Mar. Biol. Biotechnol.* **4**, 193–199.

91. Kress, C., Vandormael-Pournin, S., Baldacci, P., Cohen-Tannoudji, M., and Babinet, C. (1998). Nonpermissiveness for mouse embryonic stem (ES) cell derivation circumvented by a single backcross to 129/Sv strain: establishment of ES cell lines bearing the Omd conditional lethal mutation. *Mamm. Genome* **9**, 998–1001.

92. Hong, Y., Winkler, C., and Schartl, M. (1998b). Efficiency of cell culture derivation from blastula embryos and of chimera formation in the medaka *(Oryzias latipes)* depends on donor genotype and passage number. *Dev. Gene Evol.* **208**, 595–602.

93. McCreath, K.J., Howcroft, J., Campbell, K.H., Colman, A., Schnieke, A.E., and Kind, A.J. (2000). Production of gene-targeted sheep by nuclear transfer from cultures somatic cells. *Nature* **405**, 1004–1005.

94. Klug, M.G., Soonpa, M.H., Koh, G.Y., and Field, L.J. (1996). Genetically selected cardiomyocytes from differentiating embryonic stem cells form stable intracardiac grafts. *J. Clin. Invest.* **98**, 216–224.

95. Kolossov, E., Fleischmann, B.L., Lui, Q., Bloch, W., Viachenko-Karpinski, S., Manzke, O., Ji, G.J., Bohlen, H., Addicks, K., and Hescheler, J. (1998). Functional characteristics of ES cell-derived cardiac precursor cells identified by tissue-specific expression of the green fluorescent protein. *J. Cell Biol.* **143**, 2045–2056.

96. Li, M., Pevny, L., Lovell-Badge, R., and Smith, A. (1998). Generation of purified neural precursors from embryonic stem cell lines by selection. *Curr. Biol.* **8**, 971–974.

97. Soria, B., Roche, E., Berna, G., Leon-Quinto, T., Reig, J.A., and Martin, F. (2000). Insulin-secreting cells derived from embryonic stem cells normalise glycaemia in streptozotocin-induced diabetic mice. *Diabetes* **49**, 157–162.

98. Zwaka, T.P., and Thomson, J.A. (2003). Homologous recombination in human embryonic stem cells. *Nat. Biotechnol.* **21**, 319–321.

99. Watt, F.M., and Hogan, B.L.M. (2000). Out of Eden: stem cells and their niches. *Science* **287**, 1427–1430.

100. Bacskai, B.J., Kajdasz, S.T., Christie, R.H., Carter, C., Games, D., Seubert, P., Schenk, D., and Hyman, B.T. (2001). Imaging of amyloid-β deposits in brains of living mice permits direct observation of clearance of plaques with immunotherapy. *Nat. Med.* **7**, 369–372.

101. Bacskai, B.J., Kajdasz, S.T., Mclellan, M.E., Games, D., Seubert, P., Schenk, D., and Hyman, B.T. (2002). Non-Fc-mediated mechanisms are involved in clearance of amyloid-β *in vivo* by immunotherapy. *J. Neurosci.* **22**, 7873–7878.

102. Min, J.Y., Yang, Y., Converso, K.L., Lui, L., Huang, Q., Morgan, J.P., and Xiao, Y.F. (2002). Transplantation of embryonic stem cells improves cardiac function in postinfarcted rats. *J. App. Physiol.* **92**, 288–296.

103. Gardner, R.L. (2003). Therapeutic and reproductive cloning—a scientific prospective. Cardiff Centre for Ethics, Law, and Society. Available at http://www.ccels.cardiff.ac.uk/launch/gardnerpaper.html.

104. Simerly, C., Dominko, T., Navara, C., Payne, C., Capuano, S., Gosman, G., Chong, K.Y., Takahashi, D., Chace, C., Compton, D., Hewitson, L., and Schatten, G. (2003). Molecular correlates of primate nuclear transfer. *Science* **300**, 297.

105. Terida, N., Hamazaki, T., Oka, M., Hoki, M., Mastalerz, D.M., Nakano, Y., Meyer, E.M., Morel, L., Petersen, B.E., and Scott, E.M. (2002.) Bone marrow cells adopt the phenotype of other cells by spontaneous cell fusion. *Nature* **416**, 542–545.

106. Ying, Q.L., Nichols, J., Evans, E.P., and Smith, A.G. (2002). Changing potency by cell fusion. *Nature* **416**, 545–548.

107. Vassilopoulos, G., Wang, P.R., and Russell, D.W. (2003). Transplanted bone marrow regenerates liver by cell fusion. *Nature* **422**, 901–904.

108. Wang, X., Willenbring, H., Akkari, Y., Torimaru, Y., Foster, M., Al-Dhalamy, M., Legasse, E., Finegold, M., Olson, S., and Grompe, M. (2003). Cell fusion is the principal source of bone marrow-derived hepatocytes. *Nature* **422**, 897–901.

109. Iannaccone, P.M., Taborn, G.U., Garton, R.L., Caplice, M.D., and Brenin, R.D. (1994). Pluripotential embryonic stem cells from the rat are capable of producing chimaeras. *Dev. Biol.* **163**, 288–292.

110. Ouhibi, N., Sullivan, N.F., English, J., Colledge, W.H., Evans, M.J., and Clark, N.J. (1995). Initial culture behaviour of rat blastocysts on selected feeder cell lines. *Mol. Reprod. Dev.* **40**, 311–324.

111. Stranzinger, G.F. (1996). Embryonic stem cell-like cell lines of the species rat and bovinae. *Int. J. Exp. Path.* **77**, 263–267.

25

112. Brenin, D., Look, J., Bader, M., Hubner, N., Levan, G., and Iannaccone, P. (1997). Rat embryonic stem cells: a progress report. *Transplant. Proc.* **29**, 1761–1765.

113. Vassilieva, S., Guan, K., Pich, U., and Wobus, A.M. (2000). Establishment of SSEA-1- and *Oct-4*-expressing rat embryonic stem-like cell lines and effects of cytokines of the *IL-6* family on clonal growth. *Exp. Cell Res.* **258**, 361–373.

114. Doetschman, T., Williams, P., and Maeda, N. (1988). Establishment of hamster blastocyst-derived embryonic stem (ES) cells. *Dev. Biol.* **127**, 224–227.

115. Graves, K.H., and Moreadith, R.W. (1993). Derivation and characterization of putative pluripotential stem cells from preimplantation rabbit embryos. *Mol. Reprod. Dev.* **36**, 424–433.

116. Schoonjans, L., Albright, G.M., Li, J.L., Collen, D., and Moreadith, R.W. (1996). Pluripotential rabbit embryonic stem (ES) cells are capable of forming overt coat colour chimaeras following injection into blastocysts. *Mol. Reprod. Dev.* **45**, 439–443.

117. Sukoyan, M.A., Golubitsa, A.N., Zhelezova, A.I., Shilov, A.G., Vatolin, S.Y., Maximovsky, and Serov, O.L. (1992). Isolation and cultivation of blastocyst-derived stem cell lines from American mink. *Mol. Reprod. Dev.* **33**, 418–431.

118. Sukoyan, M.A., Vatolin, S.Y., Golubitsa, A.N., Zhelezova, A.I., Semenova, L.A., and Serov, O.L. (1993). Embryonic stem cells derived from morulae, inner cell mass and blastocysts of mink: comparison of their pluripotencies. *Mol. Reprod. Dev.* **36**, 148–158.

119. Polejaeva, I.A., White, K.L., Reed, W.A., and Ellis, L.C. (1995). Isolation and long-term culture of mink and bovine embryonic-like cells. *Theriogenology* **43**, 300.

120. Polejaeva, I.A., Reed, W.A., Bunch, T.D., Ellis, L.C., and White, K.L. (1997). Prolactin-induced termination of obligate diapause of mink (*Mustela vison*) blastocysts *in vitro* and subsequent establishment of embryonic stem-like cells. *J. Reprod. Fertil.* **109**, 229–236.

121. Evans, M.J., Notarianni, E., Laurie, S., and Moor, R.M. (1990). Derivation and preliminary characterization of pluripotent cell lines from porcine and bovine blastocysts. *Theriogenol.* **33**, 125–128.

122. Notarianni, E., Galli, C., Laurie, S., Moor, R.M., and Evans, M.J. (1991). Derivation of pluripotent, embryonic stem cell lines from the pig and sheep. *J. Reprod. Fertil.* **43** (Suppl.), 255–260.

123. Saito, S., Strelchenko, N., and Niemann, H. (1992). Bovine embryonic stem cell-like cell lines cultured over several passages. *Roux's Arch. Dev. Biol.* **201**, 134–141.

124. Sims, M., and First, N.L. (1993). Production of calves by transfer of nuclei from cultured inner cell mass cells. *Proc. Natl. Acad. Sci. USA* **90**, 6143–6147.

125. Van Stekelenburg-Hamers, A.E.P., Van Achterberg, T.A.E., Rebel, H.G., Flechon, J.E., Campbell, K.H.S., Weima, S.M., and Mummery, C.L. (1995). Isolation and characterization of permanent cell lines from inner cell mass cells of bovine blastocysts. *Mol. Reprod. Dev.* **40**, 444–454.

126. Cibelli, J.B., Stice, S.L., Golueke, P.J., Kaane, J.J., Jerry, J., Blackwell, C., Ponce de leon, F.A., and Robl, J.M. (1998). Transgenic bovine chimerical offspring from somatic cell-derived stem-like cells. *Nat. Biotech.* **16**, 642–646.

127. Saito, S., Ugai, H., Sawai, K., Yamamoto, Y., Minamihashi, A., Kurosaka, K., Kobayashi, Y., Murata, T., Obata, Y., and Yokoyama, K. (2002). Isolation of embryonic stem cell lines from equine blastocysts and their differentiation *in vitro*. *FEBS Lett.* **531**, 389–396.

128. Wakamatsu, Y., Ozato, K., and Sasado, T. (1994). Establishment of a pluripotent cell line derived from a medaka (*Oryzias Latipes*) blastula embryo. *Mol. Mar. Biol. Biotechnol.* **3**, 185–191.

129. Rohwedel, J., Sehlmeyer, U., Shan, J., Meister, A., and Wobus, A.M. (1996). Primordial germ cell-derived mouse embryonic germ (EG) cells *in vitro* resemble undifferentiated stem cells with respect to differentiation capacity and cell cycle distribution. *Cell Biol. Int.* **20**, 579–587.

130. Cherny, R.A., Stokes, T.M., Merei, J., Lom, L., Brandon, M.R., and Williams, R.L. (1994). Strategies for the isolation and characterization of bovine embryonic stem cells. *Reprod. Fertil. Dev.* **6**, 569–575.

131. Shamblott, M.J., Axelman, J., Wang, S., Bugg, E.M., Littlefield, J.W., Donovan, P.J., Blumenthal, P.D., Huggins, G.R., and Gearhart, J.D. (1998). Derivation of pluripotent stem cells from cultured human primordial germ cells. *Proc. Natl. Acad. Sci. USA* **95**, 13,726–13,731.

132. Park, T.S., and Han, J.Y. (2000). Derivation and characterization of pluripotent embryonic germ cells in chicken. *Mol. Reprod. Dev.* **56**, 475–482.

133. Ledermann, B., and Burki, K. (1991). Establishment of a germ line-competent C57BL-6 embryonic stem cell line. *Exp. Cell Res.* **197**, 254–258.

134. Kawase, E., Suemori, H., Takahashi, N., Okazaki, K., Hashimoto, K., and Nakatsuji, N. (1994). Strain differences in the establishment of mouse embryonic stem (ES) cell lines. *Int. J. Dev. Biol.* **38**, 365–390.

135. Auerbach, W., Dunmore, J.H., Fairchild-Huntress, V., Fang, Q., Auerbach, A.B., Huszar, D., and Joyner, A.L. (2000). Establishment and chimera analysis of 129/SvEV- and C57BL/6-derived mouse embryonic stem cell lines. *BioTechniques* **29**, 1024–1028.

136. Schoonjans, L., Kreemers, V., Danloy, S., Moreadith, R.W., Laroche, Y., and Collen, D. (2003). Improved generation of germ line-competent embryonic stem cell lines from inbred mouse strains. *Stem Cells* **21**, 90–97.

137. Tokunaga, T., and Tsunoda, Y. (1992). Efficacious production of viable germ line chimaeras between embryonic stem (ES) cells and eight-cell stage embryos. *Dev. Growth Differ.* **34**, 561–566.

138. Yagi, T., Tokunaga, T., Furuta Y., Nada, S., Yoshida, M., Tsukada, T., Saga, Y., Takeda, N., Ikawa, Y., and Aizawa, S. (1993). A novel ES cell line, TT2, with high germ line-differentiating potential. *Anal. Biochem.* **214**, 70–76.

139. Noben-Trauth, N., Kohler, G., Burki, K., and Ledermann, B. (1996). Efficient targeting of the *IL-4* gene in a BALB/c embryonic stem cell line. *Transgenic Res.* **5**, 487–491.

140. Dinkel, A., Aicher, W.K., Warnatz, K., Burki, K., Eibel, H., and Ledermann, B. (1999). Efficient generation of transgenic BALB/c mice using BALB/c embryonic stem cells. *J. Immunol. Methods* **223**, 255–260.

141. Roach, M.L., Stock, J.L., Byrum, R., Koller, B.H., and McNeish, J.D. (1995). A new embryonic stem cell line from DBA/1lacJ mice allows genetic modification of a murine model of human inflammation. *Exp. Cell Res.* **221**, 520–525.

142. Kitani, H., Takagi, N., Atsumi, T., Kawakura, K., Imamura, K., Goto, S., Kusakabe, M., and Fukuta, K. (1996). Isolation of a germ line-transmissible embryonic stem cell line from C3H/He mice. *Zoolog. Sci.* **13**, 865–871.

143. Suda, Y., Suzuki, M., Ikawa, Y., and Aizawa, S. (1987). Mouse embryonic stem cells exhibit indefinite proliferative potential. *J. Cell Physiol.* **133**, 197–201.

3

Molecular Facets of Pluripotency

Fatima Cavaleri and Hans Schöler

Introduction

Early mammalian embryogenesis is characterized by a gradual restriction in the developmental potential of the cells that constitute the embryo. The zygote and single blastomeres from a two- to four-cell embryo exhibit a totipotent phenotype. As the embryo continues to cleave, the blastomeres lose the potential to differentiate into all cell lineages of the embryo. The blastocyst is the first landmark of the embryo in which cell lineage restriction is apparent. At this stage, the outer cells of the embryo compact into the trophectoderm (TE) from which the placenta will derive. The inner cells, called the inner cell mass (ICM), will generate all cell lineages of the embryo proper, but they cannot contribute to the trophoblast and thus are widely considered to be pluripotent. Once isolated and cultured *in vitro* under permissive conditions, the ICM may be propagated as an embryonic stem (ES) cell line. These cells are the *in vitro* substitutes for embryos in the search for the genetic switches and molecular mechanisms required to ensure pluripotency. Mutations affecting the ability of ES cells to self-renew or differentiate and contribute to distinct cell lineages provide the necessary tools to unravel the molecular network underlying pluripotency.

In an attempt to define the molecular basis underlying pluripotency, we will focus our attention on four main areas:

1. Influence of extracellular factors on pluripotency and self-renewal (ligands, cytokines, and receptors)
2. Signaling pathways activated in pluripotent cells (Jak-STAT and ERK cascades)
3. Gene transcriptional programs operating in pluripotent cells (mainly Oct4 and its target genes)
4. Gene function during development of the early mammalian embryo

Cellular Models to Study Pluripotency

Three types of pluripotent cell lines are currently available as cellular models to unravel the mechanisms of pluripotency: embryonal carcinoma (EC), ES, and embryonic germ (EG) cells.

EC CELLS

EC cells historically are the first pluripotent stem cells derived from mouse embryonic or fetal tissues. EC cells are self-renewing, undifferentiated cells derived from teratocarcinomas—gonadal malignant tumors containing undifferentiated cells mixed with various differentiated tissues of the three primary germ layers. Teratocarcinomas, first observed as naturally developing tumors in certain strains of mice, were derived from preimplantation–pregastrulating embryos or primordial germ cells (PGCs) grafted ectopically *in vivo*.[1] EC cells can reform teratocarcinomas *in vivo* and differentiate *in vitro* when cultured in suspension. They provide a suitable model system to study cellular commitment and differentiation, but they have one major disadvantage: EC cells are tumor cells, and consequently, they are typically aneuploid. Although they could integrate into a developing embryo and contribute to adult tissues,[2,3] their contribution was extremely poor, lacking consistency and reproducibility. Most importantly, EC cell contribution to the germ line was shown to be a rare event.

ES CELLS

The derivation of EC cells set the stage for the derivation and handling of ES cells. In 1981, two groups[4,5] reported the establishment of pluripotent cell lines from blastocyst-stage mouse embryos. The capability of ES cells to form teratocarcinomas upon subcutaneous injection into syngeneic mice *in vivo* and to differentiate into tissues of all germ layers from embryoid bodies *in vitro* was considered proof of their pluripotentiality. Although prone to discard the Y-chromosome, ES cells are, in general, euploid and constitute an ideal, direct, *in vitro* link to and from the embryo. In 1984, Bradley showed that pluripotent ES cells could be used efficiently to alter the genome of the mouse.[6] A few years later, the foundation of modern mouse developmental genetics was established with the generation of genetically modified mice derived from ES cells manipulated by retroviral or homologous recombination methods.[7–10]

EG CELLS

In addition to EC and ES cells, a third type of pluripotent stem cell, the EG cell, has been isolated from the mouse. Migratory PGCs form colonies that are morphologically indistinguishable from ES cell colonies when grown on feeder cells in the presence of serum and a cocktail of growth factors, namely leukemia inhibitory factor (LIF), basic fibroblast growth factor (bFGF), and stem cell factor.[11] Like ES cells, EG cells show full developmental capacity, being able to differentiate into derivatives–lineages of all germ layers *in vitro,* form teratocarcinomas *in vivo,* and contribute to all tissues of chimeric mice, including the germ line, upon injection into host blastocysts.[12–14]

In summary, pluripotent, murine, embryo-derived ES and EG cells exhibit unique properties that make them an extremely powerful model for unveiling the molecular basis of pluripotency both *in vitro* and *in vivo:*

- Unlimited self-renewal: they can be grown in large numbers and passaged indefinitely *in vitro*
- Stable karyotype
- Refractoriness to senescence (i.e., they are virtually immortal)
- Highly efficient and reproducible differentiation potential: they can generate derivatives of all three embryonic germ layers both *in vitro* and *in vivo*
- Germ line colonization
- Clonogenicity: they grow as separate colonies that can be expanded as independent subclones following genetic manipulations;
- High versatility to genetic manipulation without loss of pluripotency, as introduction of foreign DNA does not affect their ability to fully integrate into the founder tissue of a host embryo or to colonize its germ line.

Stem Cell Environment: Cytokines and Pluripotency

STEM CELL NICHE

In many cases, the culture of stem cells has been compromised by the paucity of knowledge regarding their cellular environment or niche. Hematopoietic stem cells, for example, were identified more than 40 years ago,[15] but culture conditions remain to be established to ensure their maintenance *in vitro.* In addition, they might require complicated three-dimensional arrangements of specific stromal cells to proliferate.

ES CELL NICHE

In contrast, ES cells are easy to handle technically. The establishment of the first murine ES cell lines was achieved by culturing early embryos on a layer of mitotically inactivated mouse fibroblasts.[4] Without such a "feeder" layer, cultured embryonic cells would not remain pluripotent, suggesting that fibroblasts either promote self-renewal, suppress differentiation, or both.

LIF AND OTHER CYTOKINES

Fibroblasts maintain the pluripotency of ES cells by secreting a factor, identified as LIF[16,17] and also known as differentiation inhibiting activity.[18] LIF is a member of the interleukin-6 family of cytokines, including *IL-6,* oncostatin M (OSM), ciliary neurotrophic factor (CNTF) and cardiotrophin-1 (CT-1).[19] Members of the *IL-6* family of cytokines are structurally and functionally related. They act on a variety of cells (i.e., they are pleiotropic) and can mediate proliferation, differentiation, or both according to the target cell types.

For example, LIF, OSM, and *IL-6* can induce myeloma growth and inhibit macrophage differentiation of M1 cells.[19] The redundancy in biological function is mainly caused by the structural similarity of the receptor complex involved in signal transduction (see the next section).

REDUNDANT CYTOKINE FUNCTIONS AND DEVELOPMENT

The absence of a developmental phenotype in *IL-6-,* LIF-, and CNTF-null mice confirms that *IL-6*-related cytokines indeed have redundant functions.[20–22] However, LIF-mutant females are infertile, as the interaction between the embryo and the uterine wall (decidual reaction) strictly depends on a surge of estrogen on the fourth day of gestation, which coincides with a surge in LIF production by the uterus.[21] As a consequence, LIF$^{-/-}$ females fail to support embryo implantation. LIF$^{-/-}$ embryos can implant and develop to term in a normal uterus.

ES cell self-renewal dependence on the cytokine supply can be attributed to several factors: LIF may influence the rate of cell proliferation or cell cycle progression and act on the stem cell phenotype by activating a signaling cascade that operates on the up- or down-regulation of genes exclusively expressed in "pluripotent" or differentiated cells, respectively. Although it does not appear that LIF affects cell proliferation,[23] analysis of the ES cell expression profile does not favor either of the two previously mentioned explanations, because LIF withdrawal triggers the disappearance of pluripotent markers and the appearance of differentiated markers within 24 hours.[24–26] A complete and systematic analysis of the target genes lying downstream of the LIF-induced signaling pathways is necessary to clarify the cytokine *modus operandi* on the ES cell phenotype.

Cytokine-Receptor Binding on ES Cells: Multiple Relay Stations

STRUCTURE

The receptors involved in the *IL-6* cytokine family signaling cascade belong to the cytokine receptor class I family. The extracellular domain of all members of cytokine receptor class I family is composed of a variable number of fibronectin type III modules.[27] Two of the fibronectin modules are conserved among all members of the family and constitute the cytokine-binding module.[19] The amino (N)-terminal fibronectin module is characterized by four positionally conserved cysteine residues, whereas the carboxy (C)-terminal module is distinguished by a WSXWS motif.[28,29] The cytoplasmic domain of the receptor contains three conserved motifs, called Box 1, Box 2, and Box 3, found in a proximal to distal location from the cell membrane, and lacks intrinsic kinase activity. These three subdomains are responsible for transmitting the extracellular signal to the cytoplasm.

DIMERIZATION

Binding of the *IL-6* family of cytokines to their cognate receptors leads to homodimerization of gp130 or heterodimerization of gp30 with the cytokine cognate receptor. For example, the *IL-6/IL-6 receptor (IL-6R)* and the *IL-11/IL-11R* complexes induce gp130 homodimerization. Both LIF and CT-1 bind to LIFR and induce LIFR/gp130 heterodimerization. CNTF engages LIFR/gp130 as a signaling competent complex through an association with CNTF/CNTFR, whereas OSM engages the LIFR/gp130 or OSMR/gp130 by binding to the gp130 portion of the heterodimers (Fig. 3–1). Gp130 is the common component of the described receptor complexes critical for signal transduction, thereby explaining the observed redundancy in cytokine functions.

LIF AND LIFR

LIF and LIFR exhibit a reciprocal pattern of expression in the mouse blastocysts. The cytokine is expressed in the TE and the receptor is expressed in the ICM.[30] This pattern of distribution was suggestive of a paracrine interaction between the trophoblast and the ICM, whereby the production of LIF by the trophoblast could sustain the pluripotent ICM.

EXPRESSION OF CYTOKINE RECEPTORS AND LIGANDS

Although gp130 is widely expressed in various tissues, ligand-specific receptor components display a more restricted expression. LIFR, OSMR, and CNTFR are expressed in ES cells, and as a consequence, CT-1, OSM, CNTF, and LIF are interchangeable in preventing ES cell differentiation and supporting ES cell derivation and ES cell maintenance in culture.[31–34] *IL-6* and *IL-11* cannot substitute for CT-1, OSM, and CNTF, as the *IL-6* and *IL-11* receptors are not expressed in ES cells. However, *IL-6* can prevent ES differentiation if delivered with a soluble form of the *IL-6* receptor, which retains ligand-binding activity and the capability to induce gp130 homodimerization[34] (Fig. 3–1).

GENETIC STUDIES

LIFR-null embryos die shortly after birth and exhibit reduced bone mass and profound loss of motor neurons as compared to their wild-type counterparts.[35,36] Embryos homozygous for the gp130 mutation die between 12 and 18 days postcoitus (dpc) because of placental, myocardial, hematological, and neurological disorders.[37,38] CNTFR-deficient mice exhibit perinatal death and display profound motor neuron deficits.[39]

RECEPTOR GENE FUNCTION IN ES CELLS AND DIAPAUSE

The late embryonic lethality of gp130$^{-/-}$ fetuses is in disaccord with the gp130 requirement for ES cell self-renewal *in vitro*.[40] Delayed or quiescent blastocysts were used for the initial ES cell derivation experiments.[4] Lactating females can conceive while still nursing their pups, but they cannot support blastocyst implantation because they do not produce estrogen on the fourth day of gestation. As a consequence, embryonic development is arrested; it can resume under favorable conditions for optimal development. This phenomenon, called diapause, can be artificially induced by ovariectomy following fertilization. The embryos reach the blastocyst stage, hatch from the zona pellucida, and float in the uterus in a quiescent status for up to 4 weeks. In this scenario, the epiblast, which normally preserves its pluripotent status for about 3 days (from 3.5 dpc, when it forms, to 6.5 dpc, when gastrulation starts), can be maintained for longer periods and resumes development when an estrogen-rich environment is established.

The possibility that cytokine receptors may have an embryonic function in the quiescent embryo state was investigated.[41] LIFR$^{-/-}$ and gp130$^{-/-}$ delayed embryos are unable to resume embryogenesis after 12 and 6 days of diapause,

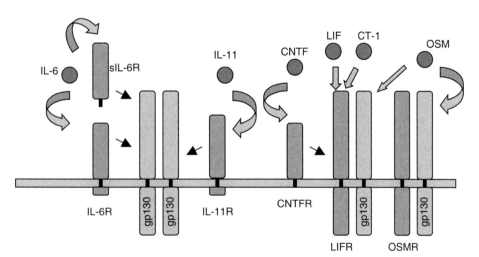

Figure 3–1. *Cytokine receptor complexes that have the common subunit Gp130. IL-6/IL-6R and IL-11/IL-11R complexes induce gp130 homodimerization. Both LIF and CT-1 bind to LIFR and induce LIFR/gp130 heterodimerization. CNTF engages LIFR/gp130 as a signaling competent complex through an association with CNTF/CNTFR, whereas OSM engages the LIFR/gp130 or OSMR/gp130 by binding to the gp130 portion of the heterodimers. SIL-6R stands for the soluble form of the receptor.*

respectively. The number of cells that constitute the ICM of delayed gp130$^{-/-}$ blastocysts is gradually reduced by apoptosis during the 6-day period of diapause. Moreover, ICMs isolated from delayed gp130-null blastocysts cannot form a pluripotent outgrowth *in vitro,* as they differentiate exclusively into parietal endoderm.

Thus, it appears that maintenance of the epiblast during diapause is temporally dependent on different cytokines and that gp130 plays a more critical role than LIFR in this process. Two models may explain why epiblast cells enter apoptosis in the absence of gp130 signaling:

1. Gp130 relays a cell survival signal from the extracellular compartment to the nucleus. This model is supported by the antiapoptotic activity of the transcription factor STAT3 in a variety of cells[42] (for a review, see Hirano *et al.*[43]).
2. Gp130 suppresses epiblast differentiation. In the absence of a gp130 signal, epiblast cells may differentiate inappropriately as shown by their endoderm formation and consequently die.

Signal Transduction: Cascades to the Stem Cell Nucleus

Homo- or heterodimerization of gp130 results in the activation of receptor-associated kinases of the Janus family, Jak1, Jak2, and Tyk2. These tyrosine kinases constitutively interact with the conserved regions Box 1and Box 2 of gp130.[44,45] The receptor complex is inactive until ligand-induced receptor dimerization brings the associated Jak kinases within sufficient proximity to allow transphosphorylation and activation of the kinase catalytic domain.[46–48] Activated Jaks phosphorylate specific tyrosines on the intracellular domain of gp130, creating docking sites for the recruitment of Src homology domain 2 (SH2) proteins to the activated receptor complex. When gp130 is phosphorylated, several signaling pathways are activated involving STAT1 and STAT3, the SH2-domain containing tyrosine phosphatase (SHP-2), extracellular signal receptor kinases (ERK1 and ERK2) or mitogen-activated kinases (MAPK), growth-factor receptor-bound protein 2 (Grb2), Grb2-associated binder protein 1 (Gab1), and phosphatidylinositol-3 kinase (for a review, see Heinrich *et al.*, Kolch, and Vanhaesebroeck *et al.*[49–51]).

STAT: Latent Transcription Factors Transmitting Signals

STAT FAMILY

STAT proteins belong to a group of latent cytoplasmic transcription factors that play a central role in transmitting signals from the membrane to the nucleus, hence their name (signal transducers and activators of transcription). Seven STAT proteins have been identified in the mouse (STAT1 to STAT6, including STAT5a and STAT5b). With the exception of STAT4, which is restricted to myeloid cells and testes,[52] STAT factors are expressed ubiquitously in the embryo. They are activated in many cell types by various cytokines,

growth factors, and interferons, and they are substrates for tyrosine kinases of the Src[53] and Jak families (for a review, see Hirano *et al.*[43]).

STRUCTURE

STAT proteins have several conserved structural and functional domains. A tetramerization and a leucine zipper-like domain are located at the N terminus, followed by a DNA binding domain, a Src homology domain 3-like region (SH3, proline-rich motif binding domain), an SH2, a critical site of tyrosine phosphorylation (Y705 in STAT3), and a C-terminal transactivation domain. No evidence has emerged to suggest an SH3 function.

The SH2 domain plays three important roles:

- Recruitment to activated receptor complexes
- Interaction with Jaks
- STAT dimerization and DNA binding

REGULATION

The regulation of STAT signaling occurs mostly at the post-translational level and involves both tyrosine and serine phosphorylation.

Phosphorylation of the conserved tyrosine (Y701 in STAT1 and Y705 in STAT3) results in the dimerization of STAT1/STAT3 through the intermolecular interaction of the SH2 domains and the domain containing the phosphorylated tyrosine. STAT1 and STAT3 homo- and heterodimers translocate to the nucleus, where they activate gene transcription by binding to specific DNA sequences (TT). Consistent with the requirement for dimerization-induced activation, the consensus binding sites are symmetrical dyad sequences. To achieve maximal transcriptional activity, the C-terminal transactivation domain of both STAT1 and STAT3 requires phosphorylation at Serine 727 by MAPK family members, suggesting a cross talk between MAPK and Jak/STAT pathways.[54,55]

STAT3

STAT3 was identified originally as an acute response factor that, upon *IL-6*-family cytokine stimulation, induces the expression of a variety of genes, referred to as acute response genes, whose expression dramatically increases with tissue injury and inflammation.[52]

Targeted disruption of the *STAT3* gene *in vivo* leads to embryonic lethality.[56] *STAT3*-null embryos develop into elongated egg cylinders, but they degenerate around embryonic day (E) 7.0. At this stage, wild-type embryos start to express *STAT3* in the visceral endoderm. Embryonic lethality is then explained as a consequence of the failure to establish metabolic exchanges between the embryo and the maternal blood. *STAT3* thus plays a unique, crucial role during embryonic development that cannot be compensated for by other members of the *STAT* family.

LIF AND STAT3

The initial studies conducted on LIF-dependent transcriptional activation in ES cells showed the induction of a DNA-binding activity that correlated with LIF treatment.[57,58] Steady-state levels of STAT1, -3, -5, and -6 were unaffected by LIF treatment. In contrast, coimmunoprecipitation experiments indicated that STAT3 was a component of the tyrosine-phosphorylated complex that formed upon LIF induction. In addition, tyrosine kinase inhibitors were shown to impair the formation of the activated STAT3 complex and to change the morphology of undifferentiated ES cells to a differentiated phenotype.[58]

ES CELL SELF-RENEWAL AND THE UNDIFFERENTIATED STATE

Identification of STAT3 as a key determinant of ES cell self-renewal came from the elegant studies conducted in Smith's lab[40] and Yokota's lab.[59] Granulocyte colony-stimulating factor receptor (G-CSFR) belongs to the class I family of cytokine receptors and is not expressed in ES cells. To characterize the functional role of the receptor intracellular domains or amino acid residues involved in signal transduction, chimeric receptors constituted of the extracellular domain of G-CSFR fused to the transmembrane and cytoplasmic region of gp130 or LIFR were engineered.[40] G-CSFR/gp130 and G-CSFR can support ES cell self-renewal at higher and lower efficiency, respectively, whereas the G-CSFR/LIFR chimera cannot support the formation of stem cell colonies. This result suggests that gp130 is an essential component in signaling self-renewal in ES cells and that G-CSFR and gp130 intracellular domains activate common signaling pathways.

The intracellular domain of gp130 harbors four consensus YXXQ motifs whose phosphorylated tyrosines were shown to function as docking sites for STAT3.[60] Single or double mutation of these tyrosine residues (Y126, 173, 265, and 275, enumeration starting from the transmembrane domain) did not affect self-renewal appreciably (Fig. 3–2). Rather, mutations of Y265/275 abolished STAT3-induced binding activity and formation of undifferentiated colonies. These data demonstrate that STAT3 docking sites are essential in mediating transmission of the signal from gp130 to STAT3 in self-renewing ES cells, although the tyrosine residues are not functionally equivalent. Moreover, conditional expression of STAT3F, containing a phenylalanine substituting for Tyrosine 705, caused complete differentiation of ES cells even in the presence of LIF.

In the paper by Matsuda et al., STAT3 activation was shown to be sufficient to maintain the undifferentiated status of mouse embryonic cells.[59] To uncouple STAT activation from any signaling pathway induced at a membrane receptor by extracellular factors, the authors constructed a fusion protein composed of the entire STAT3 coding region and the ligand-binding domain of the estrogen receptor. The STAT3ER chimeric protein was specifically phosphorylated at Tyrosine 705 in the presence of the synthetic steroid ligand, 4-hydroxytamoxifen (4HT). Parental ES cells and ES cells expressing STAT3ER were grown in the presence of LIF or 4HT. The compact colonies formed by STAT3ER ES cells in the presence of either LIF or 4HT clearly demonstrated that STAT3 activation is sufficient to maintain the undifferentiated phenotype of ES cells. Most importantly, besides being morphologically undifferentiated, cells grown for 1 month in 4HT widely contributed to all tissues of chimeric mice.

STAT3-INDEPENDENT ES CELL SELF-RENEWAL

The striking paradox created by STAT3- or gp130-null phenotypes and the strict dependence on gp130–STAT3 signaling pathways for the maintenance of pluripotent ES cells is suggestive of the existence of alternative pathways governing pluripotency in vivo. Dani et al. presented evidence of STAT3-independent signaling pathways operating in self-renewing ES cells.[61] When ES cells are grown at high density in the absence of LIF, the newly differentiated cells start synthesizing LIF, which, in turn, allows the expansion of undifferentiated cells.[62] To eliminate the LIF-dependent pathways of self-renewal, a LIF-deficient ES cell line was generated. Strikingly, LIF$^{-/-}$ cells can still produce undifferentiated colonies, though at a lower efficiency than wt or heterozygous lines when induced to differentiate. ES cell renewal factor (ESRF) can support the pluripotential character of ES cells upon blastocyst injection. Interestingly, ESRF operate using neither LIFR nor gp130 because it is effective on LIFR-deficient ES cells and is not blocked by anti-gp130 antibodies. STAT3 is not induced in the presence of ESRF.

SHP-2–ERK Signaling

STAT1 and STAT3 are only two of the downstream effector molecules induced by cytokine signaling via gp130. LIF treatment of ES cells increases MAPK activity[58] and induces phosphorylation of ERK1 and ERK2[63] (for a review on the MAPK pathway, see Kolch[50]). The bridging factor between the cytokine receptor and MAPK is the widely expressed tyrosine phosphatase SHP-2.

SHP-2 STRUCTURE

SHP-2 contains two amino-terminal SH2 domains and a C-terminal catalytic domain. SHP-2 interacts with the intracellular domain of gp130 through phosphorylated Tyrosine 118, located inside the consensus YSTV sequence.[42] Recruitment to the activated receptor induces SHP-2 phosphorylation, which leads to an increase in phosphatase activity by preventing an intramolecular interaction between the SH2 and the catalytic domain of SHP-2.[64] In BAF-B03 cells, the mutation of gp130 Tyrosine 118 into phenylalanine was shown to block SHP-2 phosphorylation and induction of ERK2 activation.[42]

SHP-2–ERK SIGNALING AND ES CELLS

G-CSFR-responsive ES cells provided an excellent tool for establishing the role of SHP-2–ERK signaling in ES cell propagation.[40] A mutant G-CSFR–gp130 chimeric receptor that cannot be phosphorylated on Y118 (and that, consequently, cannot induce SHP-2 phosphorylation) does not impair the self-renewal of ES cells (Fig. 3–2). In contrast, the mutated chimera renders ES cells more sensitive to G-CSF, as they can be maintained at a lower G-CSF concentration (1000-fold less) than that required by ES cells expressing the unmodified receptor. Moreover, the signal started at the phosphorylated Y118 mediates attenuation of activated STAT3, as shown by slower turnover of phosphorylated STAT3.

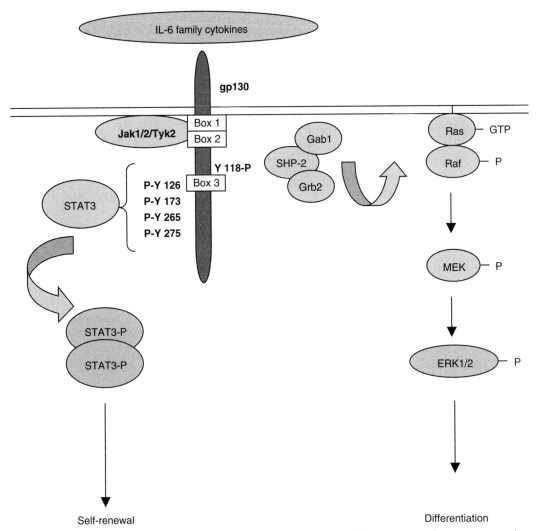

Figure 3–2. *Signaling pathways induced by the IL-6 cytokine family.* Following gp130 hetero- or homodimerization, activated Jaks phosphorylate the intracellular domain of gp130 on Y 126, 173, 265, 275, and 118 (P denotes phosphorylated status). STAT3 association with phosphorylated Y126–275 leads to STAT3 phosphorylation, dimerization, and translocation to the stem cell nucleus. Association of SHP-2 with phosphorylated Y118 leads, through adaptor proteins, to activation of the Ras pathway and translocation of ERK1/2 to nucleus. STAT3 activation induces ES cell self-renewal, whereas ERK activation causes cell differentiation.

Enhanced ES cell self-renewal is observed when a catalytically inactive SHP-2 is overexpressed or ERK phosphorylation is chemically blocked. These results indicate that SHP-2 and ERK activation is not required for the maintenance of self-renewal signaling; rather, they inhibit it. This conclusion is confirmed by enhanced LIF sensitivity and increased proliferation rates observed in ES cells, and in embryoid bodies derived thereof, expressing a ΔSH2–SHP-2 protein.[65] However, cardiac–epithelial differentiation of SHP-2 mutant cells is inhibited and delayed, indicating that SHP-2 plays a positive role in ES cell differentiation. In conclusion, ES cell self-renewal is a consequence of the precise balance of antagonistic signaling pathways.

SHP-2 COMMUNICATES WITH ERKS

Activated ERKs undergo nuclear translocation, which enables them to modulate the activities of transcription factors that govern proliferation, differentiation, and cell survival (for a review, see Peyssonnaux *et al.*[66]). SHP-2 interaction with two adaptor molecules, Grb2 and Gab1, provides two alternative routes that couple cytokines to the activation of ERK pathways.

SHP-2/Grb2 association leads to Ras activation through the GTP–GDP exchange protein SOS.[50] SHP-2 has also been shown to associate with the scaffold Grb2-associated binder protein Gab1 and PI3-kinase and to activate ERK MAPK using a Ras-dependent pathway.[67]

GRB2 AND GAB1 ADAPTOR PROTEINS

Like most adaptor proteins, Grb2 contains SH2 and SH3 domains. The SH2 domain mediates Grb2 binding to SHP-2, and the SH3 domain mediates interaction with SOS.[68] Tyrosine phosphorylation of Gab1 following stimulation with cytokines depends on the gp130 site (Y118) docking SHP-2, but it is independent of the gp130 C-terminal domain interacting with STAT3. Gp130-mediated ERK2 activation is enhanced by Gab1 expression and inhibited by a dominant-negative Ras.[67]

FUNCTIONAL ABLATION OF GRB2 IN ES CELLS

Null mutation of the *Grb2* gene leads to embryonic lethality around 7.5 dpc.[69] The differentiation potential of *Grb2*-null ICM cells is compromised as cultured blastocysts lack either visceral or parietal endodermal cells. The ability of *Grb2* to support endoderm differentiation is abrogated by mutation in the SH2 or SH3 domain. Interestingly, the transformation of *Grb2*-deficient ES cells with an activated variant of Ras restores endoderm differentiation, indicating that the Grb2–Ras pathway is essential for early specification of the endoderm tissues.

Consequences of LIFR/gp130 Interaction at the Gene Expression Level

The phenotype of a particular cell type is the culmination of a well-defined and unique pattern of gene expression characterized by the activation of some genes and the repression of others. Therefore, elucidation of the molecular basis of a pluripotency is based primarily on the identification of the key transcription factors involved in regulating gene expression at the pluripotent "state." In a simplistic model, genes that promote and maintain an undifferentiated cellular state would be expressed in pluripotent cells, and those that are activated during stem cell differentiation would be repressed. Conversely, in terminally differentiated cells, pluripotency-related genes would be silenced, whereas those required for the differentiated cell state would be expressed. Elements that influence the transcriptional regulation of gene expression include epigenetic modifications of the genome, such as methylation and histone deacetylation, which determine what types of interactions are allowed between DNA and transcription factors and modulating cofactors.

Oct4: Key Transcription Factor Required for Pluripotency

Oct4 is a transcription factor belonging class V of POU factors. The POU family of transcription factors binds to the octamer motif ATGC(A/T)AAT found in the regulatory domains of cell type-specific as well as ubiquitous genes.[70] POU factors have a common conserved DNA-binding domain, called the POU domain, which was originally identified in the transcription factors Pit1, Oct1, Oct2, and Unc86.[71] The POU domain is comprised of two structurally independent subdomains—the POU-specific domain (POU$_S$) and the homeodomain (POU$_H$)—connected by a flexible linker of variable length.

The POU domain of Oct4 is characterized by several properties that confer on the Oct4 protein an impressive versatility in the operational mode of transcriptional regulation:

- Flexible amino acid–base interactions, allowing recognition of moderately variable cognate DNA elements
- Variable orientation, spacing, and positioning of DNA-tethered POU subdomains relative to each other on the DNA, as shown by the different arrangement on the palindromic Oct factor recognition sequences[72]
- Cooperative binding of the two subdomains to the DNA
- Interaction with other transcription factors and regulatory modulators
- Posttranslational modifications modulating Oct4 transactivation in various cell types[73,74]

The POU domain binds to DNA through interaction of the third "recognition" helix of the POU$_H$ with bases in the DNA major groove at the 3'A/TTTA-rich portion of the octamer site. The POU$_H$ domain has a structure similar to other homeodomains. The POU$_S$ domain exhibits a site-specific, high-affinity DNA-binding and -bending capability.[75] Both the POU$_S$ and the POU$_H$ subdomains function as structurally independent units[76] with cooperative high-affinity DNA-binding specificity.[77,78] Functional cooperation between the two subdomains may occur indirectly through the DNA[73] by overlapping base contacts from the two subdomains.[79]

In addition to the DNA-binding function, both the POU$_H$ and the POU$_S$ subdomains can participate in protein–protein interactions.[71,80] In ES cells, Oct4 activates gene transcription irrespective of the distance of the octamer motif from the transcriptional initiation site.[81,82] However, Oct4 can transactivate only from a proximal location in differentiated cells. In this scenario, interaction between the adenovirus protein E1A or human papillomavirus E7 oncoprotein and the Oct4 POU domain is sufficient for Oct4 to elicit transcriptional activation from remote binding sites.[83] E1A and E7 proteins would therefore mimic unidentified ES cell-specific coactivators that serve a similar function in pluripotent cells.

Two domains spanning the N- and C-terminal portion of Oct4 protein define the transactivation capacity of the POU transcription factor.[80,81,84] The N-terminal region (N domain) is a proline- and acid residue–rich region, whereas the C-terminal domain (C domain) is a region rich in proline, serine, and threonine residues. The N domain can function as an activation domain in heterologous cell systems. However, the C domain of Oct4 exhibits a POU domain-mediated cell type-specific function.[74] Intramolecular interactions between the POU domain and the C domain may lead to cell type-specific interactions with different cofactors or kinases. An interesting regulation model of the C domain predicts that association between the Oct4 POU domain and other factors can alter the phosphorylation status of the protein and ultimately modulate the activity of the C domain.[74]

OCT4 EXPRESSION

Mouse Oct4

Oct4, otherwise designated Oct3, or POU5F1, is a maternally inherited transcript that is developmentally regulated in mice. It is expressed at low levels in all blastomeres until the four-cell stage,[85] at which time the gene undergoes zygotic activation[86] resulting in high Oct4 protein levels in the nuclei of all blastomeres until compaction.[85] After cavitation, Oct4 expression is maintained only in the ICM of the blastocyst and is downregulated in the differentiated TE.[81,87,88] Following implantation, Oct4 expression is restricted to the primitive ectoderm (epiblast), although it is transiently expressed at high levels in cells of the forming hypoblast (primitive endoderm).[70,85] During gastrulation, starting at 6.0–6.5 dpc, Oct4 expression is down-regulated in the epiblast in an anterior–posterior manner. From 8.5 dpc onward, Oct4 is restricted to precursors of the gametes or PGCs. Oct4 is also expressed in undifferentiated mouse ES, EG, and EC cell lines.[13,81,87,89] ES and EC cell treatment with the differentiation-inducing agent retinoic acid (RA) triggers rapid Oct4 down-regulation in both cell types.[81,87,90] Oct4 is not expressed in differentiated tissues. Recently, a very low amount of Oct4 messenger RNA was detected in multipotent adult precursor cells and human breast cancer cells.[91,92]

Humans Oct4

Oct4 is highly expressed in ICM cells compared to TE cells in discarded human embryos.[93] It is also expressed in pluripotent human EC and ES–EG cell lines.[94–96]

MOLECULAR OCT4 FUNCTION

Gene inactivation experiments clearly indicate that Oct4 plays a determinant role in the specification of mouse pluripotent cells.[97] However, Oct4 function is not confined to pluripotent cells. Extrapolation of the data obtained by manipulating Oct4 expression in ES cells indicates that this transcription factor is a master regulator of cell fate in all three tissues of a preimplantation embryo.[98]

Embryos Lacking Oct4

Oct4-deficient embryos die at the peri-implantation stage and form empty decidua (or implantation sites) that contain trophoblastic cells but are devoid of yolk sac or embryonic structures.[97] The embryos develop up to the 3.5 dpc blastocyst stage with an unaltered number of cells in the ICM or trophoblastic compartment compared with wild-type embryos, suggesting that in the absence of Oct4 protein, during early stages of development, cell proliferation is not affected. In vitro cultures of cells immunosurgically isolated from the inner region of Oct4-deficient 4 dpc blastocysts contain trophoblastic giant cells but not pluripotent cells or extraembryonic endoderm. These findings are consistent with the concept that Oct4 is essential in the establishment of the ICM pluripotency.

ES Cells with Low and High Levels of Oct4

Based on Oct4 expression levels during the first two events of cell lineage commitment in the early embryo, it is not entirely surprising that a critical amount of Oct4 has been reported recently to be crucial for the maintenance of ES cell self-renewal.[98]

ES cells containing a conditional expression system to variably express Oct4 helped to determine the cellular phenotype linked to high or low amounts of Oct4 protein.[98] Briefly, ES cells in which both endogenous Oct4 alleles had been inactivated[99] were maintained as ES cells by tetracycline-regulated transactivator constructs activating a transgene expressing Oct4.[100] A decrease below 50% compared to the endogenous level of Oct4 found in undifferentiated ES cells resulted in the commitment of ES cells to TE lineages, containing both proliferating and endoduplicating giant cells based on the culture conditions.[98] This result is consistent with the phenotype of Oct4[−/−] embryos[97] and the observation that trophoblastic differentiation of outer cells of the morula is accompanied by Oct4 down-regulation.[81,82,87] In contrast, an increase beyond the 50% threshold of Oct4 leads to the concomitant differentiation of ES cells into extraembryonic endoderm and mesoderm. Interestingly, LIF withdrawal leads to the specification of the same cell lineages. Less subtle changes in the level of Oct4 (an increase or decrease) do not affect ES cell self-renewal. In conclusion, the precise level of Oct4 protein governs commitment of embryonic cells along three distinct cell fates (self-renewal, TE, or extraembryonic endoderm and mesoderm).

The conditional Oct4-null ES cell line was used in a complementation essay to establish which domains of the Oct4 protein are sufficient to maintain ES cells.[101] The complementation assay was based on the ability of a proper Oct4 molecule to rescue the self-renewal capability of cells that would otherwise differentiate because of Oct4 down-regulation. Oct4 is the only POU protein to have the ability to rescue the self-renewing phenotype, as Oct2 and Oct6 have no effect on cell fate in this system. A truncated Oct4 protein containing the Oct4 POU domain and either the N or the C domain can support ES cell self-renewal like its wild-type counterpart. Furthermore, gene expression analysis revealed that Oct4 transactivation domains, though equivalent in sustaining the undifferentiated stem cell phenotype, elicit activation of different target genes. It would be interesting then to determine the consequences of either N or C domain deletion on pluripotency and embryo development in vivo.

REGULATION OF OCT4 EXPRESSION

Use of Oct4/LacZ transgenes has allowed the identification of two distinct enhancer elements reciprocally driving the cell type-specific expression of Oct4.[89] The distal enhancer (DE), located approximately 5 Kb upstream the promoter, regulates Oct4 expression in preimplantation embryos (morula and ICM), PGCs, and in ES, F9 EC, and EG cells. However, the DE is inactive in cells of the epiblast. The proximal enhancer (PE), located approximately 1.2 Kb upstream, directs Oct4 expression in the epiblast, including Oct4 down-regulation in the anterior to posterior direction after gastrulation, and in P19 EC cells, including RA-dependent Oct4 down-regulation[102] (Fig. 3–3). Two similar inverted elements, the 2A site of the

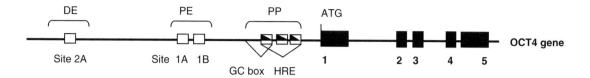

Upstream regulator

DE	PE			
Site 2A	Site 1A 1B	GC box HRE	1	2 3 4 5

OCT4 gene

DE	PE
Preimplantation embryo: oocyte through morula stage	Postimplantation embryo: Embryonic ectoderm
Post-implantation embryo: PGCs	P19 EC cells
ES cells EG cells F9 EC cells	

Figure 3-3. *Genomic structure of the Oct4 gene.* Open boxes indicate the conserved regions included in the proximal enhancer (PE) and distal enhancer (DE). Black boxes indicate the five exons of the gene. The cell specificity conferred by the two enhancers is also depicted.

DE and the 1A site of the PE, are bound by transcription factors *in vivo* in undifferentiated ES and EC cells. Upon RA-induced differentiation, protection of these two areas is lost.[103] These data suggest that these two elements are involved in regulating *Oct4* transcription, probably through local signals, cell type-specific factors, or both.

The *Oct4* gene comprises a TATA-less promoter containing a GC-rich Sp1-like sequence and three hormone response element half sites: (HRE) R1, R2, and R3.[104–106] *Oct4* and steroidogenic factor-1 (SF1) expression patterns are inversely correlated to that of the germ cell nuclear factor (GCNF) in P19 cells. Both SF1 and GCNF are orphan nuclear receptors. During RA-induced differentiation of P19 cells, SF1/Oct4 down-regulation is followed temporally first by GCNF up-regulation and then by induction of the orphan receptors ARP-1/COUP-TFII and EAR-3/COUP-TFI, which act as negative regulators of *Oct4* promoter-driven transcription.[105, 107–109] SF1 binding to a site overlapping the R3 and part of the flanking R2 repeat in undifferentiated P19 cells can activate the *Oct4* promoter in synergism with retinoic acid receptor.[110] GCNF binds to the R2 repeat *in vivo* and represses transcription driven by the proximal enhancer–promoter (PEP) in P19 cells (Fig. 3–3).

Analysis of GCNF-deficient embryos has emphasized the effect of GCNF-induced repression of the *Oct4* gene.[109,111] Low GCNF expression is detected in the whole mouse embryo at 6.5 dpc. At 7.5 dpc, increasing GCNF and decreasing *Oct4* mRNA levels are observed in neural folds and at the posterior of the embryo. As mentioned previously, at the end of gastrulation, *Oct4* is maintained only in PGCs at the base

of the allantois. In 8.0–8.5 dpc GCNF-deficient embryos, *Oct4* mRNA is detected in the putative hindbrain region and posterior of the embryo. This indicates that loss of GCNF leads to loss of *Oct4* repression in somatic cells and loss of GCNF-induced restriction of *Oct4* in the germ line. The same phenotype is observed in GCNF-deficient mice containing a targeted deletion of the DNA-binding domain of GCNF.[112] These findings thus implicate GCNF in the restriction of the mammalian germ line and embryonic cell potency.

DNA methylation constitutes an important mechanism of gene expression regulation during embryogenesis. A global loss of DNA methylation occurs during cleavage prior to the 16-cell stage.[113] Following implantation, a wave of *de novo* DNA methylation occurs in all genes, except those containing CpG islands.[114–116] *In vivo* analysis of the PEP region of the *Oct4* gene reveals that *Oct4* is not methylated from the blastula stage up to 6.25 dpc, a time during which other genes undergo *de novo* methylation.[117] Interestingly, a *cis*-specific demethylation element exists within the *Oct4* PE. Mutational analysis shows that site 1A within the PE is involved in preventing methylation. The presence of this *cis*-specific demodification element causes demethylation of sequences that had been methylated prior to their introduction into EC cells and protects them from *de novo* methylation *in vivo*. Interestingly, methylated PE sequences induce a decrease in transcriptional activation of both a reporter gene and the endogenous *Oct4* in P19 cells. According to the model proposed by Gidekel and Bergman,[117] binding of transacting factors to the PE element offers protection against *de novo* methylation, which can begin soon after gastrulation when these factors are down-regulated. At the end of gastrulation, these factors would be present only in the germ cell lineage, the sole lineage to express *Oct4* by 8.5 dpc.

TARGET GENES OF OCT4

A few putative Oct4 target genes have been identified to date and are briefly discussed in this chapter (Fig. 3–4). Human chorionic gonadotropin (hCG) is required for implantation and maintenance of pregnancy. HCG is secreted by the TE of peri-implantation blastocysts.[118–120] *Oct4* has been shown to silence the expression of α- and β-subunit genes of hCG in human choriocarcinoma cells. Oct4 binding to a unique octamer motif (ACAATAATCA) in the hCGβ–305/–249 promoter considerably reduces both hCGβ–mRNA and protein levels in JAr cells.[121] Although Oct4 is a potent inhibitor of hCGα expression, no octamer-binding site has been identified in the promoter region of hCGα.[122]

Like CG in humans, tau interferon (*IFN-τ*) is needed to prevent the regression of the maternal corpus luteum during the early stages of pregnancy in ruminant species.[123] In cattle, members of the multigene *IFN-τ* family are expressed in the TE from the blastocyst stage to the beginning of the placentation process. Expression of the *IFN-τ* gene is activated by an Ets-2 enhancer located in the promoter region at −79/−70.[124] *IFN-τ* repression by Oct4 is specific, as neither Oct1 nor Oct2 interferes with Ets-2–induced activation of the *IFN-τ* promoter in JAr cells. The mechanism of repression is based on protein–protein interactions between the Oct4 POU domains and the region localized between the activation and the DNA-binding domain of Ets-2. These data, taken together with the observation that reduced Oct4 protein level triggers differentiation of murine ES cells into TE,[98] suggest that the silencing of *Oct4* in the TE is a prerequisite for up-regulation of *hCGs* and *IFN-τ*.

The *Rex1 (Zfp-42)* gene, which encodes a zinc-finger protein, is expressed at high levels in ES and EC cells and is down-regulated upon RA treatment.[125] Both processes are

mediated by the octamer motif located in the promoter region of *Rex1*.[126] Low levels of Oct4 protein are sufficient to activate the *Rex1* promoter in P19 RA-differentiated cells, whereas high Oct4 or Oct6 levels inhibit transcription in F9 cells. Distinct Oct4 protein domains elicit the observed effects, suggesting different molecular mechanisms of Oct4-mediated transcriptional activation and repression.[25]

Expression of the platelet-derived growth factor α receptor *(PDGFαR)* in undifferentiated human EC Tera2 cells depends on a canonical octamer motif within the gene promoter.[127] Mutation of the octamer site has been shown to decrease the promoter activity and *PDGFαR* expression.

OCT4 DOES NOT PLAY *SOLO*

Regulation of the *FGF4* and *UTF* genes has provided insight into an Oct4-induced activation model based on partnership with the transcription factor Sox2.[128–130]

Sox2 belongs to the Sox (Sry-related HMG box-containing) family of proteins that bind to DNA through the 79-amino acid high mobility group (HMG) domain. In contrast to most DNA-binding proteins, which access DNA through the major groove, the HMG box interacts with the minor groove of the DNA helix and, as a consequence, induces a dramatic bend in the DNA molecule. As a result of this energetically high-cost interaction, Sox proteins bind to DNA with a high dissociation constant. Sox2 is coexpressed with Oct4 in the ICM of preimplantation embryos, ES and EC cells, and germ cells.[128,131]

Distinct regulatory elements govern *FGF4* gene expression in the mouse ICM, myotomes, and developing limb.[132] *FGF4* expression in the ICM and ES–EC cells is conferred by a distal enhancer localized in the 3′ UTR of the gene. Oct4 (or Oct1) and Sox2 bind to their respective cognate sites in the embryonic enhancer and form a unique ternary complex that elicits strong synergistic transcriptional activation.[128] Formation of an active ternary complex is highly dependent on the spatial arrangement of the adjacent Sox- and Oct-binding sites

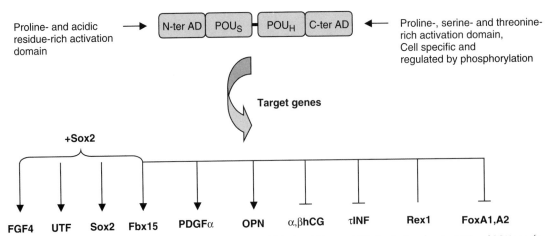

Figure 3–4. *Oct4 protein functional domains.* Shown are N-terminal (N-ter) and C-terminal (C-ter) activation domains (AD) and POU specific (POU$_S$) and homeodomains (POU$_H$). Also shown is the effect of Oct4 on the transcription of its target genes (the arrow depicts activation, and the blunt-end line depicts repression).

on the DNA, because the insertion of three base pairs between the Sox and Oct recognition sequences of the *FGF4* gene severely impairs the enhancer function.[133] The C-terminal domains of both Sox2 and Oct4 contribute to the functional activity of Sox2/Oct4 complex.[129] Activity of the Oct4 C domain requires a Sox2/Oct4 complex. The synergistic action of Sox2 and Oct4 results from two distinct yet concerted events. The first event involves cooperative binding of Sox2 and Oct4 to the DNA via their respective DNA-binding domains. The tethering of each factor to the enhancer region on *FGF4* ameliorates the intrinsic activity of the activation domains of each protein. Upon formation of the ternary Sox2/Oct4 complex, novel DNA–protein and protein–protein interactions induce conformational changes that may lead to activation of latent domains and constitute a new, distinct platform for the recruitment of other coactivators (for a review, see Dailey *et al.*[134]). In line with this model, synergistic activation of *FGF4* transcription by Sox2 and Oct4 in HeLa cells is mediated by p300, a potential bridging factor, which should promote enhancer–promoter interactions.[135] The embryonic *FGF4* enhancer sequences are conserved in the mouse and human genes.[136–138]

ES cell–specific expression of *UTF1* is regulated by the synergistic action of Sox2 and Oct4. The binding sites for these two factors are arranged with no intervening spacing in the second intron of *UTF1* gene.[130,139] Interestingly, one base difference in the canonical octamer-binding sequence enables the recruitment of an active Sox2/Oct4 complex and prevents binding of a transcriptionally inactive complex containing Oct1 or Oct6. The sequence ACTAGCAT (canonical sequence ATTA/TGCAT) is recognized specifically by Oct4; Oct1 and Oct6 can bind to it only by exploiting half of the 3′ adjacent Sox site (AACAATG). The POU$_H$ domain of Oct4 is essential for Oct4 to exhibit unique DNA-binding ability on the *UTF1* consensus sequence.

A noncanonical binding site for Oct4 and Sox2 has been found in the 3′ regulatory region of the *Sox2* gene, called SRR2, and is involved in *Sox2* expression in ES–EC cells.[140] *Sox2* and Oct4 or Oct6 can bind simultaneously, but not cooperatively, to SRR2. Oct6 or Oct4 (but not Oct1) have been shown to slightly increase *Sox2*-dependent transcription of the *Sox2* gene.

The F-box containing protein 15 (Fbx15) is expressed predominantly in ES cells. Embryonic expression of Fbx15 results from the cooperative binding of Oct4 and Sox2 to cognate sites juxtaposed in the ES cell-specific enhancer. Mutation of either binding site abolishes the activity of the enhancer.[141]

Analysis of Sox2-deficient embryos supports the hypothesis that functional association between Oct4 and Sox2 constitutes a new paradigm of gene activation in the early embryo.[131] Sox2-deficient embryos fail to survive shortly after implantation, at 6.0 dpc, with abnormal implants showing disorganized extraembryonic tissues and lacking Oct4+ epiblast cells. At the egg cylinder stage, Sox2 is expressed in the epiblast and in the adjacent extraembryonic ectoderm (ExE) of wild-type embryos. Postimplantation lethality cannot be attributed to a

lack of Sox2 expression in ExE, as wild-type ES cells can rescue development in Sox2-deficient mice.

Immunosurgically isolated Sox2-null ICMs are diverted to a trophectodermal and endodermal phenotype. In Sox2-deficient blastocysts, Oct4 expression is detected by RT-PCR, indicating that a pluripotent ICM can be specified but not maintained. However, complete lack of Sox2 function is not feasible during early development, as maternal Sox2 protein persists throughout preimplantation development. A *Sox2*-null ES cell line cannot be established, confirming that Sox2 plays a role in the maintenance of pluripotent stem cells.

The structural flexibility of the linker sequence between the two independent POU subdomains endows Oct4 with the ability to form homodimers on specific DNA sequences. A novel palindromic Oct-factor recognition element (PORE), composed of an inverted pair of homeodomain-binding sites separated by five base pairs (ATTTGaaatgCAAAT), has been identified in the first intron of the EC–ES cell-specific *OPN* gene enhancer.[142]

OPN is an extracellular phosphoprotein that binds to specific integrins and modulates cell migration and adhesion of the primitive endoderm cells (for a review, see Denhardt *et al.*[143]). In the mouse embryo, *OPN* is coexpressed with Oct4 in the ICM, and in the forming primitive endoderm at 4.0 dpc,[142] and is down-regulated in the epithelial hypoblast of E4.5 embryos. In EC and ES cells, OPN expression is inversely correlated with Sox2 protein levels.

The POU transcription factors Oct1, Oct6, and Oct4 bind to the DNA PORE element as monomers, homodimers, and heterodimers. The Oct4 monomer does not elicit transcriptional activation via the PORE in EC cells. Rather, activation of gene transcription is highly dependent on Oct4 dimerization on the PORE. Mutation in the palindromic element of either homeodomain-binding site drastically impairs dimerization and transcriptional activation. Interestingly, Sox2 represses Oct4-mediated *OPN* gene transactivation by binding to the cognate site adjacent to the PORE in the *OPN* intron. Sox2 may interfere with Oct4 dimer formation.[142]

Dimerization on the PORE creates a specific conformational surface that may be suitable for interaction with unidentified coactivators.[72] Oct1- or Oct2-PORE dimers can interact and synergize transcriptional activation in conjunction with the lymphoid specific coactivator OBF-1.[144] According to a model of the PORE Oct4 dimer structure, Isoleucine 21 (I 21) of the POU$_S$ and Serine 107 (S107) of the POU$_H$ of two distinct Oct4 molecules make specific contact in the PORE dimer interface.[72] Mutation of either residue impairs dimerization on the PORE element. S107 corresponds to a conserved phosphorylation site identified in Oct1 and Pit1.[145,146] Phosphorylation of this serine has been shown to influence Oct1 binding to DNA[146] and may provide an additional level of regulation of Oct4 dimer activity. Mutation of S107 into glutamate might structurally mimic a phosphorylated serine.

To date, *OPN* is the only known Oct4 target gene to be transcriptionally regulated by Oct4 dimers. Mutant mice with impaired dimerization of the Oct4 protein might be valuable in identifying new Oct4 dimer target genes and the function of these genes during early development.

Nanog

A recent report has highlighted the importance of a new player on the stage of pluripotency.[147,148] Nanog, a divergent homeodomain factor, is expressed *in vivo* in the interior cells of compacted morulae, in the ICM or epiblast of a preimplantation blastocyst, and in postmigratory germ cells. *In vitro*, Nanog is a marker for all pluripotent cell lines, from ES (both murine and human) to EG and EC cells. Hence the name Nanog, after the Celtic land of the ever-young Tir nan Og.

Nanog-deficient embryos die soon after implantation because of a failure in the specification of the pluripotent epiblast, which is diverted to endodermal fate. Similarly, *Nanog* deletion in ES cells causes differentiation into parietal–visceral endoderm lineages. These data demonstrate that *Nanog* is essential for maintenance of a pluripotent phenotype both *in vivo* and *in vitro* and that endoderm specification depends on *Nanog* down-regulation.

Nanog overexpression renders ES cells independent of LIF/STAT3 stimulation for self-renewal. LIF and *Nanog* have independent effects on the propagation of undifferentiated vs differentiated cells. The differentiation potential of ES cells overexpressing *Nanog* is both reduced and retarded, but removal of the *Nanog* transgene reverses the cells' status to that of the parental stem cell. *Nanog* expression does not seem to be regulated by Oct4, but the two homeodomain proteins work in concert to maintain a pluripotent phenotype.

FoxD3, *FGF4, FGFR2,* and β-Integrin

Genes whose disruption causes pre- or postimplantation embryonic lethality are the best candidates as gatekeepers of early development.

FoxD3, a transcription factor belonging to the forkhead family, is expressed in mouse and human ES cells and during mouse embryogenesis in the epiblast and neural crest cells.[149–151] *FoxD3*-deficient blastocysts exhibit a regular pattern of *Oct4, Sox2,* and *FGF4* expression at 3.5 dpc. Nevertheless, mutant mouse embryos die at 6.5 dpc, showing a smaller epiblast; extended proximal, extraembryonic, endodermic, and ectodermic tissues; and a lack of a primitive streak compared with wild-type embryos.[152] These results indicate that FoxD3 is required for maintenance of the epiblast but not for differentiation of extraembryonic tissues. This has been confirmed by the observation that FoxD3-deficient ICMs fail to expand after prolonged culture *in vitro*. Oct4 and FoxD3 proteins interact in solution, and Oct4 inhibits FoxD3 activation of the *FoxA1* and *FoxA2* endodermal promoters in a heterologous cell system.[153]

FGF4 is produced by ICM cells and was first postulated to function in an autocrine fashion to promote the proliferation and expansion of the ICM.[154] Later, it was discovered that it was involved in the patterning of the extraembryonic ectoderm by stimulating the proliferation of trophoblast stem cells.[155,156] *FGF4-* and FGF receptor 2 *(FGFR2)*-null embryos cannot form an egg cylinder and die soon after implantation.[157,158] When cultured *in vivo,* their ICMs fail to expand and eventually degenerate. Although *FGFR2* ES cells have not been derived to date, *FGF4*-deficient ES cells proliferate in the absence of the growth factor, suggesting that at least *in vitro FGF4* is not required for ES cell proliferation.[155]

β-Integrin-deficient embryos lack a proper TE epithelium and blastocyst cavity; consequently, they fail to implant at the preimplantation stage.[159]

Genetic deletion of *B-myb,*[160] *Taube Nuss,*[161] and *Chk1*[162] lead to early embryonic lethality and severe defects in the outgrowth of the ICM. This phenotype can be attributed to inactivation of housekeeping genes, either involved in proliferation or cell cycle checkpoints or apoptosis. These processes affect the ICM more that TE cells because of the difference in the proliferation rate of the two cell lineages.

Genetic Model for Molecular Control of Pluripotency

Oct4 cannot be considered a master gene for pluripotency, since it cannot prevent the differentiation of ES cells upon LIF withdrawal. This finding implies that Oct4 and LIF probably activate two different pathways of gene activation, with the second relying on STAT3. The fact that both Oct4 up-regulation and LIF withdrawal lead to the same pattern of ES cell differentiation can be explained by assuming a cross talk between both pathways.

Niwa has suggested a model of the known molecular mechanisms controlling ES cell phenotype[98] (for a review, see Niwa[163]), which is outlined here. Oct4 target genes can be subdivided into three groups:

- Those activated by Oct4 and Sox2 *(FGF4* and *UTF)* (group A).
- Those repressed by Oct4 *(hCG-α and -β)* (group B).
- Those activated by Oct4 but repressed by a squelching mechanism when Oct4 is overexpressed *(Rex1)* (group C). This last group of genes is considered to comprise the cross talk junction between the Oct4 and the LIF–STAT3 signaling pathway, as they should be coactivated by Oct4 and unidentified X-factors that lie downstream the STAT3 activation cascade.

STAT3 is hypothesized to activate ES "state" genes, to suppress endodermal–mesodermal genes, or both. As already described, activated STAT3 and subtle changes in *Oct4* expression are compatible with maintenance of a pluripotent ES cell fate. To achieve a pluripotent status, group A and C genes need to be activated and group B genes need to be silenced by Oct4. Group B genes are activated only when Oct4 expression falls below the 50% threshold and are specific for the TE lineages. A 50% increase in the expression of Oct4, or LIF withdrawal, induces down-regulation of group C genes, either by squelching of the X-coactivators lying downstream of the STAT3 pathway or by down-regulation of a STAT3-induced transcriptional program, leading to a differentiation into mesoderm–endoderm.

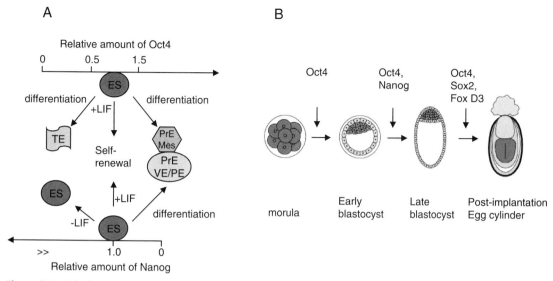

Figure 3–5. Molecular network operating in ES cells and early embryos (A) Model of the integrated roles of Oct4, Nanog, and LIF on embryonic stem (ES) cell fate specification according to different Oct4 and Nanog levels. (B) Model depicting the role of Oct4, Nanog, Sox2, and FoxD3 during early mouse development. (Mes: mesoderm, PE: parietal endoderm, PrE: primitive endoderm, TE: trophectoderm, and VE: visceral endoderm.)

The validity of this model is supported by the existence of the E1A-like activities postulated to exist in ES cells,[164] which may likely represent the mentioned X-coactivators. Nanog would be incorporated within this model as an essential determinant of pluripotency that induces activation of ES state genes, repression of visceral–parietal state genes, or both (Fig. 3–5A). Identification of Oct4 coactivators and *Nanog/ STAT3* target genes is required to enrich and validate the described transcriptional network.

In vivo, Oct4 is essential for the specification of a pluripotent ICM. Nanog and Oct4 would be critical for maintenance of the epiblast during formation of the hypoblast. Post-implantation maintenance of the epiblast would be dependent on Oct4, Sox2, and FoxD3 (Fig. 3–5B).

Plenty of questions regarding the mechanisms of pluripotency remain unanswered. How are the Oct4, STAT3, and Nanog transcriptional pathways regulated, and how do they cross talk? Are other genes present that regulate pluripotency? And in particular, is there one master gene controlling pluripotency? Discovery of such a gene would be the panacea of modern human regenerative medicine, as it would obviate the need for human cloning with all its genetic implications and ethical considerations. However, it appears that pluripotency is most likely achieved through the combination of properly sequenced processes that control chromatin accessibility, chromatin modifications, and activation and repression of specific genes. This is further complicated by potential sensitivity to subtle changes in gene expression levels.

The advent of DNA microchip technology has granted scientists an easy and rapid method of comparing the gene expression profiles of pluripotent and differentiated cells. In the last three years, several reports have obliterated the old concept that adult stem cells are restricted in their potential to only generate cell lineages of their tissue of origin (for a review, see Preston *et al.*[165]). However, it appears that adult stem cell plasticity is mostly linked to environmental cues of the early embryonic blastocyst milieu. The transdifferentiation potential of adult stem cells *in vitro* is very low and inefficient. In addition, the genetic manipulation of adult stem cells using homologous recombination has not been reported.

Euploid pluripotent ES cell lines have been derived from human blastocysts,[166] which may eventually help to create a renewable source of donor cells with reduced immunogenicity for use in transplantation therapy. We are far from using human ES cells in clinical trials. However, investigating the molecular mechanisms underlying pluripotency using the mouse model is the simplest tool available for scientists that will eventually lead to human ES cell-based therapy.

REFERENCES

1. Stevens, L.C., and Little, C.C. (1954). Spontaneous testicular teratomas in an inbred strain of mice. *Proc. Natl. Acad. Sci. USA* **40,** 1080–1087.

2. Brinster, R.L. (1974). The effect of cells transferred into the mouse blastocyst on subsequent development. *J. Exp. Med.* **140,** 1049–1056.

3. Mintz, B., and Illmensee, K. (1975). Normal genetically mosaic mice produced from malignant teratocarcinoma cells. *Proc. Natl. Acad. Sci. USA* **72,** 3585–3589.

4. Evans, M.J., and Kaufman, M.H. (1981). Establishment in culture of pluripotential cells from mouse embryos. *Nature* **292,** 154–156.

5. Martin, G.R. (1981). Isolation of a pluripotent cell line from early mouse embryos cultured in medium conditioned by teratocarcinoma stem cells. *Proc. Natl. Acad. Sci. USA* **78,** 7634–7638.

6. Bradley, A., Evans, M., Kaufman, M.H., and Robertson, E. (1984). Formation of germ line chimaeras from embryo-derived teratocarcinoma cell lines. *Nature* **309,** 255–256.

7. Robertson, E., Bradley, A., Kuehn, M., and Evans, M. (1986). Germ line transmission of genes introduced into cultured pluripotential cells by retroviral vector. *Nature* **323,** 445–458.

8. Gossler, A., Doetschman, T., Korn, R., Serfling, E., and Kemler, R. (1986). Transgenesis by means of blastocyst-derived embryonic stem cell lines. *Proc. Natl. Acad. Sci. USA* **83,** 9065–9069.

9. Doetschman, T., Gregg, R.G., Maeda, N., Hooper, M.L., Melton, D.W., Thompson, S., and Smithies, O. (1987). Targeted correction of a mutant *HPRT* gene in mouse embryonic stem cells. *Nature* **330,** 576–578.

10. Thomas, K.R., and Capecchi, M.R. (1987). Site-directed mutagenesis by gene targeting in mouse embryo-derived stem cells. *Cell* **51,** 503–512.

11. Matsui, Y., Zsebo, K., and Hogan, B.L. (1992). Derivation of pluripotential embryonic stem cells from murine primordial germ cells in culture. *Cell* **70,** 841–847.

12. Labosky, P.A., Barlow, D.P., and Hogan, B.L. (1994). Mouse embryonic germ (EG) cell lines: transmission through the germ line and differences in the methylation imprint of insulin-like growth factor 2 receptor *(Igf2r)* gene compared with embryonic stem (ES) cell lines. *Development* **120,** 3197–3204.

13. Labosky, P.A., Barlow, D.P., and Hogan, B.L. (1994). Embryonic germ cell lines and their derivation from mouse primordial germ cells. *Ciba Foundation Symposium* **182,** 157–168; discussion 168–178.

14. Stewart, C.L., Gadi, I., and Bhatt, H. (1994). Stem cells from primordial germ cells can reenter the germ line. *Dev. Biol.* **161,** 626–628.

15. Till, J., and McCulloch, E. (1961). A direct measurement of the radiation sensitivity of normal mouse bone marrow cells. *Radiat. Res.* **14,** 1419–1430.

16. Smith, A.G., and Hooper, M.L. (1987). Buffalo rat liver cells produce a diffusible activity which inhibits the differentiation of murine embryonal carcinoma and embryonic stem cells. *Dev. Biol.* **121,** 1–9.

17. Smith, A.G. Heath, J.K., Donaldson, D.D., Wong, G.G., Moreau, J., Stahl, M., and Rogers, D.. (1988). Inhibition of pluripotential embryonic stem cell differentiation by purified polypeptides. *Nature* **336,** 688–690.

18. Smith, A.G. Nichols, J., Robertson, M., and Rathjen, P.D.. (1992). Differentiation inhibiting activity (DIA/LIF) and mouse development. *Dev. Biol.* **151,** 339–351.

19. Taga, T., and Kishimoto, T. (1997). Gp130 and the interleukin-6 family of cytokines. *Annu. Rev. Immunol.* **15,** 797–819.

20. Kopf, M., Baumann, H., Freer, G., Freudenberg, M., Lamers, M., Kishimoto, T., Zinkernagel, R., Bluethmann, H., and Kohler, G. (1994). Impaired immune and acute-phase responses in interleukin-6-deficient mice. *Nature* **368,** 339–342.

21. Stewart, C.L., Kaspar, P., Brunet, L.J., Bhatt, H., Gadi, I., Kontgen, F., and Abbondanzo, S.J. (1992). Blastocyst implantation depends on maternal expression of leukemia inhibitory factor. *Nature* **359,** 76–79.

22. Masu, Y., Wolf, E., Holtmann, B., Sendtner, M., Brem, G., and Theonen, H. (1993). Disruption of the *CNTF* gene results in motor neuron degeneration. *Nature* **365,** 27–32.

23. Raz, R., Lee, C.K., Cannizzaro, L.A., d'Eustachio, P., and Levy, D.E.. (1999). Essential role of STAT3 for embryonic stem cell pluripotency. *Proc. Natl. Acad. Sci. USA* **96,** 2846–2851.

24. Scherer, C.A., Chen, J., Nachabeh, A., Hopkins, N., and Ruley, H.E. (1996). Transcriptional specificity of the pluripotent embryonic stem cell. *Cell Grow. Diff.* **7,** 1393–1401.

25. Ben-Shushan, E., Thompson, J.R., Gudas, J.L., and Bergman, Y. (1998). *Rex-1,* a gene encoding a transcription factor expressed in the early embryo, is regulated via *Oct-3/4* and Oct-6 binding to an octamer site and a novel protein, Rox-1, binding to an adjacent site. *Mol. Cell. Biol.* **18,** 1866–1878.

26. Lake, J., Rathjen, J., Remiszewski, J., and Rathjen, P.D. (2000). Reversible programming of pluripotent cell differentiation. *J. Cell Science* **113,** 555–566.

27. Patthy, L. (1990). Homology of a domain of the growth hormone–prolactin receptor family with type III modules of fibronectin. *Cell* **61,** 13–14.

28. Bazan, J.F. (1990). Structural design and molecular evolution of a cytokine receptor superfamily. *Proc. Natl. Acad. Sci. USA* **87,** 6934–6938.

29. Bazan, J.F. (1991). WKS motifs and the cytokine receptor framework of tissue factor [comment]. *Trends Biochem. Sci.* **16,** 329.

30. Nichols, J., Davidson, D., Taga, T., Yoshida, K., Chambers, I., and Smith, A. (1996). Complementary tissue-specific expression of LIF and LIF-receptor mRNAs in early mouse embryogenesis. *Mech. Dev.* **57,** 123–131.

31. Yoshida, K., Chambers, I., Nichols, J., Smith, A., Saito, M., Yasukawa, K., Shoyab, M., Taga, T., and Kishimoto, T. (1994). Maintenance of the pluripotential phenotype of embryonic stem cells through direct activation of gp130 signaling pathways. *Mech. Dev.* **45,** 163–171.

32. Conover, J.C., Ip, N.Y., Poueymirou, W.T., Bates, B., Goldfarb, M.P., DeChiara, T.M., and Yancopoulos, G.D. (1993). Ciliary neurotrophic factor maintains the pluripotentiality of embryonic stem cells. *Development* **119,** 559–565.

33. Wolf, E., Kramer, R., Polejaeva, I., Thoenen, H., and Brem, G. (1994). Efficient generation of chimeric mice using embryonic stem cells after long-term culture in the presence of ciliary neurotrophic factor. *Transgen. Res.* **3,** 152–158.

34. Nichols, J., Chambers, I., and Smith, A. (1994). Derivation of germ line competent embryonic stem cells with a combination of interleukin-6 and soluble interleukin-6 receptor. *Exp. Cell Res.* **215,** 237–239.

35. Li, M., Sendtner, M., and Smith, A. (1995). Essential function of LIF receptor in motor neurons. *Nature* **378,** 724–727.

36. Ware, C.B., Horowitz, M.C., Renshaw, B.R., Hunt, J.S., Liggitt, D., Koblar, S.A., Gliniak, B.C., McKenna, H.J., Papayannopoulou, T., and Thoma, B. (1995). Targeted disruption of the low-affinity leukemia inhibitory factor receptor gene causes placental, skeletal, neural, and metabolic defects and results in perinatal death. *Development* **121,** 1283–1299.

37. Nakashima, K., Wiese, S., Yanagisawa, M., Arakawa, H., Kimura, N., Hisatsune, T., Yoshida, K., Kishimoto, T., Sendtner, M., and Taga, T. (1999). Developmental requirement of gp130 signaling in neuronal survival and astrocyte differentiation. *J. Neurosci.* **19,** 5429–5434.

38. Yoshida, K., Taga, T., Saito, M., Suematsu, S., Kumanogoh, A., Tanaka, T., Fujiwara, H., Hirata, M., Yamagami, T., Nakahata, T., Hirabayashi, T., Yoneda, Y., Tanaka, K., Wang, W.Z., Mori, C., Shiota, K., Yoshida, N., and Kishimoto, T. (1996). Targeted disruption of gp130, a common signal transducer for the interleukin 6 family of cytokines, leads to myocardial and hematological disorders. *Proc. Natl. Acad. Sci. USA* **93,** 407–411.

39. DeChiara, T.M., Vejsada, R., Poueymirou, W.T., Acheson, A., Suri, C., Conover, J.C., Friedman, B., McClain, J., Pan, L., and

Stahl, N. (1995). Mice lacking the CNTF receptor, unlike mice lacking CNTF, exhibit profound motor neuron deficits at birth. *Cell* **83**, 313–322.

40. Niwa, H., Burdon, T., Chambers, I., and Smith, A. (1998). Self-renewal of pluripotent embryonic stem cells is mediated via activation of STAT3. *Genes Dev.* **12**, 2048–2060.

41. Nichols, J., Chambers, I., Taga, T., and Smith, A. (2001). Physiological rationale for responsiveness of mouse embryonic stem cells to gp130 cytokines. *Development* **128**, 2333–2339.

42. Fukada, T., Hibi, M., Yamanaka, Y., Takahashi-Tezuka, M., Fujitani, Y., Yamaguchi, T., Nakajima, K., and Hirano, T. (1996). Two signals are necessary for cell proliferation induced by a cytokine receptor gp130: Involvement of STAT3 in antiapoptosis. *Immunity* **5**, 449–460.

43. Hirano, T., Ishihara, K., and Hibi, M. (2000). Roles of STAT3 in mediating the cell growth, differentiation, and survival signals relayed through the *IL-6* family of cytokine receptors. *Oncogene* **19**, 2548–2556.

44. Murakami, M., Narazaki, M., Hibi, M., Yawata, H., Yasukawa, K., Hamaguchi, M., Taga, T., and Kishimoto, T. (1991). Critical cytoplasmic region of the interleukin 6 signal transducer gp130 is conserved in the cytokine receptor family. *Proc. Natl. Acad. Sci. USA* **88**, 11,349–11,353.

45. Darnell, J.E., Jr., Kerr, I.M., and Stark, G.R. (1994). Jak-STAT pathways and transcriptional activation in response to IFNs and other extracellular signaling proteins. *Science* **264**, 1415–1421.

46. Lutticken, C., Wegenka, U.M., Yuan, J., Buschmann, J., Schinlder, C., Ziemiecki, A., Harpur, A.G., Wilks, A.F., Yasukawa, K., and Taga, T. (1994). Association of transcription factor APRF and protein kinase Jak1 with the interleukin-6 signal transducer gp130. *Science* **263**, 89–92.

47. Matsuda, T., Yamanaka, Y., and Hirano, T. (1994). Interleukin-6-induced tyrosine phosphorylation of multiple proteins in murine hematopoietic lineage cells. *Biochem. Biophys. Res. Comm.* **200**, 821–828.

48. Stahl, N., Boulton, T.G., Farruggella, T., Ip, N.Y., Davis, S., Witthuhn, B.A., Quelle, F.W., Silvennoinen, O., Barbeiri, G., and Pellegrini, S. (1994). Association and activation of Jak–Tyk kinases by CNTF–LIF–OSM–IL-6-β receptor components. *Science* **263**, 92–95.

49. Heinrich, P.C., Behrmann, I., Muller-Newen, G., Schaper, F., and Graeve, L. (1998). Interleukin-6-type cytokine signaling through the gp130/Jak/STAT pathway. *Biochem. J.* **334 (Pt. 2)**, 297–314.

50. Kolch, W. (2000). Meaningful relationships: the regulation of the Ras/Raf/MEK/ERK pathway by protein interactions. *Biochem. J.* **351 (Pt. 2)**, 289–305.

51. Vanhaesebroeck, B., and Alessi, D.R. (2000). The PI3K–PDK1 connection: more than just a road to PKB. *Biochem. J.* **346 (Pt. 3)**, 561–576.

52. Zhong, Z., Wen, Z., and Darnell, Jr., J.E. (1994). Stat3: a STAT family member activated by tyrosine phosphorylation in response to epidermal growth factor and interleukin-6. *Science* **264**, 95–98.

53. Cao, X., Tay, A., Guy, G.R., and Tan, Y.H. (1996). Activation and association of Stat3 with Src in v-Src-transformed cell lines. *Mol. Cell. Biol.* **16**, 1595–1603.

54. Wen, Z., Zhong, Z., and Darnell, Jr., J.E. (1995). Maximal activation of transcription by Stat1 and Stat3 requires both tyrosine and serine phosphorylation. *Cell* (1995). **82**, 241–250.

55. Chung, J., Uchida, E., Grammer, T.C., and Blenis, J. (1997). STAT3 serine phosphorylation by ERK-dependent and -independent pathways negatively modulates its tyrosine phosphorylation. *Mol. Cell. Biol.* **17**, 6508–6516.

56. Takeda, K., Noguchi, K., Shi, W., Tanaka, T., Matsumoto, M., Yoshida, N., Kishimoto, T., and Akira, S. (1997). Targeted disruption of the mouse *Stat3* gene leads to early embryonic lethality. *Proc. Natl. Acad. Sci. USA* **94**, 3801–3804.

57. Hocke, G.M., Cui, M.Z., and Fey, G.H. (1995). The LIF response element of the α2 macroglobulin gene confers LIF-induced transcriptional activation in embryonal stem cells. *Cytokine* **7**, 491–502.

58. Boeuf, H., Hauss, C., Graeve, F.D., Baran, N., and Kedinger, C. (1997). Leukemia inhibitory factor-dependent transcriptional activation in embryonic stem cells. *J. Cell Biol.* **138**, 1207–1217.

59. Matsuda, T., Nakamura, T., Nakao, K., Arai, T., Katsuki, M., Heike, T., and Yokota, T. (1999). STAT3 activation is sufficient to maintain an undifferentiated state of mouse embryonic stem cells. *EMBO J.* **18**, 4261–4269.

60. Stahl, N., Farruggella, T.J., Boulton, T.G., Zhong, Z., Darnell, J.E., Jr., and Yancopoulos, G.D. (1995). Choice of STATs and other substrates specified by modular tyrosine-based motifs in cytokine receptors. *Science* **267**, 1349–1353.

61. Dani, C., Chambers, I., Johnstone, S., Robertson, M., Ebrahimi, B., Saito, M., Taga, T., Li, M., Burdon, T., Nichols, J., and Smith A. (1998). Paracrine induction of stem cell renewal by LIF-deficient cells: a new ES cell regulatory pathway. *Dev. Biol.* **203**, 149–162.

62. Rathjen, P.D., Nichols, J., Toth, S., Edwards, D.R., Heath, J.K., and Smith, A.G. (1990). Developmentally programmed induction of differentiation inhibiting activity and the control of stem cell populations. *Genes Dev.* **4**, 2308–2318.

63. Burdon, T., Chambers, I., Stracey, C., Niwa, H., and Smith, A. (1999). Signaling mechanisms regulating self-renewal and differentiation of pluripotent embryonic stem cells. *Cells Tissues Organs* **165**, 131–143.

64. Hof, P., Pluskey, S., Dhe-Paganon, S., Eck, M.J., and Shoelson, S.E. (1998). Crystal structure of the tyrosine phosphatase SHP-2. *Cell* **92**, 441–450.

65. Qu, C.K., and Feng, G.S. (1998). Shp-2 has a positive regulatory role in ES cell differentiation and proliferation. *Oncogene* **17**, 433–439.

66. Peyssonnaux, C., and Eychene, A. (2001). The Raf/MEK/ERK pathway: new concepts of activation. *Biol. Cell* **93**, 53–62.

67. Takahashi-Tezuka, M., Yoshida, Y., Fukada, T., Ohtani, T., Yamanaka, Y., Nishida, K., Nakajima, K., Hibi, M., and Hirano, T. (1998). Gab1 acts as an adapter molecule linking the cytokine receptor gp130 to ERK mitogen-activated protein kinase. *Mol. Cell. Biol.* **18**, 4109–4117.

68. Feng, S., Chen, J.K., Yu, H., Simon, J.A., and Schreiber, S.L. (1994). Two binding orientations for peptides to the Src SH3 domain: development of a general model for SH3-ligand interactions. *Science* **266**, 1241–1247.

69. Cheng, A.M., Saxton, T.M., Sakai, R., Kulkarni, S., Mbamalu, G., Vogel, W., Tortorice, C.G., Cardiff, R.D., Cross, J.C., Muller, W.J., and Pawson, T. (1998). Mammalian Grb2 regulates multiple steps in embryonic development and malignant transformation. *Cell* **95**, 793–803.

70. Scholer, H.R. (1991). Octamania: The POU factors in murine development. *Trends Genet.* **7**, 323–329.

71. Brehm, A., Ohbo, K., Zwerschke, W., Botquin, V., Jansen-Durr, P., and Scholer, H.R. (1999). Synergism with germ line transcription factor Oct-4: viral oncoproteins share the ability to mimic a stem cell-specific activity. *Mol. Cell. Biol.* **19**, 2635–2643.

72. Remenyi, A., Tomilin, A., Pohl, E., Lins, K., Philippsen, A., Reinbold, R., Scholer, H.R., and Wilmanns, M. (2001). Differential dimer activities of the transcription factor Oct-1 by DNA-induced interface swapping. *Mol. Cell* **8**, 569–580.

73. Herr, W., and Cleary, M.A. (1995). The POU domain: versatility in transcriptional regulation by a flexible two-in-one DNA-binding domain. *Genes Dev.* **9**, 1679–1693.

74. Brehm, A., Ohbo, K., and Scholer, H. (1997). The carboxy-terminal transactivation domain of Oct-4 acquires cell specificity through the POU domain. *Mol. Cell. Biol.* **17**, 154–162.

75. Verrijzer, C.P., van Oosterhout, J.A., van Weperen, W.W., and van der Vliet, P.C. (1991). POU proteins bend DNA via the POU-specific domain. *EMBO J.* **10**, 3007–3014.

76. Botfield, M.C., Jancso, A., and Weiss, M.A. (1992). Biochemical characterization of the Oct-2 POU domain with implications for bipartite DNA recognition. *Biochemistry* **31**, 5841–5848.

77. Verrijzer, C.P., Alkema, M.J., van Weperen, W.W., Van Leeuwen, H.C., Strating, M.J., and van der Vliet, P.C. (1992). The DNA binding specificity of the bipartite POU domain and its subdomains. *EMBO J.* **11**, 4993–5003.

78. Pomerantz, J.L., and Sharp, P.A. (1994). Homeodomain determinants of major groove recognition. *Biochemistry* **33**, 10,851–10,858.

79. Klemm, J.D., Rould, M.A., Aurora, R., Herr, W., and Pabo, C.O. (1994). Crystal structure of the Oct-1 POU domain bound to an octamer site: DNA recognition with tethered DNA-binding modules. *Cell* **77**, 21–32.

80. Vigano, M.A., and Staudt, L.M. (1996). Transcriptional activation by Oct-3: Evidence for a specific role of the POU-specific domain in mediating functional interaction with Oct-1). *Nucleic Acids Res.* **24**, 2112–2118.

81. Okamoto, K., Okazawa, H., Okuda, A., Sakai, M., Muramatsu, M., and Hamada, H. (1990). A novel octamer binding transcription factor is differentially expressed in mouse embryonic cells. *Cell* **60**, 461–472.

82. Scholer, H.R., Ruppert, S., Suzuki, N., Chowdhury, K., and Gruss, P. (1990). New type of POU domain in germ line-specific protein Oct-4. *Nature* **344**, 435–439.

83. Scholer, H.R., Ciesiolka, T., and Gruss, P. (1991). A nexus between Oct-4 and E1A: Implications for gene regulation in embryonic stem cells. *Cell* **66**, 291–304.

84. Imagawa, M., Miyamoto, A., Shirakawa, M., Hamada, H., and Muramatsu, M. (1991). Stringent integrity requirements for both transactivation and DNA-binding in a transactivator, Oct3. *Nucleic Acids Res.* **19**, 4503–4508.

85. Palmieri, S.L., Peter, W., Hess, H., and Scholer, H.R. (1994). Oct-4 transcription factor is differentially expressed in the mouse embryo during establishment of the first two extra-embryonic cell lineages involved in implantation. *Dev. Biol.* **166**, 259–267.

86. Yeom, Y.I., Ha, H.S., Balling, R., Scholer, H.R., and Artzt, K. (1991). Structure, expression, and chromosomal location of the *Oct-4* gene. *Mech. Dev.* **35**, 171–179.

87. Rosner, M.H., Vigano, M.A., Ozato, K., Timmons, P.M., Poirier, F., Rigby, P.W., and Staudt, L.M. (1990). A POU-domain transcription factor in early stem cells and germ cells of the mammalian embryo. *Nature* **345**, 686–692.

88. Scholer, H.R., Dressler, G.R., Balling, R., Rohdewohld, H., and Gruss, P. (1990). Oct-4: A germ line-specific transcription factor mapping to the mouse t-complex. *EMBO J.* **9**, 2185–2195.

89. Yeom, Y.I., Fuhrmann, G., Ovitt, C.E., Brehm, A., Ohbo, K., Gross, M. (1996). Germ line regulatory element of Oct-4 specific for the totipotent cycle of embryonal cells. *Development* **122**, 881–894.

90. Scholer, H.R., Balling, R., Hatzopoulos, A.K, Suzuki, N., and Gruss, P. (1989). Octamer-binding proteins confer transcriptional activity in early mouse embryogenesis. *EMBO J.* **8**, 2551–2557.

91. Jiang, Y., Jahagirdar, B.N., Reinhardt, R.L., Schwartz, R.E., Keene, C.D., Ortiz-Gonzalez, X.R., Reyes, M., Lenvik, T., Lund, T., Blackstad, M., Du, J., Aldrich, S., Lisberg, A., Low, W.C., Largaespada, D.A., and Verfaillie, C.M. (2002). Pluripotency of mesenchymal stem cells derived from adult marrow [comment]. *Nature* **418**, 41–49.

92. Jin, T., Branch, D.R., Zhang, X., Qi, S., Youngson, B., and Goss, P.E. (1999). Examination of POU homeobox gene expression in human breast cancer cells. *Int. J. Cancer* **81**, 104–112.

93. Hansis, C., Grifo, J.A., and Krey, L.C. Oct-4 expression in inner cell mass and trophectoderm of human blastocysts. *Mol. Human Reprod.* (2000). **6**, 999–1004.

94. Pera, M.F., Cooper, S., Mills, J., and Parrington, J.M. (1989). Isolation and characterization of a multipotent clone of human embryonal carcinoma cells. *Differentiation* **42**, 10–23.

95. Reubinoff, B.E., Pera, M.F., Fong, C.Y., Trounson, A., and Bongso, A. (2000). Embryonic stem cell lines from human blastocysts: somatic differentiation *in vitro* [comment]. [Erratum appears in *Nat. Biotechnol.* (2000). **18**, 559]. *Nat. Biotechnol.* **18**, 399–404.

96. Shamblott, M.J., Axelman, J., Wang, S., Bugg, E.M., Littlefield, J.W., Donovan, P.J., Blumenthal, P.D., Huggins, G.R., and Gearhart, J.D. (1998). Derivation of pluripotent stem cells from cultured human primordial germ cells. [Erratum appears in *Proc. Nat. Acad. Sci. USA* (1999). **96**, 1162]. *Proc. Natl. Acad. Sci. USA* **95**, 13,726–13,731.

97. Nichols, J., Zevnik, B., Anastassiadis, K., Niwa, H., Klewe-Nenenius, D., Chambers, I., Scholer, H.R., and Smith, A. (1998). Formation of pluripotent stem cells in the mammalian embryo depends on the POU transcription factor Oct4. *Cell* **95**, 379–391.

98. Niwa, H., Miyazaki, J., and Smith, A.G. (2000). Quantitative expression of *Oct-3/4* defines differentiation, dedifferentiation, or self-renewal of ES cells [comment]. *Nat. Genet.* **24**, 372–376.

99. Mountford, P., Zevnik, B., Duwel, A., Nichols, J., Li, M., Dani, C., Robertson, M., Chambers, I., and Smith, A. (1994). Dicistronic targeting constructs: Reporters and modifiers of mammalian gene expression. *Proc. Natl. Acad. Sci. USA* **91**, 4303–4307.

100. Gossen, M., and Bujard, H. (1992). Tight control of gene expression in mammalian cells by tetracycline-responsive promoters. *Proc. Natl. Acad. Sci. USA* **89**, 5547–5551.

101. Niwa, H., Masui, S., Chambers, I., Smith, A.G., and Miyazaki, J. (2002). Phenotypic complementation establishes requirements for specific POU domain and generic transactivation function of *Oct-3/4* in embryonic stem cells. *Mol. Cell. Biol.* **22**, 1526–1536.

102. Okazawa, H., Okamoto, K., Ishino, F., Ishino-Kaneko, T., Takeda, S., Toyoda, Y., Muramatsu, M., and Hamada, H. (1991). The *oct3* gene, a gene for an embryonic transcription factor, is controlled by a retinoic acid repressible enhancer. *EMBO J.* **10**, 2997–3005.

103. Minucci, S., Botquin, V., Yeom, Y.I., Dey, A., Sylvester, I., Zand, D.J., Ohbo, K., Ozato, K., and Scholer, H.R. (1996). Retinoic acid-mediated down-regulation of *Oct3/4* coincides with the loss of promoter occupancy *in vivo*. *EMBO J.* **15**, 888–899.

104. Pikarsky, E., Sharir, H., Ben-Shushan, E., and Bergman, Y. (1994). Retinoic acid represses *Oct-3/4* gene expression through several retinoic acid-responsive elements located in the promoter–enhancer region. *Mol. Cell. Biol.* **14,** 1026–1038.

105. Schoorlemmer, J., van Puijenbroeck, A., van Den Eijnden, M., Jonk, L., Pals, C., and Kruijer, W. (1994). Characterization of a negative retinoic acid response element in the murine Oct4 promoter. *Mol. Cell. Biol.* **14,** 1122–1136.

106. Sylvester, I., and Scholer, H.R. (1994). Regulation of the *Oct-4* gene by nuclear receptors. *Nucleic Acids Res.* **22,** 901–911.

107. Ben-Shushan, E., Sharir, H., Pikarsky, E., and Bergman, Y. (1995). A dynamic balance between ARP-1/COUP-TFII, EAR-3/COUP-TFI, and retinoic acid receptor–retinoid X receptor heterodimers regulates *Oct-3/4* expression in embryonal carcinoma cells. *Mol. Cell. Biol.* **15,** 1034–1048.

108. Fuhrmann, G., Sylvester, I., and Scholer, H.R. (1999). Repression of Oct-4 during embryonic cell differentiation correlates with the appearance of TRIF, a transiently induced DNA-binding factor. *Cell. Mol. Biol.* **45,** 717–724.

109. Fuhrmann, G., Chung, A.C., Jackson, K.J., Hummelke, G., Baniahmad, A., Sutter, J., Sylvester, I., Scholer, H.R., and Cooney, A. (2001). Mouse germ line restriction of Oct4 expression by germ cell nuclear factor. *Dev. Cell* **1,** 377–387.

110. Barnea, E., and Bergman, Y. (2000). Synergy of SF1 and RAR in activation of *Oct-3/4* promoter. *J. Biol. Chem.* **275,** 6608–6619.

111. Chung, A.C., Katz, D., Pereira, F.A., Jackson, K.J., DeMayo, F.J., Cooney, A.J., and O''Malley, B.W. (2001). Loss of orphan receptor germ cell nuclear factor function results in ectopic development of the tail bud and a novel posterior truncation. *Mol. Cell. Biol.* **21,** 663–677.

112. Lan, Z.J., Chung, A.C., Xu, X., DeMayo, F.J., and Cooney, A.J. (2002). The embryonic function of germ cell nuclear factor is dependent on the DNA binding domain. *J. Biol. Chem.* **277,** 50,660–50,667.

113. Jaenisch, R. (1997). DNA methylation and imprinting: why bother? [comment]. *Trends Genet.* **13,** 323–329.

114. Kafri, T., Ariel, M., Brandeis, M., Shemer, R., Urven, L., McCarrey, J., Cedar, H., and Razin, A. (1992). Developmental pattern of gene-specific DNA methylation in the mouse embryo and germ line. *Genes Dev.* **6,** 705–714.

115. Brandeis, M., Frank, D., Keshet, I., Siegfried, Z., Mendelsohn, M., Nemes, A., Temper, V., Razin, A., and Cedar, H. (1994). Sp1 elements protect a CpG island from *de novo* methylation. *Nature* **371,** 435–438.

116. Macleod, D., Charlton, J., Mullins, J., and Bird, A.P. (1994). Sp1 sites in the mouse *Aprt* gene promoter are required to prevent methylation of the CpG island. *Genes Dev.* **8**(19), 2282–2292.

117. Gidekel, S., and Bergman, Y. (2002). A unique developmental pattern of *Oct-3/4* DNA methylation is controlled by a *cis*-demodification element. *J. Biol. Chem.* **277,** 34,521–34,530.

118. Hay, D.L., and Lopata, A. (1988). Chorionic gonadotropin secretion by human embryos *in vitro*. *J. Clin. Endocrin. Met.* **67,** 1322–1324.

119. Dokras, A., Sargent, I.L., Ross, C., Gardner, R.L., and Barlow, D.H. (1991). The human blastocyst: morphology and human chorionic gonadotrophin secretion *in vitro*. *Human Reprod.* **6,** 1143–1151.

120. Seshagiri, P.B., and Hearn, J.P. (1993). *In vitro* development of *in vivo*-produced rhesus monkey morulae and blastocysts to hatched, attached, and postattached blastocyst stages: Morphology and early secretion of chorionic gonadotrophin. *Human Reprod.* **8,** 279–287.

121. Liu, L., and Roberts, R.M. (1996). Silencing of the gene for the beta subunit of human chorionic gonadotropin by the embryonic transcription factor *Oct-3/4*. *J. Biol. Chem.* **271,** 16,683–16,689.

122. Liu, L., Leaman, D., Villalta, M., and Roberts, R.M. (1997). Silencing of the gene for the alpha-subunit of human chorionic gonadotropin by the embryonic transcription factor *Oct-3/4*. *Mol. Endocrin.* **11,** 1651–1658.

123. Ezashi, T., Ghosh, D., and Roberts, R.M. (2001). Repression of Ets-2-induced transactivation of the tau interferon promoter by Oct-4. *Mol. Cell. Biol.* **21,** 7883–7891.

124. Ezashi, T., Ealy, A.D., Ostrowski, M.C., and Roberts, R.M. (1998). Control of interferon-tau gene expression by Ets-2. *Proc. Nat. Acad. Sci. USA* **95,** 7882–7887.

125. Rogers, M.B., Hosler, B.A., and Gudas, L.J. (1991). Specific expression of a retinoic acid-regulated, zinc-finger gene, *Rex-1,* in preimplantation embryos, trophoblast, and spermatocytes. *Development* **113,** 815–824.

126. Hosler, B.A., LaRosa, G.J., Grippo, J.F., and Gudas, L.J. (1989). Expression of *REX-1*, a gene containing zinc-finger motifs, is rapidly reduced by retinoic acid in F9 teratocarcinoma cells. *Mol. Cell. Biol.* **9,** 5623–5629.

127. Kraft, H.J., Mosselman, S., Smits, H.A., Hohenstein, P., Piek, E., Chen, Q., Artzt, K., and van Zoelen, E.J. (1996). Oct-4 regulates alternative platelet-derived growth factor α receptor gene promoter in human embryonal carcinoma cells. *J. Biol. Chem.* **271,** 12,873–12,878.

128. Yuan, H., Corbi, N., Basilico, C., and Dailey, L. (1995). Developmental-specific activity of the *FGF-4* enhancer requires the synergistic action of Sox2 and Oct-3. *Genes Dev.* **9,** 2635–2645.

129. Ambrosetti, D.C., Scholer, H.R., Dailey, L., and Basilico, C. (2000). Modulation of the activity of multiple transcriptional activation domains by the DNA binding domains mediates the synergistic action of Sox2 and Oct-3 on the fibroblast growth factor-4 enhancer. *J. Biol. Chem.* **275,** 23,387–23,397.

130. Nishimoto, M., Fukushima, A., Okuda, A., and Muramatsu, M. (1999). The gene for the embryonic stem cell coactivator UTF1 carries a regulatory element which selectively interacts with a complex composed of Oct-3/4 and Sox-2. *Mol. Cell. Biol.* **19,** 5453–5465.

131. Avilion, A.A., Nicolis, S.K, Pevny, L.H., Perez, L., Vivian, N., and Lovell-Badge, R. (2003). Multipotent cell lineages in early mouse development depend on *SOX2* function. *Genes Dev.* **17,** 126–140.

132. Fraidenraich, D., Lang, R., and Basilico, C. (1998). Distinct regulatory elements govern *Fgf4* gene expression in the mouse blastocyst, myotomes, and developing limb. *Dev. Biol.* **204,** 197–209.

133. Ambrosetti, D.C., Basilico, C., and Dailey, L. (1997). Synergistic activation of the fibroblast growth factor 4 enhancer by *Sox2* and *Oct-3* depends on protein–protein interactions facilitated by a specific spatial arrangement of factor binding sites. *Mol. Cell. Biol.* **17,** 6321–6329.

134. Dailey, L., and Basilico, C. (2001). Coevolution of HMG domains and homeodomains and the generation of transcriptional regulation by Sox/POU complexes. *J. Cell. Phys.* **186,** 315–328.

135. Nowling, T.K., Johnson, L.R., Wiebe, M.S., and Rizzino, A. (2000). Identification of the transactivation domain of the transcription factor *Sox-2* and an associated coactivator. *J. Biol. Chem.* **275,** 3810–3818.

136. Brookes, S., Smith, R., Thurlow, J., Dickson, C., and Peters, G. (1989). The mouse homologue of *hst*/k-FGF: Sequence, genome organization, and location relative to int-2. *Nucleic Acids Res.* **17,** 4037–4045.

137. Taira, M., Yoshida, T., Miyagawa, K., Sakamoto, H., Terada, M., and Sugimura, T. (1987). cDNA sequence of human transforming gene *hst* and identification of the coding sequence required for transforming activity. *Proc. Natl. Acad. Sci. USA* **84,** 2980–2984.

138. Yoshida, T., Miyagawa, K., Odagiri, H., Sakamoto, H., Little, P.F., Terada, M., and Sugimura, T. (1987). Genomic sequence of *hst,* a transforming gene encoding a protein homologous to fibroblast growth factors and the int-2-encoded protein. [Erratum appears in *Proc. Nat. Acad. Sci. USA* (1988). **85,** 1967]. *Proc. Natl. Acad. Sci. USA* **84,** 7305–7309.

139. Okuda, A., Fukushima, A., Nishimoto, M., Orimo, A., Yamagishi, T., Nabeshima, Y., Kuro-o, M., Boon, K., Keaveney, M., Stunnenberg, H.G., and Muramatsu, M. (1998). *UTF1,* a novel transcriptional coactivator expressed in pluripotent embryonic stem cells and extraembryonic cells. *EMBO J.* **17,** 2019–2032.

140. Tomioka, M., Nishimoto, M., Miyagi, S., Katayanagi, T., Fukui, N., Niwa, H., Muramatsu, M., and Okuda, A. (2002). Identification of *Sox-2* regulatory region, which is under the control of *Oct-3/4–Sox-2* complex. *Nucleic Acids Res.* **30,** 3202–3213.

141. Tokuzawa, Y., Kaiho, E., Maruyama, M., Takahashi, K., Mitsui, K., Maeda, M., Niwa, H., and Yamanaka, S. (2003). *Fbx15* is a novel target of *Oct4/3* but is dispensable for embryonic stem cell self-renewal and mouse development. *Mol. Cell. Biol.* **23,** 2699–2708.

142. Botquin, V., Hess, H., Fuhrmann, G., Anastassiadis, C., Gross, M.K., Vriend, G., and Scholer, H.R. (1998). New POU dimer configuration mediates antagonistic control of an osteopontin preimplantation enhancer by *Oct-4* and *Sox-2. Genes Dev.* **12,** 2073–2090.

143. Denhardt, D.T., Butler, W.T., Chambers, A.F., and Senger, D.R. (eds.) (1995). Osteopontin: Role in cell signaling and adhesion. *In* "Annals of the New York Academy of Sciences," Vol. 760. New York Academy of Sciences, New York.

144. Tomilin, A., Remenyi, A., Lins, K., Bak, H., Leidel, S., Vriend, G., Wilmanns, M., and Scholer, H.R. (2000). Synergism with the coactivator OBF-1 (OCA-B, BOB-1) is mediated by a specific POU dimer configuration. *Cell* **103,** 853–864.

145. Kapiloff, M.S., Farkash, Y., Wegner, M., and Rosenfeld, M.G. (1991). Variable effects of phosphorylation of Pit-1 dictated by the DNA response elements. *Science* **253,** 786–789.

146. Segil, N., Roberts, S.B., and Heintz, N. (1991). Mitotic phosphorylation of the *Oct-1* homeodomain and regulation of *Oct-1* DNA-binding activity. *Science* **254,** 1814–1816.

147. Chambers, I., Colby, D., Robertson, M., Nichols, J., Lee, S., Tweedie, S., and Smith, A. (2003). Functional expression cloning of Nanog, a pluripotency sustaining factor in embryonic stem cells. *Cell* **113,** 643–655.

148. Mitsui, K., Tokuzawa, Y., Itoh, H., Segawa, K., Murakami, M., Takahashi, K., Maruyama, M., Maeda, M., and Yamanaka, S. (2003). The homeoprotein Nanog is required for maintenance of pluripotency in mouse epiblast and ES cells. *Cell* **113,** 631–642.

149. Labosky, P.A., and Kaestner, K.H. (1998). The winged-helix transcription factor Hfh2 is expressed in neural crest and spinal cord during mouse development. *Mech. Dev.* **76,** 185–190.

150. Hromas, R., Ye, H., Spinella, M., Dmitrovsky, E., Xu, D., and Costa, R. (1999). Genesis, a winged-helix transcriptional repressor, has embryonic expression limited to the neural crest and stimulates proliferation *in vitro* in a neural development model. *Cell Tissue Res.* **297,** 371–382.

151. Dottori, M., Gross, M.K., Labosky, P., and Goulding, M. (2001). The winged-helix transcription factor Foxd3 suppresses interneuron differentiation and promotes neural crest cell fate. *Development* **128,** 4127–4138.

152. Hanna, L.A., Foreman, R.K., Tarasenko, I.A., Kessler, D.S., and Labosky, P.A. (2002). Requirement for Foxd3 in maintaining pluripotent cells of the early mouse embryo. *Genes Dev.* **16,** 2650–2661.

153. Guo, Y., Costa, R., Ramsey, H., Starnes, T., Vance, G., Robertson, K., Kelley, M., Reinbold, R., Scholer, H., and Hromas, R. (2002). The embryonic stem cell transcription factors *Oct-4* and FoxD3 interact to regulate endodermal-specific promoter expression. *Proc. Natl. Acad. Sci. USA* **99,** 3663–3667.

154. Rappolee, D.A., Basilico, C., Patel, Y., and Werb, Z. (1994). Expression and function of *FGF-4* in peri-implantation development in mouse embryos. *Development* **120,** 2259–2269.

155. Wilder, P.J., Kelly, D., Brigman, K., Peterson, C.L., Nowling, T., Gao, Q.S., McComb, R.D., Capecchi, M.R., and Rizzino, A. (1997). Inactivation of the *FGF-4* gene in embryonic stem cells alters the growth and/or the survival of their early differentiated progeny. *Dev. Biol.* **192,** 614–629.

156. Tanaka, S., Kunath, T., Hadjantonakis, A.K., Nagy, A., and Rossant, J. (1998). Promotion of trophoblast stem cell proliferation by *FGF4. Science* **282,** 2072–2075.

157. Feldman, B., Poueymirou, W., Papaionnou, V.E., DeChiara, T.M., and Goldfarb, M. (1995). Requirement of *FGF-4* for postimplantation mouse development. *Science* **267,** 246–249.

158. Arman, E., Haffner-Krausz, R., Chen, Y., Heath, J.K., and Lonai, P. (1998). Targeted disruption of fibroblast growth factor (FGF) receptor 2 suggests a role for FGF signaling in pregastrulation mammalian development. *Proc. Natl. Acad. Sci. USA* **95,** 5082–5087.

159. Larue, L., Ohsugi, M., Hirchenhain, J., and Kemler, R. (1994). E-cadherin-null mutant embryos fail to form a trophectoderm epithelium. *Proc. Natl. Acad. Sci. USA* **91,** 8263–8267.

160. Tanaka, Y., Patestos, N.P., Maekawa, T., and Ishii, S. (1999). *B-myb* is required for inner cell mass formation at an early stage of development. *J. Biol. Chem.* **274,** 28,067–28,070.

161. Voss, A.K., Thomas, T., Petrou, P., Anastassiadis, K., Scholer, H., and Gruss, P. (2000). *Taube nuss* is a novel gene essential for the survival of pluripotent cells of early mouse embryos. *Development* **127,** 5449–5461.

162. Takai, H., Naka, K., Okada, Y., Watanabe, M., Harada, N., Saito, S., Anderson, C.W., Appella, E., Nakanishi, M., Suzuki, H., Nagashima, K., Sawa, H., Ikeda, K., and Motoyama, N. (2002). Chk2-deficient mice exhibit radioresistance and defective p53-mediated transcription. *EMBO J.* **21,** 5195–5205.

163. Niwa, H. (2001). Molecular mechanism to maintain stem cell renewal of ES cells. *Cell Struc. Func.* **26,** 137–148.

164. La Thangue, N.B., and Rigby, P.W. (1987). An adenovirus E1A-like transcription factor is regulated during the differentiation of murine embryonal carcinoma stem cells. *Cell* **49,** 507–513.

165. Preston, S.L., Alison, M.R., Forbes, S.J., Direkze, N.C., Poulsom, R., and Wright, N.A. (2003). The new stem cell biology: Something for everyone. *Mol. Pathol.* **56,** 86–96.

166. Thomson, J.A., Itskovitz-Eldor, J., Shapiro, S.S., Waknitz, M.A., Swiergiel, J.J., Marshall, V.S., and Jones, J.M. (1998). Embryonic stem cell lines derived from human blastocysts [comment]. [Erratum appears in *Science* (1998). **282,** 1827]. *Science* **282,** 1145–1147.

4

Mechanisms of Stem Cell Self-Renewal

Hitoshi Niwa

Self-renewal of embryonic stem (ES) cells is achieved by symmetrical cell division while maintaining pluripotency. This can be modulated by extrinsic factors such as a cytokine leukemia inhibitory factor (LIF) for mouse ES cells. External signals control gene expression by regulating transcription factors. *Oct-3/4* acts as a pivotal player in determining self-renewal or differentiation. However, it is still a mystery as to how self-renewal is achieved, since cell-cycle regulation, apoptosis, and telomerase activity have not been analyzed well in ES self-renewal. More information is needed to reach a better understanding of self-renewal in ES cells.

If a question can be put at all, then it can also be answered.

Ludwig Wittgenstein

Stem cells show mystical qualities to us. As a result, we feel that even if all possible scientific questions are answered, the main problem of stem cells has not been touched at all. However, what we can only ask proper questions and seek answers for them. We believe that if it can be said at all, it can be said clearly.

Self-Renewal of Pluripotent Stem Cells

The capacities for self-renewal and differentiation are the two characteristic potentials of stem cells. Self-renewal can be defined as making a complete phenocopy of stem cells through mitosis, which means at least one daughter cell generated by mitosis possesses the same capacity of self-renewal and differentiation. In stem cell self-renewal, symmetric cell division generates two stem cells; asymmetric cell division results in one stem cell and either one differentiated progeny or a stem cell with a restricted capacity for differentiation. Self-renewal by symmetric cell division is often observed in transient stem cells appearing in early embryonic development to increase body size. In contrast, self-renewal by asymmetric cell division can be found in permanent stem cells in embryos in later developmental stages and in adults to maintain the homeostasis of the established body plan.

ES cells are pluripotent stem cells derived from pre- or peri-implantation embryos (Fig. 4–1). The first ES cell lines were established from the mouse inner cell mass (ICM) of

blastocyst-stage embryos in 1981.[1,2] A pluripotent stem cell population appears only transiently during early embryogenesis, so competency for deviation of ES cells exists in a very narrow range of developmental stages.[3] In the case of mouse development, the pluripotent stem cell population is first seen as ICM by segregation of trophectoderm during the formation of blastocyst at 3.5 days postcoitus (dpc). At 4.5 dpc, a primitive endoderm layer can be seen at the surface of ICM, and the remaining pluripotent cell population covered by primitive endoderm is designated as epiblast. After implantation, epiblast cells start to proliferate rapidly and increase in size. At 6.0 dpc, apoptotic cell death eliminates the central part of the epiblast, resulting in the formation of an epithelialized monolayer of pluripotent stem cells designated as primitive ectoderm[4] (Fig. 4–2). Primitive ectoderm undergoes differentiation to embryonic germ layers through gastrulation, and it is there that cells lose pluripotency. After 7.0 dpc, only primordial germ cells retain latent pluripotency, which can be shown by the establishment of embryonic germ (EG) cells *in vitro*.[5]

ES cells are not equivalent to the pluripotent stem cells in the ICM, although they are directly derived from the ICM. The ICM pluripotent stem cells divide slowly. In the delayed blastocyst generated by ovariectomy after fertilization, the doubling time of ICM–epiblast cells is estimated at 96 hours or longer. However, mouse ES cells grow more rapidly than these cells, and they display a doubling time of 12 to 14 hours. Such rapid growth of pluripotent stem cells is observed only in the epiblast after implantation, and it may be triggered by the signals from the primitive endoderm and extraembryonic ectoderm. Their doubling time at 5.0 dpc is 11 to 12 hours, almost the same as ES cells, and reaches 4–5 hours at 6.0 dpc.[6] Because the epithelial characteristics and altered pluripotency are evident in primitive ectoderm that cannot be found in ES cells, ES cells are most similar to the pluripotent stem cells in the epiblast at 5.0 dpc. Expression patterns of stage-specific marker genes also suggest that the pattern in ES cells is most similar to the epiblast between 4.75–5.0 dpc.[7]

Molecular Mechanism to Retain ES Cell Self-Renewal

The ability of continuous self-renewal *in vitro* is one of the characteristic phenotypes of ES cells. As found in the case of other cellular phenotypes, it should be regulated by transcriptional control in the nucleus by extracellular signals[8] (Fig. 4–3). At the molecular level, self-renewal can be defined

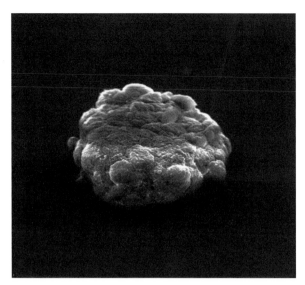

Figure 4–1. *Scanning Electromicroscope View of Mouse ES Cells.* Mouse ES cells form compact colonies in which cells are in tight contact.

techniques, such as coculture with feeder cells,[11] were developed to improve the proper self-renewal of EC cells *in vitro*.

One of the first mouse ES cell lines was established by the culture of ICM on feeder layers in the presence of an EC-conditioned medium,[1] and another was derived from delayed blastocysts cultured on feeder cells.[2] The role of feeder cells as a source of soluble growth factors was suggested by the efficient replacement of such cells with a medium conditioned by buffalo rat liver cells.[12] It was then that a cytokine LIF was identified as a responsible factor mediating this phenomenon.[13] LIF had been originally identified as a cytokine inducing differentiation and preventing self-renewal of the particular leukemia cell line M1,[14] but against ES cells it exhibited the opposite effect—inhibition of differentiation while retaining the capacity for self-renewal. Using recombinant LIF, researchers can maintain ES cells with pluripotency on gelatinized dishes during long-term culture *in vitro*. Moreover, new ES cell lines can be established under such conditions from blastocysts of the genetic background named 129,[15] indicating that the presence of LIF is sufficient to maintain ES cell self-renewal in this case.

What is the role of LIF in keeping ES cell self-renewal? Since the removal of LIF results in differentiation mainly toward primitive endoderm,[16,17] one of its effects on ES cells is to inhibit differentiation. Reports have suggested that the action of LIF is limited to inhibiting differentiation without stimulating proliferation,[18,19] but it is still hard to state this clearly because all of these experiments were done under crude experimental conditions in the presence of fetal calf serum (FCS) in the culture medium.

LIF belongs to the *IL-6* cytokine family, whose members share the transmembrane glycoprotein gp130 as a common component for signal transduction of their receptors.[20] The high-affinity LIF receptor consists of a heterodimer of gp130 and LIF receptor-β (LIFRβ).[21] LIFRβ possesses its own cytoplasmic domain homologous to that of gp130, but our experiment using the chimeric molecules consisting of the extracellular domain of granulocyte colony-stimulating factor receptor and the intracellular domain of either gp130 or LIFRβ revealed that only gp130 is responsible for signal integration to retain ES cell self-renewal.[16] One of the major

as the combinatorial phenomenon of keeping pluripotency and stimulating cellular proliferation.

EXTRACELLULAR SIGNALS FOR ES CELL SELF-RENEWAL

Prior to the establishment of ES cells in routine culture, researchers manipulated embryonal carcinoma (EC) cells. EC cells are pluripotent stem cells derived from a particular type of tumor, teratocarcinoma. This tumor consists of tissues derived from multiple, and often all three, germ layers. Teratocarcinomas are derived from ectopically migrated primordial germ cells,[9] and they continuously grow by self-renewal and differentiation of the remaining pluripotent stem cells. Because many different types of cell lines had been established from various tumors, such an interesting characteristic of teratocarcinomas intrigued researchers and spurred them to establish pluripotent cell lines. In their efforts to do so, several important strategies for the culture of pluripotent stem cells were developed. The first EC cell line from a mouse teratocarcinoma was established in 1970.[10] Thereafter, several

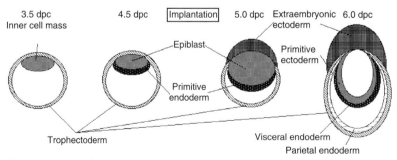

Figure 4–2. *Peri-Implantation Development of Mouse Embryos.* A pluripotent cell population is in the inner cell mass (ICM), epiblast, and primitive ectoderm. ES cells are most similar to the epiblast in their characteristics, although they are normally derived from the ICM.

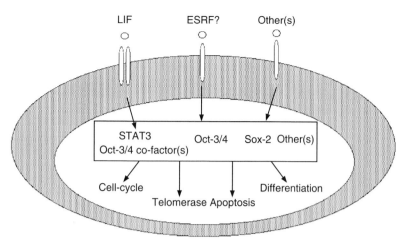

Figure 4–3. *Molecular Mechanism Governing ES Cell Self-Renewal.* The mechanism can be divided into three categories: extrinsic factors, transcriptional regulators, and effectors.

pathways of signal transduction using gp130 is the JAK–STAT pathway, and its importance in ES cells has been shown by a series of genetic manipulations.[16,22–24] We demonstrated that the blockage of activation of the signal transduction molecule STAT3 by overexpression of its dominant-negative mutant in the presence of LIF induces differentiation similar to that induced by the withdrawal of LIF, indicating that STAT3 activation is essential for LIF action.[16] On the other hand, Matsuda *et al.* showed that activation of STAT3 is sufficient to maintain ES cell self-renewal in the absence of LIF.[23] They transduced ES cells with the chimeric molecule consisting of STAT3 and the ligand-binding domain of the mutant estrogen receptor, which can be dimerized by the artificial estrogen derivative tamoxifen. Their results showed that self-renewal of these ES cells can be maintained by tamoxifen without LIF as efficiently as with LIF.

Although the LIF action on mouse ES cells is drastic, its physiological action during development appears to be restricted. Elimination of the function of LIF,[25] gp130,[26] LIFRβ,[27,28] or STAT3[29] by gene targeting did not interfere with the self-renewal of pluripotent stem cells during early embryogenesis. The role of gp130 in the pluripotent cell phenotype was only evident when the delayed blastocysts were carefully analyzed. The ICM of delayed blastocysts normally maintains pluripotency, but gp130[−/−] blastocysts could not maintain pluripotency during the delayed period.[30] Since the maintenance of blastocysts in the uterus without implantation is a characteristic feature in rodents,[30] the responsiveness of ES cells to gp130 signaling has its origin in this adaptive physiological function. Moreover, it may be the reason why LIF do not show obvious effects on ES cells of other species, especially primates. However, the function of the gp130–STAT3 pathway in germ cell development is evolutionarily conserved, since it can be found in invertebrates.[31,32] This may suggest that the role of this system in rodent ES cells is a small evolutionary cooption derived from the maintenance of germ cells.[33]

Although LIF is the only extrinsic factor to date for promoting ES cell self-renewal, its action is not unique. It was reported that the activity of a medium conditioned by parietal endoderm cells could replace LIF for short-term culture without activating STAT3, indicating that a different molecular mechanism can support ES cell self-renewal in the absence of LIF.[34] Unfortunately, it remains a mystery as to what kind of signals mediate this phenomenon, since the responsible substance named ES cell renewal factor (ESRF) has not been identified. It is clear that neither LIF nor ESRF is sufficient to maintain ES cell self-renewal because the culture to detect their activity always contains FCS, a cocktail of several soluble factors. FCS can be replaced by artificial chemical components, but such a simple replacement is limited in the presence of feeder cells.[35] In the feeder-free condition, ES cells can be maintained in high-density culture conditions[36] but not in clonal-density conditions, indicating that a community effect is evident under such conditions.[37] Since this community effect is masked in the presence of FCS or feeder cells, it can be conducted by soluble factors and may be replaced by cell–cell interaction using adherent molecules.

TRANSCRIPTIONAL REGULATION FOR ES CELL SELF-RENEWAL

STAT3

STAT3, activated by LIF, acts as a transcriptional regulator in nuclei. However, its function is not commonly found in various pluripotent stem cells. Many mouse and human EC cell lines propagate in an LIF-independent manner, as found in primate ES cells,[38] and overexpression of dominant-negative STAT3 in LIF-independent EC cells does not affect their self-renewal.[16] These data clearly rule out the possibility that independence against exogenous LIF is not simply caused by the presence of autocrine or intracellular activation of its signal transduction pathway. In mouse ES cells, we previously proposed that STAT3 might activate the expression of a partner of *Oct-3/4*, which has yet to be identified, to maintain ES cell self-renewal[17] (see later sections of this chapter).

Oct-3/4

The molecular mechanism governing self-renewal and differentiation of pluripotent stem cells was first characterized using EC cells because of their longer history and convenience of culture *in vitro*. Many EC cell lines have been adapted to *in vitro* culture in the presence of FCS without particular supplemental factors such as feeders. These EC cells undergo differentiation synchronously with chemical inducers such as all-*trans* retinoic acid,[39] so many trials have been done using these EC cells to identify genes involving the transition from self-renewal to differentiation. In 1990, three different groups identified the same gene, which encodes a transcription factor of the POU family, by its specific expression in undifferentiated stem cells followed by down-regulation during differentiation.[40–42] This gene is *Oct-3/4,* initially reported as *Oct-3* or *Oct-4*, encoded by *Pou5f1*. *Oct-3/4* expression is tightly restricted in stem cell populations during development. Its expression is detectable in totipotent and pluripotent cells—such as fertilized eggs, all blastomeres of morula, the ICM of blastocysts, the epiblast, and the primitive ectoderm—and then restricted in latent pluripotent cells in germ cell lineage, although retention of expression in differentiating cells is observed at 8.5 dpc, especially in neural cell lineage.[43,44] The function of *Oct-3/4* in pluripotent stem cells was initially analyzed by a conventional gene-targeting strategy.[45] Heterozygous *Oct-3/4*-deficient animals developed normally, but homozygous embryos obtained by their intercross exhibited developmental defects at the peri-implantation stage. The homozygous embryo was never recovered at the egg cylinder stage after implantation; however, implantation was not affected since homozygous embryos could be recovered from swelling deciduas at 5.0 dpc, and it was observed at the blastocyst stage at close-to-expected Mendelian frequency. However, when the ICM was isolated by immunosurgery[46] and cultured *in vitro,* cells underwent differentiation to trophectoderm, whereas the ICM derived from wild-type or heterozygous blastocysts formed a stem cell clump surrounded by parietal endoderm. These data indicated that the function of *Oct-3/4* was essential in establishing the proper pluripotency in the ICM of blastocysts, but it was still unclear whether its function was necessary for the self-renewal of established pluripotent stem cells.

Functional analyses of *Oct-3/4* in ES cells revealed their unique characteristics.[17] Loss-of-function phenotype of *Oct-3/4* evaluated by the combination of gene-targeting and tetracycline-inducible transgene expression revealed that its function is essential for the continuous propagation of stem cell populations. Moreover, loss of *Oct-3/4* function strictly determines the differentiated fate of ES cells toward trophectoderm, which is merely observed in normal culture conditions, as found in the ICM of *Oct-3/4*-null embryos. Once the essential nature of the *Oct-3/4* function in ES cell self-renewal was established, the next question was its sufficiency; however, this question was hard to address. Unexpectedly, overexpression of *Oct-3/4* induces differentiation toward primitive endoderm lineage. Careful estimation of the threshold level to induce differentiation using tetracycline-regulatable transgenesis revealed that only a 50% increase over the normal expression level is sufficient. It was reported that overexpression of *Oct-3/4* represses its transcriptional activation using a squelching mechanism,[47] and high-level expression of *Oct-3/4* is detected in primitive endoderm imaged on the surface of the ICM at 4.5 dpc,[44] suggesting that the phenomenon observed in ES cells might have some physiological significance. Therefore, *Oct-3/4* can be regarded as a three-way switch to determine three different cell fates—pluripotent stem cells, primitive endoderm, and trophectoderm—in a dose-dependent manner.[8] The original question about its sufficiency in ES cell self-renewal was finally addressed in *Oct-3/4*-null ES cells maintained by a tetracycline-regulatable *Oct-3/4* transgene. In these ES cells, *Oct-3/4* expression is maintained after the withdrawal of LIF, but they undergo normal differentiation events toward primitive endoderm in the absence of LIF, indicating that *Oct-3/4* expression is not sufficient to continue self-renewal without LIF. This result also revealed that the LIF–STAT3 axis does not form linear cascade with *Oct-3/4* to maintain ES cell self-renewal, since loss of *Oct-3/4* induces differentiation to trophectoderm in the presence of LIF.[17]

In contrast to STAT3, such *Oct-3/4* function appears to be common in various pluripotent stem cells. Stem cell-specific expression of *Oct-3/4* is reported in primate ES cell lines,[48] and overexpression of *Oct-3/4* induces differentiation in various mouse EC cell lines.[49] However, *Oct-3/4* may be an evolutionarily new component of the genome because it can be found only in mammals. In zebra fish, the diverse POU family member POU2 was identified as an ortholog of *Oct-3/4,*[50] indicating its rapid evolution in vertebrates because of the absence of *Oct-3/4*- and POU2-like sequences in invertebrate genomes.[51]

Sox-2

Sox-2 is a member of the Sry-related transcription factor family.[52] Its function in ES cells was first identified in relation to *Oct-3/4*. When the fibroblast growth factor-4 (*Fgf-4*) gene was identified as a possible target of *Oct-3/4,*[53] its enhancer element specifically active in pluripotent stem cells was analyzed. It possesses binding elements for the *Sox* family members as well as the POU family members. Subsequently, the *Sox* family members expressed in ES cells were surveyed, and *Sox-2* was identified.[54] *Sox-2* can be regarded as one of the cofactors of *Oct-3/4,* since it activates the transcription of target genes, such as *Fgf-4,*[54] *Utf-1,*[55] *Fbx-15,*[56] and *Lefty-1,*[57] in cooperation with *Oct-3/4*. Moreover, *Sox-2* expression is regulated by *Oct-3/4* and *Sox-2,* indicating that a positive feedback mechanism may be involved in the maintenance of ES cell self-renewal.[58]

Recently, *Sox-2* function in pluripotent stem cells was analyzed *in vivo* by gene targeting.[59] Heterozygous *Sox-2*-deficient embryos develop normally, but homozygous embryos stop development in the peri-implantation stage, as found in *Oct-3/4* mutants. However, the precise point at which they exhibit abnormalities is slightly later than the point in *Oct-3/4* mutants (abnormal embryos without an epiblast can be recovered at 6.0 dpc). A homozygous blastocyst looks healthier than that of *Oct-3/4* mutants, and the isolated ICM generates primitive endoderm as well as trophectoderm. Such a delay of abnormal phenotype may be caused by the persistence of maternal transcripts as discussed in the report, but it will be necessary to confirm the precise role of *Sox-2* in ES cells, as we did for *Oct-3/4*.

Nanog

Nanog (also reported as ENK) is a new member of the transcription factors whose functions are essential for keeping self-renewal.[60,61,62] It encodes an NK2-family homeobox transcription factor and is named for Tir Na Nog, the name of the land of the ever-young in Celtic myth, because its forced expression in mouse ES cells allow self-renewal in the absence of LIF. However, Nanog expression is not regulated by Stat3 directly, and Nanog cannot replace the function of *Oct-3/4*, so its function is still mysterious. Loss of function in the embryo resulted in the peri-implantation lethality, and that in ES cells induced differentiation to parietal endoderm-like cells with up-regulation of Gata-6. Since overexpression of Gata-6 triggers a similar differentiation event and its expression is up-regulated after withdrawal of LIF or Stat3 activity, one of the possible function of Nanog might be the repression of Gata-6 expression.

Transcription Factors Involving ICM Outgrowth

Many possible transcriptional factors have been reported in the involvement in self-renewal of pluripotent stem cells. It was reported that overexpression of the homeobox transcription factor Pem replaces the LIF dependency of mouse ES cells,[63] but strong expression of Pem is observed in differentiated cell types such as extraembryonic tissues,[64] and Pem-null animals develop normally without abnormality in pluripotent stem cells during early embryogenesis.[65] In contrast, inhibition of Ehox activity results in the maintenance of a stem cell phenotype in limiting concentrations of LIF, but it will be necessary to confirm its function *in vivo*.[66]

A defect of ICM outgrowth found in *Oct-3/4* or *Sox-2* mutant embryos might be regarded as a landmark of gene function in pluripotent cell populations. However, such a phenotype may not always reflect the abnormality of pluripotent stem cells themselves. For example, a mutation of the signal transduction adapter protein Disabled-2 (Dab-2) resulted in a defect of ICM outgrowth in which only primitive endoderm cells were maintained after one week.[67] However, Dab-2 expression is detectable in primitive endoderm but not in the ICM, and the homozygous embryos that die at 5.5 dpc exhibit abnormal migration of primitive endoderm cells. Why do Dab-2-null embryos show a growth defect of pluripotent cell clumps? We think that it might be because of the functional deficiency of primitive endoderm cells essential

for maintaining pluripotent cells as epiblast. Similar dissociation between abnormal phenotype in ICM outgrowth and function in pluripotent stem cells was evident more clearly in *Fgf-4*. Homozygous *Fgf-4*-null embryos showed a defect in ICM outgrowth,[68] but ES cells lacking *Fgf-4* function were established by serial gene targeting.[69] Therefore, not only a cell-autonomous defect but also a non–cell-autonomous defect can produce the defect of ICM outgrowth; we think that the case of the forkhead family transcription factor, Foxd3,[70] may be the latter case because its function on differentiation of primitive endoderm has been pointed out in ES cells.[71]

EFFECTOR MOLECULES TO RETAIN ES CELL SELF-RENEWAL

Prevention of Differentiation

To maintain ES cell self-renewal, entering the differentiation process should be strictly prevented. During differentiation, expression of various genes is up-regulated in a lineage-specific manner. The GATA family transcription factors Gata-4 and Gata-6 are specifically up-regulated during differentiation to primitive endoderm induced by overexpression of *Oct-3/4* or withdrawal of LIF.[17] Their function in primitive endoderm differentiation *in vivo* was confirmed by gene targeting. Loss of Gata-4 resulted in functional deficiency in visceral endoderm,[72,73] whereas loss of Gata-6 affected differentiation of primitive endoderm.[74] Interestingly, ectopic expression of either Gata-4 or Gata-6 in ES cells activates expression of endogenous Gata-4 and Gata-6 and induces differentiation toward parietal endoderm.[75] These data strongly suggest that one of the functions of *Oct-3/4* in maintaining ES cell self-renewal is the prevention of differentiation by repressing genes inducing differentiation. In the case of GATA factors, repression may occur indirectly by activation of a repressor. In contrast, genes involving trophectoderm differentiation, such as the homeobox transcription factor Cdx-2, may be directly inhibited by *Oct-3/4* because their expression is rapidly up-regulated as *Oct-3/4* is repressed.[17] We observed that ectopic expression of Cdx-2 induced differentiation toward trophectoderm,[76] indicating the significance of a gatekeeper function of *Oct-3/4*.

Maintenance of Stem Cell Proliferation

Proliferation of ES cells is achieved through their self-renewal. As in other cell types, it should be regulated by controlling the cell cycle; however, as described in the next section, cell-cycle regulation in ES cells is unusual.[19] For example, it may lack a major break of cell cycle, since the retinoblastoma gene is kept in an inactivated state.[77] Unfortunately, no *Oct-3/4* target gene involving cell-cycle regulation has been identified. STAT3 can activate several genes involving cell-cycle regulation, such as c-*myc* in M1 leukemia cells[78] and MCF7 cells,[79] but none of them has been identified as the targets in ES cells.

Recently, a novel Ras family member was identified by its specific expression in ES cells.[80] This gene, *E-Ras,* encodes a constitutively active form and stimulates phosphatidylinositol-3-OH kinase. Loss of ERas activity in ES cells results in slow proliferation and poor tumorigenicity after transplantation, suggesting that its function is not essential but important for rapid proliferation of mouse ES cells.

Unlimited propagation requires the maintenance of telomeres. ES cells possess a constitutive telomerase activity, and loss of this activity results in limited growth.[81] ES cells lacking detectable telomerase activity by deletion of telomerase RNA showed a reduced growth ratio after more than 300 divisions and almost zero after 450 cell divisions. Since the induction of differentiation results in the reduction of telomerase activity, maintenance of this activity should be coupled with maintenance of ES cell self-renewal.

Regulation of apoptosis is also important for continuous growth of stem cells. Since stem cells have the proliferative ability for self-renewal *in vivo,* they must strictly control it to reduce the incidence of tumorigenesis. Undifferentiated ES cells show a higher incidence of apoptosis against various stresses, such as ultraviolet irradiation, blockage of cell cycle, and oxidative stress, than differentiated cells. Such high susceptibility to apoptosis may contribute to keeping the mutation ratio in undifferentiated cells as low as in the differentiated cells by eliminating the cells that might be damaged. Function of the tumor suppressor gene *p53* in ES cells contributes to hypersensitivity to UV irradiation,[82] but the contribution of the *p53*-independent pathway was also suggested.[83,84]

Self-Renewal as a Marker of "Stemness"

Since self-renewal is a common feature of stem cells, the molecular mechanism governing it might be shared among different types of stem cells, and it could be regarded as a marker of "stemness."[85] However, at present, stocked information for each stem cell line is still too little to highlight their overlap. Although *Oct-3/4* expression is observed in pluripotent stem cells, such as ES, EC, and EG cells,[8] a faint level of expression, 1/1000 of ES cells, was reported in multipotent adult progenitor cells.[86] It may not have functional significance, since a 50% reduction induces differentiation, or it may be significant if 1 in 1000 cells expresses the level of *Oct-3/4* found in ES cells. No other stem cells express detectable levels of *Oct-3/4,* although neural stem cells express *Sox-2* at the level found in ES cells. Even if the molecule is not shared, the principle such as a gatekeeper function might be shared by different transcription factors in different stem cells.

Summary

ES cell self-renewal has been analyzed in the past two decades using mouse ES cells, and many principal molecules have been identified. The isolation of human ES cells has accelerated studies on ES cells of various organisms except rodents, and they have revealed both the common and different characteristics of these ES cell lines with different origins. Since we now know that there is some difference in the mechanism to maintain self-renewal between human and mouse ES cells, we will need to characterize human ES cells carefully in comparison to mouse ES cells for their future application on regenerative medicine. However, although our knowledge is still far from complete in understanding the molecular mechanisms governing self-renewal, ES cells can be regarded as one of the best characterized among stem cells. Therefore, results from ES cell studies can provide good models for other stem cell systems.

REFERENCES

1. Martin, G.R. (1981). *Proc. Natl. Acad. Sci. USA* **78,** 7634–7638.
2. Evans, M.J., and Kaufman, M.H. (1981). *Nature* **292,** 154–156.
3. Brook, F.A., and Gardner, R.L. (1997). *Proc. Natl. Acad. Sci. USA* **94,** 5709–5712.
4. Coucouvanis, E., and Martin, G.R. (1995). *Cell* **83,** 279–287.
5. Matsui, Y., Toksoz, D., Nishikawa, S., Williams, D., Zsebo, K., and Hogan, B.L. (1991). *Nature* **353,** 750–752.
6. Snow, M.H.L. (1977). *J. Embryo. Exp. Morph.* **42,** 293–303.
7. Pelton, T.A., Sharma, S., Schulz, T.C., Rathjen, J., and Rathjen, P.D. (2002). *J. Cell Sci.* **115,** 329–339.
8. Niwa, H. (2001). *Cell Struct. Funct.* **26,** 137–148.
9. Andrew, P.W., Przyborski, S.A., and Thomson, J.A. (2001). *In* "Stem Cell Biology," (D.R. Marshak *et al.,* eds.), pp. 231–266. Cold Spring Harbor Laboratory Press, New York.
10. Kahn, B.W., and Ephrussi, B. (1970). *J. Natl. Cancer Inst.* **44,** 1015–1029.
11. Martin, G.R., and Evans, M.J. (1975). *Proc. Natl. Acad. Sci. USA* **72,** 1441–1445.
12. Smith, A.G., and Hooper, M.L. (1987). *Dev. Biol.* **121,** 1–9.
13. Smith, A.G., Heath, J.K., Donaldson, D.D., Wong, G.G., Moreau, J., Stahl, M., and Rogers, D. (1988). *Nature* **336,** 688–690.
14. Tomida, M., Yamamoto-Yamaguchi, Y., and Hozumi, M. (1984). *J. Biol. Chem.* **259,** 10,978–10,982.
15. Nichols, J., Evans, E.P., and Smith, A.G. (1990). *Development* **110,** 1341–1348.
16. Niwa, H., Burdon, T., Chambers, I., and Smith, A. (1998). *Genes Dev.* **12,** 2048–2060.
17. Niwa, H., Miyazaki, J., and Smith, A.G. (2000). *Natl. Genet.* **24,** 372–376.
18. Zandstra, P.W., Le, H.V., Daley, G.Q., Griffith, L.G., and Lauffenburger, D.A. (2000). *Biotechnol. Bioeng.* **69,** 607–617.
19. Burdon, T., Smith, A., and Savatier, P. (2002). *Trends Cell Biol.* **12,** 432–438.
20. Taga, T., and Kishimoto, T. (1997). *Annu. Rev. Immunol.* **15,** 797–819.
21. Gearing, P.D., Gough, N.M., King, J.A., Hilton, D.J., Nicola, N.A., Simpson, R.J., Nice, E.C., Kelso, A., and Metcalf, D. (1987). *EMBO J.* **6,** 3995–4002.
22. Boeuf, H., Hauss, C., Graeve, F.D., Baran, N., and Kedinger, C. (1997). *J. Cell Biol.* **138,** 1207–1217.
23. Matsuda, T., Nakamura, T., Nakao, K., Arai, T., Katsuki, M., Heike, T., and Yokota, T. (1999). *EMBO J.* **18,** 4261–4269.
24. Raz, R., Lee, C.K., Cannizzaro, L.A., d'Eustachio, P., and Levy, D.E. (1999). *Proc. Natl. Acad. Sci. USA* **96,** 2846–2851.
25. Stewart, C.L., Kaspar, P., Brunet, L.J., Bhatt, H., Gadi, I., Kontgen, F., and Abbondanzo, S.J. (1992). *Nature* **359,** 76–79.
26. Yoshida, K., Taga, T., Saito, M., Suematsu, S., Kumanogoh, A., Tanaka, T., Fujiwara, H., Hirata, M., Yamagami, T., Nakahata, T., Hirabayashi, T., Yoneda, Y., Tanaka, K., Wang, W.Z., Mori, C.,

Shiota, K., Yoshida, N., and Kishimoto, T. (1996). *Proc. Natl. Acad. Sci. USA* **93**, 407–411.

27. Ware, C.B., Horowitz, M.C., Renshaw, B.R., Hunt, J.S., Liggitt, D., Koblar, S.A., Gliniak, B.C., McKenna, H.J., Papayannoupoulou, T., Thoma, B., Cheng, L., Donovan, P.J., Peschon, J.J., Bartlett, P.F., Willis, C.R., Wright, B.D., Carpenter, M.K., Davidson, B.L., and Gearing, D.P. (1995). *Development* **121**, 1283–1299.

28. Li, M., Sendtner, M., and Smith, A. (1995). *Nature* **378**, 724–727.

29. Takeda, K., Noguchi, K., Shi, W., Tanaka, T., Matsumoto, M., Yoshida, N., Kishimoto, T., and Akira, S. (1997). *Proc. Natl. Acad. Sci. USA* **94**, 3801–3804.

30. Nichols, J., Chambers, I., Taga, T., and Smith, A. (2001). *Development* **128**, 2333–2339.

31. Kiger, A.A., Jones, D.L., Schulz, C., Rogers, M.B., and Fuller, M.T. (2001). *Science* **294**, 2542–2545.

32. Tulina, N., and Matunis, E. (2001). *Science* **294**, 2546–2549.

33. Pires-daSilva, A., and Sommer, R.J. (2003). *Natl. Rev. Genet.* **4**, 39–49.

34. Dani, C., Chambers, I., Johnstone, S., Robertson, M., Ebrahimi, B., Saito, M., Taga, T., Li, M., Burdon, T., Nichols, J., and Smith, A. (1998). *Dev. Biol.* **203**, 149–162.

35. Goldsborough, M.D., Tilkins, M.L., Lobo-Alfonso, J., Morrison, J.R., Stevens, M.E., Meneses, J., Pedersen, R., Koller, B., and Latour, A. (1998). *Focus* **20**, 8–12.

36. Ward, C.M., Stern, P., Willington, M.A., and Flenniken, A.M. (2002). *Lab. Invest.* **82**, 1765–1767.

37. Ogawa, K., Matsui, H., Ohtsuka, S., and Niwa, H. (2004). *Genes Cells* (in press).

38. Schuringa, J.J., van der Schaaf, S., Vellenga, E., Eggen, B.J., and Kruijer, W. (2002). *Exp. Cell Res.* **274**, 119–129.

39. Pfeiffer, S.E., Jakob, H., Mikoshiba, K., Dubois, P., Guenet, J.L., Nicolas, J.F., Gaillard, J., Chevance, G., and Jacob, F. (1981). *J. Cell Biol.* **88**, 57–66.

40. Okamoto, K., Okazawa, H., Okuda, A., Sakai, M., Muramatsu, M., and Hamada, H. (1990). *Cell* **60**, 461–472.

41. Rosner, M.H., Vigano, M.A., Ozato, K., Timmons, P.M., Poirier, F., Rigby, P.W., and Staudt, L.M. (1990). *Nature* **345**, 686–692.

42. Schöler, H.R., Ruppert, S., Suzuki, N., Chowdhury, K., and Gruss, P. (1990). *Nature* **344**, 435–439.

43. Schöler, H.R., Dressler, G.R., Balling, R., Rohdewohld, H., and Gruss, P. (1990). *EMBO J.* **9**, 2185–2195.

44. Palmieri, S.L., Peter, W., Hess, H., and Schöler, H.R. (1994). *Dev. Biol.* **166**, 259–267.

45. Nichols, J., Zevnik, B., Anastassiadis, K., Niwa, H., Klewe-Nebenius, D., Chambers, I., Scholer, H., and Smith, A. (1998). *Cell* **95**, 379–391.

46. Solter, D., and Knowles, B.B. (1975). *Proc. Natl. Acad. Sci. USA* **72**, 5099–5102.

47. Schöler, H.R., Ciesiolka, T., and Gruss, P. (1991). *Cell* **66**, 291–304.

48. Zwaka, T.P., and Thomson, J.A. (2003). *Natl. Biotechnol.* **21**, 319–321.

49. Iwamatsu, Y., and Niwa H. (unpublished).

50. Reim, G., and Brand, M. (2002). *Development* **129**, 917–933.

51. Sekita, Y. *et al.* (unpublished).

52. Kamachi, Y., Uchikawa, M., and Kondoh, H. (2000). *Trends Genet.* **16**, 182–187.

53. Schoorlemmer, J., and Kruijer, W. (1991). *Mech. Dev.* **36**, 75–86.

54. Yuan, H., Corbi, N., Basilico, C., and Dailey, L. (1995). *Genes Dev.* **9**, 2635–2645.

55. Nishimoto, M., Fukushima, A., Okuda, A., and Muramatsu, M. (1999). *Mol. Cell. Biol.* **19**, 5453–5465.

56. Tokuzawa, Y., Kaiho, E., Maruyama, M., Takahashi, K., Mitsui, K., Maeda, M., Niwa, H., and Yamanaka, S. (2003). *Mol. Cell. Biol.* **23**, 2699–2708.

57. Fukui. N., and Niwa H. (unpublished).

58. Tomioka, M., Nishimoto, M., Miyagi, S., Katayanagi, T., Fukui, N., Niwa, H., Muramatsu, M., and Okuda, A. (2002). *Nucleic Acids Res.* **30**, 3202–3213.

59. Avilion, A.A., Nicolis, S.K., Pevny, L.H., Perez, L., Vivian, N., and Lovell-Badge, R. (2003). *Genes Dev.* **17**, 126–140.

60. Wang, S.H., Tsai, M.S., Chiang, M.F., and Li, H. (2003). *Gene Expr. Patterns* **3**, 99–103.

61. Mitsui, K., Tokuzawa, Y., Itoh, H., Segawa, K., Murakami, M., Takahashi, K., Maruyama, M., Maeda, M., and Yamanaka, S. (2003). The homeoprotein Nanog is required for maintenance of pluripotency in mouse epiblast and ES cells. *Cell* **113**, 631–642.

62. Chambers, I., Colby, D., Robertson, M., Nichols, J., Lee, S., Tweedie, S., and Smith, A. (2003). Functional expression cloning of Nanog, a pluripotency sustaining factor in embryonic stem cells. *Cell* **113**, 643–655.

63. Fan, Y., Melhem, M.F., and Chaillet, J.R. (1999). *Dev. Biol.* **210**, 481–496.

64. Lin, T.P., Labosky, P.A., Grabel, L.B., Kozak, C.A., Pitman, J.L., Kleeman, J., and MacLeod, C.L. (1994). *Dev. Biol.* **166**, 170–179.

65. Pitman, J.L., Lin, T.P., Kleeman, J.E., Erickson, G.F., and MacLeod, C.L. (1998). *Dev. Biol.* **202**, 196–214.

66. Jackson, M., Baird, J.W., Cambray, N., Ansell, J.D., Forrester, L.M., and Graham, G.J. (2002). *J. Biol. Chem.* **277**, 38,683–38,692.

67. Yang, D.H., Smith, E.R., Roland, I.H., Sheng, Z., He, J., Martin, W.D., Hamilton, T.C., Lambeth, J.D., and Xu, X.X. (2002). *Dev. Biol.* **251**, 27–44.

68. Feldman, B., Poueymirou, W., Papaioannou, V.E., DeChiara, T.M., and Goldfarb, M. (1995). *Science* **267**, 246–249.

69. Wilder, P.J., Kelly, D., Brigman, K., Peterson, C.L., Nowling, T., Gao, Q.S., McComb, R.D., Capecchi, M.R., and Rizzino, A. (1997). *Dev. Biol.* **192**, 614–629.

70. Hanna, L.A., Foreman, R.K., Tarasenko, I.A., Kessler, D.S., and Labosky, P.A. (2002). *Genes Dev.* **16**, 2650–2661.

71. Guo, Y., Costa, R., Ramsey, H., Starnes, T., Vance, G., Robertson, K., Kelley, M., Reinbold, R., Scholer, H., and Hromas, R. (2002). *Proc. Natl. Acad. Sci. USA* **99**, 3663–3667.

72. Kuo, C.T., Morrisey, E.E., Anandappa, R., Sigrist, K., Lu, M.M., Parmacek, M.S., Soudais, C., and Leiden, J.M. (1997). *Genes Dev.* **11**, 1048–1060.

73. Molkentin, J.D., Lin, Q., Duncan, S.A., and Olson, E.N. (1997). *Genes Dev.* **11**, 1061–1072.

74. Morrisey, E.E., Tang, Z., Sigrist, K., Lu, M.M., Jiang, F., Ip, H.S., and Parmacek, M.S. (1998). *Genes Dev.* **12**, 3579–3590.

75. Fujikura, J., Yamato, E., Yonemura, S., Hosoda, K., Masui, S., Nakao, K., Miyazaki, J.I., and Niwa, H. (2002). *Genes Dev.* **16**, 784–789.

76. Niwa, H. (unpublished).

77. Savatier, P., Huang, S., Szekely, L., Wiman, K.G., and Samarut, J. (1994). *Oncogene* **9**, 809–818.

78. Minami, M., Inoue, M., Wei, S., Takeda, K., Matsumoto, M., Kishimoto, T., and Akira, S. (1996). *Proc. Natl. Acad. Sci. USA* **93**, 3963–3966.

79. Zhang, F., Li, C., Halfter, H., and Liu, J. (2003). *Oncogene* **22**, 894–905.

80. Takahashi, K., Mitsui, K., and Yamanaka, S. (2003). *Nature* **423**, 541–545.

81. Niida, H., Shinkai, Y., Hande, M.P., Matsumoto, T., Takehara, S., Tachibana, M., Oshimura, M., Lansdorp, P.M., and Furuichi, Y. (2000). *Mol. Cell. Biol.* **20,** 4115–4127.

82. Sabapathy, K., Klemm, M., Jaenisch, R., and Wagner, E.F. (1997). *EMBO J.*, **16,** 6217–6229.

83. Corbet, S.W., Clarke, A.R., Gledhill, S., and Wyllie, A.H. (1999). *Oncogene*, **18,** 1537–1544.

84. Aladjem, M.I., Spike, B.T., Rodewald, L.W., Hope, T.J., Klemm, M., Jaenisch, R., and Wahl, G.M. (1998). *Curr. Biol.* **8,** 145–155.

85. Ramalho-Santos, M., Yoon, S., Matsuzaki, Y., Mulligan, R.C., and Melton, D.A. (2002). *Science* **298,** 597–600.

86. Jiang, Y., Jahagirdar, B.N., Reinhardt, R.L., Schwartz, R.E., Keene, C.D., Ortiz-Gonzalez, X.R., Reyes, M., Lenvik, T., Lund, T., Blackstad, M., Du, J., Aldrich, S., Lisberg, A., Low, W.C., Largaespada, D.A., and Verfaillie, C.M. (2002). *Nature* **418,** 41–49.

5

Cell-Cycle Control in Embryonic Stem Cells

Pierre Savatier and Anna Malashicheva

Introduction

Mouse embryonic stem (ES) cells are the *in vitro* counterpart of the epiblast cells of the early postimplantation embryo. ES cells are highly pluripotent in that they can generate all cell types of the adult organism, which reflects the central role of the epiblast as the founder tissue of the whole embryo in rodents.[1] Mouse ES cells display unusual proliferative properties.[2] Their derivation does not rely on any immortalizing agent, they cannot enter a quiescence state, they do not undergo senescence, and they can proliferate without apparent limit. They also can multiply in the absence of serum and are not subject to contact inhibition or anchorage dependence. These are features of transformed cells, and, indeed, ES cells are tumorigenic in that they produce teratocarcinomas when injected into adult mice. Human ES cells are also immortal and can form tumors *in vivo,* suggesting that, besides pluripotency, infinite life span and unrestricted growth are intrinsic features of all ES cells. These are remarkable phenomena in that ES cells are genotypically wild type, as demonstrated by their ability to fully integrate into the developing embryo and to generate healthy adults. ES cells in this respect contrast all other types of neoplastic cells, the growth of which appears to be associated with genetic lesions in growth-controlling protooncogenes and tumor suppressor genes. Some fundamental differences in the expression or regulation of cell-cycle control genes—more specifically, in those regulating the G_1–S transition in response to mitogenic signals—are likely to underlie the growth properties of mouse ES cells. Here, we review current data on the control of the mitotic cycle of mouse ES cells and epiblast cells, and we describe the possible relationships among cell-cycle control, self-renewal, and pluripotency.

Mouse ES Cells Lack Control of G1 Associated with a Functional RB Pathway

The proliferation of mammalian cells is controlled largely during the G_1 phase of their growth cycles. The decision to initiate a new round of DNA synthesis is dependent upon phosphorylation and functional inactivation of the retinoblastoma protein (RB) (Fig. 5–1). Hypophosphorylated (G_1-specific) RB inhibits the expression of genes required for S-phase entry by sequestering the E2F family of transcription factors. During progression through the G_1 phase, RB is sequentially phosphorylated by complexes of cyclins and cyclin-dependent kinases (CDKs). Of prime importance are D-type cyclins (cyclin D1, D2, or D3), forming complexes with CDK4 and CDK6, and cyclin E, forming complexes with CDK2.[3] Primary phosphorylation by cyclin D-CDK4/6 complexes displaces histone deacetylases from RB. This derepresses transcription of the *cyclin E* and the *cdc25A* genes. Cdc25A phosphatase removes inhibitory phosphates from CDK2. The resulting cyclin E-CDK2 complex then completes RB phosphorylation, leading to E2F release, target gene activation, and S-phase entry.[4–6] The relevance of the cyclin D-CDK4/6 → RB-E2F circuitry—also called the RB pathway—in G_1 control is illustrated by its disruption in many types of human tumors.[6–9] A second pathway involves the c-*myc* protooncogene, which directly stimulates transcription of the genes encoding cyclin E and cdc25A to generate cyclin E-CDK2 kinase. The Myc and RB pathways are now thought to be two parallel and cooperative G_1–S control pathways converging on cyclin E-CDK2 kinase, the activity of which determines entry into S phase.[10, 11]

The cyclin D-CDK4/6 → RB-E2F pathway appears to be operative in virtually all cell types. In contrast, the control of the ES cell cycle is likely to be markedly different. ES cells display a very short G_1 phase of approximately 1.5 hours, during which hypophosphorylated—G_1-specific—RB is virtually undetectable. RB is thus likely to be rephosphorylated immediately after mitosis in ES cells.[12] An important issue, therefore, is whether ES cells are subject to G_1 regulation by RB. Several pieces of evidence support the notion that the cyclin D-CDK4/6 → RB-E2F pathway does not regulate the ES cell cycle:

1. Cyclin D1 and cyclin D3 are expressed at low levels in ES cells; cyclin D2 is not expressed. CDK4-associated kinase activity is barely detectable. Differentiation induced by the withdrawal of leukemia inhibitory factor (LIF) or by the formation of embryoid bodies results in strong expression of the three D-type cyclins and robust CDK4-associated kinase activity.[13] The relatively low levels of D-type cyclins in ES cells compared to their differentiated derivatives reflects the situation in epiblast cells, which do not express appreciable D-type cyclins until gastrulation commences.[14]

Handbook of Stem Cells
Volume 1

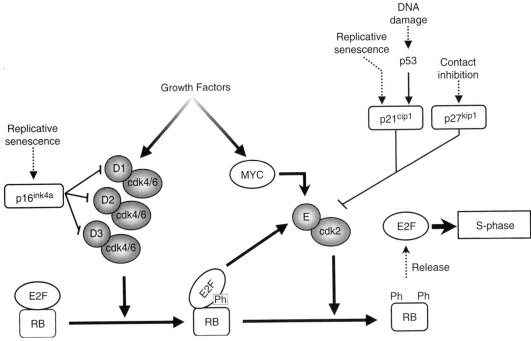

Figure 5-1. Molecular pathways leading to control of RB phosphorylation and S-phase entry in somatic cells.

2. ES cells are refractory to the growth inhibitory activity of p16[ink4a].[13] p16[ink4a] is a specific inhibitor of CDK4 and CDK6 that acts by preventing the association of D-type cyclins with the CDKs.[15] Resistance to p16[ink4a]-mediated growth inhibition is a common feature of cancer cells whose RB pathway has been disrupted.[16, 17] It was recently shown that cyclin D3-CDK6, the most abundant cyclin D-CDK4/6 type complex in ES cells, are resistant to the growth inhibitory activity of p16[ink4a].[18] Withdrawal of LIF and subsequent differentiation is accompanied by sensitization to p16[ink4a]-mediated growth inhibition, indicating that RB control of G$_1$ is imposed during differentiation.[13]

3. The inactivating disruptions in all three retinoblastoma-gene family members (*RB* and its two cognates, *p107* and *p130*) do not seem to compromise ES cell proliferation, but they reduce differentiation in experimental teratocarcinomas.[19, 20] This further indicates that RB dependence is only acquired as ES cells undergo differentiation.

4. ES cells share striking similarities in proliferative behavior with embryonic fibroblasts harboring the triple knockout (*TKO*) of the three retinoblastoma gene family members (*Rb$^{-/-}$, p107$^{-/-}$,* and *p130$^{-/-}$*).[19, 20] Both *TKO* murine embryonic fibroblasts (MEFs) and ES cells fail to arrest in G$_1$ at confluence. In normal fibroblasts, this phenomenon, known as contact inhibition, is accompanied by increased p27[kip1] (an inhibitor of cyclin E-CDK2 kinase) levels, decreased cyclin D1 levels, and an accumulation of hypophosphorylated

RB leading to G$_1$ arrest.[21] ES cells and *TKO* MEF also escape replicative senescence and are immortal.[19, 20] In normal cells, replicative senescence and G$_1$ arrest are associated with an accumulation of hypophosphorylated RB arising from inhibition of CDK4 and CDK6 kinases[22] by p16[ink4a] and from inhibition of CDK2 by p21[cip1].[23] Finally, both ES cells and *TKO* MEFs fail to arrest in G$_1$ following DNA damage.[19, 20, 24, 25] In normal cells, growth arrest in G$_1$ is strictly dependent on a functional RB pathway.[26, 27]

Together, these data strongly support the notion that ES cells lack RB control in G$_1$. This control is likely to be restored when ES cells commit to differentiation. Lack of RB control suggests that the Myc pathway could play a critical role in the promotion of the G$_1$–S transition of ES cells.

Mouse ES Cells Lack Control of G1 Associated with Ras/ERK Signaling

Extracellular regulated kinase (ERK)-type mitogen-activated protein kinases (MAPKs) regulate a variety of cellular responses and have well-documented roles in the control of proliferation in most, if not all, nontransformed somatic cell types. The ERK pathway is engaged through the recruitment of the Grb2 adaptor–SOS guanine nucleotide exchange factor complex to activated receptors. This promotes activation of Ras, which then initiates a cascade of transphosphorylations that culminates in ERK activation. Active ERKs undergo

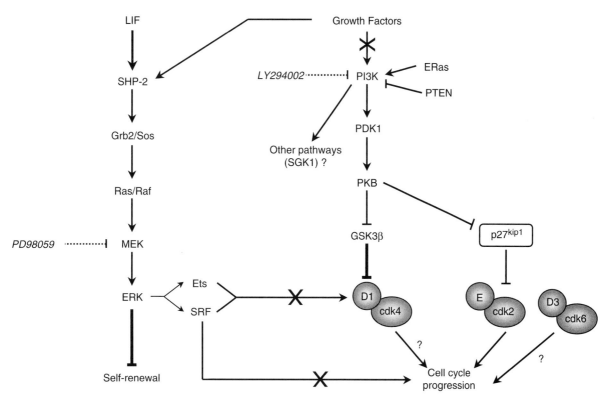

Figure 5–2. Ras- and PI3K-dependent signaling pathways regulating self-renewal and cell cycle progression in response to growth factor stimulation in ES cells. PD98059 and LY294002 are pharmacological inhibitors of MEK and PI3K, respectively.

nuclear translocation, which enables them to up-regulate the activity of growth-promoting transcription factors such as Elk, Ets, Myc, and serum response factor (SRF).

Several lines of evidence support the notion that ES cells do not rely on Ras/ERK signaling for proliferation control (Fig. 5–2):

1. Grb2-deficient ES cells proliferate and self-renew normally, but they display strongly impaired differentiation. Reintroduction of either a Grb2-SOS chimeric protein or an activated form of Ras into Grb2$^{-/-}$ ES cells restores normal differentiation, indicating that Ras dependence is only acquired at the onset of differentiation.[28]

2. In ES cells, the Grb2-SOS complex is recruited to the activated gp130 receptor using the protein phosphatase SHP-2. Elimination of the SHP-2 binding site from gp130 receptor blocks coupling to Ras and inactivates ERK signaling, yet it does not impair proliferation.[29] Similarly, specific restriction of ERK activity by pharmacological inhibition of MEK, the upstream activator of ERK, does not alter the cell-cycle kinetics.[30] Therefore, ERK activity appears to be fully dispensable for ES cell proliferation. Suppression of ERK activity enhances self-renewal, suggesting that

Ras/ERK signaling has a prodifferentiative effect on the ES cell.[29]

3. The SRF transcription factor, a direct target of activated ERKs, is an important regulator of somatic cell proliferation in response to serum stimulation. SRF regulates the expression of growth-promoting transcription factors like c-fos and Egr-1.[31] C-fos, with c-jun and ets, is a critical regulator of cyclin D1 expression.[32–34] Thus, SRF and its targets are thought to play an important role in activating the cyclin D-CDK4/6 → RB-E2F pathway in response to growth-factor stimulation. SRF-deficient ES cells have a normal proliferation rate despite the severely impaired serum-dependent expression of c-fos and Egr-1.[31] Thus, the SRF function is dispensable in the ES cell.

Together, these data provide evidence that the cascade that operates in most cells—which begins with extracellular mitogens, transduces signals through the Ras/ERK pathway, and leads to regulation of cyclin-CDK complexes and RB phosphorylation—is not engaged in ES cells.

The Ras/ERK pathway seems to be dedicated largely to driving RB phosphorylation in somatic cells.[35] Hence, inhibitors of this pathway have a strong cytostatic effect on the proliferation of normal cells but only a minimal effect on tumorigenic cells whose growth has escaped RB control.[36–38] Therefore, the resistance of ES cells to disruption of Ras/ERK signaling further indicates that the ES cell lack RB control in the G_1 phase.

PI3K Signaling Contributes to Regulation of the ES Cell Cycle

Increased levels of 3′-phosphorylated phosphoinositides are frequently associated with growth factor and cytokine signaling. This occurs through receptor-mediated translocation of PI3K to the cell membrane. The PI3K products $PI(3,4)P_2$ and $PI(3,4,5)P_3$ activate several signal transducers, including the serine–threonine kinases phosphoinositide-dependent kinase 1 (PDK1) and protein kinase B (PKB/Akt). The tumor suppressor PTEN, which removes the phosphate from the 3′ position of 3′-phosphoinositides, is a negative regulator of this pathway. Coordinate localization of the lipid-bound kinase at the membrane facilitates PDK1-mediated phosphorylation of PKB, which then modulates the expression of key regulators of the cell cycle. In particular, PKB decreases the rate of degradation of cyclin D1,[39] whereas it increases the rate of degradation of $p27^{kip1}$, an inhibitor of the G_1–S transition.[40] Both result in promotion of G_1 transit in response to mitogenic stimulation.

Data show that ES cells differ from other cell types both in the regulation of PI3K activity and in the downstream signaling cascades that it activates (Fig. 5–2). Specific pharmacological inhibition of PI3K activity in ES cells increases the proportion of cells in G1. This is accompanied by down-regulation of cyclin D1 expression.[30] Moreover, the genetic disruption of p85α results in G_1 growth retardation and up-regulation of the $p27^{kip1}$ inhibitor.[41] Conversely, ES cells lacking PTEN exhibit an accelerated transit through G_1, which appears to be caused by an increase in the rate of degradation of the $p27^{kip1}$ inhibitor.[42] Therefore, ES cells appear to be dependent on PI3K activity for proliferation. Interestingly, this activity is not impaired by serum starvation in ES cells.[30] This suggests that PI3K activity does not depend on mitogenic stimulation, a finding consistent with the evidence that serum starvation does not induce ES cell growth arrest.[31] One possible activator of PI3K is the product of the Ras-like gene, *Eras*. Eras is expressed in mouse ES cells, where it interacts with PI3K but not with Raf. Eras-null ES cells display attenuated PI3K signaling, as well as impaired growth that is rescued by forced expression of active PI3K. Eras is therefore a novel pathway that activates PI3K in ES cells.[43]

PI3K-dependent signals that influence the proliferation of ES cells have not been defined. PKB would seem to be a likely candidate, but ES cells lacking the upstream activator PDK1 are viable.[44] These ES cells exhibit negligible activation of PKB and fail to activate other targets of PDK1. These data point to the possibility that PI3K may influence ES cell growth through a PDK1/PKB-independent pathway. The PKB-related protein serum and glucocorticoid-induced kinase 1 (SGK1) might fulfill this role.[45, 46]

ES Cell-Cycle Machinery Is Constitutively Active

EXPRESSION OF CYCLIN D1 IS NOT DEPENDENT ON MITOGENIC STIMULATION IN ES CELLS

Cyclin D1 is an essential regulator of the G_1–S transition in response to growth factor stimulation in somatic cells. As we have described, ES cells express a low cyclin D1 level. Furthermore, regulation of cyclin D1 expression differs between ES cells and other cells (see Fig. 5–2). First, the Ras/ERK pathway, central to the transcriptional activation of cyclin D1 expression in somatic cells,[32, 33, 47, 48] does not contribute to the regulation of cyclin D1 expression in ES cells,[30] a finding consistent with the evidence that ERK signaling does not promote ES cell proliferation. Second, the steady-state level of cyclin D1 protein is critically regulated by PI3K signaling in ES cells[30] like in other cells. PI3K-dependent regulation of the cyclin D1 protein level occurs mostly through the regulation of the glycogen synthase kinase 3β-dependent rate of degradation.[39] Unlike somatic cells, however, PI3K activity seems to be uncoupled from persistent mitogenic stimulation in ES cells.[30] Thus, neither PI3K activity nor cyclin D1 expression is down-regulated after serum starvation. Together, these data lead us to the conclusion that expression of cyclin D1 is disconnected from mitogenic signals transduced by tyrosine kinase receptors in ES cells. Constitutive, albeit low, expression of cyclin D1 could contribute to constitutive phosphorylation of RB. Alternatively, the functional significance of cyclin D-CDK4 complexes in ES cells may be to sequester[49] $p27^{kip1}$ and to prevent this inhibitor from acting on cyclin E-CDK2 kinase.[15]

ABSENCE OF CELL-CYCLE-REGULATED CDK2 ACTIVITY IN MOUSE ES CELLS

Cyclin-CDK complexes become activated at precise points of the cell cycle in somatic cells. The cyclin D-CDK4/6 complexes are formed during the G_2 phase that precedes mitosis. They are maintained throughout the subsequent G1 phase, and their level drops abruptly when cells enter the S phase. The cyclin E-CDK2 complexes are present during the late G_1 phase. Activity of these complexes drops at the beginning of the S phase. Then CDK2 forms new complexes with cyclin A to regulate DNA replication. The cyclin A-CDK2 complexes are progressively replaced by cyclin B1-CDC2 complexes during transit through the G_2 phase. The level of those latter complexes collapse before reentry into G_1. Precise temporal control of these cyclin-CDK kinase activities is crucial in establishing transitions from one cell-cycle phase to the next and in ensuring that cell-cycle events are executed in the correct order.[3, 11] The cell-cycle regulation of cyclin D, E, A, and B1 levels plays a critical role in this process (Fig. 5–3).

The periodic expression of cyclin-CDK complexes and the subsequent regulation of cell-cycle progression appears to be operative in all cell types. The ES cell-cycle clock is likely to be markedly different. ES cells display vastly elevated cyclin E-, cyclin A-, and cyclin B-associated kinase activities, and both cyclin E and cyclin A are expressed at levels well

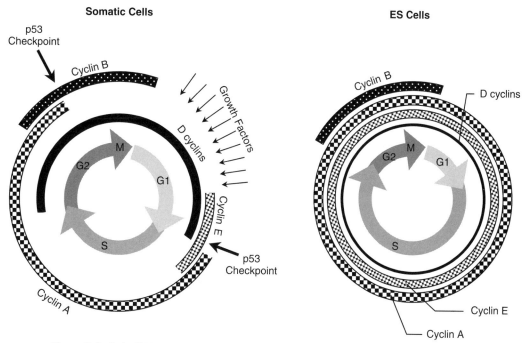

Figure 5–3. Cyclin-CDK expression patterns during cell-cycle progression in somatic cells and mouse ES cells.

beyond those seen in other primary and transformed mouse cell lines. Furthermore, cyclin E-CDK2- and cyclin A-CDK2-associated kinase activities show no obvious periodicity during cell-cycle progression. Only cyclin B1-CDC2-associated kinase activity is clearly cell-cycle dependent, being most active in G_2–M.[30]

These data provide evidence that cyclin E-CDK2 and cyclin A-CDK2 kinases are constitutively active in the ES cell. This observation provides a satisfactorily explanation to the previous finding that ES cell are able to proliferate actively despite Pow cyclin D-associated CDK activity. Hence, high cyclin E activity in breast cancer cell lines can completely substitute for cyclin D-associated CDK activities.[50] Similarly, enforced expression of cyclin E renders somatic cells resistant to growth inhibition by p16[ink4a],[51] whereas constitutive cyclin E-CDK2 activity in fibroblasts is associated with anchorage-independent growth,[52] another property exhibited by mouse ES cells.

E2F TARGET GENES ARE NOT CELL-CYCLE REGULATED IN MOUSE ES CELLS

Upon release from the block imposed by the hypophosphorylated (G_1-specific) form of the RB family members, the free E2F transcription factors up-regulate the expression of a several genes involved in cell-cycle progression (i.e., *cyclin E*, c-*myc*, B-*myb*, and *Cdc2*) as well as in DNA replication. The activation of these *E2F* target genes is therefore tightly linked to the temporal activation of cyclin D-CDK4/6 and cyclin E-CDK2; together, they are crucial in controlling the kinetics of transit through G_1- and S-phase entry in somatic

cells.[4, 53] ES cells again appear different in that E2F4, the predominant form of E2F activity in ES cells,[54] is almost exclusively in the free, active form and that strong E2F4 DNA-binding activity is present throughout the cell cycle. Furthermore, ES cells do not display cell-cycle–dependent expression of the *E2F* target genes.[30]

As the CDK activities associated with the G1–S transition are ectopically active and the target genes of these activities are constitutively expressed throughout the cell cycle, the ES cell mitotic cycle appears to be constitutively primed for DNA replication. It has been proposed that ES cells lack the G_1 checkpoint (also called the restriction point),[30] defined as the point in G_1 when a cell becomes irreversibly committed to S phase and no longer requires growth factor stimulation. Loss of the G_1 checkpoint is often associated with transformation in cancer cells.[11]

Mouse ES Cells Lack p53-Dependent Checkpoints

Following DNA damage or nucleotide depletion, the cell cycle is arrested in G_1 and in G_2. Arrest in G_1 prevents aberrant replication of damaged DNA, and arrest in G_2 allows cells to avoid segregation of defective chromosomes. Both checkpoints crucially rely on the p53 transcription factor, which becomes stabilized upon DNA damage and regulates the transcription of several genes, among which is the *p21*[*waf1/cip1*] CDK inhibitor capable of silencing cyclin E-CDK2 and cyclin B-CDC2. This leads to the accumulation of the growth suppressive form of RB[10, 11, 15, 27, 55] (Fig. 5–1).

ES cells do not undergo cell-cycle arrest at the G_1 and G_2 checkpoints in response to DNA damage or nucleotide depletion, although they synthesize abundant quantities of transcriptionally active p53.[24, 25] Several factors may account for the inability of ES cells to arrest growth at the G_1–S or G_2–M transitions. First, the p53 protein in ES cells is mainly, if not exclusively, cytoplasmic, and it translocates inefficiently to the nucleus upon DNA damage. Second, ectopically expressed nuclear p53 appears unable to activate p21[waf1/cip1] expression and to trigger cell-cycle arrest. Hence, ES cells have an effective mechanism for rendering them refractory to p53 function.[24] In addition, growth arrest at the G_1–S transition following DNA damage relies crucially on the RB pathway,[19, 20, 26] and, as we have explained, this pathway is not functional in ES cells.

Therefore, ES cells appear to lack the p53-dependent G_1 and G_2 checkpoints that characterize normal somatic cells. The question arises of how these cells maintain genome integrity in the absence of cell-cycle checkpoints. After DNA damage, ES cells undergo p53-dependent apoptosis,[25] so there is a suggestion that the function of p53 in ES cells is to trigger apoptosis, thereby efficiently eliminating all cells with damaged DNA.

Unrestricted Proliferation and Self-Renewal

As we have described, ES cells have an unorthodox cell cycle in which most of the G_1 control pathways operative in other cell types are absent. Uncoupling the G_1 phase of the cell cycle from extrinsic stimuli helps to explain the rapid proliferative rate of ES cells as well as their ability to form teratocarcinomas when placed in a heterologous environment *in vivo*.[2] Hence, loss of functional RB and p53 pathways, constitutive PI3K activity, or ectopic cyclin E-CDK2 kinase activity—four features of the ES cell mitotic cycle—is often associated with tumor growth.[7, 8, 50, 56]

It is tempting to speculate that constitutive transit through G_1 may actively sustain the undifferentiated state. Indeed, P19 embryonal carcinoma cells display increased sensitivity to retinoic acid-induced differentiation during the G_1 phase,[57] suggesting that ES cells are particularly vulnerable to differentiation inducers while they progress from mitosis to the next S phase. Hypophosphorylated (G_1-specific) RB contributes to differentiation in certain cell types, where it participates in complex formation with differentiation-promoting transcription factors such as MyoD, myogenin, NF-IL6, and C/EBP.[58–61] Constitutive phosphorylation of RB would therefore protect the ES cell from differentiation-promoting factors.

The STAT3 transcription factor may contribute to activation of the G_1–S transition. On the one hand, STAT3 is known to be a critical regulator of ES cell self-renewal in response to activation of the gp130 receptor by LIF.[62, 63] On the other hand, STAT3 is known to promote entry into the S phase in some types of differentiated cells, and it activates expression of specific cell-cycle regulators including junB, Myc, and

Pim-1.[63–65] JunB and Myc are transcriptional activators of the *cyclin A* and *cyclin E* gene, respectively.[10, 66] Pim-1 is a serine–threonine kinase that phosphorylates and activates Cdc25A, thereby potentiating the accumulation of active cyclin E-CDK2 and cyclin A-CDK2 kinases.[67] Therefore, the LIF/gp130/STAT3 pathway may suppress differentiation by up-regulating expression of key regulators of the G_1–S transition.[2]

Cell-Cycle Control in the Early Postimplantation Mouse Embryo

The lack of control over the G_1–S transition in ES cells—and the gain of this control during differentiation—is likely to reflect a similar phenomenon in the early postimplantation embryo. Epiblast is the founder tissue of the whole embryo in rodents. Epiblast cells are highly proliferating ($t_{1/2}$ = 9–11 hours) and potentially tumorigenic.[68, 69] The onset of gastrulation (6.5 days postcoitus) is associated with an increase in the proliferation rate of epiblast cells as well as with the start of differentiation within the embryo proper. Hence, most cells of the gastrulation embryo (pluripotent epiblast, mesoderm, and endoderm cells) have a cell cycle of 7–7.5 hours[70, 71] and a G_1 phase of 1.5–2 hours. But the cells of the primitive streak divide every 3–3.5 hours with a further shortening of all three phases of the cell cycle: G1 (<30 min.), S (2–2.75 hours), and G_2 (<20 min.).[72] Therefore, the commitment of epiblast progenitors to become mesoderm and endoderm is associated with a very short cell cycle during transit through the primitive streak (Fig. 5–4).

Epiblast cells of the pregastrulation embryo do not express D-type cyclins. Expression of cyclin D1 is activated first in the whole epiblast of the gastrulating embryo. Expression of cyclin D2 (superimposed on that of cyclin D1) is activated next and coincides with the transit of epiblast progenitors through the primitive streak.[14] Thus, activation of cyclin D1 and cyclin D2 expression coincides first with the increase in the growth rate of the epiblast cells taking place at the onset of gastrulation (cyclin D1) and second with the further increase in the growth rate occurring when epiblast cells migrate through the primitive streak (cyclin D2). The activation of cyclin D1 expression takes place in the pluripotent epiblast prior to commitment to ectoderm, mesoderm, and endoderm lineages, suggesting that the gain of cyclin D1-associated functions is a prerequisite for differentiation.

It is tempting to speculate that activation of cyclin D1 expression in the pluripotent epiblast of the gastrulating embryo reflects the acquisition of G_1–S regulation by tyrosine kinase receptors and the downstream Ras cascade. This is corroborated by the genetic disruption of Grb2 or SRF, both of which result in severe developmental defects. Grb2-deficient ES cells are unable to contribute to epiblast development in the gastrulating embryo.[28] SRF-deficient embryos display severe gastrulation defects, evidenced by the lack of primitive streak formation and of any mesodermal cells.[73] Thus, pluripotent ES cells are likely to become Ras dependent at the onset of gastrulation.

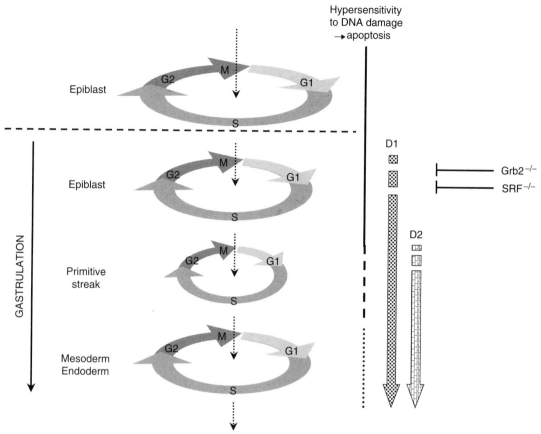

Figure 5–4. Variations of cell-cycle kinetics and expression patterns of cyclin D_1 and cyclin D_2 in the pregastrulation and gastrulation mouse embryo.

As we have explained, ES cells lack the DNA damage checkpoints and sustain extensive apoptosis after treatment with DNA damaging agents.[24, 25] A similar situation is observed in the gastrulation embryo, where irradiation does not induce growth arrest. Rather, epiblast cells undergo extensive apoptosis. This apoptotic response is not observed in the extraembryonic tissues and is observed only at very low levels in the mesoderm and endoderm.[74] It seems, therefore, that commitment of pluripotent epiblast cells to differentiation into mesoderm or endoderm coincides with a major change in the fate of DNA-damaged cells. It is tempting to speculate that this commitment is associated with the gain of DNA damage checkpoints in the G_1 and G_2 phases of the cell cycle.

Summary

The epiblast cells of the early postimplantation embryo and the ES cells share extensive similarities regarding their cell-cycle features. Both display an unusual cell-cycle distribution with few cells in the G_1 and G_2 phases, they do not rely on Grb2-dependent signaling and on SRF-dependent transcription, and they do not seem to undergo cell-cycle arrest—a prerequisite to DNA repair—after DNA damage. Together,

these results point to some fundamental differences in the regulation of the mitotic cycle in mouse ES cells. This might simply reflect the requirement of rapidly producing sufficient cell numbers to initiate gastrulation. As we have explained, it is possible that the cell-cycle properties of ES cells might also be involved in sustaining the undifferentiated state. If this is the case, then these properties should be shared with the ES cells of other species. It will be instructive to determine whether primate ES cells exhibit the cell-cycle features of their rodent counterparts, particularly in light of a report that human ES cells have a markedly reduced proliferation rate compared to mouse ES cells.[75]

ACKNOWLEDGMENTS

Anna Malashicheva is a recipient of a fellowship from the Ligue Nationale contre le Cancer.

REFERENCES

1. Smith, A.G. (2001). Embryo-derived stem cells: of mice and men. *Annu. Rev. Cell Dev. Biol.* **17,** 435–462.

2. Burdon, T., Smith, A., and Savatier, P. (2002). Signaling, cell cycle, and pluripotency in embryonic stem cells. *Trends Cell Biol.* **12,** 432–438.

3. Weinberg, R.A. (1995). The retinoblastoma protein and cell-cycle control. *Cell* **81,** 323–330.

4. Dyson, N. (1998). The regulation of E2F by pRB-family proteins. *Genes Dev.* **12,** 2245–2262.

5. Harbour, J.W., and Dean, D.C. (2000). The Rb/E2F pathway: expanding roles and emerging paradigms. *Genes Dev.* **14,** 2393–2409.

6. Nevins, J.R. (2001). The Rb/E2F pathway and cancer. *Hum. Mol. Genet.* **10,** 699–703.

7. Sherr, C.J. (1996). Cancer cell cycles. *Science* **274,** 1672–1677.

8. Bartkova, J., Lukas, J., and Bartek, J. (1997). Aberrations of the G1- and G1–S-regulating genes in human cancer. *Prog. Cell Cycle Res.* **3,** 211–220.

9. Bartek, J., Bartkova, J., and Lukas, J. (1997). The retinoblastoma protein pathway in cell-cycle control and cancer. *Exp. Cell Res.* **237,** 1–6.

10. Bartek, J., and Lukas, J. (2001). Pathways governing G1–S transition and their response to DNA damage. *FEBS Lett.* **490,** 117–122.

11. Blagosklonny, M.V., and Pardee, A.B. (2002). The restriction point of the cell cycle. *Cell Cycle* **1,** 103–110.

12. Savatier, P., Huang, S., Szekely, L., Wiman, K.G., and Samarut, J. (1994). Contrasting patterns of retinoblastoma protein expression in mouse embryonic stem cells and embryonic fibroblasts. *Oncogene* **9,** 809–818.

13. Savatier, P., Lapillonne, H., van Grunsven, L.A., Rudkin, B.B., and Samarut, J. (1996). Withdrawal of differentiation inhibitory activity–leukemia inhibitory factor up-regulates D-type cyclins and cyclin-dependent kinase inhibitors in mouse embryonic stem cells. *Oncogene* **12,** 309–322.

14. Wianny, F., Real, F.X., Mummery, C.L., Van Rooijen, M., Lahti, J., Samarut, J., and Savatier, P. (1998). G1-phase regulators, cyclin D1, cyclin D2, and cyclin D3: Up-regulation at gastrulation and dynamic expression during neurulation. *Dev. Dyn.* **212,** 49–62.

15. Sherr, C.J., and Roberts, J.M. (1999). CDK inhibitors: positive and negative regulators of G1-phase progression. *Genes Dev.* **13,** 1501–1512.

16. Medema, R.H., Herrera, R.E., Lam, F., and Weinberg, R.A. (1995). Growth suppression by p16ink4 requires functional retinoblastoma protein. *Proc. Nat. Acad. Sci. USA* **92,** 6289–6293.

17. Lukas, J., Parry, D., Aagaard, L., Mann, D.J., Bartkova, J., Strauss, M., Peters, G., and Bartek, J. (1995). Retinoblastoma-protein-dependent cell-cycle inhibition by the tumor suppressor p16. *Nature* **375,** 503–506.

18. Takahashi, K., Mitsui, K., and Yamanaka, S. (2003). Role of Eras in promoting tumour-like properties in mouse embryonic stem cells. *Nature* **423,** 541–545.

19. Dannenberg, J.H., van Rossum, A., Schuijff, L., and te Riele, H. (2000). Ablation of the retinoblastoma gene family deregulates G(1) control causing immortalization and increased cell turnover under growth-restricting conditions. *Genes Dev.* **14,** 3051–3064.

20. Sage, J., Mulligan, G.J., Attardi, L.D., Miller, A., Chen, S., Williams, B., Theodorou, E., and Jacks, T. (2000). Targeted disruption of the three Rb-related genes leads to loss of G(1) control and immortalization. *Genes Dev.* **14,** 3037–3050.

21. St. Croix, B., Sheehan, C., Rak, J.W., Florenes, V.A., Slingerland, J.M., and Kerbel, R.S. (1998). E-cadherin-dependent growth suppression is mediated by the cyclin-dependent kinase inhibitor p27(KIP1). *J. Cell Biol.* **142,** 557–571.

22. Stein, G.H., and Dulic, V. (1998). Molecular mechanisms for the senescent cell-cycle arrest. *J. Investig. Dermatol. Symp. Proc.* **3,** 14–18.

23. Brown, J.P., Wei, W., and Sedivy, J.M. (1997). Bypass of senescence after disruption of *p21CIP1/WAF1* gene in normal diploid human fibroblasts. *Science* **277,** 831–834.

24. Aladjem, M.I., Spike, B.T., Rodewald, L.W., Hope, T.J., Klemm, M., Jaenisch, R., and Wahl, G.M. (1998). ES cells do not activate p53-dependent stress responses and undergo p53-independent apoptosis in response to DNA damage. *Curr. Biol.* **8,** 145–155.

25. Prost, S., Bellamy, C.O., Clarke, A.R., Wyllie, A.H., and Harrison, D.J. (1998). p53-independent DNA repair and cell-cycle arrest in embryonic stem cells. *FEBS Lett.* **425,** 499–504.

26. Harrington, E.A., Bruce, J.L., Harlow, E., and Dyson, N. (1998). pRB plays an essential role in cell-cycle arrest induced by DNA damage. *Proc. Natl. Acad. Sci. USA* **95,** 11,945–11,950.

27. Brugarolas, J., Moberg, K., Boyd, S.D., Taya, Y., Jacks, T., and Lees, J.A. (1999). Inhibition of cyclin-dependent kinase 2 by p21 is necessary for retinoblastoma protein-mediated G1 arrest after gamma irradiation. *Proc. Natl. Acad. Sci. USA* **96,** 1002–1007.

28. Cheng, A.M., Saxton, T.M., Sakai, R., Kulkarni, S., Mbamalu, G., Vogel, W., Tortorice, C.G., Cardiff, R.D., Cross, J.C., Muller, W.J., and Pawson, T. (1998). Mammalian Grb2 regulates multiple steps in embryonic development and malignant transformation. *Cell* **95,** 793–803.

29. Burdon, T., Stracey, C., Chambers, I., Nichols, J., and Smith, A. (1999). Suppression of SHP-2 and ERK signaling promotes self-renewal of mouse embryonic stem cells. *Dev. Biol.* **210,** 30–43.

30. Jirmanova, L., Afanassieff, M., Gobert-Gosse, S., Markossian, S., and Savatier, P. (2002). Differential contributions of ERK and PI3-kinase to the regulation of cyclin D1 expression and to the control of the G1–S transition in mouse embryonic stem cells. *Oncogene* **21,** 5515–5528.

31. Schratt, G., Weinhold, B., Lundberg, A.S., Schuck, S., Berger, J., Schwarz, H., Weinberg, R.A., Ruther, U., and Nordheim, A. (2001). Serum response factor is required for immediate-early gene activation yet is dispensable for proliferation of embryonic stem cells. *Mol. Cell Biol.* **21,** 2933–2943.

32. Albanese, C., Johnson, J., Watanabe, G., Eklund, N., Vu, D., Arnold, A., and Pestell, R.G. (1995). Transforming p21ras mutants and c-Ets-2 activate the cyclin D1 promoter through distinguishable regions. *J. Biol. Chem.* **270,** 23,589–23,597.

33. Kerkhoff, E., and Rapp, U.R. (1998). Cell-cycle targets of Ras/Raf signaling. *Oncogene* **17,** 1457–1462.

34. Brown, J.R., Nigh, E., Lee, R.J., Ye, H., Thompson, M.A., Saudou, F., Pestell, R.G., and Greenberg, M.E. (1998). Fos family members induce cell-cycle entry by activating cyclin D1. *Mol. Cell Biol.* **18,** 5609–5619.

35. Lukas, J., Bartkova, J., and Bartek, J. (1996). Convergence of mitogenic signaling cascades from diverse classes of receptors at the cyclin D-cyclin-dependent kinase-pRb-controlled G1 checkpoint. *Mol. Cell Biol.* **16,** 6917–6925.

36. Peeper, D.S., Upton, T.M., Ladha, M.H., Neuman, E., Zalvide, J., Bernards, R., DeCaprio, J.A., and Ewen, M.E. (1997). Ras signaling linked to the cell-cycle machinery by the retinoblastoma protein. *Nature* **386,** 177–181.

37. Leone, G., DeGregori, J., Sears, R., Jakoi, L., and Nevins, J.R. (1997). Myc and Ras collaborate in inducing accumulation of active cyclin E/Cdk2 and E2F. *Nature* **387,** 422–426.

38. Mittnacht, S., Paterson, H., Olson, M.F., and Marshall, C.J. (1997). Ras signaling is required for inactivation of the tumor suppressor pRb cell-cycle control protein. *Curr. Biol.* **7,** 219–221.

39. Diehl, J.A., Cheng, M., Roussel, M.F., and Sherr, C.J. (1998). Glycogen synthase kinase-3beta regulates cyclin D1 proteolysis and subcellular localization. *Genes Dev.* **12**, 3499–3511.

40. Liang, J., Zubovitz, J., Petrocelli, T., Kotchetkov, R., Connor, M.K., Han, K., Lee, J.H., Ciarallo, S., Catzavelos, C., Beniston, R., Franssen, E., and Slingerland, J.M. (2002). PKB/Akt phosphorylates p27, impairs nuclear import of p27 and opposes p27-mediated G1 arrest. *Nat. Med.* **8**, 1153–1160.

41. Hallmann, D., Trumper, K., Trusheim, H., Ueki, K., Kahn, C.R., Cantley, L.C., Fruman, D.A., and Horsch, D. (2003). Altered signaling and cell-cycle regulation in embryonal stem cells with a disruption of the gene for phosphoinositide 3-kinase regulatory subunit p85α. *J. Biol. Chem.* **278**, 5099–5108.

42. Sun, H., Lesche, R., Li, D.M., Liliental, J., Zhang, H., Gao, J., Gavrilova, N., Mueller, B., Liu, X., and Wu, H. (1999). PTEN modulates cell-cycle progression and cell survival by regulating phosphatidylinositol 3-, 4-, and 5-trisphosphate and Akt/protein kinase B signaling pathway. *Proc. Natl. Acad. Sci. USA* **96**, 6199–6204.

43. Faast, R., White, J., Cartwright, P., Sarcevic, B., and Dalton, S. (2004). Cdk6-cyclin D3 activity in murine ES cells is resistant to inhibition by p16(INK4a). *Oncogene* **23**, 491–502.

44. Williams, M.R., Arthur, J.S., Balendran, A., van der Kaay, J., Poli, V., Cohen, P., and Alessi, D.R. (2000). The role of 3-phosphoinositide-dependent protein kinase 1 in activating AGC kinases defined in embryonic stem cells. *Curr. Biol.* **10**, 439–448.

45. Kobayashi, T., and Cohen, P. (1999). Activation of serum- and glucocorticoid-regulated protein kinase by agonists that activate phosphatidylinositide 3-kinase is mediated by 3-phosphoinositide-dependent protein kinase-1 (PDK1) and PDK2. *Biochem. J.* **339 (Pt. 2),** 319–328.

46. Park, J., Leong, M.L., Buse, P., Maiyar, A.C., Firestone, G.L., and Hemmings, B.A. (1999). Serum and glucocorticoid-inducible kinase (SGK) is a target of the PI 3-kinase-stimulated signaling pathway. *EMBO J.* **18**, 3024–3033.

47. Winston, J.T., Coats, S.R., Wang, Y.Z., and Pledger, W.J. (1996). Regulation of the cell-cycle machinery by oncogenic *Ras*. *Oncogene* **12**, 127–134.

48. Aktas, H., Cai, H., and Cooper, G.M. (1997). Ras links growth factor signaling to the cell-cycle machinery via regulation of cyclin D1 and the Cdk inhibitor p27KIP1. *Mol. Cell Biol.* **17**, 3850–3857.

49. Savatier, P. (Unpublished data).

50. Gray-Bablin, J., Zalvide, J., Fox, M.P., Knickerbocker, C.J., DeCaprio, J.A., and Keyomarsi, K. (1996). Cyclin E, a redundant cyclin in breast cancer. *Proc. Natl. Acad. Sci. USA* **93**, 15,215–15,220.

51. Lukas, J., Herzinger, T., Hansen, K., Moroni, M.C., Resnitzky, D., Helin, K., Reed, S.I., and Bartek, J. (1997). Cyclin E-induced S phase without activation of the pRb/E2F pathway. *Genes Dev.* **11**, 1479–1492.

52. Fang, F., Orend, G., Watanabe, N., Hunter, T., and Ruoslahti, E. (1996). Dependence of cyclin E-CDK2 kinase activity on cell anchorage. *Science* **271**, 499–502.

53. Helin, K. (1998). Regulation of cell proliferation by the E2F transcription factors. *Curr. Opin. Genet. Dev.* **8**, 28–35.

54. Humbert, P.O., Rogers, C., Ganiatsas, S., Landsberg, R.L., Trimarchi, J.M., Dandapani, S., Brugnara, C., Erdman, S., Schrenzel, M., Bronson, R.T., and Lees, J.A. (2000). E2F4 is essential for normal erythrocyte maturation and neonatal viability. *Mol. Cell* **6**, 281–291.

55. Zhou, B.B., and Elledge, S.J. (2000). The DNA damage response: putting checkpoints in perspective. *Nature* **408**, 433–439.

56. Barre, B., Avril, S., and Coqueret, O. (2003). Opposite regulation of myc and p21waf1 transcription by STAT3 proteins. *J. Biol. Chem.* **278**, 2990–2996.

57. Mummery, C.L., van den Brink, C.E., and de Laat, S.W. (1987). Commitment to differentiation induced by retinoic acid in P19 embryonal carcinoma cells is cell-cycle dependent. *Dev. Biol.* **121**, 10–19.

58. Gu, W., Schneider, J.W., Condorelli, G., Kaushal, S., Mahdavi, V., and Nadal-Ginard, B. (1993). Interaction of myogenic factors and the retinoblastoma protein mediates muscle cell commitment and differentiation. *Cell* **72**, 309–324.

59. Novitch, B.G., Spicer, D.B., Kim, P.S., Cheung, W.L., and Lassar, A.B. (1999). pRb is required for MEF2-dependent gene expression as well as cell-cycle arrest during skeletal muscle differentiation. *Curr. Biol.* **9**, 449–459.

60. Chen, P.L., Riley, D.J., Chen-Kiang, S., and Lee, W.H. (1996). Retinoblastoma protein directly interacts with and activates the transcription factor NF-IL6. *Proc. Natl. Acad. Sci. USA* **93**, 465–469.

61. Chen, P.L., Riley, D.J., Chen, Y., and Lee, W.H. (1996). Retinoblastoma protein positively regulates terminal adipocyte differentiation through direct interaction with C/EBPs. *Genes Dev.* **10**, 2794–2804.

62. Niwa, H., Burdon, T., Chambers, I., and Smith, A. (1998). Self-renewal of pluripotent embryonic stem cells is mediated via activation of STAT3. *Genes Dev.* **12**, 2048–2060.

63. Matsuda, T., Nakamura, T., Nakao, K., Arai, T., Katsuki, M., Heike, T., and Yokota, T. (1999). STAT3 activation is sufficient to maintain an undifferentiated state of mouse embryonic stem cells. *EMBO J.* **18**, 4261–4269.

64. Fukada, T., Ohtani, T., Yoshida, Y., Shirogane, T., Nishida, K., Nakajima, K., Hibi, M., and Hirano, T. (1998). STAT3 orchestrates contradictory signals in cytokine-induced G1 to S cell-cycle transition. *Embo. J.* **17**, 6670–6677.

65. Shirogane, T., Fukada, T., Muller, J.M., Shima, D.T., Hibi, M., and Hirano, T. (1999). Synergistic roles for Pim-1 and c-Myc in STAT3-mediated cell-cycle progression and antiapoptosis. *Immunity* **11**, 709–719.

66. Andrecht, S., Kolbus, A., Hartenstein, B., Angel, P., and Schorpp-Kistner, M. (2002). Cell-cycle-promoting activity of JunB through cyclin A activation. *J. Biol. Chem.* **277**, 35,961–35,968.

67. Mochizuki, T., Kitanaka, C., Noguchi, K., Muramatsu, T., Asai, A., and Kuchino, Y. (1999). Physical and functional interactions between Pim-1 kinase and Cdc25A phosphatase. Implications for the Pim-1-mediated activation of the c-Myc signaling pathway. *J. Biol. Chem.* **274**, 18,659–18,666.

68. Snow, M.H.L. (1977). Gastrulation in the mouse: growth and regionalization of the epiblast. *J. Embryol. Exp. Morphol.* **42**, 293–303.

69. Solter, D., Dominis, M., and Damjanov, I. (1980). Cell-cycle analysis in the mouse egg cylinder. *Int. J. Cancer* **25**, 341–349.

70. Poelmann, R.E. (1981). Differential mitosis and degeneration patterns in relation to the alterations in the shape of the embryonic ectoderm of early postimplantation mouse embryos. *J. Embryol. Exp. Morphol.* **55**, 33–51.

71. Lawson, K.A., Meneses, J.J., and Pedersen, R.A. (1991). Clonal analysis of epiblast fate during germ layer formation in the mouse embryo. *Development* **113**, 891–911.

72. Mac Auley, A., Werb, Z., and Mirkes, P.E. (1993). Characterization of the unusually rapid cell cycles during rat gastrulation. *Development* **117,** 873–883.

73. Arsenian, S., Weinhold, B., Oelgeschlager, M., Ruther, U., and Nordheim, A. (1998). Serum response factor is essential for mesoderm formation during mouse embryogenesis. *EMBO J.* **17,** 6289–6299.

74. Heyer, B.S., MacAuley, A., Behrendtsen, O., and Werb, Z. (2000). Hypersensitivity to DNA damage leads to increased apoptosis during early mouse development. *Genes Dev.* **14,** 2072–2084.

75. Amit, M., Carpenter, M.K., Inokuma, M.S., Chiu, C.P., Harris, C.P., Waknitz, M.A., Itskovitz-Eldor, J., and Thomson, J.A. (2000). Clonally derived human embryonic stem cell lines maintain pluripotency and proliferative potential for prolonged periods of culture. *Dev. Biol.* **227,** 271–278.

Chromatin-Modifying Factors and Transcriptional Regulation During Development

Scott Bultman, Nathan Montgomery, and Terry Magnuson

Introduction

CHROMATIN AND TRANSCRIPTIONAL REGULATION DURING DEVELOPMENT

Regulation of gene expression is inherently more complicated in eukaryotes than in prokaryotes because the transcriptional machinery must recognize a chromatin template instead of naked DNA.[1,2] Consequently, chromatin-modifying factors play crucial roles in transcriptional regulation and must be involved in many biological processes, including the ability of stem cells to proliferate and differentiate into genetically identical but functionally diverse cell types.

Although sequence-specific transcription factors are necessary for transcription of downstream target genes, they are usually not sufficient because the RNA polymerase II holoenzyme is so large that it cannot access DNA in the context of nucleosomes or higher-order chromatin structures (Fig. 6–1). However, transcriptional activators bound to specific promoters can recruit protein complexes up to 2 megadalton (MDa), which covalently modify N-terminal histone tails or use ATPase activity to alter the conformation, position, or both of nucleosomes.[3,4] As a result, these promoters adopt an "open" chromatin configuration capable of binding the RNA polymerase II holoenzyme so that transcription can be initiated. This open state is responsible for characteristic DNase I hypersensitive sites. Conversely, transcriptional repressors can recruit similar or identical complexes to other loci to establish a "closed" chromatin configuration that cannot be transcribed. In addition to being involved in transcriptional initiation, chromatin-modifying factors often maintain the gene expression profiles required to fully execute a program of differentiation from committed progenitor cells through numerous cell divisions to terminal differentiation. Considering their role in both establishing and maintaining transcriptional states, chromatin-modifying factors should play an important role in many aspects of normal development and physiology. Numerous mutations in chromatin-modifying factors generated by gene targeting in the mouse confer embryonic-lethal phenotypes, confirming this supposition[5] (Table 6–1). As described in

this chapter, the biological significance of chromatin-modifying factors is also clearly demonstrated by normal and abnormal epigenetic events that have been documented in cloning experiments.

IMPORTANCE OF CHROMATIN IN HEREDITY IS UNDERSCORED BY UNEXPECTED COAT COLORS AND DEVELOPMENTAL DEFECTS IN CLONED ANIMALS

The first cloned cat, called Cc for either copy cat or carbon copy, is particularly interesting because she has different coat-color markings than her genetic donor despite being genetically identical[6] (Fig. 6–2). This observation indicates that DNA sequence alone is not sufficient to confer certain genetic traits. Instead, a heritable influence must exist that is not based on DNA sequence. This influence, referred to as epigenetics, is not as well understood as the genetic code, but it is becoming increasingly clear that it involves the ability of a chromatin structure to affect transcription at the level of individual genes, clusters of genes, or even whole chromosomes. In the case of Cc, the apparent paradox of her unexpected coat-color markings can be reconciled by an epigenetic event called X-chromosome inactivation. Female mammals have two X-chromosomes, whereas males have only one. Consequently, one of the two X-chromosomes is inactivated stochastically on a cell-by-cell basis in females during early embryogenesis and maintained in a clonal manner throughout the numerous cell divisions that occur during development. The primary goal of this process is to achieve the same level of X-linked gene activity in females as males (i.e., dosage compensation), but the stochastic nature of X-chromosome inactivation also results in individual females having unique distributions of cells, where one X-chromosome is inactivated. This mosaicism is usually not visible, but it can be readily observed in Cc because her two X-chromosomes carry different alleles of a pigmentation gene partly responsible for calico coat color. The allele conferring orange color was inactivated in a different subset of pigment-producing cells (i.e., melanocytes) than the subset in the cat from which she was derived, so Cc had a different pattern of orange, black, and white coloration.

Not surprisingly, cloning is an inefficient process compared to *in vitro* fertilization or more conventional embryological manipulations. Cc was the only clone to survive of more than

Handbook of Stem Cells
Volume 1
Copyright © 2004 by Academic Press

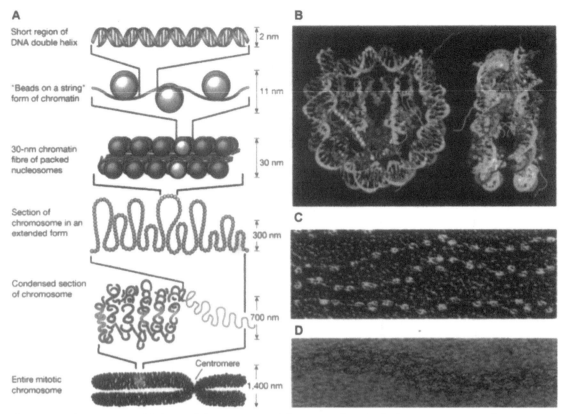

Figure 6–1. *Chromatin structure.* (A) Schematic of chromatin structure. 147-bp segments of DNA (top level) wrap 1.65 times around histone octamers to form nucleosomes (second level). Arrays of nucleosomes assemble into 30-nm solenoid structures (third level), considered to be the fundamental unit of higher-order chromatin. Extensive looping (fourth level) and condensation (fifth level) brought about by various proteins, including high-mobility group members, results in the configuration of the interphase nucleus, which undergoes further condensation to yield metaphase chromosome during mitosis (bottom panel). After returning to interphase, some regions of the genome remain highly condensed and are referred to as heterochromatin.[132,241] (B) X-ray crystal structure of nucleosome at 2.8 angstroms resolution viewed down the DNA superhelix axis (left) or orthogonal to the DNA superhelix axis.[241] Molecular mass is 206 kDa and consists of DNA wrapped around the periphery of an H3–H4 tetramer flanked by two H2A–H2B dimers. The structure of N-terminal histone tails cannot be elucidated in this crystal structure but protrude away and contact neighboring nucleosomes. (C) Electron micrograph of nucleosomes as beads on a string as depicted in the second level of part a. (D) Electron micrograph of 30-nm solenoid structure as depicted in the third level of part a. Parts A and B reproduced with permission from *Nature*. (Please see CD-ROM for color version of this figure.)

200 nuclear transfer attempts,[6] consistent with success rates from less than 1% to 3% for cattle, sheep, goats, pigs, and mice.[7–12] Many clones fail to reach the blastocyst stage and successfully implant into the uterus. Clones that progress beyond this stage often die *in utero* because of placental defects or die shortly after birth with increased birth weight, respiratory distress, and/or cardiovascular defects. Furthermore, although it is too soon to assess the long-term health of cloned cattle, sheep, goats, and pigs that have survived, cloned mice are known to have impaired immune systems, become obese, and die prematurely.[13,14] Cloned obese mice can be bred to genetically identical individuals of the same inbred strain, and their progeny are not predisposed to obesity, providing additional evidence that epigenetics is an important determinant in the health of cloned animals.[13]

Unlike X-chromosome inactivation, which occurred normally in Cc, the embryonic and postnatal lethality and the adult obesity in many other clones is probably caused by abnormal epigenetic events stemming from inappropriate chromatin structure, leading to deregulated expression of *Oct4* and many other genes.[15] This notion is supported by evidence that cloned embryos sometimes exhibit aberrant patterns of DNA methylation at CpG dinucleotides and abnormal expression of both imprinted and nonimprinted genes.[16–20] Many more chromatin-based abnormalities will probably be detected using chromatin immunoprecipitation (ChIP) assays.

CHROMATIN, ZYGOTIC GENOME ACTIVATION, AND CLONING SUCCESS

Despite the low success rate, it is remarkable that cloning is ever able to work. After a nucleus from a somatic cell is transferred into oocyte cytoplasm, the chromatin structure must undergo rapid and extensive reprogramming to facilitate a genomewide expression profile similar to that of an early embryo. These changes must occur within minutes or hours in a cloning experiment, whereas reprogramming normally takes

TABLE 6–1
Phenotypes of Chromatin-Modifying Protein Knockout Mice

	DNA Methyltransferases
Dnmt1	Midgestation lethality, global hypomethylation loss of imprinting, and defects in stochastic X-inactivation[174,229,245]
Dnmt3a	Runted at birth with postnatal lethality around 4 weeks and spermatogenesis defects[38,231]
Dnmt3b	Mid- to late gestation lethality (E14.5–E18.5) with defective growth, neural tube development, and centromeric DNA methylation[38]
Dnmt3a, 3b	Midgestation lethality (E11.5), defective somitogenesis[38]
Dnmt3L	Male infertility and maternal effect lethality at midgestation (E10.5) with loss of maternal imprints and neural tube defects[230,231]

	Methyl-CpG-Binding Proteins
Mbd1	Subtle neurological defects[246]
Mdb2	Defective maternal behavior[247]
Mbd3	Embryonic defects beginning at implantation with perigastrulation lethality (E8.5)[247]
Mecp2	Postnatal death at 6–12 weeks with multiple neurological defects[248,249]

	Histone Acetyltransferases
Gcn5(Pcaf-b)	Midgestation lethality (E9.5–E11.5), defective embryonic mesoderm[250,251]
Pcaf	Viable with no apparent phenotypes[250,251]
p300	Midgestation lethality (E9–E11.5), exencephaly, and cardiac and cell proliferation defects[252]
Cbp	Midgestation lethality (E9.5–E10.5) and neural tube, hematopoietic, and vascular defects[253]
p300+/−, Cbp+/−	Midgestation lethality and exencephaly[252]

	Histone Deacetylases
Hdac1	Midgestation lethality (E10.5) with proliferation defects[254]
Hdac9	Viable with no apparent phenotypes at birth but cardiac hypertrophy by 8 months[255]
Sir2a	Neonatal lethality in inbred mice and sterility in outbred mice[256]

	Histone Methyltransferases
G9a	Midgestation lethality (E9.5–E12.5), severe developmental delay, incomplete chorioallantoic fusion, massive apoptosis, and loss of euchromatic histone H3-K9 methylation[257]
Suv39h1, 2	Low-penetrance late-gestation lethality, growth retarded, male hypogonadism, genome instability and tumor prone, and loss of histone H3-K9 methylation in pericentric heterochromatin[138]

	Histone Variants
H2AX	Low body weight with male infertility and radiation sensitivity[70]
H2AZ	Peri-implantation lethality (E4.5–E6.5)[258]
H3.3a	Low penetrance neonatal lethality, low body weight, neuromuscular defects, and reduced copulatory behavior[259]
H1 subtypes	No phenotypes in single or even double mutants[260,261]
Prm1+/−	Apparent male infertility (failed germ line transmission in targeting chimeras)[262]
Prm2+/−	Apparent male infertility (failed germ line transmission in targeting chimeras)[262]

	SWI/SNF
Brm	Viable and fertility with modest increase in weight[263]
Brg1	Implantation stage lethality (E4.5)[91]
Brg1+/−	Predisposition to exencephaly and tumor formation[91]
Baf47(Snf5/Ini1)	Implantation stage lethality (E3.5–E5.5)[264]

Continued

TABLE 6–1—cont'd
Phenotypes of Chromatin-Modifying Protein Knockout Mice

SWI/SNF—cont'd	
Baf47(Snf5/Ini1)[+/−]	Predisposition to rhabdoid tumors[93]
Baf155(Srg3)	Implantation stage lethality[95]
Baf155(Srg3)[+/−]	Predisposition to exencephaly[95]
Lsh	Neonatal lethality, low body weight, renal lesions, and global DNA hypomethylation[105,107]

Polycomb Group Proteins	
Eed	Perigastrulation lethality (E8.5), defective embryonic mesoderm production, imprinted X-inactivation, and autosomal imprinting[176, 199, 204, 207]
Eed[hypo/hypo]	Homeotic transformations[203, 204]
Ezh2(Enx1)	Two phenotypic classes with embryonic lethality around implantation (E5.5) or at gastrulation stages (E8.5)[201]
Bmi1	Postnatal death with homeotic transformations, hematopoietic defects, ataxia and seizures, and proliferation defects[210,265]
M33	Homeotic transformations, cell proliferation defects, and male-to-female sex reversal[266,267]
Mel18(Zfp144)	Postnatal death at 4 weeks and homeotic transformations[268]
Ring1a	Homeotic transformations[269]
Mph1(Edr1/Rae28)	Neonatal lethality with homeotic transformations and defects in neural crest derivatives[270]
Ring1b (Rnf2)	Gastrulation stage lethality (E7.5) and defective embryonic mesoderm production[208]

Trithorax Group Proteins	
Mll	Midgestation embryonic lethality (E11.5–E14.5) with Hox gene misregulation and hematopoietic defects[271,272]

High-mobility Group Proteins	
Hmgi-c (Pygmy)	Dwarfism[273]
Hmgb1	Neonatal lethality because of hypoglycemia[274]
Hmgb2	Reduced male fertility associated with Sertoli cell defects and sperm immotility[275]
Sry	Male-to-female sex reversal[276]

Sperm Nucleus Decondensation–Protamine-histone Conversion	
Npm2	Apparent maternal-effect gene, most embryos dying by the two-cell or blastocyst stage, with decondensed chromatin[277]

place in the germ line during spermatogenesis and oogenesis over weeks or months. Therefore, incomplete or aberrant reprogramming in clones is expected. In this regard, nuclei from more differentiated cell types should require more extensive reprogramming and be less efficient donors, and this hypothesis has been borne out experimentally. The percentage of mouse clones that developed to term with nuclei from blastomeres of two-, four-, and eight-cell (i.e., morula) stage embryos decreased from 22% to 14% to 8%, respectively.[21,22] Survival decreased to between 2–11% for embryonic stem (ES) cells and 1–3% for somatic cells from adults.[22] This reduction in competency occurs later in cattle, as the percentage of bovine clones that developed to term from morulae, fetal fibroblast, and adult fibroblast nuclei was 28%, 13%, and 5%, respectively.[22, 23] The difference in timing may be because zygotic genome activation (ZGA) occurs earlier in mice (primarily at the two-cell stage) than in cattle (the morula stage).[24] As a result, less time and fewer cell cycles are available for transferred mouse nuclei to respond to signals from the oocyte cytoplasm by making wholesale changes in the chromatin structure before transcription should be initiated.

In the initial stages of a cloning experiment, changes in chromatin structure are thought to be accompanied by the loss of many proteins from remodeled donor nuclei and by the acquisition of many other proteins from the egg cytoplasm. For example, when nuclei from tadpole-derived cells are introduced into enucleated Xenopus laevis eggs, more than 90% of TATA-binding protein (TBP) is rapidly lost from the nuclear matrix, and there is a concomitant appearance of other proteins.[25] Many changes of this sort will undoubtedly require

Figure 6–2. *Evidence of epigenetic inheritance in a mammalian clone. Photograph of the cloned cat, Cc (right), and her genetic donor (left). Photograph courtesy of Pat Sullivan, Associated Press. (Please see CD-ROM for color version of this figure.)*

chromatin-modifying factors instead of occurring passively. In fact, the large size of *Xenopus* eggs made them amenable to biochemical analyses and made it possible to determine that the ISWI chromatin-remodeling complex acts in an adenosine 5′-triphosphate (ATP)-dependent manner to remove TBP from remodeled nuclei.[25] This result suggests that ISWI might be required at the onset of ZGA in normal embryos and the remodeling events that occur in cloned embryos. However, even the former possibility is difficult to validate using conventional mutagenesis and breeding strategies because female heterozygotes often express the wild-type allele during oogenesis and deposit wild-type gene product into mutant, haploid eggs. After fertilization in the mouse, most maternal mRNAs are degraded at the two-cell stage, but the corresponding proteins can persist until the blastocyst or egg cylinder stages before being degraded or diluted from repeated cell divisions. The presence of maternally loaded, wild-type protein may explain why few, if any, knockouts arrest or die in the early cleavage stages and may account for why embryos with targeted mutations in "housekeeping" genes often survive to around implantation.

To overcome this problem, the oocyte-specific zona pellucida 3 *(Zp3)* promoter can be used in Cre–*loxP* conditional gene targeting. Using this approach, female mice have been created that carry a *Brg1$^{Zp3–Cre}$* conditional mutation that inactivates a subset of SWI/SNF-related chromatin-remodeling complexes similar to ISWI in primary oocytes.[26] When these females are bred to wild-type males, oogenesis, fertilization, and the second meiotic division occur normally. The resulting heterozygous embryos are viable but arrest at the onset of ZGA between the one- and four-cell stages (usually at the two-cell stage). This very early developmental block occurs in heterozygous embryos derived from *Brg1$^{-/-}$* oocytes but not *Brg1$^{+/-}$* oocytes, indicating that *Brg1$^{Zp3–Cre}$* is a maternal-effect mutation. In addition, zygotic transcripts are present at

50% of normal levels. Together, the ISWI biochemistry and *Brg1* genetic approaches demonstrate that ATPase chromatin-remodeling complexes are required at the onset of ZGA and may be involved in some of the remodeling events that occur during the early steps of the cloning process.

RATIONAL APPROACHES TOWARD IMPROVING PROSPECTS FOR CLINICAL APPLICATIONS OF STEM CELLS AND THERAPEUTIC CLONING

Over the last few years, chromatin research has made tremendous progress by using genetic, biochemical, and molecular approaches in a range of model organisms. An important theme that has emerged from these multidisciplinary efforts is that DNA methylation, histone modifications, and ATPase chromatin-remodeling complexes are functionally interdependent. It is becoming evident that these interactions also apply to DNA replication and repair during interphase of the cell cycle, chromosome segregation in mitosis, and recombination in meiosis. A second important theme is that chromatin-modifying factors from each of these three general categories underlie some of the most well-studied epigenetic processes: position-effect variegation (PEV), X-chromosome inactivation, Polycomb group (Pc-G) silencing, trithorax group (trx-G) activation, and monoallelic expression in both genomic imprinting and allelic exclusion. Recent work has provided considerable insight into the molecular mechanisms and has revealed striking similarities.

Not only is this body of work significant from a basic research perspective, but it also has important implications for stem cell transplantation procedures and therapeutic cloning in the clinical setting.[27] A better understanding of chromatin condensation and relaxation in normal development and physiology could be used to reprogram cells more efficiently. Normally, chromatin-modifying factors participate in cell fate determination and subsequent steps in a lineage leading to terminal differentiation. Considering the reversible nature of the chromatin structure, it may prove possible to coax a lineage in the opposite direction. Starting with differentiated cells, it might be possible to acquire stem cells or cells with progenitor cell characteristics. These methodologies should not be restricted to the derivation of ES cells but should apply to other cell types as well. For example, lymphocytes might be dedifferentiated to hematopoietic stem cells, muscle to myoblasts, and postmitotic neurons to neuronal progenitor cells. In fact, reprogramming within a lineage might be more efficient than creating ES-like cells. Cell fusion-independent transdifferentiation might also be possible. Undoubtedly, these types of approaches will be technically challenging, but success has been achieved in the opposite direction. Recently, Sonic hedgehog and other factors have been used to convert ES cells into motor neurons and dopaminergic neurons that function *in vivo*.[28–31]

In the sections that follow, we review what is currently known about DNA methylation, the histone code, and ATPase chromatin-remodeling complexes (see the sections "DNA Methylation," "Histone Code," and "ATPase Chromatin-Remodeling Complexes," respectively). Subsequently, we describe the role of these factors in PEV, X-chromosome inactivation, Pc-G silencing and trx-G activation, and monoallelic expression (see the sections "Position-Effect Variegation," "X-Chromosome Inactivation," "Polycomb and Trithorax Groups," and "Monoallelic Expression: Imprinting and Allelic Exclusion," respectively).

Chromatin-Modifying Factors

DNA METHYLATION

Most DNA methylation in mammalian cells occurs at cytosines of CpG dinucleotides, which are symmetrically methylated on complimentary strands of DNA. Cytosine methylation, like all forms of nucleotide alkylation, promotes base deamination and is mutagenic.[32] As a result, CpG dinucleotides are underrepresented fivefold in the mammalian genome.[33] A notable exception is CpG islands, stretches of DNA greater than 200 base pairs with an unusually high frequency of CpG dinucleotides often situated at the 5′ ends of genes.[34] By definition, CpG islands are unmethylated in the germ line, and they often remain unmethylated in somatic tissues.[35]

Dynamic changes in DNA methylation during embryogenesis suggest that methylation may play an important role in cell fate specifications (Fig. 6–3). Shortly after fertilization, the male pronucleus is rapidly demethylated. Blocking DNA replication does not inhibit demethylation, which indicates this demethylation is caused by an as yet unidentified demethylase.[36] Interestingly, the maternal genome is resistant to this active demethylation, perhaps because the paternal genome becomes accessible to demethylases during the protamine-to-histone conversion. From the two-cell stage to the blastocyst stage, DNA methyltransferases are largely excluded from nuclei, and both the paternal and maternal genomes undergo passive demethylation, such that implantation-stage embryos are largely demethylated. Important exceptions to this globally demethylated state are imprinted genes and certain retroviral-like elements, which maintain their methylation status. After implantation, cells of the mouse embryo proper are remethylated. In contrast, mouse extraembryonic cells experience only modest remethylation,[5] suggesting that DNA methylation plays a less prominent role in these tissues.

Independent waves of demethylation and remethylation also occur in the germ line. Primordial germ cells (PGCs) are actively demethylated in both sexes beginning around mouse embryonic day (E) 10.5 and finishing by E12.5.[37] This demethylation erases the parental legacy of alleles and is critical in imprinting, but it may have a more general role in resetting the totipotent state. Male germ cells are remethylated late in embryonic development during the leptotene stage of meiosis; female germ cells are remethylated postnatally, around P6, during oocyte maturation.[5]

Several DNA methyltransferase enzymes have been identified and characterized. These enzymes are separated into two functional classes. DNMT3A and DNMT3B are *de novo* methyltransferases responsible for remethylation in both somatic and germ cells.[38] *De novo* methyltransferase activity

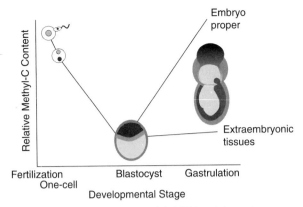

Figure 6–3. *Dynamic changes in global DNA methylation during mouse embryogenesis. At fertilization, both gametes are hypermethylated. Shortly after fertilization, the male pronucleus is actively demethylated. Because DNA methyltransferases are initially excluded from the nucleus, passive demethylation occurs from the one-cell to the blastocyst stages. After implantation, embryonic tissues undergo pronounced remethylation and level off at gastrulation. Remethylation is limited in extraembryonic tissues. Figure adapted from Li.[5] (Please see CD-ROM for color version of this figure.)*

may be stimulated by DNMT3L, which resembles DNMT3A and DNMT3B but lacks the methyltransferase catalytic domain and thus is thought to lack methyltransferase activity of its own. DNMT3L colocalizes with DNMT3A and DNMT3B and potentiates DNMT3A activity *in vitro*.[39] DNMT3L also interacts with histone deacetlyases[40,41] and may recruit and restrict *de novo* methyltransferases to substrates packaged in only certain chromatin conformations.

DNMT1 represents the second functional class. It is a maintenance methyltransferase that prefers hemimethylated templates and is recruited to hemimethylated DNA after replication through an association with proliferating cell nuclear antigen (PCNA), the replication fork clamp.[32] Once recruited, it propagates the methylated state by copying methylation onto the nascent strand. Accordingly, *Dnmt1* knockout mice fail to maintain the high levels of methylation generated by postimplantation methylation and die during midgestation with numerous developmental defects.[5]

DNA methylation is not inherently repressive, and the transcriptional consequences of DNA methylation appear to be mediated by interplay with other epigenetic mechanisms. Cytosine methylation alters the substrate presented to DNA-binding proteins, imposing allosteric constraints that favor some interactions but block others.[42] Methylated CpG dinucleotides in and around promoters often block transcriptional activator binding and recruit chromatin-modifying enzymes that promote higher-order, repressive chromatin conformations.[42] Methyl-CpG-binding proteins, such as MBD2 and MeCP2, can recruit histone deacetylases (HDACs),[43, 44] histone methyltransferases (HMTs),[45] and ATP-dependent nucleosome-remodeling complexes,[43] which all work in concert to restrict access of the general transcription machinery to the DNA. Importantly, even though DNA methylation is generally considered a repressive mark, this is not universally true. DNA methylation can promote transcription by disrupting factors that bind to *cis*-acting insulator elements that separate genes and their requisite enhancers (see the section "Monoallelic Expression: Imprinting and Allelic Exclusion"). Therefore, the transcriptional consequences of DNA methylation are context dependent, often promoting repression but in other cases facilitating activation.

The importance of DNA methylation to cell physiology is perhaps best illustrated by the pathologies that result when the processes of establishing and reading these marks go awry. Much as the exquisite fidelity of DNA replication is not absolute, somatic cells accumulate epimutations during aging and carcinogenesis. A variety of tumor suppressors, including *RB* and *p16,* are silenced by aberrant methylation of promoter CpG islands in human tumors,[32] and mutations in *Dnmt3b* cause a complex disease called immunodeficiency, centromeric region instability, and facial abnormalities (ICF).[42] In other diseases, methylation patterns are maintained more or less appropriately, but the cellular machinery responsible for recognizing those marks is disrupted. For instance, mutation of *MECP2* causes a neurological disorder known as Rett syndrome, and mice mutant for *Mbd2* exhibit behavioral defects, including compromised maternal nurturing of pups.[5]

HISTONE CODE

DNA methylation is important for the proper expression of many genes and is perturbed in some diseases, but it cannot account for many other aspects of transcriptional regulation. First, most CpG islands are unmethylated, regardless of whether or not the associated gene is expressed.[35] Second, many cell types are properly specified despite having globally hypomethylated genomes in *Dnmt1*[−/−] embryos.[5] Lethality does not occur until closer to midgestation at E9.5–10.5. Third, and perhaps most importantly, the nematode *Caenorhabditis elegans* lacks detectable cytosine methylation, and the fruit fly *Drosophila melanogaster* has only trace levels restricted to the earliest stages of embryogenesis.[35] Thus, evolutionary conserved mechanisms other than DNA methylation must be crucial for transcriptional regulation.

In this regard, histones are intimately associated with DNA and are among the most abundant and highly conserved proteins from yeast to human. Not only have the amino acid sequences and three-dimensional structures been conserved to a remarkable extent but so have a variety of posttranslational modifications. These modifications are covalent and consist of acetylation, methylation, phosphorylation, ubiquitination, and polyribosylation of specific residues of H2A, H2B, H3, and H4, usually in the N-terminal tails that protrude away from nucleosomes. For example, Fig. 6–4 shows the position and nature of modifications that occur on H3 N-terminal tails. Each of these modifications either promotes or inhibits transcription. The situation is complicated because some of the opposing modifications inhibit each other and are therefore mutually exclusive. All of these modifications and the interplay that occurs among them are referred to as the histone code.[46–50] Briefly, enzymes such as histone acetyltransferases

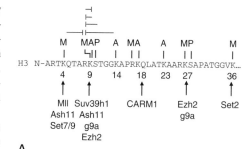

HAT	Histone target	Class	HDAC	Yeast homolog
PCAF	H3, H4	I	HDAC1, 2, 3, 8	Rpd3
CREBBP	All	II	HDAC4, 5,6, 7, 9	Hda1
P300	All	III	hSIRT1-7	Sir2
Tip60	H2A, H3, H4			
MOZ/ZNF220				
HBO/MYST2	H3, H4			
SRC1/NCOA1	H3, H4			
GRIP1/NCOA2				
TAFII250	H2A, H3			
MYST1	H2A, H3, H4			
ATF2	H2B, H4			
GCN5L2	H2A, H3			
MORF	H3, H4			

Figure 6–4. *Covalent modifications of histones. (A) Methylation (M), acetylation (A), and phosphorylation (P) of specific amino acids on an H3 N-terminal tail. The positions of lysines (K) are indicated. Except for K36, which functions in a context-dependent manner, all of the modifications either promote or inhibit transcription. Moreover, K9 methylation is mutually exclusive with certain neighboring modifications (indicated above). Histone methyltransferases are shown below the residues they are able to modify. (B) Mammalian histone acetyltransferases (HATs) and their histone substrates, which usually include multiple sites on N-terminal tails. (C) Three classes of mammalian histone deacetylases (HDACs), which are grouped according to their relationship with yeast HDACs, oppose HATs. Parts b and c adapted from Drs. M. Bunger and T. Archer. (Please see CD-ROM for color version of this figure.)*

(HATs) and HMTs write the code by introducing specific modifications. These modifications then serve as docking sites for proteins that read and execute the code. For example, acetylated lysines can be recognized by the bromodomains of subunits of ATPase-remodeling complexes to promote transcription.[51–55] In contrast, certain methylated lysines can be bound by the chromodomain of heterochromatin protein 1 or (HP1) or Pc-G proteins to facilitate higher order chromatin structures that inhibit transcription.[56, 57] Considerable interplay and a two-way flow of epigenetic information also occurs between histone modifications and DNA methylation. For example, just as DNA methylation can influence histone deacetylation, genetic screens in *Arabidopsis* and *Neurospora* have uncovered mutations in HMTs *(DIM5* and *Kryptonite)* that influence DNA methylation.[58–60] It seems likely that this will also be the case in mammals, especially since mutations in other putative chromatin-modifying factors perturb DNA methylation (see the section "ATPase Chromatin-Remodeling Complexes").

Covalent modifications of histones must be labile so that the transcriptional status of a particular gene can be reversed. HATs are counteracted by HDACs, and kinases are counteracted by phosphatases. However, an exception may be histone methylation. Even though lysines can be mono-, di-, or trimethylated and gene activity increases when histone 3 lysine 4 (H3-K4) is converted from a di- to a trimethyl state,[61] no histone demethylases have been identified that can remove these methyl groups or groups from other lysine or arginine residues.[48,62] Instead, there has been speculation that the most N-terminal amino acids, including methylated residues, might sometimes be proteolytically cleaved.[62] Such a mechanism would not be precise or dynamic but would reverse the effect of methylation until new histones are synthesized and assembled into nucleosomes during S phase. However, it is also possible that clipped tails might serve as a signal to be replaced by histone variants. Unlike core histones, many histone variants are expressed during G_1 and G_2 of the cell cycle and can be incorporated into nucleosomes of nondividing cells where they confer unique properties. For example, H3.3 differs from H3 at only four amino acids but has been associated with rDNA arrays and other transcriptionally active loci.[63]

Although the histone code is usually thought of in terms of transcriptional regulation, it is anticipated that it will also be important for many other processes including DNA repair, replication, mitosis, and recombination. In fact, evidence of this already exists. Aurora kinases phosphorylate H3-S10 for chromosome condensation at the onset of mitosis.[64,65] It is possible that *Su(var)3-6* counteracts this process, since it encodes a Ser/Thr phosphatase required for mitosis.[66] In other mutants, nucleotide excision repair,[67] VDJ recombination in lymphocytes,[68] apoptosis,[69] and other processes are affected. Histone variants come into play here, too. CENP-A replaces H3 at centromeres and is important for kinetochores and the separation of sister chromatids. H2AX is phosphorylated and localized to double-strand breaks during DNA repair and might also be involved in VDJ recombination of immunoglobulin and T-cell receptors in lymphocytes.[70,71] Protamines replace histones in sperm so that the haploid genome can be packaged compactly.

Something else often overlooked is that some enzymes that write the histone code also covalently modify proteins unrelated to histones. For example, the CARM1 HMT methylates the KIX domains of p300 and CBP, two highly related HAT paralogs, which has important consequences in the regulation of nuclear receptor genes.[72] Furthermore, p300 and CBP are not just targets but are themselves known to acetylate nonhistone substrates. They acetylate the zinc-finger transcription factor EKLF, which increases its affinity for ATPase chromatin-remodeling complexes and enables it to be a more potent transcriptional activator of β globin.[73] They also acetylate the p53 tumor suppressor protein, which potentiates its ability to act as a transcriptional activator[74, 75] and acetylate the BCL6 transcriptional repressor, which inhibits its ability to recruit HDACs.[76] Many more instances are probably forthcoming and may obfuscate the histone code. One should consider this issue when evaluating mutant phenotypes or other functional data. Finally, to address the magnitude of this issue, the percentage of HAT or HMT activity devoted to histone substrates could be estimated using genetic

approaches in yeast or biochemical–proteomic methods in mammalian cells.

ATPase CHROMATIN-REMODELING COMPLEXES

In addition to enzymes that covalently modify histones, a second evolutionarily conserved mechanism that modulates chromatin structure is carried out by ATPase chromatin-remodeling complexes. Genetic screens in the budding yeast *Saccharomyces cerevisiae* identified mutants unable to switch mating types (swi) or use sucrose as an energy source (sucrose nonfermenter, or snf) and led to the discovery of the first complex called SWI/SNF.[77–79] The SWI/SNF complex consists of 11 subunits with an apparent molecular mass of 1.15 MDa (recently revised from 2 MDa).[80] It does not possess significant DNA-binding ability of its own but is recruited to promoters by sequence-specific transcription factors.[81] The energy derived from ATP hydrolysis allows the complex to alter the conformation and position of nucleosomes.[82] DNA–histone contacts are broken, and histone octamers can be slid several hundred base pairs upstream or downstream.[4,82] As a result, a core promoter can be made nucleosome-free and accessible to the RNA polymerase II holoenzyme so that transcription can be initiated. SWI/SNF can have the opposite effect at other loci and inhibit transcription.[83–86] Gene expression profiling with whole-genome oligonucleotide arrays demonstrated that approximately 300 genes, or about 5% of the total number in the yeast genome, are regulated positively or negatively by SWI/SNF complexes.[83, 87] These genes are not linked, indicating that SWI/SNF complexes act at the level of individual genes instead of chromosomal regions.[87] Much work using single nucleosomes or nucleosome arrays assembled *in vitro* as templates in assays has provided insight into the mechanism of SWI/SNF function, but there is a caveat: It is not clear whether SWI/SNF complexes ever encounter nucleosomes as beads on a string in the nucleus, because chromatin exists as 30-nm solenoid structures and more highly condensed structures *in vivo* (Fig. 6–1). Therefore, SWI/SNF or something else must first act upon and relax these higher-order structures.

SWI/SNF-related complexes have been conserved throughout evolution and have been characterized extensively in flies, mice, and humans. Because of duplication and divergence events, mammals have additional subunits that result in heterogeneity among complexes in different tissues and cell types.[88–90] Targeted mutations of several SWI/SNF-related genes confer peri-implantation lethality (Table 6–1), suggesting that the corresponding gene products do function together in a complex. In addition, *Brg1* and *Baf47/Snf5* heterozygotes are tumor prone,[91–94] and *Brg1* and *Baf155* heterozygotes are predisposed to exencephaly.[91, 95] However, it is seems possible that one or more of these factors function outside of canonical SWI/SNF-related complexes. The BRG1 catalytic subunit has biochemical activity on its own and is known to physically associate with RB, TRP53, nuclear hormone receptors, and several lineage-restricted transcription factors. In addition, BRG1, BAF155, BAF170, and BAF47/SNF5 comprise a minimal complex with significant activity *in vitro*[96] and have been identified as components of nuclear receptor corepressor.[97]

Additional ATPase chromatin-remodeling complexes have been characterized that are distinct from SWI/SNF, although each one has a catalytic subunit with sequence similarity to the DNA-dependent ATPase domain of SWI2/SNF2[4,98,99] (Fig. 6–5). At this point, more similarities than differences have been identified among the various complexes *in vitro*, and it is not clear whether the differences are relevant *in vivo*. Therefore, it is not clear why such diversity has been selected during evolution, but it is tempting to speculate. Some complexes may modulate higher order chromatin structure[100]; other complexes might act on nucleosome arrays. Different complexes could act at distinct promoters or overlap at a large subset of loci. In the latter case, any two complexes might perform fundamentally different tasks at the same promoter to influence transcriptional initiation, or one could act downstream to influence transcriptional elongation. Precedent for this sort of division of labor comes from recent reports that the yeast Set1 and Set2 HMTs are recruited to coding regions by a transcriptional elongation complex.[101]

The diversity of chromatin-remodeling complexes is likely to be even greater than realized. Numerous SWI2/SNF2-related genes have been identified by reduced stringency hybridization or genome sequencing projects, and some of these genes probably encode "orphan" catalytic subunits of complexes that await identification and purification.[102,103]

Some of these putative catalytic subunits have interesting properties, such as the ability to regulate DNA methylation. A targeted mutation of lymphoid-specific helicase *(Lsh)* results in a 50–70% reduction in cytosine methylation throughout the genome.[104–106] Homozygotes die shortly after birth, possibly because of renal failure (the gene is lymphoid specific in adults but widely expressed in embryos),[107] indicating that the expression and activity of *de novo* and maintenance DNA methyltransferases are unaffected. Instead, Lsh1 is expressed during S phase and may facilitate localization of Dnmt1 to hemimethylated DNA following replication or protect against demethylase activity.[105, 106] Mutations in *ATRX*, another SWI2/SNF2-like gene, reduce DNA methylation in rDNA arrays and other repeats and result in mental retardation, α-thalassemia, and fertility defects in humans.[106,108]

SWI/SNF-related complexes also work with HAT complexes. Sequence-specific transcription factors can recruit HAT complexes to promoters to acetylate histone tails. Acetylated lysine residues can then serve as docking sites for bromodomains of SWI2/SNF2-related catalytic subunits, resulting in increased affinity of SWI/SNF-related complexes for their chromatin targets.[53,109–111] At other loci or at different stages of the cell cycle (late mitosis), the order is reversed, with SWI/SNF-related complexes recruited first and HAT complexes second.[112–114] Genetic interactions between

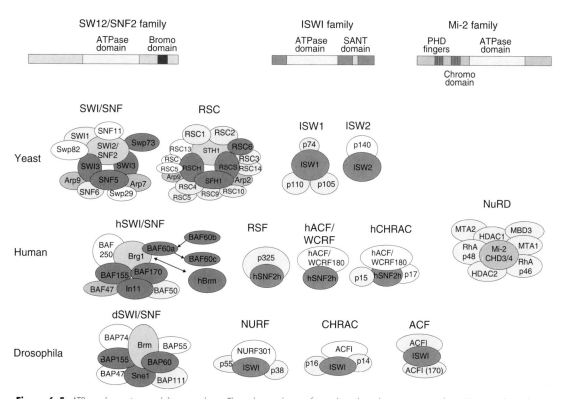

Figure 6–5. *ATPase chromatin-remodeling complexes. Three distinct classes of complexes based upon corresponding ATPase catalytic subunits (top). Complexes in the SWI2/SNF2 and ISWI families are conserved among yeast, human, and Drosophila, whereas the Mi-2 family consists of vertebrate NURD complexes. Reproduced with permission from Cell.[4] (Please see CD-ROM for color version of this figure.)*

SWI/SNF *(swi2/snf2)* and HAT *(gcn5)* mutations in yeast indicate that the coordinated recruitment of their gene products must be important *in vivo*. Compared to single mutants, double mutants exhibit synergistic effects in the deregulated expression of downstream target genes, grow very slowly with mitotic defects on some backgrounds, and are not viable on others.[115–117] It is possible that these phenotypes are not entirely caused by transcriptional deregulation because, much like histone-modifying enzymes, ATPase chromatin-remodeling complexes have been implicated in DNA repair, replication, recombination, and mitosis.[103,118]

Epigenetic Processes

POSITION-EFFECT VARIEGATION

Chromatin and Molecular Basis or PEV

Shortly after discovering the mutagenic properties of X-irradiation, Müller described the isolation of several radiation-induced mutations of the *D. melanogaster* white *(w)* eye-color gene in 1930.[119] Interestingly, the mutant eyes contained patches of wild-type cells with red pigmentation intermingled with patches of mutant cells lacking pigmentation and appearing white. Six years later it was demonstrated that the X-rays induced a chromosomal rearrangement in each mutant line, such as an inversion in *In(1)w^{m4}* (abbreviated *w^{m4}* for white mottled 4) (Fig. 6–6), that resulted in heterochromatin being juxtaposed with the *w* locus.[120] The regulatory elements and coding sequence of the *w* gene were not perturbed in any of these mutants, but heterochromatin would spread across the breakpoint and silence transcription in a subset of eye progenitor cells during development. In contrast, the heterochromatin would not spread far enough to reach the *w* gene in

other eye progenitor cells, and it would be transcribed at wild-type levels. Clonal expansion of these cell populations subsequently produced patches of white and red eye color, respectively. This silencing process must be stochastic because even genetically identical flies exhibit unique patterns of white and red coloration. This epigenetic process, which has been documented at other loci in *D. melanogaster* and in other organisms, is appropriately called position-effect variegation (PEV).

Because *w^{m4}* is such a visual example of PEV, it served as the foundation of genetic screens to identify genes that modify the extent of heterochromatin spreading in PEV.[121–123] *E(var)* mutations were recovered that enhance PEV, resulting in increased heterochromatin spreading, and that cause the *w* gene to be silenced in a greater percentage of eye cells. Therefore, *E(var)* mutants have eyes that are whiter than typical *w^{m4}* flies (Fig. 6–6). In contrast, *Su(var)* mutations were recovered that suppress PEV, inhibiting the spread of heterochromatin, and that cause the *w* gene to be transcribed in a greater percentage of eye cells. These mutants have eyes that are redder than *w^{m4}* and therefore that more closely resemble wild type. In these screens, most of the *E(var)s* and *Su(var)s* were isolated as dominant mutations. When homozygous, more than half of these mutations were lethal, indicating that most corresponding gene products are essential.[122]

Although *E(var)* and *Su(var)* gene products are not strictly defined by conserved features, most that have been characterized at the molecular level contain domains or motifs present in Pc-G, trx-G, or other chromatin-modifying factors. The connection between PEV and chromatin has also been strengthened by observations that histone, HAT, HDAC, Pc-G, and trx-G mutations can behave as *E(var)s* or *Su(var)s*.[124–129] On a mechanistic level, the most significant progress has come from the analysis of *Suv39h1* and *HP1α*, mammalian orthologs of *D. melanogaster Su(var)3-9* and *Su(var)2-5* (which encodes HP1), respectively. Suv39h1 methylates the lysine 9 residue of histone H3 (H3-K9) in pericentric regions of the genome,[130] and this covalent modification serves as a docking site for the chromodomain of HP1α[56, 57, 131–133] (Fig. 6–7B). HP1α is a structural component of heterochromatin, and, once situated at a particular H3-K9 residue, it is thought to use a second domain, called the chromo shadow domain, to directly or indirectly bind another Suv39h1 molecule.[133, 134] This recruitment step results in H3-K9 methylation at an adjacent nucleosome and is followed by more HP1α binding, thereby creating a feedback loop such that heterochromatin can propagate or spread over megabase intervals throughout pericentric regions. This feedback loop is quite dynamic[135, 136] and is also able to maintain pericentric regions as heterochromatin throughout the numerous cell divisions that occur during embryogenesis and in adults. This form of cellular memory is accomplished by the HP1α chromo shadow domain directly interacting with the molecular chaperone chromatin assembly factor (CAF-1), which is localized to replication forks by PCNA during S phase and which incorporates newly synthesized histones into nascent nucleosomes.[132,137]

The importance of *Suv39h1* and *Suv39h2* (a closely related paralog) have been confirmed by gene targeting.[138] Single

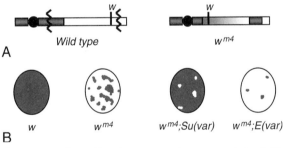

Figure 6–6. *Drosophila white gene and genetic analysis of PEV.* (A) Schematic of *Drosophila melanogaster* X-chromosome. The white *(w)* eye-color gene is located at a distal position in wild type (left) but juxtaposed with pericentric heterochromatin because of an inversion (the position of which is indicated by squiggles) in *w^{m4}* (right). Black represents centromere, dark represents pericentric heterochromatin, white represents euchromatin, and the gray gradient shows the spreading of pericentric heterochromatin to different extents in *w^{m4}*, silencing the *w* gene in some cells but not others. (B) Schematic of *Drosophila melanogaster* eye-color phenotypes. The wild-type *w* allele confers red eyes. Patches of red and white are intermingled in *w^{m4}*, corresponding to ommatidia, where *w* is transcriptionally active or silenced, respectively. Second-site mutations modify the *w^{m4}* phenotype, with some resulting in decreased spreading of heterochromatin and a higher percentage of red *(Su(var))* or increased spreading of heterochromatin and a higher percentage of white *(E(var))*. (Please see CD-ROM for color version of this figure.)

mutants do not exhibit a detectable phenotype, but double homozygotes often die during fetal development. As expected from the preceding model, double mutants are devoid of H3-K9 methylation in pericentric regions, but not elsewhere, which results in chromosomal instability in somatic tissues and the germ line. As a result, surviving double mutants are runted, prone to B-cell lymphomas, and infertile. Neither *HP1α* nor two other *HP1*-related genes have been knocked out yet in the mouse, but mutations in *Drosophila Su(var)2-5* are lethal.

RNAi and Sequence Specificity of PEV

Suv39h1 does not exhibit any specificity other than that it methylates H3-K9, so what directs its activity to histone tails located in pericentric chromosomal regions, known to be particularly rich in heterochromatin, but not to other regions of the genome? Work from the *Schizosaccharomyces pombe* counterparts of *Su(var)3-9 (Clr4)* and *HP1 (Swi6)* suggest that an RNAi-like mechanism is crucial[139–142] (Fig. 6–7A). In wild-type fission yeast, DNA repeats that are highly enriched in pericentric regions are transcribed bidirectionally to produce 1.4- and 2.4-kbp double-stranded transcripts processed by dicer into approximately 22 nucleotide sense and antisense RNAs.[143] Similar to short interfering RNAs (siRNAs) or microRNAs, these RNA oligonucleotides physically associate with argonaute and other, as yet unidentified, proteins to comprise RNA-induced silencing complexes (RISC). However, unlike

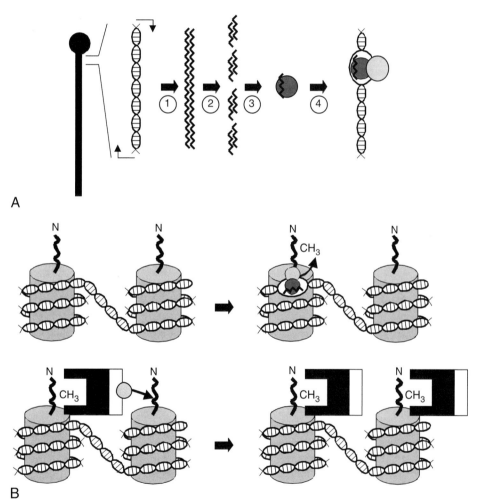

Figure 6–7. *Mosaic coat color in t(X;7) mice.* (A) Schematic of mouse chromosomes X (gray) and 7 (blue). The coat-color genes pink-eyed dilution *(p)* and albino *(c)* are located on chromosome 7. A reciprocal t(X;7) translocation fuses the two chromosomes (right). Translocation breakpoints are indicated with squiggles. (B) Schematic of t(X;7) coat-color mosaicism. Gray and white circles represent pigmented and unpigmented melanocytes, respectively. Intact X and chromosome 7 are shown to the left of X;7 derivatives. The white segment of the intact chromosome 7 represents *p* and *c* mutations (i.e., the cells are heterozygous for both genes). The black box indicates the inactivated X chromosome. Pigment cells that inactivate the translocated X silence the only functional *p* and *c* alleles and do not produce pigment. Cells that inactivate the intact X maintain expression of the *p* and *c* genes on the translocated chromosome and produce pigment. (Please see CD-ROM for color version of this figure.)

conventional siRNAs, which move to the cytoplasm to bind and degrade cognate mRNAs,[144,145] the heterochromatin derived siRNAs remain in the nucleus. It is thought that they direct the RISCs to the corresponding DNA repeats and enable Clr4 to methylate H3-K9 followed by Swi6 binding (Fig. 6–7A).

Just how siRNAs-RISC recruit Clr4 to pericentric repeats is not yet clear and could be direct or indirect. The most direct

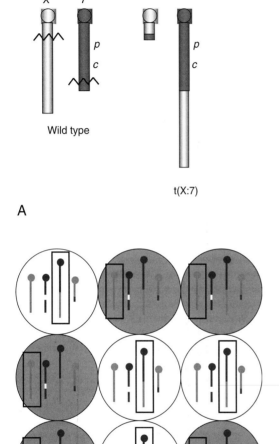

A

B

Figure 6–8. *Specificity and propagation of epigenetic marks in PEV.* (A) Specificity: DNA repeats in pericentric region are transcribed bidirectionally (1). Double-stranded RNAs are cleaved by dicer (2) and processed by RNAi-like machinery (3) to yield RNA oligonucleotides that associate with argonaute and other proteins (gray circle). RNA oligonucleotides are thought to interact with the segment of pericentric repeat that served as the template (4) and to directly or indirectly recruit Clr4 histone methyltransferase (white circle). (B) Propagation: Clr4 methylates H3-K9 (CH3) (upper right panel), which serves as a docking site for the chromodomain of Swi6 (black part of box) (lower left panel). The chromo shadow domain of Swi6 (white part of box) is thought to directly or indirectly recruit more Clr4, which methylates H3-K9 on the adjacent nucleosome (barrel) (lower left). Recruitment of more Swi6 to the nascent H3-K9 methyl group enables the next nucleosome to be modified (lower right panel). (Please see CD-ROM for color version of this figure.)

possibility is that the Clr4 chromodomain binds processed dsRNAs and might be part of RISC. Precedent comes from an HAT involved in *Drosophila* dosage compensation, MOF, that uses an RNA-binding chromodomain to bind dsRNA to specifically methylate H4-K16 of the male X-chromosome.[146,147] More direct evidence comes from HP1α itself, where a hinge region between the chromo- and the chromo shadow domains has been shown to bind RNA.[148] A less direct connection would have Clr4 interacting with another protein that binds siRNAs or some other component of RISC. The least direct possibility is that the siRNAs-RISC directly or indirectly targets an HDAC instead of Clr4 to the repeats. This model is supported by the aforementioned role of MOF in dosage compensation and is attractive because H3-K9 and H3-K14 must be deacetylated before H3-K9 can be methylated.[133,149] Histone acetylation status might also provide an explanation for why Clr4-Swi6 spreading does not extend beyond pericentric regions and silence more distal chromosomal regions. Insulators partition the genome into functional domains and are associated with particularly high H3-K9 and H3-K14 acetylation levels.[150, 151] In this case, a strong insulator refractory to deacetylation would preclude Clr4 from having a template to methylate and prevent ectopic spreading of heterochromatin.

The studies described previously could be performed in a straightforward manner in *S. pombe* because the genes encoding the RNAi machinery exist as singletons. However, there is mounting evidence that RNAi-like-directed changes in chromatin structure exist in other organisms and might not be restricted to pericentric heterochromatin. dsRNAs with homology to transgenes can mediate DNA methylation and transcriptional silencing of transgenes in plants.[42, 152] In addition, mutations in *Pc-G* genes perturb RNAi and cosuppression in both *D. melanogaster* and *C. elegans.*[153–156] *Pc*-G gene products have been implicated in chromatin structure and transcriptional silencing but not RNA degradation or posttranscriptional regulation, so these results suggest that RNA-directed silencing may not be carried out entirely at the posttranscriptional level but might also influence chromatin structure and act at the transcriptional level. This notion is supported by the finding that RNAi decreases hnRNA levels in addition to mRNA.[157]

Although RNAi is thought to have arisen as a defense against RNA viruses and the mobilization of transposable elements, it is tempting to speculate that siRNAs may play a more general role in regulation of gene expression. It is conceivable that siRNAs provide sequence specificity to other enzymes involved in chromatin modifications. Except for E(Z) interacting with PHO, no DNA methyltransferases or HMTs have been shown to interact with sequence-specific activators or repressors. Ironically, Jacob and Monod proposed that the *lac* repressor might encode an RNA molecule and that RNAs might have an important role regulating operons,[158] but this notion was never embraced and was subsequently dismissed as a possible mechanism for eukaryotic transcriptional regulation.

X-CHROMOSOME INACTIVATION

Similar to *Drosophila* PEV, certain chromosomal rearrangements result in mosaic silencing of coat-color genes in female mice.[159, 160] However, whereas *w* is juxtaposed to pericentric regions in *w^m4*, the pink-eye dilution *(p)* and albino coat-color *(c)* loci are juxtaposed to the X-chromosome in t(X;7) translocations (Fig. 6–8). Because a stochastic choice is made to silence one of the two X-chromosomes to achieve dosage compensation in a process called X-chromosome inactivation, some cells choose to inactivate the translocated X and therefore silence *p* and *c*. Other cells choose to inactivate the intact X and express *p* and *c*. As with PEV, this choice is made early in development (around implantation) and then propagated clonally.

Strikingly, the similarities between PEV and X-chromosome inactivation extend to molecular and mechanistic levels; both employ noncoding RNAs that direct similar chromatin modifications. In the case of X-chromosome inactivation, repressive epigenetic marks are targeted by *Xist,* a 17-kb, untranslated RNA transcribed from the inactive but not the active X-chromosome. After being transcribed, *Xist* does not diffuse away from the inactive X (Xi) but coats the chromosome in *cis,* which may allow it to directly or indirectly localize chromatin-modifying complexes to the Xi. Complementary genetic approaches underscore *Xist's* role in X-inactivation; a targeted mutation in *Xist* inhibits inactivation of the mutated chromosome,[161] and *Xist* expressed from an autosomal transgene can lead to ectopic inactivation of the transgenic autosome,[162] similar to t(X;7) translocations. Thus, *Xist* is both necessary and sufficient to initiate long-range silencing in *cis.* Because of this potent silencing capability, cells must count their X-chromosomes and repress *Xist* on one X-chromosome, the active X (Xa), per diploid cell. In the mouse, *Xist* repression on the Xa is accomplished by expression of *Tsix,* another large untranslated RNA partially antisense to *Xist.*[163] However, it is not clear whether *Tsix* is used in all mammals, and even in the mouse the exact mechanism by which *Tsix* blocks *Xist* is not known.

The Xi is cytologically distinguishable as a late replicating, condensed heterochromatin at the nuclear periphery.[164, 165] In recent years, antibodies have been developed that detect histone marks and chromatin-associated proteins, some of which are enriched on the heterochromatic Xi and underrepresented on the Xa. Histones associated with the Xi are hypoacetylated, hypomethylated at H3-K4, and hypermethylated at H3-K9 and H3-K27. All of these marks are consistent with repressive higher order chromatin conformations such as those found in pericentric heterochromatin.[166–171] Additionally, some reports have suggested that the histone variant macroH2A is enriched on the Xi and that a separate variant H2A.Z is excluded from the Xi.[172,173] Finally, in mouse embryonic tissues, the Xi is DNA hypermethylated relative to the Xa.[163] However, the Xi is not hypermethylated in mouse extraembryonic tissues, which undergo imprinted rather than stochastic X-inactivation.[174] This discrepancy is consistent with a more prominent role for DNA methylation in the embryo proper (see the section "DNA Methylation").

Critically, this wealth of colocalization data has important caveats. First, the Xi is itself a condensed structure in the nucleus. Thus, it is not always clear whether the marks and proteins apparently enriched on the X are any more concentrated than bulk histones.[175] Additionally, colocalization data

is dependent upon the specificity of the antibodies used in the assays. For instance, it is not clear whether histone H3 is truly hypermethylated at K9 on the Xi as previously suggested[167–169] or whether the α-H3-K9 met antibodies simply cross-react with methylated H3-K27 residues known to be enriched on the Xi.[170,171] Most importantly, in most cases, the appropriate mouse mutants have not been generated to determine whether the marks or variants are necessary for X-inactivation.

In vitro ES cell differentiation models of X-inactivation have defined a sequence of epigenetic modifications that appear to help initiate and maintain stochastic X-inactivation (Fig. 6–9). This program is initiated by *Xist* and involves the ordered recruitment of Polycomb group proteins, HDACs, histone variants, and DNA methyltransferases. In at least two cases, functional data with mouse mutants has verified that certain steps are required for X-inactivation.[174,176]

Importantly, several genes on the Xi escape X-chromosome inactivation. These loci contain epigenetic marks enriched on the Xa (e.g., histone hyperacetylation), are biallelically expressed, and replicate synchronously with the corresponding Xa alleles, indicating that they escape all aspects of X-inactivation.[177] Most of these genes reside in the pseudoautosomal region that carries functional homologs on the Y-chromosome. Thus, these genes are essentially diploid in both males and females, precluding any need for dosage compensation. Other genes escape X-inactivation despite lacking homologs on the Y. Organisms appear to be less sensitive to dosage of these gene products. Presumably, escaping genes are protected from the spread of repressive chromatin marks by flanking insulator elements. However, the mechanisms of escape are poorly understood.

X- and Y-chromosomes are also silenced during male germ line development, a process called meiotic sex chromosome inactivation (MSCI). MSCI not only renders sex chromosomes transcriptionally inert but also is required for synapsis of the pseudoautosomal regions of the sex chromosomes.[178] There appear to be important differences between female somatic X-inactivation and male germ line X-inactivation. Unlike X-inactivation, MSCI is not dependent upon *Xist.*[179] Instead, one of the earliest identified features of MSCI is sex chromosome-specific enrichment of the phosphorylated histone variant γH2AX, also known to colocalize double-strand breaks. *H2AX* loss-of-function mutations compromise MSCI and sex chromosome synapsis.[178]

POLYCOMB AND TRITHORAX GROUPS

Pc-G Silencing

Genetic screens in *Drosophila* have identified many *Pc*-G genes required for the proper expression of homeotic genes.[180–184] (Table 6–2). Whereas gap and pair-rule gene products are required to establish homeotic gene expression, Pc-G factors are required for maintenance. Not unexpectedly, these distinct classes of regulatory factors act in concert. Gap and pair-rule genes encode DNA-binding factors that bind to enhancers and promoters of homeotic genes in the *Antennapedia* (ANT-C) and *bithorax* (BX-C) complexes and, in so doing, directly activate or repress transcription.

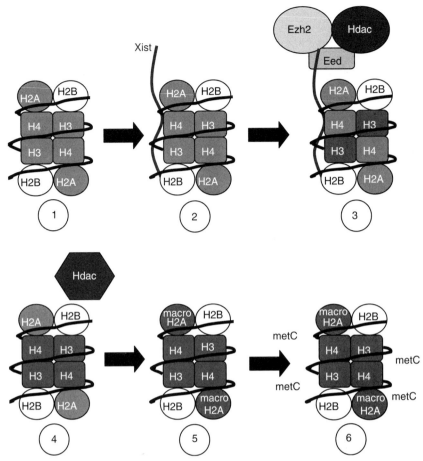

Figure 6–9. *Sequential epigenetic marks during X-chromosome inactivation.* For all histones (H2A, H2B, H3, and H4), light gray represents covalent modifications or variants associated with transcriptional activity, and dark gray represents transcriptional repression. H2B is white because no covalent modifications or variants are known to be enriched on the inactive X-chromosome (Xi). (A) Initially, both X-chromosomes are H3 and H4 hyperacetylated, H3-K4 hypermethylated, and DNA hypomethylated. (B) *Xist* coats one of the two X-chromosomes, which is destined to be the Xi, as the first step of the inactivation process. (C) Next, the Eed–Ezh2–Hdac complex is recruited and mediates H3 deacetylation and H3-K9 and H3-K27 methylation. Concomitant with these Pc-G-mediated modifications, H3-K4 is demethylated. Subsequently, (D) H4 is deacetylated, and (E) macroH2A replaces H2A in many nucleosomes on the Xi. (F) Finally, CpGs on the Xi become methylated. (Please see CD-ROM for color version of this figure.)

However, these genes are transiently expressed, and the corresponding gene products decay by midembryogenesis, yet homeotic gene expression is properly maintained throughout the remainder of development. Some gap and pair-rule proteins that repress transcription are thought to directly or indirectly recruit Pc-G factors before decaying.[185] These Pc-G factors assemble into at least two complexes and alter chromatin structure. In so doing, the Pc-G complexes act as a form of cellular memory to keep inactive homeotic genes in a permanent "off" state over the course of many cell divisions. This regulation is crucial for proper anterior–posterior (A–P) patterning because homeotic genes, which are expressed in stem cell populations in the imaginal discs, control cell fate decisions in the head, the three thorax segments, and the eight abdominal segments.

Accordingly, Pc-G mutants exhibit ectopic homeotic gene expression and A–P patterning defects. Going back to the original genetic screens, many Pc-G mutants were isolated as heterozygotes that have two or three thorax number one segments (T1-T1-T3 or T1-T1-T1) instead of the normal T1-T2-T3 pattern. These T2-to-T1 and T3-to-T1 homeotic transformations are most evident in male flies because mating structures, called sex combs, normally found only on the first pair of legs emanating from T1 are found on the first two or all three pairs of legs. This observation accounts for the names of quite a few *Pc-G* genes: Polycomb *(Pc)*, extra sex combs *(esc)*, additional sex combs *(Asx)*, sex combs on the midleg *(Scm)*, posterior sex combs *(Psc)*, etc. Moreover, when many of these same mutations are made homozygous, homeotic gene expression is altered to a greater extent, homeotic

TABLE 6–2
Pc-G Genes Characterized at the Molecular Level

Drosophila Gene	Abbreviation	Mouse Ortholog(s)	Domain–Motif	Proposed Function
Polycomb	Pc	Mpc1/M33, MPc2, Mpc3	Chromodomain	PRC1, binds-H3-K9 and H3-K27
Polyhomeotic	ph	Mph1/Rae28 Mph2, Mph3	Zinc finger, SAM/SPM domain	PRC1, oligomerization
Posterior sex combs	Psc	Bmi1, Mel18	RING finger	PRC1
dRING	dRING	Ring1a, Ring1b/Rnf2	RING finger	PRC1
Sex comb on midleg	Scm	Scmh1, Scmh2	Zinc fingers, SAM/SPM domain	PRC1
Zeste	z	ND	Helix–turn–helix, leucine zipper	PRC1, binds DNA
Heat shock cognate 4	hsc4	Hsc4	ATPase domain	PRC1, putative chaperone
Suppressor of zeste 2	Su(z)2	Bmi1, Mel18	RING finger	ND
Polycomb-like	Pcl	Mpcl1, Mpcl2/M96	PHD fingers	ND
Enhancer of zeste	E(z)	Ezh1/Enx2, Ezh2/Enx1	SET domain	E(Z)-ESC complex, HMT
Extra sex combs	esc	Eed	WD40 repeats	E(Z)-ESC complex
Suppressor of zeste 12	Su(z)12	Su(z)12h1	Zinc finger	E(Z)-ESC complex
Pleiohomeotic	pho	YY1	Zinc finger	E(Z)-ESC complex, binds DNA
Enhancer of Polycomb	E(Pc)	Epc1	ND	ND
Cramped	crm	ND	ND	Interacts with PCNA
Additional sex combs	Asx	Asxl1, Asxl2	Cysteine cluster	ND
Multisex combs	mxc	Ssb	RNA-binding domains	ND

transformations are more severe and widespread, expression of other types of genes is perturbed, and embryonic or larval lethality often result. In addition, robust genetic interactions among mutations in distinct Pc-G genes exacerbate these mutant phenotypes.

The first suggestion that Pc-G factors might modulate the chromatin structure came from the molecular analysis of PC and the realization that it shares a chromodomain with HP1.[186] More recently, E(Z) has been shown to share a SET domain with SU(VAR)3-9 and have HMT activity.[187–190] Coupled with conventional chromatography and protein–protein interaction data, these observations have led to a model analogous to Suv39h/Clr4 and HP1/Swi6 in PEV.[184,187–189,191] (Fig. 6–10). Like PEV, one Pc-G member interacts with PCNA and may facilitate the reestablishment of repressive complexes following DNA replication[192] (Table 6–2). It is also possible that the spreading of Pc-G silencing is blocked by insulator elements.[193, 194] However, there are some differences. Pc-G complexes are distributed more widely throughout the genome—with antibodies detecting about 100 sites on polytene chromosomes—than Suv39h/Clr4 and HP1/Swi6, which are primarily restricted to pericentric regions. Pc-G complexes also act more locally. They apparently spread over tens of kilobases to around 100 kb, whereas Suv39h/Clr4 and HP1/Swi6 spread over megabasepair intervals. Both of these differences could be caused partly by cis-acting elements, called Polycomb response elements (PREs), which are enriched in the ANT-C and BX-C and can be bound by a Pc-G member (PHO) that associates with E(Z)-ESC complex.[195–197] It also is not clear how other Pc-G factors contribute to the silencing process.

Mammalian Pc-G gene products are more numerous because of duplication and divergence events during vertebrate evolution, but they comprise similar complexes and perform similar roles in development.[181, 198] Null mutations of Ezh2, Eed, and YY1, all of which encode components of the first complex, result in early embryonic lethality[199–201] (Tables 6–1 and 6–2). However, it is clear that the function of this complex is not restricted to early embryogenesis but is instead involved in a variety of biological processes in many tissues.

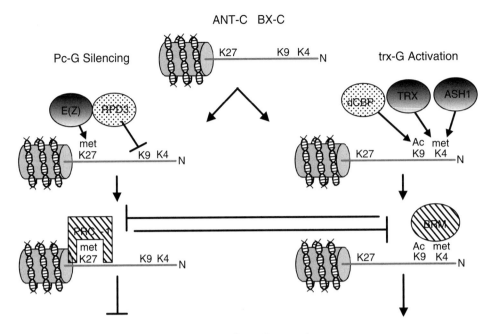

Figure 6–10. *Homeotic gene regulation by polycomb and trithorax groups.* Schematic illustrating antagonistic roles of Pc-G silencing and trx-G activation in homeotic gene regulation. A single nucleosome in the ANT-C or BX-C is shown with an H3 N-terminal tail projecting to the right (top panel). Pc-G silencing is initiated by the addition of repressive covalent modifications: E(Z) methylates (met) K27, and RPD3 deacetylates K9 (upper left). PRC1 complex binds metK27 (lower left). Trx-G activation is initiated by the addition of other covalent modifications: TRX and ASH1 methylate (met) K4, and dCBP acetylates (Ac) K9 (upper right). An SWI/SNF-related BRM complex is recruited to K4-methylated, K9-acetylated nucleosomes (lower right). PRC1 and BRM recruitment are mutually exclusive[242] (lower panels). Whereas PRC1 recruitment represses homeotic gene transcription, BRM promotes expression (bottom panel). See Tables 6–2 and 6–3 and selected references for additional subunits in these complexes.[188,189,218–224,242–244] (Please see CD-ROM for color version of this figure.)

An *Ezh2* conditional mutation in B-cells demonstrated that the wild-type gene product is required for VDJ recombination.[68] *Ezh2* is also overexpressed in human prostate cancer tumors, and, conversely, RNAi down-regulation of *Ezh2* inhibits the proliferation of prostate cancer cells *in vitro*.[202] Although *Eed* null mutants exhibit severe A–P patterning defects during gastrulation,[199] they die before many *Hox* genes are expressed. However, an ENU-induced hypomorph mutant line misexpresses *Hox* genes[203] and exhibits homeotic transformations.[204] It also has placental defects[203] and has been implicated in T-cell lymphomas.[205] It has also become clear that *Eed* plays a role in X-chromosome inactivation[171, 176, 206] and genomic imprinting.[207]

In contrast, null mutations of *Pc*-G genes that encode components of the mammalian PRC1 complex do not confer embryonic-lethal phenotypes. *MPc2/M33/Cbx2, Bmi1, Mel18,* and *Rae28/Mph1* homozygotes exhibit altered *Hox* gene expression and homeotic transformations, manifest by changes in vertebral identities, as well as cell proliferation defects in the hematopoietic system[181, 198] (Tables 6–1 and 6–2). One exception is *Ring1B/Rnf2,* but although null mutants die during gastrulation,[208] hypomorphs are viable and exhibit altered *Hox* gene expression and homeotic transformations.[209] Of all these genes, *Bmi1* is particularly noteworthy because it

inhibits the *Ink4a* tumor suppressor locus[210] and is required for continued proliferation of hematopoietic stem cells.[211,212] It also regulates proliferation in more differentiated cells in several hematopoietic lineages. Gain-of-function mutations down-regulate both *Ink4a* gene products (the p16 and p19 cyclin-dependent kinase inhibitors) and cooperate with *c-Myc* in B- and T-cell lymphomas.[213,214] Conversely, loss-of-function mutations lead to increased expression of p16 and p19 and decreased proliferation of erythrocytes, resulting in anemia. Moreover, this phenotype is suppressed by an *Ink4a* targeted mutation.

Trx-G Activation

Genetic screens in *Drosophila* identified loss-of-function mutations in *trx* and several other genes that suppress dominant *Pc* mutant phenotypes.[215] This *trx* group of genes also encode proteins that have a variety of interesting domains and motifs, some of which are shared with *Pc*-G members, but have the opposite effect on transcription (Table 6–3). For example, the TRX protein has a SET domain, just like E(Z), but methylates H3-K4 instead of H3-K9/H3-K27 and is involved in transcriptional activation of homeotic genes instead of transcriptional repression[187,216–218] (Fig. 6–10). Consequently, mutations in *trx* or other *trx*-G genes result in

TABLE 6-3
Trx-G Genes Characterized at the Molecular Level

Drosophila Gene	Abbreviation	Mouse Ortholog(s)	Domain–Motif	Proposed Function
Trithorax	trx	Mll/All/Hrx, Mll2	SET domain, PHD finger	TAC1 complex, HMT, binds histone
Trithorax-like	trl	ND	Zinc fingers, POZ domains	DNA-binding GAGA factor
Kismet	kis	ND	ATPase domain, chromodomain	ND
Domino	dom	ND	ATPase domain, PEST domain	ND
Brahma	brm	Brm, Brg1	ATPase domain, bromodomain,	SWI/SNF complex, catalytic subunit
Moira	mor	Baf155, Baf170	SANT domain, leucine zipper	SWI/SNF complex
Osa	osa	Baf250	ARID domain	SWI/SNF complex
Snf5 related 1	snr1	Baf47/Snf5/INI1	Putative coiled-coil domain	SWI/SNF complex
Zeste	z	ND	Helix–turn–helix, leucine zipper	Interacts with SWI/SNF, binds DNA
Taranis	tara	Trip-Br	NLS	ND
Absent, small, or homeotic discs 1	ash1	Ash1l	PHD finger, bromodomain, SET domain	Ash1 complex, HMT
Absent, small, or homeotic discs 2	ash2	Ash2l	PHD finger	Ash2 complex
Female sterile (1) homeotic	fs(1)h	ND	Bromodomains	ND
Tonalli	tna	ND	SP-RING finger	Sumoylation possibly
Modifier of mdg4	mod(mdg4)	ND	BTB domain	Binds su(Hw) insulator element

decreased homeotic gene expression instead of ectopic expression. Of course, that trx-G and Pc-G counteract each other at the molecular level is not surprising, considering that the two groups have an antagonistic relationship at the genetic level.

Genetic and molecular interactions among other trx-G genes, which encode various chromatin-modifying factors, are common and important at the mechanistic level. TRX physically binds to another HMT called ASH1,[219,220] and both TRX and ASH1 bind to the dCBP HAT.[221,222] TRX also binds to a subunit of an SWI/SNF-related complex, called SNR1,[223] which includes OSA, brahma (BRM), and moira (MOR).[224] Like Suv39 and HP1 or E(Z) and PC, TRX, ASH1, or both may provide a covalently modified histone interface for the BRM complex (Fig. 6–10). Mammalian counterparts of trx-G genes are important for many aspects of development, ranging from implantation to Hox gene expression, erythropoiesis, and neural tube closure at midgestation to postnatal fitness and cancer prevention[198] (Table 6–3). With respect to Hox gene regulation, trx-G and Pc-G factors counteract each other just as they do in Drosophila.[225]

MONOALLELIC EXPRESSION: IMPRINTING AND ALLELIC EXCLUSION

Mammals are diploid for all autosomal loci, inheriting one copy of each gene from each parent. Presumably, most genes use both alleles. However, for a growing subset of characterized genes, only one allele is used per cell, a process termed monoallelic expression. For genes subject to monoallelic expression, each cell is functionally hemizygous, expressing either the maternally or paternally inherited allele but not both.

The best-studied type of monoallelic expression is imprinting, whereby genes are expressed according to their parental origin. For example, only maternally inherited copies of H19 are expressed (paternal alleles are silenced), and only paternally inherited copies of Igf2 are expressed. Such parent-of-origin expression explains the inability of mammalian parthengenotes, gynegenotes, and androgenotes, as well as certain uniparental disomies, to develop to term.[226–228] Imprinted genes tend to be tightly linked. To date, more than 10 clusters encompassing roughly 60 imprinted genes have been identified in the mouse (see http://www.mgu.har.mrc.ac.uk/imprinting/all_impmaps.html). From these data, many researchers have estimated that the mouse and human genomes contain somewhere between a hundred and many hundred imprinted genes. However, these estimates may substantially underestimate the actual number of imprinted genes for a variety of reasons. First, most imprinted genes that have been characterized to date were uncovered by Cattanach and Searles' work with uniparental disomies in mice carrying translocations.[228] Because these translocations only covered part of the mouse genome, there are large regions of the genome that have not been assayed for parent-of-origin effects. Additionally, many genes are imprinted only in certain tissues, and many others produce no phenotype when biallelically silenced or expressed. Sequencing ESTs from a variety of tissues from F1 hybrids would be a more comprehensive way of identifying imprinted genes.

Imprinted genes are associated with regions of DNA that are differentially methylated in sperm and oocytes. These regions, termed imprinting control regions (ICRs), appear to regulate entire imprinting clusters. Targeted deletion of ICRs lead to loss of imprinting of all of the genes in the cluster. Additionally, $Dnmt1^{-/-}$ embryos exhibit loss of imprinting (biallelic expression or silencing) of almost all imprinted genes,[229] and the progeny of $Dnmt3L^{-/-}$, and $Dnmt3a^{-/-}$, $Dnmt3b^{+/-}$ double mutant females exhibit loss of imprinting of maternally imprinted genes.[230,231] Additionally, the promoters of imprinted genes are themselves often differentially DNA methylated on maternal versus paternal alleles. These findings have led to a general consensus that DNA methylation is a critical part of the biochemical imprint that distinguishes maternal and paternal alleles at imprinted loci.

Some ICRs contain binding sites for methylation-sensitive insulators. At the $H19/Igf2$ imprinting cluster on mouse chromosome 7, the ICR includes clustered bindings sites for the insulator CTCF (Fig. 6–11). Here, allele-specific methylation drives allele-specific, methylation-sensitive, insulator binding, which reciprocally regulates $H19$ and $Igf2$ by blocking maternal $Igf2$ association with its downstream enhancer[232,233] (Fig. 6–11). Other ICRs are associated with noncoding RNAs. At the imprinted cluster on mouse chromosome 17, the non-coding, paternally transcribed Air RNA acts in cis to silence reciprocally imprinted genes, including $Igf2r$.[234] Such a phenomenon is reminiscent of silencing of the X-chromosome by $Xist$, but the mechanism of RNA-mediated silencing at imprinted loci is poorly understood.

During germ line development, imprints must be erased and then reestablished so that all ICRs in each gamete have gender-appropriate epigenetic marks. Lee *et al.* were able to analyze the timing of imprint erasure by monitoring imprinting in clones derived from mouse PGC nuclei.[235] Clones derived from E12.5 or E13.5 PGC nuclei die at midgestation and exhibit loss of differential methylation of all genes analyzed. Moreover, transcript levels from imprinted genes were consistent with loss of imprinted expression. Conversely, clones derived from E11.5 PGC nuclei developed much further and exhibited appropriate differential DNA methylation of many genes analyzed. Thus, the work by Lee *et al.* suggests that PGC imprint erasure begins as cells reach the genital ridges at around E11.5, concomitant with genomic demethylation. One caveat to this work is that imprinted expression was assayed by quantifying transcripts; future work will need to use allele-specific transcript detection methods to verify these results. Although similar cloning experiments have not been performed with later stage germ cells, analysis of DNA methylation suggests that male germ cells reestablish imprints late in embryogenesis during leptonema, and female germ cells reestablish imprints around P6, during oocyte growth.[5]

Recently, additional epigenetic marks that distinguish parental alleles at imprinted loci have begun to emerge. Nucleosomes associated with active alleles tend to be hyper-acetylated on the tails of H3 and H4 and methylated at H3-K4.[236] Conversely, histones associated with silenced alleles tend to be hypoacetylated and methylated at lysine 9 of histone H3.[236] The enzymes responsible for these modifications at imprinted loci are largely undefined. Loss-of-function mutations in the Pc-G gene Eed lead to biallelic expression of several imprinted genes, including $Mash2$ and $Cdkn1c$ in the Beckwith-Wiedemann syndrome (BWS) imprinting cluster on mouse chromosome 7.[207] EED associates with EZH2, an

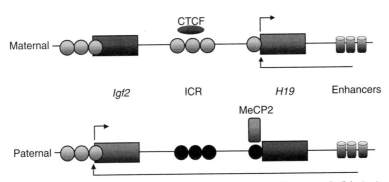

Figure 6–11. *Coordinated transcription of two imprinted genes.* The maternal allele (top) includes an ICR between $Igf2$ and $H19$ that is unmethylated (three circles) and binds CTCF (oval), which blocks the association of $Igf2$ with enhancers (three barrels) downstream of $H19$, leading to $Igf2$ silencing (top left and bottom right boxes). Because the CTCF-binding sites do not separate $H19$ and these enhancers, $H19$ is transcribed (arrow). The paternal allele ICR (bottom) is methylated (three black circles) and cannot bind CTCF, which facilitates interaction between $Igf2$ and its downstream enhancers, leading to $Igf2$ transcription (arrow). Conversely, $H19$ promoter is methylated (one black circle), recruits MeCP2 (box), and is silenced (top left and bottom right boxes). Current models postulate that $Igf2$ has a greater affinity than $H19$ for the downstream enhancers; therefore, in the absence of CTCF insulation, $Igf2$ outcompetes $H19$ for these enhancers. (Please see CD-ROM for color version of this figure.)

HMT with activity directed against H3-K9 and H3-K27.[237] Future work will need to address allele-specific association of the latter mark at imprinted loci. Interestingly, allele-specific DNA methylation remains intact at affected genes in *Eed*−/− embryos.[207] This observation suggests that covalent histone modifications at imprinted loci are either parallel to or downstream of DNA methylation. Consistent with this model, MeCP2 recruits histone H3-K9 methyltransferase activity to the maternally silenced allele of the imprinted gene *H19*.[45] This finding indicates that allele-specific DNA methylation may drive allele-specific transcriptionally repressive chromatin marks.

In prominent models, imprints are established during germ line development and then propagated and spread in postfertilization cells. Often overlooked, and potentially more relevant to developmental abnormalities in clones, parental genomes remain partitioned in early embryos. It has long been known that male and female pronuclei remain separate until the completion of the first mitosis. Surprisingly, parental genomes continue to be compartmentalized even after the pronuclei fuse. Haaf and colleagues tracked parental genomes in preimplantation embryos by staining sperm nuclei with bromodeoxyuridine.[238] These studies indicate that parental genomes remain compartmentalized in the nucleus at least until implantation. Neither the functional significance of this compartmentalization nor the consequences of disrupting it are known. However, the existence of such compartments indicates that parent-of-origin epigenetic marks could be applied *de novo* in postfertilization cells.

Imprinted genes are a subset of a much larger number of genes that are monoallelically expressed. For many monoallelically expressed genes, the active allele is determined not by parent-of-origin as in imprinting but by allelic exclusion, where a stochastic choice dictates one allele to be active and one to be silent. Our understanding of allelic exclusion lags our understanding of imprinting, because the mosaic nature of the process requires analyses to be performed at the level of single cells (i.e., expression analyses of a mosaic tissue will suggest biallelic expression). The technical obstacles to studying allelic exclusion also make it difficult to estimate what fraction of the genome might be subject to such regulation; what work has been done has concentrated on odorant and pheromone receptors, which number just under 1000 in human and just over 1000 in mouse, and several immunological molecules, including the immunoglobulin loci and the T-cell receptor. At these loci, alleles are distinguished not only by expression state but also by DNA methylation status, DNase I hypersensitivity, and replication asynchrony. Generally, active alleles are hypomethylated, DNase I hyperaccessible, and early replicating, whereas silent alleles are hypermethylated, DNase I hypoaccessible, and late replicating. Replication asynchrony is established around implantation, long before antigen receptor rearrangement or the onset of odorant receptor expression and roughly coincident with other stochastic epigenetic choices, including X-inactivation.[239] Also similar to X-inactivation, the epigenetic states dictated by implantation-stage choice are propagated through mitoses to generate clonal populations of cells.[239] Finally, allelic exclusion choice may not occur at the level of individual genes as anticipated but at the level of entire chromosomes. The early replicating alleles of any two linked genes subject to allelic exclusion appear to always be on the same chromosome.[240] Essentially, many or all chromosomes may be subject to processes mechanistically similar to X-inactivation, but a much higher proportion of genes may escape on autosomes. Future work will need to extend the replication assays and determine whether transcriptionally active alleles are always on the same chromosome.

Summary

Drawing upon several models of epigenetic inheritance, much has been learned about chromatin-modifying factors and how they act and interact to regulate transcription. It is becoming increasing clear that these factors and their corresponding epigenetic marks dictate developmental potentials. The present challenge is to better understand chromatin-remodeling mechanisms in cell fate decisions, cell proliferation and differentiation, and plasticity. In addition to providing considerable insight into many aspects of embryogenesis and postnatal development, this knowledge should prove valuable for improving the prospects of stem cell technologies in the clinical setting.

REFERENCES

1. Struhl, K. (1999). Fundamentally different logic of gene regulation in eukaryotes and prokaryotes. *Cell* **98,** 1–4.
2. Lemon, B., and Tjian, R. (2000). Orchestrated response: a symphony of transcription factors for gene control. *Genes Dev.* **14,** 2551–2569.
3. Fry, C.J., and Peterson, C.L. (2001). Chromatin-remodeling enzymes: who's on first? *Curr. Biol.* **11,** R185–R197.
4. Narlikar, G.J., Fan, H.Y., and Kingston, R.E. (2002). Cooperation between complexes that regulate chromatin structure and transcription. *Cell* **108,** 475–487.
5. Li, E. (2002). Chromatin modification and epigenetic reprogramming in mammalian development. *Nat. Rev. Genet.* **3,** 662–673.
6. Shin, T., Kraemer, D., Pryor, J., Liu, L., Rugila, J., Howe, L., Buck, S., Murphy, K., Lyons, L., and Westhusin, M. (2002). A cat cloned by nuclear transplantation. *Nature* **415,** 859.
7. Wilmut, I., Schnieke, A.E., McWhir, J., Kind, A.J., and Campbell, K.H. (1997). Viable offspring derived from fetal and adult mammalian cells. *Nature* **385,** 810–813.
8. Kato, Y., Tani, T., Sotomaru, Y., Kurokawa, K., Kato, J., Doguchi, H., Yasue, H., and Tsunoda, Y. (1998). Eight calves cloned from somatic cells of a single adult. *Science* **282,** 2095–2098.
9. Wakayama, T., Perry, A.C., Zuccotti, M., Johnson, K.R., and Yanagimachi, R. (1998). Full-term development of mice from enucleated oocytes injected with cumulus cell nuclei. *Nature* **394,** 369–374.
10. Baguisi, A., Behboodi, E., Melican, D.T., Pollock, J.S., Destrempes, M.M., Cammuso, C., Williams, J.L., Nims, S.D., Porter, C.A., Midura, P. *et al.* (1999). Production of goats by somatic cell nuclear transfer. *Nat. Biotechnol.* **17,** 456–461.

11. Polejaeva, I.A., Chen, S.H., Vaught, T.D., Page, R.L., Mullins, J., Ball, S., Dai, Y., Boone, J., Walker, S., Ayares, D.L. *et al.* (2000). Cloned pigs produced by nuclear transfer from adult somatic cells. *Nature* **407,** 86–90.

12. Onishi, A., Iwamoto, M., Akita, T., Mikawa, S., Takeda, K., Awata, T., Hanada, H., and Perry, A.C. (2000). Pig cloning by microinjection of fetal fibroblast nuclei. *Science* **289,** 1188–1190.

13. Tamashiro, K.L., Wakayama, T., Akutsu, H., Yamazaki, Y., Lachey, J.L., Wortman, M.D., Seeley, R.J., D'Alessio, D.A., Woods, S.C., Yanagimachi, R. *et al.* (2002). Cloned mice have an obese phenotype not transmitted to their offspring. *Nat. Med.* **8,** 262–267.

14. Ogonuki, N., Inoue, K., Yamamoto, Y., Noguchi, Y., Tanemura, K., Suzuki, O., Nakayama, H., Doi, K., Ohtomo, Y., Satoh, M. *et al.* (2002). Early death of mice cloned from somatic cells. *Nat. Genet.* **30,** 253–254.

15. Boiani, M., Eckardt, S., Scholer, H.R., and McLaughlin, K.J. (2002). Oct4 distribution and level in mouse clones: consequences for pluripotency. *Genes Dev.* **16,** 1209–1219.

16. Bourc'his, D., Le Bourhis, D., Patin, D., Niveleau, A., Comizzoli, P., Renard, J.P., and Viegas-Pequignot, E. (2001). Delayed and incomplete reprogramming of chromosome methylation patterns in bovine cloned embryos. *Curr. Biol.* **11,** 1542–1546.

17. Dean, W., Santos, F., Stojkovic, M., Zakhartchenko, V., Walter, J., Wolf, E., and Reik, W. (2001). Conservation of methylation reprogramming in mammalian development: aberrant reprogramming in cloned embryos. *Proc. Natl. Acad. Sci. USA* **98,** 13,734–13,738.

18. Humpherys, D., Eggan, K., Akutsu, H., Hochedlinger, K., Rideout, W.M., 3rd, Biniszkiewicz, D., Yanagimachi, R., and Jaenisch, R. (2001). Epigenetic instability in ES cells and cloned mice. *Science* **293,** 95–97.

19. Kang, Y.K., Koo, D.B., Park, J.S., Choi, Y.H., Chung, A.S., Lee, K.K., and Han, Y.M. (2001). Aberrant methylation of donor genome in cloned bovine embryos. *Nat. Genet.* **28,** 173–177.

20. Kang, Y.K., Park, J.S., Koo, D.B., Choi, Y.H., Kim, S.U., Lee, K.K., and Han, Y.M. (2002). Limited demethylation leaves mosaic-type methylation states in cloned bovine preimplantation embryos. *EMBO J.* **21,** 1092–1100.

21. Cheong, H.T., Takahashi, Y., and Kanagawa, H. (1993). Birth of mice after transplantation of early cell-cycle stage embryonic nuclei into enucleated oocytes. *Biol. Reprod.* **48,** 958–963.

22. Wilmut, I., Beaujean, N., de Sousa, P.A., Dinnyes, A., King, T.J., Paterson, L.A., Wells, D.N., and Young, L.E. (2002). Somatic cell nuclear transfer. *Nature* **419,** 583–586.

23. Heyman, Y., Chavatte-Palmer, P., LeBourhis, D., Camous, S., Vignon, X., and Renard, J.P. (2002). Frequency and occurrence of late gestation losses from cattle cloned embryos. *Biol. Reprod.* **66,** 6–13.

24. Thompson, E.M. (1996). Chromatin structure and gene expression in the preimplantation mammalian embryo. *Reprod. Nutr. Dev.* **36,** 619–635.

25. Kikyo, N., Wade, P.A., Guschin, D., Ge, H., and Wolffe, A.P. (2000). Active remodeling of somatic nuclei in egg cytoplasm by the nucleosomal ATPase ISWI. *Science* **289,** 2360–2362.

26. Bultman, S., Gebuhr, T., and Magnuson, T. (Unpublished data).

27. Hadjantonakis, A.K., and Papaioannou, V.E. (2002). Can mammalian cloning combined with embryonic stem cell technologies be used to treat human diseases? *Genome Biol.* **3,** R1023.

28. Chung, S., Sonntag, K.C., Andersson, T., Bjorklund, L.M., Park, J.J., Kim, D.W., Kang, U.J., Isacson, O., and Kim, K.S. (2002). Genetic engineering of mouse embryonic stem cells by Nurr1 enhances differentiation and maturation into dopaminergic neurons. *Eur. J. Neurosci.* **16,** 1829–1838.

29. Cassidy, R., and Frisen, J. (2002). Embryonic stem cells: taming the fountain of youth. *Curr. Biol.* **12,** R705– R706.

30. Kim, J.H., Auerbach, J.M., Rodriguez-Gomez, J.A., Velasco, I., Gavin, D., Lumelsky, N., Lee, S.H., Nguyen, J., Sanchez-Pernaute, R., Bankiewicz, K. *et al.* (2002). Dopamine neurons derived from embryonic stem cells function in an animal model of Parkinson's disease. *Nature* **418,** 50–56.

31. Wichterle, H., Lieberam, I., Porter, J.A., and Jessell, T.M. (2002). Directed differentiation of embryonic stem cells into motor neurons. *Cell* **110,** 385–397.

32. Rountree, M.R., Bachman, K.E., Herman, J.G., and Baylin, S.B. (2001). DNA methylation, chromatin inheritance, and cancer. *Oncogene* **20,** 3156–3165.

33. Waterston, R.H., and Lindblad-Toh, K., and Birney, E., and Rogers, J., and Abril, J.F., and Agarwal, P., and Agarwala, R., and Ainscough, R., and Alexandersson, M., and An, P. *et al.* (2002). Initial sequencing and comparative analysis of the mouse genome. *Nature* **420,** 520–562.

34. Gardiner-Garden, M., and Frommer, M. (1987). CpG islands in vertebrate genomes. *J. Mol. Biol.* **196,** 261–282.

35. Bird, A. (2002). DNA methylation patterns and epigenetic memory. *Genes Dev.* **16,** 6–21.

36. Mayer, W., Niveleau, A., Walter, J., Fundele, R., and Haaf, T. (2000). Demethylation of the zygotic paternal genome. *Nature* **403,** 501–502.

37. Hajkova, P., Erhardt, S., Lane, N., Haaf, T., El-Maarri, O., Reik, W., Walter, J., and Surani, M.A. (2002). Epigenetic reprogramming in mouse primordial germ cells. *Mech. Dev.* **117,** 15–23.

38. Okano, M., Bell, D.W., Haber, D.A., and Li, E. (1999). DNA methyltransferases Dnmt3a and Dnmt3b are essential for *de novo* methylation and mammalian development. *Cell* **99,** 247–257.

39. Chedin, F., Lieber, M.R., and Hsieh, C.L. (2002). The DNA methyltransferase-like protein DNMT3L stimulates *de novo* methylation by Dnmt3a. *Proc. Natl. Acad. Sci. USA* **99,** 16,916–16,921.

40. Deplus, R., Brenner, C., Burgers, W.A., Putmans, P., Kouzarides, T., de Launoit, Y., and Fuks, F. (2002). Dnmt3L is a transcriptional repressor that recruits histone deacetylase. *Nucleic Acids Res.* **30,** 3831–3838.

41. Aapola, U., Liiv, I., and Peterson, P. (2002). Imprinting regulator DNMT3L is a transcriptional repressor associated with histone deacetylase activity. *Nucleic Acids Res.* **30,** 3602–3608.

42. Jones, P.A., and Takai, D. (2001). The role of DNA methylation in mammalian epigenetics. *Science* **293,** 1068–1070.

43. Feng, Q., and Zhang, Y. (2001). The MeCP1 complex represses transcription through preferential binding, remodeling, and deacetylating methylated nucleosomes. *Genes Dev.* **15,** 827–832.

44. Jones, P.L., Veenstra, G.J., Wade, P.A., Vermaak, D., Kass, S.U., Landsberger, N., Strouboulis, J., and Wolffe, A.P. (1998). Methylated DNA and MeCP2 recruit histone deacetylase to repress transcription. *Nat. Genet.* **19,** 187–191.

45. Fuks, F., Hurd, P.J., Wolf, D., Nan, X., Bird, A.P., and Kouzarides, T. (2003). The methyl-CpG-binding protein MeCP2 links DNA methylation to histone methylation. *J. Biol. Chem.* **278,** 4035–4040.

46. Strahl, B.D., and Allis, C.D. (2000). The language of covalent histone modifications. *Nature* **403,** 41–45.

47. Turner, B.M. (2000). Histone acetylation and an epigenetic code. *Bioessays* **22,** 836–845.

48. Jenuwein, T., and Allis, C.D. (2001). Translating the histone code. *Science* **293,** 1074–1080.

49. Berger, S.L. (2002). Histone modifications in transcriptional regulation. *Curr. Opin. Genet. Dev.* **12,** 142–148.

123. Schotta, G., Ebert, A., Dorn, R., and Reuter, G. (2003). Postion-effect variegation and the genetic dissection of chromatin regulation in *Drosophila. Semin. Cell Dev. Biol.* **14,** 67–75.

124. Moore, G.D., Procunier, J.D., Cross, D.P., and Grigliatti, T.A. (1979). Histone gene deficiencies and position-effect variegation in *Drosophila. Nature* **282,** 312–314.

125. Mottus, R., Reeves, R., and Grigliatti, T.A. (1980). Butyrate suppression of position-effect variegation in *Drosophila melanogaster. Mol. Gen. Genet.* **178,** 465–469.

126. Moore, G., Sinclair, D., and Grigliatti, T. (1983). Histone gene multiplicity and position-effect variegation in *Drosophila melanogaster. Genetics* **105,** 327–344.

127. Farkas, G., Gausz, J., Galloni, M., Reuter, G., Gyurkovics, H., and Karch, F. (1994). The trithorax-like gene encodes the *Drosophila* GAGA factor. *Nature* **371,** 806–808.

128. De Rubertis, F., Kadosh, D., Henchoz, S., Pauli, D., Reuter, G., Struhl, K., and Spierer, P. (1996). The histone deacetylase RPD3 counteracts genomic silencing in *Drosophila* and yeast. *Nature* **384,** 589–591.

129. Sinclair, D.A., Clegg, N.J., Antonchuk, J., Milne, T.A., Stankunas, K., Ruse, C., Grigliatti, T.A., Kassis, J.A., and Brock, H.W. (1998). Enhancer of Polycomb is a suppressor of position-effect variegation in *Drosophila melanogaster. Genetics* **148,** 211–220.

130. Rea, S., Eisenhaber, F., O'Carroll, D., Strahl, B.D., Sun, Z.W., Schmid, M., Opravil, S., Mechtler, K., Ponting, C.P., Allis, C.D. *et al.* (2000). Regulation of chromatin structure by site-specific histone H3 methyltransferases. *Nature* **406,** 593–599.

131. Eissenberg, J.C. (2001). Molecular biology of the chromo domain: an ancient chromatin module comes of age. *Gene* **275,** 19–29.

132. Felsenfeld, G., and Groudine, M. (2003). Controlling the double helix. *Nature* **421,** 448–453.

133. Richards, E.J., and Elgin, S.C. (2002). Epigenetic codes for heterochromatin formation and silencing: rounding up the usual suspects. *Cell* **108,** 489–500.

134. Brasher, S.V., Smith, B.O., Fogh, R.H., Nietlispach, D., Thiru, A., Nielsen, P.R., Broadhurst, R.W., Ball, L.J., Murzina, N.V., and Laue, E.D. (2000). The structure of mouse HP1 suggests a unique mode of single peptide recognition by the shadow chromo domain dimer. *EMBO J.* **19,** 1587–1597.

135. Cheutin, T., McNairn, A.J., Jenuwein, T., Gilbert, D.M., Singh, P.B., and Misteli, T. (2003). Maintenance of stable heterochromatin domains by dynamic HP1 binding. *Science* **299,** 721–725.

136. Festenstein, R., Pagakis, S.N., Hiragami, K., Lyon, D., Verreault, A., Sekkali, B., and Kioussis, D. (2003). Modulation of heterochromatin protein 1 dynamics in primary mammalian cells. *Science* **299,** 719–721.

137. Murzina, N., Verreault, A., Laue, E., and Stillman, B. (1999). Heterochromatin dynamics in mouse cells: interaction between chromatin assembly factor 1 and HP1 proteins. *Mol. Cell* **4,** 529–540.

138. Peters, A.H., O'Carroll, D., Scherthan, H., Mechtler, K., Sauer, S., Schofer, C., Weipoltshammer, K., Pagani, M., Lachner, M., Kohlmaier, A. *et al.* (2001). Loss of the Suv39h histone methyltransferases impairs mammalian heterochromatin and genome stability. *Cell* **107,** 323–337.

139. Hall, I.M., Shankaranarayana, G.D., Noma, K., Ayoub, N., Cohen, A., and Grewal, S.I. (2002). Establishment and maintenance of a heterochromatin domain. *Science* **297,** 2232–2237.

140. Jenuwein, T. (2002). Molecular biology: an RNA-guided pathway for the epigenome. *Science* **297,** 2215–2218.

141. Volpe, T.A., Kidner, C., Hall, I.M., Teng, G., Grewal, S.I., and Martienssen, R.A. (2002). Regulation of heterochromatic silencing and histone H3 lysine-9 methylation by RNAi. *Science* **297,** 1833–1837.

142. Zilberman, D., Cao, X., and Jacobsen, S.E. (2003). Argonaute4 control of locus-specific siRNA accumulation and DNA and histone methylation. *Science* **299,** 716–719.

143. Ketting, R.F., Fischer, S.E., Bernstein, E., Sijen, T., Hannon, G.J., and Plasterk, R.H. (2001). Dicer functions in RNA interference and in synthesis of small RNA involved in developmental timing in *C. elegans. Genes Dev.* **15,** 2654–2659.

144. Tuschl, T., Zamore, P.D., Lehmann, R., Bartel, D.P., and Sharp, P.A. (1999). Targeted mRNA degradation by double-stranded RNA *in vitro. Genes Dev.* **13,** 3191–3197.

145. Hammond, S.M., Bernstein, E., Beach, D., and Hannon, G.J. (2000). An RNA-directed nuclease mediates posttranscriptional gene silencing in *Drosophila* cells. *Nature* **404,** 293–296.

146. Akhtar, A., Zink, D., and Becker, P.B. (2000). Chromodomains are protein–RNA interaction modules. *Nature* **407,** 405–409.

147. Akhtar, A., and Becker, P.B. (2000). Activation of transcription through histone H4 acetylation by MOF, an acetyltransferase essential for dosage compensation in *Drosophila. Mol. Cell* **5,** 367–375.

148. Muchardt, C., Guilleme, M., Seeler, J.S., Trouche, D., Dejean, A., and Yaniv, M. (2002). Coordinated methyl and RNA binding is required for heterochromatin localization of mammalian HP1α. *EMBO Rep.* **3,** 975–981.

149. Nakayama, J., Rice, J.C., Strahl, B.D., Allis, C.D., and Grewal, S.I. (2001). Role of histone H3 lysine 9 methylation in epigenetic control of heterochromatin assembly. *Science* **292,** 110–113.

150. Litt, M.D., Simpson, M., Gaszner, M., Allis, C.D., and Felsenfeld, G. (2001). Correlation between histone lysine methylation and developmental changes at the chicken beta-globin locus. *Science* **293,** 2453–2455.

151. Litt, M.D., Simpson, M., Recillas-Targa, F., Prioleau, M.N., and Felsenfeld, G. (2001). Transitions in histone acetylation reveal boundaries of three separately regulated neighboring loci. *EMBO J.* **20,** 2224–2235.

152. Mette, M.F., Aufsatz, W., van der Winden, J., Matzke, M.A., and Matzke, A.J. (2000). Transcriptional silencing and promoter methylation triggered by double-stranded RNA. *EMBO J.* **19,** 5194–5201.

153. Pal-Bhadra, M., Bhadra, U., and Birchler, J.A. (1997). Cosuppression in *Drosophila:* gene silencing of Alcohol dehydrogenase by *white-Adh* transgenes is Polycomb dependent. *Cell* **90,** 479–490.

154. Kelly, W.G., and Fire, A. (1998). Chromatin silencing and the maintenance of a functional germ line in *Caenorhabditis elegans. Development* **125,** 2451–2456.

155. Pal-Bhadra, M., Bhadra, U., and Birchler, J.A. (1999). Cosuppression of nonhomologous transgenes in *Drosophila* involves mutually related endogenous sequences. *Cell* **99,** 35–46.

156. Dudley, N.R., Labbe, J.C., and Goldstein, B. (2002). Using RNA interference to identify genes required for RNA interference. *Proc. Natl. Acad. Sci. USA* **99,** 4191–4196.

157. Montgomery, M.K., Xu, S., and Fire, A. (1998). RNA as a target of double-stranded RNA-mediated genetic interference in *Caenorhabditis elegans. Proc. Natl. Acad. Sci. USA* **95,** 15,502–15,507.

158. Jacob, F., and Monod, J. (1961). On the regulation of gene activity. *Cold Spring Harbor Lab. Symp.* 193–202.

159. Cattanach, B.M. (1974). Position effect variegation in the mouse. *Genet. Res.* **23,** 291–306.

160. Russell, L.B. (1963). Mammalian X-chromosome action: inactivation limited in spread and in region of origin. *Science* **140,** 976–978.

161. Penny, G.D., Kay, G.F., Sheardown, S.A., Rastan, S., and Brockdorff, N. (1996). Requirement for Xist in X-chromosome inactivation. *Nature* **379,** 131–137.

162. Lee, J.T., and Jaenisch, R. (1997). Long-range *cis* effects of ectopic X-inactivation centers on a mouse autosome. *Nature* **386,** 275–279.

163. Plath, K., Mlynarczyk-Evans, S., Nusinow, D.A., and Panning, B. (2002). Xist RNA and the mechanism of X-chromosome inactivation. *Annu. Rev. Genet.* **36,** 233–278.

164. Morishima, A., Grumbach, M.M., and Taylor, J.H. (1962). Asynchronous duplication of human chromosomes and the origin of sex chromatin. *Proc. Natl. Acad. Sci. USA* **48,** 756–763.

165. Barr, M.L., and Carr, D.H. (1961). Correlations between sex chromatin and sex chromosomes. *Acta Cytol.* **6,** 34–35.

166. Jeppesen, P., and Turner, B.M. (1993). The inactive X-chromosome in female mammals is distinguished by a lack of histone H4 acetylation, a cytogenetic marker for gene expression. *Cell* **74,** 281–289.

167. Heard, E., Rougeulle, C., Arnaud, D., Avner, P., Allis, C.D., and Spector, D.L. (2001). Methylation of histone H3 at Lys-9 is an early mark on the X-chromosome during X-inactivation. *Cell* **107,** 727–738.

168. Peters, A.H., Mermoud, J.E., O'Carroll, D., Pagani, M., Schweizer, D., Brockdorff, N., and Jenuwein, T. (2002). Histone H3 lysine 9 methylation is an epigenetic imprint of facultative heterochromatin. *Nat. Genet.* **30,** 77–80.

169. Boggs, B.A., Cheung, P., Heard, E., Spector, D.L., Chinault, A.C., and Allis, C.D. (2002). Differentially methylated forms of histone H3 show unique association patterns with inactive human X-chromosomes. *Nat. Genet.* **30,** 73–76.

170. Plath, K., Fang, J., Mlynarczyk-Evans, S.K., Cao, R., Worringer, K.A., Wang, H., de la Cruz, C.C., Otte, A.P., Panning, B., and Zhang, Y. (2003). Role of histone H3 lysine 27 methylation in X-inactivation. *Science* **300,** 131–135.

171. Silva, J., Mak, W., Zvetkova, I., Appanah, R., Nesterova, T.B., Webster, Z., Peters, A.H., Jenuwein, T., Otte, A.P., and Brockdorff, N. (2003). Establishment of histone h3 methylation on the inactive X-chromosome requires transient recruitment of eed-enx1 Polycomb group complexes. *Dev Cell* **4,** 481–495.

172. Costanzi, C., and Pehrson, J.R. (1998). Histone macroH2A1 is concentrated in the inactive X-chromosome of female mammals. *Nature* **393,** 599–601.

173. Rangasamy, D., Berven, L., Ridgway, P., and Tremethick, D.J. (2003). Pericentric heterochromatin becomes enriched with H2A.Z during early mammalian development. *EMBO J.* **22,** 1599–1607.

174. Sado, T., Fenner, M.H., Tan, S.S., Tam, P., Shioda, T., and Li, E. (2000). X-inactivation in the mouse embryo deficient for Dnmt1: distinct effect of hypomethylation on imprinted and random X-inactivation. *Dev Biol.* **225,** 294–303.

175. Cohen, D.E., and Lee, J.T. (2002). X-chromosome inactivation and the search for chromosomewide silencers. *Curr. Opin. Genet. Dev.* **12,** 219–224.

176. Wang, J., Mager, J., Chen, Y., Schneider, E., Cross, J.C., Nagy, A., and Magnuson, T. (2001). Imprinted X-inactivation maintained by a mouse Polycomb group gene. *Nat. Genet.* **28,** 371–375.

177. Heard, E., Clerc, P., and Avner, P. (1997). X-chromosome inactivation in mammals. *Annu. Rev. Genet.* **31,** 571–610.

178. Fernandez-Capetillo, O., Mahadevaiah, S.K., Celeste, A., Romanienko, P.J., Camerini-Otero, R.D., Bonner, W.M., Manova, K., Burgoyne, P., and Nussenzweig, A. (2003). H2AX is required for chromatin remodeling and inactivation of sex chromosomes in male mouse meiosis. *Dev Cell* **4,** 497–508.

179. McCarrey, J.R., Watson, C., Atencio, J., Ostermeier, G.C., Marahrens, Y., Jaenisch, R., and Krawetz, S.A. (2002). X-chromosome inactivation during spermatogenesis is regulated by an Xist–Tsix-independent mechanism in the mouse. *Genesis,* **34,** 257–266.

180. Simon, J. (1995). Locking in stable states of gene expression: transcriptional control during *Drosophila* development. *Curr. Opin. Cell Biol.* **7,** 376–385.

181. Jacobs, J., and van Lohuizen, M. (1999). Cellular memory of transcriptional states by Polycomb group proteins. *Semin. Cell Dev. Biol.* **10,** 227–235.

182. Gebuhr, T.C., Bultman, S.J., and Magnuson, T. (2000). Pc-G/trx-G and the SWI/SNF connection: developmental gene regulation through chromatin remodeling. *Genesis* **26,** 189–197.

183. Mahmoudi, T., and Verrijzer, C.P. (2001). Chromatin silencing and activation by Polycomb and trithorax group proteins. *Oncogene* **20,** 3055–3066.

184. Orlando, V. (2003). Polycomb, epigenomes, and control of cell identity. *Cell* **112,** 599–606.

185. Kehle, J., Beuchle, D., Treuheit, S., Christen, B., Kennison, J.A., Bienz, M., and Muller, J. (1998). dMi-2, a hunchback-interacting protein that functions in Polycomb repression. *Science* **282,** 1897–1900.

186. Paro, R., and Hogness, D.S. (1991). The Polycomb protein shares a homologous domain with a heterochromatin-associated protein of *Drosophila*. *Proc. Natl. Acad. Sci. USA* **88,** 263–267.

187. Czermin, B., Melfi, R., McCabe, D., Seitz, V., Imhof, A., and Pirrotta, V. (2002). Drosophila enhancer of Zeste/ESC complexes have a histone H3 methyltransferase activity that marks chromosomal Polycomb sites. *Cell* **111,** 185–196.

188. Kuzmichev, A., Nishioka, K., Erdjument-Bromage, H., Tempst, P., and Reinberg, D. (2002). Histone methyltransferase activity associated with a human multiprotein complex containing the Enhancer of Zeste protein. *Genes Dev.* **16,** 2893–2905.

189. Muller, J., Hart, C.M., Francis, N.J., Vargas, M.L., Sengupta, A., Wild, B., Miller, E.L., O'Connor, M.B., Kingston, R.E., and Simon, J.A. (2002). Histone methyltransferase activity of a *Drosophila* Polycomb group repressor complex. *Cell* **111,** 197–208.

190. Yeates, T.O. (2002). Structures of SET domain proteins: Protein lysine methyltransferases make their mark. *Cell* **111,** 5–7.

191. Simon, J.A., and Tamkun, J.W. (2002). Programming off and on states in chromatin: mechanisms of Polycomb and trithorax group complexes. *Curr. Opin. Genet. Dev.* **12,** 210–218.

192. Yamamoto, Y., Girard, F., Bello, B., Affolter, M., and Gehring, W.J. (1997). The *cramped* gene of *Drosophila* is a member of the Polycomb group, and interacts with *mus209,* the gene encoding proliferating cell nuclear antigen. *Development* **124,** 3385–3394.

193. Gerasimova, T.I., and Corces, V.G. (1998). Polycomb and trithorax group proteins mediate the function of a chromatin insulator. *Cell* **92,** 511–521.

194. Mallin, D.R., Myung, J.S., Patton, J.S., and Geyer, P.K. (1998). Polycomb group repression is blocked by the *Drosophila* suppressor of Hairy-wing [su(Hw)] insulator. *Genetics* **148,** 331–339.

195. Brown, J.L., Mucci, D., Whiteley, M., Dirksen, M.L., and Kassis, J.A. (1998). The *Drosophila* Polycomb group gene

pleiohomeotic encodes a DNA-binding protein with homology to the transcription factor YY1. *Mol. Cell* **1**, 1057–1064.

196. Mihaly, J., Mishra, R., and Karch, F. (1998). A conserved sequence motif in Polycomb-response elements. *Mol. Cell* **1**, 1065–1066.

197. Fritsch, C., Brown, J.L., Kassis, J.A., and Muller, J. (1999). The DNA-binding Polycomb group protein pleiohomeotic mediates silencing of a *Drosophila* homeotic gene. *Development* **126**, 3905–3913.

198. Gould, A. (1997). Functions of mammalian Polycomb group- and trithorax group-related genes. *Curr. Opin. Genet. Dev.* **7**, 488–494.

199. Faust, C., Schumacher, A., Holdener, B., and Magnuson, T. (1995). The eed mutation disrupts anterior mesoderm production in mice. *Development* **121**, 273–285.

200. Donohoe, M.E., Zhang, X., McGinnis, L., Biggers, J., Li, E., and Shi, Y. (1999). Targeted disruption of mouse Yin Yang 1 transcription factor results in peri-implantation lethality. *Mol. Cell Biol.* **19**, 7237–7244.

201. O'Carroll, D., Erhardt, S., Pagani, M., Barton, S.C., Surani, M.A., and Jenuwein, T. (2001). The Polycomb group gene *Ezh2* is required for early mouse development. *Mol. Cell Biol.* **21**, 4330–4336.

202. Varambally, S., Dhanasekaran, S.M., Zhou, M., Barrette, T.R., Kumar-Sinha, C., Sanda, M.G., Ghosh, D., Pienta, K.J., Sewalt, R.G., Otte, A.P., Rubin, M.A., and Chinnaiyan, A.M. (2002). The Polycomb group protein EZH2 is involved in progression of prostate cancer. *Nature* **419**, 624–629.

203. Wang, J., Mager, J., Schnedier, E., and Magnuson, T. (2002). The mouse Pc-G gene *eed* is required for *Hox* gene repression and extraembryonic development. *Mamm. Genome* **13**, 493–503.

204. Schumacher, A., Faust, C., and Magnuson, T. (1996). Positional cloning of a global regulator of anterior–posterior patterning in mice. *Nature* **384**, 648.

205. Richie, E.R., Schumacher, A., Angel, J.M., Holloway, M., Rinchik, E.M., and Magnuson, T. (2002). The Polycomb group gene *eed* regulates thymocyte differentiation and suppresses the development of carcinogen-induced T-cell lymphomas. *Oncogene* **21**, 299–306.

206. Mak, W., Baxter, J., Silva, J., Newall, A.E., Otte, A.P., and Brockdorff, N. (2002). Mitotically stable association of Polycomb group proteins eed and enx1 with the inactive X-chromosome in trophoblast stem cells. *Curr. Biol.* **12**, 1016–1020.

207. Mager, J., Montgomery, N.D., de Villena, F.P., and Magnuson, T. (2003). Genome imprinting regulated by the mouse Polycomb group protein Eed. *Nat. Genet.* **33**, 502–507.

208. Voncken, J.W., Roelen, B.A., Roefs, M., de Vries, S., Verhoeven, E., Marino, S., Deschamps, J., and van Lohuizen, M. (2003). Rnf2 (Ring1b) deficiency causes gastrulation arrest and cell cycle inhibition. *Proc. Natl. Acad. Sci. USA* **100**, 2468–2473.

209. Suzuki, M., Mizutani-Koseki, Y., Fujimura, Y., Miyagishima, H., Kaneko, T., Takada, Y., Akasaka, T., Tanzawa, H., Takihara, Y., Nakano, M., Masumoto, H., Vidal, M., Isono, K., and Koseki, H. (2002). Involvement of the Polycomb group gene *Ring1B* in the specification of the anterior–posterior axis in mice. *Development* **129**, 4171–4183.

210. Jacobs, J.J., Kieboom, K., Marino, S., DePinho, R.A., and van Lohuizen, M. (1999). The oncogene and Polycomb group gene *bmi-1* regulates cell proliferation and senescence through the ink4a locus. *Nature* **397**, 164–168.

211. Lessard, J., and Sauvageau, G. (2003). Bmi-1 determines the proliferative capacity of normal and leukemic stem cells. *Nature* **423**, 255–260.

212. Park, I.K., Qian, D., Kiel, M., Becker, M.W., Pihalja, M., Weissman, I.L., Morrison, S.J., and Clarke, M.F. (2003). Bmi-1 is required for maintenance of adult self-renewing hematopoietic stem cells. *Nature* **423**, 302–305.

213. van Lohuizen, M., Verbeek, S., Scheijen, B., Wientjens, E., van der Gulden, H., and Berns, A. (1991). Identification of cooperating oncogenes in *E mu-myc* transgenic mice by provirus tagging. *Cell* **65**, 737–752.

214. Haupt, Y., Bath, M.L., Harris, A.W., and Adams, J.M. (1993). *Bmi-1* transgene induces lymphomas and collaborates with myc in tumorigenesis. *Oncogene* **8**, 3161–3164.

215. Kennison, J.A., and Tamkun, J.W. (1988). Dosage-dependent modifiers of Polycomb and antennapedia mutations in *Drosophila. Proc. Natl. Acad. Sci. USA* **85**, 8136–8140.

216. Katsani, K.R., Arredondo, J.J., Kal, A.J., and Verrijzer, C.P. (2001). A homeotic mutation in the trithorax SET domain impedes histone binding. *Genes Dev.* **15**, 2197–2202.

217. Milne, T.A., Briggs, S.D., Brock, H.W., Martin, M.E., Gibbs, D., Allis, C.D., and Hess, J.L. (2002). MLL targets SET domain methyltransferase activity to *Hox* gene promoters. *Mol. Cell* **10**, 1107–1117.

218. Nakamura, T., Mori, T., Tada, S., Krajewski, W., Rozovskaia, T., Wassell, R., Dubois, G., Mazo, A., Croce, C.M., and Canaani, E. (2002). ALL-1 is a histone methyltransferase that assembles a supercomplex of proteins involved in transcriptional regulation. *Mol. Cell* **10**, 1119–1128.

219. Rozovskaia, T., Tillib, S., Smith, S., Sedkov, Y., Rozenblatt-Rosen, O., Petruk, S., Yano, T., Nakamura, T., Ben-Simchon, L., Gildea, J., Croce, C.M., Shearn, A., Canaani, E., and Mazo, A. (1999). Trithorax and ASH1 interact directly and associate with the trithorax group-responsive bxd region of the Ultrabithorax promoter. *Mol. Cell Biol.* **19**, 6441–6447.

220. Beisel, C., Imhof, A., Greene, J., Kremmer, E., and Sauer, F. (2002). Histone methylation by the *Drosophila* epigenetic transcriptional regulator Ash1. *Nature* **419**, 857–862.

221. Bantignies, F., Goodman, R.H., and Smolik, S.M. (2000). Functional interaction between the coactivator *Drosophila* CREB-binding protein and ASH1, a member of the trithorax group of chromatin modifiers. *Mol. Cell Biol.* **20**, 9317–9330.

222. Petruk, S., Sedkov, Y., Smith, S., Tillib, S., Kraevski, V., Nakamura, T., Canaani, E., Croce, C.M., and Mazo, A. (2001). Trithorax and dCBP acting in a complex to maintain expression of a homeotic gene. *Science* **294**, 1331–1334.

223. Rozenblatt-Rosen, O., Rozovskaia, T., Burakov, D., Sedkov, Y., Tillib, S., Blechman, J., Nakamura, T., Croce, C.M., Mazo, A., and Canaani, E. (1998). The C-terminal SET domains of ALL-1 and Trithorax interact with the INI1 and SNR1 proteins, components of the SWI/SNF complex. *Proc. Natl. Acad. Sci. USA* **95**, 4152–4157.

224. Kal, A.J., Mahmoudi, T., Zak, N.B., and Verrijzer, C.P. (2000). The *Drosophila* brahma complex is an essential coactivator for the trithorax group protein zeste. *Genes Dev.* **14**, 1058–1071.

225. Hanson, R.D., Hess, J.L., Yu, B.D., Ernst, P., van Lohuizen, M., Berns, A., van der Lugt, N.M., Shashikant, C.S., Ruddle, F.H., Seto, M., and Korsmeyer, S.J. (1999). Mammalian trithorax and Polycomb group homologues are antagonistic regulators of homeotic development. *Proc. Natl. Acad. Sci. USA* **96**, 14,372–14,377.

226. Surani, M.A., and Barton, S.C. (1983). Development of gynogenetic eggs in the mouse: implications for parthenogenetic embryos. *Science* **222**, 1034–1036.

227. McGrath, J., and Solter, D. (1984). Completion of mouse embryogenesis requires both the maternal and paternal genomes. *Cell* **37**, 179–183.

228. Cattanach, B.M., and Kirk, M. (1985). Differential activity of maternally and paternally derived chromosome regions in mice. *Nature* **315**, 496–498.

229. Li, E., Bestor, T.H., and Jaenisch, R. (1992). Targeted mutation of the DNA methyltransferase gene results in embryonic lethality. *Cell* **69**, 915–926.

230. Bourc'his, D., Xu, G.L., Lin, C.S., Bollman, B., and Bestor, T.H. (2001). Dnmt3L and the establishment of maternal genomic imprints. *Science* **294**, 2536–2539.

231. Hata, K., Okano, M., Lei, H., and Li, E. (2002). Dnmt3L cooperates with the Dnmt3 family of *de novo* DNA methyltransferases to establish maternal imprints in mice. *Development* **129**, 1983–1993.

232. Bartolomei, M.S., and Tilghman, S.M. (1992). Parental imprinting of mouse chromosome 7. *Semin. Dev. Biol.* **3**, 107–117.

233. Drewell, R.A., Goddard, C.J., Thomas, J.O., and Surani, M.A. (2002). Methylation-dependent silencing at the H19 imprinting control region by MeCP2. *Nucleic Acids Res.* **30**, 1139–1144.

234. Sleutels, F., Zwart, R., and Barlow, D.P. (2002). The noncoding Air RNA is required for silencing autosomal-imprinted genes. *Nature* **415**, 810–813.

235. Lee, J., Inoue, K., Ono, R., Ogonuki, N., Kohda, T., Kaneko-Ishino, T., Ogura, A., and Ishino, F. (2002). Erasing genomic-imprinting memory in mouse clone embryos produced from day 11.5 primordial germ cells. *Development* **129**, 1807–1817.

236. Fournier, C., Goto, Y., Ballestar, E., Delaval, K., Hever, A.M., Esteller, M., and Feil, R. (2002). Allele-specific histone lysine methylation marks regulatory regions at imprinted mouse genes. *EMBO J.* **21**, 6560–6570.

237. Cao, R., Wang, L., Wang, H., Xia, L., Erdjument-Bromage, H., Tempst, P., Jones, R.S., and Zhang, Y. (2002). Role of histone H3 lysine 27 methylation in Polycomb group silencing. *Science* **298**, 1039–1043.

238. Mayer, W., Smith, A., Fundele, R., and Haaf, T. (2000). Spatial separation of parental genomes in preimplantation mouse embryos. *J. Cell Biol.* **148**, 629–634.

239. Mostoslavsky, R., Singh, N., Tenzen, T., Goldmit, M., Gabay, C., Elizur, S., Qi, P., Reubinoff, B.E., Chess, A., Cedar, H., and Bergman, Y. (2001). Asynchronous replication and allelic exclusion in the immune system. *Nature* **414**, 221–225.

240. Singh, N., Ebrahimi, F.A., Gimelbrant, A.A., Ensminger, A.W., Tackett, M.R., Qi, P., Gribnau, J., and Chess, A. (2003). Coordination of the random asynchronous replication of autosomal loci. *Nat. Genet.* **33**, 339–341.

241. Luger, K., Mader, A.W., Richmond, R.K., Sargent, D.F., and Richmond, T.J. (1997). Crystal structure of the nucleosome core particle at 2.8 A resolution. *Nature* **389**, 251–260.

242. Shao, Z., Raible, F., Mollaaghababa, R., Guyon, J.R., Wu, C.T., Bender, W., and Kingston, R.E. (1999). Stabilization of chromatin structure by PRC1, a Polycomb complex. *Cell* **98**, 37–46.

243. Ng, J., Hart, C.M., Morgan, K., and Simon, J.A. (2000). A *Drosophila* ESC-E(Z) protein complex is distinct from other Polycomb group complexes and contains covalently modified ESC. *Mol. Cell Biol.* **20**, 3069–3078.

244. Saurin, A.J., Shao, Z., Erdjument-Bromage, H., Tempst, P., and Kingston, R.E. (2001). A *Drosophila* Polycomb group complex includes Zeste and dTAFII proteins. *Nature* **412**, 655–660.

245. Li, E., Beard, C., and Jaenisch, R. (1993). Role for DNA methylation in genomic imprinting. *Nature* **366**, 362–365.

246. Zhao, X., Ueba, T., Christie, B.R., Barkho, B., McConnell, M.J., Nakashima, K., Lein, E.S., Eadie, B.D., Willhoite, A.R., Muotri, A.R. *et al.* (2003). Mice lacking methyl-CpG binding protein 1 have deficits in adult neurogenesis and hippocampal function. *Proc. Natl. Acad. Sci. USA* **100**, 6777–6782.

247. Hendrich, B., Guy, J., Ramsahoye, B., Wilson, V.A., and Bird, A. (2001). Closely related proteins MBD2 and MBD3 play distinctive but interacting roles in mouse development. *Genes Dev.* **15**, 710–723.

248. Chen, R.Z., Akbarian, S., Tudor, M., and Jaenisch, R. (2001). Deficiency of methyl-CpG-binding protein-2 in CNS neurons results in a Rett-like phenotype in mice. *Nat. Genet.* **27**, 327–331.

249. Guy, J., Hendrich, B., Holmes, M., Martin, J.E., and Bird, A. (2001). A mouse Mecp2-null mutation causes neurological symptoms that mimic Rett syndrome. *Nat. Genet.* **27**, 322–326.

250. Xu, W., Edmondson, D.G., Evrard, Y.A., Wakamiya, M., Behringer, R.R., and Roth, S.Y. (2000). Loss of Gcn5l2 leads to increased apoptosis and mesodermal defects during mouse development. *Nat. Genet.* **26**, 229–232.

251. Yamauchi, T., Yamauchi, J., Kuwata, T., Tamura, T., Yamashita, T., Bae, N., Westphal, H., Ozato, K., and Nakatani, Y. (2000). Distinct but overlapping roles of histone acetylase PCAF and of the closely related PCAF-B–GCN5 in mouse embryogenesis. *Proc. Natl. Acad. Sci. USA* **97**, 11,303–11,306.

252. Yao, T.P., Oh, S.P., Fuchs, M., Zhou, N.D., Ch'ng, L.E., Newsome, D., Bronson, R.T., Li, E., Livingston, D.M., and Eckner, R. (1998). Gene dosage-dependent embryonic development and proliferation defects in mice lacking the transcriptional integrator p300. *Cell* **93**, 361–372.

253. Oike, Y., Takakura, N., Hata, A., Kaname, T., Akizuki, M., Yamaguchi, Y., Yasue, H., Araki, K., Yamamura, K., and Suda, T. (1999). Mice homozygous for a truncated form of CREB-binding protein exhibit defects in hematopoiesis and vasculo–angiogenesis. *Blood,* **93**, 2771–2779.

254. Lagger, G., O'Carroll, D., Rembold, M., Khier, H., Tischler, J., Weitzer, G., Schuettengruber, B., Hauser, C., Brunmeir, R., Jenuwein, T. *et al.* (2002). Essential function of histone deacetylase 1 in proliferation control and CDK inhibitor repression. *EMBO J.* **21**, 2672–2681.

255. Zhang, C.L., McKinsey, T.A., Chang, S., Antos, C.L., Hill, J.A., and Olson, E.N. (2002). Class II histone deacetylases act as signal-responsive repressors of cardiac hypertrophy. *Cell* **110**, 479–488.

256. McBurney, M.W., Yang, X., Jardine, K., Hixon, M., Boekelheide, K., Webb, J.R., Lansdorp, P.M., and Lemieux, M. (2003). The mammalian SIR2alpha protein has a role in embryogenesis and gametogenesis. *Mol. Cell Biol.* **23**, 38–54.

257. Tachibana, M., Sugimoto, K., Nozaki, M., Ueda, J., Ohta, T., Ohki, M., Fukuda, M., Takeda, N., Niida, H., Kato, H. *et al.* (2002). G9a histone methyltransferase plays a dominant role in euchromatic histone H3 lysine 9 methylation and is essential for early embryogenesis. *Genes Dev.* **16**, 1779–1791.

258. Faast, R., Thonglairoam, V., Schulz, T.C., Beall, J., Wells, J.R., Taylor, H., Matthaei, K., Rathjen, P.D., Tremethick, D.J., and Lyons, I. (2001). Histone variant H2A.Z is required for early mammalian development. *Curr. Biol.* **11**, 1183–1187.

259. Couldrey, C., Carlton, M.B., Nolan, P.M., Colledge, W.H., and Evans, M.J. (1999). A retroviral gene trap insertion into the histone *3.3A* gene causes partial neonatal lethality, stunted growth, neuromuscular deficits, and male subfertility in transgenic mice. *Hum Mol. Genet.* **8**, 2489–2495.

260. Sirotkin, A.M., Edelmann, W., Cheng, G., Klein-Szanto, A., Kucherlapati, R., and Skoultchi, A.I. (1995). Mice develop

normally without the H1(0) linker histone. *Proc. Natl. Acad. Sci. USA* **92,** 6434–6438.

261. Fan, Y., Sirotkin, A., Russell, R.G., Ayala, J., and Skoultchi, A.I. (2001). Individual somatic H1 subtypes are dispensable for mouse development even in mice lacking the H1(0) replacement subtype. *Mol. Cell Biol.* **21,** 7933–7943.

262. Cho, C., Willis, W.D., Goulding, E.H., Jung-Ha, H., Choi, Y.C., Hecht, N.B., and Eddy, E.M. (2001). Haploinsufficiency of protamine-1 or -2 causes infertility in mice. *Nat. Genet.* **28,** 82–86.

263. Reyes, J.C., Barra, J., Muchardt, C., Camus, A., Babinet, C., and Yaniv, M. (1998). Altered control of cellular proliferation in the absence of mammalian brahma (SNF2α). *EMBO J.* **17,** 6979–6991.

264. Guidi, C.J., Sands, A.T., Zambrowicz, B.P., Turner, T.K., Demers, D.A., Webster, W., Smith, T.W., Imbalzano, A.N., and Jones, S.N. (2001). Disruption of Ini1 leads to peri-implantation lethality and tumorigenesis in mice. *Mol. Cell Biol.* **21,** 3598–3603.

265. van der Lugt, N.M., Domen, J., Linders, K., van Roon, M., Robanus-Maandag, E., te Riele, H., van der Valk, M., Deschamps, J., Sofroniew, M., van Lohuizen, M. (1994). Posterior transformation, neurological abnormalities, and severe hematopoietic defects in mice with a targeted deletion of the *bmi-1* protooncogene. *Genes Dev.* **8,** 757–769.

266. Core, N., Bel, S., Gaunt, S.J., Aurrand-Lions, M., Pearce, J., Fisher, A., and Djabali, M. (1997). Altered cellular proliferation and mesoderm patterning in Polycomb-M33-deficient mice. *Development* **124,** 721–729.

267. Katoh-Fukui, Y., Tsuchiya, R., Shiroishi, T., Nakahara, Y., Hashimoto, N., Noguchi, K., and Higashinakagawa, T. (1998). Male-to-female sex reversal in M33 mutant mice. *Nature* **393,** 688–692.

268. Akasaka, T., Kanno, M., Balling, R., Mieza, M.A., Taniguchi, M., and Koseki, H. (1996). A role for *mel-18,* a Polycomb group-related vertebrate gene, during the anterior–posterior specification of the axial skeleton. *Development* **122,** 1513–1522.

269. del Mar Lorente, M., Marcos-Gutierrez, C., Perez, C., Schoorlemmer, J., Ramirez, A., Magin, T., and Vidal, M. (2000). Loss- and gain-of-function mutations show a Polycomb group function for Ring1A in mice. *Development* **127,** 5093–5100.

270. Takihara, Y., Tomotsune, D., Shirai, M., Katoh-Fukui, Y., Nishii, K., Motaleb, M.A., Nomura, M., Tsuchiya, R., Fujita, Y., Shibata, Y. *et al.* (1997). Targeted disruption of the mouse homologue of the *Drosophila* polyhomeotic gene leads to altered anterior–posterior patterning and neural crest defects. *Development* **124,** 3673–3682.

271. Yu, B.D., Hess, J.L., Horning, S.E., Brown, G.A., and Korsmeyer, S.J. (1995). Altered Hox expression and segmental identity in Mll-mutant mice. *Nature* **378,** 505–508.

272. Yagi, H., Deguchi, K., Aono, A., Tani, Y., Kishimoto, T., and Komori, T. (1998). Growth disturbance in fetal liver hematopoiesis of Mll-mutant mice. *Blood,* **92,** 108–117.

273. Zhou, X., Benson, K.F., Ashar, H.R., and Chada, K. (1995). Mutation responsible for the mouse pygmy phenotype in the developmentally regulated factor HMGI-C. *Nature* **376,** 771–774.

274. Calogero, S., Grassi, F., Aguzzi, A., Voigtlander, T., Ferrier, P., Ferrari, S., and Bianchi, M.E. (1999). The lack of chromosomal protein Hmg1 does not disrupt cell growth but causes lethal hypoglycemia in newborn mice. *Nat. Genet.* **22,** 276–280.

275. Ronfani, L., Ferraguti, M., Croci, L., Ovitt, C.E., Scholer, H.R., Consalez, G.G., and Bianchi, M.E. (2001). Reduced fertility and spermatogenesis defects in mice lacking chromosomal protein Hmgb2. *Development* **128,** 1265–1273.

276. Gubbay, J., Collignon, J., Koopman, P., Capel, B., Economou, A., Munsterberg, A., Vivian, N., Goodfellow, P., and Lovell-Badge, R. (1990). A gene mapping to the sex-determining region of the mouse Y-chromosome is a member of a novel family of embryonically expressed genes. *Nature* **346,** 245–250.

277. Burns, K.H., Viveiros, M.M., Ren, Y., Wang, P., DeMayo, F.J., Frail, D.E., Eppig, J.J., and Matzuk, M.M. (2003). Roles of NPM2 in chromatin and nucleolar organization in oocytes and embryos. *Science* **300,** 633–636.

Regulation of Hypoxic Genes in Differentiating Stem Cells

Fiona A. Mack and M. Celeste Simon

Early embryonic development occurs within a low oxygen (O_2) or hypoxic environment. To facilitate continued growth within the hypoxic environment, the cardiovascular and hematopoietic systems are formed and placentation occurs to meet the O_2 requirements of the embryo. Cellular responses to changes in O_2 concentrations are primarily mediated by the heterodimeric transcription factor (HIF), consisting of an α-subunit (HIF-α) and a β-subunit (ARNT). HIF regulates the expression of O_2-responsive genes involved in energy metabolism, O_2 transport, vasculogenesis, angiogenesis, and hematopoiesis. Loss of HIF activity in $Arnt^{-/-}$ embryos results in lethality cause by cardiovascular, hematopoietic, and placental defects. Although genetic studies have allowed the observation of hypoxic effects on embryonic development and overall pattern formation, *in vitro* studies using stem cell populations present with mammalian blastocysts have provided a powerful tool for analyzing hypoxic effects on cellular differentiation and proliferation. In particular, this chapter focuses on the effects of HIF activity in the lineage pathways of hematopoietic (including hemangioblast formation) and trophoblast stem (TS) cells. These results have vast implications for clinical treatment tissue ischemia pathologies, such as cardiac dysfunction and preeclampsia; cancer therapeutics; and the propagation of stem cells for transplantation studies.

Introduction

Research into the factors that define early development has mainly focused on the effects of diffusible proteins. This work has led to the hypothesis that a gradient of a diffusible signal or morphogen can functionally regulate a variety of developmental processes, including cellular differentiation and overall pattern formation. Within this model of development, all cells are able to respond equivalently to the signal; however, exposure to varying concentrations of the signal elicits different changes, which determine the identity of the cell. Although this research has provided vital information about essential early genes and the carefully orchestrated events that create a multicellular organism, other environmental morphogens have not been as thoroughly examined. Prior to

the development of the mammalian placenta, both O_2 and nutrients are limited within the growing embryo. However, this is also a period considerable cellular proliferation and differentiation; in particular, the cardiovascular and hematopoietic systems form at this time. The function of these organ systems is to monitor and respond to the physiological needs of the growing embryo; their formation is also tightly regulated by the physiology of the surrounding environment. The inability of the early embryo to sense an O_2 gradient results in cardiovascular and hematopoietic defects, along with embryonic lethality. Furthermore, these defects appear to be caused by the improper differentiation of the stem cell populations. Low O_2 or hypoxia has been found to promote embryonic stem cell proliferation and differentiation and is therefore required for early embryonic development.

Isolation of multipotential stem cells from the murine embryo has allowed the study of a variety of differentiation pathways in embryogenesis and organogenesis. Differentiation of mammalian blastocysts begins as early as day 3.5 post coitum, defining two cell layers: the trophectoderm and the inner cell mass (ICM) (Fig. 7–1). Cells within the trophectoderm are restricted in their differentiation pathways and only create placental cell types and extraembryonic ectoderm. The formation of specialized cells within the placenta can be modeled *in vitro* by isolating and propagating TS cells.[1] Within the ICM exists a second stem cell population, embryonic stem (ES) cells incapable of forming trophectoderm, form all cell types within the embryo and extraembryonic mesoderm. Both stem cell populations must balance proliferation with differentiation to accommodate the rapid growth of the embryo and yet meet the physiological demands of this process. In addition to embryonic growth occurring in a low O_2 uterine environment, an O_2 gradient is generated as the embryo grows. Therefore, the stem cell populations within the embryo must also be able to sense and adapt to the low O_2 environment. This chapter seeks to analyze the role of O_2 gradients and hypoxia within the differentiation of ES cells and TS cells and its implications in the future use of stem cells for clinical exploitation.

Oxygen Regulated Gene Expression

HIF TARGET GENES

Under low O_2, the energy needs of a cell are maintained by switching from oxidative phosphorylation as the primary

Handbook of Stem Cells
Volume 1

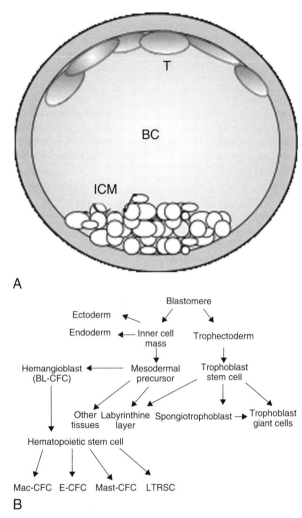

A

B

Figure 7–1. Stems cells of the mammalian blastocysts, showing (A) a schematic of embryonic day (E)3.5 blastocysts (ICM: Inner Cell Mass, BC: Blastocoel Cavity, and T: Trophectoderm) and (B) a summary of hypoxia regulated lineage pathways.

generator of adenosine 5′-triphosphate (ATP) to glycolysis, a process known as the Pasteur effect. To compensate for the reduced ATP-generating capacity of glycolysis, both glucose transporters and glycolytic enzymes are induced by hypoxia. To increase O_2 delivery to the entire organism, hypoxia promotes blood vessel formation and remodeling (vasculogenesis and angiogenesis). Hypoxia also induces vessel vasodilation and increases the production of red blood cells to improve O_2 carrying capacity. One key regulator of both cellular and systemic changes to O_2 concentration is the hypoxia inducible factor (HIF), which consists of an α-subunit (HIF-α) and a β-subunit, also called the aryl hydrocarbon receptor nuclear translocator (ARNT).[2,3] HIF activates directly or indirectly the expression of many O_2 responsive genes involved in energy metabolism, O_2 delivery, vasculogenesis, angiogenesis, and hematopoiesis, including erythropoietin (EPO), transferrin, transferrin receptor, vascular endothelial growth factor (VEGF) and VEGF receptors Flk-1 and Flt- 1, and platelet-derived growth factor-β.[4–10] In addition, HIF regulates the expression of genes necessary for cellular proliferation and survival.[6,11–13]

HIF POST TRANSLATION REGULATION

HIF activity is regulated at multiple levels. The ARNT subunits are constitutively transcribed and translated, while the HIF-α subunits are highly regulated by protein stability. During normal O_2 conditions (21%), HIF-α subunits are targeted for ubiquitin-mediated degradation through the 26S proteasome by binding to an E3 ubiquitin ligase containing the von Hippel-Lindau tumor suppressor protein (pVHL).[14] pVHL binding requires the hydroxylation of key proline residues within the O_2-dependent degradation domain of HIF-α.[15,16] This modification is accomplished by a recently defined, evolutionarily conserved family of prolyl hydroxylase, which are not only O_2 dependent but also require iron and a metabolic substrate α-ketoglutarate.[17,18] Furthermore, HIF transactivation is achieved by the recruitment of coactivators, p300 and CBP, to the c-terminal activation domain of HIF-α.[21–25] This interaction is inhibited by an additional O_2-regulated hydroxylation event on an asparagine residue within the c-terminal activation domain. Therefore, under low O_2, HIF-α subunits stabilized, translocate into the nucleus, and dimerize with ARNT to form the transcriptionally active HIF complex.[19,20]

Active HIF in response to low O_2 can be found within nearly all cells types, including the stem cell populations of ES and TS cells, suggesting that it is the main regulator of O_2 homeostasis. Although many models exist to explain how a cell can sense changes in O_2 concentrations, an exact mechanism is unknown. HIF transcriptional activity can be detected around 5% O_2 and increases exponentially as O_2 levels decrease.[26] This is well within the physiologic range of O_2 in which many cells and tissues exists, including the uterine environment of developing mammalian embryos.[27–29]

Early Embryonic Development

DEVELOPMENT OF THE VASCULAR SYSTEM

The cardiovascular system is the first organ to become functional and is crucial for the continued growth of the embryo. The effects of hypoxia on the development of this system have been reviewed elsewhere[30,31] and will only be briefly mentioned here. Note that many of the molecules that promote vascular development are essential for the development of the hematopoietic system and the placenta. These parallels are not surprising for at least two reasons: First, data exists that suggests a common precursor to both endothelial and hematopoietic cells, called the hemangioblast.[32] Second, during placental development TS cells differentiate, adopting certain endothelial cell characteristics, in terms of invasion and adhesion, to facilitate endovascularization within the maternal decidua.[33,34] Furthermore, many of the genes that regulate these processes are direct HIF transcriptional targets or indirectly regulated by O_2 concentrations.

Shortly after gastrulation, the vascular system initiates the *de novo* formation and aggregation of endothelial precursor cells or angioblasts within the embryo proper and the formation of blood islands in the visceral yolk sac, a process known as vasculogenesis. Within the yolk sac, these primitive endothelial cells aggregate to form a capillary plexus, a honeycombed network of blood vessels containing primitive erythroblasts. A similar process occurs concurrently within the embryo to vascularize the head mesenchyme and lateral plate mesoderm.[35] The development of a mature vascular system containing venules, veins, arteries, and arterioles requires a dynamic process of vessel remodeling, termed angiogenesis. This process includes the proliferation and sprouting of new vessels from preexisting ones, the pruning of excess branches, and the enlargement of endothelial tubes to form major vessels. Mature vessels also require the recruitment of supporting cells, including pericytes and smooth muscles cells.

Although the initial events leading to angioblast specification are not known, subsequent events appear to be increased expression of VEGF and its receptors VEGFR2 and VEGFR1, the protein products of the *Flk-1* and *Flt-1* genes, respectively. *Flk-1* expression is the earliest known marker of developing endothelial and hematopoietic lineages.[36] However, later in development, the expression of *Flk-1* is restricted to endothelial cell precursors.[37] *In vitro* studies demonstrate that *Flk-1+* cells isolated from differentiated ES cells are capable of producing both hematopoietic and endothelial lineages.[37,38] *Flk-1−/−* mice die around embryonic day (E)9 and lack both blood vessels and hematopoietic cells.[39] Therefore, *Flk-1* is essential for the development of embryonic vasculature. *Flt-1* mutants also die early in development but harbor defects in primary vessel formation and organization, indicative of an overgrowth of endothelial cells.[40,41] These observations have led to the conclusion that *Flt-1* signaling pathways play an inhibitory role in early endothelial development by sequestering VEGF, thereby modulating the ligand's effects. Mutations of VEGF are also highly lethal; *Vegf+/−* embryos die early in gestation with reduced size and functional blood vessels.[42,43] Conditional knockouts of the *Vegf* gene, leading to reduced VEGF signaling, result in neonatal lethality and reduced organ vascularization.[44] Hypermorphic alleles of *Vegf*, which increase VEGF expression by two- to threefold, also result in embryonic lethality between E12.5–14 because of severe defects in heart development caused by abnormal vasculogenesis.[45] The effects of VEGF on vascular development are therefore highly dose dependent.

ROLE OF HYPOXIA IN EARLY EMBRYONIC DEVELOPMENT

Although the effects of VEGF and VEGF signaling imply a role for hypoxia in embryonic development, genetic evidence provides the strongest link between HIF activity and early embryonic vasculature and growth. *Arnt−/−* ES cells fail to activate hypoxia responsive genes involved in metabolism and vasculogenesis, such as *Glut1*, *Pgk*, and *Vegf*.[46] During embryonic development, the loss of ARNT results in lethality around (E)9.5–10.5 because of vascular remodeling defects

within embryonic structures, similar to *Vegf−/−* embryos. Embryonic lethality appeared to be a result of a lack of embryonic vasculature within the placenta.[46–48] To ensure that the vascular defects within *Arnt−/−* embryos were not secondary to the placentation defects, homozygous embryos were produced by aggregating mutant ES cells with wild-type tetraploid embryos, which are created by fusing diploid (E)1.5 blastocysts.[49] Within this assay, ES cells will comprise the embryo proper and extraembryonic mesoderm (i.e., blood vessels) because the tetraploid cells can only develop into extraembryonic structures, such as the placenta and yolk sac endoderm. Although tetraploid aggregation rescued the placentation defect, the *Arnt−/−* embryo still exhibited lethality around (E)10.6 because of yolk sac vascular and cardiac defects.[48] Loss of HIF-1α does not completely recapitulate the *Arnt−/−* phenotype; *Hif-1α−/−* embryos exhibit lethality at (E)9.0, showing significant cell death and reduced vascular development.[4,50] Loss of HIF-2α can result in embryonic lethality between (E)9.5–12.5 because of vascular remodeling defects.[51] However, these effects appear to be background dependent; other studies have shown that *Hif-2α−/−* embryos die mid-gestation, presumably from cardiac dysfunction caused by reduced catecholamine synthesis.[52]

Although the induction of HIF has been thoroughly examined in cancer and disease states such as ischemia, the early developmental consequences of HIF overexpression have not been determined. Transgenic overexpression of HIF in the epidermis results in a hypervascularity phenotype distinct from overexpression of VEGF, implying that hypoxic signaling promotes mature vessel formation with the recruitment of supporting cells.[53] Loss of HIF antagonist pVHL also results in constitutive HIF stabilization and activation of downstream target genes in tumors and ES cells.[14,54–56] *Vhl−/−* embryos are growth retarded and exhibit lethality between (E)9.5–10.5 because of placental vascular defects.[57] HIF activity is therefore critical for normal embryonic development, and simply the inability to respond to changes in the O_2 environment can lead to lethality.

Early Hematopoiesis

HEMANGIOBLAST FORMATION

The development of the early vasculature is spatially and temporally linked to early hematopoiesis. As mesodermal cells are generated, they migrate to a region destined to become the yolk sac about 12 hours after the onset of gastrulation.[58] As stated previously, these aggregates form blood islands, which contain both hematopoietic and endothelial precursor cells. Given the close physical relationship between hematopoietic and endothelial development, it has been suggested that both are derived from a common precursor cell, termed the hemangioblast.[32,38] The idea of the hemangioblast is supported by the observation that both endothelial and hematopoietic cells express common genetic markers such as *Flk-1, CD34, CD31, Flt-1, Scl, Tie-2,* and *Gata 2*.[36,59–66] The existence of a hemangioblast is also supported by genetic evidence: *Flk−/−* mutant mice exhibit both vascular and hematopoietic defects,[67–70] and loss of SCL leads to defects in primitive and definitive hematopoiesis, along with aberrant yolk sac vasculature.[71–73] Similarly, hypoxia and HIF target gene expression have significant effects on the generation and proliferation of both hematopoietic and endothelial cells.[43,68,74–77] Isolation of the hemangioblast *in vivo* from embryos has been elusive because of its proposed transient nature, possibly existing within the yolk between days 6.5 and 7 after gestation.[38,78] Formal proof of its existence has been based on experiments that use an *in vitro* model to differentiate ES cells into hematopoietic and endothelial precursor cells.

In vitro ES cell differentiation assays have lead to the identification of a blast colony-forming cell (BL-CFC), which has the potential to produce both endothelial and hematopoietic cells and is therefore considered the putative hemangioblast.[38] BL-CFCs come from *Flk-1+* cells, and upon addition of VEGF protein, their formation and proliferation is increased.[38,78,79] In addition to VEGF signaling, hemangioblast survival and proliferation requires SCL, a basic helix-loop-helix polypeptide. *Scl−/−* embryoid bodies (three-dimensional structures containing differentiated ES cells) fail to generate BL-CFCs; instead, they produce colonies intermediate between mesoderm and hematopoietic lineages.[80] The time frame of hemangioblast formation is brief, occurring between days 2.5 and 3.5 of differentiation. Preliminary studies have shown that BL-CFCs can be isolated from the primitive streak of embryos.[58] These colonies contain both primitive and definitive hematopoietic precursors as well as adherent cells expressing PECAM, a marker indicative of endothelial lineages. These results confirm the assumption that the early yolk sac contains the hemangioblast populations whose formation can be modeled *in vitro*.

HYPOXIC EFFECTS ON HEMANGIOBLASTS FORMATION

Given the requirements of the VEGF and VEGF receptor *Flk-1* for hemangioblast formation, the effects of hypoxia on these populations of cells was examined. Culture of embryoid bodies (EBs) under 3% O_2 not only increased the formation of BL-CFCs but also altered their kinetics of formation from mesoderm precursors.[81] Under normoxia (21% O_2), transitional colonies, which express mesodermal markers as well as hematopoietic and endothelial markers,[80] were formed between days 2 and 2.5 of EB differentiation. BL-CFCs were not found until day 3.0. Hypoxia promoted the formation of BL-CFCs as early as day 2, which persisted until day 2.75 and decreased the numbers of transitional colony. The requirement of HIF transcriptional activity was also analyzed using a genetic model. *Arnt−/−* EBs were able to form BL-CFCs *in vitro*, although their numbers were significantly less than wild-type controls. Loss of HIF signaling resulted in a concomitant increase in the numbers of 2° EBs and transitional colonies formed, indicating the presence of more mesodermal precursors unable to completely differentiate. Although the addition of VEGF to wild-type cultures promoted a decrease in the formation of transitional colonies and an increase in blast colony formation, VEGF had no effect on the proliferation of *Arnt−/−* BL-CFCs. Furthermore, the defect in BL-CFC formation appears secondary to a decrease in the expression of *Flk-1+*

cells in *Arnt−/−* EBs.[81] These genetic studies demonstrate a role for HIF as early as the initial fate decision of mesodermal stem cells. Future experiments may suggest a universal role of hypoxia in the lineage progression of ectoderm- and endoderm-derived tissues by performing similar *in vitro* differentiation assays using ES cells.

EARLY HEMATOPOIETIC DEVELOPMENT

Primitive hematopoiesis occurs extraembryonically within the yolk sac leading to the production of primitive nucleated red blood cells expressing embryonic forms of globin. *In vitro* and transplantation studies demonstrate that multiple hematopoietic lineages can arise within this region. Primitive erythroid cells are detected as early as (E)7.0 and persist until (E)9.0. Myeloid progenitors begin to form at (E)8.25 and persist until yolk sac hematopoiesis begins to decline between (E)11–12. With the decline in yolk sac hematopoiesis begins the rise of definitive hematopoietic cells within the para-aorta-splanchnopleura region of the embryo. This region gives rise to the aorta, gonads, and mesonephros (AGM) regions and will later become the fetal liver. The AGM is thought to be the site of the generation of long-term repopulating stem cells (LTRSC), responsible for the continued renewal of hematopoietic cells in the adult.[58] LTRSCs may also be present within the yolk sac, establishing a second cohort of definitive hematopoietic cells within the embryo.[82] Nevertheless, the fetal liver is the predominant site of definitive hematopoiesis, including erythropoiesis, myelopoiesis, and lymphopoiesis, in the embryo. Shortly after birth and within the adult, the bone marrow becomes the primary site of hematopoiesis.

The association between the hematopoietic system and vascular development has already been established from hemangioblast studies; therefore, it is not surprising that the genes that affect vascular development also affect hematopoiesis. The expression of *Scl*, originally cloned as a T-cell oncogene, is critical for the development of both hematopoietic and endothelial lineages.[65,71–73,80] Mutation within transforming growth factor β-1 (TGFβ-1), result in embryonic lethality from improper endothelial and hematopoietic development.[83] Furthermore, VEGF signaling is essential not only for vascular development but also for blood island formation and hematopoiesis.[39] In chimera experiments, *Flk-1* mutant ES cells were unable to contribute to primitive hematopoiesis within the embryonic yolk sac and definitive hematopoiesis in adult.[68] The hematopoietic and vascular defects within *Flk-1* mutant mice appears to be caused by the mislocalization of precursors cells, which were unable to migrate to the yolk sac.[68] *In vitro, Flk-1* mutant ES cells are able to differentiate into some hematopoietic progenitors, circumventing cell migration defects.[69,70] Exogenous expression of VEGF increases the colony-forming rates of adult wild-type hematopoietic stem cells (HSCs) and restores the ability of VEGF-deficient HSCs to form colonies *in vitro*. VEGF seems to promote HSC survival through an internal autocrine loop, as suggested by an experiment in which administration of extracellular VEGF inhibitors had minor effect on HSC survival.[84] Furthermore, the survival aspects of VEGF signaling appear to be mediated through the activation of antiapoptotic pathways.[84,85] In addition to the necessity of VEGF and VEGF signaling for hematopoietic development, other hypoxia responsive genes have been examined. EPO expression is induced by hypoxia and is the essential regulator of erythroid differentiation and proliferation.[2,8,75,86,87] Loss of EPO or the EPO receptor in mice leads to a decrease in circulating erythrocytes and fetal liver hypocellularity.[75,76]

ROLE OF HYPOXIC SIGNALING IN EARLY HEMATOPOIESIS

Further genetic evidence for the role of HIF in hematopoiesis comes from the analysis of clonogenic assays of $Arnt^{-/-}$ yolk sacs. Lack of $Arnt$ leads to a decrease in all hematopoietic progenitors assayed, including erythroid, macrophage, megakaryocyte, and granulocyte lineages.[74] This phenotype can be recapitulated in vitro by differentiating ES cells into EBs and selecting for the production of hematopoietic progenitors. Upon the removal of the leukemia inhibitory factor from the culture media, ES cells begin to differentiate into EBs, spherical structures that contain the derivatives of all three germ layers.[88,89] Within these EBs, hematopoiesis can occur in a time frame similar to the development in the yolk sac.[90] Primitive erythropoiesis can be detected as early as day 3.5 of differentiation. Shortly thereafter, additional hematopoietic progenitors begin to be generated, macrophages by day 4.5, definitive erythroid by day 5.0 and mast cells by day 9. The EB assay provides a unique tool in which both genetic and environmental factors that regulate hematopoietic development and precursor formation can be analyzed. $Arnt^{-/-}$ ES cells assayed within the EB system were deficient in the generation of hematopoietic progenitors similar to the yolk sac clonogenic assays.[74] However, the addition of exogenous VEGF rescued the hematopoietic defect of $Arnt^{-/-}$ ES cells, implying a cell extrinsic effect in hematopoietic development. Furthermore, exposure of wild-type cells to hypoxia promoted the proliferation of all hematopoietic progenitors in these in vitro assays.[74]

Early hematopoiesis in the embryo occurs within an overall hypoxic environment; the maintenance, survival, or both of adult HSC is also dependent upon hypoxia. Hematopoietic stems cells within adult animals are also though to reside in a gradient of O_2 concentrations within bone marrow.[91] Hypoxia has been found to maintain the proliferation potential of progenitor cells; more committed cells are not preserved in low O_2 environments.[91,92] Analogous effects of hypoxia on hematopoiesis can be seen within human systems; low O_2 increases the formation of blast-forming unit erythroid (BFU-E) colonies within 14-day clonogenic assays.[93] Shorter hypoxic incubation increased the formation of both BFU-E and colony-forming unit granulocyte/macrophage (CFU-GM) colonies.[94] These effects may be mediated by hypoxia-induced cytokine production from the bone marrow stroma. One limitation of these experiments is the inability to assess the effects of hypoxia on HSCs alone because the material used within these assays—umbilical cord blood, mobilized peripheral blood, and bone marrow progenitors—contain a variety of cells. Recently, Danet et al.[95] has shown that hypoxia preferentially expands human HSCs (defined as cells being capable of continued proliferation and multilineage repopulation of bone marrow in immune compromised mice) after 4 days in culture at 1.5% O_2. Currently, clinical studies exist that seek to use stem cells for bone marrow repopulation in cases of genetic disease or as a component of cancer therapy. Hypoxic culture conditions may therefore have profound effects on the expansion of human hematopoietic stem cells ex vivo for transplantation experiments.

Placental Development

FORMATION OF MURINE PLACENTA

Placenta formation begins when the metabolic and O_2 needs of the embryo surpass what can be supplied by the yolk sac. Although the organization of a placenta can differ from mammalian species to mammalian species, two basic functions are universal. First, TS cells, specialized epithelial cells, differentiate to form structures, which provide a large surface to facilitate nutrient and gas exchange between maternal and fetal blood. Second, TS cells invade the uterus to produce growth factors, cytokine, and hormones that further promote the delivery of nutrients and increase blood flow to the embryo. Within the mouse, placenta formation begins with the fusion of the allantois with extraembryonic chorion derived from the polar trophectoderm. As fetal blood vessels migrate into this region, TS cells that reside in the chorion begin to differentiate and fuse to form syncytiotrophoblast. This region, the labyrinthine layer, is characterized by the interdigitation of maternal and fetal blood vessels, providing the function of nutrient and gas exchange. Placenta formation can therefore be a model for the development of a vascular structure (Fig. 7–2). Concurrent with labyrinthine formation, a second cell type, trophoblast giant cells derived from stem cells within ectoplacental cone, invade and anchor into the uterine wall. Trophoblast giant cells are in direct contact with maternal blood sinus and are therefore exposed to high concentrations of O_2. These giant cells, so called because within the murine placenta they can obtain ploidy up to 1024N because of multiple rounds of endoreduplication, form the boundary between fetal and maternal tissues. Trophoblast giant cells also secrete a multitude of factors that promote angiogenesis and vasoactivity.[96] Between the labyrinthine and giant cell layers resides a third cell type: the spongiotrophoblast population, analogous to human column cytotrophoblast. Placenta formation can therefore be viewed as a dynamic process requiring the spatially and temporally coordinated differentiation of a stem cell population into the highly specialized cell types.

HIF ACTIVITY IN PLACENTAL FORMATION

Given the primary function of the placenta to deliver O_2 and nutrient to the embryo, it is likely that similar physiological stimuli, which regulate embryonic vascularization, can regulate placenta formation. O_2, in addition to regulating the

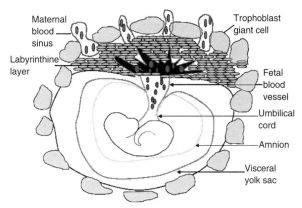

Figure 7–2. Schematic of murine (E)9.5 placenta.

growth and formation of vascular and hematopoietic cells, drives placental cells proliferation and differentiation. Human trophoblasts cells proliferate under hypoxia and fail to differentiate into an invasive phenotype.[97] Furthermore, culture under 21% O_2 stops human trophoblast proliferation and restores normal differentiation.[98] Early placentation is thought to occur in a relatively hypoxic environment, thereby promoting stem cell proliferation. Increased blood flow to the placenta would therefore expose the stem cells to higher O_2 concentrations, leading to growth arrest and differentiation. The expression of HIF within the placenta supports this theory. Within early pregnancy, the expression of HIF-1α is high and parallels that of TGFβ-3, an inhibitor of trophoblast differentiation. After 9 weeks, the expression of both drops as placental O_2 levels increase, suggesting that HIF regulates trophoblast differentiation.[97] HIF also seems to be highly expressed during preeclampsia, a pathology of pregnancy thought to result from decreased O_2 tension with the placenta.[99,100]

HYPOXIC REGULATION OF TS CELL DIFFERENTIATION

To clearly assess the role of hypoxia in placental development, a genetic approach must be taken. As stated earlier, $Arnt^{-/-}$ mice lack HIF activity, which results in embryonic lethality between (E)9.5–10.5. $Arnt^{-/-}$ placentas lack fetal blood vessels within the labyrinthine layer and are less invasive than controls. The aberrant architecture of $Arnt^{-/-}$ placentas is caused by an expansion of the giant cell population and a concomitant decrease in the spongiotrophoblast population.[48] *In vitro* analysis of murine TS cells revealed an increase in proliferation under hypoxia; a similar response is seen when human cytotrophoblasts are cultured under low O_2.[101] Hypoxia also promoted the differentiation of TS cells into spongiotrophoblasts and induced the expression of TGFβ-3 within murine and human trophoblast cells.[48,97] $Arnt^{-/-}$ TS cells lacked detectable levels of spongiotrophoblast lineage marker 4311 and appeared to have a greater propensity to form polyploidy giant cells in undifferentiating conditions. Hypoxia therefore affects the cell fate determination of

TS cells, possibly by inhibiting cellular differentiation by the induction of TGFβ-3 signaling.

The inability to activate HIF target genes is detrimental to placental development, so it appears to be overexpression of these genes. Lack of pVHL results in the dysregulation of HIF target genes expression in tumor-derived cell lines and mouse ES cells, thereby mimicking a constant hypoxic state.[14,54–56] $Vhl^{-/-}$ mice also exhibit embryonic lethality around (E)9.5–10.5 because of the vascular defects within the placenta.[57] The embryonic endothelium fails to invade into the maternal decidua, resulting in a lack of a labyrinthine layer. Expression of the trophoblast giant cell marker Pl Lac is decreased in addition to aberrant expression of 4311+ spongiotrophoblast cells in $Vhl^{-/-}$ placenta (Mack, unpublished). Therefore, trophoblast cells must also be able to sense an O_2 gradient for proper cellular differentiation and placental architecture.

GROWTH FACTOR SIGNALING TO HIF

In addition to low O_2, HIF transcriptional activity can be regulated by a variety of growth factors and cytokines. Insulin, insulin-like growth factor, fibroblast growth factor, and interleukin-1β all increase HIF-1α protein expression, HIF DNA binding activity, and target gene expression under normoxia.[102] During early development, growth factor signaling may also augment HIF transcriptional activity. The conjunction of these two signaling pathways may in turn affect cellular differentiation. A function for basal normoxic levels of HIF activation is suggested by the phenotype of $Arnt^{-/-}$ TS cells. Wild-type TS cells express an abundance of HIF-1α protein under 21% O_2 when compared to ES cells. $Arnt^{-/-}$ TS cells exhibit reduced proliferation and harbor adhesion defects under normoxic conditions, implying a role for HIF activity even under normoxia.[103] The effects of normoxic HIF levels mediated by growth factor signals may provide further insight into the developmental requirements of HIF activity.

Summary

Nearly all cell types respond to hypoxia; however, the O_2 gradient in which stem cells reside has profound effects on cellular differentiation, cellular migration, and pattern formation. The use of stem cells *in vitro* has allowed the elucidation of the complex molecule pathways that facilitate these events. These studies have also highlighted commonalities between stem cells within the embryo that develop both hematopoietic and vascular lineages and those within the trophectoderm that generate vascular and trophoblastic components of the placenta. Enabling us to gain further insight into the role of hypoxia in development, analogous events occur during disease states such as cancer, cardiac dysfunction, and pathologies of pregnancy. Stem cell research may therefore have profound implications for a variety of clinical studies: Inhibitors of HIF activity may be therapeutic for cancers that overexpress HIF; during pregnancy, HIF levels may be used as a diagnostic tool for preeclampsia detection; and hypoxia could be used to maintain and propagate stem cells *ex vivo*, further enhancing their clinical application.

REFERENCES

1. Tanaka, S., Kunath, T., Hadjantonakis, A.K., Nagy, A., and Rossant, J. (1998). Promotion of trophoblast stem cell proliferation by FGF4. *Science* **282**, 2072–2075.

2. Wenger, R.H., and Gassmann, M. (1997). Oxygen(s) and the hypoxia-inducible factor-1. *Biol. Chem.* **207**, 609–616.

3. Wang, G.L., Jiang, B.H., Rue, E.A., and Semenza, G.L. (1995). Hypoxia-inducible factor 1 is a basic-helix-loop-helix-PAS heterodimer regulated by cellular O_2 tension. *Proc. Natl. Acad. Sci. U. S. A.* **92**, 5510–5514.

4. Iyer, N.V., Kotch, L.E., Agani, F., Leung, S.W., Laughner, E., Wenger, R.H., Gassmann, M., Gearhart, J.D., Lawler, A.M., Yu, A.Y., and Semenza, G.L. (1998). Cellular and developmental control of O_2 homeostasis by hypoxia-inducible factor 1 alpha. *Genes Dev.* **12**, 149–162.

5. Ryan, H.E., Poloni, M., McNulty, W., Elson, D., Gassmann, M., Arbeit, J.M., and Johnson, R.S. (2000). Hypoxia-inducible factor-1alpha is a positive factor in solid tumor growth. *Cancer Res.* **60**, 4010–4015.

6. Carmeliet, P., Dor, Y., Herbert, J.M., Fukumura, D., Brusselmans, K., Dewerchin, M., Neeman, M., Bono, F., Abramovitch, R., Maxwell, P., Koch, C.J., Ratcliffe, P., Moons, L., Jain, R.K., Collen, D., and Keshet, E. (1998). Role of HIF-1alpha in hypoxia-mediated apoptosis, cell proliferation and tumor angiogenesis. *Nature* **394**, 485–490.

7. Gerber, H.P., Condorelli, F., Park, J., and Ferrara, N. (1997). Differential transcriptional regulation of the two vascular endothelial growth factor receptor genes. *Flt-1,* but not *Flk-1/KDR,* is up-regulated by hypoxia. *J. Biol. Chem.* **272**, 23,659–23,667.

8. Wood, S.M., Wiesener, M.S., Yeates, K.M., Okada, N., Pugh, C.W., Maxwell, P.H., and Ratcliffe, P.J. (1998). Selection and analysis of a mutant cell line defective in the hypoxia-inducible factor-1 alpha-subunit (HIF-1alpha). Characterization of hif-1alpha-dependent and independent hypoxia-inducible gene expression. *J. Biol. Chem.* **273**, 8360–8368.

9. Wood, S.M., Gleadle, J.M., Pugh, C.W., Hankinson, O., and Ratcliffe, P.J. (1996). The role of the aryl hydrocarbon receptor nuclear translocator (ARNT) in hypoxic induction of gene expression. Studies in ARNT-deficient cells. *J. Biol. Chem.* **271**, 15,117–15,123.

10. Tacchini, L., Bianchi, L., Bernelli-Zazzera, A., and Cairo, G. (1999). Transferrin receptor induction by hypoxia. HIF-1 mediated transcriptional activation and cell-specific post-transcriptional regulation. *J. Biol. Chem.* **274**, 24,142–24,146.

11. Bruick, R.K. (2000). Expression of the gene encoding the proapoptotic Nip3 protein is induced by hypoxia. *Proc. Natl. Acad. Sci. U. S. A.* **97**, 9082–9087.

12. Sowter, H.M., Ratcliffe, P.J., Watson, P., Greenberg, A.H., and Harris, A.L. (2001). HIF-1-dependent regulation of hypoxic induction of the cell death factors BNIP3 and NIX in human tumors. *Cancer Res.* **61**, 6669–6673.

13. Goda, N., Ryan, H.E., Khadivi, B., McNulty, W., Rickert, R.C., and Johnson, R.S. (2003). Hypoxia-inducible factor 1alpha is essential for cell cycle arrest during hypoxia. *Mol. Cell Biol.* **23**, 359–369.

14. Maxwell, P.H., Wiesener, M.S., Chang, G.W., Clifford, S.C., Vaux, E.C., Cockman, M.E., Wykoff, C.C., Pugh, C.W., Maher, E.R., and Ratcliffe, P.J. (1999). The tumor suppressor protein VHL targets hypoxia-inducible factors for oxygen-dependent proteolysis. *Nature* **399**, 271–275.

15. Ivan, M., Kondo, K., Yang, H., Kim, W., Valiando, J., Ohh, M., Salic, A., Asara, J.M., Lane, W.S., and Kaelin, W.G., Jr. (2001). HIF-alpha targeted for VHL-mediated destruction by proline hydroxylation: implications for O_2 sensing. *Science* **292**, 464–468.

16. Jaakkola, P., Mole, D.R., Tian, Y.M., Wilson, M.I., Gielbert, J., Gaskell, S.J., Kriegsheim, A., Hebestreit, H.F., Mukherji, M., Schofield, C.J., Maxwell, P.H., Pugh, C.W., and Ratcliffe, P.J. (2001). Targeting of HIF-alpha to the von Hippel-Lindau ubiquitylation complex by O_2-regulated prolyl hydroxylation. *Science* **292**, 468–472.

17. Bruick, R.K., and McKnight, S.L. (2001). A conserved family of prolyl-4-hydroxylases that modify HIF. *Science* **294**, 1337–1340.

18. Epstein, A.C., Gleadle, J.M., McNeill, L.A., Hewitson, K.S., O'Rourke, J., Mole, D.R., Mukherji, M., Metzen, E., Wilson, M.I., Dhanda, A., Tian, Y.M., Masson, N., Hamilton, D.L., Jaakkola, P., Barstead, R., Hodgkin, J., Maxwell, P.H., Pugh, C.W., Schofield, C.J., and Ratcliffe, P.J. (2001). *C. elegans* EGL-9 and mammalian homologs define a family of dioxygenases that regulate HIF by prolyl hydroxylation. *Cell* **107**, 43–54.

19. Kallio, P.J., Wilson, W.J., O'Brien, S., Makino, Y., and Poellinger, L. (1999). Regulation of the hypoxia-inducible transcription factor 1alpha by the ubiquitin-proteasome pathway. *J. Biol. Chem.* **274**, 6519–6525.

20. Tanimoto, K., Makino, Y., Pereira, T., and Poellinger, L. (2000). Mechanism of regulation of the hypoxia-inducible factor-1 alpha by the von Hippel-Lindau tumor suppressor protein. *EMBO J.* **19**, 4298-4309.

21. Arany, Z., Huang, L.E., Eckner, R., Bhattacharya, S., Jiang, C., Goldberg, M.A., Bunn, H.F., and Livingston, D.M. (1996). An essential role for p300/CBP in the cellular response to hypoxia. *Proc. Natl. Acad. Sci. U. S. A.* **93**, 12,969–12,973.

22. Jiang, B.H., Zheng, J.Z., Leung, S.W., Roe, R., and Semenza, G.L. (1997). Transactivation and inhibitory domains of hypoxia-inducible factor 1alpha. Modulation of transcriptional activity by oxygen tension. *J. Biol. Chem.* **272**, 19,253–19,260.

23. Pugh, C.W., O'Rourke, J.F., Nagao, M., Gleadle, J.M., and Ratcliffe, P.J. (1997). Activation of hypoxia-inducible factor-1; definition of regulatory domains within the alpha subunit. *J. Biol. Chem.* **272**, 11,205–11,214.

24. Ebert, B.L., and Bunn, H.F. (1998). Regulation of transcription by hypoxia requires a multiprotein complex that includes hypoxia-inducible factor 1, an adjacent transcription factor, and p300/CREB binding protein. *Mol. Cell Biol.* **18**, 4089–4096.

25. Carrero, P., Okamoto, K., Coumailleau, P., O'Brien, S., Tanaka, H., and Poellinger, L. (2000). Redox-regulated recruitment of the transcriptional coactivators CREB-binding protein and SRC-1 to hypoxia-inducible factor 1alpha. *Mol. Cell Biol.* **20**, 402–415.

26. Jiang, B.H., Semenza, G.L., Bauer, C., and Marti, H.H. (1996). Hypoxia-inducible factor 1 levels vary exponentially over a physiologically relevant range of O_2 tension. *Am. J. Physiol.* **271**, C1172–C1180.

27. Intaglietta, M., Johnson, P.C., and Winslow, R.M. (1996). Microvascular and tissue oxygen distribution. *Cardiovasc. Res.* **32**, 632–643.

28. Kaufman, D.L., and Mitchell, J.A. (1994). Intrauterine oxygen tension during the oestrous cycle in the hamster: patterns of change. *Comp. Biochem. Physiol. Comp. Physiol.* **107**, 673–678.

29. Mitchell, J.A., and Yochim, J.M. (1968). Intrauterine oxygen tension during the estrous cycle in the rat: its relation to uterine respiration and vascular activity. *Endocrinology* **83**, 701–705.

30. Maltepe, E., and Simon, M.C. (1998). Oxygen, genes, and development: an analysis of the role of hypoxic gene regulation during murine vascular development. *J. Mol. Med.* **76,** 391–401.

31. Ramirez-Bergeron, D.L., and Simon, M.C. (2001). Hypoxia-inducible factor and the development of stem cells of the cardiovascular system. *Stem Cells* **19,** 279–286.

32. Sabin, F.R. (1920). Studies on the origin of blood vessels and red corpuscles as seen in living blastoderm of the chick during the second day of incubation. *Contrib. Embryol.* **9,** 213–262.

33. Zhou, Y., Genbacev, O., Damsky, C.H., and Fisher, S.J. (1998). Oxygen regulates human cytotrophoblast differentiation and invasion: implications for endovascular invasion in normal pregnancy and in preeclampsia. *J. Reprod. Immunol.* **39,** 197–213.

34. Zhou, Y., Fisher, S.J., Janatpour, M., Genbacev, O., Dejana, E., Wheelock, M., and Damsky, C.H. (1997). Human cytotrophoblasts adopt a vascular phenotype as they differentiate. A strategy for successful endovascular invasion? *J. Clin. Invest.* **99,** 2139–2151.

35. Rossant, J., and Howard, L. (2002). Signaling pathways in vascular development. *Annu. Rev. Cell Dev. Biol.* **18,** 541–573.

36. Yamaguchi, T.P., Dumont, D.J., Conlon, R.A., Breitman, M.L., and Rossant, J. (1993). *Flk-1,* an *Flt*-related receptor tyrosine kinase is an early marker for endothelial cell precursors. *Development* **118,** 489–498.

37. Yamashita, J., Itoh, H., Hirashima, M., Ogawa, M., Nishikawa, S., Yurugi, T., Naito, M., and Nakao, K. (2000). *Flk-1*-positive cells derived from embryonic stem cells serve as vascular progenitors. *Nature* **408,** 92–96.

38. Choi, K., Kennedy, M., Kazarov, A., Papadimitriou, J.C., and Keller, G. (1998). A common precursor for hematopoietic and endothelial cells. *Development* **125,** 725–732.

39. Shalaby, F., Rossant, J., Yamaguchi, T.P., Gertsenstein, M., Wu, X.F., Breitman, M.L., and Schuh, A.C. (1995). Failure of blood-island formation and vasculogenesis in *Flk-1*-deficient mice. *Nature* **376,** 62–66.

40. Fong, G.H., Rossant, J., Gertsenstein, M., and Breitman, M.L. (1995). Role of the *Flt-1* receptor tyrosine kinase in regulating the assembly of vascular endothelium. *Nature* **376,** 66–70.

41. Fong, G.H., Zhang, L., Bryce, D.M., and Peng, J. (1999). Increased hemangioblast commitment, not vascular disorganization, is the primary defect in *Flt-1* knock-out mice. *Development* **126,** 3015–3025.

42. Carmeliet, P., Ferreira, V., Breier, G., Pollefeyt, S., Kieckens, L., Gertsenstein, M., Fahrig, M., Vandenhoeck, A., Harpal, K., Eberhardt, C., Declercq, C., Pawling, J., Moons, L., Collen, D., Risau, W., and Nagy, A. (1996). Abnormal blood vessel development and lethality in embryos lacking a single VEGF allele. *Nature* **380,** 435–439.

43. Ferrara, N., Carver-Moore, K., Chen, H., Dowd, M., Lu, L., O'Shea, K.S., Powell-Braxton, L., Hillan, K.J., and Moore, M.W. (1996). Heterozygous embryonic lethality induced by targeted inactivation of the VEGF gene. *Nature* **380,** 439–442.

44. Gerber, H.P., Hillan, K.J., Ryan, A.M., Kowalski, J., and Keller, G.A. (1999). VEGF is required for growth and survival in neonatal mice. *Development* **126,** 1149–1159.

45. Miquerol, L., Langille, B.L., and Nagy, A. (2000). Embryonic development is disrupted by modest increases in vascular endothelial growth factor gene expression. *Development* **127,** 3941–3946.

46. Maltepe, E., Schmidt, J.V., Baunoch, D., Bradfield, C.A., and Simon, M.C. (1997). Abnormal angiogenesis and responses to glucose and oxygen deprivation in mice lacking the protein ARNT. *Nature* **386,** 403–407.

47. Kozak, K.R., Abbott, B., and Hankinson, O. (1997). ARNT-deficient mice and placental differentiation. *Dev. Biol.* **191,** 297–305.

48. Adelman, D.M., Gertsenstein, M., Nagy, A., Simon, M.C., and Maltepe, E. (2000). Placental cell fates are regulated in vivo by HIF-mediated hypoxia responses. *Genes Dev.* **14,** 3191–3203.

49. Nagy, A., and Rossant, J. (1996). Targeted mutagenesis: analysis of phenotype without germ line transmission. *J. Clin. Invest.* **97,** 1360–1365.

50. Ryan, H.E., Lo, J., and Johnson, R.S. (1998). HIF-1a is required for solid tumor formation and embryonic vascularization. *EMBO J.* **17,** 3005–3015.

51. Peng, J., Zhang, L., Drysdale, L., and Fong, G.H. (2000). The transcription factor EPAS-1/hypoxia-inducible factor 2alpha plays an important role in vascular remodeling. *Proc. Natl. Acad. Sci. U. S. A.* **97,** 8386–8391.

52. Tian, H., Hammer, R.E., Matsumoto, A.M., Russell, D.W., and McKnight, S.L. (1998). The hypoxia-responsive transcription factor EPAS1 is essential for catecholamine homeostasis and protection against heart failure during embryonic development. *Genes Dev.* **12,** 3320–3324.

53. Elson, D.A., Thurston, G., Huang, L.E., Ginzinger, D.G., McDonald, D.M., Johnson, R.S., and Arbeit, J.M. (2001). Induction of hypervascularity without leakage or inflammation in transgenic mice overexpressing hypoxia-inducible factor-1alpha. *Genes Dev.* **15,** 2520–2532.

54. Iliopoulos, O., Levy, A.P., Jiang, C., Kaelin, W.G., Jr., and Goldberg, M.A. (1996). Negative regulation of hypoxia-inducible genes by the von Hippel-Lindau protein. *Proc. Natl. Acad. Sci. U. S. A.* **93,** 10,595–10,599.

55. Krieg, M., Haas, R., Brauch, H., Acker, T., Flamme, I., and Plate, K.H. (2000). Up-regulation of hypoxia-inducible factors HIF-1alpha and HIF-2alpha under normoxic conditions in renal carcinoma cells by von Hippel-Lindau tumor suppressor gene loss of function. *Oncogene* **19,** 5435–5443.

56. Mack, F.A., Rathmell, W.K., Arsham, A.M., Gnarra, J., Keith, B., and Simon, M.C. (2003). Loss of pVHL is sufficient to cause HIF dysregulation in primary cells but does not promote tumor growth. *Cancer Cell* **3,** 75–88.

57. Gnarra, J.R., Ward, J.M., Porter, F.D., Wagner, J.R., Devor, D.E., Grinberg, A., Emmert-Buck, M.R., Westphal, H., Klausner, R.D., and Linehan, W.M. (1997). Defective placental vasculogenesis causes embryonic lethality in VHL-deficient mice. *Proc. Natl. Acad. Sci. U. S. A.* **94,** 9102–9107.

58. Lacaud, G., Robertson, S., Palis, J., Kennedy, M., and Keller, G. (2001). Regulation of hemangioblast development. *Ann. NY Acad. Sci.* **938,** 96–107; discussion 108.

59. Young, P.E., Baumhueter, S., and Lasky, L.A. (1995). The sialomucin CD34 is expressed on hematopoietic cells and blood vessels during murine development. *Blood* **85,** 96–105.

60. Watt, S.M., Gschmeissner, S.E., and Bates, P.A. (1995). PECAM-1: its expression and function as a cell adhesion molecule on hemopoietic and endothelial cells. *Leuk. Lymphoma* **17,** 229–244.

61. Eichmann, A., Corbel, C., Nataf, V., Vaigot, P., Breant, C., and Le Douarin, N.M. (1997). Ligand-dependent development of the endothelial and hemopoietic lineages from embryonic mesodermal cells expressing vascular endothelial growth factor receptor 2. *Proc. Natl. Acad. Sci. U. S. A.* **94,** 5141–5146.

62. Kabrun, N., Buhring, H.J., Choi, K., Ullrich, A., Risau, W., and Keller, G. (1997). *Flk-1* expression defines a population of early embryonic hematopoietic precursors. *Development* **124,** 2039–2048.

63. Fong, G.H., Klingensmith, J., Wood, C.R., Rossant, J., and Breitman, M.L. (1996). Regulation of *Flt-1* expression during mouse embryogenesis suggests a role in the establishment of vascular endothelium. *Dev. Dyn.* **207**, 1–10.

64. Sato, T.N., Tozawa, Y., Deutsch, U., Wolburg-Buchholz, K., Fujiwara, Y., Gendron-Maguire, M., Gridley, T., Wolburg, H., Risau, W., and Qin, Y. (1995). Distinct roles of the receptor tyrosine kinases Tie-1 and Tie-2 in blood vessel formation. *Nature* **376**, 70–74.

65. Kallianpur, A.R., Jordan, J.E., and Brandt, S.J. (1994). The SCL/TAL-1 gene is expressed in progenitors of both the hematopoietic and vascular systems during embryogenesis. *Blood* **83**, 1200–1208.

66. Orkin, S.H. (1992). GATA-binding transcription factors in hematopoietic cells. *Blood* **80**, 575–581.

67. Shalaby, F., Rossant, J., Yamaguchi, T.P., Gertsenstein, M., Wu, X.F., Breitman, M.L., and Schuh, A.C. (1995). Failure of blood-island formation and vasculogenesis in *Flk-1*-deficient mice. *Nature* **376**, 62–66.

68. Shalaby, F., Ho, J., Stanford, W.L., Fischer, K.D., Schuh, A.C., Schwartz, L., Bernstein, A., and Rossant, J. (1997). A requirement for *Flk-1* in primitive and definitive hematopoiesis and vasculogenesis. *Cell* **89**, 981–990.

69. Hidaka, M., Stanford, W.L., and Bernstein, A. (1999). Conditional requirement for the *Flk-1* receptor in the *in vitro* generation of early hematopoietic cells. *Proc. Natl. Acad. Sci. U. S. A.* **96**, 7370–7375.

70. Schuh, A.C., Faloon, P., Hu, Q.L., Bhimani, M., and Choi, K. (1999). *In vitro* hematopoietic and endothelial potential of *Flk-1*(−/−) embryonic stem cells and embryos. *Proc. Natl. Acad. Sci. U. S. A.* **96**, 2159–2164.

71. Robb, L., Lyons, I., Li, R., Hartley, L., Kontgen, F., Harvey, R.P., Metcalf, D., and Begley, C.G. (1995). Absence of yolk sac hematopoiesis from mice with a targeted disruption of the SCL gene. *Proc. Natl. Acad. Sci. U. S. A.* **92**, 7075–7079.

72. Shivdasani, R.A., Mayer, E.L., and Orkin, S.H. (1995). Absence of blood formation in mice lacking the T-cell leukaemia oncoprotein tal-1/SCL. *Nature* **373**, 432–434.

73. Visvader, J.E., Fujiwara, Y., and Orkin, S.H. (1998). Unsuspected role for the T-cell leukemia protein SCL/tal-1 in vascular development. *Genes Dev.* **12**, 473–479.

74. Adelman, D.M., Maltepe, E., and Simon, M.C. (1999). Multilineage embryonic hematopoiesis requires hypoxic ARNT activity. *Genes Dev.* **13**, 2478–2483.

75. Wu, H., Liu, X., Jaenisch, R., and Lodish, H.F. (1995). Generation of committed erythroid BFU-E and CFU-E progenitors does not require erythropoietin or the erythropoietin receptor. *Cell* **83**, 59–67.

76. Lin, C.S., Lim, S.K., D'Agati, V., and Costantini, F. (1996). Differential effects of an erythropoietin receptor gene disruption on primitive and definitive erythropoiesis. *Genes Dev.* **10**, 154–164.

77. Phillips, P.G., Birnby, L.M., and Narendran, A. (1995). Hypoxia induces capillary network formation in cultured bovine pulmonary microvessel endothelial cells. *Am. J. Physiol.* **268**, L789–L800.

78. Kennedy, M., Firpo, M., Choi, K., Wall, C., Robertson, S., Kabrun, N., and Keller, G. (1997). A common precursor for primitive erythropoiesis and definitive hematopoiesis. *Nature* **386**, 488–493.

79. Faloon, P., Arentson, E., Kazarov, A., Deng, C.X., Porcher, C., Orkin, S., and Choi, K. (2000). Basic fibroblast growth factor positively regulates hematopoietic development. *Development* **127**, 1931–1941.

80. Robertson, S.M., Kennedy, M., Shannon, J.M., and Keller, G. (2000). A transitional stage in the commitment of mesoderm to hematopoiesis requiring the transcription factor SCL/tal-1. *Development* **127**, 2447–2459.

81. Ramirez-Bergeron, D.L., Adelman, D.M., Cowden, K.D., and Simon, M.C. (2003). Hypoxia enhances mesoderm and hemangioblast specification during early embryonic development. *Development* (Submitted).

82. Palis, J., Robertson, S., Kennedy, M., Wall, C., and Keller, G. (1999). Development of erythroid and myeloid progenitors in the yolk sac and embryo proper of the mouse. *Development* **126**, 5073–5084.

83. Dickson, M.C., Martin, J.S., Cousins, F.M., Kulkarni, A.B., Karlsson, S., and Akhurst, R.J. (1995). Defective hematopoiesis and vasculogenesis in transforming growth factor-beta 1 knock out mice. *Development* **121**, 1845–1854.

84. Gerber, H.P., Malik, A.K., Solar, G.P., Sherman, D., Liang, X.H., Meng, G., Hong, K., Marsters, J.C., and Ferrara, N. (2002). VEGF regulates hematopoietic stem cell survival by an internal autocrine loop mechanism. *Nature* **417**, 954–958.

85. Larrivee, B., Lane, D.R., Pollet, I., Olive, P.L., Humphries, R.K., and Karsan, A. (2003). VEGFR-2 induces survival of hematopoietic progenitor cells. *J. Biol. Chem.* **30**, 30.

86. Bunn, H.F., and Poyton, R.O. (1996). Oxygen sensing and molecular adaptation to hypoxia. *Physiol. Rev.* **76**, 839–885.

87. Semenza, G.L., Nejfelt, M.K., Chi, S.M., and Antonarakis, S.E. (1991). Hypoxia-inducible nuclear factors bind to an enhancer element located 3′ to the human erythropoietin gene. *Proc. Natl. Acad. Sci. U. S. A.* **88**, 5680–5684.

88. Keller, G.M. (1995). *In vitro* differentiation of embryonic stem cells. *Curr. Opin. Cell Biol.* **7**, 862–869.

89. Schmitt, R.M., Bruyns, E., and Snodgrass, H.R. (1991). Hematopoietic development of embryonic stem cells *in vitro*: cytokine and receptor gene expression. *Genes Dev.* **5**, 728–740.

90. Keller, G., Kennedy, M., Papayannopoulou, T., and Wiles, M.V. (1993). Hematopoietic commitment during embryonic stem cell differentiation in culture. *Mol. Cell Biol.* **13**, 473–486.

91. Cipolleschi, M.G., Dello Sbarba, P., and Olivotto, M. (1993). The role of hypoxia in the maintenance of hematopoietic stem cells. *Blood* **82**, 2031–2037.

92. Cipolleschi, M.G., Rovida, E., Ivanovic, Z., Praloran, V., Olivotto, M., and Dello Sbarba, P. (2000). The expansion of murine bone marrow cells preincubated in hypoxia as an *in vitro* indicator of their marrow-repopulating ability. *Leukemia* **14**, 735–739.

93. Cipolleschi, M.G., D'Ippolito, G., Bernabei, P.A., Caporale, R., Nannini, R., Mariani, M., Fabbiani, M., Rossi-Ferrini, P., Olivotto, M., and Dello Sbarba, P. (1997). Severe hypoxia enhances the formation of erythroid bursts from human cord blood cells and the maintenance of BFU-E *in vitro*. *Exp. Hematol.* **25**, 1187–1194.

94. Quinlan, D.P., Jr., Rameshwar, P., Qian, J., Maloof, P.B., Mohr, A.M., Hauser, C.J., and Livingston, D.H. (1998). Effect of hypoxia on the hematopoietic and immune modulator preprotachykinin-I. *Arch. Surg.* **133**, 1328–1334.

95. Danet, G.H., Pan, Y., Luongo, J.L., Bonnet, D.A., and Simon, C. (2003). Expansion of human scid-repopulation cells under hypoxic conditions. *J. Clin. Invest.* **112**, 126–135.

96. Cross, J.C., Hemberger, M., Lu, Y., Nozaki, T., Whiteley, K., Masutani, M., and Adamson, S.L. (2002). Trophoblast functions, angiogenesis and remodeling of the maternal vasculature in the placenta. *Mol. Cell Endocrinol.* **187**, 207–212.

97. Caniggia, I., Mostachfi, H., Winter, J., Gassmann, M., Lye, S.J., Kuliszewski, M., and Post, M. (2000). Hypoxia-inducible factor-1 mediates the biological effects of oxygen on human trophoblast differentiation through TGF-beta(3). *J. Clin. Invest.* **105,** 577–587.

98. Genbacev, O., Zhou, Y., Ludlow, J.W., and Fisher, S.J. (1997). Regulation of human placental development by oxygen tension. *Science* **277,** 1669–1672.

99. Rajakumar, A., Doty, K., Daftary, A., Harger, G., and Conrad, K.P. (2003). Impaired oxygen-dependent reduction of HIF-1alpha and -2alpha proteins in preeclamptic placentae. *Placenta* **24,** 199–208.

100. Rajakumar, A., Whitelock, K.A., Weissfeld, L.A., Daftary, A.R., Markovic, N., and Conrad, K.P. (2001). Selective overexpression of the hypoxia-inducible transcription factor, HIF-2alpha, in placentas from women with preeclampsia. *Biol. Reprod.* **64,** 499–506.

101. Genbacev, O., Joslin, R., Damsky, C.H., Polliotti, B.M., and Fisher, S.J. (1996). Hypoxia alters early gestation human cytotrophoblast differentiation/invasion *in vitro* and models the placental defects that occur in preeclampsia. *J. Clin. Invest.* **97,** 540–550.

102. Semenza, G. (2002). Signal transduction to hypoxia-inducible factor 1. Biochem. *Pharmacol.* **64,** 993–998.

103. Cowden-Dahl, K., Mack, F., and Simon, M.C. Personal communication.

8

Regulation of Gap Junction Protein Genes in Differentiating ES cells

Masahito Oyamada, Yumiko Oyamada, and Tetsuro Takamatsu

Gap junctions are cell–cell communicating junctions that consist of multimeric proteins called connexins and mediate the exchange of low-molecular-weight metabolites and ions between contacting cells. Gap junctional communication has long been hypothesized to play a crucial role in the maintenance of homeostasis, morphogenesis, cell differentiation, and growth control in multicellular organisms. The recent discovery that human genetic disorders are associated with mutations in connexin genes and experimental data on connexin knockout mice have provided direct evidence that gap junctional communication is essential for tissue functions and organ development. In the early developmental stages, cells differentiating in a similar direction communicate freely using gap junctions, whereas communication becomes restricted between cell populations with different fates. Investigations of gap junctional communication and connexin expression have shown that the expression of multiple connexins is differentially regulated during the differentiation of embryonic stem (ES) cells *in vitro,* such as cardiomyocyte differentiation and neuronal differentiation. However, the molecular mechanisms by which connexin expression is regulated are largely unknown. The importance of understanding the regulation of connexin expression in differentiating ES cells is increasingly recognized—not only in developmental biology but also in regenerative medicine employing cell transplantation in which ES cells are used as a cell source.

Introduction

Gap junctions are specialized cell–cell junctions that directly link the cytoplasm of neighboring cells. They mediate the direct transfer of low-molecular-weight (<1000 daltons) metabolites and ions, including second messengers such as cyclic adenosine-mono-phosphate, inositol trisphosphate, and Ca^{2+}, between adjacent cells. Therefore, it has long been hypothesized that gap junctional intercellular communication plays a crucial role in the maintenance of homeostasis, morphogenesis, cell differentiation, and growth control in multicellular organisms. Recent discoveries of human genetic

disorders caused by mutations in gap junction protein (connexin) genes and experimental data on connexin knockout mice provide direct evidence that gap junctional intercellular communication is essential for tissue functions and organ development, and that its dysfunction causes diseases.[1] Here, we will briefly introduce the gap junction structure, connexin genes, and gap junctional communication in embryogenesis and development. We will then summarize data on the regulation of connexin genes in differentiating ES cells.

Gap Junctions and Connexin Genes

The name "gap" junction is derived from a uniform narrow gap, 2–4 nm, between the membranes of two adjacent cells observed under an electron microscope. However, the important feature of gap junctions is their intercellular channels, which allow small molecules to pass directly from the inside of one cell to the inside of the other. A gap-junctional intercellular channel is formed by two connexon hemichannels; each connexon consists of six subunits of connexin (Fig. 8–1). Studies using fluorescent molecules of various sizes have shown that molecules with a molecular weight lower than 1000 can pass, suggesting that the maximal functional pore size for the channel is about 1.5 nm in diameter in mammalian cells.

Thus far, 21 human genes and 20 mouse genes for connexins have been identified.[2] The different nomenclature systems used for connexins include one employing molecular masses and one employing Greek letters. In the molecular mass nomenclature, the generic term connexin (Cx) is used for the protein family, with an indication of species (as necessary) and a numeric suffix designating the predicted molecular mass in kilodaltons. Thus, the 43-kD protein from human heart is termed *human connexin43* (hCx43). On the other hand, when Greek-letter nomenclature is used, the connexin gene family is divided into alpha, beta, chi, and epsilon classes based on sequence similarities. Cx43 corresponds to gap junction protein α-1 in this system. The Human Genome Organisation (HUGO) nomenclature is based upon the Greek-letter nomenclature; for example, gap junction protein α-1 is termed Gja1. For better comparison, both nomenclature systems are used to describe the human and mouse gap junction protein genes listed in Table 8–1.

Most connexin genes, with several exceptions, are composed of two exons, the second of which contains the whole coding region and is separated from the first exon by an

Handbook of Stem Cells
Volume 1
Copyright © 2004 by Academic Press
All rights of reproduction in any form reserved.

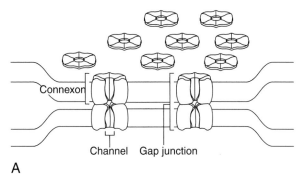

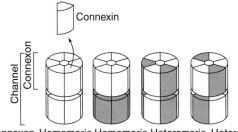

Connexon Homomeric Homomeric Heteromeric Heteromeric
Channel Homotypic Heterotypic Homotypic Heterotypic

B

Figure 8–1. Gap junctions in (A) a three-dimensional drawing and (B) different combinations of connexins to make a gap junction channel.

intron. The reading frames of hCx31.3, hCx36, hCx40.1, mCx36, mCx39, and mCx57 have been shown to be located on the first and second exons, which are interrupted by an intron.[2]

It has been demonstrated that each connexin shows tissue- or cell-type–specific expression and that most organs and many cell types express more than one connexin (Table 8–1). Some connexins, such as Cx32 and Cx43, are expressed in cells of many types, but other connexins, such as Cx33 and Cx50, are expressed only in specific organs (e.g., Cx33 and Cx50 are expressed in the testis and lens, respectively). There is growing evidence that a single gap junction channel can be made of different connexins, i.e., two connexons each consisting of different types of connexins can form a heterotypic gap junction channel, whereas one connexon containing different types of connexins can form a heteromeric gap junction channel (Fig. 8–1B).[3] Distinct electrophysiological and ion-selective properties have been shown not only for homotypic gap junction channels made of different connexins but also between homotypic and heterotypic gap junction channels.[4]

Gap Junctional Communication in Embryogenesis and Development

As summarized in Table 8–2, the recent discovery that certain human genetic disorders are caused by mutations in connexin genes and experimental data on connexin knockout mice provide direct evidence that gap junctional intercellular

communication is essential for tissue functions and organ development. Gap junctional intercellular communication is also believed to be critical for regulation of early developmental events. A plausible hypothesis is that as specific groups of cells in the embryo assume their distinct identities and begin to differentiate, they uncouple from the surrounding tissue. It is possible, in other words, that cells differentiating in a similar direction can communicate freely, whereas communication between cell populations with different fates is restricted. To test this hypothesis, investigations have been carried out by different laboratories, using various organisms including mouse, chick, frog, mollusk, and nematode embryos, to characterize changes in the pattern of gap junctional communication in the embryo as development progresses.[5,6] Gap junctional communication during embryonal development can be demonstrated by using microelectrode impalements to monitor the cell-to-cell movement of ions (ionic coupling). It also can be shown by microinjection of small-molecular-weight fluorescent dyes, such as Lucifer yellow, into a single cell and observation of the subsequent dye spread into the surrounding cells (dye coupling). It has been revealed that in many instances, cell–cell coupling is established within the first few cleavages and results in the entire embryo becoming interconnected as a syncytium. However, as development progresses, dye coupling delineates boundaries defining restrictions in gap junctional communication that effectively segregate the developing embryo or tissue into several "communication compartment" domains. Thus, cells lying within a communication compartment are well coupled, exhibiting both ionic and dye coupling, whereas there is little or no coupling between cells situated across a compartment border. Such restriction of gap junctional communication and the segregation of cells into communication compartment domains are almost always associated with embryogenesis and development.

For example, Lo and Gilula[7] have shown that, in the mouse embryo, gap junctional intercellular communication is first present at the late eight-cell stage and that all cells in the preimplantation embryo are interconnected by gap junctions. However, as development progresses, the postimplantation mouse embryo subdivides into two global communication compartments: Dye coupling studies show that the inner cell mass-derived embryo and the trophectoderm-derived placental precursor cell are each segregated into separate communication compartment domains.[8–10] As development proceeds, dye coupling is demonstrated to become restricted to smaller groups of cells. For example, in the 7.5-d mouse embryo (at the primitive streak or gastrulation stage), cells within all three germ layers are well dye coupled, but there is little or no dye transfer between germ layers, indicating that each is a separate communication compartment. From the pattern of dye movement within the embryonic ectoderm and mesoderm, it is further suggested that cells in each of these germ layers may be subdivided into smaller communication compartments.

Next, an important question arises as to how such restrictions in gap junctional coupling are established. Because each

TABLE 8–1
Connexin Genes[b]

Human			Mouse	
Name			Name	
Molecular Mass Nomenclature	HUGO (Greek letter) Nomenclature	Chromosomal Locus	Molecular Mass Nomenclature	Expressed Organ or Cell Types
hCx25	—	6	—	—
hCx26[a]	GJB2	13q11–q12	mCx26[a]	Breast, cochlea, placenta, hepatocytes, keratinocytes
hCx30	GJB6	13q12	mCx30	Brain, cochlea, keratinocytes
hCx30.3	GJB4	1p35–p34	mCx30.3	Keratinocytes
hCx31	GJB3	1p34	mCx31	Placenta, keratinocytes
hCx31.1	GJB5	1p35.1	mCx31.1	Keratinocytes
hCx31.3 (hCx30.2)	GJE1	7q22.1	mCx29	Brain, spinal cord, Schwann cells
hCx31.9	GJC1 (GJA11)	17q21.1	mCx30.2	—
hCx32	GJB1	Xq13.1	mCx32	Hepatocytes, oligodendrocytes, Schwann cells
—	—	—	mCx33	Sertoli cells
hCx36	GJA9	15q13.2	mCx36	Neurons, pancreatic β-cells
hCx37	GJA4	1p35.1	mCx37	Endothelium, granulosa cells
hCx38	GJA2	—	—	—
hCx40	GJA5	1q21.1	mCx40	Cardiac conduction system, endothelium
hCx40.1	—	—	mCx39	—
hCx43	GJA1	6q21–q23.2	mCx43	Many cell types
hCx45	GJA7	17q21.31	mCx45	Cardiac conduction system, smooth muscle cells
hCx46	GJA3	13q11–q12	mCx46	Lens
hCx47	GJA12	1q41–q42	mCx47	Brain, spinal cord
hCx50	GJA8	1q21.1	mCx50	Lens
hCx59	GJA10	1p34	—	—
hCx62	—	6q15–q16	mCx57	Ovary

[a]Orthologous genes of human and mouse connexin genes are listed in the same line.
[b]A modified nomenclature to coordinate the Greek letter nomenclature with the molecular mass nomenclature was recently proposed.[2]

connexin gene exhibits different spatially restricted patterns of expression in the embryo and adult tissues, segregation of cells into communication compartments may also arise from the differential expression of different connexin genes. However, little research has been done to clarify this hypothesis. Ruangvoravat and Lo[11] reported that in the early postimplantation mouse embryo, in which gap junctional communication is restricted to two global compartments, Cx43 is expressed exclusively in the inner cell mass-derived embryonic compartment and not in the trophectoderm-derived extraembryonic compartment.

Connexin Expression and Gap Junctional Communication in ES Cells

The *in vitro* differentiation system using ES cells provides a useful model to study gap junctional communication and connexin expression at the early stage of cell differentiation. Investigations of gap junctional communication and connexin expression have been carried out by different laboratories using pluripotent stem cell lines, including ES cells and embryonal carcinoma (EC) cells, i.e., H6, F9, and p19. The available data are summarized in the next section.

TABLE 8–2
Human Genetic Diseases Linked to Mutations in Connexin Genes and Connexin Knockout Mice

Human		Mouse	
Human Connexins (HUGO Nomenclature)	Human Genetic Diseases	Mouse Connexins	Phenotypes of Connexin Knockout Mice
hCx26 (GJB2)	Sensorineuronal deafness, palmoplantar keratoderma	mCx26	Die *in utero*, presumably because of placental dysfunction
hCx30 (GJB6)	Sensorineuronal deafness, hydrotic ectodermal dysplasia	mCx30	Hearing impairment
hCx30.3 (GJB4)	Erythrokeratodermia variabilis	mCx30.3	—
hCx31 (GJB3)	Sensorineuronal deafness, erythrokeratodermia variabilis	mCx31	Placenta, keratinocytes
hCx32 (GJB1)	X-linked Charcot-Marie-Tooth disease	mCx32	Abnormal glycogen metabolism, high incidences of liver tumors, abnormalities of peripheral nerve myelin
hCx36 (GJA9)	—	mCx36	Visual deficits
hCx37 (GJA4)	—	mCx37	Female sterility caused by ovarian dysfunction
hCx40 (GJA5)	—	mCx40	Abnormal cardiac conduction
hCx43 (GJA1)	Oculodentodigital dysplasia	mCx43	Cardiac malformation
hCx45 (GJA7)	—	mCx45	Die on ED 10.5 because of endocardial cushion defect or altered blood vessel formation
hCx46 (GJA3)	Zonular pulverulent cataract-3	mCx46	Nuclear cataracts
hCx50 (GJA8)	Zonular pulverulent cataract-1	mCx50	Nuclear cataracts, microphthalmia

GAP JUNCTIONAL COMMUNICATION AND CONNEXIN EXPRESSION IN PLURIPOTENT EMBRYONAL CARCINOMA CELLS

Formation of cell–cell junctions including gap junctions in aggregated embryonal carcinoma cells *in vitro* was first reported by Strum *et al.*[12] Under the action of supplemental calcium, H6 mouse EC cell aggregates undergo compaction similar to mouse embryonic cell compaction *in vivo*. At the 24th hour of aggregation, there is a 20-fold increase in the size of the largest gap junctions in compacted aggregates compared with the size in uncompacted aggregates.

Nishi *et al.*[13] studied the expression of products from three different connexin genes (Cx26, Cx32, and Cx43) in the mouse ES cell line CCE and during differentiation of the F9 EC cell line. In the presence of the leukemia inhibitory factor, undifferentiated ES cells express Cx43 mRNA but neither Cx26 nor Cx32, and Cx43 is localized to regions of cell–cell contact. During the differentiation of F9 cells into two different populations, i.e., parietal endoderm- and visceral endoderm-like cells, expression of Cx26, Cx32, and Cx43 is modulated. Undifferentiated F9, parietal endoderm-like, and visceral endoderm-like cells express Cx43 at very high levels. Cx26 is most abundant in the visceral endoderm-like cells, less abundant in the undifferentiated F9 cells, and barely detectable in parietal endoderm-like cells. Cx32 is detected only in the visceral endoderm-like cells. In addition, Hennemann et al.[14] detected four connexin cDNAs coding for mouse—Cx31, Cx31.1, Cx43, and Cx45—with a low level of Cx32 mRNA in a cDNA library from F9 cells. Van der Heyden et al.[15] treated F9 cells first with retinoic acid to form primitive (epithelial) or visceral endoderm and then with parathyroid hormone–related peptide to induce the transition to parietal (mesenchymal) endoderm. They demonstrated that Cx43 mRNA and protein expression levels, protein phosphorylation, and subcellular localization are dynamically regulated during F9 cell differentiation.

IN VITRO CARDIOMYOCYTE DIFFERENTIATION OF ES CELLS

Doetschman et al.[16] first reported that cystic embryoid bodies produced by ES cell lines develop rhythmically contracting, intercalated disc-containing myocardial cells in vitro, and subsequent studies on the expression of cardiac-specific genes, proteins, action potentials, and ionic channels support the conclusion that an in vitro system for differentiation of ES cells into cardiac myocytes can reproduce the cardiomyocyte development from uncommitted embryonal cells to highly specialized cellular phenotypes of the myocardium.[17] Thus, several studies on gap junctional communication and connexin expression during cardiomyocyte differentiation have been performed using this system.[18–20] Our data are shown here.

We studied the expression of connexin genes and gap junctional intercellular communication during in vitro cardiomyocyte differentiation of mouse ES cells.[18,20] When the hanging drop culture method for cardiomyocytic differentiation of ES cells in vitro is used without leukemia inhibitory factor, beating cells with somewhat cylindroid morphology are first observed in about 20% of the plated embryoid bodies at day 7 of culture. At day 9, 84% of the embryoid bodies showed beating, and this level was maintained during the observation period (up to 14 days). During the cardiomyocytic differentiation of ES cells in vitro, differential regulation of Cx40, Cx43, and Cx45 expressed in cardiomyocytes in vivo takes place. Reverse transcription-polymerase chain reaction analysis for the expression of Cx40, Cx43, and Cx45 was carried out, and the results were compared with those for heart-specific genes such as myosin heavy chain-alpha (MHC-α), MHC-β, and myosin light chain-2v (MLC-2v) (Fig. 8–2). Cx40 transcripts are not found in undifferentiated ES cells, and they are barely detectable in 3- and 5-day-old embryoid bodies. A significant increase of Cx40 transcripts is observed with the appearance of beating cells at day 7. Cx40 transcripts are also found in samples from microdissected contracting myocytes at day 14, as are MHC-α transcripts. In contrast, the expression of the major cardiac gap junction genes Cx43 and Cx45 is observed even in undifferentiated ES cells (day 0 of the culture), and these levels do not differ significantly before and after the appearance of beating cardiomyocytes (Fig. 8–2).

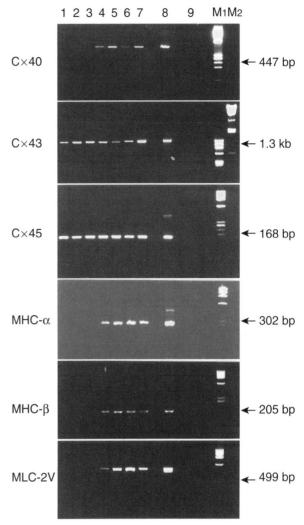

Figure 8–2. Expression of connexins and heart-specific genes during ES cell differentiation into cardiomyocytes in vitro measured by RT-PCR: Lane 1, undifferentiated ES cells; lanes 2–7, embryoid bodies on days 3, 5, 7, 9, 11, and 13; lane 8, sample from a mouse heart as a positive control; and lane 9, negative control. The sample with no RNA was reverse transcribed and PCR amplified; M1 is the molecular weight marker. The product of φX 174 plasmid DNA cut by HaeIII; M2 is the molecular weight marker. The product of λphage DNA was cut by HindIII. (Reprinted from Oyamada et al.[18] with permission from Elsevier.)

Analysis of gap junctional communication measured by microinjection of Lucifer yellow shows that undifferentiated ES cells are dye coupled with each other (mean ± SD; 5.3 ± 4.8 cells/injection, n = 18), although not all the ES cells in each colony are dye coupled. No communication is observed between STO feeder cells and undifferentiated ES cells. Dye transfer is observed among both the beating and nonbeating cells of embryoid body outgrowths. The extent of dye coupling is not significantly different in the undifferentiated ES cells, embryoid body outgrowth cells at day 5 (mean ± SD; 2.7 ± 1.2 cells/injection, n = 16) of culture, or beating cells at days 7 (mean ± SD; 2.7 ± 2.4 cells/injection, n = 7),

10 (mean ± SD; 4.0 ± 2.3 cells/injection, n = 11), and 18 (mean ± SD; 6.0 ± 4.8 cells/injection, n = 8) of culture. Interestingly, when dye is injected into a beating cell at the border, dye spread is restricted to neighboring beating cells (Fig. 8–3). Taken with the fact that prebeating cells at day 5 and the beating cells at day 7 have the least dye coupling, these data suggest that a compartmentalization of dye spread occurs during cardiomyocytic differentiation of ES cells *in vitro*. Calcium imaging using the fluorescent probe fluo 3 with confocal microscopy demonstrates that Ca^{2+} transients are synchronized among ES cell–derived beating cells (Fig. 8–4).

Immunofluorescent staining for Cx43 MHC-α/β demonstrates that Cx43 protein is localized not only in beating cells but also in surrounding nonbeating cells, whereas MHC-α/β is positive exclusively in the beating cells in the embryoid body outgrowth. Thus, the compartmentalization of dye spread during cardiomyocytic differentiation of ES cells may not result from the expression pattern of Cx43 in differentiating ES cells. Our recent study using an *in vitro* cardiomyocyte differentiation system of p19 mouse embryonal carcinoma

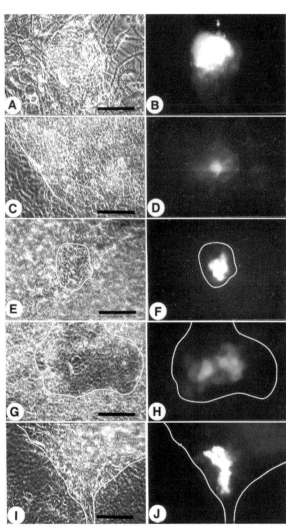

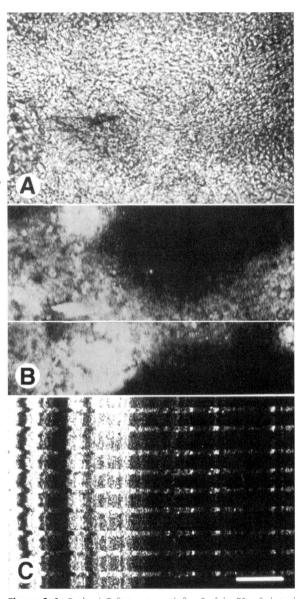

Figure 8–3. Gap junctional intercellular communication measured by the microinjection-dye transfer method with Lucifer yellow in undifferentiated ES cells cocultured with (B) STO cells, (D) cells of embryoid body outgrowth at day 5, and ES cell-derived beating cardiomyocytes at (F) day 7, (H) day 10, and (J) day 18. (A, C, E, G, and I) show the phase-contrast micrographs of the cells. (A) and (B) are taken from the same field, as are (C) and (D), (E) and (F), (G) and (H), (I) and (J). White-line borders are marked between beating cardiomyocytes and nonbeating cells. The scale bar is 25 mm. (Reprinted from Oyamada et al.[18] with permission from Elsevier.)

Figure 8–4. Confocal Ca^{2+} imaging with fluo 3 of the ES cell–derived cardiomyocytes at day 16, showing (A) the phase-contrast micrograph and (b) the two-dimensional confocal mode. This picture was taken when a Ca^{2+} transient occurred in the cells. (C) The line scan-mode analysis runs along the line indicated in (B). The horizontal scale bar is 100 μm; the vertical scale bar is 0.7 s. (Reprinted from Oyamada et al.[18] with permission from Elsevier.)

cells transfected with an enhanced green fluorescent protein-expression vector driven by an MHC-α promoter has demonstrated that most Cx40+ spots are localized in MHC-α+ cardiomyocytes, whereas Cx43+ spots are present not only in MHC-α+ cardiomyocytes but also in MHC-α−noncardiomyocytes.[20a] Thus, the establishment of a communication compartment may be related to the expression and localization of Cx40.

Knockout mice lacking Cx43 die just after birth because of cardiac malformation, indicating that Cx43 has an essential role in heart development. To determine whether lack of Cx43 expression and function influences the early stage of cardiomyocytic differentiation, the capacity to differentiate *in vitro* into cardiomyocytes of Cx43 knockout (Cx43$^{-/-}$) mouse ES cells was compared with that of wild-type ES cells.[20] *In vitro*, Cx43$^{-/-}$ ES cells differentiate into spontaneously contracting cardiomyocytes similar to the wild-type cells, although they show weak Lucifer yellow dye coupling at all stages of *in vitro* differentiation. Cx43 gene knockout does not significantly change the time course, the frequency of cardiomyocytic differentiation of ES cells *in vitro*, or expression of cardiac-specific genes. The loss of Cx43 expression does not lead to compensatory up-regulation of expression of other cardiac connexin genes, such as Cx40 and Cx45. Redundancy of the connexin gene family during the early stages of cardiomyocytic differentiation is suggested.

Banach et al.[21] recently reported that the developmental change of the conduction velocity in Cx43$^{-/-}$ ES cell–derived cardiomyocytes is different from that in wild-type ES cell-derived cardiomyocytes. At the onset of beating, both cell lines exhibit similar, slow-conduction velocities. However, the developmental increase of the conduction velocity in cultures at the later time in the wild type is threefold that in the Cx43$^{-/-}$ cell line.

In addition to mouse ES cells, data on gap junctional communication and connexin expression recently became available for human ES cells.[22] The human ES cell differentiating system generates spontaneously contracting areas in embryoid bodies, similar to those of mouse ES cells. Morphological analysis revealed an isotropic tissue of early-stage cardiac phenotype and distribution of Cx43 and Cx45 along the cell borders. High-resolution activation maps demonstrated the presence of a functional syncytium that is probably made of gap-junctional communication.

IN VITRO NEURAL DIFFERENTIATION OF PLURIPOTENT ES CELLS

Belliveau et al.[23] showed that differentiation of neurons and glial cells from pluripotent stem cells involves specific connexin expression in each cell type. They examined the expression of connexin genes during neural differentiation of the p19 EC cell line induced by retinoic acid. Untreated p19 cells express Cx26 and Cx43 but not Cx32. Treatment with retinoic acid induces the p19 cells to differentiate first into neurons and then into astrocytes. Retinoic acid decreases Cx43 mRNA, protein, and functional gap junctions, whereas Cx26

mRNA is not affected by retinoic acid treatment. Cx26 is detectable at sites of cell–cell and cell–neurite contact of MAP2+ neurons. On the other hand, Cx43 is expressed in glial fibrillary acidic protein-positive astrocytes.

Duval et al.[24] reported that during *in vitro* differentiation of embryonic neural progenitor cells (neurospheres), three distinct communication compartments are established: coupled proliferating cells in the neurosphere, uncoupled cells undergoing neuronal or oligodendrocytic differentiation, and coupled differentiating astrocytes. Lucifer yellow microinjection analysis revealed that cells located in neurospheres are strongly dye coupled, regardless of the differentiation time. On the cell layers formed by differentiated cells migrating out of the neurosphere, only astrocytes are coupled.

Transcriptional Regulation of Connexin Genes

The molecular mechanisms by which connexin expression is transcriptionally regulated are largely unknown. However, some information on ubiquitous and tissue-specific regulation of connexin genes exists.[25] For example, in many of the human and rodent connexin genes, putative or confirmed binding sites (consensus sequences) for transcription factors are identified in the promoter regions of the connexin genes. Sp-1 binding sites are found in rat and human Cx43, rat Cx26, rat Cx32, and rat Cx40 genes. TATA consensus sequence is present in mouse Cx43, rat Cx40, and mouse Cx37 genes. Activator protein 1 binding site is present in rat and human Cx43 genes and rat Cx40 genes.

Concerning tissue-specific regulation of connexin genes, it has been shown that the cardiac transcription factors Tbx5 and Nkx-2.5 interact with the binding site in the Cx40 promoter and directly activate Cx40 gene expression. In heterozygous knockout mice for Tbx5, Cx40 transcription is markedly decreased.[26] In transgenic mice expressing a DNA binding-impaired mutant of Nkx-2.5, expression of Cx40 and Cx43 is dramatically reduced in the transgenic heart.[27]

It has also been reported that Cx31 expression in keratinocytes and ES cells is regulated by different *cis*-regulatory elements, i.e., Cx31 expression in keratinocytes is regulated by a basal promoter, whereas its expression in ES cells depends on the intron sequence and the basal promoter.[28]

Perspectives

As described previously, little information is available on connexin expression in differentiating ES cells. Nevertheless, the importance of understanding the regulation of connexin expression in differentiating ES cells can be recognized not only in developmental biology but also in regenerative medicine. For example, cell transplantation therapy has been discussed as an innovative strategy for the treatment of heart failure after myocardial infarction. In this therapy, to improve the function of the diseased heart, it is necessary for grafted cardiomyocytes to display orderly and synchronous mechanical contractions coincident with the host myocardium.[29]

Thus, gap junctional communication between grafted and host cardiomyocytes plays an important role, and regulation of expression and localization of connexins is surely involved. Vascular endothelial growth factor that increases Cx43 expression in an autocrine fashion[30] is reported to enhance functional improvement of postinfarcted hearts by transplantation of differentiating ES cells.[31]

ACKNOWLEDGMENTS

This work was supported by grants-in-aid for scientific research from the Ministry of Education, Culture, Sports, Science, and Technology in Japan.

We are grateful to Aki Tominaga for her help with the manuscript and figure preparation and to Ramona Ratliff for advice on English usage.

REFERENCES

1. White, T.W., and Paul, D.L. (1999). Genetic diseases and gene knockouts reveal diverse connexin functions. *Annu. Rev. Physiol.* **61,** 283–310.
2. Sohl, G., and Willecke, K. (2003). An update on connexin genes and their nomenclature in mouse and man. *Cell Commun Adhes.* **10,** 173–180.
3. Kumar, N.M., and Gilula, N.B. (1996). The gap junction communication channel. *Cell* **84,** 381–388.
4. Verselis, V., and Veenstra, R. (2000). Gap junction channels: permeability and voltage gating. *In* "Advances in Molecular and Cell Biology: Gap Junctions," (E.L. Hertzberg, ed.), pp. 129–192. JAI Press, Stamford, CT.
5. Lo, C.W., and Gulula, N.B. (2000). Gap junctions in development. *In* "Advances in Molecular and Cell Biology: Gap Junctions," (E.L. Hertzberg, ed.), Vol. 30, pp. 193–219. JAI Press, Stamford, CT.
6. Levin, M. (2002). Isolation and community: a review of the role of gap junctional communication in embryonic patterning. *J. Membr. Biol.* **185,** 177–192.
7. Lo, C.W., and Gilula, N.B. (1979). Gap junctional communication in the preimplantation mouse embryo. *Cell* **18,** 399–409.
8. Lo, C.W., and Gilula, N.B. (1979). Gap junctional communication in the postimplantation mouse embryo. *Cell* **18,** 411–422.
9. Kalimi, G.H., and Lo, C.W. (1988). Communication compartments in the gastrulating mouse embryo. *J. Cell Biol.* **107,** 241–255.
10. Kalimi, G.H., and Lo, C.W. (1989). Gap junctional communication in the extraembryonic tissues of the gastrulating mouse embryo. *J. Cell Biol.* **109,** 3015–3026.
11. Ruangvoravat, C.P., and Lo, C.W. (1992). Connexin 43 expression in the mouse embryo: localization of transcripts within developmentally significant domains. *Dev. Dyn.* **194,** 261–281.
12. Strum, J.M., Kartha, S., and Felix, J.S. (1984). Junction formation in aggregated embryonal carcinoma cells. *Dev. Biol.* **105,** 93–101.
13. Nishi, M., Kumar, N.M., and Gilula, N.B. (1991). Developmental regulation of gap junction gene expression during mouse embryonic development. *Dev. Biol.* **146,** 117–130.
14. Hennemann, H., Schwarz, H., and Willecke, K. (1992). Characterization of gap junction genes expressed in F9 embryonic carcinoma cells: molecular cloning of mouse connexin31 and -45 cDNAs. *Eur. J. Cell Biol.* **57,** 51–58.
15. van der Heyden, M.A., Veltmaat, J.M., Hendriks, J.A., Destree, O.H., and Defize, L.H. (2000). Dynamic connexin43 expression and gap junctional communication during endoderm differentiation of F9 embryonal carcinoma cells. *Eur. J. Cell Biol.* **79,** 272–282.
16. Doetschman, T.C., Eistetter, H., Katz, M., Schmidt, W., and Kemler, R. (1985). The *in vitro* development of blastocyst-derived embryonic stem cell lines: formation of visceral yolk sac, blood islands, and myocardium. *J. Embryol. Exp. Morphol.* **87,** 27–45.
17. Boheler, K.R., Czyz, J., Tweedie, D., Yang, H.T., Anisimov, S.V., and Wobus, A.M. (2002). Differentiation of pluripotent embryonic stem cells into cardiomyocytes. *Circ. Res.* **91,** 189–201.
18. Oyamada, Y., Komatsu, K., Kimura, H., Mori, M., and Oyamada, M. (1996). Differential regulation of gap junction protein (connexin) genes during cardiomyocytic differentiation of mouse embryonic stem cells *in vitro. Exp. Cell Res.* **229,** 318–326.
19. Westfall, M.V., Pasyk, K.A., Yule, D.I., Samuelson, L.C., and Metzger, J.M. (1997). Ultrastructure and cell–cell coupling of cardiac myocytes differentiating in embryonic stem cell cultures. *Cell Motil. Cytoskeleton* **36,** 43–54.
20. Oyamada, M., Oyamada, Y., Komatsu, K., Mori, M., and Takamatsu, T. (2000). *In vitro* cardiomyocytic differentiation of mouse embryonic stem cells deficient in gap junction protein connexin43. *Cardiac Vasc. Regen.* **1,** 54–64.
20a. Oyamada, *et al.* (unpublished).
21. Banach, K., Halbach, M.D., Hu, P., Hescheler, J., and Egert, U. (2003). Development of electrical activity in cardiac myocyte aggregates derived from mouse embryonic stem cells. *Am. J. Physiol. Heart Circ. Physiol.* **284,** H2114–H2123.
22. Kehat, I., Gepstein, A., Spira, A., Itskovitz-Eldor, J., and Gepstein, L. (2002). High-resolution electrophysiological assessment of human embryonic stem cell-derived cardiomyocytes: a novel *in vitro* model for the study of conduction. *Circ. Res.* **91,** 659–661.
23. Belliveau, D.J., Bechberger, J.F., Rogers, K.A., and Naus, C.C. (1997). Differential expression of gap junctions in neurons and astrocytes derived from p19 embryonal carcinoma cells. *Dev. Genet.* **21,** 187–200.
24. Duval, N., Gomes, D., Calaora, V., Calabrese, A., Meda, P., and Bruzzone, R. (2002). Cell coupling and Cx43 expression in embryonic mouse neural progenitor cells. *J. Cell Sci.* **115,** 3241–3251.
25. Beyer, E.C., and Willecke, K. (2000). Gap junction genes and their regulation. *In* "Advances in Molecular and Cell Biology: Gap Junctions," (E.L. Hertzberg, ed.), Vol. 30, pp. 1–30. JAI Press, Stamford, CT.
26. Bruneau, B.G., Nemer, G., Schmitt, J.P., Charron, F., Robitaille, L., Caron, S., Conner, D.A., Gessler, M., Nemer, M., Seidman, C.E., and Seidman, J.G. (2001). A murine model of Holt-Oram syndrome defines roles of the T-box transcription factor Tbx5 in cardiogenesis and disease. *Cell* **106,** 709–721.
27. Kasahara, H., Wakimoto, H., Liu, M., Maguire, C.T., Converso, K.L., Shioi, T., Huang, W.Y., Manning, W.J., Paul, D., Lawitts, J., Berul, C.I., and Izumo, S. (2001). Progressive atrioventricular conduction defects and heart failure in mice expressing a mutant Csx/Nkx-2.5 homeoprotein. *J. Clin. Invest.* **108,** 189–201.
28. Plum, A., Hallas, G., and Willecke, K. (2002). Expression of the mouse gap junction gene Gjb3 is regulated by distinct mechanisms in embryonic stem cells and keratinocytes. *Genomics* **79,** 24–30.

29. Matsushita, T., Oyamada, M., Kurata, H., Masuda, S., Takahashi, A., Emmoto, T., Shiraishi, I., Wada, Y., Oka, T., and Takamatsu, T. (1999). Formation of cell junctions between grafted and host cardiomyocytes at the border zone of rat myocardial infarction. *Circulation* **100,** II262– II268.

30. Pimentel, R.C., Yamada, K.A., Kleber, A.G., and Saffitz, J.E. (2002). Autocrine regulation of myocyte Cx43 expression by VEGF. *Circ. Res.* **90,** 671–677.

31. Yang, Y., Min, J.Y., Rana, J.S., Ke, Q., Cai, J., Chen, Y., Morgan, J.P., and Xiao, Y.F. (2002). VEGF enhances functional improvement of postinfarcted hearts by transplantation of ESC-differentiated cells. *J. Appl. Physiol.* **93,** 1140–1151.

9

Cell Fusion and the Differentiated State

Penny A. Johnson and Peter W. Andrews

Introduction

Cell fusion recently surfaced as an issue and concern in analysing data from experiments designed to demonstrate the pluripotency of various adult stem cells.[1,2] However, the phenomenon of spontaneous cell fusion has been known for a considerable time, and experimentally induced cell fusion has been widely used for years, both for genetic analysis and for studies of the differentiated and determined states.

Following an initial observation by Barski et al.,[3] Sorieul and Ephrussi[4] found that the coculture of two mouse cell lines with differing marker chromosomes resulted in the appearance of a significant proportion (up to 10%) of spontaneously derived hybrid cells during about 3 months of continuous culture. Subsequently, Littlefield[5] showed that it was possible to use specific drug selection techniques to isolate such hybrid cells. Based on the earlier studies of Szybalski and Smith,[6] he introduced the hypoxanthine-aminopterin-thymidine (HAT) selection system to eliminate parental cells separately deficient in hypoxanthine phosphoribosyl transferase (HPRT) and thymidine kinase (TK). Genetic complementation resulting in expression of both enzymes allowed for survival of the hybrids. In a seminal paper using this approach to isolate spontaneous hybrids between diploid human fibroblasts and mouse L-cells, Weiss and Green[7] reported a substantial loss of human chromosomes but the retention of mouse chromosomes.

In a separate line of work, Okada[8] reported that HVJ, a mouse virus of the myxovirus group, induces cell fusion and the formation of giant polynuclear cells. Harris and Watkins[9] then showed that the UV-inactivated Sendai virus would induce cell fusion with the formation of heterokaryons that contain nuclei from two different cells. Subsequently, Pontecorvo[10] discovered that polyethylene glycol (PEG) was a more convenient agent for inducing cell fusion events.

The combination of techniques for producing hybrid cells with the common phenomenon of loss of human chromosomes in mouse–human hybrids, and with new techniques for chromosome identification, has provided a powerful approach to human genetics. Thus, by correlating the expression of human traits in such hybrids with the retention of particular human chromosomes, individual human genes could be located on specific chromosomes or even parts of chromosomes.[11,12]

Hybrid Cells and Differentiated Phenotypes

Contemporary with the development of techniques for producing hybrid cells, Gurdon et al.[13,14] demonstrated that a nucleus obtained from a differentiated cell of a tadpole, when transferred to an enucleated frog oocyte, supported the development of an adult frog. The general conclusion from these studies was that all differentiated cells retain full genetic potential for development and that the differentiated states of functionally distinct cell types must therefore arise from differential regulation of gene activity. What, then, would be the result of combining the genomes from different cell types in a single hybrid cell?

In 1965, Harris[15] described the behaviour of different nuclei in heterokaryons formed between various cell types. The most striking of these combinations was the fusion of HeLa cells with mature chicken erythrocytes in which, unlike mammalian erythrocytes, the chromatin is condensed and the nucleus is inactive. In the resulting heterokaryons, the chicken erythrocyte nuclei became active for both DNA and RNA synthesis and reexpressed chicken-specific genes.[16]

This result was confirmed and shown to be the result of cytoplasmic factors by Ladda and Estenson,[17] who found that chicken erythrocyte nuclei are also reactivated when introduced into enucleated cytoplasms. Furthermore, the reactivated chicken nucleus in cells reconstituted with fibroblast cytoplasm supported synthesis of chicken globin.[18]

However, attempts to discern general rules from the fusion of cells of different phenotypes proved difficult. Despite the results with erythrocyte heterokaryons, an early conclusion was that the fusion of cells expressing two distinct states of differentiation frequently resulted in the loss of those differentiated functions in the hybrid cells.[19] For example, hybrids formed between fibroblasts and melanomas did not produce melanin,[20] and globin synthesis was not inducible in hybrids between fibroblasts and Friend erythroleukemia cells.[21] On the other hand, hybrids between human leukocytes and mouse liver tumour cell lines sometimes expressed liver-specific proteins from the human genome contributed by the fibroblasts.[22] Similarly, rat hepatoma–mouse lymphocyte or fibroblast hybrids often expressed mouse albumin.[23,24] Separately, Minna et al.[25] produced hybrids between neuroblastoma cells, which exhibit a variety of neural features, and mouse L-cells, which are long-established, immortalised fibroblastoid cells. In their

Handbook of Stem Cells
Volume 1

experiments, the hybrid cells did retain at least some of the neural features of the neuroblastoma parental cells, notably their electrical activity.

Apart from attempting to investigate the control of specific differentiated states, Harris and his colleagues, in particular, sought to use cell hybridisation to establish the mode of genetic control of the transformed state of cancer cells. In a long series of experiments, Harris et al.[26] sought to discover whether the genetic changes that underlie the transformed state of tumour cells were the result of the loss or gain of gene function. In a conclusion that presaged the identification of tumour suppressor genes, they reported that malignancy acted as a recessive trait at the cellular level, as fusion of malignant cells with nonmalignant partners resulted in the formation of nonmalignant hybrid cells in which malignancy reappeared with subsequent chromosome loss. Clearly such a result is not always the case, as might be inferred from our current knowledge of oncogenes as well as tumour suppressor genes. Perhaps the most notable exception to this rule was the formation of immortal and tumorigenic "hybridomas" that produced monoclonal antibodies following the fusion of terminally differentiated plasma cells and a lymphoid cell line.[27]

Generally, it seemed that hybrids of cells with distinct phenotypes did not express a hybrid phenotype. Rather, they tended to express genes associated with one or other of the parent cells but not both. For example, Conscience et al.[28] described mouse hepatoma–Friend erythroleukemia hybrids, which continued expressing liver functions but in which globin expression was extinguished. Furthermore, in some cases, the gene expression typical of one parental phenotype was activated from the genome of the other parental cell. However, no clear rules emerged as to which phenotype would predominate.

The mechanisms by which one phenotype predominates over another in such hybrids largely remains poorly understood. In some cases, at least, the genome of one contributing nucleus retained the capacity for reactivation of its tissue-specific genes even when extinguished in the initial hybrid cells. For example, Weiss et al.[29] reported that in Chinese hamster fibroblast–rat hepatoma hybrids, rat liver functions were extinguished, only to reappear in some subclones on subsequent passage, possibly because of the loss of particular chromosomes. This result implies a stable modification to the genome responsible for the maintenance of its epigenetic state and not erased in hybrid cells. In other situations, experiments with phenomena such as imprinting and X-inactivation indicate that DNA methylation and histone acetylation can play a role in the heritable regulation of gene activity. Similar mechanisms are likely to play a role in the maintenance of a stable differentiated phenotype and might underlie results such as these.

On the other hand, dynamic regulatory factors must also be important, because the early heterokaryon experiments clearly suggest that any repression of gene activity can be overcome by diffusible factors. Perhaps the earliest and clearest identification of a factor that can play a role in the dynamic regulation of gene activity was the discovery of the helix–loop–helix transcription factor, MyoD. The presence of MyoD alone, introduced into a cell by transfection with appropriate expression vectors, is sufficient to activate muscle-specific genes from several distinct cell types.[30] MyoD is also subject to positive autoregulation so that, once expressed in a cell, it tends to maintain its own expression, thus establishing a dynamic system for the maintenance of the muscle-differentiated state.[31]

Nevertheless, and not surprisingly, even this story is not so simple. In some cells, MyoD is not sufficient to activate muscle gene expression[32]; other somatic cell hybrid experiments show that MyoD itself is subject to negative regulators specified by loci elsewhere in the genome.[33] If these patterns of regulation also apply to other key regulatory genes, it would not be unexpected that the outcome of fusion experiments between distinct types of differentiated cells would depend on the parental cells, the interactions of structural modifications to chromatin and DNA, and the dynamic, diffusible regulatory factors pertinent to those cells.

Hybrids of Pluripotent Cells

The behavior of hybrids of pluripotent cells has attracted considerable interest ever since lines of embryonal carcinoma (EC) cells were established in vitro. Indeed, the first description of established cultures of mouse EC cells by Finch and Ephrussi[34] reported the outcome of hybrids between the EC cells and fibroblasts; in those experiments, the fibroblast phenotype predominated.

EC cells are the malignant, pluripotent stem cells of teratocarcinomas, which occur spontaneously in male mice of the 129 strain and in young human males, as testicular tumours of germ cell origin.[35,36] Teratocarcinomas may contain an array of differentiated cell types corresponding to somatic cells of any of the three germ layers of the developing embryo or to extraembryonic cell types of the yolk sac or the trophoblast (in humans but not mice).[37,38] The stem cell status of EC cells was first clearly demonstrated experimentally by the landmark study by Kleithsmith and Pierce,[39] and the relation of these cells to the inner cell mass or primitive ectoderm of the early stages of embryonic development, at least in the mouse, became evident through a series of studies during the 1970s.[40,41] Those studies laid the foundations for the derivation of embryonic stem (ES) cells directly from the blastocyst of both mouse[42,43] and primate, including human, embryos.[44,45] ES cells are evidently the "normal" counterparts of tumour-derived EC cells in both mice and humans.[46] A closely related pluripotent cell type is the embryonic germ (EG) cell, lines of which have been derived from cultures of primordial germ cells from the genital ridges of both mouse and human embryos.

In 1976, Miller and Ruddle initiated a long series of experiments by several groups to investigate the consequences of fusing EC cells with somatic, differentiated cells. In their experiments[47,48] hybrids of EC cells with thymocytes retained an EC phenotype. Others found similar results in fusions of EC cells with various lymphoid cells. Typically, the hybrids extinguished differentiated markers of the lymphoid parents and retained pluripotency.[50,51] In several cases in which the parental EC cells had lost their ability to differentiate (nullipotent EC cells), the hybrids regained that ability.[52–55] The most likely explanation for this result is that the nullipotent EC cells had accumulated mutations that limited their ability to differentiate; such mutations would be expected to provide EC cells with a strong selective advantage because differentiation is typically accompanied by the loss of extended growth potential. Fusion with a wild-type cell could then allow genetic complementation and restore pluripotency, provided that the overall phenotype of the hybrid was that of an EC cell. Recently, we have fused a pluripotent human EC cell line, NTERA2, with a nullipotent line, 2102Ep.[56] In that case, the hybrid cells did retain an ability to differentiate, suggesting that "loss-of-function" recessive mutations in 2102Ep were principally responsible for its inability to differentiate. However, although the hybrids differentiated, they did not give rise to neural differentiation, as the parental NTERA2 cells are well documented to do. Thus, the 2102Ep cells had evidently acquired dominant mutations that interfered with expression of that particular lineage in NTERA2 cells.

One circumstance in which the extinction of the somatic cell genes was variable was expression of the class 1 major histocompatibility complex (MHC) antigens. In mouse EC cells, the MHC antigens of the H2 complex are typically not expressed,[57,58] although they are expressed in human EC cells.[59] In some hybrids with lymphoid cells, expression of the somatic parent's H2 genes was suppressed; in others, it was not.[52,60] In fusions of mouse EC cells with human lymphoid cells, most human chromosomes are lost, as generally occurs in mouse–human hybrids, and the hybrids retained an EC phenotype. However, in those retaining human chromosome 6, the human MHC antigens of the human lymphocyte antigen complex remained active.[61]

Not all combinations of EC cells with somatic cells resulted in hybrids expressing an EC phenotype. Generally, hybrids with fibroblasts or fibroblastoid cells yielded fibroblastoid hybrids,[50,52,62,63] as originally reported by Finch and Ephrussi.[34] In some hybrid combinations, for example, EC cell–hepatomas, both phenotypes were extinguished.[64] However, intriguing results were obtained in EC cell–Friend erythroleukemia cell hybrids. Such hybrids generally expressed the phenotype of the erythroleukemia cells and were inducible for globin expression, which was specified by the EC-derived genome as well as the erythroleukemia genome.[65,66] Nevertheless, when the EC cell parent was tetraploid, some hybrids retained an EC phenotype. Apparently, an increased dosage of the EC genome was sufficient to overcome the dominant effect of the erythroleukemia cell.

Reprogramming Somatic Cell Nuclei with EC, ES, or EG Cell Cytoplasm

Not only in frogs but also in mammals,[67–71] nuclear transfer into enucleated eggs has resulted in the birth of live animals and illustrates the plasticity of nuclei derived from fully differentiated somatic cells. The ability of the egg or oocyte to "reprogram" the somatic cell nucleus to such a profound extent is remarkable. These experiments raised the prospect of deriving embryonic stem cells genetically identical to a prospective patient, who might receive transplants of differentiated derivatives of those stem cells to replace diseased or damaged tissues. However, the technique is demanding and inaccessible for many researchers, and the availability of human donor eggs is limited and ethically problematic. An attractive alternative for both study and practical application would be to "reprogram" somatic cells using pluripotent ES, EG, or EC cells. However, despite the extensive earlier studies of EC–somatic cell hybrids, none clearly demonstrated reprogramming of the genome derived from the somatic cell parent. It was formally possible that the somatic genome was silenced and that maintenance of the pluripotent state was actively dependent upon continued gene expression from the EC cell-derived genome alone.

To investigate the issue of nuclear reprogramming further, Tada et al.[72] fused murine EG cells with thymocytes from transgenic mice carrying a neo^R/lacZ transgene. From this fusion, EG–thymocyte hybrids expressing lacZ and drug resistance were isolated. They retained the morphology of the EG partner. Furthermore, when injected into blastocysts, the lacZ-expressing hybrids contributed to the development of tissues corresponding to all three germ layers. Similar experiments were conducted using transgenic mouse thymocytes engineered to express green fluorescent protein (GFP) under the transcriptional control of the Oct-4 promoter.[73] Because Oct-4 is transcribed exclusively in germ cells, early embryos, and ES and EC cells, GFP should only be expressed when reprogramming of the thymocyte nucleus occurred. As expected, the Oct-4-driven GFP gene was transcriptionally silent in the parental thymocytes but activated in the resulting ES–thymocyte hybrids. In addition, in both ES and EG hybrids with female thymocytes and in similar EC hybrids,[74] reactivation of the inactive thymocyte X-chromosome was observed. That the ability for reprogramming is conserved between species was demonstrated in reciprocal fusions using mouse or human EC cells and cells of lymphocytic origin.[75] Hybrids formed from fusion of the human T-cell line, CEM C7A, to mouse p19 EC cells expressed the endogenous human Oct-4 and Sox2 genes and adopted the morphology of the murine EC cells, with a high nuclear: cytoplasm ratio, prominent nucleoli, and growth in tight, well-defined adherent colonies.[75] In the murine EC–human T-lymphocytes, there was considerable heterogeneity of expression between colonies and within a single colony over time. Thus, expression of human markers of cells of endoderm (collagen IV, laminin B1) and ectoderm (nestin) origin was noted in colonies that also expressed Oct-4 and Sox2. These data suggest that cross-species reprogramming had occurred in the hybrids and that subsequent spontaneous differentiation resulted in the human partner expressing the potential to adopt a fate not previously available to it.[75] The reciprocal cross, using human 2102Ep EC cells and murine thymocytes, resulted in expression of the endogenous murine Oct-4 gene (unpublished data). Collectively, these data demonstrate that the ability to reprogram somatic nuclei is not the exclusive domain of the egg and oocyte but can also be achieved by pluripotent ES, EG, and EC cells.

Interestingly, in the experiments by Tada et al.,[72,73] although both EG and ES cells were shown to be capable of reprogramming thymocytes, the two cell types displayed different capacities for erasure of imprints. Imprinted genes are those for which the maternal and paternal alleles exhibit differential expression in somatic cells. Imprinting is established during gametogenesis and most likely involves methylation at specific loci. After fertilisation, the imprinted pattern of those specific genes is retained in all cells of the developing embryo except that, necessarily, such imprints are erased in the primordial germ cells (PGCs) and are reinstated prior to the completion of gametogenesis in preparation for the next generation. Thus, in ES cells derived from the blastocyst, monoallelic expression of imprinted genes is evident, but imprinting is absent from EG cells that have been derived from PGC after imprints have been erased. In EG–thymocyte hybrids, the H19 and p57Kip2 loci, normally methylated on the paternal allele and preferentially expressed from the maternal allele in thymocytes, were denuded of the paternal imprints. Similarly, the maternally methylated Peg1/Mest allele was demethylated in the EG–thymocyte hybrids, and both maternal and paternal alleles were expressed. Furthermore, ordinarily methylated but not imprinted genes, such as Aprt, Pgk2, and globin, were demethylated in these hybrids just as they are in PGCs. Thus, the EG cells appeared to possess the same capacity as PGC to erase imprints. By contrast, methylation at the imprinted loci, H19 and Igf2r, was maintained in ES–thymocyte hybrids.[73] Similarly, Forejt et al.[76] found that imprinting was not erased in EC–thymocyte hybrids, although the nonimprinted allele, normally silent in thymocytes, was expressed in the hybrids. These data strongly suggested that although extensive remodelling of the chromatin sufficient to establish pluripotency occurred, reprogramming did not extend to imprinting if the pluripotent partner itself retained imprinting. Tada et al.[73] further demonstrated that erasure of imprints is dominant in ES–EG hybrids.

These observations on epigenetic imprinting in stem cell hybrids have relevance to the development of embryos derived after somatic nuclear transfer to enucleated oocytes, and fusions using ES, EG, and EC cells may serve as useful models of the process. The efficiency with which somatic nuclei generate living clones is notoriously low. Dolly the sheep, the first mammal cloned from a fully differentiated adult cell nucleus, was the single success in more than 300 nuclear transfer experiments.[67,71] Epigenetic abnormalities because of inappropriate imprinting are probably one important reason for the poor success rate and questionable health of clones living to term. Bortvin et al.[77] demonstrated that a constellation of 70–80 genes is inappropriately expressed in mouse embryos cloned from adult nuclei. In addition, many cloned embryos are subject to developmental abnormalities indicative of faulty imprinting at several loci.[78] During normal embryogenesis, PGCs, which eventually differentiate into male or female gametes, are erased of imprinting; during the

development of the gametes in embryos resulting from normal fertilisation, correct imprinting is reestablished. However, because a cloned individual does not result from fertilisation by mature sperm of an egg but rather from a donated diploid nucleus injected into an enucleate egg, the process of erasure and reinstatement of correct imprinting never occurs. The cell fusion experiments using ES, EG, and EC cells previously described may help to elucidate the process of imprinting and reprogramming and to provide further information about why embryo cloning is a risky and inefficient process.

Cell Fusion and the Demonstration of Stem Cell Plasticity

Recently, there have been a myriad of discussions and reports regarding adult stem cells and what appears to be their capacity not only to regenerate their own tissue of origin but also to regenerate lineages other than those from which they derive. Thus haematopoietic stem cells and mesenchymal stem cells have been observed to generate neurons,[79] muscle,[80] hepatocytes,[81–83] and a host of other tissues.[84] Similarly, foetal neural cells have been reported to create haematopoietic and other tissues.[85,86] A degree of controversy has surrounded these reports, and scientists have been at pains to design experiments that unequivocally demonstrate a single such adult stem cell can generate cells of more than one lineage.

Cell fusion occurs spontaneously under appropriate conditions in vivo, as well as in vitro, and in vivo can be a normal physiological process during the development of several organs and tissues. For example, myoblast–myoblast and myoblast–myotube fusions occur as part of normal skeletal muscle development,[87,88] and fusion of trophoblast cells to form the giant cells occurs in the development of the placenta.[89] Recent genetic studies in Drosophila and Caenorhabditis elegans have determined some of the genes required for developmental fusion events.[90]

The existence of genetically regulated, physiologically relevant cell fusion in vivo, as well as evidence of reprogramming of somatic cells following cell fusion, may confound many of the observations of adult stem cell plasticity. Two separate examples have recently reported that spontaneous fusion of cells, in the absence of an external fusogenic agent, can occur between populations of pluripotent stem cells and other cell types kept in cocultures, echoing the much earlier observations of Barski and Ephrussi. Terada et al.[1] used mixed cultures of murine ES and genetically tagged bone marrow cells under conditions favouring the outgrowth of hybrids to demonstrate that ES–bone marrow hybrids could be isolated at a frequency of 10^{-5}–10^{-6}. Spontaneous fusion was dependent on the presence of IL-3 and the leukaemia inhibitory factor, which obligate cytokines for haematopoietic lineages and the maintenance of pluripotency and self-renewal in ES cells, respectively. In similar experiments using mixed cultures of murine ES and genetically marked cells taken from fetal and adult mouse brain, Ying et al.[2] observed spontaneous hybrid formation at 10-fold frequency. In both reports, resulting hybrids displayed the morphology and pluripotency of the

ES partner. Where once the somatic partner in these hybrids was restricted in its developmental fate to producing the repertoire of haematopoietic lineages or central nervous system lineages, respectively, fusion with the ES cell allowed expression of new potential fates. These spontaneously formed hybrid cells were capable of contributing to all three germ layers after injection into blastocysts. Thus in any demonstration of lineage plasticity of adult stem cells, it becomes important to rule out the possibility of fusion with another endogenous pluripotent stem cell that reprograms the test cell.

A further development in cell fusion has recently been documented in two reports[91,92] examining the nature of hepatocytes derived from haematopoietic stem cells, previously one of the most robust arguments for adult stem cell plasticity.[82] Using mice engineered to be susceptible to liver degeneration through tyrosinaemia because of ablation of the fumarylacetoacetate hydrolase gene, Lagasse and co-workers elegantly demonstrated unequivocal regeneration of hepatocytes from transplanted, lineage-depleted bone marrow. However, ordinarily, the liver contains a subset of polyploid cells, suggesting that cell fusion may be a characteristic feature of this organ. The two follow-up studies report that the hepatocyte outgrowth as a result of haematopoietic stem cell transplantation was almost certainly because of fusion of haematopoietic cells with preexisting hepatocytes. In the study by Wang et al.,[92] some of the regenerated liver cells were diploid rather than tetraploid, as would be expected when two diploid cells fuse. This suggests that it is possible to generate a diploid cell from a tetraploid hybrid and still maintain the reprogrammed phenotype.

The identity of the fusion partner derived from bone marrow was not determined in these reports; nevertheless, the authors speculate that it is probably not the haematopoietic stem cell itself but a later progenitor. In the liver regeneration model, the authors speculate that the haematopoietic partner cells are phagocytic Kupffer cells,[91] macrophages, B- or T-cells,[92] a view supported by finding that liver regeneration occurred after the haematopoietic lineages had been repopulated. However, because liver injury did not mobilise a similar response, it is unlikely that this is a generalised response to tissue damage;[93] rather, it may be the result of the artificial constraints of the experimental design. Others have observed indications of engraftment in distant tissues by cells introduced during the transplantation of donated organs or tissues. For example, Y-chromosome-positive cells with apparent neuronal[94] or cardiomyocyte[95] function have been noted in the brains and hearts, respectively, of female bone marrow transplant recipients. These observations have been interpreted as evidence of transdifferentiation of the incoming donor cells and subsequent population of host organs. However, given the findings described previously, it now seems plausible that these may have been the result of spontaneous fusion[96] of host and donor cells.

Summary

The study and use of cell fusion has an extensive history. It has been an invaluable tool in somatic cell genetics, and it has

highlighted the complexity of the mechanisms that regulate the maintenance of the determined and differentiated states. Although it is difficult to make strong claims that the study of cell hybrids has contributed substantially to understanding those mechanisms, the ability of pluripotent stem cells to reprogram somatic nuclei to a primitive, pluripotent state increases the potential of achieving somatic cell reprogramming in an efficient manner for therapeutic purposes without resorting to nuclear transfer to oocytes—so-called therapeutic cloning. The phenomenon of spontaneous fusion is also an issue that now has to be addressed in the analysis of any claims for plasticity of otherwise lineage-restricted, adult stem cells.

ACKNOWLEDGMENTS

This work was supported partly by grants from the Wellcome Trust, Yorkshire Cancer Research and the BBSRC.

REFERENCES

1. Terada, N., Hamazaki, T., Oka, M., Hoki, M., Mastalerz, D.M., Nakano, Y., Meyer, E.M., Morel, L., Petersen, B.E., Scott, E.W. (2002). Bone marrow cells adopt the phenotype of other cells by spontaneous cell fusion. *Nature* **416**, 542–545.

2. Ying, Q.L., Nichols, J., Evans, E.P., and Smith, A.G. (2002). Changing potency by spontaneous fusion. *Nature* **416**, 545–548.

3. Barski, G., Sorieul, S., and Cornefert, F. (1960). Production dans des cultures *in vitro* de deux souche cellulaires en association, de cellules de charactere "hybrids." *C.R. Acad. Sci. (Paris)* **251**, 1825–1830.

4. Sorieul, S., and Ephrussi, B. (1961). Karyological demonstration of hybridisation of mammalian cells *in vitro*. *Nature* **190**, 653–654.

5. Littlefield, J.W. (1964). Selection of hybrids from matings of fibroblasts *in vitro* and their presumed recombinants. *Science* **145**, 709–710.

6. Szybalski, W., and Smith, M.J. (1959). Genetics of human cell lines: I. 8-Azaguanine resistance, a selective "single step" marker. *Proc. Soc. Exp. Biol. Med.* **101**, 662–666.

7. Weiss, M.C., and Green, H. (1967). Human–mouse hybrid cell lines containing partial complements of human chromosomes and functioning human genes. *Proc. Natl. Acad. Sci. USA* **58**, 1104–1111.

8. Okada, Y. (1962). Analysis of giant polynuclear cell formation caused by HJV virus from Ehrlich's ascites tumour cells. *Exp. Cell Res.* **26**, 98–107.

9. Harris, H., and Watkins, J.F. (1965). Hybrid cells derived from mouse and man; artificial heterokaryons of mammalian cells from different species. *Nature* **205**, 640–646.

10. Pontecorvo, G. (1975). Production of mammalian somatic cell hybrids by means of polyethylene glycol treatment. *Somatic Cell Genet.* **1**, 397–400.

11. Nabholz, M., Miggiano, V., and Bodmer, W. (1969). Genetic analysis with human–mouse somatic cell hybrids. *Nature* **223**, 358–363.

12. Ruddle, F.H., Chapman, V.M., Chen, T.R., and Klebe, R.J. (1970). Genetic analysis with man–mouse somatic cell hybrids: linkage between human lactate dehydrogenase A and B and peptidase B. *Nature* **227**, 251–257.

13. Gurdon, J.B. (1962). The developmental capacity of nuclei taken from intestinal epithelial cells of feeding tadpoles. *J. Embryol. Exp. Morph.* **10**, 622–640.

14. Gurdon, J.B., and Uehlinger, V. (1966). "Fertile" intestine nuclei. *Nature* **210**, 1240–1241.

15. Harris, H. (1965). Behaviour of differentiated nuclei in heterokaryons of animal cells from different species. *Nature* **206**, 583–588.

16. Harris, H., Sidebottom, E., Grace, D.M., and Bramwell, M.E. (1969). The expression of genetic information: a study with hybrid animal cells. *J. Cell Science* **4**, 499–525.

17. Ladda, R.L., and Estenson, R.D. (1970). Introduction of a heterologous nucleus into enucleated cytoplasms of cultivated mouse L-cells. *Proc. Natl. Acad. Sci. USA* **67**, 1528–1533.

18. Ege, T., Zeuthen, J., and Ringertz, N.R. (1975). Reactivation of chick erythrocyte nuclei after fusion with enucleated cells. *Somatic Cell Genet.* **1**, 65–80.

19. Davidson, R.L. (1973). Control of the differentiated state in somatic cell hybrids. *Symp. Soc. Dev. Biol.* **31**, 295–328.

20. Davidson, R., Ephrussi, B., and Yamamoto, K. (1968). Regulation of melanin synthesis in mammalian cells, as studied by somatic hybridization: I. Evidence for negative control. *J. Cell Physiol.* **72**, 115–127.

21. Deisseroth, A., Velez, R., Burk, R.D., Minna, J., Anderson, W.F., and Nienhuis, A. (1976). Extinction of globin gene expression in human fibroblast–mouse erythroleukemia cell hybrids. *Somatic Cell Genet.* **2**, 373–384.

22. Darlington, G.J., Bernard, H.P., and Ruddle, F.H. (1974). Human serum albumin phenotype activation in mouse hepatoma–human leukocyte cell hybrids. *Science* **185**, 859–862.

23. Malawista, S.E., and Weiss, M.C. (1974). Expression of differentiated functions in hepatoma cell hybrids: high frequency of induction of mouse albumin production in rat hepatoma–mouse lymphoblast hybrids. *Proc. Natl. Acad. Sci. USA* **71**, 927–931.

24. Peterson, J.A., and Weiss, M.C. (1972). Expression of differentiated functions in hepatoma cell hybrids: Induction of mouse albumin production in rat hepatoma–mouse fibroblast hybrids. *Proc. Natl. Acad. Sci. USA* **69**, 571–575.

25. Minna, J., Nelson, P., Peacock, J., Glazer, D., and Nirenberg, M. (1971). Genes for neuronal properties expressed in neuroblastoma–L cell hybrids. *Proc. Natl. Acad. Sci. USA* **68**, 234–239.

26. Weiner, F., Klein, G., and Harris, H. (1971). The analysis of malignancy by cell fusion: III. Hybrids between diploid fibroblasts and other tumour cells. *J. Cell Sci.* **8**, 681–692.

27. Kohler, G., and Milstein, C. (1975). Continuous cultures of fused cells secreting antibody of predefined specificity. *Nature* **256**, 495–497.

28. Conscience, J.F., Ruddle, F.H., Skoultchi, A., and Darlington, G.J. (1977). Somatic cell hybrids between Friend erythroleukemia cells and mouse hepatoma cells. *Somatic Cell Genet.* **3**, 157–172.

29. Weiss, M.C., Sparkes, R.S., and Bertolotti, R. (1975). Expression of differentiated functions in hepatoma cell hybrids: IX. Extinction and reexpression of liver-specific enzymes in rat hepatoma–Chinese hamster fibroblast hybrids. *Somatic Cell Genet.* **1**, 27–40.

30. Weintraub, H., Tapscott, S.J., Davis, R.L., Thayer, M.J., Adam, M.A., Lassar, A.B., and Miller, A.D. (1989). Activation of muscle-specific genes in pigment, nerve, fat, liver, and fibroblast cell lines by forced expression of MyoD. *Proc. Natl. Acad. Sci. USA* **86**, 5434–5438.

31. Thayer, M.J., Tapscott, S.J., Davis, R.L., Wright, W.E., Lassar, A.B., and Weintraub, H. (1989). Positive autoregulation of the myogenic determination gene MyoD1. *Cell* **58**, 241–248.

32. Schafer, B.W., Blakely, B.T., Darlington, G.J., and Blau, H.M. (1990). Effect of cell history on response to helix–loop–helix family of myogenic regulators. *Nature* **344**, 454–458.

33. Thayer, M.J., and Weintraub, H. (1990). Activation and repression of myogenesis in somatic cell hybrids: evidence for transnegative regulation of MyoD in primary fibroblasts. *Cell* **63**, 23–32.

34. Finch, B.W., and Ephrussi, B. (1967). Retention of multiple developmental potentialities by cells of a mouse testicular teratocarcinomas during prolonged culture *in vitro* and their extinction upon hybridisation with cells of permanent lines. *Proc. Natl. Acad. Sci. USA* **57**, 615–621.

35. Stevens, L.C. (1967). The biology of teratomas. *Adv. Morphol.* **6**, 1–31.

36. Skakkebaek, N.E., Berthelsen, J.G., Giwercman, A., and Müller, J. (1987). Carcinoma *in situ* of the testis: Possible origin from gonocytes and precursor of all types of germ cell tumours except spermatocytoma. *Int. J. Androl.* **10**, 19–28.

37. Damjanov, I., and Solter, D. (1974). Experimental teratoma. *Curr. Top. Path.* **59**, 69–130.

38. Mostofi, F.K., and Price, E.B. (1973). "Atlas of Tumour Pathology: Tumours of the male genital system," Second series, Fascicle 8. Armed Forces Institute of Pathology, Washington DC.

39. Kleinsmith, L.J., and Pierce, G.B. (1964). Multipotentiality of single embryonal carcinoma cells. *Cancer Res.* **24**, 1544–1552.

40. Jacob, F. (1978). Mouse teratocarcinoma and mouse embryo. *Proc. Roy. Soc. (Lond)* **B201**, 249–270.

41. Martin, G.R. (1980). Teratocarcinomas and mammalian embryogenesis. *Science* **209**, 768–776.

42. Evans, M.J., and Kaufman, M.H. (1981). Establishment in culture of pluripotential cells from mouse embryos. *Nature* **292**, 154–156.

43. Martin, G.R. (1981). Isolation of a pluripotent cell line from early mouse embryos cultured in medium conditioned by teratocarcinoma stem cells. *Proc. Natl. Acad. Sci. USA* **78**, 7634–7638.

44. Thomson, J.A., Kalishman, J., Golos, T.G., Durning, M., Harris, C.P., Becker, R.A., and Hearn, J.P. (1995). Isolation of a primate embryonic stem cell line. *Proc. Natl. Acad. Sci. USA* **92**, 7844–7848.

45. Thomson, J.A., Itskovitz-Eldor, J., Shapiro, S.S., Waknitz, M.A., Swiergiel, J.J., Marshall, V.S., and Jones, J.M. (1998). Embryonic stem cell lines derived from human blastocysts. *Science* **282**, 1145–1147.

46. Andrews, P.W. (2002). From teratocarcinomas to embryonic stem cells. *Phil. Trans. R. Soc. (Lond)* **B357**, 405–417.

47. Miller, R.A., and Ruddle, F.H. (1976). Pluripotent teratocarcinomas–thymus somatic cell hybrids. *Cell* **9**, 45–55.

48. Miller, R.A., and Ruddle, F.H. (1977). Properties of teratocarcinoma–thymus somatic cell hybrids. *Somatic Cell Genet.* **3**, 247–261.

49. Miller, R.A., and Ruddle, F.H. (1977). Teratocarcinoma–Friend erythroleukemia cell hybrids resemble their pluripotent embryonal carcinoma parent. *Dev. Biol.* **56**, 157–173.

50. Rousset, J.P., Dubois, P., Lasserre, C., Aviles, D., Fellous, M., and Jami, J. (1979). Phenotype and surface antigens of mouse teratocarcinoma–fibroblast cell hybrids. *Somatic Cell Genet.* **5**, 739–752.

51. Rousset, J.P., Jami, J., Dubois, P., Aviles, D., and Ritz, E. (1980). Developmental potentialities and surface antigens of mouse teratocarcinoma–lymphoid cell hybrids. *Somatic Cell Genet.* **6**, 419–433.

52. Andrews, P.W., and Goodfellow, P.N. (1980). Antigen expression by somatic cell hybrids of a murine embryonal carcinoma cell with thymocytes and L-cells. *Somatic Cell Genet.* **6**, 271–284.

53. Rousset, J.P., Bucchini, D., and Jami, J. (1983). Hybrids between F9 nullipotent teratocarcinomas and thymus cells produce multi-differentiated tumours in mice. *Dev. Biol.* **96**, 331–336.

54. Rosenstraus, M.J., Balint, R.F., and Levine, A.J. (1980). Pluripotency of somatic cell hybrids between nullipotent and pluripotent embryonal carcinoma cells. *Somatic Cell Genet.* **6**, 555–565.

55. Atsumi, T., Shirayoshi, Y., Takeichi, M., and Okada, T.S. (1982). Nullipotent teratocarcinoma cells acquire the pluripotency for differentiation by fusion with somatic cells. *Differentiation* **23**, 83–86.

56. Duran, C., Talley, P.J., Walsh, J., Pigott, C., Morton, I., and Andrews, P.W. (2001). Hybrids of pluripotent and nullipotent human embryonal carcinoma cells: partial retention of a pluripotent phenotype. *Int. J. Cancer* **93**, 324–332.

57. Artzt, K., and Jacob, F. (1974). Absence of serologically detectable H2 on primitive teratocarcinoma cells in culture. *Transplantation* **17**, 632–634.

58. Morello, D., Gachelin, G., Dubois, P., Tanigaki, N., Pressman, D., and Jacob, F. (1978). Absence of reaction of a xenogenic anti-H2 serum with mouse embryonal carcinoma cells. *Transplantation* **26**, 119–125.

59. Andrews, P.W., Bronson, D.L., Wiles, M.V., and Goodfellow, P.N. (1981). The expression of major histocompatibility antigens by human teratocarcinoma derived cells lines. *Tissue Antigens* **17**, 493–500.

60. Gmür, R., Solter, D., and Knowles, B.B. (1980). Independent regulation of H2-K and H2-D gene expression in murine teratocarcinomas somatic cell hybrids. *J. Exp. Med.* **151**, 1349–1358.

61. Benham, F.J., Quintero, M.A., and Goodfellow, P.N. (1983). Human–mouse hybrids with an embryonal carcinoma phenotype continue to transcribe HLA-A,B,C. *EMBO J.* **2**, 1963–1968.

62. Jami, J., Failly, C., and Ritz, E. (1973). Lack of expression of differentiation in mouse teratoma–fibroblast somatic cell hybrids. *Exp. Cell Res.* **76**, 191–199.

63. McBurney, M.W., and Strutt, B. (1979). Fusion of embryonal carcinoma cells to fibroblast cells, cytoplasts, and karyoplasts: developmental properties of viable fusion products. *Exp. Cell Res.* **124**, 171–180.

64. Litwack, G., and Croce, C.M. (1979). Somatic cell hybrids between totipotent mouse teratocarcinoma and rat hepatoma cells. *J. Cell Physiol.* **101**, 1–8.

65. McBurney, M.W. (1977). Haemoglobin synthesis in cell hybrids formed between teratocarcinomas and Friend erythroleukemia cells. *Cell* **12**, 653–662.

66. McBurney, M.W., Featherstone, M.S., and Kaplan, H. (1978). Activation of teratocarcinoma-derived haemoglobin genes in teratocarcinoma–Friend cell hybrids. *Cell* **15**, 1323–1330.

67. Campbell, K.H., McWhir, J., Ritchie, W.A., and Wilmut, I. (1996). Sheep cloned by nuclear transfer from a cultured cell line. *Nature* **380**, 64–66.

68. Wells, D.N., Misica, P.M., Day, A.M., Peterson, A.J., and Tervit, H.R. (1998). Cloning sheep from cultured embryonic cells. *Reprod. Fertil. Dev.* **10**, 615–626.

69. Polejaeva, I.A., Chen, S.H., Vaught, T.D., Page, R.L., Mullins, J., Ball, S., Dai, Y., Boone, J., Walker, S., Ayares, D.L., Colman, A., and Campbell, K.H. (2000). Cloned pigs produced by nuclear transfer from adult somatic cells. *Nature* **407**, 86–90.

70. Wakayama, T., Rodriguez, I., Perry, A.C., Yanagimachi, R., and Mombaerts, P. (1999). Mice cloned from embryonic stem cells. *Proc. Natl. Acad. Sci. USA* **96**, 14,984–14,989.

71. Wilmut, I., Schnieke, A.E., McWhir, J., Kind, A.J., and Campbell, K.H. (1997). Viable offspring derived from fetal and adult mammalian cells. *Nature* **385**, 810–813.

72. Tada, M., Tada, T., Lefebvre, L., Barton, S.C., and Surani, M.A. (1997). Embryonic germ cells induce epigenetic reprogramming of somatic nucleus in hybrid cells. *EMBO J.* **16**, 6510–6520.

73. Tada, M., Takahama, Y., Abe, K., Nakatsuji, N., and Tada, T. (2001). Nuclear reprogramming of somatic cells by *in vitro* hybridization with ES cells. *Curr. Biol.* **11**, 1553–1558.

74. Takagi, N., Yoshida, M.A., Sugawara, O., and Sasaki, M. (1983). Reversal of X-inactivation in female mouse somatic cells hybridized with murine teratocarcinoma stem cells *in vitro*. *Cell* **34**, 1053–1062.

75. Flasza, M., Shering, A.F., Andrews, P.W., Talley, P., and Johnson, P.A. (2003). Reprogramming in interspecies embryonal carcinoma– somatic cell hybrids induces expression of pluripotency and differentiation markers. *Cloning Stem Cells* **5**, 339–354.

76. Forejt, J., Saam, J.R., Gregorova, S., and Tilghman, S.M. (1999). Monoallelic expression of reactivated imprinted genes in embryonal carcinoma cell hybrids. *Exp. Cell Res.* **252**, 416–422.

77. Bortvin, A., Eggan, K., Skaletsky, H., Akutsu, H., Berry, D.L., Yanagimachi, R., Page, D.C., and Jaenisch, R. (2003). Incomplete reactivation of Oct-4-related genes in mouse embryos cloned from somatic nuclei. *Development* **130**, 1673–1680.

78. Rideout, I.W., Eggan, K., and Jaenisch, R. (2001). Nuclear cloning and epigenetic reprogramming of the genome. *Science* **293**, 1093–1098.

79. Brazelton, T.R., Rossi, F.M., Keshet, G.I., and Blau, H.M. (2000). From marrow to brain: expression of neuronal phenotypes in adult mice. *Science* **290**, 1775–1779.

80. Ferrari, G., Cusella-De Angelis, G., Coletta, M., Paolucci, E., Stornaiuolo, A., Cossu, G., and Mavilio, F. (1998). Muscle regeneration by bone marrow-derived myogenic progenitors. *Science* **279**, 1528–1530.

81. Alison, M.R., Poulsom, R., Jeffery, R., Dhillon, A.P., Quaglia, A., Jacob, J., Novelli, M., Prentice, G., Williamson, J., and Wright, N.A. (2000). Hepatocytes from nonhepatic adult stem cells. *Nature* **406**, 257.

82. Lagasse, E., Connors, H., Al-Dhalimy, M., Reitsma, M., Dohse, M., Osborne, L., Wang, X., Finegold, M., Weissman, I.L., and Grompe, M. (2000). Purified hematopoietic stem cells can differentiate into hepatocytes *in vivo*. *Nat. Med.* **6**, 1229–1234.

83. Theise, N.D., Nimmakayalu, M., Gardner, R., Illei, P.B., Morgan, G., Teperman, L., Henegariu, O., and Krause, D.S. (2000). Liver from bone marrow in humans. *Hepatology* **32**, 11–16.

84. Krause, D.S., Theise, N.D., Collector, M.I., Henegariu, O., Hwang, S., Gardner, R., Neutzel, S., and Sharkis, S.J., (2001). Multiorgan, multilineage engraftment by a single bone marrow-derived stem cell. *Cell* **105**, 369–377.

85. Bjornson, C.R., Rietze, R.L., Reynolds, B.A., Magli, M.C., and Vescovi, A.L. (1999). Turning brain into blood: a hematopoietic fate adopted by adult neural stem cells *in vivo*. *Science* **283**, 534–537.

86. Clarke, D.L., Johansson, C.B., Wilbertz, J., Veress, B., Nilsson, E., Karlstrom, H., et al. (2000). Generalized potential of adult neural stem cells. *Science* **288**, 1660–1663.

87. Hughes, S.M., and Blau, H.M. (1992). Muscle fibre pattern is independent of cell lineage in postnatal rodent development. *Cell* **68**, 659–671.

88. Taylor, M.V. (2002). Muscle differentiation: how two cells become one. *Curr. Biol.* **12**, R224–R228.

89. Bischof, P., Meisser, A., and Campana, A. (2000). Paracrine and autocrine regulators of trophoblast invasion—a review. *Placenta* **21 Suppl. A,** S55–S60.

90. Witze, E., and Rothman, J.H. (2002). Cell fusion: An efficient sculptor. *Curr. Biol.* **12,** R467–R469.

91. Vassilopoulos, G., Wang, P.R., and Russell, D.W. (2003). Transplanted bone marrow regenerates liver by cell fusion. *Nature* **422,** 901–904.

92. Wang, X., Willenbring, H., Akkari, Y., Torimaru, Y., Foster, M., Al-Dhalimy, M., Lagasse, E., Finegold, M., Olson, S., and Grompe, M. (2003). Cell fusion is the principal source of bone marrow-derived hepatocytes. *Nature* **422,** 897–901.

93. Wang, X., Montini, E., Al-Dhalimy, M., Lagasse, E., Finegold, M., and Grompe, M. (2002). Kinetics of liver repopulation after bone marrow transplantation. *Am. J. Pathol.* **161,** 565–574.

94. Mezey, E., Key, S., Vogelsang, G., Szalayova, I., Lange, G.D., and Crain, B. (2003). Transplanted bone marrow generates new neurons in human brains. *Proc. Natl. Acad. Sci. USA* **100,** 1364–1369

95. Deb, A., Wang, S., Skelding, K.A., Miller, D., Simper, D., and Caplice, N.M. (2003). Bone marrow-derived cardiomyocytes are present in adult human heart: a study of gender-mismatched bone marrow transplantation patients. *Circulation* **107,** 1247–1249.

96. Pells, S., Di Domenico, A.I., Callagher, E.J., and McWhir, J. (2002). Multipotentiality of neuronal cells after spontaneous fusion with embryonic stem cells and nuclear reprogramming *in vitro. Cloning Stem Cells* **4,** 331–338.

Nuclear Cloning and Epigenetic Reprogramming

Zhongde Wang, Alexander Meissner, and Rudolf Jaenisch

Introduction

Successful cloning by nuclear transfer (NT) requires the reprogramming of a differentiated genome into a totipotent state that can reinitiate normal embryogenesis (Fig. 10–1). Embryonic genes silenced in the donor nucleus must be reactivated, and donor nucleus specific genes detrimental to the totipotent state need to be silenced. A chromatin structure that ensures such gene expression patterns has to be established in the donor genome. This process, broadly defined as epigenetic reprogramming, must occur within hours to a few days following NT to allow the development of a reconstructed embryo. Faulty epigenetic reprogramming in cloned embryos leads to widespread irregularities in gene expression that might result in the developmental abnormalities and embryonic lethality frequently observed in cloning.[1] Indeed, cloning by NT is characterized by extremely low efficiency in all species to which this technique has been applied.[2] Most clones die before birth, and the rare clones that survive to term or adulthood display a range of developmental abnormalities. Among these abnormalities are circulatory problems, respiratory distress, obesity, immune dysfunction, kidney or brain malformation, and early death.[3–8] Notably, an increase in placental and birth weight, a cross-species phenotype referred to as large offspring syndrome (LOS), is often observed.[9–11] At present, little is known about the events that take place during reprogramming and the molecules in the egg cytoplasm responsible for this process.

A better understanding of the molecular mechanisms governing epigenetic reprogramming would provide great insights into the developmental abnormalities associated with cloning. In this chapter, we discuss recent advances in understanding the molecular and cellular aspects of epigenetic reprogramming following NT. We begin by reviewing the role of DNA methylation, a key epigenetic modification known to control normal development and gene expression. Then, we discuss the aberrant DNA methylation patterns observed in clones and how they might lead to abnormalities in the animals. Finally, we review what is known about factors that may affect epigenetic reprogramming.

Epigenetics and Epigenetic Reprogramming in Cloning

After fertilization, the genetic content of a zygote is inherited by all somatic cells of the developing organism. However, only a subset of the genes is active in a given cell type. For normal development to proceed, it is essential to turn on the appropriate genes and turn off genes not required in a particular cell. This process generally involves DNA methylation and chromatin modifications that impose stable but reversible marks on the genome. Such stable alterations resulting in differential gene expression are often referred to as *epigenetic.*[12]

Because each somatic nucleus within an organism has acquired a certain tissue-specific epigenetic state during development, cloning from somatic cells requires the resetting of a differentiated nucleus to a totipotent, embryonic ground state.[11] One likely explanation for cloning-associated abnormalities is inadequate epigenetic reprogramming of the donor genome. Microarray experiments have shown that hundreds of genes are abnormally expressed in newborn cloned animals.[1] Furthermore, DNA methylation patterns in cloned preimplantation embryos and in tissues from cloned animals have been shown to be aberrant compared with controls. The most direct evidence for the notion that cloning phenotypes are epigenetic rather than genetic comes from the observation that the abnormal phenotypes of cloned animals are not transmitted to their offspring.[7,13]

DNA METHYLATION DURING NORMAL DEVELOPMENT

DNA methylation provides heritable information to the DNA that is not encoded in the nucleotide sequence. In higher eukaryotes, DNA methylation is the only covalent modification of the DNA. It occurs at position 5 of the pyrimidine ring of cytosines and is almost exclusively restricted to CpG dinucleotides in somatic cells.[14] In contrast, embryonic stem (ES) cells and early embryos seem to contain significant amounts of non-CpG methylation (mostly CpA).[15,16] Currently, the functional role of this non-CpG methylation is not clear.

DNA methylation has been implicated to participate in a diverse range of cellular functions and pathologies, including tissue-specific gene expression, cell differentiation, genomic imprinting, X-chromosome inactivation, regulation of chromatin structure, carcinogenesis, and aging.[17–22] In general, methylation is found in CpG-poor regions; CpG-rich areas (CpG islands) seem to be protected from this modification and are generally associated with active genes.[23] This is consistent with the fact that methylated CpG islands are found on the

Handbook of Stem Cells
Volume 1
Copyright © 2004 by Academic Press

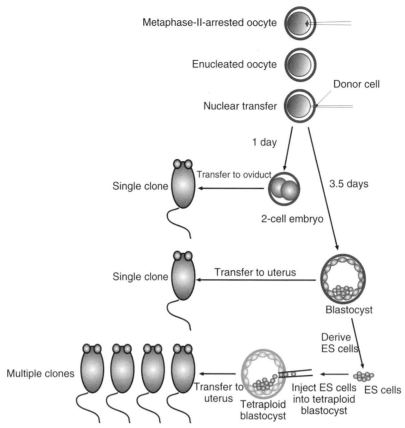

Figure 10-1. *Generation of cloned mice.* The metaphase spindle is removed from a metaphase-II-arrested oocyte using micromanipulators. Then the donor nucleus is injected directly into the cytoplasm. Three different approaches to subsequently generate cloned mice are depicted. First, to minimize the time in culture 2-cell embryos can be transferred to the oviduct of a recipient female. Second, to further assess the developmental potential of the reconstructed embryos in vitro, clones can be cultured until the blastocyst stage (day 3.5) and then be transferred to the uterus of a recipient female. Finally, ES cells can be derived from the Inner Cell Mass (ICM) of the cloned blastocyst and by using tetraploid embryo complementation, multiple identical clones that are solely derived from the donor ES cells can be generated.[70]

inactive X-chromosome and on the silenced allele of imprinted genes.[24–26] The methyl group is positioned in the major groove of the DNA, where it can easily be detected by proteins interacting with the DNA.[18] The effects of DNA methylation on chromatin structure and gene expression are likely mediated by a family of proteins that share a highly conserved methyl CpG-binding domain (MBD).[27] Two of these, Mecp2 and Mbd1, have been suggested to be involved in transcriptional repression[28–30] based on biochemical observations that they form complexes with histone deacetylases and other proteins important for chromatin structure.[31–34]

DNA methylation patterns are extremely dynamic in early mammalian development. Within 1–2 cell divisions after fertilization, a wave of global demethylation takes place. It has been suggested that the paternal genome is actively demethylated during the period of protamine–histone exchange and that the maternal genome subsequently becomes demethylated, presumably through a passive DNA replication

mechanism.[35,36] By the morula stage, methylation is found only in some repetitive elements and imprinted genes.[35,37,38] After implantation, genomewide methylation levels increase dramatically, establishing a differential pattern between the cells of the inner cell mass and those of the trophectoderm[36] and resulting in the formation of methylation patterns found in the adult.[39] Primordial germ cells (PGC) also undergo global demethylation. Importantly, in contrast to demethylation during preimplantation, all parental-specific epigenetic marks are erased in the PGC by embryonic day 13–14. As a result, PGC and diploid germ cells are the only cell types in which the paternal and maternal genomes are equivalent. Upon initiation of gametogenesis, PGC remethylation begins, and the parental-specific methylation patterns that will code for monoallelic expression of imprinted genes are established.[35,40]

Maintenance and establishment of DNA methylation is accomplished by at least three independent catalytically active DNA methyltransferases: Dnmt1, Dnmt3a, and Dnmt3b.[19,41]

There are two isoforms of Dnmt1, an oocyte-specific isoform (Dnmt1o) and a somatic isoform. Somatic Dnmt1 is often referred to as the "maintenance" methyltransferase because it is believed to be the enzyme responsible for copying methylation patterns after DNA replication. The oocyte-specific isoform of Dnmt1 is believed to be responsible for maintaining but not for establishing maternal imprints. The Dnmt3 family (Dnmt3a, 3b, 3l, and several isoforms) is required for the *de novo* methylation that occurs after implantation, for the *de novo* methylation of newly integrated retroviral sequences in mouse ES cells,[41,42] and for the establishment of imprints (Dnmt3l).[43] It was recently shown that Dnmt3a has a strong preference for unmethylated DNA.[44]

The essential role of DNA methylation in mammalian development is highlighted by the fact that mutant mice lacking each of the enzymes (generated by gene targeting) are not viable and die either during early embryonic development (Dnmt1 and Dnmt3b) or shortly after birth (Dnmt3a).[19,42,45] The knockout of Dnmt3l leads to male infertility and the failure to establish imprints in female eggs.[43,46] Disruption of Dnmt2 did not reveal any obvious effects on genomic DNA methylation.[47] The biological role of Dnmt2 is still elusive; however, a possible role in centromere function has been suggested.[41]

ABNORMAL DNA METHYLATION PATTERNS IN CLONES

Considering the fundamental role of DNA methylation in development, it seems likely that any NT embryo will need to recapitulate a functional pattern of epigenetic modifications to proceed through normal embryogenesis. Several groups have investigated DNA methylation patterns in NT embryos and reported finding abnormalities in DNA methylation.[48–53] In cloned bovine embryos, satellite sequence methylation levels are closer to the donor cells than to control embryos.[50] However, methylation patterns of single-copy gene promoters in cloned bovine blastocysts appeared to be normally demethylated.[50] In addition, the satellite sequences, not the single-copy genes, showed more methylation in the trophectoderm than in the inner cell mass of cloned bovine blastocysts[51] (reviewed by Han *et al.*[54]). Using antibodies against 5-methyl cytosine, two independent studies showed that the cloned bovine embryos did not undergo global demethylation in early embryogenesis and even showed precocious *de novo* methylation,[49] with abnormally hypomethylated euchromatin and abnormally hypermethylated centromeric heterochromatin.[53] These findings suggest that different chromosomal regions might respond differently to demethylation in the egg cytoplasm. Interestingly, when the same satellite sequences examined in bovine[50] were analyzed in a different species (porcine), methylation levels at the blastocyst stage of cloned embryos were more comparable to those of fertilized control embryos,[55] suggesting species-specific differences. A recent study that analyzed several imprinted genes in cloned murine blastocysts showed that most of the examined genes displayed aberrant methylation and expression patterns.[56]

It would be interesting to know if aberrant methylation patterns during preimplantation development contribute to the low

efficiency of generating clones and to what extent the clones can tolerate such variation. Unfortunately, analyzing the methylation status in preimplantation embryos provides only indirect correlations, preventing satisfactory resolution of this question.

To establish a potential correlation between global DNA methylation levels and the developmental potential of cloned embryos, Cezar *et al.*[57] compared the genomewide methylation status among spontaneously aborted cloned fetuses, live cloned fetuses, and adult clones in bovine. When genomewide cytosine methylation levels were measured by reverse-phase HPLC, they found that a significant number of aborted fetuses lacked detectable levels of 5-methylcytosine. In contrast, when seemingly healthy adult, lactating clones were compared to similarly aged lactating cows produced by artificial insemination, comparable DNA methylation levels were observed. The authors suggested that survivability of cloned cattle is related to the global DNA methylation status. All evidence suggests that a correct global methylation status is required for development. However, subtle changes might be compatible with normal development and result only in minor or no phenotypes. For example, by applying restriction landmark genome scanning (RLGS) in two seemingly healthy cloned mice, it was shown that methylation patterns at several sites in each clone differed from those in the controls.[52]

The reason for the frequent abnormal DNA methylation patterns in cloned embryos is still unclear. It is likely that, because of the epigenetic difference between the somatic donor cell and the gametes, the somatic nucleus responds differently to the egg cytoplasm, affecting subsequent events during embryogenesis. For example, the highly coordinated demethylation process in the pronuclei of the maternal and paternal genome upon fertilization might not happen appropriately in the somatic donor genome following NT. It is not clear whether all of the somatic epigenetic marks imposed by DNA methylation during differentiation can be removed from the donor nucleus. Any failure to demethylate the DNA sequences normally demethylated during early cleavage stages of development might be stably passed on to progeny cells. Another possible explanation for the aberrant methylation patterns in clones may result from the ectopic expression of the somatic form of Dnmt1 in the egg- and cleavage-stage cloned embryos. In the mouse oocyte and preimplantation embryo, the oocyte-specific form (Dnmt1o), but not the longer somatic form, is expressed. It has been shown that a translocation of Dnmt1o between nucleus and cytoplasm is tightly regulated during murine preimplantation development.[58,59] In contrast, cloned preimplantation mouse embryos were reported to aberrantly express the somatic form of the Dnmt1 gene, and the translocation of Dnmt1o was absent.[60] As mentioned previously, DNA methyltransferases (Dnmt1, 3a, 3b, and 3l) play important roles in setting up and maintaining DNA methylation patterns. It is reasonable to speculate that dysregulation of any of these enzymes in clones may alter DNA methylation patterns. These abnormal DNA methylation patterns could result in embryo lethality or phenotypic abnormality. Little is known about the developmental role of dynamic changes in DNA methylation during preimplantation, although recently the importance of early embryonic methylation patterns in setting up the structural profile of the genome was shown.[22] This suggests that the failure to establish correct methylation patterns early in development might have far-reaching effects on the chromatin structure. Interestingly, mouse embryos deficient for Dnmt1 and Dnmt3b die around embryonic day 9.5,[42,45] but Lsh mutant mice die only after birth, despite showing a substantial loss of methylation throughout the genome.[61]

Factors That May Affect Epigenetic Reprogramming in Cloning

Studies have shown that epigenetic reprogramming seems to be incomplete in most, if not all, of the clones. In this section, we discuss some of the aspects of the donor genome shown to directly affect cloning efficiency. In addition, we discuss the role of the recipient egg cytoplasm in reprogramming a donor genome.

EPIGENETIC STATE OF THE DONOR GENOME

Mature gametes have the full potential to initiate embryogenesis as a result of epigenetic modifications acquired during gametogenesis. In contrast, cloning shortcuts this process by omitting all the epigenetic modifications acquired during germ cell development. A somatic donor nucleus has an epigenetic state radically different from that of the zygote.

Cloning Efficiency and Developmental Stage of the Donor Cell

Clones have been successfully produced using cells derived from different developmental stages in several species. An active research topic has been whether cloning efficiency depends on the developmental stages of the animals from which the donor cells are used. In amphibians, the developmental stage of a donor cell directly correlates with cloning efficiency. Cells from undifferentiated blastula were found to be more efficient to clone than cells from differentiated gastrula, neurula, or tail bud stage cells.[62] As a result, no frog has been cloned from an adult donor cell so far. In mammals, however, the comparison of somatic cells from different

stages of mammalian development has generated controversial results. For example, in bovine, the development of clones both at preimplantation (blastocyst formation rate) and at postimplantation stages are similar when fetal, newborn, and adult cells were compared, irrespective of the donor cell types used.[63,64] Yet others have shown that blastocysts generated from cultured bovine fetal cells have higher success rates for both pregnancy and calving compared to those derived from cultured adult cells.[65] An unexplained exception found in these experiments was that among all the fetal and adult cells compared, adult cumulus cells produced the highest pregnancy and calving rates.[65]

In mice, Wakayama *et al.* found a consistent difference in the cloning efficiency between embryonic cells (2.4%), fetal cells (1.0% for female and 2.2% for male), and adult cells (0.5% for female and 1.7% for male) (reviewed by Wakayama *et al.*[66]). In rabbits, it was found that nuclei from morula cells and fetal fibroblasts are more efficient than the nuclei from fibroblasts derived from young or aged animals when used to produce cloned blastocysts.[67] Because cells from different tissues and even from the same tissue at a particular stage of development are not necessarily in the same epigenetic state, we believe that the comparison is only informative if the exact differentiation state of the donor cells is known.

Cloning Efficiency and the Differentiation State of the Donor Cell

Our laboratory recently compared cloned blastocysts derived from mouse ES and cumulus cells for the extent of epigenetic reprogramming by monitoring the activation of Oct-4 and 10 other embryonic genes. Significantly, all ES clones expressed these genes normally, but 38% of the cumulus cell derived clones failed to do so.[68] In addition, it was found that blastocysts derived from ES cells develop to term between a 10-fold and 20-fold higher efficiency than those derived from somatic cells[69,70] (Table 10–1). Because ES cells express Oct-4 and other pluripotency genes, they likely require little or no epigenetic reprogramming following NT to support embryogenesis.

This raised the question of whether fully differentiated cells have the potential to be reprogrammed. Somatic tissues

TABLE 10–1
Differentiation States of Donor Cells and Their Cloning Efficiencies

Donor Cell Types	Percentage of NT Embryos Developed to Morula or Blastocyst Stage	Percentage of Clones Developed to Term per Transferred Blastocysts	References
ES cell	10–20%	30–50%	Rideout *et al.*, 2000; Eggan *et al.*, 2001 and 2002
Cumulus cell or fibroblast	60–70%	1–3%	Wakayama *et al.*, 1998 and 1999
B- or T-cell	4%	ND	Hochedlinger *et al.*, 2002; Jaenisch *et al.*, 2003

harbor cell types with different epigenetic states, such as somatic stem cells, progenitor cells, and fully differentiated cells. Because no definitive marker for the differentiation state of a donor cells was used in previous somatic cell cloning experiments, the possibility that most somatic clones produced thus far were derived from rare adult stem cells could not be excluded. To clarify these issues, our laboratory recently cloned mice from fully differentiated B and T cells in which the genetic rearrangements of the immunoglobulin and TCR genes were used as stable markers for the identity and differentiation state of the donor cells.[71] This result is the first unequivocal demonstration that fully differentiated cells have the potential to be reprogrammed to a totipotent state. However, the cloning efficiency was very low by using these donor cells, and mice could not be produced by directly transferring the cloned blastocysts into uteri of recipient mice. Rather, in a first step, ES cells were derived from the cloned blastocysts; monoclonal mice were generated in a second step by injecting the cloned ES cells into tetraploid blastocysts (see Fig. 10–1).

It was also found that B and T cells are much less efficient than other types of somatic cells (cumulus and fibroblast cells) in the production of cloned blastocysts (reviewed by Jeanisch et al.[72]; see Table 1). This observation, along with the results obtained from the comparison of cloning efficiencies between somatic cells and ES cells, suggests that the differentiation state of the donor genome has a direct effect on epigenetic reprogramming. It will be interesting to determine whether fully differentiated cells from other tissues are different in their cloning efficiency. These experiments might help to understand the effect of tissue-specific epigenetic modifications on the reprogramming process.

Donor Cell Type-Specific Abnormalities in Clones. Several groups have compared cells derived from different tissues to investigate whether cloning phenotypes are donor cell-type specific.[1,7,8,63] In bovine, for example, it was found that calves cloned from cumulus and oviduct cells were not overweight, as frequently observed in clones from other cell types.[63] It was found that mice cloned from Sertoli cells tend to die prematurely from hepatic failure, tumors, or both,[8] whereas mice cloned from cumulus cells often become obese.[7] These findings in mammals have extended the discoveries reported in early amphibian cloning experiments, in which cloning phenotypes were found to be correlated with the donor cell types used for NT (reviewed by Hochedlinger et al.[73]). Consistent with these studies, our laboratory has recently shown through microarray experiments that a subset of genes, which were abnormally expressed in cloned animals, were donor cell-type specific.[1] This is the first molecular evidence showing that the tissue origins of donor cells could directly influence their epigenetic reprogramming.

Environmental Effects on the Donor Genome

It is widely established that epigenetic states can be influenced by environmental cues, both *in vitro* and *in vivo*.[12] For example, the DNA methylation status in mouse tissues can be affected by diet[74] and aging.[75] Moreover, it has been shown that imprinted gene expression in ES cells can be altered during cell culture.[76] Thus, cloning from cells in which imprinting marks have been altered would result in abnormal imprinted gene expression in the cloned animals. This is because parental-specific imprinting patterns can be established only during germ cell development, not by any of the postzygotic developmental stages. Indeed, mice cloned from mouse ES cells showed abnormal expression patterns for some of the examined imprinted genes.[48,76] Cell culture effects were also found in somatic cell cloning experiments, in which different porcine fibroblast subclones derived from the same primary cell line resulted in different developmental potential when used as nuclear donors.[77] Because it is known that methylation is progressively lost during *in vitro* culture of fibroblasts,[78] such variation among cell lines in producing clones could be the result of changes in DNA methylation.

Genetic Background of the Donor Genome

Our laboratory investigated the influence of genetic background on cloning efficiency by comparing mouse ES cells with either inbred or hybrid backgrounds as donor cells. Results showed that F1 hybrid ES cells were more efficient than inbred ES cells to clone. Although all of the inbred clones that survived to term died at birth because of respiratory distress, a certain percentage of F1 clones survived.[69] However, because similar differences were also found between mice entirely derived from inbred ES and those derived from F1 ES cells by ES–tetraploid complementation,[69] the beneficial effect from the more heterogeneous genetic background of F1 ES cells is not limited to cloning. Therefore, it is possible that the respiratory disstress experienced by most inbred clones at their births was caused by their delayed development rather than by a failure of epigenetic reprogramming.

Cell Cycle Stage of the Donor Genome and Reprogramming Efficiency

It has been suggested that donor cells arrested at G0 of the cell cycle are crucial for cloning somatic cells by NT.[79] However, mammals have been cloned from G1 and M phase donor cells.[6,80–82] To investigate which cell cycle stage is more advantageous in reprogramming a somatic nucleus, a recent study compared the development of bovine clones produced from fibroblasts either at the G0 (high-confluence treatment) or G1 ("shake-off" treatment) stage of the cell cycle.[83] There was no difference in the blastocyst formation rate of these two groups. However, when postimplantation development of these clones was examined in 50 recipients, five calves were obtained from clones derived from G1 cells, but none of the G0 clones survived beyond 180 days of gestation. The authors suggested that the donor cell cycle stage is important for the development of clones—in particular, that G1 cells are more amenable to supporting late gestation stage development. The underlying mechanisms for the correlation between donor cell cycle and cloning efficiency remain elusive.

RECIPIENT CYTOPLASM

Mature eggs in most mammalian species are arrested at the metaphase of the second meiosis (MII), caused by high levels of maturation promoting factor (MPF) activity. Upon fertilization or by some artificial stimuli, MPF activity in the eggs starts to decline, releasing eggs from the MII arrest to finish the cell cycle. This process is commonly referred to as egg activation.[84] Both unactivated (MII, high MPF activity) eggs and activated eggs (low MPF activity) have been used as recipients for cloning experiments in mammals. The transfer of an interphase nucleus into an enucleated MII egg results in premature chromosome condensation (PCC) and nuclear envelope breakdown (NEBD), which is induced by high levels of MPF activity in the MII eggs.[85] PCC and NEBD could cause chromosome damage if a nucleus with an incompatible cell cycle stage is transferred into the MII egg.[85,86] Elongated chromosomes with single- and double-stranded chromatids will form by PCC when G0/G1 and G2 phase nuclei, respectively, are transferred into MII eggs. In these situations, no DNA damage seems to occur. When mitotic chromosomes were transferred into MII cytoplasm, the chromosomes remained condensed.[87] However, extensive chromosome fragmentation, termed *pulverization,* occurred when an S phase nucleus was used. Thus, to maintain a normal diploid genome in the cloned embryos, coordination between the cell cycle stage of the donor nucleus and the recipient egg needs to be considered. These observations suggested that a donor nucleus at any cell cycle stage, with the exception of S phase, is compatible with an egg arrested at the MII stage of oogenesis.[88,89]

On the other hand, some reports suggest that activated eggs could be considered "universal recipients."[85,88] This is because activated eggs have lost MPF activity and do not induce PCC and NEBD, irrespective of the cell cycle stage of the donor cells; consequently, chromatin damage is avoided.[85] Indeed, cloned goats,[90] sheep,[85] and cows[91] have been produced using activated eggs as recipients. However, no mouse was cloned when nuclei from cleavage mouse embryos were transferred into enucleated zygotes.[92] Furthermore, when somatic cell nuclei (cumulus cells) were transferred to enucleated zygotes, severe chromosome damage occurred in all of the cloned embryos, and the authors suggested that endonuclease activity of the recipient cytoplasm was responsible for the fragmentation of the donor chromatin.[66,93] At present, there is no evidence that activated eggs can be used as "universal recipients," particularly not in mice. However, these different observations of mouse and farm animals remain unsolved.

In addition to the cell cycle compatibility between donor nucleus and recipient cytoplasm, which is important for maintaining intact diploid genomes of cloned embryos, the potential difference in reprogramming activities in the unactivated and activated egg cytoplasm needs to be considered. Several studies have been performed to address this issue. In bovine, one study found that although a cloned calf could be produced from cumulus cells using MII eggs, all clones arrested before or at the eight-cell stage when activated eggs were used.[82]

Similarly, another group found that bovine somatic clones (from skin fibroblasts) could be produced only by MII eggs, but not by activated eggs.[94] Interestingly, the latter study also found that embryonic nuclei (from blastomeres) can be reprogrammed by both MII and activated eggs.[94] This differential requirement for the egg cytoplasmic environment by somatic and embryonic nuclei is consistent with the idea that different epigenetic states of donor nuclei require different degrees of reprogramming.

It is believed that the MPF activity, present in unactivated eggs but not in activated eggs, is important for the reprogramming of somatic genomes.[95,96] It was also proposed that an MII egg allows more time than a zygote for the donor nucleus to be remodeled before the first cell cycle starts.[97] Others speculated that the enucleated zygotes fail to reprogram somatic genomes because reprogramming activities associated with pronuclei are removed during the zygote enucleation step.[98]

In summary, it remains unclear how the egg cytoplasm reprograms a differentiated genome. Identifying the molecular nature of the reprogramming activity might help to improve cloning efficiency.

Summary

Accumulated evidence suggests that incomplete epigenetic reprogramming probably occurs in all clones. In this chapter, we discussed faulty epigenetic reprogramming in clones, as well as the factors that may affect reprogramming. We only focused on the abnormalities of DNA methylation patterns in clones, because the potential roles of other chromatin modifications such as histone acetylation and methylation in NT have yet to be addressed in more detail (reviewed by Li,[43] Urnov et al.,[99] and Vignon et al.[100]).

Despite our limited understanding of epigenetic reprogramming, we know that even fully differentiated cells can be reprogrammed by the egg cytoplasm to a totipotent or less differentiated state.[71] Thus, a somatic cell nucleus from a patient could be transferred into an enucleated egg to produce ES cells possessing the potential to differentiate into different somatic cells useful for cell therapy (reviewed by Hochedlinger and Jaenisch[101]). We believe that the abnormalities found in clones will unlikely interfere with the therapeutic applications of NT because problems inherent in the NT technology do not impede the generation of functional cells for tissue repair. In our laboratory, we successfully derived ES cells from tissue isolated from an immune-deficient adult mouse by cloning and subsequently repaired the gene responsible for the disease.[102] This result established a paradigm for the treatment of a genetic disorder by combining NT with gene therapy.

ACKNOWLEDGMENTS

We would like to thank Konrad Hochedlinger, Kevin Eggan, Caroline Beard, Robert Blelloch, and Teresa Holm for critical reading of the manuscript. Zhongde Wang is supported by a postdoctoral fellowship from The Lalor Foundation; Alexander Meissner is supported by a Boehringer Ingelheim Ph.D. fellowship; and this work is supported by the National Cancer Institute grant CA84198 to Rudolf Jaenisch.

REFERENCES

1. Humpherys, D., Eggan, K., Akutsu, H., Friedman, A., Hochedlinger, K., Yanagimachi, R., Lander, E.S., Golub, T.R., and Jaenisch, R. (2002). Abnormal gene expression in cloned mice derived from embryonic stem cell and cumulus cell nuclei. *Proc. Natl. Acad. Sci. USA* **99**, 12,889–12,894.

2. Roslin Institute. (2002). Somatic Cell Nuclear Transfer (Cloning) Efficiency. *Available online at* http://www.roslin.ac.uk/public/webtablesGR.pdf.

3. Cibelli, J.B., Campbell, K.H., Seidel, G.E., West, M.D., and Lanza, R.P. (2002). The health profile of cloned animals. *Natl. Biotechnol.* **20**, 13–14.

4. Hill, J.R., Roussel, A.J., Cibelli, J.B., Edwards, J.F., Hooper, N.L., Miller, M.W., Thompson, J.A., Looney, C.R., Westhusin, M.E., Robl, J.M., and Stice, S.L. (1999). Clinical and pathologic features of cloned transgenic calves and fetuses (13 case studies). *Theriogenology* **51**, 1451–1465.

5. Lanza, R.P., Cibelli, J.B., Blackwell, C., Cristofalo, V.J., Francis, M.K., Baerlocher, G.M., Mak, J., Schertzer, M., Chavez, E.A., Sawyer, N., Lansdorp, P.M., and West, M.D. (2000). Extension of cell life span and telomere length in animals cloned from senescent somatic cells. *Science* **288**, 665–669.

6. Ono, Y., Shimozawa, N., Ito, M., and Kono, T. (2001). Cloned mice from fetal fibroblast cells arrested at metaphase by a serial nuclear transfer. *Biol. Reprod.* **64**, 44–50.

7. Tamashiro, K.L., Wakayama, T., Akutsu, H., Yamazaki, Y., Lachey, J.L., Wortman, M.D., Seeley, R.J., D'Alessio, D.A., Woods, S.C., Yanagimachi, R., and Sakai, R.R. (2002). Cloned mice have an obese phenotype not transmitted to their offspring. *Natl. Med.* **8**, 262–267.

8. Ogonuki, N., Inoue, K., Yamamoto, Y., Noguchi, Y., Tanemura, K., Suzuki, O., Nakayama, H., Doi, K., Ohtomo, Y., Satoh, M., Nishida, A., and Ogura, A. (2002). Early death of mice cloned from somatic cells. *Natl. Genet.* **30**, 253–254.

9. McEvoy, T.G., Sinclair, K.D., Young, L.E., Wilmut, I., and Robinson, J.J. (2000). Large offspring syndrome and other consequences of ruminant embryo culture *in vitro:* relevance to blastocyst culture in human ART. *Hum. Fertil. (Cambridge)* **3**, 238–246.

10. Young, L.E., Sinclair, K.D., and Wilmut, I. (1998). Large offspring syndrome in cattle and sheep. *Rev. Reprod.* **3**, 155–163.

11. Rideout, W.M., III, Eggan, K., and Jaenisch, R. (2001). Nuclear cloning and epigenetic reprogramming of the genome. *Science* **293**, 1093–1098.

12. Jaenisch, R., and Bird, A. (2003). Epigenetic regulation of gene expression: how the genome integrates intrinsic and environmental signals. *Natl. Genet.* **33 Suppl.,** 245–254.

13. Shimozawa, N., Ono, Y., Kimoto, S., Hioki, K., Araki, Y., Shinkai, Y., Kono, T., and Ito, M. (2002). Abnormalities in cloned mice are not transmitted to the progeny. *Genesis* **34**, 203–207.

14. Clark, S.J., Harrison, J., and Frommer, M. (1995). CpNpG methylation in mammalian cells. *Natl. Genet.* **10**, 20–27.

15. Ramsahoye, B.H., Biniszkiewicz, D., Lyko, F., Clark, V., Bird, A.P., and Jaenisch, R. (2000). Non-CpG methylation is prevalent in embryonic stem cells and may be mediated by DNA methyltransferase 3a. *Proc. Natl. Acad. Sci. USA* **97**, 5237–5242.

16. Haines, T.R., Rodenhiser, D.I., and Ainsworth, P.J. (2001). Allele-specific non-CpG methylation of the Nf1 gene during early mouse development. *Dev. Biol.* **240**, 585–598.

17. Jaenisch, R. (1997). DNA methylation and imprinting: why bother? *Trends Genet.* **13**, 323–329.

18. Jeltsch, A. (2002). Beyond Watson and Crick: DNA methylation and molecular enzymology of DNA methyltransferases. *Chembiochem.* **3**, 274–293.

19. Robertson, K.D., and Wolffe, A.P. (2000). DNA methylation in health and disease. *Natl. Rev. Genet.* **1**, 11–19.

20. Gaudet, F., Hodgson, J.G., Eden, A., Jackson-Grusby, L., Dausman, J., Gray, J.W., Leonhardt, H., and Jaenisch, R. (2003). Induction of tumors in mice by genomic hypomethylation. *Science* **300**, 489–492.

21. Eden, A., Gaudet, F., Waghmare, A., and Jaenisch, R. (2003). Chromosomal instability and tumors promoted by DNA hypomethylation. *Science* **300**, 455.

22. Hashimshony, T., Zhang, J., Keshet, I., Bustin, M., and Cedar, H. (2003). The role of DNA methylation in setting up chromatin structure during development. *Natl. Genet.* **34**, 187–192.

23. Cross, S.H., and Bird, A.P. (1995). CpG islands and genes. *Curr. Opin. Genet. Dev.* **5**, 309–314.

24. Neumann, B., and Barlow, D.P. (1996). Multiple roles for DNA methylation in gametic imprinting. *Curr. Opin. Genet. Dev.* **6**, 159–163.

25. Razin, A., and Cedar, H. (1994). DNA methylation and genomic imprinting. *Cell* **77**, 473–476.

26. Riggs, A.D., and Pfeifer, G.P. (1992). X-chromosome inactivation and cell memory. *Trends Genet.* **8**, 169–174.

27. Wade, P.A. (2001). Methyl CpG-binding proteins and transcriptional repression. *Bioessays* **23**, 1131–1137.

28. Fujita, N., Takebayashi, S., Okumura, K., Kudo, S., Chiba, T., Saya, H., and Nakao, M. (1999). Methylation-mediated transcriptional silencing in euchromatin by methyl-CpG binding protein MBD1 isoforms. *Mol. Cell Biol.* **19**, 6415–6426.

29. Fujita, N., Shimotake, N., Ohki, I., Chiba, T., Saya, H., Shirakawa, M., and Nakao, M. (2000). Mechanism of transcriptional regulation by methyl-CpG binding protein MBD1. *Mol. Cell Biol.* **20**, 5107–5118.

30. Nan, X., Campoy, F.J., and Bird, A. (1997). MeCP2 is a transcriptional repressor with abundant binding sites in genomic chromatin. *Cell* **88**, 471–481.

31. Jones, P.L., Veenstra, G.J., Wade, P.A., Vermaak, D., Kass, S.U., Landsberger, N., Strouboulis, J., and Wolffe, A.P. (1998). Methylated DNA and MeCP2 recruit histone deacetylase to repress transcription. *Natl. Genet.* **19**, 187–191.

32. Nan, X., Ng, H.H., Johnson, C.A., Laherty, C.D., Turner, B.M., Eisenman, R.N., and Bird, A. (1998). Transcriptional repression by the methyl CpG-binding protein Mecp2 involves a histone deacetylase complex. *Nature* **393**, 386–389.

33. Wade, P.A., Gegonne, A., Jones, P.L., Ballestar, E., Aubry, F., and Wolffe, A.P. (1999). Mi-2 complex couples DNA methylation to chromatin remodeling and histone deacetylation. *Natl. Genet.* **23**, 62–66.

34. Zhang, Y., Ng, H.H., Erdjument-Bromage, H., Tempst, P., Bird, A., and Reinberg, D. (1999). Analysis of the NuRD subunits reveals a histone deacetylase core complex and a connection with DNA methylation. *Genes Dev.* **13**, 1924–1935.

35. Reik, W., Dean, W., and Walter, J. (2001). Epigenetic reprogramming in mammalian development. *Science* **293**, 1089–1093.

36. Santos, F., Hendrich, B., Reik, W., and Dean, W. (2002). Dynamic reprogramming of DNA methylation in the early mouse embryo. *Dev. Biol.* **241**, 172–182.

37. Walsh, C.P., Chaillet, J.R., and Bestor, T.H. (1998). Transcription of IAP endogenous retroviruses is constrained by cytosine methylation. *Natl. Genet.* **20,** 116–117.

38. Sanford, J.P., Clark, H.J., Chapman, V.M., and Rossant, J. (1987). Differences in DNA methylation during oogenesis and spermatogenesis and their persistence during early embryogenesis in the mouse. *Genes Dev.* **1,** 1039–1046.

39. Turker, M.S. (1999). The establishment and maintenance of DNA methylation patterns in mouse somatic cells. *Semin. Cancer Biol.* **9,** 329–337.

40. Lucifero, D., Mertineit, C., Clarke, H.J., Bestor, T.H., and Trasler, J.M. (2002). Methylation dynamics of imprinted genes in mouse germ cells. *Genomics* **79,** 530–538.

41. Bestor, T.H. (2000). The DNA methyltransferases of mammals. *Hum. Mol. Genet.* **9,** 2395–2402.

42. Okano, M., Bell, D.W., Haber, D.A., and Li, E. (1999). DNA methyltransferases Dnmt3a and Dnmt3b are essential for *de novo* methylation and mammalian development. *Cell* **99,** 247–257.

43. Li, E. (2002). Chromatin modification and epigenetic reprogramming in mammalian development. *Natl. Rev. Genet.* **3,** 662–673.

44. Yokochi, T., and Robertson, K.D. (2002). Preferential methylation of unmethylated DNA by mammalian *de novo* DNA methyltransferase Dnmt3a. *J. Biol. Chem.* **277,** 11,735–11,745.

45. Li, E., Bestor, T.H., and Jaenisch, R. (1992). Targeted mutation of the DNA methyltransferase gene results in embryonic lethality. *Cell* **69,** 915–926.

46. Bourc'his, D., Xu, G.L., Lin, C.S., Bollman, B., and Bestor, T.H. (2001). Dnmt3l and the establishment of maternal genomic imprints. *Science* **294,** 2536–2539.

47. Okano, M., Xie, S., and Li, E. (1998). Dnmt2 is not required for *de novo* and maintenance methylation of viral DNA in embryonic stem cells. *Nucleic Acids Res.* **26,** 2536–2540.

48. Dean, W., Bowden, L., Aitchison, A., Klose, J., Moore, T., Meneses, J.J., Reik, W., and Feil, R. (1998). Altered imprinted gene methylation and expression in completely ES cell-derived mouse fetuses: association with aberrant phenotypes. *Development* **125,** 2273–2282.

49. Dean, W., Santos, F., Stojkovic, M., Zakhartchenko, V., Walter, J., Wolf, E., and Reik, W. (2001). Conservation of methylation reprogramming in mammalian development: aberrant reprogramming in cloned embryos. *Proc. Natl. Acad. Sci. USA* **98,** 13,734–13,738.

50. Kang, Y.K., Koo, D.B., Park, J.S., Choi, Y.H., Chung, A.S., Lee, K.K., and Han, Y.M. (2001). Aberrant methylation of donor genome in cloned bovine embryos. *Natl. Genet.* **28,** 173–177.

51. Kang, Y.K., Park, J.S., Koo, D.B., Choi, Y.H., Kim, S.U., Lee, K.K., and Han, Y.M. (2002). Limited demethylation leaves mosaic-type methylation states in cloned bovine pre-implantation embryos. *EMBO J.* **21,** 1092–1100.

52. Ohgane, J., Wakayama, T., Kogo, Y., Senda, S., Hattori, N., Tanaka, S., Yanagimachi, R., and Shiota, K. (2001). DNA methylation variation in cloned mice. *Genesis* **30,** 45–50.

53. Bourc'his, D., Le Bourhis, D., Patin, D., Niveleau, A., Comizzoli, P., Renard, J.P., and Viegas-Pequignot, E. (2001). Delayed and incomplete reprogramming of chromosome methylation patterns in bovine cloned embryos. *Curr. Biol.* **11,** 1542–1546.

54. Han, Y.M., Kang, Y.K., Koo, D.B., and Lee, K.K. (2003). Nuclear reprogramming of cloned embryos produced *in vitro*. *Theriogenology* **59,** 33–44.

55. Kang, Y.K., Koo, D.B., Park, J.S., Choi, Y.H., Kim, H.N., Chang, W.K., Lee, K.K., and Han, Y.M. (2001). Typical demethylation events in cloned pig embryos: clues on species–specific differences

in epigenetic reprogramming of a cloned donor genome. *J. Biol. Chem.* **276,** 39,980–39,984.

56. Mann, M.R., Chung, Y.G., Nolen, L.D., Verona, R.I., Latham, K.E., and Bartolomei, M.S. (2003). Disruption of imprinted gene methylation and expression in cloned preimplantation stage mouse embryos. *Biol. Reprod.* **69,** 902–914.

57. Cezar, G.G., Bartolomei, M.S., Forsberg, E.J., First, N.L., Bishop, M.D., and Eilertsen, K.J. (2003). Genomewide epigenetic alterations in cloned bovine fetuses. *Biol. Reprod.* **68,** 1009–1014.

58. Howell, C.Y., Bestor, T.H., Ding, F., Latham, K.E., Mertineit, C., Trasler, J.M., and Chaillet, J.R. (2001). Genomic imprinting disrupted by a maternal effect mutation in the Dnmt1 gene. *Cell* **104,** 829–838.

59. Ratnam, S., Mertineit, C., Ding, F., Howell, C.Y., Clarke, H.J., Bestor, T.H., Chaillet, J.R., and Trasler, J.M. (2002). Dynamics of Dnmt1 methyltransferase expression and intracellular localization during oogenesis and preimplantation development. *Dev. Biol.* **245,** 304–314.

60. Chung, Y.G., Ratnam, S., Chaillet, J.R., and Latham, K.E. (2003). Abnormal regulation of DNA methyltransferase expression in cloned mouse embryos. *Biol. Reprod.* **69,** 146–153.

61. Dennis, K., Fan, T., Geiman, T., Yan, Q., and Muegge, K. (2001). Lsh, a member of the SNF2 family, is required for genomewide methylation. *Genes Dev.* **15,** 2940–2944.

62. Gurdon, J.B. (1963). Nuclear transplantation in amphibia and the importance of stable nuclear changes in cellular differentiation. *Q. Rev. Biol.* **38,** 54–78.

63. Kato, Y., Tani, T., and Tsunoda, Y. (2000). Cloning of calves from various somatic cell types of male and female adult, newborn, and fetal cows. *J. Reprod. Fertil.* **120,** 231–237.

64. Hill, J.R., Winger, Q.A., Long, C.R., Looney, C.R., Thompson, J.A., and Westhusin, M.E. (2000). Development rates of male bovine nuclear transfer embryos derived from adult and fetal cells. *Biol. Reprod.* **62,** 1135–1140.

65. Forsberg, E.J., Strelchenko, N.S., Augenstein, M.L., Betthauser, J.M., Childs, L.A., Eilertsen, K.J., Enos, J.M., Forsythe, T.M., Golueke, P.J., Koppang, R.W., Lange, G., Lesmeister, T.L., Mallon, K.S., Mell, G.D., Misica, P.M., Pace, M.M., Pfister-Genskow, M., Voelker, G.R., Watt, S.R., and Bishop, M.D. (2002). Production of cloned cattle from *in vitro* systems. *Biol. Reprod.* **67,** 327–333.

66. Wakayama, T., and Perry, A.C.F. (2002). Cloning of mice. *In* "Cloning," (J.B. Cibelli *et al.,* ed.) pp. 301–342. Academic Press, Burlington.

67. Galat, V., Lagutina, I., Mezina, M., Prokofiev, M.I., and Zakhartchenko, V. (2002). Effect of donor cell age on the efficiency of nuclear transfer in rabbits. *Reprod. Biomed. Online* **4,** 32–37.

68. Bortvin, A., Eggan, K., Skaletsky, H., Akutsu, H., Berry, D.L., Yanagimachi, R., Page, D.C., and Jaenisch, R. (2003). Incomplete reactivation of Oct-4-related genes in mouse embryos cloned from somatic nuclei. *Development* **130,** 1673–1680.

69. Eggan, K., Akutsu, H., Loring, J., Jackson-Grusby, L., Klemm, M., Rideout, W.M., III, Yanagimachi, R., and Jaenisch, R. (2001). Hybrid vigor, fetal overgrowth, and viability of mice derived by nuclear cloning and tetraploid embryo complementation. *Proc. Natl. Acad. Sci. USA* **98,** 6209–6214.

70. Rideout, W.M., Wakayama, T., Wutz, A., Eggan, K., Jackson-Grusby, L., Dausman, J., Yanagimachi, R., and Jaenisch, R. (2000). Generation of mice from wild-type and targeted ES cells by nuclear cloning. *Natl. Genet.* **24,** 109–110.

71. Hochedlinger, K., and Jaenisch, R. (2002). Monoclonal mice generated by nuclear transfer from mature B and T donor cells. *Nature* **415,** 1035–1038.

126

72. Jeanisch, R., Eggan, K., Humpherys, D., Rideout, W., and Hochedlinger, K. (2002). Nuclear cloning, stem cells, and genomic reprogramming. *Cloning Stem Cells* **4,** 389–396.

73. Hochedlinger, K., and Jaenisch, R. (2002). Nuclear transplantation: lessons from frogs and mice. *Curr. Opin. Cell Biol.* **14,** 741–748.

74. Friso, S., Choi, S.W., Girelli, D., Mason, J.B., Dolnikowski, G.G., Bagley, P.J., Olivieri, O., Jacques, P.F., Rosenberg, I.H., Corrocher, R., and Selhub, J. (2002). A common mutation in the 5,10-methylenetetrahydrofolate reductase gene affects genomic DNA methylation through an interaction with folate status. *Proc. Natl. Acad. Sci. USA* **99,** 5606–5611.

75. Issa, J.P. (2000). CpG-island methylation in aging and cancer. *Curr. Top Microbiol. Immunol.* **249,** 101–118.

76. Humpherys, D., Eggan, K., Akutsu, H., Hochedlinger, K., Rideout, W.M., III, Biniszkiewicz, D., Yanagimachi, R., and Jaenisch, R. (2001). Epigenetic instability in ES cells and cloned mice. *Science* **293,** 95–97.

77. Kuhholzer, B., Hawley, R.J., Lai, L., Kolber-Simonds, D., and Prather, R.S. (2001). Clonal lines of transgenic fibroblast cells derived from the same fetus result in different development when used for nuclear transfer in pigs. *Biol. Reprod.* **64,** 1695–1698.

78. Wilson, V.L., and Jones, P.A. (1983). DNA methylation decreases in aging but not in immortal cells. *Science* **220,** 1055–1057.

79. Wilmut, I., Schnieke, A.E., McWhir, J., Kind, A.J., and Campbell, K.H. (1997). Viable offspring derived from fetal and adult mammalian cells. *Nature* **385,** 810–813.

80. Wakayama, T., Rodriguez, I., Perry, A.C., Yanagimachi, R., and Mombaerts, P. (1999). Mice cloned from embryonic stem cells. *Proc. Natl. Acad. Sci. USA* **96,** 14,984–14,989.

81. Cibelli, J.B., Stice, S.L., Golueke, P.J., Kane, J.J., Jerry, J., Blackwell, C., Ponce de Leon, F.A., and Robl, J.M. (1998). Cloned transgenic calves produced from nonquiescent fetal fibroblasts. *Science* **280,** 1256–1258.

82. Tani, T., Kato, Y., and Tsunoda, Y. (2000). Developmental potential of cumulus cell-derived culture frozen in a quiescent state after nucleus transfer. *Theriogenology* **53,** 1623–1629.

83. Kasinathan, P., Knott, J.G., Moreira, P.N., Burnside, A.S., Jerry, D.J., and Robl, J.M. (2001). Effect of fibroblast donor cell age and cell cycle on development of bovine nuclear transfer embryos *in vitro. Biol. Reprod.* **64,** 1487–1493.

84. Wu, H., He, C.L., and Fissore, R.A. (1998). Injection of a porcine sperm factor induces activation of mouse eggs. *Mol. Reprod. Dev.* **49,** 37–47.

85. Campbell, K.H., Loi, P., Otaegui, P.J., and Wilmut, I. (1996). Cell cycle coordination in embryo cloning by nuclear transfer. *Rev. Reprod.* **1,** 40–46.

86. Barnes, F.L., Collas, P., Powell, R., King, W.A., Westhusin, M., and Shepherd, D. (1993). Influence of recipient oocyte cell cycle stage on DNA synthesis, nuclear envelope breakdown, chromosome constitution, and development in nuclear transplant bovine embryos. *Mol. Reprod. Dev.* **36,** 33–41.

87. Alberio, R., Motlik, J., Stojkovic, M., Wolf, E., and Zakhartchenko, V. (2000). Behavior of M-phase synchronized blastomeres after nuclear transfer in cattle. *Mol. Reprod. Dev.* **57,** 37–47.

88. Campbell, K.H., Alberio, R., Lee, J.H., and Ritchie, W.A. (2001). Nuclear transfer in practice. *Cloning Stem Cells* **3,** 201–208.

89. Oback, B., and Wells, D. (2002). Practical aspects of donor cell selection for nuclear cloning. *Cloning Stem Cells* **4,** 169–174.

90. Baguisi, A., Behboodi, E., Melican, D.T., Pollock, J.S., Destrempes, M.M., Cammuso, C., Williams, J.L., Nims, S.D., Porter, C.A., Midura, P., Palacios, M.J., Ayres, S.L., Denniston, R.S., Hayes, M.L., Ziomek, C.A., Meade, H.M., Godke, R.A., Gavin, W.G., Overstrom, E.W., and Echelard, Y. (1999). Production of goats by somatic cell nuclear transfer. *Natl. Biotechnol.* **17,** 456–461.

91. Stice, S.L., Keefer, C.L., and Matthews, L. (1994). Bovine nuclear transfer embryos: oocyte activation prior to blastomere fusion. *Mol. Reprod. Dev.* **38,** 61–68.

92. McGrath, J., and Solter, D. (1983). Nuclear transplantation in mouse embryos. *J. Exp. Zool.* **228,** 355–362.

93. Wakayama, T., Shinkai, Y., Tamashiro, K.L., Niida, H., Blanchard, D.C., Blanchard, R.J., Ogura, A., Tanemura, K., Tachibana, M., Perry, A.C., Colgan, D.F., Mombaerts, P., and Yanagimachi, R. (2000). Cloning of mice to six generations. *Nature* **407,** 318–319.

94. Du, F., Sung, L.Y., Tian, X.C., and Yang, X. (2002). Differential cytoplast requirement for embryonic and somatic cell nuclear transfer in cattle. *Mol. Reprod. Dev.* **63,** 183–191.

95. Szollosi, D., Czolowska, R., Szollosi, M.S., and Tarkowski, A.K. (1988). Remodeling of mouse thymocyte nuclei depends on the time of their transfer into activated, homologous oocytes. *J. Cell Sci.* **91 (Pt. 4),** 603–613.

96. Wakayama, T., and Yanagimachi, R. (2001). Effect of cytokinesis inhibitors, DMSO, and the timing of oocyte activation on mouse cloning using cumulus cell nuclei. *Reproduction* **122,** 49–60.

97. Solter, D. (2000). Mammalian cloning: advances and limitations. *Natl. Rev. Genet.* **1,** 199–207.

98. Polejaeva, I.A., Chen, S.H., Vaught, T.D., Page, R.L., Mullins, J., Ball, S., Dai, Y., Boone, J., Walker, S., Ayares, D.L., Colman, A., and Campbell, K.H. (2000). Cloned pigs produced by nuclear transfer from adult somatic cells. *Nature* **407,** 86–90.

99. Urnov, F.D., and Wolffe, A.P. (2002). The nucleus. *In* "Cloning," (J.B. Cibelli *et al.*, eds.) pp. 47–84. Academic Press, Burlington.

100. Vignon, X., Zhou, Q., and Renard, J.P. (2002). Chromatin as a regulative architecture of the early developmental functions of mammalian embryos after fertilization or nuclear transfer. *Cloning Stem Cells* **4,** 363–377.

101. Hochedlinger, K., and Jaenisch, R. (In press.)

102. Rideout, W.M., III, Hochedlinger, K., Kyba, M., Daley, G.Q., and Jaenisch, R. (2002). Correction of a genetic defect by nuclear transplantation and combined cell and gene therapy. *Cell* **109,** 17–27.

11

Origin, Early Patterning, and Fate of the Mouse Epiblast

Anne Camus, Aitana Perea-Gomez, and Jérôme Collignon

Introduction

The epiblast can first be identified as a tissue at the late blastocyst stage, at embryonic day 4.0 (E4.0), when it consists of no more than 30 apolar cells. The epiblast is known to generate extraembryonic mesoderm and all fetal cell lineages, including the germ line. This pluripotency is its most distinctive property. It has to be distinguished from the totipotency of the blastomeres of earlier cleavage-stage embryos, which can produce all embryonic and extraembryonic cell lineages of the conceptus, including the trophectoderm. This chapter reviews what is known about the formation, the patterning, and the fate of the epiblast in the mouse embryo. It presents the latest findings in the field and attempts to complement earlier reviews.[1–6] An important aspect of the establishment of the epiblast lineage, no doubt critical in the regulation of its differentiation, is the role of chromatin modifications in the regulation of gene expression. This is not covered in this chapter, but relevant information can be found in Chapter 6 of this book and in several reviews.[7–9]

Origin and Properties of the Mouse Epiblast

FORMATION OF THE EPIBLAST

The major differences between the development of mice and that of other vertebrates at early stages is the slow pace of the first cleavages and their asynchrony. The first plane of cleavage is meridional, more or less parallel to the animal–vegetal (AV) axis, which is marked by the position of the second polar body at the animal pole of the zygote (Fig. 11–1). The zygotic genome starts to be expressed at the end of the two-cell stage, 36 hours after fertilization. At the beginning of the eight-cell stage, individual blastomeres are still clearly visible, but as they become polarized and flattened in a process called compaction, the whole embryo takes a more spherical shape. The compaction results in the fourth and fifth division cleavage producing either outer polar cells or inner apolar cells. Aggregation experiments have shown that unlike inner cells,

outer cells rapidly lose their totipotence (reviewed by Pedersen[10]). They will essentially form the trophectoderm, which will contribute exclusively to extraembryonic structures. This is the first apparent lineage segregation in mouse development. Trophectoderm cells secrete a fluid that, trapped inside by tight junctions established between outer cells, contributes to the formation and the expansion of a cavity termed the blastocoel. The inner cells remain together, positioned on one side of the hollow sphere of trophectoderm cells, where they form the inner cell mass (ICM). The trophectoderm overlying the ICM is called the polar trophectoderm. Interaction with the ICM is critical for polar trophectoderm cells to remain diploid and to proliferate. In contrast, cells, from the mural component of the trophectoderm, lining the blastocoel, stop dividing and become polyploid. The embryo at this stage is called a blastocyst. Its AV axis is inherited from the zygote. Its embryonic–abembryonic axis is perpendicular to the AV axis, and together they define the plane of bilateral symmetry of the blastocyst (Fig. 11–1, reviewed by Gardner[5] and Zernicka-Goetz[6]). Between E3.5 and E4.5, the primitive endoderm (PrE) differentiates at the blastocoelic surface of the ICM. The remainder of the ICM can then be called epiblast, or embryonic ectoderm. The polar trophectoderm will produce the extraembryonic ectoderm (ExE). At this stage, the embryo hatches from the zona pellucida and implants in the uterine wall. PrE cells see their developmental fates restricted to extraembryonic tissues (visceral and parietal endoderm), whereas epiblast cells retain the potential to generate all embryonic cell lineages. By the late gastrula stage, the epiblast will have produced both embryonic and extraembryonic mesoderm, germ cells, definitive endoderm, neuroectoderm, and surface ectoderm (reviewed by Tam and Behringer[1]).

EARLY ALLOCATION OF CELLS TO THE ICM

The potency of cleavage-stage blastomeres was examined in the mouse either by reducing their number using disaggregation–reaggregation techniques, or aggregating morulae to form giant embryos. These classic studies showed that despite drastic alterations, development could proceed and lead to normal animals (reviewed by Pedersen[10]). These regulative abilities suggested that early blastomeres, at least up to the differentiation of the trophectoderm, were equivalent. This data, with the apparent late onset of embryonic polarity, seemed to make the possibility of an early specification of the blastomeres irrelevant to the actual patterning of the embryo (reviewed by

Handbook of Stem Cells
Volume 1

Anne Camus, Aitana Perea-Gomez, and Jérôme Collignon

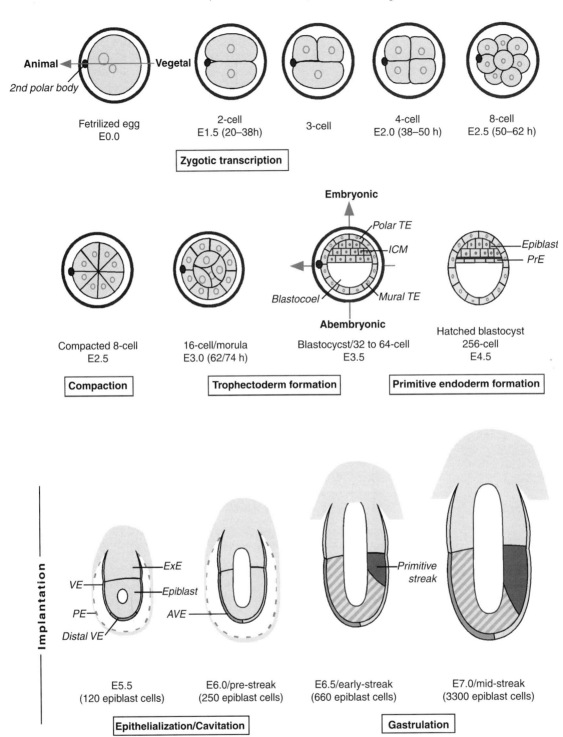

Figure 11-1. *Mouse development from fertilization to gastrulation.* The first lineage to be determined is the trophectoderm at the morula stage. At E4.5, a second extraembryonic lineage, the primitive endoderm, is located at the blastocoelic surface of the inner cell mass. After implantation, epiblast cells retain their pluripotency until the mid- to late streak stage and produce the three definitive germ layers during gastrulation (TE, trophectoderm; PrE, primitive endoderm; PE, parietal endoderm; VE, visceral endoderm; AVE, anterior visceral endoderm; and ExE, extraembryonic ectoderm).

Gardner[5] and Zernicka-Goetz[6]). However, recent work has shown that in most embryos, the two blastomeres of the two-cell stage do not contribute equally to the different cell lineages that constitute the blastocyst.[11,12] The study of this phenomenon has brought new insights into the early allocation of precursors to the epiblast lineage.

Lineage studies using nonintrusive labeling techniques demonstrated that the embryonic–abembryonic axis is set up at the two-cell stage, orthogonal to the first plane of cleavage of the zygote.[11,12] This suggested that when development proceeds unperturbed, the embryonic and abembryonic halves of the blastocyst are predominantly made of descendants from either one or the other two-cell stage blastomere. Labeling studies showed that the clonal boundary between descendants of the two-cell blastomeres is maintained at least up to the early blastocyst stage.[12,13] What can account for the different fates of the two-cell blastomeres? Because cell divisions become asynchronous as early as the two-cell stage, an early dividing and a late dividing blastomere can be distinguished. Piotrowska's labeling study confirmed an earlier hypothesis that early dividing blastomeres contributed more descendants to the ICM than late dividing ones.[12,14,15] This suggested that a shorter cell cycle inherited by the descendants of the early dividing blastomere could result in an apparent prepattern of the two-cell stage embryo. Labeling studies showed that the sperm entry position (SEP) often predicted the early dividing blastomere as well as the position of the first plane of cleavage.[12,16,17] The possibility that the sperm may contribute to the patterning of a mammalian embryo has some appeal because it echoes its role in some other vertebrates and could be seen as a trace of an ancient patterning mechanism. In contrast to what happens in wild-type embryos, clonal analysis of two-cell blastomere descendants in parthenogenetic embryos found no difference in their respective fates.[13] This further supported the notion that sperm contributes to the patterning of the blastocyst. In addition, ablation of the cortical region at the SEP disturbed the customary embryonic–abembryonic patterning of two-cell blastomeres descendants.[13] The role of the SEP in embryo patterning, however, is disputed. Davies and Gardner found no consistent relationship between the SEP and the orientation of the first plane of cleavage.[18] Other studies suggest that a shorter cell cycle may not be determinant for the preferential contribution of one blastomere to the ICM.[13,19] Live imaging of developing *in vitro*–fertilized embryos may help to resolve these issues.

SEGREGATION OF THE EPIBLAST LINEAGE

The PrE appears as an epithelium on the blastocoelic surface of the ICM at the late blastocyst stage (E4.5). A basal lamina separating the PrE from the epiblast is promptly synthesized (Fig. 11–1). Cell lineage–tracing studies in chimeric embryos have found that by this stage, the potential of PrE cells and epiblast cells has become restricted to their respective lineages.[20,21] This is the second lineage segregation event in mouse development. Labeling studies have shown that 1 day earlier, at the early blastocyst stage, ICM cells lining the blastocoel frequently comprise descendants from both

blastomeres of the two-cell stage embryo.[12] Cell lineage studies showed that these ICM cells produce either PrE descendants or epiblast, mixed clones remaining a rarity.[22,23] This implies that PrE specification is nearing completion but also that the ICM is still a mixture of both types of precursors. This would suggest that the formation of the PrE does not result from a simple induction of the top layer of the ICM to adopt an endodermal fate. Instead, it could involve an early specification event in a subset of ICM cells and a subsequent cell-sorting mechanism, bringing endoderm precursors to the blastocoelic surface. Genetic analysis may support this hypothesis. Gata6 is a zinc-finger transcription factor placed by functional studies at the top of the genetic cascade that controls the establishment of the PrE and the differentiation of its derivatives.[24,25] *Gata6* is expressed at the early blastocyst stage in a subset of ICM cells, salt-and-pepper fashion, before becoming uniformly expressed in the PrE layer when it forms at E4.5.[25] Although the dynamic of *Gata6* expression in the ICM is suggestive of a cell-sorting mechanism, this has not been formally proven. The inactivation of the signal transduction adapter protein encoded by *Disabled2 (Dab2),* a direct target of Gata6,[26] however, completes the picture. In *Dab2* mutant embryos, PrE cells are specified, but they do not form an epithelial layer separated from the epiblast.[27] Instead, they are found embedded in the epiblast, suggesting they failed to reach its blastocoelic surface. The authors propose that *Dab2*-mutant PrE cells fail to respond to extracellular cues normally involved in positioning them. Interestingly, embryos mutant for *γ1-laminin,* which cannot assemble a basal lamina, have a similar phenotype.[28]

MOLECULAR CONTROL OF PLURIPOTENTIALITY

Embryonic stem (ES) cells are pluripotent cells derived from cultured blastocysts. They can be maintained undifferentiated in culture for extended periods of time, expanded, reintroduced in an embryonic context, and found to contribute to all embryonic lineages (reviewed by Smith[29]). Their pluripotency corresponds to that of the epiblast at the late blastocyst stage, when it looses the ability to form PrE. They have been used extensively to investigate the molecular basis of pluripotentiality. A specific feature of mouse gestation may have facilitated the derivation of ES cell lines in this species. Female mice can delay the implantation of blastocysts and keep their development on hold for up to 3 or 4 weeks, a situation termed diapause. This occurs when fertilization happens while they are still nursing a litter, or it can be induced experimentally by a postfertilization ovariectomy. The molecular pathway involved in this phenomenon also operates in ES cells. The self-renewing capacity of ES cells has been found to depend on the secretion by cocultured feeder cells of a cytokine, called LIF, that signals via the gp130/LIF receptor complex. The transduction of this signal operates through a JAK pathway to activate the transcription regulator Stat3, which suppress differentiation in ES cells (Fig. 11–2). Interestingly, the inactivation of LIF or gp130/LIFR in the embryo does not result in early developmental defects, but it prevents mutant blastocysts from recovering from diapause (reviewed by

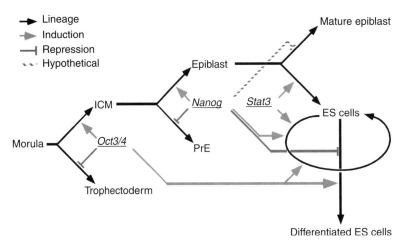

Figure 11–2. *Molecular control of pluripotentiality.* The names of the genes are underlined. See the section "Molecular Control of Pluripotentiality" for comments.

Smith[29]). The epiblast may therefore rely on a gp130 independent pathway for its expansion during unperturbed development but switches to the gp130 pathway when implantation must be delayed. This suggests that ES cells may represent a specific state of the epiblast. ES cells have nevertheless helped to demonstrate that growth and differentiation can be separated and the critical role of extrinsic factors in controlling progression of the latter.

Cellular pluripotentiality is, however, clearly dependent on the presence of intrinsic factors. The expression of Oct-3–4, a POU family transcription factor, in early blastomeres, ICM cells, epiblast cells, germ cells, and ES cells was suggestive of a possible role in determining pluripotentiality. In its absence, ICM cells become nonproliferating trophoblast cells.[30] Oct-3–4, therefore, acts in ICM cells to prevent their differentiation into trophectoderm (Fig. 11–2). *In vitro* studies suggest the Oct-3–4 relationship with pluripotentiality is complex, as its presence is required to maintain the self-renewing capacity of ES cells, but that it promotes their differentiation into extraembryonic endoderm when transiently expressed at higher levels.[31] Another function of Oct-3–4 in ICM cells is to activate Fgf4 production to promote in a paracrine fashion the maintenance and proliferation of a trophoblast stem-cell population in the adjacent polar trophectoderm.

Nanog, a divergent homeodomain-containing transcription factor, was recently identified as another determinant of pluripotentiality. Its expression is first detected in inner cells of morula-stage embryos, remains on in ICM cells and off in trophoblast cells at the blastocyst stage, becomes restricted to the epiblast after PrE differentiation, and is downregulated at implantation.[32,33] It was also found in primordial germ cells and in some cultured pluripotent cell lines. The ICM of embryos deficient for Nanog differentiate completely into parietal endoderm (PE) but not into trophoblast.[33]

Thus, Nanog may be required later than Oct-3–4 for maintenance of pluripotency in epiblast progenitors (Fig. 11–2). ES cells deficient for *Nanog* also lost pluripotentiality and produced extraembryonic endoderm.[32,33] However, forced expression of *Nanog* in ES cells could bypass their requirement for the LIF/Stat3 pathway. These cells maintained *Oct-3–4* expression and a self-renewing capacity that resisted attempts to promote differentiation.[32,33] The induction of *Nanog* expression is independent of that of *Oct-3–4* as it was readily detected in *Oct-3–4^{-/-}* mutant embryos. The main function of Nanog seems to be to fend off PrE differentiation. The onset of its expression fittingly corresponds to the timing of specification of this tissue, as suggested by the expression of *Gata6*. Given the opposite effects of *Oct-3–4* and *Nanog* regarding PrE differentiation, it will be interesting to investigate how they might regulate *Gata6* expression.

Two other transcription factors have been found to play roles in the maintenance of the epiblast, but genetic studies suggest their activity is required somewhat later. Sox2 is an HMG box-containing transcription factor. Its inactivation leads to a failure to maintain the epiblast beyond the time of PrE differentiation.[34] As a result, the mutant conceptus contains only PE cells and trophoblast cells. The activation of *Fgf4* transcription in the epiblast, possibly required for the maintenance of the polar trophectoderm lineage, is dependent on the association of Oct-3–4 with Sox2.[35] An earlier role of *Sox2* within the ICM could be masked by the persistence of maternal protein up to the blastocyst stage. Foxd3 is a winged helix–forkhead family transcription factor also known to interact with *Oct-3–4*. *Foxd3^{-/-}* mutant blastocysts look normal and still express *Oct-3–4*, *Sox2*, and *Fgf4*, but their ICM cells fail to expand when developed in culture.[36] However, mutant embryos do not present overt abnormalities before E6.5. The role of *Foxd3* seems to be in the maintenance of epiblast progenitors.

EPITHELIALIZATION OF THE EPIBLAST

The PrE differentiates to form the visceral endoderm (VE) and PE. PE cells migrate out of the PrE to line the entire blastocoelic cavity (Fig. 11–1). They secrete extracellular matrix components that assemble to form a specialized membrane called Reichert's membrane, which surrounds the embryo. VE cells cover the epiblast and ExE. At early postimplantation stages, the trophectoderm, Reichert's membrane, and the VE constitute an ensemble that filters and transports nutrients and waste, essential for the survival and growth of the embryo (reviewed by Bielinska et al.[37]). Complex interactions take place between the VE and the underlying ExE and epiblast that drive reciprocal maintenance and differentiation. Functional studies of genes involved in the differentiation of the VE have helped to characterize this interdependency. Thus, deficiencies for the nuclear factors Gata6, vHNF1, and HNF4 all result in early embryonic lethality caused by a primary defect in VE differentiation and an associated degenerescence of the epiblast.[24,25,38–40] Failure to assemble or differentiate a proper VE also results in cavitation defects. In both the *Dab2* and the *γl-laminin* mutants, for example, the proamniotic cavity doesn't form in the epiblast.[27,28] The proamniotic cavity is normally formed shortly after implantation by a process that involves epithelialization of the epiblast cells attached to the basal lamina and possibly apoptosis of medial epiblast cells (Fig.11–1).[41] Embryoid bodies have been used to model the formation of the proamniotic cavity *in vitro* to identify the interactions and the molecules involved. Embryoid bodies form when aggregates of ES cells are cultured in suspension for a few days.[42] They have an outer layer of endoderm surrounding a core of epiblast-like cells, separated by a basal lamina. After a few days in culture, they cavitate in a fashion similar to that of the embryo, except that once epithelialization has occurred, a greater number of cells are left in the middle to undergo apoptosis.[41] Mutant studies and *in vitro* studies have shown that the differentiation of the VE, which depends both directly and indirectly on bone morphogenetic protein (BMP) and Indian hedgehog signaling, is required for the cavitation of the epiblast.[25,27,43,44] Defective interactions with the basal lamina, caused by loss-of-function mutations in γ1-laminin, β1-integrin, or Integrin Linked Kinase (ILK), prevent epiblast cells from becoming polarized and forming an epithelium.[28,45–47] The assembly of the basal lamina also has a positive feedback effect on the differentiation of the VE.[48] It had been postulated that a signal promoting cell death in epiblast cells was delivered by the VE,[41] but mutant studies have brought little evidence to support this hypothesis or even warrant the necessity for such a signal. It seems possible that the epithelialization of the epiblast cells could create a barrier, lowering the flow of nutrients for the few epiblast cells remaining unattached to the basal lamina, thereby triggering their apoptosis.

Attached to the basal lamina, with their apical side bordering the proamniotic cavity, epiblast cells form a tall, columnar pseudo-stratified epithelium. When they divide, epiblast cells have to relinquish contact with the basal lamina, and mitosis occurs at the apical surface of the layer. Lineage tracing of sister cells has shown that they easily become separated when they reestablish contact with the basal lamina, and clonal analysis of their descendants found that this results in the absence of coherent clonal growth in the epiblast up to the gastrulation stage.[49] This cell-mingling effect is linked to the high proliferation rate of the epiblast, which numbers 30 cells at the late blastocyst stage (E 4.0) and a few thousand at the midstreak stage (E 6.75).[50] In contrast, VE cells form a shorter epithelium, which maintains coherent clonal growth throughout these stages.[23,49,51] These data suggest that any possible positional cue to embryonic polarity, inherited from preimplantation stages, is more likely to be maintained in an extraembryonic tissue than in the epiblast at the early egg-cylinder stage. Clonal analysis of descendants from cells of the top layer of the ICM at the early blastocyst stage has been informative in that respect. Labeled cells that became PrE cells were more likely to contribute to distal VE if they were originally close to the animal pole of the blastocyst.[22] Conversely, endoderm precursors close to the vegetal pole were more likely to contribute to VE covering the extraembryonic region. This study suggests that the spatial organization of the blastocyst prefigures the proximal–distal polarity of the postimplantation embryo.[22]

Postimplantation Patterning of Epiblast Cells

LATE COMMITMENT OF EPIBLAST CELLS

Fate mapping by clonal analysis in the early gastrula has demonstrated that the developmental fates and morphogenetic movements of cell populations in different regions of the epiblast are predictable during gastrulation. However, the progeny of individual cells can contribute to a variety of embryonic and extraembryonic tissues in all three germ layers.[1,52–54] Therefore, at this stage, epiblast cells are not irreversibly committed or restricted to any tissue lineage. Acquisition of a more restricted cell fate and lineage determination is likely to take place when gastrulation is completed (from E7.5 onward). Cells exhibit progressive restriction in their potency as they become committed to a precise developmental fate and differentiate.

Major decisions about lineage allocation are made during gastrulation when the single-layered epiblast is transformed into the three primary germ layers of the embryo: the endoderm, the mesoderm, and the ectoderm (Fig. 11–1, reviewed by Tam and Behringer[1]). Posterior and proximal–lateral epiblast cells delaminate and ingress through the primitive streak (PS) as it forms proximally at the posterior side of the embryo. They are subsequently allocated to either the mesoderm or the endoderm germ layers. Fate mapping studies of the PS have revealed a regionalization of cell fate. The type of mesoderm produced depends on the time and the position at which cells ingress though the PS (reviewed by Tam and Behringer[1]). The first cells to go through the streak mainly generate extraembryonic mesoderm. Subsequently, as the PS elongates toward the distal tip of the embryo, cells emerging from the anterior, the middle, and the posterior region of the streak, respectively, contribute to anterior mesoderm and definitive endoderm, paraxial mesoderm, and lateral mesoderm (Fig. 11–3A). This sequential recruitment of epiblast cells to distinct mesodermal fates between the mid- and late gastrula stage also reflects the regionalized expression of mesoderm-inducing and -regionalizing factors (FGF, Wnt, and TGF-β) along the proximal–distal axis of the PS. Progenitors of different mesodermal lineages may therefore be differently specified, depending on the combination of mesoderm-inducing factors they are exposed to during their passage through the PS. Whether this regionalization reflects any restriction in cell potency can be directly tested by heterotopic transplantations. Such experiments assess the developmental plasticity of the transplanted cells when confronted with a different environment. When reintroduced into the epiblast, newly formed mesodermal cells can reingress through the PS and produce all mesoderm types formed by pluripotent epiblast cells apart from lateral mesoderm.[55] These experiments indicate that cellular ingression through the PS does not result in a dramatic restriction of lineage potency.

Distal and anterior epiblast cells do not migrate through the PS. They expand anteriorly and laterally and form the ectoderm germ layer.[52,56,57] At early gastrulation stages, these epiblast cells are not committed to a particular fate as descendants of a single cell can colonize the neuroectoderm, the surface ectoderm, and the amnion ectoderm (Fig. 11–3A). Heterotopic transplantations during early gastrulation stages further revealed their developmental plasticity. Distal epiblast cells of early streak embryos, fated to become ectoderm, can contribute to extraembryonic mesoderm, lateral mesoderm, and primordial germ cells when grafted in the proximal region.[58] In contrast, anterior epiblast cells of late streak embryos grafted in ectopic positions mainly produce neural tissue, indicating that neuroectoderm specification might have occurred at the late streak stage.[56] In vitro culture of germ layer explants provides a useful assay to test ectoderm specification, defined as the behavior of this tissue when grown in isolation.[59,60] The homeobox gene Otx2 is widely expressed in the epiblast prior to gastrulation but becomes progressively restricted to the anterior end of the embryo by late gastrulation and ultimately marks the anterior neuroectoderm. Anterior epiblast explants maintain Otx2 expression in culture only when dissected from midstreak stage embryos onward, indicating that anterior neural identity might be specified after this stage.[60] In vitro culture of anterior epiblast explants has also demonstrated that the expression of engrailed genes is specified by midstreak stage, at least 12 hours before their onset of expression in the midbrain region of the neural tube at the early somite stage.[59] In addition explant–recombination assays provided evidence that anterior mesendoderm-derived signals are critical for establishing neural regional identity in the anterior ectoderm at mid- to late streak stages.[59,60] These studies suggest that the specification of anterior epiblast cells into a neuroectodermal fate occurs around the midstreak stage. Nevertheless, anterior ectoderm cells retain developmental plasticity after their specification. Indeed, when

recombined with VE, cells of the anterior epiblast at the late streak stage can be respecified and can adopt posterior mesodermal fates.[61] Fgf signaling can also change the fate of anterior epiblast from ectoderm to mesoderm. Anterior epiblast explants treated with Fgf2 subsequently express molecular markers consistent with a differentiation into paraxial and axial mesoderm.[62]

In contrast, cells from the organizer are committed to their fate much earlier. The 1924 pioneering embryological experiments of Spemann and Mangold in the amphibian embryo first demonstrated that cells of the dorsal blastopore lip have the ability to induce a complete secondary axis when ectopically grafted onto the ventral side of a host embryo (reviewed by Harland and Gerhart[63]). Distinguishable from other cell populations, the organizer is defined by a unique combination of inductive, morphogenetic, and patterning properties that influence the surrounding host tissues to differentiate into a duplicated axis. Cell populations with developmental and functional properties similar to the Spemann–Mangold organizer have been identified in other vertebrates, such as zebra fish, bird, and mouse. In the mouse, heterotopic transplantation of the organizer cell population to the lateral region of the late streak stage embryo leads to axis duplication[65–68] (reviewed by Camus and Tam[64]). The organizer mainly produces the axial mesoderm (notochord) and the floor plate of the neural tube. Induced host tissues differentiate into neural tissue, paraxial mesoderm (somites), and gut endoderm with different anterior–posterior characteristics. These organizer transplantation studies provide the ultimate demonstration of the competence and plasticity of the ectoderm layer of the embryo at the end of gastrulation.

Based on cell fate and axis-inducing activity, three populations of cells with organizing activities have been identified in the embryo during gastrulation. They represent the successive identities of the organizer: The early gastrula organizer is made up of a few cells in the posterior epiblast at the early streak stage; the midgastrula organizer comprises cells of the anterior tip of the PS at midstreak stage; and finally, the node, an ectoderm and endoderm two-layered structure, is found at the anterior extremity of the fully extended PS[65–67,69] (Fig. 11–3A). Regardless of the gastrulation stage the donor organizer is derived from, transplantations studies reveal that differentiation of the organizer cells is regulated autonomously. When transplanted to an ectopic site, the organizer population always self-differentiates and influences neighboring host tissues to change their fate.

Cell fate analysis of these distinct organizer populations indicates that they undergo significant changes in their cellular composition during gastrulation.[69] This study suggests that the gastrula organizer is composed of transiently recruited precursors. Most of them are allocated to various anterior–posterior levels of the axial mesendoderm as the embryo develops. Gene expression analysis has revealed that the gastrula organizer expresses different combinations of organizer-specific genes during gastrulation (reviewed by Camus et al.[64]). Whether the changes in lineage potency and molecular properties of the organizer population during gastrulation

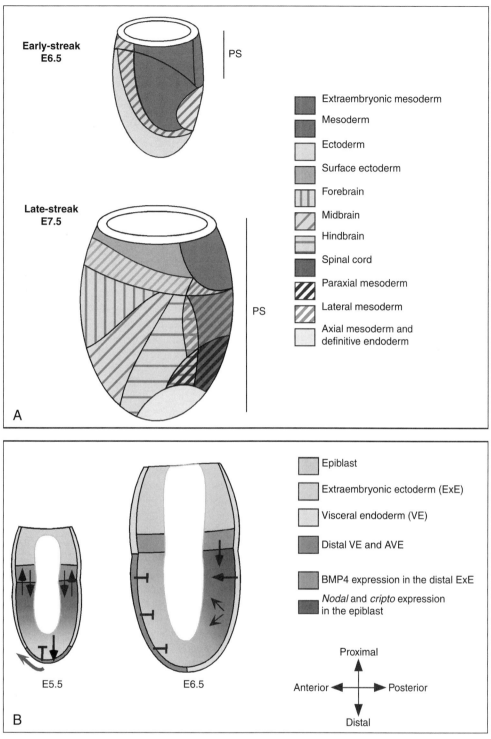

Figure 11-3. *Fate map and early patterning of epiblast cells.* (A) In the fate map of epiblast cells at the early streak and late streak stages, a black vertical bar represents the extent of the primitive streak (PS). Only the epiblast layer of the embryo is represented. Epiblast cells recruited into the proximal PS at the early streak stage generate predominantly extraembryonic mesoderm. Lateral mesoderm and paraxial mesoderm cells arise at more distal positions as the PS extends. The anterior–distal region of the PS contains the precursors of axial mesendoderm cells, the organizer derivatives. In the anterior region, at the late streak stage, epiblast cells have been specified to form neuroectoderm with different anterior–posterior identities. (B) Proximal–distal and anterior–posterior patterning of the epiblast is shown. At E5.5, Nodal signaling from the epiblast is required to specify distal visceral endoderm (VE) cells. Distal VE cells express Nodal antagonists that inhibit Nodal action in the distal epiblast. Reciprocal interactions between the epiblast and the extraembryonic ectoderm (ExE) reinforce Nodal signaling in the proximal epiblast. At E6.5, anterior visceral endoderm cells repress Nodal and possibly Wnt expression in the anterior epiblast. Signals derived from the posterior VE, the posterior ExE, or both may contribute to induce, maintain, or both the PS in the posterior epiblast region. During gastrulation, signals derived from the organizer are required for the patterning of adjacent tissues.

135

reflect significant differences in axis-inducing activity has not yet been clearly demonstrated. Together, these results indicate that the mouse gastrula organizer is a dynamic cell population. The chick gastrula organizer, Hensen's node, is also composed of transiently recruited precursors that acquire and lose organizer gene expression as they coast through the node region. Embryological experiments have demonstrated that reciprocal interactions between Hensen's node and its neighboring tissues ensure the maintenance of an organizer cell state in a fixed spatial domain with dynamic cellular composition.[70] Whether similar interactions between the middle region and the anterior region of the PS regulate the organizer cell state in the mouse embryo is unknown.

INTERACTIONS WITH EXTRAEMBRYONIC LINEAGES ESTABLISH EPIBLAST POLARITY BEFORE GASTRULATION

Because of the cell-mingling phenomenon characterized within the epiblast at pregastrula stages, it is generally assumed that any spatial information derived from early polarity cues would be transmitted to the epiblast by extraembryonic tissues.[22,49,51] Genetic data, experimental embryology, and results from chimera experiments have provided compelling evidence that reciprocal interactions between the extraembryonic and embryonic lineages establish and reinforce early patterning in the mouse embryo (reviewed by Beddington and Robertson[2] and Lu et al.[3]).

A subset of VE cells at the distal tip of the embryo starts to express a specific repertoire of genes at E5.5. It comprises the homeobox gene Hex as well as Cerl and Lefty1, which encode secreted proteins.[71–74] Between E5.5 and E6.0, their distal domain of expression is displaced proximally to a position opposite of where the PS will eventually form, marking for the first time the anterior of the embryo. Lineage-tracing studies demonstrated that this shift in the position of the expression domain is the consequence of a unidirectional movement of distal VE cells toward the anterior[71,75,76] (Fig. 11–3B). These cells express additional markers once they have reached their anterior position (reviewed by Beddington et al.,[2] Perea-Gomez et al.,[4] and Camus et al.[64]). This group of cells was therefore called anterior visceral endoderm, or AVE (Fig. 11–3B). These findings demonstrated that the VE is patterned along the proximal–distal axis of the embryo at E5.5 and along the anterior–posterior axis from E6.0. Could this proximal–distal patterning of the VE prefigure the establishment of the anterior–posterior axis in the epiblast? Gene expression analyses indicate that the ExE is also patterned along the proximal–distal axis at early stages before gastrulation. The TGF-β-secreted molecule Bmp4 and the T-box genes Eomesodermin (Eomes) and Brachyury (T) are expressed specifically in the distal ExE cells abutting the proximal epiblast at E6.0[77–79] (Fig. 11–3B). In the epiblast, two factors required for PS and mesoderm formation, the TGF-β molecule Nodal and its coreceptor Cripto, first found throughout the epiblast at E5.0, see their expression progressively restricted to a proximal region by E5.75.[80,81] The secreted molecule Wnt3, involved in PS formation, is also detected in the proximal epiblast adjacent to the ExE at this

stage.[82] By E6.25, the expression of Nodal, Cripto, and Wnt3 becomes circumscribed to the posterior epiblast, where genes involved in mesoderm migration, such as T and Fgf8, are then induced and where the PS arises at E6.5 (Fig. 11–3B). Together, these studies have led to the proposal that the proximal–distal polarity of the early postimplantation embryo is transformed into the anterior–posterior polarity of the gastrulating embryo through asymmetric cell movements in the VE and posterior restriction of proximal epiblast markers (reviewed by Beddington et al.[2]).

The establishment of a proximal–distal pattern and its transformation into the anterior–posterior axis of the gastrula stage embryo has been shown to depend on signals from the ExE and the VE that modulate Nodal signaling in the epiblast. Nodal is a major player in early embryonic patterning. Mouse embryos bearing a mutation in the Nodal gene fail to express other proximal epiblast markers and do not form a PS. In addition, AVE specification is abolished in Nodal[−/−] mutants.[80,83–85] Nodal signals via a complex formed by type II and type I serine-threonine kinase receptors (Act RIIA, Act RIIB, ALK 4, ALK 7) and EGF-CFC cofactors (cripto or cryptic). The activated receptor complex phosphorylates Smad2 and Smad3, which associate with Smad4 and translocate to the nucleus. There, they cooperatively regulate the transcription of target genes with other DNA-binding proteins, such as the forkhead transcription factor Foxh1 (reviewed by Whitman[86]). The expression of Nodal in the epiblast, extremely dynamic, is under the control of two cis-regulatory elements characterized by transgenesis. The 5′ proximal epiblast enhancer (PEE) controls Nodal expression in the proximal epiblast and in the PS at later stages. The intronic asymmetric enhancer (ASE), containing two Foxh1-binding sites, is involved in a positive feedback loop that activates Nodal expression throughout the epiblast and in the VE.[87,88]

Recent studies have suggested that reciprocal interactions between the ExE and the proximal epiblast region are likely to establish a proximal–distal gradient of Nodal signaling in the prestreak stage mouse embryo.[85,89] Compound mutants, chimera analysis, and tissue-explants studies have demonstrated that the proprotein convertases Spc1 and Spc4 produced by distal ExE cells are required to cleave the immature form of Nodal secreted by adjacent proximal epiblast cells. Spc1 and Spc4 therefore directly potentiate Nodal signaling in the proximal epiblast of the pregastrula embryo.[89] Moreover, Beck et al. have proposed that Spc1 and Spc4 regulate Nodal activity in the epiblast indirectly by stimulating the induction of BMP4 in the ExE. In turn, BMP4 would signal to the epiblast, leading to the amplification of the expression of the Nodal coreceptor Cripto in cells adjacent to the ExE.[89] Previous mutant analysis suggested that Nodal signaling is involved at early stages in regulating and maintaining BMP4 expression in the ExE.[85] These findings therefore indicate that reciprocal tissue interactions are essential for the establishment of proximal–distal patterning (Fig. 11–3B).

Similar interactions involving the regulation of Nodal signaling have been described between the epiblast and the VE.

Analysis of mutant embryos indicates that the initial specification of distal VE cells requires high levels of Nodal signal produced in the epiblast and transduced by Smad2 in the VE[85,90–92] (Fig. 11–3B). *Nodal* expression in the VE is also likely activated, via the autoregulatory element ASE, by Nodal produced in the epiblast.[85,90] In addition to Nodal signals, the transcription factors Otx2, Foxa2, and Lhx1 and the Wnt signal transducer β-catenin are required for correct specification of distal VE cells.[93–96] Little is known about the mechanisms that drive the distal-to-anterior movement of VE cells between E5.5 and E6.0.[76] However, in mutant embryos in which Nodal signaling is attenuated, AVE markers such as *Hex* are still expressed in distal positions at E6.5. This indicates that distal VE cells fail to move anteriorly in the absence of high Nodal levels.[81,91,92,97] A similar phenotype has been observed in mouse embryos lacking β-catenin.[96] Lineage-tracing analysis and transgenic rescue experiments have demonstrated that Otx2 is required in the VE for its distal to anterior movement.[94,95]

Ablation of the AVE provided evidence of a role for this tissue in patterning the anterior epiblast fated to generate the anterior neuroectoderm and surface ectoderm.[98] Analyses of chimeric embryos with a mutant VE and a wild-type epiblast have demonstrated that Foxa2, Lhx1, Otx2, and Nodal are required in the AVE to ensure proper development of anterior neural structures (reviewed by Beddington *et al.*[2]). Based on these findings and with the knowledge that an ectopically grafted organizer (early gastrula organizer or node) can only induce a secondary axis lacking anterior neural structures, the AVE has been proposed as the mouse equivalent of the amphibian head organizer, likely to play a central role in the induction of anterior neural tissues. However, transplantation studies, germ-layer explant assays, and genetic studies have clearly demonstrated that the AVE alone cannot induce anterior neuroectoderm but rather can impart anterior fate on the adjacent epiblast by repressing the action of posterior signals[68,82,94] (reviewed by Perea-Gomez *et al.*[4]).

The first evidence of an early role of the distal VE and the AVE cells in regulating the expression of posterior markers in the epiblast came from explant recombination experiments. The AVE of early to midstreak stage embryos does not induce anterior neuroectoderm markers but can significantly reduce the expression of *T* and *Cripto* in epiblast explants. This repressing activity is abolished in *Otx2*-mutant AVE.[94] Results from genetic analyses are consistent with these observations (reviewed by Perea-Gomez *et al.*[4]). Inactivation of genes required for AVE specification, such as the signal transducer Smad2 or the transcription factors Foxa2 and Lhx1, results in the enlargement of proximal–posterior fates throughout the epiblast and the severe reduction or absence of distal–anterior epiblast derivatives.[90,93] The action of the AVE in epiblast patterning is partly mediated by two secreted proteins, Cerl and Lefty1, that function as extracellular Nodal antagonists (reviewed by Whitman[86]). *Cerl* and *Lefty1* expression is first detected in the distal VE and then in the AVE prior to gastrulation.[73,74,99] Interestingly, the expression of these two Nodal antagonists in the VE is most likely dependent on

Nodal itself as part of a negative feedback loop.[85,90,91] *Cerl*[−/−], *Lefty1*[−/−] compound mutants, and chimeric embryos lacking Cerl and Lefty1 expression in the VE show supernumerary primitive streaks.[99] These results indicate that Cerl and Lefty1 are required in the AVE to restrict the action of Nodal signals involved in PS induction and mesoderm formation (Fig. 11–3B). These findings strengthen the hypothesis that the main function of the AVE is to provide repressing signals that prevent the anterior epiblast from adopting a posterior fate under the influence of signals such as Nodal. Subsequent interactions between anterior epiblast and anterior mesendoderm tissues derived from the organizer allow anterior neural development to proceed (reviewed by Martinez-Barbera and Beddington[100]).

Nodal may not be the only signal antagonized by AVE cells. Wnt3 is required downstream of Nodal for PS formation in the posterior epiblast. Moreover, ectopic or deregulated Wnt signaling leads to axis duplication at early gastrulation stages.[101–103] Interestingly, the Wnt antagonist Dkk1 is expressed in the AVE, and biochemical data suggest that the secreted protein Cerl might also function as a Wnt antagonist.[104,105] This is consistent with the suggestion that another role of the AVE would be to antagonize Wnt signals in the epiblast. However the capacity of Dkk1 and Cerl to restrict the extent of Wnt signaling in the epiblast has not been demonstrated so far.

Because interactions between AVE and epiblast clearly contribute to the anterior–posterior patterning, a role for posterior VE cells in patterning the posterior epiblast is conceivable. Although asymmetric gene expressions have been reported in the posterior VE, no evidence so far indicates that posterior VE cells have such a role.[3]

COMPLEX INTERACTIONS BETWEEN DISTINCT SIGNALING PATHWAYS DURING EPIBLAST PATTERNING

A network of signaling pathways regulates the migration and the differentiation of epiblast cells during gastrulation. Genetic studies and experimental embryology have provided effective tools for investigating connecting points in this network and characterizing some of the interactions that govern the determination of different cell fates.

In the posterior region, epiblast cells that delaminate through the PS region produce a variety of mesoderm and endoderm types under the influence of different signaling pathways. Recent studies have suggested that, as in other vertebrate embryos, graded levels of Nodal signaling in the posterior epiblast could govern the generation of distinct PS derivatives (extraembryonic mesoderm, embryonic mesoderm, and definitive endoderm).[86,106] Characterization of *Nodal* hypomorph mutants displaying different degrees of Nodal activity have indicated that epiblast cells are sensitive to the level of Nodal signaling.[97] Loss of function of its downstream mediator Foxh1, its modulator Arkadia, or of the Spc1 and Spc4 Nodal convertases does not abolish mesoderm formation, but it impairs the generation of axial mesoderm and definitive endoderm.[89,91,107,108] These results indicate that Nodal signals for the formation of axial mesendoderm tissues derived from the organizer must be higher than those for the formation of more posterior–lateral mesoderm tissues. Negative regulators of the pathway are also likely to contribute to the establishment of a gradient of Nodal activity. Thus, the combined loss-of-function of the Nodal antagonists Cerl and Lefty1 or of the transcriptional corepressor Drap1 lead to the expansion of axial mesendoderm derivatives at the expense of paraxial mesoderm.[99,109] A recent study provided compelling evidence that graded Nodal signaling is also required for the specification within the organizer region of the anterior definitive endoderm and prechordal plate progenitors. When Nodal activity is specifically lowered in the proximal–posterior epiblast because of the exclusive deletion of the *cis*-regulatory element PEE of the *Nodal* gene, the anterior definitive endoderm and prechordal plate are missing.[110] A similar phenotype has been observed when Smad2 activity is removed from the epiblast by a conditional inactivation strategy. Interestingly, in both of these mutants, the node, the notochord, and the floor plate develop normally. In contrast, inactivation of one copy of *Smad3* in the context of the *Smad2*-deficient epiblast leads to a failure to specify all organizer derivatives, including the notochord.[110] Together, these results indicate that graded Nodal signaling in the posterior epiblast contributes to mesoderm and endoderm patterning, requiring increasing levels of Nodal for posterior–lateral mesoderm, notochord, prechordal plate, and anterior endoderm formation. Recent evidence suggests that the Wnt signaling pathway is also involved in the choice between endoderm and mesoderm fates. Indeed, conditional deletion of *β-catenin* in the epiblast results in endoderm cells adopting precardiac mesoderm cell fate[111] (reviewed by Tam *et al.*[112]).

The analysis of the targeted disruption of *Fgf receptor 1 (Fgfr1)* provides a vivid illustration of the interactions between the major signaling pathways. *Fgfr1* expression is detected throughout the epiblast at pregastrulation stages and subsequently into the posterior part of the PS. *Fgfr1*-mutant embryos display a severe reduction of lateral and paraxial mesoderm and an apparent expansion of the axial mesendoderm.[113,114] Chimeras analyses indicated that *Fgfr1*[-/-] cells fail to undergo the epithelial to mesenchymal transition, accumulate in the PS, and form ectopic neural tubes.[115,116] Therefore, incorrectly specified mesoderm precursors are able to respond to neuralizing signals and to change their fate accordingly. Further molecular analysis of the chimeric embryos and explant assays provided remarkable insights into the downstream targets of the Fgfr1 pathway and the mechanisms by which Fgfr1 signaling controls both the patterning of mesoderm cells and morphogenesis.[117] Expression of the T-box gene *Tbx6* is dramatically reduced in *Fgfr1*-mutant embryos. The phenotype of *Tbx6* mutants is similar to that of *Fgfr1* in that cells fated to form paraxial mesoderm differentiate into ectopic neural tubes.[118] *Fgfr1* might therefore act through *Tbx6* for the patterning of paraxial mesoderm cells. The expression of the zinc-finger transcription factor Snail is also missing in *Fgfr1* mutant cells. Snail normally represses the expression of the cell adhesion molecule E-cadherin. As a result, *Fgfr1*[-/-] cells have abnormally high levels of E-cadherin,

which accounts for their failure to achieve the epithelial to mesenchymal transition. Ciruna and Rossant[117] have reported that this defect also indirectly affects Wnt signaling and the patterning of mesoderm cells. Indeed, in mutant cells with high levels of E-cadherin, β-catenin is sequestered at the cell membrane, and its nuclear function in mediating Wnt signaling is impaired. In accordance with this finding, Fgfr1-deficient embryos do not express T, a direct target of Wnt signaling, in the regions of the PS fated to generate lateral and paraxial mesoderm. These observations can be related to the phenotype of *Wnt3a* mutants in which *T* expression is also missing and cells fated to produce the paraxial mesoderm form ectopic neural tubes.[119] These studies provide evidence that interactions between the FGF and the Wnt pathways play an essential role in morphogenesis and in the patterning of mesoderm cells by regulating both cell adhesion and cell fate determination.

How cells integrate different signals and modulate their response accordingly is a key issue. The study of a gene called *Churchill (ChCh),* recently characterized in the chick, provides an example of a possible mechanism.[120] It encodes a zinc-finger protein that may play a pivotal role in altering the response of epiblast cells to Fgf signaling. During gastrulation, Nodal signaling and Fgf signaling cooperate to induce *T* and *Tbx6L* in the epiblast and to regulate cell ingression through the PS. However, continued exposure to Fgf signaling induces *ChCh* in the epiblast, subsequently leading to the activation of Smad-interacting-protein 1 (Sip1) that blocks further mesoderm induction. Concomitantly, *ChCh*-expressing epiblast cells become sensitive to neural-inducing signals emanating from the node. This study therefore suggests that *ChCh* functions as a switch determining the response of epiblast cells to Fgf signaling.

Summary

Although it is difficult to reconstruct past events from today's observations, it appears likely that the evolution of viviparity in the mammalian lineage was made possible by that of pluripotentiality. To survive and develop *in utero*, the mammalian embryo has to develop an extraembryonic interface that feeds and protects embryonic precursors. However, these embryonic precursors have to possess a protection of their own, dependent on intrinsic factors, because they must remain unresponsive to the signals that first promote the differentiation of extraembryonic lineages. A subsequent release of this intrinsic blockage to differentiation may allow signals from the extraembryonic tissues to initiate the patterning of the embryo. On the assumption that positional cues inherited from the egg play a role in patterning the embryo, extraembryonic tissues constitute the most likely vessel to carry them until the epiblast becomes receptive. When it does, a network of signaling pathways coordinates the growth, the specification, and the migration of the different cell populations that compose the embryo. The first overt signs of embryonic differentiation, marking the establishment of the anterior–posterior axis, become apparent quite late in development in comparison to other vertebrates. As differentiation is always associated with a loss in developmental potency, this correlates with the prolonged undifferentiated state of the epiblast.

What lies ahead is the relentless characterization of the molecular and cellular interactions that govern the establishment, the maturation, and the differentiation of the epiblast. Beyond this, we need a deeper understanding of what goes on outside of the cell, within its cytoplasm, and in its nucleus while it is exposed to the signals that impinge on its fate in the embryo. What is, for example, the range of the secreted signaling molecules and of their antagonists? How are graded levels of a particular signal generated, and how are they read and integrated by individual cells? One key challenge will be to correlate these events with specific changes in the status of the chromatin. These studies will no doubt contribute to the stem cell field, bringing valuable insights into the mechanisms that control their differentiation toward a given lineage.

ACKNOWLEDGMENTS

We thank Dr. R. Pedersen for the opportunity to write this chapter. We are grateful to Drs. J. Aghion and D. Saberan-Djoneidi for critical reading of the manuscript, and to Drs. C. Chazaud and M. Zernicka-Goetz for helpful discussions. We would like to acknowledge M. Barre for help with the figures. Our laboratory receives support from the Centre National de la Recherche Scientifique, the Ministère de la Recherche (ACI grant), the Fondation pour la Recherche Médicale, and the Association pour la Recherche contre le Cancer (ARC 5456).

REFERENCES

1. Tam, P.P., and Behringer, R.R. (1997). Mouse gastrulation: the formation of a mammalian body plan. *Mech. Dev.* **68,** 3–25.
2. Beddington, R.S., and Robertson, E.J. (1999). Axis development and early asymmetry in mammals. *Cell* **96,** 195–209.
3. Lu, C.C., Brennan, J., and Robertson, E.J. (2001). From fertilization to gastrulation: axis formation in the mouse embryo. *Curr. Opin. Genet. Dev.* **11,** 384–392.
4. Perea-Gomez, A., Rhinn, M., and Ang, S.L. (2001). Role of the anterior visceral endoderm in restricting posterior signals in the mouse embryo. *Int. J. Dev. Biol.* **45,** 311–320.
5. Gardner, R.L. (2001). The initial phase of embryonic patterning in mammals. *Int. Rev. Cytol.* **203,** 233–290.
6. Zernicka-Goetz, M. (2002). Patterning of the embryo: the first spatial decisions in the life of a mouse. *Development* **129,** 815–829.
7. Strahl, B.D., and Allis, C.D. (2000). The language of covalent histone modifications. *Nature* **403,** 41–45.
8. Reik, W., Dean, W., and Walter, J. (2001). Epigenetic reprogramming in mammalian development. *Science* **293,** 1089–1093.
9. Jaenisch, R., and Bird, A. (2003). Epigenetic regulation of gene expression: how the genome integrates intrinsic and environmental signals. *Nat. Genet.* **33 Suppl.,** 245–254.
10. Pedersen, R.A. (1986) Potency, lineage, and allocation in preimplantation mouse embryos. *In* "Experimental Approaches to Mammalian Embryonic Development" (J. Rossant and R.A. Pedersen, eds.), pp. 3–33. Cambridge University Press, Cambridge.

11. Gardner, R.L. (2001). Specification of embryonic axes begins before cleavage in normal mouse development. *Development* **128,** 839–847.
12. Piotrowska, K., Wianny, F., Pedersen, R.A., and Zernicka-Goetz, M. (2001). Blastomeres arising from the first cleavage division have distinguishable fates in normal mouse development. *Development* **128,** 3739–3748.
13. Piotrowska, K., and Zernicka-Goetz, M. (2002). Early patterning of the mouse embryo—contributions of sperm and egg. *Development* **129,** 5803–5813.
14. Kelly, S.J., Mulnard, J.G., and Graham, C.F. (1978). Cell division and cell allocation in early mouse development. *J. Embryol. Exp. Morphol.* **48,** 37–51.
15. Garbutt, C.L., Johnson, M.H., and George, M.A. (1987). When and how does cell division order influence cell allocation to the inner cell mass of the mouse blastocyst? *Development* **100,** 325–332.
16. Piotrowska, K., and Zernicka-Goetz, M. (2001). Role for sperm in spatial patterning of the early mouse embryo. *Nature* **409,** 517–521.
17. Plusa, B., Piotrowska, K., and Zernicka-Goetz, M. (2002). Sperm entry position provides a surface marker for the first cleavage plane of the mouse zygote. *Genesis* **32,** 193–198.
18. Davies, T.J., and Gardner, R.L. (2002). The plane of first cleavage is not related to the distribution of sperm components in the mouse. *Hum. Reprod.* **17,** 2368–2379.
19. Fujimori, T., Kurotaki, Y., Miyazaki, J.I., and Nabeshima, Y.I. (2003). Analysis of cell lineage in two- and four-cell mouse embryos. *Development* **130,** 5113–5112.
20. Gardner, R.L., and Rossant, J. (1979). Investigation of the fate of 4–5 day post-coitum mouse inner cell mass cells by blastocyst injection. *J. Embryol. Exp. Morphol.* **52,** 141–152.
21. Gardner, R.L. (1982). Investigation of cell lineage and differentiation in the extraembryonic endoderm of the mouse embryo. *J. Embryol. Exp. Morphol.* **68,** 175–198.
22. Weber, R.J., Pedersen, R.A., Wianny, F., Evans, M.J., and Zernicka-Goetz, M. (1999). Polarity of the mouse embryo is anticipated before implantation. *Development* **126,** 5591–5598.
23. Zernicka-Goetz, M. (Personal communication).
24. Morrisey, E.E., Tang, Z., Sigrist, K., Lu, M.M., Jiang, F., Ip, H.S., and Parmacek, M.S. (1998). GATA6 regulates HNF4 and is required for differentiation of visceral endoderm in the mouse embryo. *Genes Dev.* **12,** 3579–3590.
25. Koutsourakis, M., Langeveld, A., Patient, R., Beddington, R., and Grosveld, F. (1999). The transcription factor GATA6 is essential for early extraembryonic development (corrected and republished). *Development* **126,** 723–732.
26. Morrisey, E.E., Musco, S., Chen, M.Y., Lu, M.M., Leiden, J.M., and Parmacek, M.S. (2000). The gene encoding the mitogen-responsive phosphoprotein Dab2 is differentially regulated by GATA-6 and GATA-4 in the visceral endoderm. *J. Biol. Chem.* **275,** 19,949–19,954.
27. Yang, D.H., Smith, E.R., Roland, I.H., Sheng, Z., He, J., Martin, W.D., Hamilton, T.C., Lambeth, J.D., and Xu, X.X. (2002). Disabled-2 is essential for endodermal cell positioning and structure formation during mouse embryogenesis. *Dev. Biol.* **251,** 27–44.
28. Smyth, N., Vatansever, H.S., Murray, P., Meyer, M., Frie, C., Paulsson, M., and Edgar, D. (1999). Absence of basement membranes after targeting the LAMC1 gene results in embryonic lethality due to failure of endoderm differentiation. *J. Cell Biol.* **144,** 151–160.
29. Smith, A.G. (2001). Embryo-derived stem cells: of mice and men. *Annu. Rev. Cell Dev. Biol.* **17,** 435–462.

30. Nichols, J., Zevnik, B., Anastassiadis, K., Niwa, H., Klewe-Nebenius, D., Chambers, I., Scholer, H., and Smith, A. (1998). Formation of pluripotent stem cells in the mammalian embryo depends on the POU transcription factor Oct-4. *Cell* **95,** 379–391.

31. Niwa, H., Miyazaki, J., and Smith, A.G. (2000). Quantitative expression of Oct-3–4 defines differentiation, dedifferentiation or self-renewal of ES cells. *Nat. Genet.* **24,** 372–376.

32. Chambers, I., Colby, D., Robertson, M., Nichols, J., Lee, S., Tweedie, S., and Smith, A. (2003). Functional expression cloning of Nanog, a pluripotency sustaining factor in embryonic stem cells. *Cell* **113,** 643–655.

33. Mitsui, K., Tokuzawa, Y., Itoh, H., Segawa, K., Murakami, M., Takahashi, K., Maruyama, M., Maeda, M., and Yamanaka, S. (2003). The homeoprotein Nanog is required for maintenance of pluripotency in mouse epiblast and ES cells. *Cell* **113,** 631–642.

34. Avilion, A.A., Nicolis, S.K., Pevny, L.H., Perez, L., Vivian, N., and Lovell-Badge, R. (2003). Multipotent cell lineages in early mouse development depend on SOX2 function. *Genes Dev.* **17,** 126–140.

35. Ambrosetti, D.C., Basilico, C., and Dailey, L. (1997). Synergistic activation of the fibroblast growth factor 4 enhancer by Sox2 and Oct-3 depends on protein–protein interactions facilitated by a specific spatial arrangement of factor binding sites. *Mol. Cell Biol.* **17,** 6321–6329.

36. Hanna, L.A., Foreman, R.K., Tarasenko, I.A., Kessler, D.S., and Labosky, P.A. (2002). Requirement for Foxd3 in maintaining pluripotent cells of the early mouse embryo. *Genes Dev.* **16,** 2650–2661.

37. Bielinska, M., Narita, N., and Wilson, D.B. (1999). Distinct roles for visceral endoderm during embryonic mouse development. *Int. J. Dev. Biol.* **43,** 183–205.

38. Chen, W.S., Manova, K., Weinstein, D.C., Duncan, S.A., Plump, A.S., Prezioso, V.R., Bachvarova, R.F., and Darnell, J.E., Jr. (1994). Disruption of the HNF-4 gene, expressed in visceral endoderm, leads to cell death in embryonic ectoderm and impaired gastrulation of mouse embryos. *Genes Dev.* **8,** 2466–2477.

39. Coffinier, C., Thepot, D., Babinet, C., Yaniv, M., and Barra, J. (1999). Essential role for the homeoprotein vHNF1/HNF1beta in visceral endoderm differentiation. *Development* **126,** 4785–4794.

40. Barbacci, E., Reber, M., Ott, M.O., Breillat, C., Huetz, F., and Cereghini, S. (1999). Variant hepatocyte nuclear factor 1 is required for visceral endoderm specification. *Development* **126,** 4795–4805.

41. Coucouvanis, E., and Martin, G.R. (1995). Signals for death and survival: a two-step mechanism for cavitation in the vertebrate embryo. *Cell* **83,** 279–287.

42. Robertson, E. (1987) Embryo-derived stem cell lines. *In* "Teratocarcinomas and Embryonic Stem Cells, a Practical Approach" (E. Robertson, ed.), pp. 71–112. IRL Press, Oxford.

43. Coucouvanis, E., and Martin, G.R. (1999). BMP signaling plays a role in visceral endoderm differentiation and cavitation in the early mouse embryo. *Development* **126,** 535–546.

44. Maye, P., Becker, S., Kasameyer, E., Byrd, N., and Grabel, L. (2000). Indian hedgehog signaling in extraembryonic endoderm and ectoderm differentiation in ES embryoid bodies. *Mech. Dev.* **94,** 117–132.

45. Murray, P., and Edgar, D. (2000). Regulation of programmed cell death by basement membranes in embryonic development. *J. Cell Biol.* **150,** 1215–1221.

46. Li, S., Harrison, D., Carbonetto, S., Fassler, R., Smyth, N., Edgar, D., and Yurchenco, P.D. (2002). Matrix assembly, regulation, and survival functions of laminin and its receptors in embryonic stem cell differentiation. *J. Cell Biol.* **157,** 1279–1290.

47. Sakai, T., Li, S., Docheva, D., Grashoff, C., Sakai, K., Kostka, G., Braun, A., Pfeifer, A., Yurchenco, P.D., and Fassler, R. (2003). Integrin-linked kinase (ILK) is required for polarizing the epiblast, cell adhesion, and controlling actin accumulation. *Genes Dev.* **17,** 926–940.

48. Murray, P., and Edgar, D. (2001). Regulation of the differentiation and behavior of extraembryonic endodermal cells by basement membranes. *J. Cell Sci.* **114,** 931–939.

49. Gardner, R.L., and Cockroft, D.L. (1998). Complete dissipation of coherent clonal growth occurs before gastrulation in mouse epiblast. *Development* **125,** 2397–2402.

50. Snow, M.H. (1977). Gastrulation in the mouse: growth and regionalization of the epiblast. *J. Embryol. Exp. Morphol.* **42,** 293–303.

51. Lawson, K.A., and Pedersen, R.A. (1987). Cell fate, morphogenetic movement, and population kinetics of embryonic endoderm at the time of germ layer formation in the mouse. *Development* **101,** 627–652.

52. Lawson, K.A., Meneses, J.J., and Pedersen, R.A. (1991). Clonal analysis of epiblast fate during germ layer formation in the mouse embryo. *Development* **113,** 891–911.

53. Lawson, K.A., and Pedersen, R.A. (1992). Clonal analysis of cell fate during gastrulation and early neurulation in the mouse. *Ciba Found Symp.* **165,** 3–21.

54. Lawson, K.A., and Hage, W.J. (1994). Clonal analysis of the origin of primordial germ cells in the mouse. *Ciba Found. Symp.* **182,** 68–84.

55. Tam, P.P., Parameswaran, M., Kinder, S.J., and Weinberger, R.P. (1997). The allocation of epiblast cells to the embryonic heart and other mesodermal lineages: the role of ingression and tissue movement during gastrulation. *Development* **124,** 1631–1642.

56. Beddington, R.S. (1982). An autoradiographic analysis of tissue potency in different regions of the embryonic ectoderm during gastrulation in the mouse. *J. Embryol. Exp. Morphol.* **69,** 265–285.

57. Quinlan, G.A., Williams, E.A., Tan, S.S., and Tam, P.P. (1995). Neuroectodermal fate of epiblast cells in the distal region of the mouse egg cylinder: implication for body plan organization during early embryogenesis. *Development* **121,** 87–98.

58. Tam, P.P., and Zhou, S.X. (1996). The allocation of epiblast cells to ectodermal and germ line lineages is influenced by the position of the cells in the gastrulating mouse embryo. *Dev. Biol.* **178,** 124–132.

59. Ang, S.L., and Rossant, J. (1993). Anterior mesendoderm induces mouse Engrailed genes in explant cultures. *Development* **118,** 139–149.

60. Ang, S.L., Conlon, R.A., Jin, O., and Rossant, J. (1994). Positive and negative signals from mesoderm regulate the expression of mouse Otx2 in ectoderm explants. *Development* **120,** 2979–2989.

61. Belaoussoff, M., Farrington, S.M., and Baron, M.H. (1998). Hematopoietic induction and respecification of A–P identity by visceral endoderm signaling in the mouse embryo. *Development* **125,** 5009–5018.

62. Burdsal, C.A., Flannery, M.L., and Pedersen, R.A. (1998). Fgf2 alters the fate of mouse epiblast from ectoderm to mesoderm *in vitro. Dev. Biol.* **198,** 231–244.

63. Harland, R., and Gerhart, J. (1997). Formation and function of Spemann's organizer. *Annu. Rev. Cell Dev. Biol.* **13,** 611–667.

64. Camus, A., and Tam, P.P. (1999). The organizer of the gastrulating mouse embryo. *Curr. Top. Dev. Biol.* **45,** 117–153.

65. Beddington, R.S. (1994). Induction of a second neural axis by the mouse node. *Development* **120,** 613–620.

66. Sulik, K., Dehart, D.B., Iangaki, T., Carson, J.L., Vrablic, T., Gesteland, K., and Schoenwolf, G.C. (1994). Morphogenesis of the murine node and notochordal plate. *Dev. Dyn.* **201,** 260–278.

67. Tam, P.P., Steiner, K.A., Zhou, S.X., and Quinlan, G.A. (1997). Lineage and functional analyses of the mouse organizer. *Cold Spring Harb. Symp. Quant. Biol.* **62,** 135–144.

68. Tam, P.P., and Steiner, K.A. (1999). Anterior patterning by synergistic activity of the early gastrula organizer and the anterior germ layer tissues of the mouse embryo. *Development* **126,** 5171–5179.

69. Kinder, S.J., Tsang, T.E., Wakamiya, M., Sasaki, H., Behringer, R.R., Nagy, A., and Tam, P.P. (2001). The organizer of the mouse gastrula is composed of a dynamic population of progenitor cells for the axial mesoderm. *Development* **128,** 3623–3634.

70. Joubin, K., and Stern, C.D. (1999). Molecular interactions continuously define the organizer during the cell movements of gastrulation. *Cell* **98,** 559–571.

71. Thomas, P.Q., Brown, A., and Beddington, R.S. (1998). Hex: a homeobox gene revealing peri-implantation asymmetry in the mouse embryo and an early transient marker of endothelial cell precursors. *Development* **125,** 85–94.

72. Rodriguez, T.A., Casey, E.S., Harland, R.M., Smith, J.C., and Beddington, R.S. (2001). Distinct enhancer elements control Hex expression during gastrulation and early organogenesis. *Dev. Biol.* **234,** 304–316.

73. Stanley, E.G., Biben, C., Allison, J., Hartley, L., Wicks, I.P., Campbell, I.K., McKinley, M., Barnett, L., Koentgen, F., Robb, L., and Harvey, R.P. (2000). Targeted insertion of a lacZ reporter gene into the mouse Cer1 locus reveals complex and dynamic expression during embryogenesis. *Genesis* **26,** 259–264.

74. Juan, H., and Hamada, H. (2001). Roles of Nodal–Lefty regulatory loops in embryonic patterning of vertebrates. *Genes Cells* **6,** 923–930.

75. Rivera-Perez, J.A., Mager, J., and Magnuson, T. (2003). Dynamic morphogenetic events characterize the mouse visceral endoderm. *Dev. Biol.* **261,** 470–487.

76. Srinivas, S., Rodriguez, T., Clements, M., Smith, J.C., and Beddington, R.S. (2004). Active cell migration drives the unilateral movements of the anterior visceral endoderm. *Development.* **131,** 1157–1164.

77. Lawson, K.A., Dunn, N.R., Roelen, B.A., Zeinstra, L.M., Davis, A.M., Wright, C.V., Korving, J.P., and Hogan, B.L. (1999). Bmp4 is required for the generation of primordial germ cells in the mouse embryo. *Genes Dev.* **13,** 424–436.

78. Russ, A.P., Wattler, S., Colledge, W.H., Aparicio, S.A., Carlton, M.B., Pearce, J.J., Barton, S.C., Surani, M.A., Ryan, K., Nehls, M.C., Wilson, V., and Evans, M.J. (2000). Eomesodermin is required for mouse trophoblast development and mesoderm formation. *Nature* **404,** 95–99.

79. Perea-Gomez, A., Camus, A., Moreau, A., Grieve, K., Moneron, G., Dubois, A., Cibert, C., and Collignon, J. (2004). Initiation of gastrulation in the mouse embryo is preceded by an apparent shift in the orientation of the anterior-posterior axis. *Curr. Biol.* **14,** 197–207.

80. Varlet, I., Collignon, J., and Robertson, E.J. (1997). Nodal expression in the primitive endoderm is required for specification of the anterior axis during mouse gastrulation. *Development* **124,** 1033–1044.

81. Ding, J., Yang, L., Yan, Y.T., Chen, A., Desai, N., Wynshaw-Boris, A., and Shen, M.M. (1998). Cripto is required for correct orientation of the anterior–posterior axis in the mouse embryo. *Nature* **395,** 702–707.

82. Liu, P., Wakamiya, M., Shea, M.J., Albrecht, U., Behringer, R.R., and Bradley, A. (1999). Requirement for Wnt3 in vertebrate axis formation. *Nat. Genet.* **22,** 361–365.

83. Zhou, X., Sasaki, H., Lowe, L., Hogan, B.L., and Kuehn, M.R. (1993). Nodal is a novel TGF-β-like gene expressed in the mouse node during gastrulation. *Nature* **361,** 543–547.

84. Conlon, F.L., Lyons, K.M., Takaesu, N., Barth, K.S., Kispert, A., Herrmann, B., and Robertson, E.J. (1994). A primary requirement for Nodal in the formation and maintenance of the primitive streak in the mouse. *Development* **120,** 1919–1928.

85. Brennan, J., Lu, C.C., Norris, D.P., Rodriguez, T.A., Beddington, R.S., and Robertson, E.J. (2001). Nodal signaling in the epiblast patterns the early mouse embryo. *Nature* **411,** 965–969.

86. Whitman, M. (2001). Nodal signaling in early vertebrate embryos: themes and variations. *Dev. Cell* **1,** 605–617.

87. Norris, D.P., and Robertson, E.J. (1999). Asymmetric and node-specific Nodal expression patterns are controlled by two distinct cis-acting regulatory elements. *Genes Dev.* **13,** 1575–1588.

88. Saijoh, Y., Adachi, H., Sakuma, R., Yeo, C.Y., Yashiro, K., Watanabe, M., Hashiguchi, H., Mochida, K., Ohishi, S., Kawabata, M., Miyazono, K., Whitman, M., and Hamada, H. (2000). Left–right asymmetric expression of Lefty2 and Nodal is induced by a signaling pathway that includes the transcription factor FAST2. *Mol. Cell* **5,** 35–47.

89. Beck, S., Le Good, J.A., Guzman, M., Ben Haim, N., Roy, K., Beermann, F., and Constam, D.B. (2002). Extraembryonic proteases regulate Nodal signaling during gastrulation. *Nat. Cell Biol.* **4,** 981–985.

90. Waldrip, W.R., Bikoff, E.K., Hoodless, P.A., Wrana, J.L., and Robertson, E.J. (1998). Smad2 signaling in extraembryonic tissues determines anterior–posterior polarity of the early mouse embryo. *Cell* **92,** 797–808.

91. Yamamoto, M., Meno, C., Sakai, Y., Shiratori, H., Mochida, K., Ikawa, Y., Saijoh, Y., and Hamada, H. (2001). The transcription factor Foxh1 (FAST) mediates Nodal signaling during anterior–posterior patterning and node formation in the mouse. *Genes Dev.* **15,** 1242–1256.

92. Norris, D.P., Brennan, J., Bikoff, E.K., and Robertson, E.J. (2002). The Foxh1-dependent autoregulatory enhancer controls the level of Nodal signals in the mouse embryo. *Development* **129,** 3455–3468.

93. Perea-Gomez, A., Shawlot, W., Sasaki, H., Behringer, R.R., and Ang, S. (1999). HNF3beta and Lim1 interact in the visceral endoderm to regulate primitive streak formation and anterior–posterior polarity of the mouse embryo. *Development* **126,** 4499–4511.

94. Kimura, C., Yoshinaga, K., Tian, E., Suzuki, M., Aizawa, S., and Matsuo, I. (2000). Visceral endoderm mediates forebrain development by suppressing posteriorizing signals. *Dev. Biol.* **225,** 304–321.

95. Perea-Gomez, A., Lawson, K.A., Rhinn, M., Zakin, L., Brulet, P., Mazan, S., and Ang, S.L. (2001). Otx2 is required for visceral endoderm movement and for the restriction of posterior signals in the epiblast of the mouse embryo. *Development* **128,** 753–765.

96. Huelsken, J., Vogel, R., Brinkmann, V., Erdmann, B., Birchmeier, C., and Birchmeier, W. (2000). Requirement for beta-catenin in anterior–posterior axis formation in mice. *J. Cell Biol.* **148,** 567–578.

97. Lowe, L.A., Yamada, S., and Kuehn, M.R. (2001). Genetic dissection of Nodal function in patterning the mouse embryo. *Development* **128,** 1831–1843.

98. Thomas, P., and Beddington, R. (1996). Anterior primitive endoderm may be responsible for patterning the anterior neural plate in the mouse embryo. *Curr. Biol.* **6,** 1487–1496.

99. Perea-Gomez, A., Vella, F.D., Shawlot, W., Oulad-Abdelghani, M., Chazaud, C., Meno, C., Pfister, V., Chen, L., Robertson, E., Hamada, H., Behringer, R.R., and Ang, S.L. (2002). Nodal antagonists in the anterior visceral endoderm prevent the formation of multiple primitive streaks. *Dev. Cell* **3,** 745–756.

100. Martinez-Barbera, J.P., and Beddington, R.S. (2001). Getting your head around Hex and Hesx1: forebrain formation in mouse. *Int. J. Dev. Biol.* **45,** 327–336.

101. Popperl, H., Schmidt, C., Wilson, V., Hume, C.R., Dodd, J., Krumlauf, R., and Beddington, R.S. (1997). Misexpression of Cwnt8C in the mouse induces an ectopic embryonic axis and causes a truncation of the anterior neuroectoderm. *Development* **124,** 2997–3005.

102. Zeng, L., Fagotto, F., Zhang, T., Hsu, W., Vasicek, T.J., Perry, W.L., Lee, J.J., Tilghman, S.M., Gumbiner, B.M., and Constantini, F. (1997). The mouse Fused locus encodes Axin, an inhibitor of the Wnt signaling pathway that regulates embryonic axis formation. *Cell* **90,** 181–192.

103. Ishikawa, T.O., Tamai, Y., Li, Q., Oshima, M., and Taketo, M.M. (2003). Requirement for tumor suppressor Apc in the morphogenesis of anterior and ventral mouse embryo. *Dev. Biol.* **253,** 230–246.

104. Glinka, A., Wu, W., Delius, H., Monaghan, A.P., Blumenstock, C., and Niehrs, C. (1998). Dickkopf-1 is a member of a new family of secreted proteins and functions in head induction. *Nature* **391,** 357–362.

105. Piccolo, S., Agius, E., Leyns, L., Bhattacharyya, S., Grunz, H., Bouwmeester, T., and De Robertis, E.M. (1999). The head inducer Cerberus is a multifunctional antagonist of Nodal, BMP, and Wnt signals. *Nature* **397,** 707–710.

106. Chen, Y., and Schier, A.F. (2001). The zebra fish Nodal signal Squint functions as a morphogen. *Nature* **411,** 607–610.

107. Hoodless, P.A., Pye, M., Chazaud, C., Labbe, E., Attisano, L., Rossant, J., and Wrana, J.L. (2001). Foxh1 (Fast) functions to specify the anterior primitive streak in the mouse. *Genes Dev.* **15,** 1257–1271.

108. Episkopou, V., Arkell, R., Timmons, P.M., Walsh, J.J., Andrew, R.L., and Swan, D. (2001). Induction of the mammalian node requires Arkadia function in the extraembryonic lineages. *Nature* **410,** 825–830.

109. Iratni, R., Yan, Y.T., Chen, C., Ding, J., Zhang, Y., Price, S.M., Reinberg, D., and Shen, M.M. (2002). Inhibition of excess Nodal signaling during mouse gastrulation by the transcriptional corepressor DRAP1. *Science* **298,** 1996–1999.

110. Vincent, S.D., Dunn, N.R., Hayashi, S., Norris, D.P., and Robertson, E.J. (2003). Cell fate decisions within the mouse organizer are governed by graded Nodal signals. *Genes Dev.* **17,** 1646–1662.

111. Lickert, H., Kutsch, S., Kanzler, B., Tamai, Y., Taketo, M.M., and Kemler, R. (2002). Formation of multiple hearts in mice following deletion of beta-catenin in the embryonic endoderm. *Dev. Cell* **3,** 171–181.

112. Tam, P.P., Kanai-Azuma, M., and Kanai, Y. (2003). Early endoderm development in vertebrates: lineage differentiation and morphogenetic function. *Curr. Opin. Genet. Dev.* **13,** 393–400.

113. Yamaguchi, T.P., Harpal, K., Henkemeyer, M., and Rossant, J. (1994). Fgfr1 is required for embryonic growth and mesodermal patterning during mouse gastrulation. *Genes Dev.* **8,** 3032–3044.

114. Deng, C.X., Wynshaw-Boris, A., Shen, M.M., Daugherty, C., Ornitz, D.M., and Leder, P. (1994). Murine Fgfr1 is required for early postimplantation growth and axial organization. *Genes Dev.* **8,** 3045–3057.

115. Ciruna, B.G., Schwartz, L., Harpal, K., Yamaguchi, T.P., and Rossant, J. (1997). Chimeric analysis of fibroblast growth factor receptor-1 (Fgfr1) function: a role for Fgfr1 in morphogenetic movement through the primitive streak. *Development* **124,** 2829–2841.

116. Deng, C., Bedford, M., Li, C., Xu, X., Yang, X., Dunmore, J., and Leder, P. (1997). Fibroblast growth factor receptor-1 (Fgfr1) is essential for normal neural tube and limb development. *Dev. Biol.* **185,** 42–54.

117. Ciruna, B., and Rossant, J. (2001). FGF signaling regulates mesoderm cell fate specification and morphogenetic movement at the primitive streak. *Dev. Cell* **1,** 37–49.

118. Chapman, D.L., and Papaioannou, V.E. (1998). Three neural tubes in mouse embryos with mutations in the T-box gene Tbx6. *Nature* **391,** 695–697.

119. Yoshikawa, Y., Fujimori, T., McMahon, A.P., and Takada, S. (1997). Evidence that absence of Wnt-3a signaling promotes neuralization instead of paraxial mesoderm development in the mouse. *Dev. Biol.* **183,** 234–242.

120. Sheng, G., dos Reis, M., and Stern, C.D. (2003). Churchill, a zinc finger transcriptional activator, regulates the transition between gastrulation and neurulation. *Cell.* **115,** 603–613.

Differentiation in Early Development

Susana M. Chuva de Sousa Lopes and Christine L. Mummery

Introduction

During the first cleavage divisions, totipotent blastomeres of the mammalian embryo segregate and eventually become committed to the extraembryonic, somatic and germ line lineages losing developmental potency. In mice and humans, pluripotent embryonic cells can be isolated from early embryos and maintained in culture as embryonic stem (ES) cells.[1,2] In this chapter, we review the development of the mammalian embryo during preimplantation and the earliest postimplantation stages as a basis for understanding developmental potency of ES cells, although it is important to realize that, despite nearly 40 years of research, a number of basic questions on early mammalian development still remain unanswered. On the one hand, this is due to the small size of early mammalian embryos and the effort that is required to obtain them in the large numbers necessary, until recently, for analysis of gene and protein expression. On the other hand, it is because implantation (and later placentation), through which the embryo establishes (and maintains) a physical connection with the mother, makes embryos relatively inaccessible; it has not been possible to mimic implantation *in vitro* or monitor these developmental stages *in vivo*. However, advances in techniques for analysis of gene expression in small sample sizes, *in vitro* fertilization, clonal analysis of cultured embryos, and the use of genetic markers are providing new clues on key developmental events and allowing important questions to be addressed.

Among the most important recent conclusions is the realization that early mammalian development in terms of timing and mechanisms of axis formation is not as entirely distinct from that in lower vertebrates as was previously thought.

Preimplantation Development

In mammals, fertilization occurs in the oviduct, where sperm encounters and fuses with the oocyte. As a result the oocyte nucleus, which had been arrested in metaphase II, completes meiosis and the two parental pronuclei fuse to form the diploid zygotic nucleus (Fig. 12–1A). Progressive demethylation of both paternal and maternal genomes begins after fertilization

leading later to epigenetic reprogramming (reviewed by reference 3). Transcription of the embryonic genome starts at the two-cell stage in mice[4] and at the four- to eight-cell stage in humans.[5] Until then the embryo relies solely on maternal mRNA, but after activation of the embryonic genome, maternal transcripts are rapidly degraded although maternally encoded proteins may still be present and functionally important. The embryo continues cleaving without visible growth (Fig. 12–1).

CELL POLARIZATION OCCURS DURING COMPACTION

At the eight-cell stage in mice and 8- to 16-cell stage in humans, the embryo undergoes a process known as compaction to become a morula, a compact smooth spherical structure (Fig. 12–1D). All blastomeres flatten, maximize their contacts, and become polarized. Their cytoplasm forms two distinct zones: the apical domain accumulates endosomes, microtubules, and microfilaments,[6–8] whereas the nucleus moves to the basal domain.[9] Furthermore, gap junctions form basally ensuring communication between blastomeres,[10–13] and numerous microvilli[14] and tight junctions are formed apically.[10,11]

The next cleavage plane of the blastomeres is perpendicular to their axis of polarity, resulting in two cells with different phenotypes. One daughter cell is located inside the embryo, is small and apolar, and contains only basolateral elements. The other daughter cell is located at the surface of the embryo, is larger and polar, and contains the entire apical domain of the progenitor cell and some basolateral elements. These polar cells inherit the region containing the tight junctions thereby creating a physical barrier between the inner apolar cells and the maternal environment.[11,15]

BLASTOCYST FORMATION (CAVITATION)

After compaction, the presumptive trophectoderm (TE) cells form the outer layer of the embryo. Intercellular contacts strengthen between these cells and a true epithelium is formed. This thin single cell layer develops a continuum of junctional complexes, including gap junctions, desmosomes, and tight junctions.[11,15] Furthermore, the composition of the basal and apical membranes becomes more distinct, with Na+/K+-ATPases accumulating in the basal membrane.[16,17] These ion pumps actively transport sodium ions into the embryo, which leads to accumulation of water molecules, possibly via aquaporins.[18] A fluid-filled cavity, the blastocoelic cavity, is thus created on one side of the embryo[19] in a process known as

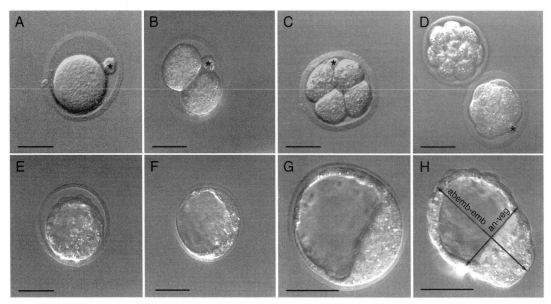

Figure 12–1. *Mouse preimplantation development.* After fertilization the two parental pronuclei fuse to form the zygote (A). The embryo cleaves, forming a two-cell (B), four-cell (C), and eight-cell embryo. The embryo then undergoes compaction to become a smooth spherical structure, the morula (D). Note that the second polar body remains attached to the embryo (*). The blastocoelic cavity then develops on one side of the embryo to form an early blastocyst (E). The cavity enlarges occupying most of the expanded blastocyst (F, G). Around embryonic day (E) 4.5, the late blastocyst reaches the uterus, "hatches" from the zona pellucida, and is ready to implant (H). The late blastocyst consists of three cell subpopulations: the trophectoderm, the inner cell mass, and the primitive endoderm. In the blastocyst three axes can be defined: the embryonic–abembryonic (abemb-emb), the animal–vegetal (an-veg), and a third axis on the same plane but perpendicular to the an-veg axis. (Photomicrographs courtesy of B. Roelen.)

cavitation (Fig. 12–1E). The presumptive inner cell mass (ICM) cells stay closely associated during this process, not only because of gap junctions, tight junctions, and interdigitating microvilli between the cells but also because processes from TE cells fix the ICM to one pole of the embryo and partially isolate it from the blastocoel.[15] The intercellular permeability seal of the TE cells prevents fluid loss and as a consequence the blastocoelic cavity gradually expands to occupy most of the blastocyst between the 64- and 128-cell stage (Fig. 12–1E to G). At this stage, the embryo is not radially symmetric around the embryonic–abembryonic axis but is bilaterally symmetric (slightly oval). The outer TE layer and the ICM are composed of descendants of the outer and inner cell population of the morula, respectively. The TE in turn consists of two subpopulations: the polar TE contacts the ICM and the mural TE surrounds the blastocoelic cavity. The TE descendants give rise to extraembryonic structures such as the placenta but do not contribute to the embryo proper. The cells of the ICM that contact the blastocoelic cavity differentiate to primitive endoderm, also an extraembryonic tissue. Furthermore, the ICM gives rise not only to the embryo proper but also to the visceral yolk sac, amnion, and the allantois, a structure that will form the umbilical cord. An overview of cell lineage relationships in the early mouse is shown in Fig. 12–2. During preimplantation development (3 to 4 days in mice, 5 to 7 days in humans) the embryo has traveled through the oviduct inside the zona pellucida, a

protective glycoprotein coat. Reaching the uterus, the blastocyst "hatches" from the zona pellucida and is ready to implant (Fig. 12–1H). Stages of mouse and human preimplantation development are summarized in Table 12–1.

AXIS SPECIFICATION DURING PREIMPLANTATION IN THE MOUSE

In lower vertebrates the body axes are already specified in the undivided egg or very soon thereafter (reviewed by reference 20), whereas in mammalian embryos, axis specification was thought to be completed only during gastrulation. This view was supported by the observation that the mammalian embryo is extremely plastic, ignoring disturbances such as the removal or reaggregation of blastomeres. The prevailing concept, therefore, became one of no embryonic prepatterning before gastrulation (reviewed by reference 21). Recent studies, however, have suggested that the mammalian zygote may in fact be polarized and the body axes specified at the time of fertilization similar to lower vertebrates. In the mouse zygote, the position of the animal pole, marked by the second polar body,[22] or the sperm entry point, which triggers Ca^{2+} waves,[23,24] have been discussed as defining the plane of first cleavage.[25–27] However, it is still unclear whether the positions of these two cues are directly responsible for the zygote polarity and subsequent position of the first cleavage plane.[25,28] Alternatively, zygote polarity and the positions of the second polar body and the sperm entry point might be determined by

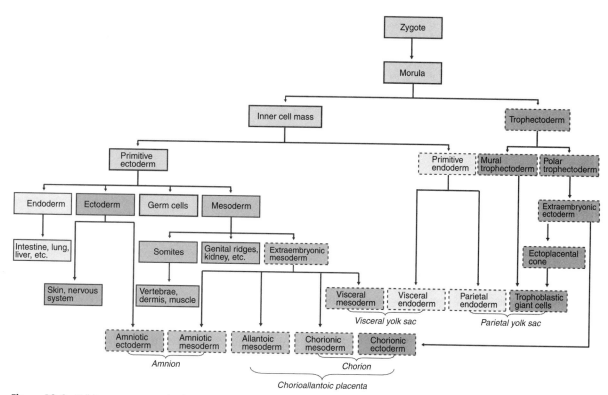

Figure 12–2. *Cell lineages in mouse development.* All extraembryonic tissues are enclosed by hatched lines, whereas embryonic tissues are enclosed by solid lines. (Adapted from references 98 and 144.)

TABLE 12–1
Summary of Mouse and Human Preimplantation Development

Stage (M)	Time	Stage (H)	Time	Developmental Processes
Zygote	0–20 h	zygote–2 cell	0–60 h	Axis determination
2-cell	20–38 h	4–8 cell	60–72 h	Activation of embryo genome
4-cell	38–50 h			
8-cell	50–62 h	8–16 cell	~ 3.5 d	Compaction
16-cell	62–74 h		~ 4.0 d	Two phenotypically different cells emerge
32-cell	~ 3.0 d	32 cell	~ 4.5 d	Blastocoelic cavity forms (cavitation)
64-cell	~ 3.5 d		~ 5.5 d	Blastocyst consists of two cell populations (ICM and TE)
128–256-cell	~ 4.5 d	166–286 cell	~ 6.0 d	Part of ICM differentiates to PrE; hatching, followed by implantation

During mouse and human development the timing of each cleavage division is dependent on environmental factors (*in vitro* versus *in vivo*), individual variation, and mouse strain. The cleavage times presented here are ranges from several published sources. For references see text and references 97–100. d, days; h, hours; H, human; ICM, inner cell mass; M, mouse; PrE, primitive endoderm; TE, trophectoderm.

an intrinsic asymmetry already present in the oocyte. The oocyte has for example an asymmetric distribution of mitochondria[29,30] and other factors including leptin and Stat3.[31]

The first cleavage plane coincides with the embryonic-abembryonic boundary of the blastocyst and interestingly the fates of the two blastomeres are distinguishable and can be anticipated. The blastomere containing the sperm entry site generally divides first[25] and contributes preferentially to the embryonic region of the blastocyst, whereas its sister cell preferentially forms the abembryonic region.[25,28,32] Parthenogenic eggs that do not contain a sperm entry point are able to divide and develop to blastocysts, although there is no tendency for the two blastomeres to follow different fates.[33] This indicates that although during normal development the site of sperm penetration correlates with the later spatial arrangement of the blastocyst, it is not essential for patterning the embryo.

There is a clear topographic relationship between the blastocyst and the zygote. The blastocyst has three defined axes,[34,35] which correlate with the position of the second polar body and the plane of the first cleavage. Although the blastocyst axes also correlate with the three axes of the uterine horn, a relationship with the body axes of the future fetus is less clear, but such a relationship has been suggested (reviewed by references 36 and 37).

DEVELOPMENTAL POTENCY OF THE EARLY MOUSE EMBRYO

In the mouse, both blastomeres of a two-cell stage embryo transplanted separately into foster mothers develop into identical mice.[38] To assess the developmental potential of each blastomere of four-cell and eight-cell mouse embryos, Kelly[39] combined isolated blastomeres with genetically distinguishable blastomeres of the same age, creating chimeric composites. Each blastomere was shown to contribute extensively to both embryonic and extraembryonic tissues (TE and visceral yolk sac) and generate viable and fertile mice. This indicated that at these developmental stages all blastomeres are still totipotent. However, although isolated four-cell and eight-cell stage blastomeres could generate blastocysts and implant, they were incapable of generating viable fetuses.[40,41] This may be explained by the fact that a defined number of cell divisions (five) occurs before blastocyst formation. Thus, in contrast to the normal 32-cell blastocyst, isolated blastomeres from four-cell and eight-cell embryos resulted in 16-cell and 8-cell blastocysts, respectively. According to Tarkowski and Wróblewska,[40] it is the position of a cell in the blastocyst that determines its fate: cells at the surface of the embryo become TE, whereas cells enclosed in the embryo become ICM. Blastocysts generated from isolated four- and eight-cell blastomeres contain progressively fewer cells in the ICM, making it likely that a minimum number of ICM cells is necessary for survival beyond the blastocyst stage.

Although different phenotypically, the two cell subpopulations in the 16-cell morula are still plastic and able to produce cells of the other lineage provided they are at the correct position in the embryo, that is, inside or at its surface. Cells of the

ICM of 32- and 64-cell embryos are also still capable of contributing to all tissues of the conceptus (embryonic and extraembryonic) and are thus totipotent (reviewed by reference 42). The potency of TE cells has been difficult to determine because TE cells are not easy to isolate (tightly connected with each other) and because they are not readily integrated inside the embryo (low adhesiveness). After the 64-cell stage, the ICM loses totipotency.[43]

Once the embryo has implanted (up to embryonic day [E] 7.0), the ability of embryonic cells (including the primordial germ cells formed slightly later in development) to contribute to the embryo when introduced directly into a host blastocyst is lost.[44,45] Remarkably, when introduced into adult syngeneic adult mice, epiblast cells are able to generate teratocarcinomas containing a spectrum of differentiated tissues and an embryonal carcinoma (EC) stem cell population. EC cells are then able to form mouse chimeras when introduced into blastocysts,[46–48] suggesting that, although pluripotency is lost in the epiblast, it can be regain to a certain extent. Similarly, primordial germ cells isolated from E8.5 mouse embryos cultured to become embryonic germ (EG) cells and adult hematopoietic and neural stem cells are able to regain pluripotency and can contribute to the embryo when introduced into blastocysts.[49–51]

GENES IMPORTANT DURING PRE-IMPLANTATION MOUSE DEVELOPMENT

Before implantation, the embryo is relatively self-sufficient and can for example develop in vitro in simple culture media without growth factors supplements (reviewed by reference 52). Of particular importance during preimplantation development are genes that regulate activation of the embryonic genome, the cell cycle, compaction, cavitation, and hatching (reviewed by reference 53). However, only relatively few mutations (specific gene deletions, insertions, and more extensive genetic abnormalities) have been reported to result in preimplantation lethality (Table 12–2). The reasons for this are not clear, but one may be that the initial presence of maternal transcripts in the zygote effectively results in maternal rescue. Ablation of specific maternal transcripts in the zygote is not always feasible using conventional knockout techniques because deficiency in candidate genes often results in lethality before adulthood. To date, only a limited number of maternal-effect genes involved in preimplantation development have been identified (see Table 12–2).

Interestingly, most genes transcribed during preimplantation development are detected immediately after genome activation and continue to be transcribed resulting in mRNA accumulation (reviewed by reference 54). Therefore, to trigger the different specific developmental events during preimplantation, post-transcriptional regulation may play an important role.

ES cells are derived from the ICM; therefore, it is not surprising that ES and ICM cells express common genes. Some of these genes have been described as being necessary for maintaining the undifferentiated phenotype of ES cells and could be expected to play important roles in the segregation of

TABLE 12–2
Lethal Mouse Mutations Affecting Differentiation During Early Development

Gene/Locus	Mutant Phenotype	References
Zar1	Zygote arrest	Wu et al., 2003[101]
Hsf1	Zygote to 2-cell stage arrest	Christians et al., 2000[102]
NPM2	Zygote to 2-cell stage arrest	Burns et al., 2003[103]
Mater	2-cell stage arrest	Tong et al., 2000[104]
Tcl1	4- to 8-cell stage arrest	Narducci et al., 2002[105]
Stella	Failure to form blastocysts	Payer et al., 2003[106]
Wt1 (Wilms' tumor 1)	Zygotes fail to undergo mitosis (background dependent)	Kreidberg et al., 1999[107]
C25H (pid)	2- to 6-cell stage embryos fail to undergo mitosis	Lewis, 1978[108]
Tgfb1	2- to 4-cell arrest (background dependent)	Kallapur et al., 1999[109]
E-cadherin (uvomorulin)	Defects in compaction	Larue et al., 1994;[110] Riethmacher et al., 1995[111]
Trb (Traube)	Defects in compaction	Thomas et al., 2000[112]
Mdn (morula decompaction)	Defects in compaction	Cheng and Costantini, 1993[113]
Om (ovum mutant)	Failure to form blastocysts (background dependent)	Wakasugi et al., 1967[114]; Baldacci et al., 1992[115]
SRp20	Failure to form blastocysts	Jumaa et al., 1999[116]
t12, tw32	Failure to form blastocysts	Bennett, 1975[117]; Smith, 1956[118]
Thp (hairpin)	Failure to form blastocysts	Babiarz, 1983[119]
Ts (Tail short)	Failure to form blastocysts	Paterson, 1980[120]
α-E-catenin	Failure to form blastocysts (TE defect)	Torres et al., 1997[121]
Vav	Blastocysts fail to hatch	Zmuidzinas et al., 1995[122]
Os (oligosyndactyly)	Metaphase arrest at the early blastocyst stage	Van Valen, 1966[123]; Magnuson and Epstein, 1984[124]
Brg1	Abnormal blastocyst development (fail to hatch)	Bultman et al., 2000[125]
Ax (lethal nonagouti)	Abnormal blastocyst development	Papaioannou and Mardon, 1983[126]
l(5)-1	Abnormal blastocyst development	Papaioannou, 1987[127]
twPa-1	Abnormal blastocyst development	Guenet et al., 1980[128]
PL16	Abnormal blastocyst development	Sun-Wada et al., 2000[129]
CpG binding protein (CGBP)	Abnormal blastocyst development	Carlone and Skalnik, 2001[130]
Thioredoxin (Txn)	Abnormal blastocyst development	Matsui et al., 1996[131]
Gpt	Abnormal blastocyst development	Marek et al., 1999[132]
Ltbp2	Abnormal blastocyst development	Shipley et al., 2000[133]
Hbath-J	Decreased TE cell number	Hendrey et al., 1995[134]
Ay (lethal yellow)	Defects in TE formation	Papaioannou and Gardner, 1979[135]
Evx1	Defects in TE formation	Spyropoulos and Capecchi, 1994[136]
Eomes (Eomesodermin)	Defects in TE formation	Russ et al., 2000[66]
Cdx2	Defects in TE formation	Chawengsaksophak et al., 1997[65]
Egfr	Defects in ICM formation (background dependent)	Threadgill et al., 1995[137]
β1 integrin	Defects in ICM formation	Stephens et al., 1995[138]; Fässler and Meyer, 1995[139]
Lamc1	Defects in ICM formation	Smyth et al., 1999[140]
B-myb	Defects in ICM formation	Tanaka et al., 1999[62]

Continued

TABLE 12–2, cont'd
Lethal Mouse Mutations Affecting Differentiation During Early Development

Gene/Locus	Mutant Phenotype	References
Fgf4	Defects in ICM formation	Feldman *et al.*, 1995[141]
Fgfr2	Defects in ICM formation	Arman *et al.*, 1998[142]
Taube Nuss (Tbn)	Defects in ICM formation	Voss *et al.*, 2000[61]
Oct4 (Oct3, Pou5f1)	Defects in ICM formation	Nichols *et al.*, 1998[60]
Nanog	Defects in ICM formation	Mitsui *et al.*, 2003[63]; Chambers *et al.*, 2003[64]

The table is divided in three sections. The top lists maternal-effect genes. Embryos lacking these genes develop normally in heterozygous but not homozygous mothers. The middle section includes genes and loci that when deleted cause embryonic lethality before implantation. The lower section includes genes and loci that when deleted cause embryonic lethality during implantation but before the formation of the egg cylinder. Embryos deficient in most of these genes develop to normal blastocysts and are able to hatch and implant, but the whole embryo or selectively the TE or ICM (ICM- or primitive endoderm-derived cells) degenerates soon thereafter leading to resorption. Extensive genetic abnormalities are not included in the table (for a review see reference 143).

ICM, inner cell mass; TE, trophectoderm.

the pluripotent ICM from the differentiated TE cell population. However, when deleted in the mouse most of those genes appear to be crucial during implantation or gastrulation but not during the preimplantation period, when both ICM and TE are formed. Most pertinent in this respect are the genes for leukemia inhibitory factor (LIF) and LIF receptors. Although mouse ES cells are highly dependent on LIF for maintenance of pluripotency in culture, neither deletion of receptor nor ligand genes appear to affect pluripotency of the ICM at the blastocyst stage.[55–57] Interestingly, *in vivo* LIF appears important for regulation of implantation (see the section on implantation).

The POU transcription factor Oct4 has the best-characterized involvement in regulating potency in mammals. Oct4 is initially expressed by all blastomeres, but expression becomes restricted to the ICM as the blastocyst forms (Fig. 12–3). Thereafter, a transient up-regulation of Oct4 occurs in the ICM cells that differentiate to primitive endoderm (reviewed by reference 58). Interestingly, expression levels of Oct4 in mouse ES cells also regulate early differentiation choices mimicking events in the blastocyst: mouse ES cells lacking *Oct4* differentiate to TE, whereas a two-fold increase in Oct4 expression leads to endoderm and mesoderm formation.[59] Mouse embryos deficient in *Oct4* are unable to form mature ICM and die around implantation time.[60] Other genes described as being involved in cell fate determination during preimplantation development include *Taube nuss, B-myb, Nanog, Cdx2,* and *Eomes* (see Table 12–2). Both *Taube nuss* and *B-myb* homozygous-deficient mice develop to normal blastocysts. At the time of implantation, however, *Taube nuss*[-/-] ICM cells undergo massive apoptosis and the embryo becomes a ball of trophoblast cells[61]; in *B-myb* knockout mice the ICM also degenerates, but the reason for this is unclear.[62] *Taube nuss* and *B-myb* seem to be necessary for ICM survival, whereas *Oct4* is required for establishment and maintenance of the ICM identity but not cell survival. *Nanog* is expressed exclusively in the ICM, whereas *Oct4* prevents TE differentiation. *Nanog* prevents differentiation of ICM to primitive

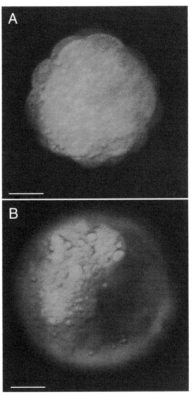

Figure 12–3. *Oct4 expression at morula and blastocyst stages.* GFP expression driven by distal elements of the Oct4 promoter (kindly supplied by H. Schöler) was used here to mimic endogenous Oct4 expression. In the morula, all blastomeres express high levels of Oct4 (A). In the early blastocyst, the inner cell mass express high levels of Oct4, whereas weaker expression is observed in trophectoderm cells (B).

endoderm. In agreement, *Nanog*[-/-] blastocysts are formed but the ICM in culture differentiates into endoderm.[63,64] In contrast, *Cdx2* and *Eomes* appear to be involved in trophoblast development, and embryos lacking these genes die soon after implantation probably because of defects in the trophoblast lineage.[65,66]

From Implantation to Gastrulation

The mechanisms used by the mammalian embryo to implant are species dependent, contrasting with the general developmental steps during the preimplantation period. In addition, an intimate and highly regulated cross talk between mother and mammalian embryo makes implantation a complex process.

Reaching the uterus, the blastocyst hatches from the zona pellucida and the TE cells become adhesive, expressing integrins that enable the embryo to bind the extracellular matrix (ECM) of the uterine wall (reviewed by reference 67). The mouse embryo adheres to the uterine wall via the mural TE cells of the abembryonic region and is slighted tilted.[34,68] In contrast, human embryos bind through the embryonic region. Once attached to the uterus, trophoblast cells secrete enzymes that digest the ECM[69,70] allowing them to infiltrate and start uterine invasion. At the same time, the uterine tissues surrounding the embryo undergo a series of changes collectively known as the decidual response. These include formation of a spongy structure known as decidua, vascular changes leading to the recruitment of inflammatory and endothelial cells to the implantation site, and apoptosis of the uterine epithelium (reviewed by reference 71).

THE MURINE TROPHECTODERM AND PRIMITIVE ENDODERM CELLS

Apoptosis occurring in the uterine wall gives TE cells the opportunity to invade the decidua by phagocytosing dead epithelial cells. At about E5.0, the mural TE cells cease division but continue endoreduplicating their DNA to become primary trophoblastic giant cells.[72] This cell population is joined by polar TE cells that migrate around the embryo and similarly become polytene (secondary trophoblastic giant cells). However, other polar TE cells continue dividing and remain diploid, giving rise to the ectoplacental cone and the extraembryonic ectoderm that pushes the ICM into the blastocoelic cavity (Fig. 12–4).

During implantation, the primitive endoderm layer forms two subpopulations: the visceral endoderm (VE) and the parietal endoderm (PE), both extraembryonic tissues.[73] The VE is a polarized epithelium closely associated with the extraembryonic ectoderm and the ICM (Fig. 12–4A); later in development it contributes to the visceral yolk sac. PE cells migrate largely as individual cells over the TE (Fig. 12–4A) and secrete large amounts of ECM to form a thick basement membrane known as Reichert's membrane. The PE cells together with the trophoblastic giant cells and Reichert's membrane form the parietal yolk sac.

DEVELOPMENT OF THE MURINE INNER CELL MASS TO THE EPIBLAST

The ICM located between the recently formed extraembryonic ectoderm and the VE gives rise to all cells of the embryo proper. During implantation, the ICM organizes into a pseudo-stratified columnar epithelium (also referred to as primitive or

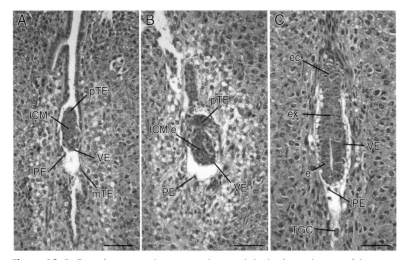

Figure 12–4. *Tissue formation and movements during and shortly after implantation of the mouse embryo (E5.0–E5.5). During implantation, cell division rate in the embryo increases, leading to rapid growth (A–C). The primitive endoderm cells segregate into visceral endoderm (VE) and parietal endoderm (PE). The polar trophectoderm cells (pTE) form the ectoplacental cone (ec) and the extraembryonic ectoderm (ex). pTE cells together with mural trophectoderm cells (mTE) contribute to form the trophoblastic giant cells (TGC). The inner cell mass (ICM) cavitates and organizes into an epithelium known as the epiblast (e).*

embryonic ectoderm, epiblast, or egg cylinder) surrounding a central cavity, the proamniotic cavity (Fig. 12–4). Signals from the VE, including BMPs, are responsible for apoptosis in the core of the epiblast leading to its cavitation.[74,75] Between E5.5 and E6.0, the proamniotic cavity expands to the extraembryonic ectoderm, forming the proamniotic canal (Fig. 12–5).

After implantation, a wave of *de novo* methylation occurs leading to epigenetic reprogramming (finished by E6.5). This affects the entire genome to different extents in embryonic and extraembryonic lineages (reviewed by reference 3). After implantation, the rate of cell division increases, followed by rapid growth. At E4.5, the ICM consists of approximately 20–25 cells, at E5.5 the epiblast has about 120 cells, and at E6.5 it consists of 660 cells.[76]

At E6.5, gastrulation starts with the formation of a morphologically visible structure in the future posterior side of the embryo, the primitive streak. During this complex process the three definitive germ layers are formed; the germ line is set aside; and extraembryonic mesoderm that contributes to the visceral yolk sac, placenta, and umbilical cord is generated.[43] An overview of tissue formation and movement during mouse gastrulation is shown in Fig. 12–6.

THE HUMAN EMBRYO

Human development during implantation and gastrulation is significantly different from that of the mouse. Briefly, the human trophoblast cells invade the uterine tissue and form the syncytiotrophoblast, a tissue similar to the mouse giant trophoblast cells. However, the trophoblast cells that contact the ICM and the blastocoelic cavity stay single cells, remain diploid, and are known as cytotrophoblasts. These cells proliferate and fuse with the syncytiotrophoblast. In humans, no structure equivalent to the murine extraembryonic ectoderm is formed.

Human primitive endoderm cells, also known as hypoblast cells, form on the surface of the ICM and proliferate, and some migrate to line the blastocoelic cavity leading to the formation of the primary yolk sac and Heuser's membrane. The human primary yolk sac is not equivalent to the murine parietal yolk sac, although both are transient structures. Moreover, it is still unclear whether human embryos develop a PE-like cell type.[77] Paralleling the formation of the murine Reichert's membrane, a spongy layer of acellular material known as the extraembryonic reticulum is formed between cytotrophoblast and Heuser's membrane. Thereafter, the extraembryonic reticulum is invaded by extraembryonic mesoderm. The origin of this tissue in humans is still uncertain. The extraembryonic mesoderm proliferates to line both Heuser's membrane and cytotrophoblast. The extraembryonic reticulum then breaks down and is replaced by a fluid-filled cavity, the chorionic cavity.

A new wave of hypoblast proliferation generates cells that contribute to the formation of the definitive yolk sac. This new structure displaces the primary yolk sac, which buds off and breaks up into small vesicles that remain present in the abembryonic pole. The definitive yolk sac in humans is equivalent to the visceral yolk sac in the mouse.

The human ICM organizes into a pseudostratified columnar epithelium and cavitates, producing the amniotic cavity.

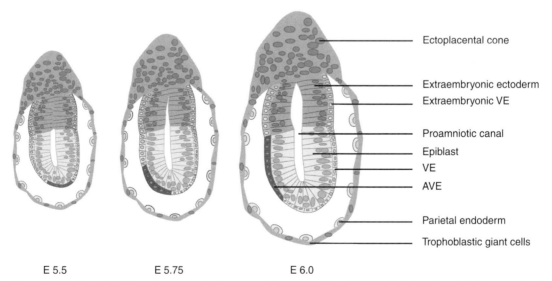

E 5.5　　　　E 5.75　　　　E 6.0

Ectoplacental cone

Extraembryonic ectoderm
Extraembryonic VE

Proamniotic canal
Epiblast
VE
AVE

Parietal endoderm
Trophoblastic giant cells

Figure 12–5. *Tissue formation and movements in the pregastrulation mouse embryo (E5.5–E6.0). During this period, the extraembryonic ectoderm organizes into an epithelium. The proamniotic cavity initially restricted to the epiblast now expands into the extraembryonic ectoderm, forming the proamniotic canal. At E5.5, the most distal visceral endoderm cells (red) express a different set of markers than the surrounding visceral endoderm (VE). These distal VE cells move from the distal tip to surround the prospective anterior part of the epiblast and form the anterior visceral endoderm (AVE). The VE surrounding the extraembryonic ectoderm consists of a columnar epithelium, whereas the VE cells surrounding the epiblast are more flattened. (Adapted from reference 94.)*

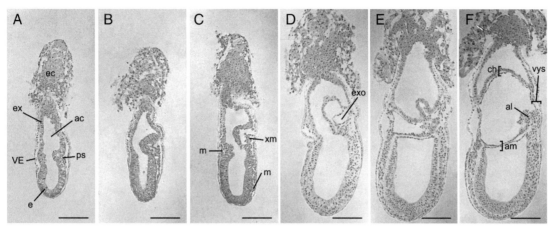

Figure 12–6. *Tissue formation and movements during the gastrulation of the mouse embryo (E6.5–E7.5). Gastrulation begins with the formation of the primitive streak (ps) in the posterior side of the E6.5 embryo at the junction of the extraembryonic ectoderm (ex) and epiblast (e) (A). As more cells ingress through the streak, it elongates toward the distal tip of the embryo, between epiblast and visceral endoderm (VE) (B). While the newly formed embryonic mesoderm (m) moves distally and laterally to surround the whole epiblast, the extraembryonic mesoderm (xm) pushes the extraembryonic ectoderm upward and to the center (C, D). The extraembryonic mesoderm develops lacunae, creating a mesoderm-lined cavity known as exocoelom (exo). The exocoelom enlarges, and, as a consequence, the tissue at the border of extraembryonic and embryonic ectoderm fuses, dividing the pro-amniotic cavity (ac) in two and forming the amnion (am) and the chorion (ch) (E). The layer of extraembryonic mesoderm and the visceral endoderm together form the visceral yolk sac (vys). At the posterior side of the embryo the allantois (al) and the primordial germ cells are formed (E, F). The extraembryonic ectoderm and ectoplacental cone (ec) are derived from the trophectoderm. The definitive endoderm cells intercalate with the visceral endoderm in the region of the streak but also form a larger patch of cells at the distal part of the embryo. This patch of cells moves anteriorly, displacing the anterior visceral endoderm, which moves toward the extraembryonic region of the embryo. For the lineages of early mouse development see Fig. 12–2.*

The ICM cells that lie on the hypoblast are known as the epiblast and will give rise to the embryo proper. The ICM cells that contact the trophoblast form the amnion. The human embryo forms a bilaminar embryonic disc, similar to chick embryos, and patterns of cell movement during gastrulation are conserved between chick and humans.

With such diversity in extraembryonic structures supporting the development of the ICM in mice and humans, it is not surprising that ES cells derived from mice and humans are not similar. They differ in developmental potency, for example, in their ability to differentiate to TE. Human ES cells can form TE in culture,[78] but under normal circumstances mouse ES cells do not (although see also the section on the role of extraembryonic tissues in patterning the mouse embryo).[79] Furthermore, mouse ES cells in culture have recently been shown to develop into cells with primordial germ cell properties. In turn, these cells can develop into sperm- or oocyte-like cells.[80–82] The potential of these cells to fertilize or to be fertilized and generate viable mice is still unknown. It is not yet known whether human ES cells have this potential to form primordial germ cells in culture. Mouse and human ES cells also express different cell surface markers[83]; have different requirements in culture for self renewal; and respond differently to growth and differentiation cues, the most striking being the response to LIF (reviewed by reference 83).

IMPLANTATION: MATERNAL VERSUS EMBRYONIC FACTORS

In mice, the presence of the blastocyst in the uterus is sufficient to trigger ovarian production of progesterone and estrogen. These two hormones are absolutely required for embryo survival as they prime the uterus for implantation and decidualization. The uterus starts producing LIF and members of the epidermal growth factor (EGF) family, including EGF, heparin-binding EGF, transforming growth factor-alpha (TGFα), and amphiregulin. Those molecules together with Hoxa10 induce the production of cyclo-oxygenase (COX) enzymes, the rate-limiting enzymes in the production of prostaglandins. The embryo on the other hand also produces important molecules that act in autocrine and paracrine ways. With a few exceptions, all of these factors and corresponding receptors play crucial roles during this period and when deleted in the mouse lead to lethality during or soon after implantation (reviewed by references 52 and 84).

The suppression of the maternal immune response is also essential during implantation but still incompletely understood. TE cells, the only cell population of the conceptus that physically contacts maternal cells, have developed several mechanisms to avoid rejection (reviewed by reference 71). Examples are the production of numerous factors and enzymes, including indoleamine 2,3-dioxygenase (IDO)[85] by the TE cells that suppress the maternal immune system and the lack of polymorphic class I and II major histocompatability complex (MHC) antigens in TE cells.

THE ROLE OF EXTRAEMBRYONIC TISSUES IN PATTERNING THE MOUSE EMBRYO

Extraembryonic tissues not only are necessary for nutrition and regulating implantation during development[86] but also play crucial roles in patterning the embryo before and during gastrulation. Unequivocal evidence for this comes from the analysis of chimeric embryos generated from blastocysts colonized with ES cells.[79] In chimeras, ES cells preferentially colonize epiblast-derived tissues. It is, therefore, possible to generate embryos with extraembryonic tissues of one genotype and epiblast-derived tissues of another genotype. For example, nodal is expressed embryonically and extraembryonically (depending on the developmental stage). Furthermore, *nodal* deficient embryos fail to gastrulate.[87,88] It was, thus, initially difficult to distinguish embryonic from extraembryonic functions. However, when *nodal*[-/-] ES cells were introduced into wild-type blastocysts, the extraembryonic tissues were wild-type, whereas epiblast-derived tissue lacked *nodal*. The developing chimera was essentially normal until mid-gestation, suggesting that the presence of *nodal* (exclusively) in the extraembryonic tissues is sufficient to rescue embryonic patterning.[89]

In contrast to the extensive mixing of epiblast cells, labeled primitive endoderm cells develop as more coherent clones, consistent with the function of the VE in embryo patterning. The primitive endoderm cells in the vicinity of the second polar body preferentially form VE cells surrounding the epiblast, whereas cells away from the second polar body preferentially form VE cells surrounding the extraembryonic ectoderm.[90]

At E5.5, the most distal VE cells are characterized by the expression of the homeobox gene *Hex*.[91] This cell population migrates toward the prospective anterior side of the embryo during the next day of development producing an endodermal stripe known as the anterior visceral endoderm (AVE) (Fig. 12–5). The AVE is, thus, the first clear landmark of an anterior–posterior axis in the embryo, preceding the formation of the primitive streak, at the opposite side of the embryo during gastrulation.

Before gastrulation, the extraembryonic ectoderm signals to the proximal epiblast, inducing expression of several genes important for posterior proximal identity. In contrast, signals from the distal VE (and later the anteriorly migrating AVE) seem to inhibit the expression of that same set of genes, restricting in this way the posterior fate (reviewed by references 92–94).

Both VE and VE-like cell lines secrete signals that are able to induce differentiation of mouse and human ES cells at least toward cardiomyocytes[95,96] (Chuva de Sousa Lopes, unpublished results). Making use of the tissues or sequences of signal transduction pathways used by the embryo for its own patterning and differentiation might be an efficient way to study and even direct ES cell differentiation.

ACKNOWLEDGMENTS

We are grateful to J. Korving, M. Reijnen, L. Tertoolen, J. Heinen, and F. Vervoordeldonk for technical assistance and B. Roelen and L. Defize for careful reading and useful comments on the manuscript. S.M.C.S.L. was supported by Fundação para a Ciência e Tecnologia, Portugal (SFRH/BD/827/2000).

REFERENCES

1. Evans, M.J., and Kaufman, M.H. (1981). Establishment in culture of pluripotential cells from mouse embryos. *Nature* **292**, 154–156.

2. Thomson, J.A., Itskovitz-Eldor, J., Shapiro, S.S., Waknitz, M. A., Swiergiel, J.J., Marshall, V.S., and Jones, J.M. (1998). Embryonic stem cell lines derived from human blastocysts. *Science* **282**, 1145–1147.

3. Reik, W., Dean, W., and Walter, J. (2001). Epigenetic reprogramming in mammalian development. *Science* **293**, 1089–1093.

4. Flach, G., Johnson, M.H., Braude, P.R., Taylor, R.A., and Bolton, V.N. (1982). The transition from maternal to embryonic control in the 2-cell mouse embryo. *EMBO J.* **1**, 681–686.

5. Braude, P., Bolton, V., and Moore, S. (1988). Human gene expression first occurs between the four- and eight-cell stages of preimplantation development. *Nature* **332**, 459–461.

6. Reeve, W. J. (1981). Cytoplasmic polarity develops at compaction in rat and mouse embryos. *J. Embryol. Exp. Morphol.* **62**, 351–367.

7. Johnson, M.H., and Maro, B. (1984). The distribution of cytoplasmic actin in mouse 8-cell blastomeres. *J. Embryol. Exp. Morphol.* **82**, 97–117.

8. Fleming, T.P., and Pickering, S.J. (1985). Maturation and polarization of the endocytotic system in outside blastomeres during mouse preimplantation development. *J. Embryol. Exp. Morphol.* **89**, 175–208.

9. Reeve, W.J., and Kelly, F.P. (1983). Nuclear position in the cells of the mouse early embryo. *J. Embryol. Exp. Morphol.* **75**, 117–139.

10. Ducibella, T., and Anderson, E. (1975). Cell shape and membrane changes in the eight-cell mouse embryo: prerequisites for morphogenesis of the blastocyst. *Dev. Biol.* **47**, 45–58.

11. Magnuson, T., Demsey, A., and Stackpole, C.W. (1977). Characterization of intercellular junctions in the preimplantation mouse embryo by freeze-fracture and thin-section electron microscopy. *Dev. Biol.* **61**, 252–261.

12. Lo, C.W., and Gilula, N.B. (1979). Gap junctional communication in the preimplantation mouse embryo. *Cell* **18**, 399–409.

13. Sheth, B., Fesenko, I., Collins, J.E., Moran, B., Wild, A.E., Anderson, J.M., and Fleming, T.P. (1997). Tight junction assembly during mouse blastocyst formation is regulated by late expression of ZO-1 alpha+ isoform. *Development* **124**, 2027–2037.

14. Reeve, W.J., and Ziomek, C.A. (1981). Distribution of microvilli on dissociated blastomeres from mouse embryos: evidence for surface polarization at compaction. *J. Embryol. Exp. Morphol.* **62**, 339–350.

15. Ducibella, T., Albertini, D.F., Anderson, E., and Biggers, J.D. (1975). The preimplantation mammalian embryo: characterization of intercellular junctions and their appearance during development. *Dev. Biol.* **45**, 231–250.

16. Watson, A.J., and Kidder, G.M. (1988). Immunofluorescence assessment of the timing of appearance and cellular distribution of Na/K-ATPase during mouse embryogenesis. *Dev. Biol.* **126**, 80–90.

17. Watson, A.J., Damsky, C.H., and Kidder, G.M. (1990). Differentiation of an epithelium: Factors affecting the polarized distribution of Na+,K(+)-ATPase in mouse trophectoderm. *Dev. Biol.* **141**, 104–114.

18. Offenberg, H., Barcroft, L.C., Caveney, A., Viuff, D., Thomsen, P.D., and Watson, A.J. (2000). mRNAs encoding aquaporins are present during murine preimplantation development. *Mol. Reprod. Dev.* **57**, 323–330.

19. Wiley, L.M. (1984). Cavitation in the mouse preimplantation embryo: Na/K-ATPase and the origin of nascent blastocoele fluid. *Dev. Biol.* **105**, 330–342.

20. Gurdon, J.B. (1992). The generation of diversity and pattern in animal development. *Cell* **68**, 185–199.

21. Papaioannou, V.E., and Ebert, K.M. (1986). Comparative aspects of embryo manipulation in mammals. *In* "Experimental Approaches to Mammalian Embryonic Development" (J. Rossant and R.A. Pedersen, eds.), pp. 67–96. Cambridge University Press, Cambridge, UK.

22. Plusa, B., Grabarek, J.B., Piotrowska, K., Glover, D.M., and Zernicka-Goetz, M. (2002). Site of the previous meiotic division defines cleavage orientation in the mouse embryo. *Nat. Cell Biol.* **4**, 811–815.

23. Kline, D., Mehlmann, L., Fox, C., and Terasaki, M. (1999). The cortical endoplasmic reticulum (ER) of the mouse egg: localization of ER clusters in relation to the generation of repetitive calcium waves. *Dev. Biol.* **215**, 431–442.

24. Deguchi, R., Shirakawa, H., Oda, S., Mohri, T., and Miyazaki, S. (2000). Spatiotemporal analysis of Ca(2+) waves in relation to the sperm entry site and animal-vegetal axis during Ca(2+) oscillations in fertilized mouse eggs. *Dev. Biol.* **218**, 299–313.

25. Piotrowska, K., and Zernicka-Goetz, M. (2001). Role for sperm in spatial patterning of the early mouse embryo. *Nature* **409**, 517–521.

26. Plusa, B., Piotrowska, K., and Zernicka-Goetz, M. (2002). Sperm entry position provides a surface marker for the first cleavage plane of the mouse zygote. *Genesis* **32**, 193–198.

27. Davies, T.J., and Gardner, R.L. (2002). The plane of first cleavage is not related to the distribution of sperm components in the mouse. *Hum. Reprod.* **17**, 2368–2379.

28. Piotrowska, K., Wianny, F., Pedersen, R.A., and Zernicka-Goetz, M. (2001). Blastomeres arising from the first cleavage division have distinguishable fates in normal mouse development. *Development* **128**, 3739–3748.

29. Van Blerkom, J., and Runner, M. N. (1984). Mitochondrial reorganization during resumption of arrested meiosis in the mouse oocyte. *Am. J. Anat.* **171**, 335–355.

30. Calarco, P.G. (1995). Polarization of mitochondria in the unfertilized mouse oocyte. *Dev. Genet.* **16**, 36–43.

31. Antczak, M., and Van Blerkom, J. (1997). Oocyte influences on early development: the regulatory proteins leptin and STAT3 are polarized in mouse and human oocytes and differentially distributed within the cells of the preimplantation stage embryo. *Mol. Hum. Reprod.* **3**, 1067–1086.

32. Gardner, R.L. (2001). Specification of embryonic axes begins before cleavage in normal mouse development. *Development* **128**, 839–847.

33. Piotrowska, K., and Zernicka-Goetz, M. (2002). Early patterning of the mouse embryo—contributions of sperm and egg. *Development* **129**, 5803–5813.

34. Smith, L.J. (1980). Embryonic axis orientation in the mouse and its correlation with blastocyst relationships to the uterus. Part 1. Relationships between 82 hours and 4 1/4 days. *J. Embryol. Exp. Morphol.* **55**, 257–277.

35. Gardner, R.L. (1990). Location and orientation of implantation. *In* "Establishing a Successful Human Pregnancy" (R. G. Edwards, ed.), pp. 225–238. Raven Press, New York.

36. Gardner, R.L. (2002). Patterning is initiated before cleavage in the mouse. *Ann. Anat.* **184**, 577–581.

37. Zernicka-Goetz, M. (2002). Patterning of the embryo: the first spatial decisions in the life of a mouse. *Development* **129**, 815–829.

38. Tsunoda, Y., and McLaren, A. (1983). Effect of various procedures on the viability of mouse embryos containing half the normal number of blastomeres. *J. Reprod. Fertil.* **69**, 315–322.

39. Kelly, S.J. (1977). Studies of the developmental potential of 4- and 8-cell stage mouse blastomeres. *J. Exp. Zool.* **200**, 365–376.

40. Tarkowski, A.K., and Wróblewska, J. (1967). Development of blastomeres of mouse eggs isolated at the 4- and 8-cell stage. *J. Embryol. Exp. Morphol.* **18**, 155–180.

41. Rossant, J. (1976). Postimplantation development of blastomeres isolated from 4- and 8-cell mouse eggs. *J. Embryol. Exp. Morphol.* **36**, 283–290.

42. Pedersen, R.A. (1986). Potency, lineage, and allocation in preimplantation mouse embryos. *In* "Experimental Approaches to Mammalian Embryonic Development" (J. Rossant and R.A. Pedersen, eds.), pp. 3–33. Cambridge University Press, Cambridge, UK.

43. Gardner, R.L., and Rossant, J. (1979). Investigation of the fate of 4-5 day post-coitum mouse inner cell mass cells by blastocyst injection. *J. Embryol. Exp. Morphol.* **52**, 141–152.

44. Gardner, R.L., Lyon, M.F., Evans, E.P., and Burtenshaw, M.D. (1985). Clonal analysis of X-chromosome inactivation and the origin of the germ line in the mouse embryo. *J. Embryol. Exp. Morphol.* **88**, 349–363.

45. Donovan, P.J. (1994). Growth factor regulation of mouse primordial germ cell development. *Curr. Top. Dev. Biol.* **29**, 189–225.

46. Brinster, R.L. (1974). The effect of cells transferred into the mouse blastocyst on subsequent development. *J. Exp. Med.* **140**, 1049–1056.

47. Mintz, B., and Illmensee, K. (1975). Normal genetically mosaic mice produced from malignant teratocarcinoma cells. *Proc. Natl. Acad. Sci. U. S. A.* **72**, 3585–3589.

48. Papaioannou, V.E., McBurney, M.W., Gardner, R.L., and Evans, M.J. (1975). Fate of teratocarcinoma cells injected into early mouse embryos. *Nature* **258**, 70–73.

49. Stewart, C.L., Gadi, I., and Bhatt, H. (1994). Stem cells from primordial germ cells can reenter the germ line. *Dev. Biol.* **161**, 626–628.

50. Geiger, H., Sick, S., Bonifer, C., and Muller, A.M. (1998). Globin gene expression is reprogrammed in chimeras generated by injecting adult hematopoietic stem cells into mouse blastocysts. *Cell* **93**, 1055–1065.

51. Clarke, D.L., Johansson, C.B., Wilbertz, J., Veress, B., Nilsson, E., Karlstrom, H., Lendahl, U., and Frisen, J. (2000). Generalized potential of adult neural stem cells. *Science* **288**, 1660–1663.

52. Hardy, K., and Spanos, S. (2002). Growth factor expression and function in the human and mouse preimplantation embryo. *J. Endocrinol.* **172**, 221–236.

53. Warner, C.M., and Brenner, C.A. (2001). Genetic regulation of preimplantation embryo survival. *Curr. Top. Dev. Biol.* **52**, 151–192.

54. Kidder, G.M. (1992). The genetic program for preimplantation development. *Dev. Genet.* **13**, 319–325.

55. Stewart, C.L., Kaspar, P., Brunet, L.J., Bhatt, H., Gadi, I., Kontgen, F., and Abbondanzo, S.J. (1992). Blastocyst implantation depends on maternal expression of leukaemia inhibitory factor. *Nature* **359**, 76–79.

56. Ware, C.B., Horowitz, M.C., Renshaw, B.R., Hunt, J.S., Liggitt, D., Koblar, S.A., Gliniak, B.C., McKenna, H.J., Papayannopoulou, T., Thoma, B., Linzhao, C., Donovan, P.J., Peschon, J.J., Bartlett, P.F., Willis, C.R., Wright, B.D., Carpenter, M.K., Davison, B.L., and Gearing, D.P. (1995). Targeted disruption of the low-affinity leukemia inhibitory factor receptor gene causes placental, skeletal, neural and metabolic defects and results in perinatal death. *Development* **121**, 1283–1299.

57. Yoshida, K., Taga, T., Saito, M., Suematsu, S., Kumanogoh, A., Tanaka, T., Fujiwara, H., Hirata, M., Yamagami, T., Nakahata, T., Hirabayashi, T., Yoneda, Y., Tanaka, K., Wang, W.Z., Mori, C., Shiota, K., Yoshida, N., and Kishimoto, T. (1996). Targeted disruption of gp130, a common signal transducer for the interleukin 6 family of cytokines, leads to myocardial and hematological disorders. *Proc. Natl. Acad. Sci. U. S. A.* **93**, 407–411.

58. Schöler, H.R. (1991). Octamania: the POU factors in murine development. *Trends Genet.* **7**, 323–329.

59. Niwa, H., Miyazaki, J., and Smith, A.G. (2000). Quantitative expression of Oct-3/4 defines differentiation, dedifferentiation or self-renewal of ES cells. *Nat. Genet.* **24**, 372–376.

60. Nichols, J., Zevnik, B., Anastassiadis, K., Niwa, H., Klewe-Nebenius, D., Chambers, I., Scholer, H., and Smith, A. (1998). Formation of pluripotent stem cells in the mammalian embryo depends on the POU transcription factor Oct4. *Cell* **95**, 379–391.

61. Voss, A. K., Thomas, T., Petrou, P., Anastassiadis, K., Scholer, H., and Gruss, P. (2000). Taube nuss is a novel gene essential for the survival of pluripotent cells of early mouse embryos. *Development* **127**, 5449–5461.

62. Tanaka, Y., Patestos, N.P., Maekawa, T., and Ishii, S. (1999). B-myb is required for inner cell mass formation at an early stage of development. *J. Biol. Chem.* **274**, 28,067–28,070.

63. Mitsui, K., Tokuzawa, Y., Itoh, H., Segawa, K., Murakami, M., Takahaschi, K., Maruyama, M., Maeda, M., and Yamanaka, S. (2003). The homeoprotein Nanog is required for maintenance of pluripotency in mouse epiblast and ES cells. *Cell.* **113**, 631–642.

64. Chambers, I., Colby, D., Robertson, M., Nichols, J., Lee, S., Tweedie, S., and Smith, A. (2003). Functional expression cloning of Nanog, a pluripotent sustaining factor in embryonic stem cells. *Cell.* **113**, 643–655.

65. Chawengsaksophak, K., James, R., Hammond, V.E., Kontgen, F., and Beck, F. (1997). Homeosis and intestinal tumours in Cdx2 mutant mice. *Nature* **386**, 84–87.

66. Russ, A.P., Wattler, S., Colledge, W.H., Aparicio, S.A., Carlton, M.B., Pearce, J.J., Barton, S.C., Surani, M.A., Ryan, K., Nehls, M.C., Wilson, V., and Evans, M.J. (2000). Eomesodermin is required for mouse trophoblast development and mesoderm formation. *Nature* **404**, 95–99.

67. Wang, J., and Armant, D.R. (2002). Integrin-mediated adhesion and signaling during blastocyst implantation. *Cells Tissues Organs* **172**, 190–201.

68. Smith, L.J. (1985). Embryonic axis orientation in the mouse and its correlation with blastocyst relationships to the uterus. II. Relationships from 4 1/4 to 9 1/2 days. *J. Embryol. Exp. Morphol.* **89**, 15–35.

69. Strickland, S., Reich, E., and Sherman, M.I. (1976). Plasminogen activator in early embryogenesis: enzyme production by trophoblast and parietal endoderm. *Cell* **9**, 231–240.

70. Brenner, C.A., Adler, R.R., Rappolee, D.A., Pedersen, R.A., and Werb, Z. (1989). Genes for extracellular-matrix-degrading metalloproteinases and their inhibitor, TIMP, are expressed during early mammalian development. *Genes Dev.* **3**, 848–859.

71. Cross, J.C., Werb, Z., and Fisher, S.J. (1994). Implantation and the placenta: key pieces of the development puzzle. *Science* **266**, 1508–1518.

72. Varmuza, S., Prideaux, V., Kothary, R., and Rossant, J. (1988). Polytene chromosomes in mouse trophoblast giant cells. *Development* **102**, 127–134.

73. Gardner, R.L. (1982). Investigation of cell lineage and differentiation in the extraembryonic endoderm of the mouse embryo. *J. Embryol. Exp. Morphol.* **68**, 175–198.

74. Coucouvanis, E., and Martin, G.R. (1995). Signals for death and survival: a two-step mechanism for cavitation in the vertebrate embryo. *Cell* **83**, 279–287.

75. Coucouvanis, E., and Martin, G.R. (1999). BMP signaling plays a role in visceral endoderm differentiation and cavitation in the early mouse embryo. *Development* **126**, 535–546.

76. Snow, M.H.L. (1977). Gastrulation in the mouse: growth and regionalization of the epiblast. *J. Embryol. Exp. Morphol.* **42**, 293–303.

77. Luckett, W.P. (1978). Origin and differentiation of the yolk sac and extraembryonic mesoderm in presomite human and rhesus monkey embryos. *Am. J. Anat.* **152**, 59–98.

78. Xu, R.H., Chen, X., Li, D.S., Li, R., Addicks, G.C., Glennon, C., Zwaka, T.P., and Thomson, J.A. (2002). BMP4 initiates human embryonic stem cell differentiation to trophoblast. *Nat. Biotechnol.* **20**, 1261–1264.

79. Beddington, R.S., and Robertson, E.J. (1989). An assessment of the developmental potential of embryonic stem cells in the midgestation mouse embryo. *Development* **105**, 733–737.

80. Hübner, K., Fuhrman, G., Christenson, L.K., Kehler, J., Reinbold, R., De la Fuente, R., Wood, J., Strauss, J.T., III, Boiani, M., and Schöler, H. (2003). Derivation of oocytes from mouse embryonic stem cells. *Science.* **300**, 1251–1256.

81. Toyooda, Y., Tsunekawa, N., Akasu, R., and Noce, T. (2003). Embryonic stem cells can form germ cells in vitro. *Proc Natl. Acad. Sci. U.S.A.* **100**, 11457–11462.

82. Geijsen, N., Horoschak, M., Kim, K., Gribnau, J., Eggan, K., and Daley, G.Q. (2004). Derivation of embryonic germ cells and male gametes from embryonic stem cells. *Nature.* **427**, 148–154.

83. Pera, M.F., Reubinoff, B., and Trounson, A. (2000). Human embryonic stem cells. *J. Cell Sci.* **113**, 5–10.

84. Paria, B.C., Song, H., and Dey, S.K. (2001). Implantation: molecular basis of embryo-uterine dialogue. *Int. J. Dev. Biol.* **45**, 597–605.

85. Munn, D.H., Zhou, M., Attwood, J.T., Bondarev, I., Conway, S.J., Marshall, B., Brown, C., and Mellor, A.L. (1998). Prevention of allogeneic fetal rejection by tryptophan catabolism. *Science* **281**, 1191–1193.

86. Rossant, J. (1986). Development of extraembryonic cell lineages in the mouse embryo. *In* "Experimental Approaches to Mammalian Embryonic Development" (J. Rossant and R.A. Pedersen, ed.), pp. 97–120. Cambridge University Press, Cambridge, UK.

87. Conlon, F.L., Barth, K.S., Robertson, E.J. (1991). A novel retrovirally induced embryonic lethal mutation in the mouse: assessment of the developmental fate of embryonic stem cells homozygous for the 413.d proviral integration. *Development* **111**, 969–981.

88. Conlon, F.L., Lyons, K.M., Takaesu, N., Barth, K.S., Kispert, A., Herrmann, B., Robertson, E.J. (1994). A primary requirement for nodal in the formation and maintenance of the primitive streak in the mouse. *Development* **120**, 1919–1928.

89. Varlet, I., Collignon, J., Robertson, E.J. (1997). Nodal expression in the primitive endoderm is required for specification of the anterior axis during mouse gastrulation. *Development* **124**, 1033–1044.

90. Weber, R.J., Pedersen, R.A., Wianny, F., Evans, M.J., and Zernicka-Goetz, M. (1999). Polarity of the mouse embryo is anticipated before implantation. *Development* **126**, 5591–5598.

91. Thomas, P.Q., Brown, A., and Beddington, R.S. (1998). Hex: a homeobox gene revealing peri-implantation asymmetry in the mouse embryo and an early transient marker of endothelial cell precursors. *Development* **125**, 85–94.

92. Beddington, R.S., and Robertson, E.J. (1998). Anterior patterning in mouse. *Trends Genet.* **14**, 277–284.

93. Beddington, R.S., and Robertson, E.J. (1999). Axis development and early asymmetry in mammals. *Cell* **96**, 195–209.

94. Lu, C.C., Brennan, J., and Robertson, E.J. (2001). From fertilization to gastrulation: axis formation in the mouse embryo. *Curr. Opin. Genet. Dev.* **11**, 384–392.

95. Mummery, C., Ward, D., van den Brink, C.E., Bird, S.D., Doevendans, P.A., Opthof, T., Brutel, de la Riviere, Tertoolen, L., van der, Heyden M., and Pera, M. (2002). Cardiomyocyte differentiation of mouse and human embryonic stem cells. *J. Anat.* **200**, 233–242.

96. Mummery, C., Ward-van Oostwaard, D., Doevendans, P., Spijker, R., van den Brink, S., Hassink, R., van der Heyden, M., Opthof, T., Pera, M., Brutel de la Riviere, A., Passier, R., Tertoolen, L. (2003). Differentiation of human embryonic stem cells to cardiomyocytes; the role of co-culture with visceral endoderm-like cells. *Circulation* **107**, 2733–2740.

97. Collins, J.E., and Fleming, T.P. (1995). Epithelial differentiation in the mouse preimplantation embryo: making adhesive cell contacts for the first time. *Trends Biochem. Sci.* **20**, 307–312.

98. Hogan, B., Beddington, R., Costantini, F., Lacy, E. (1994). "Manipulating the Mouse Embryo: A Laboratory Manual," 2nd ed. Cold Spring Harbor Laboratory Press, New York.

99. Fong, C.Y., and Bongso, A. (1999). Comparison of human blastulation rates and total cell number in sequential culture media with and without co-culture. *Hum. Reprod.* **14**, 774–781.

100. Larsen, W.J. (1997). "Human Embryology," 2nd ed. Churchill Livingstone, New York.

101. Wu, X., Viveiros, M.M., Eppig, J.J., Bai, Y., Fitzpatrick, S.L., and Matzuk, M.M. (2003). Zygote arrest 1 (Zar1) is a novel maternal-effect gene critical for the oocyte-to-embryo transition. *Nat. Genet.* **33**, 187–191.

102. Christians, E., Davis, A.A., Thomas, S.D., and Benjamin, I.J. (2000). Maternal effect of Hsf1 on reproductive success. *Nature* **407**, 693–694.

103. Burns, K., Viuenos, M.M., Ren, Y., Wang, P., DeMayo, F.J., Frail, D.E., Eppig, J.J., and Matzuk, M.M. (2003). Roles of NPMZ in chromatin and nucleolar organization in oocytes and embryos. *Science* **300**, 633–636.

104. Tong, Z.B., Gold, L., Pfeifer, K.E., Dorward, H., Lee, E., Bondy, C.A., Dean, J., and Nelson, L.M. (2000). Mater, a maternal effect gene required for early embryonic development in mice. *Nat. Genet.* **26**, 267–268.

105. Narducci, M.G., Fiorenza, M.T., Kang, S.M., Bevilacqua, A., Di Giacomo, M., Remotti, D., Picchio, M.C., Fidanza, V.,

Cooper, M.D., Croce, C.M., Mangia, F., Russo, G. (2002). TCL1 participates in early embryonic development and is overexpressed in human seminomas. *Proc. Natl. Acad. Sci. U. S. A.* **99**, 11,712–11,717.

106. Payer, B., Saitou, M., Barton, S.C., Thresher, R., Dixon, J.P.C., Zahn, D., Colledge, W.H., Carlton, M.B.L., Nakano, T., and Azim Surani, M. (2003). Stella is a maternal effect gene required for normal early development in mice. *Curr. Biol.* **13**, 2110–2117.

107. Kreidberg, J.A., Natoli, T.A., McGinnis, L., Donovan, M., Biggers, J.D., and Amstutz, A. (1999). Coordinate action of Wt1 and a modifier gene supports embryonic survival in the oviduct. *Mol. Reprod. Dev.* **52**, 366–375.

108. Lewis, S.E. (1978). Developmental analysis of lethal effects of homozygosity for the c25H deletion in the mouse. *Dev. Biol.* **65**, 553–557.

109. Kallapur, S., Ormsby, I., and Doetschman, T. (1999). Strain dependency of TGFbeta1 function during embryogenesis. *Mol. Reprod. Dev.* **52**, 341–349.

110. Larue, L., Ohsugi, M., Hirchenhain, J., and Kemler, R. (1994). E-cadherin null mutant embryos fail to form a trophectoderm epithelium. *Proc. Natl. Acad. Sci. U. S. A.* **91**, 8263–8267.

111. Riethmacher, D., Brinkmann, V., and Birchmeier, C. (1995). A targeted mutation in the mouse E-cadherin gene results in defective preimplantation development. *Proc. Natl. Acad. Sci. U. S. A.* **92**, 855–859.

112. Thomas, T., Voss, A.K., Petrou, P., and Gruss, P. (2000). The murine gene, Traube, is essential for the growth of preimplantation embryos. *Dev. Biol.* **227**, 324–342.

113. Cheng, S.S., and Costantini, F. (1993). Morula decompaction (mdn), a preimplantation recessive lethal defect in a transgenic mouse line. *Dev. Biol.* **156**, 265–277.

114. Wakasugi, N., Tomita, T., and Kondo, K. (1967). Differences of fertility in reciprocal crosses between inbred strains of mice. DDK, KK and NC. *J. Reprod. Fertil.* **13**, 41–50.

115. Baldacci, P.A., Richoux, V., Renard, J.P., Guenet, J.L., and Babinet, C. (1992). The locus Om, responsible for the DDK syndrome, maps close to Sigje on mouse chromosome 11. *Mamm. Genome* **2**, 100–105.

116. Jumaa, H., Wei, G., and Nielsen, P.J. (1999). Blastocyst formation is blocked in mouse embryos lacking the splicing factor SRp20. *Curr. Biol.* **9**, 899–902.

117. Bennett, D. (1975). The T-locus of the mouse. *Cell* **6**, 441–454.

118. Smith, L.J. (1956). A morphological and histochemical investigation of a preimplantation lethal (t12) in the house mouse. *J. Exp. Zool.* **132**, 51–83.

119. Babiarz, B.S. (1983). Deletion mapping of the T/t complex: evidence for a second region of critical embryonic genes. *Dev. Biol.* **95**, 342–351.

120. Paterson, H.F. (1980). In vivo and in vitro studies on the early embryonic lethal tail-short (Ts) in the mouse. *J. Exp. Zool.* **211**, 247–256.

121. Torres, M., Stoykova, A., Huber, O., Chowdhury, K., Bonaldo, P., Mansouri, A., Butz, S., Kemler, R., and Gruss, P. (1997). An alpha- E-catenin gene trap mutation defines its function in preimplantation development. *Proc. Natl. Acad. Sci. U. S. A.* **94**, 901–906.

122. Zmuidzinas, A., Fischer, K.D., Lira, S. A., Forrester, L., Bryant, S., Bernstein, A., and Barbacid, M. (1995). The vav proto-oncogene is required early in embryogenesis but not for hematopoietic development in vitro. *EMBO J.* **14**, 1–11.

123. Van Valen, P. (1966). Oligosyndactylism, an early embryonic lethal in the mouse. *J. Embryol. Exp. Morphol.* **15**, 119–124.

124. Magnuson, T., and Epstein, C.J. (1984). Oligosyndactyly: a lethal mutation in the mouse that results in mitotic arrest very early in development. *Cell* **38**, 823–833.

125. Bultman, S., Gebuhr, T., Yee, D., La Mantia, C., Nicholson, J., Gilliam, A., Randazzo, F., Metzger, D., Chambon, P., Crabtree, G., and Magnuson, T. (2000). A Brg1 null mutation in the mouse reveals functional differences among mammalian SWI/SNF complexes. *Mol. Cell* **6**, 1287–1295.

126. Papaioannou, V.E. and Mardon, H. (1983). Lethal nonagouti (ax): Description of a second embryonic lethal at the agouti locus. *Dev. Genet.* **4**, 21–29.

127. Papaioannou, V.E. (1987). Description of an embryonic lethal gene, l(5)-1, linked to Wsh. *Dev. Genet.* **8**, 27–34.

128. Guenet, J.L., Condamine, H., Gaillard, J., and Jacob, F. (1980). twPa-1, twPa-2, twPa-3: Three new t-haplotypes in the mouse. *Genet. Res.* **36**, 211–217.

129. Sun-Wada, G., Murata, Y., Yamamoto, A., Kanazawa, H., Wada, Y., and Futai, M. (2000). Acidic endomembrane organelles are required for mouse postimplantation development. *Dev. Biol.* **228**, 315–325.

130. Carlone, D.L., and Skalnik, D.G. (2001). CpG binding protein is crucial for early embryonic development. *Mol. Cell Biol.* **21**, 7601–7606.

131. Matsui, M., Oshima, M., Oshima, H., Takaku, K., Maruyama, T., Yodoi, J., and Taketo, M.M. (1996). Early embryonic lethality caused by targeted disruption of the mouse thioredoxin gene. *Dev. Biol.* **178**, 179–185.

132. Marek, K.W., Vijay, I.K., and Marth, J.D. (1999). A recessive deletion in the GlcNAc-1-phosphotransferase gene results in peri-implantation embryonic lethality. *Glycobiology* **9**, 1263–1271.

133. Shipley, J.M., Mecham, R.P., Maus, E., Bonadio, J., Rosenbloom, J., McCarthy, R.T., Baumann, M.L., Frankfater, C., Segade, F., and Shapiro, S.D. (2000). Developmental expression of latent transforming growth factor beta binding protein 2 and its requirement early in mouse development. *Mol. Cell Biol.* **20**, 4879–4887.

134. Hendrey, J., Lin, D., and Dziadek, M. (1995). Developmental analysis of the Hba(th-J) mouse mutation: effects on mouse peri-implantation development and identification of two candidate genes. *Dev. Biol.* **172**, 253–263.

135. Papaioannou, V., and Gardner, R.L. (1979). Investigation of the lethal yellow Ay/Ay embryo using mouse chimaeras. *J. Embryol. Exp. Morphol.* **52**, 153–163.

136. Spyropoulos, D.D., and Capecchi, M.R. (1994). Targeted disruption of the even-skipped gene, evx1, causes early postimplantation lethality of the mouse conceptus. *Genes Dev.* **8**, 1949–1961.

137. Threadgill, D.W., Dlugosz, A.A., Hansen, L.A., Tennenbaum, T., Lichti, U., Yee, D., LaMantia, C., Mourton, T., Herrup, K., Harris, R.C., Barnard, J.A., Yuspa, S.H., Coffey, R.J., Magnuson, T. (1995). Targeted disruption of mouse EGF receptor: effect of genetic background on mutant phenotype. *Science* **269**, 230–234.

138. Stephens, L.E., Sutherland, A.E., Klimanskaya, I.V., Andrieux, A., Meneses, J., Pedersen, R.A., and Damsky, C.H. (1995). Deletion of beta 1 integrins in mice results in inner cell mass failure and peri-implantation lethality. *Genes Dev.* **9**, 1883–1895.

139. Fässler, R., and Meyer, M. (1995). Consequences of lack of beta 1 integrin gene expression in mice. *Genes Dev.* **9**, 1896–1908.

140. Smyth, N., Vatanseuer, H.S., Murray, P., Meyer, M., Frie, C., Paulsson, M., and Edgar, D. (1998). Absence of basement membrane after targeting the *LAMC1* gene results in embryonic lethality due to failure of endoderm differentiation. *J. Cell. Biol.* **144**, 151–160.

141. Feldman, B., Poueymirou, W., Papaioannou, V.E., DeChiara, T.M., and Goldfarb, M. (1995). Requirement of FGF-4 for postimplantation mouse development. *Science* **267**, 246–249.

142. Arman, E., Haffner-Krausz, R., Chen, Y., Heath, J.K., and Lonai, P. (1998). Targeted disruption of fibroblast growth factor (FGF) receptor 2 suggests a role for FGF signaling in pregastrulation mammalian development. *Proc. Natl. Acad. Sci. U. S. A.* **95**, 5082–5087.

143. Magnuson, T. (1986). Mutations and chromosomal abnormalities: How are they useful for studying genetic control of early mammalian development. *In* "Experimental Approaches to Mammalian Embryonic Development" (J. Rossant and R.A. Pedersen, eds.), pp. 437–474. Cambridge University Press, Cambridge, UK.

144. Gardner, R.L. (1983). Origin and differentiation of extraembryonic tissues in the mouse. *Int. Rev. Exp. Pathol.* **24**, 63–133.

13

Drosophila Female Germline Stem Cells

Haifan Lin

Introduction

Germline stem cells in the *Drosophila* ovary provide an excellent opportunity to study the defining mechanisms of stem cells. These stem cells have been unambiguously identified by genetic, laser ablation, and cell biological analyses.[1-4] Like other stem cells, they possess the ability to self-renew and to produce a large number of differentiated progeny (reviewed in references 5 and 6). Particularly, their self-renewing division is characterized by an invariant and stereotypic pattern of asymmetry that generates a daughter stem cell and a differentiated daughter cell.[4,7,8] These properties, combined with the powerful genetic, cell biological, molecular, and genomic methods that are uniquely available in *Drosophila*, render these stem cells an effective model for stem cell research.

Fundamental questions in stem cell biology can be readily addressed using the *Drosophila* ovarian germline stem cell as a model. For example, how is the stem cell fate initially established in a tissue? What are mechanisms that control the self-renewal of stem cells? What are mechanisms that cause the differentiation of stem cell daughters? What is the relationship between the totipotency of the germline and the pluripotency of stem cells? These questions are pivotal to the understanding of stem cell biology.

Over the past several years we have witnessed remarkable progress in understanding stem cell behavior and its underlying molecular mechanisms. This surge of progress stems partly from the successful culture and directed differentiation of human embryonic stem cells and the transplantation experiments that implicate the ability of mammalian tissue stem cells to transdifferentiate. Moreover, it benefits significantly from mechanistic studies in model systems such as *Drosophila, Caenorhabditis elegans,* and *Arabidopsis* that effectively combine genetic, cell biological, and molecular approaches.[9,10] Owing to a concerted effort involving diverse experimental systems and approaches, the field is now poised to address stem cell behavior and its underlying mechanism in a systematic fashion. In this chapter, I summarize the latest progress on *Drosophila* ovarian germline stem cell research and evaluate its general significance to stem cell biology.

Germline Stem Cells in the *Drosophila* Ovary: A Descriptive Narrative

Germline stem cells in the *Drosophila* ovary reside at the tip of the ovariole, the functional unit of the ovary (Fig. 13–1, reviewed in reference 8). A *Drosophila* ovary typically contains 16–18 ovarioles. Each ovariole consists of an anterior structure called the germarium and a string of progressively more differentiated egg chambers posterior to the germarium. The tip of the germarium contains a single stack of postmitotic somatic cells called terminal filament cells (Fig. 13–1). At the base of the terminal filament are several squamous epithelial cells that cap the underlying two to three germline stem cells and, thus, are called cap cells. The germarium can be divided into three regions (Fig. 13–1). Region 1 contains mitotically active germline cells, region 2 contains differentiating germline cysts, and region 3 contains a newly formed egg chamber. Germline stem cells are the most apically located germ cells in region 1, in direct contact with the somatic cap cells at the apex.

Germline stem cells divide asymmetrically in parallel to the germarial axis such that the daughter stem cell remains apposed to cap cells, whereas the differentiating daughter cell, the cystoblast, is displaced one cell away from cap cells[4,7] (Fig. 13–2). The cystoblast then undergoes four rounds of asymmetric divisions with incomplete cytokinesis to form a germline cyst containing 16 cells called cystocytes. Cystocytes within a cyst are interconnected in an invariant pattern by cytoplasmic bridges called ring canals. As the cyst moves to region 2 of the germarium, it becomes enveloped by follicle cells produced by two to three somatic stem cells located in this region to form an egg chamber[11] (Figs. 13–1 and 13–2). Meanwhile, within the cyst, one of the two cystocytes with four ring canals differentiates into the oocyte, whereas the other 15 cystocytes differentiate into nurse cells. The oocyte then relocates to the posterior region of the cyst, which defines the anterio–posterior axis of the egg chamber and of the future embryo. The polarized egg chamber eventually buds off the germarium, joins the pre-existing linear array of egg chambers to form an ovariole, and eventually develops into a mature egg (reviewed in reference 1). Thus, an ovariole resembles an assembly line, with each egg chamber representing a differentiated and precisely patterned structure derived from a single germline stem cell division. Moreover, the position of the egg chamber along the ovariole corresponds to its birth order and developmental stage, serving as a ideal record of germline stem cell division.

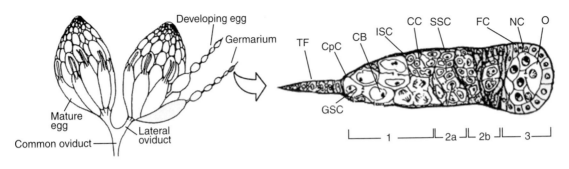

Drosophila ovaries

Germarium

Figure 13–1. The *Drosophila* ovary and germarium. The *Drosophila* ovary (left) is composed of 16–18 beads-on-a-string structures called ovarioles. An ovariole is a functional unit of oogenesis, starting with the germarium and followed by a string of successively developed egg chambers. The germarium (right) includes regions 1–3. The germline stem cells (GSCs) are basal to the terminal filament (TF) and in contact with cap cells (CpC). A GSC divides asymmetrically to produce a cystoblast (CB), which then further divides with incomplete cytokinesis to produce a germline cyst containing interconnected cystocytes (CC). These mitotic events occur in region 1. In region 2, intracyst transport of certain RNA, proteins, and organelles occurs, leading to the differentiation of 15 nurse cells (NC) and an oocyte (O) within each cyst. In region 3, a differentiated germline cyst becomes completely enveloped by a monolayer of follicle cells (FC) to form an egg chamber. ISC, nonmitotic inner sheath cells; SSC, somatic stem cell. (Adapted from reference 8.)

These attributes render *Drosophila* oogenesis an ideal model to study stem cell division and its resulting tissue lineage.

Intercellular Regulation of Germline Stem Cell Division: The Stem Cell Niche Theory

Like many other developmental processes, the division of *Drosophila* female germline stem cells is controlled by both intercellular and intracellular mechanisms. Recent studies have highlighted the essential role of intercellular mechanisms in particular, which constitutes a microenvironment, the so-celled stem cell niche, in regulating the self-renewing division of female germline stem cells (reviewed in reference 12). This section summarizes current knowledge of these intercellular mechanisms and the stem cell niche theory.

THE NICHE THEORY: A BRIEF OVERVIEW

A key feature of germline stem cells, like any other tissue stem cells, is that they reside in the Shangri-La, the idyllic hideaway, of their tissues. Here they thrive to self-renew and to produce numerous daughter cells that will differentiate and age as they leave the paradise. The concept of such a Shangri-La, that is, of a defined stem cell–supporting locale in the tissue, is now generally called the stem cell niche.

Conceptually, a stem cell niche should include three components: the localized signaling cells and an extracellular matrix that regulate stem cell fate, the effective range covered by the signaling, and the signaling target, that is, the stem cells. This definition is the "conceptual definition." Current literature, however, frequently restricts the definition of the stem cell niche to include only the signaling cells, presumably for the simplicity of discussing stem cell niches in an experimental context.[10,13] It is this minimal definition that is used in this chapter.

The concept of a stem cell niche was first proposed over 3 decades ago for the human hematopoietic system. In this system, an inductive microenvironment—the hematopoietic organ stroma—provides factors that maintain hematopoietic stem cells and excludes factors that induce their differentiation.[14] Similar models have also been proposed for epidermis, intestinal epithelium, neural system, and gonads in mammals.[5,15–17] For example, in human and mice, epidermal stem cells are located in a bulged region in the hair follicle. The bulge-associated dermal pallila cells, whose fate regulated by Wnt signaling, appear to induce epidermal stem cells to maintain their fate.[18] In the small intestine, epithelial stem cells are located near the bottom of the crypt, with their adjacent mesenchymal cells providing a potential niche. In the testis, the Sertoli cells, in direct contact with spermatogonial stem cells, are probably a key component of the niche.

How can a stem cell niche be defined experimentally? At present, there is no straightforward answer. A stringent assay is based on whether introduced stem cells can repopulate an empty niche.[10] This assay may not work for those niches whose property depends on the constant existence of stem cells. An alternative assay is to determine whether disrupting the niche or its signaling function will cause stem cell loss. This can be effectively applied in genetic models such as *Drosophila,* as discussed in this chapter.

Although the identification of stem cell niches is an arduous endeavor in mammalian systems, it can be more readily accomplished in simpler experimental organisms such as the *Drosophila* ovary. Indeed, it has been implicated in *Drosophila* that the self-renewing property of germline stem cells is regulated by somatic signaling (reviewed in reference 5). Studies of such somatic regulation in the past several years have led to a series of exciting discoveries that provide valuable insights into the structure, function, and signaling pathways of the stem cell niche. The following sections summarize these discoveries and evaluate their general significance.

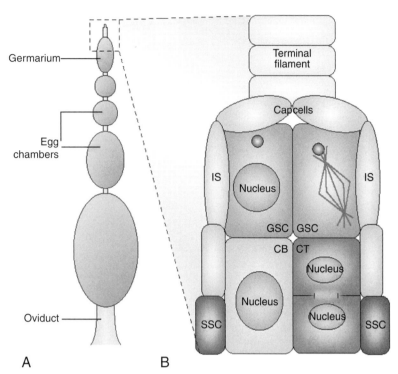

Figure 13–2. *Asymmetric division of germline stem cells in the germarium.* (A) A schematic drawing of an *Drosophila* ovariole. (B) A magnified view of the boxed region of the germarium in (A). The tip of the germarium contains a single stack of postmitotic somatic cells called terminal filament cells. At the base of the terminal filament are several squamous cap cells that cap the two to three germline stem cells (GSCs). Cap and terminal filament cells form the stem cell niche. A GSC divides asymmetrically with regard to its niche, producing one daughter cell that will remain in contact with the niche as a stem cell while the other daughter cell will leave the niche and differentiate as a cystoblast (CB).[4,7] This divisional asymmetry is ensured through the anchorage of one pole of the mitotic spindle by a cytoplasmic organelle called the spectrosome (the small orange sphere in panel B).[4,59,82] Following GSC division, the cystoblast undergoes four rounds of mitosis with incomplete cytokinesis to generate a 16-cell cyst (CT). Meanwhile, two to three somatic stem cells (SSCs), residing in the middle region, produce prefollicle cells that form an epithelium surrounding the 16-cell cyst to produce an egg chamber.[11] SSCs are separated from their signaling source by two to five inner sheath cells (IS) that may extend the niche for SSCs from signaling cells (see main text). As the egg chamber buds off the germarium, some prefollicle cells form an interfollicular stalk that connects the newly formed egg chamber to the germarium. Thus, the germline and somatic stem cells together are responsible for the generation and maintenance of the ovary as an organ. (Adapted from reference 12.) (Please see CD-ROM for color version of this figure.)

THE ESSENTIAL FUNCTION OF THE *DROSOPHILA* OVARIAN STEM CELL NICHE

In the *Drosophila* ovary, the germline stem cell niche is composed of terminal filament cells and cap cells[19] (Fig. 13–2). Germline stem cells divide asymmetrically with respect of the niche, producing a daughter stem cell that remains in contact with the cap cell and a daughter cell called the cystoblast that leaves the niche and differentiates.

This ovarian niche is essential for the self-renewing division of germline stem cells; however, different cells in the niche appear to have different functions. Laser ablation of most terminal filament cells, except for a few at the base, increased the rate of germline stem cell division.[3] This indicates that these terminal filament cells might negatively regulate the proliferation of germline stem cells. Although it remains elusive how this negative regulation occurs, it is tempting to imagine that these terminal filament cells prevent the overprogression of oogenesis at the expense of the female's own well-being.

Recently, it has been shown that dietary conditions, by acting through the insulin signaling pathway, regulate the division rate of both germline and somatic stem cells in the ovary.[20] It is conceivable that some terminal filament cells are involved in mediating these signals from outside the niche to modulate the divisional rate of germline and somatic stem cells.

Just as it is difficult to determine how signaling from beyond the niche is sensed by stem cells, it is likewise very difficult to determine directly how niche cells maintain germline stem cells. This is challenging for two reasons. First, it is not yet feasible to ablate cap cells because of their squamous shape and their extensive contact with germline stem cells. Second, it has not been possible to remove a gene specifically from all cap and terminal filament cells by genetic mosaic analysis because of their polyclonal origin. Despite these difficulties, the identification and analysis of genes that are specifically expressed in cap and terminal filament cells has provided an effective alternative to examine the function of these niche cells in regulating germline stem cell division.

In this regard, the analysis of the *fs(1)Yb (Yb)* gene has provided the strongest evidence for the essential role of cap and terminal filament cells as a niche in maintaining germline stem cell division[21] (Fig. 13–1). *Yb, hedgehog (hh)*, and *engrailed (en)* are the only genes known to be specifically expressed in the cap and terminal filament cells[19,21,22] (Szakmary and Lin, unpublished data). Among them, the role of *en* in oogenesis has not been explored, whereas removing *hh* expression during oogenesis causes only a minor defect in germline stem cell maintenance[23] (see the section on signaling). However, loss of *Yb* function depletes functional germline stem cells.[21] Germline stem cells in *Yb*-null mutant females either differentiate into germline cysts without any division or undergo limited aberrant divisions, therefore losing the ability to self-renew. Consistent with its niche-cell-specific expression pattern, removing *Yb* function from the germline does not affect germline stem cell division. Together, these results not only suggest that *Yb* is required in terminal filament and cap cells to maintain germline stem cells but also reveal the essential role of the niche in regulating the self-renewing division of germline stem cells.

The essential role of the niche in germline stem cell maintenance is also supported by the analysis of several other genes that are not specifically expressed in these cells (Fig. 13–1, Table 13–1). The *piwi* gene, which encodes a highly basic novel protein, is expressed in both germline and somatic cells, including terminal filament cells and cap cells.[24] The *piwi* mutants phenocopy *Yb* mutants, indicating that *piwi* is essential for germline stem cell maintenance. Interestingly, removing *piwi* from the germline does not affect the maintenance of germline stem cells, but eliminating *piwi* expression in the cap and terminal filament cells by mutation of *Yb* is sufficient to cause a *piwi* phenotype.[23–25] This further indicates that probably only the niche-cell expression of *piwi* is required for germline stem cell maintenance. In addition to Piwi, DE-cadherin (encodes by *shotgun*), and β-catenin (encoded by *armadillo*)

TABLE 13–1
Key Genes Involved in Niche Signaling in the Fly Gonad

Gene	Protein	Expression	Function	Reference
fs(1)Yb	Novel	Cap/TF-specific	Essential for ovarian GSC and SSC self-renewal	21,23
Hh	Signal	Cap/TF-specific	Essential for ovarian SSC division, minor role in GSC division	19,23,35
Ptc	Hh receptor	All germarial cells	Suppresses ovarian SSC and GSC division	19,34,35
Piwi	eIF2C-like	Ubiquitous	Cap/TF expression essential for GSC self-renewal	24,83
Dpp	TGFβ-like	Inner sheath cells, cap cells	Promotes ovarian GSC self-renewal, but restricts the proliferation of gonialblasts and spermatogonia	27,28
Punt	Dpp receptor	Ovary: GSC, etc. Testis: somatic cyst cells	Promotes ovarian GSC self-renewal, but restricts the proliferation of gonialblasts and spermatogonia	27
mad/med	Transcription factor	Ovarian GSC, etc.	Dpp effector, promotes ovarian GSC self-renewal	27
Shn	Transcription factor	Ubiquitous	Dpp effector, restricts the proliferation of gonialblasts and spermatogonia	84
Shotgun	DE-cadherin	Ubiquitous, preferentially at Cap–GSC interface	Essential for ovarian GSC and SSC self-renewal	26,36
Arm	β-catenin	Ubiquitous, preferentially at Cap–GSC interface	Essential for ovarian GSC and SSC self-renewal	26,36
Zpg	Innexin 4	Germline-specific	Required for early germ cell or GSC survival and differentiation	33
Upd	Ligand	Hub cell-specific	Acts through JAK-STAT to maintain GSC and SSCs in testes	85,86
jak, stat	Signal transducers	GSCs, SSCs, at least	Required to maintain GSCs and SSCs	85,86
Raf	Signal transducer	Somatic cyst cells, at least	Restricts the proliferation of gonialblasts and spermatogonia	87
Egfr	Receptor	Somatic cyst cells, at least	Restricts the proliferation of gonialblasts and spermatogonia	88

GSC, germline stem cell; SSC, somatic stem cell; TF, terminal filament cell.

fs (1) Yb, female sterile (1) Yb; *hh*, hedgehog; *ptc*, patched; *dpp*, decapentaplegic; *mad*, mothers against dpp; *med*, medea; *shn*, shnurri; *arm*, armadillo; *zpg*, zero population growth; *jak*, janus kinase; *egfr*, epidermal growth factor receptor; *upd*, unpaired; *stat*, signal-transducer and activator of transcription; *elF2c*, eukaryotic translational initiation factor.

are expressed in all somatic and germline cells, with a high level of protein accumulation at the cap cell–stem cell interface.[26] Removing DE-cadherin or β-catenin from germline stem cells causes a failure in their self-renewal. This indicates that adherens junctions, probably those between cap and stem cells, are required for germline stem cell maintenance. Finally, *decapentaplegic (dpp)*, which encodes a TGFβ-like signaling molecule, is also essential for germline stem cell maintenance.[27] Although the soma-dependence of *dpp* has not been tested by clonal analysis and its putative expression in cap cells awaits further confirmation, *dpp* is expressed in inner sheath cells, other posterior germarial cells, and possibly in cap cells.[28]

THE CENTRAL ROLE OF CAP CELLS IN THE *DROSOPHILA* OVARIAN STEM CELL NICHE

In the stem cell niche, cap cells seem to have a crucial function in regulating the self-renewing ability of germline stem cells. Although this statement cannot be tested directly by ablation or clonal analyses for reasons mentioned previously, it is supported by four lines of evidence. First, cap cells are in direct contact with germline stem cells; failure in anchoring one pole of the stem cell spindle toward the cap cells affects the asymmetry of the stem cell division.[4] Second, mutations in *Yb* completely eliminate *hh* expression in cap cells but only partially affect *hh* expression in terminal filament cells.[23] Because the *Yb*-dependent expression of *hh* is essential for somatic stem cell maintenance and is involved in germline stem cell maintenance (see later discussion), the absolute requirement of *Yb* for *hh* expression in cap cells further indicates that cap cells might be the key signaling cells. Third, ablation of most of the terminal filament cells increases the rate of germline stem cell division.[3] This indicates that only cap cells, possibly together with a few cells in the base of the terminal filament proper, might be required for germline stem cell maintenance. Thus, cap cells probably constitute the central component of the niche that is required for stem cell maintenance in the germline. The fourth line of evidence comes from the study of the DE-cadherin and β-catenin as mentioned previously.[27] Although these proteins are ubiquitously present in the germarium, their preferential accumulation at the cap–stem cell interface and their requirement for the germline stem cell maintenance also support the central role of cap cells in the niche.

As expected, the size of the germline stem cell niche is correlated to the number of stem cells in the germline. Germaria with one, two, and three germline stem cells have niches containing an average of 4.2, 5.3, and 6.6 cap cells.[28] When a stem cell is lost, another stem cell will divide symmetrically along the cap cells, repopulating stem cells in the niche.[28] These interesting observations lend further support to the idea that cap cells are the central component of the niche.

SIGNALING FROM THE *DROSOPHILA* OVARIAN STEM CELL NICHE

The molecular nature of somatic signaling from the niche is being revealed at a rapid pace (Fig. 13–3). Dpp is the *Drosophila*

homologue of bone morphogenetic protein (BMP) 2/4. Loss of *dpp* function causes depletion of germline stem cells, whereas overexpressing *dpp* produces germline tumors containing numerous cells that resemble stem cells.[27] Genetic clonal analyses on the receptors and downstream transducers of the *dpp* signal, such as *punt* (encoding a type II receptor) and Mad/Med (encoding a dimeric transcription activator), show that the Dpp signal is directly received by germline stem cells.

Yb and Piwi appear to be part of a different signaling pathway (Fig. 13–3). This is mainly based on the following reasons. First, Yb is required for the expression of Piwi and the Hh signal in cap and terminal filament cells[23] but is not required for *dpp* expression (Szakmary and Lin, unpublished data). This suggests that Dpp expression is not regulated by Yb. Second, although *Yb* and *piwi* mutants have a germline stem cell depletion phenotype that is similar to *dpp* mutants, overexpression of *Yb* or *piwi* in somatic cells increases the number of germline stem-like cells by 2.5-fold.[25] This increase, unlike the tumorous phenotype caused by *dpp* overexpression, corresponds more proportionally to the increase in the *Yb* and *piwi* expression level that is induced by heat-shock. So, *Yb/piwi*-mediated signaling from the niche seems to modulate the rate of germline stem cell division in a dose-dependent fashion, whereas *dpp* may operate via a very different mechanism, possibly by regulating the asymmetric fate of the two daughter cells.

Then what are the signaling molecules produced by the Yb/Piwi-mediated pathway? Yb and Piwi proteins themselves are unlikely signaling molecules. Yb is a novel protein that does not contain obvious transmembrane domain or a signal peptide. Piwi is the founding member of the Piwi (also known as Argonaute) family of proteins, which encode basic proteins sharing homology with eIF2C (a eukaryotic translational initiation factor and have crucial roles in stem cell division, gametogenesis, and RNA silencing in the animal and plant kingdoms.[24,29–31] A mouse homologue of Piwi, called Miwi, forms a complex with the mRNA of its target genes to regulate spermiogenesis.[32] In the *Drosophila* germarium, Piwi is a nucleoplasmic protein present in both germline and somatic cells, including cap and terminal filament cells.[25] Piwi might, therefore, be involved in RNA-related activities in the nucleus, and so, like Yb, it is probably not secreted.

A known signaling molecule produced by the Yb/Piwi-mediated pathway is Hh (Fig. 13–1). Hh is specifically expressed in the niche cells[19]; a deficiency in *hh* causes germline stem cell defects at a low frequency (20%), whereas overexpressing *hh* in somatic cells causes a slight (56%) increase in germline stem cell numbers.[23] This suggests that *hh* has a minor role in germline stem cell division. Hh expression in the niche cells requires Yb, but not Piwi,[23] indicating that Hh and Piwi representing bifurcating branches of the pathway downstream of Yb (Fig. 13–3). Interestingly, forced expression of *hh* in a *Yb* mutant or overexpression of *hh* in *piwi* mutant can rescue the *Yb* and *piwi* mutant phenotype, respectively.[23] Therefore, Hh could be a safeguard mechanism that is downstream of Yb and can compensate for Piwi deficiency. The germline stem cell defect in a *Yb* mutant can also

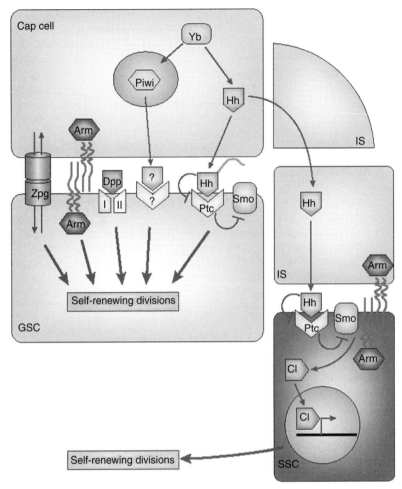

Figure 13–3 *Somatic signaling pathways in the Drosophila ovarian stem cell niche.* A model summarizing the known niche–stem cell interactions as presented in the text. Innexin (or Zero population growth [Zpg]) also exists at the interface between germ cells and between germ cells and follicle cells, which is not shown in this illustration. GSC, germline stem cell; IS, inner sheath cell; SSC, somatic stem cell. Abbreviation of the signaling components is identical to those in the text. (Adapted from reference 12.) (Please see CD-ROM for color version of this figure.)

be rescued by generating *patched (ptc)*-deficient germline stem cells in *Yb* or *piwi* mutants.[23] As Ptc is the receptor of Hh, and Ptc activity is repressed by Hh, the results of the rescue experiments indicate that Hh exerts its function by acting through Ptc on the germline stem cells.

Because Piwi is not required for Hh expression,[23] the Piwi branch of the pathway should lead to the production of yet more signals that are essential for germline stem cell maintenance. Such signals could be cytokines, extracellular matrix molecules, or cell–cell junctional molecules. The requirement of the DE-cadherin and β-catenin for germline stem cell maintenance (discussed above) underscores the importance of cell–cell adhesion in the maintenance of stem cell fate.[26]

In addition to the cell–cell adhesion mechanism, signaling from the niche through gap junctions might be required to maintain germline stem cells. The *zero population growth (zpg)* gene encodes a germline–specific gap junction protein,

innexin 4, that is found on germ cell surfaces, both those adjacent to cap and other somatic cells and those adjacent to other germ cells.[33] The *zpg*-null mutant contains small numbers of aberrant germ cells that presumably resemble stem cells or their immediate daughter cells but lack germ cells in the later stages of differentiation. This led to the conclusion that Zpg is required for the survival and differentiation of early germ cells. An alternative possibility is that the *zpg* mutation affects normal physiology of germline stem cells: stem cells in the mutant undergo aberrant divisions and produce a limited number of ill-differentiated germ cells that undergo cell death. Consequently, functional germline stem cells are lost. Consistent with this explanation, *zpg* mutants do not display germline tumor phenotype, as would be expected if *zpg* is only required for the survival and differentiation of stem cell daughters. Thus, the *zpg* phenotype indicates the possibility that gap junctions between germline stem cells and their contacting somatic cells is important for the normal stem cell function.

Studies reviewed in this section point to three salient features of the fly ovarian niche. First, it produces in parallel several signaling molecules that are required for maintaining the stem cell fate in the germline. These signaling molecules include cytokines and also, possibly, small molecules that pass through gap junctions. Second, cell–cell adhesion is an integral part of the niche. Third, the niche seems to reflect a balancing act of two opposing components: the proximal component (cap cells) that are essential for stem cell maintenance and the distal component (most, if not all, terminal filament cells) that negatively regulates stem cell division.

THE DUAL FUNCTION OF THE *DROSOPHILA* OVARIAN STEM CELL NICHE

An additional feature of the ovarian niche in *Drosophila* is that it regulates both germline and somatic stem cells.[23] In the germarium, in addition to two to three germline stem cells at the apex, there are two to three somatic stem cells that reside in the middle region (Figs. 13–1 to 13–3). These cells produce prefollicle cells that form an epithelium that surrounds the interconnected daughter cells of cystoblasts to form an egg chamber.[11] The egg chamber then buds off from the germarium, joining pre-existing egg chambers to form an ovariole. The coordination between germline and somatic stem cell divisions is essential for ovary formation and oogenesis, because uncoupled proliferation of germline and somatic stem cells disrupts egg chamber formation and ovariole morphogenesis.[19]

Such coordinated regulation involves a bifurcating signaling pathway that is mediated by *Yb*, which is expressed in terminal filament and cap cells[21] (Szakmary and Lin, unpublished data; Fig. 13–3). *Yb* is required for both germline and somatic stem cell divisions.[23] Loss of *Yb* function eliminates germline stem cells and correspondingly reduces somatic stem cell division, whereas *Yb* overexpression increases germline stem cell number and causes somatic stem cell to overproliferate. *Yb* achieves this dual-controlling role by regulating the expression of *piwi* and *hh* in the niche cells. The *piwi*-mediated pathway is at least primarily required for germline stem cell lineage, because the loss-of-function and overexpression phenotypes of *piwi* are indistinguishable from those of *Yb*, at least with regard to the germline. Complementary to *piwi*, the *hh*-mediated pathway is primarily required for somatic stem cell division.[19,23,34,35] The *hh* deficiency markedly reduces somatic stem cell division, whereas *hh*-overexpression causes over-division of somatic stem cells.[19,23,34,35] Hh regulates target cells by binding to its receptor Patched (Ptc) on the surface of the target cells. This binding releases the suppression of a membrane protein called Smoothened (Smo) by Ptc, which allows Smo to act through an intracellular signal transduction pathway to activate the transcription factor Cubitus interruptus (Ci, a Gli1 homologue), thus leading to transcriptional activation of specific genes in the target cells. In the fly ovary, this signaling pathway is critical in controlling somatic stem cell division. Somatic stem cells that are deficient in Ptc mimics *hh*-overexpression phenotype,[34] whereas somatic stem

cells deficient in Smo mimic the *hh* mutant phenotype.[19,23,34,35] These results indicate that Hh regulates somatic stem cell division by binding directly to Ptc on the stem cell surface. Interestingly, somatic stem cells are not in direct contact with cap cells; they are separated by several postmitotic epithelial cells called inner sheath cells (Figs. 13–1 to 13–3). The Hh molecules produced by cap cells must travel through this extended "arm" of the niche to reach somatic stem cells. These observations indicate that the Piwi- and Hh-mediated bifurcating signaling pathways control germline stem cell and somatic stem cell division, respectively, with Hh signaling also having a minor effect in germline stem cell division.

Another important feature of the ovarian niche is that it involves cadherin-mediated cell adhesion for anchoring both somatic and germline stem cells.[36] DE-cadherin and β-catenin also accumulate in the junctions between somatic stem cells and their neighboring cells and between the rest of germarial cells. Somatic stem cells deficient in DE-cadherin cannot be maintained in the ovary. It is possible that cadherin-mediated cell adhesion is a general mechanism for anchoring stem cells to their niches.

Many complex tissues and all organs are composed of two or more distinctive types of constituent cells derived from their corresponding stem cells or precursor cells. The coordinated division of these stem/precursor cells within an organ is crucial for organogenesis and homeostasis. The studies in the fly gonads for the first time unequivocally demonstrate that a common niche can regulate the coordinated behavior of two distinct populations of stem cells within an organ. Moreover, these studies also reveal the molecular pathways underlying such regulation. Does such a dual-functional niche exist in mammalian systems? The fly studies reviewed here provide a conceptual guide to search for such niches in other systems (see the section on new insights into stem cells).

FORMATION AND PERSISTENCE OF THE OVARIAN STEM CELL NICHE

The ovarian stem cell niche is formed at the onset of oogenesis in the prepupal stage, accompanied by the initiation of asymmetric division of germline stem cells.[1,37] Specifically, terminal filament formation is initiated at the late third instar larval and completed at the prepupal stages, with the number of cells in each terminal filament increasing gradually to eight or nine in a progressive fashion across the ovary. Cap cell formation is initiated at the larval–pupal transition and continues to the prepupal stage (0–4 hours after pupation), at which stage germline stem cells initiate asymmetric divisions. Once the niche are formed, it is apparently stable and retains *dpp* signaling ability for up to 18 days after the resident germline stem cells are forced to differentiate and exit the niche by ectopically expressing the *bam* gene[38] (see the section on asymmetrically expressed and/or segregated cell fate regulators). This is a significant portion of the adult life span. Therefore, other stem cell niches might also be stable while empty. For example, empty yet stable niches may exist in the mammalian testis, because transplanted germline stem cells from other mice or even from primates can colonize the testes of infertile recipient mice. It is, thus, possible that niches independent of target stem cells is an intrinsic property of stem cell niches in tissues. Such a property may render the tissue more potential to regenerate following a catastrophic event that reduces or eliminates the resident stem cells.

Intracellular Mechanisms: The Question of Asymmetry

An implicit assumption of stem cells requires that they posses a robust cell cycle program that is tightly regulated by signaling from the niche. For asymmetrically dividing stem cells such as female germline stem cells in *Drosophila,* it is also important to have an intracellular asymmetry-generating mechanism that gives rise to the divergent fates of the two daughter cells. The asymmetric mechanism may consist of cell fate regulators and a cellular machinery responsible for their asymmetric expression or segregation. In general, less is known about the intracellular mechanisms that regulate germline stem cell division. Despite this, rapid progress in the past several years has revealed multiple facets of the intracellular mechanisms.

CELL CYCLE MACHINERY

Relatively little is known about how cell-cycle regulators control stem cell division. Germline stem cells in *Drosophila* are not exceptional in this case. Cyclin A and Roughex, an inhibitor of the S-phase function of the cyclin A–cyclin-dependent kinase 1 (Cdk1) complex, regulate the normal progression of male meiosis, whereas cyclin E controls the female nurse cell endocycle. However, their potential roles in germline stem cell division have not been addressed.[39] Likewise, Cyclin D and Cdk4 are not essential for fertility.[40] The only cyclins known to be required for female fertility are cyclin B and B3.[41] Germline clonal analysis suggests that cyclin B may be required for germline stem cell division (Zhong Wang and H. Lin, unpublished data).

In addition to cyclins, the *shut-down (shu)* gene might link germline stem cell cycle to extrinsic signaling.[42] The *shu* mutant displays *piwi/Yb* like phenotype; however, the mutation is germline-dependent. Thus, *shu* appears to encode a cell-autonomous factor essential for the self-renewal of the germline stem cells and oogenesis. Consistent with this, the *shu* RNA and protein are strongly expressed in the germline stem cells and in 16-cell cysts. The *shu* RNA is also present in the germ cells throughout embryogenesis. The Shu protein shares similarity to the heat-shock protein-binding immunophilins. Both immunophilins and Shu contain an FK506-binding protein domain and a tetratricopeptide repeat. In plants, high-molecular-weight immunophilins have been shown to regulate cell divisions in the root meristem in response to extracellular signals. These results suggest that Shu may regulate the mitoses of germ cells in the germarium. These preliminary observations provide unique opportunities for genetic dissection of regulation of germline stem cell division by the cell cycle machinery.

ASYMMETRICALLY EXPRESSED AND/OR SEGREGATED CELL FATE REGULATORS

The generation of bifurcating cell fates during *Drosophila* germline stem cell division is expected to be regulated by factors that are differentially expressed and/or segregated between the two daughter cells. Such a differential gene expression could be controlled at the DNA or genetic information level, such as gene conversion during mating-type switch in the yeasts.[43] However, this level of regulation is unlikely to occur in germline stem cells because these cells need to maintain their genome to produce gametes of the same genetic constitution. If such regulation happens, it would have to be reverted precisely. However, differential gene expression can be manifested at the level of asymmetric DNA replication (like what occurs in the fission yeast[44]), epigenetic modification of the chromatin, transcription, post-transcriptional RNA processing, translation, and post-translational processing of the protein products. Especially, the epigenetic regulation is likely involved given that a suppressor of *piwi, P[wA]4-4,* is an epigenetic suppressor that does not correspond to a conventional protein-coding gene but to a subtelomeric heterochromatic repeat at the subtelomeric region of the third chromosome.[45] At present, it is not known whether *P[wA]4-4* functions in the niche cells or the stem cells.

In addition to epigenetic regulation, transcriptional regulation appears to play a key role in germline stem cell division. For example, the putative transcription factor Stonewall (Stwl) is required for preoogenic development and for the maintenance of female germline stem cells. Some *stwl* germaria are germlineless, whereas others display a rapid decrease in egg chamber production, in addition to subsequent oogenic defects.[46] These defects suggest that Stwl is involved in multiple steps of germline development. It has been found that removing one copy of the *similar, tango,* or *serendipity-δ* gene will restore the self-renewing division of germline stem cells in *piwi* mutants.[45] Similar and Tango are two bHLH family proteins known to function as heterodimers, whereas Serendipity-δ is a Cys-2/His-2 zinc finger transcription factor. These findings reveal a dosage-sensitive transcriptional mechanism involved in regulating germline stem cell division, even though it remains to be determined whether such a mechanism acts cell autonomously in the germline.

In *Drosophila,* asymmetrically segregating cell fate determinants have not been clearly demonstrated for germline stem cells, even though such factors (e.g., Numb and Prospero) have been identified in neuroblasts (reviewed in reference 47). Despite this, several *Drosophila* genes have recently been shown to be required cell autonomously for either the maintenance of female germline stem cells or the proper differentiation of cystoblasts. Among them, *pumilio (pum)* is essential for germline stem cell maintenance. The *pum* mutant females often contain abnormal numbers of germline stem cells at the onset of oogenesis, because of the requirement of *pum* during preoogenic germline development.[48] Moreover, those germline stem cells that presumably have formed fail to maintain themselves during oogenesis.[49] Pum is an RNA binding protein known to mediate translational repression in the embryo.[50]

It is present at a high level in germline stem cells but a low level in cystoblasts.[48,49] Thus, Pum may be an asymmetrically expressed cell fate regulator that selectively suppresses the translation of certain RNAs in the stem cell to prevent it from differentiation. Several *pum* homologues have been identified in mammals and are expressed in the testis (e.g., reference 51), suggesting that a *pum*-like mechanism may exist in mammalian spermatogonial stem cells as well.

The binding partner of *pum* in the embryo, *nanos (nos),* is also involved in germline maintenance. It has been reported that *nos* mutations block germline cyst development in adult ovaries without the immediately loss of germline, and thus *nos* has been suggested to function in the differentiation of cystoblasts and germline cysts.[49] However, this reported phenotype is likely a mild manifestation of the failure in germline maintenance, either due to the hypomorphic nature of the mutation or slightly redundant role of *nos* in the process. In these reported ovarioles, 69% of the newly eclosed *nos* mutant adult ovaries are germlineless.[49] This defect indicates a failure in germline proliferation and/or maintenance before and/or during oogenesis. Removing *nos* activity during oogenesis causes germline stem cell depletion.[52] Thus, *nos* is also directly involved in germline stem cell maintenance.

In contrast to *pum* and *nos*, the *bag of marbles (bam)* gene is required to promote stem cell differentiation in both sexes.[53] The *bam* mutant germ cells fail to differentiate, but instead proliferate like stem cells or ill-differentiated germline cells.[53] Heat shock-induced ectopic expression of *bam* is sufficient to eliminate germline stem cells.[54] Because *bam* mRNA and the cytoplasmic form of the BAM protein (Bam-C) are only expressed in the cystoblast but not in germline stem cells, it is likely that Bam is an asymmetrically expressed cell-autonomous regulator for the cystoblast fate.

Like *bam,* the *benign gonial cell neoplasm (bgcn)* gene seems to be another cell-autonomous factor required for determining the cystoblast fate. Mutations of *bgcn* block the differentiation of cystoblasts, causing *bam*-like phenotype.[55] In addition, *bgcn* mutations dominantly enhance a *bam* mutant phenotype. This reveals the likely functional interdependence of these two genes.[56] The *bgcn* mRNA is expressed in a small number of germline cells in the germarium, including the stem cells.[56] The *bgcn* gene encodes a protein that is related to the DExH-box family of RNA-dependent helicases but lacks critical residues for ATPase and helicase functions. Hence, it is possible that Bgcn and Bam may be involved in regulating the translation of the cystoblast differentiation genes.

CELLULAR MACHINERY FOR ASYMMETRIC LOCALIZATION AND ORIENTATION

Because *Drosophila* germline stem cells divide in a stereotypic fashion of asymmetry for self-renewal, it is crucial to have a cellular mechanism that ensures the proper segregation and localization of cytoplasmic components between the two daughter cells. The *Drosophila* cytoskeletal systems are known to play a crucial role in asymmetric segregation and localization of cell fate determinants and in spindle orientation during mitosis (reviewed in reference 47; also see references 57 and 58).

In *Drosophila* ovarian germline stem cells, the cytoskeleton has been shown to play an important role in the asymmetric germline stem cell divisions.[59] As mentioned in the beginning of this chapter, the spectrosome, an organelle enriched in membrane skeletal proteins, ensures the divisional asymmetry both by defining the mitotic spindle orientation and by localizing cell fate and cell cycle molecules such as Bam and cyclin A to the organelle. At telophase, the spectrosome grows in size and elongates toward the future cystoblast and eventually becomes asymmetrically bisected by delayed cytokinesis occurring at the next cell cycle. Delayed cytokinesis may be a common feature of germline stem cell division, because it is also seen for dividing spermatogonial stem cells in both *Drosophila* and mammals.

It is important to point out that, even if the spectrosome is important for the asymmetry of germline stem cell division, such asymmetry does not seem to be essential for the self-renewal of germline stem cells in the *Drosophila* ovary. In the absence of the spectrosome and its descendent structure, the fusome, a normal number of egg chambers, although ill-differentiated, are still produced.[7] This likely reflects the fact that, although germline stem cell divisions are randomly oriented without the spectrosome, the topology of the stem cell niche still allows about 50% of the daughter cells to be included in the niche. Consequently, a self-renewing stem cell population of is still maintained in the germline. Thus, without the spectrosome, the germline stem cells in the *Drosophila* ovary lose the "stereotypic stem cell" quality that self-renews during each cell cycle but become "populational stem cells" that self-renew on a stochastic basis. The function of the spectrosome thus may be to guarantee that each stem cell division is properly asymmetric to generate a functional germline stem cell and cystoblast. Therefore, the study of the spectrosome has revealed the important role of membrane skeletal proteins in establishing a divisional asymmetry. These proteins may play a similar role in other stem cell systems.

Then, what links the spindle pole to the spectrosome? What orients the spectrosome toward the cap cell? The answer to these questions partly lies in cytoplasmic dynein.[60] In germline cysts, cytoplasmic dynein is required to link one pole of the mitotic spindle to the fusome. Given the structural similarities between the fusome and the spectrosome, it is likely that cytoplasmic dynein plays the same role in germline stem cells. Studying how the spectrosome is anchored near cap cells should help revealing how somatic signaling induces the polarity in the target stem cells.

New Insights into Stem Cells: Lessons from the Fly Ovary

Recent studies on female germline stem cells in *Drosophila* have yielded exciting insights not only on the structure and function of the stem cell niche but also on intracellular mechanisms that regulate stem cell division. What can we learn about stem cell mechanisms in mammalian systems from the fly research? An in-depth comparison between the fly and mammalian stem cells at the mechanistic level requires a parallel understanding of mammalian stem cell systems. Current knowledge on intracellular mechanisms in both *Drosophila* and mammalian systems is too fractional for a meaningful comparison. However, the intercellular mechanisms discovered in the fly ovary have generated some guiding principles for the stem cell niche concept.

Several mammalian stem cell niches have been identified. For example, the skin stem cell niche has been effectively localized to the bulge of the hair follicle in humans and mice.[61,62] The Wnt and Sonic Hedgehog (Shh) pathways, among others, are important in inducing the competence of the niche.[18,63] The overall configuration and function of the hair follicle niche seem to be very similar to the ovarian and testicular niches in *Drosophila*. Another mammalian niche being characterized is that of hematopoietic stem cells. The physical features of the hematopoietic stem cell niche within bone marrow have recently been defined as a group of spindle-shaped N-cadherin[+] CD45[−] osteoblasts.[64,65] It also has been shown in mice that bone morphogenetic protein (BMP) and the Steel/c-Kit signaling pathways, via direct contact between stromal cells and hematopoietic stem cells, are essential for hematopoiesis.[64,65,66] Recently, the Wnt, Shh, and Notch pathways have also been demonstrated to be important for regulating hematopoietic stem cell division.[67,68] There is also ample evidence to indicate that stem cell niches exist in other epithelia[10] and in the testis[5] and possibly in neural,[69] muscular,[70] hepatic,[71] pancreatic,[72] and other systems. It seems that most, if not all, mammalian stem cells, have their niches.[10,13]

Despite the encouraging progress as reviewed previously, mammalian stem cell niches are extremely difficult to study because of their complexity. In many tissues, stem cells have not been unambiguously identified. As a result, remarkably little is known about what exactly constitutes a mammalian stem cell niche or whether such a niche indeed exists for all types of stem cells. This paucity of knowledge underscores the importance of stem cell study in simpler model systems such as *Drosophila* and *C. elegans*. At this early stage, some general comparisons can be made between *Drosophila* and mammalian stem cell niches, and some lessons can be learned from the fly ovary.

First, the structure of fly niches suggests that a mammalian niche does not necessarily need to be complicated to fulfill its function. It is possible that one or a few stromal cells will suffice to regulate hematopoietic stem cell division or that epidermal stem cell division may only require a very small number of dermal cells in the hair follicle bulge. Similar scenarios in other stem cell systems can be easily imagined.

Second, dual-functional niches might exist in mammalian systems. For example, the same stromal cells in the bone marrow might control the division of both hematopoietic and mesenchymal stem cells. In another example, a subset of dermal cells in the olfactory epithelium might regulate the division of both epithelial stem cells and olfactory neuronal stem cells. Such dual-functional niches, yet to be identified in mammalian systems, might be crucial in organogenesis and in regulating the homeostasis of tissues and organs.

Third, conserved signaling pathways might be involved in different stem cell systems, although their function in each stem cell system might be different. For instance, in flies, the *dpp* signaling pathway plays opposite roles in female and male germline stem cell systems. In mammals, BMP8b, a Dpp homologue, is required for the initiation and maintenance of germline stem cells,[73] just as Dpp is in *Drosophila* oogenesis. However, unlike the situation in the fly, BMP8b is expressed in germ cells instead of somatic niche cells.[73] In another example, the JAK-STAT pathway has very different functions in oogenesis and spermatogenesis in *Drosophila*. By the same token, although this pathway has been implicated in maintaining embryonic stem cells in mammals,[74] it might perform alternative functions in tissue stem cell systems. In fact, the Steel/c-Kit signaling pathway is required for the maintenance of hematopoietic stem cells but promotes differentiation of spermatogenic stem cells.[66] These differences, although striking, tend to be understated by the review literature.

Finally, a stem cell niche may contain tissue- and species-specific mechanisms. For example, a mammalian homologue of Yb has not been identified. This indicates that Yb-like molecules might be specific to flies. In the fly, *Yb*-mediated signaling is required female-specifically; *Yb*-null mutations do not display a male phenotype.[21] Such tissue-specific components of the niche mechanism are expected to exist in mammalian tissue stem-cell systems as well. The tissue-specific signaling from a niche might in turn lead to the transcription of overlapping sets of genes in different stem cells as has been reported recently.[75,76]

Is there any property of a mammalian niche not yet hinted at by the current study of the fly niches? The answer is yes. There is emerging evidence to indicate that the environment of mammalian stem cells not only regulates their self-renewing division but also restricts the lineage of their differentiation to that of the host tissue. For example, isolated single embryonic cells often exhibit more developmental flexibility than extended masses of tissue.[77] Similarly, adult hepatic stem cells can transdifferentiate into pancreatic endocrine hormone-producing cells *in vitro* under appropriate culture conditions.[78] Also, on migration to skeletal muscles, transplanted hematopoietic stem cells appear to contribute to muscle regeneration,[79] although a later study suggests that such events are either rare or are due to the impurity of the stem cells.[80] Current research in *Drosophila* has not shed light on how a niche restricts the differentiation potential of stem cells. In addition, some mammalian stem cells use apoptosis as a routine mechanism to remove excess stem cells and their differentiated daughter cells,[81] but this does not seem to be the case in *Drosophila*. In the future, studying mutant conditions that lead to transdifferentiation and aberrant apoptosis of *Drosophila* stem cells should help to understand the mechanisms underlying these processes in mammalian stem cell systems.

Concluding Remarks

Germline stem cells in the *Drosophila* ovary offer great opportunities for addressing fundamental questions of stem cell biology. They are one of the few types of stem cells that have been unambiguously identified, thus overcoming the stem-cell "identity crisis" that has been severely hampering research in the field. Moreover, these stem cells can be effectively studied by combined genetic, cell biological, molecular, and genomic approaches that are uniquely available in *Drosophila*. Finally, the pluripotency of stem cells in adult tissues may be a partial manifestation of the totipotency of the germline. By choosing to study stem cells in the germline, one has placed oneself in a unique position that allows both stem cell and germline biology to be effectively explored.

Recent works in germline stem cells in *Drosophila* have clearly defined the microenvironment, or the stem cell niche, and its key function as a Shangri-La that allows the stem cells to thrive. Furthermore, important instructive signaling pathways from the niche have been identified. This knowledge has provided a platform for systematic analysis of the formation and self-renewing division of these stem cells. The general implication of these studies to other stem cell systems is becoming increasingly obvious.

Elucidation of the mechanisms that underlie the self-renewing division of germline stem cells in *Drosophila* is occurring at an exciting rate. New genetic, genomic, and proteomic screens will identify more genes involved in germline stem cell mechanisms. Meanwhile, further analysis of known genes and pathways involved in germline stem cell division will reveal exactly how cell–cell signaling and intracellular events occur in an orchestrated manner to ensure the stem cell character. These genetic and molecular analyses will also reveal how germline stem cell division and maintenance are related to general cell cycle and germline mechanisms. The knowledge gained from these studies is illuminating our understanding of the self-renewing mechanisms of tissue stem cells in general.

ACKNOWLEDGMENTS

I thank past and current members of the laboratory for their enthusiasm and contributions to the understanding of germline stem cells. I am indebted to Drs. Seth Findley and Tora Smulders-Srinivasan for critical reading of the manuscript. Part of this chapter is adapted from reference 12. The author is supported by NIH grants HD33760 and HD42012.

REFERENCES

1. King, R.C. (1970). "Ovarian Development in *Drosophila melanogaster*." Academic Press, New York.
2. Wieschaus, E., and Szabad, J. (1979). The development and function of the female germline in *Drosophila melanogaster*, a cell lineage study. *Dev. Biol.* **68**, 29–46.
3. Lin, H., and Spradling, A. (1993). Germline stem cell division and egg chamber development in transplanted *Drosophila* germaria. *Dev. Biol.* **159**, 140–152.
4. Deng, W., and Lin, H. (1997). Spectrosomes and fusomes are essential for anchoring mitotic spindles during asymmetric germ cell divisions and for the microtubule-based RNA transport during oocyte specification in *Drosophila. Dev. Biol.* **189**, 79–94.
5. Lin, H. (1997). The tao of stem cells in the germline. *Annu. Rev. Genet.* **31**, 455–491.
6. Lin, H. (1998). The self-renewing mechanism of stem cells in the germline. *Cur. Opin. Cell Biol.* **10**, 687–693.
7. Lin, H., and Spradling, A.C. (1997). A novel group of *pumilio* mutations affects the asymmetric division of germline stem cells in the *Drosophila* ovary. *Development* **124**, 2463–2476.
8. Deng, W., and Lin, H. (2001). Asymmetric germ cell division and oocyte determination during *Drosophila* oogenesis. *Int. Rev. Cytol.* **203**, 93–138.
9. Benfey, P.N. (1999). Stem cells: a tale of two kingdoms. *Curr Biol.* **9**, R171–172.
10. Spradling, A., Drummond-Barbosa, D., and Kai, T. (2001). Stem cells find their niche. *Nature* **414**, 98–104.
11. Margolis, J., and Spradling, A.C. (1995). Identification and behavior of epithelial stem cells in the *Drosophila* ovary. *Development* **121**, 3797–3807.
12. Lin, H. (2002). The stem-cell niche theory: lessons from flies. *Nature Rev. Genet.* **3**, 931–940.
13. Watt, F.M., and Hogan, B.L. (2000). Out of Eden: stem cells and their niches. *Science* **287**, 1427–1430.
14. Trenton, J.J. (1970). Influence of hematopoietic organ stroma (hematopoietic inductive microenvironments) on stem cell differentiation. *In* "Regulation of Hematopoietic Stem Cells" (A.S. Gordon, ed.), pp. 161–185. Appleton-Century-Crofts, New York.
15. Hall, P.A., and Watt, F.M. (1989). Stem cells: the generation and maintenance of cellular diversity. *Development* **106**, 619–633.
16. Potten, C.S., and Loeffler, M. (1990). Stem cells: attributes, cycles, spirals, pitfalls and uncertainties lessons for and from the crypt. *Development* **110**, 1001–1020.
17. Morrison, S.J., Shah, N.M., and Anderson, D.J. (1997). Regulatory mechanisms in stem cell biology. *Cell* **88**, 287–298.
18. Fuchs, E., Merrill, B.J., Jamora, C., and DasGupta, R. (2001). At the roots of a never-ending cycle. *Dev. Cell* **1**, 13–25.
19. Forbes, A.J., Lin, H., Ingham, P.W., and Spradling, A.C. (1996). *hedgehog* is required for the proliferation and specification of ovarian somatic cells prior to egg chamber formation in *Drosophila. Development* **122**, 1125–1135.
20. Drummond-Barbosa, D., and Spradling, A.C. (2001). Stem cells and their progeny respond to nutritional changes during *Drosophila* oogenesis. *Dev. Biol.* **231**, 265–278.
21. King, F.J., and Lin, H. (1999). Somatic signaling mediated by *fs(1)Yb* is essential for germline stem cell maintenance during *Drosophila* oogenesis. *Development* **126**, 1833–1844.
22. Forbes, A.J., Nakano, Y., Taylor, A.M., and Ingham, P.W. (1993). Genetic analysis of hedgehog signaling in the *Drosophila* embryo. *Development Suppl* 115–124.
23. King, F.J., Szakmary, A., Cox, D.N., and Lin, H. (2001). *Yb* modulates the divisions of both germline and somatic stem cells through *piwi-* and *hh*-mediated mechanisms in the *Drosophila* ovary. *Mol. Cell* **7**, 497–508.
24. Cox, D.N., Chao, A., Baker, J., Chang, L., Qiao, D., and Lin, H. (1998). A novel class of evolutionarily conserved genes defined by *piwi* are essential for stem cell self-renewal. *Genes Dev.* **12**, 3715–3727.
25. Cox, D.N., Chao, A., and Lin, H. (2000). *piwi* encodes a nucleoplasmic factor whose activity modulates the number and division rate of germline stem cells. *Development* **127**, 503–514.
26. Song, X., Zhu, C.H., Doan, C., and Xie, T. (2002). Germline stem cells anchored by adherens junctions in the *Drosophila* ovary niches. *Science* **296**, 1855–1857.

27. Xie, T., and Spradling, A.C. (1998). *decapentaplegic* is essential for the maintenance and division of germline stem cells in the *Drosophila* ovary. *Cell* **94,** 251–260.

28. Xie, T., and Spradling, A.C. (2000). A niche maintaining germline stem cells in the *Drosophila* ovary. *Science* **290,** 328–330.

29. Bohmert, K., Campus, I., Bellini, C., Bouchez, D., Caboche, M., and Benning, C. (1998). *AGO1* defines a novel locus of *Arabidopsis* controlling leaf development. *EMBO J.* **17,** 170–180.

30. Moussian, B., Schoof, H., Haecker, A., Jurgens, G., and Laux, T. (1998). Role of the *ZWILLE* gene in the regulation of central shoot meristem cell fate during *Arabidopsis* embryogenesis. *EMBO J.* **17,** 1799–1809.

31. Tabara, H., Sarkissian, M., Kelly, W.G., Fleenor, J., Grishok, A., Timmons, L., Fire, A., and Mello, C.C. (1999). The *rde-1* gene, RNA interference, and transposon silencing in *C. elegans*. *Cell* **99,** 123–132.

32. Deng, W., and Lin, H. (2002). *miwi*, a murine homolog of *piwi*, encodes a cytoplasmic protein essential for spermatogenesis. *Dev. Cell* **2,** 819–830.

33. Tazuke, S.I., Schulz, C., Gilboa, L., Fogarty, M., Mahowald, A.P., Guichet, A., Ephrussi, A., Wood, C.G., Lehmann, R., and Fuller, M.T. (2002). A germline-specific gap junction protein required for survival of differentiating early germ cells. *Development* **129,** 2529–2539.

34. Forbes, A.J., Spradling, A.C., Ingham, P.W., and Lin, H. (1996b). The role of segment polarity genes during early oogenesis in *Drosophila*. *Development* **122,** 3283–3294.

35. Zhang, Y., and Kalderon, D. (2001). Hedgehog acts as a somatic stem cell factor in the *Drosophila* ovary. *Nature* **410,** 599–604.

36. Song, X., and Xie, T. (2002). DE-cadherin-mediated cell adhesion is essential for maintaining somatic stem cells in the *Drosophila* ovary. *Proc. Natl. Acad. Sci. USA* **99,** 14813–14818.

37. Zhu, C.H., and Xie, T. (2003). Clonal expansion of ovarian germline stem cells during niche formation in *Drosophila*. *Development* **130,** 2579–2588.

38. Kai, T., and Spradling, A. (2003). An empty *Drosophila* stem cell niche reactivates the proliferation of ectopic cells. *Proc. Natl. Acad. Sci. USA* **100,** 4633–4638.

39. Gonczy, P., Thomas, B.J., and DiNardo, S. (1994). Roughex is a dose-dependent regulator of the second meiotic division during *Drosophila* spermatogenesis. *Cell* **77,** 1015–1025.

40. Meyer, C.A., Jacobs, H.W., Datar, S.A., Du, W., Edgar, B.A., Lehner, C.F. (2000). *Drosophila* Cdk4 is required for normal growth and is dispensable for cell cycle progression. *EMBO J.* **19,** 4533–4542.

41. Jacobs, H.W., Knoblich, J.A., Lehner, C.F. (1998). *Drosophila* Cyclin B3 is required for female fertility and is dispensable for mitosis like Cyclin B. *Genes Dev.* **12,** 3741–3751.

42. Munn, K., and Steward, R. (2000). The *shut-down* gene of *Drosophila melanogaster* encodes a novel FK506-binding protein essential for the formation of germline cysts during oogenesis. *Genetics* **156,** 245–256.

43. Klar, A.J.S., and Bonaduce, M.J. (1993). The mechanism of fission yeast mating-type interconversion: evidence for two types of epigenetically inherited chromosomal imprinted events. *Cold Spring Harbor Symp. Quant. Biol.* **58,** 457–465.

44. Dalgaard, J.Z., and Klar, A.J. (2001). Does *S. pombe* exploit the intrinsic asymmetry of DNA synthesis to imprint daughter cells for mating-type switching? *Trends Genet.* **17,** 153–157.

45. Smulders-Srinivasan, T.K., and Lin, H. (2003). Screens for *piwi* suppressors in *Drosophila* identify dosage-dependent regulators of germline stem cell division. *Genetics* **165,** 1971–1991.

46. Akiyama, T. (2002). Mutations of *stonewall* disrupt the maintenance of female germline stem cells in *Drosophila melanogaster*. *Dev. Growth Differ.* **44,** 97–102.

47. Lin, H., and Schagat, T. (1997). Neuroblasts: a model for asymmetric division of stem cells. *Trends Genet.* **13,** 33–39.

48. Parisi, M.P., and Lin, H. (1999). The *Drosophila pumilio* gene encodes two functional protein isoforms that play multiple roles in germline development, gametogenesis, oogenesis and embryogenesis. *Genetics* **153,** 235–250.

49. Forbes, A., and Lehmann, R. (1998). Nanos and Pumilio have critical roles in the development and function of *Drosophila* germline stem cells. *Development* **125,** 679–690.

50. Murata, Y., and Wharton, R.P. (1995). Binding of Pumilio to maternal hunchback mRNA is required for posterior patterning in *Drosophila* embryos. *Cell* **80,** 747–756.

51. Nagase, T., Seki, N., Ishikawa, K., Ohira, M., Kawarrabayasi, Y., Ohara, O., Tanaka, A., Kotani, H., Miyajima, N., and Nomura, N. (1996). Prediction of the coding sequences of unidentified human genes. VI. The coding sequences of 80 new genes (KIAA0201-KIAA0280) deduced by analysis of cDNA clones from cell line KG-1 and brain. *DNA Res.* **3,** 321–329.

52. Wang, Z., and Lin, H. (2004). *nanos* maintains germline stem cell self-renewal by preventing differentiation. *Science* **303,** 2016–2019.

53. McKearin, D.M., and Spradling, A.C. (1990). *Bag-of-marbles:* a *Drosophila* gene required to initiate both male and female gametogenesis. *Genes Dev.* **4,** 2242–2251.

54. Ohlstein, B., and McKearin, D. (1997). Ectopic expression of the *Drosophila* Bam protein eliminates oogenic germline stem cells. *Development* **124,** 3651–3662.

55. Gateff, E. (1982). "Gonial Cell Neoplasm of Genetic Origin Affecting Both Sexes of *Drosophila melanogaster*. Alan R. Liss, New York.

56. Ohlstein, B., Lavoie, C.A., Vef, O., Gateff, E., and McKearin, D.M. (2000). The *Drosophila* cystoblast differentiation factor, benign gonial cell neoplasm, is related to DExH-box proteins and interacts genetically with bag-of-marbles. *Genetics* **155,** 1809–1819.

57. Albertson, R., and Doe, C.Q. (2003). Dlg, Scrib and Lgl regulate neuroblast cell size and mitotic spindle asymmetry. *Nat. Cell Biol.* **5,** 166–170.

58. Cai, Y., Yu, F., Lin, S., Chia, W., Yang, X. (2003). Apical complex genes control mitotic spindle geometry and relative size of daughter cells in *Drosophila* neuroblast and pI asymmetric divisions. *Cell* **112,** 51–62.

59. Lin, H., Yue, L., and Spradling, A.S. (1994). The *Drosophila* fusome, a germline-specific organelle, contains membrane skeletal proteins and functions in cyst formation. *Development* **120,** 947–956.

60. McGrail, M., and Hays, T.S. (1997). The microtubule motor cytoplasmic dynein is required for spindle orientation during germline cell divisions and oocyte differentiation in *Drosophila*. *Development* **124,** 2409–2419.

61. Cotsarelis, G., Sun, T.T., and Lavker, R.M. (1990). Label-retaining cells reside in the bulge area of pilosebaceous unit: implications for follicular stem cells, hair cycle, and skin carcinogenesis. *Cell* **61,** 1329–1337.

62. Taylor, G., Lehrer, M.S., Jensen, P.J., Sun, T.T., and Lavker, R.M. (2000). Involvement of follicular stem cells in forming not only the follicle but also the epidermis. *Cell* **102,** 451–461.

63. Oro, A.E., Higgins, K.M., Hu, Z., Bonifas, J.M., Epstein, E.H., Jr., and Scott, M.P. (1997). Basal cell carcinomas in mice overexpressing *sonic hedgehog*. *Science* **276,** 817–821.

64. Zhang, J., Niu, C., Ye, L., Huang, H., He, X., Tong, W.G., Ross, J., Haug, J., Johnson, T., Feng, J.Q., Harris, S., Wiedemann, L.M., Mishima, Y., and Li, L. (2003). Identification of the haematopoietic stem cell niche and control of the niche size. *Nature* **425,** 836–841.

65. Calvi, L.M., Adams, G.B., Weibrechet, K.W., Webber, J.M., Olson, D.P., Knight, M.C., Martin, R.P., Schipani, E., Divieti, P., Bringhurst, F.R., Milner, L.A., Kronenberg, H.M., and Scadden, D.T. (2003). Osteoblastic cell regulate the haematopoietic stem cell niche. *Nature* **425,** 841–846.

66. Besmer, P. (1991). The kit ligand encoded at the murine *Steel* locus: a pleiotropic growth and differentiation factor. *Curr Opin Cell Biol.* **3,** 939–946.

67. Reya, T., Morrison, S.J., Clarke, M.F., and Weissman, I.L. (2001). Stem cells, cancer, and cancer stem cells. *Nature* **414,** 105–111.

68. Reya, T., Duncan, A.W., Ailles, L., Domen, J., Scherer, D.C., Willert, K., Hintz, L., Nusse, R., and Weissman, I.L. (2003). A role for Wnt signalling in self-renewal of haematopoietic stem cells. *Nature* **423,** 409–414.

69. Temple, S. (2001). The development of neural stem cells. *Nature* **414,** 112–117.

70. Goldring, K., Partridge, T., and Watt, D. (2002). Muscle stem cells. *J. Pathol.* **197,** 457–467.

71. Forbes, S., Vig, P., Poulsom, R., Thomas, H., and Alison, M. (2002). Hepatic stem cells. *J. Pathol.* **197,** 510–518.

72. Gu, G., Dubauskaite, J., and Melton, D.A. (2002). Direct evidence for the pancreatic lineage: NGN3+ cells are islet progenitors and are distinct from duct progenitors. *Development* **129,** 2447–2457.

73. Zhao, G.Q., Deng, K., Labosky, P.A., Liaw, L., and Hogan, B.L. (1996). The gene encoding bone morphogenetic protein 8B is required for the initiation and maintenance of spermatogenesis in the mouse. *Genes Dev.* **10,** 1657–1669.

74. Matsuda, T., Nakamura, T., Nakao, K., Arai, T., Katsuki, M., Heike, T., and Yokota, T. (1999). STAT3 activation is sufficient to maintain an undifferentiated state of mouse embryonic stem cells. *EMBO J.* **18,** 4261–4269.

75. Ramalho-Santos, M., Yoon, S., Matsuzaki, Y., Mulligan, R.C., and Melton, D.A. (2002). "Stemness": transcriptional profiling of embryonic and adult stem cells. *Science* **298,** 597–600.

76. Ivanova, N.B., Dimos, J.T., Schaniel, C., Hackney, J.A., Moore, K.A., and Lemischka, I.R. (2002). A stem cell molecular signature. *Science* **298,** 601–604.

77. Gurdon, J.B. (1988). A community effect in animal development. *Nature* **336,** 772–774.

78. Yang, L., Li, S., Hatch, H., Ahrens, K., Cornelius, J.G., Petersen, B.E., and Peck, A.B. (2002). In vitro trans-differentiation of adult hepatic stem cells into pancreatic endocrine hormone-producing cells. *Proc. Natl. Acad. Sci. USA* **99,** 8078–8083.

79. Gussoni, E., Soneoka, Y., Strickland, C.D., Buzney, E.A., Khan, M.K., Flint, A.F., Kunkel, L.M., and Mulligan, R.C. (1999). Dystrophin expression in the mdx mouse restored by stem cell transplantation. *Nature* **401,** 390–394.

80. Wagers, A.J., Sherwood, R.I., Christensen, J.L., and Weissman, I.L. (2002). Little evidence for developmental plasticity of adult hematopoietic stem cells. *Science* **297,** 2256–2259.

81. de Rooij, D.G. (2001). Proliferation and differentiation of spermatogonial stem cells. *Reproduction* **121,** 347–354.

82. Lin, H., and Spradling, A. (1995). Fusome asymmetry and oocyte determination. *Dev. Genet.* **16,** 6–12.

83. Cox, D.N. (1999). Function of the *Drosophila piwi* gene in the self-renewing division of germline stem cells and in germline development. Ph.D. Dissertation thesis, Duke University, Durham, NC.

84. Matunis, E., Tran, J., Gonczy, P., Caldwell, K., and DiNardo, S. (1997). *punt* and *schnurri* regulate a somatically derived signal that restricts proliferation of committed progenitors in the germline. *Development* **124,** 4383–4391.

85. Kiger, A.A., Jones, D.L., Schulz, C., Rogers, M.B., and Fuller, M.T. (2001). Stem cell self-renewal specified by JAK-STAT activation in response to a support cell cue. *Science* **294,** 2542–2545.

86. Tulina, N., and Matunis, E. (2001). Control of stem cell self-renewal in *Drosophila* spermatogenesis by JAK-STAT signaling. *Science* **294,** 2546–2549.

87. Tran, J., Brenner, T.J., and DiNardo, S. (2000). Somatic control over the germline stem cell lineage during *Drosophila* spermatogenesis. *Nature* **407,** 754–757.

88. Kiger, A.A., White-Cooper, H., and Fuller, M.T. (2000). Somatic support cells restrict germline stem cell self-renewal and promote differentiation. *Nature* **407,** 750–754.

Regulation of Stem Cell Self-renewal Versus Differentiation by a Support Cell Niche: Lessons from the *Drosophila* Male Germ Line

D. Leanne Jones, Yukiko M. Yamashita, Cordula Schulz, and Margaret T. Fuller

The *Drosophila* male germ line is emerging as a powerful model system in which to study the molecular and cellular mechanisms that regulate self-renewal and differentiation of adult stem cells. In addition to the many existing mutants and sequenced genome, a variety of genetic tools developed for *Drosophila* have allowed analysis of male germ line stem cell (GSC) behavior at the molecular level. Using these approaches, several genes, molecular pathways, and mechanisms have been identified that play an instructive role either in male GSC self-renewal or in stem cell daughter differentiation. Most importantly, the ability to identify and study *Drosophila* male GSCs *in vivo* has allowed contributions of the support cell microenvironment, or the stem cell niche, toward regulating stem cell behavior to be assessed. *Drosophila* female GSCs, which are also being studied intensively (see Chapter 13 in this volume), provide a powerful model system for many of the same reasons, allowing comparison of the mechanisms that regulate different stem cell populations in the same organism.

The male germ line is a classic stem cell system. Division of male GSCs supports production of sperm throughout reproductive life. Transplantation experiments in mammals have shown that male GSCs can reconstitute a host depleted of endogenous stem cells.[1,2] Unlike hematopoietic or epidermal stem cells, male GSCs give rise to only one differentiated cell type, the male gametes. This relative simplicity with respect to lineage may help lay bare the essential mechanisms regulating stem cell self-renewal and differentiation by pruning away complications arising from the many downstream fate decisions involved in specifying different lineages among the differentiating progeny characteristic of more complex systems like the blood or epidermis.

In this chapter we describe the normal behavior of *Drosophila* male GSCs and the anatomy of the stem cell niche. We then review genetic experiments and the results of mutant screens that have provided insight into the molecular mechanisms that regulate stem cell self-renewal and differentiation in this system. In a separate chapter in the companion volume of this series,[3] we compare the *Drosophila* male and female GSC systems with respect to paradigms that they suggest for the role of the niche and regulation of adult stem cell behavior in other organisms and tissues.

The *Drosophila* Male Germ Line Stem Cell System

In adult *Drosophila melanogaster* testes, an average of 9 GSCs lie at the apical tip in a ring closely surrounding a cluster of postmitotic somatic cells called the hub (Figs. 14–1A and 14–2).[4] Male GSCs initiate the first self-renewing divisions in the testes by late embryogenesis and maintain production of sperm throughout development and adult life. As in many other stem cell systems, the frequency of division of *Drosophila* male GSCs is low, with an average of only one stem cell in division per 5–10 testes (<2% of stem cells) in newly eclosed adult males.[5]

When a *Drosophila* male GSC divides, it normally gives rise to one cell that remains next to the hub and retains stem cell identity and one cell, called a gonialblast, which is displaced away from the hub and will initiate differentiation.[4,6,7] The gonialblast and its progeny undergo four rounds of synchronous cell division, giving rise to a cluster of 16 spermatogonia (Figs. 14–1A and C and Fig. 14–2). The spermatogonial divisions are comparable to the transit amplifying divisions described in blood, skin, intestinal epithelial and many other stem cell lineages. In *Drosophila,* as in mammalian spermatogenesis, cytokinesis is incomplete and the spermatogonia derived from a single gonialblast remain interconnected by cytoplasmic bridges, providing a convenient marker to distinguish spermatogonia from gonialblasts and stem cells, which both exist and divide as single cells. Interestingly, the number of rounds of spermatogonial divisions differs among species, precisely four in *D. melanogaster,* three in *Drosophila hydei,*[8] and five in *Drosophila pseudoobscura,* suggesting that the mechanism that specifies the number of transient amplifying divisions is under genetic control.[9]

After completing the transit amplifying mitotic divisions, the differentiating germ cells cease mitosis and become spermatocytes, which grow 25 times in volume, initiate a robust and cell type–specific gene expression program, and undergo meiosis, again with incomplete cytokinesis (Fig. 14–1A). Over the next 5 days, almost every subcellular component of the resulting haploid spermatids is remodeled to produce the terminally differentiated product of the lineage, mature sperm. The whole process of spermatogenesis from stem cell to sperm takes approximately 10 days in *D. melanogaster.*[10] Most of the stages of germ cell differentiation can be easily visualized in whole testes, where cells in the first half of spermatogenesis are displayed sequentially from apical tip to the middle third of the testis, or in squashed preparations, where the differentiating germ cells are spilled out of an opened

testis and can be observed either by phase contrast light microscopy[9] or fixed and stained for immunofluorescence (Figs. 14–1B and 14–2C).

Male GSCs were functionally identified as stem cells *in situ* using genetic systems for inducible, site-specific recombination that allow regulated induction of marked clones of wild type cells at low frequency[11] (Fig. 14–1C). Similar genetic strategies can be used to generate marked clones of homozygous mutant cells in an otherwise heterozygous animal allowing tests of cell autonomy and examination of the effects of mutants that cause early lethality in a whole animal (e.g., see reference 12).

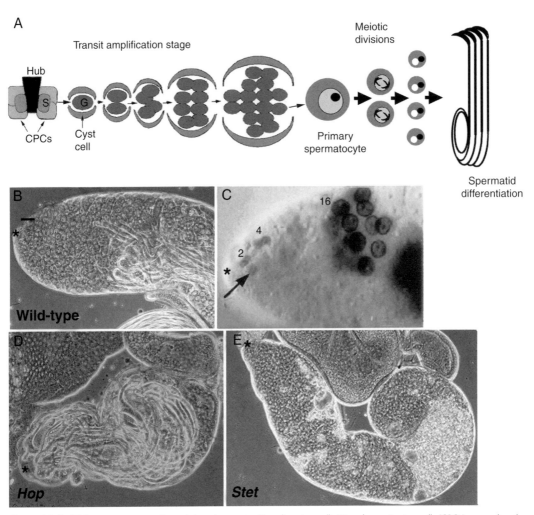

Figure 14–1. (A) Spermatogenesis in *Drosophila melanogaster.* Germ line stem cells (S) and somatic stem cells (CPCs) surrounding the apical hub divide asymmetrically, giving rise to one daughter cell that retains stem cell identity, while the other daughter cell initiates differentiation as a gonialblast (G) or cyst cell. The gonialblast undergoes transit amplifying mitotic divisions to produce a cyst of 16 interconnected spermatogonia, which then initiate differentiation as spermatocytes. The subsequent meiotic divisions produce haploid spermatids, which terminally differentiate to produce mature sperm. (B) A wild type testis tip visualized using phase-contrast optics. (Bar) Region containing amplifying spermatogonia. (C) Functional demonstration of stem cell identity by lineage tracing using Flp recombinase-mediated clonal induction to generate a marked germ line stem cell (arrow).[11] Cysts of 2, 4, and 16 differentiating germ cells produced from the marked germ line clone are visible. (Adapted from reference 7.) (D) Phase-contrast image of a *hop* mutant testis in which all early germ cells have been lost due to a failure in stem cell self-renewal. (E) *stet* mutant testis in which germ line stem cells do not differentiate properly due to failure of somatic cyst cells to encapsulate germ cells, resulting in accumulation of early germ cells. Images in B, D, and E (*) apical hub, and images are at the same approximate magnification. (Please see CD-ROM for color version of this figure.)

Male GSCs can be visualized in the context of their normal anatomic position by expressing either green fluorescent protein (GFP) (Fig. 14–2B), Tubulin:GFP, or other fusion proteins under control of a germ line–specific gene expression system based on the *D. nanos (nos)* promoter and the yeast transcriptional activator GAL4.[13,14] This same system, which drives expression in male GSCs through the early spermatocyte stage, also provides a useful tool for assessing the effects of forced expression of wild type or altered proteins of interest on GSC behavior.

Male GSCs in the *Drosophila* testis are flanked by a second population of stem cells: the somatic cyst progenitor cells (CPCs) (Figs. 14–1A and 14–2A and D). The CPCs sit adjacent and just distal to the GSCs and extend narrow processes up past the GCSs to touch the apical hub (Figs. 14–2D and 14–3). The CPCs also self-renew and give rise to a differentiating cell population: the somatic cyst cells.

Two cyst cells enclose each gonialblast and continue to envelope its differentiating progeny throughout the process of spermatogenesis. The cyst cells do not divide again, but co-differentiate with the germ cells they enclose.[7] The somatic cyst cells, which may be the functional equivalent of mammalian Sertoli cells, play a major role in ensuring spermatogonial differentiation and the transition from spermatogonia to spematocyte.[15–17]

Signaling from a Support Cell Niche Specifies Stem Cell Self-renewal

One of the critical questions in the adult stem cell field concerns the mechanisms that regulate the decision between self-renewal and differentiation. Adult stem cells have two fundamental properties: a long-term capacity to divide and the ability to produce daughter cells that either retain stem cell

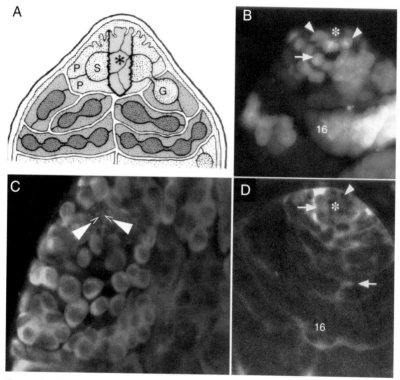

Figure 14–2. (A) Schematic section through the germinal proliferation center at the apical tip of the *Drosophila* testis. (*) Hub, (S) germ line stem cell, (P) cyst progenitor cell, and (G) gonialblast. (Adapted from reference 4.) (B) Male GSCs around the hub visualized live in a testis from a *nosGAL4, UAS-gfp* fly. To generate this genotype, flies carrying a transgene with the *Drosophila nanos (nos)* promoter driving expression of the yeast transcriptional activator GAL4 fused with the VP16 transcriptional activation domain are mated with flies carrying a transgene with a cDNA encoding the GFP reporter cloned downstream of multiple copies of the yeast upstream activating sequence (UAS) to which GAL4 binds.[13,14,35] In the resulting males, the GFP reporter is expressed specifically in early male germ cells from GSCs through the early spermatocyte stage (arrowheads). Germ line stem cells adjacent to the hub (arrow). Gonialblast displaced away from the hub. (C) Immunofluorescence image of germ cells stained with an antibody to the germ cell specific protein Vasa and hub cells stained with an antibody to the membrane associated protein Fasciclin III (arrowheads). Germ line stem cells surrounding the hub. (D) Cyst cells marked by expressing GFP under the *patched* promoter (*ptcGAL4; UAS-gfp*), using the same technique as described for (B) (arrowhead). Germ line stem cell (arrows). Cyst cells surrounding germ line cysts.[14] (Please see CD-ROM for color version of this figure.)

D. Leanne Jones, Yukiko Yamashita, Cordula Schulz, and Margaret T. Fuller

identity or initiate differentiation along the appropriate lineage(s). The balance between self-renewal and initiation of differentiation is crucial. If too many daughter cells initiate differentiation, the stem cell population may be depleted. Conversely, if too many daughter cells maintain stem cell identity, the stem cell population may expand out of proportion, providing a pool of proliferative, incompletely differentiated cells that could mutate and become tumorigenic. However, when needed, the ability of stem cells to divide symmetrically to increase stem cell number may be important for recovery from wounding or other damage to stem cell populations. Recent work on the mechanisms that regulate stem cell maintenance and self-renewal in the *Drosophila* male and female germ lines has shed important light on this central question in stem cell biology, identifying critical cell–cell signaling pathways required for stem cell self-renewal and/or maintenance (reviewed in references 3, 18, and 19).

The population of male GSCs in the *Drosophila* testis is maintained by mechanisms that ensure a reliably asymmetric outcome of male GSC divisions. Normally the daughter cell that retains contact with the apical hub self-renews stem cell identity, while the daughter cell displaced away from the hub initiates differentiation. Molecular mechanisms underlying the stereotyped behavior of male GSCs and their

differentiating progeny have been identified through analysis of *Drosophila* mutants that cause either GSC loss (Fig. 14–1D) or overproliferation of early germ cells at the expense of differentiation (Fig. 14–1E).

Recent work has revealed that the somatic hub at the apical tip of the testis serves as a niche that supports self-renewal of the GSCs via activation of the Janus kinase (JAK)-signal transducer and activator of transcription (STAT) pathway within the adjacent germ cells[12,20] (Fig. 14–3). JAKs are non-receptor tyrosine kinases that mediate signaling downstream of many mammalian cytokine and growth factor receptors, in part by phosphorylation and activation of STAT (reviewed in reference 21). *D. melanogaster* has a single JAK kinase encoded by the *hopscotch (hop)* gene and a single known STAT, encoded by *stat92E*. Hop and Stat92E act together in a variety of essential developmental processes, including embryonic segmentation, larval production of blood cells, and border cell migration during oogenesis.[22,23] The ligand, Upd, has been shown to act upstream of *hop* and *stat92E* genetically and to activate Hop kinase activity *in vitro*.[24] Upd binds to the receptor Domeless (Dome), which contains some homology to the interleukin (IL)-6 and IL-3 family of cytokine receptors in vertebrates, raising the possibility that the *Drosophila upd, Dome, hop,* and *stat92E* genes

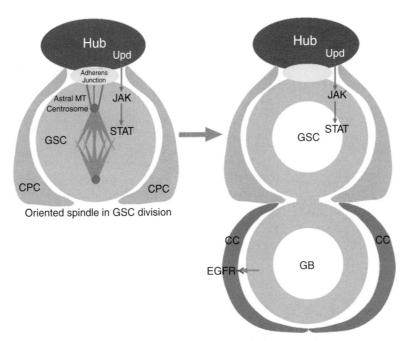

Figure 14–3. Both extrinsic and intrinsic determinants are involved in ensuring the asymmetric outcome of stem cell divisions. The signaling ligand Upd, secreted from the apical hub, specifies germ line stem cell (GSC) identity by activating the JAK-STAT pathway within the GSCs. Two cyst progenitor cells (CPCs), which function as somatic stem cells, surround each GSC. After stem cell division, one daughter cell maintains contact with the hub and retains stem cell identity, while the other is displaced away from the hub and initiates the differentiation program as a gonialblast (GB) or cyst cell (CC), respectively. Cyst cells enclose gonialblasts and later stages to promote proper differentiation. Epidermal growth factor receptor (EGFR) function in somatic cells is required for ensuring germ cell differentiation. The mitotic spindle is oriented perpendicular to the hub during GSC division to ensure an asymmetric outcome of the stem cell division. (Please see CD-ROM for color version of this figure.)

encode components of an ancestral IL-6 type signaling pathway.[25,26]

The important role played by JAK-STAT signaling in stem cell self-renewal in the male germ line was initially revealed by a special missense allele of the *Drosophila* JAK kinase *hopscotch (hop)*. Males carrying a viable, male sterile *hop* allele[27] with an amino acid substitution in the putative receptor binding domain[28,29] exhibit loss of the early stages of spermatogenesis[12,20] (Fig. 14–1D). Initial round(s) of spermatogenesis proceed, and testes from newly eclosed *hop* mutant males have a number of elongating spermatid bundles. However, GSCs are lost, perhaps as early as the first few rounds of spermatogenesis, which initiate near the end of embryogenesis.[12,20] The signal for stem cell self-renewal is transduced from the activated JAK via STAT. Analysis of clones of germ cells homozygous mutant for *stat92E* in an otherwise *stat92E/+* animal revealed that *stat92E* activity was required autonomously in the germ line for stem cell self-renewal.[12,20] Presumably, stem cell identity is specified at least in part by transcriptional targets of activated STAT.

The signaling ligand for the *Drosophila* JAK-STAT pathway, Upd, is normally expressed in the somatic apical hub cells, suggesting that the apical hub may serve as a stem cell niche, instructing the adjacent germ cells to self-renew stem cell identity by providing a local source of the critical signaling ligand (Fig. 14–3). Consistent with this hypothesis, ectopic expression of *upd* in early germ cells resulted in enlarged testes containing many small cells resembling GSCs and gonialblasts. This uncontrolled early germ cell proliferation and accumulation of cells expressing stem cell markers was not dependent on contact with the apical hub, presumably because Upd ligand expressed and secreted by the early germ cells themselves can activate JAK-STAT signaling in an autocrine loop. These data suggest that *upd*, which is normally expressed in the hub cells, is an essential molecular component of the stem cell niche, specifying maintenance and self-renewal of stem cell identity in adjacent germ cells. Experiments in tissue culture suggest that the Upd protein associates tightly with the extracellular matrix after secretion, potentially restricting its diffusion.[24] If diffusion of secreted Upd protein is also restricted *in vivo,* only cells that maintain direct contact with apical hub cells may normally receive sufficient levels of Upd to retain stem cell identity. Consistent with a spatially limited range for the Upd signal from the niche, STAT protein was detected in the nucleus only in those germ cells directly adjacent to the apical hub.[30] JAK-STAT pathway activation in response to Upd secreted from the hub may also directly or indirectly regulate self-renewal of the somatic stem cells, the CPCs.[12,20] If Upd secreted from the apical hub does signal directly to specify somatic stem cell self-renewal, then the requirement for this signal for both germ line and somatic stem cell self-renewal may provide a mechanism to coordinate in space two different stem cell populations that produce differentiating daughter cells that must work together (see reference 3 for further discussion).

Orientation of Stem Cell Division with Respect to the Niche Ensures an Asymmetric Outcome

The reliably asymmetric outcome of GSC divisions in *Drosophila* testes may also be regulated by mechanisms that orient the division plane in GSCs. Direct observation of dividing GSCs expressing GFP α-tubulin revealed that the mitotic spindle is consistently oriented perpendicular to the hub, with one of the two spindle poles positioned near the region of GSC cortex where the stem cell contacts the hub[5] (Fig. 14–3). Orientation of GSCs toward the hub is maintained throughout the cell cycle. In early interphase, the single centrosome is located between the nucleus and the region of cortex where the GSC touches the hub. When the centrosome duplicates, one daughter centrosome remains next to the hub while the other migrates to the opposite side of the GSC nucleus to set up the oriented spindle. Function of the integral centrosomal protein Centrosomin (Cnn) is required for normal centrosome positioning and spindle orientation in GSCs, suggesting a role for centrosomes and/or astral microtubules in maintaining GCS orientation toward the hub. The average number of stem cells around the hub increased in *cnn* mutant males, although hub diameter remained the same, suggesting that misoriented GSC spindles can lead to symmetric divisions where both daughters of a GSC self-renew stem cell identity.[5]

If the asymmetric outcome of stem cell divisions within a niche is regulated by orientation of the division plane, the cell intrinsic mechanisms that specify spindle orientation in the stem cell are of paramount importance for controlling the balance between stem cell self-renewal and differentiation. The effects of *cnn* mutants on centrosome position in interphase and spindle orientation during mitosis and the normal close attachment of one spindle pole to a region of the GSC next to the hub suggest that a specialized region of the GSC cell cortex adjacent to the hub might provide a polarity cue or anchor toward which astral microtubules from the centrosome and spindle pole orient (Fig. 14–3). Immunofluorescence and ultrastructural analysis both indicate a specialized region of the GSC cortex where the stem cell contacts the hub: high levels of DE-cadherin, encoded by the *Drosophila* gene *shotgun*, and β-catenin, encoded by the *Drosophila* gene *armadillo*, mark the GSC–hub interface,[5] and GSCs attach to hub cells by localized adherens junctions.[31] Homologues of the tumor suppressor gene *Adenomatous Polyposis Coli (APC)*, encoded by the *Drosophila* genes *apc1* and *apc2*, are also involved in the mechanisms that polarize male GSCs toward the niche. Apc1 protein localizes to the centrosomes in late G_2/prophase, whereas Apc2 protein is concentrated at the interface between GSCs and the hub. Both interphase centrosome positioning and spindle orientation were perturbed in flies carrying mutations in *apc1* or *apc2*. Together, these observations suggest a model where astral microtubules extending from the centrosome are captured by a protein complex containing Apc2 localized to the GSC cortex at the cell–cell junctional complex with the hub.[5] Thus, the normally asymmetric outcome of male GSC divisions is controlled by a combination of extrinsic factor(s) that specify stem cell identity and intrinsic cellular machinery acting at the centrosome and cell cortex to orient the cell division plane with respect to the signaling microenvironment. Together, the concerted actions of these intercellular and intracellular mechanisms govern the normally asymmetric choice of cell fates by placing one daughter within the stem cell niche to maintain stem cell identity and the other out of the stem cell niche to initiate the differentiation program (Fig. 14–3).

Attachment to the Niche and Stem Cell Maintenance

Physical attachment to the niche may be a feature of many adult stem cell systems, with the kind of junctional complex depending on the nature of the niche. *Drosophila* male and female GSCs attach directly to somatic niche cells by adherens junctions, and *Drosophila* E-cadherin concentrates at the GSC cortex where GSCs interface with the hub.[5,32,33] When male GSCs are made homozygous null mutant for *shot-gun,* using Flp recombinase-mediated clonal induction, the mutant stem cells are gradually lost from the testis tip.[34] Similar experiments revealed that *DE*-cadherin is also required in *Drosophila* female GSCs for stem cell maintenance.[32] In some stem cell systems in mammals, the level of integrins such as $\beta 1$ and $\alpha 6$ is increased in stem cells, - suggesting that attachment to a basal lamina may be important in holding stem cells close to self-renewal signals emanating from surrounding support cells.[3] The somatic CPCs in the *Drosophila* testis have cytoplasmic extensions between the individual GSCs that contact the hub (Figs. 14–2D and 14–3). These cytoplasmic extensions may anchor the somatic stem cells to the hub and also help hold the GSCs within the niche.

Guardian Cells and the Larger Neighborhood of the Niche Help Ensure Proper Differentiation

Although signals from the hub specify self-renewal of stem cell identity, other signals from the microenvironment also play roles in regulating the fate of daughters of stem cell divisions in the *Drosophila* male germ line. Interactions between germ cells and somatic cyst cells appear to restrict expression of stem cell characteristics and ensure that stem cell daughters displaced away from the hub initiate differentiation. Thus, the somatic cyst cells play an important guardian role, preventing accumulation of early germ cells with ambiguous identity.[16,17,35]

Somatic cyst cells require activation of the epidermal growth factor receptor (EGFR) signal transduction pathway for normal differentiation of the early germ cells they enclose (Fig. 14–3). Loss of function of the EGF receptor or the downstream effector Raf in somatic cells resulted

in expansion in the number of early germ cells because of unrestricted mitotic divisions.[16,17] The early germ cells that accumulated under these conditions often showed mixed identity. Some cells still expressed the stem cell marker escargot *(esg)*; many maintained spherical spectrosomes or divided as single cells, characteristics of stem cells or gonialblasts; while some were interconnected and had small branched fusomes reminiscent of spermatogonia. The transition from the spermatogonial transit amplifying divisions to the spermatocyte stage also appeared to depend on activation of the EGFR signaling pathway in the somatic cells, as testes from males carrying a temperature-sensitive allele of the *Egfr* accumulated cysts of interconnected spermatogonia that continued to divide beyond the normal four rounds of transit amplifying divisions.[17] Activation of TGFβ signaling also plays a role in the transition from the spermatogonial transit amplifying divisions to spermatocyte differentiation.[15]

Recent results suggest that a ligand secreted by early male germ cells may activate the EGFR signaling pathway in the somatic cyst cells.[35] The *Drosophila stet* gene encodes a homologue of *rhomboid (rho),* a transmembrane protease[36] that plays an essential role in EGFR signaling. Rho proteolytically cleaves and activates the major EGFR ligand *spitz (spi)* in the signaling cell (reviewed in reference 37). In males mutant for *stet,* somatic cyst cells fail to properly encapsulate germ cells, and early germ cells at mixed stages of differentiation accumulate, much as in EGFR mutant males. Mosaic analysis demonstrated that wild type function of *stet* is required in the germ cells for normal germ cell enclosure by somatic cyst cells and germ cell differentiation[35] (Fig. 14–1E), whereas function of the *Egfr* and its downstream effector *Draf* are required in the soma.[16,17] Together these results suggest that as one of the earliest steps of differentiation, germ cells send an EGF class signal that activates the EGFR on the surface of neighboring somatic cyst cells (Fig. 14–3), causing the somatic cells to send out processes to envelope the germ cells. The somatic cyst cells then in turn play a guardian role, sending signals of an as yet unknown nature back to the germ cells to ensure that they properly embark on the spermatogonial differentiation program.

In addition to signaling via ligand–receptor based systems such as the Upd-JAK-Stat and EGFR pathways, intercellular communication through gap junctions appears to play an important role in the survival and differentiation of early germ cells in *Drosophila*. Loss of function mutations in the *zero population growth (zpg)* gene, which encodes a germ line–specific gap junction protein, result in loss of early germ cells at the beginning of differentiation in both males and females.[38] Zpg protein is concentrated on the germ cell–soma interface in males and females and between adjacent germ cells in developing egg chambers, suggesting that transfer of small molecules and nutrients from surrounding support cells to germ cells via gap junctions may be essential for gametogenesis.[38] In addition, the presence of gap junctions between female GSCs and adjacent support cells, coupled with loss of female GSCs over time, suggests that signaling via gap junctions may be required for stem cell maintenance or that gap junctions may physically help maintain GSCs in their niche.[38]

Stem Cells in a Niche: Lessons from *Drosophila*

A general picture of how the stem cell niche mechanism might work to control stem cell number and maintain the correct balance between self-renewal and differentiation is beginning to emerge from work on *Drosophila* male and female GSCs. This process involves complex cross talk between intercellular and intracellular mechanisms (Fig. 14–3). First, the size or number of stem cell niches defines the correct number of stem cells by sending short-range signal(s) for self-renewal or maintenance to the neighboring stem cells. Second, cell–cell adhesion between supporting niche cells and stem cells enables stem cells to remain tightly associated with the niche. Third, stem cells are polarized with respect to the niche. Either localized signals from the niche or the geometry of the cell adhesion junctions between stem cells and the niche could provide polarity cues to orient stem cells toward the niche. Finally, stem cells polarized through contact with the niche can orient their mitotic spindles to ensure the normally asymmetric outcome of stem cell divisions by reliably placing one daughter cell firmly within the niche, where it can both maintain its attachment and come under the influence of the self-renewal signal(s), while placing the other daughter cell outside of the niche. Attachment to, orientation toward, and signaling from a supporting niche may also play important roles in regulating stem cell number, self-renewal, and differentiation in tissues maintained by stem cell populations in mammals.

ACKNOWLEDGMENTS

The authors would like to thank Salli Tazuke, Tony Mahowald, Amy Kiger, and Thomas Fellner for many helpful discussions. Y.M.Y is a JSPS fellow, and D.L.J is a Lilly fellow of the Life Sciences Research Foundation. This work was supported by NIH grant 1P01 DK53074, subproject#4, to M.T.F.

REFERENCES

1. Brinster, R.L. (2002). Germline stem cell transplantation and transgenesis. *Science* **296**, 2174–2176.
2. Ogawa, T., Dobrinski, I., Avarbock, M.R., and Brinster, R.L. (2000). Transplantation of male germ line stem cells restores fertility in infertile mice. *Nat. Med.* **6**, 29–34.
3. Jones, D.L., and Fuller, M.T. (2004). Stem cell niches. *In* "Handbook of Adult and Fetal Stem Cells," Vol. 1. (Lanza, R., ed.) Academic Press, San Diego, CA.
4. Hardy, R.W., Tokuyasu, K.T., Lindsley, D.L., and Garavito, M. (1979). The germinal proliferation center in the testis of Drosophila melanogaster. *J. Ultrastruct. Res.* **69**, 180–190.
5. Yamashita, Y., Jones, D.L., and Fuller, M.T. (2003) Orientation of asymmetric stem cell division by the APC tumor suppressor and centrosome. *Science* **301**, 1547–1550.
6. Harris, B.B. (1929). The effects of aging of X-rayed males upon mutation frequency in *Drosophila*. *J. Hered.* **20**, 229–302.
7. Gönczy, P., and DiNardo, S. (1996). The germ line regulates somatic cyst cell proliferation and fate during Drosophila spermatogenesis. *Development* **122**, 2437–2347.
8. Hennig, W. (1985). Y Chromosome function and spermatogenesis in *Drosophila hydei*. *Adv. Genet.* **23**, 179–234.
9. Fuller, M.T. (1993). Spermatogenesis. *In* "The Development of *Drosophila melanogaster*" (M. Bate and A. Martinez-Arias, eds.), pp. 71–147. Cold Spring Harbor Laboratory Press, New York.
10. Lindsley, D., and Tokuyasu, K.T. (1980). Spermatogenesis. *In* "Genetics and Biology of Drosophila" (M. Ashburner and T.R.F. Wright, eds.), pp. 225–294. Academic Press, New York.
11. Xu, T., and Rubin, G.M. (1993). Analysis of genetic mosaics in developing and adult *Drosophila* tissues. *Development* **117**, 1223–1237.
12. Kiger, A.A., Jones, D.L., Schulz, C., Rogers, M.B., and Fuller, M.T. (2001). Stem cell self-renewal specified by JAK-STAT activation in response to a support cell cue. *Science* **294**, 2542–2545.
13. Van Doren, M., Williamson, A.L., and Lehmann, R. (1998). Regulation of zygotic gene expression in Drosophila primordial germ cells. *Curr. Biol.* **8**, 243–246.
14. Kiger, A.A., and Fuller, M.T. (2001). Male germ line stem cells. *In* "Stem Cells Biology" (D. Gottlieb, R. Gardner, and D. Marshak, eds.), pp. 149–187. Cold Spring Harbor Laboratory Press, New York.
15. Matunis, E., Tran, J., Gonczy, P., Caldwell, K., and DiNardo, S. (1997). punt and schnurri regulate a somatically derived signal that restricts proliferation of committed progenitors in the germline. *Development* **124**, 4383–4391.
16. Tran, J., Brenner, T.J., and DiNardo, S. (2000). Somatic control over the germline stem cell lineage during Drosophila spermatogenesis. *Nature* **407**, 754–757.
17. Kiger, A.A., White-Cooper, H., and Fuller, M.T. (2000). Somatic support cells restrict germline stem cell self-renewal and promote differentiation. *Nature* **407**, 750–754.
18. Spradling, A., Drummond-Barbosa, D., and Kai, T. (2001). Stem cells find their niche. *Nature* **414**, 98–104.
19. Lin, H. (2002). The stem-cell niche theory: lessons from flies. *Nat. Rev. Genet.* **3**, 931–940.
20. Tulina, N., and Matunis, E. (2001). Control of stem cell self-renewal in Drosophila spermatogenesis by JAK-STAT signaling. *Science* **294**, 2546–2549.
21. Ihle, J.N., Stravapodis, D., Parganas, E., Thierfelder, W., Feng, J., Wang, D., and Teglund, S. (1998). The roles of Jaks and Stats in cytokine signaling. *Cancer J. Sci. Am.* **4** (Suppl 1), S84–91.
22. Zeidler, M.P., Bach, E.A., and Perrimon, N. (2000). The roles of the Drosophila JAK/STAT pathway. *Oncogene* **19**, 2598–2606.
23. Silver, D.L., and Montell, D.J. (2001). Paracrine signaling through the JAK/STAT pathway activates invasive behavior of ovarian epithelial cells in Drosophila. *Cell* **107**, 831–841.
24. Harrison, D.A., McCoon, P.E., Binari, R., Gilman, M., and Perrimon, N. (1998). Drosophila unpaired encodes a secreted protein that activates the JAK signaling pathway. *Genes Dev.* **12**, 3252–3263.
25. Brown, S., Hu, N., and Hombria, J.C. (2001). Identification of the first invertebrate interleukin JAK/STAT receptor, the Drosophila gene domeless. *Curr. Biol.* **11**, 1700–1705.

26. Chen, H.W., Chen, X., Oh, S.W., Marinissen, M.J., Gutkind, J.S., and Hou, S.X. (2002). *mom* identifies a receptor for the Drosophila JAK/STAT signal transduction pathway and encodes a protein distantly related to the mammalian cytokine receptor family. *Genes Dev.* **16,** 388–398.

27. Dybas, L.K., Harden, K.D., Machnick, J.L., and Geer, B.W. (1983). Male fertility in *Drosophila melanogaster*: Lesions of spermatogenesis associated with male-sterile mutations of the *vermilion* region. *J. Exp. Zool.* **226,** 293–302.

28. Luo, H., Asha, H., Kockel, L., Parke, T., Mlodzik, M., and Dearolf, C.R. (1999). The Drosophila Jak kinase hopscotch is required for multiple developmental processes in the eye. *Dev. Biol.* **213,** 432–441.

29. Richter, M.F., Dumenil, G., Uze, G., Fellous, M., and Pellegrini, S. (1998). Specific contribution of Tyk2 JH regions to the binding and the expression of the interferon alpha/beta receptor component IFNAR1. *J. Biol. Chem.* **273,** 24723–24729.

30. Matunis, E. (personal communication).

31. Mahowald, A.P. (personal communication).

32. Song, X., Zhu, C.H., Doan, C., and Xie, T. (2002). Germline stem cells anchored by adherens junctions in the Drosophila ovary niches. *Science* **296,** 1855–1857.

33. Mahowald, A.P. (personal communication).

34. Jones, D.L., *et al.* (in preparation).

35. Schulz, C., Wood, C.G., Jones, D.L., Tazuke, S.I., and Fuller, M.T. (2002). Signaling from germ cells mediated by the rhomboid homolog stet organizes encapsulation by somatic support cells. *Development* **129,** 4523–4534.

36. Urban, S., Lee, J.R., and Freeman, M. (2001). Drosophila rhomboid-1 defines a family of putative intramembrane serine proteases. *Cell* **107,** 173–182.

37. Klambt, C. (2002). EGF receptor signalling: Roles of star and rhomboid revealed. *Curr. Biol.* **12,** R21–23.

38. Tazuke, S.I., Schulz, C., Gilboa, L., Fogarty, M., Mahowald, A.P., Guichet, A., Ephrussi, A., Wood, C.G., Lehmann, R., and Fuller, M.T. (2002). A germline-specific gap junction protein required for survival of differentiating early germ cells. *Development* **129,** 2529–2539.

39. Brand, A.H., and Perrimon, N. (1993). Targeted gene expression as a means of altering cell fates and generating dominant phenotypes. *Development* **118,** 401–415.

15

Spermatogonial Stem Cells in the Rat and Mouse

David L. Garbers, Nikolaus Schultz, Zhuoru Wu, and F. Kent Hamra

Introduction

An ability to culture and genetically manipulate spermatogonial stem cells in culture could lead to direct germ line transmission of modified genomes, methods to correct male infertility, and a means to rapidly screen for germ cell–directed contraceptives (Fig. 15–1). Although most genetic models revolve around the mouse, principally because of the ability to maintain pluripotency of embryonic stem (ES) cells in culture, the laboratory rat is one of the most comprehensively studied mammals. Expansion of technology to produce genetically modified rats, or other animal species, would likely represent a significant advance in biology and medicine. In the absence of pluripotent ES cells, an alternative would be germ line transmission through the targeting of male germ cells in culture, followed by testicular transplantation, colonization, and subsequent production of genetically modified mature spermatozoa for fertilization. A second and similar approach would be to genetically modify male germ cells in culture and induce differentiation to spermatids followed by the production of genetically modified pups through egg intracytoplasmic injection.

The understanding of how spermatogonial stem cells renew themselves and commit to differentiation has progressed slowly, in part due to the lack of *in vitro* culture system to facilitate their study. The established method of evaluating spermatogonial stem cell character has been to transfer cells to recipient males and determine testis colonization activity.[1,2] This is an effective means by which to evaluate stem cell activity,[3–5] although it is relatively slow and labor-intensive. A more general stem cell transcriptional profile, as has been suggested for stem cells as diverse as neural, hemapoietic and embryonic, may dictate "stemness" for the spermatogonial stem cell as opposed to a cadre of specifically expressed genes.[6,7] Whatever the case, the establishment of molecular markers to reliably define spermatogonial stem cells in culture would be particularly important for the field.

Transcript Profile of the Developing Testis

As the testis matures, seminiferous tubules change from being dominated by Sertoli cells and gonocytes to being occupied principally by differentiating spermatogonia, spermatocytes, and spermatids.[8–11] Thus, it can be speculated that the relative levels of various testicular transcripts will change as a function of testis age. Transcripts enriched in various somatic cells and gonocytes/spermatogonial stem cells should dominate the early testis, and mRNA enriched in differentiating germ cells should be most abundant in later stages of testicular development (Fig. 15–2). The actual relative transcript abundance of testis transcripts is demonstrated in Fig. 15–3 as a hierarchical tree. In the work of Schultz *et al.*[12] a total of 21,374 transcripts were identified as present at some point in time in the developing mouse testis (day 1 postnatal to adult). Transcripts present in Sertoli and interstitial cell cultures were subtracted to yield a germ cell–enriched mRNA profile. About 3794 transcripts, or 3486 putative genes, changed at least three-fold compared with postnatal day one. An interesting facet of their studies was that almost 4% of the mouse genome appeared dedicated to male germ cell expression, with more than 99% of the testis-specific genes first being expressed coincident with or following meiosis. Thus, many of the genes are apparently associated with late spermatocyte or spermatid development or with mature sperm function. A number of the sperm-specific genes have been disrupted and have been shown to cause male infertility.[12] In contrast, only a small number of genes of the testis were testis-specific at ages at which gonocytes or spermatogonial stem cells are prevalent. Thus, most of the gene transcripts associated with the spermatogonial stem cell or gonocyte also seem present in other cell types, a conclusion consistent with the results of those studying other types of stem cells.[6,7]

Maintenance of Spermatogonial Stem Cell Activity in Culture

A number of groups have defined conditions to maintain spermatogonial stem cells *in vitro* for relatively short periods of time based on the ability of these cultured cells to form colonies after transplantation to a testis.[13–20] Mouse embryonic fibroblast (MEF) feeder layers were initially shown as beneficial for the maintenance of mouse spermatogonial stem cell activity,[13] but more recent work shows that even on this feeder layer, mouse stem cell activity is reduced rapidly and substantially.[17,19] A variety of other cell feeder layers have been recently evaluated for effectiveness at maintaining mouse spermatogonial stem cell activity in culture. The most effective feeder layer cells were OP9 bone marrow stroma and L fibroblast cell lines, which more than doubled stem cell

Targeting Male Germ Stem Cells

✦ Correction of male infertility

✦ Development of specific male contraceptives

✦ Development of methods to modify genomes of animal models other than the mouse

✦ Introduction of genes in animals for the production of important medical products

✦ Direct correction of defective genes in the male germ cell

✦ Development of methods to select against defective genes in germ cell cultures.

✦ Gene targeting through homologous recombination in species other than the mouse

✦ Gene trapping or enhancer trapping to define gene function in species other than the mouse

Figure 15-1. Medical and biologic implications and importance of research targeting the spermatogonial stem cell.

activity after 1 week in culture based on colonization of recipient testes.[17] Growth factors in the transforming growth factor beta (TGFβ) family, such as bone morphogenetic protein-4 and activin-A, appear to accelerate the time-dependent loss of stem cell activity when cultured on MEFs.[17] In contrast, high concentrations of glial cell line–derived neurotrophic factor

significantly reduce stem cell loss.[17] In the case of the rat, a population of spermatogonial stem cells were obtained by selection on collagen and laminin and shown to be essentially devoid of differentiated germ cells or somatic cells.[16,20] Greater than 90% of the germ cells were characterized as type A spermatogonia.[20] These cells could be maintained on MSC-1 Sertoli cell feeder layers for more than 20 days without losses in stem cell activity based on testis colonization.[20] MSC-1, mouse Sertoli feeder lines were initially derived from transgenic mice expressing SV40 T-antigen under the control of the Müllerian inhibitory substance promoter and display characteristics similar to nontransformed Sertoli cells.[21] In similar medium, but with MEFs as feeder cells, rat germ cells retain germ cell character,[20] but substantial losses of stem cell activity are seen as a function of time in culture.[15,20] Between 75 and 90% of rat spermatogonial stem cell activity is lost after only 5 days in culture on MEFs.[15,20] That some cell feeder layers are able to maintain germ stem cell character more effectively than others suggests that feeder layers actively participate in stem cell maintenance. Conceivably some feeder layers may produce factors that maintain stem cell activity, reminiscent of mouse ES cells growing on embryonic fibroblasts producing myeloid leukemia inhibiting factor,[22,23] or some feeder layer cells fail to produce "differentiation" factors. Recently, the combination of MEF feeder cells and factor-supplemented medium were reported to support the growth of spermatogonial stem cells from neonatal mice in culture.[18,19] In marked contrast to other reports, these studies suggest that spermatogonial stem cells are capable of maintaining a steady state of stem cell renewal after multiple passages in culture.

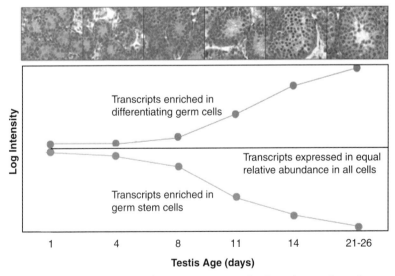

Figure 15-2. Relative abundance of testicular transcripts predicted as a function of testicular age. (Top): Histological sections of mouse testes collected at different ages. Germ cells begin entering meiosis between days 11 and 14. (Bottom): Predicted average transcript profiles for mRNA enriched in gonocytes/spermatogonial stem cells or enriched in germ cells later in development as a function of testis age. (Please see CD-ROM for color version of this figure.)

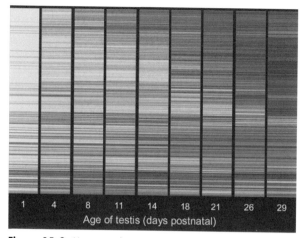

Figure 15–3. Heat map showing transcript expression as a function of testis age in the mouse. Affymetrix-murine genome U74v 2A, B, and C microarrays were used to identify transcripts expressed in the testes of mice at developmental time points spanning the first waves of spermatogenesis (postnatal days 1, 4, 8, 11, 14, 18, 21, 26, and 29). About 10,000 transcripts are represented. Please see CD-ROM for color version of this figure and a full description of the color code that quantifies the relative changes in gene expression.

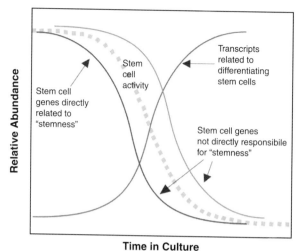

Figure 15–4. Hypothetical relative transcript accumulation as a function of time after stem cells are placed in an environment in which stem cell activity disappears coincident with differentiation. The model assumes that gene expression is the major determinant of "stemness." If stemness is determined principally by posttranslational modifications, the time course of the gene expression profile, or even the steady-state level of transcripts, may have little relevance to maintenance of stemness. (Please see CD-ROM for color version of this figure.)

Signature of the Spermatogonial Stem Cell

The spermatogonial stem cell in mammals has not been unequivocally identified through the use of germ cell-specific molecular markers or by other means.[24–28] Mouse testicular cells characterized as side scatter[lo], α6-integrin[+], β1-integrin[+], Thy-1[+], CD24[+], CD9[+], ckit[-], αv-intergrin[-], MHC-Ia/β2M[-], sca-1[-], CD34[-], and cKit[-] have been sorted and shown as enriched for spermatogonial stem cells based on testicular colonization.[29–32] However, these gene products are also relatively abundant in other stem cells and in populations of differentiated germ cells and other testicular cells.[20] Other transcripts specifically present in germ cells (e.g., *Dazl*, *Vasa*) are expressed at many stages of germ cell development[33,34] and, therefore, are not specific signatures for the spermatogonial stem cell.

In recent work, the transcript profiles of spermatogonial stem cells have been compared with the profiles of germ cells that are in the process of losing stem cell character as they differentiate.[20] These studies were facilitated by the use of a transgenic rat line that expresses green fluorescent protein (GFP) exclusively in the germ line.[20a] Through the use of these GFP-marked cells, a rapid separation of germ cells from somatic cells is possible. The major goals of these studies were to define gene transcripts that change before or coincident with a loss of stem cell activity. If stemness is primarily defined by gene expression and not posttranslational regulation, then as shown in the hypothetical model in Fig. 15–4, the most important stemness transcripts will not necessarily be those identified in a comparison of highly differentiated

cells to stem cells but those that disappear (or possibly appear) before or coincident with losses of stem cell activity. Some or all of these genes are potentially required for stem cell maintenance. A list of 248 genes that fit these criteria are given in Fig. 15–5.[20] These genes were used to develop a stem cell index, which is the average cumulative transcript expression for these 248 genes.[20] The authors suggested, based on an analysis of mouse testis, and cultures of rat and mouse male germ cells, that the stem cell index adequately predicts stemness and the relative abundance of stem cells in a mixed population of cells.[20] Figure 15–6 illustrates labeling of 10-day-old spermatogonial stem cell cultures on MSC-1 feeder cells using an antibody to one the genes *(Egr3)* listed in Fig. 15–5. The Egr3 antibody reacts only weakly with germ cells cultured on MEF feeder cells where stem cell activity has been lost.[20] Thus, Egr3 or possibly other probes to genes listed in Fig. 15–5 may now define stem cells in culture.

Genome Modification of Mouse and Rat Male Germ Stem Cells

Several methods to modify the male germ cell at the genomic level have been attempted. *In vivo* transfection, in which liposome/DNA complexes are injected into seminiferous tubules, or DNA is injected into the seminiferous tubules followed by *in vivo* electroporation has been shown to yield transgene expression in the transfected cells,[35–38] but stable incorporation of the foreign DNA in the spermatogonial stem cells has not been consistently accomplished in these studies.

Apoptosis
Casp7, Card10, Pmaip1, Sgk3

Cell cycle
Cables1

Cell adhesion and cytoskeleton
Enc1, Efemp2, Epb4, 1l4a, Gsn, Lamb2, Mbp, Nid2, Punc, Reln, Scarb1, Spock1, Snap91, Sdc2, Sdc4, Thbs4, Tubb5, Utrn, Waspip, Cldn4, Cryga, Myof1f, Tjp2, and 2 EST clusters

Channels and transporters
Abcd4, Cacna1g, Epb4, 1l4b, Rlbp1, Slc22a3, Slc25a13, Nxf7, and 1 EST cluster

DNA modification and repair
Dnmt3a, Polg2

Metabolism and biosynthesis
Ampd2, Gus, Elovl4, Elovl6, Enpep, Prep, Pccb, Smox, Neu2, Psmb9, and 3 EST clusters

Translation and posttranslational modification
Galnt2 and 1 EST cluster

RNA binding and modification
Rbpms, and 4 EST clusters

Signal transduction
Adcy6, F2r (Thrombin receptor) Dusp6, Fgfr3, Gfra1 (GDNF receptor alpha1), H2-M3, Igbp1, ck, Ltbp1, Ptgfrn, Ppp3ca, Ptprg, Ptprk, Rab12, Sema4d, Stard13, Sh3d19, Stat2, Spry4, Chrna4, Cnp1, Ephb3, Ret, Hak-pending, Tbc1d8, and 5 EST clusters

Transcriptional regulation
Aebp1, Ank2, Ankrd6, Bcl6b, Egr3, Foxo1, Hey1, Irf1, Lmo4, Midn, Nr1d1, Pbx2, Ski, Satb1, Sox13, Tcfe3, Zfp278, Bhlhb3, Egr4, Foxa2, Klf3, Pou3f1, Sall4, and 9 EST clusters

Other
Asb13, Btbd3, Emb, Gig1, H19, Lphn1, Tera, Tpbg, C1gbp

Unknown EST clusters (68)

Figure 15–5. A list of gene transcripts that decrease before or coincident with a loss of spermatogonial stem cell activity as assessed by ability to colonize a recipient testis. Some or all of these genes are candidates for the maintenance of spermatogonial stem cell character (also see reference 20). (Please see CD-ROM for color version of this figure.)

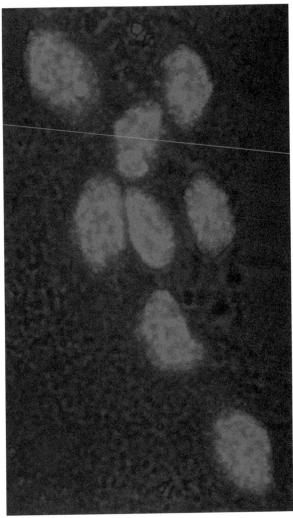

Figure 15–6. Rat spermatogonial stem-like cells stain positive with Egr3 antibody. Antibody to one of the transcripts (Egr3) represented in Fig. 15–5 reacts with male germ cells (light gray) in cultures containing high stem cell activity (10-day germ cell culture on MSC-1 Sertoli cells). As the single cells divide and form long chains, the Egr3 signal disappears. (Please see CD-ROM for color version of this figure.)

In a recent study, plasmid DNA that encoded a modified yellow fluorescent protein (EYFP) containing a mitochondrial localization signal peptide was injected into the seminiferous tubules of 14-day-old mice; subsequent electroporation *in vivo* resulted in formation of spermatozoa expressing the transgene.[39] The EYFP-positive spermatozoa were selected and after intracytoplasmic sperm injection (ICSI), a high percentage of pups inherited the transgene. The transgene was also transmitted to subsequent generations.[39] Whether transfected germ cells included stem cells is not clear. In other experiments designed to introduce new genes into testicular germ cells, various viral vectors have been administered through the hepatic artery, by intramuscular injection, or by direct injection into the testis. Although somatic cells of the testis were transduced after these procedures, no evidence was garnered to show successful transduction of germ cells.[40–46] These findings, however, do suggest minimal risks of germ line integration after the use of viral vectors in gene therapy.

The only established method to deliver transgenes directly into the male germ line is through retroviral-mediated gene delivery into spermatogonial stem cells. Brinster and colleagues first reported successful retroviral infection of mouse and rat spermatogonial stem cells *in vivo* or *in vitro*[14,15,47] and showed that transgenic mice could be formed carrying the retroviral transgene.[48] A transmission rate of about 4.5% was achieved and the transgene was transmitted to and expressed in subsequent generations.[48] Transgenic rats also have been produced using cultures of spermatogonial stem cells that were transduced with a lentiviral GFP-expression vector.[16] A single male rat transplanted with the transduced stem cells was able to transmit the viral transgene to ~30% of the total progeny and to 50% of the progeny derived from the cultured stem cells.[16] Based on a transgene marking the cultures of donor cells (MT-lacZ) all pups inheriting the lentiviral transgene originated from the transplanted spermatogonial stem cells and were able to transmit both transgenes to subsequent generations.[16]

Differentiation of Male Germ Cells *In Vitro*

In the adult, spermatogonia are categorized as type A and type B.[24–28] The type A cells are further divided into A single; A paired; A aligned; and A1, A2, A3, and A4.[25–28] The type B form from the type A spermatogonia and then differentiate to form spermatocytes and spermatids.[8,9] Although molecular signatures for the spermatogonial stem cell relative to the other germ cells have been difficult to establish, it is known that expression of the receptor-tyrosine kinase KIT results in a loss of spermatogonial stem cell activity based on ability to colonize a recipient testis.[29,30] Likewise, it has been suggested that the ligand for KIT, stem cell factor (SCF), is essential for differentiation and proliferation of male germ cells,[49,50] in part because of its ability to prevent apoptosis.[51–53] In support of an important role of (SCF) in differentiation, an immortalized germ cell line expressing telomerase is stimulated to progress through meiosis and form apparent spermatids in response to (SCF) in culture.[54] Primary cultures of spermatogonial stem cells can be stimulated to differentiate into pairs, chains, and germ cell colonies, but the numbers that progress through meiosis is generally negligible.[18,20,55] Recently, however, after 100 days in culture bovine spermatogonia have been reported to differentiate into spermatocytes and spermatids based on various marker proteins.[55]

Summary

Development of technology to expand spermatogonial stem cells in culture, which might then be conditionally stimulated to produce differentiated gametes, would no doubt lead to the valuable use of such cells in both medicine and agriculture (Fig. 15–1). The identification of molecular markers for the spermatogonial stem cell would most certainly accelerate the development of such technology, because conditions that support stem cell renewal could be more quickly evaluated relative to testicular transplantation assays. A review of the field suggests that molecular markers for spermatogonial stem cells have now been identified, but whether some or many of these transcripts are essential for stem cell maintenance is not known. Aside from the development of methods to maintain and possibly expand spermatogonial stem cells in culture, the conditional stimulation of differentiation is also important. A cell line obtained by the Dym group[54] seems the most attractive germ cell system in which to study and eventually

understand the differentiation process. Once achieved with a cell line, the process could possibly be recapitulated in primary cultures of male germ cells.

ACKNOWLEDGMENTS

This work was supported by the Cecil H. and Ida Green Center for Reproductive Biology Sciences and the Howard Hughes Medical Institute and grant HD36022 from the National Institutes of Health.

REFERENCES

1. Brinster, R.L., and Zimmermann, J.W. (1994). Spermatogenesis following male germ-cell transplantation. *Proc. Natl. Acad. Sci. U.S.A.* **91**, 11298–11302.
2. Brinster, R.L. (2002). Germline stem cell transplantation and transgenesis. *Science* **296**, 2174–2176.
3. Dobrinski, I., Ogawa, T., Avarbock, M.R., and Brinster, R.L. (1999). Computer assisted image analysis to assess colonization of recipient seminiferous tubules by spermatogonial stem cells from transgenic donor mice. *Mol. Reprod. Dev.* **53**, 142–148.
4. Nagano, M., Avarbock, M.R., and Brinster, R.L. (1999). Pattern and kinetics of mouse donor spermatogonial stem cell colonization in recipient testes. *Biol. Reprod.* **60**, 1429–1436.
5. Nagano, M.C. (2003). Homing efficiency and proliferation kinetics of male germ line stem cells following transplantation in mice. *Biol. Reprod.* **69**, 701–707.
6. Ramalho-Santos, M., Yoon, S., Matsuzaki, Y., Mulligan, R.C., and Melton, D.A. (2002). "Stemness": transcriptional profiling of embryonic and adult stem cells. *Science* **298**, 597–600.
7. Ivanova, N.B., Dimos, J.T., Schaniel, C., Hackney, J.A., Moore, K.A., and Lemischka, I.R. (2002). A stem cell molecular signature. *Science* **298**, 601–604.
8. Clermont, Y., and Perey, B. (1957). Quantitative study of the cell population of the seminiferous tubules in immature rats. *Am. J. Anat.* **100**, 241–267.
9. Clermont, Y. (1972). Kinetics of spermatogenesis in mammals: Seminiferous epithelium cycle and spermatogonial renewal. *Physiol. Rev.* **52**, 198–236.
10. Bellve, A.R., Cavicchia, J.C., Millette, C.F., O'Brien, D.A., Bhatnagar, Y.M., Dym, M. (1977). Spermatogenic cells of the prepuberal mouse. Isolation and morphological characterization. *J. Cell Biol.* **74**, 68–85.
11. McLean, D.J., Friel, P.J., Johnston, D.S., and Griswold, M.D. (2003). Characterization of spermatogonial stem cell maturation and differentiation in neonatal mice. *Biol. Reprod.* **69**, 2085–2091.
12. Schultz, N., Hamra, F.K., and Garbers, D.L. A multitude of genes expressed solely in meiotic or post-meiotic spermatogenic cells offers a myriad of contraceptive targets. *Proc. Natl. Acad. Sci. U.S.A.* **100**, 12201–12206.
13. Nagano, M., Avarbock, M.R., Leonida, E.B., Brinster, C.J., and Brinster, R.L. (1998). Culture of mouse spermatogonial stem cells. *Tissue Cell* **30**, 389–397.
14. Nagano, M., Shinohara, T., Avarbock, M.R., and Brinster, R.L. (2000). Retrovirus-mediated gene delivery into male germ line stem cells. *FEBS Lett.* **475**, 7–10.

15. Orwig, K.E., Avarbock, M.R., and Brinster, R.L. (2002). Retrovirus-mediated modification of male germline stem cells in rats. *Biol. Reprod.* **67**, 874–879.

16. Hamra, F.K., Gatlin, J., Chapman, K.M., Grellhesl, D.M., Garcia, J.V., Hammer, R.E., and Garbers, D.L. (2002). Production of transgenic rats by lentiviral transduction of male germ-line stem cells. *Proc. Natl. Acad. Sci. U.S.A.* **99**, 14931–14936.

17. Nagano, M., Ryu, B.Y., Brinster, C.J., Avarbock, M.R., and Brinster, R.L. (2003). Maintenance of mouse male germ line stem cells in vitro. *Biol. Reprod.* **68**, 2207–2214.

18. Kanatsu-Shinohara, M., Ogonuki, N., Inoue, K., Miki, H., Ogura, A., Toyokuni, S., and Shinohara, T. (2003). Long-term proliferation in culture and germline transmission of mouse male germline stem cells. *Biol. Reprod.* **69**, 612–616.

19. Jeong, D., McLean, D.J., and Griswold, M.D. (2003). Long-term culture and transplantation of murine testicular germ cells. *J. Androl.* **24**, 661–669.

20. Hamra, F.K., Schultz, N., Chapman, K.M., Grellhesl, D.M., Cronkhite, J.T., Hammer, R.E., and Garbers, D.L. (2004). Defining the spermatogonial stem cell. *Dev. Biol.* **269**, 393–410.

20a. Cronkhite, Garbers, and Hammer, unpublished.

21. McGuinness, M.P., Linder, C.C., Morales, C.R., Heckert, L.L., Pikus, J., and Griswold, M.D. (1994). Relationship of a mouse Sertoli cell line (MSC-1) to normal Sertoli cells. *Biol. Reprod.* **51**, 116–124.

22. Smith, A.G., and Hooper, M.L. (1987). Buffalo rat liver cells produce a diffusible activity which inhibits the differentiation of murine embryonal carcinoma and embryonic stem cells. *Dev. Biol.* **121**, 1–9.

23. Williams, R.L., Hilton, D.J., Pease, S., Willson, T.A., Stewart, C.L., Gearing, D.P., Wagner, E.F., Metcalf, D., Nicola, N.A., and Gough, N.M. (1988). Myeloid leukaemia inhibitory factor maintains the developmental potential of embryonic stem cells. *Nature* **336**, 684–687.

24. Clermont, Y., and Leblond, C.P. (1953). Renewal of spermatogonia in the rat. *Am. J. Anat.* **93**, 475–502.

25. Huckins, C. (1971). The spermatogonial stem cell population in adult rats. I. Their morphology, proliferation and maturation. *Anat. Rec.* **169**, 533–557.

26. Oakberg, E.F. (1971). Spermatogonial stem-cell renewal in the mouse. *Anat. Rec.* **169**, 515–531.

27. de Rooij, D.G., and Russell, L.D. (2000). All you wanted to know about spermatogonia but were afraid to ask. *J. Androl.* **21**, 776–798.

28. de Rooij, D.G. (2001). Proliferation and differentiation of spermatogonial stem cells. *Reproduction* **121**, 347–354.

29. Shinohara, T., Avarbock, M.R., and Brinster, R.L. (1999). beta1- and alpha6-integrin are surface markers on mouse spermatogonial stem cells. *Proc. Natl. Acad. Sci. U.S.A.* **96**, 5504–5509.

30. Shinohara, T., Orwig, K.E., Avarbock, M.R., and Brinster, R.L. (2000). Spermatogonial stem cell enrichment by multiparameter selection of mouse testis cells. *Proc. Natl. Acad. Sci. U. S. A.* **97**, 8346–8351.

31. Kubota, H., Avarbock, M.R., and Brinster, R.L. (2003). Spermatogonial stem cells share some, but not all, phenotypic and functional characteristics with other stem cells. *Proc. Natl. Acad. Sci. U.S.A.* **100**, 6487–6492.

32. Kanatsu-Shinohara, M., Toyokuni, S., and Shinohara, T. (2004) CD9 Is a surface marker on mouse and rat male germline stem cells. *Biol. Reprod.* **70**, 70–75.

33. Reijo, R.A., Dorfman, D.M., Slee, R., Renshaw, A.A., Loughlin, K.R., Cooke, H., and Page, D.C. (2000). DAZ family proteins exist throughout male germ cell development and transit from nucleus to cytoplasm at meiosis in humans and mice. *Biol. Reprod.* **63**, 1490–1496.

34. Noce, T., Okamoto-Ito, S., and Tsunekawa, N. (2001). Vasa homolog genes in mammalian germ cell development. *Cell Struct. Funct.* **26**, 131–136.

35. Yamazaki, Y., Fujimoto, H., Ando, H., Ohyama, T., Hirota, Y., and Noce, T. (1998). In vivo gene transfer to mouse spermatogenic cells by deoxyribonucleic acid injection into seminiferous tubules and subsequent electroporation. *Biol. Reprod.* **59**, 1439–1444.

36. Yamazaki, Y., Yagi, T., Ozaki, T., and Imoto, K. (2000). In vivo gene transfer to mouse spermatogenic cells using green fluorescent protein as a marker. *J. Exp. Zool.* **286**, 212–218.

37. Kim, J.H., Jung-Ha, H.S., Lee, H.T., and Chung, K.S. (1997). Development of a positive method for male stem cell-mediated gene transfer in mouse and pig. *Mol. Reprod. Dev.* **46**, 515–526.

38. Muramatsu, T., Shibata, O., Ryoki, S., Ohmori, Y., and Okumura, J. (1997). Foreign gene expression in the mouse testis by localized in vivo gene transfer. *Biochem. Biophys. Res. Commun.* **233**, 45–49.

39. Huang, Z., Tamura, M., Sakurai, T., Chuma, S., Saito, T., and Nakatsuji, N. (2000). In vivo transfection of testicular germ cells and transgenesis by using the mitochondrially localized jellyfish fluorescent protein gene. *FEBS Lett.* **487**, 248–251.

40. Ikawa, M., Tergaonkar, V., Ogura, A., Ogonuki, N., Inoue, K., and Verma, I.M. (2002). Restoration of spermatogenesis by lentiviral gene transfer: offspring from infertile mice. *Proc. Natl. Acad. Sci. U.S.A.* **99**, 7524–7529.

41. Blanchard, K.T., and Boekelheide, K. (1997). Adenovirus-mediated gene transfer to rat testis in vivo. *Biol. Reprod.* **56**, 495–500.

42. Hall, S.J., Bar-Chama, N., Ta, S., and Gordon, J.W. (2000). Direct exposure of mouse spermatogenic cells to high doses of adenovirus gene therapy vector does not result in germ cell transduction. *Hum. Gene Ther.* **11**, 1705–1712.

43. Arruda, V.R., Fields, P.A., Milner, R., Wainwright, L., De Miguel, M.P., Donovan, P.J., Herzog, R.W., Nichols, T.C., Biegel, J.A., Razavi, M., Dake, M., Huff, D., Flake, A.W., Couto, L., Kay, M.A., and High, K.A. (2001). Lack of germline transmission of vector sequences following systemic administration of recombinant AAV-2 vector in males. *Mol. Ther.* **4**, 586–592.

44. Peters, A.H., Drumm, J., Ferrell, C., Roth, D.A., Roth, D.M., McCaman, M., Novak, P.L., Friedman, J., Engler, R., and Braun, R.E. (2001). Absence of germline infection in male mice following intraventricular injection of adenovirus. *Mol. Ther.* **4**, 603–613.

45. Kanatsu-Shinohara, M., Ogura, A., Ikegawa, M., Inoue, K., Ogonuki, N., Tashiro, K., Toyokuni, S., Honjo, T., and Shinohara, T. (2002). Adenovirus-mediated gene delivery and in vitro microinsemination produce offspring from infertile male mice. *Proc. Natl. Acad. Sci. U.S.A.* **99**, 1383–1388.

46. Ye, X., Gao, G.P., Pabin, C., Raper, S.E., and Wilson, J.M. (1998). Evaluating the potential of germ line transmission after intravenous administration of recombinant adenovirus in the C3H mouse. *Hum. Gene Ther.* **9**, 2135–2142.

47. Nagano, M., Watson, D.J., Ryu, B.Y., Wolfe, J.H., and Brinster, R.L. (2002). Lentiviral vector transduction of male germ line stem cells in mice. *FEBS Lett.* **524**, 111–115.

48. Nagano, M., Brinster, C.J., Orwig, K.E., Ryu, B.Y., Avarbock, M.R., and Brinster, R.L. (2001). Transgenic mice produced by retroviral transduction of male germ-line stem cells. *Proc. Natl. Acad. Sci. U.S.A.* **98**, 13090–13095.

49. Dym, M., Jia, M.C., Dirami, G., Price, J.M., Rabin, S.J., Mocchetti, I., and Ravindranath, N. (1995). Expression of c-kit receptor and its autophosphorylation in immature rat type A spermatogonia. *Biol. Reprod.* **52**, 8–19.

50. Feng, L.X., Ravindranath, N., and Dym, M. (2000). Stem cell factor/c-kit up-regulates cyclin D3 and promotes cell cycle progression via the phosphoinositide 3-kinase/p70 S6 kinase pathway in spermatogonia. *J. Biol. Chem.* **275**, 25572–25576.

51. Sette, C., Dolci, S., Geremia, R., and Rossi, P. (2000). The role of stem cell factor and of alternative c-kit gene products in the establishment, maintenance and function of germ cells. *Int. J. Dev. Biol.* **44**, 599–608.

52. Dirami, G., Ravindranath, N., Pursel, V., and Dym, M. (1999). Effects of stem cell factor and granulocyte macrophage-colony stimulating factor on survival of porcine type A spermatogonia cultured in KSOM. *Biol. Reprod.* **61**, 225–230.

53. Yan, W., Suominen, J., and Toppari, J. (2000). Stem cell factor protects germ cells from apoptosis in vitro. *J. Cell Sci.* **113** (Pt 1), 161–168.

54. Feng, L.X., Chen, Y., Dettin, L., Pera, R.A., Herr, J.C., Goldberg, E., and Dym, M. (2002). Generation and in vitro differentiation of a spermatogonial cell line. *Science* **297**, 392–395.

55. Izadyar, F., Den Ouden, K., Creemers, L.B., Posthuma, G., Parvinen, M., and De Rooij, D.G. (2003). Proliferation and differentiation of bovine type A spermatogonia during long-term culture. *Biol. Reprod.* **68**, 272–281.

Primordial Germ Cells in Mouse and Human

Dame Anne McLaren

Introduction

WHAT ARE PRIMORDIAL GERM CELLS?

The germ cell lineage terminates in the differentiation of the gametes (eggs and spermatozoa). In mammals the lineage arises in the extraembryonic mesoderm at the posterior end of the primitive streak. From here the germ cells migrate to the two genital ridges, which later form the gonads. During this period they proliferate at a steady rate and are known as primordial germ cells (PGCs). Once in the genital ridges they may be termed gonocytes. Proliferation ceases in the male genital ridge when the germ cells transiently arrest in G_0/G_1 as prospermatogonia and in the female genital ridge when they enter prophase of the first meiotic division as oocytes. These events, which occur before birth in both mouse and human, mark the initiation of the lengthy processes of spermatogenesis and oogenesis, respectively, and the end of the primordial phase of germ cell development.

PRIMORDIAL GERM CELLS ARE NOT STEM CELLS

Stem cells are commonly defined as cells with a choice: they can divide to form either two cells like themselves (self-renewal) or one cell like themselves and one that is embarking on a pathway of differentiation (asymmetric division). PGCs do not at any stage constitute a stem cell population: each of the cell divisions that they undergo (9 or 10 in the mouse, more in the human) moves them further along their developmental trajectory. At a later stage in the male germ cell lineage a true stem cell population forms: spermatogenic stem cells in the testis divide slowly to form a self-renewing population throughout the lifetime of the male, giving rise to waves of proliferating spermatogonia that enter meiosis as spermatocytes, then differentiate into spermatids and finally into mature spermatozoa. PGCs can give rise *in vitro* to pluripotent stem cell populations that will proliferate indefinitely, given appropriate culture conditions (embryonic germ cells [EGCs]), but PGCs *in vivo* are not stem cells.

Handbook of Stem Cells
Volume 1
Copyright © 2004 by Academic Press
All rights of reproduction in any form reserved.

Origin of the Germ Cell Lineage

IDENTIFICATION OF PRIMORDIAL GERM CELLS

In many mammals, including mouse[1] and human,[2] PGCs can be readily identified by staining for alkaline phosphatase activity. Tissue nonspecific alkaline phosphatase (TNAP) is expressed in many tissues, but, throughout the primordial period, activity is markedly higher in germ cells than in the surrounding somatic cells. The function of the enzyme is not clear, because disruption of the *Tnap* gene does not appear to affect germ cell development.[3] PGCs have also been identified histologically and by electron microscopy and also more recently by a variety of genetic markers (see the section on gene expression below). The allantois, once it has started to grow, forms a convenient landmark for spotting the cluster of PGCs at its base (about 8 days post coitum [dpc] in the mouse). The earliest stage at which the cluster was identified, in the same location but before an allantois was apparent, was 7.25 dpc,[4] in mid-gastrulation.

EARLY STUDIES

The failure to identify germ cells in the mouse embryo by morphology, alkaline phosphatase activity, or any other feature at any stage of development earlier than mid-gastrulation was frustrating because in many invertebrates and lower vertebrates the germ line could be traced back to very early development, even to the egg. In *Drosophila* the germ line derives from the pole plasm, incorporated in the pole cells,[5] the first cells to form; in *Caenorhabditis elegans* the germ cell determinants (P granules) present in the egg are asymmetrically segregated during the first four cell divisions, to form the germ line[6]; in *Xenopus* and other anuran amphibia the germplasm apparent in the egg can be following into the germ cells as they form.[7] Expression of homologues of the germ line–specific gene *Vasa* is localized in "germ plasm" from early cleavage stages onward in both zebrafish[8] and chick.[9] No such lineage could be detected in the mouse or any other mammal. Chimera studies were unable to identify any cells in the preimplantation embryo that were uniquely associated with the germ line. Circumstantial evidence had led some early workers to assert that the germ cell lineage in mammals had an extraembryonic origin. Subsequently however, various lines of evidence, in particular the transplantation studies of Gardner and Rossant,[10] established beyond doubt that the ancestors of the germ cell lineage were to be found in the epiblast, which is derived from the inner cell mass of the blastocyst, not from the outer trophectoderm.

TIME AND PLACE OF LINEAGE DETERMINATION

Fate-mapping of the mouse epiblast was achieved by injection of a long-lasting fluorochrome into single epiblast cells of embryos removed from the uterus in early gastrulation. Subsequent culture of the embryo for 48 hours revealed the tissue fate of the clonal descendants of the injected cell.[11] It was found that only the most proximal cells of the epiblast, those close to the extraembryonic ectoderm, included PGCs among their descendants. No clone consisted only of PGCs, proving that at the time of injection (6.0 or 6.5 dpc), the germ cell lineage was not determined (lineage restricted).[12] Indeed, PGCs never constituted more than a small proportion of each marked clone, and marked PGCs only made up a small proportion of the total number of TNAP-positive PGCs. Clonal analysis revealed that the most likely time of germ cell determination was 7.2 dpc, approximately the time at which a TNAP-positive cluster of putative germ cells had first been identified in the extraembryonic mesoderm.

Clones without any PGCs contained more cells than those with PGCs, and the fewer the PGCs the larger was the total number of cells. This suggested that germ cell determination was associated with an increase in cell doubling time. Best-fit analysis gave a doubling time of about 16 hours for PGCs, in contrast to 6–7 hours for the surrounding somatic extra-embryonic mesoderm cells.[12] For the period 8.5–13.5 dpc, counts of PGCs on successive days had given a similar figure of 16 hours for PGC doubling time.[13]

In Amphibia, the germ cell lineage can be traced back to the egg in frogs and toads (Anura), but in Urodeles it is induced in mid-gastrulation, in the mesoderm, similar to mammals. It has been proposed that the urodele/mammal mode of development is the more primitive. The early-determination mode, characterized by germplasm, must then have been derived several different times in evolution.[14] This view is supported by the expression pattern of germ line–specific genes such as *Vasa* and *Dazl*, which are similar in urodeles and mammals and also in primitive fishes[15] but very different in *Anura*, chick, zebrafish, *Drosophila*, and *Caenorhabditis*.

SIGNALING FACTORS

Bmp4 homozygous mutants die around the time of gastrulation. Using a strain combination that survived until late gastrulation, Lawson *et al.*[16] observed that the homozygotes had no allantois and no PGCs. BMP4 protein known to act as a signaling molecule is normally expressed in the extraembryonic ectoderm. Chimeras made between normal embryonic stem (ES) cells and *Bmp4*-negative embryos, in which the epiblast contained both cell types but the extraembryonic tissues were all BMP4-negative, also lacked both allantois and PGCs. Hence *Bmp4* expression in the extraembryonic ectoderm is required for the establishment of the germ cell lineage, implicating a *Bmp4*-dependent signal to the immediately adjacent proximal epiblast cells. *Bmp8b* mutants have a reduced number of PGCs, suggesting that BMP8b is also involved in signaling, perhaps in interaction with BMP4. The molecular details of the signaling pathway have still to be established.

Further evidence that signaling from the extraembryonic ectoderm is required for germ cell determination comes from experiments in which distal epiblast cells, which would normally give rise to neurectoderm, were transplanted at 6.5 dpc to a proximal location.[17] Some of the PGCs that formed expressed the genetic marker carried by the donor embryo. This finding suggests that all epiblast cells in early gastrulation have the potential to develop into PGCs, if they receive the appropriate signals. Signals emanating from the extraembryonic ectoderm predispose the neighboring epiblast cells to a germ cell fate but they do not determine that fate, because the clonal analysis referred to in the previous section on time and place of lineage determination showed that only a small proportion of the descendants of any proximal epiblast cell became PGCs. Once the cells have passed through the primitive streak and reached the cluster region, a further signal or signals may be required to complete the determination process, halt further movement, and slow down the cell cycle.

GENE EXPRESSION

For decades, the high level of expression of *Tnap* was the only useful genetic marker for the initial stages of the mammalian germ cell lineage. *Oct4*[18] is expressed diffusely during gastrulation, so PGCs are not distinguished from the surrounding tissues until about 8.0 dpc. Other useful PGC markers (*SSEA1, Mouse Vasa Homolog, Dazl*) are expressed somewhat later.

Saitou *et al.*[19] made single-cell cDNA libraries from the cluster region of 7.0–7.5 dpc mouse embryos. PGC libraries could be distinguished from somatic cell libraries by the relatively high level of expression of *Tnap* and the absence of expression of *Hoxb4*, previously reported from *in situ* data to be present only in somatic cells. Two new germ cell–specific genes were isolated from the PGC libraries. These were termed *Fragilis* and *Stella* (also isolated as *Pgc7*[20]). *Fragilis* is expressed from about 6.0 dpc on, in the proximal region of the epiblast. Its expression pattern shifts as the epiblast cells move toward the primitive streak, and by 7.2 dpc it is concentrated around the cluster region. Once the PGCs begin to move away, *Fragilis* is down-regulated, although it comes on again later. *In vitro*, *Fragilis* expression can be induced in any epiblast tissue, if placed in proximity to extraembryonic ectoderm. It belongs to a widely distributed family of interferon-inducible genes, of which other members code for proteins showing homotypic adhesion and changes in cell cycle regulation. *Stella*, in contrast, is a novel gene, not part of a gene family. It carries a nuclear-localization signal. It is up-regulated in the cluster region, where *Fragilis* expression is strongest, at the time when PGCs can first be visualized. *Stella* maintains its PGC-specific expression during germ cell migration and into the genital ridges; thus, it provides a valuable new germ-cell–specific genetic marker.

Migration

ROUTE

As the germ cell cluster breaks up, at about 8.0 dpc, the PGCs appear to migrate actively into the visceral endoderm, which carries them along as it invaginates to form the hind gut. Although initially ventral, they become distributed around the hind gut and pass dorsally into the genital ridges, through the body wall, or up the dorsal mesentery and round the coelomic angle at 10.0–11.0 dpc. The entire period of migration can now be visualized on a video of PGCs carrying a transgenic green fluorescent protein marker.[21] The PGCs show locomotory behavior throughout, which is nondirectional in the wall of the hind gut where they are carried along passively but strongly directional as they leave the hind gut and enter the genital ridges. Once in the ridges, the locomotory behavior ceases.

GUIDANCE MECHANISMS

Nothing is known of the mechanism that encourages the PGCs to enter the visceral endoderm (rather than the allantois, or some other extraembryonic mesodermal region) as the cluster breaks up. Contact guidance may play a part in facilitating exit from the endodermal hind gut wall, because the adhesion properties (particularly to laminin) change at this time. As the PGCs move toward the genital ridges, they have been reported to contact one another through long cellular processes, forming a loose network.[22] The molecular nature of the directional signal that attracts them toward the genital ridges has yet to be elucidated, but in zebrafish there is recent evidence that the chemokine-receptor pair stromal cell–derived factor 1 (SDF-1) and it G-protein–coupled receptor (CXCR4) act to guide migrating PGCs.[23]

GENE EXPRESSION

Certain gene products need to be present if PGC migration is to take place normally.[24] Abnormal migration patterns are readily detected, because they result in subfertility or sterility. Two classic mouse mutants, *White-spotting* and *Steel*, both show sterility in the homozygous condition and defects in hematopoiesis and pigment cell migration. *White-spotting (W)* codes for c-kit, a cell surface receptor; *Steel (SL)* codes for its ligand, stem cell factor. If either element of this signal transduction pathway is defective, PGC migration is disturbed, proliferation is affected, apoptosis occurs, and few germ cells reach the genital ridges. Other genes known to be required for normal PGC migration include *gcd (germ cell deficient)*, *β1 integrin*, and *Fgf8*.

Germ Cells in the Genital Ridge

PHENOTYPE

Mouse PGCs migrate actively into the genital ridges between 10.5 and 11.5 dpc. Soon after entry into the ridges their motile phenotype changes to a rounded shape, they up-regulate

E-cadherin, movement ceases, and they form loose groups. Gene expression changes; *Mvh (mouse vasa homolog)* and *Gcna (germ cell nuclear antigen)* act as useful germ cell markers at this stage. Proliferation continues for another couple of days, with a doubling time of about 16 hours. However, by 12.5 dpc, germ cells in both female and male embryos are entering the premeiotic cell cycle, and meiotic genes such as *Scp3 (synaptonemal complex protein 3)* are up-regulated.[25]

A detailed quantitative study of germ cells in the human fetal ovary, before and during entry into meiosis, was made by Baker.[26]

SEX DETERMINATION

In a female genital ridge, the germ cells proceed at about 13.5 dpc into prophase of the first meiotic division, passing through leptotene, zygotene, and pachytene stages before arresting in diplotene, in primordial follicles, shortly after birth. Germ cells enter into first meiotic prophase at the same time in ectopic locations outside the genital ridge, such as in the adrenal primordium, in female but also in male embryos. Germ cells isolated from both male and female embryos at 11.5 dpc or earlier will enter meiosis at this time also in cultured aggregates of lung tissue[27] or even on a feeder layer *in vitro*.[28] These observations indicate that germ cell entry into meiosis occurs cell autonomously, at a time that appears to be intrinsic rather than determined by an extrinsic signal.

In the male genital ridge, in contrast, the germ cells at about 13.5 dpc down-regulate meiotic genes such as *Scp3* and enter mitotic arrest in G_1/G_0[29] as prospermatogonia. This change in cell fate determination is not cell autonomous but is induced by the somatic cells, probably the Sertoli cells, of the male genital ridge. The somatic signal that blocks entry into meiosis has not yet been identified but possible candidates are prostaglandin D and LDL. In XY embryos, the testis-determining gene on the Y chromosome *(Sry)* is expressed in the supporting cell lineage for about 36 hours, from 10.5 to 12.0 dpc. *Sox9*, the presumed target of *Sry*, is expressed from 11.5 dpc on and is required for the differentiation of Sertoli cells from the supporting cell lineage and for their subsequent maintenance. By 12.5 dpc, germ cells in the male genital ridge are enclosed in cords, lined with Sertoli cells, and surrounded by peritubular myoid cells that have migrated in from the mesonephric region in response to an *Sry*-dependent signal.[30] Germ cells removed from a female genital ridge at 12.5 dpc or earlier and aggregated with somatic tissue from a 12.5 dpc male genital ridge will enter mitotic arrest rather than meiotic prophase, but by 13.5 dpc they are already committed to the female pathway of development. The male germ cells, however, are already committed to the male pathway by 12.5 dpc and develop as prospermatogonia even when aggregated with female genital ridge cells.[31]

X CHROMOSOME REACTIVATION

In female mammals, one or other of the two X chromosomes, at random, is inactivated during gastrulation in all cells of the somatic lineages and also in the germ cell lineage.

During germ cell migration, therefore, PGCs in both male and female embryos have just a single X chromosome active (dosage compensation). Once in the genital ridges, however, the silent X in XX germ cells is reactivated[32] and remains active throughout oogenesis, in human oocytes[33] and in mouse oocytes. Reactivation occurs not only in the female genital ridge but also in XX germ cells experimentally introduced into a male genital ridge.[34] *Xist* is involved in the initiation of X chromosome inactivation: expressed on the inactive X, it produces a stable transcript that coats the whole chromosome and can be visualized by RNA fluorescent *in situ* hybridization (FISH). Once the germ cells are in the genital ridge, *Xist* is down-regulated and the transcript disappears,[35] consistent with reactivation of the silent X chromosome.

EPIGENETIC CHANGES

Methylation patterns are imposed during gastrulation on the nascent somatic cell lineages but not on PGCs, perhaps because of their extraembryonic birth place. Global methylation in PGCs is still further decreased once the germ cells are in the genital ridges. Imprinted genes (i.e., genes in which only the paternal or only the maternal allele is expressed but not both) are characterized by differential methylation at specific CpG sites.[36] Genes shown to be imprinted in the mouse are not necessarily imprinted in the human (e.g., *Igf2r*).[37] In the germ cell lineage, the previous genomic imprint has to be erased, and a new imprint is established according to the sex of the embryo. The differential site-specific methylation in some imprinted genes has been examined in mouse germ cells by bisulfite sequencing. It decreases during PGC migration or shortly after entry into the genital ridges. At 10.5 dpc, some site-specific methylation is present, much less at 11.5 dpc, and very little at 12.5 dpc.[38] New imprints are established after birth: in the female germ line, for example, different imprinted genes acquire their new methylation pattern at different stages of oogenesis. Nuclear transfer experiments, using nuclei from male germ cells at 14.5–16.5 dpc, or nuclei from female neonatal oocytes, have established that these imprint-free genomes cannot support normal fetal development, but development was significantly improved when 11.5 dpc male germ cells (still retaining some imprints) were used as nuclear donors.[39] Obata *et al.*[40] have shown that 12.5 dpc female germ cells are able to complete meiosis and genomic imprinting *in vitro*. Their nuclei are then capable of supporting development to full term after transfer to an enucleated mature oocyte, followed by *in vitro* fertilization.

CELL AUTONOMOUS OR INDUCED?

As we have seen, many features of PGCs change once they have entered the genital ridges. To what extent is entry into the genital ridge causal, involving signals that emanate from the somatic tissues? We know that this is so for the block to entry into meiosis in the male genital ridge (see the section on sex determination) and also for the expression of *Mvh*, which depends on contact with genital ridge somatic tissue.[41] Conversely, we know that entry of germ cells into first meiotic prophase occurs cell autonomously unless they are exposed to 12.5 dpc or later male genital ridge tissue (see the section on sex determination); also expression of *Gcna* occurs cell autonomously, at a preprogrammed time, apparently requiring neither entry into the genital ridges nor even migration.[42] As yet we have no evidence bearing on this question, in relation either to X chromosome reactivation or to epigenetic changes.

Embryonic Germ Cells

EMBRYONIC GERM CELL DERIVATION

Early attempts to establish long-term cultures of mouse PGCs met with little success, even when feeder cells were used. Chromosomally stable stem cells were eventually obtained by combining three growth factors in the cultures: stem cell factor (SCF), fibroblast growth factor 2 (bFGF), and leukemia inhibitory factor (LIF). These stem cells were termed embryonic germ cells (EGCs) to distinguish them from embryonic stem (ES) cells. EGCs, like ES cells, proved capable of indefinite proliferation in culture and were pluripotent both *in vitro* in embryoid bodies and *in vivo* in chimeras in which they colonized all cell lineages including the germ line. EGC lines have been derived from PGCs before and during migration (8.5, 9.5 dpc) and also from PGCs in the genital ridge but only up to 12.5 dpc. EGC lines have also been derived in some other mammalian species, including from human PGCs.[43] Like mouse EGCs, human EGCs show high levels of alkaline phosphatase activity and express SSEA1. They also express SSEA4, TRA-1-60, and TRA-1-81. (See Chapter 42.)

XIST EXPRESSION

In PGCs, *Xist* may code for a stable transcript (migrating XX PGCs) or expression may be entirely absent (XY PGCs; XX PGCs after X chromosome reactivation in the genital ridge). In either case, undifferentiated EGC lines derived from the PGCs are characterized by an unstable *Xist* transcript, visualized by RNA FISH as a small dot overlying the locus. A similar situation is seen in ES cells. Once the EGCs or ES cells start to differentiate, the unstable transcript disappears and is replaced by a stable transcript or absence of expression, as appropriate.

EPIGENETIC CHANGES

The epigenetic status of imprinted genes in EGCs might be expected to reflect that in the PGCs from which they were derived. However, this is not so. Site-specific differential methylation proved to be absent from most imprinted genes, in EGC lines derived not only from 11.5 but also from 9.5 dpc germ cells.[44] This apparent conflict with the PGC data can be resolved if one assumes that the epigenetic changes involved in erasure of imprints continue after the cells are put into culture, reaching an imprint-free state once the EGC line is established. When these imprint-free EGCs have been used for making chimeras, some of the chimeras have shown growth retardation and skeletal defects (ribs and spine). Germ line transmission, however, has been reported with EGCs derived from 11.5 dpc PGCs.[45] The methylation status of most of the imprinted genes remained unchanged in fibroblasts derived by *in vivo* differentiation of EGCs in chimeras. In human EGC lines, the epigenetic status of undifferentiated cells has not been examined, but after differentiation to fibroblast-like cells, three imprinted genes showed monoallelic expression (as in normal somatic tissues), and the fourth, *Igf2*, showed some relaxation of imprinting.[46] These results suggest that there may be a considerable difference in the timing of imprint erasure between humans and mice. Relative to colonization of the genital ridge, entry into meiosis is also later and less well synchronized in the human than in the mouse.[26]

REFERENCES

1. Chiquoine, A.D. (1954). The identification, origin, and migration of the primordial germ cells in the mouse embryo. *Anat. Rec.* **118**, 135–146.
2. Witschi, E. (1948). Migration of the germ cells of human embryo from the yolk sac to the primitive gonadal folds. *Contrib. Embryol. Carnegie Inst.* **32**, 67–80.
3. MacGregor, G.R., Zambrowicz, B.P., and Soriano, P. (1995). Tissue non-specific alkaline phosphatase is expressed in both embryonic and extraembryonic lineages during mouse embryogenesis but is not required for migration of primordial germ cells. *Development* **121**, 1487–1496.
4. Ginsburg, M., Snow, M.H.L., and McLaren, A. (1990). Primordial germ cells in the mouse embryo during gastrulation. *Development* **110**, 521–528.
5. Illmensee, K., and Mahowald, A.P. (1974). Transplantation of polar plasm in *Drosophila*: induction of germ cells at the anterior pole of the egg. *Proc. Natl. Acad. Sci. U.S.A.* **71**, 1016–1020.
6. Strome, S., and Wood, W.B. (1982). Immunofluorescence visualization of germ-line-specific cytoplasmic granules in embryos, larvae, and adults of *Caenorhabditis elegans*. *Proc. Natl. Acad. Sci.* **79**, 1558–1562.
7. Mahowald, A.P., and Hennen, S. (1971). Ultrastructure of the "germ plasm" in eggs and embryos of *Rana pipiens*. *Dev. Biol.* **24**, 37–53.
8. Knaut, H., Pelegri, F., Bohmann, K., Schwarz, H., and Nusslein-Volhard, C. (2000). Zebrafish *vasa* RNA but not its protein is a component of the germ plasm and segregates asymmetrically before germ line specification. *J. Cell Biol.* **149**, 875–888.
9. Tsunekawa, N., Naito, M., Sakai, Y., Nishida, T., and Noce, T. (2000). Isolation of chicken *vasa* gene homolog and tracing the origin of primordial germ cells. *Development* **127**, 2741–2750.
10. Gardner, R.L., and Rossant, J. (1979). Investigation of the fate of 4.5 day post-coitum inner cell mass cells by blastocyst injection. *J. Embryol. Exp. Morphol.* **52**, 141–152.
11. Lawson, K.A., Meneses, J.J., and Pedersen, R.A. (1991). Clonal analysis of epiblast fate during germ layer formation in the mouse embryo. *Development* **113**, 891–911.
12. Lawson, K.A., and Hage, W.J. (1994). Clonal analysis of the origin of primordial germ cells in the mouse. *In* "Ciba Foundation Symposium 182, Germ Line Development" (J. Marsh and J. Goode, eds.), pp. 68–91. Wiley & Sons, Chichester, England.
13. Tam, P., and Snow, M.H.L. (1981). Proliferation and migration of primordial germ cells during compensatory growth in the mouse embryo. *J. Embryol. Exp. Morphol.* **64**, 133–147.
14. Johnson, A.D., Crother, B., White, M.E., Patient, R., Bachvarova, R.F., Drum, M., and Masi, T. (2003). Regulative germ cell

15. Johnson, A.D., Drum, M., Bachvarova, R.F., Masi, T., White, M.E., and Crother, M.I. (2003). Evolution of predetermined germ cells in vertebrate embryos: implications for macro-evolution. *Evol. Dev.* **5**, 414–431.
16. Lawson, K.A., Dunn, R.R., Roelen, B.A., Zeinstra, L.M., Davis, A.M., Wright, C.V., Korving, J.P., and Hogan, B.L. (1999). Bmp4 is required for the generation of primordial germ cells in the mouse embryo. *Genes Dev.* **13**, 424–436.
17. Tam, P.P., and Zhou, S.X. (1996). The allocation of epiblast cells to ectodermal and germ-line lineages is influenced by the position of the cells in the gastrulating mouse embryo. *Dev. Biol.* **178**, 124–132.
18. Schöler, H.R., Dressler, G.R., Balling, R., Rohdewohld, H., and Gruss, P. (1990). Oct-4: A germline-specific transcription factor mapping to the mouse t-complex. *EMBO J.* **9**, 2185–2195.
19. Saitou, M., Barton, S., and Surani, M.A. (2002). A molecular programme for the specification of germ cell fate in mice. *Nature* **418**, 293–300.
20. Sato, M., Kimura, T., Kurokawa, K. Fujita, Y., Abe, K., Masuhara, M., Yasunaga, T., Ryo, A., Yamamoto, M., and Nakano, T. (2002). Identification of PGC7, a new gene expressed specifically in preimplantation embryos and germ cells. *Mech. Dev.* **113**, 91–94.
21. Molyneaux, K.A., Stallock, J., Schaible, K., and Wylie, C. (2001). Time-lapse analysis of living mouse germ cell migration. *Dev. Biol.* **240**, 488–498.
22. Gomperts, M., Garcia-Castro, M., Wylie, C., and Heasman, J. (1994). Interactions between primordial germ cells play a role in their migration in mouse embryos. *Development* **120**, 135–141.
23. Kunwar, P.S., and Lehmann, R. (2003). Germ-cell attraction. *Nature* **421**, 226–227.
24. Wylie, C. (1999). Germ cells. *Cell* **96**, 165–174.
25. Di Carlo, A.D., Travia, G., and De Felici, M. (2000). The meiotic specific synaptonemal complex protein SCP3 is expressed by female and male primordial germ cells of the mouse embryo. *Int. J. Dev. Biol.* **44**, 241–244.
26. Baker, T.G. (1963). A quantitative cytological study of germ cells in human ovaries. *Proc. Roy. Soc. B* **158**, 417–433.
27. McLaren, A., and Southee, D. (1997). Entry of mouse embryonic germ cells into meiosis. *Dev. Biol.* **187**, 107–113.
28. Chuma, S., and Nakatsuji, N. (2001). Autonomous transition into meiosis of mouse fetal germ cells *in vitro* and its inhibition by gp130-mediated signalling. *Dev. Biol.* **229**, 468–479.
29. McLaren, A. (1984). Meiosis and differentiation of mouse germ cells. *In* "38th Symposium of the Society of Experimental Biology. Controlling Events in Meiosis" (C.W. Evans and H.G. Dickinson, eds.), pp. 7–23. Company of Biologists, Cambridge, UK.
30. McLaren, A. (1998). Gonad development: assembling the mammalian testis. *Curr. Biol.* **8**, R175–R177.
31. Adams, I.R., and McLaren, A. (2002). Sexually dimorphic development of mouse primordial germ cells: switching from oogenesis to spermatogenesis. *Development* **129**, 1155–1164.
32. Monk, M., and McLaren, A. (1981). X-chromosome activity in foetal germ cells of the mouse. *J. Embryol. Exp. Morphol.* **63**, 75–84.
33. Gartler, S.M., Liskay, R.M., and Gant, N. (1973). Two functional X-chromosomes in human foetal oocytes. *Exp. Cell Res.* **82**, 464–466.
34. McLaren, A., and Monk, M. (1981). X-chromosome activity in the germ cells of sex-reversed mouse embryos. *J. Reprod. Fertil.* **63**, 533–537.

35. Nesterova, T.B. Mermoud, J.E., Hilton, K., Pehrson, J., Surani, M.A., McLaren, A., and Brockdorff, N. (2002). *Xist* expression and macroH2A1.2 localisation in mouse primordial and pluripotent embryonic germ cells. *Differentiation* **69,** 216–225.

36. Surani, M.A. (1998). Imprinting and the initiation of gene silencing in the germ cell line. *Cell* **93,** 309–312.

37. Killian, J.K., Nolan, C.M., Wylie, A.A., Li, T., Vu, T.H., Hoffman, A.R., and Jirtle, R.L. (2001). Divergent evolution in M6P/IGF2R imprinting from the Jurassic to the Quaternary. *Hum. Mol. Genet.* **10,** 1721–1728.

38. Hajkova, P., Erhardt, S., Lane, N., Haaf, T., El-Maarri, O., Reik, W., Walter, J., and Surani, M.A. (2002). Epigenetic reprogramming in mouse primordial germ cells. *Mech. Dev.* **117,** 15–23.

39. Lee, J., Inoue, K., Ono, R., Ogonuki, N., Kohda, T., Kanego-Ishino, T., Ogura, A., and Ishino, F. (2002). Erasing genomic imprinting memory in mouse clone embryos produced from day 11.5 primordial germ cells. *Development* **15,** 1807–1817.

40. Obata, Y., Kono, T., and Hatada, I. (2002). Maturation of mouse fetal germ cells *in vitro. Nature* **418,** 497–498.

41. Toyooka, Y., Tsunekawa, N., Takahashi, Y., Matsui, Y., Satoh, M., and Noce, T. (2000). Expression and intracellular localization of mouse Vasa-homologue protein during germ cell development. *Mech. Dev.* **93,** 139–149.

42. Richards, A.J., Enders, G.C., and Resnick, J.L. (1999). Differentiation of murine premigratory primordial germ cells in culture. *Nature* **359,** 550–551.

43. Shamblott, M.J., Axelman, J., Wang, S., Bugg, E.M., Littlefield, J.W., Donovan, P.J., Blumenthal, P.D., Huggins, G.R., and Gearhart, J.D. (1998). Derivation of pluripotent stem cells from cultured human primordial germ cells. *Proc. Natl. Acad. Sci. U.S.A.* **95,** 13,726–13,731.

44. Durcova-Hills, G., Ainscough, J.E., and McLaren, A. (2001). Pluripotential stem cells derived from migrating primordial germ cells. *Differentiation* **68,** 220–226.

45. Tada, T., Tada, M., Hilton, K., Barton, S.C., Sado, T., Takagi, N., and Surani, M.A. (1998). Epigenotype switching of imprintable loci in embryonic germ cells. *Dev. Genes Evol.* **207,** 551–561.

46. Onyango, P., Jiang, S., Uejima, H., Shamblott, M.J., Gearhart, J.D., Cui, H., and Feinberg, A.P. (2002). Monoallelic expression and methylation of imprinted genes in human and mouse embryonic germ cell lineages. *Proc. Natl. Acad. Sci. U.S.A.* **99,** 10,599–10,604.

Stem Cells in Extraembryonic Lineages

Tilo Kunath and Janet Rossant

Introduction

The establishment of mouse embryonic stem (ES) cells provided an excellent model to study embryonic lineages in culture and *in vivo*.[1, 2] These pluripotent cells can contribute to all embryonic tissues, including the germ line, in chimeras.[3, 4] Furthermore, tissues from all three germ layers have been successfully formed from ES cells in culture.[5–10] These abilities have made ES cells an attractive culture system for studying the regulators of lineage-specific determination and differentiation. However, the inability of ES cells to differentiate into cells of the trophoblast lineage has precluded them from being a cell culture model for this essential extraembryonic lineage. The establishment of trophoblast stem (TS) cell lines from mouse blastocysts and early trophoblast tissue has provided such a model.[11, 12] TS cells can be grown indefinitely in culture, can differentiate into trophoblast subtypes, and can contribute exclusively to the trophoblast lineage in chimeras. This chapter reviews development of the extraembryonic trophoblast lineage in the mouse, considers evidence for the existence and the location of trophoblast progenitor populations *in vivo,* and describes the work that led to the establishment of TS cell lines. Some applications of this cell culture system are reviewed here; detailed protocols for the establishment and maintenance of TS cell lines can be found in chapter 45 of this volume. Finally, the extraembryonic endoderm lineage is briefly described.

Trophoblast Lineage

TROPHOBLAST DEVELOPMENT

An early priority of all mammalian embryos is to establish the extraembryonic lineages. The first such lineage to form is the trophoblast. In the mouse, this occurs by embryonic day (E) 3.5 when the preimplantation morula embryo cavitates to form the blastocyst. The outer sphere of 40–50 trophectoderm (TE) cells of the early blastocyst contains the sole precursors of the entire trophoblast lineage. An eccentrically located clump of cells within the trophectodermal sphere is the inner cell mass (ICM). One day later, a second extraembryonic lineage, primitive endoderm (PrE), forms at the exposed surface

of the ICM. The remainder of the ICM is the primitive ectoderm or epiblast. These three lineages are the foundations for development of the entire conceptus and two of them (TE and PrE) are restricted to the extraembryonic lineages. The primitive ectoderm will also produce several extraembryonic lineages tissues, such as the amnion, the allantois, and the mesodermal compartment of the definitive yolk sac[13, 14] (Fig. 17–1).

The derivatives of the trophoblast lineage are essential for the survival of the embryo in the maternal uterine environment. It mediates implantation into the uterus and establishes a barrier for nutrient and waste exchange. It comprises a major portion of the placenta, where trophoblast cells take on endocrine and immunological roles in addition to the primary task of supplying the embryo with nutrient-rich blood and removing wastes. A role in embryo patterning is also beginning to emerge for this versatile lineage.[15]

As mentioned previously, the trophoblast lineage is unambiguously present at blastocyst formation as the TE. There is a distinction between TE in contact with the ICM, or polar TE, and TE surrounding the blastocoel, or mural TE. The most distal or abembryonic cells in the mural TE are the first to differentiate into primary trophoblast giant cells followed by cells lateral to the border of the ICM.[16] The giant cells are aptly named, since they reach extraordinary sizes and possess very high DNA contents.[17] These cells undergo rounds of DNA synthesis (S phase) without intervening mitoses in a process known as endoreduplication.[18] The giant cells express several genes of the prolactin family, including Placental lactogen I *(PL-I)* early in giant cell differentiation[19]; later, they express *PL-II.*[20]

Proliferating TE cells at the proximal region of the conceptus generate several trophoblast structures. At E6.5, trophoblast tissue in direct contact with the embryonic ectoderm forms the extraembryonic ectoderm (ExE). These cells are diploid and highly proliferative. Continuous with the ExE and immediately above it is the ectoplacental cone (EPC). The rate of proliferation in this tissue is less than in ExE, but the cells are still diploid.[21] The EPC loses expression of several genes associated with ExE, such as *Fgfr2, Cdx2,* and Eomesodermin *(Eomes),*[22–24] and it initiates expression of other genes, such as *Tpbp* (formerly *4311).*[25, 26] The outer periphery of the EPC has a lower mitotic index than the core, and these outer cells contribute secondary giant cells to the growing parietal yolk sac as well as to the placenta itself[27] (Fig. 17–2). During gastrulation, posterior mesoderm migrates into the extraembryonic region and becomes associated with

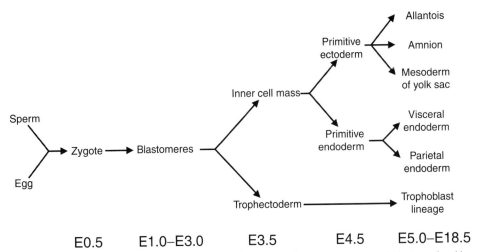

Figure 17–1. *Extraembryonic lineages during mouse development.* After fertilization, the zygote divides to produce blastomeres that eventually segregate into two lineages at blastocyst formation (E3.5): inner cell mass and trophectoderm. About 1 day later, the inner cell mass is further subdivided into the primitive ectoderm (or epiblast) and primitive endoderm. The primitive ectoderm will form all three germ layers of the embryo proper (not shown) and will contribute to several extraembryonic tissues: the allantois, the amnion, and the mesodermal part of the definitive (or visceral) yolk sac. The primitive endoderm differentiates into two major types of extraembryonic endoderm: visceral and parietal endoderm. The trophectoderm is the precursor to all trophoblast lineages in the placenta as well as to the giant cell layer of the parietal yolk sac. (Please see CD-ROM for color version of this figure.)

trophoblast tissue of the ExE to form the chorion. This trophoblast tissue is now referred to as chorionic ectoderm (ChE) (Fig. 17–2). At E8.5–9.0, the mesoderm-derived allantois fuses with the chorion, which further fuses with the base of the EPC, resulting in occlusion of the EPC cavity. These are the initial steps for forming a mature chorioallantoic placenta (Fig. 17–2). In this mature tissue, the extraembryonic mesoderm and ChE combine to form the labyrinth, the site of nutrient and waste exchange with the maternal blood supply. The EPC differentiates into the spongiotrophoblast, a supporting tissue in intimate contact with the labyrinthine trophoblast. Peripheral giant cells are in direct contact with the maternal decidua and are the invasive cells of the trophoblast. The maternal vasculature invades the spongiotrophoblast layer, and the endothelium is replaced with endovascular trophoblast as it enters the labyrinth.[28]

Numerous genetic mutants have been characterized that affect various aspects of placental development, and they have been summarized in two recent reviews.[29, 30] A few mutants of note are described here. The T-box gene, *Eomes,* is expressed in the TE of the blastocyst and the ExE of the early postimplantation embryo.[22, 31] A homozygous null mutation in this gene resulted in an embryonic lethal phenotype at the peri-implantation stage. Blastocysts implanted into the uterus but developed no further. The phenotype was caused by a cell-autonomous role for *Eomes* in trophoblast tissue as determined by chimeric analysis.[31] The *Cdx2* mutation may have a

similar defect to *Eomes*[−/−], since the gene is also expressed in early trophoblast derivatives,[24] and the knockout results in lethality at the time of implantation.[32] However, the precise phenotype has not been reported yet. The orphan nuclear receptor, *Errβ*, is expressed in the ExE and the ChE.[33] Targeted deletion of this gene resulted in embryonic lethality at E9.5 with a failure of the chorion and an overproduction of giant cells.[34] This gene is not required for the initial period of trophoblast proliferation, but it is required for its maintenance. The bHLH gene, *Hand1,* has an essential role in trophoblast giant cells. This gene is expressed in giant cells and functionally promotes their differentiation.[35] *Hand1*-deficient embryos die of placental failure because of a block in giant cell differentiation.[36] The lessons from these and other mutations point to the importance of lineage-specific transcription factors during trophoblast development.

FGF SIGNALING AND TROPHOBLAST PROGENITOR CELLS *IN VIVO*

The polar TE at the embryonic pole of the blastocyst remains diploid and proliferative, and the mural TE differentiates into postmitotic giant cells. Sustained proliferation of polar TE cells is dependent on interactions with the ICM and later with the epiblast. Transplanting an ectopic ICM to the mural TE region inhibits giant cell differentiation and induces a zone of proliferation. The dividing cells were determined by genetic markers to be of TE origin and not from the transplanted ICM.[37]

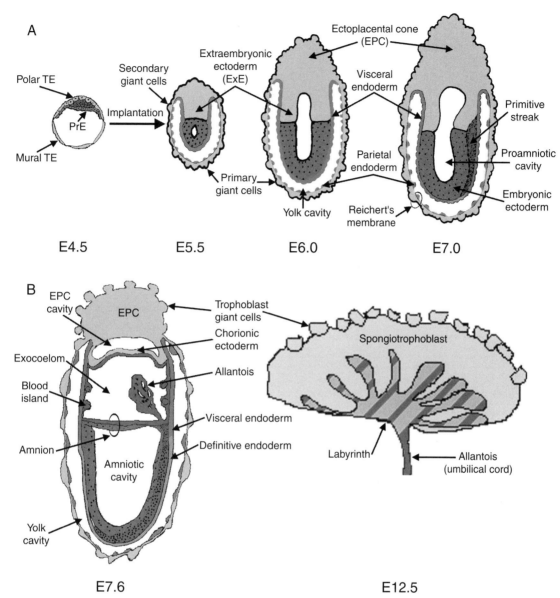

Figure 17–2. *Postimplantation development.* (A) Implantation to gastrulation. Based on their relative position to the inner cell mass, the trophectoderm (TE) cells of the E4.5 blastocyst have segregated into mural and polar TE. The polar TE grows into the blastocoel to produce the extraembryonic ectoderm and outward to form the ectoplacental cone (EPC). The mural TE differentiates into primary giant cells. Secondary giant cells line the outer surface of the EPC and contribute cells peripherally to the growing parietal yolk sac. At E6.5, the primitive streak forms at the posterior region of embryonic ectoderm adjacent to the extraembryonic ectoderm. By E7.0, definitive endoderm is beginning to emerge from the leading edge of the primitive streak. The primitive endoderm expands to line the entire surface of the former blastocoel, now known as the yolk cavity. The cells adjacent to the giant cell layer differentiate into parietal endoderm, and the cells in contact with the extraembryonic ectoderm and embryonic ectoderm become visceral endoderm. (B) Later development of extraembryonic lineages. By E7.5, posterior mesoderm has moved into the extraembryonic region and contributed to the chorion, amnion, and visceral yolk sac tissues. Three cavities are now present: the EPC cavity, the exocoelom, and the amniotic cavity. The interaction of visceral endoderm and extraembryonic mesoderm induces blood islands in the definitive yolk sac region. The allantois, emerging from the posterior end of the embryo into the exocoelom, fuses with the chorion that also combines with the EPC to form the chorioallantoic placenta (E12.5). Chorionic ectoderm and mesoderm combined with allantoic mesoderm generate the labyrinth. The spongiotrophoblast is mostly derived from the EPC. The definitive endoderm has replaced most of the visceral endoderm in the embryonic region after E7.5. (Please see CD-ROM for color version of this figure.)

A model emerged whereby trophoblast proliferation was dependent on signals from the ICM, and in the absence of this stimulus, the default pathway of giant cell differentiation would ensue.[38, 39] In agreement with this, the trophoblast-derived ExE and EPC differentiate into giant cells when explanted into culture.[27, 40] Contact with embryonic ectoderm, by placing the ExE or EPC into the amniotic cavities of E7.5 embryos ("embryonic pocket" culture), inhibited giant cell differentiation of the ExE only.[40] Thus, the trophoblast tissue nearest the epiblast, the ExE, can respond to proliferation signals from the embryo, but the more distal EPC is refractory to them. This is the first indication of where the trophoblast progenitors may reside *in vivo.*

Clues to the identity of the embryo-derived signal came from expression and genetic studies of the fibroblast growth factor (FGF) signaling pathway. Embryos mutant for the *Fgf4* gene die shortly after implantation.[41] Since this ligand is expressed in the ICM,[42] it could have an autocrine function in maintaining ICM cells, a paracrine role in the proliferation of polar TE cells, or both. The reciprocal expression pattern of *Fgfr2* in the TE and the ExE lent support for the latter model.[22, 23] Two different targeted deletions of the *Fgfr2* gene resulted in different phenotypes on the same genetic background. The deletion of exon 9, the alternatively spliced IIIc exon, resulted in a peri-implantation lethal phenotype similar to the *Fgf4* mutation.[43] Surprisingly, deletion of the complete Ig III loop (exons 7, 8, and 9) resulted in a less severe phenotype, with lethality occurring at E10.5 because of a failure of the placental labyrinth.[44] The IIIc deletion could be a dominant–negative mutation, since there is a possibility that a soluble FGFR2 IIIb variant is produced. However, heterozygous mice were normal and fertile.[43] On the other hand, the complete Ig III deletion might be a hypomorphic allele. They show by Western analysis that a truncated protein with the remaining two Ig loops and a complete intracellular domain is produced.[44] Although it cannot bind FGF ligands, it may participate in some ligand-independent signaling. Regardless of which *Fgfr2* allele is the complete loss-of-function mutation, an essential role for FGF signaling in trophoblast development is unmistakable. An *Fgfr2 IIIb* isoform-specific knockout resulted in a phenotype that did not have trophoblast defects as reported for the two *Fgfr2*-null alleles. The mice died at birth with severe lung and limb abnormalities.[45] In addition, the placental rescue of an *Fgfr2*-null allele by tetraploid aggregation resulted in a phenocopy of the *IIIb*-specific mutation.[46] This implicates the IIIc isoform of FGFR2 as the trophoblast-specific receptor and predicts that a *IIIc*-specific mutation should show trophoblast defects similar to one of the null mutations. The *Grb2* and *FRS2α* mutations may also have defects in the initial period of proliferation of the polar TE by disabling the FGF signal transduction pathway.[47, 48] *Grb2* is an adaptor for several signal pathways, but *FRS2α* is specific to FGF signaling.

Based on gene expression studies, FGF-dependent trophoblast progenitors are likely present from E3.5 to E8.5 (for 5 days). *Fgfr2* expression is down-regulated in the ChE by E8.5, and *Eomes*, an essential gene for the early trophoblast,

is also repressed.[22] A more precise prediction of when and where early trophoblast progenitors reside came from studies on the distribution of activated diphosphorylated mitogen-activated protein kinase (dpMAPK) during early development.[49] These studies revealed regions of the embryo where MAPK was activated, a common target in several signal transduction pathways. The early ExE (E5.5) was positive for dpMAPK, but most of the epiblast and visceral endoderm (VE) were not. The region of ExE positivity become more restricted to the trophoblast cells closest to the epiblast as development continued. This ring of dpMAPK staining persisted in the ChE after gastrulation occurred and contact with the epiblast was lost. The MAPK activation in ExE and ChE was attributed to FGF signaling, since a specific inhibitor (SU5402) abolished staining in this region and not others.[49] The dpMAPK+ trophoblast cells in the ExE–ChE may be progenitors for the entire trophoblast lineage, but they only exist for a fraction (<25%, or 5 of 19 days) of embryogenesis. In this situation, it may be more appropriate to refer to this subset of trophoblast cells as multipotent progenitors. Nevertheless, we refer to the FGF-dependent cultured cell lines derived from this tissue as stem cells, just as ES cell lines are considered stem cells. In their established culture conditions, ES and TS cells can be maintained in their respective primitive states from which they can differentiate into several cell types.

As will be detailed later in this chapter, FGF-dependent TS cell lines can be derived from blastocysts and early postimplantation trophoblast tissue. Recent work by Uy *et al.* used TS cell line derivations as an assay to determine which tissues could generate the characteristic TS cell cultures.[50] Although this may not precisely determine where the multipotent progenitors exist *in vivo,* it should definitively exclude regions and embryological times in which they do *not* exist. The ability to derive TS cell lines was demonstrated for embryos from the early blastocyst stage to as late as the 10-somite pair stage (~E8.0). From postimplantation embryos, TS cell lines could only be derived from ExE or ChE and not from the EPC or embryonic tissues; they could not be derived from trophoblast tissue at later stages.[50] It was also noted that TS cell lines could be derived from all regions of the ExE, including the cells adjacent to the EPC (farthest from the epiblast). Later in development, the ChE, a trophoblast tissue not in direct contact with the epiblast, efficiently produced TS cell lines.[50] This suggested that the inductive FGF signal supplied by the embryo at this stage is diffusible over a long range or that it is produced from other tissues, such as the extraembryonic mesoderm or endoderm. The areas of dpMAPK positivity and the regions where TS cell lines could be derived did not coincide. TS cell cultures could be obtained from ExE cells distant from the epiblast and regions of the chorion that were not positive for dpMAPK. However, *Fgfr2* expression did persist in these dpMAPK− regions, suggesting that cells could respond to an FGF signal but were not doing so *in vivo.* For this reason, trophoblast cells in ExE–ChE that are positive for dpMAPK may more accurately represent the trophoblast progenitor population *in vivo.*

The current model proposes that FGF4 produced by the ICM is necessary for the proliferative maintenance of the polar TE and that the lack of FGF signaling in the mural region results in giant cell differentiation. After implantation, the epiblast continues to produce FGF4 that signals to the overlying ExE, resulting in MAPK activation and maintenance of the trophoblast progenitor population. The FGFR2 IIIc isoform is predicted to be the trophoblast-specific FGF receptor *in vivo*. Essential transcription factors for the maintenance of this population include *Cdx2, Eomes,* and *Errβ*. After gastrulation and the formation of the chorion, portions of the ChE remain positive for dpMAPK, but the source and identity of the FGF signal is unclear at this point (Fig. 17–3).

The FGF-dependent progenitors are not present after chorioallantoic fusion, but the placenta is still required to undergo a substantial increase in size and is likely under the control of different signaling pathways. The TGFβ signaling pathway activated by Nodal is a possible candidate for this signal. An insertional mutation at the *nodal* locus resulted in a placental defect with excessive giant cell formation and a lack of spongiotrophoblast and labyrinth development.[51] Unlike *Fgfr2* or the transcription factors *Cdx2, Eomes,* and *Errβ*, *nodal* is not expressed in the early ExE or ChE. Its expression in the placenta is specific to the spongiotrophoblast layer

(an EPC descendant), begins at E9.5, and continues until term.[52] Interestingly, a compound null–hypomorph *nodal* mutation resulted in a less severe placental defect in which the giant cell and spongiotrophoblast layers were expanded at the expense of the labyrinth.[52] This suggests that Nodal-dependent progenitors may be residing in the labyrinth and that the source of the proliferative signal has shifted from the embryo to the spongiotrophoblast.

TS Cell Lines

DERIVATION OF TS CELL LINES

The culture of ExE or EPC tissue in most conditions resulted in giant cell differentiation.[21, 40] This led to the proposal that the default state of early trophoblast tissue is giant cells.[38] The accumulating evidence that FGF signaling was important for trophoblast development and could prevent giant cell transformation, led Dr. Satoshi Tanaka to revisit ExE explant cultures. Not only did FGF4 reduce giant cell formation in ExE explants, it also reduced the amount of EPC-like differentiation. Encouraged by these results, ExE from E6.5 embryos was disaggregated into single cells and plated on embryonic fibroblasts (EMFIs) in the presence of FGF4 and its essential cofactor heparin. This resulted in the formation of flat

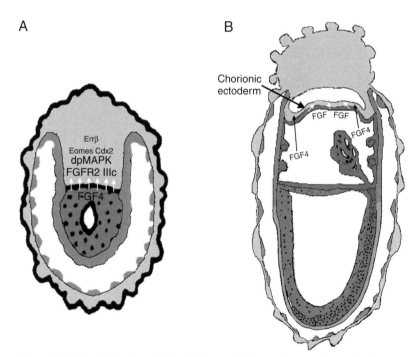

Figure 17–3. *Model of early trophoblast development.* (A) During early postimplantation development, FGF4 produced by the epiblast signals to the overlying extraembryonic ectoderm (white arrows) using the FGFR2 IIIc isoform. This leads to activation of the MAPK pathway, as indicated by diphosphorylated MAPK (dpMAPK). Downstream transcription factors essential for the maintenance of this lineage include Eomes, Cdx2, and Errβ. (B) After gastrulation, the chorionic ectoderm is far from the embryo proper but maintains dpMAPK activity. FGF4 may be diffusing over a long range, or a different FGF may be supplied by the underlying extraembryonic mesoderm. (Please see CD-ROM for color version of this figure.)

epithelial colonies that could be passaged indefinitely. Identical cell lines could also be derived from E3.5 blastocyst outgrowths. Chapter 45 of this volume provides detailed protocols on the derivation and maintenance of these TS cell lines.

TS cell lines expressed *Fgfr2* and the transcription factors characteristic of trophoblast progenitors *in vivo: Cdx2, Eomes,* and *Errβ.* Removal of FGF4, heparin, or the EMFIs resulted in giant cell differentiation (Fig. 17–4A and 17–4B) and complete down-regulation of these four markers. During the differentiation process, markers of intermediate trophoblast tissue, such as *Mash2* and *Tpbp* were expressed. The cell culture–derived giant cells exhibited increased ploidy and expressed the giant cell marker, *Pl-I,* like their *in vivo* counterparts.[12] TS cells did not express the ES cell or early epiblast marker *Oct4,* the mesoderm marker *Brachyury,* or the endoderm marker *Hnf-4.*[53–55] FACS analysis and visual inspection of the cultures revealed that TS cells cultures are heterogeneous even when grown in stem cell conditions (Fig. 17–4C and 17–4D). TS cell cultures could also be maintained in EMFI-conditioned medium, suggesting that EMFIs produce a soluble factor or factors important for TS cell self-renewal.

The developmental potential of TS cells was tested in chimeras generated by blastocyst injections. Green fluorescent protein (GFP)-transgenic TS cells were analyzed in chimeras from E6.5 to term (E18.5). All chimeras had TS cell contributions exclusively in trophoblast tissues (Fig. 17–4E and 17–4F). There were no examples of contributions to the embryo proper or to the visceral yolk sac and amnion, two extraembryonic membranes that do not contain trophoblast cells. In addition, all subtypes of the trophoblast lineage could be colonized. In early embryos, GFP-TS cells were in the ExE, EPC, and giant cells. In older conceptuses, the labyrinth and spongiotrophoblast had GFP-TS cell contributions.[12] The exclusive, tissue-specific restriction observed in chimeras indicates that TS cells are committed to the trophoblast lineage and retain the potential to differentiate into its many cell types.

Although TS cells can produce some remarkable chimeras with high contributions to the trophoblast lineage, improvements in its efficiency are required before this can be used as a routine assay to test the potential of manipulated TS cell lines. The percentage of observing chimeras from the most efficient method (blastocyst injection) is 45% of embryos recovered. However, the chance of obtaining *high-contribution* chimeras is between 5 and 10%. There may be several reasons for this low efficiency. First, the heterogeneity of the TS cell cultures suggests that only a fraction of the cells may be true stem cells. Any method to identify cells with greater stem cell potential and separate them from non–stem cells should improve the efficiency and extent of contribution during chimera production. Diploid cells can be separated from higher ploidy cells by fluorescence-activated cell sorting (FACS) with Hoechst 33342 dye, and a reduction in heterogeneity is observed by morphology and FACS analysis. However, this procedure only excludes one of the trophoblast subtypes: polyploid giant cells. A more precise method of isolation—for example, FACS for a specific cell-surface marker such as FGFR2 or high-efflux properties such as the side population[56]—should further narrow the stem cell window. To date, attempts to rescue a genetic trophoblast defect by TS cell chimerism have not been reported, but identifying and isolating TS cells with maximum developmental potential should help in this area.

TS CELLS AS MODELS OF TROPHOBLASTS

The TS cell culture system was used to investigate the role of the orphan nuclear receptor, ERRβ, through the use of a small molecule inhibitor. Diethylstilbestrol (DES) is a synthetic estrogen that is a potent agonist for the classical estrogen receptors, ERα and ERβ. It was demonstrated that DES has the opposite effect on the three ER-related receptors: ERRα, ERRβ, and ERRγ. ERRs are constitutively active transcription factors and do not require a ligand for activation.[57] Since TS cells and ExE express high levels of *Errβ,* the effects of DES treatment were investigated. DES specifically induced TS cell differentiation toward a trophoblast giant cell phenotype, and estradiol had no effect.[58] To investigate the effect of DES treatment on trophoblast tissue *in vivo,* pregnant mice were fed DES during early placentation (E4.5 to 8.5), and their placentas were examined at E9.5. Strikingly, the DES-treated placentas did not have the usual trilayered placenta consisting of spongiotrophoblast, labyrinth, and giant cells. Instead, they consisted of multiple layers of giant cells similar to *Errβ*-mutant placentas.[34, 58] This strongly suggested that the effects of DES in the placenta and in TS cells are mediated through only one of the ERRs: ERRβ. This illustrates that ERRβ is essential for the maintenance of TS cells in culture and the trophoblast progenitor population *in vivo.*

In an effort to identify novel trophoblast-specific genes, a cDNA microarray analysis was performed by comparing TS cell, ES cell, and EMFI RNA. Total RNA from these samples was used to prepare cDNA hybridized to the NIA mouse 15K cDNA clone set[59] in the laboratory of Minoru Ko and colleagues. Lists of genes particular to each cell type were generated, and several novel trophoblast lineage genes were investigated further by Northern blotting. Two novel genes *(Mm. 3590* and *Mm. 46582)* and a *Greul1*-homolog[60] were specifically expressed in TS cells and giant cells but not ES cells or EMFIs. These genes were considered trophoblast-lineage genes and not TS cell-specific genes, since they were all expressed in giant cells.[61]

Since the first report of TS cell lines, several laboratories have used this stem cell culture system for a diverse array of studies. A very interesting result was obtained when *Oct4* was conditionally repressed in ES cells. The *Oct4*-repressed cells transformed into trophoblast giant cells at the expense of embryonic lineages that ES cells normally produce under differentiative conditions. Even more striking was the establishment of TS cell cultures when FGF4 was added to ES cells during the down-regulation of *Oct4.*[62] This implicated Oct4 as a major repressor of the trophoblast lineage. Avilion *et al.* used the derivation of TS cell lines as an assay to determine the necessity of the high-mobility group box transcription

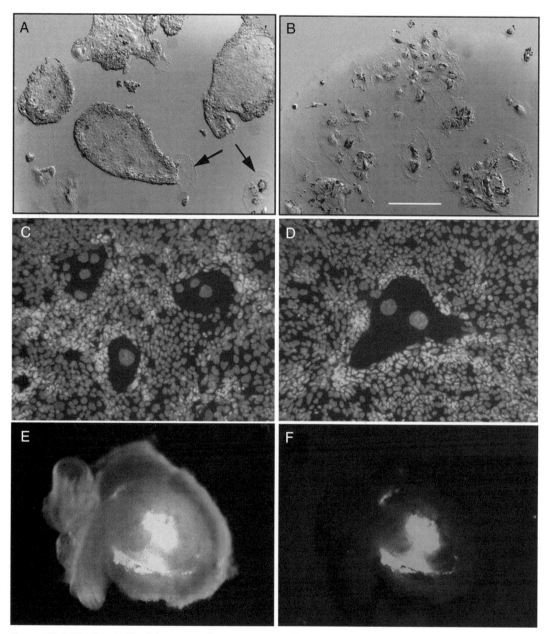

Figure 17–4. *TS cells and a TS cell chimera.* TS cells grown in (A) stem cell and (B) differentiative conditions. (A) Differential interference contrast (DIC) micrograph of several TS cell colonies grown in stem cell conditions. They form tight epithelial sheets with occasional differentiated giant cells (arrows) at their periphery. (B) DIC micrograph of six-day differentiated TS cells showing a drastic change in cell morphology to the characteristic giant cells. The bar is 50 μm. (C and D) Two examples of confluent stem cell cultures of TS cells stained with Hoechst 33342. The huge nuclei and vast cytoplasm of the giant cells are evident. There are also cells with intermediate sized nuclei (dots in panel C, for example). (E and F) An E8.5 TS cell chimera generated by blastocyst injection of green fluorescent protein–TS cells. The embryo with placenta was observed under UV fluorescence with (E) partial bright-field and (F) dark-field optics. (Please see CD-ROM for color version of this figure.)

factor, *Sox2,* for this lineage. They determined that *Sox2* is an essential gene for the trophoblast lineage, since null TS cells could not be derived.[63] Adelman *et al.* derived TS cells mutant for the hypoxia-responsive transcription factor *Arnt.* They went on to show that *Arnt*−/− TS cells were deficient in forming the intermediate EPC-like trophoblast cells during differentiation in culture.[64] Yan *et al.* used TS cells to study the effects of retinoic acid (RA) treatment in culture. They also found that TS cells skipped the intermediate *Mash2+* trophoblast subtype and differentiated directly into giant cells when treated with RA.[65] Ma *et al.* found that transfection of TS cells with *nodal* decreases giant cell formation and that JunB activity increases it.[52] Female TS cells were used by Mak *et al.* to show that paternally imprinted X-chromosome inactivation observed in the female trophoblast lineage *in vivo* is maintained in TS cells. Furthermore, the imprinting is maintained by stable association of the polycomb proteins, Eed and Enx1, with the inactive X-chromosome.[66] The role of α7 integrin in trophoblast attachment to different extracellular substrates was investigated with the TS cell culture system.[67] Suppressor of cytokine signaling 3 *(SOCS3)*-mutant TS cells were derived and shown to have an increased tendency to form giant cells at the expense of EPC-like cells, similar to the phenotype observed for the *SOC3*−/− placenta *in vivo.*[68] A targeted mutation against the mitochondrial transmembrane guanosine triphosphatase, mitofusin 2 *(Mfn2),* resulted in a giant cell defect and lethality by E11.5. *Mfn2*−/− TS cell lines were derived and shown to have severe morphological defects in their mitochondria. They were spherical and small, instead of the long mitochondrial tubules observed in wild-type TS cells.[69] Finally, Shiota *et al.* compared the DNA methylation status of CpG islands in TS cells and differentiated TS cells (giant cells) using the restriction-landmark genomic-scanning method.[70] These various reports illustrate that TS cell lines provide a useful model to study the trophoblast lineage in the mouse.

Extraembryonic Endoderm Lineage

EXTRAEMBRYONIC ENDODERM DEVELOPMENT

The PrE lineage first makes its appearance on the blastocoelic surface of the ICM at E4.5. The developmental path taken by the PrE depends on the tissue it interacts with. The PrE in contact with the extraembryonic and embryonic ectoderm differentiates into VE, and the PrE in contact with the trophoblast giant cell layer differentiates into parietal endoderm (PE) (Fig. 17–2). The PE collaborates with the giant cell layer to form the intervening Reichert's membrane. The combination of the PE, giant cells, and a thick basement membrane is the parietal yolk sac. The VE is a complex lineage with roles in nutrient delivery, embryonic cavitation, anterior induction, and hemangioblast induction.[71]

Once the initial PrE cells are established, the GATA factors, GATA4 and GATA6, are major players in the maintenance and elaboration of this lineage. *GATA4*-mutant embryos form VE but express elevated levels of *GATA6,* suggestive of some functional redundancy.[72,73] The embryos die around

E9.5 with heart defects. The *GATA6* mutation is more severe, with serious VE defects and lethality occurring between E5.5–7.5.[74] An instructive role for these proteins in extraembryonic endoderm specification was shown by ectopic expression in ES cells.[75]

The transition of VE to PE first occurs at the periphery of the ICM as the cells migrate onto the inner surface of the mural TE at the blastocyst stage. The VE grows as an epithelial layer with coherent growth,[76] and the PE cells grow individually and scatter on the giant layer as they lay down matrix proteins. The differentiation of VE to PE is considered by some to be the first epithelial-to-mesenchymal transition in development.[77] Studies in embryonal carcinoma cells identified cyclic adenosine monophosphate as an inducer of PE, if the cells were first differentiated into VE by RA treatment.[78] The ligand, parathyroid hormone-related protein (PTHrP), was later suggested to be an endogenous inducer of PE.[79] PTHrP is produced by the giant cell layer, and PE cells express its receptor, the G-protein–coupled receptor, type I PTHrP-R, at high levels.[80,81] The zinc-finger transcription factor, Snail, was identified as an immediate early target of PTHrP signaling in ES cells and was shown to be expressed in PE *in vivo.*[82] *Snail* and the highly related gene, *Slug,* are important for epithelial–mesenchymal transitions in several species.[83–85] In *Snail*−/− embryos, the initial mesoderm is formed, but it remains epithelial-like in agreement with the defined role of *Snail* in epithelial–mesenchymal transitions. *Snail*−/− embryos are smaller than wild-type littermates at E7.5 and die before E8.5.[86] A phenotype in the VE-to-PE transition was not reported on, but such a defect would not be inconsistent with the time of lethality.

EXTRAEMBRYONIC ENDODERM PROGENITORS?

PrE is considered to be the progenitor of both VE and PE, but this primitive cell type only persists one day after implantation (E5.5). After this point, both extraembryonic endoderm layers (VE and PE) continue to grow extensively. Chimera studies have shown that PrE cells have the potential to contribute to both VE and PE in a single chimera.[14] Observations, such as the sequential appearance of VE cells followed by PE cells during the differentiation of ES and EC cells, have biased opinions on how these cell types arise *in vivo.* These observations led to a model in which VE cells continually produce more PE cells in the marginal zone (the proximal region of yolk cavity). However, these experiments do not conclusively prove such a relationship *in vivo.* It is possible that the VE and PE layers have separate and self-sufficient cell populations after an early point in development (e.g., by E6.5). One possibility is that PE progenitors exist at the distal tip of the parietal yolk sac and that they contribute descendants that migrate up toward the marginal zone. The VE layer may have a similar progenitor zone to maintain its population. Mitotic indices in both tissues measured at E7.5 were similar.[87] An alternative theory puts extraembryonic endoderm stem cells in the marginal zone between the VE and the PE. Although this region has been proposed to be the site of VE-to-PE transition,[87] direct lineage analysis of these cells have not been performed. Real-time imaging of embryo–embryo chimeras (harboring different fluorescent transgenes) should answer some of these questions.

Summary

Gene expression studies (e.g., *Eomes*), TS cell line derivation potential, and MAPK activity in the embryo have led to a precise prediction of when and where trophoblast multipotent progenitors exist *in vivo*. The ExE cells close to the epiblast and a discrete population of ChE are the most likely locations for these early progenitors. However, by E8.5, the FGF-dependent progenitors do not exist and may be replaced by a different class of multipotent cells. The extraembryonic VE and PE layers exhibit substantial growth during development, but a defined progenitor or stem cell population has yet to be identified in this cell lineage.

REFERENCES

1. Evans, M.J., and Kaufman, M.H. (1981). Establishment in culture of pluripotential cells from mouse embryos. *Nature* **292**, 154–156.
2. Martin, G.R. (1981). Isolation of a pluripotent cell line from early mouse embryos cultured in medium conditioned by teratocarcinoma stem cells. *Proc. Nat. Acad. Sci. USA* **78**, 7634–7638.
3. Bradley, A., Evans, M., Kaufman, M.H., and Robertson, E. (1984). Formation of germ line chimaeras from embryo-derived teratocarcinoma cell lines. *Nature* **309**, 255–256.
4. Beddington, R.S., and Robertson, E.J. (1989). An assessment of the developmental potential of embryonic stem cells in the midgestation mouse embryo. *Development* **105**, 733–737.
5. Hescheler, J., Fleischmann, B.K., Lentini, S., Maltsev, V.A., Rohwedel, J., Wobus, A.M., and Addicks, K. (1997). Embryonic stem cells: a model to study structural and functional properties in cardiomyogenesis. *Cardiovasc. Res.* **36**, 149–162.
6. Jones, E.A., Tosh, D., Wilson, D.I., Lindsay, S., and Forrester, L.M. (2002). Hepatic differentiation of murine embryonic stem cells. *Exp. Cell Res.* **272**, 15–22.
7. Yamashita, J., Itoh, H., Hirashima, M., Ogawa, M., Nishikawa, S., Yurugi, T., Naito, M., and Nakao, K. (2000). Flk1+ cells derived from embryonic stem cells serve as vascular progenitors. *Nature* **408**, 92–96.
8. Ying, Q.L., Stavridis, M., Griffiths, D., Li, M., and Smith, A. (2003). Conversion of embryonic stem cells into neuroectodermal precursors in adherent monoculture. *Nat. Biotechnol.* **21**, 183–186.
9. Strubing, C., Ahnert-Hilger, G., Shan, J., Wiedenmann, B., Hescheler, J., and Wobus, A.M. (1995). Differentiation of pluripotent embryonic stem cells into the neuronal lineage *in vitro* gives rise to mature inhibitory and excitatory neurons. *Mech. Dev.* **53**, 275–287.
10. Ema, M., Faloon, P., Zhang, W.J., Hirashima, M., Reid, T., Stanford, W.L., Orkin, S., Choi, K., and Rossant, J. (2003). Combinatorial effects of Flk1 and Tal1 on vascular and hematopoietic development in the mouse. *Genes Dev.* **17**, 380–393.
11. Kunath, T., Strumpf, D., Tanaka, S., and Rossant, J. (2001). Trophoblast stem cells. *In* "Stem Cell Biology," (D.R. Marshak *et al.*, eds.), pp. 267–287. Cold Spring Harbor Laboratory Press, Cold Spring Harbor, NY.
12. Tanaka, S., Kunath, T., Hadjantonakis, A.K., Nagy, A., and Rossant, J. (1998). Promotion of trophoblast stem cell proliferation by FGF4. *Science* **282**, 2072–2075.
13. Snell, G.D., and Stevens, L.C. (1966). Early embryology. *In* "Biology of the Laboratory Mouse," (E.L. Green, ed.), pp. 205–245. McGraw-Hill, New York, NY.
14. Gardner, R.L. (1982). Investigation of cell lineage and differentiation in the extraembryonic endoderm of the mouse embryo. *J. Embryol. Exp. Morphol.* **68**, 175–198.
15. Beck, S., Le Good, J.A., Guzman, M., Ben Haim, N., Roy, K., Beermann, F., and Constam, D.B. (2002). Extraembryonic proteases regulate Nodal signaling during gastrulation. *Nat. Cell Biol.* **4**, 981–985.
16. Dickson, A.D. (1963). Trophoblastic giant cell transformation of mouse blastocysts. *J. Reprod. Fertil.* **6**, 465–466.
17. Barlow, P.W., and Sherman, M.I. (1972). The biochemistry of differentiation of mouse trophoblast: studies on polyploidy. *J. Embryol. Exp. Morphol.* **27**, 447–465.
18. Edgar, B.A., and Orr-Weaver, T.L. (2001). Endoreplication cell cycles: more for less. *Cell* **105**, 297–306.
19. Faria, T.N., Ogren, L., Talamantes, F., Linzer, D.I., and Soares, M.J. (1991). Localization of placental lactogen-I in trophoblast giant cells of the mouse placenta. *Biol. Reprod.* **44**, 327–331.
20. Yamaguchi, M., Ogren, L., Endo, H., Thordarson, G., Bigsby, R.M., and Talamantes, F. (1992). Production of mouse placental lactogen-I and placental lactogen-II by the same giant cell. *Endocrinology* **131**, 1595–1602.
21. Rossant, J., and Ofer, L. (1977). Properties of extraembryonic ectoderm isolated from postimplantation mouse embryos. *J. Embryol. Exp. Morphol.* **39**, 183–194.
22. Ciruna, B.G., and Rossant, J. (1999). Expression of the T-box gene Eomesodermin during early mouse development. *Mech. Dev.* **81**, 199–203.
23. Haffner-Krausz, R., Gorivodsky, M., Chen, Y., and Lonai, P. (1999). Expression of Fgfr2 in the early mouse embryo indicates its involvement in preimplantation development. *Mech. Dev.* **85**, 167–172.
24. Beck, F., Erler, T., Russell, A., and James, R. (1995). Expression of Cdx-2 in the mouse embryo and placenta: possible role in patterning of the extraembryonic membranes. *Dev. Dyn.* **204**, 219–227.
25. Lescisin, K.R., Varmuza, S., and Rossant, J. (1988). Isolation and characterization of a novel trophoblast-specific cDNA in the mouse. *Genes Dev.* **2**, 1639–1646.
26. Guillemot, F., Nagy, A., Auerbach, A., Rossant, J., and Joyner, A.L. (1994). Essential role of Mash-2 in extraembryonic development. *Nature* **371**, 333–336.
27. Ilgren, E.B. (1981). On the control of the trophoblastic giant cell transformation in the mouse: homotypic cellular interactions and polyploidy. *J. Embryol. Exp. Morphol.* **62**, 183–202.
28. Adamson, S.L., Lu, Y., Whiteley, K.J., Holmyard, D., Hemberger, M., Pfarrer, C., and Cross, J.C. (2002). Interactions between trophoblast cells and the maternal and fetal circulation in the mouse placenta. *Dev. Biol.* **250**, 358–373.
29. Cross, J.C. (2000). Genetic insights into trophoblast differentiation and placental morphogenesis. *Semin. Cell Dev. Biol.* **11**, 105–113.
30. Rossant, J., and Cross, J.C. (2001). Placental development: Lessons from mouse mutants. *Nat. Rev. Genet.* **2**, 538–548.

31. Russ, A.P., Wattler, S., Colledge, W.H., Aparicio, S.A., Carlton, M.B., Pearce, J.J., Barton, S.C., Surani, M.A., Ryan, K., Nehls, M.C., Wilson, V., Evans, M.J. (2000). Eomesodermin is required for mouse trophoblast development and mesoderm formation. *Nature* **404,** 95–99.

32. Chawengsaksophak, K., James, R., Hammond, V.E., Kontgen, F., and Beck, F. (1997). Homeosis and intestinal tumors in Cdx2-mutant mice. *Nature* **386,** 84–87.

33. Pettersson, K., Svensson, K., Mattsson, R., Carlsson, B., Ohlsson, R., and Berkenstam, A. (1996). Expression of a novel member of estrogen-response element-binding nuclear receptors is restricted to the early stages of chorion formation during mouse embryogenesis. *Mech. Dev.* **54,** 211–223.

34. Luo, J., Sladek, R., Bader, J.A., Matthyssen, A., Rossant, J., and Giguere, V. (1997). Placental abnormalities in mouse embryos lacking the orphan nuclear receptor ERRβ. *Nature* **388,** 778–782.

35. Cross, J.C., Flannery, M.L., Blanar, M.A., Steingrimsson, E., Jenkins, N.A., Copeland, N.G., Rutter, W.J., and Werb, Z. (1995). Hxt encodes a basic helix–loop–helix transcription factor that regulates trophoblast cell development. *Development* **121,** 2513–2523.

36. Riley, P., Anson-Cartwright, L., and Cross, J.C. (1998). The Hand1 bHLH transcription factor is essential for placentation and cardiac morphogenesis. *Nat. Genet.* **18,** 271–275.

37. Gardner, R.L., Papaioannou, V.E., and Barton, S.C. (1973). Origin of the ectoplacental cone and secondary giant cells in mouse blastocysts reconstituted from isolated trophoblast and inner cell mass. *J. Embryol. Exp. Morphol.* **30,** 561–572.

38. Gardner, R.L., and Johnson, M.H. (1972). An investigation of inner cell mass and trophoblast tissues following their isolation from the mouse blastocyst. *J. Embryol. Exp. Morphol.* **28,** 279–312.

39. Gardner, R.L., and Papaioannou, V.E. (1975). Differentiation in the trophectoderm and inner cell mass. *In* "The Early Development of Mammals," (M. Balls *et al.,* eds.), pp. 107–132. Cambridge University Press, Cambridge.

40. Rossant, J., and Tamura-Lis, W. (1981). Effect of culture conditions on diploid to giant cell transformation in postimplantation mouse trophoblast. *J. Embryol. Exp. Morphol.* **62,** 217–227.

41. Feldman, B., Poueymirou, W., Papaioannou, V.E., DeChiara, T.M., and Goldfarb, M. (1995). Requirement of FGF-4 for postimplantation mouse development. *Science* **267,** 246–249.

42. Niswander, L., and Martin, G.R. (1992). Fgf-4 expression during gastrulation, myogenesis, and limb and tooth development in the mouse. *Development* **114,** 755–768.

43. Arman, E., Haffner-Krausz, R., Chen, Y., Heath, J.K., and Lonai, P. (1998). Targeted disruption of fibroblast growth factor (FGF) receptor 2 suggests a role for FGF signaling in pregastrulation mammalian development. *Proc. Natl. Acad. Sci. USA* **95,** 5082–5087.

44. Xu, X., Weinstein, M., Li, C., Naski, M., Cohen, R.I., Ornitz, D.M., Leder, P., and Deng, C. (1998). Fibroblast growth factor receptor 2 (FGFR2)-mediated reciprocal regulation loop between FGF8 and FGF10 is essential for limb induction. *Development* **125,** 753–765.

45. De Moerlooze, L., Spencer-Dene, B., Revest, J., Hajihosseini, M., Rosewell, I., and Dickson, C. (2000). An important role for the IIIb isoform of fibroblast growth factor receptor 2 (FGFR2) in mesenchymal–epithelial signaling during mouse organogenesis. *Development* **127,** 483–492.

46. Arman, E., Haffner-Krausz, R., Gorivodsky, M., and Lonai, P. (1999). Fgfr2 is required for limb outgrowth and lung-branching morphogenesis. *Proc. Natl. Acad. Sci. USA* **96,** 11,895–11,899.

47. Cheng, A.M., Saxton, T.M., Sakai, R., Kulkarni, S., Mbamalu, G., Vogel, W., Tortorice, C.G., Cardiff, R.D., Cross, J.C., Muller, W.J., and Pawson, T. (1998). Mammalian Grb2 regulates multiple steps in embryonic development and malignant transformation. *Cell* **95,** 793–803.

48. Hadari, Y.R., Gotoh, N., Kouhara, H., Lax, I., and Schlessinger, J. (2001). Critical role for the docking-protein FRS2-α in FGF receptor-mediated signal transduction pathways. *Proc. Natl. Acad. Sci. USA* **98,** 8578–8583.

49. Corson, L.B., Yamanaka, Y., Lai, K.M.V., and Rossant, J. (2003). Spatial and temporal patterns of ERK signaling during mouse embryogenesis. *Development* (In press).

50. Uy, G.D., Downs, K.M., and Gardner, R.L. (2002). Inhibition of trophoblast stem cell potential in chorionic ectoderm coincides with occlusion of the ectoplacental cavity in the mouse. *Development* **129,** 3913–3924.

51. Iannaccone, P.M., Zhou, X., Khokha, M., Boucher, D., and Kuehn, M.R. (1992). Insertional mutation of a gene involved in growth regulation of the early mouse embryo. *Dev. Dyn.* **194,** 198–208.

52. Ma, G.T., Soloveva, V., Tzeng, S.J., Lowe, L.A., Pfendler, K.C., Iannaccone, P.M., Kuehn, M.R., and Linzer, D.I. (2001). Nodal regulates trophoblast differentiation and placental development. *Dev. Biol.* **236,** 124–135.

53. Palmieri, S.L., Peter, W., Hess, H., and Scholer, H.R. (1994). Oct-4 transcription factor is differentially expressed in the mouse embryo during establishment of the first two extraembryonic cell lineages involved in implantation. *Dev. Biol.* **166,** 259–267.

54. Duncan, S.A., Manova, K., Chen, W.S., Hoodless, P., Weinstein, D.C., Bachvarova, R.F., and Darnell, J.E., Jr. (1994). Expression of transcription factor HNF-4 in the extraembryonic endoderm, gut, and nephrogenic tissue of the developing mouse embryo: HNF-4 is a marker for primary endoderm in the implanting blastocyst. *Proc. Natl. Acad. Sci. USA* **91,** 7598–7602.

55. Wilkinson, D.G., Bhatt, S., and Herrmann, B.G. (1990). Expression pattern of the mouse *T* gene and its role in mesoderm formation. *Nature* **343,** 657–659.

56. Goodell, M.A., Brose, K., Paradis, G., Conner, A.S., and Mulligan, R.C. (1996). Isolation and functional properties of murine hematopoietic stem cells that are replicating *in vivo.* *J. Exp. Med.* **183,** 1797–1806.

57. Giguere, V. (2002). To ERR in the estrogen pathway. *Trends Endocrinol. Metab.* **13,** 220–225.

58. Tremblay, G.B., Kunath, T., Bergeron, D., Lapointe, L., Champigny, C., Bader, J.A., Rossant, J., and Giguere, V. (2001). Diethylstilbestrol regulates trophoblast stem cell differentiation as a ligand of orphan nuclear receptor ERRβ. *Genes Dev.* **15,** 833–838.

59. Kargul, G.J., Dudekula, D.B., Qian, Y., Lim, M.K., Jaradat, S.A., Tanaka, T.S., Carter, M.G., and Ko, M.S. (2001). Verification and initial annotation of the NIA mouse 15K cDNA clone set. *Nat. Genet.* **28,** 17–18.

60. Borchers, A.G., Hufton, A.L., Eldridge, A.G., Jackson, P.K., Harland, R.M., and Baker, J.C. (2002). The E3 ubiquitin ligase GREUL1 anteriorizes ectoderm during *Xenopus* development. *Dev. Biol.* **251,** 395–408.

61. Tanaka, T.S., Kunath, T., Kimber, W.L., Jaradat, S.A., Stagg, C.A., Usuda, M., Yokota, T., Niwa, H., Rossant, J., and Ko, M.S. (2002). Gene expression profiling of embryo-derived stem cells reveals candidate genes associated with pluripotency and lineage specificity. *Genome Res.* **12,** 1921–1928.

62. Niwa, H., Miyazaki, J., and Smith, A.G. (2000). Quantitative expression of Oct-3/4 defines differentiation, dedifferentiation, or self-renewal of ES cells. *Nat. Genet.* **24,** 372–376.

63. Avilion, A.A., Nicolis, S.K., Pevny, L.H., Perez, L., Vivian, N., and Lovell-Badge, R. (2003). Multipotent cell lineages in early mouse development depend on SOX2 function. *Genes Dev.* **17**, 126–140.

64. Adelman, D.M., Gertsenstein, M., Nagy, A., Simon, M.C., and Maltepe, E. (2000). Placental cell fates are regulated *in vivo* by HIF-mediated hypoxia responses. *Genes Dev.* **14**, 3191–3203.

65. Yan, J., Tanaka, S., Oda, M., Makino, T., Ohgane, J., and Shiota, K. (2001). Retinoic acid promotes differentiation of trophoblast stem cells to a giant cell fate. *Dev. Biol.* **235**, 422–432.

66. Mak, W., Baxter, J., Silva, J., Newall, A.E., Otte, A.P., and Brockdorff, N. (2002). Mitotically stable association of Polycomb group proteins Eed and Enx1 with the inactive X-chromosome in trophoblast stem cells. *Curr. Biol.* **12**, 1016–1020.

67. Klaffky, E., Williams, R., Yao, C.C., Ziober, B., Kramer, R., and Sutherland, A. (2001). Trophoblast-specific expression and function of the integrin-α7 subunit in the peri-implantation mouse embryo. *Dev. Biol.* **239**, 161–175.

68. Takahashi, Y., Carpino, N., Cross, J.C., Torres, M., Parganas, E., and Ihle, J.N. (2003). SOCS3: an essential regulator of LIF receptor signaling in trophoblast giant cell differentiation. *EMBO J.* **22**, 372–384.

69. Chen, H., Detmer, S.A., Ewald, A.J., Griffin, E.E., Fraser, S.E., and Chan, D.C. (2003). Mitofusins Mfn1 and Mfn2 coordinately regulate mitochondrial fusion and are essential for embryonic development. *J. Cell Biol.* **160**, 189–200.

70. Shiota, K., Kogo, Y., Ohgane, J., Imamura, T., Urano, A., Nishino, K., Tanaka, S., and Hattori, N. (2002). Epigenetic marks by DNA methylation specific to stem, germ, and somatic cells in mice. *Genes Cells* **7**, 961–969.

71. Bielinska, M., Narita, N., and Wilson, D.B. (1999). Distinct roles for visceral endoderm during embryonic mouse development. *Int. J. Dev. Biol.* **43**, 183–205.

72. Kuo, C.T., Morrisey, E.E., Anandappa, R., Sigrist, K., Lu, M.M., Parmacek, M.S., Soudais, C., and Leiden, J.M. (1997). GATA4 transcription factor is required for ventral morphogenesis and heart tube formation. *Genes Dev.* **11**, 1048–1060.

73. Molkentin, J.D., Lin, Q., Duncan, S.A., and Olson, E.N. (1997). Requirement of the transcription factor GATA4 for heart tube formation and ventral morphogenesis. *Genes Dev.* **11**, 1061–1072.

74. Morrisey, E.E., Tang, Z., Sigrist, K., Lu, M.M., Jiang, F., Ip, H.S., and Parmacek, M.S. (1998). GATA6 regulates HNF4 and is required for differentiation of visceral endoderm in the mouse embryo. *Genes Dev.* **12**, 3579–3590.

75. Fujikura, J., Yamato, E., Yonemura, S., Hosoda, K., Masui, S., Nakao, K., Miyazaki, J., and Niwa, H. (2002). Differentiation of embryonic stem cells is induced by GATA factors. *Genes Dev.* **16**, 784–789.

76. Gardner, R.L., and Cockroft, D.L. (1998). Complete dissipation of coherent clonal growth occurs before gastrulation in mouse epiblast. *Development* **125**, 2397–2402.

77. Verheijen, M.H., and Defize, L.H. (1999). Signals governing extraembryonic endoderm formation in the mouse: involvement of the type 1 parathyroid hormone-related peptide (PTHrP) receptor, p21Ras, and cell adhesion molecules. *Int. J. Dev. Biol.* **43**, 711–721.

78. Strickland, S., Smith, K.K., and Marotti, K.R. (1980). Hormonal induction of differentiation in teratocarcinoma stem cells: Generation of parietal endoderm by retinoic acid and dibutyryl cAMP. *Cell* **21**, 347–355.

79. Van de Stolpe, A., Karperien, M., Lowik, C.W., Juppner, H., Segre, G.V., Abou-Samra, A.B., de Laat, S.W., and Defize, L.H. (1993). Parathyroid hormone-related peptide as an endogenous inducer of parietal endoderm differentiation. *J. Cell Biol.* **120**, 235–243.

80. Karperien, M., Lanser, P., de Laat, S.W., Boonstra, J., and Defize, L.H. (1996). Parathyroid hormone related peptide mRNA expression during murine postimplantation development: evidence for involvement in multiple differentiation processes. *Int. J. Dev. Biol.* **40**, 599–608.

81. Karperien, M., van Dijk, T.B., Hoeijmakers, T., Cremers, F., Abou-Samra, A.B., Boonstra, J., de Laat, S.W., and Defize, L.H. (1994). Expression pattern of parathyroid hormone–parathyroid hormone-related peptide receptor mRNA in mouse postimplantation embryos indicates involvement in multiple developmental processes. *Mech. Dev.* **47**, 29–42.

82. Veltmaat, J.M., Orelio, C.C., Ward-Van Oostwaard, D., Van Rooijen, M.A., Mummery, C.L., and Defize, L.H. (2000). Snail is an immediate early target gene of parathyroid hormone-related peptide signaling in parietal endoderm formation. *Int. J. Dev. Biol.* **44**, 297–307.

83. Nieto, M.A., Sargent, M.G., Wilkinson, D.G., and Cooke, J. (1994). Control of cell behavior during vertebrate development by *Slug*, a zinc-finger gene. *Science* **264**, 835–839.

84. Cano, A., Perez-Moreno, M.A., Rodrigo, I., Locascio, A., Blanco, M.J., del Barrio, M.G., Portillo, F., and Nieto, M.A. (2000). The transcription factor snail controls epithelial–mesenchymal transitions by repressing E-cadherin expression. *Nat. Cell Biol.* **2**, 76–83.

85. Carl, T.F., Dufton, C., Hanken, J., and Klymkowsky, M.W. (1999). Inhibition of neural crest migration in *Xenopus* using antisense slug RNA. *Dev. Biol.* **213**, 101–115.

86. Carver, E.A., Jiang, R., Lan, Y., Oram, K.F., and Gridley, T. (2001). The mouse snail gene encodes a key regulator of the epithelial–mesenchymal transition. *Mol. Cell Biol.* **21**, 8184–8188.

87. Hogan, B.L., and Newman, R. (1984). A scanning electron microscope study of the extraembryonic endoderm of the eighth-day mouse embryo. *Differentiation* **26**, 138–143.

18

Neurogenesis in the Vertebrate Embryo

Chris Kintner and Naoko Koyano-Nakagawa

Introduction

A long-standing quest in the field of developmental biology is to determine how the diverse cell types that comprise the central nervous system (CNS) are generated during embryonic development. This issue has been difficult to address not only because the CNS is comprised of different cell types such as neurons and glia but also because the cellular composition of neural tissue varies enormously depending on its position along the body axis. Nonetheless, recent studies, mainly in the developing spinal cord, have revealed a rudimentary picture of the mechanisms that govern cell-type diversity in the vertebrate CNS. An important insight from these studies is that many of these mechanisms act in the early embryo when neural precursors first arise. In this chapter, we describe the early events that govern the formation of neural precursors and their differentiation into neurons in the developing vertebrate CNS. We first explain how the precursor cells for the CNS arise in the vertebrate embryo and how they differ from those for other developmental lineages. We next describe the role of the proneural genes as critical regulatory factors that promote the differentiation of neural precursors into neurons. Finally, we explain how the process of neural patterning may control the fate of neural precursors by regulating the activity of the proneural genes. The general model emphasized in this chapter is (1) that neural precursors in the CNS are already restricted in their fate when they form in the embryo as a consequence of the patterning processes that specify their position along the neuraxes and (2) that patterning genes trigger the proneural gene cascade at the proper time and place, thus determining patterns of neuronal differentiation. This model is likely to influence future studies of cell-type diversification in CNS development with the goal of manipulating embryonic and adult stem cells to restore damaged neural tissue in a therapeutic setting.

Embryonic Induction and the Establishment of Neural Tissue

The progenitor cells for the vertebrate CNS first appear in development with the formation of the neural plate from a

portion of the ectoderm (also known as the epiblast) during gastrulation (Fig. 18–1). The neural plate subsequently forms a tube consisting of neuroepithelial cells (NECs) arranged around a central lumen that extends along the anterior–posterior axis (Fig. 18–2A, B). In addition to the neural plate, the ectoderm also forms the neural crest, a migrating population of precursors that move throughout the embryo, generating both neural and nonneural cell types. In addition, ectodermal cells produce placodal structures that contain neural precursors for sensory ganglia as well as neurons in the ear and nose. Finally, other regions of the ectoderm contain precursors for nonneural tissue, most prominently in ventral regions where they generate the skin. Thus, neural precursors arise in the vertebrate embryo at gastrulae stages when the ectoderm is subdivided into regions with different developmental fates, a process governed by inductive tissue interactions between the ectoderm and another region called the organizer.

In their classic experiment, Mangold and Spemann showed that the ventral ectoderm of a host embryo could be induced to form a complete nervous system when exposed to a transplanted piece of tissue called the organizer.[1] Subsequently, this process, called neural induction, has been described in chick[2] and mouse embryos,[3] suggesting that it is a key feature of neural tissue formation in all vertebrates, including, by extension, human embryos. Additional embryological experiments were subsequently instrumental in showing that neural tissue is specified during neural induction by two sets of signals.[1] One set neuralizes the ectodermal cells, thus causing them to form nerve cells rather than skin cells. A second set patterns the neuralized ectoderm, thus determining subregions that will form nerve cells of a brain type or spinal cord type, for example. As these two sets of signals have been identified and studied, it has become clear that neuralization and patterning are intimately linked. Indeed, the idea that a generic neural lineage exists is likely to be misleading because position plays such a prominent and early role in specifying cell fate in the CNS. To explain this, one needs to consider how neuralizing and patterning signals act during neural induction.

Neuralization of the Ectoderm

In amphibians, the ectoderm can be easily isolated from blastula-stage embryos and placed in culture, where it differentiates into skin but not into neural tissue. However, dissociating

Handbook of Stem Cells
Volume 1

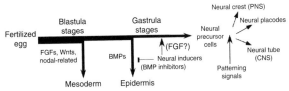

Figure 18-1. *Default model of neural induction.* Following fertilization, a region of the early embryo generates the ectoderm or epiblast, which responds to patterning signals as development progresses from left to right. At blastula stages, these signals include ones that induce mesodermal derivatives in posterior regions of the embryo using growth factors such as FGF, Wnts, and nodal-related families. At gastrulae stages, the ectoderm on the ventral side is induced to become epidermis by BMP signaling. However, a region of ectoderm avoids BMP signaling through inhibitors produced by the organizer, producing neural tissue. This neural tissue responds to a variety of patterning signals that divide it into different neural fates.

the isolated ectoderm into individual cells has been known since the experiments of Holtfreter to "induce" neural differentiation,[4] suggesting that ectodermal cells can generate neural precursors even in the absence of inductive signals from the organizer. A molecular understanding of this phenomenon was uncovered in *Xenopus* embryos during the study of signaling molecules that play prominent roles in axis determination.[5,6] One of these is the bone morphogenetic proteins (BMPs): members of the TGF-β superfamily of growth factors that play a key role in patterning the embryo along the dorsal–ventral axis.[7] Surprisingly, the inhibition of BMP signaling has been found to be the critical event required for converting ectoderm into neural tissue[8] (Fig. 18–1). When reagents that block the BMP signaling pathway are introduced into isolated ectoderm, they effectively convert it into neural tissue. Conversely, adding back BMPs as soluble ligands to dissociated ectodermal cells effectively blocks neural differentiation and promotes the formation of epidermal tissue. Finally, BMP inhibitors such as noggin, chordin, and follistatin have been identified that bind and antagonize BMP signaling extracellularly. These inhibitors are potent neural inducers, are expressed at quite high levels in organizer tissues, and underlie the molecular basis of organizer activity revealed in Mangold and Spemann's experiment.[9–11] These observations have led to the so-called default model for neural induction in which ectoderm is neuralized when inhibitors produced by the organizer block BMP signaling before and during gastrulation[12] (Fig. 18–1).

The default model also takes into account that growth factor signaling is required for the production of other embryonic cell lineages, such as those that generate mesodermal derivatives.[13] Induction of mesodermal derivatives occurs before gastrulation, mediated by different families of growth factors such as the Wnts, the fibroblast growth factors (FGFs), and the nodal-related members of the TGF-β superfamily[14,15] (Fig. 18–1). Significantly, ectoderm can be induced to produce mesodermal tissue if exposed to these factors at the appropriate stage. Thus, embryonic cells may only generate neural tissue if they avoid a series of signaling events that promote their differentiation along nonneural lineages (Fig. 18–1).

A major caveat to the default model is that other signaling pathways may act during neural induction to neuralize the ectoderm. For example, genetic experiments in mice show that some neural tissue forms even when neural induction has been disabled by mutations in the BMP inhibitors or by removal of the organizer.[16,17] This remaining neural tissue is an indication that additional pathways operate in embryos to specify neural tissue. Other results in chick experiments suggest that FGF is more effective than BMP inhibitors at inducing neural tissue in epiblast cells adjacent to the neural plate.[18–20] In *Xenopus* embryos, the ectoderm also forms neural tissue when exposed to FGF at the appropriate stage,[21,22] although whether or not FGF is normally required for neural induction remains controversial.[23,24] FGF action in this case may be mediated through Smad10, whose function is critical for the formation of neural precursors in *Xenopus* embryos.[25] In addition, FGF signaling is required for maintaining neural precursor cells in culture and for regulating their differentiation *in vivo*.[26,27] Together, these results point to a role for FGF signaling in the formation of neural precursors as a means of regulating their differentiation. The Wnt signaling pathway has also been implicated in the formation of neural precursors in early embryos. Reagents that block Wnt signaling in frog embryos antagonize neural tissue formation,[28] and blocking Wnt signaling in chick embryos allows the epiblast to respond to FGF and form neural tissue.[29] Inhibiting Wnt activity in ES cells also potentiates neural cell formation.[30] In summary, these results may indicate that the inhibition of BMP signaling is not sufficient for embryonic cells to form neural tissue. Nonetheless, they do not necessarily mean that the default model is incorrect. With further study, for example, these other pathways may contribute to neural induction in the same way as the BMP inhibitors: by preventing BMP activity[31] or the activity of other signals that promote a nonneural state.

Neural Patterning

The neuroectoderm of the neural plate produces the NECs of the neural tube, thus forming the neural progenitors that will generate the various neurons and glia that comprise the CNS. As the neural tube forms, the NECs are morphologically homogeneous, perhaps giving the mistaken impression that they are generic neural precursors at this stage. To the contrary, their homogenous appearance belies NECs status as an already diverse population of progenitor cells as a result of neural patterning. To illustrate this point, the following description will focus on the spinal cord, where perhaps the most is known about how patterning influences the formation and fate of neural precursors.

As NECs form the neural plate, they are exposed to a variety of signals that specify their position within the nervous system along two major cardinal axes. In the spinal cord, one of these axes, dorsal–ventral (D–V), depends largely on signals produced by two specialized midline structures, one at the ventral pole of neural tube (the floor plate)[32] and the other at the dorsal pole (the roof plate) (Fig. 18–2B). By acting as morphogens, the signals produced by these so-called organizing centers subdivide the NECs of the neural tube into domains with different developmental fates.[33] Specifically, the floor plate cells secrete a protein, called Sonic hedgehog (Shh, Fig. 18–2B), which induces or suppresses at different concentration thresholds the expression of genes, usually ones encoding homeodomain (HD) transcription factors, in NECs lying at different positions in the ventral spinal cord (Fig. 18–2C).[34] In this manner, the gradient of Shh activity subdivides the ventral NECs into at least five distinct areas by activating–suppressing the expression of different transcription factors, which then sharpen into nonoverlapping zones by cross-repression[35] (Fig. 18–2C). NECs in one of these zones (pMN, Fig. 18–2C) produce somatic motor neurons, and those in the other zones produce various classes of interneurons. These patterning events along the D–V axis take place in the context of a similarly complex patterning of the neural tube along a second orthogonal anterior–posterior (A–P) axis that also begins at neural plate stages.[36] Although the signals and target genes mediating this patterning are less understood, it is clear that they intersect with D–V patterning to generate a Cartesian coordinate system in which NECs express a unique code of transcription factors that determine cell fate at each point along the neuraxes. This code, for example, ensures that motor neurons form in response to Shh in a ventral domain along the entire spinal cord but that different motor neuron subtypes form at each A–P axial level.[37] In summary, neural patterning of the ventral spinal cord as well as other regions of the neural tube sets up a diverse pattern of gene expression within NECs that is already apparent when they form at neural plate stages. This pattern of gene expression is thought to be a major determinant of NEC fate, dictating when and where neurons and glia form.

Proneural Gene Cascade: A Downstream Target of Neural Patterning

How then does patterning of the NECs described previously dictate precise patterns of neuronal differentiation? The key finding addressing this question has come from the discovery of a class of basic helix–loop–helix (bHLH) proteins encoded by the so-called proneural genes. As transcriptional activators, the proneural proteins are thought to activate gene expression necessary both for the differentiation of precursors into neurons and for neuronal cell-type specification, thus acting as a molecular switch of differentiation (Table 18–1).

The vertebrate proneural bHLH genes fall into two families based on the homology to bHLH genes originally identified in *Drosophila* as mutations that block neural differentiation (Table 18–1).[38] One smaller family consists of those related to the *Drosophila* achaete–scute genes, such as *Mash1*. The second, larger family encodes proteins related to *Drosophila* atonal and can be subdivided structurally into three subfamilies: the neurogenin (Ngn)-like, the NeuroD-like, and the atonal-like. Expression of these different subfamilies occurs in precise spatial and temporal patterns both within the dividing NECs and within cells that have initiated

neuronal differentiation. When eliminated by targeted mutation, loss of specific proneural bHLH genes results in deletion of specific populations of neurons.[39–41] However, the loss of neurons is likely to be much more severe when multiple members are simultaneously eliminated, indicating that the proneural genes have overlapping function as found in *Drosophila*.[42] Because of this genetic redundancy, it is difficult to test experimentally whether all neuronal differentiation is driven by proneural gene action. However, in gain-of-function experiments, proneural proteins are potent inducers of neuronal differentiation when ectopically expressed not only in neural precursors but also in some nonneural tissues.[43]

The proneural proteins function to initiate many of the physiological changes that occur when NECs undergo terminal neuronal differentiation (Table 18–1). One such function is to promote cell-cycle exit, an irreversible set of events incurred by all NECs as they form neurons.[44] NECs initiate cell-cycle exit when their nuclei move to the lateral edge of ventricular zone, where they enter the G_0 phase and eventually delaminate out of the neuroepithelium (Fig. 18–2D). Ectopic expression of the proneural proteins in NECs or in tissue culture models of NECS causes rapid cell-cycle arrest, although some subtypes of proneural proteins promote this transition better than others.[44,45] The mechanism by which the proneural proteins initiate irreversible cell-cycle exit appears to be quite complex and is an area of active research.[46,47] This mechanism may involve direct protein–protein interactions with cell-cycle machinery or alternatively transcriptional changes in expression of genes that encode cell-cycle regulators, such as cyclin-dependent kinase inhibitors p21, p16, and p27.[44]

Proneural proteins also function to activate the expression of genes associated with all subtypes of neurons, such as those that encode neuronal isoforms of the cytoskeletal proteins, channels involved in membrane excitability, and proteins involved in axon guidance. Significantly, genes encoding the proneural proteins are expressed in neural precursors and in committed neurons but often are transient in expression and lost as neurons mature.[38] Thus, proneural proteins may initiate expression of panneuronal genes directly then maintain expression indirectly by activating a downstream transcriptional network. This network may include not only transcriptional activators of the neuronal genes but also transcriptional repressors that relieve the repression of neuronal genes. For example, transcriptional enhancers for many of the panneuronal differentiation genes contain binding sites for a repressor, called REST/NRSF, which acts to extinguish the expression of these genes in nonneuronal cells as well as in neuronal precursors.[48] This repression is presumably blocked in neurons by a mechanism involving the proneural proteins.

Another function associated with the proneural proteins during neuronal differentiation is the inhibition of gene expression required for astroglia or oligodendrocytes differentiation.[38] Neural precursors first generate neurons then switch to produce both types of glia at later stages, suggesting that glial differentiation genes need to be repressed in neural precursors during neurogenesis. Studies using cultured neural stem cells indicate that the proneural proteins inhibit astroglia

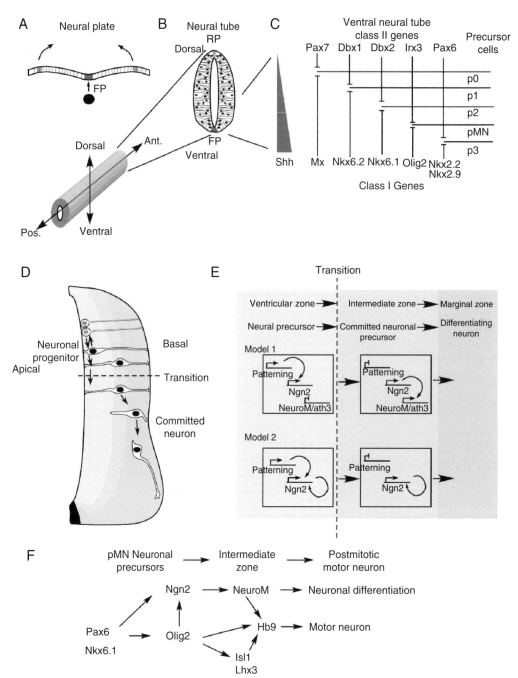

Figure 18-2. *Patterning and neurogenesis in the ventral spinal cord.* (A) The neural plate forms during gastrulation as a thickening of the ectoderm into a neuroepithelium, at which time patterning along the dorsal–ventral axis begins with the establishment of the floor plate (FP) and the roof plate (RP). (B) As the neural plate forms a neural tube, the NECs are patterned by signals emanating in part from the floor and roof plates. (C) In ventral spinal cord, this patterning consists of a gradient of Shh secreted by the floor plate, which activates–suppresses the expression of the class I and II homeodomain proteins (one exception is Olig2, a bHLH repressor) in a concentration dependent fashion. Mx is a hypothetical protein that has been proposed to contribute to ventral patterning by analogy with other class I proteins. (D) Neurogenesis within the neural tube is organized along a third developmental axis that corresponds to the apical–basal orientation of the neuroepithelium. Progenitor cells consist of NECs localized along the apical surface of the ventricular zone (no shading) within which their nucleus transverses during the cell cycle. During cell division, the two daughter cells separate at the apical surface, with recent studies suggesting that they maintain contact with the basal surface.[98] A precursor undergoes neuronal differentiation when its nucleus migrates laterally (light gray), exiting the cell cycle. Terminal neuronal differentiation is likely to be completed when a precursor delaminates from the neuroepithelium by detaching from ventricular surface, and migrating laterally into the marginal zone (dark gray shading). (E) Expression of proneural genes during the different phases of neurogenesis as shown by shading used in part D. Proneural genes such as the neurogenins are expressed in dividing precursors within the ventricular zone (no shading). Neuronal commitment occurs in the intermediate zone (light gray shading) when the levels of neurogenin are sufficiently high (in model 2) or when a downstream bHLH gene is activated (model 1). In either case, commitment causes the precursor to make the transition to a postmitotic

TABLE 18–1
Known Functions or Expression Patterns of bHLH Proteins in Neuronal Differentiation

Group	Subgroup	bHLH name	Comments	References
Acheate–scute	Acheate–scute-like	Mash1	Required for autonomic neuronal differentiation	100, 101
			Autonomic and olfactory neuron differentiation	102
			Coordination of differentiation in ventral forebrain	103, 104
			Determination gene in olfactory sensory neurons	105, 106
			Promotes neuronal fate and inhibits astrocytic fate in cortical progenitors	59
			Negative indirect autoregulation of the promoter	107
			Retinal development	108, 109
		Xash1	*Xenopus* homolog of Mash1, expressed in anterior regions of the CNS	110
		Cash1	Chick homolog of Mash1 and Xash1; has similar expression pattern	111
		Xash3	Only in *Xenopus*, early neural plate expression	112–114
		Cash4	Only in chick, early proneural gene in posterior CNS	115
	Nscl-like	Nscl1, Nscl2	Expressed during "late" phases of neuronal commitment	116–120
Atonal	Neurogenin-like	Xngn1	Promotes neurogenesis in both neuroectoderm and ectoderm; overexpression in developing embryos induces various downstream targets such as Ath-3, Xcoe2, Delta, MyT1, NeuroD, Tubulin, Neurofilament, Hes6, XETOR, and NKL	58, 84, 86, 91, 121–123
		Ngn1/NeuroD3/Math4C	Sensory lineage	124, 125
			Required for proximal cranial sensory ganglia	126
			Neurogenesis in developing dorsal root ganglia	127
			Specification of dorsal interneurons by crossinhibition with Math1	128
			Differentiation in olfactory sensory neurons	105, 106
			Inhibits gliogenesis	49
		Ngn2/Math4A	Required for epibranchial placode-derived cranial sensory ganglia	129
			Promotes neuronal fate and inhibits astrocytic fate in cortical progenitors	59
			Induced by and cross-regulates with Pax6	42, 60
		Ngn3	Promotes gliogenesis in the spinal cord	130
	NeuroD-like	NeuroD/β2	Converts *Xenopus* ectoderm into neurons	43
			Cell fate, determination, differentiation, and survival in neural retina	93, 131–133
			Required for differentiation of the granule cells in cerebellum and hippocampus	134
			Survival of inner ear sensory neurons	135
			Neurite outgrowth	136
		NeuroD2/NDRF	Required for development and survival of CNS neurons	39

Continued

Figure 18–2. cont'd, neuron (light gray shading) that undergoes terminal neuronal differentiation (dark gray shading). (F) Integration of neuronal differentiation with neuronal subtype specification. In the ventral spinal cord, patterning leads to expression of both the proneural protein Ngn2 and HD transcription factors, which cooperate to activate the expression of the motor neuron determinate HB9. This cooperation integrates a program of neuronal differentiation promoted by Ngn2, and perhaps NeuroM, along with a program of motor neuron differentiation. (Part C is adapted from Shirasaki *et al.*[36]). (Please see CD-ROM for color version of this figure.)

TABLE 18–1
Known Functions or Expression Patterns of bHLH Proteins in Neuronal Differentiation—cont'd

Group	Subgroup	bHLH name	Comments	References
		Math2/Nex1	Expressed in postmitotic cells of the brain	137
			Induces differentiation of PC12 cells and expression of GAP-43 gene	138, 139
		Xath2	Expressed in postmitotic cells of stage 32+ Xenopus dorsal telencephalon	140
		Math3/NeuroD4/ NeuroM	Expressed in transition stage in neurogenesis	141
			Amacrine cell specification in the retina	142
			Cooperates with Lim-HD proteins to specify motor neurons	57
		Xath3	Converts ectoderm into a neural fate	143
			Promotes sensory neuron marker expression	144
	Atonal-like	Math1	Required for cerebellar granule neuron development	145
			Required for generation of inner ear hair cells	146
			Required for proprioceptor pathway development	147
			Specification of dorsal interneuron subpopulation	128
		Xath1	Expressed in hindbrain; induces neuronal differentiation in ectoderm	148
		Math5	Promotes retinal ganglion cell fate through brn-3b	41
			Retinogenesis, regulated by Pax6	149, 150
		Xath5	Retinal ganglion cell fate	47, 151
			Regulates neurogenesis in olfactory placode	152
		Math6	Promotes neuronal fate at the expense of glial fate	153
Olig	Olig-like	Olig1, Olig2	Specification of motor neurons and oligodendrocytes	61, 62, 154–157
			Motor neurons specification in combination with ngn2	57
		Olig3	Transiently expressed in different types of progenitors of embryonic CNS	158
E12	E12	E12/E47	Dimerization partner of various bHLH proteins	38

differentiation in neural precursors not by binding DNA but by competing for critical coactivators required to induce the expression of glial genes such as glial fibrillary acidic protein.[49] In addition, proneural proteins can interfere with growth factor induction of glial differentiation by binding to and inhibiting components of the CNTF signaling pathway. Ectopic expression of proneural proteins also suppresses the formation of oligodendrocyte precursors that normally arise within discrete regions of the neural tube after neurogenesis is largely complete.[50] Thus, one function of the proneural proteins is to prevent cells from expressing genes necessary for glial differentiation while activating those required for neuronal differentiation.

Finally, the proneural proteins are involved not only in promoting changes associated with generic neuronal differentiation but also in activating gene expression required for neuronal subtype specification.[38] Since proneural proteins fall into several subfamilies with distinct sequence differences, one

possibility is that a given subfamily is specialized to promote the differentiation of a particular type of neuron. Indeed, in *Drosophila* there is strong evidence that the achaete–scute class of proneural proteins induces one type of external sense organ and the atonal class induces another.[51] Similar differences have been described for vertebrate proneural proteins, suggesting that they are designed partly to activate different downstream targets associated with neuronal cell-type specification.[52,53] The best-understood example of this occurs during the specification of motor neurons using the expression of an HD transcription factor called HB9 (Fig. 18–2F). Expression of HB9 is only activated where neural precursors in the ventral neural tube exit the cell cycle and produce motor neurons[54,55] (intermediate zone in Fig. 18–2D). Analysis of the enhancer required for this activation reveals an element with closely aligned binding sites for proneural proteins as well as for two HD proteins, Islet1 and Lhx2, know to be required for motor neuron differentiation.[56,57] Binding of these factors cooperatively activates expression of HB9, thus driving motor neuron differentiation. Significantly, although some proneural proteins can cooperate to activate HB9 expression, others cannot. Similar links have been made between the patterning of NECs and the expression of proneural proteins in the dorsal spinal cord.[52] In this case, neighboring domains of NECs produce different classes of interneurons by expressing distinct members of the proneural bHLH family. Thus, these observations strongly suggest that proneural proteins function to execute generic neuronal differentiation as well as to activate the downstream targets genes needed for neuronal cell-type specification.[38]

Potential Links Between Neural Patterning and Neurogenesis Control

Because the proneural proteins behave as a molecular "switch" that promotes neuronal differentiation, how their activity is regulated has important consequences for determining the fate of NECs. In some cases, the key element in this switch is a bHLH cascade in which the expression of one class of proneural protein in NECs can trigger neuronal differentiation by activating the expression of a downstream proneural gene (Fig. 18–2E, model 1). Alternatively, the key element may be in the form of a threshold in which only high levels of proneural gene expression in NECs are sufficient to trigger neuronal differentiation (Fig. 18–2E, model 2). In either case, sufficiently high activity of proneural proteins in NECs promotes exit from the cell cycle and terminal neuronal differentiation.[58] Conversely, if the activity or expression of proneural proteins is inhibited, NECs seem to revert to a ground state in which they have the option to divide and either become a neuron at a later time or serve as the source of progenitor cells for various glia at even later stages (Fig. 18–2D). Thus, proneural protein activity is not only a key factor in determining the onset and duration of neurogenesis but is also key in maintaining proper balance between the number of NECs that undergo terminal neuronal differentiation and the number that are retained in a progenitor mode, thus maintaining a progenitor cell pool for later-born neurons or for glia.[59] Not surprisingly, many of the factors that control the fate of NECs seem to converge on the expression or activity of the bHLH proteins, including the patterning genes described previously.

Analysis of the enhancer that drives expression of the proneural gene, Ngn2, in the spinal cord has revealed several discrete elements responsible for different spatial and temporal expression patterns in NECs.[42,60] These elements are likely to be driven by transcription factors whose expression is spatially restricted in NECs during neural patterning. For example, in the ventral spinal cord, the first neurons to be generated are motor neurons, and their generation in chick spinal cord is correlated with the early expression of Ngn2 within a narrow ventral domain of NECs. As already explained, this region of NECs is patterned by Shh signaling, which induces the expression of a key transcription factor, called Olig2, within the motor neuron–producing area of ventral NECs (Fig. 18–2C and F).

When ectopically expressed in the embryonic spinal cord, Olig2 induces ectopic motor neuron differentiation and does so partly by inducing ectopic and precocious expression of Ngn2.[61,62] Significantly, motor neurons arise in response to ectopic Olig2 with kinetics similar to those they normally do in the ventral neural tube. Expressing high levels of Ngn2 along with Olig2 short-circuits this time course, resulting in rapid motor neuron differentiation. Thus, the interactions among the patterning gene, Olig2, and the proneural protein, Ngn2, seems to be key in promoting motor neuron differentiation. Since Olig2 is a bHLH repressor,[61] its regulation of Ngn2 expression seems to be indirect, perhaps through the regulation of inhibitors of proneural gene expression such as those described in later sections of this chapter.

Thus, the general emerging principle is that the fate of NECs during neurogenesis is established using interactions between patterning genes and proneural proteins. The remaining challenge is to determine how the bHLH cascade is engaged in a myriad of ways to produce the appropriate number and types of neurons that comprise each region of the CNS along the neuraxes. This challenge, although daunting in its complexity, is likely to revolve around the large number of factors that seem to regulate the expression or activity of the proneural proteins.

Regulation of Proneural Protein Expression and Activity

One striking feature of the bHLH proteins is their ability to feedback and autoactivate expression of themselves or to activate a downstream bHLH gene (Fig. 18–2E). As a result, direct or indirect changes in the strength of this positive feedback loop is one avenue that can be exploited during the process of patterning to control neuronal differentiation (Fig. 18–3). The following section reviews some of the prominent regulators of the bHLH cascade that have been described and are likely to be the focus of future research in this area.

Members of the Id family of bHLH proteins contain a dimerization domain but are unable to bind DNA.[63] Since the proneural proteins bind DNA as heterodimers with the ubiquitously expressed E proteins, they are inactivated when they instead form nonfunctional dimers with the Id proteins. Targeted mutations in Id1 and Id3 causes premature neuronal differentiation in mice, demonstrating these proteins negatively regulate the differentiation of neural precursors, most likely by inhibiting the activity of the proneural proteins.[64] The factors critical in regulating the expression of Id proteins are not known, but one potentially significant input is repression of these genes by the patterning genes that promote neurogenesis. In addition, expression of these genes are likely to be a target of the Notch signaling pathway, which plays a prominent role in regulating neurogenesis as described later in this chapter.

A well-established family of proteins that negatively regulate neurogenesis are the bHLH transcriptional repressors called Esr, Hes, Her, Hrt, and Hey, depending on their species of origin and the subfamily classification of their structure.[65]

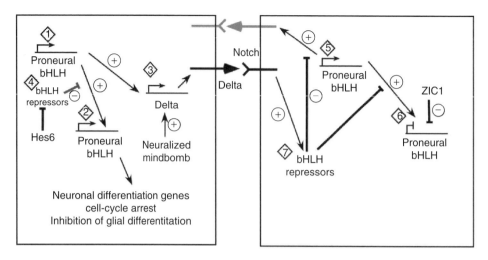

Differentiating neuron   Inhibited precursor

Figure 18–3. *Possible points of regulation of the bHLH cascade by patterning genes.* Differentiation of NECs depends on the bHLH cascade whose activity can be regulated in ways that promote neuronal differentiation, as shown on the left, or which keep the cell in a precursor state, as shown on the right. The bHLH proteins activate the expression of Delta (left panel), thus inhibiting neuronal differentiation noncell autonomously by activating the Notch receptor in neighboring cells (right panel). Products encoded by the patterning genes can potentially influence the activity of the proneural proteins in a variety of ways, as indicated by the numbers enclosed in diamonds. They can promote neuronal differentiation by promoting the expression of the neurogenins (1), the downstream bHLH (2), or the expression or activity of Delta (3), thereby enhancing lateral inhibition. Alternatively, neuronal differentiation can be enhanced by inhibiting the activity of proteins such as the bHLH repressors (4) that inhibit the activity of the bHLH proteins and thus neuronal differentiation. Patterning genes may prevent neuronal differentiation by inhibiting the activity of the neurogenins (5) or the downstream bHLHs (6), as shown for Zic1. Finally, patterning may inhibit neurogenesis by promoting the expression of the bHLH repressors (7).

Many of these genes were isolated and named based on homology to genes in *Drosophila*, called Hairy or Enhancer of Split, which play important roles in regulating proneural genes during fly neural development. Functional analysis of these bHLH repressors show that they potentially antagonize the activity of the proneural proteins by several mechanisms: interacting directly protein to protein,[66] competing with the proneural proteins for their binding sites (the E-box) in DNA,[67] or binding distinct DNA elements (the N-box or high-affinity repressor sites) in enhancers targeted by the proneural proteins.[68] An extremely large body of literature highlights the importance of bHLH repressors as potent regulators of the proneural proteins during neurogenesis. For example, targeted mutations of Hes1 or Hes5 in the mouse results in precocious and increased numbers of precursors undergoing neuronal differentiation,[69] and ectopic expression of these factors in *Xenopus* or zebra fish strongly inhibits neurogenesis in gain-of-function experiments.[70] In some cases, the bHLH repressors seem to regulate neurogenesis within relatively uniform domains of NECs.[71] In other cases, the expression of the repressor bHLH proteins is controlled by the Notch signaling pathway during a local patterning process, called lateral inhibition, which influences the ability of NECs to undergo differentiation.[72]

During lateral inhibition, the expression of the bHLH repressors are likely to be directly regulated by the Notch signal transduction pathway through binding sites for a DNA-binding protein referred to here as Suppressor of Hairless, or Su(H).[73]

In the absence of Notch signaling, Su(H) acts as a transcriptional repressor thought to actively inhibit the expression of the bHLH repressors.[74] However, upon Notch receptor activation by ligand binding, the Notch intracellular domain (ICD) is released from the membrane, moves to the nucleus, and converts Su(H) from a repressor into an activator, thus rapidly inducing gene expression.[75] As a consequence, activating the Notch pathway induces the expression of repressor bHLH genes and thereby inhibits neurogenesis, and inhibiting the Notch pathway enhances the levels of neuronal differentiation within a pool of neural precursors.[76] Significantly, the proneural proteins are potent activators of a least one Notch ligand related to *Drosophila* Delta.[58,77] Thus, proneural proteins not only promote neuronal differentiation cell autonomously but also, by activating Delta, inhibit neuronal differentiation in their neighbors noncell autonomously (Fig. 18–3).

The interaction of the proneural proteins with the Notch pathway appears to be a critical factor in determining the number of neurons generated from NECs within a given region of the neural tube.[72] As a result, one can imagine a scenario where patterning genes act by targeting the activity of the Notch pathway, perhaps by targeting several proteins known to be Notch modulators. Activity of the Notch receptor, for example, is modulated by posttranslational modification mediated by glycosyltransferases encoded by the vertebrate homologs of the *Drosophila Fringe* gene.[78] The *Fringe* homologs are dynamically expressed within neural precursor populations, where they may influence the activity of the Notch pathway. Another Notch modulator expressed in neural precursors is a small ankyrin repeat protein, called NRARP, which promotes the turnover of Notch ICD.[79] Indeed, numerous mechanisms have been proposed to change the half-life of Notch ICD, thus altering the efficacy of Notch activity.[80,81] Finally, another potential mechanism of modulating Notch activity is by changing the activity, expression, or both of the ligands. In this respect, an important factor in ligand activity appears to be their removal from the cell surface following ubiquitination by specific E3 ligases.[82,83] In all, modulation of Notch activity is likely to be one way in which the output of the patterning genes could target the activity of the proneural proteins during neurogenesis.

In addition to negative regulators of proneural protein activity, the patterning genes could influence neurogenesis by regulating the expression of genes whose products promote the activity of proneural proteins. For example, proneural proteins induce the expression of a bHLH protein, called Hes6, distantly related to the repressor bHLH proteins described previously.[84,85] As a target of the proneural proteins, Hes6 is expressed ubiquitously in neural precursors in regions where neuronal differentiation occurs within neurogenic epithelium. However, in contrast to the other repressors bHLH protein, Hes6 promotes neurogenesis in ectopic expression experiments, and it seems to do so by antagonizing the activity of the repressor bHLH proteins. Thus targeting Hes6, a repressor of repressors, could conceivably be a means of regulating the efficacy of the bHLH cascade. A similar scenario applies to the HLH proteins called EBF/Olf-1/Coe, whose expression is activated in neural precursors by the proneural bHLH proteins and which can promote neurogenesis in some assays.[86,87] How these transcription factors modulate the activity of the proneural proteins is not known, but their expression is a potential target of regulation by patterning genes.

Another significant class of transcription factors that may link patterning and the bHLH cascade fall into a family of related Kruppel-like C2H2 zinc-finger proteins, including Gli1-3, Zic1-5, and Nkl. The *Gli* genes are the vertebrate homologs of *Drosophila Cubiutis Interruptus*, the downstream transcriptional mediators of Shh.[88] Given the importance of Shh signaling in regulating neurogenesis in the spinal cord as well as in other regions of the CNS, the Gli proteins are likely to have a role in regulating the bHLH cascade. Indeed both the Gli proteins as well as the closely related Zic and NKL proteins have been shown to have both positive and negative effects on neurogenesis when overexpressed in *Xenopus* embryos.[89–91] The mechanism by which these transcription factors regulate neurogenesis is mostly unknown. A major exception was revealed by the analysis of a proneural gene in chick and mouse called *Math1* and *Cath1,* respectively.[92] *Cath1/Math1* is expressed in NECs in the dorsal neural tube where it drives the differentiation of dorsal interneurons. The neuronal enhancer of *Math1* contains a site for autoregulation as well as a binding site for Zic1, which inhibits the activity of the autoregulatory site.[93] In this manner, Zic1 prevents *Math1* from activating its own promoter and inducing neuronal differentiation. How Zic1 is

regulated in this case is not fully understood, but interestingly, the expression of other proneural genes does not appear to respond to Zic1 in the spinal cord. Thus, the Gli/Zic/Nkl family of proteins could contribute to the temporal and regional regulation of the proneural proteins as a downstream consequence of patterning.

The patterning of NECs may also result in changes in proneural protein activity by mechanisms involving posttranslational modifications. For example, bHLH proteins can be regulated by phosphorylation; a specific example of this regulation has been demonstrated for the proneural protein, NeuroD, in *Xenopus* embryos.[93] *Xenopus* NeuroD contains a consensus phosphorylation site for the regulatory kinase, GSK3β, that, when mutated, dramatically changes NeuroD's ability to promote neuronal differentiation. One possibility is that GSK3β regulates this using Wnt signaling, thereby changing the efficacy of proneural activity. Proneural activity might also be regulated by targeted protein turnover using degradation by the ubiquitin-proteasome pathway. Although this form of regulation has not been examined thoroughly in the context of neurogenesis, it is likely that proneural proteins, like other bHLH transcription factors, will be targeted by ubiquitin ligases for degradation in a regulated manner.[94,95] Finally, a relatively new and exciting level of regulation is likely to occur at the level of RNA. The recent identification of small, interfering microRNAs provides a compelling means of coordinated regulation of gene expression during differentiation. Finally, regulation of RNA activity during neurogenesis may occur through RNA-binding proteins, many of which are expressed in neural precursors in response to proneural gene activity.[96–98] Future work will undoubtedly uncover additional links with the patterning of neural precursors and the regulation of proneural activity at both the RNA and protein levels.

Summary

The development of the CNS can be represented as a series of fate choices progressively made by embryonic cells in response to both intrinsic and extrinsic cues. One of the first fate decisions is made in the ectoderm, where cells form the NECs of the neural plate rather than differentiating into nonneural tissues. This choice apparently can occur by default, suggesting that embryonic cells can form NECs in the absence of extrinsic instructions. However, a key process during neural induction is neural patterning during which a complex network of gene expression is established along the neuraxis, thereby specifying the position and subsequent fate of NECs. These complex genetic networks, many of which involve HD transcription factors, dictate patterns of neurogenesis by controlling when and where NECs undergo neuronal differentiation. Significantly, the patterning genes appear to regulate neurogenesis by converging on the activity of the proneural bHLH proteins, which function as molecular switches to initiate neuronal differentiation by promoting cell-cycle arrest, expression of neuronal differentiation genes, suppression of glial differentiation genes, and activation of neuronal subtype genes.

Thus, the neural precursors for the CNS initially choose their fate by default, but neural patterning is instrumental in instructing their subsequent neuronal fate by establishing a complex code of gene expression that drives the bHLH cascade at the proper time and place.

REFERENCES

1. Hamburger, V. (1988). "The Heritage of Experimental Embryology: Hans Spemann and the Organizer." Oxford University Press, Oxford.
2. Streit, A., and Stern, C.D. (1999). Neural induction. A bird's eye view. *Trends Genet.* **15**, 20–24.
3. Beddington, R.S. (1994). Induction of a second neural axis by the mouse node. *Development* **120**, 613–620.
4. Holtfreter, J. (1944). Neural differentiation of ectoderm through exposure to saline solution. *J. Exp. Zool.* **95**, 307–340.
5. Hemmati-Brivanlou, A., and Melton, D.A. (1994). Inhibition of activin receptor signaling promotes neuralization in *Xenopus*. *Cell* **77**, 273–281.
6. Hemmati-Brivanlou, A., Kelly, O.G., and Melton, D.A. (1994). Follistatin, an antagonist of activin, is expressed in the Spemann organizer and displays direct neuralizing activity. *Cell* **77**, 283–295.
7. Dale, L., and Wardle, F.C. (1999). A gradient of BMP activity specifies dorsal–ventral fates in early *Xenopus* embryos. *Semin. Cell Dev. Biol.* **10**, 319–326.
8. Harland, R. (2000). Neural induction. *Curr. Opin. Genet. Dev.* **10**, 357–362.
9. Sasal, Y., Lu, B., Steinbelsser, H., and De Robertis, E.M. (1995). Regulation of neural induction by the Chd and Bmp-4 antagonistic patterning signals in *Xenopus*. *Nature* **378**, 419.
10. Lamb, T.M., Knecht, A.K., Smith, W.C., Stachel, S.E., Economides, A.N., Stahl, N., Yancopolous, G.D., and Harland R.M. (1993). Neural induction by the secreted polypeptide noggin. *Science* **262**, 713–718.
11. Oelgeschlager, M., Kuroda, H., Reversade, B., and De Robertis, E.M. (2003). Chordin is required for the Spemann organizer transplantation phenomenon in *Xenopus* embryos. *Dev. Cell* **4**, 219–230.
12. Weinstein, D.C., Hemmati-Brivanlou, A. (1997). Neural induction in *Xenopus laevis*: evidence for the default model. *Curr. Opin. Neurobiol.* **7**, 7–12.
13. Smith, J.C. (1995). Mesoderm-inducing factors and mesodermal patterning. *Curr. Opin. Cell Biol.* **7**, 856–861.
14. Munoz-Sanjuan, I., and Hemmati Brivanlou, A. (2001). Early posterior–ventral fate specification in the vertebrate embryo. *Dev. Biol.* **237**, 1–17.
15. Schier, A.F., and Shen, M.M. (2000). Nodal signaling in vertebrate development. *Nature* **403**, 385–389.
16. Klingensmith, J., Ang, S.L., Bachiller, D., and Rossant, J. (1999). Neural induction and patterning in the mouse in the absence of the node and its derivatives. *Dev. Biol.* **216**, 535–549.
17. Bachiller, D., Klingensmith, J., Kemp, C., Belo, J.A., Anderson, R.M., May, S.R., McMahon, J.A., McMahon, A.P., Harland, R.M., Rossant, J., and De Robertis, E.M. (2000). The organizer factors Chordin and Noggin are required for mouse forebrain development. *Nature* **403**, 658–661.
18. Streit, A., Lee, K.J., Woo, I., Roberts, C., Jessell, T.M., and Stern, C.D. (1998). Chordin regulates primitive streak development

and the stability of induced neural cells but is not sufficient for neural induction in the chick embryo. *Development* **125**, 507–519.
19. Streit, A., Berliner, A.J., Papanayotou, C., Sirulnik, A., and Stern, C.D. (2000). Initiation of neural induction by FGF signaling before gastrulation. *Nature* **406**, 74–78.
20. Wilson, S.I., Graziano, E., Harland, R., Jessell, T.M., and Edlund, T. (2000). An early requirement for FGF signaling in the acquisition of neural cell fate in the chick embryo. *Curr. Biol.* **10**, 421–429.
21. Lamb, T.M., and Harland, R.M. (1995). Fibroblast growth factor is a direct neural inducer, which combined with noggin generates anterior–posterior neural pattern. *Development* **121**, 3627–3636.
22. Kengaku, M., and Okamoto, H. (1993). Basic fibroblast growth factor induces differentiation of neural tube and neural crest lineages of cultured ectoderm cells from *Xenopus* gastrula. *Development* **119**, 1067–1078.
23. Kroll, K.L., and Amaya, E. (1996). Transgenic *Xenopus* embryos from sperm nuclear transplantations reveal FGF signaling requirements during gastrulation. *Development* **122**, 3173–3183.
24. Holowacz, T., and Sokol, S. (1999). FGF is required for posterior neural patterning but not for neural induction. *Dev. Biol.* **205**, 296–308.
25. LeSueur, J.A., Fortuno, E.S., 3rd, McKay, R.M., and Graff, J.M. (2002). Smad10 is required for formation of the frog nervous system. *Dev. Cell* **2**, 771–783.
26. Diez del Corral, R., Breitkreuz, D.N., and Storey, K.G. (2002). Onset of neuronal differentiation is regulated by paraxial mesoderm and requires attenuation of FGF signaling. *Development* **129**, 1681–1691.
27. Mathis, L., Kulesa, P.M., and Fraser, S.E. (2001). FGF receptor signaling is required to maintain neural progenitors during Hensen's node progression. *Nat. Cell Biol.* **3**, 559–566.
28. Baker, J.C., Beddington, R.S., and Harland, R.M. (1999). Wnt signaling in *Xenopus* embryos inhibits bmp4 expression and activates neural development. *Genes Dev.* **13**, 3149–3159.
29. Wilson, S.I., Rydstrom, A., Trimborn, T., Willert, K., Nusse, R., Jessell, T.M., and Edlund, T. (2001). The status of Wnt signaling regulates neural and epidermal fates in the chick embryo. *Nature* **411**, 325–330.
30. Willert, K., Brown, J.D., Danenberg, E., Duncan, A.W., Weissman, I.L., Reya, T., Yates, J.R., 3rd, and Nusse, R. (2003). Wnt proteins are lipid-modified and can act as stem cell growth factors. *Nature* **423**, 448–452.
31. Bainter, J.J., Boos, A., and Kroll, K.L. (2001). Neural induction takes a transcriptional twist. *Dev. Dyn.* **222**, 315–327.
32. Yamada, T., Placzek, M., Tanaka, H., Dodd, J., and Jessell, T.M. (1991). Control of cell pattern in the developing nervous system: polarizing activity of the floor plate and notochord. *Cell* **64**, 635–647.
33. Jessell, T.M. (2000). Neuronal specification in the spinal cord: inductive signals and transcriptional codes. *Nat. Rev. Genet.* **1**, 20–29.
34. Briscoe, J., Pierani, A., Jessell, T.M., and Ericson, J. (2000). A homeodomain protein code specifies progenitor cell identity and neuronal fate in the ventral neural tube. *Cell* **101**, 435–445.
35. Muhr, J., Andersson, E., Persson, M., Jessell, T.M., and Ericson J. (2001). Groucho-mediated transcriptional repression establishes progenitor cell pattern and neuronal fate in the ventral neural tube. *Cell* **104**, 861–873.
36. Shirasaki, R., and Pfaff, S,L. (2002). Transcriptional codes and the control of neuronal identity. *Annu. Rev. Neurosci.* **25**, 251–281.

37. Ericson, J., Muhr, J., Jessell, T.M., and Edlund, T. (1995). Sonic hedgehog: a common signal for ventral patterning along the rostrocaudal axis of the neural tube. *Int. J. Dev. Biol.* **39,** 809–816.

38. Bertrand, N., Castro D.S., and Guillemot, F. (2002). Proneural genes and the specification of neural cell types. *Nat. Rev. Neurosci.* **3,** 517–530.

39. Olson, J.M., Asakura, A., Snider, L., Hawkes, R., Strand, A., Stoeck, J., Hallahan, A., Pritchard, J., and Tapscott, S.J. (2001). NeuroD2 is necessary for development and survival of central nervous system neurons. *Dev. Biol.* **234,** 174–187.

40. Schwab, M.H., Bartholomae, A., Heimrich, B., Feldmeyer, D., Druffel-Augustin, S., Goebbels, S., Naya, F.J., Zhao, S., Frotscher, M., Tsai, M.J., and Nave, K.A. (2000). Neuronal basic helix-loop-helix proteins (NEX and BETA2/Neuro D) regulate terminal granule cell differentiation in the hippocampus. *J. Neurosci.* **20,** 3714–3724.

41. Wang, S.W., Kim, B.S., Ding, K., Wang, H., Sun, D., Johnson, R.L., Klein, W.H., and Gan, L. (2001). Requirement for math5 in the development of retinal ganglion cells. *Genes Dev.* **15,** 24–29.

42. Scardigli, R., Schuurmans, C., Gradwohl, G., and Guillemot, F. (2001). Crossregulation between Neurogenin2 and pathways specifying neuronal identity in the spinal cord. *Neuron* **31,** 203–217.

43. Lee, J.E., Hollenberg, S.M., Snider, L., Turner, D.L., Lipnick, N., and Weintraub, H. (1995). Conversion of *Xenopus* ectoderm into neurons by NeuroD, a basic helix-loop-helix protein. *Science* **268,** 836–844.

44. Farah, M.H., Olson, J.M., Sucic, H.B., Hume, R.I., Tapscott, S.J., and Turner, D.L. (2000). Generation of neurons by transient expression of neural bHLH proteins in mammalian cells. *Development* **127,** 693–702.

45. Lo, L., Dormand, E., Greenwood, A., and Anderson, D.J. (2002). Comparison of the generic neuronal differentiation and neuron subtype specification functions of mammalian achaete–scute and atonal homologs in cultured neural progenitor cells. *Development* **129,** 1553–1567.

46. Souopgui, J., Solter, M., and Pieler, T. (2002). XPak3 promotes cell-cycle withdrawal during primary neurogenesis in *Xenopus laevis*. *EMBO J.* **21,** 6429–6439.

47. Ohnuma, S., Hopper, S., Wang, K.C., Philpott, A., and Harris, W.A. (2002). Coordinating retinal histogenesis: Early cell-cycle exit enhances early cell fate determination in the *Xenopus* retina. *Development* **129,** 2435–2446.

48. Jones, F.S., and Meech, R. (1999). Knockout of REST/NRSF shows that the protein is a potent repressor of neuronally expressed genes in nonneural tissues. *Bioessays* **21,** 372–376.

49. Sun, Y., Nadal-Vicens, M., Misono, S., Lin, M.Z., Zubiaga, A., Hua, X., Fan, G., and Greenberg, M.E. (2001). Neurogenin promotes neurogenesis and inhibits glial differentiation by independent mechanisms. *Cell* **104,** 365–376.

50. Ross, S.E., Greenberg, M.E., and Stiles, C.D. (2003). Basic helix–loop–helix factors in cortical development. *Neuron.* **39,** 13–25.

51. Jarman, A.P., Grau, Y., Jan, L.Y., and Jan, Y.N. (1993). *Atonal* is a proneural gene that directs chordotonal organ formation in the *Drosophila* peripheral nervous system. *Cell* **73,** 1307–1321.

52. Helms, A.W., and Johnson, J.E. (2003). Specification of dorsal spinal cord interneurons. *Curr. Opin. Neurobiol.* **13,** 42–49.

53. Parras, C.M., Schuurmans, C., Scardigli, R., Kim, J., Anderson, D.J., and Guillemot, F. (2002). Divergent functions of the proneural genes *Mash1* and *Ngn2* in the specification of neuronal subtype identity. *Genes Dev.* **16,** 324–338.

54. Tanabe, Y., William, C., and Jessell, T.M. (1998). Specification of motor neuron identity by the MNR2 homeodomain protein. *Cell* **95,** 67–80.

55. Arber, S., Han, B., Mendelsohn, M., Smith, M., Jessell, T.M., and Sockanathan, S. (1999). Requirement for the homeobox gene *Hb9* in the consolidation of motor neuron identity. *Neuron* **23,** 659–674.

56. Thaler, J.P., Lee, S.K., Jurata, L.W., Gill, G.N., and Pfaff, S.L. (2002). LIM factor Lhx3 contributes to the specification of motor neuron and interneuron identity through cell-type-specific protein–protein interactions. *Cell* **110,** 237–249.

57. Lee, S.K., and Pfaff, S.L. (2003). Synchronization of neurogenesis and motor neuron specification by direct coupling of bHLH and homeodomain transcription factors. *Neuron* **38,** 731–745.

58. Ma, Q., Kintner, C., and Anderson D.J. (1996). Identification of neurogenin, a vertebrate neuronal determination gene. *Cell* **87,** 43–52.

59. Nieto, M., Schuurmans, C., Britz, O., and Guillemot, F. (2001). Neural bHLH genes control the neuronal versus glial fate decision in cortical progenitors. *Neuron* **29,** 401–413.

60. Scardigli, R., Baumer, N., Gruss, P., Guillemot, F., and Le Roux, I. (2003). Direct and concentration-dependent regulation of the proneural gene *Neurogenin2* by Pax6. *Development* **130,** 3269–3281.

61. Novitch, B.G., Chen, A.I., and Jessell, T.M. (2001). Coordinate regulation of motor neuron subtype identity and panneuronal properties by the bHLH repressor Olig2. *Neuron* **31,** 773–789.

62. Mizuguchi, R., Sugimori, M., Takebayashi, H., Kosako, H., Nagao, M., Yoshida, S., Nabeshima, Y., Shimamura, K., and Nakafuku, M. (2001). Combinatorial roles of olig2 and neurogenin2 in the coordinated induction of panneuronal and subtype-specific properties of motoneurons. *Neuron* **31,** 757–771.

63. Yokota, Y. (2001). Id and development. *Oncogene* **20,** 8290–8298.

64. Lyden, D., Young, A.Z., Zagzag, D., Yan, W., Gerald, W., O'Reilly, R., Bader, B.L., Hynes, R.O., Zhuang, Y., Manova, K., and Benezra, R. (1999). Id1 and Id3 are required for neurogenesis, angiogenesis and vascularization of tumor xenografts. *Science* **401,** 670–677.

65. Davis, R.L., and Turner, D.L. (2001). Vertebrate hairy and enhancer of split-related proteins: transcriptional repressors regulating cellular differentiation and embryonic patterning. *Oncogene* **20,** 8342–8357.

66. Sasai, Y., Kageyama, R., Tagawa, Y., Shigemoto, R., and Nakanishi, S. (1992). Two mammalian helix-loop-helix factors structurally related to *Drosophila* hairy and enhancer of split. *Genes Dev.* **6,** 2620–2634.

67. Jennings, B.H., Tyler, D.M., and Bray, S.J. (1999). Target specificities of *Drosophila* enhancer of split basic helix-loop-helix proteins. *Mol. Cell Biol.* **19,** 4600–4610.

68. Giagtzoglou, N., Alifragis, P., Koumbanakis, K.A., and Delidakis, C. (2003). Two modes of recruitment of E(spl) repressors onto target genes. *Development* **130,** 259–270.

69. Ohtsuka, T., Ishibashi, M., Gradwohl, G., Nakanishi, S., Guillemot, F., and Kageyama, R. (1999). Hes1 and Hes5 as notch effectors in mammalian neuronal differentiation. *EMBO J.* **18,** 2196–2207.

70. Takke, C., Dornseifer, P., v. Weizsacker, E., and Campos-Ortega, J.A. (1999). *Her4*, a zebra fish homologue of the *Drosophila* neurogenic gene *E(spl)*, is a target of Notch signaling. *Development* **126,** 1811–1821.

71. Geling, A., Itoh, M., Tallafuss, A., Chapouton, P., Tannhauser, B., Kuwada, J.Y., Chitnis, A.B., and Bally-Cuif, L. (2003). bHLH

transcription factor Her5 links patterning to regional inhibition of neurogenesis at the midbrain–hindbrain boundary. *Development* **130,** 1591–1604.

72. Lewis, J. (1998). Notch signaling and the control of cell fate choices in vertebrates. *Semin. Cell Dev. Biol.* **9,** 583–589.

73. Barolo, S., and Posakony, J.W. (2002). Three habits of highly effective signaling pathways: principles of transcriptional control by developmental cell signaling. *Genes Dev.* **16,** 1167–1181.

74. Kao, H.Y., Ordentlich, P., Koyano-Nakagawa, N., Tang, Z., Downes, M., Kintner, C.R., Evans, R.M., and Kadesch, T. (1998). A histone deacetylase corepressor complex regulates the Notch signal transduction pathway. *Genes Dev.* **12,** 2269–2277.

75. Weinmaster, G. (1997). The ins and outs of Notch signaling. *Mol. Cell Neurosci.* **9,** 91–102.

76. Chitnis, A., and Kintner, C. (1995). Neural induction and neurogenesis in amphibian embryos. *Perspect. Dev. Neurobiol.* **3,** 3–15.

77. Hans, S., and Campos-Ortega, J.A. (2002). On the organization of the regulatory region of the zebra fish *deltaD* gene. *Development* **129,** 4773–4784.

78. Hicks, C., Johnston, S.H., diSibio, G., Collazo, A., Vogt, T. F., and Weinmaster, G. (2000). Fringe differentially modulates Jagged1 and Delta1 signaling through Notch1 and Notch2. *Nat. Cell Biol.* **2,** 515–520.

79. Lamar, E., Deblandre, G., Wettstein, D., Gawantka, V., Pollet, N., Niehrs, C., and Kintner, C. (2001). Nrarp is a novel intracellular component of the Notch signaling pathway. *Genes Dev.* **15,** 1885–1899.

80. Fryer, C.J., Lamar, E., Turbachova, I., Kintner, C., and Jones, K.A. (2002). Mastermind mediates chromatin-specific transcription and turnover of the Notch enhancer complex. *Genes Dev.* **16,** 1397–1411.

81. Lai, E.C. (2002). Protein degradation: four E3s for the notch pathway. *Curr. Biol.* **12,** R74–78.

82. Deblandre, G.A., Lai, E.C., and Kintner, C. (2001). *Xenopus* neuralized is an ubiquitin ligase that interacts with XDelta1 and regulates Notch signaling. *Dev. Cell* **1,** 795–806.

83. Itoh, M., Kim, C.H., Palardy, G., Oda, T., Jiang, Y. J., Maust, D., Yeo, S.Y., Lorick, K., Wright, G.J., Ariza-McNaughton, L., Weissman, A.M., Lewis, J., Chandrasekharappa, S.C., and Chitnis, A.B. (2003). Mind bomb is a ubiquitin ligase that is essential for efficient activation of Notch signaling by Delta. *Dev. Cell* **4,** 67–82.

84. Koyano-Nakagawa, N., Kim, J., Anderson, D., and Kintner, C. (2000). Hes6 acts in a positive feedback loop with the neurogenins to promote neuronal differentiation. *Development* **127,** 4203–4216.

85. Bae, S., Bessho, Y., Hojo, M., and Kageyama, R. (2000). The bHLH gene *Hes6,* an inhibitor of Hes1, promotes neuronal differentiation. *Development* **127,** 2933–2943.

86. Dubois, L., Bally-Cuif, L., Crozatier, M., Moreau, J., Paquereau, L., and Vincent, A. (1998). XCoe2, a transcription factor of the Col/Olf-1/EBF family involved in the specification of primary neurons in *Xenopus. Curr. Biol.* **8,** 199–209.

87. Pozzoli, O., Bosetti, A., Croci, L., Consalez, G.G., and Vetter, M.L. (2001). Xebf3 is a regulator of neuronal differentiation during primary neurogenesis in *Xenopus. Dev. Biol.* **233,** 495–512.

88. Koebernick, K., and Pieler, T. (2002). Gli-type zinc finger proteins as bipotential transducers of Hedgehog signaling. *Differentiation* **70,** 69–76.

89. Brewster, R., Lee, J., and Ruiz i Altaba, A. (1998). Gli/Zic factors pattern the neural plate by defining domains of cell differentiation. *Nature* **393,** 579–583.

90. Mizuseki, K., Kishi, M., Matsui, M., Nakanishi, S., and Sasai, Y. (1998). *Xenopus* Zic-related-1 and Sox-2, two factors induced by chordin, have distinct activities in the initiation of neural induction. *Development* **125,** 579–587.

91. Lamar, E., Kintner, C., and Goulding, M. (2001). Identification of NKL, a novel Gli-Kruppel zinc-finger protein that promotes neuronal differentiation. *Development* **128,** 1335–1346.

92. Ebert, P.J., Timmer, J.R., Nakada, Y., Helms, A.W., Parab, P.B., Liu, Y., Hunsaker, T.L., and Johnson, J.E. (2003). Zic1 represses Math1 expression via interactions with the Math1 enhancer and modulation of Math1 autoregulation. *Development* **130,** 1949–1959.

93. Moore, K.B., Schneider, M.L., and Vetter, M.L. (2002). Posttranslational mechanisms control the timing of bHLH function and regulate retinal cell fate. *Neuron* **34,** 183–195.

94. Hirata, H., Yoshiura, S., Ohtsuka, T., Bessho, Y., Harada, T., Yoshikawa, K., and Kageyama, R. (2002). Oscillatory expression of the bHLH factor Hes1 regulated by a negative feedback loop. *Science* **298,** 840–843.

95. Sriuranpong, V., Borges, M.W., Strock, C.L., Nakakura, E.K., Watkins, D.N., Blaumueller, C.M., Nelkin, B.D., and Ball, D.W. (2002). Notch signaling induces rapid degradation of achaete–scute homolog 1. *Mol. Cell Biol.* **22,** 3129–3139.

96. Perron, M., Furrer, M.P., Wegnez, M., and Theodore, L. (1999). *Xenopus* elav-like genes are differentially expressed during neurogenesis. *Mech. Dev.* **84,** 139–142.

97. Park, H.C., Hong, S.K., Kim, H.S., Kim, S.H., Yoon, E.J., Kim, C.H., Miki, N., and Huh, T.L. (2000). Structural comparison of zebra fish Elav/Hu and their differential expressions during neurogenesis. *Neurosci. Lett.* **279,** 81–84.

98. Sakakibara, S., Nakamura, Y., Satoh, H., and Okano, H. (2001). RNA-binding protein Musashi2, developmentally regulated expression in neural precursor cells and subpopulations of neurons in mammalian CNS. *J. Neurosci.* **21,** 8091–8107.

99. Das, T., Payer, B., Cayouette, M., and Harris, W.A. (2003). *In vivo* time-lapse imaging of cell divisions during neurogenesis in the developing zebra fish retina. *Neuron* **37,** 597–609.

100. Sommer, L., Shah, N., Rao, M., and Anderson D.J. (1995). The cellular function of MASH1 in autonomic neurogenesis. *Neuron* **15,** 1245–1258.

101. Lo, L.C., Tiveron, M.C., and Anderson, D.J. (1998). MASH1 activates expression of the paired homeodomain transcription factor Phox2a and couples panneuronal and subtype-specific components of autonomic neuronal identity. *Development* **125,** 609–620.

102. Guillemot, F., Lo, L. C., Johnson, J.E., Auerbach, A., Anderson, D.J., and Joyner, A.L. (1993). Mammalian achaete–scute homolog 1 is required for the early development of olfactory and autonomic neurons. *Cell* **75,** 463–476.

103. Horton, S., Meredith, A., Richardson, J.A., and Johnson, J.E. (1999). Correct coordination of neuronal differentiation events in ventral forebrain requires the bHLH factor MASH1. *Mol. Cell Neurosci.* **14,** 355–369.

104. Casarosa, S., Fode, C., and Guillemot, F. (1999). Mash1 regulates neurogenesis in the ventral telencephalon. *Development* **126,** 525–534.

105. Cau, E., Casarosa, S., and Guillemot, F. (2002). Mash1 and Ngn1 control distinct steps of determination and differentiation in the olfactory sensory neuron lineage. *Development* **129,** 1871–1880.

106. Cau, E., Gradwohl, G., Fode, C., and Guillemot, F. (1997). Mash1 activates a cascade of bHLH regulators in olfactory neuron progenitors. *Development* **124,** 1611–1621.

107. Meredith, A., and Johnson, J.E. (2000). Negative autoregulation of Mash1 expression in CNS development. *Dev. Biol.* **222,** 336–346.

108. Tomita, K., Nakanishi, S., Guillemot, F., and Kageyama, R. (1996). Mash1 promotes neuronal differentiation in the retina. *Genes Cells* **1,** 765–774.

109. Ahmad, I., Dooley, C.M., and Afiat, S. (1998). Involvement of Mash1 in EGF-mediated regulation of differentiation in the vertebrate retina. *Dev. Biol.* **194,** 86–98.

110. Ferreiro, B., Skoglund, P., Bailey, A., Dorsky, R., and Harris, W.A. (1993). XASH1, a *Xenopus* homolog of achaete–scute: a proneural gene in anterior regions of the vertebrate CNS. *Mech. Dev.* **40,** 25–36.

111. Jasoni, C.L., Walker, M.B., Morris, M.D., and Reh, T.A. (1994). A chicken achaete–scute homolog (CASH-1) is expressed in a temporally and spatially discrete manner in the developing nervous system. *Development* **120,** 769–783.

112. Ferreiro, B., Kintner, C., Zimmerman, K., Anderson, D., and Harris, W.A. (1994). *XASH* genes promote neurogenesis in *Xenopus* embryos. *Development* **120,** 3649–3655.

113. Turner, D.L., and Weintraub, H. (1994). Expression of achaete–scute homolog 3 in *Xenopus* embryos converts ectodermal cells to a neural fate. *Genes Dev.* **8,** 1434–1447.

114. Zimmerman, K., Shih, J., Bars, J., Collazo, A., and Anderson D.J. (1993). XASH-3, a novel *Xenopus* achaete–scute homolog, provides an early marker of planar neural induction and position along the mediolateral axis of the neural plate. *Development* **119,** 221–232.

115. Henrique, D., Tyler, D., Kintner, C., Heath, J.K., Lewis, J.H., Ish-Horowicz, D., and Storey, K.G. (1997). Cash4, a novel achaete–scute homolog induced by Hensen's node during generation of the posterior nervous system. *Genes Dev.* **11,** 603–615.

116. Begley, C.G., Lipkowitz, S., Gobel, V., Mahon, K.A., Bertness, V., Green, A.R., Gough, N.M., and Kirsch, I.R. (1992). Molecular characterization of *NSCL*, a gene encoding a helix-loop-helix protein expressed in the developing nervous system. *Proc. Natl. Acad. Sci. U. S. A.* **89,** 38–42.

117. Duncan, M.K., Bordas, L., Dicicco-Bloom, E., and Chada, K.K. (1997). Expression of the helix-loop-helix genes *Id-1* and *NSCL-1* during cerebellar development. *Dev. Dyn.* **208,** 107–114.

118. Uittenbogaard, M., Peavy, D.R., and Chiaramello, A. (1999). Expression of the bHLH gene *NSCL-1* suggests a role in regulating cerebellar granule cell growth and differentiation. *J. Neurosci. Res.* **57,** 770–781.

119. Haire, M.F., and Chiaramello, A. (1996). Transient expression of the basic helix-loop-helix protein NSCL-2 in the mouse cerebellum during postnatal development. *Brain Res. Mol. Brain Res.* **36,** 174–178.

120. Kruger, M., and Braun, T. (2002). The neuronal basic helix-loop-helix transcription factor NSCL-1 is dispensable for normal neuronal development. *Mol. Cell Biol.* **22,** 792–800.

121. Bellefroid, E.J., Bourguignon, C., Hollemann, T., Ma, Q., Anderson, D.J., Kintner, C., and Pieler, T. (1996). X-MyT1, a *Xenopus* C2HC-type zinc finger protein with a regulatory function in neuronal differentiation. *Cell* **87,** 1191–1202.

122. Talikka, M., Perez, S.E., and Zimmerman, K. (2002). Distinct patterns of downstream target activation are specified by the helix-loop-helix domain of proneural basic helix-loop-helix transcription factors. *Dev. Biol.* **247,** 137–148.

123. Cao, Y., Zhao, H., and Grunz, H. (2002). XETOR regulates the size of the proneural domain during primary neurogenesis in *Xenopus laevis*. *Mech. Dev.* **119,** 35–44.

124. Perez, S.E., Rebelo, S., and Anderson, D.J. (1999). Early specification of sensory neuron fate revealed by expression and function of neurogenins in the chick embryo. *Development* **126,** 1715–1728.

125. Zirlinger, M., Lo, L.C., McMahon, J., McMahon, A.P., and Anderson D.J. (2002). Transient expression of the bHLH factor neurogenin-2 marks a subpopulation of neural crest cells biased for a sensory but not a neuronal fate. *Proc. Natl. Acad. Sci. U. S. A.* **99,** 8084–8089.

126. Ma, Q., Chen, Z., del Barco Barrantes, I., de la Pompa, J.L., and Anderson, D.J. (1998). Neurogenin1 is essential for the determination of neuronal precursors for proximal cranial sensory ganglia. *Neuron* **20,** 469–482.

127. Ma, Q., Fode, C., Guillemot, F., and Anderson, D.J. (1999). Neurogenin1 and neurogenin2 control two distinct waves of neurogenesis in developing dorsal root ganglia. *Genes Dev.* **13,** 1717–1728.

128. Gowan, K., Helms, A.W., Hunsaker, T.L., Collisson, T., Ebert, P.J., Odom, R., and Johnson, J.E. (2001). Crossinhibitory activities of Ngn1 and Math1 allow specification of distinct dorsal interneurons. *Neuron* **31,** 219–232.

129. Fode, C., Gradwohl, G., Morin, X., Dierich, A., LeMeur, M., Goridis, C., and Guillemot, F. (1998). The bHLH protein Neurogenin 2 is a determination factor for epibranchial placode-derived sensory neurons. *Neuron* **20,** 483–494.

130. Lee, J., Wu, Y.Y., Qi, Y.C., Xue, H.P., Liu, Y., Scheel, D., German, M., Qiu, M.S., Guillemot, F., and Rao, M. (2003). Neurogenin3 participates in gliogenesis in the developing vertebrate spinal cord. *Dev. Biol.* **253,** 84–98.

131. Morrow, E.M., Furukawa, T., Lee, J.E., and Cepko, C.L. (1999). NeuroD regulates multiple functions in the developing neural retina in rodent. *Development* **126,** 23–36.

132. Yan, R.T., and Wang, S.Z. (1998). NeuroD induces photoreceptor cell overproduction *in vivo* and *de novo* generation *in vitro*. *J. Neurobiol.* **36,** 485–496.

133. Ahmad, I., Acharya, H.R., Rogers, J.A., Shibata, A., Smithgall, T.E., and Dooley, C.M. (1998). The role of NeuroD as a differentiation factor in the mammalian retina. *J. Mol. Neurosci.* **11,** 165–178.

134. Miyata, T., Maeda, T., and Lee, J.E. (1999). NeuroD is required for differentiation of the granule cells in the cerebellum and hippocampus. *Genes Dev.* **13,** 1647–1652.

135. Kim, W.Y., Fritzsch, B., Serls, A., Bakel, L.A., Huang, E.J., Reichardt, L.F., Barth, D.S., and Lee, J.E. (2001). NeuroD-null mice are deaf due to a severe loss of the inner ear sensory neurons during development. *Development* **128,** 417–426.

136. Cho, J.H., Kwon, I.S., Kim, S., Ghil, S.H., Tsai, M.J., Kim, Y.S., Lee, Y.D., and Suh-Kim, H. (2001). Overexpression of BETA2/NeuroD induces neurite outgrowth in F11 neuroblastoma cells. *J. Neurochem.* **77,** 103–109.

137. Bartholoma, A., and Nave, K.A. (1994). NEX-1, a novel brain-specific helix-loop-helix protein with autoregulation and sustained expression in mature cortical neurons. *Mech. Dev.* **48,** 217–228.

138. Uittenbogaard, M., Martinka, D.L., and Chiaramello, A. (2003). The basic helix-loop-helix differentiation factor Nex1/MATH-2 functions as a key activator of the *GAP-43* gene. *J. Neurochem.* **84,** 678–688.

139. Uittenbogaard, M., and Chiaramello, A. (2002). Constitutive overexpression of the basic helix-loop-helix Nex1/MATH-2 transcription factor promotes neuronal differentiation of PC12 cells and neurite regeneration. *J. Neurosci. Res.* **67,** 235–245.

140. Taelman, V., Opdecamp, K., Avalosse, B., Ryan, K., and Bellefroid, E.J. (2001). *Xath2*, a bHLH gene expressed during a late transition stage of neurogenesis in the forebrain of *Xenopus* embryos. *Mech. Dev.* **101**, 199–202.

141. Roztocil, T., Matter-Sadzinski, L., Alliod, C., Ballivet, M., and Matter, J.M. (1997). NeuroM, a neural helix-loop-helix transcription factor, defines a new transition stage in neurogenesis. *Development* **124**, 3263–3272.

142. Inoue, T., Hojo, M., Bessho, Y., Tano, Y., Lee, J.E., and Kageyama, R. (2002). Math3 and NeuroD regulate amacrine cell fate specification in the retina. *Development* **129**, 831–842.

143. Takebayashi, K., Takahashi, S., Yokota, C., Tsuda, H., Nakanishi, S., Asashima, M., and Kageyama, R. (1997). Conversion of ectoderm into a neural fate by *ATH-3*, a vertebrate basic helix-loop-helix gene homologous to *Drosophila* proneural gene atonal. *EMBO J.* **16**, 384–395.

144. Perron, M., Opdecamp, K., Butler, K., Harris, W.A., and Bellefroid, E.J. (1999). X-ngnr-1 and Xath3 promote ectopic expression of sensory neuron markers in the neurula ectoderm and have distinct inducing properties in the retina. *Proc. Natl. Acad. Sci. U. S. A.* **96**, 14,996–15,001.

145. Ben-Arie, N., Bellen, H.J., Armstrong, D.L., McCall, A.E., Gordadze, P.R., Guo, Q., Matzuk, M.M., and Zoghbi, H.Y. (1997). Math1 is essential for genesis of cerebellar granule neurons. *Nature* **390**, 169–172.

146. Bermingham, N.A., Hassan, B.A., Price, S.D., Vollrath, M.A., Ben-Arie, N., Eatock, R.A., Bellen, H.J., Lysakowski, A., and Zoghbi, H.Y. (1999). *Math1*, an essential gene for the generation of inner ear hair cells. *Science* **284**, 1837–1841.

147. Bermingham, N.A., Hassan, B.A., Wang, V.Y., Fernandez, M., Banfi, S., Bellen, H.J., Fritzsch, B., and Zoghbi, H.Y. (2001). Proprioceptor pathway development is dependent on MATH1. *Neuron* **30**, 411–422.

148. Kim, P., Helms, A.W., Johnson, J.E., and Zimmerman, K. (1997). XATH-1, a vertebrate homolog of *Drosophila* atonal, induces a neuronal differentiation within ectodermal progenitors. *Dev. Biol.* **187**, 1–12.

149. Brown, N.L., Patel, S., Brzezinski, J., and Glaser, T. (2001). Math5 is required for retinal ganglion cell and optic nerve formation. *Development* **128**, 2497–2508.

150. Brown, N.L., Kanekar, S., Vetter, M.L., Tucker, P.K., Gemza, D.L., and Glaser, T. (1998). Math5 encodes a murine basic helix-loop-helix transcription factor expressed during early stages of retinal neurogenesis. *Development* **125**, 4821–4833.

151. Kanekar, S., Perron, M., Dorsky, R., Harris, W.A., Jan, L.Y., Jan, Y.N., and Vetter, M.L. (1997). Xath5 participates in a network of bHLH genes in the developing *Xenopus* retina. [Erratum appears in *Neuron* (1998). **21**, following 1221.] *Neuron* **19**, 981–994.

152. Burns, C.J., and Vetter, M.L. (2002). Xath5 regulates neurogenesis in the *Xenopus* olfactory placode. *Dev. Dyn.* **225**, 536–543.

153. Inoue, C., Bae, S.K., Takatsuka, K., Inoue, T., Bessho, Y., and Kageyama, R. (2001). *Math6*, a bHLH gene expressed in the developing nervous system, regulates neuronal versus glial differentiation. *Genes Cells* **6**, 977–986.

154. Zhou, Q., and Anderson, D.J. (2002). The bHLH transcription factors OLIG2 and OLIG1 couple neuronal and glial subtype specification. *Cell* **109**, 61–73.

155. Zhou, Q., Choi, G., and Anderson, D.J. (2001). The bHLH transcription factor Olig2 promotes oligodendrocyte differentiation in collaboration with Nkx2.2. *Neuron* **31**, 791–807.

156. Sun, T., Echelard, Y., Lu, R., Yuk, D., Kaing, S., Stiles, C.D., and Rowitch, D.H. (2001). Olig bHLH proteins interact with homeodomain proteins to regulate cell fate acquisition in progenitors of the ventral neural tube. *Curr. Biol.* **11**, 1413–1420.

157. Lu, Q.R., Sun, T., Zhu, Z.M., Ma, N., Garcia, M., Stiles, C.D., and Rowitch, D.H. (2002). Common developmental requirement for Olig function indicates a motor neuron–oligodendrocyte connection. *Cell* **109**, 75–86.

158. Takebayashi, H., Ohtsuki, T., Uchida, T., Kawamoto, S., Okubo, K., Ikenaka, K., Takeichi, M., Chisaka, O., and Nabeshima Y. (2002). Nonoverlapping expression of Olig3 and Olig2 in the embryonic neural tube. *Mech. Dev.* **113**, 169–174.

19

Neural Crest Cells

Paul A. Trainor, Marianne Bronner-Fraser, and Robb Krumlauf

Neural crest cells are a migratory cell population that produces a range of differentiation fates including neurons, glia, cartilage, bone, pigment cells, and connective tissue during embryonic development. Neural crest cell patterning is achieved through a combination of cell intrinsic information acquired in the neural tube during their formation and cell extrinsic events, which influence their subsequent migration and differentiation. Neural crest cells are remarkably plastic; combined with their multipotency and limited capacity for self-renewal, they exhibit many of the hallmarks of stem cells. Stem cells are regarded as self-renewing progenitor cells that can generate one or more specialized cell types. The major issues in stem cell biology concern the determination of "stemness" (i.e., the capacity for self-renewal) and how distinct derivatives are generated from the same stem cell population, whether by cell-intrinsic or cell-extrinsic cues. These same issues have been the focus of the neural crest field for decades, and our knowledge of neural crest cell development can therefore contribute a great deal to the understanding of stem cell patterning. In this chapter, we describe recent advances in our understanding of neural crest cell formation and patterning in relation to stem cells, which has important implications for stem cell therapy and tissue engineering.

Introduction

During vertebrate development, the central nervous system (CNS) arises from a group of neuroepithelial cells that originate from the ectodermal germ layer. Though originally a flat "neural plate" in the midline of the embryo, these cells subsequently invaginate to form a "neural tube" that runs along the body axis from head to tail. The neural tube is initially composed of a single layer of cells. However, as development proceeds and extensive cell division occurs, the neural tube becomes multilayered, with precursor cells dividing in the medial portion of the neural tube adjacent to the central cavity, termed ventricles in the head. This region becomes the "ventricular zone" and contains dividing progenitors, including neural stem cells. After cells complete their terminal mitoses and generate neuroblasts or glioblasts, they move laterally and

subsequently differentiate into a multitude of neurons and support cells. The neural tube expands in the head to form the brain and in the trunk to form the spinal cord. Thus, the neural tube generates the entire vertebrate CNS.

The vertebrate peripheral nervous system derives from two sources: the neural crest and the ectodermal placodes. Both cell populations are migratory, form at the border between neural plate and nonneural ectoderm, and generate some identical derivatives such as sensory neurons. However, placodes are confined to the head, and neural crest cells form along the whole rostrocaudal axis. Neural crest cells delaminate from the neural tube and migrate extensively (Fig. 19–1) to form sensory and autonomic neurons, neuroendocrine cells, glia, and melanocytes. In addition, they produce smooth muscle, dermis, cartilage, dentine, and bone (Fig.19–2). Placodes are discrete regions of thickened columnar epithelium on the head that ingress to form portions of cranial ganglia and sense organs.

Neural crest cells first become morphologically detectable when they emigrate from the neural tube, undergoing an epithelial to mesenchymal conversion to form a migrating cell population (Fig. 19–1). However, they are initially part of the dorsal neural tube itself. This leads to the intriguing question of how neural crest cells form and become different from other neural tube cells. Cell lineage studies have demonstrated that a single neuroepithelial cell in the dorsal neural tube can produce migrating neural crest cells that form multiple differentiated cell types as disparate as sympathetic ganglion cells, sensory ganglion cells, and melanocytes.[1] Thus, the original precursor was "multipotent" with respect to its potential to form neural crest derivatives. Interestingly, the same cell can contribute not only to the neural crest but also to dorsal neural tube–derived cells, including sensory interneurons and roof plate cells.[1] This result reveals that a cell in the dorsal neural tube is not only a neural crest cell precursor but also a neural tube precursor, suggesting a shared lineage between the neural tube and the neural crest. Furthermore, when a notochord was grafted adjacent to the dorsal neural tube in combination with lineage analysis, neural crest derivatives plus both dorsal and ventral neural tube derivatives were found to arise from the same clone.[2] This raises the intriguing possibility that what is often referred to as a "premigratory neural crest cell" in the dorsal neural tube actually represents a neural stem cell with broad potential to form both peripheral and central nervous system derivatives and possibly nonneuronal cells (such as pigment cells).

Formation and Migration of Neural Crest Cells

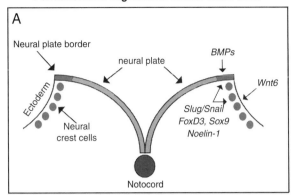

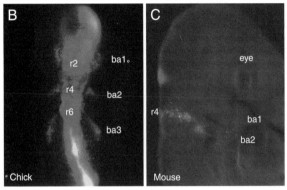

Figure 19-1. *Neural crest cell formation and migration.* (A) Neural crest cells are generated at the neural plate border, the junction between the neural plate and surface ectoderm. Both the surface ectoderm through Wnt6 and the neural plate through BMPs can induce neural crest cell formation. It remains to be determined whether Wnt and BMP signaling act during neural crest induction synergistically or independently to generate individual lineages within the neural crest. During their formation, neural crest cells express the transcriptional repressors Snail/Slug, which regulate the epithelial to mesenchymal transition and delamination of neural crest cells from the neural tube. Numerous genes, including Foxd3, Sox9, and Noelin-1, are also expressed in either the premigratory or the migratory neural crest cells. Cranial neural crest cells in (B) chick and (C) mouse embryos migrate ventrolaterally in discrete, segregated streams from specific rhombomeres (r) in the neural tube into the adjacent branchial arches (ba). (See color plate 1.)

Neural Crest Derivatives

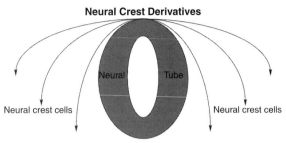

Cell type and tissue contributions

Sensory neurons	Spinal ganglia
Cholinergic neurons	Thyroid gland
Adrenergic neurons	Ultimobranchial body
Rohon-Beard cells	Adrenal gland
Schwann cells	Teeth
Glial cells	Dentine
Chromaffin cells	Connective tissue
Parafollicular cells	Adipose tissue
Calcitonin producing cells	Smooth muscles
Melanocytes	Cardiac septa
Chondroblasts, chondrocytes	Dermis
Osteoblasts, osteocytes	Cornea
Odontoblasts	Endothelia
Fibroblasts	Adipocytes
Cardiac mesenchyme	Mesenchymal cells
Striated myoblasts	Smooth myoblasts

Figure 19-2. *Neural crest cell derivatives.* Neural crest cells are a multipotent population derived from the dorsal edge of the neural tube that migrates extensively and generates an array of distinct cell fates specific for their axial origins. The primary difference between cranial and trunk neural crest cells is the ability of cranial neural crest cells to produce hard mesenchymal tissues such as bone, cartilage, and the odontoblasts of the teeth. Stem cells are a self-renewing pluripotent cell population, and hence, neural crest cells exhibit many of the hallmarks of a stem cell population. (See color plate 2.)

tube, can become neural crest cells if given appropriate signals. Such experiments reveal the remarkable flexibility in cell fates displayed by the vertebrate nervous system during development.

Induction of the Neural Crest

Although the first morphological evidence of the neural crest as a separate population occurs as these cells initiate migration, a variety of molecular markers are expressed at the border of the neural and nonneural ectoderm in a region that fate-maps to the formation of neural crest (Fig. 19-1A). For example, the zinc-finger transcription factor, Slug, is one of the earliest known neural crest markers[8] and is expressed in the neural folds as they elevate and close to form the neural tube. A variety of other transcription factors, including *Sox9*, *Foxd3*,[9,10] and various members of the *Zic*, *Msx*, and *Pax* gene families are known to be expressed in neural crest cells and are important for neural crest specification (reviewed by LaBonne and Bronner-Fraser[11]). Furthermore, a genomics approach has recently been used to characterize a variety of genes expressed in newly induced neural crest cells, presenting a molecular profile of less than 100 genes that are up-regulated with induction of this cell population.[12] Thus, combinations of multiple genes functioning cooperatively are necessary to generate the neural crest forming ability.

Even migrating neural crest cells labeled after they have left the neural tube have the capacity to contribute to multiple neural crest lineages.[3] Cultured neural crest cells from mammalian embryos are multipotent and have the capacity to self-renew, at least for a limited time.[4] Thus, migratory neural crest cells retain stem cell properties (see later sections).

After leaving the neural tube, neural crest cells do not normally contribute to the CNS. However, even migrating neural crest cells can adopt the fates of their neighbors after engraftment into the ventral neural tube, forming floor plate and motor neurons.[5] Similarly, neural tube-derived cells from older embryos will migrate and differentiate into neural crest cell derivatives after transplantation onto neural crest cell migration pathways.[6,7] Thus, it seems that many cells, likely those within the ventricular zone of the neural

How then does the neural crest become induced at the border between the neural plate and the nonneural ectoderm? There is increasing evidence suggesting that induction of this population occurs well before the process of neural tube closure and may likely initiate during gastrulation. Neural crest induction appears to occur through a tissue interaction between the neural plate (presumptive CNS) and nonneural ectoderm (presumptive epidermis) (see Fig. 19–1A). Rollhäuser-terHorst[13] and more recently Moury and Jacobson[14] juxtaposed presumptive epidermis and neural plate in Urodeles and found that neural crest cells were generated *de novo*. In avian embryos, similar juxtaposition of nonneural ectoderm and early neural plate tissue also induces the formation of neural crest cells.[15] This can occur with neural plate tissue taken from early stages (stage 4) just after neural plate formation, as well as with later stage intermediate neural plate derived from the closing neural plate (stage 10). The neural plate is competent to respond to neural crest induction during a restricted period of time, declining precipitously after the 10 somite stage.[16] Later neural plate plus epidermis, but not early neural plate plus epidermis, expresses dorsal neural tube markers such as *Wnt1* and *Wnt3a* in addition to neural crest markers.[17] Furthermore, the addition of bone morphogenetic proteins (BMPs) to neural plates neurons at stages after the neural plate has lost competence to form neural crest cells leads to differentiation of different populations of dorsal sensory neurons.[18]

Little is known about what factors render the neural plate and neural tube competent to respond to neural crest-inducing factors. One glycoprotein, called Noelin-1, may be a competence factor, because it appears to have the ability to prolong neural crest production.[19] Initially, *Noelin-1* is expressed in a graded pattern in the closing neural tube, but it subsequently becomes restricted to the dorsal neural folds and migrating neural crest. Overexpression of *Noelin-1* causes an excess of neural crest emigration and extends the time that the neural tube is competent to generate as well as to regenerate neural crest cells *in vivo*. Thus, *Noelin-1* may play a role in regulating the production of neural crest cells by the neural tube.

The molecular basis of neural crest induction is beginning to be understood. This inductive interaction requires both a source of inducer (the ectoderm) and a competent receiving tissue (the neural plate). Several molecules have been implicated in neural crest cell formation, including members of the TGF-β superfamily (dorsalin, BMP4), fibroblast growth factors (FGFs), and, more recently, Wnts. Neural crest-inducing ability was first demonstrated for Dorsalin-1,[20] which is able to induce neural crest cells from naïve neural plates *in vitro*, and hence, to substitute for nonneural ectoderm. However, it is expressed transiently and relatively late in the neural tube, ruling out a role in initial neural crest induction at the neural plate border. Subsequently, Liem *et al.*[18] showed that BMP4 can induce the formation of neural crest cells from neural plate explants *in vitro* in the presence of N2/F12 medium. A complication is that BMP4 is expressed transiently in the ectoderm flanking the neural plate and is then down-regulated

from the ectoderm and up-regulated in the neural folds and dorsal neural tube.[21,22] Furthermore, blocking BMP signaling has no effect on neural crest formation prior to the elevation of the neural folds, when BMP is no longer expressed in the ectoderm.[23] This suggests that BMPs function in the neural folds or the dorsal neural tube, playing a secondary role in maintaining an already induced neural crest population rather than in the induction process itself.

In *Xenopus*, FGFs play a role in the neural crest induction cascade,[24] inducing neural crest markers in neuralized animal caps.[25] Conversely, dominant negative FGF receptor (dnFgfr) inhibits neural crest formation without affecting formation of the neural plate.[26] However, embryos overexpressing a dominant negative FGF receptor have normal neural crest derivatives.[27,28] One possibility is that FGF signals influence neural crest formation indirectly by functioning through the Wnt pathway.[29]

Wnt genes have recently come to the forefront as playing important roles in neural crest cell induction.[21,29,30] In *Xenopus*, *Wnt1* and *Wnt3a* dramatically increase the number of neural crest cells when injected into the embryo or introduced into neuralized animal caps. A complication is that *Wnt1* and *Wnt3a* are expressed in the dorsal neural tube only after neural tube closure. However, other Wnts may be expressed in the mesoderm underlying the neural folds. In avian embryos, a dominant negative Wnt construct (dnWnt) blocks neural crest formation when introduced at the neural plate border or into the closing neural tube. This suggests that a Wnt or Wnts are necessary for both early neural crest induction and later maintenance of the population. Furthermore, the addition of a soluble form of Wnt is sufficient to induce neural crest cells in naïve neural plate tissue in a defined saline medium with no other additives. In contrast, BMP4 can only induce neural crest in a medium supplemented with other growth factors (N2/F12, which contains insulin-like and other growth factors). Importantly, *Wnt6* is expressed in the ectoderm adjacent to the open neural plate, neural folds, and closed neural tube (Fig. 19–1A). Thus, it has the correct spatial and temporal expression pattern in the ectoderm to mediate neural crest induction. These results show that Wnts are both necessary and sufficient to account for the induction of neural crest in the avian embryo at the open neural plate stage.[21]

It is clear from the experiments referenced here that neural crest induction is likely to occur using multiple factors that operate sequentially and sometimes cooperatively. Although it has been assumed that neural crest induction has an endpoint (i.e., when the neural plate can no longer responds to inductive signals to form neural crest), progenitors with neural crest-forming ability persist in the ventricular zone through embryogenesis and perhaps into adulthood. Similar to the endpoint, little is known about when and how the process of neural crest induction begins. Although it has been assumed that this occurs at the open neural plate stage, there is increasing evidence to suggest that neural crest induction may initiate during gastrulation. Furthermore, there may be important species differences that need to be explored and explained to obtain an encompassing picture of the molecular mechanisms underlying this fascinating process.

Axial Patterning and Plasticity of Neural Crest Cells

Neural crest cell derivatives generate a variety of cell types and structures along the anterior–posterior (A–P) axis of the vertebrate embryo (Fig. 19–2). This raises the issue of how and when they acquire different regional characteristics. Gene expression studies have shown that the *Hox* family of transcription factors display ordered and nested domains of expression in cranial and trunk neural crest cells as they migrate from the neural tube.[31,32] Based on the highly conserved roles of *Hox* genes in the regulation of axial pattering and the specification of regional identity in many animal tissues and species (reviewed by McGinnis and Krumlauf [33,34]), it has been postulated that *Hox* expression provides a combinatorial code that specifies the A–P character of neural crest cells.[31,32,35] Gain- and loss-of-function experiments in several vertebrates have confirmed this hypothesis and highlighted the critical role *Hox* genes play in patterning neural crest cells.[36,37]

The best evidence for primary roles of *Hox* genes in regulating the A–P identity of neural crest cells is seen in cranial regions. At the level of the hindbrain, the vertebrate CNS is organized into a series of lineage-restricted segmental units, called rhombomeres.[38] The formation of these segments is part of a fundamental mechanism that allows adjacent cell populations in the hindbrain to separate from each other, receive local signals, and adopt unique identities from their neighbors. Each rhombomere generates a unique part of the mature adult CNS. This segmental organization is also important for establishing the proper patterns of cranial neural crest cell formation and their pathways of migration.[39–44] There are three main streams of cranial neural crest cells that emigrate from rhombomeres: r1–r2, r4, and r6 into the first, second, and third branchial arches, respectively (Fig. 19–1B and C; Fig. 19–3). Segments r3 and r5 generate fewer migratory neural crest cells than the adjacent even-numbered rhombomeres, partly because of inhibitory signals generated by interactions between r3, r5, and surrounding tissues.[39,45] The neural crest cells that do arise from r3 and r5 migrate in rostral or caudal directions to join the three main streams of cells emerging from r1–r2, r4, and r6.[39,40] Transposition experiments in mouse and chick embryos have demonstrated that restrictive signals in the arch environment create crest-free zones adjacent to r3 and r5 by preventing infilling from other migrating crest cell populations.[39,45–47] This underscores the importance of tissue interactions and environmental signals in modulating the induction and migration of cranial neural crest cells.

The nature of the signals that restrict the ability of r3 and r5 to generate neural crest cells or inhibit their migration are largely unknown. BMP4 and Wnt signaling has been shown to influence the survival of neural crest cells generated by r3 and r5 in the chick;[43,44,48] however, this process does not appear to function in the mouse.[39] The transient segmental patterns of

apoptosis over r3 and r5 in the chick may therefore represent a species-specific phenomenon. In the chick, neural crest cells emigrate after closure of the neural tube; in the mouse, they emerge at neural groove stages before closure.[41] It may be important to clear cells positioned between the surface ectoderm and neural tube, which are unable to successfully migrate into the periphery, as they could disrupt signaling between these tissues. In fact, inhibiting odd-numbered rhombomere apoptosis in chick embryos leads to atavistic muscle attachment sites.[49] Analysis of cell movements in *ErbB4* mouse mutants using cell grafting, lineage tracing, and whole embryo culture has revealed that *ErbB4* is essential for restricting the infilling of migratory neural crest cells derived from r4 into the region adjacent to r3 (Fig. 19–3).[47] Intriguingly, this *ErbB4*-dependent defect in crest migration has been shown to be nonautonomous.[47] Wild-type cells grafted into r4 of *ErbB4* mutants undergo abnormal migration and move rostrally into the territory adjacent to r3. *ErbB4* itself is expressed in r3 and not in the adjacent arch environment, and its neuregulin receptor is active in r4. This implies that the loss of *ErbB4* in r3 alters interactions between r3 and the surrounding tissues, such that some inhibitory cues are not properly generated. In more lateral regions, blocking Eph receptor signaling has been shown to perturb neural crest migration, indicating it is coupled to the regulation of crest cell movements[50] (Fig. 19–3).

Mice containing targeted mutations in *Hox* genes have defects in cranial neural crest derivatives. *Hoxa2* is expressed in crest cells emigrating from r4 into the second branchial arch.[32,51] Homozygous null mutants of *Hoxa2* have a respecification of second arch elements toward a first arch identity in the absence of any segmental defects in r4 itself.[52–54] Consistent with this, knock down of expression of *Hoxa2* in combination with *Hoxb2* in zebra fish also transforms second arch neural crest derivatives to a first arch identity.[55] Conversely, ectopic expression of *Hoxa2* in more anterior cranial crest cells of several vertebrates leads to the transformation of first arch structures posteriorly toward a second arch identity.[56–58] This demonstrates the role of *Hoxa2* as a homeotic selector gene involved in the specification of cranial neural crest cells into a second arch fate. Neural crest defects have been detected in other *Hox* mutants, confirming that *Hox* genes generate a combinatorial code for A–P patterning of cranial crest populations.[36,37,59] With respect to neural crest cells generated in the trunk, there is little insight into whether *Hox* genes directly pattern their properties. This may reflect that *Hox* genes regulate the positional identity of somites and their derivatives;[34,37,60] hence, the majority of the analyses of *Hox* mutants has concentrated on defects in somites and vertebrate. Conditional mutations of *Hox* genes in the neural tube and neural crest would be helpful in probing roles for these genes in the head-versus-trunk neural crest cells.

The phenotypes observed by alteration of *Hoxa2* suggest a primary role for *Hoxa2* directly in the crest cells, as opposed to indirect influences mediated by changes in regional identity of r4 before the cells migrate. Regulatory analysis of *Hoxa2* expression in transgenic mice has shown that distinct *cis*

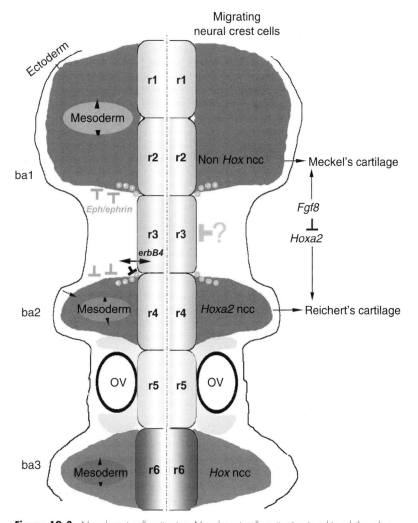

Figure 19-3. *Neural crest cell patterning.* Neural crest cells patterning is achieved through a combination of the information acquired in the neural tube during their formation and the influence of the environmental tissues they contact during their migration and differentiation. Interestingly, neural crest cells, mesoderm, ectoderm, and endoderm derived from the same axial level contribute to the formation of the same branchial arch (ba) in a conserved pattern. The mesoderm forms the myogenic cores of the branchial arches, which are enveloped by neural crest cells and are then surrounded by the surface ectoderm and endoderm. The cranial mesoderm is involved in maintaining the anterior–posterior character of migrating neural crest cells. The endoderm and ectoderm, respectively, influence neural crest cell differentiation into skeletogenic and tooth derivatives. It is important to note that *Hox* genes are not expressed in the first branchial arch, where Meckel's cartilage is one of the primary derivatives. In contrast, the second arch, which generates Reichert's cartilage, does express *Hox* genes; *Hoxa2* in particular is the primary determinant of second arch fate. In experiments in which *Hoxa2* is suppressed in the first arch either by null mutation or by ectopic sources of *FGf8*, such as the isthmus, the second arch identity is transformed into that of a first arch. Conversely, when *Hoxa2* is overexpressed in the first arch, its identity is transformed into that of a second arch. Therefore, it is crucial to keep *Hox*-expressing neural crest cells segregated from non–*Hox*-expressing neural crest cells. This is achieved through *ErbB4* signaling from the neural tube with Eph and ephrin signaling as well as yet unidentified signals, which restrict the lateral migration of neural crest cells from rhombomeres (r) 3 and 5. (See color plate 3.)

elements direct expression in the neural crest cells and hindbrain segments.[51] Further support for the independent specification of regional identity in neural crest cells and hindbrain segments comes from defects seen in *Hoxb1* and *Hoxa1* mutant mice. Mutation of *Hoxb1*, which is segmentally expressed in r4,[61] transforms r4 to an r2-like character, but neural crest elements in the second branchial arch are unaffected.[62–64] In *Hoxa1* mutants, minor hypoplasias in some neural crest–derived elements have been attributed to segmentation defects in the hindbrain that result in the loss of r5, a reduction of r4, and a misplaced otocyst, all of which could alter neural crest migration.[65–67] However the majority of the second arch crest-derived elements are not affected in *Hoxa1* mutants. Recent lineage-tracing studies have shown a dramatically reduced level of neural crest cell migration from r4 in *Hoxa1* mutants.[68] The reduced number of crest cells from r4 appears to be compensated for in later developmental stages, as the number of cells in the second arch and patterning of its elements are similar to wild-type animals later in gestation. This illustrates the regulative ability of neural crest cells and shows that a fixed number of early migrating cells are not essential to generate normally patterned structures.

In *Hoxb1* and *Hoxa1* double mutants, there is a complete loss of second arch neural crest–derived structures, even though these components were unaffected in the single mutants.[64,68–70] These defects could arise through effects on the neural crest itself or other tissues in which these genes are expressed (CNS, mesoderm, surface ectoderm, and endoderm). Compound mutants in which *Hoxb1* and *Hoxa1* were selectively eliminated together only in the CNS by targeted disruption of control regions demonstrated that the defects in second arch crest cells arise from a failure in neural crest formation.[68] In the absence of *Hoxb1* and *Hoxa1*, cells in r4 fail to adopt any regional character and are unable to respond to local signals that induce the formation of migratory neural crest. Cells from wild-type embryos grafted into these mutants are capable of generating neural crest cells, showing that the appropriate inductive signals are in the double mutants.[68] This is surprising because it is generally assumed that the events leading to the induction of crest from the midbrain to spinal cord regions (see "Induction of the Neural Crest") are not dependent upon the establishment of specific A–P characters. However, the genetic data in the mouse illustrates that there is a synergy between *Hoxa1* and *Hoxb1* in regional control of neural crest formation and implies that A–P patterning and induction of neural crest must be coupled in some manner. It will be important to determine whether this applies along the entire A–P axis. In the *Hoxa1–Hoxb1* double mutants, it is interesting that expression of markers for placodes (*Ngn2*), pharyngeal pouches (*Pax1*) and surface ectoderm signaling systems (*Fgf8, Fgf3, Shh,* and *Bmp7*) are properly activated in the absence of crest formation and migration into the second branchial arch.[68] Similar results are seen upon surgical ablation of crest cells in the chick embryo.[71] These results imply that interactions with and signals from the neural crest cells are not necessary to initiate localized expression of these components or to set up the A–P and proximal–distal regionalization of the branchial arches.

One of the most intriguing questions in neural crest cell biology relates to the timing and cell autonomy of the regulatory programs that govern the differentiation and patterning of this pluripotential population. In the trunk, the somites are the major segmental building blocks of bone and connective tissue. However, in the head, this role is taken over by the cranial neural crest cells, and there has been great interest in the nature of the patterning information that directs their morphogenesis during craniofacial development. Landmark transposition experiments in avian embryos by Noden[72] provided evidence that cranial neural crest cells might contain a prepattern before they emigrate from the neural tube. When neural crest primordia from the first branchial arch are grafted more posteriorly in place of those for the second or third branchial arches, crest cells are generated by the grafted tissue, and they migrate into the arch immediately adjacent to the graft.[72] Hence, they are not attracted back to their normal first arch environment. The surprising finding in such transpositions is that the neural crest cells derived from the grafted tissue differentiate into ectopic proximal first arch skeletal elements. The muscle cell types and attachments are also characteristic of those in the first arch. The generation of duplicated first-arch structures in an ectopic environment suggests a model in which neural crest cells possess a program that prepatterns their morphogenesis and sends spatial information to other cell types and tissues in the arch.

This research focused attention on the early patterning mechanisms established in the midbrain and hindbrain before emigration of neural crest cells. Based on the patterns of gene expression in hindbrain segments and on cranial neural crest[31,32,61] and craniofacial defects in targeted *Hox* mutants,[34,35,37,38] the *Hox* family of transcription factors appeared to be logical candidates for participating in any potential prepatterning mechanism for neural crest. However, analysis of *Hoxa2* neural crest expression demonstrated that this domain is generated by *cis* elements separate from those involved in modulating rhombomeric expression in the hindbrain.[51] Therefore, the expression domain of *Hoxa2* critical for patterning the second brachial arch is not established first in the hindbrain and then passively maintained in the neural crest cells during migration. New signals and inputs are required to activate *Hoxa2* in neural crest cells as they delaminate. One of these components is a member of the *AP2* transcription factor family.[51] *AP2* genes are globally expressed in migrating neural crest cells and play diverse functional roles in their development.[73–75] Therefore, other factors must restrict the activation of *Hoxa2* anterior to the second branchial arch and integrate environmental signals from the arches that modulate neural crest cell expression.[51,76,77]

Furthermore, an extensive series of transposition, ablation, and regeneration experiments in chick embryos have revealed context- and time-dependent influences on the ability to establish, maintain, and reprogram *Hox* expression in rhombomeres and cranial neural crest cells.[47,76,78–97] Some of these experiments are supportive of the prepatterning model and cell autonomy of *Hox* expression; other analyses; strongly argue for plasticity in crest patterning and *Hox* expression. Recent experiments aimed at resolving these conflicting points of view have begun to clarify this issue of autonomy versus plasticity. Transposing single or small numbers of rhombomeric cells from one segment into an ectopic segmental location in mouse[96] or zebra fish[91] embryos clearly demonstrates plasticity and reprogramming of *Hox* gene expression (reviewed by Trainor et al.[36,76]). This work shows that cells within the hindbrain are continually assessing their environment and that they maintain the ability to change their fate in response to signals in ectopic segmental locations. Interestingly, this plasticity can be masked when larger groups of cells are transposed, indicating there are community effects or interactions between the host and grafted cells that modulate cell fate.[36,96] If sufficient numbers of cells are transposed to an ectopic location, they can reinforce each other and maintain their original A–P character. Such community effects would therefore explain data arguing for autonomy of *Hox* expression and prepatterning when entire rhombomeres or groups of segments were grafted.[36,76,83,86,88,94,97] Cell–cell interactions in the grafted tissue would maintain expression in ectopic locations, giving the impression of cell autonomy. This plasticity in rhombomeric and CNS cells means that critical A–P patterning programs are established at these stages but that these programs have the ability to be altered by environmental signals.

In the transpositions of small groups of cells, the patterns of *Hox* expression in migrating cranial neural crest cells derived from the graft were found to be completely plastic.[36,76,91,96] Neural crest cells failed to initiate expression appropriate to their axial level of origin, and when migratory neural crest cells from one arch were transposed to another, they rapidly down-regulated their *Hox* expression.[96] Therefore, in an ectopic arch environment, cranial neural crest cells are unable to initiate or maintain their proper A–P patterning program based on restricted *Hox* expression. However, when neural crest cells from the second branchial arch were grafted into the first arch environment in combination with second arch mesoderm, the neural crest cells maintained their original patterns of *Hox* expression.[96] This demonstrates that signals from the head mesoderm in the second arch help r4-derived neural crest cells establish or maintain their proper genetic program of positional identity (see Fig. 19–3). The mesodermal signals appear to be permissive rather than instructive, as neural crest cells from other arches that interact with mesoderm from the second branchial arch do not change their fate.

There is an interesting difference in the plasticity of cranial neural crest cells and rhombomeric cells. When transposed along the A–P axis, rhombomeric cells will either maintain their original identity or adopt that of their new location depending upon the community effects.[91,96] However, transposed cranial neural crest cells in mice and zebra fish fail to activate their normal patterns of *Hox* expression; consequently, they are able to contribute to structures in the branchial arches, indicating they are not simply eliminated by cell death.[91] These results suggest that although cranial neural crest cell precursors may be programmed in the hindbrain before emigration, they are still competent to receive signals from mesoderm or other tissues (ectoderm and endoderm) in their prospective branchial arch. This enables them to adopt the proper regional identity.

The plasticity or lack of prepatterning for *Hox* expression in cranial neural crest cells raises the question of how ectopic first-arch structures can be generated in transposition experiments.[72] Community effects may play a role in preserving the original A–P character, as these experiments were done with large blocks of tissues. However, another contributing factor

appears to be the influence of the organizing tissues such as the isthmus, which expresses *Fgf8*.[98] In transpositions of presumptive first-arch neural crest primordia, the rostral limit of the grafted tissue generally extends to the isthmus (midbrain–hindbrain junction). The isthmus acts as an organizing center and through *Fgf8* is able to induce regional midbrain identities in ectopic locations.[98–101] Recent experiments performing transpositions of first arch crest primordia with and without the isthmus have demonstrated that duplicated first-arch structures are only detected in grafts that contained the isthmus.[102] Isthmus grafts express *Fgf8* among many other factors, which in turn represses *Hoxa2* expression in neural crest cells, thereby generating a first arch fate.[36,102] Hence, in contrast to prepatterning, these results suggests a model in which ectopic first-arch structures arise because the grafts contain a regional signal that patterns crest and the crest cells are capable of responding to that signal. This again points to the critical role for environmental influences in elaborating the distinct programs of regional identity in cranial neural crest.[36,39,76,97,102] Therefore, neural crest cell patterning relies on a balance between signals acquired in the neuroepithelium during their formation and their competency to respond to environmental signals they receive from the tissues they contact during their migration and differentiation.

There is amazing morphological diversity in vertebrate craniofacial development, even though many common mechanisms underlie head patterning. What are the tissues and signals that contribute to this diversity? Recent experiments have illustrated that neural crest cells are an important source of information that can modulate interspecies variation in head derivatives.[103] As described previously, a program for specifying A–P patterning and regional identity is established in the hindbrain before crest cells emigrate, and this pathway is elaborated by appropriate signals in the surrounding arch environment. By exchanging the same presumptive neural crest primordia for an arch between ducks and quails, Schneider and Helms[103] have demonstrated through interspecies transplantations that differences in beak morphology correlate with species-specific neural crest cell programs. Hence, in these species, the donor neural crest primordia have established an autonomous program for a distinct morphology that will respond to evolutionary conserved signals in the host environment. This elegantly illustrates the importance of establishing fine-grained genetic programs in the CNS that can be modulated for evolutionary diversity.

Neural Crest and Stem Cells

Stem cells are defined as clonogenic self-renewing progenitor cells that can generate one or more specialized cell types.[104] Classically in vertebrates, there are two distinct groups of stem cells. The first group consists solely of embryonic stem (ES) cells, derived from the inner cell mass of the blastocyst. ES cells are totipotent and capable of generating all the differentiated cell types in the body. The second group consists of organ- or tissue-specific stem cells, which are derivatives of

ES cells. These stem cells are multipotent rather than totipotent and construct tissues and organs *de novo*. In adults, they maintain continuous cellular turnover and provide regenerative capacity in certain tissues. The phenotypic example of the second group is the hematopoietic stem cell, which generates all the cell types that make up the blood and immune systems.

A cardinal feature of stem cells is their ability to self-renew, that is, to divide so that each produces at least one daughter cell that maintains the multipotent character of its parent.[105] Probably the most important question in stem cell biology today is, What determines the self-renewing capacity? Studies of stem cell self-renewal require the identification of factors that promote stem cell division. It is possible that single growth factors promote cell division and maintain the stem cell state. However, not all factors that make stem cells divide are self-renewal factors. They could, for example, promote differentiation. Conversely, there could be factors that maintain the stem cell state but do not promote cell division.[104] One such example is Notch signaling, which can maintain neuroepithelial progenitors in a multipotent state without influencing proliferation (reviewed by Artavanis-Tsakonas *et al.*[106]). The maintenance of stem cell state or character therefore involves at least three distinct functions. First, there must be an inhibition of overt differentiation. Second, there has to be maintenance of proliferative capacity. Third, there needs to be maintenance of multipotency.

The other major issues being addressed in stem cell biology concern the differentiation of stem cells. For instance, how do stem cells choose their fates? To what degree do intrinsic cell autonomous programs versus extrinsic environmental signals influence lineage fate choices and specification? Are stem cells and their properties fixed and unchangeable, or are they plastic and adaptable? Stem cells *in vivo* are likely to encounter multiple simultaneous instructive signals. How do they interpret this information? Many of these issues have been tackled in great depth by the neural crest cell community during the past two decades, and interestingly, there are substantial similarities between neural crest cells and stem cells. Our knowledge of neural crest cell patterning therefore has a lot to offer toward understanding stem cell development and regulation, particularly in the area of cell-intrinsic versus cell-extrinsic regulation and specification of cell lineage and fate. Neural crest cell development is regulated by the interplay of intrinsic or autonomous signals received during their formation in the neural tube, balanced with the extrinsic environmental signals that they receive during their migration, which ultimately determines neural crest cell fate.

Neural crest cells are a multipotent embryonic migratory cell population, which give rise to a range of fates.[107] With a limited capacity for self-renewal, neural crest cells are regarded as stem cells or stem cell–like. The neural crest has been an attractive system for investigating the mechanisms underlying cell lineage specification, and one of the major issues in the field concerns how an apparently homogeneous population of nondifferentiated cells becomes channeled into distinct developmental pathways. As explained previously,

neural crest cells exhibit an inherent plasticity or flexibility, which incidentally is one of the hallmarks of stems cells.

Multipotent, self-renewing neural crest stem cell progenitors of autonomic neurons and glia were first identified in the peripheral nervous system by *in vitro* subcloning experiments.[108] Neural crest stem cells do not generally generate sensory neurons and therefore contribute to only a subset of neural crest derivatives *in vivo*.[42,108] It's important to note the clear distinction in the differentiation ability of cranial versus trunk neural crest cells. *In vivo*, cranial neural crest cells generate cartilage, bone, and connective tissue, among many other cell types; trunk neural crest cells do not. Therefore, these neural crest stem cells are probably representative only of trunk and not of cranial neural crest stem cells. One would expect cranial neural crest stem cells to exhibit a wider differentiative capacity. Nonetheless, the differentiation of neural crest stem cells can be promoted by specific instructive extracellular signals. Neuregulin-1 promotes Schwann cell differentiation, BMP2/4 promotes autonomic neuronal and smooth muscle, and TGF-β promotes smooth muscle differentiation (Fig. 19–4).[109,110] In the peripheral nervous system, Notch signaling can restrict neural crest stem cell differentiation to nonneural fates while concomitantly promoting gliogenesis.[105] The inhibition of neuronal differentiation does not necessarily maintain multipotency, which is indicative of a requirement for other genes in this process.

Sox10 is one gene that could fulfill such a role. *Sox10* is expressed initially in early migrating neural crest cells and is maintained in satellite glia and Schwann cell precursors (Fig. 19–4). At the same time, it is down-regulated in neuronal derivatives.[111] Excess BMP2 or TGF-β down-regulates *Sox10* in neural crest stem cells, which is believed to mimic the normal process of lineage restriction during neural crest cell development. Conversely, the constitutive expression of *Sox10* in neural crest stem cells prevents BMP2 and TGF-β from extinguishing gliogenic potential.[112] *Sox10* therefore maintains the neurogenic potential of neural crest stem cells. Additionally, *Sox10* has been shown to inhibit proliferative arrest in neural crest stem cells, and it is critical for the induction of the transcriptional determinants of autonomic neurogenesis.[113] Given this combination of functions, the role of *Sox10* in neural crest stem cells therefore seems to be synonymous with maintenance of the stem cell state. This, however, raises the issue of whether other Sox proteins contribute to the maintenance of tissue-specific stem cell properties.

The *Sox* genes are a large family of transcriptional regulators that contain a conserved high mobility group, DNA-binding domain.[114] *Sox2* is particularly notable because it is expressed in the first stem cell populations within the early mouse embryo, namely, the inner cell mass cells of the blastocysts from which ES cells are derived. Interestingly, *Sox2* is also expressed in the uncommitted dividing stem cells and precursor cells of the developing fetal and adult CNSs, which suggests a potential role for *Sox2* in maintaining stem cell character.[115–117] Unlike *Sox10*, *Sox2* is not expressed in migrating neural crest cells, and although it may not be a neural crest stem cell marker, it could be a more general stem cell marker.

Stem Cell Maintenance and Differentiation

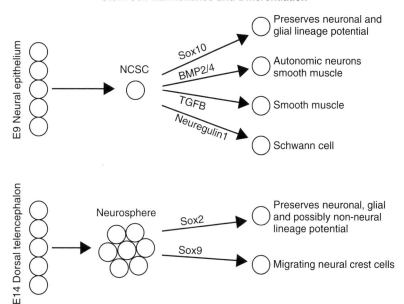

Figure 19–4. *Stem cells maintenance and differentiation.* Neural crest stem cells (NCSC) can be isolated from embryonic day (E) 9 neural epithelium, and their subsequent differentiation can be regulated by several cell extrinsic factors *in vitro. Sox10* preserves neuronal and glial lineage potential in neural crest stem cells; BMP2/4 promotes autonomic neuron and smooth muscle differentiation. TGF-β also promotes smooth muscle differentiation, in contrast to Neuregulin, which regulates Schwann cell differentiation. Neurospheres can also be generated from E14 dorsal telencephalons, in which case, *Sox2* appears to be able to preserve neuronal glial and possibly non-neural lineage potential. High-level *Sox2*-expressing neurospheres maintain their undifferentiated state and exhibit a reduced capacity to generate neural crest cells when transplanted into the murine neural plates at the time of neural crest cell formation. In contrast, *Sox9* promotes the differentiation of neurospheres into migrating neural crest cells when low-level *Sox2*-expressing neurospheres are grafted into the neural plates of E8 mouse embryos. The *Sox* gene family may therefore regulate the transition of a stem cell from totipotent to multipotent.

In clonal density assays of cells isolated from the embryonic dorsal telencephalon either expressing or not expressing *Sox2*, only *Sox2*-expressing cells divided and generated secondary neurospheres. No secondary neurospheres were obtained from cells lacking *Sox2,* which is suggestive of *Sox2* playing a crucial role in the self-renewal capacity exhibited by neural stem cells. In differentiation assays, low-level *Sox2*-expressing neural stem cells primarily undergo gliogenesis. In contrast, neural stem cells selected for high levels of *Sox2* primarily produce neurons and radial glia, implying that high levels of *Sox2* are important for the self-renewal of stem cells and may define a stem cell type within the CNS. *Sox2* therefore may be crucial not only for the establishment but also for the maintenance of the undifferentiated neural stem cell state.[118]

Given the obvious similarities between stem cells and neural crest cells, an important issue to be addressed is whether neural stem cells can generate or regenerate migrating cranial neural crest cells *in vivo* by transplantation into the vertebrate embryonic neural plate. Neural stem cells are broadly classified as multipotent, self-renewing progenitor cells. In the CNS, these cells generate neurons, astrocytes, and oligodendrocytes. In the peripheral nervous system, they generate neurons, Schwann cells, and other derivatives, such as smooth muscle cells.[104] Cranial neural crest cells, however, produce a much broader range of cell fates than neural stem cells, including, cartilage, bone, connective tissue, and many of the sensory components of the peripheral nervous system.

Cranial neural crest cells migrate in discrete, segregated streams from the neural tube into the adjacent pharyngeal arches.[39–42] Cranial neural crest cell migration and patterning relies on a balance between the signals they acquire in the neural tube during their formation and their competency to respond to the signals they contact in the environment during their migration and differentiation[39,46,47,96] (see "Axial Patterning and Plasticity of Neural Crest Cells"). Of interest is whether neural stem cells would generate neural crest cells that migrate along the appropriate pathways, respecting the normally neural crest–free territories.[39,46] Therefore, to further characterize the multipotentiality and phenotypic plasticity of neural stem cells, recent experiments have challenged their potential to generate migrating neural crest cells. Both low- and high-level *Sox2* expressing neural stem cells were transplanted into r2 of neural plates in embryonic day 8.25 (5 somite stage) mouse embryos. During normal development, r2-derived neural crest cells migrate ventrolaterally into the first branchial arch. Neural stem cells expressing low or high levels of *Sox2* were both transplanted into r2 and readily incorporated into the neural plate as a cohort of cells with minimal intermingling with their immediate neighbors. Remarkably low *Sox2*-expressing neural stem cells exhibited a differentiative competency to generate migrating neural crest cells as evidenced by DiI lineage tracing. Not only were these neural stem cells able to respond appropriately to neural crest–inducing signals, but they also migrated along the designated neural crest pathway and populated the full proximo–distal extent of the first arch.[119] This suggests that neural stem cells can correctly interpret local embryonic positional cues and generate neural crest cells that also follow appropriate migratory cues. In contrast, neural stem cells selected for high levels of *Sox2* expression, when transplanted into r2, generate very few migrating neural crest cells. These results are consistent with the role of *Sox2* as a stem cell maintenance signal, inhibitory to differentiation. It will be interesting to determine whether neural stem cells are competent to acquire appropriate A–P positional information (i.e., *Hox* code) following transplantation. Studies in progress in both avians and mammals are assessing the long-term differentiative fates of the neural stem cell–derived neural crest cells, as it remains to be seen whether neural stem cells derived from the CNS can produce nonneural derivatives. Based on the location of the transplanted cells after delamination from the neural tube and migration into the distal region of the branchial arches, with the clear role of the branchial arch environment in influencing neural crest cell differentiation, we would expect that these cells will be competent given the right conditions to differentiate into connective tissue as well as the hard tissues of the head, including cartilage, bone, and the odontoblasts of the teeth.

A recent study strongly supports this notion and highlights the influence of extrinsic environmental factors in stem cell differentiation. Mammalian ES cells as well as both fetal and adult neural stem cells can all generate cartilage, bone, and the odontoblasts of the teeth if they are recombined with embryonic oral epithelium and then cultured as explants under kidney capsules.[120]

In such experiments, which demonstrate that neural stem cells have the potential to produce non-neural derivatives, it is important to note that these cells are usually generated as "neurospheres," spheres of multipotent progenitors that grow out of mixed populations of CNS cells in bFGF-containing media.[121] Such neurospheres are thought of as CNS stem cells, but because the stem cells have only ever been studied in culture, it is not certain whether they have properties similar to normal CNS stem cells *in vivo*. For instance, neurosphere cells have been observed to generate blood cells upon transplantation into irradiated mice,[122] skeletal muscle upon coculture with a myogenic cell lines or upon transplantation into regenerating muscle *in vivo*,[123] or derivatives of all three germ layers upon injections into blastocysts or early chick embryos.[124] The implication is that CNS stem cells possibly retain a much broader developmental potential than is usually observed *in vivo*. One caveat, however, is that perhaps

CNS progenitors lose patterning information and acquire a broader developmental potential as a result of being cultured in high concentrations of mitogens such as bFGF.[121] Such a dedifferentiation program has been previously observed in the demonstration that primordial germ cells become totipotent when cultured in growth factors such as bFGF and leukemia inhibitory factor (LIF). Primordial germ cells normally only produce germ cells; if transplanted into blastocysts, they do not detectably contribute to any somatic tissue. However, when primordial germ cells are first cultured in a bFGF- and LIF-containing medium and then transplanted into blastocysts, they can produce all somatic tissues as well as the germ line.[125,126] Similarly, additional evidence for dedifferentiation followed by redifferentiation has been provided by studies of neural crest–derived melanocytes, which lose their pigment and differentiate into glial cells upon clonal expansion in the presence of endothelin-3.[127,128] There is the possibility, however, that the *in vitro* cultivation necessary to isolate neural stem cells leads to their reprogramming.

These results challenge our notion of lineage restriction. The question remains as to whether pluripotent neural stem cells that generate neural derivatives *in situ*, do so only because they are located in the brain. Perhaps the only reason neural stem cells do not make blood or liver during normal development is that they are incapable of accessing the hematopoietic or hepatic microenvironments. These important questions will remain unanswered until CNS neural stem cells, purified from uncultured neural tissue, are tested for their ability to generate non-neuronal derivatives. Unfortunately, it may never be possible to truly address this question adequately. The nature of the stem cell niche is that the niche anchors and maintains the stem cell in place. The removal of the prospective stem cell from its niche environment could cause it to deregulate immediately and lose its spatial patterning information and regional identity. Hence, dissociation of the neuroepithelium necessary to isolate CNS neural stem cells might artificially expand the developmental capacities of these stem cells, even without the influence of expansion culture, and in doing so, it would facilitate the so-called dedifferentiation that has been observed in various transplantation assays. To date, therefore, it is not known whether neural stem cells correspond to normal CNS stem cells or whether their developmental potential has been broadened in culture. The implication, however, is that unexpectedly broad developmental potential may be a general phenomenon of progenitor cells given the right circumstances or conditions.

Significantly, an intriguing phenomenon may have been uncovered in which the developmental potential of cells can be reprogrammed under specific culture conditions or after transplantation without reflecting the normal developmental lineage relationships. It is critical both scientifically and clinically to understand this phenomenon, which poses the question as to whether differentiation is primarily environmentally regulated. This is one of the issues currently under intense investigation in the neural crest field, which makes neural crest cell development such a pertinent and analogous system for understanding stem cell patterning.

The possibility that any multipotential (or stem cell–like) cell population can respond to the appropriate positional cues to generate specific cell tissues and types, such as bone and the odontoblasts of teeth, has incredibly important implications in the possible treatment of craniofacial abnormalities. Craniofacial abnormalities constitute at least one third of all congenital abnormalities and are largely considered the consequence of defects in the formation, proliferation, migration, and differentiation of neural crest cells. The formation, migration, and early differentiation of neural crest cells *in vivo* occurs primarily between the third and eighth weeks of human gestation. There has been much talk about the potential use of stem cells not only in treating neurological disorders such as Alzheimer's and Parkinson's disease but also in possibly treating heart defects and congenital craniofacial abnormalities. The possibility of treating craniofacial abnormalities using stem cell therapy safely *in utero* during this critical period of gestation period remains an almost impossible dream. Not only are enormous advances in fetal surgery required but so are methods for detecting the early onset of craniofacial abnormalities. In the head, nearly all the cartilage, bone, and teeth are derived from neural crest cells, and it's intriguing that tooth and bone formation can be induced in stem cells without passing through a neural crest intermediate. Irrespective of the so-called dedifferentiation phenomenon, the remarkable demonstration that neural stem cells are competent under the right conditions to generate the hard tissues of the head opens the door for neural stem cell–derived tissue engineering as an alternative approach in the treatment of congenital craniofacial abnormalities.

ACKNOWLEDGMENTS

The authors wish to thank Morphoula Remboutsika, Robin Lovell-Badge, James Briscoe, and Paul Sharpe for contributing results to this manuscript prior to their publication. This work was supported by research funds from the Stowers Institute to Robb Krumlauf and Paul A. Trainor, by a Basil O'Connor Fellowship from the March of Dimes to Paul A. Trainor, and by an HFSP International Network Research Grant (RG0146/2000B) to Marianne Bronner-Fraser and Robb Krumlauf.

REFERENCES

1. Bronner-Fraser, M., and Fraser, S. (1988). Cell lineage analysis reveals multipotency of some avian neural crest cells. *Nature* **335**, 161–164.
2. Artinger, K.B., and Bronner-Fraser, M. (1993). Delayed formation of the floor plate after ablation of the avian notochord. *Neuron* **11**, 1147–1161.
3. Fraser, S.E., and Bronner-Fraser, M. (1991). Migrating neural crest cells in the trunk of the avian embryo are multipotent. *Development* **112**, 913–920.
4. Shah, N.M., and Anderson, D.J. (1997). Integration of multiple instructive cues by neural crest stem cells reveals cell-intrinsic biases in relative growth factor responsiveness. *Proc. Natl. Acad. Sci. USA* **94**, 11,369–11,374.
5. Ruffins, S., Artinger, K.B., and Bronner-Fraser, M. (1998). Early migrating neural crest cells can form ventral neural tube derivatives when challenged by transplantation. *Dev. Biol.* **203**, 295–304.
6. Sharma, K., Korade, Z., and Frank, E. (1995). Late-migrating neuroepithelial cells from the spinal cord differentiate into sensory ganglion cells and melanocytes. *Neuron* **14**, 143–152.
7. Korade, Z., and Frank, E. (1996). Restriction in cell fates of developing spinal cord cells transplanted to neural crest pathways. *J. Neurosci.* **16**, 7638–7648.
8. Nieto, M.A., Sargent, M.G., Wilkinson, D.G., and Cooke, J. (1994). Control of cell behavior during vertebrate development by slug, a zinc finger gene. *Science* **264**, 835–839.
9. Sasai, N., Mizuseki, K., and Sasai, Y. (2001). Requirement of Foxd3-class signaling for neural crest determination in Xenopus. *Development* **128**, 2525–2536.
10. Spokony, R.F., Aoki, Y., Saint-Germain, N., Magner-Fink, E., and Saint-Jeannet, J.P. (2002). The transcription factor Sox9 is required for cranial neural crest development in Xenopus. *Development* **129**, 421–432.
11. LaBonne, C., and Bronner-Fraser, M. (1998). Induction and patterning of the neural crest, a stem cell-like precursor population. *J. Neurobiol.* **36**, 175–189.
12. Gammill, L.S., and Bronner-Fraser, M. (2002). Genomic analysis of neural crest induction. *Development* **129**, 5731–5741.
13. Rollhäuser-ter-Horst, J. (1979). Artificial neural crest formation in amphibia. *Anat. Embryol. (Berl.)* **157**, 113–120.
14. Moury, J.D., and Jacobson, A.G. (1989). Neural fold formation at newly created boundaries between neural plate and epidermis in the axolotl. *Dev. Biol.* **133**, 44–57.
15. Selleck, M.A., and Bronner-Fraser, M. (1995). Origins of the avian neural crest: the role of neural plate-epidermal interactions. *Development* **121**, 525–538.
16. Basch, M.L., Selleck, M.A., and Bronner-Fraser, M. (2000). Timing and competence of neural crest formation. *Dev. Neurosci.* **22**, 217–227.
17. Dickinson, M.E., Selleck, M.A., McMahon, A.P., and Bronner-Fraser, M. (1995). Dorsalization of the neural tube by the non-neural ectoderm. *Development* **121**, 2099–2106.
18. Liem, K.F., Jr., Tremml, G., and Jessell, T.M. (1997). A role for the roof plate and its resident TGF-β-related proteins in neuronal patterning in the dorsal spinal cord. *Cell* **91**, 127–138.
19. Barembaum, M., Moreno, T.A., LaBonne, C., Sechrist, J., and Bronner-Fraser, M. (2000). Noelin-1 is a secreted glycoprotein involved in generation of the neural crest. *Nat. Cell Biol.* **2**, 219–225.
20. Basler, K., Edlund, T., Jessell, T.M., and Yamada, T. (1993). Control of cell pattern in the neural tube: regulation of cell differentiation by Dorsalin-1, a novel TGF beta family member. *Cell* **73**, 687–702.
21. Garcia-Castro, M.I., Marcelle, C., and Bronner-Fraser, M. (2002). Ectodermal Wnt function as a neural crest inducer. *Science* **13**, 13.
22. Watanabe, Y., and Le Douarin, N.M. (1996). A role for Bmp4 in the development of subcutaneous cartilage. *Mech. Dev.* **57**, 69–78.
23. Selleck, M.A., Garcia-Castro, M.I., Artinger, K.B., and Bronner-Fraser, M. (1998). Effects of Shh and Noggin on neural crest formation demonstrate that BMP is required in the neural tube but not ectoderm. *Development* **125**, 4919–4930.
24. Monsoro-Burq, A.H., Fletcher, R.B., and Harland, R.M. (2003). Neural crest induction by paraxial mesoderm in Xenopus embryos requires FGF signals. *Development* **130**, 3111–3124.

25. Mayor, R., Morgan, R., and Sargent, M.G. (1995). Induction of the prospective neural crest of Xenopus. *Development* **121,** 767–777.

26. Mayor, R., Guerrero, N., and Martinez, C. (1997). Role of FGF and noggin in neural crest induction. *Dev. Biol.* **189,** 1–12.

27. Godsave, S.F., and Durston, A.J. (1997). Neural induction and patterning in embryos deficient in FGF signaling. *Int. J. Dev. Biol.* **41,** 57–65.

28. Amaya, E., Musci, T.J., and Kirschner, M.W. (1991). Expression of a dominant negative mutant of the FGF receptor disrupts mesoderm formation in *Xenopus* embryos. *Cell* **66,** 257–270.

29. LaBonne, C., and Bronner-Fraser, M. (1998). Neural crest induction in *Xenopus:* evidence for a two-signal model. *Development* **125,** 2403–2414.

30. Saint-Jeannet, J.P., He, X., Varmus, H.E., and Dawid, I.B. (1997). Regulation of dorsal fate in the neuraxis by Wnt1 and Wnt3a. *Proc. Natl. Acad. Sci. USA* **94,** 13,713–13,718.

31. Hunt, P., Wilkinson, D., and Krumlauf, R. (1991). Patterning the vertebrate head: murine Hox 2 genes mark distinct subpopulations of premigratory and migrating neural crest. *Development* **112,** 43–51.

32. Hunt, P., Gulisano, M., Cook, M., Sham, M., Faiella, A., Wilkinson, D., Boncinelli, E., and Krumlauf, R. (1991). A distinct Hox code for the branchial region of the head. *Nature* **353,** 861–864.

33. McGinnis, W., and Krumlauf, R. (1992). Homeobox genes and axial patterning. *Cell* **68,** 283–302.

34. Krumlauf, R. (1994). Hox genes in vertebrate development. *Cell* **78,** 191–201.

35. Krumlauf, R. (1993). Hox genes and pattern formation in the branchial region of the vertebrate head. *Trends Genet.* **9,** 106–112.

36. Trainor, P.A., and Krumlauf, R. (2001). Hox genes, neural crest cells and branchial arch patterning. *Curr. Opin. Cell Biol.* **13,** 698–705.

37. Maconochie, M.K., Nonchev, S., Morrison, A., and Krumlauf, R. (1996). Paralogous Hox genes: Function and regulation. *Annu. Rev. Genet.* **30,** 529–556.

38. Lumsden, A., and Krumlauf, R. (1996). Patterning the vertebrate neuraxis. *Science* **274,** 1109–1115.

39. Trainor, P.A., Sobieszczuk, D., Wilkinson, D., and Krumlauf, R. (2002). Signaling between the hindbrain and paraxial tissues dictates neural crest migration pathways. *Development* **129,** 433–442.

40. Sechrist, J., Serbedzija, G.N., Scherson, T., Fraser, S.E., and Bronner-Fraser, M. (1993). Segmental migration of the hindbrain neural crest does not arise from its segmental generation. *Development* **118(3),** 691–703.

41. Köntges, G., and Lumsden, A. (1996). Rhombencephalic neural crest segmentation is preserved throughout craniofacial ontogeny. *Development* **122,** 3229–3242.

42. Le Douarin, N., and Kalcheim, C. (1999). "The Neural Crest," 2nd ed. Cambridge University Press, Cambridge.

43. Graham, A., Heyman, I., and Lumsden, A. (1993). Even-numbered rhombomeres control the apoptotic elimination of neural crest cells from odd-numbered rhombomeres in the chick hindbrain. *Development* **119,** 233–245.

44. Graham, A., Francis-West, P., Brickell, P., and Lumsden, A. (1994). The signaling molecule Bmp4 mediates apoptosis in the rhombencephalic neural crest. *Nature* **372,** 684–686.

45. Golding, J.P., Dixon, M., and Gassmann, M. (2002). Cues from neuroepithelium and surface ectoderm maintain neural crest-free regions within cranial mesenchyme of the developing chick. *Development* **129,** 1095–1105.

46. Farlie, P.G., Kerr, R., Thomas, P., Symes, T., Minichiello, J., Hearn, C.J., and Newgreen, D. (1999). A paraxial exclusion zone creates patterned cranial neural crest cell outgrowth adjacent to rhombomeres 3 and 5. *Dev. Biol.* **213,** 70–84.

47. Golding, J., Trainor, P., Krumlauf, R., and Gassman, M. (2000). Defects in pathfinding by cranial neural crest cells in mice lacking the neuregulin receptor Erbb4. *Nat. Cell Biol.* **2,** 103–109.

48. Ellies, D.L., Church, V., Francis-West, P., and Lumsden, A. (2000). The Wnt antagonist cSFRP2 modulates programmed cell death in the developing hindbrain. *Development* **127,** 5285–5295.

49. Ellies, D.L., Tucker, A.S., Lumsden, A. (2002). Apoptosis of premigratory neural crest cells in rhombomeres 3 and 5: consequences for patterning of the branchial region. *Dev. Biol.* **251,** 118–128.

50. Smith, A., Robinson, V., Patel, K., and Wilkinson, D.G. (1997). The EphA4 and EphB1 receptor tyrosine kinases and ephrin-B2 ligand regulate targeted migration of branchial neural crest cells. *Curr. Biol.* **7,** 561–570.

51. Maconochie, M., Krishnamurthy, R., Nonchev, S., Meier, P., Manzanares, M., Mitchell, P., and Krumlauf, R. (1999). Regulation of Hoxa2 in cranial neural crest cells involves members of the Ap2 family. *Development* **126,** 1483–1494.

52. Gendron-Maguire, M., Mallo, M., Zhang, M., and Gridley, T. (1993). Hoxa2 mutant mice exhibit homeotic transformation of skeletal elements derived from cranial neural crest. *Cell* **75,** 1317–1331.

53. Gavalas, A., Davenne, M., Lumsden, A., Chambon, P., and Rijli, F. (1997). Role of Hoxa2 in axon pathfinding and rostral hindbrain patterning. *Development* **124,** 3693–3702.

54. Rijli, F.M., Mark, M., Lakkaraju, S., Dierich, A., Dolle, P., and Chambon, P. (1993). A homeotic transformation is generated in the rostral branchial region of the head by disruption of Hoxa-2, which acts as a selector gene. *Cell* **75,** 1333–1349.

55. Hunter, M.P., and Prince, V.E. (2002). Zebra fish Hox paralogue group 2 genes function redundantly as selector genes to pattern the second pharyngeal arch. *Dev. Biol.* **247,** 367–389.

56. Pasqualetti, M., Ori, M., Nardi, I., and Rijli, F.M. (2000). Ectopic Hoxa2 induction after neural crest migration results in homeosis of jaw elements in *Xenopus. Development* **127,** 5367–5378.

57. Grammatopoulos, G.A., Bell, E., Toole, L., Lumsden, A., and Tucker, A.S. (2000). Homeotic transformation of branchial arch identity after Hoxa2 overexpression. *Development* **127,** 5355–5365.

58. Couly, G., Grapin-Botton, A., Coltey, P., Ruhin, B., and Le Douarin, N.M. (1998). Determination of the identity of the derivatives of the cephalic neural crest: incompatibility between Hox gene expression and lower jaw development. *Development* **128,** 3445–3459.

59. Rijli, F., Gavalas, A., and Chambon, P. (1998). Segmentation and specification in the branchial region of the head: the role of Hox selector genes. *Int. J. Dev. Biol.* **42,** 393–401.

60. Kessel, M., and Gruss, P. (1991). Homeotic transformations of murine prevertebrae and concomitant alteration of Hox codes induced by retinoic acid. *Cell* **67,** 89–104.

61. Wilkinson, D.G., Bhatt, S., Cook, M., Boncinelli, E., and Krumlauf, R. (1989). Segmental expression of Hox-2 homeobox-containing genes in the developing mouse hindbrain. *Nature* **341,** 405–409.

62. Goddard, J., Rossel, M., Manley, N., and Capecchi, M. (1996). Mice with targeted disruption of Hoxb1 fail to form the motor nucleus of the VIIth nerve. *Development* **122,** 3217–3228.

63. Studer, M., Lumsden, A., Ariza-McNaughton, L., Bradley, A., and Krumlauf, R. (1996). Altered segmental identity and

abnormal migration of motor neurons in mice lacking Hoxb1. *Nature* **384,** 630–635.

64. Studer, M., Gavalas, A., Marshall, H., Ariza-McNaughton, L., Rijli, F., Chambon, P., and Krumlauf, R. (1998). Genetic interaction between Hoxa1 and Hoxb1 reveal new roles in regulation of early hindbrain patterning. *Development* **125,** 1025–1036.

65. Chisaka, O., Musci, T., and Capecchi, M. (1992). Developmental defects of the ear, cranial nerves and hindbrain resulting from targeted disruption of the mouse homeobox gene Hox-1.6. *Nature* **355,** 516–520.

66. Lufkin, T., Dierich, A., LeMeur, M., Mark, M., and Chambon, P. (1991). Disruption of the Hox-1.6 homeobox gene results in defects in a region corresponding to its rostral domain of expression. *Cell* **66,** 1105–1119.

67. Mark, M., Lufkin, T., Vonesch, J.L., Ruberte, E., Olivo, J.C., Dollé, P., Gorry, P., Lumsden, A., and Chambon, P. (1993). Two rhombomeres are altered in Hoxa1 mutant mice. *Development* **119,** 319–338.

68. Gavalas, A., Trainor, P., Ariza-McNaughton, L., and Krumlauf, R. (2001). Synergy between Hoxa1 and Hoxb1: the relationship between arch patterning and the generation of cranial neural crest. *Development* **128,** 3017–3027.

69. Rossel, M., and Capecchi, M. (1999). Mice mutant for both Hoxa1 and Hoxb1 show extensive remodeling of the hindbrain and defects in craniofacial development. *Development* **126,** 5027–5040.

70. Gavalas, A., Studer, M., Lumsden, A., Rijli, F., Krumlauf, R., and Chambon, P. (1998). Hoxa1 and Hoxb1 synergize in patterning the hindbrain, cranial nerves and second pharyngeal arch. *Development* **125,** 1123–1136.

71. Veitch, E., Begbie, J., Schilling, T.F., Smith, M.M., and Graham, A. (1999). Pharyngeal arch patterning in the absence of neural crest. *Curr. Biol.* **9,** 1481–1484.

72. Noden, D. (1983). The role of the neural crest in patterning of avian cranial skeletal, connective, and muscle tissues. *Dev. Biol.* **96,** 144–165.

73. Zhang, J., Hagopian-Donaldson, S., Serbedzija, G., Elsemore, J., Plehn-Dujowich, D., McMahon, A.P., Flavell, R.A., and Williams, T. (1996). Neural tube, skeletal and body wall defects in mice lacking transcription factor Ap2. *Nature* **381,** 238–241.

74. Mitchell, P.J., Timmons, P.M., Hébert, J.M., Rigby, P.W.J., and Tjian, R. (1991). Transcription factor Ap2 is expressed in neural crest cell lineages during mouse embryogenesis. *Genes Dev.* **5,** 105–119.

75. Schorle, H., Meier, P., Buchert, M., Jaenisch, R., and Mitchell, P.J. (1996). Transcription factor AP-2 is essential for cranial closure and craniofacial development. *Nature* **381,** 235–238.

76. Trainor, P., and Krumlauf, R. (2000). Patterning the cranial neural crest: Hindbrain segmentation and Hox gene plasticity. *Nat. Rev. Neurosci.* **1,** 116–124.

77. Tümpel, S., Maconochie, M., Wiedemann, L.M., and Krumlauf, R. (2002). Conservation and diversity in the *cis*-regulatory networks that integrate information controlling expression of Hoxa2 in hindbrain and cranial neural crest cells in vertebrates. *Dev. Biol.* **246,** 45–56.

78. Couly, G.F., Grapin-Bottom, A., Coltey, P., and Le Douarin, N.M. (1996). The regeneration of the cephalic neural crest, a problem revisited: the regenerating cells originate from the contralateral or from the anterior and posterior neural folds. *Development* **122,** 3393–3407.

79. Diaz, C., and Glover, J. (1996). Appropriate pattern formation following regulative regeneration in the hindbrain neural tube. *Development* **122,** 3095–3105.

80. Gould, A., Itasaki, N., and Krumlauf, R. (1998). Initiation of rhombomeric Hoxb4 expression requires induction by somites and a retinoid pathway. *Neuron* **21,** 39–51.

81. Grapin-Botton, A., Bonnin, M.A., Ariza-McNaughton, L., Krumlauf, R., and LeDouarin, N.M. (1995). Plasticity of transposed rhombomeres: Hox gene induction is correlated with phenotypic modifications. *Development* **121,** 2707–2721.

82. Grapin-Botton, A., Bonnin, M.A., and Le Douarin, N. (1997). Hox gene induction in the neural tube depends on three parameters: competence, signal supply and paralogue group. *Development* **124,** 849–859.

83. Guthrie, S., Muchamore, I., Kuroiwa, A., Marshall, H., Krumlauf, R., and Lumsden, A. (1992). Neuroectodermal autonomy of Hox-2.9 expression revealed by rhombomere transpositions. *Nature* **356,** 157–159.

84. Hunt, P., Clarke, J.D.W., Buxton, P., Ferretti, P., and Thorogood, P. (1998). Stability and plasticity of neural crest patterning and branchial arch Hox code after extensive cephalic crest rotation. *Dev. Biol.* **198,** 82–104.

85. Hunt, P., Ferretti, P., Krumlauf, R., and Thorogood, P. (1995). Restoration of normal Hox code and branchial arch morphogenesis after extensive deletion of hindbrain neural crest. *Dev. Biol.* **168,** 584–597.

86. Itasaki, N., Sharpe, J., Morrison, A., and Krumlauf, R. (1996). Reprogramming Hox expression in the vertebrate hindbrain: influence of paraxial mesoderm and rhombomere transposition. *Neuron* **16,** 487–500.

87. Kulesa, P., Bronner-Fraser, M., and Fraser, S. (2000). *In ovo* time-lapse analysis after dorsal neural tube ablation shows rerouting of chick hindbrain neural crest. *Development* **127,** 2843–2852.

88. Kuratani, S.C., and Eichele, G. (1993). Rhombomere transposition repatterns the segmental organization of cranial nerves and reveals cell-autonomous expression of a homeodomain protein. *Development* **117,** 105–117.

89. Yntema, C., and Hammond, W. (1945). Depletions and abnormalities in the cervical sympathetic system of the chick following extirpation of the neural crest. *J. Exp. Zool.* **100,** 237–263.

90. Simon, H., Hornbruch, A., and Lumsden, A. (1995). Independent assignment of antero–posterior and dorso–ventral positional values in the developing chick hindbrain. *Curr. Biol.* **5,** 205–214.

91. Schilling, T. (2001). Plasticity of zebra fish Hox expression in the hindbrain and cranial neural crest hindbrain. *Dev. Biol.* **231,** 201–216.

92. Scherson, T., Serbedzija, G., Fraser, S., and Bronner-Fraser, M. (1993). Regulative capacity of the cranial neural tube and neural crest. *Development* **118,** 1049–1061.

93. Saldivar, J.R., Sechrist, J.W., Krull, C.E., Ruffin, S., and Bronner-Fraser, M. (1997). Dorsal hindbrain ablation results in the rerouting of neural crest migration and the changes in gene expression, but normal hyoid development. *Development* **124,** 2729–2739.

94. Saldivar, J., Krull, C., Krumlauf, R., Ariza-McNaughton, L., and Bronner-Fraser, M. (1996). Rhombomere of origin determines autonomous versus environmentally regulated expression of Hoxa3 in the avian embryo. *Development* **122,** 895–904.

95. McKee, G., and Ferguson, M. (1984). The effects of mesencephalic neural crest cell extirpation on the development of chicken embryos. *J. of Anat.* **139,** 491–512.

96. Trainor, P., and Krumlauf, R. (2000). Plasticity in mouse neural crest cells reveals a new patterning role for cranial mesoderm. *Nat. Cell Biol.* **2,** 96–102.

97. Prince, V., and Lumsden, A. (1994). Hoxa-2 expression in normal and transposed rhombomeres: independent regulation in the neural tube and neural crest. *Development* **120,** 911–923.

98. Crossley, P.H., Martinez, S., and Martin, G.R. (1996). Midbrain development induced by Fgf8 in the chick embryo. *Nature* **380**, 66–68.

99. Irving, C., and Mason, I. (1999). Regeneration of isthmic tissue is the result of a specific and direct interaction between rhombomere 1 and midbrain. *Development* **126**, 3981–3989.

100. Irving, C., and Mason, I. (2000). Signaling by Fgf8 from the isthmus patterns the anterior hindbrain and establishes the anterior limit of Hox gene expression. *Development* **127**, 177–186.

101. Martinez, S., Marin, F., Nieto, M.A., and Puelles, L. (1995). Induction of ectopic *engrailed* expression and fate change in avian rhombomeres: intersegmental boundaries as barriers. *Mech. of Dev.* **51**, 289–303.

102. Trainor, P.A., Ariza-McNaughton, L., and Krumlauf, R. (2002). Role of the isthmus and FGFs in resolving the paradox of neural crest plasticity and prepatterning. *Science* **295**, 1288–1291.

103. Schneider, R.A., and Helms, J.A. (2003). The cellular and molecular origins of beak morphology. *Science* **299**, 565–568.

104. Anderson, D.J. (2001). Stem cells and pattern formation in the nervous system: the possible versus the actual. *Neuron* **30**, 19–35.

105. Morrison, S.J., Shah, N.M., and Anderson, D.J. (1997). Regulatory mechanisms in stem cell biology. *Cell* **88**, 287–298.

106. Artavanis-Tsakonas, S., Rand, M.D., and Lake, R.J. (1999). Notch signaling: cell fate control and signal integration in development. *Science* **284**, 770–776.

107. Noden, D.M. (1982). Patterns and organization of craniofacial skeletogenic and myogenic mesenchyme: a perspective. *Prog. Clin. Biol. Res.* **101**, 167–203.

108. Stemple, D.L., and Anderson, D.J. (1992). Isolation of a stem cell for neurons and glia from the mammalian neural crest. *Cell* **71**, 973–985.

109. Shah, N.M., Groves, A.K., and Anderson, D.J. (1996). Alternative neural crest cell fates are instructively promoted by TGF-β superfamily members. *Cell* **85**, 331–343.

110. Shah, N.M., Marchionni, M.A., Isaacs, I., Stroobant, P., and Anderson, D.J. (1994). Glial growth factor restricts mammalian neural crest stem cells to a glial fate. *Cell* **77**, 349–360.

111. Pusch, C., Hustert, E., Pfeifer, D., Sudbeck, P., Kist, R., Roe, B., Wang, Z., Balling, R., Blin, N., and Scherer, G. (1998). The SOX10/Sox10 gene from human and mouse: sequence, expression, and transactivation by the encoded HMG domain transcription factor. *Hum. Genet.* **103**, 115–123.

112. Kim, J., Lo, L., Dormand, E., and Anderson, D.J. (2003). SOX10 maintains multipotency and inhibits neuronal differentiation of neural crest stem cells. *Neuron* **38**, 17–31.

113. Paratore, C., Eichenberger, C., Suter, U., and Sommer, L. (2002). Sox10 haploinsufficiency affects maintenance of progenitor cells in a mouse model of Hirschsprung disease. *Hum. Mol. Genet.* **11**, 3075–3085.

114. Wilson, M., and Koopman, P. (2002). Matching SOX: partner proteins and co-factors of the SOX family of transcriptional regulators. *Curr. Opin. Genet. Dev.* **12**, 441–446.

115. Zappone, M.V., Galli, R., Catena, R., Meani, N., De Biasi, S., Mattei, E., Tiveron, C., Vescovi, A.L., Lovell-Badge, R., Ottolenghi, S., and Nicolis, S.K. (2000). Sox2 regulatory sequences direct expression of a (beta)-geo transgene to telencephalic neural stem cells and precursors of the mouse embryo, revealing regionalization of gene expression in CNS stem cells. *Development* **127**, 2367–2382.

116. Rex, M., Orme, A., Uwanogho, D., Tointon, K., Wigmore, P.M., Sharpe, P.T., and Scotting, P.J. (1997). Dynamic expression of chicken Sox2 and Sox3 genes in ectoderm induced to form neural tissue. *Dev. Dyn.* **209**, 323–332.

117. Sasai, Y. (2001). Roles of Sox factors in neural determination: Conserved signaling in evolution? *Int. J. Dev. Biol.* **45**, 321–326.

118. Remboutsika, M., and Lovell-Badge, R. (Personal communication).

119. Trainor, P.A., Remboutsika, M., and Lovell-Badge, R. (Personal communication).

120. Sharpe, P. (Personal communication).

121. Palmer, T.D., Markakis, E.A., Willhoite, A.R., Safar, F., and Gage, F.H. (1999). Fibroblast growth factor-2 activates a latent neurogenic program in neural stem cells from diverse regions of the adult CNS. *J. Neurosci.* **19**, 8487–8497.

122. Bjornson, C.R., Rietze, R.L., Reynolds, B.A., Magli, M.C., and Vescovi, A.L. (1999). Turning brain into blood: a hematopoietic fate adopted by adult neural stem cells *in vivo*. *Science* **283**, 534–537.

123. Galli, R., Borello, U., Gritti, A., Minasi, M.G., Bjornson, C., Coletta, M., Mora, M., De Angelis, M.G., Fiocco, R., Cossu, G., and Vescovi, A.L. (2000). Skeletal myogenic potential of human and mouse neural stem cells. *Nat. Neurosci.* **3**, 986–991.

124. Clarke, D.L., Johansson, C.B., Wilbertz, J., Veress, B., Nilsson, E., Karlstrom, H., Lendahl, U., and Frisen, J. (2000). Generalized potential of adult neural stem cells. *Science* **288**, 1660–1663.

125. Matsui, Y., Zsebo, K., and Hogan, B.L. (1992). Derivation of pluripotential embryonic stem cells from murine primordial germ cells in culture. *Cell* **70**, 841–847.

126. Donovan, P.J. (1994). Growth factor regulation of mouse primordial germ cell development. *Curr. Top. Dev. Biol.* **29**, 189–225.

127. Dupin, E., Real, C., Glavieux-Pardanaud, C., Vaigot, P., and Le Douarin, N.M. (2003). Reversal of developmental restrictions in neural crest lineages: transition from Schwann cells to glial-melanocytic precursors *in vitro*. *Proc. Natl. Acad. Sci. USA* **100**, 5229–5233.

128. Dupin, E., Glavieux, C., Vaigot, P., and Le Douarin, N.M. (2000). Endothelin 3 induces the reversion of melanocytes to glia through a neural crest-derived glial-melanocytic progenitor. *Proc. Natl. Acad. Sci. USA* **97**, 7882–7887.

20

Melanocytes

Toshiyuki Yamane, Hitomi Aoki, Tsutomu Motohashi, and Takahiro Kunisada

Introduction

Melanocytes or their precursors melanoblasts are derived from the neural crest cells. After extensive migration, they finally reside in the skin, inner ear, and uveal tract as highly dendritic, heavily pigmented cells; they are generally located in the epidermal basal cell layer of these areas, including hair follicles.[1] Genetic observations indicate that steel factor (SLF, also known as MGF or stem cell factor)[2] and endothelin 3 (ET3)[3] are essential environmental factors for the early stages of melanocyte development.

In this chapter, we describe the culture system and give a short protocol for inducing the differentiation of embryonic stem (ES) cells into cells of the melanocyte lineage. The most noteworthy features of *in vitro* differentiation of ES cells are that the entire process of melanocyte development can be seen in a culture dish and that this process can thus be easily manipulated experimentally. Because there are well-established techniques to introduce or knockout genes in ES cells, the culture system we established provides a fast and easy way to examine functions of the genes of interest that might affect neural crest or melanocyte development. This system also provides a good tool to examine how environmental factors act in the development of the neural crest and melanocytes by adding or blocking these factors.

Melanocytes from ES Cells

INTRODUCTION TO OUR CULTURE SYSTEM

Mouse ES cells are derived from the inner cell mass of preimplantation blastocysts. In the presence of leukemia inhibitory factor, they can divide unlimited in culture without differentiating into cells of a more mature state. ES cells become integrated into fetal development when put back into the embryo, and they are able to generate all kinds of cells in the body.[4] Their contribution to coat color in chimeric mice gives apparent evidence for the existence of ES cell-derived melanocytes *in vivo*.

ES cells can also differentiate into cells of various lineages in a culture dish where a differentiation-inducing environment exists.[5] Earlier, we established a culture system that supports

the differentiation of melanocytes from ES cells.[6, 7] By culturing ES cells on a monolayer of bone marrow-derived ST2 stromal cells for three weeks in a medium containing certain additives (see the section "Important Factors for the Differentiation into Melanocytes"), they efficiently differentiate into melanocytes in culture.

The term "stromal cells" is used to designate the feeder cells that support blood cell development. ST2 was originally established as a cell line that supports both myelopoiesis and B-cell lymphopoiesis.[8] However, ES cells also grow and differentiate on ST2 stromal cells and generate cells of various other lineages, including blood cells, endothelial cells, and cardiac muscle cells in medium containing fetal calf serum (FCS), even if no additional growth factors or cytokines are added.[9] ST2 stromal cells themselves have some potential to differentiate into cells of other lineages, including the adipocyte and osteoblast. But they can never generate pigmented cells because they were derived from an albino mouse.[6]

In our system, we inoculate a small amount of a single-cell suspension of ES cells on an ST2 monolayer. Each single ES cell grows by piling up and thus forms a colony. The efficient generation of melanocytes is achievable when ES cells are grown at a low cell density. This sharp dependency of melanocyte induction on the number of inoculated cells is indicated in Fig. 20–1. It is preferable when there are only about 8 colonies per 1 cm^2 (80 colonies per well in six-well plates) or less, because each colony sometimes spreads to become 3 mm in diameter.

IMPORTANT FACTORS FOR DIFFERENTIATION INTO MELANOCYTES

In the medium supplemented with serum only, ES cells generate a small number of melanocyte colonies by 3 weeks in culture on ST2 cells. The addition of dexamethasone (Dex), a synthetic glucocorticoid, dramatically increases the number of melanocytes by two orders of magnitude. Various factors known to promote melanogenesis, which include basic fibroblast growth factor (bFGF), cholera toxin (CT), 12-*O*-tetradecanoyl phorbol acetate, 1a, 25-dihydroxyvitamin D$_3$, or combinations of these factors, increase the number of melanocytes synergistically with Dex. But these factors do not support much melanogenesis from ES cells when added alone or in combinations in the absence of Dex. Thus, Dex is the most important additive in our culture system. We use the culture containing Dex, bFGF, and CT as the standard condition. Under this condition, pigmented melanocytes start to appear at day 12 or 13 after establishment of the culture.

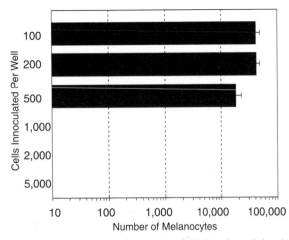

Figure 20–1. Relationship of the number of D3 ES cells seeded to the number of melanocytes induced. In this six-well plate condition, 1000 or more ES cells per well did not induce melanocytes.

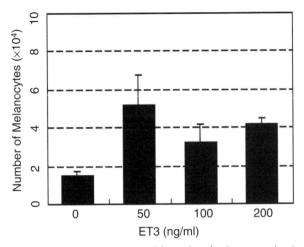

Figure 20–2. ET3 concentration and the number of melanocytes induced from D3 ES cells. About two-fold induction was observed at 50 to 200 ng/ml.

The numbers of melanocyte reach 50,000 cells per well (six-well plate) by 3 weeks in culture.

Dex is effective at concentrations of more than 10^{-8} mol/L, and it is required during a later phase in the culture. The presence of this factor only during days 12–21 is sufficient for the full induction of melanocytes. Dex may also induce some biological responses to stromal cells, but as yet we do not know which cells, ST2 cells or ES-derived ones, respond to Dex.

Signals from SLF and ET3 are essential for melanocyte lineage development. The number of melanocytes increases only slightly when SLF is added to the standard culture. But this does not mean that SLF is not important for melanocyte formation from ES cells, because ST2 stromal cells in the culture produce a sufficient amount of SLF for melanocyte differentiation. Antagonistic antibodies specific for c-Kit (the receptor for SLF: ACK2) nearly abolish the generation of melanocytes in culture. The addition of ET3 augments the melanocyte formation five-fold in the culture supplemented only with Dex, and two-fold under the standard condition. Interestingly, BQ788, a selective endothelin-B receptor antagonist, reduces the number of melanocytes by two orders of magnitude under culture conditions with only Dex as an additive, but BQ788 has only a slight effect under the standard condition.[10] Thus, bFGF and CT might substitute for the requirements of ET3 in culture. Still, ET3 reproducibly increases the final number of mature melanocytes and stimulates the pigmentation of the individual melanocytes. Therefore, 50 to 100 ng/ml of ET3 may be added to the standard medium. The addition of ET3 also helps to reduce the serum lot dependency of the culture system. Dose dependency of melanocytes induced from D3 ES cells upon the ET3 concentration is shown in Fig. 20–2.

COURSE OF DIFFERENTIATION

In the standard condition, pigmented melanocytes appear at day 12 or 13 after culture setup, and their number continues to

increase to three weeks of culture. The mRNAs for melanogenic markers *(Trp-1, Trp-2,* and *tyrosinase)* are first detected around day 6 of culture, and their levels continue to increase after this time. Cells containing microphthalmia-associated transcription factor proteins are also detected immunohistochemically around day 6. These observations show that melanoblasts start to appear as early as day 6 of the differentiation process. We examined the time at which SLF-dependent melanoblasts appear in the culture by using ACK2. The addition of ACK2 until day 9 decreased the number of melanocytes to 30% of the control. By adding it until day 12, the generation of melanocytes was nearly abolished. As expected from mRNA analysis, the addition for the initial 6 days had little effect. Thus, c-Kit-dependent melanoblasts appear around day 6 and increase their maximum number by day 12. The presence of dendritic or bipolar c-Kit+ cells was confirmed by immunohistochemical staining. These cells disappear by adding ACK2, but they are still present in colonies derived from SCL$^{-/-}$ ES cells, which lack blood cells (the most likely other source of c-Kit-expressing cells). Thus, these c-Kit^{+} cells are most likely melanoblasts. The timeline of melanogenesis from ES cells is summarized in Fig. 20–3. It is noteworthy that the timeline of melanocyte lineage development from ES cells corresponds to that of melanocyte development *in vivo* because D3 ES cells, the line we mainly use, were derived from an embryonic day (E) 3.5 blastocyst.[5]

SELF-RENEWING MELANOBLASTS

In our culture system, melanocytes are generated in colonies containing heterogenous populations of cells. Blood cells, endothelial cells, cardiac muscle cells, and cells of unidentified other cell lineages are observed at the same time. However, we found that melanocyte lineage cells can be selectively propagated by dissociating growing colonies into single cells and replating suspensions of them on fresh ST2 monolayers at the low cell density (<50 cells/cm^2) in the

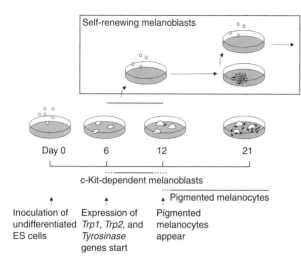

Figure 20–3. Schedule of the melanocyte development from ES cells.

standard condition. At this density, single cells proliferate and form round colonies. These round colonies derived from single cells reach 5 mm in diameter by 2 weeks of culture and consist of melanoblast-like cells and a small percentage of pigmented melanocytes (Fig. 20–4). These colonies seem to reach their maximum size 2 weeks after replating, but the proportion of pigmented mature melanocytes increases after this time. Melanoblast-like cells are detected among these replated cells as early as day 6, and they increase in number for the next 3 days. These cells can be also detected on day 12, but their number had already reached a plateau at day 9. The frequency of these melanoblast-like colony-forming cells is 0.018 at day 9.

These replated cells seem to be melanoblasts, because no colonies are generated if the cultures are pretreated with ACK2 before replating. Furthermore, these colonies grow in

Figure 20–4. Melanocytes induced in the secondary colonies derived from melanoblasts of the first melanocyte culture. The small arrow indicates mature melanocytes; the large arrow indicates slightly pigmented melanocytes; and the arrowheads indicate nonpigmented dendritic cells, supposedly a melanoblast.

an SLF-dependent manner after the replating since ACK2 blocks this step, too.

Interestingly, these replated cells can grow again when the colonies are dissociated and seeded on fresh ST2 monolayers. Single cells form colonies of similar size by two weeks in culture. Even in these colonies, only some of the cells become pigmented mature cells. This cycle can be repeated at least once. These characteristics suggest that the replatable cells are immature self-renewing precursors. Because these precursors still possess the potential to differentiate, we might call these precursors melanoblastic "stem cells." These cells lose their potential to grow after being frozen.

Methods

DIFFERENTIATION OF ES CELLS INTO MELANOCYTES

1. Prepare confluent ST2 feeder layers in six-well plates. ST2 cells are maintained in RPMI 1640 supplemented with 5% FCS, 50 μM 2-ME, 50 units/ml streptomycin, and 50-μg/ml penicillin. Usually, confluent ST2 cells split 1:4 reach the confluent state after three to four days in a 10-cm dish. Just when they reach this confluent state, the cells should be passaged for the next use. Avoid long-time maintenance of ST2 cells (more than 12 passages from the original stock).
2. Allow ES cells to grow to a subconfluent.
3. Harvest ES cells and seed them at the appropriate cell density, so that approximately 80 colonies are generated per well. Plating efficiency varies by the lot of serum. Supplement them with 10^{-7} M Dex, 20 pM bFGF, 10-pM CT, and optionally 100-ng/ml ET3 (final concentration).
4. Change the culture medium every 2 or 3 days and maintain the culture for 3 weeks. Mature melanocytes are identified after trypsinization as pigmented cells by bright-field, not phase-contrast, microscopy

MEDIUM

α-Minimum essential medium (α-MEM: Gibco BRL Cat. No. 11900-024) supplemented with 10% FCS, 50 units/ml streptomycin, and 50-μg/ml penicillin. Select a lot of FCS that supports melanocyte generation.

REFERENCES

1. Nordlund, J.J., Boissy, R.E., Hearing, V.J., King, R.A., and Ortonne, J.P., (eds.) (1998). "The Pigmentary System," Oxford University Press, New York, NY.
2. Galli, S.J., Zsebo, K.M., and Geissler, E.N. (1993) The Kit ligand, stem cell factor. *Adv. Immunol.* **55,** 1–96.
3. Baynash, A.G., Hosoda, K., Giaid, A., Richardson, J.A., Emoto, N., Hammer, R.E., and Yanagisawa, M. (1994). Interaction of endothelin-3 with endothelin-B receptor is essential for development of epidermal melanocytes and enteric neurons. *Cell* **79,** 1277–1285.
4. Nagy, A., Rossant, J., Nagy, R., Abramow-Newerly, W., and Roder, J.C. (1993). Derivation of completely cell culture-derived mice from early-passage embryonic stem cells. *Proc. Natl. Acad. Sci. USA* **90,** 8424–8428.

5. Doetschman, T.C., Eistetter, H., Katz, M., Schmidt, W., and Kemler, R. (1985). The *in vitro* development of blastocyst-derived embryonic stem cell lines: formation of visceral yolk sac, blood islands, and myocardium. *J. Embryol. Exp. Morphol.* **87,** 27–45.

6. Yamane, T., Hayashi, S.I., Mizoguchi, M., Yamazaki, H., and Kunisada, T. (1999). Derivation of melanocytes from embryonic stem cells in culture. *Dev. Dyn.* **216,** 450–458.

7. Yamane, T., Hayashi, S.I., and Kunisada, T. (2002). Embryonic stem cells as a model to study melanocyte lineage. *In* "Embryonic Stem Cells: Methods and Protocols (Methods in Molecular Biology)," (K. Turksen, ed.), Vol. 185, pp. 261–268. Humana Press, Totowa, NJ.

8. Ogawa, M., Nishikawa, S., Ikuta, K., Yamamura, F., Naito, M., Takahashi, K., and Nishikawa, S.I. (1988). B–cell ontogeny in murine embryo studied by a culture system with the monolayer of a stromal cell clone, ST2: B-cell progenitor develops first in the embryonal body rather than in the yolk sac. *EMBO J.* **7,** 1337–1343.

9. Hemmi, H., Okuyama, H., Yamane, T., Nishikawa, S.I., Nakano, T., Yamazaki, H., Kunisada, T., and Hayashi, S.I. (2001). Temporal and spatial localization of osteoclasts in colonies from embryonic stem cells. *Biochem. Biophys. Res. Commun.* **280,** 526–534.

10. (Unpublished observation).

21

Nervous System

Lorenz Studer

Introduction

Over the last few years, embryonic stem (ES) cells have emerged as a powerful tool to study brain development and function *in vitro* and *in vivo*. The recent isolation of human ES cells has further stimulated ES cell research directed toward cell-therapeutic applications, assessing the potential ES cells as a source of a range of somatic cell types affected by disease. The central nervous system (CNS) has been proposed as one of the prime targets for ES cell-based therapies because of early successes in directing ES cells toward neural fates, experience with fetal tissue transplantation in neurodegenerative diseases, and the devastating nature of many CNS diseases that often lack efficient alternative treatments. Some of the most striking advantages of ES cells over any other cell type are extensive self-renewal capacity and differentiation potential, access to the earliest stages of neural development, and ease of inducing stable genetic manipulations.

The mammalian brain is one of the most complex biological structures known. The study of brain function in the normal and diseased brain is therefore a daunting task. However, an understanding of the basic elements that produce the extraordinary cell diversity in the brain is an important step toward that end. Developmental biology taught us that all the cells of the CNS are derived from a small set of neuroepithelial cells that sequentially generate the various neuronal and glial subtypes that comprise the CNS and peripheral nervous system (PNS). ES cells provide a powerful model system for studying developmental neurobiology and for testing hypotheses on how neural identity and regional specification is established and on how neural stem cells decide to undergo neuronal or glial differentiation programs. The protocol for the directed differentiation of ES cells into specific neuronal or glial subtypes can serve as a cell-based developmental screen to identify novel genes involved in specific aspects of CNS development and to assess the role of known genes under conditions that can bypass the embryonic lethality often observed when studying gene function *in vivo*. This interplay between ES cells and developmental biology is mutually beneficial and will hopefully not only result in novel insights for basic biology but also provide a comprehensive framework of differentiation

strategies for cell therapeutic applications. Although work with mouse ES cells has achieved several of these goals, human ES cell work significantly lags the mouse work. It will be essential to narrow this gap soon to fulfill some of the promises of stem cell research for medical applications.

This review provides a short introduction on neural development followed by a section on neural stem cells, contrasting their advantages and limitations for both basic and clinical applications with the use of ES cells. Subsequently, I introduce the various strategies available for inducing neural differentiation in mouse ES cells and give various examples for neuronal, glial, and neural crest specification *in vitro*. This section is followed by a brief summary of published work on lineage selection using surface makers and cell type-specific promoters, a strategy that can be used as an alternative or in parallel to directed differentiation protocols. A synopsis of the current studies of neural differentiation in human and nonhuman primate ES cells is followed by more general remarks on the potential for ES cells to address developmental questions using cell-based screens. The final section summarizes recent work with ES cells for cell-therapeutic applications in preclinical models of neural disease.

Neural Development

A basic understanding of neural development is a prerequisite for developing rational strategies of stem cell differentiation. The neural plate is derived from the dorsal ectoderm and is induced by "organizer" signals derived from the underlying notochord. The dominant model of neural induction is the default hypothesis. This hypothesis states that that neural tissue is formed spontaneously in the absence of bone morphogenetic protein (BMP) signaling during early gastrulation, and exposure to BMP signals causes epidermal differentiation.[1] Accordingly, signals emanating from the organizer essential for neural induction are BMP inhibitors such as chordin,[2] noggin,[3] follistatin,[4] and cerberus. However, there is also strong evidence that fibroblast growth factor (FGF) signals emanating from precursors of the organizer prior to gastrulation are essential for a "prepattern" of neural induction through activation of Sox3 and early response to neural induction (ERNI).[5] Recent studies have identified Churchill (ChCh), a zinc-finger transcriptional activator induced by low doses of FGF signaling, that inhibits the mesoendoderm-inducing effects of FGF and sensitizes cells to BMP signals, thereby acting as a switch from gastrulation to neurulation.[6] Other essential players during

Handbook of Stem Cells
Volume 1

neural induction are insulin-like growth factor (IGF)[7] and Wnt signaling.[8,9]

After the formation of the neural plate, cells undergo a well-defined set of morphological and molecular changes leading to the formation of neural folds and neural tube closure. This is followed by orchestrated waves of neural proliferation and differentiation. Of particular importance in determining specific neural fates are signals that provide regional identity both in the anterior–posterior (A–P) and in the dorsal–ventral (D–V) axis and that define domains of distinct expression of homeodomain proteins and basic helix-loop-helix (bHLH) transcription factors. The leading hypothesis of A–P axis specification states that anterior fates are established as defaults during early neural induction, and FGF, Wnt, and retinoid signals are essential for establishing posterior cell fates (for a review, see Lumsden and Krumlauf[10]). D–V identity is determined by the antagonistic action of Sonic hedgehog (SHH) secreted ventrally form the notochord and floor plate and of BMPs from the roof plate (for a review, see Jessell[11]). There is ample evidence from explant studies[12–14]—and more recently from ES cell differentiation studies[15–19]—that confirm such a concentration-dependent role of SHH to define specific progenitor domains within the neural tube by activating class II genes in the ventral spinal cord.[20] However, genetic studies with SHH/Gli3,[21–23] or SHH/Rab23,[24] double-mutant mice have shown that D–V patterning can occur in the absence of SHH questioning an exclusive role for SHH gradients in D–V patterning. Recent work demonstrated that the timing of D–V patterning is controlled by the antagonistic action of FGF and retinoid signals[25] with FGF signals inhibiting the establishment D–V homeodomain transcription factors.[25] Other findings suggested a more specific role for FGFs in inhibiting dorsal gene expression[26] and identified retinoids as an activator of class I genes[26] essential for D–V patterning. A SHH-antagonistic concentration-dependent role for BMPs in dorsal–neural patterning has been proposed from work with explants *in vitro* (e.g., see Dickinson *et al.*[27] and Liem *et al.*[28]) and partly confirmed in ES cell differentiation studies.[17] Although some *in vivo* data from genetic ablation studies[29] and work in transgenic mice that overexpress the BMP receptor type 1a (BMPR1a/Alk3) under control of the regulatory elements of the *nestin* gene[30] are compatible with a dorsal patterning role for BMPs, loss-of-function studies of BMPR1b suggested a much more limited role for BMPs in determining selectively choroids plexus fate.[31] In addition to BMPs, Wnt signals might contribute to dorsal neural patterning, particularly the establishment of the neural crest.[32]

Subsequent differentiation of patterned neural precursor cells occurs in a stereotypic fashion with neurons being born first followed by astroglial and oligodendroglial differentiation. Onset of neuronal differentiation is controlled through inhibition of the Notch pathway that represses proneural bHLH genes (for review, see Gaiano and Fishell[33] and Tanigaki *et al.*[34]). Astrocytic fate is established using activation of Jak/Stat signals, which exert an instructive role on multipotent neural progenitor to drive astrocytic differentiation.[35,36] However, recent insights into the neurogenic properties

of radial glial[37] cells as well as the identification of adult neural stem cells as cell-expressing astrocytic markers[38] suggest a more complex and dynamic interaction between neural stem cell and astrocytic fates. Oligodendrocytes were believed to derive from bipotent glial precursors termed O2A progenitors[39] or from other glially committed precursors.[40] However, data recently emerged that suggest a lineage relationship between motor neurons and oligodendrocytes in the spinal cord[41,42] as well as γ-aminobutyric acidergic (GABAergic) neurons and oligodendrocytes in the forebrain[43,44] by their shared requirement for expression of the bHLH gene *Olig* 2. A review of the developmental signals that control the various neuronal subtypes is beyond the scope of this chapter, but some of the necessary signals will be described in the individual headings under the section "Derivation of ES Cell-Derived Neurons." Excellent reviews on the specification of catecholaminergic and neurons,[45] ventral and dorsal spinal cord neuron subtypes,[46,47] forebrain patterning,[48,49] and forebrain cell types[50,51] are available for more in-depth information on this topic.

Neural Stem Cells

The isolation of neural stem cells provided a first step toward developing rational strategies of *in vitro* neuronal and glial differentiation. Neural stem cell culture systems had significant influence on protocols of directed neural differentiation from ES cells. I therefore briefly highlight some of the basic neural stem cell techniques with a view toward explaining commonalities and discrepancies between the two *in vitro* differentiation strategies. Neural stem cells have been isolated from both the developing and the adult brain (for review, see Gage[52] and McKay[53]). More than 10 years of intensive research has convincingly demonstrated the capacity of neural stem cells for self-renewal and multilineage differentiation into neurons, astrocytes, and oligodendrocytes, the three major CNS lineages. However, although many tissue-specific stem cells, such as hematopoietic stem cells, are capable of differentiation into all progeny within an organ system,[54] neural stem cells do not efficiently generate all neuronal subtypes in the adult brain. They are largely limited to the production of GABA and glutamatergic neurons after long-term expansion.[55,56] Early attempts at isolating and propagating neural stem cells *in vitro* were based purely on selective growth and proliferation condition. The most common method is the neurosphere culture system.[57–59] Under these conditions, neural precursors are grown at low density and allowed to proliferate as free-floating spheres in the presence of epidermal growth factor (EGF) and FGF-2. Human neurospheres cultures are typically supplemented with leukemia inhibitory factor (LIF)[60] in addition to EGF and FGF-2. Neurospheres can be formed from single cells, and the capacity for neurosphere formation is often used as an assay to test stem cell properties of neural cells. For example the isolation of prospectively identified neural stem cells based on surface markers such as AC133,[61] Lex1,[62] or combinations of surface markers[63] was largely developed on the ability of the cells to form neurospheres *in vitro*.

These data need to be interpreted cautiously, as neurosphere formation is not necessarily a true test of stemness and neurospheres do contain many differentiated cells in addition to the presumptive progenitor–stem cell population. Recent studies have demonstrated that neurospheres are formed more efficiently from transit amplifying populations than from true stem cells in the adult subventricular zone.[64]

An alternative approach to the neurosphere technology is the growth of neural precursor–stem cells as monolayer culture attached on a matrix—typically fibronectin or laminin—in the presence of FGF-2.[65–67] These conditions are more amenable to study of the precise lineage relationship, and they allow precise manipulations at the single-cell level. Complete lineage trees for single cortical stem cells have been worked out under such conditions.[68] Among the most important limitations of current neural stem cell technology are the limited *in vitro* control of neural patterning and neuronal subtype specification.

The derivation of midbrain dopamine neurons has served as a model for these difficulties. Functional midbrain dopamine neurons can be derived from short-term-expanded precursor cells isolated from the early rodent and human midbrain.[69,70] However, long-term expansion causes a dramatic loss in the efficiency of midbrain dopamine neuron generation.[71] Several strategies have been developed in an attempt to overcome these problems, ranging from exposure and complex growth factor cocktails[72,73] to changes in oxygen levels[74] and transgenic expression of Nurr1,[75,76] a key transcription factor during midbrain dopamine neuron development.[77–79] However, none of these approaches has succeeded in deriving midbrain dopamine neurons that exhibit full functionality *in vitro* and *in vivo* from naïve, long-term-expanded neural stem cells. Although the mechanisms of the restricted neuronal differentiation potential remain to be elucidated, the cell types most difficult to derive from neural stem cells are neurons born at developmental stages prior to stem cell isolation. This suggests that the competence of the precursor population to generate these neuronal subtypes might be lost or that the environmental cofactors required for appropriate neuron subtype specification are missing. Alternatively, the mitogens used for propagation of the neural precursor cells might select for progeny incapable of generating early neuronal subtypes, bias competent precursors into a noncompetent state, or directly deregulate the neural patterning state as recently suggested for FGF-2-expanded precursors in the spinal cord.[80] Possible solutions might consist of isolating neural stem cells at an earlier developmental state and defining conditions that allow these cells to retain early competency for patterning factors, identifying growth factors that do not bias neuronal subtype or that are able to reinduce competence in later precursors, or introducing novel patterning strategies that can bypass current limitations in neuronal subtype potential. One early example in this direction is the growth of midbrain-derived precursors in the absence of FGF2 but in the presence of SHH and FGF8 as well as TGFβ-3,[81] a combination capable of increasing midbrain dopamine neurons generated *in vitro* but still with limited capacity for cell expansion. Although these problems continue to hamper *in vitro* differentiation studies with primary neural stem cells, ES cells offer a simple and efficient alternative solution to overcoming such concerns.

Neural Differentiation of Mouse ES Cells

ES cells are capable of virtually unlimited *in vitro* proliferation at the undifferentiated stage, overcoming many problems associated with the instability of stem cell phenotype observed in tissue-specific stem cells including neural stem cells. In addition to proliferation potential, ES cells offer many important advantages for both basic and applied research, such as ease of genetic manipulation, access to the earliest stages of neural development, and comprehensive differentiation potential. The cell fate potential of ES cells is most vividly illustrated upon injection of ES cells into the developing blastocyst, where ES progeny contributes to all tissues including the germ line. Neural differentiation has been one of the best-studied *in vitro* differentiation pathways in ES cell research. This is partly because of the ease by which ES cells generate neural progeny but also because of the potential of neural progeny for cell-therapeutic applications in the CNS. The use of ES cells in regenerative medicine received a significant boost about 5 years ago when human ES cells and embryonic germ (EG) cells were first isolated.[82–84]

NEURAL INDUCTION

The initial requirement for generating defined neural subtypes from ES cells is appropriate control of neural induction. There are at least three main strategies for using ES cells *in vitro* to induced neural differentiation in mouse ES cells: embryoid body (EB)-based systems, stromal feeder-mediated neural induction, and protocols based on default differentiation into neural fates (Fig. 21–1).

EB-Based Protocols

EBs are formed upon aggregation of ES cells in suspension cultures. The interactions of cells within the EB causes cell differentiation in a framework that mimics normal development, particularly the steps of gastrulation. Accordingly, derivatives of all three germ layers can be found in EBs[85] (for a review, see Weiss *et al.*[86]), and EB culture is often used as a first screening tool to demonstrate pluripotency of putative ES cell lines. Although the derivation of neural progeny is inefficient under basic EB conditions, several protocols have been developed to enhance neural induction and to select and expand EB-derived neural precursors.

The first EB-mediated neural differentiation protocol was based on exposure to retinoic acid (RA) for 4 days after EBs had been formed for 4 days in the absence of RA (the so-called 4⁻/4⁺ protocol[87]). RA is a vitamin A derivative released primarily by surrounding mesodermal cells, and it exhibits a strong neural induction and patterning effect (for a review, see Maden[88]). Many variations on the basic protocol have been developed.[89–91] However, no clear mechanistic understanding of the action of RA in EBs has emerged, and the overall cell composition under these conditions

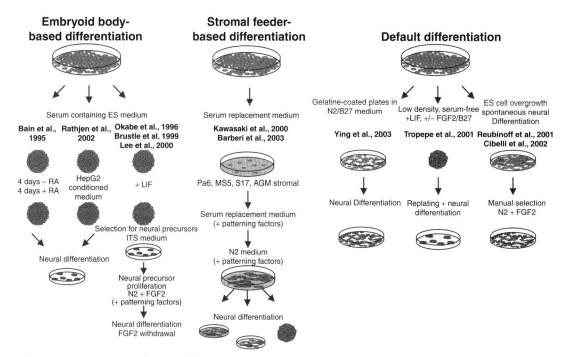

Figure 21–1. *Basic techniques for inducing neural differentiation in ES cells in vitro. (A) Embryoid body-based protocols are initiated by the aggregation of undifferentiated ES cells. Neural differentiation is promoted by exposure to RA, hepatocarcinoma cell line (HepG2)-conditioned medium, or neural selection in defined medial. Classic studies are cited for each of the three main EB-based strategies. (B) Stromal feeder-mediated differentiation is obtained upon plating undifferentiated ES cells at low density on stromal feeder cell lines derived from the bone marrow of the AGM region of the embryo. Serum-free conditions are required throughout the protocol. Conditions can be readily adapted to achieve neural subtype-specific differentiation for a large number of CNS cell types. Classic studies are cited for PA6- and MS5-mediated differentiation. (C) Default neural differentiation is achieved by reducing endogenous BMP signals using plating cells at low density under minimal medium conditions or in the presence of the BMP antagonist noggin. Neurally committed cells can also be mechanically isolated and propagated from plates exhibiting spontaneous neural differentiation after overgrowth of ES cells. (Please see CD-ROM for color version of this figure.)*

remains heterogeneous. One major additional concern in RA-based neural induction protocols is the concomitant effect of RA on A–P patterning mediated through activating the *Hox* gene cascade.[92]

An alternative EB-based strategy is the exposure to conditioned medium derived from the hepatocarcinoma cell line (HepG2), which appears to induce neuroectodermal fate directly.[93] Accordingly, HepG2-treated aggregates do not express endodermal or mesodermal markers but directly generate neural progeny expressing progenitor markers such as Sox1, Sox2, and nestin. The active component within an HepG2-conditioned medium remains to be isolated. Some evidence indicates that at least two separable components are responsible for this activity, and one of these components is apparently a known extracellular matrix molecule.[93] Unlike the RA protocols, HepG2 conditions are not thought to bias neural subtype composition toward specific A–P or D–V fates. However, no detailed studies are available that have addressed this issue experimentally or developed neural subtype-specific protocols.

A third strategy for achieving neural induction is an RA-free EB-based protocol that subjects EB progeny to neural-selective growth conditions.[16,94,95] Neural selection from EB progeny is achieved under minimal growth conditions in a serum-free medium supplemented with insulin, transferrin, and selenite (ITS medium). Under these conditions, most EB-derived cells die, and a distinct population of immature cells emerges that expresses increasing levels of the intermediate filament nestin. These nestin⁺ precursors can be replated and directed toward various neuronal and glial fates using a combination of patterning, survival, and lineage-promoting factors (see the sections "Derivation of ES Cell-Derived Neurons" and "ES Cell-Derived Glia"). This technique is quite robust and highly modular for generating a variety of neural subtypes (see later sections of this chapter). Moreover, commercially available kits provide a simple entry point for setting up the system. However, ES cell line-specific differences in the efficiency of neural induction can occur, particularly at stage III of differentiation (selection of nestin⁺ precursors from EBs in ITS medium) and can be limiting for some applications.[15,96]

Stromal Feeder-Mediated Neural Induction

Bone marrow-derived stromal cell lines have been used for years to support the growth of undifferentiated hematopoietic stem cells,[97–100] acting partly through expression of the membrane protein mKirre, a mammalian homolog of the *kirre* gene of *Drosophila melanogaster.*[101]

More recently, it has been reported that many stromal cell lines that support hematopoietic stem cell growth exhibit neural-inducing properties in coculture with mouse ES cells[15,102,103] Stromal cell lines with the highest efficiencies of neural induction are typically at the preadipocytic stage of differentiation. Although most of these cell lines were isolated from the bone marrow (e.g., PA-6, MS5, and S17), stromal cells derived from the aorta–gonad–mesonephros (AGM) region were found to induce neural differentiation equally well in mouse ES and nuclear transfer ES cells.[15] The inducing effect does not require the survival of the stromal cells, as similar or increased neural inducing activity is observed upon paraformaldehyde fixation.[102] The main activity resides within the cell surface of the stromal cells and does not diffuse efficiently over long distances.[102] The molecular nature of this inducing activity of stromal-derived cells remains unknown, but preliminary data suggest that it does not involve BMP or Wnt signaling. The efficiency and robustness of neural induction using stromal feeder cells is extremely high compared to alternative protocols,[15] and differentiation appears to occur without any bias toward regional specification or neuronal-versus-glial fate choice.[15,17]

Neural Differentiation by Default

Coculture-free, direct neural differentiation protocols are based on the default hypothesis proposing that in the absence of cell–cell signaling, particularly in the absence of exposure to BMPs, ectodermal cells will adopt a neural fates.[1] Two independent studies with mouse ES cells confirmed that under minimal conditions, in the absence of BMP but in the presence of a required endogenous FGF signal, neural induction does occur in nonadherent[104] or adherent[105] monocultures. Interference with FGF signaling using dominant–negative or gene targeting approaches prevents neural differentiation in either system, confirming an confirm the early role for FGF in neural induction suggested by *in vivo* studies.[5] The development of more refined culture systems will be particularly useful for defining the minimal molecular requirements that drive neural fate specification in early development. Maintenance of undifferentiated mouse ES cells in the absence of serum but in the presence of BMP4 and LIF[106] will be an additional important step toward that end. However, the efficacy of default monoculture approach in comparison to EB and stromal feeder protocols has not been determined. Furthermore, although these systems appear highly defined at the time of plating, the heterogeneity of cell types starts to appear quickly after initiation of differentiation even under monoculture conditions.

DERIVATION OF ES CELL-DERIVED NEURONS

Neuronal differentiation occurs rapidly upon neural induction of mouse ES cells. The efficiency of neuronal-versus-glial differentiation varies widely. Neuronal subtype specification can be influenced by the mode of neuronal induction. This is particularly the case for the RA induction protocol known to induce the *Hox* gene cascade in a dose-dependent fashion and to promote hindbrain and spinal cord fates at the expense of forebrain differentiation. The basic strategy for achieving neuronal subtype differentiation relies on the application of signals that mimic early patterning events in the embryo to define A–P and D–V domains within the body axis of the developing embryo. A–P patterning is thought to involve factors that actively posteriorize regional identity, including RA, FGFs, and Wnts. D–V patterning is thought to be controlled by the antagonistic action of SHH and BMP signals. Although early mouse ES cell differentiation strategies yielded neurons that were poorly characterized and typically of GABA or glutamatergic origin, more refined protocols have been developed recently for many neuronal subtypes. Protocols for a selection of neuronal subtypes are described in more detail later in this chapter.

Midbrain Dopaminergic Neurons

Derivation of midbrain dopamine neurons from ES cells has been of particular interest because of the clinical potential for dopamine neuron transplants in the treatment of Parkinson's disease (for review, see Bjorklund *et al.*[107] and Dunnett and Bjorklund[108]). Protocols for the dopaminergic differentiation of mouse ES cells closely follow findings obtained in explant studies that identified FGF8 and SHH as critical factors in midbrain dopamine neuron specification.[14,109–111] The effect of SHH/FGF8 on ES cell-derived neural precursors was first described using an EB-based five-step differentiation protocol.[16] Under these conditions, up to 34% of all neurons expressed tyrosine hydroxylase (TH), the rate-limiting enzyme in the synthesis of dopamine. However, the effect of SHH and FGF8 was relatively modest and did not exceed that of another dopamine neuron-promoting factor, ascorbic acid (AA, vitamin C).[16,71] A further increase in dopamine neuron yield was obtained in ES cells overexpressing Nurr1.[18] Nearly 80% of all neurons express TH under these conditions, and expression of midbrain dopaminergic markers remains stable even after transgenic expression of Nurr1 has been silenced. Midbrain dopaminergic differentiation was also obtained using coculture of ES cells on the stromal feeder cell line (PA6).[102] PA6 cells mediated neural induction, yielding dopaminergic differentiation in up to 16% of all neurons without requiring exposure to exogenous SHH and FGF8 but in the presence of AA. These results were initially interpreted as PA6 exhibiting a specific action promoting dopamine neuron fate in addition to its neural-inducing properties.[112] However, later studies demonstrated that there is no irreversible bias toward the generation of midbrain dopamine neurons using PA6 but that neural precursors derived under these conditions remain highly amenable to A–P and D–V patterning.[15,17] When combining stromal feeder-mediated neural induction with exposure to SHH/FGF8, about 50% of all neurons express TH15 without requiring any transgene, such as Nurr1, to further push dopamine neuron phenotype.

Numbers of TH neurons need to be interpreted carefully in all *in vitro* differentiation studies, as TH is an unreliable marker for identifying dopamine neuron. TH is also expressed in other catecholaminergic neurons including noradrenergic and adrenergic cells, and it is induced in many cell types under various conditions including cell stress, hypoxia, and exposure to a variety of growth hormones. It is therefore essential that studies reporting on the derivation of midbrain dopamine neurons provide additional markers and evidence of dopamine neuron function *in vitro* and *in vivo*. A detailed description of all these parameters can be found in a recent review.[113] The derivation of TH neurons has also been achieved using a monolayer, default neural induction protocol.[105] However, efficiency of dopamine neuron induction, characterization of midbrain phenotype, and *in vitro* and *in vivo* functionality using a default neural induction protocol have not yet been reported.

Serotonergic Neurons

The developmental origin of serotonergic neurons is closely related to that of midbrain dopamine neurons. Both neuronal subtypes are dependent on signals emanating from the isthmic organizer.[45] Accordingly, serotonergic neurons are a major "contaminating" neuronal subtypes in protocols aimed at the derivation of midbrain dopaminergic cells. Protocols specifically designed to increase serotonergic-versus-dopaminergic differentiation have been based on the exposure to FGF4. Application of exogenous FGF4 preceding FGF8 and SHH application ectopically induces serotonergic neurons in explant culture.[14] Although application of FGF4 to neural precursors in the presence of FGF2 at stage IV (neural precursor cell proliferation) of the multistep EB differentiation protocol does not yield a significant increase in serotonergic differentiation,[16] FGF4 added in the absence of FGF2 causes a dramatic shift from dopaminergic to serotonergic differentiation.[18] Efficient derivation of hindbrain serotonergic neurons using stromal feeder-mediated neural induction also involves early FGF4 exposure in the absence of FGF2, followed by FGF2, FGF8, and SHH application.[15] Novel strategies to refine serotonergic differentiation protocols might use novel, basic developmental insights that demonstrated the importance of the transcription factor Lmx1b in serotonergic differentiation.[114] They also may use studies of zebra fish in which several novel genes have been isolated that affect the proportion of dopaminergic-versus-serotonergic neurons, including the elongation factor foggy[115] and the zinc-finger protein named too few.[116] Although cell therapy might be not a primary goal for optimizing serotonergic differentiation protocols, the derivation of ES cell-derived serotonin neurons may provide insights into brain development and offer an unlimited source of cells for pharmacological screens in a neurotransmitter system involved in various psychiatric disorders.[117–120]

Motor Neurons

Development of spinal motor neurons has been studied in great detail using a variety of mouse loss-of-function and chick gain-of-function models as well as explant culture systems (for review, see Jessell[11] and Lee and Pfaff[46]). A more advanced understanding of the developmental signals involved in motor neuron specification and a wealth of reagents available for their phenotypic characterization make the derivation of motor neurons from ES cells an obvious target. Early studies have demonstrated that cells expressing markers of motor neurons can be generated using an EB induction protocol with RA exposure (2⁻/7⁺).[90] More systematic approaches of using RA exposure with exogenous SHH to promote ventral fates have yielded ES cell-derived motor neurons at high efficiency and have demonstrated how developmental pathways can be harnessed to direct ES cell fate *in vitro*.[19] By creating an ES cell line, which expresses GFP under the control of the motor neuron-specific gene HB9, these ES cell-derived motor neurons could also be readily identified and purified. The *in vivo* properties of ES cell-derived motor neurons were demonstrated upon transplantation into the spinal cord of early chick embryos. ES cell-derived motor neurons were detected in the ventral spinal cord, extended axons, and innervated nearby muscle targets.[19]

Efficient derivation of motor neurons has also been achieved using stromal feeders such as PA6[17] or MS5 cells[15] with SHH and RA treatment. The next challenges for *in vitro* motor neuron differentiation protocols will be the selective generation of motor neurons of distinct A–P and columnar identity. Recent insights from developmental biology studies will provide a good starting point.[121,122] The potential of ES cell-derived motor neurons for future therapeutic applications in spinal cord injury or amyotrophic lateral sclerosis (ALS, Lou Gehrig's disease) will heavily rely on the ability to generate precise motor neuron subtypes *in vitro*. Additional requirements are controlling axonal outgrowth, target selection, and specificity of muscle innervation. One particularly useful approach might be the genetic or pharmacological manipulation of ES cell-derived motor neurons to overcome growth inhibitors in an adult environment, a strategy used successfully to overcome growth inhibition of primary dorsal-root ganglion cells upon activation of the cyclic adenosine monophosphate pathway.[123,124]

GABA Neurons

GABA cells are the main inhibitor neuron type within the brain and are found at high densities in basal forebrain structures, particularly in the striatum. The presence of GABAergic neurons during ES cell differentiation *in vitro* has been reported under various conditions including the classic 4⁻/4⁺ EB-based differentiation protocols,[87] which yield yields approximately 25% GABA neurons.[125] Interestingly, protocols with shorter periods of RA-free EB formation followed by extended RA treatment (2⁻/7⁺) select for motor neurons rather than GABA neurons.[90] This suggests that the timing of RA application might be crucial for neural fate specification. The presence of GABA neurons has also been reported under default neural induction conditions.[105]

Directed differentiation to GABA neurons has been achieved using a stromal feeder-based approach.[15] Neural induction on MS5 is followed by neural precursor proliferation in FGF2 and subsequent exposure to SHH and FGF8. The delayed application of FGF8 and SHH promotes ventral forebrain identities as determined by the expression of the forebrain-specific marker FOXG1B (BF-1, see Tao and Lai[126]) and increases GABAergic differentiation.[15] In addition to forebrain striatal and cortical GABA neurons, there are many other types of GABA neurons in various brain regions, including the thalamus,[127] midbrain,[128] and cerebellum.[129] It remains to be determined whether there will be common differentiation strategies that can be used to derive these various GABAergic subtypes from ES cells or whether diversity in the expression of region-specific markers will be reflected in the culture conditions. GABA neurons are highly relevant for a variety of neurological disorders, including Huntington's disease, epilepsy, and stroke.

Glutamate Neurons

Glutamate neurons can be readily obtained at high efficiencies from mouse ES cells. For example, in the Bain protocol,[87] approximately 70% of all neurons are glutamatergic, and ES cell-derived neurons with N-methyl-D-aspartate (NMDA) and non-NMDA receptor subtypes have been described.[130] Similar neuron subtype compositions have been obtained with various related protocols.[91,131] More detailed physiological data on glutamatergic neurons have been reported after coculture of ES cell-derived neurons on hippocampal brain slices.[132] Interestingly, this study suggested a possible bias toward establishing AMPA- over NMDA-type synaptic contacts.[132] There is currently no detailed data on the derivation of glutamatergic neurons using stromal feeder or default neural differentiation protocols.

Other Neuronal and Neural Subtypes

The presence of about 5% glycinergic neurons has been reported using the classic 4⁻/4⁺ EB protocol.[87,125] However, directed differentiation into this main inhibitory neuronal subtype in the spinal cord has not been demonstrated. Other interesting neural types generated from ES cells are precursors of the otic anlage.[133] These precursors were obtained by culturing EBs for 10 days in EGF and IGF followed by bFGF expansion. After transplantation of these precursors *in vivo*, differentiation was observed into cells expressing markers of mature hair cells.[133] Derivation of radial glial cells from mouse ES cells[134] provides another interesting assay system to probe neuronal and glial lineage relationships in early neural development.

Neural Crest Differentiation

The neural crest is a transient structure formed from the most dorsal aspects of the neural tube of the vertebrate embryo. It contains migratory cells that form the PNS including sensory, sympathetic, and enteric ganglia; large parts of the facial skeleton; as well as various other cell types including Schwann cells, melanocytes, and adrenomedullary cells. ES cells provide a powerful assay to study neural crest development *in vitro*. The main strategy for deriving neural crest-like structures from ES cells is based on the exposure to BMPs (BMP2, BMP4, or BMP7) following neural induction. The feasibility of this approach was recently demonstrated for mouse and partly nonhuman primate ES cells using the PA6

stromal feeder cell system.[17] This study showed the development of sensory as well as sympathetic neurons in a BMP dose-dependent manner. The derivation of smooth muscle cells required growth in chicken extract with BMP withdrawal. No melanocytes or Schwann cells could be obtained under these conditions.[17]

Another recent study suggests efficient neural crest induction, including Schwann cell differentiation, using an EB-based, multistep differentiation protocol with BMP2 treatment.[135] Neural crest formation has also been reported in HepG2-mediated neural differentiation protocols upon exposure to staurosporine,[93] previously reported to induce avian neural crest development.[136] However, characterization of neural crest progeny was limited to morphological observations and expression of Sox10, a marker expressed during neural crest development but also during glial development in the CNS. Future studies are required to define conditions for deriving all neural crest lineages *in vitro* and to validate stability and function of neural crest phenotypes *in vivo*.

DERIVATION OF ES CELL-DERIVED GLIA

Neural progenitors derived from mouse ES cells can be readily differentiated into astrocytic and oligodendroglial progeny under conditions similar to those described from primary neural precursors. The first reports on the glial differentiation of mouse ES cells were based on the 4⁻/4⁺ EB protocols[87,89,91] or multistep EB differentiation protocols.[94] Most of the glial progeny under these conditions are astrocytes, with only few immature oligodendrocytes present. However, subsequent studies have defined conditions for the selective generation of both astrocytes and oligodendrocytes.

Oligodendrocytes

Highly efficient differentiation into oligodendrocytes was reported first using a modified multistep, EB-based protocol.[95] ES cell-derived neural precursors were expanded with FGF2 followed by FGF2⁺EGF and FGF2⁺platelet-derived growth factor (PDGF). These conditions yielded a population of A2B5⁺ glial precursors capable of differentiation into both astrocytic (~36% glial fibrillary acidic protein-positive, or GFAP⁺) and oligodendrocytic (~38% O4⁺) progeny upon mitogen withdrawal. The 4⁻/4⁺ EB–RA induction protocol has recently been optimized for the production of oligodendrocytic progeny. This study[137] demonstrated efficient selection of neural progeny by both positive (Sox1–enhanced green fluorescent protein, or EGFP) and negative (Oct4–herpesvirus thymidine kinase) selection and oligodendrocytic differentiation in RA-induced EBs after expansion in FGF2 followed by dissociation and replating in serum-free medium containing FGF2 and SHH. The final step involved SHH and FGF2 withdrawal and the addition of PDGF and thyroid hormone (T3). Under these conditions, approximately 50% of all cells express oligodendroglial markers. Optimized conditions for oligodendrocyte differentiation using HepG2 or default neural differentiation protocols have not yet been reported. However, stromal feeder-mediated induction, initially thought to bias toward neuronal progeny,[102] can be readily adapted to derive oligodendrocytes at very high efficiencies and without requiring genetic selection.[15]

Astrocytes

Highly efficient differentiation of ES cells into astrocytes has been recently reported using stromal feeder-mediated neural induction followed by sequential exposure to FGF2, bFGF/EGF, EGF/CNTF, and ciliary neurotrophic factor (CNTF). More than 90% of all cells expressed the astrocytic marker GFAP under these conditions.[15] Significant numbers of GFAP cells were also obtained using HepG2-mediated neural differentiation[93] or multistep EB protocols.[95] Glial progenitors obtained with a multistep EB protocol were recently "transplanted" *in vitro* into hippocampal slices and revealed that full physiological maturation of ES cell-derived astrocytes can be achieved upon interaction with an appropriate host environment.[138] Under these conditions, ES cell-derived astrocytes integrated seamlessly into host astrocytic networks tightly coupled by gap junctions.

LINEAGE SELECTION

Lineage selection based on surface markers or the cell type-specific expression of promoter-driven selectable markers provides an alternative approach to directed *in vitro* differentiation protocols. The use of genetic markers in ES cells is particularly attractive because of ease of inducing stable genetic modifications and the availability of large libraries of transgenic and gene-targeted mice and ES cells. Efficient purification of neural progeny from mouse ES cells *in vitro* was demonstrated through positive selection using a Sox1-EGFP knockin cell line[139] and combined with negative selectable marker controlled by endogenous Oct4 locus.[137] Other ES lines successfully used for the genetic identification and purification of neural precursor and neuronal and glial progeny *in vitro* include a tau-EGFP knockin cell line,[131] a GFAP transgenic line,[140] GAD-lacZ knockin ES cells,[141] BF1-lacZ knockin ES cells,[15] and ES cell lines driven under the regulatory elements of the *Nestin* gene.[142,143] Promoter-driven lineage selection for motor neuron fate *in vitro* includes ES cell lines expressing EGFP in the Olig2 locus[144] or as a transgene under the *HB9* promoter.[19]

Neural Differentiation of Human and Nonhuman Primate ES Cells

Neural differentiation potential was readily observed when primate ES or ES-like cells were first established in both monkey[145] and human ES cells[82,83] as well as in human EG cells[84] and monkey parthenogenetic stem cells.[146] However, the derivation of purified populations of neural progeny from human ES cells required more systematic studies. A highly efficient protocol for the neural differentiation of human ES cells was based on a modified multistep EB approach.[147] ES cells are aggregated for a short time (approximately 4 days) and subsequently replated under serum-free conditions in the presence of FGF-2. Under these conditions, neural precursors can be readily identified based on the formation of multilayered

epithelia termed rosettes. It was suggested that such rosettes might mimic neural tube-like structures *in vitro*. These neural precursor cells can be enzymatically separated from the surrounding cell types and grown to purity under neurosphere-like conditions in the presence of FGF-2. Differentiated neural progeny derived from these neurosphere-like structures are neurons and astrocytes. The main neuronal subtypes are GABAergic and glutamatergic phenotypes[147] (see also Studer[148]). A similar spectrum of differentiated progeny was obtained when human ES cell-derived neural precursors were obtained after spontaneous neural differentiation by overgrowth of undifferentiated cells.[149] Rosette-like structures were manually isolated under microscopic view and subsequently grown and passaged under neurosphere-like conditions. A third strategy that yielded differentiated cell populations enriched for neural precursors was based on a modified EB–RA induction protocol, followed by lineage selection in attached cultures using serum-free conditions and supplementation with bFGF.[150]

Protocols that yield better control over neuronal subtype specification are still in development, but the first examples have been provided for deriving midbrain-like dopamine neurons from nonhuman primate ES cells.[98,146,151] Interestingly, PA6-mediated neural induction caused differentiation into retinal-pigment epithelial cells[98] in addition to neural differentiation and the derivation of TH[+] neurons. A bias toward eye differentiation was not observed with standard mouse ES cell protocols using stromal feeder cells. However, more systematic efforts have identified conditions that yield eye-like differentiation in mouse ES cells,[152] suggesting that eye phenotypes are can be obtained not only with human ES cells but also mouse ES cells.

One interesting difference between human and mouse ES cell differentiation is the presence of large numbers of rosette-like structures during the early stages of neural differentiation in human ES cells. These structures are rarely observed during mouse ES cell differentiation. A better understanding of the developmental nature of these structures may give important hints about how to optimize neuronal subtype specification *in vitro*. D–V patterning in vertebrates occurs during the time of neural tube formation, and distinct transcription factor domains are established by the time of neural tube closure. The presence or absence of such domains in cultured rosettes will an important factor in determining whether D–V identity has been established or whether these structures remain sensitive to patterning strategies.

Developmental Perspectives

Highly reproducible *in vitro* differentiation protocols and an increasing number of available ES reporter cell lines provide powerful tools for establishing cell-based developmental screens. In addition, large-scale gene-trapping approaches have yielded ES cells lines mutant for a large proportion of all the genes within the mouse genome (see *http://baygenomics. ucsf.edu/* and *http://www.lexicon-genetics.com*). Several ES cell-based *in vitro* differentiation screens have been carried out to assay for genes involved in neural–neuronal induction. One such screen using kinase-directed combinatorial libraries has identified a molecule with potent inhibitory activity for GSK3β during neural differentiation of mouse ES and P19 cells.[153] The result suggested that activation of Wnt signaling through increased β-catenin levels and activation of downstream targets, including LEF1/TCF1, increases neuronal differentiation. In agreement with these findings, previous studies have shown that Wnt1 is downstream target during RA-mediated neural differentiation of P19 cells and that Wnt1 is sufficient to trigger neural differentiation in these cells. In contrast, a recent report identified the Wnt antagonist Sfrp2 during neural differentiation of EBs exposed to RA.[154] This study used functional gene screening of RA-treated and control EBs through subtraction hybridization followed by episomal expression of differentially expressed cDNAs. The discrepancy between the two approaches on role of Wnt signaling during neural differentiation *in vitro* reflects differences in the assays used. It underscores the importance of using better-defined, developmentally based *in vitro* differentiation systems that allow careful interpretation of the findings in such screens. The availability of more comprehensive genomic tools will facilitate the establishment of detailed gene expression profiles under all *in vitro* ES cell differentiation conditions that will complement the few existing data sets.[155] Early gene-trapping studies that used *in vitro* differentiation screens prior to or instead of *in vivo* studies (e.g., see Xiong et al.[156] and Baker et al.[157]) may also see a revival using refined neural differentiation protocols. The availability of high-throughput functional genomic approaches such as RNAi-based gene knockdowns screens in *Dosophilia*[158,159] and *C. elegans*[160,161] could be readily adapted to ES cell *in vitro* differentiation systems and may provide unprecedented opportunities for studying neural development using cell-based differentiation systems. Such approaches could be of particular importance in studying human neural development when no appropriate *in vivo* alternatives exist.

Therapeutic Perspectives

One of the driving forces behind deciphering the developmental program that controls cell fate specification is the hope that such insights could be harnessed for generating specialized cells for therapy. However, despite the excitement about the potential of ES cells in neural repair, there are few examples in which such approaches have been tested in animal models of disease.

PARKINSON'S DISEASE

One of the most widely discussed applications is the derivation of unlimited numbers of dopamine neurons from human ES cells for the treatment of Parkinson's disease. This disease is a particularly attractive for cell transplantation because of the relatively defined pathology that mainly affects midbrain dopamine neurons and the largely unknown etiology that currently precludes causative treatment. At the onset of clinical symptoms, most midbrain dopamine neurons have already

died, providing further rationale for a cell replacement approach. The first ES cell-based study that showed functional improvement in 6OHDA lesioned rats, an animal model of Parkinson's disease, was based on the transplantation of low numbers of largely undifferentiated mouse ES cells isolated after short-term differentiation in EB cultures.[162] Spontaneous differentiation into large numbers of neurons with midbrain dopamine characteristics was observed. However, the clinical relevance of this approach is rather limited because of the high rate of tumor formation (>50% of the animals with surviving grafts developed teratomas).

Remarkable functional improvement was obtained after transplantation of dopamine neurons derived from mouse ES cells overexpressing Nurr1.[18] This study was based on a multistep EB differentiation protocol. In addition, to behavioral restoration in 6OHDA lesioned rats, this study demonstrated *in vivo* functionality using electrophysiological recordings from grafted dopamine neurons in acute brain slices obtained from the grafted animals. However, transgenic expression of Nurr1 raises safety concerns that may preclude clinical translation. Functional recovery with dopamine neurons derived from naïve mouse ES cells was recently reported.[15] This study demonstrated functional improvement *in vivo* after grafting dopamine neurons derived from ES and nuclear transfer ES cells using stromal feeder-mediated differentiation. Successful grafting of nuclear transfer ES cell-derived dopamine neurons provided a first example of therapeutic cloning in neural disease.[15] Differentiation of human ES cells into midbrain dopamine neurons has not yet been reported. However, it is likely such protocols will become available within the next few years to be tested in rodent and primate models of Parkinson's disease.

Several issues remain to be addressed before clinical trials with human ES cell-derived dopamine neurons should be initiated. Twenty years of fetal tissue research have demonstrated that fetal midbrain dopamine neurons can survive and function long term (more than 10 years[163]) in the brain of Parkinson's patients. However, these studies have also shown limited efficacy in placebo-controlled clinical trials and demonstrated potential for side effects.[164,165] Stem cells will have to learn from the fetal tissue transplantation trials and better define and address the critical parameters that can take cell therapy in Parkinson's disease to the next level.[107] The derivation of highly purified populations of *substantia nigra*-type dopamine neurons from human ES cells will be an important first step on this road.

HUNTINGTON'S DISEASE

Similar to Parkinson's disease, the pathology in Huntington's disease preferentially affects selective neuronal subtypes, particularly GABAergic medium spiny neurons, the main neuron subtype in the striatum. Fetal tissue transplantation trials[166–168] provide experience on how to design stem cell-based approaches for the treatment of Huntington's disease. However, unlike in Parkinson's disease, grafted cells are required not to reconnect to local targets within the striatum but to project from the striatum to the targets in the globus pallidus and the substantia nigra pars reticulata. Data on whether fetal tissue grafts have been able to reestablish such long-distance connections in patients remains controversial. Although the identification of the molecular defect in Huntington's disease as a unstable expansion of cytosine-adenine-guanine repeats in the *IT15* gene suggests many alternative therapeutic approaches to the use of cell transplantation, it also provides the research community with genetic models of the disease[169] that allow careful evaluation of all strategies. ES cell-derived GABAergic neurons have not yet been tested in any animal model of Huntington's disease, but the *in vitro* derivation of GABA neurons with forebrain characteristics has been achieved at high efficiencies.[15] Another interesting avenue for stem cells in Huntington's disease is the derivation of human ES cells with Huntington's disease mutations from embryos discarded after preimplantation diagnostics. Such Huntington's disease ES cell lines could provide invaluable insights into the selective vulnerability of the striatal GABAergic cell population.

SPINAL CORD INJURY AND OTHER MOTOR NEURON DISORDERS

Traumatic or degenerative injuries to the spinal cord are often devastating and irreversible. Cell replacement using stem cells has been touted as a prime application of stem cell research. However, the complexity of cell therapy in spinal cord injury is enormous and far from resolved. Motor neurons are one of the main cell types affected by spinal cord injuries and by various degenerative diseases such as ALS. The efficient derivation of motor neurons from mouse ES cells has been demonstrated with both EB-based[19] and stromal feeder protocols.[15,17] However, the functionality of ES cell-derived neurons *in vivo* has only been addressed using xenografts into the developing chick spinal cord.[19] The behavior of ES cell-derived motor neurons in the adult CNS and in animal models of spinal cord injury or disease has not been tested.

Prior to the availability of directed differentiation protocols, there have been reports on functional improvement in animal models of spinal cord injury after grafting ES cell-derived progeny.[170] In one such study, dissociated $4^-/4^+$ mouse EBs derived from D3 or Rosa26 ES cells were transplanted into the spinal cord 9 days after a crush injury. The grafted cells differentiated *in vivo* into oligodendrocytes, neurons, and astrocytes, and they induced significant functional improvement in Basso, Beattie, and Bresnahan (BBB) scores over those of sham-injected animals. However, the mechanism by which functional improvement was obtained remains controversial.[171] Based on the ability for efficient differentiation into oligodendrocytes *in vivo,* it was suggested that remyelination of denuded axons might be a key factor.[172] Functional improvement was also reported after grafting EB-derived cells obtained from human EG cells.[173] EB cell populations derived from human EG cells were implanted into the cerebrospinal fluid (CSF) of rats after virus-induced neuronopathy and motor neuron degeneration, a model of ALS. Although a very small number of transplanted cells started to express markers compatible with motor neuron fate, most cells differentiated into neural progenitor or glial cells. It was concluded that the

functional improvement was caused by enhancing host neuron survival and function rather than reestablishing functional connections from graft-derived motor neurons. Future studies will have to bridge the gap between the increasing knowledge about controlling *in vitro* differentiation from ES cell to motor neuron progeny and the limited information from *in vivo* studies based on grafting poorly defined cell populations.

STROKE

Little work has been done with ES cell-derived progeny in animal models of stroke. A recent study showed that grafted ES cells can survive in a rat stroke model induced by transient ischemia using occlusion of the middle cerebral artery. The goal of this study was noninvasive imaging of the grafted cells using high-resolution MRI after transfection with ultrasmall, superparamagnetic iron-oxide particles.[174] The authors provided evidence for extensive migration of the grafted cells along the corpus callosum toward the ischemic lesion. However, no phenotypic analyses of the differentiated cell types were performed, and no functional effects were measured. Cell transplantation efforts for the treatment of stroke are complicated by the multiple cell types affected and the variability of the affected cell populations depending on stroke location.

DEMYELINATION

The capacity of mouse ES cell-derived progeny to remyelinate *in vivo* has been demonstrated after transplantation of highly purified ES cell-derived glial progenitors into the spinal cord of *md* rats[95] that lack the X-linked gene encoding myelin proteolipid protein, an animal model of Pelizaeus-Merzbacher syndrome. This study showed impressive *in vivo* differentiation results and yielded large grafts comprised of myelinating oligodendrocytes. However, the grafted cells were not able to extend the short life span of these animals precluding detailed functional analyses. A second study demonstrated that remyelination after grafting purified oligosphere cultures derived from $4^-/4^+$ EBs into the spinal cord of shiverer mice or into the chemically demyelinated spinal cord.[175]

Important challenges are the derivation of functional oligodendrocytes from human ES cells and the demonstration of functional benefits *in vivo,* including strategies to obtain remyelination over more extended CNS regions. Transplantation of ES cell-derived oligodendrocytes into models of multiple sclerosis will be of particular clinical interest. However a successful approach will require sophisticated strategies to overcome host-mediated factors that prevent oligodendrocytes maturation[176] as well as strategies that address the autoimmune nature of the disease.

OTHER DISEASES

Several disease models approached with fetal neural progenitors have not yet been tested using ES cell-based approaches. These include epilepsy and enzymatic deficiencies such as lysosomal storage diseases. Other CNS disorders such as Alzheimer's disease have been touted as future applications for ES cell therapy. However, at the current stage of research, the challenges for cell therapy in Alzheimer's disease seem to be overwhelming, and it appears more likely that the role for ES cells might be providing cellular models of disease rather than replacing cells. Some early attempts toward this goal have studied neural differentiation in ES cells that exhibit the disease causing the mutant of amyloid precursor protein (APP) knocked into the endogenous APP locus.[177]

Summary

The development of protocols that allow the directed differentiation from ES cells to specific neural fates provides an essential basis for all cell-based approaches in neural repair. Although these protocols are becoming routine for mouse ES cells, work with human ES cells lags behind. However, it is likely that these difficulties will be overcome within the next few years and that some of the first clinical ES cell applications of will be within the CNS. Beyond the role in regenerative medicine, ES cell *in vitro* differentiation protocols will become an essential tool for gene discovery and serve as a routine assay of neural development. The availability of libraries of ES cells with specific mutations or expressing specific transgenes will a great asset for such studies. *In vitro* ES cell differentiation will also provide unlimited sources of defined neural subtypes for pharmacological assays in drug screening and toxicology. However, one of the most important contributions might be the availability of a basic research tool that allows us to unravel step by step the complex signals that govern the development of single pluripotent ES cells to the amazing diversity of cell types that comprise the mammalian CNS.

REFERENCES

1. Munoz-Sanjuan, I., and Brivanlou, A.H. (2002). Neural induction, the default model, and embryonic stem cells. *Nat. Rev. Neurosci.* **3**, 271–280.
2. Sasai, Y., Lu, B., Steinbeisser, H., and De Robertis, E.M. (1995). Regulation of neural induction by the Chd and Bmp-4 antagonistic patterning signals in *Xenopus*. *Nature* **377**, 757.
3. Lamb, T.M., Knecht, A.K., Smith, W.C., Stachel, S.E., Economides, A.N., Stahl, N., Yancopoulos, G.D., and Harland, R.M. (1993). Neural induction by the secreted polypeptide noggin. *Science* **262**, 713–718.
4. Hemmati Brivanlou, A., Kelly, O.G., and Melton, D.A. (1994). Follistatin, an antagonist of activin, is expressed in the Spemann organizer and displays direct neuralizing activity. *Cell* **77**, 283–295.
5. Streit, A., Berliner, A.J., Papanayotou, C., Sirulnik, A., and Stern, C.D. (2000). Initiation of neural induction by FGF signaling before gastrulation. *Nature* **406**, 74–78.
6. Sheng, G., dos Reis, M., and Stern, C.D. (2003). Churchill, a zinc-finger transcriptional activator, regulates the transition between gastrulation and neurulation. *Cell* **115**, 603–613.
7. Pera, E.M., Wessely, O., Li, S.Y., and De Robertis, E.M. (2001). Neural and head induction by insulin-like growth factor signals. *Dev. Cell* **1**, 655–665.
8. Wilson, S.I., Rydstrom, A., Trimborn, T., Willert, K., Nusse, R., Jessell, T.M., and Edlund, T. (2001). The status of Wnt signaling regulates neural and epidermal fates in the chick embryo. *Nature* **411**, 325–330.
9. Baker, J.C., Beddington, R.S., and Harland, R.M. (1999). Wnt signaling in *Xenopus* embryos inhibits bmp4 expression and activates neural development. *Genes Dev.* **13**, 3149–3159.
10. Lumsden, A., and Krumlauf, R. (1996). Patterning the vertebrate neuraxis. *Science* **274**, 1109–1115.
11. Jessell, T.M. (2000). Neuronal specification in the spinal cord: inductive signals and transcriptional codes. *Natl. Rev. Genet.* **1**, 20–29.
12. Ericson, J., Muhr, J., Placzek, M., Lints, T., Jessell, T.M., and Edlund, T. (1995). Sonic hedgehog induces the differentiation of ventral forebrain neurons: a common signal for ventral patterning within the neural tube. *Cell* **81**, 747–756.
13. Roelink, H., Porter, J.A., Chiang, C., Tanabe, Y., Chang, D.T., Beachy, P.A., and Jessell, T.M. (1995). Floor plate and motor neuron induction by different concentrations of the amino-terminal cleavage product of Sonic hedgehog autoproteolysis. *Cell* **81**, 445–455.
14. Ye, W.L., Shimamura, K., Rubenstein, J.R., Hynes, M.A., and Rosenthal, A. (1998). FGF and Shh signals control dopaminergic and serotonergic cell fate in the anterior neural plate. *Cell* **93**, 755–766.
15. Barberi, T., Klivenyi, P., Calingasan, N.Y., Lee, H., Kawamata, H., Loonam, K., Perrier, A.L., Bruses, J., Rubio, M.E., Topf, N., Tabar, V., Harrison, N.L., Beal, M.F., Moore, M.A., and Studer, L. (2003). Neural subtype specification of fertilization and nuclear transfer embryonic stem cells and application in Parkinsonian mice. *Nat. Biotechnol.* **21**, 1200–1207.
16. Lee S.H., Lumelsky, N., Studer, L., Auerbach, J.M., and McKay, R.D. (2000). Efficient generation of midbrain and hindbrain neurons from mouse embryonic stem cells. *Nat. Biotechnol.* **18**, 675–679.
17. Mizuseki, K., Sakamoto, T., Watanabe, K., Muguruma, K., Ikeya, M., Nishiyama, A., Arakawa, A., Suemori, H., Nakatsuji, N., Kawasaki, H., Murakami, F., and Sasai, Y. (2003). Generation of neural crest-derived peripheral neurons and floor plate cells from mouse and primate embryonic stem cells. *Proc. Natl. Acad. Sci. U. S. A.* **100**, 5828–5833.
18. Kim, J.H., Auerbach, J.M., Rodriguez-Gomez, J.A., Velasco, I., Gavin, D., Lumelsky, N., Lee, S.H., Nguyen, J., Sanchez-Pernaute, R., Bankiewicz, K., and McKay, R. (2002). Dopamine neurons derived from embryonic stem cells function in an animal model of Parkinson's disease. *Nature* **418**, 50–56.
19. Wichterle, H., Lieberam, I., Porter, J.A., and Jessell, T.M. (2002). Directed differentiation of embryonic stem cells into motor neurons. *Cell* **110**, 385–397.
20. Briscoe, J., Pierani, A., Jessell, T.M., and Ericson, J. (2000). A homeodomain protein code specifies progenitor cell identity and neuronal fate in the ventral neural tube. *Cell* **101**, 435–445.
21. Rallu, M., Machold, R., Gaiano, N., Corbin, J.G., McMahon, A.P., and Fishell, G. (2002). Dorsoventral patterning is established in the telencephalon of mutants lacking Gli3 and hedgehog signaling. *Development* **129**, 4963–4974.
22. Persson, M., Stamataki, D., te Welscher, P., Andersson, E., Bose, J., Ruther, U., Ericson, J., and Briscoe, J. (2002). Dorsal–ventral patterning of the spinal cord requires Gli3 transcriptional repressor activity. *Genes Dev.* **16**, 2865–2878.
23. Litingtung, Y., and Chiang, C. (2000). Specification of ventral neuron types is mediated by an antagonistic interaction between shh and gli3. *Nat. Neurosci.* **3**, 979–985.
24. Eggenschwiler, J.T., Espinoza, E., and Anderson, K.V. (2001). Rab23 is an essential negative regulator of the mouse Sonic hedgehog signaling pathway. *Nature* **412**, 194–198.

25. Diez del Corral, R., Olivera-Martinez, I., Goriely, A., Gale, E., Maden, M., and Storey, K. (2003). Opposing FGF and retinoid pathways control ventral neural pattern, neuronal differentiation, and segmentation during body axis extension. *Neuron* **40,** 65–79.

26. Novitch, B.G., Wichterle, H., Jessell, T.M., and Sockanathan, S. (2003). A requirement for retinoic acid-mediated transcriptional activation in ventral–neural patterning and motor neuron specification. *Neuron* **40,** 81–95.

27. Dickinson, M.E., Selleck, M.A., McMahon, A.P., and Bronner-Fraser, M. (1995). Dorsalization of the neural tube by the nonneural ectoderm. *Development* **121,** 2099–2106.

28. Liem, K.F., Tremml, G., Roelink, H., and Jessell, T.M. (1995). Dorsal differentiation of neural plate cells induced by BMP-mediated signals from epidermal ectoderm. *Cell* **82,** 969–979.

29. Lee, K.J., Dietrich, P., and Jessell, T.M. (2000). Genetic ablation reveals that the roof plate is essential for dorsal interneuron specification. *Nature* **403,** 734–740.

30. Panchision, D.M., Pickel, J.M., Studer, L., Lee, S.H., Turner, P., Hazel, T.G., and McKay, R.D. (2001). Sequential actions of BMP receptors control neural precursor cell production and fate. *Genes Dev.* **15,** 2094–2110.

31. Hebert, J.M., Mishina, Y., and McConnell, S.K. (2002). BMP signaling is required locally to pattern the dorsal telencephalic midline. *Neuron* **35,** 1029–1041.

32. Garcia-Castro, M.I., Marcelle, C., and Bronner-Fraser, M. (2002). Ectodermal Wnt function as a neural crest inducer. *Science* **297,** 848–851.

33. Gaiano, N., and Fishell, G. (2002). The role of notch in promoting glial and neural stem cell fates. *Annu. Rev. Neurosci.* **25,** 471–490.

34. Tanigaki, K., Nogaki, F., Takahashi, J., Tashiro, K., Kurooka, H., and Honjo, T. (2001). Notch1 and Notch3 instructively restrict bFGF-responsive multipotent neural progenitor cells to an astroglial fate. *Neuron* **29,** 45–55.

35. Rajan, P., and McKay, R.D. (1998). Multiple routes to astrocytic differentiation in the CNS. *J. Neurosci.* **18,** 3620–3629.

36. Bonni, A., Sun, Y., NadalVicens, M., Bhatt, A., Frank, D.A., Rozovsky, I., Stahl, N., Yancopoulos, G.D., and Greenberg, M.E. (1997). Regulation of gliogenesis in the central nervous system by the JAK-STAT signaling pathway. *Science* **278,** 477–483.

37. Noctor, S.C., Flint, A.C., Weissman, T.A., Wong, W.S., Clinton, B.K., and Kriegstein, A.R. (2002). Dividing precursor cells of the embryonic cortical ventricular zone have morphological and molecular characteristics of radial glia. *J. Neurosci.* **22,** 3161–3173.

38. Doetsch, F., Caille, I., Lim, D.A., Garcia-Verdugo, J.M., and Alvarez-Buylla, A. (1999). Subventricular zone astrocytes are neural stem cells in the adult mammalian brain. *Cell* **97,** 703–716.

39. French-Constant, C., and Raff, M.C. (1986). Proliferating bipotential glial progenitor cells in adult rat optic nerve. *Nature* **319,** 499–502.

40. Rao, M.S., Noble, M., and Mayer-Proschel, M. (1998). A tripotential glial precursor cell is present in the developing spinal cord. *Proc. Natl. Acad. Sci. U. S. A.* **95,** 3996–4001.

41. Zhou, Q., and Anderson, D.J. (2002). The bHLH transcription factors OLIG2 and OLIG1 couple neuronal and glial subtype specification. *Cell* **109,** 61–73.

42. Lu, Q.R., Sun, T., Zhu, Z.M., Ma, N., Garcia, M., Stiles, C.D., and Rowitch, D.H. (2002). Common developmental requirement for Olig function indicates a motor neuron–oligodendrocyte connection. *Cell* **109,** 75–86.

43. He, W., Ingraham, C., Rising, L., Goderie, S., and Temple, S. (2001). Multipotent stem cells from the mouse basal forebrain contribute GABAergic neurons and oligodendrocytes to the cerebral cortex during embryogenesis. *J. Neurosci.* **21,** 8854–8862.

44. Yung, S.Y., Gokhan, S., Jurcsak, J., Molero, A.E., Abrajano, J.J., and Mehler, M.F. (2002). Differential modulation of BMP signaling promotes the elaboration of cerebral cortical GABAergic neurons or oligodendrocytes from a common sonic hedgehog-responsive ventral forebrain progenitor species. *Proc. Natl. Acad. Sci. U. S. A.* **99,** 16,273–16,278.

45. Goridis, C., and Rohrer, H. (2002). Specification of catecholaminergic and serotonergic neurons. *Nat. Rev. Neurosci.* **3,** 531–541.

46. Lee, S.K., and Pfaff, S.L. (2001). Transcriptional networks regulating neuronal identity in the developing spinal cord. *Nat. Neurosci.* **4,** 1183–1191.

47. Caspary, T., and Anderson, K.V. (2003). Patterning cell types in the dorsal spinal cord: what the mouse mutants say. *Nat. Rev. Neurosci.* **4,** 289–297.

48. Rallu, M., Corbin, J.G., and Fishell, G. (2002). Parsing the prosencephalon. *Nat. Rev. Neurosci.* **3,** 943–951.

49. Puelles, L., and Rubenstein, J.L. (2003). Forebrain gene expression domains and the evolving prosomeric model. *Trends Neurosci.* **26,** 469–476.

50. Wilson, S.W., and Rubenstein, J.L.R. (2000). Induction and dorsoventral patterning of the telencephalon. *Neuron* **28,** 641–651.

51. Rubenstein, J.L. (2000). Intrinsic and extrinsic control of cortical development. *Novartis. Found. Symp.* **228,** 67–75.

52. Gage, F.H. (2000). Mammalian neural stem cells. *Science* **287,** 1433–1438.

53. McKay, R.D. (1997). Stem cells in the central nervous system. *Science* **276,** 66–71.

54. Spangrude, G.J., Heimfeld, S., and Weissman, I.L. (1988). Purification and characterization of mouse hematopoietic stem cells. *Science* **241,** 58–62.

55. Caldwell, M.A., He, X.L., Wilkie, N., Pollack, S., Marshall, G., Wafford, K.A., and Svendsen, C.N. (2001). Growth factors regulate the survival and fate of cells derived from human neurospheres. *Nat. Biotechnol.* **19,** 475–479.

56. Jain, M., Armstrong, R.J., Tyers, P., Barker, R.A., and Rosser, A.E. (2003). GABAergic immunoreactivity is predominant in neurons derived from expanded human neural precursor cells *in vitro*. *Exp. Neurol.* **182,** 113–123.

57. Reynolds, B.A., and Weiss, S. (1992). Generation of neurons and astrocytes from isolated cells of the adult mammalian central nervous system. (See comments). *Science* **255,** 1707–1710.

58. Kilpatrick, T.J., and Bartlett, P.F. (1993). Cloning and growth of multipotential neural precursors: requirements for proliferation and differentiation. *Neuron* **10,** 255–265.

59. Gritti, A., Cova, L., Parati, E.A., Galli, R., and Vescovi, A.L. (1995). Basic fibroblast growth factor supports the proliferation of epidermal growth factor-generated neuronal precursor cells of the adult mouse CNS. *Neurosci. Lett.* **185,** 151–154.

60. Galli, R., Pagano, S.F., Gritti, A., and Vescovi, A.L. (2000). Regulation of neuronal differentiation in human CNS stem cell progeny by leukemia inhibitory factor. *Dev. Neurosci.* **22,** 86–95.

61. Uchida, N., Buck, D.W., He, D.P., Reitsma, M.J., Masek, M., Phan, T.V., Tsukamoto, A.S., Gage, F.H., and Weissman, I.L. (2000). Direct isolation of human central nervous system stem cells. *Proc. Natl. Acad. Sci. U. S. A.* **97,** 14,720–14,725.

62. Capela, A., and Temple, S. (2002). LeX/ssea-1 is expressed by adult mouse CNS stem cells, identifying them as nonependymal. *Neuron* **35**, 865–875.

63. Rietze, R.L., Valcanis, H., Brooker, G.F., Thomas, T., Voss, A.K., and Bartlett, P.F. (2001). Purification of a pluripotent neural stem cell from the adult mouse brain. *Nature* **412**, 736–739.

64. Doetsch, F., Petreanu, L., Caille, I., Garcia-Verdugo, J.M., and Alvarez-Buylla, A. (2002). EGF converts transit amplifying neurogenic precursors in the adult brain into multipotent stem cells. *Neuron* **36**, 1021–1034.

65. Davis, A.A., and Temple, S. (1994). A self-renewing multipotential stem cell in embryonic rat cerebral cortex. *Nature* **372**, 263–266.

66. Johe, K.K., Hazel, T.G., Müller, T., Dugich-Djordjevic, M.M., and McKay, R.D. (1996). Single factors direct the differentiation of stem cells from the fetal and adult central nervous system. *Genes Dev.* **10**, 3129–3140.

67. Palmer, T.D., Ray, J., and Gage, F.H. (1995). FGF-2-responsive neuronal progenitors reside in proliferative and quiescent regions of the adult rodent brain. *Mol. Cell Neurosci.* **6**, 474–486.

68. Qian, X.M., Shen, Q., Goderie, S.K., He, W.L., Capela, A., Davis, A.A., and Temple, S. (2000). Timing of CNS cell generation: a programmed sequence of neuron and glial cell production from isolated murine cortical stem cells. *Neuron* **28**, 69–80.

69. Studer, L., Tabar, V., and McKay, R.D. (1998). Transplantation of expanded mesencephalic precursors leads to recovery in Parkinsonian rats. *Nat. Neurosci.* **1**, 290–295.

70. Sanchez-Pernaute, R., Studer, L., Bankiewicz, K.S., Major, E.O., and McKay, R.D. (2001). *In vitro* generation and transplantation of precursor-derived human dopamine neurons. *J. Neurosci. Res.* **65**, 284–288.

71. Yan, J., Studer, L., and McKay, R.D. (2001). Ascorbic acid increases the yield of dopaminergic neurons derived from basic fibroblast growth factor expanded mesencephalic precursors. *J. Neurochem.* **76**, 307–311.

72. Carvey, P.M., Ling, Z.D., Sortwell, C.E., Pitzer, M.R., McGuire, S.O., Storch, A., and Collier, T.J. (2001). A clonal line of mesencephalic progenitor cells converted to dopamine neurons by hematopoietic cytokines: a source of cells for transplantation in Parkinson's disease. *Exp. Neurol.* **171**, 98–108.

73. Ling, Z.D., Potter, E.D., Lipton, J.W., Carvey, P.M. (1998). Differentiation of mesencephalic progenitor cells into dopaminergic neurons by cytokines. *Exp. Neurol.* **149**, 411–423.

74. Studer, L., Csete, M., Lee, S.H., Kabbani, N., Walikonis, J., Wold, B., and McKay, R.D. (2000). Enhanced proliferation, survival, and dopaminergic differentiation of CNS precursors in lowered oxygen. *J. Neurosci.* **20**, 7377–7383.

75. Wagner, J., Akerud, P., Castro, D.S., Holm, P.C., Canals, J.M., Snyder, E.Y., Perlmann, T., and Arenas, E. (1999). Induction of a midbrain dopaminergic phenotype in Nurr1-overexpressing neural stem cells by type 1 astrocytes. *Nat. Biotechnol.* **17**, 653–659.

76. Kim, J.Y., Koh, H.C., Lee, J.Y., Chang, M.Y., Kim, Y.C., Chung, H.Y., Son, H., Lee, Y.S., Studer, L., McKay, R., and Lee, S.H. (2003). Dopaminergic neuronal differentiation from rat embryonic neural precursors by Nurr1 overexpression. *J. Neurochem.* **85**, 1443–1454.

77. Zetterström, R.H., Solomin, L., Jansson, L., Hoffer, B.J., Olson, L., and Perlmann, T. (1997). Dopamine neuron agenesis in Nurr1-deficient mice. *Science* **276**, 248–250.

78. Saucedo-Cardenas, O., Quintana-Hau, J.D., Le, W.D., Smidt, M.P., Cox, J.J., DeMayo, F., Burbach, J.H., and Conneely, O.M. (1998). Nurr1 is essential for the induction of the dopaminergic phenotype and the survival of ventral mesencephalic late dopaminergic precursor neurons. *Proc. Natl. Acad. Sci. U. S. A.* **95**, 4013–4018.

79. Castillo, S.O., Baffi, J.S., Palkovits, M., Goldstein, D.S., Kopin, I.J., Witta, J., Magnuson, M.A., and Nikodem, V.M. (1998). Dopamine biosynthesis is selectively abolished in substantia nigra ventral–tegmental area but not in hypothalamic neurons in mice with targeted disruption of the *Nurr1* gene. *Mol. Cell Neurosci.* **11**, 36–46.

80. Gabay, L., Lowell, S., Rubin, L., and Anderson, D.J. (2003). Deregulation of dorsoventral patterning by FGF confers trilineage differentiation capacity on CNS stem cells *in vitro*. *Neuron* **40**, 485–499.

81. Farkas, L.M., Dunker, N., Roussa, E., Unsicker, K., and Krieglstein, K. (2003). Transforming growth factor-beta(s) are essential for the development of midbrain dopaminergic neurons *in vitro* and *in vivo*. *J. Neurosci.* **23**, 5178–5186.

82. Thomson, J.A., Itskovitz-Eldor, J., Shapiro, S.S., Waknitz, M.A., Swiergiel, J.J., Marshall, V.S., and Jones, J.M. (1998). Embryonic stem cell lines derived from human blastocysts. *Science* **282**, 1145–1147.

83. Reubinoff, B.E., Pera, M.F., Fong, C.Y., Trounson, A., and Bongso, A. (2000). Embryonic stem cell lines from human blastocysts, somatic differentiation *in vitro*. *Nat. Biotechnol.* **18**, 399–404.

84. Shamblott, M.J., Axelman, J., Wang, S., Bugg, E.M., Littlefield, J.W., Donovan, P.J., Blumenthal, P.D., Huggins, G.R., and Gearhart, J.D. (1998). Derivation of pluripotent stem cells from cultured human primordial germ cells. *Proc. Natl. Acad. Sci. U. S. A.* **95**, 13,726–13,731.

85. Doetschman, T.C., Eistetter, H., Katz, M., Schmidt, W., and Kemler, R. (1985). The *in vitro* development of blastocyst-derived embryonic stem cell lines: formation of visceral yolk sac, blood islands, and myocardium. *J. Embryol. Exp. Morphol.* **87**, 27–45.

86. Weiss, M.J., and Orkin, S.H. (1996). *In vitro* differentiation of the murine embryonic stem cells: new approaches to old problems. *J. Clin. Invest.* **97**, 591–595.

87. Bain, G., Kitchens, D., Yao, M., Huettner, J.E., and Gottlieb, D.I. (1995). Embryonic stem cells express neuronal properties *in vitro*. *Dev. Biol.* **168**, 342–357.

88. Maden, M. (2002). Retinoid signaling in the development of the central nervous system. *Nat. Rev. Neurosci.* **3**, 843–853.

89. Fraichard, A., Chassande, O., Bilbaut, G., Dehay, C., Savatier, P., and Samarut, J. (1995). *In vitro* differentiation of embryonic stem cells into glial cells and functional neurons. *J. Cell Sci.* **108**, 3181–3188.

90. Renoncourt, Y., Carroll, P., Filippi, P., Arce, V., and Alonso, S. (1998). Neurons derived *in vitro* from ES cells express homeoproteins characteristic of motoneurons and interneurons. *Mech. Dev.* **79**, 185–197.

91. Strübing, C., Ahnert-Hilger, G., Shan, J., Wiedenmann, B., Hescheler, J., and Wobus, A.M. (1995). Differentiation of pluripotent embryonic stem cells into the neuronal lineage *in vitro* gives rise to mature inhibitory and excitatory neurons. *Mech. Dev.* **53**, 275–287.

92. Krumlauf, R. (1994). *Hox* genes in vertebrate development. *Cell* **78**, 191–201.

93. Rathjen, J., Haines, B.P., Hudson, K.M., Nesci, A., Dunn, S., and Rathjen, P.D. (2002). Directed differentiation of pluripotent cells to neural lineages: homogeneous formation and differentiation of a neurectoderm population. *Development* **129**, 2649–2661.

94. Okabe, S., Forsberg-Nilsson, K., Spiro, A.C., Segal, M., and McKay, R.D. (1996). Development of neuronal precursor cells and functional postmitotic neurons from embryonic stem cells *in vitro*. *Mech. Dev.* **59**, 89–102.

95. Brustle, O., Jones, K.N., Learish, R.D., Karram, K., Choudhary, K., Wiestler, O.D., Duncan, I.D., and McKay, R.D. (1999). Embryonic stem cell-derived glial precursors: A source of myelinating transplants. *Science* **285**, 754–756.

96. Wakayama, T., Tabar, V., Rodriguez, I., Perry, A.C., Studer, L., and Mombaerts, P. (2001). Differentiation of embryonic stem cell lines generated from adult somatic cells by nuclear transfer. *Science* **292**, 740–743.

97. Collins, L.S., and Dorshkind, K. (1987). A stromal cell line from myeloid long-term bone marrow cultures can support myelopoiesis and B-lymphopoiesis. *J. Immunol.* **138**, 1082–1087.

98. Croisille, L., Auffray, I., Katz, A., Izac, B., Vainchenker, W., and Coulombel, L. (1994). Hydrocortisone differentially affects the ability of murine stromal cells and human marrow-derived adherent cells to promote the differentiation of CD34++/CD38– long-term culture-initiating cells. *Blood* **84**, 4116–4124.

99. Nakano, T., Kodama, H., and Honjo, T. (1994). Generation of lymphohematopoietic cells from embryonic stem cells in culture. *Science* **265**, 1098–1101.

100. Sutherland, H.J., Eaves, C.J., Lansdorp, P.M., Thacker, J.D., and Hogge, D.E. (1991). Differential regulation of primitive human hematopoietic cells in long-term cultures maintained on genetically engineered murine stromal cells. *Blood* **78**, 666–672.

101. Ueno, H., Sakita-Ishikawa, M., Morikawa, Y., Nakano, T., Kitamura, T., and Saito, M. (2003). A stromal cell-derived membrane protein that supports hematopoietic stem cells. *Nat. Immunol.* **4**, 457–463.

102. Kawasaki, H., Mizuseki, K., Nishikawa, S., Kaneko, S., Kuwana, Y., Nakanishi, S., Nishikawa, S., and Sasai, Y. (2000). Induction of midbrain dopaminergic neurons from ES cells by stromal cell-derived inducing activity. *Neuron* **28**, 31–40.

103. Kawasaki, H., Suemori, H., Mizuseki, K., Watanabe, K., Urano, F., Ichinose, H., Haruta, M., Takahashi, M., Yoshikawa, K., Nishikawa, S.I., Nakatsuji, N., and Sasai, K. (2002). Generation of dopaminergic neurons and pigmented epithelia from primate ES cells by stromal cell-derived inducing activity. *Proc. Natl. Acad. Sci. U. S. A.* **99**, 1580–1585.

104. Tropepe, V., Hitoshi, S., Sirard, C., Mak, T.W., Rossant, J., and van der Kooy, D. (2001). Direct neural fate specification from embryonic stem cells: a primitive mammalian neural stem cell stage acquired through a default mechanism. *Neuron* **30**, 65–78.

105. Ying, Q.L., Stavridis, M., Griffiths, D., Li, M., and Smith, A. (2003). Conversion of embryonic stem cells into neuroectodermal precursors in adherent monoculture. *Nat. Biotechnol.* **21**, 183–186.

106. Ying, Q.L., Nichols, J., Chambers, I., and Smith, A. (2003). BMP induction of Id proteins suppresses differentiation and sustains embryonic stem cell self-renewal in collaboration with STAT3. *Cell* **115**, 281–292.

107. Bjorklund, A., Dunnett, S.B., Brundin, P., Stoessl, A.J., Freed, C.R., Breeze, R.E., Levivier, M., Peschanski, M., Studer, L., and Barker, R. (2003). Neural transplantation for the treatment of Parkinson's disease. *Lancet. Neurol.* **2**, 437–445.

108. Dunnett, S.B., and Bjorklund, A. (1999). Prospects for new restorative and neuroprotective treatments in Parkinson's disease. *Nature* **399**, A32–A39.

109. Ye, W.L., Bouchard, M., Stone, D., Liu, X.D., Vella, F., Lee, J., Nakamura, H., Ang, S.L., Busslinger, M., and Rosenthal, A. (2001). Distinct regulators control the expression of the mid–hindbrain organizer signal FGF8. *Nat. Neurosci.* **4**, 1175–1181.

110. Hynes, M., Poulsen, K., Tessier-Lavigne, M., and Rosenthal, A. (1995). Control of neuronal diversity by the floor plate: contact-mediated induction of midbrain dopaminergic neurons. *Cell* **80**, 95–101.

111. Hynes, M., Porter, J.A., Chiang, C., Chang, D., Tessier-Lavigne, M., Beachy, P.A., and Rosenthal, A. (1995). Induction of midbrain dopaminergic neurons by Sonic hedgehog. *Neuron* **15**, 35–44.

112. Hynes, M., and Rosenthal, A. (2000). Embryonic stern cells go dopaminergic. *Neuron* **28**, 11–14.

113. Perrier, A.L., and Studer, L. (2003). Making and repairing the mammalian brain: *In vitro* production of dopaminergic neurons. *Semin. Cell Dev. Biol.* **14**, 181–189.

114. Ding, Y.Q., Marklund, U., Yuan, W., Yin, J., Wegman, L., Ericson, J., Deneris, E., Johnson, R.L., and Chen, Z.F. (2003). Lmx1b is essential for the development of serotonergic neurons. *Nat. Neurosci.* **6**, 933–938.

115. Guo, S., Yamaguchi, Y., Schilbach, S., Wada, T., Lee, J., Goddard, A., French, D., Handa, H., and Rosenthal, A. (2000). A regulator of transcriptional elongation controls vertebrate neuronal development. *Nature* **408**, 366–369.

116. Levkowitz, G., Zeller, J., Sirotkin, H.I., French, D., Schilbach, S., Hashimoto, H., Hibi, M., Talbot, W.S., and Rosenthal, A. (2003). Zinc-finger protein too few controls the development of monoaminergic neurons. *Nat. Neurosci.* **6**, 28–33.

117. Coyle, N., Jones, I., Roberson, E., Lendon, C., and Craddock, N. (2000). Variation at the serotonin transporter gene influences susceptibility to bipolar affective puerperal psychosis. *Lancet.* **356**, 1490–1491.

118. Lesch, K.P., Bengel, D., Heils, A., Sabol, S.Z., Greenberg, B.D., Petri, S., Benjamin, J., Muller, C.R., Hamer, D.H., and Murphy, D.L. (1996). Association of anxiety-related traits with a polymorphism in the serotonin transporter gene regulatory region. *Science* **274**, 1527–1531.

119. Ogilvie, A.D., Battersby, S., Bubb, V.J., Fink, G., Harmar, A.J., Goodwin, G.M., and Smith, C.A.D. (1996). Polymorphism in serotonin transporter gene associated with susceptibility to major depression. *Lancet.* **347**, 731–733.

120. Asberg, M., Thoren, P., Traskman, L., Bertilsson, L., and Ringberger, V. (1976). "Serotonin depression": a biochemical subgroup within the affective disorders? *Science* **191**, 478–480.

121. Sockanathan, S., Perlmann, T., and Jessell, T.M. (2003). Retinoid receptor signaling in postmitotic motor neurons regulates rostrocaudal positional identity and axonal projection pattern. *Neuron* **40**, 97–111.

122. Dasen, J.S., Liu, J.P., and Jessell, T.M. (2003). Motor neuron columnar fate imposed by sequential phases of Hox-c activity. *Nature* **425**, 926–933.

123. Qiu, J., Cai, D., Dai, H., McAtee, M., Hoffman, P.N., Bregman, B.S., and Filbin, M.T. (2002). Spinal axon regeneration induced by elevation of cyclic AMP. *Neuron* **34**, 895–903.

124. Neumann, S., Bradke, F., Tessier-Lavigne, M., and Basbaum, A.I. (2002). Regeneration of sensory axons within the injured spinal cord induced by intraganglionic cAMP elevation. *Neuron* **34**, 885–893.

125. Gottlieb, D.I. (2002). Large-scale sources of neural stem cells. *Annu. Rev. Neurosci.* **25**, 381–407.

126. Tao, W., and Lai, E. (1992). Telencephalon-restricted expression of BF-1, a new member of the HNF-3–forkhead gene family in the developing rat brain. *Neuron* **8**, 957–966.

127. Houser, C.R., Vaughn, J.E., Barber, R.P., and Roberts, E. (1980). GABA neurons are the major cell type of the nucleus reticularis thalami. *Brain Res.* **200,** 341–354.

128. Ribak, C.E., Vaughn, J.E., Saito, K., Barber, R., and Roberts, E. (1976). Immunocytochemical localization of glutamate decarboxylase in rat *substantia nigra. Brain Res.* **116,** 287–298.

129. Hatten, M.E., Francois, A.M., Napolitano, E., and Roffler-Tarlov, S. (1984). Embryonic cerebellar neurons accumulate [3H]-gamma-aminobutyric acid: visualization of developing gamma-aminobutyric acid-utilizing neurons *in vitro* and *in vivo. J. Neurosci.* **4,** 1343–1353.

130. Finley, M.F., Kulkarni, N., and Huettner, J.E. (1996). Synapse formation and establishment of neuronal polarity by P19 embryonic carcinoma cells and embryonic stem cells. *J. Neurosci.* **16,** 1056–1065.

131. Wernig, M., Tucker, K.L., Gornik, V., Schneiders, A., Buschwald, R., Wiestler, O.D., Barde, Y.A., and Brustle, O. (2002). Tau EGFP embryonic stem cells: an efficient tool for neuronal lineage selection and transplantation. *J. Neurosci. Res.* **69,** 918–924.

132. Benninger, F., Beck, H., Wernig, M., Tucker, K.L., Brustle, O., and Scheffler, B. (2003). Functional integration of embryonic stem cell-derived neurons in hippocampal slice cultures. *J. Neurosci.* **23,** 7075–7083.

133. Li, H., Roblin, G., Liu, H., and Heller, S. (2003). Generation of hair cells by stepwise differentiation of embryonic stem cells. *Proc. Natl. Acad. Sci. U. S. A.* **100,** 13,495–13,500.

134. Liour, S.S., and Yu, R.K. (2003). Differentiation of radial glia-like cells from embryonic stem cells. *Glia* **42,** 109–117.

135. Gossrau, G., Wernig, M., and Brustle, O. (2003). Neural crest fates in differentiating embryonic stem cell cultures. *Soc. Neurosci. Abstr.* **347,** 8.

136. Newgreen, D.F., and Minichiello, J. (1996). Control of epitheliomesenchymal transformation: II—Cross-modulation of cell adhesion and cytoskeletal systems in embryonic neural cells. *Dev. Biol.* **176,** 300–312.

137. Billon, N., Jolicoeur, C., Ying, Q.L., Smith, A., and Raff, M. (2002). Normal timing of oligodendrocyte development from genetically engineered, lineage-selectable mouse ES cells. *J. Cell Sci.* **115,** 3657–3665.

138. Scheffler, B., Schmandt, T., Schroder, W., Steinfarz, B., Husseini, L., Wellmer, J., Seifert, G., Karram, K., Beck, H., Blumcke, I., Wiestler, O.D., Steinhauser, C., and Brustle, O. (2003). Functional network integration of embryonic stem cell-derived astrocytes in hippocampal slice cultures. *Development* **130,** 5533–5541.

139. Li, M., Pevny, L., Lovell-Badge, R., and Smith, A. (1998). Generation of purified neural precursors from embryonic stem cells by lineage selection. *Curr. Biol.* **8,** 971–974.

140. Tang, F., Shang, K., Wang, X., and Gu, J. (2002). Differentiation of embryonic stem cell to astrocytes visualized by green fluorescent protein. *Cell Mol. Neurobiol.* **22,** 95–101.

141. Westmoreland, J.J., Hancock, C.R., and Condie, B.G. (2001). Neuronal development of embryonic stem cells: a model of GABAergic neuron differentiation. *Biochem. Biophys. Res. Commun.* **284,** 674–680.

142. Lenka, N., Lu, Z.J., Sasse, P., Hescheler, J., and Fleischmann, B.K. (2002). Quantitation and functional characterization of neural cells derived from ES cells using nestin enhancer-mediated targeting *in vitro. J. Cell Sci.* **115,** 1471–1485.

143. Andressen, C., Stocker, E., Klinz, F.J., Lenka, N., Hescheler, J., Fleischmann, B., Arnhold, S., and Addicks, K. (2001). Nestin-specific green fluorescent protein expression in embryonic stem cell-derived neural precursor cells used for transplantation. *Stem Cells* **19,** 419–424.

144. Xian, H.Q., McNichols, E., St. Clair, A., and Gottlieb, D.I. (2003). A subset of ES cell-derived neural cells marked by gene targeting. *Stem Cells* **21,** 41–49.

145. Thomson, J.A., Kalishman, J., Golos, T.G., Durning, M., Harris, C.P., Becker, R.A., and Hearn, J.P. (1995). Isolation of a primate embryonic stem cell line. *Proc. Natl. Acad. Sci. U. S. A.* **92,** 7844–7848.

146. Cibelli, J.B., Grant, K.A., Chapman, K.B., Cunniff, K., Worst, T., Green, H.L., Walker, S.J., Gutin, P.H., Vilner, L., Tabar, V., Dominko, T., Kane, J., Wettstein, P.J., Lanza, R.P., Studer, L., Vrana, K.E., and West, M.D. (2002). Parthenogenetic stem cells in nonhuman primates. *Science* **295,** 819.

147. Zhang, S.C., Wernig, M., Duncan, I.D., Brustle, O., and Thomson, J.A. (2001). *In vitro* differentiation of transplantable neural precursors from human embryonic stem cells. *Nat. Biotechnol.* **19,** 1129–1133.

148. Studer, L. (2001). Stem cells with brainpower. *Nat. Biotechnol.* **19,** 1117–1118.

149. Reubinoff, B.E., Itsykson, P., Turetsky, T., Pera, M.F., Reinhartz, E., Itzik, A., and Ben Hur, T. (2001). Neural progenitors from human embryonic stem cells. *Nat. Biotechnol.* **19,** 1134–1140.

150. Carpenter, M.K., Inokuma, M.S., Denham, J., Mujtaba, T., Chiu, C.P., and Rao, M.S. (2001). Enrichment of neurons and neural precursors from human embryonic stem cells. *Exp. Neurol.* **172,** 383–397.

151. Vrana, K.E., Hipp, J.D., Goss, A.M., McCool, B., Riddle, D., Walker, S.J., Wettstein, P.G., Studer, L., Tabar, V., Cunniff, K., Chapman, K., Vilner, L., West, M.D., Grant, K.A., and Cibelli, J.B. (2003). Nonhuman primate parthenogenetic stem cells. *Proc. Natl. Acad. Sci. U. S. A.* **100,** 11,911–11,916.

152. Ooto, S., Haruta, M., Honda, Y., Kawasaki, H., Sasai, Y., and Takahashi, M. (2003). Induction of the differentiation of lentoids from primate embryonic stem cells. *Invest. Ophthalmol. Vis. Sci.* **44,** 2689–2693.

153. Ding, S., Wu, T.Y., Brinker, A., Peters, E.C., Hur, W., Gray, N.S., and Schultz, P.G. (2003). Synthetic small molecules that control stem cell fate. *Proc. Natl. Acad. Sci. U. S. A.* **100,** 7632–7637.

154. Aubert, J., Dunstan, H., Chambers, I., and Smith, A. (2002). Functional gene screening in embryonic stem cells implicates Wnt antagonism in neural differentiation. *Nat. Biotechnol.* **20,** 1240–1245.

155. Bain, G., Mansergh, F.C., Wride, M.A., Hance, J.E., Isogawa, A., Rancourt, S.L., Ray, W.J., Yoshimura, Y., Tsuzuki, T., Gottlieb, D.I., and Rancourt, D.E. (2000). ES cell neural differentiation reveals a substantial number of novel ESTs. *Funct. Integr. Genomics* **1,** 127–139.

156. Xiong, J.W., Battaglino, R., Leahy, A., and Stuhlmann, H. (1998). Large-scale screening for developmental genes in embryonic stem cells and embryoid bodies using retroviral entrapment vectors. *Dev. Dyn.* **212,** 181–197.

157. Baker, R.K., Haendel, M.A., Swanson, B.J., Shambaugh, J.C., Micales, B.K., and Lyons, G.E. (1997). *In vitro* preselection of gene-trapped embryonic stem cell clones for characterizing novel developmentally regulated genes in the mouse. *Dev. Biol.* **185,** 201–214.

158. Kiger, A., Baum, B., Jones, S., Jones, M., Coulson, A., Echeverri, C., and Perrimon, N. (2003). A functional genomic analysis of cell morphology using RNA interference. *J. Biol.* **2,** 27.

159. Lum, L., Yao, S., Mozer, B., Rovescalli, A., Von Kessler, D., Nirenberg, M., and Beachy, P.A. (2003). Identification of Hedgehog pathway components by RNAi in *Drosophila* cultured cells. *Science* **299,** 2039–2045.

160. Gonczy, P., Echeverri, C., Oegema, K., Coulson, A., Jones, S.J., Copley, R.R., Duperon, J., Oegema, J., Brehm, M., Cassin, E., Hannak, E., Kirkham, M., Pichler, S., Flohrs, K., Goessen, A., Leidel, S., Alleaume, A.M., Martin, C., Ozlu, N., Bork, P., and Hyman, A.A. (2000). Functional genomic analysis of cell division in *C. elegans* using RNAi of genes on chromosome III. *Nature* **408,** 331–336.

161. Lee, S.S., Lee, R.Y., Fraser, A.G., Kamath, R.S., Ahringer, J., and Ruvkun, G. (2003). A systematic RNAi screen identifies a critical role for mitochondria in *C. elegans* longevity. *Nat. Genet.* **33,** 40–48.

162. Bjorklund, L.M., Sanchez-Pernaute, R., Chung, S., Andersson, T., Chen, I.Y., McNaught, K.S., Brownell, A.L., Jenkins, B.G., Wahlestedt, C., Kim, K.S., and Isacson, O. (2002). Embryonic stem cells develop into functional dopaminergic neurons after transplantation in a Parkinson rat model. *Proc. Natl. Acad. Sci. U. S. A.* **4,** 2344–2349.

163. Piccini, P., Brooks, D.J., Bjorklund, A., Gunn, R.N., Grasby, P.M., Rimoldi, O., Brundin, P., Hagell, P., Rehncrona, S., Widner, H., and Lindvall, O. (1999). Dopamine release from nigral transplants visualized *in vivo* in a Parkinson's patient. *Nat. Neurosci.* **2,** 1137–1140.

164. Freed, C.R., Greene, P.E., Breeze, R.E., Tsai, W.Y., DuMouchel, W., Kao, R., Dillon, S., Winfield, H., Culver, S., Trojanowski, J.Q., Eidelberg, D., and Fahn, S. (2001). Transplantation of embryonic dopamine neurons for severe Parkinson's disease. *N. Engl. J. Med.* **344,** 710–719.

165. Olanow, C.W., Goetz, C.G., Kordower, J.H., Stoessl, A.J., Sossi, V., Brin, M.F., Shannon, K.M., Nauert, G.M., Perl, D.P., Godbold, J., and Freeman, T.B. (2003). A double-blind controlled trial of bilateral fetal nigral transplantation in Parkinson's disease. *Annu. Neurol.* **54,** 403–414.

166. Freeman, T.B., Cicchetti, F., Hauser, R.A., Deacon, T.W., Li, X.J., Hersch, S.M., Nauert, G.M., Sanberg, P.R., Kordower, J.H., Saporta, S., and Isacson, O. (2000). Transplanted fetal striatum in Huntington's disease: phenotypic development and lack of pathology. *Proc. Natl. Acad. Sci. U. S. A.* **97,** 13,877–13,882.

167. Bachoud-Levi, A.C., Bourdet, C., Brugieres, P., Nguyen, J.P., Grandmougin, T., Haddad, B., Jeny, R., Bartolomeo, P., Boisse, M.F., Dalla Barba, G., Degos, J.D., Ergis, A.M., Lefaucheur, J.P., Lisovoski, F., Pailhous, E., Remy, P., Palfi, S.,

Defer, G.L., Cesaro, P., Hantraye, P., and Peschanski, M. (2000). Safety and tolerability assessment of intrastriatal neural allografts in five patients with Huntington's disease. *Exp. Neurol.* **161,** 194–202.

168. Gaura, V., Bachoud-Levi, A.C., Ribeiro, M.J., Nguyen, J.P., Frouin, V., Baudic, S., Brugieres, P., Mangin, J.F., Boisse, M.F., Palfi, S., Cesaro, P., Samson, Y., Hantraye, P., Peschanski, M., and Remy, P. (2003). Striatal neural grafting improves cortical metabolism in Huntington's disease patients. *Brain* **127 (Pt. 1),** 65–72.

169. Menalled, L.B., and Chesselet, M.F. (2002). Mouse models of Huntington's disease. *Trends Pharmacol. Sci.* **23,** 32–39.

170. McDonald, J.W., Liu, X.Z., Qu, Y., Liu, S., Mickey, S.K., Turetsky, D., Gottlieb, D.I., and Choi, D.W. (1999). Transplanted embryonic stem cells survive, differentiate, and promote recovery in injured rat spinal cord. *Nat. Med.* **5,** 1410–1412.

171. Privat, A., Ribotta, M.G., and Orsal, D. (2000). What is a functional recovery after spinal cord injury? *Nat. Med.* **6,** 358.

172. McDonald, J.W., Gottlieb, D.I., and Choi, D.W. (2000). Reply to "What is a functional recovery after spinal cord injury?" *Nat. Med.* **6,** 358.

173. Kerr, D.A., Llado, J., Shamblott, M.J., Maragakis, N.J., Irani, D.N., Crawford, T.O., Krishnan, C., Dike, S., Gearhart, J.D., and Rothstein, J.D. (2003). Human embryonic germ cell derivatives facilitate motor recovery of rats with diffuse motor neuron injury. *J. Neurosci.* **23,** 5131–5140.

174. Hoehn, M., Kustermann, E., Blunk, J., Wiedermann, D., Trapp, T., Wecker, S., Focking, M., Arnold, H., Hescheler, J., Fleischmann, B.K., Schwindt, W., and Buhrle, C. (2002). Monitoring of implanted stem cell migration *in vivo*: a highly resolved *in vivo* magnetic resonance imaging investigation of experimental stroke in rat. *Proc. Natl. Acad. Sci. U. S. A.* **99,** 16,267–16,272.

175. Liu, S., Qu, Y., Stewart, T.J., Howard, M.J., Chakrabortty, S., Holekamp, T.F., McDonald, J.W. (2000). Embryonic stem cells differentiate into oligodendrocytes and myelinate in culture and after spinal cord transplantation. *Proc. Natl. Acad. Sci. U. S. A.* **97,** 6126–6131.

176. John, G.R., Shankar, S.L., Shafit-Zagardo, B., Massimi, A., Lee, S.C., Raine, C.S., and Brosnan, C.F. (2002). Multiple sclerosis: reexpression of a developmental pathway that restricts oligodendrocyte maturation. *Nat. Med.* **8,** 1115–1121.

177. Abe, Y., Kouyama, K., Tomita, T., Tomita, Y., Ban, N., Nawa, M., Matsuoka, M., Niikura, T., Aiso, S., Kita, Y., Iwatsubo, T., and Nishimoto, I. (2003). Analysis of neurons created from wild-type and Alzheimer's mutation knockin embryonic stem cells by a highly efficient differentiation protocol. *J. Neurosci.* **23,** 8513–8525.

22

Sensory Epithelium of the Eye and Ear

Constance Cepko and Donna M. Fekete

Introduction

Humans rely heavily on both vision and hearing. Unfortunately, both deteriorate with age, partly because of the death of cells in the primary sensory organs, the eye and the ear. In addition, the frequency of disease genes that affect one or both of these modalities is relatively high.[1-3] Stem cells able to replace some of the dying cells, either *in situ* or through engraftment, have been a hope for some time. In part, this is because there are few effective therapies for diseases of these tissues. Work aimed at identifying retinal and otic stem cells has been undertaken with more energy in the last several years because of the exciting findings for stem cells elsewhere in the body. Here, we review these recent findings in the context of normal development.

Introduction to Progenitor and Stem Cells in the Retina

The retina has served as a model of central nervous system (CNS) anatomy, physiology, and development.[4, 5] Most studies aimed at understanding its development have concerned the production of the retinal neurons and glia from retinal progenitor cells. These cells were originally shown by lineage analysis to be multipotent throughout development, capable of generating both neurons and glia, even in a single, terminal cell division (reviewed by Cepko *et al.*[6]). Retinal progenitor cells do not appear to be totipotent except for the earliest progenitor cells, when clones can comprise all retinal cell types. Moreover, retinal progenitor cells do not appear to be able to proliferate extensively *in vivo*[7] or following explantation and exposure to different culture conditions (e.g., see Lillien *et al.*[8] and Jensen *et al.*[9]). Recent studies have been aimed at finding retinal stem cells. These studies have been conducted along the two lines established in the search for stem cells elsewhere in the CNS. One approach has been to search for mitotic cells capable of generating retinal neurons in the adult *in vivo*. The other approach has been to culture cells in growth factors. Both types of experiments have begun to yield promising answers, but much more needs to be done.

The Optic Vesicle Generates Diverse Cell Types That Can Undergo Transdifferentiation

To appreciate some of the intriguing observations concerning retinal stem cells, a review of the tissues that derive from the optic vesicle is needed.[10, 11] The optic vesicle is an evagination of the neural tube where the diencephalon and telencephalon meet. The vesicle at first protrudes as a simple evagination when the neural tube forms. Soon thereafter, the vesicle undergoes an invagination to form a two-layered optic cup. The outer cup will form a nonneural structure, the retinal pigmented epithelium (RPE), as well as with other support structures of the eye (Fig. 22–1). The RPE is a single layer of epithelial cells heavily pigmented to capture stray light that passes through the retina. It performs several support functions, including such highly specialized functions as the isomerization of *trans* to *cis* retinal to allow the photopigments, the opsins, to continue to capture light. The RPE expresses many specific gene products. A recent transcriptome analysis conducted using serial analysis of gene expression (SAGE) showed that 40% of the RPE SAGE tags did not have a corresponding cDNA in GenBank.[12] This is a much higher rate of unknowns than seen in other tissues (e.g., the human retina).

The inner wall of the optic cup forms the neural retina (Fig. 22–1). The primary sensory cells are the photoreceptors (PRs), which comprise two types, the rods and the cones. The rods are active under dim light, and the cones are active under daylight conditions. In addition, there are several types of interneurons, horizontal cells, amacrine cells, and bipolar cells and an output neuron, the retinal ganglion cell. The retina also has one glial cell that spans the retinal layers, the Müller glial cell. During the early phase of retinal neurogenesis, retinal progenitor cells produce the various retinal neurons in a conserved fashion, typically beginning with production of ganglion cells and finishing with production of rod PRs, bipolar interneurons, and Müller glia (reviewed by Altshuler *et al.*[13]). The production of these cells begins in the center of the retina and proceeds to the retinal periphery, or margin. In amphibians and teleost fish, there is continual growth at the margin throughout the life of the animal in a region termed the ciliary marginal zone, or CMZ.[14-16] In addition, in fish, there is a late wave of production of rod PRs as the retina expands.[17]

The developmental sequence at the periphery of the retina is complex and not at all understood at a molecular level,

Handbook of Stem Cells
Volume 1

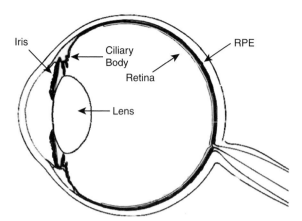

Figure 22–1. The eye is a complex tissue, developing from cells originating from the neural tube, the neural crest, the surface ectoderm, and the mesoderm. The retina is the neurosensory tissue that originates from the inner layer of the optic cup, and the RPE originates from the outer optic cup layer. Both the inner and outer optic cup layers contribute to the formation of the ciliary body and iris. The ciliary body also comprises cells from the neural crest, which form the ciliary muscle. The iris muscles derive from the outer layer of the optic cup. Stem cells have been isolated from the ciliary body[37, 45] and iris,[46] and Muller glia in the retina have been found to divide and generate neurons in the early posthatch chick.[29]

although it is an important region for stem cells. The margin is the fold that develops following invagination of the primary optic vesicle. Following the initial formation of the morphologically simple folds at the periphery, where the presumptive RPE and retina meet, some rather unusual morphogenetic events, including transdifferentiation, take place to form several anterior support structures for the eye. The ciliary body, with the associated pars plicata and pars plana, as well as the iris, form from this area (Fig. 22–1). The pars plana and plicata each comprise two epithelial layers, one pigmented and one unpigmented. They are the site of attachment of the zonules, or suspensory ligaments of the lens. The unpigmented epithelial layer of the pars plicata and plana is continuous with the retina, and the pigmented layer is continuous with the RPE. The tight apposition of these two epithelial layers allows regulation of secretion from the ciliary body, as it is highly vascularized with a rather leaky type of blood vessel. Beyond secretion of aqueous (through the pars plicata) and vitreous (through the pars plana humor), the ciliary body also controls the shape of the lens. Neural crest–derived muscles form within the ciliary body and contract and relax the ligaments surrounding the lens during lens accommodation.

The iris is the shutter that opens and closes to allow more or less light to penetrate the eye. It includes a pigmented epithelial layer derived from the margin of the optic cup that is continuous with the RPE. It also has an initially unpigmented epithelial layer, the inner or posterior layer of epithelium, which is continuous with the retina. This layer gradually becomes pigmented, however, and additional pigmentation of the iris is contributed by neural crest–derived melanocytes. Remarkably, the pupil is opened and closed by muscles that

derive from the margin of the optic cup, the only ectodermally derived muscles in the body. This occurs because of transdifferentiation as initially pigmented cells separate from the epithelial sheet, proliferate, and form muscles. Thus, the retinal margin develops to serve several functions, and most of these diverse cell types derive from both the outer and the inner walls of the early optic cup.

Classical embryological experiments with birds, fish, amphibians, and mammals revealed a great deal of plasticity among the ocular tissues. For example, extirpation of most—but importantly, not all—of the retina leads to transdifferentiation of the RPE into the retina.[18] This capacity exists only until embryonic day (E) 4 in chickens[18] and E14 in mice.[19, 20] In urodeles, it can occur throughout life.[21–23] In chicks, it was found to be induced by fibroblast growth factor (FGF) in RPE cultures.[24, 25] *In vivo*, it is not clear if FGF is involved in the initial distinction between the retina and RPE, but delivery of FGF8 *in vivo* can trigger transdifferentiation.[26] Wolffian regeneration in newts is a remarkable process by which the dorsal iris can regenerate a lens,[27] originally not derived from the optic vesicle but from the surface ectoderm. This type of regeneration has not been seen in birds or mammals. All of these examples reveal that end-stage differentiated cells are not necessarily committed or irreversibly differentiated. Perhaps most remarkably, as explained later in this chapter, the pigmented cells derived from this area of the optic cup display broad developmental potential in adult mammals in that they are the source of retinal stem cells.

In vivo Neurogenesis in the Posthatch Chicken

A search for stem cells in the developed retina was recently conducted by Fischer and Reh in the chicken.[28,29] Retinal neurogenesis in most of the chick retina is complete by E12.[30] Fischer and Reh examined the posthatch chick (i.e., >E21) for the incorporation of bromodeoxyuridine (BrdU).[28] They found that two areas could be labeled. In a normal retina without injury, the P7 retina was labeled in the ciliary margin, reminiscent of the aforementioned findings for amphibians and fish.[28] These cells were followed using their BrdU label and were found to incorporate into the inner nuclear layer (INL), generating bipolar and amacrine neurons. No cells were found in the outer nuclear layer (ONL), the layer containing PRs. Antigens consistent with the INL fates were also observed. The newly generated cells appeared progressively more centrally as harvests were made later and later. These findings suggest that the CMZ cells were generating more retinal neurons to accommodate additional growth of the eye, previously thought to occur only through an expansion of the volume of the vitreous cavity, and stretching of the retinal tissue. However, this does not occur throughout the life of the chicken as it does in amphibians and fish, since the growth stops a few weeks posthatch. The number of mitotic cells within the CMZ was not increased following injection of a toxin, *N*-methyl–D-aspartate (NMDA), unlike the response seen in the *Xenopus* eye.[31] However, injection of 100-ng doses of epidermal growth factor (EGF), insulin, or insulin-like growth factor 1 (IGF-1), but not FGF, did increase the mitotic activity in this area. In addition, if insulin was applied with FGF2, cells with gene expression profiles and processes consistent with the ganglion cell fate were observed.[32]

Another site of BrdU incorporation in the posthatch chick could be identified following application of the toxin NMDA, which primarily targets amacrine cells.[29] If BrdU was applied two days after injection of NMDA at P7, incorporation of BrdU into Müller glial cells in the central retina was observed. Labeling with BrdU at 1 day or 3 days following toxin administration led to few BrdU-labeled cells. It thus appears that a process triggered by toxin administration requires approximately 2 days to stimulate one or two rounds of cell division. This response is also developmentally limited, as few BrdU-labeled cells were observed after P14, and the response was lost in a central-to-peripheral manner, similar to the initial wave of neurogenesis in the retina. Müller glial cells do possess the ability to undergo *reactive gliosis,* a phenomenon associated with various types of retinal damage in adult mammals and birds.[33] Reactive gliosis occurs in astrocytes throughout the CNS and is characterized by limited cell division; expression of intermediate filament proteins, such as vimentin and glial fibrillary acidic protein (GFAP); and increased process outgrowth.[34] It has not been established that this type of cell division leads to production of neurons elsewhere in the CNS or in the retina of adult birds.

The BrdU-labeled Müller glial cells induced by toxin treatment were found in the ONL and INL, whereas Müller glial nuclei are typically only found in the INL. Some of these BrdU-labeled cells coexpressed two markers of retinal progenitor cells, Chx10 and Pax6, and some expressed a bHLH gene, *CASH-1,* a marker of early retinal progenitor cells. A small percentage (<10%) of the BrdU+ cells subsequently were found to have neuronal morphology and to express markers of amacrine cells and bipolar cells. Transiently, however, many cells expressed a neurofilament (NF) marker, normally expressed on horizontal and ganglion cells in the retina. This appeared to be transient as the number of NF+ cells decreased, and markers and morphology consistent with mature ganglion and horizontal cells were not seen. Researchers did not find markers of PR cells. Many of the BrdU-labeled cells persisted in what appeared to be an arrested state for at least 12 days. They explored the possibility that the *in vivo* environment was limited for production of PR cells by culturing the toxin-treated retinas, but they were similarly unable to observe the genesis of PR cells, though they did find that toxin-treated retinas proliferated *in vitro* more than the untreated controls.

The division of Müller glia, following by genesis of neurons in the chick, can also be stimulated by growth factors in the absence of added toxins.[35] Application of both insulin and FGF2 by intraocular injection, starting at P7 and continuing for 3 days, led to the production of many mitotic Müller glial cells. Fourteen days after the last injection, some BrdU+ cells showed markers of amacrine and perhaps ganglion cells, and others showed markers of Müller glia. Similar to the findings following NMDA injections, no markers of PR cells were observed. To explore whether the type of toxin, and thus the target cell killed by the toxin, combined with growth factor injection might give a more specific replacement of the targeted cells, researchers injected several types of toxins with insulin and FGF2.[36] When ganglion cells were targeted by the toxins, kainic acid, or colchicine, more cells with ganglion cell markers were observed. These studies lead to the hope that replacement of the specific cells that die in various retinal diseases, such as ganglion cells in glaucoma, might be effectively replaced following stimulation of stem cells with the right cocktail of factors.

Ahmad *et al.,*[37] as well as Kubota and colleagues,[38] have searched for proliferation in the uninjured retina of mammals. Ahmad *et al.* injected 4-week-old rats intraperitoneally with BrdU for 5 days. The only incorporation that they report was in the ciliary margin—that is, no labeling of Müller glial cells was observed. Kubota *et al.*[38] examined opossum and mouse (as well as quail) and found no incorporation in centrally located Müller glia. Kubota *et al.* did find some incorporation of BrdU in the ciliary margin of quail, though less than in the chicken, and a few labeled cells in the ciliary margin of the opossum, but they found no labeled cells in the ciliary margin in the mouse.

Radial glial cells, astrocytes, and Müller glia have been shown to share some antigens with progenitor cells (e.g., see Linser *et al.,*[39] Doetsch *et al.,*[40] and Lendahl *et al.*[41]). This resemblance is more extensive that previously appreciated. We systematically analyzed gene expression in the developing and mature murine retina.[42] We found that there were 85 genes preferentially expressed in Müller glia in the mature retina. Of these genes, the majority were also found in retinal progenitor cells. Some of these genes, such as cyclin D3, undoubtedly reflect that Müller cells retain the ability to divide but other genes are more enigmatic. Nonetheless, the studies from Fisher and Reh mentioned previously and the SAGE data argue that Müller glia should be explored further as a source of cells that might replace dying neurons. This notion is in keeping with the idea that radial glial cells elsewhere in the developing CNS,[43] as well as astrocytes in the mature forebrain,[40] can serve as neuronal progenitor cells and stem cells, respectively.

Growth of Retinal Neurospheres from the Ciliary Margin of Mammals

Reynolds and Weiss demonstrated in 1992 that cultures of CNS tissue in the presence of EGF, FGF, or both would lead to balls of cells with indefinite proliferation capacity, or *neurospheres.*[44] Neurospheres were subsequently shown to produce neurons, astrocytes, and oligodendrocytes and were thus identified as originating from neural stem cells. Several groups have applied these protocols to the retina. Cultures from ocular tissues of mouse, rat, human, and cow have been made using FGF and EGF.[45, 46] Retinal neurospheres have been recovered and appear to have cells with indefinite proliferation potential, multipotency, and possibly totipotency.

Tropepe et al.[45] reported that the ciliary body from adult mice had the most enriched source of retinal stem cells. They examined E14 RPE and retina and adult retina, RPE, iris, and ciliary body for production of neurospheres in the presence of FGF, EGF, or both. They were unable to recover any neurospheres with the proliferative capacity of stem cells from the embryonic or adult retina or from the adult iris, RPE, and ciliary muscle. A few neurospheres were recovered from the embryonic RPE, which included the peripheral margin, the precursor to the ciliary body. In the adult, neurospheres were only recovered from the pigmented cells of the ciliary body (Fig. 22–1), termed the pigmented ciliary margin (PCM). Although there was some recovery from the E14 RPE, the number per eye increased 10-fold in the adult PCM compared to the entire RPE of the E14 retina. This curious finding suggests that these cells are formed at the end of development and not the beginning, the opposite of what one might have predicted. Alternatively, during the maturation of the PCM, there is an expansion of a few early stem cells. Tropepe et al. found that the stem cells were either rare or hard to culture, as only 0.6% of the adult PCM-plated cells would produce a neurosphere in the presence of FGF2. They did not require exogenous FGF, as they could arise, albeit at a reduced frequency, in its absence. This was presumably because of endogenous FGF, as addition of anti-FGF antibody reduced the formation of neurospheres.

As the PCM neurospheres originated with the pigmented cells of the ciliary body, it was of interest to determine if pigment was necessary for their ability to be stem cells. This was examined in albinos, where they were isolated at a comparable frequency to that of pigmented animals.[45] The RPE and ciliary body normally do not express Chx10. However, upon the genesis of neurospheres, cells began to express this retinal marker. If cultured under conditions that favor differentiation, the cells turned on markers of PRs, bipolar cells, and glia. However, no markers of amacrine and horizontal cell interneurons, or of ganglion cells, were seen. It is significant that rhodopsin, a definitive marker of a PR cell, can be expressed. Rhodopsin is not expressed by other CNS neurospheres or neural cell lines derived from other CNS locations.[47] Retinal progenitor cells normally do not make oligodendrocytes, and the oligodendrocyte marker, O4, was not observed.

There is a naturally occurring null allele of the paired-type homeobox gene, Chx10, in mice (orj). This mutant has a retina and RPE approximately 10-fold smaller than wild-type mice, with an expanded ciliary margin.[48] When cultures were made from the ciliary margin of orj, approximately fivefold more neurospheres were recovered.[45] These spheres were approximately $\frac{1}{3}$ the size of the wild-type spheres, in keeping with the finding that Chx10 is required for the full proliferation of retinal progenitor cells. Thus, Chx10 must be involved with the allocation or regulation of the number of stem cells in the PCM.

Ahmad et al. also report the isolation of retinal neurospheres from the ciliary body of rats,[37] and Tropepe et al. reported such results from postmortem human and bovine

eyes.[45] The rat neurospheres were dependent upon FGF2 and could not be recovered from the retina, the RPE, or the nonpigmented portion of the ciliary epithelium. Haruta et al. also isolated retinal stem cells from the rat eye, but they used iris tissue rather than ciliary margin tissue.[46] As shown in Fig. 22–1, the iris and ciliary body are adjacent to each other at the margin of the eye. The iris cells were cultured as an explant in the presence of FGF, rather than as dissociated cells. Tropepe et al. had reported previously that, unlike the ciliary body cells, dissociated cells from the iris did not generate neurospheres.[45] Cells that migrated out of the iris explants were able to express some neural markers, such as NF200, but not PR-specific markers. However, if the cells were transduced with crx, a homeobox gene important in PR differentiation,[49, 50] approximately 10% of the cells expressed rhodopsin and recoverin, two markers of PR cells. The ciliary body-derived neurospheres can generate cells bearing the same retinal markers, including rhodopsin, without transduction of crx. The difference may be caused by culture conditions. The ciliary body-derived cells can be grown as spheres, and this environment may support PR development without a need for crx transduction. When Haruta et al. cultured ciliary body-derived cells as monolayers, as they cultured iris-derived cells, the ciliary body–derived cells did not express PR markers.[46]

Haruta et al. point out that tissue from the iris can be readily obtained for autologous grafts.[46] It is far more difficult to obtain tissue from the ciliary body, with an accompanying risk of damage to the ciliary body. However, as Tropepe et al. reported that postmortem human and bovine PCM could produce spheres at low frequency, it is possible that humans could be used as a source of donor cells. This would not be as immunologically compatible as an autologous graft, but it nonetheless might suffice, as it is still not clear how well tolerated retinal grafts might be.[51]

That the pigmented ciliary body and iris cells are the source of retinal stem cells is rather surprising. It was expected that the periphery of the eye might be the area where stem cells would reside, as this is the location of stem cells in amphibians and fish. In the CMZ of amphibians and fish, the nonpigmented cells contiguous with the retinal epithelium, located nearest to the retina, make more retinal cells. However, stem cells have not been recovered from this area in mammals. An alternative prediction might have been that retinal stem cells would be the RPE cells. As explained previously, the RPE is quite plastic early in development in mammals and chicks and throughout life in urodeles, maintaining the ability to make retinal cells in response to certain conditions. However, the adult mammalian RPE has not been shown to generate neurospheres when cultured under the conditions described previously. Moreover, even the embryonic RPE does not supply many neurospheres in the neurosphere culture conditions. In contrast to the preceding predictions, the most robust source of retinal stem cells in the adult mammal is the ciliary body pigmented cells. These cells are immediately adjacent to, and contiguous with, the RPE, but they are not RPE cells, at least in terms of function, as described previously. We do not have markers that would help to further define them. They derive from the outer walls of the optic cup, and the inner walls normally produce the retina in normal development. It should be noted, however, that whether the iris stem cells are derived from the inner or outer walls of the optic cup is not clear at this time. Although the iris stem cells are pigmented, both the inner and outer walls of the optic cup normally develop pigmentation in the iris. Both iris- and ciliary body-derived stem cells are pigmented, which may provide a useful marker for their prospective isolation.

Prospects for Stem Cell Therapy in the Retina

A large number of the diseases of the retina are caused by degeneration of PR cells. Approximately 40% of the genes identified as human disease genes that lead to blindness are rod specific.[1] Many of these diseases nonetheless lead to the loss of cone PR cells. This nonautonomous death of cones is the reason for loss of daylight, high-acuity vision. Thus, replacement of dying rods, or the retardation of the death of rods, might prevent or slow the death of cones. Replacement of dying cones themselves is another potential therapeutic approach. This is particularly appropriate when the etiology of the disease is not clear, as is the case in the most prevalent disease, age-related macular degeneration. The source of either rod or cone PR cells could be the endogenous stem cells themselves. The best scenario would be the stimulation of the division of Müller glia, which are distributed through the retina, followed by the induction of PR differentiation. Unfortunately, as noted previously, Müller glia have not been observed to generate PR cells in the chick or any mammal that has been investigated. Nonetheless, future studies might lead to a manipulation that would stimulate PR production by Müller glia. A second source of PR cells might be the endogenous stem cells in the ciliary body or iris, left *in situ*. Although these cells can produce PR cells when cultured, they have not been shown to generate PR cells *in situ*. In addition, unless the cells could be made to migrate and cover the central retina, where most of our high-acuity vision occurs, they would not lead to retention or recovery of high-acuity vision. Still, if they could lead to retention of peripheral vision, some therapeutic benefit would be realized. Finally, engraftment of stem cells or of PR cells generated *in vitro* by stem cells can be attempted. The problems of graft rejection, if not an autologous graft, would have to be confronted, but they might not be as difficult to overcome as engraftment to sites in the periphery.[51] Furthermore, iris-derived cells might be used as an autologous graft. Preliminary data from Tropepe *et al.* of engraftment of the neurospheres derived from the PCM are promising. Injection of such cells into the vitreous body of postnatal day 0 rats led to the formation of many PR cells, expressing rhodopsin, in the ONL.[52] If such cells could be formed in a diseased retina, then two possible benefits might be realized. One would be to simply prevent further degeneration of endogenous PR cells, which, as mentioned previously, can die by nonautonomous processes. The second

benefit might be that the engrafted PR cells synapse with second-order neurons and provide vision themselves. To date, this has not been achieved.[53] The concern here is that the site of engraftment might not support synaptogenesis—particularly at the advanced stage when much of the retina has degenerated, likely the stage when such therapies would be attempted. Nonetheless, such strategies are worth pursuing, particularly now that there are stem cells that can be manipulated to generate retinal cells; our understanding of the processes of the development of retinal cells has similarly been advancing.

Development and Regeneration of Tissues Derived from the Inner Ear

The entire vertebrate inner ear derives from the otic placode, a thickening of the dorsolateral surface ectoderm immediately lateral to the hindbrain. Like the lens and olfactory placodes, the otic placode invaginates and pinches off to form a single-layered ball of cells, now called the otic vesicle. From this simple epithelium, a large variety of tissues and cells types arise. The otic ectoderm is neurogenic for the first-order neurons of the eighth cranial ganglion, the statoacoustic ganglion. The ganglion neuroblasts are the earliest recognizable cell type; they delaminate from the otic ectoderm at the otic cup stage even before it completes vesicle formation. The otic vesicle is also sensorigenic, generating 6–8 different sensory patches. Inner ear sensory organs subserve hearing and balance and are differentiated according to their function. There are three major classes of sensory organs: macula, crista, and acoustic. Acoustic organs vary substantially in structure and sensitivity across the vertebrates, reaching their highest complexity and frequency selectivity in the mammalian organ of Corti. In all inner ear sensory organs, the mechanosensory hair cells are interspersed among a field of supporting cells essential for hair cell survival and function. Finally, beyond the sensory patches, several types of nonsensory tissues derive from the otic epithelium. The most highly differentiated is the tissue that secretes the extracellular fluid, called endolymph, which bathes the apical surfaces of all otic epithelial cells. Endolymph contains an unusually high concentration of potassium ions. The tissue responsible for endolymph production is anatomically complex, highly vascularized, and endowed with many ion pumps and channels. Other nonsensory epithelia flank the sensory organs and may contribute, with the supporting cells, to the secretion of the specialized extracellular matrices perched above the hair cells to enhance their mechanosensitivity.

Lineage studies have yet to reveal all possible relationships among the constellation of inner ear cells, so we do not yet know if individual otic placode cells are truly pluripotent for all inner ear cell types. We are confident that mechanoreceptors and their supporting cells share a common progenitor in the bird and zebra fish inner ear[54–56] and in the regenerating salamander lateral line.[57] There is also evidence that sensory and nonsensory cells can be clonally related in the chicken ear.[54, 55] Preliminary studies in mice include a single clone with members in both the sensory saccule and nonsensory utricle.[58] Furthermore, otic neurons and sensory cells can be related in the bird.[59] To date, there is no direct evidence for the existence of a true otic stem cell—that is, one that divides asymmetrically to replicate itself while generating a daughter with an alternative cell fate or fates. Nonetheless, lineage studies indicate that multipotent progenitor cells constitute a normal feature of inner ear development, leaving open the possibility that similar cells may lurk in mature ears, where they might be poised to expand with appropriate signals or culture conditions.

A variety of growth factors and growth factor receptors have been associated with developing inner ears (reviewed by Oesterle and Warchol[60]). However, it is important to distinguish between growth factors that may regulate cell proliferation and those that may influence cell fate specification in other ways, such as the role of FGFs in otic induction.[61] Furthermore, many of the growth factor assays are performed *in vitro,* with the inherent risk that cells and tissues can change their growth factor responsiveness depending upon culture conditions (described by Oesterle and Oberholtzer[60]). For example, culturing of neonatal sensory epithelia leads to up-regulation of FGFR1/2 and IGF-1R in macular supporting cells[62] and down-regulation of EFGR in the organ of Corti.[63] This caveat notwithstanding, members of several growth factor families can enhance cell proliferation of developing otocyst or neonatal inner ear tissues, either alone or in combinations, when presented in culture. These include bombesin, EGF, FGFs, GGF2, heregulin, insulin, IGFs, PDGF, and TGFα (referenced by Oesterle *et al.*[60]; see also Zheng *et al.*[64]).

In vivo Neurogenesis in Postembryonic Animals

PROLIFERATION IN NORMALS (OR AFTER GROWTH FACTOR TREATMENT)

The vestibular maculae are involved in sensing gravity, and in fishes and amphibians these organs continue to increase in size throughout life (reviewed by Corwin and Warchol[65]). Here, we focus on the sensory organs of warm-blooded vertebrates, where there is a marked contrast between birds and mammals in the timing of inner ear organogenesis (reviewed by Corwin and Oberholtzer[66]). In both classes, sensory organs stop generating new cells approximately midway through embryogenesis.[67, 68] A notable exception is the vestibular maculae of birds, where there is ongoing addition and death of cells well beyond hatching. Cell counts or BrdU labeling have led to estimates that hair cells turn over with half-lives of 20 days,[69] 30 days,[70] or 52 days[71] in the chicken utricular macula. Within 2 weeks of hatching, nearly 500 cells in the saccular macula and 1400 cells in the utricular macula may be added per day[69] with the steady-state addition of 850 hair cells per utricle per day reached 60 days after hatching.[70] However, these numbers are apparently achieved in the absence of an amplifying progenitor. Rather, most progenitors divide once to produce a sibling pair consisting of one hair cell and one non-hair cell (presumed to be the supporting cell). BrdU+ clusters

exceeding three cells are rare 2–4 months after labeling.[71] Thus, if there is a self-renewing stem cell pool in the mature avian macula, it consists of cells that divide on an extremely slow timescale. Interestingly, the neuronal colony-forming cells of the olfactory epithelium, thought to be the true stem cell of this sensory organ, are also rare (1 in 3600 purified progenitors) and divide at a very slow rate (reviewed by Calof *et al.*[72]). Ongoing receptor cell turnover (and regeneration) in the olfactory epithelium utilizes a transient amplifying progenitor pool that in turn generates a population of immediate neuronal precursors; the latter will divide symmetrically to make differentiated olfactory receptor cells.

In contrast to lower vertebrates, in mammals the vestibular macula is quiescent from birth. So, too, are the auditory organs of both birds and mammals. For example, BrdU injections failed to label cells in the adult mouse organ of Corti.[73] However, in mice lacking the cyclin-dependent kinase inhibitors $p27^{kip1}$ or $p19^{Ink4d}$, cell turnover continues in postnatal animals.[73–75] Dividing cells are observed several weeks after birth among hair cell ($p19^{Ink4d−/−}$) or supporting cell ($p27^{kip1−/−}$) layers. Prolonged mitosis in the $p27^{kip1}$-null is accompanied by the differentiation of supernumerary hair cells and supporting cells. In both mutants, many hair cells eventually undergo apoptosis, leading to hearing loss. Nonetheless, these data suggest that the differentiated organ of Corti, which has never been shown to regenerate naturally, has the potential to harbor cells that can divide and differentiate under appropriate circumstances. In this context, it is intriguing that a subset of cells in both auditory and vestibular organs of the neonatal mouse express the neural stem cell marker, nestin (Fig. 22–2). Nestin is rapidly down-regulated about one week after birth, although it persists in nonsensory cochlear cells to day 15.[76]

Several growth factors and cytokines can affect cell proliferation in undamaged, mature inner ear sensory organs or within sheets of sensory epithelial supporting cells (reviewed by Oesterle *et al.*[60]). Insulin, IGF-1, or IL-1β enhanced proliferation of normal chicken utricular cells *in vitro,* and FGF-2 reduced proliferation. Rodent utricular cells proliferated in response to GGF2, EGF+insulin, neu differentiation factor, TGFα, or TGFα+insulin (see references by Oesterle *et al.*[60] and Zheng *et al.*[64]) but lost response to heregulin by adulthood.[77]

PROLIFERATION AFTER DESTRUCTION OF CELLS

The strongest evidence that progenitor cells reside in quiescent sensory organs of warm-blooded vertebrates comes from regeneration studies. Beginning with ground-breaking work in the late 1980s, many studies have shown that damaged sensory organs will regenerate new hair cells in chickens, largely through a proliferative mechanism (reviewed by Corwin *et al.,*[66] Cotanche *et al.,*[78] and Stone *et al.*[79]). Thus, despite the absence of ongoing turnover, supporting cells of the auditory organ (the basilar papilla) mount a vigorous mitotic response to damaging conditions: Up to 15% of them enter the cell cycle to generate both hair cells and new supporting cells. Whether supporting cells coexist alongside

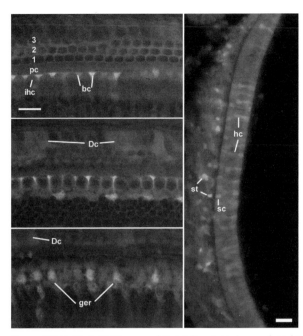

Figure 22–2. *Nestin-GFP in organ of Corti (left) and utricular macula (right) of P5 mouse. In the cochlea, GFP is seen in border cells (bc) surrounding inner hair cells (ihc), Deiters cells (Dc) surrounding outer hair cells (outer hair cell rows 1, 2, and 3 are indicated), and greater epithelial ridge cells (ger). In the utricular macula, GFP is seen in stromal cells (st), supporting cells (sc) and hair cells (hc). Figure courtesy of Ivan Lopez (UCLA).*

self-renewing stem cells remains an open question. Data suggest that only 1–4% of cycling cells in the regenerating basilar papilla will divide more than once within 3-day window after ototoxic drug treatment.[71] Even among this pool, ongoing proliferation appears to be extremely modest, although lineage analysis has not yet been performed to provide an unequivocal measure of clonal expansion. Like the basilar papilla, chicken macular cells also divide and differentiate in response to hair cell loss. The proliferation index of the drug-damaged macula rises in the presence of TGFα or TNFα.[80]

Once again, we contrast mammals to lower vertebrates: The mammalian macula has only a weak proliferative response to hair cell loss, with scant evidence that hair cells can be regenerated through a cycling intermediate. Instead, the maculae primarily restore their hair cells through direct transdifferentiation of supporting cells (reviewed by Corwin and Oberholtzer[66]) or through self-repair of sublethally damaged hair cells.[81] The limited proliferation that accompanies recovery may serve to replace transdifferentiated supporting cells rather than hair cells (see the description by Forge *et al.*[82]). Hair cell recovery is promoted by the addition of TGFα, IGF-1, retinoic acid, and brain-derived neurotrophic factor *in vivo*[83] or *in vitro*.[60] The weak proliferative response of the cultured, drug-damaged macula averaged 26 BrdU$^+$ cells per sensory organ. This proliferation was enhanced 10-fold by addition of heregulin (a member of the neuregulin family) and to a lesser extent by EGF or TGFα alone or with insulin.[64]

Neither hair cells nor supporting cells of the mammalian organ of Corti responded to heregulin, although more remote nonsensory epithelial cells of the cochlea did.

TRANSCRIPTION FACTOR REQUIREMENTS

Although many cell types are generated from otic epithelium, relatively few transcription factors have been definitively associated with cell fate specification in the ear (reviewed by Fekete and Wu[84] and Rubel and Fritzsch[85]). *NeuroD, Neurogenin-1,* and *Eya1* are essential for otic ganglion cell fate. *Brn3a/Brn3.0* is needed for ganglion cell survival and differentiation. *Math-1* is required for hair cell development and survival, and *Pou4f3/Brn3c/Brn3.1* is needed for subsequent hair cell differentiation. Ectopic delivery of *Math1* leads to ectopic production of partially differentiated hair cells in the mammalian ear, both in the adult guinea pig[86] and in cultures of postnatal rat sensory organs.[87] Thus, some cells retain the capacity to switch to a hair cell fate even into adulthood.

In Vitro Expansion of Otic Progenitors

Several groups have used immortalizing oncogenes to isolate cell lines from the developing inner ear and explore their differentiation potential (reviewed by Rivolta and Holley[88]). Efforts to expand unadulterated otic progenitor pools are just beginning, using either immature or differentiated otic epithelium as starting material. The work is presented in order based on age of the starting tissue. Several of the studies have been reported only in abstract form to date.

Work in the laboratories of Segil and Groves defined culture conditions (EGF$^+$ periotic mesenchyme) that permit E13.5 cochlear progenitors to persist in culture long after they would normally become postmitotic.[89] Mitotic progenitors generate islands of Math-1$^+$ hair cells, with numbers of hair cells continuing to increase 2 weeks after plating.[90]

Malgrange and collaborators dissociated cells from the newborn rat organ of Corti, approximately 5–6 days after sensory progenitors become postmitotic *in vivo*.[76] Filtering through fine (15-μm) nylon mesh resulted in the isolation of a population of small cells, 98% of which expressed nestin. Beginning with cell suspensions, spherical colonies called *otospheres* developed when cultured in the presence of EGF, FGF2, or both factors. After only 2 days of culturing, BrdU$^+$ progenitors expressing the hair cell marker myosin VIIA were observed, albeit in very small numbers (one per colony on average). About two cells per colony were immunopositive for the cell cycle inhibitor, p27^{kip1}, which normally labels the supporting cells of the organ of Corti. The number of myosin VIIA$^+$ cells increased to five cells per colony by 14 days, often appearing as a coherent islet. Some ultrastructural features of hair cells were evident in rare cells after both 2 and 14 days *in vitro*. Hair cell differentiation was not enhanced by switching the otospheres to "adherent" culture conditions that had been reported to induce neuronal differentiation in neurospheres. It is important to note that the method used in this study did not ensure that each otosphere originated from a single progenitor cell.

A preliminary study from another group reported successful generation of spherical cultures from mouse utricle or cochlea but only until postnatal day 6. Cells from 14- and 21-day-old sensory organs failed under similar culture conditions.[91]

Zhao reports culturing spheres from the isolated organ of Corti of adult guinea pig.[92, 93] Initially the spheres did not express nestin or the supporting cell marker, cytokeratin. Serum or EGF supplements, or long-term culture, induced nestin expression and allowed differentiation of a small number of cells as hair cells (calretinin+, myosin VIIA+, prestin+, or Brn3.1+), supporting cells (cytokeratin+ or connexin+), neurons (NF+ or βIII-tubulin+), or astrocytes (GFAP+). The appearance of differentiated hair cells was extremely rare, at less than 1% of the cells in long-term cultures.[94]

Most promising to date is the generation and differentiation of spherical cultures from single cells isolated from the utricular macula of the adult mouse. Taking their cue from the growth factor responsiveness of damaged vestibular sensory organs,[62, 83] Heller's laboratory used EGF, IGF-1, and bFGF to enhance sphere formation.[95] The combination of EGF+IGF-1 was most effective. Nestin+, sphere-forming cells could be dissociated into single cells and then expanded into new spheres through several rounds. Approximately 2.5 spheres could be formed at each passage, suggesting that a small number of cells retain sphere-renewal capability. To induce differentiation, spheres were moved to adherent culture conditions in the presence of serum, but then grown for 14 days in serum-free conditions. The cells down-regulated nestin and other markers of the early otic vesicle and up-regulated markers of several differentiated cell types. Cells expressing hair cell markers were present in up to 15% of differentiated cells. Many showed features consistent with rudimentary stereociliary bundle formation and were surrounded by cells with an expression profile consistent with supporting cells. Math-1+ cells colabeled with BrdU, indicating that these hair cells arose from a proliferative progenitor. Significantly, neurospheres grown from the subventricular zone of the mouse forebrain, cultured under identical conditions, did not generate hair cells. This suggests that the utricular stem cells have a special capacity to form inner ear mechanoreceptors. Macular-derived spheres also produced a significant percentage of cells with neuronal (6%) or astrocytic (35%) phenotypes, cell types normally absent from the macular epithelium. Spheres could also generate an array of ectoderm, mesoderm, or endoderm derivatives when the cells were delivered into the amniotic cavity of stage 4 chicken embryos. The incidence of sphere-forming stem cells was rare even under optimal growth conditions: 0.07% of plated cells. This is consistent with the absence of BrdU-labeling of adult sensory organs in the mouse and suggests that stem cells may be both rare and quiescent in vivo.

Recently, Heller's group also defined culture conditions that induced ES cells to form spheres containing many BrdU+, nestin+ cells.[96] Under growth conditions, the cells expressed nestin and markers of early otic vesicle (e.g., Pax2, BMP4, and BMP7). Under differentiating conditions, early otic markers plummeted, and markers of hair cells and supporting cells rose.

This is extremely encouraging as it suggests that it may be unnecessary to start with endogenous ear tissue to generate otic progenitors for therapeutic purposes.

Prospects for Therapy

As methods for culturing otic stem cells become established, one can ask whether the addition of different transcription factors (such as Math1) can induce differentiation of one cell type over another. Stem cells or differentiated cells derived from various sources could then be implanted back into the animal[97–99] to ask whether the cells will integrate and provide restoration of function in animal models of inner ear cell loss (reviewed by Duan et al.[100] and Holley[101]). The ear has some definite advantages for delivery of cells or gene transfer vectors, such as viruses. Surgical approaches to the fluid compartment of the inner ear provide access to the inner ear hair cells without requiring systemic delivery. For example, it is possible to inject through the round window delivering substances, such as neurotrophins, that can influence survival of sensory tissues or ganglion cells.[100, 102, 103] Delivery of cells that release soluble molecules, such as growth factors, could potentially provide functional restoration without necessarily restoring structural integrity. On the other hand, structural integration of replacement mechanoreceptors will probably be essential, even if extremely difficult, in view of the precision with which hair cell stereocilia must interact with the nonsensory matrices overlying them. Replacement of functional ganglion neurons, rather than sensory receptor cells, may be less problematic.[104] We anticipate considerable progress in these and related therapeutic approaches over the next decade, although substantial technical hurdles remain.

ACKNOWLEDGMENTS

Donna Fekete thanks S. Heller, H.B. Zhao, and T. Nakagawa for sharing unpublished data and I. Lopez for Fig. 22–2.

REFERENCES

1. Retnet. http://www.sph.uth.tmc.edu/RetNet/.
2. Li, X.C., and Friedman, R.A. (2002). Nonsyndromic hereditary hearing loss. Otolaryngol. Clin. North Am. **35,** 275–285.
3. Kramer, H.H., L.H. (2002). Molecular diagnosis of hereditary hearing impairment. Adv. Otorhinolaryngol. **61,** 11–27.
4. Dowling, J.E. (1987). "The Retina—An Approachable Part of the Brain." Harvard University Press, Cambridge, MA.
5. Rodieck, R.W. (1998). "The First Steps in Seeing." Sinauer, Sunderland, MA.
6. Cepko, C.L., Austin, C.P., Yang, X., Alexiades, M., and Ezzeddine, D. (1996). Cell fate determination in the vertebrate retina. Proc. Natl. Acad. Sci. U. S. A. **93,** 589–595.
7. Turner, D.L., Snyder, E.Y., and Cepko, C.L. (1990). Lineage-independent determination of cell type in the embryonic mouse retina. Neuron **4,** 833–845.

8. Lillien, L., and Cepko, C. (1992). Control of proliferation in the retina: temporal changes in responsiveness to FGF and TGF-α. *Development* **115,** 253–266.

9. Jensen, A.M., and Raff, M.C. (1997). Continuous observation of multipotential retinal progenitor cells in clonal density culture. *Dev. Biol.* **188,** 267–279.

10. Barishak, Y.R. (2001). "Embryology of the Eye and Its Adnexa," 2nd ed. Karger, Basel.

11. Mann, I. (1950). "The Development of the Human Eye." Grune and Stratton, New York.

12. Sharon, D., Blackshaw, S., Cepko, C.L., and Dryja, T.P. (2002). Profile of the genes expressed in the human peripheral retina, macula, and retinal pigment epithelium determined through serial analysis of gene expression (SAGE). *Proc. Natl. Acad. Sci. U. S. A.* **99,** 315–320.

13. Altshuler, D.M., Turner, D.L., and Cepko, C.L. (1991). Specification of cell type in the vertebrate retina. *In* "Development of the Visual System," (D.M.K. Lam *et al.,* eds.), pp. 37–58. MIT Press, Cambridge.

14. Hollyfield, J.G. (1968). Differential addition of cells to the retina in *Rana pipiens* tadpoles. *Dev. Biol.* **18,** 163–179.

15. Johns, P.R. (1977). Growth of the adult goldfish eye—III: Source of the new retinal cells. *J. Comp. Neurol.* **176,** 343–357.

16. Straznicky, K., and Gaze, R.M. (1971). The growth of the retina in *Xenopus laevis:* an autoradiographic study. *J. Embryol. Exp. Morphol.* **26,** 67–79.

17. Johns, P.R., and Fernald, R.D. (1981). Genesis of rods in teleost fish retina. *Nature* **293,** 141–142.

18. Coulombre, J.L., and Coulombre, A.J. (1965). Regeneration of neural retina from the pigmented epithelium in the chick embryo. *Dev. Biol.* **12,** 79–92.

19. Detwiler, S.R., and Van Dyke, R.H. (1954). The induction of neural retina from the pigment epithelial layer of the eye. *J. Exp. Zool.* **126,** 135–150.

20. Zhao, S., Rizzolo, L.J., and Barnstable, C.J. (1997). Differentiation and transdifferentiation of the retinal pigment epithelium. *Int. Rev. Cytol.* **171,** 225–266.

21. Stone, L.S. (1950). The role of retinal pigmented cells in regenerating neural retinae of adult salamander eyes. *J. Exp. Zool.* **113,** 9–31.

22. Okada, T.S. (1980). Cellular metaplasia or transdifferentiation as a model for retinal cell differentiation. *Curr. Top. Dev. Biol.* **16,** 349–380.

23. Sologub, A.A. (1968). On the capacity of eye pigmented epithelium for transformation into retina in anuran amphibian tadpoles. *Tsitologiya* **10,** 1526–1532.

24. Park, C.M., and Hollenberg, M.J. (1989). Basic fibroblast growth factor induces retinal regeneration *in vivo. Dev. Biol.* **134,** 201–205.

25. Guillemot, F., and Cepko, C. (1992). Retinal fate and ganglion cell differentiation are potentiated by acidic FGF in an *in vitro* assay of early retinal development. *Development* **114,** 743–754.

26. Vogel-Hopker, A., Momose, T., Rohrer, H., Yasuda, K., Ishihara, L., and Rapaport, D.H. (2000). Multiple functions of fibroblast growth factor 8 (FGF-8) in chick eye development. *Mech. Dev.* **94,** 25–36.

27. Reyer, R.W. (1954). Regeneration in the lens in the amphibian eye. *Q. Rev. Biol.* **29,** 1–46.

28. Fischer, A.J., and Reh, T.A. (2000). Identification of a proliferating marginal zone of retinal progenitors in postnatal chickens. *Dev. Biol.* **220,** 197–210.

29. Fischer, A.J., and Reh, T.A. (2001). Müller glia are a potential source of neural regeneration in the postnatal chicken retina. *Nat. Neurosci.* **4,** 247–252.

30. Prada, C., Puga, J., Perez-Mendez, L., Lopez, R., and Ramirez, G. (1991). Spatial and temporal patterns of neurogenesis in the chick retina. *Eur. J. Neurosci.* **3,** 559–569.

31. Reh, T.A. (1987). Cell-specific regulation of neuronal production in the larval frog retina. *J. Neurosci.* **7,** 3317–3324.

32. Fischer, A.J., Dierks, B.D., and Reh, T.A. (2002). Exogenous growth factors induce the production of ganglion cells at the retinal margin. *Development* **129,** 2283–2291.

33. MacLaren, R.E. (1996). Development and role of retinal glia in regeneration of ganglion cells following retinal injury. *Br. J. Ophthalmol.* **80,** 458–464.

34. Hatten, M.E., Liem, R.K., Shelanski, M.L., and Mason, C.A. (1991). Astroglia in CNS injury. *Glia* **16,** 779–789.

35. Fischer, A.J., McGuire, C.R., Dierks, B.D., and Reh, T.A. (2002). Insulin and fibroblast growth factor 2 activate a neurogenic program in Müller glia of the chicken retina. *J. Neurosci.* **22,** 9387–9398.

36. Fischer, A.J., and Reh, T.A. (2002). Exogenous growth factors stimulate the regeneration of ganglion cells in the chicken retina. *Dev. Biol.* **251,** 367–379.

37. Ahmad, I., Tang, L., and Pham, H. (2000). Identification of neural progenitors in the adult mammalian eye. *Biochem. Biophys. Res. Commun.* **270,** 517–521.

38. Kubota, R., Hokoc, J.N., Moshiri, A., McGuire, C., and Reh, T.A. (2002). A comparative study of neurogenesis in the retinal ciliary marginal zone of homeothermic vertebrates. *Brain Res. Dev. Brain Res.* **134,** 31–41.

39. Linser, P.J., Schlosshauer, B., Galileo, D.S., Buzzi, W.R., and Lewis, R.C. (1997). Late proliferation of retinal Müller cell progenitors facilitates preferential targeting with retroviral vectors *in vitro. Dev. Genet.* **20,** 186–196.

40. Doetsch, F., Caille, I., Lim, D.A., Garcia-Verdugo, J.M., and Alvarez-Buylla, A. (1999). Subventricular zone astrocytes are neural stem cells in the adult mammalian brain. *Cell* **97,** 703–716.

41. Lendahl, U., Zimmerman, L.B., and McKay, R.D. (1990). CNS stem cells express a new class of intermediate filament protein. *Cell* **60,** 585–595.

42. Blackshaw, S., Harpavat, S., Trimarchi, J., Li, C., Huang, H., Kuo, W.P., Weber, G., Lee, K., Fraioli, R.E., Cho, S.H., Yung, R., Asch, E., Ohno-Machado, L., Wong, W.H., and Cepko, C.L. (submitted to PLoS).

43. Kriegstein, A., and Gotz, M. (2003). Radial glia diversity: a matter of cell fate. *Glia* **43,** 37–43.

44. Reynolds, B.A., and Weiss, S. (1992). Generation of neurons and astrocytes from isolated cells of the adult mammalian central nervous system. *Science* **255,** 1707–1710.

45. Tropepe, V., Coles, B.L., Chiasson, B.J., Horsford, O.J., Elia, A.J., McInnes, R.R., and van der Kooy, D. (2000). Retinal stem cells in the adult mammalian eye. *Science* **287,** 2032–2036.

46. Haruta, M., Kosaka, M., Kanegae, Y., Saito, I., Inoue, T., Takahashi, M., Honda, Y., Kageyama, R., and Nishida, A. (2001). Induction of photoreceptor-specific phenotypes in adult mammalian iris tissue. *Nat. Neurosci.* **4,** 1163–1164.

47. Takahashi, M., Palmer, T.D., Takahashi, J., and Gage, F.H. (1998). Widespread integration and survival of adult-derived neural progenitor cells in the developing optic retina. *Mol. Cell Neurosci.* **12,** 340–348.

48. Burmeister, M., Novak, J., Liang, M.Y., Basu, S., Ploder, L., Hawes, N.L., Vidgen, D., Hoover, F., Goldman, D., Kalnins, V.I., Roderick, T.H., Taylor, B.A., Hankin, M.H., and McInnes, R.R. (1996). Ocular retardation mouse caused by Chx10 homeobox null allele: impaired retinal progenitor proliferation and bipolar cell differentiation. *Nature* **12,** 376–383.

49. Furukawa, T., Morrow, E.M., and Cepko, C.L. (1997). *Crx, a novel otx-like homeobox gene, shows photoreceptor-specific expression and regulates photoreceptor differentiation. Cell* **91**, 531–541.

50. Chen, S., Wang, Q.L., Nie, Z., Sun, H., Lennon, G., Copeland, N.G., Gilbert, D.J., Jenkins, N.A., and Zack, D.J. (1997). Crx, a novel Otx-like paired-homeodomain protein, binds to and transactivates photoreceptor cell-specific genes. *Neuron* **19**, 1017–1030.

51. Streilein, J.W., Ma, N., Wenkel, H., Ng, T.F., and Zamiri, P. (2002). Immunobiology and privilege of neuronal retina and pigment epithelium transplants. *Vision Res.* **42**, 487–495.

52. Van der Kooy, D. (Personal communication).

53. Radner, W., Sadda, S.R., Humayun, M.S., Suzuki, S., de Juan, E., Jr (2002). Increased spontaneous retinal ganglion cell activity in rd mice after neural retinal transplantation. *Invest. Ophthalmol. Vis. Sci.* **43**, 3053–3058.

54. Fekete, D.M., Muthukumar, S., and Karagogeos, D. (1998). Hair cells and supporting cells share a common progenitor in the avian inner ear. *J. Neurosci.* **18**, 7811–7821.

55. Lang, H., and Fekete, D.M. (2001). Lineage analysis in the chicken inner ear shows differences in clonal dispersion for epithelial, neuronal, and mesenchymal cells. *Dev. Biol.* **234**, 120–137.

56. Haddon, C., Jiang, Y.J., Smithers, L., and Lewis, J. (1998). Delta–Notch signaling and the patterning of sensory cell differentiation in the zebra fish ear: evidence from the mind bomb mutant. *Development* **125**, 4637–4644.

57. Balak, K.J., Corwin, J.T., and Jones, J.E. (1990). Regenerated hair cells can originate from supporting cell progeny: evidence from phototoxicity and laser ablation experiments in the lateral line system. *J. Neurosci.* **10**, 2502–2512.

58. Brigande, J.B., and Fekete, D.M. (Unpublished observations).

59. Satoh, T., and Fekete, D.M. (2003). Mechanosensory epithelial cells and ganglion cells are clonally related. *Assoc. Res. Otolaryngol. Abstr.* **26**, 118.

60. Oesterle, E.C., and Hume, C.R. (1999). Growth factor regulation of the cell cycle in developing and mature inner ear sensory epithelia. *J. Neurocytol.* **28**, 877–887.

61. Noramly, S., and Grainger, R.M. (2002). Determination of the embryonic inner ear. *J. Neurobiol.* **53**, 100–128.

62. Zheng, J.L., Helbig, C., and Gao, W.Q. (1997). Induction of cell proliferation by fibroblast and insulin-like growth factors in pure rat inner ear epithelial cell cultures. *J. Neurosci.* **17**, 216–226.

63. Zine, A., and de Ribaupierre, F. (1999). Tissue-specific levels and cellular distribution of epidermal growth factor receptors within control and neomycin-damaged neonatal rat organ of Corti. *J. Neurobiol.* **38**, 313–322.

64. Zheng, J.L., Frantz, G., Lewis, A.K., Sliwkowski, M., and Gao, W.Q. (1999). Heregulin enhances regenerative proliferation in postnatal rat utricular sensory epithelium after ototoxic damage. *J. Neurocytol.* **28**, 901–912.

65. Corwin, J.T., and Warchol, M.E. (1991). Auditory hair cells: structure, function, development, and regeneration. *Annu. Rev. Neurosci.* **14**, 301–333.

66. Corwin, J.T., and Oberholtzer, J.C. (1997). Fish n' chicks: model recipes for hair-cell regeneration? *Neuron* **19**, 951–954.

67. Ruben, R.J. (1967). Development of the inner ear of the mouse: a radioautographic study of terminal mitosis. *Acta. Oto-Laryngologica* **220 (Suppl.)**, 4–44.

68. Katayama, A., and Corwin, J.T. (1989). Cell production in the chicken cochlea. *J. Comp. Neurol.* **281**, 129–135.

69. Kil, J., Warchol, M.E., and Corwin, J.T. (1997). Cell death, cell proliferation, and estimates of hair cell life spans in the vestibular organs of chicks. *Hear. Res.* **114**, 117–126.

70. Goodyear, R.J., Gates, R., Lukashkin, A.N., and Richardson, G.P. (1999). Hair-cell numbers continue to increase in the utricular macula of the early posthatch chick. *J. Neurocytol.* **28**, 851–861.

71. Stone, J.S., Choi, Y.S., Woolley, S.M., Yamashita, H., and Rubel, E.W. (1999). Progenitor cell cycling during hair cell regeneration in the vestibular and auditory epithelia of the chick. *J. Neurocytol.* **28**, 863–876.

72. Calof, A.L., Bonnin, A., Crocker, C., Kawauchi, S., Murray, R.C., Shou, J., and Wu, H.H. (2002). Progenitor cells of the olfactory receptor neuron lineage. *Microsci. Res. Tech.* **58**, 176–188.

73. Lowenheim, H., Furness, D.N., Kil, J., Zinn, C., Gultig, K., Fero, M.L., Frost, D., Gummer, A.W., Roberts, J.M., Rubel, E.W., Hackney, C.M., and Zenner, H.P. (1999). Gene disruption of p27(Kip1) allows cell proliferation in the postnatal and adult organ of Corti. *Proc. Natl. Acad. Sci. U. S. A.* **96**, 4084–4088.

74. Chen, P., and Segil, N. (1999). p27(Kip1) links cell proliferation to morphogenesis in the developing organ of Corti. *Development* **126**, 1581–1590.

75. Chen, P., Zindy, F., Abdala, C., Liu, F., Li, X., Roussel, M.F., and Segil, N. (2003). Progressive hearing loss in mice lacking the cyclin-dependent kinase inhibitor Ink4d. *Nat. Cell Biol.* **5**, 422–426.

76. Malgrange, B., Belachew, S., Thiry, M., Nguyen, L., Rogister, B., Alvarez, M.L., Rigo, J.M., Van de Water, T.R., Moonen, G., and Lefebvre, P.P. (2002). Proliferative generation of mammalian auditory hair cells in culture. *Mech. Dev.* **112**, 79–88.

77. Hume, C.R., Kirkegaard, M., and Oesterle, E.C. (2003). ErbB expression: the mouse inner ear and maturation of the mitogenic response to heregulin. *J. Assoc. Res. Otolaryngol.* **4**, 422–443.

78. Cotanche, D.A., and Lee, K.H. (1994). Regeneration of hair cells in the vestibulocochlear system of birds and mammals. *Curr. Opin. Neurobiol.* **4**, 509–514.

79. Stone, J.S., and Rubel, E.W. (2000). Cellular studies of auditory hair cell regeneration in birds. *Proc. Natl. Acad. Sci. U. S. A.* **97**, 11,714–11,721.

80. Warchol, M.E. (1999). Immune cytokines and dexamethasone influence sensory regeneration in the avian vestibular periphery. *J. Neurocytol.* **28**, 889–900.

81. Zheng, J.L., Keller, G., and Gao, W.Q. (1999). Immuno-cytochemical and morphological evidence for intracellular self-repair as an important contributor to mammalian hair cell recovery. *J. Neurosci.* **19**, 2161–2170.

82. Forge, A., Li, L., and Nevill, G. (1998). Hair cell recovery in the vestibular sensory epithelia of mature guinea pigs. *J. Comp. Neurol.* **397**, 69–88.

83. Kopke, R.D., Jackson, R.L., Li, G., Rasmussen, M.D., Hoffer, M.E., Frenz, D.A., Costello, M., Schultheiss, P., and Van De Water, T.R. (2001). Growth factor treatment enhances vestibular hair cell renewal and results in improved vestibular function. *Proc. Natl. Acad. Sci. U. S. A.* **98**, 5886–5891.

84. Fekete, D.M., and Wu, D.K. (2002). Revisiting cell fate specification in the inner ear. *Curr. Opin. Neurobiol.* **12**, 35–42.

85. Rubel, E.W., and Fritzsch, B. (2002). Auditory system development: primary auditory neurons and their targets. *Annu. Rev. Neurosci.* **25**, 51–101.

86. Kawamoto, K., Ishimoto, S., Minoda, R., Brough, D.E., and Raphael, Y. (2003). *Math1 gene transfer generates new cochlear hair cells in mature guinea pigs in vivo. J. Neurosci.* **23**, 4395–4400.

87. Zheng, J.L., and Gao, W.Q. (2000). Overexpression of Math1 induces robust production of extra hair cells in postnatal rat inner ears. *Nat. Neurosci.* **3,** 580–586.

88. Rivolta, M.N., and Holley, M.C. (2002). Cell lines in inner ear research. *J. Neurobiol.* **53,** 306–318.

89. Deotzlhofer, A., *et al.* (2003). *In vitro* growth and differentiation of sensory hair cell progenitors from the embryonic mouse inner ear. *Assoc. Res. Otolaryngol. Abstr.* **26,** 204.

90. Segil, N. (Personal communication).

91. Licht, K., Wachs, F.P., and Strutz, J. (2003). Cultures of inner ear tissue reveal potential stem cells only within two weeks after birth in NMRI mice. *Assoc. Res. Otolaryngol. Abstr.* **26,** 259.

92. Zhao, H.B. (2001). Long-term natural culture of cochlear sensory epithelia of guinea pigs. *Neurosci. Lett.* **315,** 73–76.

93. Zhao, H.B. (2003). Multipotent differentiability of adult mammalian cochlear cells. *Assoc. Res. Otolaryngol. Abstr.* **26,** 260.

94. Zhao, H.B. (Personal communication).

95. Li, H., Roblin, G., and Heller, S. (2003). Pleuripotent stem cells from the adult mouse inner ear. *Nat. Med.* **9,** 1293–1299.

96. Li, H., Roblin, G., and Heller, S. (2003). Generation of hair cells by stepwise differentiation of embryonic stem cells. *Proc. Natl. Acad. Sci. U. S. A.* **100,** 13,495–13,500.

97. Tateya, I., Nakagawa, T., Iguchi, F., Kim, T.S., Endo, T., Yamada, S., Kageyama, R., Naito, Y., and Ito, J. (2003). Fate of neural stem cells grafted into injured inner ears of mice. *Neuroreport.* **14,** 1677–1681.

98. Iguchi, F., Nakagawa, T., Tateya, I., Kim, T.S., Endo, T., Taniguchi, Z., Naito, Y., and Ito, J. (2003). Trophic support of mouse inner ear by neural stem cell transplantation. *Neuroreport* **14,** 77–80.

99. Jurney, W.M. (2003). Survival and distribution of adult-derived stem cells transplanted into the adult mouse inner ear. *Assoc. Res. Otolaryngol. Abstr.* **26,** 262.

100. Duan, M.L., Ulfendahl, M., Laurell, G., Counter, A.S., Pyykko, I., Borg, E., and Rosenhall, U. (2002). Protection and treatment of sensorineural hearing disorders caused by exogenous factors: experimental findings and potential clinical application. *Hear. Res.* **169,** 169–178.

101. Holley, M. (2002). Application of new biological approaches to stimulate sensory repair and protection. *Br. Med. Bull.* **63,** 157–169.

102. Miller, J., Chi, D.H., O'Keefe, L.J., Kruszka, P., Raphael, Y., and Altschuler, R.A. (1997). Neurotrophins can enhance spiral ganglion cell survival after inner hair loss. *Int. J. Dev. Neurosci.* **15,** 631–643.

103. Shinohara, T., Bredberg, G., Ulfendahl, M., Pyykko, I., Olivius, N.P., Kaksonen, R., Lindstrom, B., Altschuler, R., and Miller, J.M. (2002). Neurotropic factor intervention restores auditory function in deafened animals. *Proc. Natl. Acad. Sci. U. S. A.* **99,** 1657–1660.

104. Olivius, P., Alexandrov, L., Miller, J., Ulfendahl, M., Bagger-Sjoback, D., and Kozlova, E.N. (2003). Allografted fetal dorsal root ganglion neuronal survival in the guinea pig cochlea. *Brain Res.* **979,** 1–6.

Epithelial Stem Cell Niche in the Tooth

Mark Tummers and Irma Thesleff

Teeth develop as appendages of the ectoderm, and their morphogenesis is regulated by interactions between the epithelial and the mesenchymal tissues. The enamel covering the tooth crown is the product of the dental epithelium. Human teeth do not regenerate. They have roots, which form after the crown, and grow for a limited period of time. In some animals, crown formation continues, and teeth grow throughout the lifetime. In these teeth, epithelial adult stem cells are located in a structure known as the cervical loop. This structure acts as the so-called stem cell niche for the enamel-producing ameloblasts. Fibroblast growth factor 10 (Fgf10) from the dental mesenchyme is required for the maintenance of the stem cell niche, and it apparently regulates the Notch pathway in the epithelial cells. The molecular regulation of the niche is conserved in different, continuously growing teeth. The flexible regulation of the stem cell niche conceivably accounts for differences among tooth types, such variations in crown heights and continuous growth of teeth. Although dissociated epithelial and mesenchymal cells from embryonic tooth germs can form apparently normal teeth when recombined and transplanted, it is not clear whether new teeth could be grown from stem cells.

Epithelial Stem Cell Niche

Stem cells in teeth remain elusive. There is a lack of studies focused on dental stem cells. The main reason is the same as for stem cell research in other organs: namely, the lack of a general marker for the stem cell. Recent studies comparing the gene expression of different stem cell populations show that the quest for a single marker might be in vain.[1,2] There is some overlap in gene expression among different stem cell populations, but nothing jumps out that is solely expressed in all stem cells, and we have to concede that there might be no general stem cell marker. The lack of a definitive marker forces us to address the problem of stem cells in teeth or any other organ indirectly.

The environment of the stem cell, the stem cell niche, defines the properties of the stem cell as much as the stem cell itself. The niche can be defined as the environment that sustains

the stem cell population and is instructive in the differentiation and proliferation of the progeny.[3–5] A transplanted stem cell shows a high degree of plasticity, indicating the importance of the local environment for stem cell regulation and differentiation.[6,7] This also indicates that the niches are in essence different, although there might be similarities in their regulation. In the stem cell niche of the tooth Notch, FGF and bone morphogenetic protein signaling are associated with the regulation of the niche.[8–10] To fully understand the stem cell niche of the tooth, we should look first at the morphogenesis.

Early Development of the Stem Cell Niche

The tooth is an ectodermal organ, similar to hairs, feathers, scales, beaks, nails, horns, and several types of glands. These organs consist of an epithelial and mesenchymal component, and development starts in a similar fashion. The development of the tooth starts with the initiation phase, in which the oral epithelium thickens (Fig. 23–1). This is followed by the bud stage, in which the epithelium buds into the mesenchyme. In some other epithelial–mesenchymal organs, like feathers, this budding is outward instead of inward. The bud stage is followed by a cap-and-bell stage in the tooth. In the cap stage, the epithelium folds at the site of the enamel knot, which acts as a signaling center, and starts enveloping the condensed dental mesenchyme. The epithelium that starts growing downward is called the cervical loop. You will later see that this structure acts as the niche for the epithelial stem cells in adult teeth. As for other epithelial–mesenchymal organs, the bulge is the stem cell niche of the hair follicle, and the crypt is that of the gut[11] (Fig. 23–2).

The cervical loop consists of several different epithelial compartments (Fig. 23–3). In the center is the loosely aggregated stellate reticulum, surrounded by the denser stratum intermedium. A basal layer of epithelium loops around these compartments, hence the name cervical loop. The basal layer on the outside of the cervical loop is known as the outer enamel epithelium; on the inside, it is known as the inner enamel epithelium. This basal layer is separated from the dental mesenchyme by a basal lamina. Neither the stratum intermedium nor the stellate reticulum therefore make contact with the mesenchyme, nor are they connected to the basal lamina. During the cap-and-bell stage, the cervical loop continues to grow away from the enamel knots and flees the influence sphere of the knots (Fig. 23–4). At this point, the cervical loop is an independent stem cell niche.

Handbook of Stem Cells
Volume 1

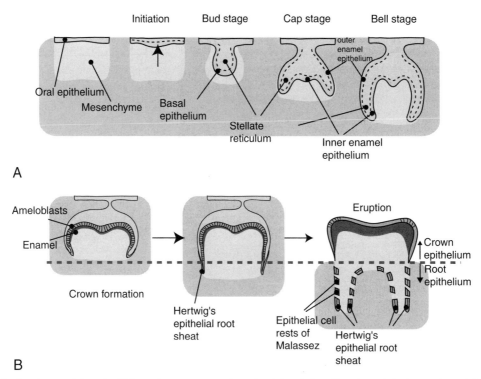

Figure 23–1. *Development of the molar.* (A) During the initiation stage, the oral epithelium thickens. Then during the bud stage, the epithelium buds into the mesenchyme. The dental mesenchyme condenses around the dental epithelium. During the cap stage, the cervical loops are formed by the outgrowth of the dental epithelium along the dental mesenchyme. This continues during the bell stage. (B) Crown formation is finished before root formation starts. The ameloblasts deposit the hard enamel characteristic of the crown. During root development, the epithelium of the cervical loop changes in its properties. It loses the stellate reticulum, and a double layer of epithelium is left, known as Hertwig's epithelial root sheath. This structure continues to grow for a while and directs root formation. It also fragments and forms islands of epithelial cells, known as the epithelial cell rests of Malassez. (Please see CD-ROM for color version of this figure.)

Location and Regulation of Stem Cells in the Continuously Growing Incisor

To better understand the functioning of the cervical loop as a stem cell niche, we have to look at a special kind of tooth, the rodent incisor. Unlike human incisors, the rodent incisor grows continuously throughout the lifetime of the animal. This continuous growth requires the presence of adult stem cells. The incisor is worn down at the tip, and new tissue is formed at the opposite end to the tooth, the so-called apical end. In a way, the story is simplified because only a single, obviously differentiated epithelial cell type is present, the enamel-producing ameloblast. Enamel is the hard matrix that covers the tooth and protects it.

In the rodent incisor, the regulation of the cervical loop is associated with Notch signaling in the epithelium and Fgf3 and Fgf10 signaling from the surrounding mesenchyme.[8] The mesenchymal FGF stimulates proliferation of the dental epithelium in the cervical loop and possibly maintains the stem cells in this area. Notch signaling has been implicated in the regulation of stem cells in many other tissues, such as neuronal and glial differentiation,[12,13] lymphocyte differentiation,[14] pancreatic differentiation,[15] and epidermal differentiation.[16]

Different compartments of the cervical loop express different genes of the *Notch* signaling pathway. *Notch* itself is expressed in the stellate reticulum and stratum intermedium in the center of the cervical loop. In the basal cell layer, *lunatic fringe* is expressed in the transit-amplifying cells, and the ligand *jagged*-1 is expressed in the differentiating ameloblasts (Fig. 23–3B).

The question is whether the epithelial stem cells are in the basal layer or in a different epithelial compartment. Stem cells are known to divide slowly. It was suggested back in 1963, based on cellular kinetics studies, that in the continuously growing molar of the rabbit, the pool of transit-amplifying cells in the inner enamel epithelium cannot be sustained by itself but probably originates from the stratum intermedium.[17] One way to detect the slowly dividing stem cells is with a Brdu pulse-chase experiment. Such experiments in the mouse incisor showed that after a chase period of 7 days, most labeled cells were in the stellate reticulum of the cervical loop.[8] The stem cells might therefore not be in the basal layer; they might be in the loosely aggregated stellate reticulum. The stem cells or their progeny have to insert themselves into the basal layer and make contact with the basal lamina, or, in short, they have to relaminate themselves (Fig. 23–3C).

Epithelial stem cell niches

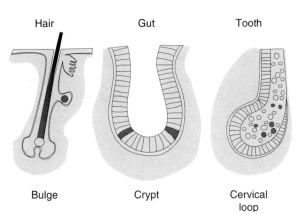

Hair   Gut   Tooth

Bulge   Crypt   Cervical loop

Figure 23-2. *Different epithelial stem cell niches and the location of the stem cells. In the hair follicle, the stem cells are located in the bulge; in the gut, they are in the crypt; and in the tooth, they are in the cervical loop. (Please see CD-ROM for color version of this figure.)*

This progeny then proliferates and differentiates while part of the basal layer.

A regulatory system must be in place that maintains the epithelial stem cell niche and the differentiation of the progeny. Fgf10 is known to stimulate epithelial proliferation and can act as a chemoattractant.[18] In the apical end of the incisor, *Fgf10* is expressed in the mesenchyme surrounding the cervical loop (Fig. 23-3). The receptors *Fgfr1b* and *Fgfr2b* are expressed in the cervical loop.[8] In Fgf10 knockouts, the cervical loop area is severely reduced in size.[9] Adding Fgf10 rescues these mutant incisors, and adding Fgf10 antibodies to the medium of wild-type incisors *in vitro* results in a similar phenotype as the knockout. Therefore, Fgf10 is required to support the epithelium of the cervical loop. It is clear that Fgf10 is definitely needed for the proliferation in this area, but it is not absolutely proven that it is required for the survival of the stem cells. Interestingly, Fgf10 also stimulates the expression of *lunatic fringe* in the basal epithelium, and it was suggested that this modulates Notch signaling in the putative stem cells in the stellate reticulum expressing *Notch*.[8]

Molar Development: Loss of the Stem Cell Niche and Root Development

In the continuously growing incisor of the mouse, the cervical loop is maintained throughout the lifetime of the animal and consequently keeps producing new tissue. However, most teeth do not grow continuously, and they have presumably lost the stem cell niche. The standard tooth model in dental research is the mouse molar. Its development is similar to human teeth. It goes through similar earlier stages of development—the initiation, bud, cap-and-bell stage—like the continuously growing incisor (Fig. 23-1). During the late bell stage, the cusp pattern of the molar crown is finalized—the entire crown shape is determined. At this point, the development differs

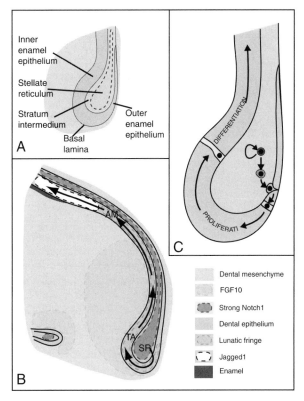

Inner enamel epithelium

Stellate reticulum

Stratum intermedium

Outer enamel epithelium

Basal lamina

A

DIFFERENTIATION

PROLIFERATI

C

B   AM   TA   SR

Dental mesenchyme
FGF10
Strong Notch1
Dental epithelium
Lunatic fringe
Jagged1
Enamel

Figure 23-3. *Cervical loop as a stem cell niche. (A) The different tissue compartments of the cervical loop. (B) Notch and FGF signaling regulates the epithelial stem cell niche. Mesenchymal Fgf10 maintains the proliferating cells and possibly the stem cells. The stem cells express Notch; the proliferating cells express lunatic fringe. Once the progeny start differentiating into ameloblast, the cells start expressing Serrate-1. (C) The stem cells possibly undergo asymmetric stem cell division in the stellate reticulum. One daughter cell remains in the stellate reticulum as a stem cell; the other one relaminates itself into the basal layer. Here, it enters the zone of proliferating cells, also known as transit-amplifying cells. Moving toward the tip of the tooth, they undergo differentiation into ameloblasts and deposit the hard enamel matrix (SR: stellate reticulum, TA: transit-amplifying cells, and AM: ameloblasts). (Please see CD-ROM for color version of this figure.)*

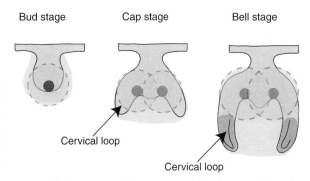

Bud stage   Cap stage   Bell stage

Cervical loop

Cervical loop

Figure 23-4. *The cervical loops are initiated by the enamel knots, the signaling centers in the early tooth. Once the cervical loops start growing away from these signaling centers during later stages of development, the cervical loops become independent stem cell niches. (Please see CD-ROM for color version of this figure.)*

significantly from the continuously growing incisor. The crown stops growing, and root development starts.[19] The cervical loop area undergoes a transformation. It loses the stellate reticulum and stratum intermedium, and only a double layer of basal epithelium, the inner and outer enamel epithelium, is left (Figs. 23–1 and 23–5). This structure is known as Hertwig's epithelial root sheath; it directs root growth and seems to have a limited growth capacity, because the root extends to a certain length and finally stops growing. The root epithelium does not differentiate into ameloblasts, and, therefore, the root surface is not covered by enamel. The limited growth capacity and the inability to produce ameloblasts suggest that the root epithelium lacks stem cells.

However, some species also have continuously growing molars, such as the rabbit, guinea pig, and some vole species (Fig. 23–5). The vole is a rodent closely related to the mouse; the early development of the molar, and the distribution of molecular markers during this development, is remarkably similar to that of the mouse molar.[20] In the sibling vole, a vole species with a continuously growing molar, the cervical loop is maintained structurally, and Notch and FGF signaling remains active, similar to the rodent incisor.[10] The stellate reticulum and stratum intermedium do not disappear after the late bell stage, as they do in the mouse molar, and the distribution of the members of the Notch signaling pathway in the epithelium and Fgf10 in the mesenchyme is identical to the distribution in the incisor. In addition, Notch signaling and Fgf10 have an identical role in the so-called intercuspal loops. The intercuspal loops are structurally similar to the cervical loop and are created by the cusp epithelium folding deep into the mesenchyme (Fig. 23–5). In the mouse molar, on the other hand, Notch and FGF signaling are switched off. Therefore, the regulation of the epithelial stem cell niche is similar in two different continuously growing tooth types, the rodent incisor and vole molar, but this regulatory setup disappears in teeth that stop growing, such as the mouse molar.

Evolutionary Implications for the Regulation of the Stem Cell Niche

There is great variation in the relative heights of the crowns and roots in different species. There are low-crowned teeth, like all human teeth and mouse molars. In these teeth, the period of crown growth is relatively short and is followed by a period of root growth. Then there are the high-crowned teeth, such as horse teeth and the molars of some vole species. Here, the period of crown growth is extended and possibly this is done by the regulation of the cervical loop and stem cell niche, that is, by maintaining this system longer. Finally, there are the continuously growing teeth in which the cervical loop is maintained throughout the lifetime of the animal. This flexible regulation of the stem cell niche could have been a relatively easy way to acquire radically different tooth types during evolution. The regulation of the stem cell niche can therefore directly dictate the characteristics of an organ. The longer the niche is maintained and differentiated progeny of the stem cells are produced, the higher the crown will be. It would be interesting to

see if a similar phenomenon occurs in other organs. Is it common that the regulation of the stem cell niche has a major influence on the function and morphology of an organ?

Morphogenesis Versus Cell Differentiation

Most stem cell research is focused on the differentiation of stem cells into various cell types. Some of these projects aim at the production of dental hard tissue, such as enamel and dentin from stem cells. Mesenchymal dental stem cells were isolated from the adult dental pulp.[21] When transplanted to muscle, these cultured dental pulp cells differentiated into odontoblasts, forming a dentine matrix. More recent results indicate that these dental pulp stem cells possess an even greater capacity for differentiation into more cell types than previously thought and that there is possibly a hierarchy of progenitors in the adult dental pulp, ranging from a small population of self-renewing cells to a larger compartment of committed progenitors.[22] The dental pulp is clearly not a uniform collection of cells. It is not clear if these dental pulp stem cells and their progeny are in a discrete niche or if they are distributed throughout the dental pulp. Also, it is not known if they have any morphogenetic potential. Notch signaling is involved in the differentiation of the mesenchymal stem cell progeny in adult dental pulp. When a hole is drilled on the molar of a rat, Notch signaling is activated.[23] Also, *Delta1* was up-regulated in the odontoblasts near the injury. The hole is then partially repaired by the dentin produced by the odontoblasts. As for epithelial dental stem cells, the HAT-7 cell line that originates from the cervical loop of the incisor is capable of producing cells that express some markers characteristic for ameloblasts.[24] Regeneration of dental hard tissue from stem cells may be feasible in the future, either *in vitro* or by transplanting the cells to patient's teeth, although the practical procedures are still difficult to imagine. However, the generation of a differentiated cell from a stem cell is a problem with a different level of complexity than the generation of a three-dimensional organ, that is, morphogenesis.

How do we go from a stem cell to a complex organ? This problem can be approached from the perspective of morphogenesis and of cell differentiation, which at first glance are closely related. Tissue recombination studies of mesenchymal and epithelial compartments of developing teeth and other organs have shown that the instructive capacity that determines the fate of neighboring tissues switches back and forth between mesenchyme and epithelium during early development.[25–28] The epithelium and mesenchyme talk to each other by reciprocal signaling during all stages of development. Many signals are transient in nature and are only active for a short period at a specific location. During the bud stage, an epithelial signaling center, the enamel knot, is created.[29,30] This transient structure will direct the shape of the crown.

But is differentiation of the stem cell progeny into the proper cell fate intimately linked with morphogenesis? Heterotopic recombination between salivary gland mesenchyme and mammary gland epithelium results in a salivary-like branching pattern.[31] Although the salivary morphogenetic

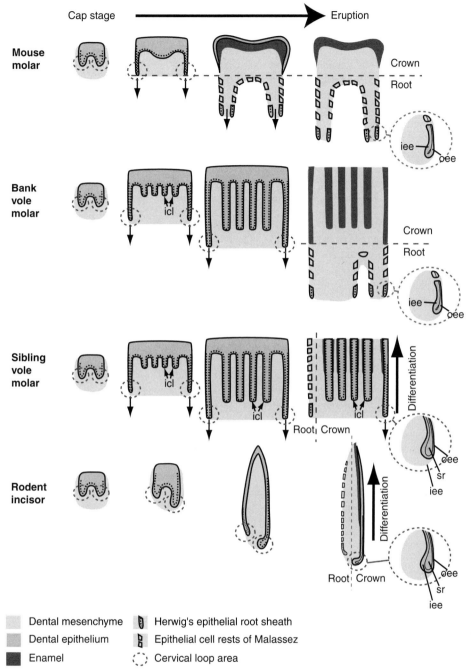

Figure 23–5. *Stem cell niche and different tooth phenotypes.* Differential regulation of the epithelial stem cell niche, the cervical loop, can result in drastically different teeth, each adapted for a specific function. The standard tooth model is the mouse molar and is similar to all human teeth. The growth of the crown is limited. Then, the cervical loop, the stem cell niche, changes appearance (stellate reticulum is lost), and root development takes place until the root reaches a certain length. The bank vole molar is an example of a high-crowned molar. The stem cell niche is maintained for a longer time, and hence, the growth period of the crown is extended. This results in higher crowns, which can sustain more wear. The period of crown growth is still followed by a period of separate root growth. In the sibling vole molar, the maintenance of the stem cell niche and the crown growth is extended indefinitely. The molar will therefore grow forever. To attach the tooth to the jawbone, a few small domains of the crown are converted into root. Therefore, root and crown development occur simultaneously and continuously. The rodent incisor follows the same system as the continuously growing molar. There is continuous and simultaneous crown and root growth (iee: inner enamel epithelium, oee: outer enamel epithelium, sr: stratum intermedium, and icl: intercuspal loop). (Please see CD-ROM for color version of this figure.)

program was followed by the mammary epithelium, the ectodermal cells differentiated according to the mammary gland-specific program. Morphogenesis and differentiation are therefore not necessarily linked together. This may result in some difficulties when stem cells will be used in the practical application of regenerating new teeth. There is the possibility that epithelial or mesenchymal stem cells are competent to participate in morphogenesis but not in differentiation of epithelial ameloblasts and mesenchymal odontoblasts.

Developmental History of the Stem Cell Niche

If we do not assume that the dental epithelial stem cells are created by dedifferentiation of already differentiated adult cells or that they migrate to the tooth from elsewhere in the embryo, we must assume that the stem cell lineage can be traced to the early stages of tooth development. We can therefore study the developmental history of the stem cell niche. The putative site of the adult epithelial stem cells is the stellate reticulum and is associated with *Notch* expression.[8] As described previously, this tissue is morphologically first seen at the bud stage, when the epithelium of the bud is divided into the outer basal layer and stellate reticulum inside it (Fig. 23–1). Some of this stellate reticulum will form the central part of the cervical loop; the remainder stays in the crown area. All the epithelium that covers the crown is eventually lost after eruption of the tooth in the oral cavity because it is then exposed. If we go back in tooth development to the initiation phase, *Notch* is already expressed in the simple oral epithelium (Fig. 23–6). This layer thickens after receiving the proper signals from the mesenchyme, and the stellate reticulum is created from the suprabasal cells. This could be the first visible representation of a tooth-specific stem cell niche. *Notch* is down-regulated in the basal layer of epithelium that makes contact with the mesenchyme. The down-regulation of *Notch* in these basal

epithelial cells is regulated by the mesenchyme.[32] Perhaps the maintenance of Notch in suprabasal cells keeps the cells in a stem cell fate. The bigger picture we can derive from all this is that the generation of the epithelial stem cell niche might be intimately associated with the induction of tooth formation. During subsequent development, mesenchymal signals may be instructive in regulating the maintenance of the niche and differentiation of the stem cells to ameloblasts.

Summary

We have made a start in the understanding of the epithelial stem cell niche in the tooth. Although this niche disappears during the development of all human teeth, it has an important role in continuously growing teeth. Flexibility in the regulation of this niche allowed for the existence of distinctly different tooth phenotypes: low-crowned, high-crowned, and continuously growing teeth. This leaves us with the view that stem cells are important not only for the regeneration and differentiation of a tissue but also for the morphogenesis of a complete organ. Evolution can create phenotypic diversity in an organ by altering the regulation of the stem cell niche.

Could we use all the information on dental stem cells to grow new teeth at will? Possibly, but we still have a long way to go. We know that teratoma tumors produce apparently normal teeth. This indicates that it must be possible to grow new teeth from multipotential stem cells under the proper conditions. Old tissue recombination studies show that the epithelial and mesenchymal cells of an early tooth germ have the capacity to form a tooth independent of the environment when transplanted or cultured *in vitro*,[26,27,33–35] even with dissociated cells.[36] If we want to grow teeth from stem cells, we would first need a reliable source of epithelial and mesenchymal dental stem cells. We also still have to find out how we can combine these two cell populations and initiate the morphogenesis of a new tooth. Further questions remain—for example, how to control the shape of the tooth and the quality of the hard tissue matrix if we want to replace missing or damaged teeth. We have also seen that there could be a direct link between initiation of tooth morphogenesis and initiation of the stem cell niche. Therefore, having stem cells is not enough to make a tooth. The paradox is that to produce a tooth, we might have to create a stem cell niche first by using stem cells.

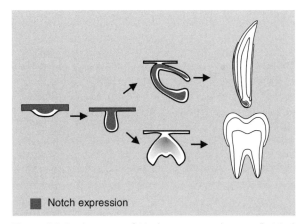

■ Notch expression

Figure 23–6. *Association of Notch expression with stem cells.* Notch expression is lost during the development of the mouse molar, which stops growing and develops roots but is maintained in the continuously growing incisor. (Please see CD-ROM for color version of this figure.)

REFERENCES

1. Ramalho-Santos, M., Yoon, S., Matsuzaki, Y., Mulligan, R.C., and Melton, D.A. (2002). "Stemness": transcriptional profiling of embryonic and adult stem cells. *Science* **298,** 597–600.
2. Ivanova, N.B., Dimos, J.T., Schaniel, C., Hackney, J.A., Moore, K.A., and Lemischka, I.R. (2002). A stem cell molecular signature. *Science* **298,** 601–604.
3. Spradling, A., Drummond-Barbosa, D., and Kai, T. (2001). Stem cells find their niche. *Nature* **414,** 98–104.
4. Watt, F.M., and Hogan, B.L. (2000). Out of Eden: stem cells and their niches. *Science* **287,** 1427–1430.

5. Nishimura, E.K., Jordan, S.A., Oshima, H., Yoshida, H., Osawa, M., Moriyama, M., Jackson, I.J., Barrandon, Y., Miyachi, Y., and Nishikawa, S. (2002). Dominant role of the niche in melanocyte stem cell fate determination. *Nature* **416,** 854–860.

6. Bjornson, C.R., Rietze, R.L., Reynolds, B.A., Magli, M.C., and Vescovi, A.L. (1999). Turning brain into blood: a hematopoietic fate adopted by adult neural stem cells *in vivo. Science* **283,** 534–537.

7. Anderson, D.J., Gage, F.H., and Weissman, I.L. (2001). Can stem cells cross lineage boundaries? *Nat. Med.* **7,** 393–395.

8. Harada, H., Kettunen, P., Jung, H.S., Mustonen, T., Wang, Y.A., and Thesleff, I. (1999). Localization of putative stem cells in dental epithelium and their association with Notch and FGF signaling. *J. Cell. Biol.* **147,** 105–120.

9. Harada, H., Toyono, T., Toyoshima, K., Yamasaki, M., Itoh, N., Kato, S., Sekine, K., and Ohuchi, H. (2002). Fgf10 maintains stem cell compartment in developing mouse incisors. *Development* **129,** 1533–1541.

10. Tummers, M., and Thesleff, I. (2003). Root or crown: a developmental choice orchestrated by the differential regulation of the epithelial stem cell niche in the tooth of two rodent species. *Development* **130,** 1049–1057.

11. Spradling, A., Drummond-Barbosa, D., and Kai, T. (2001). Stem cells find their niche. *Nature* **414,** 98–104.

12. Wang, S., and Barres, B.A. (2000). Up a notch: instructing gliogenesis. *Neuron* **27,** 197–200.

13. Lütolf, S., Radtke, F., Aguet, M., Suter, U., and Taylor, V. (2002). Notch1 is required for neuronal and glial differentiation in the cerebellum. *Development* **129,** 373–385.

14. Anderson, A.C., Robey, E.A., and Huang, Y.H. (2001). Notch signaling in lymphocyte development. *Curr. Opin. Genet. Dev.* **11,** 554–560.

15. Apelqvist, A., Li, H., Sommer, L., Beatus, P., Anderson, D.J., Honjo, T., Hrabe de Angelis, M., Lendahl, U., and Edlund, H. (1999). Notch signaling controls pancreatic cell differentiation. *Nature* **400,** 877–881.

16. Lowell, S., Jones, P., Le Roux, I., Dunne, J., and Watt, F.M. (2000). Stimulation of human epidermal differentiation by delta-notch signaling at the boundaries of stem cell clusters. *Curr. Biol.* **10,** 491–500.

17. Starkey, W.E. (1963). The migration and renewal of tritium labeled cells in the developing enamel organ of rabbits. *Br. Dent. J.* **115,** 143–153.

18. Bellusci, S., Furuta, Y., Rush, M.G., Henderson, R., Winnier, G., and Hogan, B.L. (1997). Involvement of Sonic hedgehog (Shh) in mouse embryonic lung growth and morphogenesis. *Development* **124,** 53–63.

19. Thomas, H.F. (1995). Root formation. *Int. J. Dev. Biol.* **39,** 231–237.

20. Keränen, S.V., Åberg, T., Kettunen, P., Thesleff, I., and Jernvall, J. (1998). Association of developmental regulatory genes with the development of different molar tooth shapes in two species of rodents. *Dev. Genes Evol.* **208,** 477–486.

21. Gronthos, S., Mankani, M., Brahim, J., Robey, P.G., and Shi, S. (2000). Postnatal human dental pulp stem cells (DPSCs) *in vitro* and *in vivo. PNAS* **97,** 13,625–13,630.

22. Gronthos, S., Brahim, J., Li, W., Fisher, L.W., Cherman, N., Boyde, A., DenBesten, P., Robey, P.G., and Shi, S. (2002). Stem cell properties of human dental pulp stem cells. *J. Dent. Res.* **81,** 531–535.

23. Mitsiadis, T.A., Fried, K., and Goridis, C. (1999). Reactivation of Delta-Notch signaling after injury: complementary expression patterns of ligand and receptor in dental pulp. *Exp. Cell Res.* **246,** 312–318.

24. Kawano, S., Morotomi, T., Toyono, T., Nakamura, N., Uchida, T., Ohishi, M., Toyoshima, K., and Harada, H. (2003). Establishment of dental epithelial cell line (HAT-7) and the cell differentiation dependent on Notch signaling pathway. *Connect. Tissue Res.* **43,** 409–412.

25. Dhouailly, D. (1975). Formation of cutaneous appendages in dermo–epidermal recombinations between reptiles, birds, and mammals. *Wilhelm Roux Archives* **177,** 323–340.

26. Mina, M., and Kollar, E.J. (1987). The induction of odontogenesis in nondental mesenchyme combined with early murine mandibular arch epithelium. *Arch. Oral Biol.* **32,** 123–127.

27. Lumsden, A.G. (1988). Spatial organization of the epithelium and the role of neural crest cells in the initiation of the mammalian tooth germ. *Development Supplement* **103,** 155–169.

28. Hardy, M.H. (1992). The secret life of the hair follicle. *Trends Genet.* **8,** 55–61.

29. Vaahtokari, A., Åberg, T., Jernvall, J., Keränen, S., and Thesleff, I. (1996). The enamel knot as a signaling center in the developing mouse tooth. *Mech. Dev.* **54,** 39–43.

30. Jernvall, J., and Thesleff, I. (2000). Reiterative signaling and patterning during mammalian tooth morphogenesis. *Mech. Dev.* **92,** 19–29.

31. Kratochwil, K. (1969). Organ specificity in mesenchymal induction demonstrated in the embryonic development of the mammary gland of the mouse. *Dev. Biol.* **20,** 46–71.

32. Mitsiadis, T., Lardelli, M., Lendahl, U., and Thesleff, I. (1995). Expression of Notch 1, 2, and 3 is regulated by epithelial–mesenchymal interactions and retinoic acid in the developing mouse tooth and associated with determination of ameloblast cell fate. *J. Cell Biol.* **130,** 407–418.

33. Kollar, E.J., and Baird, G.R. (1969). The influence of the dental papilla on the development of tooth shape in embryonic mouse tooth germs. *J. Embryol. Exp. Morphol.* **21,** 131–148.

34. Ruch, J.V., Karcher-Djuricic, V., and Gerber, R. (1973). Les determinismes de la morphogene et des cytodifferenciations des ebauches dentaires de souris. *Jour. Biol. Buccale* **1,** 45–56.

35. Slavkin, H.C., and Bavette, L.A., (1968). Odontogenic epithelial-mesenchymal interactions *in vitro. J. Dent. Res.* **47,** 779–785.

36. Slavkin, H.C., Beierle, J., and Bavetta, L.A. (1968). Odontogenesis: cell–cell interactions *in vitro. Nature* **217,** 269–270.

Early Embryonic Mesoderm Development

Virginia E. Papaioannou

Introduction

Mesoderm—from the Greek μέσο-ζ (middle) + δέρμα (skin). This simple descriptive name belies a multifaceted role for the middle of the three embryonic germ layers. It is the youngest layer, in evolutionary terms, and is a hallmark of the development of all complex metazoans. The mesoderm layer provided the solution to more sophisticated functions than the simple protective outer ectoderm and the absorptive inner endoderm. As organisms became larger and more complex, the mesoderm assumed functions of support, movement, circulation, and reproduction, working closely with internalized, ectoderm-derived neural and neural crest tissue as well as providing a supporting role and providing for intricate elaborations of the protective and absorptive functions of the ectoderm and endoderm. With increasingly complex modes of reproduction, all three germ layers were called into play to form novel tissues for the adaptation to different modes of oviparity, ovoviviparity, and eventually viviparity. The repertoire of tissues formed by the mesoderm is complex and varied, with many precursor cell and stem cell populations developing during embryonic life and some persisting into adulthood. The mesoderm plays a role throughout the development of the mammalian embryo, beginning from the initiation of gastrulation, the process whereby the three embryonic germ layers are formed. Here is a brief developmental history of that remarkable tissue in mammals, using the mouse as the prime example.

The mammalian embryo begins implantation into the uterus at the late blastocyst stage, when it consists of an outer layer of trophectoderm and a bilaminar inner cell mass (ICM) comprising the epiblast and the primitive endoderm (also called the hypoblast) (Fig. 24–1A). The trophectoderm is a specialized ectoderm layer that mediates contact between the embryo and the uterus and forms a major part of the placenta; it does not, however, make any cellular contribution to the body of the fetus. Similarly, the primitive endoderm layer of the ICM forms the endoderm layer of the visceral and parietal yolk sacs but does not contribute to the gut endoderm of the fetus. It is the epiblast that is the origin of the entire body of the fetus, including ectoderm-, endoderm-, and mesoderm-derived structures. These three primary layers of cells are called the definitive germ layers and arise through the process of gastrulation, a morphogenetic process that occurs within the epiblast in a specialized structure called the primitive streak.

Primitive Streak as the Origin of Mesoderm

The first mesoderm to appear in the mammalian embryo is destined to be extraembryonic in nature. One can think of this precocious appearance of mesoderm in the extraembryonic region as an adaptation to viviparity, where a functioning mesoderm-derived circulatory system is an early requirement of successful intrauterine development. In the mouse, this extraembryonic mesoderm arises from the primitive streak, although in humans it appears prior to the formation of a primitive streak. In human embryos, it is said to arise from yolk sac cells,[1] which consist at this time of cytotrophoblast and hypoblast; however, the actual origin of this tissue in humans is unknown because of the impossibility of carrying out experimental analysis. Whatever its origin, it comes to have a similar relationship to the other germ layers in the fetal membranes as it does in other mammals, including the mouse. Extraembryonic mesoderm forms and lines the extraembryonic coelom or exocoelomic cavity, providing the mesoderm component of the amnion, chorion, yolk sac, and allantois.

The primitive streak of the mouse first appears about 5.5 days postcoitus (dpc) in the epiblast at the junction between the embryonic and extraembryonic areas of the mouse egg cylinder (Fig. 24–1B), marking the posterior pole of the future embryonic body. The streak is an area in which cells of the epiblast undergo an epithelial to mesenchymal transition and commence ingressing, eventually taking up a position and spreading between the visceral endoderm and the epiblast in the embryonic region and between the visceral endoderm and the extraembryonic ectoderm in the extraembryonic region (Fig. 24–1C). The primitive streak gradually elongates with the growth of the embryo until at its maximum length, it extends from the embryonic–extraembryonic boundary to the most distal tip of the egg cylinder. The anterior end of the primitive streak is a specialized area known as the node (or Hensen's node), which appears as a bilaminar depression at the distal tip of the egg cylinder (Fig. 24–1D). The node has organizing capabilities in that it can induce a secondary neural axis in heterotopic grafting experiments.[2] The streak regresses posteriorly toward the latter part of gastrulation, becoming relatively shorter until at 9.5 dpc it is replaced by the tail bud as the source of new mesoderm in the most posterior part of the embryo.

Handbook of Stem Cells
Volume 1

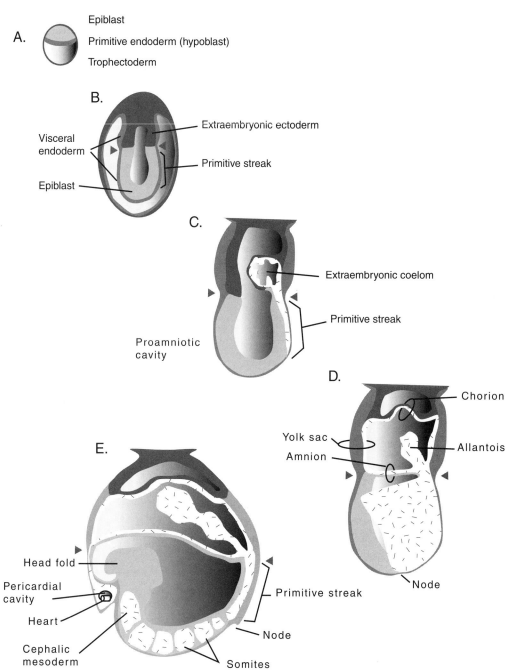

Figure 24–1. *Diagrammatic representation of midsagittal sections of mouse embryos from 4.5 to 8.5 dpc. (A) A 4.5-dpc blastocyst, just prior to implantation. (B) Early gastrula at 5.5 dpc, with the primitive streak at the posterior pole. (C) Midstreak stage embryo at 6.5–7.0 dpc, with the amniotic fold pushing across the proamniotic cavity. Intracellular spaces within the extraembryonic mesoderm coalesce to form the extraembryonic coelom. (D) A 7.5-dpc embryo with fetal membranes and allantois showing the left lateral wing of the embryonic mesoderm, which spreads between the epiblast and the visceral endoderm. (E) Headfold stage embryo at 8.5 dpc, showing embryonic and extraembryonic mesoderm. In parts B–E, stippled area represents the mesoderm, and triangles indicate the boundary between the embryonic and the extraembryonic regions. In parts C–E, the placenta and parietal yolk sac, which would surround the entire embryo, are not shown.*

Epiblast cells mostly converge on the streak, undergo the epithelial to mesenchymal conversion, ingress, and then move away from the streak between the epiblast and the endoderm. However, during the life of the streak, there is evidence that some cells have properties of stem cells for a limited time. In the anterior streak, fate mapping studies have indicated that some cells not only have progeny that differentiate as mesoderm and move away from the streak but also have progeny that remain in the streak, continuing to self-renew and retaining the potential to form new mesoderm.[3]

Fate Map of the Primitive Streak

Different types of mesoderm begin to appear upon departure from the primitive streak. The timing and order of their appearance is a closely coordinated choreography that has been revealed mostly by fate mapping studies relying on cell grafting or marking and short-term embryo culture (reviewed by Lawson[4] and Tam and Quinlan[5]). The differentiation of the different types of mesoderm into morphologically and functionally distinct cell types is presaged by differential gene expression along the length of the streak.[6] Although there is considerable overlap at the edges of the fate map boundaries, different parts of the primitive streak produce different types of mesoderm (Fig. 24–2), and the types change over time.[7]

The first mesoderm to emerge is the extraembryonic mesoderm from the posterior part of the early streak followed by the cardiac and cranial mesoderm from a more anterior part of the steak. The extraembryonic mesoderm pushes across the proamniotic cavity, carrying with it the overlying layer of extraembryonic ectoderm (Fig. 24–1C). As it does so, intercellular cavities form within the layer and coalesce into the extraembryonic coelom, effectively separating the mesoderm into two layers. This extraembryonic mesoderm will form the yolk sac mesoderm and the mesoderm of the amnion and chorion. Later, the allantois will bud out of the most posterior part of the streak and move across the extraembryonic coelom

to establish a connection with the chorion (Fig. 24–1D), forming the umbilicus.

The cranial and the cardiac mesoderm push anteriorly around the egg cylinder in the embryonic region, eventually meeting in the anterior midline. The rest of the embryonic mesoderm arises from the middle to the anterior part of the streak, producing first the lateral plate mesoderm then the intermediate and paraxial mesoderm from the midstreak region. The axial notochord arises from the node as does the head process, an anterior extension of the streak. The node contributes cells to the cranial mesoderm and the most anterior somites. As the streak regresses, production of extraembryonic mesoderm ceases, the notochord continues to be formed from the regressing node, and paraxial presomitic mesoderm continues to be produced. By the time the tail bud takes over the production of mesoderm, only lateral plate, somitic mesoderm, and notochord are being produced.[8]

Extraembryonic Mesoderm

The extraembryonic mesoderm remains closely associated with both the ectoderm and endoderm layers in the extraembryonic region, but in so doing it splits into two layers, the somatic and splanchnic layers, by the formation of a cavity between them known as the extraembryonic coelom or exocoelom. Combined with ectoderm, somatic mesoderm makes up the amnion, which remains as a nonvascular, protective membrane surrounding the fetus. Extraembryonic mesoderm makes up the mesothelial lining of the chorion, which, combined with trophectoderm derivatives, will later take part in the formation of the chorioallantoic placenta. Combined with the extraembryonic endoderm, splanchnic mesoderm makes up the yolk sac, which will form vascular endothelial cells throughout that will eventually coalesce into the vitelline circulation (Fig. 24–1D). In egg-laying vertebrates, extraembryonic mesoderm is also associated with endoderm in the allantoic sac, whereas in mammals such as mouse and human, the allantois is almost purely mesodermal with only a rudimentary endodermal component, as the allantois has lost its role as a waste retention sac. In placental mammals, the primary function of the allantois is to provide the vascular, umbilical link between mother and fetus, a role fulfilled by the mesoderm on its own.

Within the yolk sac mesoderm, vasculogenesis takes place in intimate association with hematopoiesis, or the formation of blood cells, in specialized areas called blood islands. It is here that the elusive hemangioblast is thought to reside. The hemangioblast is a common progenitor of both endothelial and hematopoietic lineages and may also be the precursor of vascular smooth muscle cells, qualifying it as a stem cell for the vascular and hematopoietic lineages.[9–11] From the yolk sac blood islands, as well as from other extraembryonic areas such as the vitelline and umbilical arteries, the hematopoietic stem cells (HSC) arise and function for a limited period during mid- to late gestation, producing the primitive blood cell lineages and seeding the embryonic hematopoietic system.[12] The embryonic hematopoietic system has its origin in multiple independent sites, including some intraembryonic sites (see the next section).

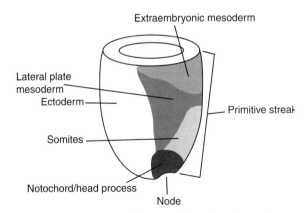

Extraembryonic mesoderm

Lateral plate mesoderm

Ectoderm

Somites

Notochord/head process

Node

Primitive streak

Figure 24–2. *Representative fate map of the mid- to late streak stage epiblast of the mouse embryo. The differently shaded areas represent the progenitors of the tissues indicated in the epiblast prior to ingression through the node or streak. The boundaries are not as sharp as indicated; rather, they have considerable margins of overlap.*

Embryonic Mesoderm

In the embryonic region of the gastrulating mouse embryo, the mesoderm moves away from the primitive streak and spreads in an anterior direction between the endoderm and epiblast layers as two lateral spreading wings of mesenchymal cells. These wings eventually meet in the anterior part of the embryo, thus forming a continuous sheet of mesoderm between the endoderm and the epiblast, which has begun to differentiate as the ectoderm layer of the embryo. At the same time, the node generates the head process, which moves anteriorly in the midline, and the notochord, which forms the axial supporting rod of the vertebrate embryo from the level of the developing forebrain to the tip of the tail.

Along the length of the embryonic axis, the mesoderm that ingresses first through the primitive streak moves the farthest from the midline and differentiates as the lateral plate. In a manner similar to the formation of the extraembryonic coelom, this mesoderm splits into two layers by the coalescence of intercellular cavities to form the intraembryonic coelom. The layers are continuous with the extraembryonic somatic and splanchnic layers of mesoderm, and the cavity is continuous with the extraembryonic coelom.

The mesoderm that ingresses next and remains closer to the midline is called the intermediate mesoderm; that ingressing later and remaining closest to the midline is known as the paraxial or somitic mesoderm. The three subdivisions—lateral plate, intermediate, and paraxial—along with the axial notochord continue to be formed progressively in an anterior-to-posterior direction as the primitive streak regresses posteriorly. Lateral plate, paraxial, and axial mesoderm are produced by the tail bud toward the end of gastrulation to make up the mesodermal structures of the tail.

Gastrulation, during which the endoderm as well as the mesoderm is produced by ingression through the primitive streak, is a dynamic process, proceeding in an anterior-to-posterior progression. While the more posterior mesoderm is still young, the more anterior mesoderm has already begun differentiating, taking on specific mesodermal identities commensurate with its axial level and position in the embryo. The morphological subdivisions of mesoderm—cranial, cardiac, paraxial, axial, lateral plate, and intermediate mesoderm—all have distinct fates, and most interact with endoderm- or ectoderm-derived tissue during subsequent stages of organogenesis. In addition, mesoderm throughout the embryo forms endothelial cells as the basis for the circulatory system and the definitive HSC arise from embryonic mesoderm from the aorta–gonad–mesonephros region,[13] providing blood cells in addition to those derived from the extraembryonic region to seed the fetal liver and eventually the adult sites of hematopoiesis: the thymus, spleen, omentum, and bone marrow.

CRANIAL AND CARDIAC MESODERM

In the head region, unlike other regions of the embryo where bone is derived exclusively from mesoderm, the bones of the cranium, face, and neck are formed from ectoderm-derived neural crest cells as well as mesoderm. The muscles of the face and neck, with the exception of the iris muscles, are derived from the anterior paraxial mesoderm. The cardiac mesoderm progenitors are initially in the most anterior region of the gastrulating embryo within the splanchnic mesoderm layer, but they come to lie in a ventral position caudal to the cranial region with the formation of the anterior head fold and the lateral body folds, which shape the embryonic body (Fig. 24–1E). The pericardial cavity, within which the heart develops, forms by the coalescence of extracellular spaces between mesoderm cells as the endothelial heart tubes come together to form the primitive heart tube. Although the heart is an exclusively mesoderm-derived tissue, it is thought that its differentiation is induced by the associated anterior visceral endoderm (see Schultheiss and Lassar[14] for review). As the vascular network forms throughout the mesoderm of the embryo, it connects with the pulsating heart and with the extraembryonic vascular network, eventually forming a complete circulatory system with intraembryonic and extraembryonic components.

LATERAL PLATE

With the formation of the anterior, posterior, and lateral body folds, the somatic and splanchnic layers of mesoderm with their associated ectoderm and endoderm, respectively, gradually gather on the ventral side of the embryo to meet at the umbilicus. This closes the connection between the extraembryonic coelom and the intraembryonic coelom, which later forms the abdominal and pleural cavities within the embryo. Thus the somatic and splanchnic mesoderm layers of the lateral plate completely line the body cavities and form the serous membranes.

In association with the endoderm, the splanchnic mesodermal layer of the lateral plate also takes part in the formation of the gut-associated derivatives of the respiratory and digestive systems: It forms the vascular components, the supporting mesenteries, and the muscular components of the gut along the length of the gut tube from the esophagus to the colon. From its position surrounding and supporting the gut, it also participates in the organogenesis of gut outpocketings forming the connective and stromal tissue of organs such as the trachea and lungs, the liver, and the pancreas.

The somatic mesoderm of the lateral plate, in association with the overlying ectoderm, forms the ventrolateral body wall, including the ventrolateral dermis. This somatic mesoderm is also the source of body wall muscles and the cells that ossify into the sternum. In addition, the lateral plate mesoderm forms the two pairs of limb buds that push out from the ventrolateral body wall. Complex interactions take place between the lateral plate mesoderm and the overlying ectoderm to form and pattern the limbs.[15,16] The bones of the limb develop from the lateral plate mesoderm, whereas cells migrate into the developing limbs from the somites to form the limb musculature.

INTERMEDIATE MESODERM

The intermediate mesoderm comes to lie in parallel ridges in the roof of the intraembryonic coelom on either side of the midline in the thoracic and abdominal regions. These ridges, known as the urogenital ridges, later form both the excretory and the reproductive organ systems.[17,18] The development of these two systems is closely interconnected. Early in development, the intermediate mesoderm in the extreme cranial end of the embryo forms a vestigial and transitory excretory system, the pronephros. Later, in the thoracic region, the mesonephros and mesonephric ducts form in the urogenital ridge. The mesonephros is transitory, but the mesonephric duct persists in male embryos and becomes part of the genital system. The definitive kidney, or metanephros, is induced in posterior intermediate mesoderm by an outgrowth of the mesonephric duct called the ureteric bud.

The gonads arise from the medial portion of the urogenital ridges from swellings called the genital or gonadal ridges, although the primordial germ cells (PGCs), the stem cells for oogonia and spermatogonia, arise from a distant site. The PGCs first appear in the posterior part of the primitive streak, migrate into the base of the allantois, then reenter the embryo to migrate along the dorsal mesentery and eventually into the gonads.[19]

PARAXIAL MESODERM

Immediately adjacent to the axis, flanking the neural tube and notochord is the paraxial mesoderm, which will form the transitory, segmental blocks of tissue called the somites (Fig. 24–1E). Throughout the process of gastrulation, the paraxial mesoderm is continuously ingressing, segmenting to form somites, and differentiating in an anterior-to-posterior progression so that by the time the tail somites are newly formed, the most anterior somites have already undergone differentiation into other structures. The regular segmentation of presomitic paraxial mesoderm involves a molecular oscillator, called the segmentation clock, which utilizes the conserved Notch signaling pathway.[20] After the initial epithelialization into segmental blocks, the somites rapidly undergo regional diversification into the dorsolateral dermomyotome and the ventromedial sclerotome. As the name implies, the dermomyotome further differentiates into the dermal component of the skin of the dorsolateral body, and into skeletal muscle, including the muscle of the limbs.[21,22] The sclerotome undergoes a further transition to mesenchymal cells and resegments around the neural tube to form the vertebrae of the axial skeleton. The resegmentation of sclerotome to form vertebrae is out of register with the original somite segmentation such that cells from the anterior part of one somite combine with cells from the posterior part of the preceding somites to form a vertebral segment.

In their differentiation, the somites are subject to the influences of multiple signals from various signaling pathways emanating from adjacent tissues. For example, Sonic hedgehog signals from the notochord and floor plate of the neural tube induce sclerotome differentiation, signals from the dorsal neural tube act to delimit the dermomyotome (Wnt signals) and dermis (neurotrophin 3), and Wnt and inhibitory bone morphogenetic protein signals from the body wall and mesoderm, respectively, act together on the

dorsolateral somite to induce limb and body wall musculature.[22–24]

NOTOCHORD

The axis of the embryo is defined by the position of the primitive streak at the posterior pole, with the epiblast dorsally located and primitive endoderm ventrally located. Cells that ingress through the node at the anterior end of the primitive streak and move cranially differentiate as a solid rod of cells called the notochord. These cells progress as far as the precordal plate, an area near where the buccopharyngeal membrane will later open as the mouth. As the primitive streak regresses in later gastrulation, notochord cells continue to ingress, forming a solid rod of mesoderm along the axis of the entire trunk and tail. It is around this structure that sclerotome-derived cells condense to form the vertebrae. The notochord makes only a small cellular contribution to the adult vertebral column, persisting only in the intervertebral disc. However, it is an important signaling center and structural component during embryogenesis of all chordate embryos.

ACKNOWLEDGMENTS

I wish to acknowledge support from the NIH (GMO 60561 and HD33082).

REFERENCES

1. Sadler, T.W. (2000). "Langman's Medical Embryology," 8th ed. Lippincott, Williams & Wilkins, Philadelphia.
2. Beddington, R.S.P. (1994). Induction of a second neural axis by the mouse node. *Development* **120,** 613–620.
3. Lawson, K.A., Meneses, J.J., and Pedersen, R.A. (1991). Clonal analysis of epiblast fate during germ layer formation in the mouse embryo. *Development* **113,** 891–911.
4. Lawson, K.A. (1999). Fate mapping the mouse embryo. *Int. J. Dev. Biol.* **43,** 773–775.
5. Tam, P.P.L., and Quinlan, G.A. (1996). Mapping vertebrate embryos. *Curr. Biol.* **6,** 104–106.
6. Nagy, A., Gertsenstein, M., Vintersten, K., and Behringer, R. (2003). "Manipulating the Mouse Embryo: A Laboratory Manual," 3rd ed. Cold Spring Harbor Laboratory Press, Cold Spring Harbor, NY.
7. Tam, P.P.L., and Beddington, R.S.P. (1987). The formation of mesodermal tissues in the mouse embryo during gastrulation and early organogenesis. *Development* **99,** 109–126.
8. Tam, P.P.L., and Tan, S.S. (1992). The somitogenetic potential of cells in the primitive streak and the tail bud of the organogenesis-stage mouse embryo. *Development* **115,** 703–715.
9. Fehling, H.J., Lacaud, G., Kubo, A., Kennedy, M., Robertson, S., Keller, G., and Kouskoff, V. (2003). Tracking mesoderm induction and its specification to the hemangioblast during embryonic stem cell differentiation. *Development* **130,** 4217–4227.
10. Choi, K., Kennedy, M., Kazarov, A., Papadimitriou, J.C., and Keller, G. (1998). A common precursor for hematopoietic and endothelial cells. *Development* **125,** 725–732.

11. Ema, M., and Rossant, J. (2003). Cell fate decisions in early blood vessel formation. *Trends Cardio. Med.* **13,** 254–259.

12. Galloway, J.L., and Zon, L.I. (2003). Ontogeny of hematopoiesis: examining the emergence of hematopoietic cells in the vertebrate embryo. *Curr. Topics Dev. Biol.* **53,** 139–158.

13. Dzierzak, E. (2003). Ontogenic emergence of definitive hematopoietic stem cells. *Curr. Opin. Hematol.* **10,** 229–234.

14. Schultheiss, T.M., and Lassar, A.B. (1999). Vertebrate heart induction. *In* "Heart Development," (R.P. Harvey *et al.,* eds.), pp. 52–62. Academic Press, San Diego.

15. Niswander, L. (2002). Interplay between the molecular signals that control vertebrate limb development. *Int. J. Dev. Biol.* **46,** 877–881.

16. Tickle, C. (2003). Patterning systems—from one end of the limb to the other. *Dev. Cell* **4,** 449–458.

17. Dressler, G.R. (2002). Development of the excretory system. *In* "Mouse Development: Patterning, Morphogenesis, and Organogenesis," (J. Rossant *et al.,* eds.), pp. 395–420. Academic Press, San Diego.

18. Swain, A., and Lovell-Badge, R. (2002). Sex determination and differentiation. *In* "Mouse Development: Patterning, Morphogenesis, and Organogenesis," (J. Rossant *et al.,* eds.), pp. 371–393. Academic Press, San Diego.

19. Anderson, R., Copeland, T.K., Scholer, H., Heasman, J., and Wylie, C. (2000). The onset of germ cell migration in the mouse embryo. *Mech. Dev.* **91,** 61–68.

20. Pourquie, O. (2001). The vertebrate segmentation clock. *J. Anat.* **199,** 169–175.

21. Buckingham, M., Bajard, L., Chang, T., Daubas, P., Hadchouel, J., Meilhac, S., Montarras, D., Rocancourt, D., and Relaix, R. (2003). The formation of skeletal muscle: From somite to limb. *J. Anat.* **202,** 59–68.

22. Duprez, D. (2002). Signals regulating muscle formation in the limb during embryonic development. *Int. J. Dev. Biol.* **46,** 915–925.

23. Gossler, A., and Hrabe de Angelis, M. (1998). Somitogenesis. *Curr. Topics Dev. Biol.* **38,** 225–287.

24. Summerbell, D., and Rigby, P. W. (2000). Transcriptional regulation during somitogenesis. *Curr. Topics Dev. Biol.* **48,** 301–318.

Hematopoietic Stem Cells

George Q. Daley

Embryonic Stem Cells and Embryonic Hematopoiesis

Over two decades of research in mice has established that embryonic stem cells (ESCs) can give rise to all differentiated cell types in the adult organism, and are thus pluripotent. *In vitro,* ESCs undergo spontaneous aggregation and differentiate to form cystic embryoid bodies (EBs).[1–3] These teratoma-like structures consist of semi-organized tissues including contractile cardiac myocytes, striated skeletal muscle, neuronal rosettes, and hemoglobin-containing blood islands. In the last decade and a half, this *in vitro* system has been exploited to study differentiation events in a number of tissues, and has begun to be used for discovery and characterization of small molecule pharmaceuticals. The availability of ES cells from the human might make it possible to produce specific differentiated cell types for replacement cell therapies to treat a host of degenerative diseases.[4,5]

Stem cells from the embryo have fundamentally distinct properties when compared to stem cells from somatic tissues of the developed organism. The hematopoietic stem cell (HSC) is the best-characterized somatic stem cell in the adult. This rare cell residing in the bone marrow gives rise to all blood cell lineages and will reconstitute the lymphohematopoietic system when transplanted into lethally irradiated animals. Bone marrow transplantation is widely employed for the treatment of congenital, malignant, and degenerative diseases. Though adult HSCs are an important target for genetic modification, success has been limited by difficulty expressing genes in HSCs and by the challenge of maintaining and expanding HSCs in culture. Moreover, recent concerns have been raised about the safety of gene therapy with retroviruses,[6] thus harnessing ES cells as a source of HSCs would make it easier to genetically modify stem cell populations *ex vivo,* to discover small molecules that impact blood development, to study genetic and epigenetic influences on hematopoietic cell fate, and empower preclinical models for gene and cellular therapy.

A critical question is whether current methods for *in vitro* differentiation of ESCs produce HSCs capable of long-term

blood formation in adults. All protocols for *in vitro* differentiation of ES cells published to date appear to recapitulate the yolk sac stage of hematopoietic commitment, with questionable developmental maturation into adult-type somatic HSCs. The first blood cells detected in the yolk sac of the embryo and in EBs *in vitro* are primitive nucleated erythrocytes.[7] These cells express embryonic forms of hemoglobin with a left-shifted oxyhemoglobin dissociation curve, adapted to the low oxygen environment of the embryo. Embryonic forms of hemoglobin serve as markers of primitive, embryonic erythropoiesis. Later in development, both yolk sac and EBs produce a variety of more differentiated myeloid cell types and enucleated red blood cells that express adult globins and are typical of circulating mature blood. This suggests that yolk sac precursors are capable of making the transition from the primitive to definitive hematopoietic programs,[3] but the extent to which yolk sac–derived progenitors contribute long-term to hematopoiesis in the adult remains controversial. Experimental manipulation of yolk sac blood progenitors can reveal a latent potential for hematopoietic engraftment in adults. When marked yolk sac cells from one embryo are transplanted into other embryos, yolk sac progenitors can contribute to blood formation in the adult,[8] yet yolk sac progenitors fail to engraft if injected directly into the adult.[9,10] However, when directly injected into the liver of myeloablated newborn mice, highly purified CD34+/c-Kit+ progenitors isolated from mouse yolk sac will provide long-term blood production throughout adulthood.[11,12] Apparently, the newborn liver retains the embryonic hematopoietic microenvironment and supports the developmental maturation of the yolk sac stem cells. Yolk sac cells can also engraft in irradiated mice if they are first cultured on a supportive stromal cell line taken from the aorta–gonad–mesonephros region of the embryo.[13] Here once again, the yolk sac cells can be "educated" by the stromal cells to adopt an adult profile. So indeed, hematopoietic progenitors from yolk sac appear capable of sustaining hematopoiesis in adults, but based on recent evidence from a number of groups, it appears likely that yolk sac progenitors contribute to embryonic blood formation and thereafter yield to a distinct source of definitive HSCs that arise within the embryo proper. Compelling evidence suggests that the definitive HSCs responsible for lifelong hematopoiesis arise chiefly from a separate and distinct source in the aorta–gonad–mesonephros region of the developing embryo.[14,15]

Handbook of Stem Cells
Volume 1
Copyright © 2004 by Academic Press
All rights of reproduction in any form reserved.

Blood Formation in Embryoid Bodies

As for yolk sac progenitors, it has proven exceedingly difficult to demonstrate that ES-derived hematopoietic progenitors can repopulate adult mice.[16-18] This resistance of embryonic progenitors from EBs to engraft in the adult is reminiscent of the block to engraftment observed for yolk sac progenitors, and likewise is believed to reflect the developmental immaturity of ES-derived HSCs, and the different microenvironments of the embryo and the adult.[10] Whether *in vitro* differentiation of ESCs will promote formation of AGM-like HSCs remains unresolved. In order to model hematopoietic transplantation from ES cell sources, this challenge must be overcome.

While EBs show a temporal wave of primitive followed by definitive hematopoiesis, the nature of the ES-derived HSCs has been a subject of great interest. The delineation of hematopoietic development within EBs has been pioneered by Keller *et al.*[2,3] whose seminal contributions have made the hematopoietic program among the most well-defined aspects of *in vitro* ES cell differentiation. Their work has defined the most primitive hematopoietic progenitor in EBs as the blast colony-forming cell (BL-CFC), a transient cell with both primitive erythroid potential and the capacity to generate definitive erythrocytes and multilineage myeloid colonies upon replating.[19] It also has the potential to form endothelial cells and as such has been defined as the hemangioblast. To date there is no data demonstrating lymphoid potential for this cell type.[20] Only one group has reported repopulation of irradiated adult mice with cells taken from EBs fortuitously timed to harbor the maximal number of BL-CFCs, but in this report there were no markers to demonstrate that lymphoid and myeloid cells developed from a single cell committed to the hematopoietic lineage.[17] Thus to date the relationship of the BL-CFC to definitive HSCs remains ill-defined, and whether EBs support the development of AGM-like HSCs remains an open question.

Transformation of an EB-Derived HSC by BCR/ABL

We set out to address the question of whether a lymphoid–myeloid HSC developed within differentiating EBs by attempting to transform that putative cell. We borrowed from our experience with the disease chronic myeloid leukemia (CML), the classical pathologic condition of adult hematopoietic stem cells that is caused by the BCR/ABL oncoprotein. Several biological properties unique to the BCR/ABL oncoprotein made it particularly well suited for addressing the nature of primitive blood progenitors within EBs. Induction of CML requires expression in pluripotent hematopoietic stem cells.[21-23] Multilineage hematopoiesis is monoclonal in most patients at the time of CML diagnosis, demonstrating that the fusion oncoprotein BCR/ABL endows leukemic stem cells with a competitive repopulation advantage over normal stem cells. Despite expression in a wide array of tissues, transgenic mice that carry BCR/ABL in their germ line develop only hematopoietic malignancies, reflecting the tropism of BCR/ABL for hematopoietic cell types and the sparing of nonhematopoietic tissues. Patients with CML harbor the Philadelphia chromosome translocation in both lymphoid and myeloid lineages, showing that the multilineage differentiation of stem cells is preserved despite BCR/ABL transformation.

We hypothesized that BCR/ABL would enable us to transform an ES-derived HSC, engraft mice, and determine the extent of lymphoid and myeloid differentiation *in vivo*. We introduced BCR/ABL into differentiated murine ES cells, and cultured a primitive hematopoietic blast cell that generated nucleated erythroblasts *in vitro*, mimicking yolk sac blood formation. We picked and expanded single cell clones of these cells, verified clonality by retroviral integration, injected irradiated mice, and observed successful lymphoid–myeloid engraftment in primary and secondary animals. The erythroid progenitors from engrafted mice expressed only adult globins, suggesting that the cells underwent developmental maturation to the definitive hematopoietic program *in vivo*. BCR/ABL expression enabled adult engraftment by altering the cell's homing properties, complementing a missing cytokine signal, or blocking apoptosis, allowing the ES-derivatives to acclimatize to the adult microenvironment and to differentiate into multiple hematopoietic lineages. These results provided the first definitive demonstration of the embryonic HSC (ε-HSC) that arises *in vitro* during ES differentiation.[24,25] This cell is a common progenitor of both primitive embryonic zerythropoiesis (yolk-sac type) and the definitive adult lymphoid–myeloid hematopoietic stem cell. While the BCR/ABL–transformed clones produce colonies with a comparable morphology to the BL-CFC and show primitive erythroid potential, their precise relationship to the hemangioblast is unclear, as the BCR/ABL-transformed clones do not appear to have endothelial potential.

Promoting Hematopoietic Engraftment with STAT5 and HoxB4

While BCR/ABL transformation targets a rare cell in ES cell cultures with lymphoid–myeloid developmental potential, the engrafted mice succumbed to leukemia, prompting us to explore means for isolating the ε-HSC without inducing the transformed phenotype. Our approach to generating normal, nontransformed blood progenitors from ES cells involved a combination of two strategies: 1) expression of single proteins in signaling pathways activated by BCR/ABL (e.g., STAT5), postulating that activation of downstream targets would be less disruptive to cell physiology than transformation by the complete oncoprotein; and 2) conditional expression of candidate genes using a novel ES cell line engineered to express the gene of interest from a tetracycline regulated promoter such that genetic effects could be induced and then reversed.[26,27] The Ainv15 ESC line we created expresses the tet-dependent transcriptional transactivator protein from an active genomic locus *(ROSA26)*. Any gene of interest can be inserted with high targeting efficiency into an expression cassette located within the active *HPRT* gene locus. Genes that are targeted correctly become resistant to neomycin (G418), and the inserted gene is expressed only in the presence of the potent tetracycline analogue doxycycline, and can be rapidly silenced following doxycycline removal. We chose to express the *STAT5* transcriptional regulator and the homeobox gene *HoxB4* in this system, owing to the central role of STAT5 in BCR/ABL and cytokine receptor signaling, and to extensive prior evidence from the Humphries group of the role of *Hox* genes in hematopoiesis, and the unique properties of *HoxB4,* which was previously shown to enhance hematopoietic engraftment without inducing leukemia.[28,29] We differentiated the modified ES cells into EBs, and activated gene expression by adding doxycycline to the culture medium between differentiation days 4 and 6, timed to coincide with the maximal generation of primitive multipotential hematopoietic colonies. After 6 days, the EBs were dissociated, and the cells cultured on the OP9 stromal cell line, previously shown to enhance production of hematopoietic progenitors from mES cells.[30] Expansion of hematopoietic blast cells was observed upon *STAT5* and *HoxB4* gene induction, and vigorously growing colonies of hematopoietic cells were detected only in the presence of doxycycline. These cells were harvested, plated in semi-solid media plus cytokines, and shown to produce a variety of blood cell colony types, with only the most primitive multipotential colonies significantly expanded. The cells, which also express the green fluorescent protein (GFP), were injected intravenously into irradiated syngeneic or immunodeficient mice. Contributions of GFP+ cells to the peripheral blood were then monitored by flow cytometry, and specific lymphoid and myeloid cell populations were scored by antibody staining against specific cell surface differentiation antigens, forward and side scatter properties, and by direct microscopic examination of cells cyto-centrifuged onto cover slips. In these experiments, both *STAT5* and *HoxB4*-expressing cells engrafted in mice and generated both lymphoid and myeloid populations in circulating blood. Interestingly, contributions of the *STAT5*-stimulated cells appeared to be transient, despite continued gene induction *in vivo* (through inclusion of doxycycline in the drinking water of the mice). Engraftment with *HoxB4*-expressing cells persisted in primary animals even in the absence of gene induction, and the cells of primary animals could be transplanted into secondary animals, suggesting self-renewal of a long-term reconstituting hematopoietic stem cell. Examination of peripheral blood smears from engrafted mice showed no evidence of abnormal hematopoiesis, although rare animals succumbed to hematologic malignancies from donor cells, suggesting some tendency for the genetically modified ESCs to undergo transformation *in vivo*. Retroviral delivery of *HoxB4* directly to populations of cells dissociated from EBs after 4–6 days of differentiation also succeeded in generating expanding cultures of hematopoietic cells that engrafted in irradiated mice. These data demonstrate that expression of the *STAT5* or *HoxB4* gene in differentiating cultures of ES cells yields hematopoietic engraftment in irradiated mice, with *HoxB4*

showing the most promise for stable engraftment in primary and secondary animals.[26,27]

The mechanisms by which *STAT5* and particularly *HoxB4* drive hematopoietic engraftment from ESCs remains unclear. By driving cell proliferation, both genes might serve to increase the numbers of otherwise vanishingly rare HSCs above a threshold of detection. Alternatively, *HoxB4* might be altering cell fate, a known effect of homeobox genes, by promoting a transition from primitive to definitive HSC fate. RT-PCR analysis of *HoxB4*-expressing EB-derived cells in comparison to hematopoietic progenitors isolated from precirculation yolk sac confirmed the detection of markers of definitive hematopoiesis in *HoxB4* expressing cells, including adult type globin. Moreover, *HoxB4*-transduced cells expressed *CXCR4,* the chemokine receptor implicated in hematopoietic stem cell homing to the bone marrow, and *Tel,* the transcription factor implicated in migration from the fetal liver to the adult bone marrow microenvironment. *HoxB4* appears not to be expressed in the precirculation yolk sac,[31] but is detected in primitive populations of CD34+ bone marrow cells from the adult.[29] We therefore also tested whether expression of the HoxB4 gene by retroviral infection in yolk sac progenitors would endow them with engraftment potential in adults. As for EB-derived cells, *HoxB4* expression in yolk sac progenitors induced dramatic expansion on OP9 stromal cultures and stable hematopoietic engraftment in adult mice. Yolk sac–derived progenitors could also be transplanted into secondary animals.[27] These data support the hypothesis that activation of *HoxB4* endows embryonic hematopoietic progenitors with the potential to engraft in adult hematopoietic microenvironments, and therefore may be critical to the transition from the embryonic to adult hematopoietic program.

Lymphoid potential and transient lymphoid reconstitution of engrafted immunodeficient mice has been demonstrated, showing convincingly that EB-derived cells can show full hematopoietic differentiation potential.[18,32] Native EB-cell derived hematopoietic progenitors function at best inefficiently to reconstitute the adult host, or may develop in only limited numbers under idiosyncratic culture conditions. If indeed distinct progenitors contribute to primitive yolk-sac and definitive AGM-type hematopoiesis in the embryo, then distinct progenitors might arise at spatially and temporally distinct sites during EB formation from ES cells *in vitro*. Identifying the precise culture conditions that promote differentiation of ESCs into robust adult-type definitive HSCs *in vitro* remains a critical goal.

To date, gene modification has been required to demonstrate development of lymphoid–myeloid HSCs from differentiating ES cells *in vitro*, yet even gene modification results in inefficient engraftment. Given the technical challenges and risks inherent in genetic modification, it would be preferable to derive engraftable HSCs in as natural a process as possible, by mimicking the developmental pathways of the embryo. Applying principles that specify blood formation to *in vitro* systems might enable enhanced blood formation in a safe and efficient manner.

Promoting Blood Formation *In Vitro* with Embryonic Morphogens

During gastrulation in the mouse, secreted signaling molecules induce distinct cell fates from developing mesoderm. The earliest stages of blood formation occur in the extraembryonic mesoderm of the yolk sac, where blood islands form surrounded by endothelial cells and closely opposed to the visceral (primitive) endoderm. Several of the players that regulate the transcriptional control of hematopoiesis have been identified, e.g., *SCL, AML1/CBFa2,* and several *Hox* genes, largely due to their involvement at translocation breakpoints in leukemia, and gene knockout studies of these factors has validated their role in hematopoiesis.[33,34] More recently, a small number of secreted factors have been identified that act as early embryonic inducers of mesodermal fate in the hematopoietic lineage. The most interesting of these are Hedgehog factors and bone morphogenetic protein 4 (BMP4).

Indian Hedgehog (IHH) is a member of the Hedgehog family of signaling molecules that play diverse roles in patterning early embryonic events. Baron and colleagues have shown that early hematopoietic activity in the developing murine yolk sac is dependent upon signals from the adjacent primitive/visceral endoderm, and recently they demonstrated that IHH was –produced by visceral endoderm and sufficient to mediate this induction.[35,36] IHH could respecify neuroectoderm to hematopoietic fate, and blocking IHH function by anti-HH antibodies abrogated hematopoietic development. Baron and colleagues showed that IHH induction of hematopoiesis in murine embryo explants led to expression of BMP4. BMP4, a member of the TGF-β family, has been implicated as a potent ventralizing factor and inducer of hematopoietic mesoderm in Xenopus development.[37,38] A related hedgehog factor, Sonic HH, has been shown by Bhatia *et al.* to enhance the expansion of human hematopoietic repopulating cells assayed by transplantation in immunodeficient mice.[39] BMP4 and other members of the BMP family have also been implicated in regulation of proliferation and survival of primitive human hematopoietic populations.[40] Antibodies to HH and noggin, a specific antagonist of BMP4 signaling, abrogated the proliferative effects of Sonic HH in human hematopoietic cell culture.[39] It has been shown that IHH is expressed by visceral endoderm in developing EBs,[41] and there is a single report that addition of BMP4 to differentiating cultures of rhesus ES cells augments formation of hematopoietic clusters.[42] Most recently, Bhatia *et al.* have shown that BMP4 can enhance hematopoietic potential from human ES cells.[43]

These studies offer the first hints that directed differentiation of human ES cells into HSCs might be feasible. However, numerous questions persist: will HSCs derived from hES cells function normally? Will they reconstitute normal immune function and remain nontumorigenic *in vivo*? Can immunologic issues be circumvented through nuclear replacement or gene modification? The hurdles for therapeutic applications of ES-derived cells remain high, but no matter what, the *in vitro* differentiation system will remain an important model for investigations of blood formation and embryonic development.

REFERENCES

1. Doetschman, T.C., Eistetter, H., Katz, M., Schmidt, W., and Kemler, R. (1985). The *in vitro* development of blastocyst-derived embryonic stem cell lines: formation of visceral yolk sac, blood islands, and myocardium. *J. Embryol. Exp. Morphol.* **87,** 27–45.
2. Wiles, M.V., and Keller, G. (1991). Multiple hematopoietic lineages develop from embryonic stem (ES) cells in culture. *Development* **111,** 259–267.
3. Keller, G., Kennedy, M., Papayannopoulou, T., and Wiles, M.V. (1993). Hematopoietic commitment during embryonic stem cell differentiation in culture. *Mol. Cell Biol.* **13,** 473–486.
4. Shamblott, M.J., Axelman, J., Wang, S., Bugg, E.M., Littlefield, J.W., Donovan, P.J., Blumenthal, P.D., Huggins, G.R., and Gearhart, J.D. (1998). Derivation of pluripotent stem cells from cultured human primordial germ cells. *Proc. Natl. Acad. Sci. U. S. A.* **95,** 13,726–13,731.
5. Thomson, J.A., Itskovitz-Eldor, J., Shapiro, S.S., Waknitz, M.A., Swiergiel, J.J., Marshall, V.S., and Jones, J.M. (1998). Embryonic stem cell lines derived from human blastocysts. *Science* **282,** 1145–1147.
6. Hacein-Bey-Abina, S., von Kalle, C., Schmidt, M., Le Deist, F., Wulffraat, N., McIntyre, E., Radford, I., Villeval, J.L., Fraser, C.C., Cavazzana-Calvo, M., and Fischer, A. (2003). A serious adverse event after successful gene therapy for X-linked severe combined immunodeficiency. *N. Engl. J. Med.* **348,** 255–256.
7. Palis, J., Robertson, S., Kennedy, M., Wall, C., and Keller, G. (1999). Development of erythroid and myeloid progenitors in the yolk sac and embryo proper of the mouse. *Development* **126,** 5073–5084.
8. Weissman, I., Papaioannou, V., and Gardner, R. (1978). Fetal hematopoietic origins of the adult hematolymphoid system. *In* "Differentiation of Normal and Neoplastic Hematopoietic Cells," (B C, PA M, JE T, eds.), pp. 33–47. Cold Spring Harbor, New York.
9. Toles, J.F., Chui, D.H., Belbeck, L.W., Starr, E., and Barker, J.E. (1989). Hemopoietic stem cells in murine embryonic yolk sac and peripheral blood. *Proc. Natl. Acad. Sci. U. S. A.* **86,** 7456–7459.
10. Yoder, M.C. (2001). Introduction: spatial origin of murine hematopoietic stem cells. *Blood* **98,** 3–5.
11. Yoder, M.C., and Hiatt, K. (1997). Engraftment of embryonic hematopoietic cells in conditioned newborn recipients. *Blood* **89,** 2176–2183.
12. Yoder, M.C., Hiatt, K., and Mukherjee, P. (1997). *In vivo* repopulating hematopoietic stem cells are present in the murine yolk sac at day 9.0 postcoitus. *Proc. Natl. Acad. Sci. U. S. A.* **94,** 6776–6780.
13. Matsuoka, S., Tsuji, K., Hisakawa, H., Xu, M., Ebihara, Y., Ishii, T., Sugiyama, D., Manabe, A., Tanaka, R., Ikeda, Y., Asano, S., and Nakahata, T. (2001). Generation of definitive hematopoietic stem cells from murine early yolk sac and para-aortic splanchnopleures by aorta–gonad–mesonephros region-derived stromal cells. *Blood* **98,** 6–12.
14. Godin, I., Dieterlen-Lievre, F., and Cumano, A. (1995). Emergence of multipotent hemopoietic cells in the yolk sac and para-aortic splanchnopleura in mouse embryos, beginning at

8.5 days postcoitus. (Published erratum in *Proc. Natl. Acad. Sci. U. S. A.* (1995). 92, 10,815). *Proc. Natl. Acad. Sci. USA* **92**, 773–777.

15. Medvinsky, A., and Dzierzak, E. (1996). Definitive hematopoiesis is autonomously initiated by the AGM region. *Cell* **86**, 897–906.

16. Muller, A.M., and Dzierzak, E.A. (1993). ES cells have only a limited lymphopoietic potential after adoptive transfer into mouse recipients. *Development* **118**, 1343–1351.

17. Hole, N., Graham, G.J., Menzel, U., and Ansell, J.D. (1996). A limited temporal window for the derivation of multilineage repopulating hematopoietic progenitors during embryonal stem cell differentiation *in vitro*. *Blood* **88**, 1266–1276.

18. Potocnik, A.J., Kohler, H., and Eichmann, K. (1997). Hematolymphoid *in vivo* reconstitution potential of subpopulations derived from *in vitro* differentiated embryonic stem cells. *Proc. Natl. Acad. Sci. U. S. A.* **94**, 10,295–10,300.

19. Kennedy, M., Firpo, M., Choi, K., Wall, C., Robertson, S., Kabrun, N., and Keller, G. (1997). A common precursor for primitive erythropoiesis and definitive haematopoiesis. *Nature* **386**, 488–493.

20. Choi, K., Kennedy, M., Kazarov, A., Papadimitriou, J.C., and Keller, G. (1998). A common precursor for hematopoietic and endothelial cells. *Development* **125**, 725–732.

21. Daley, G.Q., Van Etten, R.A., and Baltimore, D. (1990). Induction of chronic myelogenous leukemia in mice by the P210Bcr/Abl gene of the Philadelphia chromosome. *Science* **247**, 824–830.

22. Gishizky, M.L., Johnson-White, J., and Witte, O.N. (1993). Efficient transplantation of BCR-ABL-induced chronic myelogenous leukemia-like syndrome in mice. *Proc. Natl. Acad. Sci. U. S. A.* **90**, 3755–3759.

23. Li, S., Ilaria, R.L., Million, R.P., Daley, G.Q., and Van Etten, R.A. (1999). The P190, P210, and P230 forms of the Bcr/Abl oncogene induce a similar chronic myeloid leukemia-like syndrome in mice but have different lymphoid leukemogenic activity. *J. Exp. Med.* **189**, 1399–1412.

24. Perlingeiro, R.C., Kyba, M., and Daley, G.Q. (2001). Clonal analysis of differentiating embryonic stem cells reveals a hematopoietic progenitor with primitive erythroid and adult lymphoid–myeloid potential. *Development* **128**, 4597–4604.

25. Peters, D.G., Klucher, K.M., Perlingeiro, R.C., Dessain, S.K., Koh, E.Y., and Daley, G.Q. (2001). Autocrine and paracrine effects of an ES-cell derived, BCR/ABL-transformed hematopoietic cell line that induces leukemia in mice. *Oncogene* **20**, 2636–2646.

26. Kyba, M., Perlingeiro, R., Hoover, R., Lu, C.W., Pierce, J., and Daley, G. (2003). Enhanced hematopoietic differentiation of ES cells conditionally expressing STAT5. *Proc. Natl. Acad. Sci. U. S. A.* **100 (suppl. 1),** 11904–11910.

27. Kyba, M., Perlingeiro, R.C., and Daley, G.Q. (2002). Hoxb4 confers definitive lymphoid–myeloid engraftment potential on embryonic stem cell and yolk sac hematopoietic progenitors. *Cell* **109**, 29–37.

28. Helgason, C.D., Sauvageau, G., Lawrence, H.J., Largman, C., and Humphries, R.K. (1996). Overexpression of Hoxb4 enhances the hematopoietic potential of embryonic stem cells differentiated *in vitro*. *Blood* **87**, 2740–2749.

29. Sauvageau, G., Thorsteinsdottir, U., Eaves, C.J., Lawrence, H.J., Largman, C., Lansdorp, P.M., and Humphries, R.K. (1995). Overexpression of Hoxb4 in hematopoietic cells causes the selective expansion of more primitive populations *in vitro* and *in vivo*. *Genes Dev.* **9**, 1753–1765.

30. Nakano, T., Kodama, H., and Honjo, T. (1994). Generation of lymphohematopoietic cells from embryonic stem cells in culture. *Science* **265**, 1098–1101.

31. McGrath, K.E., and Palis, J. (1997). Expression of homeobox genes, including an insulin promoting factor, in the murine yolk sac at the time of hematopoietic initiation. *Mol. Reprod. Dev.* **48**, 145–153.

32. Potocnik, A.J., Nerz, G., Kohler, H., and Eichmann, K. (1997). Reconstitution of B-cell subsets in Rag-deficient mice by transplantation of *in vitro* differentiated embryonic stem cells. *Immunol. Lett.* **57**, 131–137.

33. Shivdasani, R.A., and Orkin, S.H. (1996). The transcriptional control of hematopoiesis. *Blood* **87**, 4025–4039.

34. Orkin, S.H. (1998). Embryonic stem cells and transgenic mice in the study of hematopoiesis. *Int. J. Dev. Biol.* **42**, 927–934.

35. Dyer, M.A., Farrington, S.M., Mohn, D., Munday, J.R., and Baron, M.H. (2001). Indian hedgehog activates hematopoiesis and vasculogenesis and can respecify prospective neurectodermal cell fate in the mouse embryo. *Development* **128**, 1717–1730.

36. Baron, M. (2001). Induction of embryonic hematopoietic and endothelial stem–progenitor cells by hedgehog-mediated signals. *Differentiation* **68**, 175–185.

37. Huber, T.L., Zhou, Y., Mead, P.E., and Zon, L.I. (1998). Cooperative effects of growth factors involved in the induction of hematopoietic mesoderm. *Blood* **92**, 4128–4137.

38. Maeno, M., Mead, P.E., Kelley, C., Xu, R.H., Kung, H.F., Suzuki, A., Ueno, N., and Zon, L.I. (1996). The role of Bmp4 and Gata2 in the induction and differentiation of hematopoietic mesoderm in *Xenopus laevis*. *Blood* **88**, 1965–1972.

39. Bhardwaj, G., Murdoch, B., Wu, D., Baker, D.P., Williams, K.P., Chadwick, K., Ling, L.E., Karanu, F.N., and Bhatia, M. (2001). Sonic hedgehog induces the proliferation of primitive human hematopoietic cells via BMP regulation. *Nat. Immunol.* **2**, 172–180.

40. Bhatia, M., Bonnet, D., Wu, D., Murdoch, B., Wrana, J., Gallacher, L., and Dick, J.E. (1999). Bone morphogenetic proteins regulate the developmental program of human hematopoietic stem cells. *J. Exp. Med.* **189**, 1139–1148.

41. Maye, P., Becker, S., Kasameyer, E., Byrd, N., and Grabel, L. (2000). Indian hedgehog signaling in extraembryonic endoderm and ectoderm differentiation in ES embryoid bodies. *Mech. Dev.* **94**, 117–132.

42. Li, F., Lu, S., Vida, L., Thomson, J.A., and Honig, G.R. (2001). Bone morphogenetic protein-4 induces efficient hematopoietic differentiation of rhesus monkey embryonic stem cells *in vitro*. *Blood* **98**, 335–342.

43. Chadwick, K., Wang, L., Li, L., Menendez, P., Murdoch, B., Rouleau, A., and Bhatia, M. (2003). Cytokines and Bmp4 promote hematopoietic differentiation of human embryonic stem cells. *Blood* **102**, 906–915.

Cell Differentiation in the Skeleton

Gerard Karsenty

The vertebrate skeleton has a complex origin. It derives from cells of both ectodermal and mesodermal tissues; it forms at hundreds of sites, some of them developing more than two days later than others during mouse embryogenesis; it can adopt a multitude of shapes and sizes; and it matures to a functional organ by following one of two distinct processes. Despite this complexity, each bone will eventually contain a similar differentiated cell type—namely, the osteoblast—solely responsible for the synthesis of an extracellular matrix able to mineralize. Thanks to the blossoming of mouse and human genetics in last 20 years, the molecular players responsible for this original complexity as well as for this final homogeneity are beginning to be known. This chapter summarizes the most recent advances in this area of developmental biology.

Introduction

The vertebrate skeleton is composed of two specialized tissues, cartilage and bone, surrounding and protecting a third one, bone marrow. Each of these two skeletal tissues contains a specific cell type of mesenchymal origin, chondrocytes in cartilage and bone, forming osteoblasts in bone. Both chondrocytes and osteoblasts fulfill unique functions critical for the growth, maintenance, and integrity of the skeleton. Chondrocytes are required for longitudinal growth of the bones; they synthesize the cartilaginous scaffolds on which osteoblasts can deposit bone matrix during both development and postnatal growth. Osteoblasts synthesize a type I collagen-rich matrix that has the unique property to become eventually mineralized. Because of this nonredundancy of function, defect of differentiation or function of either of these two cell types has tremendous consequences, reflected by the high number and frequency of genetic and acquired diseases of bone and cartilage. Given this biomedical importance, the genetic bases controlling the differentiation of chondrocytes and osteoblasts have been extensively studied. Several transcription factors as well as a complex interplay of secreted molecules have been identified that control the progression from a pluripotent progenitor to a functional cell.[1]

Skeletogenesis

Formation of the vertebrate skeleton begins with the condensation of undifferentiated cells in structures that prefigure each future skeletal element.[2] These cells originate from the sclerotome and the lateral plate mesoderm as well as from cranial neural crests.[3, 4] The latter, deriving from the dorsal margins of the cranial neural fold, are major contributors of the craniofacial skeleton.[5] The skeletal condensations, also called anlage, begin to form around 9.5 days postcoitus (dpc) during mouse development and become visible histologically around 10.5 dpc. Assembly of these skeletal condensations is orchestrated by molecules that control the migration and association of undifferentiated cells. Although some particularities exist among craniofacial, axial, and limb patterning, the pathways controlling this patterning process show many similarities. Little is known about the specific markers these cells might be expressing at this stage that could distinguish them from other mesenchymal or neural crest cells not determined to a skeletal fate. They express an extracellular matrix rich in type I collagen, hyaluronan, tenascin, and fibronectin.[6] Once formed, the skeletal condensation can evolve along two pathways to form bones, following either an intramembranous or an endochondral ossification process.[7]

Bones formed by intramembranous ossification include the frontal and parietal bones, parts of the temporal and occipital bones, most the facial bones, and the lateral part of the clavicles.[8] In these flat bones, cells of the condensations expand to form a membranous structure then differentiate directly into osteoblasts.[2, 9] They maintain then increase their secretion of type I collagen while initiating expression of noncollagenous proteins more specific of the osteoblast genetic program such as osteopontin, bone sialoprotein, and eventually osteocalcin.

In the rest of the skeleton, skeletogenesis proceeds by endochondral ossification, a multistep process. By 12.5 dpc of mouse development, skeletal condensations contain chondrocyte-like round-shaped cells expressing *type IIa collagen,* the nonchondrocyte-specific splice form of type II collagen. In the center of the condensations, cells differentiate into chondrocytes, expressing the chondrocyte-specific form of *type II collagen* (type IIb) and *aggrecan.* Between 14.5 dpc and 16.5 dpc, as the condensation elongates to create the shape of the future bone, the most inner chondrocytes differentiate into hypertrophic chondrocytes expressing *type X collagen.* In the meantime, cells at the periphery of the condensation flatten and begin to differentiate into osteoblasts that express *type I collagen*. This structure, termed the bone collar, is most apparent in the region closer to the hypertrophic zone of the condensation. The second step of the endochondral ossification process is marked by two coordinated events. While hypertrophic chondrocytes start to die through apoptosis, blood vessels invade the region they occupied, bringing in differentiating osteoblasts from the bone collar. The bone matrix synthesized by osteoblasts then replaces the cartilaginous matrix. This ossification spreads centripetally until much of the cartilage is replaced. Only a small region at either end of the growing bone will remain cartilaginous. This structure, called the growth plate cartilage, will control longitudinal growth of the bone until the end of puberty. As the newly deposited bone matrix mineralizes, osteoclast precursors coming from the blood stream invade the center of the forming structure and begin to differentiate under the influence

of factors secreted by osteoblast progenitors. They start to resorb the bone matrix, forming the internal space that will contain the bone marrow.

Skeletal Cell Determination

LIMBS MORPHOGENESIS

Our most complete knowledge of skeletal patterning and early skeletal cell determination derives from studies analyzing limbs formation (Fig. 26–1). Originally based on experiments in chickens, this wealth of knowledge is being confirmed using mouse models, demonstrating that, except for rare and minor exceptions, these mechanisms have been remarkably conserved during evolution. Formation of each limb begins with the outgrowth of a small bud of mesenchymal cells issued from the lateral plate mesoderm (LPM) covered by surface ectoderm (the ectodermal ridge, or ER). From this

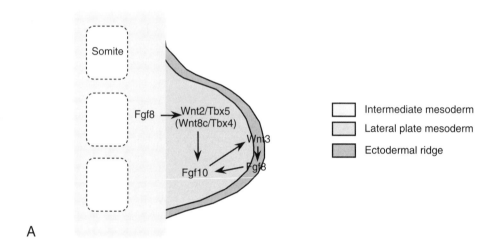

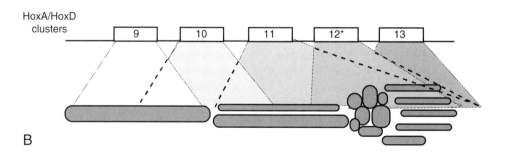

*Only in HoxD cluster

Figure 26–1. *Patterning of skeletal elements in the limbs.* (A) An initial series of interactions between FGF and Wnt signaling pathways induces limb bud formation and early outgrowth. (B) Limb skeletal elements are later specified by the proximal–distal expression of distinct genes of the Hoxa and Hoxd clusters. The area of influence of each particular set of genes (boxes) is marked with a distinct shade of gray.

LPM will derive progenitor cells of chondrocytes and other connective tissues cells such as the ones present in tendons; this, therefore, represents the first cellular determination event toward a skeletal fate. In contrast, muscles and blood vessels, for instance, will arise from progenitor cells that will eventually migrate into the developing limb bud.[10]

The initial molecular cues regulating the timing and precise localization of limb bud appearance are still poorly understood. In contrast, limb bud establishment and early growth has been well characterized, appearing to rely on a complex interplay between Wnt and fibroblast growth factor (FGF) signaling pathways (Fig. 26–1). Fgf8 produced in the intermediate mesoderm adjacent to the bud has been proposed to be a signal triggering bud outgrowth, based on the observations that this gene is transiently expressed in this region at the time of budding; FGFs can initiate the development of an additional limb bud in the flank of chicken embryos when ectopically expressed.[11, 12] Fgf8 would induce expression of *Wnt2b* in forelimb and Wnt8c in hindlimb, mesenchymes that would locally activate *Fgf10* expression. The difference in Wnt subtype activation between the upper and lower limbs would be reflected at the transcriptional level, where two distinct member of the T-box family of transcription factors, Tbx5 and Tbx4, respectively, would mediate their signal and thus contribute to limb determination.[13, 14] Fgf10 would then signal to the ER, triggering expression of *Wnt3a* in chick and *Wnt3* in mouse (one of the rare known divergences of mechanism in the two species).[15, 16] These will, in turn, locally activate *Fgf8* expression in the apical ER (AER). These Wnt, signaling cascade of activation, appear mediated by the Wnt–β-catenin canonical pathway: Misexpression of *axin*, an inhibitor of this process, and deletion of *Tcf1–Lef1*, its transcriptional effectors, impair limb outgrowth, and β-*catenin* overexpression induces FGF expression.[15, 17] What follows is a positive feedback loop allowing *Fgf8* and *Fgf10* to maintain their respective expression.[18] At the end of this inductive process, *Fgf8* is expressed throughout the AER, soon followed by expression of *Fgf4*, *Fgf9*, and *Fgf19* in a more posterior manner. These molecules are thought to direct limb buds proximal–distal extension by controlling cell number and survival.[19–21] Another secreted factor believed to influence cell survival in the condensations is Sonic hedgehog (Shh), whose absence causes a severe shortening of the distal elements of the limbs because of abnormal cell death.[22] *Shh* spatial restriction of expression to a particular region of the posterior mesenchyme, termed the zone of polarizing activity (ZPA), also defines limbs anterior–posterior axis.[23] Limb outgrowth would be regulated by a Shh–FGF feedback loop negatively regulated by bone morphogenetic protein (BMP) signaling. Indeed, gene inactivation of *Gremlin,* which encodes a BMP antagonist, results in reduced and disorganized *FGF* expression as well as loss of *Shh* expression, thereby impairing skeletal element outgrowth and specification.[24] This is also consistent with avian studies showing that BMPs promote the regression of the AER.[25] In contrast, the homeobox *Dlx5* and *Dlx6* genes would control AER maintenance in the hindlimbs by positively regulating cell proliferation.[26]

Once limb buds have been established, the main event in skeletal patterning becomes the formation of cell condensations prefiguring the future bones. This cellular condensation initially occurs by active aggregation of cells toward a center, causing a local increase in cell density without an increase in cell proliferation.[27] Changes in the extracellular matrix composition as well as in expression of surface adhesion molecules are believed to allow this process. Prior to condensation, undifferentiated mesenchymal cells secrete an extracellular matrix rich in type I collagen and hyaluronan that is thought to inhibit cell–cell interactions. An increase in hyaluronidase expression by the condensing cells would facilitate the establishment of direct contacts between them.[6] Precartilaginous condensations also transiently express adhesion molecules that facilitate the cell packing process. For instance, expression of *N-cadherin* and *NCAM,* two transmembrane glycoproteins with extracellular homotypic protein–protein interaction ability, peaks during condensation.[28] A functional redundancy among the multiple adhesion molecules expressed in condensing cells has thus been invoked to explain the normal skeletal development observed in *NCAM*-deficient mice.[29] Such abundant expression of glycosylated proteins may, however, also explain the classic observation that precartilaginous condensations can be histologically visualized by their ability to bind the lectin peanut agglutinin.[30] The genetic bases controlling the initial aggregation process are still elusive. However, double homozygote mutant mice for *Prx1* and *Prx2,* two members of the aristaless subfamily of homeobox transcription factors, display abnormal precartilaginous condensations, suggesting that they control at least part of this process.[31] It has also been shown that two receptor tyrosine kinase of the Ror family, Ror1 and Ror2, control the initial expansion of the condensation.[32, 33]

The next step of importance during skeletal patterning is the specification of skeletal elements (i.e., the definition of their final size, location, and shape). Spatial information established by the three-dimensional axis defined by the AER and ZPA are interpreted mostly by the homeobox transcription factor of the Hox family. Hox genes are arranged in four multigenic clusters in the mammalian genome; genes residing in the 5′ regions of two of them, the *Hoxa* and *Hoxd* clusters, have been implicated in regulating skeletal condensation expansion and skeletal elements morphogenesis[34, 35] (Fig. 26–1). Members of the *Hox* clusters are expressed in an anterior–posterior pattern so that the genes located most 3′ are expressed most anteriorly.[36] Deletion or misexpression experiments have shown that the abnormal expression of particular genes in particular sites often causes homeotic transformation, implicating these genes in regulating the shape of limb skeletal elements.[34, 35] In addition to Hox genes, AER and ZPA regulates the expression of *Gli* family members, both targets and transcriptional effectors of Hedgehog signaling. These genes are often ectopically expressed in polydactyly mutants such as extra toes (Xt), a mouse model of *Gli3* inactivation counting as many as eight digits per limb in the homozygous state, suggesting that they control the number of the element formed.[37–39]

AXIAL SKELETON MORPHOGENESIS

The vertebral column originates from somites that are segmented paraxial mesoderm structures lying on each side of the neural tube. These somites compartmentalize into two tissues, dermomyotomes and sclerotomes, the latter forming the vertebrae and ribs. The paired-box transcription factors Pax1 and Pax9 play a critical role in this early process, controlling proper proliferation and condensation of the precartilaginous structures in the sclerotome.[40] Their function would be directly relayed by the bagpipe-related gene Bapx1, whose deficiency causes a vertebral phenotype identical to the one observed in *Pax1* and *Pax9* double mutants.[41, 42]

Although studied in much lesser detail than limb formation, axial skeleton patterning is beginning to be understood. It appears that many pathways at work during the former process are involved in the latter, even if they do not involve identical genes. For instance, Shh controls dorsal–ventral patterning of the somites and the survival of sclerotomal cells.[43, 44] Likewise, as in limbs, initial expansion of the vertebrae anlage appears to be regulated by the receptor tyrosine kinase, *Ror1* and *Ror2*.[32, 33] Lastly, expression of particular *Hox* genes also controls the shape of particular vertebrae, and anterior or posterior shifts in expression or ablation of specific Hox genes leads to vertebral homeotic transformations.[45, 46] Interestingly, such homeotic transformations are also observed upon inactivation of another class of homeobox genes, the caudal-related *Cdx1* and *Cdx2* genes[47, 48] as well as in absence of retinoic acid (RA) signaling.[49–51] These similarities suggest an indirect pathway by which RA regulates Hox genes expression through direct control of Cdx genes.[52]

CRANIOFACIAL MORPHOGENESIS

More than 90 mouse models display skull abnormalities and craniofacial malformations, among the most frequent genetic disorders of the skeleton in humans.[53] This diversity illustrates both the molecular and morphogenetic complexity of head development. In consideration of space limitation, and because several reviews dealing with this topic were published recently,[5, 53, 54] I will only mention a few facts and outline representative examples.

In contrast to the rest of the skeleton, which originates from mesodermal derivatives, formation of the skull depends largely on neural crest cells.[5, 55, 56] Nevertheless, similarities exist in patterning regulation between the skull and the peripheral skeleton. For instance, Shh inactivation causes midline abnormalities of the face of mice and humans, indicating its involvement in cranial axis determination.[44, 57] Likewise, *Pax9* inactivation, as well as the homeodomain-containing transcription factors Dlx5 and Dlx6 inactivations, exhibit craniofacial malformations, suggesting that they contribute to skull patterning.[26, 58] Lastly, an RA–*Hox* genes cascade would play a significant role in controlling this process.[56, 59]

Chondrocyte Differentiation

The study of chondrogenesis has largely benefited from two particularities of this process. First, differentiation of chondrocytes induces significant morphological changes that facilitate the identification of distinct maturational stages. Second, most of the differentiation process is constantly recapitulated in an oriented structure in each skeletal element developing by endochondral ossification: the growth plate cartilage (Fig. 26–2). Cells at the earliest stage of maturation are small; they are located in the most distal area, termed the reserve or resting zone. They are a pool of chondrocyte progenitors. Immediately below this resting zone emerges a proliferative zone, where cells are slightly larger, flatter, and rapidly dividing. The length of these columns of rapidly dividing chondrocytes is a major determinant of bone longitudinal growth. Proliferating chondrocytes express type II collagen and aggrecan; however, the most proximal cells (also called prehypertrophic chondrocytes) express *type II collagen* at a lower level as well as *Indian hedgehog (Ihh)* and the *receptor* for *both parathyroid hormone (PTH)* and *PTH-related peptide (PTHrP)*. The most proximal zone appearing on the growth plate cartilage contains hypertrophic chondrocytes. They express *type X collagen* but not *type II collagen* and eventually undergo apoptosis.

Sox9, a member of the high mobility group (HMG) family of transcription factors is the earliest known molecule to be required for chondrocyte specification. *Sox9* was first identified as the gene inactivated in campomelic dysplasia (CD) patients, a dominant genetic disorder characterized by skeletal malformation and XY sex reversal.[60] Subsequently, Sox9 was found to activate the expression of the type II, type IX, and type XI collagen genes in chondrocytes.[61–64] Mouse genetic studies clarified the role of Sox9 during chondrogenesis.[65–67] They showed that *Sox9–/–* embryonic stem (ES) cells, but not wild-type ES cells, become excluded from the skeletal condensations, indicating that Sox9 is required for their formation. Moreover, teratomas derived from Sox9–/– ES cells, but not from wild-type ES, failed to develop cartilage in mouse chimeras, and Sox9–/– cells are abnormally sensitive to apoptotic signals. Interestingly, although *Sox9* heterozygous mutant mice are phenotypically similar to human CD

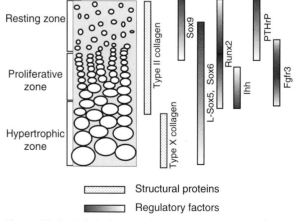

Figure 26–2. *Cell distribution and gene expression at the embryonic growth plate cartilage.*

patients, the severity of the allele insufficiency is more pronounced in mice; other abnormalities, such as expanded hypertrophic zones and premature bone mineralization, also exist in these mutant animals. These data suggest that Sox9, in addition to controlling the initial specification and survival of cells within the precartilaginous condensations, may also prevent chondrocytic hypertrophy. The latter action of Sox9 would be mediated by a PTHrP signaling pathway.[68] Two other HMG family members, L-Sox5 and Sox6, also play key roles during chondrocyte maturation. Both genes were found to be coexpressed with *Sox9* in precartilaginous condensations, but they continued to be expressed in hypertrophic chondrocytes.[69] *Sox5* and *Sox6* have redundant function *in vivo*, and single null mutant mice are virtually normal. However, targeted deletion of both L-Sox5 and Sox6 leads to late embryonic lethality because of generalized chondrodysplasia,[70] demonstrating their essential role in the control of chondrocyte differentiation.

In contrast to this group of activators, NFAT1, a member of the family of nuclear factor of activated T-cells,[71] appears to act as a repressor of chondrocyte differentiation. Indeed, its overexpression in chondrocytic cell lines suppresses the expression of chondrocyte molecular markers, and NFAT1-deficient mice develop ectopic cartilage in the joints.[72] The newly formed cartilage contains ordered and columnar chondrocytes with distinct morphologies and is eventually replaced by bone, recapitulating the process endochondral ossification.[72] FGFs, a class of secreted factors, are also involved in negatively controlling chondrocyte proliferation and differentiation. Because of the large number of FGF members expressed at every step of skeleton formation,[73] it is through the functional analysis of their receptors (FGFRs) that the role of these factors has been best characterized. *Fgfr3* inactivation in mice causes increased chondrocyte proliferation; activating mutations in *Fgfr3* are found in chondrodystrophic patients with a shortened proliferating zone at the growth plate cartilage.[74–76] These observations indicate that one or several FGFs, acting through this receptor, inhibit chondrocyte proliferation. Based on some phenotypical similarities between *Fgfr3*- and *Fgf18*-deficient mice, *Fgf18* was recently proposed to be one of these *Fgfr3* ligands in chondrocytes.[77, 78]

Chondrocyte proliferation and the rate of hypertrophy, the last stage of chondrocyte maturation, is also controlled by a negative feedback loop involving two growth factors, PTHrP and Ihh (Fig. 26–2).[79–81] PTHrP, secreted by the chondrocytes of the perichondrium, signals to the *PTHrP receptor (PPR)* expressed by proliferating chondrocytes to stimulate their proliferation. When escaping the PTHrP spatial range of activity, cells become prehypertrophic; they begin synthesizing Ihh, stop proliferating, and start differentiating in hypertrophic chondrocytes. Accordingly, chondrocyte-specific constitutive expression of *PPR* in mice causes a delay in the conversion of proliferative chondrocyte into hypertrophic chondrocyte, and an activating mutation in the human *PPR* causes Jansen metaphyseal chondrodysplasia, a short-limb dwarfism inherited disorder.[82, 83] Conversely, wild-type

chimeric mice containing *PPR*$^{-/-}$ ES cells showed premature hypertrophy of the latter.[84] The feedback part of this loop is mediated by Ihh. Its secretion by prehypertrophic chondrocytes directs cells of the perichondrium to up-regulate their synthesis of PTHrP, thereby indirectly slowing the pace of chondrocyte hypertrophy. The increase fraction of hypertrophic chondrocytes in *Ihh*-deficient mice confirmed this role.[85] Analysis of these mice as well as of mice harboring the cartilage-specific expression or inactivation of smoothened, a membrane protein required for Ihh signaling, revealed that Ihh has a direct positive activity on chondrocyte proliferation.[85, 86]

Beside this interplay of secreted molecules, one transcription factor—Runx2, formerly termed Cbfa1—has been shown to control hypertrophic differentiation. Runx2 is a transcription factor originally identified for its role as an osteoblast differentiation factor (see the next section). In addition to an absence of osteoblasts, *Runx2*-deficient mice have proximal long bones populated mostly by resting and proliferative chondrocytes, some of them enlarged; but they show no hypertrophic chondrocytes and no *type X collagen* expression.[87, 88] In contrast, targeted overexpression of *Runx2* into nonhypertrophic chondrocytes of wild-type mice or of *Runx2*-deficient mice leads to ectopic endochondral bone formation or specific rescue of the lack of hypertrophic chondrocytes, respectively.[89, 90] This rescue occurs without rescue of the arrest of osteoblast differentiation, indicating that Runx2 control of chondrocyte hypertrophy is independent of its osteoblast differentiation ability.[89]

Lastly, it has been shown that hypertrophic chondrocytes control vascular invasion, a step required for continuation of the endochondral ossification process. Indeed, cartilage resorption by Mmp9 releases VEGF, an angiogenic factor secreted by hypertrophic chondrocytes, which in turn regulates vascular invasion.[91, 92] Recently, the analysis of mice deficient for connective tissue growth factor showed that this factor would be regulating extracellular matrix remodeling and vasculogenesis through its control of VEGF and Mmp9 expression.[93]

Osteoblast Differentiation

In contrast with chondrocyte differentiation, in which all maturational stages are spatially as well as morphologically distinguishable, osteoblast differentiation is not marked by phenotypic changes *in vivo*, and osteoblasts in culture are and remain throughout their differentiation similar to fibroblasts. The only mark of differentiation is slow to appear and lies outside the cell: Only fully mature osteoblasts can produce a matrix that is subsequently mineralized.[94] This absence of morphological characteristics at the cellular level implies that one has to rely on gene expression studies to assess osteoblast differentiation. But here again the osteoblast has a poorly specific genetic program. Most of the proteins expressed by this cell type are also expressed in other cells, notably in fibroblasts. There is only one truly osteoblast-specific structural gene, osteocalcin, which is only expressed by fully differentiated osteoblasts and regulates their function.[95–97] Another particularity of osteoblast differentiation is that the events surrounding its initial occurrence during development do not take place afterward. Indeed, the process by which osteoblast precursors first appear in the bone collar, begin to differentiate, and then migrate within the core of the forming skeletal element along with invading blood vessels cannot be observed once the bones are formed. In the mature skeleton, osteoblast progenitor cells will be spread out within the bone marrow and will differentiate *in situ*.

Runx2 (formerly Cbfa1), was the first transcription factor identified as a regulator of osteoblast differentiation.[98–101] It belongs to a family of transcription factors related to runt, a regulator of neurogenesis and sexual differentiation in *Drosophila*.[102, 103] Runx2 regulates the expression of most of the major genes expressed by osteoblasts, such as *type I collagen, bone sialoprotein,* and *osteopontin*.[98, 104, 105] Importantly, *Runx2* is expressed in every osteoblast progenitor cell, regardless of its embryonic origin and of the condensation future mode of ossification. As such, Runx2 represent the first unifying event during skeletal cell differentiation. Runx2-deficient mice were generated by two groups; although normally patterned, the skeleton of these mice is entirely cartilaginous.[99, 101] The only skeletal elements missing are those formed through intramembranous ossification. At these sites, only a membranous structure exists; because there is no cartilaginous stage in the development of these structures, no cartilaginous scaffold can exist. Histologically, the skeleton of the *Runx2*-deficient mice lacks bone structures; there is no bone matrix and no osteoblasts.[99, 101, 106] Interestingly, *Runx2* heterozygous mutant mice present hypoplastic clavicles and a severe delay of the closure of the fontanelles.[101] These two features are similar to the presentation of a well-characterized human condition called cleidocranial dysplasia,[107] and mutations into the *Runx2* gene have been identified in most cleidocranial dysplasia patients.[108–110] That Runx2 haploinsufficiency results in a significant phenotype further emphasizes its importance during osteoblast differentiation. Recently, mice harboring an inactivation of *Cbf-β*—a small protein without DNA-binding and transcriptional abilities known to interact with Runx1, another Runx factor required for hematopoiesis—lethal only perinatally were analyzed.[111, 112] In contrast to the identical phenotypical abnormalities observed in Runx1-deficient and classic Cbf-β–deficient mice, these mice did not reproduce the skeletal phenotype of the Runx2-deficient mice. Their phenotype was rather similar to *Runx2* haploinsufficiency. This observation and the absence of obvious heterodimerization between Runx2 and Cbf-β *in vitro*[113] indicate that Cbf-β plays an accessory role during osteoblast differentiation.

Osx, a zinc finger-containing nuclear factor, has recently been identified as another regulator of osteoblast differentiation.[114] *Osx* is specifically expressed in osteoblasts, and *Osx*-deficient mice lack osteoblasts. *Osx* is not expressed in Runx2-null mice, yet *Runx2* is expressed normally in Osx-deficient mice, indicating that Osx acts downstream of Runx2.[114]

Besides Cbfa1 and Osx, two broadly expressed members of the Ap1 family of transcription factors, Δ*Fosb* and *fra-1*, have been reported to act as positive regulators for osteoblast differentiation.[115, 116] Δ*Fosb* is an alternative spliced transcript of *Fosb*, lacking Fosb C-terminal 101 amino acids, known to functionally differ from Fosb.[117] Generalized overexpression of Δ*Fosb* in transgenic mice leads to a postnatal osteosclerosis as a result of an increase in osteoblast differentiation.[116] Interestingly, ΔFosb was recently shown to regulate *Runx2* promoter activity in osteoblasts, establishing a functional cascade between these two transcription factors.[118] Mirroring Δ*Fosb* overexpression, forced ubiquitous expression of fra-1 causes a severe bone phenotype.[115]

Secreted molecules have also been shown to control osteoblast differentiation. For instance, in the absence Ihh, *Runx2* expression is not induced in the cells of the bone collar, and osteoblast differentiation is blocked in all skeletal elements formed by endochondral ossification.[85] These observations indicate that Ihh is a determinant of early osteoblast differentiation and suggest that this secreted factor may act through its regulation of Runx2 expression. FGFs have also been implicated in regulating osteoblast differentiation. Indeed, inactivation of *Fgf18* in mice causes a general delay of bone formation affecting skeletal elements forming by intramembranous and endochondral ossification.[77, 78]

REFERENCES

1. Karsenty, G., and Wagner, E.F. (2002). Reaching a genetic and molecular understanding of skeletal development. *Dev. Cell* **2**, 389–406.
2. Hall, B.K., and Miyake T., (2000). All for one and one for all: condensations and the initiation of skeletal development. *Bioesssays* **22**, 138–147.
3. Couly, G.F., Coltey, P.M., and Le Douarin, N.M. (1993). The triple origin of skull in higher vertebrates: a study in quail–chick chimeras. *Development* **117**, 409–429.
4. Kontges, G., and Lumsden, A. (1996). Rhombencephalic neural crest segmentation is preserved throughout craniofacial ontogeny. *Development* **122**, 3229–3242.
5. Helms, J.A., and Schneider, R.A. (2003). Cranial skeletal biology. *Nature* **423**, 326–331.
6. DeLise, A.M., Fischer, L., and Tuan, R.S. (2000). Cellular interactions and signaling in cartilage development. *Osteoarthritis Cartilage* **8**, 309–334.
7. Horton, W.A. (1993). "Cartilage Morphology," Alan R. Liss, New York.
8. Kaufman, J.M., Taelman, P., Vermeulen, A., and Vandeweghe, M. (1992). Bone mineral status in growth hormone-deficient males with isolated and multiple pituitary deficiencies of childhood onset. *J. Clin. Endocrinol. Metab.* **74**, 118–123.
9. Huang, R., Zhi, Q., Schmidt, C., Wilting, J., Brand-Saberi, B., and Christ, B. (2000). Sclerotomal origin of the ribs. *Development* **127**, 527–532.
10. Kardon, G., Campbell, J.K., and Tabin, C.J. (2002). Local extrinsic signals determine muscle and endothelial cell fate and patterning in the vertebrate limb. *Dev. Cell* **3**, 533–545.
11. Cohn, M.J., Izpisua-Belmonte, J.C., Abud, H., Heath, J.K., and Tickle, C. (1995). Fibroblast growth factors induce additional limb development from the flank of chick embryos. *Cell* **80**, 739–746.

12. Crossley, P.H., Minowada, G., MacArthur, C.A., and Martin, G.R. (1996). Roles for Fgf8 in the induction, initiation, and maintenance of chick limb development. *Cell* **84**, 127–136.

13. Rodriguez-Esteban, C., Tsukui, T., Yonei, S., Magallon, J., Tamura, K., and Izpisua Belmonte, J.C. (1999). The T-box genes Tbx4 and Tbx5 regulate limb outgrowth and identity. *Nature* **398**, 814–818.

14. Takeuchi, J.K., Koshiba-Takeuchi, K., Matsumoto, K., Vogel-Hopker, A., Naitoh-Matsuo, M., Ogura, K., Takahashi, N., Yasuda, K., and Ogura, T. (1999). Tbx5 and Tbx4 genes determine the wing–leg identity of limb buds. *Nature* **398**, 810–814.

15. Kawakami, Y., Capdevila, J., Buscher, D., Itoh, T., Rodriguez Esteban, C., and Izpisua Belmonte, J.C. (2001). Wnt signals control FGF-dependent limb initiation and AER induction in the chick embryo. *Cell* **104**, 891–900.

16. Barrow, J.R., Thomas, K.R., Boussadia-Zahui, O., Moore, R., Kemler, R., Capecchi, M.R., and McMahon, A.P. (2003). Ectodermal Wnt3–beta-catenin signaling is required for the establishment and maintenance of the apical ectodermal ridge. *Genes Dev.* **17**, 394–409.

17. Galceran, J., Farinas, I., Depew, M.J., Clevers, H., and Grosschedl, R. (1999). Wnt3a–/– like phenotype and limb deficiency in Lef1(–/–)Tcf1(–/–) mice. *Genes Dev.* **13**, 709–717.

18. Tickle, C., and Munsterberg, A. (2001). Vertebrate limb development: the early stages in chick and mouse. *Curr. Opin. Genet. Dev.* **11**, 476–481.

19. Lewandoski, M., Sun, X., and Martin, G.R. (2000). Fgf8 signaling from the AER is essential for normal limb development. *Nat. Genet.* **26**, 460–463.

20. Moon, A.M., and Capecchi, M.R. (2000). Fgf8 is required for outgrowth and patterning of the limbs. *Nat. Genet.* **26**, 455–459.

21. Mariani, F.V., and Martin, G.R. (2003). Deciphering skeletal patterning: clues from the limb. *Nature* **423**, 319–325.

22. Chiang, C., Litingtung, Y., Harris, M.P., Simandl, B.K., Li, Y., Beachy, P.A., and Fallon, J.F. (2001). Manifestation of the limb prepattern: limb development in the absence of Sonic hedgehog function. *Dev. Biol.* **236**, 421–435.

23. Riddle, R.D., R.L. Johnson, E. Laufer and C. Tabin. (1993). Sonic hedgehog mediates the polarizing activity of the ZPA. *Cell* **75**, 1401–1416.

24. Khokha, M.K., Hsu, D., Brunet, L.J., Dionne, M.S., and Harland, R.M. (2003). Gremlin is the BMP antagonist required for maintenance of Shh and FGF signals during limb patterning. *Nat. Genet.* **34**, 303–307.

25. Pizette, S., and Niswander, L. (1999). BMPs negatively regulate structure and function of the limb apical ectodermal ridge. *Development* **126**, 883–894.

26. Robledo, R.F., Rajan, L., Li, X., and Lufkin, T. (2002). The Dlx5 and Dlx6 homeobox genes are essential for craniofacial, axial, and appendicular skeletal development. *Genes Dev.* **16**, 1089–1101.

27. Summerbell, D., and Wolpert, L. (1972). Cell density and cell division in the early morphogenesis of the chick wing. *Nat. New. Biol.* **239**, 24–26.

28. Tavella, S., Raffo, P., Tacchetti, C., Cancedda, R., and Castagnola, P. (1994). NCAM and N-cadherin expression during *in vitro* chondrogenesis. *Exp. Cell Res.* **215**, 354–362.

29. Cremer, H., Lange, R., Christoph, A., Plomann, M., Vopper, G., Roes, J., Brown, R., Baldwin, S., Kraemer, P., Scheff, S., *et al.* (1994). Inactivation of the NCAM gene in mice results in size reduction of the olfactory bulb and deficits in spatial learning. *Nature* **367**, 455–459.

30. Gotz, W., Fischer, G., and Herken, R. (1991). Lectin binding pattern in the embryonal and early fetal human vertebral column. *Anat. Embryol. (Berl.)* **184**, 345–353.

31. ten Berge, D., Brouwer, A., Korving, J., Martin, J.F., and Meijlink, F. (1998). Prx1 and Prx2 in skeletogenesis: roles in the craniofacial region, inner ear, and limbs. *Development* **125**, 3831–3842.

32. DeChiara, T.M., Kimble, R.B., Poueymirou, W.T., Rojas, J., Masiakowski, P., Valenzuela, D.M., and Yancopoulos, G.D. (2000). Ror2, encoding a receptor-like tyrosine kinase, is required for cartilage and growth plate development. *Nat. Genet.* **24**, 271–274.

33. Nomi, M., Oishi, I., Kani, S., Suzuki, H., Matsuda, T., Yoda, A., Kitamura, M., Itoh, K., Takeuchi, S., Takeda, K., Akira, S., Ikeya, M., Takada, S., and Minami, Y. (2001). Loss of mRor1 enhances the heart and skeletal abnormalities in mRor2-deficient mice: redundant and pleiotropic functions of mRor1 and mRor2 receptor tyrosine kinases. *Mol. Cell Biol.* **21**, 8329–8335.

34. Zakany, J., and Duboule, D. (1999). Hox genes in digit development and evolution. *Cell Tissue Res.* **296**, 19–25.

35. Goodman, F.R. (2002). Limb malformations and the human Hox genes. *Am. J. Med. Genet.* **112**, 256–265.

36. Nelson, C.E., Morgan, B.A., Burke, A.C., Laufer, E., DiMambro, E., Murtaugh, L.C., Gonzales, E., Tessarollo, L., Parada, L.F., and Tabin, C. (1996). Analysis of Hox gene expression in the chick limb bud. *Development* **122**, 1449–1466.

37. Buscher, D., and Ruther, U. (1998). Expression profile of Gli family members and Shh in normal and mutant mouse limb development. *Dev. Dyn.* **211**, 88–96.

38. Litingtung, Y., Dahn, R.D., Li, Y., Fallon, J.F., and Chiang, C. (2002). Shh and Gli3 are dispensable for limb skeleton formation but regulate digit number and identity. *Nature* **418**, 979–983.

39. te Welscher, P., Zuniga, A., Kuijper, S., Drenth, T., Goedemans, H.J., Meijlink, F., and Zeller, R. (2002). Progression of vertebrate limb development through Shh-mediated counteraction of Gli3. *Science* **298**, 827–830.

40. Peters, H., Wilm, E., Sakai, N., Imai, K., Maas, R., and Balling, R. (1999). Pax1 and Pax9 synergistically regulate vertebral column development. *Development* **126**, 5399–5408.

41. Tribioli, C., and Lufkin, T. (1999). The murine Bapx1 homeobox gene plays a critical role in embryonic development of the axial skeleton and spleen. *Development* **126**, 5699–5711.

42. Rodrigo, I., Hill, R.E., Balling, R., Munsterberg, A., and Imai, K. (2003). Pax1 and Pax9 activate Bapx1 to induce chondrogenic differentiation in the sclerotome. *Development* **130**, 473–482.

43. Johnson, R.L., Laufer, E., Riddle, R.D., and Tabin, C. (1994). Ectopic expression of Sonic hedgehog alters dorsal–ventral patterning of somites. *Cell* **79**, 1165–1173.

44. Chiang, C., Litingtung, Y., Lee, E., Young, K.E., Corden, J.L., Westphal, H., and Beachy, P.A. (1996). Cyclopia and defective axial patterning in mice lacking Sonic hedgehog gene function. *Nature* **383**, 407–413.

45. St. Jacques, B., and McMahon, A.P. (1996). Early mouse development: lessons from gene targeting. *Curr. Opin. Genet. Dev.* **6**, 439–444.

46. Favier, B., and Dolle, P. (1997). Developmental functions of mammalian Hox genes. *Mol. Hum. Reprod.* **3**, 115–131.

47. Subramanian, V., Meyer, B.I., and Gruss, P. (1995). Disruption of the murine homeobox gene Cdx1 affects axial skeletal identities by altering the mesodermal expression domains of Hox genes. *Cell* **83**, 641–653.

48. Chawengsaksophak, K., James, R., Hammond, V.E., Kontgen, F., and Beck, F. (1997). Homeosis and intestinal tumors in Cdx2 mutant mice. *Nature* **386**, 84–87.

49. Lohnes, D., Kastner, P., Dierich, A., Mark, M., LeMeur, M., and Chambon, P. (1993). Function of retinoic acid receptor gamma in the mouse. *Cell* **73**, 643–658.

50. Lohnes, D., Mark, M., Mendelsohn, C., Dolle, P., Dierich, A., Gorry, P., Gansmuller, A., and Chambon, P. (1994). Function of the retinoic acid receptors (RARs) during development (1) craniofacial and skeletal abnormalities in RAR double mutants. *Development* **120**, 2723–2748.

51. Kaiser, M.E., Merrill, R.A., Stein, A.C., Breburda, E., and Clagett-Dame, M. (2003). Vitamin A deficiency in the late gastrula stage rat embryo results in a one to two vertebral anteriorization that extends throughout the axial skeleton. *Dev. Biol.* **257**, 14–29.

52. Houle, M., Prinos, P., Iulianella, A., Bouchard, N., and Lohnes, D. (2000). Retinoic acid regulation of Cdx1: an indirect mechanism for retinoids and vertebral specification. *Mol. Cell Biol.* **20**, 6579–6586.

53. Wilkie, A.O., and Morriss-Kay, G.M. (2001). Genetics of craniofacial development and malformation. *Nat. Rev. Genet.* **2**, 458–468.

54. Zelzer, E., and Olsen, B.R. (2003). The genetic basis for skeletal diseases. *Nature* **423**, 343–348.

55. Chai, Y., Jiang, X., Ito, Y., Bringas, P., Jr., Han, J., Rowitch, D.H., Soriano, P., McMahon, A.P., and Sucov, H.M. (2000). Fate of the mammalian cranial neural crest during tooth and mandibular morphogenesis. *Development* **127**, 1671–1679.

56. Jiang, X., Iseki, S., Maxson, R.E., Sucov, H.M., and Morriss-Kay, G.M. (2002). Tissue origins and interactions in the mammalian skull vault. *Dev. Biol.* **241**, 106–116.

57. Roessler, E., Belloni, E., Gaudenz, K., Jay, P., Berta, P., Scherer, S.W., Tsui, L.C., and Muenke, M. (1996). Mutations in the human Sonic hedgehog gene cause holoprosencephaly. *Nat. Genet.* **14**, 357–360.

58. Peters, H., Neubuser, A., Kratochwill, K., and Balling, R. (1998). Pax9-deficient mice lack pharyngeal pouch derivatives and teeth and exhibit craniofacial and limb abnormalities. *Genes Dev.* **12**, 2735–2747.

59. Morriss-Kay, G.M., and Ward, S.J. (1999). Retinoids and mammalian development. *Int. Rev. Cytol.* **188**, 73–131.

60. Foster, J.W., Dominguez-Steglich, M.A., Guioli, S., Kowk, G., Weller, P.A., Stevanovic, M., Weissenbach, J., Mansour, S., Young, I.D., Goodfellow, P.N., *et al.* (1994). Campomelic dysplasia and autosomal sex reversal caused by mutations in an SRY-related gene. *Nature* **372**, 525–530.

61. Bell, D.M., Leung, K.K., Wheatley, S.C., Ng, L.J., Zhou, S., Ling, K.W., Sham, M.H., Koopman, P., Tam, P.P., and Cheah, K.S. (1997). Sox9 directly regulates the type II collagen gene. *Nat. Genet.* **16**, 174–178.

62. Lefebvre, V., Huang, W., Harley, V.R., Goodfellow, P.N., and de Crombrugghe, B. (1997). Sox9 is a potent activator of the chondrocyte-specific enhancer of the pro alpha 1(II) collagen gene. *Mol. Cell Biol.* **17**, 2336–2346.

63. Bridgewater, L.C., Lefebvre, V., and de Crombrugghe, B. (1998). Chondrocyte-specific enhancer elements in the Col11a2 gene resemble the Col2a1 tissue-specific enhancer. *J. Biol. Chem.* **273**, 14,998–15,006.

64. Zhang, P., Jimenez, S.A., and Stokes, D.G. (2003). Regulation of human Col9a1 gene expression. Activation of the proximal promoter region by Sox9. *J. Biol. Chem.* **278**, 117–123.

65. Bi, W., Deng, J.M., Zhang, Z., Behringer, R.R., and de Crombrugghe, B. (1999). Sox9 is required for cartilage formation. *Nat. Genet.* **22**, 85–89.

66. Bi, W., Huang, W.H., Whitworth, D.J., Deng, J.M., Zhang, Z., Behringer, R., and de Crombrugghe, B. (2001). Haploinsufficiency of Sox9 results in defective cartilage primordia and premature skeletal mineralization. *Proc. Natl. Acad. Sci. U. S. A.* **98**, 6698–6703.

67. Akiyama, H., Chaboissier, M.C., Martin, J.F., Schedl, A., and de Crombrugghe, B.. (2002). The transcription factor Sox9 has essential roles in successive steps of the chondrocyte differentiation pathway and is required for expression of Sox5 and Sox6. *Genes Dev.* **16**, 2813–2828.

68. Huang, W., Chung, U.I., Kronenberg, H.M., and de Crombrugghe, B. (2001). The chondrogenic transcription factor Sox9 is a target of signaling by the parathyroid hormone-related peptide in the growth plate of endochondral bones. *Proc. Natl. Acad. Sci. U. S. A.* **98**, 160–165.

69. Lefebvre, V., Ping, L., and de Crombrugghe, B. (1998). A new long form of Sox5 (L-Sox5), Sox6 and Sox9 are coexpressed in chondrogenesis and cooperatively activate the type II collagen gene. *EMBO J.* **17**, 5718–5733.

70. Smits, P., Li, P., Mandel, J., Zhang, Z., Deng, J.M., Behringer, R., de Crombrugghe, B., and Lefebvre, V. (2001). The transcription factors L-Sox5 and Sox6 are essential for cartilage formation. *Dev. Cell* **1**, 277–290.

71. Crabtree, G.R., and Olson, E.N. (2002). NFAT signaling: choreographing the social lives of cells. *Cell* **109 (Suppl.),** S67–79.

72. Ranger, A.M., Gerstenfeld, L.C., Wang, J., Kon, T., Bae, H., Gravallese, E.M., Glimcher, M.J., and Glimcher, L.H. (2000). The nuclear factor of activated T-cells (NFAT) transcription factor NFATp (NFATc2) is a repressor of chondrogenesis. *J. Exp. Med.* **191**, 9–22.

73. Ornitz, D.M., and Marie, P.J. (2002). FGF signaling pathways in endochondral and intramembranous bone development and human genetic disease. *Genes Dev.* **16**, 1446–1465.

74. Deng, C., Wynshaw-Boris, A., Zhou, F., Kuo, A., and Leder, P. (1996). Fibroblast growth factor receptor-3 is a negative regulator of bone growth. *Cell* **84**, 911–921.

75. Colvin, J.S., Bohne, B.A., Harding, G.W., McEwen, D.G., and Ornitz, D.M. (1996). Skeletal overgrowth and deafness in mice lacking fibroblast growth factor receptor-3. *Nature Genet.* **12**, 390–397.

76. Naski, M.C., Colvin, J.S., Coffin, J.D., and Ornitz, D.M. (1998). Repression of hedgehog signaling and Bmp4 expression in growth plate cartilage by fibroblast growth factor receptor-3. *Development* **125**, 4977–4988.

77. Liu, Z., Xu, J., Colvin, J.S., and Ornitz, D.M. (2002). Coordination of chondrogenesis and osteogenesis by fibroblast growth factor 18. *Genes & Development* **16**, 859–869.

78. Ohbayashi, N., Shibayama, M., Kurotaki, Y., Imanishi, M., Fujimori, T., Itoh, N., and Takada, S. (2002). Fgf18 is required for osteogenesis and chondrogenesis in mice. *Genes Dev.* **16**, 870–879.

79. Lanske, B., Karaplis, A.C., Lee, K., Luz, A., Vortkamp, A., Pirro, A., Karperien, M., Defize, L.H., Ho, C., Mulligan, R.C., Abou-Samra, A.B., Juppner, H., Segre, G.V., and Kronenberg, H.M. (1996). PTH–PTHrP receptor in early development and Indian hedgehog-regulated bone growth. *Science* **273**, 663–666.

80. Vortkamp, A., Lee, K., Lanske, B., Segre, G.V., Kronenberg, H.M., and Tabin, C.J. (1996). Regulation of rate of cartilage differentiation by Indian hedgehog and PTH-related protein. *Science* **273**, 613–622.

81. Kronenberg, H.M. (2003). Developmental regulation of the growth plate. *Nature* **423**, 332–336.

82. Schipani, E., Kruse, K., and Juppner, H. (1995). A constitutively active mutant PTH-PTHrP receptor in Jansen-type metaphyseal chondrodysplasia. *Science* **268**, 98–100.

83. Schipani, E., Lanske, B., Hunzelman, J., Luz, A., Kovacs, C.S., Lee, K., Pirro, A., Kronenberg, H.M., and Juppner, H. (1997). Targeted expression of constitutively active receptors for parathyroid hormone and parathyroid hormone-related peptide delays endochondral bone formation and rescues mice that lack parathyroid hormone-related peptide. *Proc. Natl. Acad. Sci. U. S. A.* **94**, 13,689–13,694.

84. Chung, U.I., Lanskem B., Lee, K., Li, E., and Kronenberg, H.M. (1998). The parathyroid hormone–parathyroid hormone-related peptide receptor coordinates endochondral bone development by directly controlling chondrocyte differentiation. *Proc. Natl. Acad. Sci. U. S. A.* **95**, 13,030–13,035.

85. St. Jacques, B., Hammerschmidt, M., and McMahon, A.P. (1999). Indian hedgehog signaling regulates proliferation and differentiation of chondrocytes and is essential for bone formation. *Genes Dev.* **13**, 2072–2086.

86. Long, F., Schipani, E., Asahara, H., Kronenberg, H., and Montminy, M. (2001). The CREB family of activators is required for endochondral bone development. *Development* **128**, 541–550.

87. Inada, M., Yasui, T., Nomura, S., Miyake, S., Deguchi, K., Himeno, M., Sato, M., Yamagiwa, H., Kumura, T., and Yasui, N. (1999). Maturational disturbance of chondrocytes in Cbfa1-deficient mice. *Dev. Dyn.* **214**, 279–290.

88. Kim, I.S., Otto, F., Zabel, B., and Mundlos, S. (1999). Regulation of chondrocyte differentiation by Cbfa1. *Mech. Dev.* **80**, 159–170.

89. Takeda, S., Bonnamy, J.P., Owen, M.J., Ducy, P., and Karsenty, G. (2001). Continuous expression of Cbfa1 in nonhypertrophic chondrocytes uncovers its ability to induce hypertrophic chondrocyte differentiation and partially rescues Cbfa1-deficient mice. *Genes Dev.* **15**, 467–481.

90. Ueta, C., Iwamoto, M., Kanatani, N., Yoshida, C., Liu, Y., Enomoto-Iwamoto, M., Ohmori, T., Enomoto, H., Nakata, K., Takada, K., Kurisu, K., and Komori, T. (2001). Skeletal malformations caused by overexpression of Cbfa1 or its dominant negative form in chondrocytes. *J. Cell Biol.* **153**, 87–100.

91. Vu, T.H., Shipley, J.M., Bergers, G., Berger, J.E., Helms, J.A., Hanahan, D., Shapiro, S.D., Senior, R.M., and Werb, Z. (1998). MMP-9-gelatinase-B is a key regulator of growth plate angiogenesis and apoptosis of hypertrophic chondrocytes. *Cell* **93**, 411–422.

92. Gerber, H.P., Vu, T.H., Ryan, A.M., Kowalski, J., Werb, Z., and Ferrara, N. (1999). Vegf couples hypertrophic cartilage remodeling, ossification, and angiogenesis during endochondral bone formation. *Nat. Med.* **5**, 623–628.

93. Ivkovic, S., Yoon, B.S., Popoff, S.N., Safadi, F.F., Libuda, D.E., Stephenson, R.C., Daluiski, A., and Lyons, K.M. (2003). Connective tissue growth factor coordinates chondrogenesis and angiogenesis during skeletal development. *Development* **130**, 2779–2791.

94. Aubin, J.E. (1998). Advances in the osteoblast lineage. *Biochem. Cell Biol.* **76**, 899–910.

95. Hauschka, P.V., and Wians, F.H., Jr. (1989). Osteocalcin-hydroxyapatite interaction in the extracellular organic matrix of bone. *Anat. Rec.* **224**, 180–188.

96. Desbois, C., Hogue, D.A., and Karsenty, G. (1994). The mouse osteocalcin gene cluster contains three genes with two separate spatial and temporal patterns of expression. *J. Biol. Chem.* **269**, 1183–1190.

97. Ducy, P., Desbois, C., Boyce, B., Pinero, G., Story, B., Dunstan, C., Smith, E., Bonadio, J., Goldstein, S., Gundberg, C., Bradley, A., and Karsenty, G. (1996). Increased bone formation in osteocalcin-deficient mice. *Nature* **382**, 448–452.

98. Ducy, P., Zhang, R., Geoffroy, V., Ridall, A.L., and Karsenty, G. (1997). Osf2-Cbfa1: a transcriptional activator of osteoblast differentiation. *Cell* **89**, 747–754.

99. Komori, T., Yagi, H., Nomura, S., Yamaguchi, A., Sasaki, K., Deguchi, K., Shimizu, Y., Bronson, R.T., Gao, Y.H., Inada, M., Sato, M., Okamoto, R., Kitamura, Y., Yoshiki, S., and Kishimoto, T. (1997). Targeted disruption of Cbfa1 results in a complete lack of bone formation owing to maturational arrest of osteoblasts. *Cell* **89**, 755–764.

100. Mundlos, S., and Olsen, B.R. (1997). Diseases of the skeleton—Part I: Molecular insights into skeletal development—Transcription factors and signaling pathways. *FASEB J.* **11**, 125–132.

101. Otto, F., Thornell, A.P., Crompton, T., Denzel, A., Gilmour, K.C., Rosewell, I.R., Stamp, G.W., Beddington, R.S., Mundlos, S., Olsen, B.R., Selby, P.B., and Owen, M.J. (1997). Cbfa1, a candidate gene for cleidocranial dysplasia syndrome, is essential for osteoblast differentiation and bone development. *Cell* **89**, 765–771.

102. Duffy, J.B., and Gergen, J.P. (1991). The *Drosophila* segmentation gene runt acts as a position-specific numerator element necessary for the uniform expression of the sex-determining gene sex-lethal. *Genes Dev.* **5**, 2176–2187.

103. Gergen, J.P., and Wieschaus, E. (1986). Dosage requirements for runt in the segmentation of *Drosophila* embryos. *Cell* **45**, 289–299.

104. Ducy, P., Starbuck, M., Priemel, M., Shen, J., Pinero, G., Geoffroy, V., Amling, M., and Karsenty, G. (1999). A Cbfa1-dependent genetic pathway controls bone formation beyond embryonic development. *Genes Dev.* **13**, 1025–1036.

105. Kern, B., Shen, J., Starbuck, M., and Karsenty, G. (2001). Cbfa1 contributes to the osteoblast-specific expression of type I collagen genes. *J. Biol. Chem.* **276**, 7101–7107.

106. Hoshi, K., Komori, T., and Ozawa, H. (1999). Morphological characterization of skeletal cells in Cbfa1-deficient mice. *Bone* **25**, 639–651.

107. Sillence, D.O., Ritchie, H.E., and Selby, P.B. (1987). Animal model: skeletal anomalies in mice with cleidocranial dysplasia. *Am. J. Med. Genet.* **27**, 75–85.

108. Lee, B., Thirunavukkarasu, K., Zhou, L., Pastore, L., Baldini, A., Hecht, J., Geoffroy, V., Ducy, P., and Karsenty, G. (1997). Missense mutations abolishing DNA binding of the osteoblast-specific transcription factor Osf2–Cbfa1 in cleidocranial dysplasia. *Nat. Genet.* **16**, 307–310.

109. Mundlos, S., Otto, F., Mundlos, C., Mulliken, J.B., Aylsworth, A.S., Albright, S., Lindhout, D., Cole, W.G., Henn, W., Knoll, J.H., Owen, M.J., Mertelsmann, R., Zabel, B.U., and Olsen, B.R. (1997). Mutations involving the transcription factor Cbfa1 cause cleidocranial dysplasia. *Cell* **89**, 773–779.

110. Ducy, P. (2000). Cbfa1: a molecular switch in osteoblast biology. *Dev. Dyn.* **19**, 461–471.

111. Miller, J., Horner, A., Stacy, T., Lowrey, C., Lian, J.B., Stein, G., Nuckolls, G.H., and Speck, N.A. (2002). The core-binding factor beta subunit is required for bone formation and hematopoietic maturation. *Nat. Genet.* **32**, 645–649.

112. Yoshida, C.A., Furuichi, T., Fujita, T., Fukuyama, R., Kanatani, N., Kobayashi, S., Satake, M., Takada, K., and Komori, T. (2002).

Core-binding factor beta interacts with Runx2 and is required for skeletal development. *Nat. Genet.* **32,** 633–638.

113. Thirunavukkararsu, K., Mahajan, M., McLarren, K.W., Stifani, S., and Karsenty, G. (1998). Two domains unique to the osteoblast-specific transcription factor Osf2–Cbfa1 contribute to its trans-activation function and its inability to heterodimerize with Cbf-β. *Mol. Cell Biol.* **18,** 4197–4208.

114. Nakashima, K., Zhou, X., Kunkel, G., Zhang, Z., Deng, J.M., Behringer, R.R., and de Crombrugghe, B. (2002). The novel zinc finger-containing transcription factor osterix is required for osteoblast differentiation and bone formation. *Cell* **108,** 17–29.

115. Jochum, W., David, J.P., Elliott, C., Wutz, A., Plenk, H., Jr., Matsuo, K., and Wagner, E.F. (2000). Increased bone formation and osteosclerosis in mice overexpressing the transcription factor fra-1. *Nat. Med.* **6,** 980–984.

116. Sabatakos, G., Sims, N.A., Chen, J., Aoki, K., Kelz, M.B., Amling, M., Bouali, Y., Mukhopadhyay, K., Ford, K., Nestler, E.J., and Baron, R. (2000). Overexpression of delta Fosb transcription factor(s) increases bone formation and inhibits adipogenesis. *Nat. Med.* **6,** 985–990.

117. Mumberg, D., Lucibello, F.C., Schuermann, M., and Muller, R. (1991). Alternative splicing of Fosb transcripts results in differentially expressed mRNAs encoding functionally antagonistic proteins. *Genes Dev.* **5,** 1212–1223.

118. Zambotti, A., Makhluf, H., Shen, J., and Ducy, P. (2002). Characterization of an osteoblast-specific enhancer element in the Cbfa1 gene. *J. Biol. Chem.* **277,** 41,497–41,506.

27

Osteoclast Lineage

Toshiyuki Yamane, Hiromi Okuyama, Motokazu Tsuneto, Hiroaki Hemmi, Hidetoshi Yamazaki, and Shin-Ichi Hayashi

Introduction

Osteoclasts are hematopoietic cells that have bone resorbing activity and participate in bone remodeling and bone marrow formation. Mature functional osteoclasts are large multinuclear cells consisting of multiple osteoclasts fused with each other. Studies of spontaneously arising and gene-targeted osteopetrotic mice have identified molecules essential for osteoclastogenesis. The localization and phylogenetics of osteoclasts are thought to be strictly regulated because these cells are only detected in association with bone.

Since embryonic stem (ES) cells have the potential to differentiate into all cell lineages, it should be possible to derive any cell lineage by appropriate induction of ES cells in culture. In vitro studies allow us to manipulate the process of embryonic development and to determine exactly what is happening throughout the entire process of cell differentiation. Moreover, if embryo-like structures could be derived from single ES cells, not only the temporal appearance but also the spatial location of osteoclasts could be studied. Here, we review the biological features of osteoclast development and show our results obtained using ES cell cultures.

Osteoclast Biology

OSTEOCLAST LINEAGE

Osteoclasts, derived from hematopoietic stem cells, participate in bone remodeling and form bone marrow cavities through their bone resorbing activity.[1–4] The precursors share their characteristics with the precursors of monocytic lineage cells, such as macrophages and dendritic cells. Osteoclasts specifically express tartrate-resistant acid phosphatase (TRAP), calcitonin receptor, cathepsin K, and carbonic anhydrase II.[2] They undergo cell fusion with each other, producing large multinucleated cells containing more than 100 nuclei in some cases, and tightly attach to and resorb bone matrices.[1]

Osteoclasts are located on endosteal bone surfaces and the periosteal surface beneath the periosteum, and few are observed in locations without bone.[1,3] A lack of functional osteoclasts results in osteopetrosis, also called "marble bone disease," in which bone marrow cavities are reduced and tooth eruption does not occur.

MOLECULES ESSENTIAL FOR OSTEOCLAST DEVELOPMENT

Analyses of osteopetrotic mice have allowed the identification of molecules essential for generation of the osteoclast lineage (Table 27–1). Especially, two hematopoietic cytokines, macrophage colony-stimulating factor (M-CSF) and receptor activator of NF-κB ligand (RANKL, also named OPGL, ODF, and TRANCE),[5,6] play critical roles in osteoclast development. Mice with mutations in the gene encoding M-CSF, namely $Csf1^{op}/Csf1^{op}$ mice,[7] or in the gene encoding its receptor, Fms, namely $Csf1r$-KO (gene-disrupted) mice,[8] carry severe osteopetrosis. The M-CSF signaling may function in cell survival, because $Csf1^{op}/Csf1^{op}$ mice carrying a $Bcl2$ transgene (Tg) are cured of osteopetrosis.[9]

Mice with gene disruption of RANKL (Tnfsf11), classified in the tumor necrosis factor (TNF) superfamily, and its receptor, RANK (Tnfrsf11a), show identical osteopetrotic phenotypes.[10,11] Tg mice overexpressing a decoy receptor for RANKL, osteoprotegerin (OPG, also named OCIF; Tnfrsf11b) also harbor osteopetrosis.[12–14]

Molecules acting downstream of RANKL/RANK signaling are known to include TRAF6, NF-κB, mitogen-activated protein kinase (MAPK), and Fos, Fra-1, and Fra-2 (Table 27–1). In vitro analysis showed that the addition of inhibitors for p38 and Erk in the MAPK pathway suppresses osteoclastogenesis. Moreover, PU.1-null and dominant-negative MITF mutant ($Mitf^{mi}$) mice carry osteopetrosis. Anti-E-cadherin antibody inhibits cell fusion of osteoclasts. After cell fusion, bone resorption requires Src function.[15] Recently it was reported that lack of atypical protein kinase C (PKC) scaffold protein (Sqstm1/p62) and nuclear factor of activated T-cells, cytoplasmic, calcineurin-dependent 1 (NF-Atc1/NFAT2) resulted in osteoporosis.[16,17]

ENVIRONMENT FOR OSTEOCLAST DEVELOPMENT

Fms and RANK are expressed simultaneously on osteoclast precursor cells at particular differentiation stages. Arai et al.[18] showed that osteoclast precursors in bone marrow develop according to the following sequence: Kit+ Fms− Mac-1^{dull} multipotent cells express Fms, and subsequently they lose Kit expression and become Fms+ RANK+ Mac-1+ precursors. M-CSF, RANKL, and OPG are produced by osteoblasts

TABLE 27–1
Osteopetrotic Mice

Mutated Genes	Products	Mice	Affected Cells
Csf1	M-CSF: macrophage colony-stimulating factor	op	Stromal cells
Csf1r	M-CSF receptor–Fms	KO	Osteoclasts
Tnfsf11	RANKL: receptor activator of NF-κB ligand	KO	Stromal cells
Tnfrsf11a	RANK: receptor activator of NF-κB	KO	Osteoclasts
Tnfrsf11b	OPG: osteoprotegerin	TG	Stromal cells
Traf6	TRAF6: TNF receptor-associated factor 6	KO	Osteoclasts
Fos	Fos	KO	Osteoclasts
Fosl1	Fra-1: Fos-like antigen 1	KO	Osteoclasts
Fosl2	Fra-2: Fos-like antigen 2	KO	Osteoclasts
Src	Src	KO	Osteoclasts
Sfpi1	PU.1: SFFV proviral integration 1	KO	Osteoclasts
Mitf	MITF: microphthalmia-associated transcription factor	mi	Osteoclasts
Nfkb1, Nfkb2	NF-κB p50, p52	KO	Osteoclasts
Atp6i	H+ transporting (vacuolar proton pump) member I	oc	Stromal cells?
Ostm1	osteopetrosis associated transmembrane protein 1	gl	Osteoclasts
Acp5	TRAP: tartrate-resistant acid phosphatase	KO	Osteoclasts
Lifr	LIFR: leukemia inhibitory factor receptor	KO	Osteoclasts
Sqstm1	sequestosome 1, atypical PKC scaffold protein (p62)	KO	Osteoclasts
Nfatc1	NF-ATc1: nuclear factor of activated T-cells, cytoplasmic, calcineurin-dependent 1	KO	Osteoclasts

KO, gene-disrupted; TG, overexpressed.

and cloned stromal cells.[2,15] M-CSF is constitutively expressed, but RANKL and OPG expression is regulated by ligands for nuclear factors, parathyroid hormones (PTH and PTHrP), prostaglandins, interleukins, and cytokines.[2–4] Osteoblasts or stromal cells regulate osteoclastogenesis positively and negatively.

The phenotypes of two types of boneless KO mice, namely, runt-related transcription factor 2 (Runx2, also named Cbfal) and osterix (Osx)-gene KO mice, have yielded a key insight into osteoclast development. The transcription factor Runx2 regulates Osx expression. Therefore, Runx2(−/−) mice lack Osx-expressing cells, but Osx(−/−) mice contain Runx2-expressing cells. Runx2(−/−) but not Osx(−/−) mice lack osteoclasts in vivo,[19,20] whereas osteoclast precursors are present in Runx2(−/−) embryos. In vivo osteoclast development requires bone tissues, suggesting that the "bone" for osteoclasts is the cells expressing the Runx2 gene.

Recently, it was reported that T-cells also produce RANKL; for instance, the deterioration of rheumatoid arthritis caused by viral and bacterial infection is related to the production of RANKL by activated T-cells in the joint.[21] Myeloma cells induce RANKL expression in bone marrow stromal cells, and direct RANKL expression by myeloma cells may contribute to enhanced osteoclastogenesis in the bone microenvironment in myeloma bone disease.

Furthermore, myeloma cells inhibit the production and induce the degradation of OPG.[22]

BONE MARROW FORMATION

Phylogenetically, the osteoclast lineage first appears in Osteichthyes (bony fishes) among the vertebrates. Zebra fish in which the Fms homologue is deleted lack osteoclasts,[23] indicating that the mechanisms of osteoclastogenesis in bony fishes may be equivalent to those in mammals. Although it is not clear whether RANKL/RANK homologues are present in bony fishes, similar signaling pathways must be present because RANK shares a signaling pathway with Toll-like receptors (TLRs), which are conserved not only in vertebrates but also in invertebrates.[15]

Bone marrow cavities are rudimentary in aquatic animals, such as Xenopus (an amphibian) and Trichechiformes (a mammal). This suggests that the presence of osteoclasts is not always linked with bone marrow formation. Intramarrow hematopoiesis first appears in amphibians. The marrow in the land amphibian Rana is an active site for lympho-hematopoiesis, whereas that in aquatic amphibians such as Xenopus is inefficient. The hematopoiesis for the myeloid and erythroid lineages is initiated in rudimentary marrow cavities, and extending the cavities generates B-lymphopoiesis. Bone marrow B-lymphopoiesis is absent in osteopetrotic mice.[24]

To construct the microenvironment for B-lymphopoiesis, sufficient hematopoietic space in the bone marrow may be needed. Therefore, only the bone marrow in land vertebrates produces the B-cell lineage (Table 27–2).

Many menopausal women develop osteoporosis, which occurs because of excessive bone resorption, compared with osteogenesis. Hormonal regulation of B-lymphopoiesis and osteoclastogenesis has been reported. Since estrogen and its derivatives inhibit B-lymphopoiesis, menopausal women have increased B-lymphopoiesis in the bone marrow.[25] Early B-lineage cells are one of the sources of RANKL, and the production of RANKL by B-lineage cells may accelerate bone resorption. Intramarrow B-lymphopoiesis is regulated by the volume of hematopoietic bone marrow cavity, as described previously,[24] and osteoclast differentiation is regulated by B-lineage cell products. Although a most RANKL and M-CSF may be supplied from osteoblasts or stromal cells, the possible relationship between the B- and osteoclast lineages is noteworthy.

TISSUES IN WHICH OSTEOCLAST PRECURSORS ARE PRESENT

Mature osteoclasts, multinucleated TRAP+ cells that resorb bone matrices, are only observed in bone tissues *in vivo*. However, cells that have the potential to differentiate into mature osteoclasts are widely distributed throughout the body, including in the bone marrow, spleen, liver, lung, peritoneal cavity, and peripheral blood.[2,3] During embryonic development, yolk sacs, the aorta–gonad–mesonephros region, and fetal livers contain these precursor cells,[26] and mature TRAP+ osteoclasts are already observed on embryonic day (E) 14. As there are M-CSF and RANKL-producing cells other than osteoblasts, inhibitory molecules such as OPG may regulate osteoclastogenesis *in vivo*. Disruption of the OPG (*Tnfrsf11b*) gene results in severe osteoporosis and atherosclerosis caused by a significant increase of osteoclasts; however, osteoclasts are only present in the bone tissues,[27] suggesting that other

regulatory mechanisms must function *in vivo*. We have observed that the development of osteoclast precursors in the bone marrow and spleen, but not in the peritoneal cavity, is induced by TNF-α and M-CSF in the absence of RANKL. The responsiveness to TLR-ligands such as lipopolysaccharide is also different.[28] Thus, the osteoclast precursors maintained in each tissue may not be identical.

Osteoclastogenesis from ES Cells

STEP CULTURES FOR OSTEOCLAST INDUCTION

We established a culture system for the induction of the osteoclast lineage from undifferentiated mouse ES cells. Our step culture system is based on Nakano's coculture system[29] with cloned stromal cells (OP9 cells), as shown in Fig. 27–1. ES cells differentiate efficiently into mesodermal cells and eventually into hematopoietic cells on OP9 stromal cells. The culture medium consists of only a basic medium and fetal bovine serum (FBS). No additional growth factors or cytokines are needed. In this culture system, small clusters of immature hematopoietic cells are observable after 1 week of culture. Mature hematopoietic cells are generated after 10 days of differentiation. Small numbers of colony-forming cells in semisolid media are observed as early as day 5, but at that point, most colonies are of the erythroid and macrophage lineage. In contrast, greater numbers and more types of colonies, including granulocyte, granulocyte and macrophage, and mixed colonies, can be seen on day 10.

By replating the cultured ES cells onto ST2 stromal cells and culturing them in the presence of 1α, 25-dihydroxyvitamin D_3 [$1\alpha,25(OH)_2D_3$] and dexamethasone (Dex) for 6 days, osteoclasts can be generated.[30–32] Interestingly, osteoclast progenitors are present on day 5. This means that the appearance of osteoclast progenitors, like primitive erythrocytes, may precede that of multipotent progenitors. On day 10, more osteoclast progenitors are present. A limiting dilution assay demonstrated that one out of six cells on day 10 are osteoclast

TABLE 27–2
Phylogenetic Comparison of the Presence of Osteoclasts and B-Lymphopoiesis in Bone Marrow

Animals	Mφ	OC	BM	Intramarrow Hematopoiesis	B-lymphopoiesis
Cartilaginous fishes	Present	Absent	None	Absent	Absent
Bony fishes	Present	Present	None	Absent	Absent
Aquatic amphibians	Present	Present	Rudimentary	Present	Absent
Land amphibians	Present	Present	Present	Present	Present
Land mammals	Present	Present	Present	Present	Present
Osteopetrotic mice	Present	Absent	Rudimentary	Present	Absent
Runx2(−/−) mice	ND	Absent	None	Absent	Absent
Osx(−/−) mice	ND	Present	None	Absent	Absent
Aquatic mammals	Present	Present	Rudimentary	Present	Absent

Mφ, macrophages; OC, osteoclasts; BM, bone marrow; and ND, not determined.

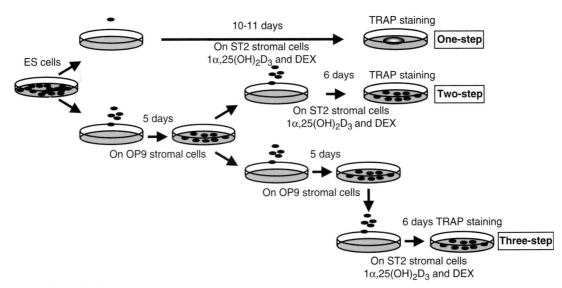

Figure 27–1. ES cell culture system for osteoclastogenesis.

progenitors.[33] It has been reported that during embryogenesis, osteoclast progenitors appear earlier in the yolk sac than in the embryo proper.[26] Our system might reflect the emergence of these osteoclast progenitors at these different stages and different locations.

ONE-STEP CULTURE FOR OSTEOCLAST DEVELOPMENT

The simplest way to induce ES cells to differentiate into osteoclasts is just by putting them in a culture containing $1\alpha,25(OH)_2D_3$ and Dex with ST2 stromal cells. We refer to this culture as a one-step culture (Fig. 27–1). Starting from single ES cells, the cells multiply and form a colony. In the colony, TRAP+ cells are observed on day 8, and on the 10th–11th day of culture, mature functional multinucleated osteoclasts that resorb bone are generated.[34] M-CSF and RANKL may be supplied by ST2 stromal cells. The osteoclastogenesis from ES cells is completely inhibited by continuous addition of OPG, or a monoclonal anti-Fms antagonistic antibody.[33] The requirement for M-CSF precedes that of RANKL, and this order of requirements is identical to that observed for early hematopoietic cells in the bone marrow.[2,15]

Interestingly, the location of mature osteoclasts in colonies is highly specific[30] (Fig. 27–2). Osteoclasts form a circle at the periphery of colonies in the one-step culture. The addition of recombinant soluble M-CSF and RANKL change the site from the periphery to the center of colonies.[34] After mature osteoclasts have been generated in cultures, if the addition of these factors is terminated, osteoclasts become located at the periphery of colonies again. These results appear to indicate that M-CSF and RANKL control the proliferation and differentiation of osteoclast precursors and that the concentrations of M-CSF and RANKL regulate the location of osteoclasts. The influence of the addition of M-CSF and RANKL on the time of the appearance of the osteoclast lineage was also observed; however, we did not find any effect.

OSTEOCLASTOGENESIS FROM ES CELLS THAT LACK HEMATOPOIETIC TRANSCRIPTION FACTORS

Results obtained with an bloodless *Tal1/Scl*-KO ES cell line showed that the Tal1 transcription factor is essential for osteoclastogenesis. However, $Gata1^{(-/Y)}$ and $Fog^{(-/-)}$ ES cells, which show abnormalities of erythroid, megakaryocyte, and mast cell development, produce normal numbers of mature osteoclasts.[33]

Interestingly, $Gata2^{(-/-)}$ ES cells give rise to reduced osteoclast development. The affected stage is a relatively early phase of hematopoiesis. ES cells are induced to differentiate into hematopoietic cells on OP9 stromal cells. On the fifth day, early hematopoietic cells are generated in cultures. These hematopoietic cells contain osteoclast precursors at a frequency of approximately 1/200 in wild-type and 1/3,000 in $Gata2^{(-/-)}$ ES cells, respectively. The frequency of osteoclast precursors from $Gata2^{(-/-)}$ ES cells is thus significantly reduced.[33] Single precursors from normal and $Gata2^{(-/-)}$ ES cells grow and differentiate into comparable numbers of osteoclasts on ST2 stromal cells. These cells are harvested on day 5 and further cultured on OP9 cells for five days. The frequency of

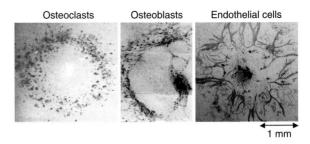

Figure 27–2. *Osteoclasts, osteoblasts, and endothelial cells in ES cell colonies.* Staining of TRAP for osteoclasts (left), alkaline phosphatase (ALP) for osteoblasts (center), and staining with anti-CD31 antibody for endothelial cells (right) were performed on days 10–11 in the one-step culture. (See color plate 4.)

osteoclast precursors the 10th day is a 20-fold increased from that on the 5th day, but the frequency of *Gata2*$^{(-/-)}$ osteoclast precursors is still one-seventh of that of wild-type precursors.[33] These results suggest that the generation of osteoclast precursors from *Gata2*$^{(-/-)}$ ES cells is mainly affected at an early hematogenetic stage within 5 days of the initiation of cultures, and after that, a lack of the *Gata2* gene does not influence osteoclastogenesis. During the first five days after the initiation of cultures, the addition of anti-Fms antibody or OPG does not affect the generation of osteoclast precursors. Surprisingly, the numbers of colony-forming cells elicited by M-CSF (CFU-M) are comparable in cultures of *Gata2*$^{(-/-)}$ and wild-type ES cells, suggesting that osteoclast precursors and CFU-M may not be identical,[33] although CFU-M has the potential to differentiate into osteoclasts in culture.[35]

KO mutations of all of these genes (*Tal1/Scl, Gata1, Fog,* and *Gata2*) are early embryonic lethal, and there have been no reports on osteoclast development in these mutants *in vivo.* The ES cell culture system enables us to assess the function of such genes in osteoclast development (Fig. 27–3).

LOCATIONS OF OSTEOCLAST, OSTEOBLAST, AND ENDOTHELIAL CELL LINEAGES IN ES CELL COLONIES

In the one-step culture, we can observe a wider range of cell lineages in a dish compared with OP9 cultures. In addition to hematopoietic lineages, at least endothelial cells, osteoblasts, myocardial cells, melanocytes, and pigmented epithelial cells are observed. Hematopoietic cells and endothelial cells share progenitor cells, called hemangioblasts, or endothelial cells are progenitor cells for hematopoietic cells. During embryogenesis, hematopoiesis and vasculogenesis are first observed in extraembryonic yolk sacs on E7.0–7.5. In the one-step culture, Kit^{high}, β2-integrin–expressing hematopoietic cells, and CD31- and Flk1-expressing endothelial cells are first observed on day 4. Mature osteoclasts are observed on E14 in embryos and on days 10–11 in culture.[34] The time required for the derivation of ES cells from blastocysts (E3.5–4.0) may

account for this difference of timing. Therefore, the program of cell differentiation in this culture system is likely to occur with precisely the same timing as embryogenesis *in vivo.*

Endothelial cells have a striking localization pattern in colonies[34] (Fig. 27–2). Vasculogenesis in *Tal1*-KO ES colonies, which lack osteoclasts, occurs normally and forms a similar pattern to that in wild-type colonies. The addition of M-CSF and RANKL changes the site of osteoclasts in the colonies but not that of endothelial cells.[36] This may mean that the pattern of endothelial cell generation is determined by the cells alone.

Bone marrow formation involves the participation of three lineages of cells. Osteoblasts build the bone, endothelial cells invade the bone, and osteoclasts resorb the bone and make the bone marrow cavity. Alkaline phosphatase-positive (ALP+) osteoblast-like cells appear on day 8 and are present at relatively inner sites of the colonies compared to osteoclasts. These two lineages of cells are closely associated and located as concentric circles.[36,37] ALP+ cells are derived from ES cells, not from the underlying ST2 stromal cells. Triple staining for putative osteoblast, osteoclast, and endothelial cell lineages is shown in Fig. 27–3.[37] Endothelial cells, osteoblasts, osteoclasts, and ST2 bone marrow stromal cells are located in an orderly pattern from the center to the outside of colonies. The locations seem to correspond to those of the bone marrow turned inside out. Even *in vitro,* there are still some rules regulating the localization of the cell lineages in colonies in the dish. These observations suggest that each cell lineage generated in the colonies has a preferred position, interacts with other lineages, and is subject to regulation of its growth and differentiation, temporally and spatially.

OSTEOCLASTOGENESIS FROM ES CELLS WITHOUT SUPPORTING STROMAL CELLS

As described in the previous section, coculture systems of single ES cells with ST2, OP9, or both stromal cells work well for the production of mature osteoclasts. However, if we want to know how undifferentiated ES cells regulate themselves and construct a tissue-like structure *in vitro,* the influence of precommitted cells in cultures has to be excluded. To induce osteoclasts under stromal cell-free conditions, at least some cells derived from the ES cells must differentiate into osteoclast precursors, and some must differentiate into supportive cells. We found that ascorbic acid is the critical reagent for osteoclastogenesis from ES cells without cloned stromal cells. The effects of ascorbic acid not only on osteoblast development (as reported) but also directed to osteoclasts may be important.[31,38] Although we have not generated osteoclasts from single ES cells yet, the development of a single ES cell culture system without stromal cells will allow us to study how organogenesis proceeds *in vitro.*

Culture Methods

ONE-STEP CULTURE ON ST2 STROMAL LAYER[30,31]

1. Prepare confluent ST2 feeder layer in 24-well plates (Note a1).
2. Grow ES cells to a subconfluent state and harvest them.

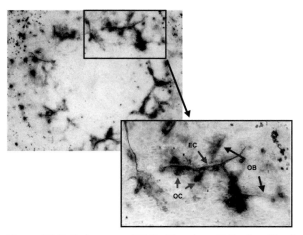

Figure 27–3. Triple staining of TRAP, ALP, and anti-CD31 of an ES cell colony on day 11 in the one-step culture on ST2 stromal cells (OC, osteoclasts; OB, putative osteoblasts; and EC, endothelial cells). (See color plate 5.)

3. Seed ES cells at the appropriate cell density (Note a2). Supplement with 10^{-8} M 1,25(OH)$_2$D$_3$ and 10^{-7} M Dex (final concentration).

4. Change the culture medium every two or three days.

Medium used: α-minimum essential medium (α-MEM: Gibco-BRL) supplemented with 10% FBS (see Note a3), 50 U/ml streptomycin, and 50 μg/ml penicillin.

Notes:

a1. ST2 cells are maintained in RPMI-1640 supplemented with 5% FBS, 50 μM 2-ME, 50 U/ml streptomycin, and 50 μg/ml penicillin.

a2. Seed ES cells so that about 20 colonies are generated per well. Plating efficiency varies according to the lot of serum.

a3. The appropriate lot of FBS must be selected.

MULTISTEP CULTURE ON OP9 STROMAL LAYER

1. Prepare confluent OP9 feeder layer in 6-well plates (Note b1).

2. Grow ES cells to a subconfluent state and harvest them.

3. Seed 10^4 ES cells per well.

4. On day 2 or 3 of differentiation, replace half of the medium with fresh medium.

5. On day 5 of differentiation, colonies that have a differentiated appearance will be observed. After washing the cultures with PBS, trypsinize them with 0.25% trypsin/0.5 mM EDTA for five minutes at 37°C. Dissociate the cell clump by pipetting up and down vigorously. After centrifugation, count ES-derived cells. Do not count OP9 cells. They are large and easily distinguished from ES cell-derived cells. About $1-2 \times 10^6$ cells are obtained per well. For two-step cultures, refer to the "Induction of Differentiation to Osteoclasts in Multistep Cultures" section. For three-step cultures, follow the steps here.

6. Seed 10^5 ES cells per well of 6-well plates containing freshly prepared OP9 layers.

7. On day 7 or 8 of differentiation, change half of the medium gently.

8. On day 10 of differentiation, hematopoietic clusters or colonies will have formed on the OP9 layers. Harvest the cultured cells by pipetting up and down. Let them stand for 4–5 minutes to precipitate the debris of OP9 stromal cells. Transfer the supernatant into a fresh tube. After centrifugation, count ES-derived cells. About 10^5 hematopoietic cells will be obtained per well. For three-step cultures, refer to the "Induction of Differentiation to Osteoclasts in Multistep Cultures" section. If you want to simultaneously analyze the other hematopoietic lineages, plate the cell suspension again onto fresh OP9 at 10^5 cells per well in 6-well plates.

Medium used: α-MEM (Gibco BRL) supplemented with 20% FCS (Note b2), 50 U/ml streptomycin, and 50 μg/ml penicillin.

Notes:

b1. OP9 are maintained in α-MEM supplemented with 20% FBS, 50 U/ml streptomycin, and 50 μg/ml penicillin.

b2. The appropriate lot of FBS must be selected.

INDUCTION OF DIFFERENTIATION TO OSTEOCLASTS IN MULTISTEP CULTURES

1. Prepare confluent ST2 feeder layers in 24-well plates (Note a1).

2. For two-step cultures (from step 5 in the "Multistep Culture on OP9 Stromal Layer" section), seed $0.5-1 \times 10^4$ cells per well. For three-step cultures (from step 12 in the "Multistep Culture on OP9 Stromal Layer" section), seed 10^3 cells per well.

3. Culture cells for six days in α-MEM supplemented with 10% FBS, 50 U/ml streptomycin, and 50 μg/ml penicillin, 10^{-8} M 1,25(OH)$_2$D$_3$ and 10^{-7} M Dex.

4. Change the culture medium every two or three days.

TRAP STAINING

1. Aspirate the culture medium.

2. Add 1 ml of 10% formalin (3.7% formaldehyde) in PBS (v/v) to each well of the plates, and fix them for 10 minutes at room temperature.

3. After washing with PBS, cover with 0.5 ml of ethanol/acetone (50:50 v/v) for exactly 1 minute at room temperature. After the treatment, immediately fill each well with PBS, aspirate the solution, and wash once more with PBS.

4. After the aspiration of PBS, cover the fixed cells with 0.25 ml of TRAP staining solution, and incubate for 10 minutes at room temperature. After red color develops, wash the plates well with water. Insufficient washing will generate high background staining.

TRAP staining solution: Acetate buffer (pH 5.0) containing 50 mM sodium acetate, 25 mg/ml naphthol AS-MX phosphate (Sigma) in a dark glass bottle at 4°C. Just before use, dissolve fast red violet LB salt (Sigma) in the volume you need at the final concentration of 0.5 mg/ml.

Summary

Osteoclasts are important cells for bone cell biology, as osteocytes and chondrocytes. It is clear phylogenetically at which point this cell lineage arises. Moreover, for assessing the hematopoietic potential of ES cells or very early embryos, the osteoclast lineage is convenient. Osteoclasts are specialized, large multinuclear cells. TRAP is a very stable enzyme, and staining for it is easy and specific. Since a majority of blood cells are nonadherent cells, it is hard to define the hematopoietic sites in culture. Osteoclasts are known to be among the most tightly adherent cells to dishes, making it possible to examine the spatial location of the cells in cultures. Macrophages are also adherent cells; however, macrophages keep the potential to differentiate into osteoclasts and dendritic

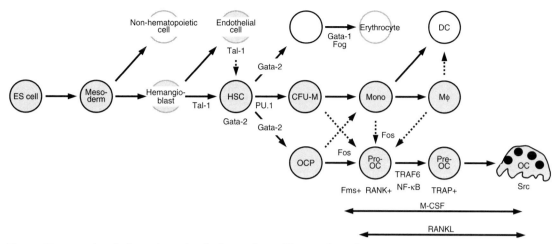

Figure 27–4. Hypothetical scheme of osteoclast development from undifferentiated ES cells (HSC, hematopoietic stem cell; Mono, monocyte; DC, dendritic cell; Mϕ, macrophage; OCP, osteoclast precursor; and OC, osteoclast).

cells, meaning that some "macrophages" may be precursor cells and change their characteristics.

Molecules essential for embryonic development, including molecules involved in Notch and Wnt signaling, regulate osteoclastogenesis directly in precursors and through supporting microenvironments *in vitro*.[39,40] A recent report showed that TNF-α, and even LPS in some conditions, can substitute for the function of RANKL in culture.[41,42] However, the authors that produced *Tnfsf11*-KO mice emphasized that RANKL/RANK is essential for osteoclastogenesis *in vivo*.[15] Open questions about the differences between *in vivo* and *in vitro* osteoclast biology remain (Fig. 27–4).

ACKNOWLEDGMENTS

We acknowledge Drs. Miya Yoshino, Takayuki Yamada, Tomomi Kurino, and Michinari Nose for critical suggestions and Drs. Tomohiro Kurosaki, Mitsuo Oshimura, and Toru Nakano for their encouragement. We thank Dr. Stuart H. Orkin for providing KO-ES cell lines. This study was supported by a Grant-in-Aid for Scientific Research (C) and Special Coordination Funds of the Ministry for Promoting Science and Technology from the Ministry of Education, Culture, Sports, Science and Technology, the Japanese government.

REFERENCES

1. Mundy, G.R., and Roodman, G.D. (1987). Osteoclast ontogeny and function. *In* "Bone and Mineral Research," (W.A. Peck, ed.), pp. 209–279. Elsevier Science Publishers, Oxford.

2. Suda, T., Udagawa, N., and Takahashi, N. (1996). Cells of bone: osteoclast generation. *In* "Principles of Bone Biology," (J.P. Bilezikian, *et al.*, eds.), pp. 87–102. Academic Press, New York.

3. Hayashi, S.I., Yamane, T., Miyamoto, A., Hemmi, H., Tagaya, H., Tanio, Y., Kanda, H., Yamazaki, H., and Kunisada, T. (1998). Commitment and differentiation of stem cells to the osteoclast lineage. *Biochem. Cell Biol.* **76**, 911–922.

4. Roodman, G.D. (1999). Cell biology of the osteoclast. *Exp. Hematol.* **27**, 1229–1241.

5. Yasuda, H., Shima, N., Nakagawa, N., Yamaguchi, K., Kinosaki, M., Mochizuki, S., Tomoyasu, A., Yano, K., Goto, M., Murakami, A., Tsuda, E., Morinaga, T., Higashio, K., Udagawa, N., Takahashi, N., and Suda, T. (1998). Osteoclast differentiation factor is a ligand for osteoprotegerin/osteoclastogenesis-inhibitory factor and is identical to Trance/RANKL. *Proc. Natl. Acad. Sci. U. S. A.* **95**, 3597–3602.

6. Lacey, D.L., Timms, E., Tan, H.L., Kelley, M.J., Dunstan, C.R., Burgess, T., Elliott, R., Colombero, A., Elliott, G., Scully, S., Hsu, H., Sullivan, J., Hawkins, N., Davy, E., Capparelli, C., Eli, A., Qian, Y.X., Kaufman, S., Sarosi, I., Shalhoub, V., Senaldi, G., Guo, J., Delaney, J., and Boyle, W.J. (1998). Osteoprotegerin ligand is a cytokine that regulates osteoclast differentiation and activation. *Cell* **93**, 165–176.

7. Yoshida, H., Hayashi, S.I., Kunisada, T., Ogawa, M., Nishikawa, S., Okamura, H., Sudo, T., Shultz, L.D., and Nishikawa, S. (1990). The murine mutation osteopetrosis is in the coding region of the macrophage colony stimulating factor gene. *Nature* **345**, 442–444.

8. Dai, X.M., Ryan, G.R., Hapel, A.J., Dominguez, M.G., Russell, R.G., Kapp, S., Sylvestre, V., and Stanley, E.R. (2002). Targeted disruption of the mouse colony-stimulating factor 1 receptor gene results in osteopetrosis, mononuclear phagocyte deficiency, increased primitive progenitor cell frequencies, and reproductive defects. *Blood* **99**, 111–120.

9. Lagasse, E., and Weissman, I.L. (1997). Enforced expression of Bcl2 in monocytes rescues macrophages and partially reverses osteopetrosis in *op/op* mice. *Cell* **89**, 1021–1031.

10. Kong, Y.Y., Yoshida, H., Sarosi, I., Tan, H.L., Timms, E., Capparelli, C., Morony, S., Oliveira-dos-Santos, A.J., Van, G., Itie, A., Khoo, W., Wakeham, A., Dunstan, C.R., Lacey, D.L., Mak, T.W., Boyle, W.J., and Penninger, J.M. (1999). OPGL is a key regulator of osteoclastogenesis, lymphocyte development, and lymph-node organogenesis. *Nature* **397**, 315–323.

11. Dougall, W.C., Glaccum, M., Charrier, K., Rohrbach, K., Brasel, K., De Smedt, T., Daro, E., Smith, J., Tometsko, M.E., Maliszewski, C.R., Armstrong, A., Shen, V., Bain, S., Cosman, D., Anderson, D., Morrissey, P.J., Peschon, J.J., and Schuh, J. (1999). RANK is essential for osteoclast and lymph node development. *Genes Dev.* **13**, 2412–2424.

12. Simonet, W.S., Lacey, D.L., Dunstan, C.R., Kelley, M., Chang, M.S., Luthy, R., Nguyen, H.Q., Wooden, S., Bennett, L., Boone, T., Shimamoto, G., DeRose, M., Elliott, R., Colombero, A., Tan, H.L., Trail, G., Sullivan, J., Davy, E., Bucay, N., Renshaw-Gegg, L., Hughes, T.M., Hill, D., Pattison, W., Campbell, P., and Boyle, W.J. (1997). Osteoprotegerin: a novel secreted protein involved in the regulation of bone density. *Cell* **89**, 309–319.

13. Yasuda, H., Shima, N., Nakagawa, N., Mochizuki, S.I., Yano, K., Fujise, N., Sato, Y., Goto, M., Yamaguchi, K., Kuriyama, M., Kanno, T., Murakami, A., Tsuda, E., Morinaga, T., and Higashio, K. (1998). Identity of osteoclastgenesis inhibitory factor (OCIF) and osteoprogerin (OPG): a mechanism by which OPG/OCIF inhibits osteoclastogenesis *in vitro*. *Endocrinology* **13**, 1329–1337.

14. Min, H., Morony, S., Sarosi, I., Dunstan, C.R., Capparelli, C., Scully, S., Van, G., Kaufman, S., Kostenuik, P.J., Lacey, D.L., Boyle, W.J., and Simonet, W.S. (2000). Osteoprotegerin reverses osteoporosis by inhibiting endosteal osteoclasts and prevents vascular calcification by blocking a process resembling osteoclastogenesis. *J. Exp. Med.* **192**, 463–474.

15. Theill, L.E., Boyle, W.J., and Penninger, J.M. (2002). RANK-L and RANK: T-cells, bone loss, and mammalian evolution. *Annu. Rev. Immunol.* **20**, 795–823.

16. Duran, A., Serrano, M., Leitges, M., Flores, J.M., Picard, S., Brown, J.P., Moscat, J., and Diaz-Meco, M.T. (2004). The atypical PKC-interacting protein p62 is an important mediator of RANK-activated osteoclastogenesis. *Dev. Cell.* **6**, 303–309.

17. Takayanagi, H., Kim, S., Koga, T., Nishina, H., Isshiki, M., Yoshida, H., Saiura, A., Isobe, M., Yokochi, T., Inoue, J., Wagner, E.F., Mak, T.W., Kodama, T., and Taniguchi, T. (2002). Induction and activation of the transcription factor NFATc1 (NFAT2) integrate RANKL signaling in terminal differentiation of osteoclasts. *Dev. Cell.* **3**, 889–901.

18. Arai, F., Miyamoto, T., Ohneda, O., Inada, T., Sudo, T., Brasel, K., Miyata, T., Anderson, D.M., and Suda, T. (1999). Commitment and differentiation of osteoclast precursor cells by the sequential expression of c-Fms and receptor activator of nuclear factor κB (RANK) receptors. *J. Exp. Med.* **190**, 1741–1754.

19. Komori, T., Yagi, H., Nomura, S., Yamaguchi, A., Sasaki, K., Deguchi, K., Shimizu, Y., Bronson, R.T., Gao, Y.H., Inada, M., Sato, M., Okamoto, R., Kitamura, Y., Yoshiki, S., and Kishimoto, T. (1997). Targeted disruption of Cbfa1 results in a complete lack of bone formation owing to maturational arrest of osteoblasts. *Cell* **89**, 755–764.

20. Nakashima, K., Zhou, X., Kunkel, G., Zhang, Z., Deng, J.M., Behringer, R.R., and de Crombrugghe, B. (2002). The novel zinc finger-containing transcription factor osterix is required for osteoblast differentiation and bone formation. *Cell* **108**, 17–29.

21. Takayanagi, H., Ogasawara, K., Hida, S., Chiba, T., Murata, S., Sato, K., Takaoka, A., Yokochi, T., Oda, H., Tanaka, K., Nakamura, K., and Taniguchi, T. (2000). T-cell-mediated regulation of osteoclastogenesis by signaling cross-talk between RANKL and IFN-γ. *Nature* **408**, 600–605.

22. Sezer, O., Heider, U., Zavrski, I., Kühne, C., and Hofbauer, L. (2003). RANK ligand and osteoprotegerin in myeloma bone disease. *Blood* **101**, 2094–2098.

23. Parichy, D.M., Ransom, D.G., Paw, B., Zon, L.I., and Johnson, S.L. (2000). An orthologue of the kit-related gene Fms is required for development of neural crest-derived xanthophores and a subpopulation of adult melanocytes in the zebra fish, *Danio rerio*. *Development* **127**, 3031–3044.

24. Tagaya, H., Kunisada, T., Yamazaki, H., Yamane, T., Tokuhisa, T., Wagner, E.F., Sudo, T., Shultz, L.D., and Hayashi, S.I. (2000). Intramedullary and extramedullary B lymphopoiesis in osteopetrotic mice. *Blood* **95**, 3363–3370.

25. Kincade, P.W., Medina, K.L., Payne, K.J., Rossi, M.I., Tudor, K.S., Yamashita, Y., and Kouro, T. (2000). Early B-lymphocyte precursors and their regulation by sex steroids. *Immunol. Rev.* **175**, 128–137.

26. Thesingh, C.W. (1986). Formation sites and distribution of osteoclast progenitor cells during the ontogeny of the mouse. *Dev. Biol.* **117**, 127–134.

27. Bucay, N., Sarosi, I., Dunstan, C.R., Morony, S., Tarpley, J., Capparelli, C., Scully, S., Tan, H.L., Xu, W., Lacey, D.L., Boyle, W.J., and Simonet, W.S. (1998). Osteoprotegerin-deficient mice develop early onset osteoporosis and arterial calcification. *Genes Dev.* **12**, 1260–1268.

28. Hayashi, S., Yamada, T., Tsuneto, M., Yamane, Y., Takahashi, M., Shultz, L.D., and Yamazaki, H. (2003). Distinct osteoclast precursors in the bone marrow and extramedullary organs characterized by responsiveness to toll-like receptor ligands and TNF-alpha. *J. Immunol.* **171**, 5130–5139.

29. Nakano, T., Kodama, H., and Honjo, T. (1994). Generation of lymphohematopoietic cells from embryonic stem cells in culture. *Science* **265**, 1098–1101.

30. Yamane, T., Kunisada, T., Yamazaki, H., Era, T., Nakano, T., and Hayashi, S.I. (1997). Development of osteoclasts from embryonic stem cells through a pathway that is c-Fms, but not c-kit, dependent. *Blood* **90**, 3516–3523.

31. Yamane, T., Kunisada, T., and Hayashi, S.I. (2002). Embryonic stem cells as a model to study osteoclast lineage. *In* "Embryonic Stem Cells: Methods and Protocols (Methods in Molecular Biology)," (K. Turksen, ed.), Vol. 185, pp. 97–106. Humana Press, Totowa, NJ.

32. Tsuneto, M., Yamane, T., Okuyama, H., Yamazaki, H., and Hayashi, S.I. (2003). *In vitro* differentiation of mouse ES cells into hematopoietic, endothelial, and osteoblastic cell lineages: a possibility of *in vitro* organogenesis. *In* "Differentiation of Embryonic Stem Cells (Methods in Enzymology)," (P.M. Wassarman *et al.*, eds.), Vol. 365, pp. 98–114. Academic Press, San Diego.

33. Yamane, T., Kunisada, T., Yamazaki, H., Nakano, T., Orkin, S.H., and Hayashi, S.I. (2000). Sequential requirements of SCL/Tal1, Gata2, macrophage colony-stimulating factor, and osteoclast differentiation factor/osteoprotegerin ligand in osteoclast development. *Exp. Hematol.* **28**, 833–840.

34. Hemmi, H., Okuyama, H., Yamane, T., Nishikawa, S.I., Nakano, T., Yamazaki, H., Kunisada, T., and Hayashi, S.I. (2001). Temporal and spatial localization of osteoclasts in colonies from embryonic stem cells. *Biochem. Biophys. Res. Commun.* **280**, 526–534.

35. Yamazaki, H., Kunisada, T., Yamane, T., and Hayashi, S.I. (2001). Presence of osteoclast precursors in the colonies cloned in the presence of hematopoietic colony-stimulating factors. *Exp. Hematol.* **29**, 68–76.

36. Okuyama, H., Tsuneto, M., Yamane, T., Yamazaki, H., and Hayashi, S. (2003). Discrete types of osteoclast precursors can be generated from embryonic stem cells. *Stem Cells.* **21**, 670–680.

37. Okuyama, H., Yamazaki, H., Yamane, T., and Hayashi, S.I. (2001). Development of osteoclast lineage cells. *Res. Adv. Blood (Global Res. Net.)* **1**, 75–84.

38. Tsuneto, M. (In preparation).

39. Yamada, T., Yamazaki, H., Yamane, T., Yoshino, M., Okuyama, H., Tsuneto, M., Kurino, T., Hayashi, S.I., and Sakano, S. (2003). Regulation of osteoclast development by Notch signaling directed to osteoclast precursors and through stromal cells. *Blood* **101,** 2227–2234.

40. Yamane, T., Kunisada, T., Tsukamoto, H., Yamazaki, H., Niwa, H., Takada, S., and Hayashi, S.I. (2001). Wnt signaling regulates hemopoiesis through stromal cells. *J. Immunol.* **161,** 765–772.

41. Kobayashi, K., Takahashi, N., Jimi, E., Udagawa, N., Takami, M., Kotake, S., Nakagawa, N., Kinosaki, M., Yamaguchi, K., Shima, N., Yasuda, H., Morinaga, T., Higashio, K., Martin, T.J., and Suda, T. (2000). Tumor necrosis factor-α stimulates osteoclast differentiation by a mechanism independent of the ODF/RANKL-RANK interaction. *J. Exp. Med.* **191,** 275–286.

42. Hayashi, S.I., Tsuneto, M., Yamada, T., Nose, M., Yoshino, M., Shultz, L.D., and Yamazaki, H. (2004). Lipopolysaccharide-induced osteoclastogenesis in Src homology 2-domain phosphatase-1-deficient viable motheaten mice. *Endocrinology.* **145,** 2721–2729.

28

Cardiomyogenic Precursor Cells in the Mammalian Embryo: Induction, Heterogeneity, and Morphogenesis

Robert G. Kelly and Richard P. Harvey

Specification, growth, differentiation, and morphogenesis of the multiple cell lineages that comprise the mammalian heart occur through highly coordinated spatial and temporal processes during development. Integration of both positive and negative signals from tissues surrounding the cardiogenic mesoderm results in progressive commitment toward a muscle fate. Differentiation occurs in a number of distinct directions that reflect the functional specificities of the chambers and other elements of the heart, and a process of *de novo* myogenesis contributes to muscularization of the intracardiac septa and valves. Whereas the initial stages of heart tube formation are accompanied by continuing allocation of cardiomyocytes at the borders of the cardiac epithelium, heart growth throughout fetal stages is driven largely by cardiomyocyte proliferation. Cardiomyocytes lose their proliferative capacity around birth, and growth and adaptation of the myocardium thereafter occurs largely through cellular hypertrophy in the presence of considerable endoreduplication but absence of cell division. Recent developments in the stem cell field have raised the exciting possibility of using stem cell therapies for repair of damaged or failing myocardium. This emerging technology will require a detailed understanding of normal cardiomyogenesis to identify the appropriate cell population or populations for engraftment and the appropriate environment in which they might be encouraged to differentiate. In this chapter we briefly review the origins and fate of myocardial progenitor cells throughout the series of events that define the embryonic heart tube and four-chambered heart. In addition, we discuss the molecular identity of conserved signaling molecules and transcription factors that drive early cardiomyogenesis and patterning and growth of the myocardium. Although the focus of this review is the embryologic origins of cardiomyocytes and their precursor cells in mammals, data from other vertebrate models are discussed where relevant to conserved mechanisms.

From Epiblast to Cardiac Crescent

Cardiomyocyte precursor cells originate in the posterior region of the embryonic epiblast before gastrulation.[1] Although unspecified, the position of these cells and the cellular movements of gastrulation dictates their future allocation to the heart progenitor zone, which lies in the anterior region of the embryo.[2,3] Heart precursor cells in the gastrula include bipotential mesodermal and endodermal progenitors,[4,5] and these cells migrate through the anterior region of the primitive streak or gastrula organiser[2] then take a lateral migratory path to form the bilateral heart-forming regions within anterior and anterior-lateral splanchnic mesoderm (reviewed in reference 6) (Fig. 28–1). Throughout these complex cellular movements, precardiac cells maintain continuity with future head mesoderm and proximity to anterior visceral endoderm and endoderm of the definitive foregut.

Multistep inductive signaling from adjacent cell layers leads to establishment of the cardiomyogenic program in precardiac mesoderm. Combinatorial signaling events activate transcription factors of the zinc finger, homeodomain, basic helix-loop-helix (bHLH), MADS-box, and T box families, which, together with positive and negative transcriptional co-factors including Myocardin and Hop1, activate the myocardial transcriptional program (reviewed in reference 7). Signaling molecules present in the primitive streak and node may initially direct mesoderm toward a cardiac fate or limit its options for adopting other fates.[8–13] Potential cardiogenic molecules expressed during gastrulation include members of the Hedgehog, Fibroblast Growth Factor (FGF), Transforming Growth Factor β (TGFβ), and Epidermal Growth Factor-Cripto/FRL-1/Cryptic (EGF-CFC) families. For example, *Sonic hedgehog (Shh)* and *Indian hedgehog (Ihh)* are expressed in the node and later within the definitive endoderm juxtaposed to cardiac mesoderm. Mouse embryos lacking Smoothened, a component of the Hedgehog receptor complex, show delayed activation of the gene encoding the cardiac homeodomain factor Nkx2-5, and abnormal heart morphology.[14] The EGF-CFC molecule, Cripto, is a co-factor for signaling through the TGFβ family member, Nodal. Cripto is expressed in the primitive streak and is required for the proper specification of precardiac mesoderm *in vitro* and

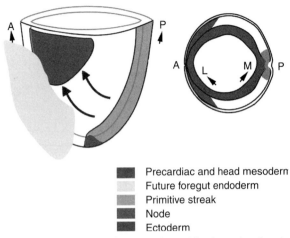

Precardiac and head mesoderm
Future foregut endoderm
Primitive streak
Node
Ectoderm

Figure 28-1. *Migration of the precardiac and head mesoderm from the primitive streak to anterior lateral regions of the embryo subsequent to gastrulation.* Precardiac mesoderm remains closely apposed to future foregut endoderm. A, anterior; L, lateral; M, medial; P, posterior. (Adapted from reference 3.)

in vivo.[15–17] The zebra fish EGF-CFC gene, *Oep,* is also required for correct specification of cardiac mesoderm.[18] *Fgf8* is expressed in the node and in the cardiac mesoderm in the mouse and anterior definitive endoderm in the chick,[19,20] whereas its relative *Fgf4* is expressed in the primitive streak.[21] Both factors are required for cell movement away from the primitive streak,[22,23] and *Fgf8* appears essential for correct cardiac specification *in vitro* and *in vivo.*[19,24]

These findings notwithstanding, separating the roles of individual factors expressed during gastrulation in mesoderm induction, cellular movements associated with gastrulation, and cardiac specification is problematic. Furthermore, future endocardial, pericardial, and epicardial cells migrate through the anterior primitive streak together with myogenic progenitor cells.[25] Although endocardial and myocardial progenitors may already be distinct at the gastrulation stage,[26] both cell types express the cardiac transcription factor genes *Mesp-1* and *Nkx2-5* at some stage in their history, potentially reflecting their common origins.[27,28]

Patterning of the embryonic myocardium may also be established during gastrulation. In the chick, future myocardial cells that traverse the primitive streak immediately caudal to the node contribute to more cranial regions of the later embryonic heart[25] (see also reference 29). Cardiac progenitors may actually pass directly through the gastrula organizer, which contains head-inducing activity and precursors of axial mesendoderm.[2] Transplantation of the node or beads soaked in Fgf4 to ectopic sites in gastrula stage chick embryos induces expression of ventricular but not atrial cardiac markers in surrounding tissue, suggesting that the node has heart-inducing capacity and a direct or indirect influence on patterning through FGFs.[13] Furthermore, overexpression of Fgf4 near the forming heart favors ventricular development.[13] Synthesis of retinoic acid in or near heart progenitors within the primitive streak or cardiac crescent also profoundly influences

cardiac patterning and is essential for correct specification of sinuatrial progenitors (reviewed in reference 30).

Specification and Differentiation Within the Cardiac Crescent

Transplantation experiments have shown that the primary requirement for activation of the cardiomyogenic program is localization of progenitor cells within the bilateral heart-forming regions.[3,31] In this location, signaling molecules originating from the anterior lateral endoderm and ectoderm activate the cardiomyogenic program (reviewed in reference 32) (Fig. 28–2). TGFβ–molecules of the bone morphogenetic protein (BMP) family, as well as FGFs and *Drosophila* wingless-homologues (Wnts), have been shown to be critical endodermal and ectodermal signals involved in induction of cardiomyogenesis (reviewed in reference 33). Extensive explant and *in vivo* analyses have revealed a major role for BMP2 and BMP4 in inducing and/or maintaining cardiomyocyte differentiation.[34–36] In a variety of settings, cardiomyocyte differentiation can be blocked by the BMP antagonist Noggin or other pathway inhibitors.[34,37,38] However, BMP signaling

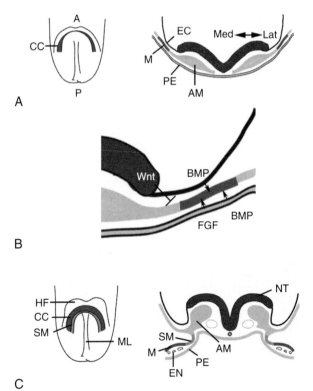

Figure 28-2. *The cardiac crescent stage.* The precardiac mesoderm is situated in the anterior lateral region of the embryo (A), apposed to pharyngeal endoderm (PE) and embryonic ectoderm (EC). Signals from adjacent cell layers regulate cardiomyocyte specification and differentiation (B). On formation of the embryonic coelom, cardiac primordia develop in lateral splanchnic mesoderm continuous with medial splanchnic mesoderm (SM) (C). Endocardial cells (EN) differentiate between the cardiac primordia and pharyngeal endoderm. A, anterior; AM, anterior mesoderm; CC, cardiac crescent; Lat, lateral; M, myocardium; Med, medial; P, posterior.

has been shown to be required at multiple stages of myocardial development subsequent to initial inductive steps, and its function in myocardium may, in part, be indirect through an essential role in endodermal differentiation.[32,37,39]

Fgf8 can substitute for the presence of anterior lateral endoderm in inducing the cardiomyogenic program in chick embryos.[19] Furthermore, Fgf8 can, together with BMP2, activate ectopic cardiomyogenesis. Combinatorial treatment of noncardiac mesoderm with BMP and FGF factors reveals that the two signaling pathways induce cardiogenesis cooperatively and that only transient exposure to FGF is required.[40,41] Cooperativity between factors impacts directly on cardiac transcription factor gene expression. BMP signaling, acting through the SMAD family of transcription factors, has been shown to activate genes encoding cardiac transcription factors GATA4, Nkx2-5, and HAND1, which are members of the zinc-finger, homeodomain, and bHLH families, respectively.[34,42] Likewise, FGF signaling, acting through the small GTPase ras, has been shown to activate *Nkx2-5* and genes encoding the MADS-box transcription factor family members, serum response factor (SRF), and Mef2c.[19,43] In zebra fish, Bmp2, together with Oep, an EGF-CFC molecule known to be involved in mesendoderm induction, activate the *gata5* gene in the cardiac zone, and Gata5 in turn is essential for activation and/or maintenance of *Nkx2-5* expression.[18,44,45] Once cardiac transcription factor genes are activated in response to extracellular signals, direct and synergistic interactions between transcription factors and cross-pathway regulation drives activation of the transcriptional program for cardiac myogenesis (reviewed in references 7 and 46). Genes encoding the sarcomeric and enzymatic machinery of the cardiomyocyte are activated at this stage as irreversible commitment to the myocardial lineage is established.[9,10,12] Additional factors produced by the underlying endodermal layer, including insulin and activin-A, appear to support differentiation of precardiac mesoderm although they are probably not primary inducers.[32,47]

The noncanonical Wnt signaling pathway in mesoderm has also been shown to be necessary for cardiogenesis in the quail and *Xenopus* models.[47,48] Biochemical studies of Wnt11 signaling in *Xenopus* have shown that cardiac induction occurs through activation of the Jun N-terminal kinase (JNK) via activation of protein kinase C (PKC), and stimulation of either kinase alone can induce cardiomyogenesis in the absence of Wnt11. Whether Wnt/PKC/JNK signaling works in parallel or upstream of BMP/FGF signaling remains to be determined.

Intersection between the endodermal and ectodermal-derived signals with additional signals restricted along the anterior-posterior and medial-lateral axes of the embryo, delimits the coordinates of precardiac mesoderm (Fig. 28–1B). Wnt signaling through the canonical β-catenin pathway represses cardiomyogenesis, both in the posterior region of the embryo and in anterior mesoderm medial to the cardiac crescent.[49–51] Wnt/β-catenin antagonists expressed in the cardiac progenitor zone are presumably present to help overcome repressive Wnt signaling from axial structures. In addition, it has recently been shown that the Wnt/β-catenin antagonists dkk-1 and Crescent also stimulate the JNK pathway, which, as noted previously, is stimulatory for cardiomyogenesis.[47] Loss of β-catenin in mouse embryos leads to formation of ectopic heart tissue, consistent with its proposed role in the canonical Wnt pathway as an inhibitor of cardiogenesis.[5] In contrast, recent findings in a mammalian *in vitro* differentiation model suggest that the Wnt/β-catenin pathway may play a positive early role in cardiogenesis, possibly through BMP induction.[52] Further refinement of the heart-forming region may come from the fact that the transcriptional responses to Fgf8 and BMPs are dose-dependent, and the concentration of these factors may be graded across the cardiac progenitor zone.[19] In summary, a combination of positive (BMP, FGF, noncanonical Wnt) and negative (Wnt/β-catenin) signaling delineates the heart-forming region in anterior lateral/splanchnic mesoderm and cooperatively induces cardiomyocyte differentiation.

The fundamentally important contribution of BMP and FGF signals to cardiomyogenesis is illustrated by their evolutionarily conserved roles in invertebrate heart induction (reviewed in reference 33). In *Drosophila,* expression of the BMP homologues Dpp and Screw in dorsal ectoderm is required for activation of the cardiomyogenic program and maintenance of expression of the essential cardiac transcription factor genes, *tinman,* the *Drosophila* homologue of *Nkx2-5,* and *pannier,* a GATA factor gene.[53] Furthermore, the FGF receptor Heartless is required for both migration of mesodermal cells dorsally, where they respond to dorsal Dpp, and for subsequent myocardial specification.[54–57] Wingless is also involved in defining the cardiomyocyte population in *Drosophila.* However, signaling occurs through the canonical Wnt/β-catenin pathway and plays a positive inductive role, apparently opposite to the situation in vertebrates.[58]

From Cardiac Crescent to Heart Tube

The precardiac mesoderm forms a highly proliferative epithelial sheet that fuses ventrally at the midline to give rise to the linear heart tube (Fig. 28–3A). This event generates an endothelium-lined myocardial trough, the latter open dorsally to pharyngeal endoderm. The ventral migration of heart progenitors occurs in close association with invagination of the foregut endoderm. The cardiac mesoderm actually migrates over the foregut endoderm, and the interposed extracellular matrix plays an important role in migration.[59–61] Ventral pharyngeal endoderm is likely to continue to play an important inductive role at this stage of heart morphogenesis, including promotion of cardiomyocyte differentiation. As the myocardial trough closes dorsally, its connection to the pharynx is called the dorsal meso-cardium (Fig. 28–3A).[62] This transient structure provides a source of myocardial cells during the rapid growth of the heart tube at this stage. Subsequently, the dorsal mesocardium breaks down and the tubular heart loops to the right (Fig. 28–3B). The direction of looping is specified by as yet unidentified embryonic laterality signals downstream of asymmetric expression of the TGFβ molecule Nodal in left lateral plate mesoderm.[63]

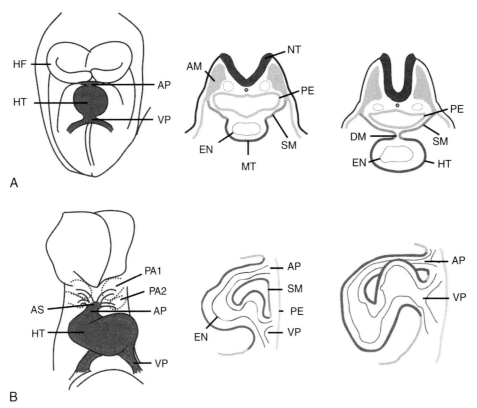

Figure 28–3. *The early heart tube and cardiac looping.* The early heart tube (HT) is a myocardial trough orientated along the anterior-posterior embryonic axis (A) with a caudal venous pole (VP) and cranial arterial pole (AP). Transverse sections reveal that the endocardial lined trough opens dorsally onto pharyngeal endoderm (PE) and is continuous with undifferentiated splanchnic (SM) and anterior (AM) mesoderm across the dorsal mesocardium (DM). The heart tube continues to elongate during rightward looping (B). At the arterial pole, myocardial cells are continuous with the aortic sac (AS) and pharyngeal arch arteries. Sagittal sections show the elongation of the heart tube and the progressive convergence of the venous and arterial poles during cardiac looping. HF, head fold; NT, neural tube; PA1 and 2, first and second pharyngeal arches. (Adapted from reference 69.)

Throughout cardiac looping, myocardial precursors are also added to the heart tube at the borders of the cardiac epithelium.[62,64,65] The addition of extracardiac cells to the growing poles of the early heart, in addition to proliferation of already differentiated cardiomyocytes, permits extremely rapid elongation of the heart tube, which in the mouse grows 5-fold in length over a period of 24 hours.[62] Myocardial differentiation of mesodermal progenitor cells is, therefore, a continuous process that initiates in the precardiac mesoderm and continues until the end of cardiac looping. At the venous pole, growth of the heart tube proceeds via continuous allocation and differentiation of cells from the caudal region of the cardiac crescent, and these give rise to the atria and sinus venosus.[29] There is an additional contribution to the body of the atrium from mesenchymal cells situated adjacent to the lung buds.[66] *Gata6* and the epitope HNK-1 are expressed in these newly differentiating cells at the venous pole of the heart.[67,68]

At the arterial pole, the heart tube grows by recruitment of extracardiac cells from splanchnic and pharyngeal mesoderm.[69] These precardiac cells constitute the anterior or secondary heart field (Fig. 28–4) and give rise to myocardium of the outflow tract and possibly also the right ventricle.[68–71]

Recruitment of these cells to a cardiomyogenic fate appears to be regulated by BMPs expressed from already differentiated cardiomyocytes at the distal pole of the heart tube.[68] The cardiac transcription factor genes *Nkx2-5* and *Gata4* are expressed in pharyngeal mesoderm adjacent to the arterial pole of the heart before activation of myocardial markers.[28,68] FGF signaling is also implicated in differentiation of anterior heart field cells. *Fgf10* is expressed in pharyngeal mesoderm dorsal to the heart (Fig. 28–4A and B) and these cells lie adjacent to pharyngeal endoderm and ectoderm expressing *Fgf8*.[70,72] *Fgf8* has been shown to be required for development of the ventricular region and arterial pole of the zebra fish heart.[24] As at the venous pole, *Gata6* and HNK-1 are expressed in cells of the pharyngeal mesoderm as they undergo transition to myocardium.[67,68] Other genes expressed in the anterior heart field include those encoding the transcription factors Islet-1 and Tbx1[73,74]; mice lacking *Tbx1* display outflow tract hypoplasia.[75,76]

Cardiomyogenesis at the arterial pole of the heart therefore appears to involve at least some of the same signals as those that induce differentiation of precardiac mesoderm in the cardiac crescent. Cells of the anterior heart field that lie in the vicinity of the caudal pharynx are apposed to both poles of

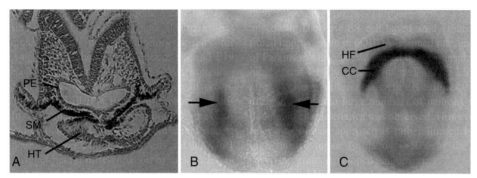

Figure 28–4. *The anterior or secondary heart field.* A transverse section through an embryo at E8.5 showing expression of β-galactosidase under transcriptional control of an *Fgf10* enhancer trap transgene in splanchnic and pharyngeal mesoderm dorsal to the heart tube (A). At the cardiac crescent stage *Fgf10* transcripts (arrows) are expressed in splanchnic mesoderm medial to differentiated cardiomyocytes of the cardiac crescent (B) that express α-cardiac actin (C). CC, cardiac crescent; HF, head fold; HT, heart tube; PE, pharyngeal endoderm; SM, splanchnic mesoderm.

the heart at terminal stages of heart tube elongation and may also contribute to inflow tract myocardium.[30] Earlier, at the cardiac crescent stage, *Fgf8* and *Fgf10* are expressed in anterior splanchnic mesoderm medial to precursor cells of the linear heart tube.[20,70] DiI labeling experiments suggest that these cells are in fact the progenitors of the anterior heart field and that cardiomyogenesis in this population is delayed with respect to differentiation within the cardiac crescent derivatives[70] (Fig. 28–4). Differential exposure to axial Wnt signals and lateral Wnt antagonists may be involved in this temporal delay. Furthermore, data from *Xenopus* suggest that activation of Notch signaling blocks differentiation of a population of *Nkx2-5*-expressing cells in lateral splanchnic mesoderm that are potentially analogous to those in the anterior heart field.[77] Thus, Notch signaling may also be involved in regulating differentiation of the anterior heart field in amniotes.

Patterning and Growth of the Embryonic Heart

After the completion of cardiac looping, the heart tube no longer grows by incorporation and differentiation of progenitor cells at the poles,[62] but by proliferation of already existing cardiomyocytes within the embryonic heart. In this section we consider briefly how the embryonic heart is patterned and how patterns of myocardial growth contribute to cardiac form.

The embryonic heart is composed of distinct evolutionary modules with different transcriptional programs.[78] The embryonic left and right ventricular chambers of the heart (Fig. 28–5) are prominent examples of such modules. Indeed, as discussed previously, the embryonic right ventricle may be formed from cells of the anterior heart field clearly after allocation of left ventricular progenitors to the heart tube from the cardiac crescent. Accordingly, the left and right ventricles show differences in the expression of a number of transcription factors and downstream genes, as well as transgenes (reviewed in reference 46). For example, the bHLH factor genes *Hand2* and *Hand1* become expressed predominantly in the right and left ventricles, respectively.[79,80] Mutation of

Hand2 in the mouse results in loss of the embryonic right ventricle because of apoptosis.[79,81] Although interpretation of the cardiac phenotype of *Hand1* mutants is complicated by its essential role in placental development, the gene appears to be necessary for formation of left ventricular progenitors.[82–84] *Nkx2-5* has been shown genetically to act upstream of *Hand1* and *Nkx2-5/Hand2* double mutant embryos do not develop either ventricular chamber.[85] The homeodomain factor *Irx4* is also expressed in the ventricular chambers and has been shown to contribute to ventricular identity.[86] *Irx4* expression is lost in *Nkx2-5/Hand2* double mutant embryos.[85] The T-box factor Tbx5 is essential for development of the atria and left ventricle, and acts in part through a direct physical interaction with Nkx2-5 on target promoters.[87,88] Another T-box factor, Tbx2, is a transcriptional repressor that has been shown to inhibit chamber-specific gene expression at the inner curvature of the looping heart through displacement of Tbx5 from Nkx2-5.[89] Additional interactions between Nkx2-5 and factors restricted to the anterior heart field are suggested by the failure of development of the arterial pole in *Nkx2-5* mutant

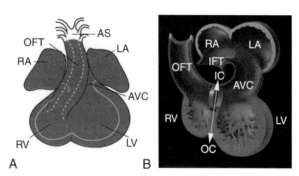

Figure 28–5. *The embryonic heart.* (A) At E10.5 the mouse heart is comprised of future left (LA) and right (RA) atria, the atrioventricular canal (AVC), future right (RV) and left (LV) ventricles, and the outflow tract (OFT). Ventricular and atrial chamber myocardium expands by ballooning morphogenesis from the outer curvature of the heart tube (B). The inner curvature (purple) maintains the gene expression pattern of the primitive heart tube. AS, aortic sac; IC, inner curvature; IFT, inflow tract; OC, outer curvature. (Adapted from reference 102.)

hearts.[90,91] Thus, complex interactions between transcriptional regulators establish the compartmental identity of the developing heart.[46] The upstream signals that initiate regionalization of the myocardium are poorly understood although, as discussed earlier, patterning of cardiac precursor cells is likely to initiate during gastrulation.

Patterns of cardiomyocyte proliferation within different cardiac compartments are related to the functional requirements of the developing heart. During fetal growth, cardiomyocyte proliferation is controlled both by intrinsic cell-cycle regulation and a continuing degree of responsiveness to external growth factors.[92,93] Proliferation of myocytes during formation of the embryonic heart tube requires FGF signaling, although FGF is not a component of later ventricular expansion.[94] Cytokines, including cardiotrophin-1, are also expressed in the developing heart and may play a role.[95] In addition to patterning the myocardium, antagonistic interactions between transcription factors also contribute to the regulation of myocardial proliferation. For example, the non-DNA binding homeodomain protein Hop1 interacts with the MADS-box containing transcription factor SRF, switching the role of SRF from a proliferative to differentiation-inducing activity.[96,97] Cardiomyocyte proliferation during the late phase of ventricular growth in zebrafish is regulated by interactions between a DNA-stimulated ATPase, Pontin, and its apparent antagonist, Reptin, often found in the same complex.[98] This complex can bind directly to β-catenin and modulate its activity on transcriptional targets, suggesting additional late roles for Wnt signaling in controlling myocardial growth.[98] Calcium influx through L-type channels has also been found to be necessary for cardiomyocyte growth in the fish heart, independent of contraction, highlighting the important but often neglected role for cellular function in generation of organ form.[99] The hearts of certain amphibia and zebra fish

have been shown to have extensive intrinsic regenerative capacity, revealing species-specific differences in the proliferative potential of adult cardiomyocytes.[100,101]

Cardiac chambers become morphologically evident as the future left and right ventricles and atrial appendages begin to balloon out from the outer curvature of the looping heart tube[102] (Fig. 28–5A and B). Chamber muscle can be regarded as a specialization of the more primitive form of myocardium found in the heart tube and its correct specification requires the coordinated activities of signaling molecules and transcription factors such as Nkx2-5 and Tbx2 (reviewed in reference 30). Once formed, there is differential growth across the ventricular wall, with a more proliferative outer compact layer and a more differentiated inner subendocardial layer that becomes trabeculated.[103–105] The trabecular myocardium is probably the force-generating myogenic component of the embryonic heart but will eventually contribute prominently to the interventricular septum and ventricular conduction system.[106] Fate mapping studies have shown that cells of the compact and trabecular layers are clonally related. As a result of the proliferation gradient, the ventricular wall is composed of the oligoclonal descendants of earlier cardiomyocytes, with intermixed clones adopting the shape of cones with their apexes orientated toward the endocardium.[104,107] Within such cones, cardiomyocyte proliferation is orientated in spindles that prefigure myofiber organization.[107] There are probably two components to differential growth across the ventricular wall. At early stages, neuregulin1 signaling from endocardial to myocardial cells plays a major role in inducing the differentiation of trabecular myocardium at the subendocardial surface (reviewed in reference 30). Later, epicardial cells derived from the so-called proepicardial organ, a component of the septum transversum, spread over the outer surface of the myocardium (Fig. 28–6A, inset). These cells influence

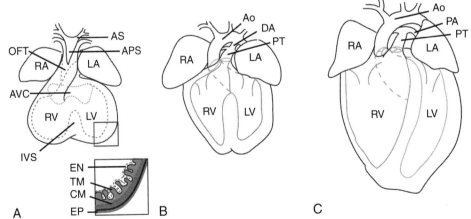

Figure 28–6. *Remodelling the embryonic heart. Septation of the embryonic heart initiates by formation of atrial and ventricular septa and rightward displacement of the atrioventricular canal (AVC) illustrated in an E11.5 mouse heart (A). The ventricular wall is comprised of inner trabeculated (TM) and outer compact (CM) myocardial layers juxtaposed to endocardial (EN) and epicardial (EP) cells, respectively (inset). Septation of the outflow tract (OFT) is achieved in part by neural crest cells of the aorticopulmonary septum that divides the distal OFT from the dorsal aortic sac (AS). By E14.5 septation is complete (B); however, the pulmonary circulation is largely bypassed during fetal development by an interatrial communication (not shown) and the ductus arteriosus (DA), shunts that are lost at birth as the definitive systemic and pulmonary circuits are established (C). Ao, aorta; IVS, interventricular septum; LA, left atrium; LV, left ventricle; PA, pulmonary arteries; PT, pulmonary trunk; RA, right atrium; RV, right ventricle.*

growth of the subepicardial ventricular myocardium and also give rise to the coronary circulation and interstitial fibroblasts. The massive expansion of the compact layer that occurs in the ventricles subsequent to trabeculation is driven by signals from the epicardium in response to multiple inputs. Recent studies show that the action of retinoic acid and erythropoietin stimulate the endocardium to express a mitogen, as yet unknown, that acts on the adjacent myocardium.[108,109]

Remodelling the Embryonic Heart Tube

Remodelling of the embryonic myocardium during the transition from a tubular heart to one with distinct chambers and parallel circulatory systems occurs during early fetal development. This involves the creation of septa within the atria, ventricles, and outflow tract and their fusion with endocardial cushion tissue in the atrioventricular canal (Fig. 28–6). Septation of the outflow tract is mediated by a subpopulation of neural crest cells that invade the arterial pole of the heart through the caudal pharyngeal arches.[110] Cardiac neural crest plays an additional role in facilitating early cardiomyocyte differentiation by blocking a proliferative signal, likely to be Fgf8, in the pharyngeal region.[111] In the absence of cardiac neural crest, elevated myocardial proliferation and impaired differentiation and contractility are observed.[72] The observation that the contribution of cells from the anterior heart field is reduced following neural crest ablation in the chick supports the hypothesis that abnormalities in cardiac differentiation at the arterial pole of the heart could represent a major component of congenital heart disease.[112] A subset of zebra fish neural crest cells has recently been shown to contribute to myocardium,[113,114] a fate that is not observed in avian or mammalian hearts.[115,116] Wnt signaling may play a role in proliferation of cardiac neural crest cells. Impaired proliferation of neural crest cells was observed in the outflow tract of mice doubly heterozygous for mutations in *Dishevelled*, encoding an intracellular mediator of Wnt signaling, and *Pitx2*, encoding an homeobox transcription factor.[117] *Pitx2* may be a target of β-catenin mediated Wnt signaling and has been shown to activate proliferation of neural crest cells through induction of the cell cycle regulator cyclin D2.[117]

During the final stages of cardiac remodeling, the septa of the outflow tract and atrioventricular canal become muscularized. The cellular basis of this process, termed myocardialization, has been investigated in explant cultures.[118] Myocardialization has been proposed to occur through one of two processes; either active invasion of mesenchymal cushions and septa by preexisting myocardium or *de novo* recruitment of mesenchyme to a myocardial fate, analogous to recruitment and differentiation of splanchnic mesodermal progenitor cells at the poles of the heart during looping. Evidence in favor of the latter mechanism suggests that myocardialization in the fetal heart may involve similar molecular signals as induction of myocardial cells at the earliest stages of heart development.[119] However, the source of mesenchymal cells in this case is likely to be cells resident in the endocardial cushions, which originally derive from the

endocardium via an epithelial to mesenchymal transition in response to myocardial signals.[120]

Summary and Perspectives

In this chapter we have seen how cardiomyogenesis depends on complex combinatorial signaling inputs. Initial cardiomyocyte specification and patterning occurs during gastrulation, whereas differentiation initiates in the precardiac mesoderm of the cardiac crescent and continues at the borders of the cardiac epithelium during heart tube formation. Differentiation subsequently shifts to the poles of the heart tube. Nevertheless, common molecular signals appear to regulate cardiomyocyte differentiation and splanchnic mesoderm remains the major source of cardiomyocytes throughout heart development. After looping is completed, growth of the myocardium occurs by proliferation of differentiated cardiomyocytes and patterns of growth directly contribute to cardiac form. A final phase of differentiation occurs during muscularization of the cardiac septa as the heart achieves its four-chambered structure.

Major questions remain. For example, does cardiogenesis proceed through continuous waves of specification and differentiation of successive progenitor populations, as discussed previously, or are there also stem cells lying within precardiac mesoderm? Are there differences in the nature of the various precursor populations and the inductive signals used at different sites of cardiomyogenesis? What are the essential extracellular signals and intracellular responses that regulate cardiomyocyte differentiation? Ongoing work will address these questions and whether our basic knowledge of developmental mechanisms can be used creatively in efforts to harness stem cells for cardiac repair in the adult.

ACKNOWLEDGMENTS

R.G.K. is an INSERM research fellow. R.P.H. is supported by grants from the National Health and Medical Research Council of Australia, the Australian Research Council, and the National Institutes of Health (USA)(NHLBI; HL68885-02).

REFERENCES

1. Parameswaran, M., and Tam, P.P. (1995). Regionalisation of cell fate and morphogenetic movement of the mesoderm during mouse gastrulation. *Dev. Genet.* **17,** 16–28.
2. Kinder, S.J., Tsang, T.E., Wakamiya, M., Sasaki, H., Behringer, R.R., Nagy, A., and Tam, P. (2001). The organiser of the mouse gastrula is composed of a dynamic population of progenitor cells for the axial mesoderm. *Development* **128,** 3623–3634.
3. Tam, P.P., Parameswaran, M., Kinder, S.J., and Weinberger, R.P. (1997). The allocation of epiblast cells to the embryonic heart and other mesodermal lineages: the role of ingression and tissue movement during gastrulation. *Development* **124,** 1631–1642.
4. Rodaway, A., and Patient, R. (2001). Mesendoderm, an ancient germ layer? *Cell* **105,** 169–172.

5. Lickert, H., Kutsch, S., Kanzler, B., Tamai, Y., Taketo, M.M., and Kemler, R. (2002). Formation of multiple hearts in mice following deletion of beta-catenin in the embryonic endoderm. *Dev. Cell* **3,** 171–181.

6. Yutzey, K.E., and Kirby, M.L. (2002). Wherefore heart thou? Embryonic origins of cardiogenic mesoderm. *Dev. Dyn.* **223,** 307–320.

7. Bruneau, B.G. (2002). Transcriptional regulation of vertebrate cardiac morphogenesis. *Circ. Res.* **90,** 509–519.

8. Sater, A.K., and Jacobson, A.G. (1990). The role of the dorsal lip in the induction of heart mesoderm in *Xenopus laevis*. *Development* **108,** 461–470.

9. Montgomery, M.O., Litvin, J., Gonzalez-Sanchez, A., and Bader, D. (1994). Staging of commitment and differentiation of avian cardiac myocytes. *Dev. Biol.* **164,** 63–71.

10. Arai, A., Yamamoto, K., and Toyama, J. (1997). Murine cardiac progenitor cells require visceral embryonic endoderm and primitive streak for terminal differentiation. *Dev. Dyn.* **210,** 344–353.

11. Yatskievych, T., Ladd, A., Antin, P. (1997). Induction of cardiac myogenesis in avian pregastrula epiblast: the role of the hypoblast and activin. *Development* **124,** 2561–2570.

12. Auda-Boucher, G., Bernard, B., Fontaine-Perus, J., Rouaud, T., Mericksay, M., and Gardahaut, M.F. (2000). Staging of the commitment of murine cardiac cell progenitors. *Dev. Biol.* **225,** 214–225.

13. Lopez-Sanchez, C., Climent, V., Schoenwolf, G.C., Alvarez, I.S., and Garcia-Martinez, V. (2002). Induction of cardiogenesis by Hensen's node and fibroblast growth factors. *Cell Tissue Res.* **309,** 237–249.

14. Zhang, X.M., Ramalho-Santos, M., and McMahon, A.P. (2001). Smoothened mutants reveal redundant roles for Shh and Ihh signaling including regulation of L/R symmetry by the mouse node. *Cell* **106,** 781–792.

15. Ding, J., Yang, L., Yan, Y.T., Chen, A., Desai, N., Wynshaw-Boris, A., and Shen, M.M. (1998). Cripto is required for correct orientation of the anterior-posterior axis in the mouse embryo. *Nature* **395,** 702–707.

16. Xu, C., Liguori, G., Adamson, E.D., and Persico, M.G. (1998). Specific arrest of cardiogenesis in cultured embryonic stem cells lacking Cripto-1. *Dev. Biol.* **196,** 237–247.

17. Xu, C., Liguori, G., Persico, M.G., and Adamson, E.D. (1999). Abrogation of the Cripto gene in mouse leads to failure of postgastrulation morphogenesis and lack of differentiation of cardiomyocytes. *Development* **126,** 483–494.

18. Reiter, J.F., Verkade, H., and Stainier, D.Y. (2001). Bmp2b and Oep promote early myocardial differentiation through their regulation of gata5. *Dev. Biol.* **234,** 330–338.

19. Alsan, B.H., and Schultheiss, T.M. (2002). Regulation of avian cardiogenesis by Fgf8 signaling. *Development* **129,** 1935–1943.

20. Crossley, P.H., and Martin, G.R. (1995). The mouse Fgf8 gene encodes a family of polypeptides and is expressed in regions that direct outgrowth and patterning in the developing embryo. *Development* **121,** 439–451.

21. Shamim, H., and Mason, I. (1999). Expression of Fgf4 during early development of the chick embryo. *Mech. Dev.* **85,** 189–192.

22. Feldman, B., Poueymirou, W., Papaioannou, V.E., DeChiara, T.M., and Goldfarb, M. (1995). Requirement of Fgf-4 for postimplantation mouse development. *Science* **267,** 246–249.

23. Sun, X., Meyers, E.N., Lewandoski, M., and Martin, G.R. (1999). Targeted disruption of Fgf8 causes failure of cell migration in the gastrulating mouse embryo. *Genes Dev.* **13,** 1834–1846.

24. Reifers, F., Walsh, E.C., Leger, S., Stainier, D.Y., and Brand, M. (2000). Induction and differentiation of the zebrafish heart requires fibroblast growth factor 8 (fgf8/acerebellar). *Development* **127,** 225–235.

25. Garcia-Martinez, V., and Schoenwolf, G.C. (1993). Primitive-streak origin of the cardiovascular system in avian embryos. *Dev. Biol.* **159,** 706–719.

26. Wei, Y., and Mikawa, T. (2000). Fate diversity of primitive streak cells during heart field formation in ovo. *Dev. Dyn.* **219,** 505–513.

27. Saga, Y., Kitajima, S., and Miyagawa-Tomita, S. (2000). Mesp1 expression is the earliest sign of cardiovascular development. *Trends Cardiovasc. Med.* **10,** 345–352.

28. Stanley, E.G., Biben, C., Elefanty, A., Barnett, L., Koentgen, F., Robb, L., and Harvey, R.P. (2002). Efficient cre-mediated deletion in cardiac progenitor cells conferred by a 3′UTR-ires-Cre allele of the homeobox gene Nkx2.5. *Int. J. Dev. Biol.* **46,** 431–439.

29. Redkar, A., Montgomery, M., and Litvin, J. (2001). Fate map of early avian cardiac progenitor cells. *Development* **128,** 2269–2279.

30. Harvey, R.P. (2002). Patterning the vertebrate heart. *Nat. Rev. Genet.* **3,** 544–556.

31. Inagaki, T., Garcia-Martinez, V.M. and Schoenwolf, G.C. (1993). Regulative ability of the prospective cardiogenic and vasculogenic areas of the primitive streak during avian gastrulation. *Dev. Dyn.* **197,** 57–68.

32. Lough, J., and Sugi, Y. (2000). Endoderm and heart development. *Dev. Dyn.* **217,** 327–342.

33. Zaffran, S., and Frasch, M. (2002). Early signals in cardiac development. *Circ. Res.* **91,** 457–469.

34. Schultheiss, T.M., Burch, J.B., and Lassar, A.B. (1997). A role for bone morphogenetic proteins in the induction of cardiac myogenesis. *Genes Dev.* **11,** 451–462.

35. Andree, B., Duprez, D., Vorbusch, B., Arnold, H.H., and Brand, T. (1998). BMP-2 induces ectopic expression of cardiac lineage markers and interferes with somite formation in chicken embryos. *Mech. Dev.* **70,** 119–131.

36. Schlange, T., Andree, B., Arnold, H.H., and Brand, T. (2000). BMP2 is required for early heart development during a distinct time period. *Mech. Dev.* **91,** 259–270.

37. Walters, M.J., Wayman, G.A., and Christian, J.L. (2001). Bone morphogenetic protein function is required for terminal differentiation of the heart but not for early expression of cardiac marker genes. *Mech. Dev.* **100,** 263–273.

38. Monzen, K., Nagai, R., and Komuro, I. (2002). A role for bone morphogenetic protein signaling in cardiomyocyte differentiation. *Trends Cardiovasc. Med.* **12,** 263–269.

39. Shi, Y., Katsev, S., Cai, C., and Evans, S. (2000). BMP signaling is required for heart formation in vertebrates. *Dev. Biol.* **224,** 226–237.

40. Lough, J., Barron, M., Brogley, M., Sugi, Y., Bolender, D.L., and Zhu, X. (1996). Combined BMP-2 and FGF-4, but neither factor alone, induces cardiogenesis in non-precardiac embryonic mesoderm. *Dev. Biol.* **178,** 198–202.

41. Barron, M., Gao, M., and Lough, J. (2000). Requirement for BMP and FGF signaling during cardiogenic induction in non-precardiac mesoderm is specific, transient, and cooperative. *Dev. Dyn.* **218,** 383–393.

42. Sparrow, D.B., Kotecha, S., Towers, N., and Mohun, T.J. (1998). Xenopus eHAND: A marker for the developing cardiovascular system of the embryo that is regulated by bone morphogenetic proteins. *Mech. Dev.* **71,** 151–163.

43. Spencer, J.A., Major, M.L., and Misra, R.P. (1999). Basic fibroblast growth factor activates serum response factor gene

expression by multiple distinct signalling mechanisms. *Mol. Cell Biol.* **19**, 3977–3988.

44. Lien, C.L., Wu, C., Mercer, B., Webb, R., Richardson, J.A., and Olson, E.N. (1999). Control of early cardiac-specific transcription of Nkx2.5 by a GATA-dependent enhancer. *Development* **126**, 75–84.

45. Reiter, J.F., Alexander, J., Rodaway, A., Yelon, D., Patient, R., Holder, N., and Stainier, D.Y. (1999). Gata5 is required for the development of the heart and endoderm in zebrafish. *Genes Dev.* **13**, 2983–2995.

46. Harvey, R.P. (2002). Molecular determinants of cardiac development and congenital disease. *In* "Mouse Development: Patterning, Morphogenesis, and Organogenesis" (J. Rossand, P.P.L. Tam, eds.), pp. 331–370. Academic Press, San Diego.

47. Pandur, P., Lasche, M., Eisenberg, L.M., and Kuhl, M. (2002). Wnt-11 activation of a non-canonical Wnt signalling pathway is required for cardiogenesis. *Nature* **418**, 636–641.

48. Eisenberg, C.A., and Eisenberg, L.M. (1999). Wnt11 promotes cardiac tissue formation of early mesoderm. *Dev. Dyn.* **216**, 45–58.

49. Marvin, M.J., Di Rocco, G., Gardiner, A., Bush, S.M., and Lassar, A.B. (2001). Inhibition of Wnt activity induces heart formation from posterior mesoderm. *Genes Dev.* **15**, 316–327.

50. Tzahor, E., and Lassar, A.B. (2001). Wnt signals from the neural tube block ectopic cardiogenesis. *Genes Dev.* **15**, 255–260.

51. Schneider, V.A., and Mercola, M. (2001). Wnt antagonism initiates cardiogenesis in *Xenopus laevis*. *Genes Dev.* **15**, 304–315.

52. Nakamura, T., Sano, M., Songyang, Z., and Schneider, M.D. (2003). A Wnt- and β-catenin-dependent pathway for mammalian cardiac myogenesis. *Proc. Natl. Acad. Sci. U. S. A.* **100**, 5834–5839.

53. Ashe, H.L., Mannervik, M., and Levine, M. (2000). Dpp signalling thresholds in the dorsal ectoderm of the Drosophila embryo. *Development* **127**, 3305–3312.

54. Beiman, M., Shilo, B.Z., and Volk, T. (1996). Heartless, a Drosophila FGF receptor homolog, is essential for cell migration and establishment of several mesodermal lineages. *Genes Dev.* **10**, 2993–3002.

55. Gisselbrecht, S., Skeath, J.B., Doe, C.Q., and Michelson, A.M. (1996). heartless encodes a fibroblast growth factor receptor (DFR1/DFGF-R2) involved in the directional migration of early mesodermal cells in the Drosophila embryo. *Genes Dev.* **10**, 3003–3017.

56. Shishido, E., Ono, N., Kojima, T., and Saigo, K. (1997). Requirements of DFR1/Heartless, a mesoderm-specific Drosophila FGF-receptor, for the formation of heart, visceral and somatic muscles, and ensheathing of longitudinal axon tracts in CNS. *Development* **124**, 2119–2128.

57. Michelson, A.M., Gisselbrecht, S., Zhou, Y., Baek, K.H., and Buff, E.M. (1998). Dual functions of the heartless fibroblast growth factor receptor in development of the Drosophila embryonic mesoderm. *Dev. Genet.* **22**, 212–229.

58. Park, M., Wu, X., Golden, K., Axelrod, J.D., and Bodmer, R. (1996). The wingless signaling pathway is directly involved in Drosophila heart development. *Dev. Biol.* **177**, 104–116.

59. Linask, K.K., and Lash, J.W. (1986). Precardiac cell migration: fibronectin localization at mesoderm-endoderm interface during directional movement. *Dev. Biol.* **114**, 87–101.

60. Suzuki, H.R., Solursh, M., and Baldwin, H.S. (1995). Relationship between fibronectin expression during gastrulation and heart formation in the rat embryo. *Dev. Dyn.* **204**, 259–277.

61. George, E.L., Georges-Labouesse, E.N., Patel-King, R.S., Rayburn, H., and Hynes, R.O. (1993). defects in mesoderm,

neural tube and vascular development in mouse embryos lacking fibronectin. *Development* **119**, 1079–1091.

62. Viragh, S., and Challice, C.E. (1973). Origin and differentiation of cardiac muscle cells in the mouse. *J. Ultrastruct. Res.* **42**, 1–24.

63. Hamada, H., Meno, C., Watanabe, D., and Saijoh, Y. (2002). Establishment of vertebrate left-right asymmetry. *Nat. Rev. Genet.* **3**, 103–113.

64. de la Cruz, M.V., Sanchez Gomez, C., Arteaga, M.M., and Arguello, C. (1977). Experimental study of the development of the truncus and the conus in the chick embryo. *J. Anat.* **123**, 661–686.

65. De Ruiter, M.C., Poelmann, R.E., Vander Plas-de Vries, I., Mentink, M.M., and Gittenberger-de Groot, A.C. (1992). The development of the myocardium and endocardium in mouse embryos. Fusion of two heart tubes? *Anat. Embryol.* **185**, 461–473.

66. Wessels, A., Anderson, R.H., Webb, S., Brown, N.A., Viragh, S., Moorman, A.F., and Lamers, W.H. (2000). Atrial development in the human heart: an immunohistochemical study with emphasis on the role of mesenchymal tissues. *Anat. Rec.* **259**, 288–300.

67. Koutsourakis, M., Langeveld, A., Patient, R., Beddington, R., and Grosveld, F. (1999). The transcription factor Gata6 is essential for early extraembryonic development. *Development* **126**, 723–732.

68. Waldo, K.L., Kumiski, D.H., Wallis, K.T., Stadt, H.A., Hutson, M.R., Platt, D.H., and Kirby, M.L. (2001). Conotruncal myocardium arises from a secondary heart field. *Development* **128**, 3179–3188.

69. Kelly, R.G., and Buckingham, M.E. (2002). The anterior heart-forming field: voyage to the arterial pole of the heart. *Trends Genet.* **18**, 210–216.

70. Kelly, R.G., Brown, N.A., and Buckingham, M.E. (2001). The arterial pole of the mouse heart forms from Fgf10-expressing cells in pharyngeal mesoderm. *Dev. Cell* **1**, 435–440.

71. Mjaatvedt, C.H., Nakaoka, T., Moreno-Rodriguez, R., Norris, R.A., Kern, M.J., Eisenberg, C.A., Turner, D., and Markwald, R.R. (2001). The outflow tract of the heart is recruited from a novel heart-forming field. *Dev. Biol.* **238**, 97–109.

72. Waldo, K., Zdanowicz, M., Burch, J., Kumiski, D.H., Stadt, H.A., Godt, R.E., Creazzo, T.L., and Kirby, M.L. (1999). A novel role for cardiac neural crest in heart development. *J. Clin. Invest.* **103**, 1499–1507.

73. Yuan, S., and Schoenwolf, G.C. (2000). Islet-1 marks the early heart rudiments and is asymmetrically expressed during early rotation of the foregut in the chick embryo. *Anat. Rec.* **260**, 204–207.

74. Chapman, D.L., Garvey, N., Hancock, S., Alexiou, M., Agulnik, S.I., Gibson-Brown, J.J., Cebra-Thomas, J., Bollag, R.J., Silver, L.M., and Papaioannou, V.E. (1996). Expression of the T-box family genes, Tbx1-Tbx5, during early mouse development. *Dev. Dyn.* **206**, 379–390.

75. Jerome, L.A., and Papaioannou, V.E. (2001). DiGeorge syndrome phenotype in mice mutant for the T-box gene, Tbx1. *Nat. Genet.* **27**, 286–291.

76. Vitelli, F., Morishima, M., Taddei, I., Lindsay, E.A., and Baldini, A. (2002). Tbx1 mutation causes multiple cardiovascular defects and disrupts neural crest and cranial nerve migratory pathways. *Hum. Mol. Genet.* **11**, 915–922.

77. Rones, M.S., McLaughlin, K.A., Raffin, M., and Mercola, M. (2000). Serrate and Notch specify cell fates in the heart field by suppressing cardiomyogenesis. *Development* **127**, 3865–3876.

78. Fishman, M., and Olson, E. (1997). Parsing the heart: genetic modules for organ assembly. *Cell* **17**, 153–156.

79. Srivastava, D., Thomas, T., Lin, Q., Kirby, M.L., Brown, D., and Olson, E.N. (1997). Regulation of cardiac mesodermal and neural crest development by the bHLH transcription factor dHAND. *Nat. Genet.* **16**, 154–160.

80. Biben, C., and Harvey, R.P. (1997). Homeodomain factor Nkx2-5 controls left/right asymmetric expression of bHLH gene eHand during murine heart development. *Genes Dev.* **11**, 1357–1369.

81. Thomas, T., Kurihara, H., Yamagishi, H., Kurihara, Y., Yazaki, Y., Olson, E.N., and Srivastava, D. (1998). A signaling cascade involving endothelin-1, dHAND and msx1 regulates development of neural-crest-derived branchial arch mesenchyme. *Development* **125**, 3005–3014.

82. Riley, P., Anson-Cartwright, L., and Cross, J.C. (1998). The Hand1 bHLH transcription factor is essential for placentation and cardiac morphogenesis. *Nat. Genet.* **18**, 271–275.

83. Riley, P.R., Gertsenstein, M., Dawson, K., and Cross, J.C. (2000). Early exclusion of hand1-deficient cells from distinct regions of the left ventricular myocardium in chimaeric mouse embryos. *Dev. Biol.* **227**, 156–168.

84. Firulli, B.A., McFadden, D.G., Lin, Q., Srivastava, D., and Olson, E.N. (1998). Heart and extra-embryonic mesoderm defects in mouse embryos lacking the bHLH transcription factor Hand1. *Nat. Genet.* **18**, 266–270.

85. Yamagishi, H., Yamagishi, C., Nakagawa, O., Harvey, R.P., Olson, E.N., and Srivastava, D. (2001). The combinatorial activities of Nkx2.5 and dHAND are essential for cardiac ventricle formation. *Dev. Biol.* **239**, 190–203.

86. Bao, Z.Z., Bruneau, B.G., Seidman, J.G., Seidman, C.E., and Cepko, C.L. (1999). Regulation of chamber-specific gene expression in the developing heart by Irx4. *Science* **283**, 1161–1164.

87. Bruneau, B.G., Nemer, G., Schmitt, J.P., Charron, F., Robitaille, L., Caron, S., Conner, D.A., Gessler, M., Nemer, M., Seidman, C.E., and Seidman, J.G. (2001). A murine model of Holt-Oram syndrome defines roles of the T-box transcription factor Tbx5 in cardiogenesis and disease. *Cell* **106**, 709–721.

88. Hiroi, Y., Kudoh, S., Monzen, K., Ikeda, Y., Yazaki, Y., Nagai, R., and Komuro, I. (2001). Tbx5 associates with Nkx2-5 and synergistically promotes cardiomyocyte differentiation. *Nat. Genet.* **28**, 276–280.

89. Habets, P.E., Moorman, A.F., Clout, D.E., van Roon, M.A., Lingbeek, M., van Lohuizen, M., Campione, M., and Christoffels, V.M. (2002). Cooperative action of Tbx2 and Nkx2.5 inhibits ANF expression in the atrioventricular canal: implications for cardiac chamber formation. *Genes Dev.* **16**, 1234–1246.

90. Lyons, I., Parsons, L.M., Hartley, L., Li, R., Andrews, J.E., Robb, L., and Harvey, R.P. (1995). Myogenic and morphogenetic defects in the heart tubes of murine embryos lacking the homeo box gene Nkx2-5. *Genes Dev.* **9**, 1654–1666.

91. Tanaka, M., Chen, Z., Bartunkova, S., Yamasaki, N., and Izumo, S. (1999). The cardiac homeobox gene Csx/Nkx2.5 lies genetically upstream of multiple genes essential for heart development. *Development* **126**, 1269–1280.

92. Burton, P.B., Raff, M.C., Kerr, P., Yacoub, M.H., and Barton, P.J. (1999). An intrinsic timer that controls cell-cycle withdrawal in cultured cardiac myocytes. *Dev. Biol.* **216**, 659–670.

93. Armstrong, M.T., Lee, D.Y., and Armstrong, P.B. (2000). Regulation of proliferation of the fetal myocardium. *Dev. Dyn.* **219**, 226–236.

94. Mima, T., Ueno, H., Fischman, D.A., Williams, L.T., and Mikawa, T. (1995). Fibroblast growth factor receptor is required for in vivo cardiac myocyte proliferation at early embryonic stages of heart development. *Proc. Natl. Acad. Sci. U. S. A.* **92**, 467–471.

95. Sheng, Z., Pennica, D., Wood, W.I., and Chien, K.R. (1996). Cardiotrophin-1 displays early expression in the murine heart tube and promotes cardiac myocyte survival. *Development* **122**, 419–428.

96. Shin, C.H., Liu, Z.P., Passier, R., Zhang, C.L., Wang, D.Z., Harris, T.M., Yamagishi, H., Richardson, J.A., Childs, G., and Olson, E.N. (2002). Modulation of cardiac growth and development by HOP, an unusual homeodomain protein. *Cell* **110**, 725–735.

97. Chen, F., Kook, H., Milewski, R., Gitler, A.D., Lu, M.M., Li, J., Nazarian, R., Schnepp, R., Jen, K., Biben, C., Runke, G., Mackay, J.P., Novotny, J., Schwartz, R.J., Harvey, R.P., Mullins, M.C., and Epstein, J.A. (2002). Hop is an unusual homeobox gene that modulates cardiac development. *Cell* **110**, 713–723.

98. Rottbauer, W., Saurin, A.J., Lickert, H., Shen, X., Burns, C.G., Wo, Z.G., Kemler, R., Kingston, R., Wu, C., and Fishman, M. (2002). Reptin and Pontin antagonistically regulate heart growth in zebrafish embryos. *Cell* **111**, 661–672.

99. Rottbauer, W., Baker, K., Wo, Z.G., Mohideen, M-A.P.K., Cantiello, H.F., and Fishman, M.C. (2001). Growth and function of the embryonic heart depend on the cardiac-specific L-type calcium channel α1 subunit. *Dev. Cell* **1**, 265–275.

100. Brockes, J.P., and Kumar, A. (2002) Plasticity and reprogramming of differentiated cells in amphibian regeneration. *Nat. Rev. Mol. Cell Biol.* **3**, 567–574.

101. Poss, K.D., Wilson, L.G., and Keating, M.T. (2002). Heart regeneration in zebrafish. *Sci. Online* **298**, 2188–2190.

102. Christoffels, V.M., Habets, P.E., Franco, D., Campione, M., de Jong, F., Lamers, W.H., Bao, Z.Z., Palmer, S., Biben, C., Harvey, R.P., and Moorman, A.F. (2000). Chamber formation and morphogenesis in the developing mammalian heart. *Dev. Biol.* **223**, 266–278.

103. Jeter, J.R., Jr., and Cameron, I.L. (1971). Cell proliferation patterns during cytodifferentiation in embryonic chick tissues: liver, heart and erythrocytes. *J. Embryol. Exp. Morphol.* **25**, 405–422.

104. Mikawa, T., Borisov, A., Brown, A.M., and Fischman, D.A. (1992). Clonal analysis of cardiac morphogenesis in the chicken embryo using a replication-defective retrovirus: I. Formation of the ventricular myocardium. *Dev. Dyn.* **193**, 11–23.

105. Pasumarthi, K.B., and Field, L.J. (2002). Cardiomyocyte cell cycle regulation. *Circ. Res.* **90**, 1044–1054.

106. Moorman, A.F., de Jong, F., Denyn, M.M., and Lamers, W.H. (1998). Development of the cardiac conduction system. *Circ. Res.* **82**, 629–644.

107. Mikawa, T., Cohen-Gould, L., and Fischman, D.A. (1992). Clonal analysis of cardiac morphogenesis in the chicken embryo using a replication-defective retrovirus. III: Polyclonal origin of adjacent ventricular myocytes. *Dev. Dyn.* **195**, 133–141.

108. Chen, T.H., Chang, T.C., Kang, J.O., Choudhary, B., Makita, T., Tran, C.M., Burch, J.B., Eid, H., and Sucov, H.M. (2002). Epicardial induction of fetal cardiomyocyte proliferation via a retinoic acid-inducible trophic factor. *Dev. Biol.* **250**, 198–207.

109. Stuckmann, I., Evans, S., and Lassar, A.B. (2003). Erythropoietin and retinoic acid, secreted from the epicardium, are required for cardiac myocyte proliferation. *Dev. Biol.* **255**, 334–349.

110. Kirby, M.L., and Waldo, K. (1995). Neural crest and cardiovascular patterning. *Circ. Res.* **77**, 211–215.

111. Farrell, M.J., Burch, J.L., Wallis, K., Rowley, L., Kumiski, D., Stadt, H., Godt, R.E., Creazzo, T.L., and Kirby, M.L. (2001). FGF-8 in the ventral pharynx alters development of myocardial calcium transients after neural crest ablation. *J. Clin. Invest.* **107,** 1509–1517.

112. Yelbuz, T.M., Waldo, K.L., Kumiski, D.H., Stadt, H.A., Wolfe, R.R., Leatherbury, L., and Kirby, M.L. (2002). Shortened outflow tract leads to altered cardiac looping after neural crest ablation. *Circulation* **106,** 504–510.

113. Li, Y.-X., Zdanowicz, M., Young, L., Kumiski, D., Leatherbury, L., and Kirby, M.L. (2003). Cardiac neural crest in zebrafish embryos contributes to myocardial cell lineage and early heart function. *Dev. Dyn.* **266,** 540–555.

114. Sato, M., and Yost, H.J. (2003). Cardiac neural crest contributes to cardiomyogenesis in zebrafish. *Dev. Biol.* **257,** 127–139.

115. Waldo, K.L., Lo, C.W., and Kirby, M.L. (1999). Connexin 43 expression neural crest patterns during cardiovascular development. *Dev. Biol.* **208,** 307–323.

116. Jiang, X., Rowitch, D.H., Soriano, P., McMahon, A.P., and Sucov, H.M. (2000). Fate of the mammalian cardiac neural crest. *Development* **127,** 1607–1616.

117. Kioussi, C., Briata, P., Baek, S.H., Rose, D.W., Hamblet, N.S., Herman, T., Ohgi, K.A., Lin, C., Gleiberman, A., Wang, J., Brault, V., Ruiz-Lozano, P., Nguyen, H.D., Kemler, R., Glass, C.K., Wynshaw-Boris, A., and Rosenfeld, M.G. (2002). Identification of a Wnt/Dvl/b-catenin Pitx2 pathway mediating cell-type-specific proliferation during development. *Cell* **111,** 673–685.

118. van den Hoff, M.J., Moorman, A.F., Ruijter, J.M., Lamers, W.H., Bennington, R.W., Markwald, R.R., and Wessels, A. (1999). Myocardialization of the cardiac outflow tract. *Dev. Biol.* **212,** 477–490.

119. van den Hoff, M.J., Kruithof, B.P., Moorman, A.F., Markwald, R.R., and Wessels, A. (2001). Formation of myocardium after the initial development of the linear heart tube. *Dev. Biol.* **240,** 61–76.

120. Markwald, R., Eisenberg, C., Eisenberg, L., Trusk, T., and Sugi, Y. (1996). Epithelial-mesenchymal transformations in early avian heart development. *Acta Anat.* **156,** 173–186.

Potential of ES Cell Differentiation Culture for Vascular Biology

Hiroshi Hisatsune, Nobuyuki Kondoh, Jun Yamashita, Satomi Nishikawa, and Shin-Ichi Nishikawa

Recent progress in vascular biology has been largely supported by two experimental systems that allow manipulation of *in vivo* angiogenesis: one is the various systems to observe neoangiogenesis and the other is gene targeting technology. The former has been useful to test both positive and negative molecules that affect the process of angiogenesis, and the latter has been used to characterize the function of a particular gene under normal circumstances. Through *in vivo* studies investigators have identified a large number of molecules involved in angiogenesis and characterized their functions in various situations including embryonic vascular development. Although this list is still expanding, a new problem has been recognized: phenotypes induced by the *in vivo* manipulations are not necessarily sufficient to specify the function of objective molecules, particularly at the cellular level. Except for such molecules as vascular endothelial growth factor (VEGF) and its receptor, whose role in development of the vascular system has been specified at both the organism and cellular levels, many of the listed molecules can be defined no further than as molecules required for vascular remodeling. An important reason for this problem is the deficit of our understanding of the function of each molecule at the cellular level. Indeed, it is difficult to describe how a given molecule is involved in the formation of a complex vascular system without knowing its function at the cellular level. Hence, development of experimental systems that enable investigators to evaluate the function of a given molecule at the cellular level is an urgent issue in this field.

Previously, most studies of the cell biology of vascular endothelial cells (EC) used endothelial cell lines that were generated and propagated *in vitro* by various methods. Although those cell lines have been useful for many purposes, it has also been widely recognized that they, although many of them are not transformed, have lost some features that are characteristics of the normal EC. In an attempt to ameliorate problems of established EC cell lines, we have prepared relatively normal EC from embryonic stem (ES) cells, because ES cells have been proven to differentiate to all somatic cells in the human body. We thus expected that EC, particularly those present in the developing embryo, may be obtained from

ES cell differentiation cultures. In this chapter, we describe our data relating to EC and its progenitor that can be prepared in the ES cell differentiation culture.

Cultures for Embryonic Stem Cell Differentiation

ES cell lines are possible because of the discovery that leukemia inhibitory factor (LIF) can inhibit differentiation of ES cells, while maintaining their proliferation. Hence, induction of ES cell differentiation is achieved by transferring immature ES cells to conditions without LIF. The most popular method for inducing ES cell differentiation has been to use embryoid body (EB) as an environment for differentiation.[1–3] By this method, ES cells are first rendered to form aggregates and transferred to the LIF(–) differentiation condition. Two epithelial cell layers, visceral endoderm on the outside and ectoderm on the inside, are spontaneously formed from these aggregates. Various cell lineages have been demonstrated to be generated within EB without addition of exogenous cytokine, indicating that EB can provide an embryo-like microenvironment that contains the necessary molecules for ES cell differentiation. Indeed, the two-layered structure with visceral endoderm and embryonic ectoderm is reminiscent of the egg-cylinder stage embryo.

Although EB culture has advantages such as ease of performance and reproducibility, a clear disadvantage of this method is that it requires a complex three-dimensional (3D) structure that is difficult to manipulate and monitor. To overcome this problem, attempts have been made to induce EB differentiation in a two-dimensional (2D) plane. In an attempt to induce ES cell differentiation to the hematopoietic cell (HPC), Nakano *et al.*[4] reported a culture of ES cells on OP9 stromal cell line. In this stromal cell–dependent culture, ES cells undergo proliferation and differentiation without forming 3D structures such as EB. In this culture, ES cells were cultured on OP9 that expressed the molecules required for proliferation and differentiation of hematopoietic stem cells. Of interest is the striking variation in the differentiation-supporting ability among stromal cell lines, particularly the repertoire of lineages generated in culture. Initially, Nakano *et al.* ascribed the activity of OP9 to support preferential differentiation to the HPC lineage to the deficit of macrophage colony-stimulating factor (M-CSF) expression in the OP9 stromal cell line (OP9 is a stromal cell line that was established

Handbook of Stem Cells
Volume 1

from the *op/op* mouse bearing a null mutation in the M-CSF gene[5]). However, later study demonstrated that OP9 can induce preferential differentiation of lateral mesoderm as compared with other stromal cell lines. Indeed, PA6, which can also support proliferation and differentiation of hematopoietic stem cells as efficiently as OP9, was shown to be defective in inducing the lateral mesoderm.[6] Instead, PA6 was shown to be an efficient stromal cell to support neuronal differentiation.[7] Hence, variation among stromal cell lines will be useful for understanding the molecular mechanisms regulating each distinct cell lineage and will provide a powerful method to steer ES cell differentiation.

Regarding the differentiation to EC and HPC, we have shown that collagen IV matrix is sufficient for ES cell differentiation to these lineages through lateral mesoderm. In this culture, ES cells are spread on a 2D plane coated by collagen IV and undergo differentiation to lateral and paraxial mesoderm.[8] This result indicates clearly that neither 3D structure nor stromal cells are required for induction of early intermediate stages from ES cells. Our study showed that ES cells spontaneously proliferate and differentiate under a simple culture condition, although the cell density is the critical factor influencing the outcome.

Because the next step for ES cell differentiation culture is to develop chemically defined culture conditions, it is significant that ES cells can undergo differentiation under a simple culture condition. Although serum-containing medium can support the differentiation to lateral mesoderm without exogenous growth factors, the mesoderm induction does not occur in the serum-free medium unless appropriate cytokines such as bone morphogenetic protein (BMP) are added (our unpublished observation). Thus, it is expected that the simplicity of this culture system will be useful to identify molecular requirements for induction of each cell lineage.

Markers for Defining Intermediate Stages During Endothelial Cell Differentiation

To date, no ES cell differentiation cultures can steer the ES cell differentiation at will to select a particular pathway, although the PA6 stromal cell line can induce as high as 90% nestin[+] cells. Nonetheless, in every currently available culture method including ours, multiple cell lineages are generated simultaneously on induction of differentiation. This situation's most significant problem is the difficulty in monitoring the events in the culture before the appearance of such cells as erythrocytes that can be characterized easily. This problem can be ameliorated if intermediate stages in a particular differentiation pathway are distinguished from other cell lineages. Although a number of stage- and lineage-specific markers have been developed for defining early intermediate stages, most markers require fixation of cells and, thus, are difficult to apply to living cells.

Basically, two methods are available to purify living cells at various intermediate stages. The first method is to use drug-based selection.[9,10] By this method, drug-resistant genes are expressed under the control of the gene regulatory unit that can direct the gene expression at a particular stage and in a particular cell lineage. After induction of ES cell differentiation, any cells of interest can be selected by adding the appropriate concentration of drug in the culture, if the drug-resistant gene is expressed specifically. The other method is to use cell sorting. To apply this technology, cells of interest have to be defined by the expression of cell surface markers that can be detected by labeled antibodies or fluorescent protein driven by a cell-specific promoter.[8] Concerning the differentiation to EC, both methods have been shown to be useful. Because any depletion of unwanted cells by drug selections requires some incubation time, drug-based selection is not suitable for selection of intermediate stages that appear only transiently. For this purpose, cell sorting technology is more useful. Moreover, cell sorting technology can combine multiple markers for the definition of the cells, which is difficult to perform by drug-based selection, although it is theoretically possible.

Although cell sorting can use multiple markers simultaneously, there few markers available for sorting intermediate stages that appear during early embryogenesis. In this context, we believe that ES cell differentiation to EC might be the best characterized process with multiple markers. As summarized in Fig. 29–1, we defined distinct intermediate stages during differentiation to EC by using multiple markers. In this scheme, mature EC is defined as the stage expressing all EC markers such as Flk1, VE-cadherin, platelet endothelial cell adhesion molecule (PECAM), and CD34. Analysis of the time course of the expression of these molecules demonstrated that they appear successively in an orderly manner. Moreover, immature stages before mesoderm differentiation are defined as cells negative in these markers but positive in E-cadherin expression that is down-regulated on mesoderm differentiation. Taken together, E-cadherin[+]Flk1[-] embryonic ectoderm cells differentiate first to E-cadherin[-]Flk1[+]VE-cadherin[-] mesoderm. This population then diverges to primitive erythrocytes, smooth muscle cells, and immature EC, but only the EC is Flk1[+]VE-cadherin[+]PECAM[-]CD34[-]. This ES population then expresses successively PECAM and eventually CD34. Each stage can be distinguished and sorted by the cell sorter, and the order of each stage during EC differentiation can be confirmed by sorting and short-term culture. As few as 2–3 days are required for completing all the process after the Flk1[+] mesoderm appears; dissection of this process can only be attained by cell sorting. Because of the short course, the process can be transferred to chemically defined condition, thereby determining the molecular requirement for differentiation. Indeed, we have recently demonstrated that this process can be supported to some extent under a serum-free condition.[11]

Utility of Embryonic Stem Cell Culture for Cell Biology of Endothelial Cells

Because a number of reliable methods for inducing EC from ES cells and markers to purify the cells in this differentiation pathway are available, EC generated from ES are now ready for cell biology use.

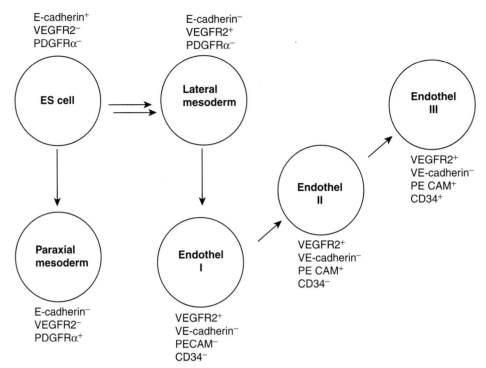

Figure 29-1. *Intermediate stages during differentiation of endothelial cells from embryonic stem (ES) cells. Five intermediate stages have been identified during differentiation of endothelial cells from ES cells. Each stage is defined in terms of the expression of the surface molecules indicated in the figure.*

CLONOGENIC ASSAY OF ENDOTHELIAL CELLS

An important system that emerged from investigation of ES cell differentiation culture is a clonogenic assay of the vascular progenitor using the OP9 stromal cell. A protocol of this method was described in detail in the report by Hirashima *et al.*[12] Briefly, the cell population that contains vascular progenitors is seeded onto the OP9 stromal cell layer. After 4–7 days of incubation, vascular progenitors form a colony that can be detected by staining with EC specific markers (Fig. 29–1). From the single-cell deposion analysis, it is likely that this assay can support clonogenic growth of even a single progenitor.[8] Moreover, this assay is effective not only for the progenitors derived from ES cells but also for those present in actual embryos.[13] In addition, a similar culture system using OP9 has been used for culturing the embryonic fragment to investigate the process of vascular development.[14]

It should be emphasized that many stromal cell lines could not be used for this assay. Indeed, as far as we have tested, no other cell lines were able to give better results than OP9 for this purpose. Because no exogenous molecules are required for this assay, it is likely that all essential molecules required for the clonogenic growth of EC such as VEGF are expressed by OP9. Our studies showed that many of the important angiogenic molecules are expressed by OP9.[12,15,16] Moreover, we think that the expression level and balance of angiogenic molecules expressed in a given cell line are important factors in determining its aptitude for the clonogenic assay.

Indeed, addition of exogenous VEGF to OP9 culture induces dispersion of the EC colony, rendering the quantification of the EC colony difficult.[12] Nonetheless, the OP9 cell line provides a suitable condition for enumerating the number of clonogenic EC progenitors from both ES cell differentiation cultures and the actual embryos. Because the proliferative capacity of EC may decrease on maturation, it should be noted that the proportion of EC progenitors clonable by this assay would decrease during embryogenesis. However, further studies are needed.

ENDOTHELIAL CELL DIVERSIFICATION

It is established that EC diversify quickly into different subsets such as arterial, venous, or capillary EC during development of the vascular system. Recent studies uncovered the molecular network involved in this process, in which Notch and Eph/Ephrin signaling pathways play key roles.[17,18] Because the failure of EC diversification resulting from defects of these signal pathways results in failure in the formation of an organized architecture of vascular network, generation of EC diversity is an essential step for vascular remodeling. Although the role of Notch and Eph/Ephrin in the vascular remodeling genes is clearly demonstrated in the mice bearing null mutations in those genes, not much has been understood concerning the function of each molecule in EC diversification. ES cell differentiation culture, in its inherent potential to deal with differentiating EC, should be the most

Hiroshi Hisatsune, Nobuyuki Kondoh, Jun Yamashita, Satomi Nishikawa, and Shin-Ichi Nishikawa

suitable experimental system to investigate the process of EC diversification. Indeed, we have demonstrated that some diversity is generated in our culture system. For instance, we are able to distinguish EC in terms of their potential to give rise to the hematopoietic cell lineage.[19,20] The number of markers that can be used for defining the diversity, however, is not enough. For instance, Eph/Ephrin and Notch regulate the process of specification of venous and arterial EC, implicating the usefulness of surface expression of these molecules in monitoring the EC diversity. However, there is still a deficiency of reliable antibodies to these molecules, which can be used for surface staining. Hence, this culture system has not gain popularity in studying EC diversification, although it should have great potential.

CELLULAR BEHAVIOR OF ENDOTHELIAL CELLS

We expect that the method of preparing EC in ES cell differentiation culture would have enormous potential in the study of the cell biologic aspect of EC behavior. Although many EC cell lines such as HUVEC are available for the cell biology of EC, it has been recognized that those cell lines have lost properties that are characteristic of EC during *in vitro* propagation. Thus, before using the EC cell lines for cell biology, the extent to which the EC cell lines represent normal EC must be determined. Another way to obtain normal EC would be to purify distinct subsets of EC from developing embryos. However, although it is theoretically possible, it is not easy to sort enough cells from the developing vascular systems of embryos. Because accumulating evidence suggests that EC prepared in the ES cell cultures maintains many properties of normal EC, this is a good, presently available method for preparing normal EC for cell biology. Moreover, as discussed previously, it is possible to differentially prepare distinct EC subsets, although further attempt to produce various markers for EC diversity is yet to be required. In this sense, we are well aware that exploitation of ES cell-derived EC may be at the very initial stage. However, some pilot studies of ours and others have already succeeded in indicating the usefulness of this method. In the final section of this chapter, we describe some examples of these studies.

As described in a previous section, OP9 provides a microenvironment that supports clonogenic proliferation of EC progenitors. A spontaneous balance of angiogenic factors established spontaneously in this culture allows EC progenitors to grow and form a round colony-like sheet in which cells adhere to each other by a VE-cadherin–mediated adherence junction. Thus, the colony-like EC sheets are useful to detect various molecules that enhance the motility of EC, because enhancement of EC motility induced the dispersion of each EC in the colony-like sheet, thereby disturbing their round shape. As shown in Fig. 29–2, stable round EC sheets are transformed into clusters of dispersed EC by addition of exogenous VEGF.[12] Moreover, we have recently shown that the VEGFR3 signal inhibits dispersion of the EC colony, probably negatively modulating the signal pathway of VEGFR2, which enhances EC motility.[15]

The cell–cell junction is another factor affecting the integrity of the EC sheet. Immunostaining of the EC sheet formed on OP9 contains both adherence junction mediated by VE-cadherin and tight junction mediated by a set of claudin (our unpublished observations). There are a number of claudins detected in the EC–EC junction, but Claudin 5 is the major molecule. Consistent with previous studies using EB, the addition of an antagonistic mAb to VE-cadherin disrupts the EC–EC junction, thereby disturbing formation of the round EC sheet. When this system is combined with various reagents that allow monitoring of various molecules associated with the cell–cell junction, more subtle change in the EC–EC junction can also be detected.

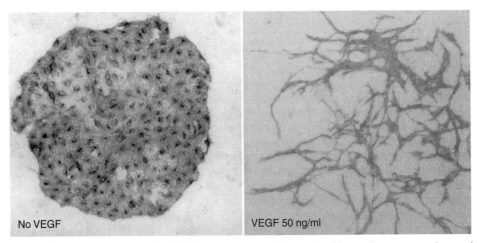

No VEGF

VEGF 50 ng/ml

Figure 29–2. *Clonogenic growth of endothelial progenitors on the OP9 stromal cell layer in the presence or absence of vascular endothelial growth factor (VEGF). VEGFR2+E-cadherin− lateral mesoderm cells (see Fig. 29–1) that were generated in vitro from embryonic stem (ES) cells were sorted and cultured on an OP9 stromal cell layer in the presence or absence of VEGF. In the absence of VEGF, the cells grew to form a round colony. Addition of VEGF induces dispersal of endothelial cells. Endothelial cells are identified by platelet endothelial cell adhesion molecule (PECAM) expression.*

Finally, this system is useful for detecting signals that induce the change of cell shape. For instance, VEGF is an effective signal. As shown in Fig. 29–2, the addition of exogenous VEGF in this culture enhances the motility of EC. In addition, the shape of EC is changed from round to elongated by this treatment. Currently, we do not know which signals induce shape changes of EC, but we expect that it would be valuable to use this culture system to screen the vasoactive substances.

Moreover, this system would be useful to screen drugs that may inhibit or enhance those three activities of EC that are detectable in this culture. For instance, it would be possible to screen drugs that show inhibitory effect on VEGF-induced EC dispersion. Such drugs may have a potential for the maintenance of the integrity of the EC layer even in the presence of a strong VEGF signal that disturbs the EC integrity. Likewise, it would be possible to find drugs that specifically affect, for instance, the cell motility, while leaving proliferation and shape unchanged.

Conclusing Remarks

In this chapter, we describe an *in vitro* system that can induce EC differentiation from ES cells and also the potential of these induced EC for cell biologic analyses of the behavior of EC. Although we have worked on this system for several years, we realize that it is still in the process of development. Nonetheless, it is important that the EC generated in this culture system behaves like the normal vascular progenitors that can be integrated in the vascular system that is induced in the *in vivo* neoangiogenesis setting. Thus, the EC supplied by this system is a rare source of normal EC. We encourage the readers to consider this system for investigating the cell biology of EC. We are ready to help you introduce this method in your work.

REFERENCES

1. Doetschman, T.C., Eistetter, H., Katz, M., Schmidt, W., and Kemler, R. (1985). The in vitro development of blastocyst-derived embryonic stem cell lines: formation of visceral yolk sac, blood islands and myocardium. *J. Embryol. Exp. Morphol.* **87,** 27–45.
2. Burkert, U., von Ruden, T., and Wagner, E.F. (1991). Early fetal hematopoietic development from in vitro differentiated embryonic stem cells. *New Biol.* **3,** 698–708.
3. Wiles, M.V., and Keller, G. (1991). Multiple hematopoietic lineages develop from embryonic stem (ES) cells in culture. *Development* **111,** 259–267.
4. Nakano, T., Kodama, H., and Honjo, T. (1994). Generation of lymphohematopoietic cells from embryonic stem cells in culture. *Science* **265,** 1098–1101.
5. Yoshida, H., Hayashi, S., Kunisada, T., Ogawa, M., Nishikawa, S., Okamura, H., Sudo, T., and Shultz, L.D. (1990). The murine mutation osteopetrosis is in the coding region of the macrophage colony stimulating factor gene. *Nature* **345,** 442–444.
6. Kataoka, H., Takakura, N., Nishikawa, S., Tsuchida, K., Kodama, H., Kunisada, T., Risau, W., Kita, T., and Nishikawa, S.I.

(1997). Expressions of PDGF receptor alpha, c-Kit and Flk1 genes clustering in mouse chromosome 5 define distinct subsets of nascent mesodermal cells. *Dev. Growth Differ.* **39,** 729–740.
7. Kawasaki, H., Mizuseki, K., Nishikawa, S., Kaneko, S., Kuwana, Y., Nakanishi, S., Nishikawa, S.I., and Sasai, Y. (2000). Induction of midbrain dopaminergic neurons from ES cells by stromal cell-derived inducing activity. *Neuron* **28,** 31–40.
8. Nishikawa, S.I., Nishikawa, S., Hirashima, M., Matsuyoshi, N., and Kodama, H. (1998). Progressive lineage analysis by cell sorting and culture identifies FLK1+VE-cadherin+ cells at a diverging point of endothelial and hemopoietic lineages. *Development* **125,** 1747–1757.
9. Li, M., Pevny, L., Lovell-Badge, R., and Smith, A. (1998). Generation of purified neural precursors from embryonic stem cells by lineage selection. *Curr. Biol.* **8,** 971–974.
10. Marchetti, S., Gimond, C., Iljin, K., Bourcier, C., Alitalo, K., Pouyssegur, J., and Pages, G. (2002). Endothelial cells genetically selected from differentiating mouse embryonic stem cells incorporate at sites of neovascularization in vivo. *J. Cell Sci.* **115,** 2075–2085.
11. Hirashima, M., Ogawa, M., Nishikawa, S., Matsumura, K., Kawasaki, K., Shibuya, M., and Nishikawa, S.I. (2003). A chemically defined culture of VEGFR2+ cells derived from embryonic stem cells reveals the role of VEGFR1 in tuning the threshold for VEGF in developing endothelial cells. *Blood* **101,** 2261–2267.
12. Hirashima, M., Kataoka, H., Nishikawa, S., and Matsuyoshi, N. (1999). Maturation of embryonic stem cells into endothelial cells in an in vitro model of vasculogenesis. *Blood* **93,** 1253–1263.
13. Fujimoto, T., Ogawa, M., Minegishi, N., Yoshida, H., Yokomizo, T., Yamamoto, M., and Nishikawa, S. (2001). Step-wise divergence of primitive and definitive haematopoietic and endothelial cell lineages during embryonic stem cell differentiation. *Genes Cells* **6,** 1113–1127.
14. Takakura, N., Watanabe, T., Suenobu, S., Yamada, Y., Noda, T., Ito, Y., Satake, M., and Suda, T. (2000). A role for hematopoietic stem cells in promoting angiogenesis. *Cell* **102,** 199–209.
15. Matsumura, K., Hirashima, M, Ogawa, M., Kubo, H., Hisatsune, H., Kondo, N., Nishikawa, S. Chiba, T., and Nishikawa, S.I. (2003). Modulation of VEGFR-2-mediated endothelial-cell activity by VEGF-C/VEGFR-3. *Blood* **101,** 1367–1374.
16. Takakura, N., Huang, X.L., Naruse, T., Hamaguchi, I., Dumont, D.J., Yancopoulos, G.D., and Suda, T. (1998). Critical role of the TIE2 endothelial cell receptor in the development of definitive hematopoiesis. *Immunity* **9,** 677–686.
17. Krebs, L.T., Xue, Y., Norton, C.R., Shutter, J.R., Maguire, M., Sundberg, J.P., Gallahan, D., Closson, V., Kitajewski, J., Callahan, R., Smith, G.H., Stark, K.L., and Gridley, T. (2000). Notch signaling is essential for vascular morphogenesis in mice. *Genes Dev.* **14,** 1343–1352.
18. Wang, H.U., Chen, Z.F., and Anderson, D.J. (1998). Molecular distinction and angiogenic interaction between embryonic arteries and veins revealed by ephrin-B2 and its receptor Eph-B4. *Cell* **93,** 741–753.
19. Ogawa, M., Kizumoto, M., Nishikawa, S., Fujimoto, T., Kodama, H., and Nishikawa, S.I. (1999). Expression of alpha4-integrin defines the earliest precursor of hematopoietic cell lineage diverged from endothelial cells. *Blood* **93,** 1168–1177.
20. Hirai, H., Ogawa, M., Suzuki, N., Yamamoto, M., Breier, G., Mazda, O., Imanishi, J., and Nishikawa, S. (2003). Hemogenic and nonhemogenic endothelium can be distinguished by the activity of fetal liver kinase (Flk)-1 promoter/enhancer during mouse embryogenesis. *Blood* **101,** 886–893.

30

Vascular Progenitor Cells in the Human Model

Sharon Gerecht-Nir and Joseph Itskovitz-Eldor

Human Vascular Development, Maintenance, and Renewal

INTRODUCTION

During the third week of human embryo development, blood vessels are formed in conjunction with blood islands within the yolk sac mesoderm. During this process, blood islands develop alongside the endoderm, which segregate into individual hemangioblasts that are surrounded by flattened endothelial precursor cells. The hemangioblasts mature into the first blood cells, whereas the endothelial precursors develop into blood vessel endothelium. At the end of the third week, the entire yolk sac, the chorionic villi, and the connecting stalk are vascularized. New vascular formation, termed vasculogenesis, takes place within the embryo on day 18. During this process, the underlying endoderm secretes substances that cause some cells of the splanchnopleuric mesoderm to differentiate into angioblasts. These mesodermal angioblasts then flatten into endothelial cells and coalesce, resulting in small vesicular structures referred to as angiocysts. The latter fuse to form networks of angioblastic cords that later unite, grow, and invade embryonic tissues to create the arterial, venous, and lymphatic channels.[1] The spread of vessel networks occurs by three processes:[1]

1. Continuous fusion of the angiocysts—vasculogenesis
2. Sprouting of new vessels from existing ones—angiogenesis
3. Assimilation of new mesodermal cells into the existing vessels' wall

Although the yolk sac is the first supplier of blood cells to the embryonic circulation, the role of blood cell production is taken over by a series of embryonic organs, such as the liver, spleen, thymus, and bone marrow. Therefore, two major concepts were suggested: the bipotential hemangioblast produces the primitive erythroid and endothelial progenitor cells, and the hemogenic endothelium gives rise to hematopoietic

stem cells and endothelial progenitors.[2] The ability of these progenitors of hematopoiesis (blood cell repopulation) or vasculogenesis or angiogenesis is yet to be determined.

VASCULOGENIC EMBRYONIC CELLS

Endothelial–Hematopoietic Cell Relationship

In human embryos, homogenic endothelium could be observed and isolated in both the extraembryonic and intraembryonic regions.[3–7] CD34+ cells were detected on a human vascular system in the yolk sac and embryo at 23 days of gestation.[3] At 35 days of gestation, CD34 was uniformly expressed at the luminal portion of the endothelial cells in developing intraembryonic blood vessels. Furthermore, in this stage, some CD34+ cells, which were round and packed into cell clusters, were found in close apposition to the endothelium in the preumbilical region of the embryo. These cells also expressed CD45 and CD31, introducing the idea that hematopoietic cells arise intrinsically in the ventral wall of human embryonic arteries.[3,4] Culture examination of the hematopoietic potential of embryonic tissue rudiments revealed that the hematopoietic potential present inside the embryo included both lymphoid and myeloid lineages, whereas the yolk sac exhibited only myelopoiesis potential, thus questioning its ability to contribute to definitive hematopoiesis in the adult human.[5] In a more recent work, endothelial cells of 3- to 6-week-old human embryos were found to express CD31, CD34, and vascular endothelial cadherin (VE-Cad). CD45 expression was restricted to hematopoietic cells, which were rarely present inside blood vessels that contained almost only erythrocytes. Furthermore, CD45+ cells disseminated in very low numbers within tissues, albeit somehow more densely in the subaortic mesenchyme.[6] Isolation of CD31+ CD34+ CD45− cells from both yolk sac and aorta was shown to possess the potential of myelolymphoid differentiation in culture.[6] Isolated CD34+ CD31− cells from an 11–12-week-old human embryo differentiated into both CD34+ CD31− and CD34+ CD31+ cells. The latter were found to be capable of forming a network of capillary-like structures.[7]

Endothelial–Smooth Muscle Cell Relationship

Evidence for the relationship between the endothelium and smooth muscle cells (SMCs) is mostly available from animal studies. Early periendothelial SMCs associated with embryonic endothelial tubes have been shown to transdifferentiate from the endothelium, up-regulating markers of the SMC phenotype[8] (both surface markers and morphology). Yamashita *et al.*[9] discovered common mouse embryonic vascular progenitors that differentiate into endothelial and SMCs by the expression of an entire set of SMC markers and the surrounding of endothelial channels when injected into chick embryos. The earliest evidence in humans was recently shown on umbilical vein endothelium–derived cells that differentiated into SMCs through *in vitro* culturing with a fibroblast growth factor.[10]

BIPOTENCY OF PROGENITORS IN ADULT PERIPHERAL BLOOD

Various studies have been preformed in an attempt to identify an adult hemangioblast, the progenitor for both endothelial and hematopoietic cells. The methodology is to isolate a specific cell population from peripheral blood and to look for any endothelial outgrowth, that is, circulating endothelial cells. Using this approach, CD34+ cells isolated from postnatal life were shown to possess endothelial features and angiogenic capabilities.[11,12] A specific fraction of those cells also expressed KDR (human Flk-1) and AC133, which indicates the existence of a population of functional endothelial precursors.[13] AC133+ circulating cells were shown to differentiate into adherent endothelial cells *in vitro* and to form new blood vessels *in vivo*.[14] A thorough examination revealed that most circulating endothelial cells, isolated by their P1H12 expression, originated from vessel walls and have limited growth capability.[15] Recently, CD34+ KDR+ cells isolated from adult bone marrow were shown to have bilineage differentiation potential: they generated hematopoietic cells, endothelial cells, and cells expressing both types of markers.[16]

There is little evidence in humans of the origin and differentiation process of SMCs. Mature bovine vascular endothelium has been shown to give rise to SMCs via "transitional" cells, co-expressing both endothelial and SMC-specific markers.[17] In humans, a recent report showed that mononuclear cells isolated from adult human peripheral buffy coat blood show either SMC or endothelial cells features, depending on specific *in vitro* culture conditions.[18]

Human Embryonic Stem Cells as a Source for Vascular Progenitors

SPONTANEOUS DIFFERENTIATION

In vivo *Differentiation*

Undifferentiated human embryonic stem cells (hESCs) form teratomas once injected into severe combined immunodeficiency (SCID) mice.[19,20] Within these teratomas various blood vessels are formed (Fig. 30–1). The small-diameter vessels located at the center of the teratomas originate in humans. Therefore, during teratoma formation from hESCs, two parallel vascular processes occur: (1) angiogenesis of host

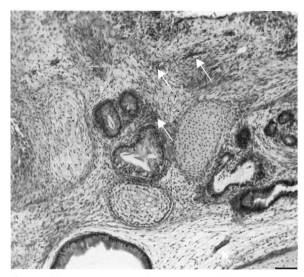

Figure 30–1. *Teratoma vasculature.* Human embryonic stem cells (hESCs) formed teratomas once injected into severe combined immunodeficiency (SCID) mice. Various blood vessels could be observed within the formed teratoma (arrows) including originated human and mouse vessels. Bar = 100 mm. (Please see CD-ROM for color version of this figure.)

vasculature into the forming human teratoma and (2) vasculogenesis of spontaneously differentiating hESCs.

In Vitro *Differentiation*

Embryoid bodies (EBs) formed from spontaneous differentiation of hESCs comprise representatives of all three embryonic layers.[21] CD34, which is considered to be an early human endothelial marker (as mentioned previously), is clearly expressed by surrounding endothelial cells that form voids within 1-month-old human EBs (Fig. 30–2). Exploring the early organization of CD34+ cells within 10- to 15-day-old EBs revealed two types of cell arrangements: the first is a typical three-dimensional (3D) vessel formation and the second is a cryptic arrangement that occasionally is difficult to associate with typical 3D vessel formation (Fig. 30–3A). However, both elongated and round cells stained for CD34, representing both endothelial and hematopoietic cells, respectively (Fig. 30–3B).

CD31 (platelet endothelial cell adhesion molecule 1 –[PECAM1]) has proven particularly useful because of its abundant early expression in mouse vascular development.[22] Levenberg *et al.* showed that CD31 is expressed in developing human EBs.[23] Exploring the early organization of CD31+ cells within 10- to 15-day-old EBs revealed only a typical 3D vessel formation in different locations within the EBs (Fig. 30–4A and B). At this time point, a few round cells, probably early hematopoietic progenitors (Fig. 30–4C), also expressed CD31. Levenberg et al.[23] also examined the kinetics of different markers during EB development. Unlike mouse ESCs, Flk1 was shown to be expressed

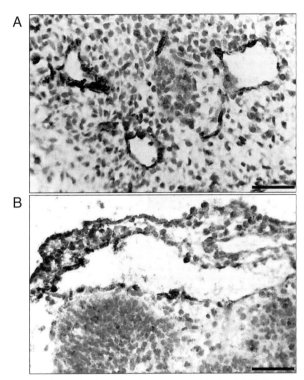

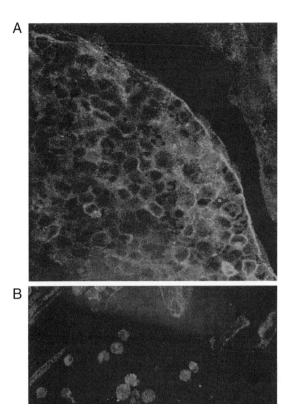

Figure 30–2. *Blood vessels in human embryoid bodies (hEBs).* Histologic sections of 1-month-old hEBs stained with anti-CD34 revealed (A) the formation of relatively small vessels and (B) larger blood vessels. Bar = 100 μm. (Please see CD-ROM for color version of this figure.)

Figure 30–3. *CD34⁺ cells in whole-mount human embryoid bodies (hEBs).* The 10- to15-day-old hEBs stained for CD34 revealed (A) occasionally cryptic, atypical vessel arrangement and (B) positive elongated and round cells (×600). (Please see CD-ROM for color version of this figure.)

in undifferentiated hESCs[23,24] and increased very slightly during differentiation.[23] In addition, other endothelial markers, namely VE-Cad and CD31, increase during the first week of human EB development.[23] Thus, to study human vasculogenesis, various vascular markers should be examined and evaluated.

INDUCED DIFFERENTIATION

Both spontaneous and induced differentiation of hESCs can occur in two-dimensional (2D) and 3D cultures, that is, cell aggregation and adherence. Approaches for the promotion of specific vascular differentiation of hESCs include the following:

1. Genetic manipulation, also known as gene targeting—*knockin* and *knockout* specific angiogenic receptors and relevant transcription factors
2. Exogenic factors—administrating the cell cultures with specific and known angiogenic and hematopoiesis factors
3. Matrix-based cultures—culturing the differentiating cells on matrices known to support vascular cell cultures
4. Co-culture—culturing the differentiating cells with specific stromal call lines that may promote vascular differentiation

Hematopoietic differentiation of hESCs was induced once hESCs were co-cultured with bone marrow cell line S17 or yolk sac endothelial cell line C166.[24] Differentiation of hESCs cultured on S17 cells resulted in the formation of various types of hematopoietic colonies and even terminally differentiated hematopoietic cells, such as erythroid cells, myeloid cells, and megakaryocytes.[24] Further enrichment of hematopoietic colony forming was achieved by sorting CD34⁺ cells from differentiating hESCs.[24]

Nishikawa and colleagues showed that during mouse development both hematopoietic and SMC differentiation are linked to the development of endothelial precursors.[25–29] Embracing their approach, induction of vascular differentiation from hESCs was examined. Different lines of hESCs

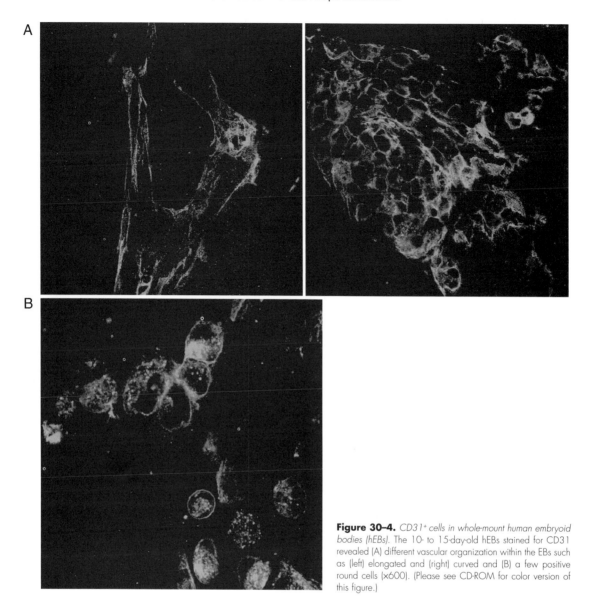

Figure 30–4. CD31+ cells in whole-mount human embryoid bodies (hEBs). The 10- to 15-day-old hEBs stained for CD31 revealed (A) different vascular organization within the EBs such as (left) elongated and (right) curved and (B) a few positive round cells (×600). (Please see CD-ROM for color version of this figure.)

were seeded on type IV collagen matrices for 14 days with differentiation medium.[9] These culture conditions induced the expression of all vascular endothelial growth factors (VEGFs): isomers and Tie2, KDR Ang2, and CD31- specific markers of endothelial cells. Some of the differentiated cells formed muscle–vascular arrangements, which were found to express smooth muscle α-actin (SMA). For the induction of a more defined population, single-cell suspensions of hESCs were used. Examination of the differentiated population revealed that the majority of the surviving cells expressed specific endothelial and endothelial–hematopoietic markers. To induce lineage-specific differentiation, administration with human VEGF, platelet-derived growth factor BB (PDGF-BB), or specific hematopoietic cytokines was examined. VEGF treatment brought about maturation of the cells into endothelial cells producing von Willebrand factor (vWF) and

with high lipoprotein metabolism.[30] Up-regulation of the expression of SMC markers was achieved once supplemented with human PDGF-BB.[30] In addition, colony formation unit assays revealed the progenitor population ability to form different hematopoietic colonies (Fig. 30–5). Formation of tube-like structures and sprouting were observed once seeding the differentiated cells within 3D collagen and matrigel gels (Fig. 30–6). Histologic sections showed the formation of a tube-like network and penetration of endothelial cells into the matrigel. Electron microscopic examination further revealed typical arrangements of the endothelial cells within the matrigel, with the typical lipoprotein capsules and Weibel-Palade bodies in the cells' cytoplasm, and the presence of lumens in the cords.[30] The presence of lumens in the cords points to the ability of the progenitor cells to differentiate into functional endothelial cells with lipoprotein metabolism and

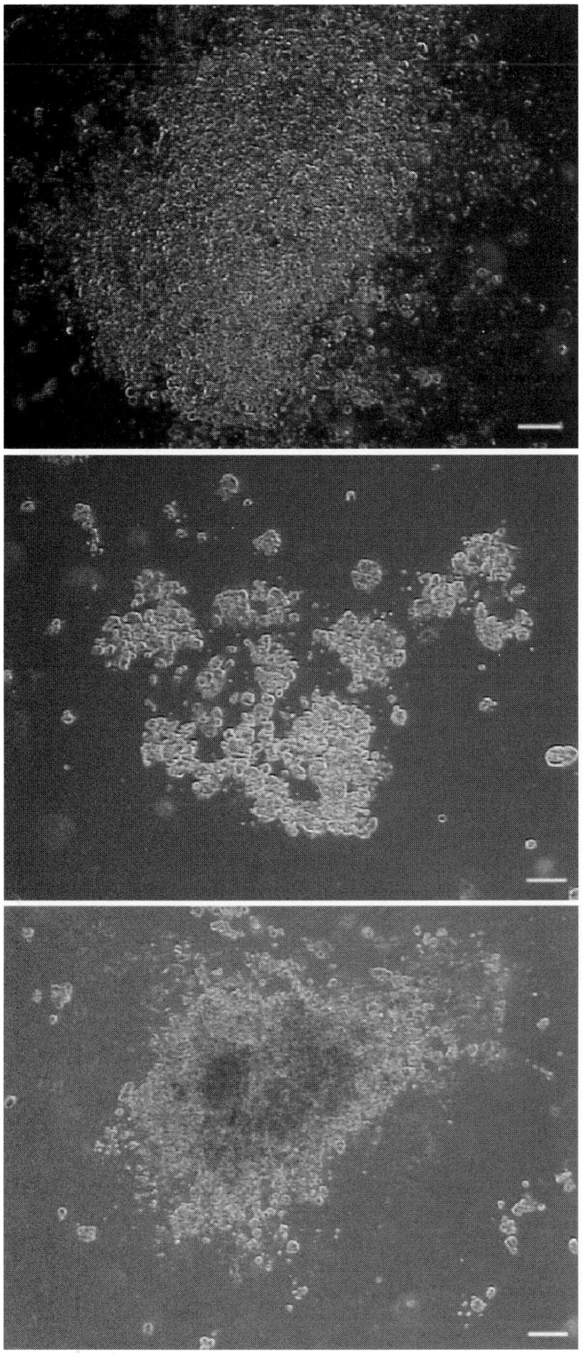

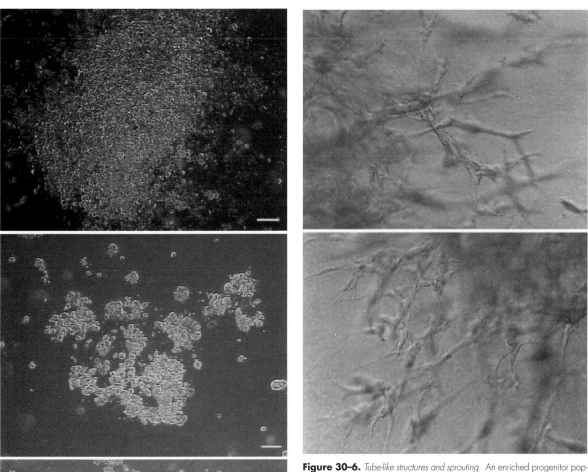

Figure 30–5. *Hematopoietic colonies.* Enriched progenitor population cultivated in semisolid media formed different types of hematopoietic colonies.

vWF production and also to form tube-like structures under sui1 conditions.

Figure 30–6. *Tube-like structures and sprouting.* An enriched progenitor population seeded within matrigel sprouted and formed vessel-like structures. Documented using Hoffman lens.

for editing. The research on human embryonic stem cells in our laboratory was partly supported by NIH grant 1Ro1Ho73798.

ACKNOWLEDGMENTS

We thank Prof. Raymond Coleman for histology instructions and assistance, Anna Ziskind for technical assistance, and Hadas O'Neill

REFERENCES

1. Larsen, W.J. (1998). "Essentials of Human Embryology," 2nd ed. Churchill Livingstone, New York.
2. Orkin, S.H., and Zon, L.I. (2002). Hematopoiesis and stem cells: plasticity versus development heterogeneity. *Nat. Immunol.* **3,** 323–328.
3. Tavian, M., Coulombel, L., Luton D., Clemente, H.S., Dieterlen-Lievre, F., and Peault, B. (1996). Aorta-associated CD34+ hematopoietic cells in the early embryo. *Blood* **87,** 67–72.
4. Tavian, M., Hallais, M.F., and Peault, B. (1999). Emergence of intraembryonic hematopoietic precursors in the pre-liver human embryo. *Development* **126,** 793–803.
5. Tavian, M., Robin, C., Coulombel, L., and Peault, B. (2001). The human embryo, but not its yolk sac, generates lympho-myeloid stem cells: mapping multipotent hematopoietic cell fate in intraembryonic mesoderm. Immunity **15,** 487–495.

6. Oberlin, E. Tavian, M., Balzsek, I., and Peault, B. (2002). Blood-forming potential of vascular endothelium in the human embryo. *Development* **129**, 4147–4157.

7. Alessandri, G., Girelli, M., Taccagni, G., Colombo, A., Nicosia, R., Caruso, A., Baronio, M., Pagano, S., Cova, L., and Parati, E. (2001). Human vasculogenesis ex vivo: embryonal aorta as a tool for isolation of endothelial cell progenitors. *Lab. Invest.* **81**, 875–885.

8. DeRuiter, M.C., Polemann, R.E., VanMunsteren, J.C., Mironoc, V., Markwald, R.R., and Gittenbereger de Groot, A.C. (1997). Embryonic endothelial cells transdifferentiate into mesenchymal cells expressing smooth muscle actins in vivo and in vitro. *Circ. Res.* **80**, 444–451.

9. Yamashita, J., Itoh, H., Hirashima, M., Ogawa, M., Nishikawa, S., Yurugi, T., Naito, M., Nakao, K., and Nishikawa, S. (2000). Flk1-positive cells derived from embryonic stem cells serve as vascular progenitors. *Nature* **408**, 92–96.

10. Ishisaki, A., Hayashi, H., Li, A.J., and Imamura, T. (2003). Human umbilical vein endothelium-derived cells retain potential to differentiate into smooth muscle-like cells. *J. Biol. Chem.* **278**, 1303–1309.

11. Asahara, T., Murohara, T., Sullivan, A., Silver, M., van der Zee, R., Li, T., Witzenbichler, B., Schatteman, G., and Isner, J.M. (1997). Isolation of putative progenitor endothelial cells for angiogenesis. *Science* **275**, 964–967.

12. Shi, Q., Rafii, S., Wu, M.H., Wijelath, E.S., Yu, C., Ishida, A., Fujita, Y., Kothari, S., Mohle, R., Sauvage, L.R., Moore, M.A., Storb, R.F., and Hammond, W.P. (1998). Evidence for circulating bone marrow-derived endothelial cells. *Blood* **92**, 362–367.

13. Peichev, M., Naiyer, A.J., Pereira, D., Zhu, Z., Lane, W.J., Williams, M., Oz, M.C., Hicklin, D.J., Witte, L., Moore, M.A., and Rafii, S. (2000). Expression of VEGFR-2 and AC133 by circulating human CD34+ cells identifies a population of functional endothelial precursors. *Blood* **95**, 952–958.

14. Gehling, U.M., Ergun, S., Schumacher, U., Wagener, C., Pantel, K., Otte, M., Schuch, G., Schafhausen, P., Mende, T., Kilic, N., Kluge, K., Schafer, B., Hossfeld, D.K., and Fiedler, W. (2000). In vitro differentiation of endothelial cells from AC133-positive progenitor cells. *Blood* **95**, 3106–3112.

15. Lin, Y., Weisdorf, D.J., Solovey, A., and Hebbel, R.P. (2000). Origins of circulating endothelial cells and endothelial outgrowth from blood. *J. Clin. Invest.* **105**, 71–77.

16. Pelosi, E., Valtieri, M., Coppola, S., Botta, R., Gabbianelli, M., Lulli, V., Marziali, G., Masella, B., Muller, R., Sgadari, C., Testa, U., Bonanno, G., and Peschle, C. (2002). Identification of the hemangioblast in postnatal life. *Blood* **100**, 3203–3208.

17. Frid, M.G., Kale, V.sA., and Stenmark, K.R. (2002). Mature vascular endothelium can give rise to smooth muscle cells via endothelial-mesenchymal transdifferentiation: in vitro analysis. *Circ. Res.* **90**, 1189–1196.

18. Simper, D., Stalboerger, P.G., Panetta, C.J., Wang, S., and Caplice, N.M. (2002). Smooth muscle progenitor cells in human blood. *Circulation* **106**, 1199–1204.

19. Thomson, J.A., Itskovitz-Eldor, J., Shapiro, S.S., Waknitz, M.A., Swiergiel, J.J., Marshall, V.S., and Jones, J.M. (1998). Embryonic stem cell lines derived from human blastocysts. *Science* **282**, 1145–1147.

20. Reubinoff, B., Pera, M., Fong, C., Trounson, A., and Bongso, A. (2000). Embryonic stem cell lines from human blastocysts: Somatic differentiation in vitro. *Nat. Biotech.* **18**, 399–404.

21. Itskovitz-Eldor, J., Schuldiner, M., Karsenti, D., Eden, A., Yanuka, O., Amit, M., Soreq, H., and Benvenisty, N. (2000). Differentiation of human embryonic stem cells into embryoid bodies comprising the three embryonic germ layers. *Mol. Med.* **6**, 88–95.

22. Vecchi, A., Garlanda, C., Lampugnani, M.G., Resnati, M., Matteucci, C., Stoppacciaro, A., Schnurch, H., Risau, W., Ruco, L., Mantovani, A., et al. (1994). Monoclonal antibodies specific for endothelial cells of mouse blood vessels. Their application in the identification of adult and embryonic endothelium. *Eur. J. Cell. Biol.* **63**, 247–254.

23. Levenberg, S. Golub, J.S., Amit, M., Itskovits-Eldor, J., and Langer, R. (2002). Endothelial cells derived from human embryonic stem cells. *Proc. Natl. Acad. Sci. U. S. A.* **99**, 4391–4396.

24. Kaufman, D.S., Hanson, E.T., Lewis, R.L., Auerbach, R., and Thomson, J.A. (2001). Hematopoietic colony-forming cells derived from human embryonic stem cells. *Proc. Natl. Acad. Sci. U. S. A.* **98**, 10716–10721.

25. Nishikawa, S.I., Nishikawa, S., Hirashima, M., Matsuyoshi, N., and Kodama, H. (1998). Progressive lineage analysis by cell sorting and culture identifies FLK+VE-cadherin+ cells at a diverging point of endothelial and hematopoietic lineages. *Development* **125**, 1747–1757.

26. Nishikawa, S.I., Nishikawa, S., Kawamoto, H., Yoshida, H., Kizumoto, M., Kataoka, H., and Katsura, Y. (1998). In vitro generation of lymphohematopoietic cells from endothelial cells purified from murine embryos. *Immunity* **8**, 761–769.

27. Fujimoto, T., Ogawa, M., Minegishi, N., Yoshida, H., Yokomizo, T., Yamamoto, M., and Nishikawa, S. (2001). Step-wise divergence of primitive and definitive hematopoietic and endothelial cell lineage during embryonic stem cell differentiation. *Genes Cells* **6**, 1113–1127.

28. Nishikawa, S.I. (2001). A complex linkage in the development pathway of endothelial and hematopoietic cells. *Curr. Opin. Cell Biol.* **13**, 673–678.

29. Fraser, S., Ogawa, M., Yu, R.T., Nishikawa, S., Yoder, M.C., and Nishikawa, S-I. (2002). Definitive hematopoietic commitment within the embryonic endothelial-cadherin+ population. *Exp. Hematol.* **30**, 1070–1078.

30. Gerecht-Nir, S., Ziskind, A., Cohen, S., and Itskovitz-Eldor, J. (2003). Human embryonic stem cells as an in vitro model for human vascular development and the induction of vascular differentiation. *Lab. Invest.* **83**, 1811–1820.

31

Differentiation of Embryonic Stem Cells into Adipose Cells

Blaine W. Phillips, Cécile Vernochet, Catherine Iéhlé, and Christian Dani

Severe obesity is the result of an increase in fat cell size in combination with increased fat cell number. Mature adipocytes do not undergo cell division and new fat cells arise from a pre-existing pool of adipose stem cells that are present irrespective of age. The development of established preadipose cell lines has facilitated the study of different steps leading to terminal differentiation of preadipocytes into adipocytes. However, these systems are limited for studying early events of differentiation because they represent cells that are already determined for the adipogenic lineage. Masters genes that commit multipotent stem cells toward adipocytes remain to be identified. *In vitro* differentiation of mouse embryonic stem (ES) cells toward the adipogenic lineage provides an alternative source of adipocytes for study in tissue culture and offers the possibility to investigate regulation of the first steps of adipose cell development. In this review we describe the sequential requirement of retinoic acid treatment and of expression of peroxisome proliferative-activated receptor gamma (PPARγ) and leukemia inhibitory factor (LIF) receptor to induce adipogenesis of ES cells. Finally, the signaling pathway involved in all-*trans*-retinoic acid (RA)-induced adipogenesis and the regulation of the differentiation of ES cells into adipocytes or osteoblasts, two closely related lineages, are discussed.

Introduction

Obesity, one of the most common health problems in the industrialized world, often leads to serious illness such as diabetes, hypertension, and cardiovascular disease. The ongoing global explosion in the incidence of obesity has thus focused attention on the development of adipose cells. It is now well established that stem cells exist in the adipose tissue[1] and an excess of their recruitment participates in the hyperplasia of the fat tissue observed in severe obesity.

The key events leading to the terminal differentiation of preadipocytes into adipocytes have been characterized in recent years by the identification of transcription factors that play a regulatory role in the differentiation process. The best

characterized transcription factors shown to be important in the development of mature adipocytes are members of the CCAAT/enhancer binding proteins (C/EBPs) and peroxisome proliferative-activated receptors (PPARs) families.[2] Several lines of evidence indicate that PPARγ plays a key role in adipogenesis. PPARγ, which is more abundant in adipocytes than in any other cell types, is a trigger of terminal differentiation of preadipocytes into adipocytes.[3] The molecular mechanisms mediating the adipogenic effect of PPARγ are starting to be resolved. For example, recent studies have identified critical cofactors for full PPARγ activity,[4] and many PPARγ target genes are known. However, master genes that commit multipotent mesenchymal stem cells toward the adipogenic lineage during the initial stages of differentiation have not yet been characterized. The development of established preadipocyte cell lines has greatly facilitated the study of the different steps leading to the terminal differentiation of preadipocytes to adipocytes (Fig. 31–1). However, these systems are limited for studying the early events of differentiation because they represent cells that are already determined for a particular lineage. *In vitro* differentiation of ES cells provides an alternative source of adipocytes for study in tissue culture and offers the possibility to investigate the regulation of the first steps of adipose cell development.[5,6]

Effect of All-*trans*–retinoic Acid and of PPARγ on the Differentiation of ES Cells in Adipocytes

ES cells have previously been shown to differentiate spontaneously into various lineages in culture.[7,8] The first morphologic observation of adipocyte-like cells derived from ES cells was reported by Field *et al.*[9] However, the number of ES cell-derived adipocytes was low because the spontaneous differentiation of ES cells into adipocytes is a rare event. Therefore, the use of ES cells for studying adipocyte development required the optimization of the culture conditions enhancing the adipocyte differentiation. A prerequisite for the commitment of ES cells into the adipogenic lineage is to treat ES cell–derived embryoid bodies (EBs) at an early phase of their differentiation with RA for a short period of time.[5,10] Two distinct phases can be distinguished in the development of the adipocyte program from ES cells. The first phase, between

Handbook of Stem Cells
Volume 1

Blaine W. Phillips, Cécile Vernochet, Catherine Iéhlé, and Christian Dani

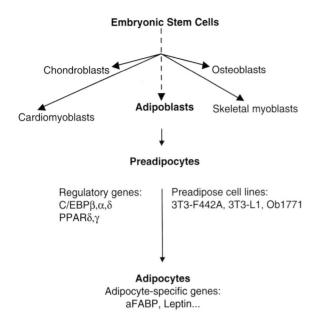

Figure 31–1. *Stages in the adipocyte development program. The names of established preadipose cell lines mainly used, genes known to play a regulatory role in terminal differentiation of preadipocytes to adipocytes, and genes specifically expressed in adipocytes are indicated. Genes involved in initial steps of differentiation have not been identified.*

day 2 and 5 after EB formation, corresponds to the permissive period for the adipogenic commitment of ES cells, which requires RA. The second phase that corresponds to the period of terminal differentiation, is influenced by adipogenic factors and requires PPARγ (see next section). Thus, RA treatment, followed by stimulation of PPARγ leads to 60–80% of EB outgrowths containing adipose cells compared with 2–5%

in the absence of treatment. After 20 days of differentiation, large adipocyte colonies developing out of the center of the EBs can be distinguished (Fig. 31–2). ES cell–derived adipocytes contain fat droplets that can be easily visualized microscopically (Fig. 31–2, left panel) or after staining with Oil Red O, a specific stain for triglycerides (Fig. 31–2, right panel).

Requirement of PPARγ and of LIF Receptor for Terminal Differentiation of ES Cells into Adipocytes

The permissive period for adipogenic commitment (between day 2–5 after EB formation) corresponds to an early period of EB development and is concomitant with peak expression of *Brachyury T* gene, a marker of nascent mesoderm.[11] Expression of *HMGIC* gene, a gene preferentially expressed in undifferentiated mesenchymal cells,[12] is weak during this period but peaks early after (Fig. 31–3). These observations are in agreement with the fact that treatment of EBs with RA during this period influences the mesenchymal differentiation of ES cells (see the section on signaling pathways involved in RA-induced adipogenesis). Expression of *PPARγ*, the master gene controlling the differentiation of preadipocytes into adipocytes is only weakly expressed during the commitment period.[13] However, expression of the *PPARγ* gene is dramatically induced during the period of terminal differentiation. The requirement of PPARγ in the development of fat cells has recently been investigated by gene targeting.[14–16] Homozygous PPARγ-deficient embryos die at mid-gestation because of a placenta defect associated with myocardial thinning. This phenotype reveals a new role of PPARγ in the development of placenta but precludes a straightforward approach to investigate the role of PPARγ in the different

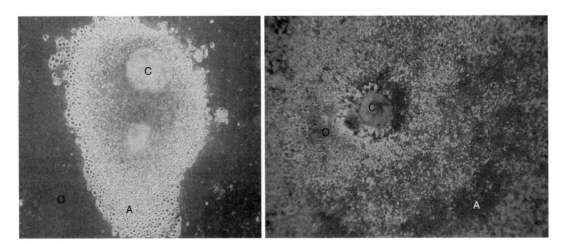

Figure 31–2. *Photomicrographic records of embryonic stem (ES) cell-derived adipocytes. A 20-day-old outgrowth derived from all-trans-retinoic acid (RA)-treated embryoid body (EB) is visualized microscopically (left panel) or after staining with Oil Red O (right panel). Adipocytes containing lipid droplets developed out of the center of the outgrowth. A, adipocytes; C, center of the EB; O, outgrowth. (Please see CD-ROM for color version of this figure.)*

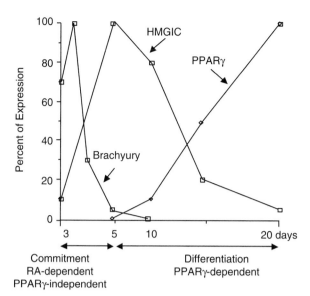

Commitment
RA-dependent
PPARγ-independent

Differentiation
PPARγ-dependent

Figure 31-3. *Expression of peroxisome proliferative-activated receptor gamma (PPARγ) and of developmental marker genes during differentiation of embryoid bodies. RNA were prepared at indicated times after embryoid formation and expression of indicated genes were determined by Northern blotting. Results are expressed by taking 100% the maximal signal obtained for each probe. Two phases can be distinguished: the commitment period that is all-trans-retinoic acid (RA)-dependent and PPARγ-independent and the second phase corresponding to the differentiation period that requires PPARγ.*

steps of development of adipose cells. Generation of PPARγ[-/-] ES-cells and of ES cells overexpressing PPARγ allowed us and others to demonstrate that PPARγ does not play a role in the RA-dependent commitment of ES cells into adipocytes but is required for the formation of mature lipid-filled adipose cells.[13,16]

LIF and its receptor (LIFR) are developmentally regulated during differentiation of preadipocytes to adipocytes. Preadipocytes, but not adipocytes, secrete functional LIF and simultaneously express LIFR. Activation of LIFR then stimulates expression of C/EBPs and promotes adipogenesis via a paracrine/autocrine manner.[17] Recently, it has been shown that selective inhibitors of the ERK pathway prevent LIF-induced adipogenesis and inhibit LIF-induced C/EBP gene expression. CAMP-responsive element binding protein/activation transcription factor-1 (CREB/ATF-1) has been identified as the transcriptional factor mediating ERK-induced C/EBP gene expression.[18] Homozygous LIFR mutant newborn die a few hours after birth[19,20] precluding, as for PPARγ, the study of the role of this receptor during the development of adipose tissue that takes place postnatally. The requirement of LIF/LIFR in adipogenesis has been investigated using mutant ES cells. LIF[-/-] ES cells undergo adipogenesis with comparable efficiency to wild-type cells, which is in agreement with studies of LIF mutant mice indicating that a lack of LIF expression does not prevent the development of adipose cells.[17] LIF belongs to the interleukin (IL)-6 cytokine family,

and a feature of members of this family is the redundancy of biologic functions.[21] The generation of LIFR[-/-] ES cells allowed us to show that this receptor is required for differentiation of ES cells into adipocytes. Importantly, addition of IL-6 together with IL-6 soluble receptor, only during the differentiation period, restores the capacity of LIFR[-/-] ES cells to undergo adipocyte differentiation. Altogether, these results strongly suggest that the gp130 signaling pathway is not involved in the commitment of ES cells into the adipogenic lineage but is required for terminal differentiation of preadipocytes into adipocytes.

GATA2 and GATA3 transcription factors are both expressed in preadipocytes, but expression is lost during maturation to fully differentiated adipocytes, suggesting that they could play a role in the regulation of adipocyte differentiation. This hypothesis has been confirmed, because GATA3 deficient ES cells exhibit an enhanced capacity to differentiate into adipocytes.[22] This work indicates that GATA3 is a negative regulator of the preadipocyte to adipocyte transition, an effect that is mediated in part by the direct suppression of the PPARγ promoter activity, and also indicates that GATA3 is not required for the lineage commitment of adipose cells. Other developmental-regulatory factors, such as members of Wnt family, have been showed to play a role in terminal differentiation of preadipocytes into adipocytes,[23] but their role in initial steps of the development of adipose cells remains to be investigated. The use of *in vitro* differentiation of ES cells to analyze the effects of mutations on adipogenesis is just beginning and master genes that commit progression from pluripotent stem cells to the adipogenic lineage have not yet been identified. One possible route to identify regulatory genes for commitment is to identify genes regulated by RA in early EBs.

Signaling Pathways Involved in All-*trans*-retinoic Acid-Induced Adipogenesis

RA cannot be omitted or substituted for commitment of ES cells into adipocytes. In either serum-containing medium or serum-free medium, RA cannot be replaced by insulin, triiodothyronine, dexamethasone, basic fibroblast growth factor (bFGF), bone morphogenetic protein-2 (BMP-2) or potent activators of PPARs.[10] However, treatment of EBs with RA leads to pleiotropic effects. It has been previously demonstrated that RA influences the differentiation of ES cells into neuronal cells, depending on the concentration and development stage of application.[24] In agreement with this report, we have observed that differentiation of ES cells into mesenchymal cells depends on the RA concentration added in the culture medium between days 2 and 5. In the absence of RA treatment, the skeletal myocyte and cardiomyocyte lineages appear spontaneously during differentiation of EBs, whereas no adipocytes and osteoblasts are detected. Low concentration of RA (10^{-8} M) gave rise subsequently to both adipocytes and skeletal myocytes but cardiomyocytes are no longer observed.[5,6] At higher concentration of RA (10^{-7} M), expression of myogenin, a skeletal myocyte specific gene, is inhibited whereas expression of ALBP, an adipocyte-specific gene, and of osteocalcin, an osteoblast-specific gene, are induced. Visualization of these different cell types by specific stains confirms these results (Fig. 31–4).

The biologic effects of RA are mediated by heterodimers formed with the different isotypes of RA receptors (RAR α, β, γ) and of the Retinoid X receptors (RXR α, β, γ). Regulation of the expression of RA-target genes could be dependent on the composition of the heterodimer. However, all isotype receptors are expressed in EBs during the permissive period for commitment (unpublished data), making unclear the identification of the receptors involved in adipocyte differentiation. This problem might be overcame by using synthetic retinoids that are selective ligands of the different RAR isotypes, to study the contribution of individual receptors to RA-dependent adipogenesis.

It has been recently reported that RA activates the ERK pathway in EBs. This effect is specific, because RA does not activate c-Jun–N-terminal kinase (JNK) and p38 mitogen-activated protein kinase (MAPK) signaling pathways. More interestingly, co-treatment of RA with a specific inhibitor of ERK signaling, prevents adipocyte formation with no effect on the differentiation of ES cells in neurons. Even more important is that the inhibition of the ERK pathway has no effect on mesenchymal differentiation in skeletal myocytes and cardiomyocytes.[25] This study indicates that ERK pathway plays an essential and specific role in RA-mediated adipogenesis of ES cells. The molecular mechanisms leading to

the phosphorylation of ERK by retinoic receptors is not known.

Regulation of the Differentiation of Embryonic Stem Cells into Adipocytes or Osteoblasts

Adipocytes and osteoblasts are derived from a common precursor cell. It has been proposed that the bone loss commonly seen during ageing or in the pathology of osteoporosis might be due, in part, to a deregulation of the normal balance between osteoblast and adipocyte differentiation. However, factors that regulate the step when mesenchymal progenitor cells are committed to become an adipocyte or an osteoblast remain elusive. *In vitro* differentiation of ES cells into both adipocytes and osteoblasts[26–28] provides a powerful system for studying the developmental switch between osteogenesis and adipogenesis.

It has recently been demonstrated that statins, members of the high-mobility group (HMG) CoA-reductase inhibitory drug family used in therapy for lowering cholesterol, have the unexpected capacity to promote bone mineral density and osteoblast differentiation.[29,30] Recently, the importance of statins in osteoblast differentiation of ES cells have been demonstrated.[27] Altogether, these results make statins potential drugs for the treatment of bone loss. However, we have more recently observed that statins also promote adipocyte differentiation in ES cells (B. Phillips and C. Dani, unpublished data). To date, there has been no large-scale study on the effect of statins treatment on adipose tissue development and on bone marrow adipocyte content. However, if this observation were confirmed *in vivo*, it would highlight a potential problem or side effect in the use of statins as antiosteoporotic agents. There are several lines of evidence indicating that statins might function through PPARγ. The promoter of PPARγ contains a functional target site for the transcriptional factor sterol response element binding protein-1-c (SREBP-1c). It is well documented that SREBP transcription factors are sensitive to cholesterol levels, thus linking PPARγ expression to statin activity. Indeed, lipid depletion induced by statins was associated with an increased expression of PPARγ in 3T3-L1 preadipose cells.[31] Although the role of PPARγ in adipogenesis cannot be disputed, its function in the process of osteogenesis is unclear. It has been shown that activation of PPARγ in MC3T3-E1 preosteoblastic cells was sufficient to promote osteogenesis; however, relatively high concentrations of PPARγ ligands appeared to inhibit this process.[32] These results are in agreement with the report showing that PPARγ was expressed in bone marrow stromal cells and that its overexpression resulted in the inhibition of osteogenesis and in the induction of adipogenesis.[33] Finally, involvement of PPARγ both in statin-induced adipogenesis and osteogenesis of ES cells has been observed (B. Phillips and C. Dani, unpublished data). Therefore, a model could be proposed in which the level of expression or of stimulation of PPARγ

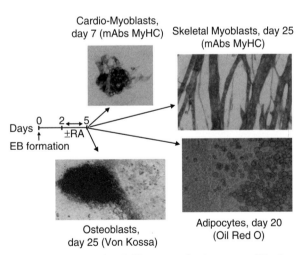

Figure 31–4. *Mesenchymal differentiation of embryonic stem (ES) cells is influenced by retinoic acid. Embryoid bodies were treated or not with all-trans-retinoic acid (RA) then outgrowths were maintained in appropriated media for terminal differentiation. Cardiomyocytes and skeletal myocytes (stained with a monoclonal antibody against myosin heavy chain) appear in the absence of RA pretreatment, whereas adipocytes (stained with Oil Red O for lipid droplets) and osteoblasts (stained with Von Kossa for bone nodules) appear in outgrowths derived from RA-treated embryoid bodies. (Please see CD-ROM for color version of this figure.)*

in stem cells determines their differentiation into adipocytes or osteoblasts.

Conclusions and Future Trends

In summary, ES cell–based differentiation represents an important model system to study the development of adipocytes, in addition to other mesenchymal and nonmesenchymal lineages. This should have impact on the field of basic research, in which genetic modifications in the cells will enable researchers to examine the contributions of signaling pathways and of individual molecules to the adipogenic differentiation program. This approach will also greatly benefit industrial research, in which the infinite differentiation capacity of ES cells holds tremendous potential to screen compound sets to find molecules that affect the development of particular lineages. The protocol used to obtain adipocyte differentiation of ES cells at a high rate is highly reproducible but is time consuming. Adipocyte differentiation is initiated by aggregation of ES cells to form EBs. The formation of EBs in mass culture by maintaining ES cells in suspension at a high density is rapid and gives rise to a high number of EBs formed. However, this method leads subsequently to a low number of outgrowths containing adipocyte colonies. The hanging drop method used for the formation of EBs[10,34] is efficient but could be difficult to fit with a high-capacity screening system. The culture conditions must be modified to allow the cultivation of large amounts of EBs with adipogenic capacity in a less time-consuming manner for routine screening A spinner flask technique has been reported to allow the cultivation of large amounts of EBs.[35] This method produced EBs that underwent endothelial differentiation and thus could serve as an *in vitro* model for evaluating the effectiveness of antiangiogenic agents. However, the ability of the cells to undergo differentiation into other lineages has yet to be investigated. Adipocytes are not the only differentiated cell types obtained in culture initiated by the hanging drop method. This allows the study of interaction of adipose cells with other cell types but could pose a problem for some applications that require pure adipocytes. Generation of purified adipocytes by a strategy of genetic selection developed by Li *et al.*[36] can be performed. In this case, a resistance gene for an antibiotic could be driven by the ALBP promoter (also named aP2), which has been shown to be specifically expressed in adipocytes both *in vitro* and *in vivo*[37] to eliminate nonadipose cells. However, to identify genes involved in adipocyte commitment, analysis of a terminal phenotype such as the formation of lipid droplets or expression of a late marker such as ALBP is not appropriate. It is necessary to follow expression of a marker of adipocyte precursors and to engineer ES cells to monitor adipocyte commitment in differentiating EBs. So far, no specific marker of adipocyte precursors has been reported in the literature. We can anticipate that, with the advent of cDNA microarray technology[38] combined with functional analysis in sophisticated, engineered ES cells[39,40] should lead in the near future to the identification of the master gene of adipogenesis.

ACKNOWLEDGMENTS

Our laboratory is supported by the Association pour la Recherche Contre le Cancer (grant n° 9982 and 4625 to C.D), the Centre National de la Recherche Scientifique (grant UMR 6543), and the Association Française contre les Myopathies. C.D is an Established Investigator of the Institut National de la Santé et de la Recherche Médicale B.P is a recipient of a Fondation pour la Recherche Medicale fellowship and C.V is a recipient of the Agence Nationale de la Recherche contre le Sida fellowship.

REFERENCES

1. Zuk, P.A., Zhu, M., Mizuno, H., Huang, J., Futrell, J.W., Katz, A.J., Benhaim, P., Lorenz, H.P., and Hedrick, M.H. (2001). Multilineage cells from human adipose tissue: implications for cell-based therapies. *Tissue Eng.* **7,** 211–228.
2. Rosen, E.D., Walkey, C.J., Puigserver, P., and Spiegelman, B.M. (2000). Transcriptional regulation of adipogenesis. *Genes Dev.* **14,** 1293–1307.
3. Tontonoz, P., Hu, E., and Spiegelman, B.M. (1995). Regulation of adipocyte gene expression and differentiation by peroxisome proliferator activated receptor gamma. *Curr. Opin. Genet. Dev.* **5,** 571–576.
4. Ge, K., Guermah, M., Yuan, C.X., Ito, M., Wallberg, A.E., Spiegelman, B.M., and Roeder, R.G. (2002). Transcription coactivator TRAP220 is required for PPAR gamma 2-stimulated adipogenesis. *Nature* **417,** 563–567.
5. Dani, C., Smith, A., Dessolin, S., Leroy, P., Staccini, L., Villageois, P., Darimont, C., and Ailhaud, G. (1997). Differentiation of embryonic stem cells into adipocytes in vitro. *J. Cell Sci.* **110,** 1279–1285.
6. Dani, C. (1999). Embryonic stem cell-derived adipogenesis. *Cells Tissues Organs* **165,** 173–180.
7. Doetschman, T.C., Eistetter, H., Katz, M., Schmidt, W., and Kemler, R. (1985). The in vitro development of blastocyst-derived embryonic stem cell lines: formation of visceral yolk sac, blood islands and myocardium. *J. Embryol. Exp. Morphol.* **87,** 27–45.
8. Smith, A. G. (2001). Embryo-derived stem cells: of mice and men. *Annu. Rev. Cell Dev. Biol.* **17,** 435–462.
9. Field, S.J., Johnson, R.S., Mortensen, R.M., Papaioannou, V.E., Spiegelman, B.M., and Greenberg, M.E. (1992). Growth and differentiation of embryonic stem cells that lack an intact c-fos gene. *Proc. Natl. Acad. Sci. U. S. A.* **89,** 9306–9310.
10. Dani, C. (2002). Differentiation of embryonic stem cells as a model to study gene function during the development of adipose cells. *Methods Mol. Biol.* **185,** 107–116.
11. Wilkinson, D.G., Bhatt, S., and Herrmann, B.G. (1990). Expression pattern of the mouse T gene and its role in mesoderm formation [see comments]. *Nature* **343,** 657–659.
12. Hirning, F.U., Wilda, M., Rippe, V., Bullerdiek, J., and Hameister, H. (1998). The expression pattern of the Hmgic gene during development. *Genes Chromosomes Cancer* **23,** 350–357.
13. Vernochet, C., Milstone, D.S., Iehle, C., Belmonte, N., Phillips, B., Wdziekonski, B., Villageois, P., Amri, E.Z., O'Donnell, P.E., Mortensen, R.M., Ailhaud, G., and Dani, C. (2002). PPARgamma-dependent and PPARgamma-independent effects on the development of adipose cells from embryonic stem cells. *FEBS Lett.* **510,** 94–98.

14. Barak, Y., Nelson, M.C., Ong, E.S., Jones, Y.Z., Ruiz, L.P., Chien, K.R., Koder, A., and Evans, R.M. (1999). PPAR gamma is required for placental, cardiac, and adipose tissue development. *Mol. Cell* **4**, 585–595.

15. Kubota, N., Terauchi, Y., Miki, H., Tamemoto, H., Yamauchi, T., Komeda, K., Satoh, S., Nakano, R., Ishii, C., Sugiyama, T., Eto, K., Tsubamoto, Y., Okuno, A., Murakami, K., Sekihara, H., Hasegawa, G., Naito, M., Toyoshima, Y., Tanaka, S., Shiota, K., Kitamura, T., Fujita, T., Ezaki, O., Aizawa, S., Nagai, R., Tobe, K., Kimura, S., and Kadowaki, T. (1999). PPAR gamma mediates high-fat diet-induced adipocyte hypertrophy and insulin resistance. *Mol. Cell* **4**, 597–609.

16. Rosen, E.D., Sarraf, P., Troy, A.E., Bradwin, G., Moore, K., Milstone, D.S., Spiegelman, B.M., and Mortensen, R.M. (1999). PPAR gamma is required for the differentiation of adipose tissue in vivo and in vitro. *Mol. Cell* **4**, 611–617.

17. Aubert, J., Dessolin, S., Belmonte, N., Li, M., McKenzie, F.R., Staccini, L., Villageois, P., Barhanin, B., Vernallis, A., Smith, A.G., Ailhaud, G., and Dani, C. (1999). Leukemia inhibitory factor and its receptor promote adipocyte differentiation via the mitogen-activated protein kinase cascade. *J. Biol. Chem.* **274**, 24,965–24,972.

18. Belmonte, N., Phillips, B.W., Massiera, F., Villageois, P., Wdziekonski, B., Saint-Marc, P., Nichols, J., Aubert, J., Saeki, K., Yuo, A., Narumiya, S., Ailhaud, G., and Dani, C. (2001). Activation of extracellular signal-regulated kinases and CREB/ATF-1 mediate the expression of CCAAT/enhancer binding proteins beta and -delta in preadipocytes. *Mol. Endocrinol.* **15**, 2037–2049.

19. Li, M., Sendtner, M., and Smith, A. (1995). Essential function of LIF receptor in motor neurons. *Nature* **378**, 724–727.

20. Ware, C.B., Horowitz, M.C., Renshaw, B.R., Hunt, J.S., Liggitt, D., Koblar, S.A., Gliniak, B.C., McKenna, H.J., Papayannopoulou, T., Thoma, B., Cheng, L., Donovan, P.J., Peschon, J., Bartlett, P., Willis, C.R., Wright, B.D., Carpenter, M.K., Davison, B.L., and Gearing, D.P. (1995). Targeted disruption of the low-affinity leukemia inhibitory factor receptor gene causes placental, skeletal, neural and metabolic defects and results in perinatal death. *Development* **121**, 1283–1299.

21. Taga, T., and Kishimoto, T. (1997). Gp130 and the interleukin-6 family of cytokines. *Annu. Rev. Immunol.* **15**, 797–819.

22. Tong, Q., Dalgin, G., Xu, H., Ting, C.N., Leiden, J.M., and Hotamisligil, G.S. (2000). Function of GATA transcription factors in preadipocyte-adipocyte transition. *Science* **290**, 134–138.

23. Ross, S.E., Hemati, N., Longo, K.A., Bennett, C.N., Lucas, P.C., Erickson, R.L., and MacDougald, O.A. (2000). Inhibition of adipogenesis by Wnt signaling. *Science* **289**, 950–953.

24. Rohwedel, J., Guan, K., and Wobus, A.M. (1999). Induction of cellular differentiation by retinoic acid in vitro. *Cells Tissues Organs* **165**, 190–202.

25. Bost, F., Caron, L., Marchetti, I., Dani, C., Le Marchand-Brustel, Y., and Binetruy, B. (2002). Retinoic acid activation of the ERK pathway is required for embryonic stem cell commitment into the adipocyte lineage. *Biochem. J.* **361**, 621–627.

26. Buttery, L.D., Bourne, S., Xynos, J.D., Wood, H., Hughes, F.J., Hughes, S.P., Episkopou, V., and Polak, J.M. (2001).

Differentiation of osteoblasts and in vitro bone formation from murine embryonic stem cells. *Tissue Eng.* **7**, 89–99.

27. Phillips, B.W., Belmonte, N., Vernochet, C., Ailhaud, G., and Dani, C. (2001). Compactin enhances osteogenesis in murine embryonic stem cells. *Biochem. Biophys. Res. Commun.* **284**, 478–484.

28. Zur Nieden, N.I., Kempka, G., and Ahr, H.J. (2003). In vitro differentiation of embryonic stem cells into mineralized osteoblasts. *Differentiation* **71**, 18–27.

29. Mundy, G., Garrett, R., Harris, S., Chan, J., Chen, D., Rossini, G., Boyce, B., Zhao, M., and Gutierrez, G. (1999). Stimulation of bone formation in vitro and in rodents by statins. *Science* **286**, 1946–1949.

30. Mundy, G.R. (2001). Statins and their potential for osteoporosis. *Bone* **29**, 495–497.

31. Fajas, L., Schoonjans, K., Gelman, L., Kim, J.B., Najib, J., Martin, G., Fruchart, J.C., Briggs, M., Spiegelman, B.M., and Auwerx, J. (1999). Regulation of peroxisome proliferator-activated receptor gamma expression by adipocyte differentiation and determination factor 1/sterol regulatory element binding protein 1: implications for adipocyte differentiation and metabolism. *Mol Cell Biol* **19**, 5495–5503.

32. Jackson, S.M., and Demer, L.L. (2000). Peroxisome proliferator-activated receptor activators modulate the osteoblastic maturation of MC3T3-E1 preosteoblasts. *FEBS Lett.* **471**, 119–124.

33. Lecka-Czernik, B., Gubrij, I., Moerman, E.J., Kajkenova, O., Lipschitz, D.A., Manolagas, S.C., and Jilka, R.L. (1999). Inhibition of Osf2/Cbfa1 expression and terminal osteoblast differentiation by PPARgamma2. *J. Cell Biochem.* **74**, 357–371.

34. Wobus, A.M., Rohwedel, J., Maltsev, V., and Hescheler, J. (1995). Development of cardiomyocytes expressing cardiac-specific genes, action potentials, and ionic channels during embryonic stem cell-derived cardiogenesis. *Ann. N. Y. Acad. Sci.* **752**, 460–469.

35. Wartenberg, M., Gunther, J., Hescheler, J., and Sauer, H. (1998). The embryoid body as a novel in vitro assay system for antian-giogenic agents. *Lab. Invest.* **78**, 1301–1314.

36. Li, M., Pevny, L., Lovell-Badge, R., and Smith, A. (1998). Generation of purified neural precursors from embryonic stem cells by lineage selection. *Curr. Biol.* **8**, 971–974.

37. Graves, R.A., Tontonoz, P., Platt, K.A., Ross, S.R., and Spiegelman, B.M. (1992). Identification of a fat cell enhancer: analysis of requirements for adipose tissue-specific gene expression. *J. Cell Biochem.* **49**, 219–224.

38. Kelly, D.L., and Rizzino, A. (2000). DNA microarray analyses of genes regulated during the differentiation of embryonic stem cells. *Mol. Reprod. Dev.* **56**, 113–123.

39. Aubert, J., Dunstan, H., Chambers, I., and Smith, A. (2002). Functional gene screening in embryonic stem cells implicates Wnt antagonism in neural differentiation. *Nat. Biotechnol.* **20**, 1240–1245.

40. Ying, Q.L., Stavridis, M., Griffiths, D., Li, M., and Smith, A. (2003). Conversion of embryonic stem cells into neuroectodermal precursors in adherent monoculture. *Nat. Biotechnol.* **21**, 183–186.

Cell Lineages and Stem Cells in the Embryonic Kidney

Gregory R. Dressler

The goal of developmental biology is to understand the genetic and biochemical mechanisms that determine cell growth and differentiation and the three-dimensional patterning of a complex organism. This knowledge can reframe the pathogenesis of human diseases such as cancer within a developmental context and can also be applied to create new therapies for the regeneration of damaged tissues. Given the emphasis on stem cells throughout this book, it would seem prudent to discuss the origin of the embryonic kidney with respect to pluripotent renal stem cells and how they may differentiate into the multiplicity of cell types found in an adult kidney. Unfortunately, no such renal embryonic stem (ES) cells have been conclusively identified. Instead, the kidney develops from a region of the embryo, over a relatively long window of time, while undergoing a sequential anterior to posterior transition that reflects in part the evolutionary history of the organ. The question then arises at what stage are cells fated to become kidney cells and when are they restricted in their developmental potential? To address these issues, it is necessary to review the early morphogenesis of the urogenital system. We can then appreciate which genes and molecular markers contribute to early renal development and what cell lineages arise from the region of the embryo devoted to creating the urogenital system.

The Anatomy of Kidney Development

For a detailed description of early renal development and nephron formation, I refer the reader to several recent reviews.[1,2] A brief summary of renal patterning and the origin of the renal progenitor cells must begin with gastrulation. In vertebrates, the process of gastrulation converts a single pluripotent sheet of embryonic tissue, the epiblast or embryonic ectoderm, into the three primary germ layers, the endoderm, the mesoderm, and the ectoderm (Fig. 32–1A). In mammals, gastrulation is marked by a furrow called the primitive streak, which extends from the posterior pole of the epiblast. Extension of the primitive streak occurs by proliferation and migration of more lateral epiblast cells to the furrow, followed by invagination through the furrow and migration back laterally under the epiblast sheet. At the most anterior end of the primitive streak is the node or organizer, called Hensen's node in the chick, and the functional equivalent to the blastopore lip or Speeman's organizer in the amphibian embryo. The node is a signaling center that expresses a potent combination of secreted factors for establishing the body axes and left–right asymmetry. The node is positioned at the anterior pole of the primitive streak at approximately the midpoint of the epiblast. The more anterior epiblast generates much of the head and central nervous system and does not undergo gastrulation in the same manner. Once the streak reaches the node, it begins to regress back to the posterior pole. During this process of primitive streak regression, the notochord is formed along the midline of the embryo and just ventral to the neural plate. The notochord is a second critical signaling center for dorsal ventral patterning of both neural plate and paraxial mesoderm. The axial mesoderm refers to the most medial mesodermal cells, which in response to regression of the streak become segmented into somites, blocks of cells surrounded by a simple epithelium. At the stage of the first somite formation, going medial to lateral, the notochord marks the midline, the somites abut the notochord on either side, and the unsegmented mesoderm is termed intermediate near the somite and lateral plate more distally (Fig. 32–1B). It is this region of intermediate mesoderm within which the kidney will form that is the primary focus of this chapter.

The earliest morphologic indication of unique derivatives arising from the intermediate mesoderm is the formation of the pronephric duct, or primary nephric duct. This single cell thick epithelial tube runs bilaterally beginning at around the 12th somite in birds and mammals. The nephric duct extends caudally until it reaches the cloaca. As it grows, it induces a linear array of epithelial tubules, which extend medio-ventrally and are thought to derive from periductal mesenchyme (Fig. 32–2). The tubules are referred to as pronephric or mesonephric, depending on their position and degree of development, and represent an evolutionarily more primitive excretory system that forms transiently in mammals until it is replaced by the adult or metanephric kidney. Along the nephric duct, there is a graded evolution of renal tubule development with the most anterior, or pronephric tubules, being very rudimentary, and the mesonephric tubules becoming well

Handbook of Stem Cells
Volume 1

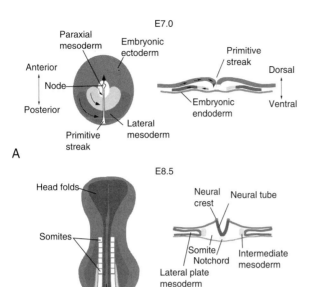

A

B

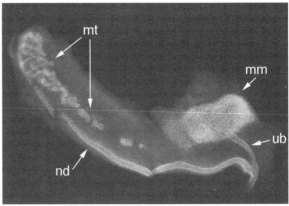

Figure 32–2. *Expression of Pax2 at the time of metanephric induction.* One side of the intermediate mesoderm–derived nephric chord was microdissected from an E11.5 mouse embryo and stained with anti-Pax2 antibodies. The micrograph shows Pax2 in the nephric duct (nd) and the ureteric bud (ub) branching from the posterior duct. Pax2 is in mesonephric tubules (mt), even those more posterior that are not connected to the nephric duct. At the posterior end, Pax2 is in the metanephric mesenchyme cells (mm), surrounding the ureteric bud, that has not yet begun to form epithelia.

Figure 32–1. *The origin of the intermediate mesoderm.* (A) At gastrulation, cells of the epiblast, or embryonic ectoderm, migrate through the primitive streak. In the mouse, the single sheet of embryonic ectoderm lines a cup-shaped egg cylinder. The left panel is a planar representation of a mouse epiblast looking down into the cup from above. The streak begins at the posterior and moves toward the anterior. Fate mapping studies indicate that lateral plate mesoderm originates from the posterior epiblast, whereas axial mesoderm is derived from more anterior epiblast cells. The intermediate mesoderm most likely originates from cells between these two regions. At the mid-streak stage, the expression of lim1 can already be detected before gastrulation in cells of the posterior epiblast. The schematic on the right is a cross section through the primitive streak, showing the formation of mesoderm as cells of the epiblast migrate toward the streak then invaginate and reverse direction underneath the epiblast sheet. (B) At the time of primitive streak regression, the notochord is formed along the ventral midline. Paraxial mesoderm begins to form segments, or somites, in an anterior to posterior direction. The lateral plate mesoderm, consists of two sheets called the somatopleure (dorsal) and the splanchnopleure (ventral). The region between the somite and the lateral plate is the intermediate mesoderm, where the first renal epithelial tube will form. (Please see CD-ROM for color version of this figure.)

developed with glomeruli and convoluted proximal tubule-like structures. In contrast, the pronephros of the zebrafish larvae is a fully developed, functional filtration unit with a single midline glomerulus.[3] Amphibian embryos such as *Xenopus laevis* have bilateral pronephric glomeruli and tubules that are functional until replaced by a mesonephric kidney in the tadpole.[4] In fact, it is not altogether obvious in mammals where to draw the distinction between pronephric tubules and mesonephric tubules. Mature mesonephric tubules are characterized by a vascularized glomerulus at the proximal end of the tubule that empties into the nephric duct; the most anterior and posterior mesonephric tubules are more rudimentary, and the most posterior tubules are not connected to the duct at all.

The adult kidney, or metanephros, is formed at the caudal end of the nephric duct when an outgrowth, called the ureteric bud or metanephric diverticulum, extends into the surrounding metanephric mesenchyme. Outgrowth or budding of the epithelia requires signals emanating from the mesenchyme. Genetic and biochemical studies indicate that outgrowth of the ureteric bud is mediated by the transmembrane tyrosine kinase RET, which is expressed in the nephric duct, and the secreted neurotrophin glial derived neurotrophic factor (GDNF), which is expressed in the metanephric mesenchyme. Once the ureteric bud has invaded the metanephric mesenchyme, inductive signals emanating from the bud initiate the conversion of the metanephric mesenchyme to epithelium (Fig. 32–3). The induced, condensing mesenchymal cells aggregate around the tips of the bud and will form a primitive polarized epithelium, the renal vesicle. Through a series of cleft formations, the renal vesicle forms first a comma then an S-shaped body, whose most distal end remains in contact with the ureteric bud epithelium and fuses to form a continuous epithelial tubule. This S-shaped tubule begins to express genes specific for glomerular podocyte cells at its most proximal end, markers for more distal tubules near the fusion with the ureteric bud epithelia, and proximal tubules markers in between. Endothelial cells begin to infiltrate the most proximal cleft of the S-shaped body as the vasculature of the glomerular tuft takes shape. At this stage, the glomerular epithelium consists of a visceral and parietal component, with the visceral cells becoming podocytes and the parietal cells the epithelia surrounding the urinary space. The capillary tuft consists of capillary endothelial cells and a specialized type of smooth muscle cell, termed the mesangial cell, whose origin remains unclear.

As these renal vesicles are generating much of epithelia of the nephron, the ureteric bud epithelia continues to undergo branching morphogenesis in response to signals derived from the mesenchyme. Branching follows a stereotypical pattern

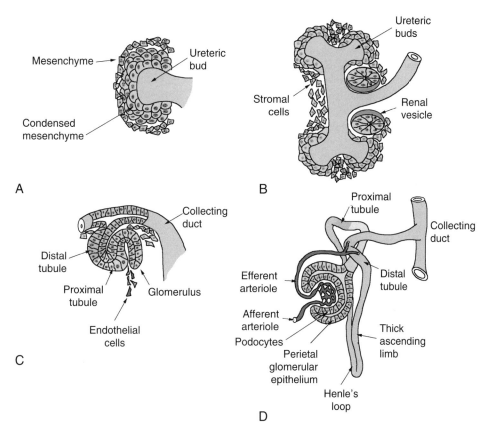

Figure 32–3. *The sequential conversion of metanephric mesenchyme to renal epithelia. A schematic of the condensation and polarization of the metanephric mesenchyme at the tips of the ureteric bud epithelia is shown. (A) Epithelial precursors aggregate at the tips, whereas stromal cells remain peripheral. (B) The initial aggregates form a primitive sphere, the renal vesicle, as branching ureteric bud epithelia cells extend outward to induce a new aggregates. Stromal cells begin to migrate into the interstitium. (C) At the S-shaped body stage, the mesenchymal derived structure is fused to the ureteric bud epithelial, which will make the collecting ducts and tubules. The proximal cleft of the S-shaped body is invaded by endothelial cells. Expression of glomerular, proximal tubule, and more distal tubule specific markers can be seen at this stage. (D) The architecture of the nephron is elaborated. Podocyte cells of the visceral glomerular epithelium contact the capillary tuft and the glomerular basement membrane is laid down. The proximal tubules become more convoluted and grow into the medullary zone to form the descending and ascending limbs of Henle's loop. The distal tubules and collecting ducts begin to express markers for more differentiated, specialized epithelia. (Please see CD-ROM for color version of this figure.)*

and results in new mesenchymal aggregates induced at the tips of the branches, as new nephrons are sequentially induced. This repeated branching and induction results in the formation of nephrons along the radial axis of the kidney, with the oldest nephrons being more medullary and the younger nephrons located toward the periphery. However, not all cells of the mesenchyme become induced and convert to epithelia, some cells remain mesenchymal and migrate to the interstitium. These interstitial mesenchymal cells, or stromal cells, are essential for providing signals that maintain branching morphogenesis of the ureteric bud and survival of the mesenchyme.

From a stem cell perspective, defining the population of cells that generate the kidney depends in part on which stage one considers. At the time of metanephric mesenchyme induction, there are at least two primary cell types, the mesenchyme and the ureteric bud epithelia. Although these cells are phenotypically distinguishable, they do express some common markers and share a common region of origin. As development progresses, it was thought that most of the epithelium of the nephron was derived from the metanephric mesenchyme, whereas the branching ureteric bud epithelium generates the collecting ducts and the most distal tubules. This view has been challenged by cell lineage tracing methods *in vitro,* which indicate some plasticity at the tips of the ureteric bud epithelium such that the two populations may intermingle.[5] Thus, at the time of induction, epithelial cells can convert to mesenchyme, just as the mesenchymal aggregates can convert to epithelia. Regardless of how the mesenchyme is induced, the cells are predetermined to make renal epithelia. Thus, their potential as renal stem cells has begun to be explored. To understand the origin of the metanephric mesenchyme, we begin with the patterning of the intermediate mesoderm.

Genes That Control Early Kidney Development

Genetic studies in the mouse have provided substantial new insights into the regulatory mechanisms underlying renal development. Although there are many genes that can affect the growth and patterning of the kidney, of particular importance with respect to potential renal stem cells are the genes that control formation of the nephric duct epithelia and proliferation and differentiation of the metanephric mesenchyme (Table 32–1).

GENES THAT DETERMINE THE NEPHROGENIC FIELD

From a perspective of stem cells and potential therapy, the adult or metanephric kidney should be a primary focus. However, the early events controlling the specification of the renal cell lineages may be common among the pronephric and mesonephric regions. Indeed, many of the same genes expressed in the pronephric and mesonephric tubules are instrumental in early metanephric development. Furthermore, the earliest events that underlie regional specification have been studied in more amenable organisms, including fish and amphibians, in which pronephric development is less transient and of functional significance.

Although formation of the nephric duct is the earliest morphologic evidence of renal development, the expression of intermediate mesodermal-specific markers precedes nephric duct formation temporally and marks the intermediate meso-derm along much of the anterior-posterior (A-P) body axis. The earliest markers specific of intermediate mesoderm are two transcription factors of the Pax family (Fig. 32–4), *Pax2* and *Pax8*, which appear to function redundantly in nephric duct formation and extension.[6] The homeobox gene *lim1* is also expressed in the intermediate mesoderm but is initially expressed in the lateral plate mesoderm before becoming more restricted.[7] Genetics implicates all three genes in some aspects of regionalization along the intermediate mesoderm. In the mouse, *Pax2* mutants begin nephric duct formation and extension but lack mesonephric tubules and the metanephros.[8] *Pax2/Pax8* double mutants have no evidence of nephric duct formation and do not express the *lim1* gene. Null mutants in *lim1* also lack the nephric duct and show reduced ability to differentiate into intermediate mesoderm specific derivatives.[7] The reduced expression of *Pax2* in *lim1* mutants could explain the inability of these cells to differentiate into urogenital epithelia. Although in *Pax2/Pax8* double null embryos,[6] the lack of lim1 expression may also be an integral part of the phenotype. Because lim1 expression precedes Pax2 and Pax8 and is spread over a wider area in the pregastrulation and postgastrulation embryo and is Pax independent, it seems likely that maintenance and restriction of lim1 expression within the intermediate mesoderm requires activation of the *Pax2/8* genes at the 5–8 somite stage. Are *Pax2/8* sufficient then to specify the renal progenitors? This question was addressed in the chick embryo by Bouchard *et al.*[6] using replication competent retroviruses expressing a Pax2b cDNA. Ectopic nephric ducts were generated within the general area of the intermediate mesoderm upon retrovirally driven Pax2b expression. These ectopic nephric ducts were not obtained with either lim1 or Pax8 alone. Strikingly, the ectopic nephric ducts paralleled the endogenous ducts and were not found in more paraxial or lateral plate mesoderm. This would suggest

TABLE 32–1
Genes that Regulate Early Kidney Cell Lineages

Gene	Expression	Mutant Phenotype	Reference
lim1	Lateral plate Nephric duct	No nephric duct, no kidneys	7
Pax2	Inter. mesoderm Nephric duct	No mesonephric tubules No metanephros	8 15
Pax2/Pax8	Inter. mesoderm	No nephric duct, no kidneys	6
WT1	Inter. mesoderm Mesenchyme	Fewer mesonephric tubules Apoptosis of mesenchyme	23
Eya1	Met. mesenchyme	No induction of mesenchyme	18
wnt4	Mesenchymal aggregates	No polarization of aggregates	24
bmp7	Ureter bud and met. mesenchyme	Developmental arrest postinduction Some branching, few nephrons	44
bf-2	Met. mesenchyme Interstitial stroma	Developmental arrest, few nephrons Limited branching	25
pod-1	Stroma and podocytes	Poorly differentiated podocytes	32
pdgf(r)	s-Shaped body	No vascularization of glomerular tuft	40

inter., intermediate; met., metanephric.

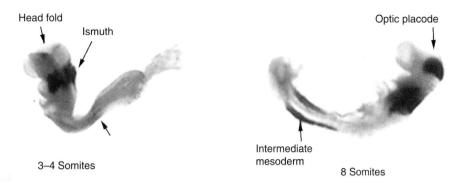

Figure 32–4. *The activation of Pax2 expression in the intermediate mesoderm. One of the earliest markers for the nephrogenic region Pax2 expression is activated around the four to five somite in the cells between the axial and lateral plate mesoderm. The embryos shown carry a Pax2 promoter driving the LacZ gene and expression is visualized by staining for beta-galactosidase activity. By the eight-somite stage, Pax2 marks the growing intermediate mesoderm even before the nephric duct is formed. Pax2 is also expressed in parts of the nervous system, especially the mid-brain–hindbrain junction, known as the rhombencephalic ismuth, and in the optic placode and cup. (Please see CD-ROM for color version of this figure.)*

that Pax2's ability to induce duct formation does require some regional competence, perhaps only in the lim1 expressing domain.

If Pax2/8 and lim1 restriction in the intermediate mesoderm are the earliest events that distinguish the nephrogenic zone from surrounding paraxial and lateral plate mesoderm, the question then remains as to how these genes are activated. In the axial mesoderm, signals derived from the ventral notochord pattern the somites along the dorsal-ventral axis. Similar notochord derived signals could also pattern mesoderm along the medio-lateral axis. However, this does not appear to be the case. In the chick embryo, the notochord is dispensable for activation of the *Pax2* gene in the intermediate mesoderm. Instead, signals derived from the somites, or paraxial mesoderm, are required for activation of Pax2.[9] It remains to be determined what these somite derived signals are, although it is worth noting that in the amphibian embryo a combination of retinoic acid and activin-A is able to activate early markers of the pronephric field including lim1.[10,11]

In addition to somite-derived signals, additional signals may be required for the formation of epithelia within the predisposed intermediate mesoderm. Activation of Pax2/8 is found more anterior to and precedes formation of the nephric duct. Thus, not all Pax2 positive cells will make the primary nephric duct. In the chick embryo, the overlying ectoderm is necessary for formation of the nephric duct, which initiates adjacent to somites 10–12, significantly more posterior to the initial Pax2 positive domain.[12] Removal of overlying ectodermal tissues, which express the secreted signaling molecule bone morphogenetic protein-4 (BMP4), blocks nephric duct formation and extension. This block can be overcome by recombinant BMP4 protein suggesting that this is indeed the essential ectodermally derived factor.

If Pax2/8 mark the entire nephric region, there must be additional factors that specify the position of elements along the A-P axis in the intermediate mesoderm. Such patterning genes could determine whether a mesonephric or metanephric

kidney is formed within the Pax2 positive domain. Among the known A-P patterning genes are members of the HOX gene family. Indeed, mice that have deleted all genes of the Hox11 paralogous group have no metanephric kidneys,[13] although it is not clear whether this is truly a shift in A-P patterning or a lack of induction. A-P patterning of the intermediate mesoderm may also depend on the FoxC family of transcription factors. *Foxc1* and *Foxc2* have similar expression domains in the presomitic and intermediate mesoderm, as early as E8.5.[14] As nephric duct extension progresses, Foxc1 is expressed in a dorso-ventral gradient with the highest levels near the neural tube and lower levels in the BMP4 positive ventro-lateral regions. In *Foxc1* homozygous null mutants the anterior boundary of the metanephric mesenchyme, as marked by GDNF expression, extends rostrally.[14] This results in a broader ureteric bud forming along the A-P axis and eventual duplication of ureters. Similar defects are observed in compound heterozygotes of *Foxc1* and *Foxc2*, indicating some redundancy and gene dosage effects. Thus, *Foxc1* and *Foxc2* may set the anterior boundary of the metanephric mesenchyme, at the time of ureteric bud outgrowth, by suppressing genes at the transcriptional level.

GENES THAT FUNCTION AT THE TIME OF METANEPHRIC INDUCTION

Pax2 and Pax8 are co-expressed in the nephric duct, but the Pax2 expression domain is broader and encompasses the mesonephric tubules and the metanephric mesenchyme. Thus, Pax8 mutants have no obvious renal phenotype, Pax2 mutants have a nephric duct but no mesonephric tubules or metanephros, and Pax2/8 double mutants lack the nephric duct completely. Thus, either Pax2 or Pax8 is enough for duct formation, but Pax2 is clearly essential for conversion of the metanephric mesenchyme into epithelia.

The Pax2 phenotype is complex. Despite the presence of a nephric duct, there is no evidence of ureteric bud outgrowth. Ureteric bud outgrowth is controlled primarily by the receptor type tyrosine kinase RET, which is expressed on the nephric duct epithelia, the secreted signaling protein GDNF, which is expressed in the metanephric mesenchyme, and the GPi linked protein GFRα1, which is expressed in both tissues. Pax2 mutants have no ureteric buds because they do not express GDNF in the mesenchyme and fail to maintain high levels of RET expression in the nephric duct.[15] Despite the lack of bud, the metanephric mesenchyme is morphologically distinguishable in Pax2 mutants. Although lacking GDNF, it does express other markers of the mesenchyme, such as Six2.[8] *In vitro* recombination experiments using Pax2 mutant mesenchyme, surgically isolated from E11 mouse embryos, and heterologous inducing tissues indicate that *Pax2* mutants are unable to respond to inductive signals.[15] Thus, *Pax2* is necessary for specifying the region of intermediate mesoderm destined to undergo mesenchyme-to-epithelium conversion. In humans, the necessity of Pax2 function is further underscored because the loss of a single *Pax2* allele is associated with renal-coloboma syndrome, which is characterized by hypoplastic kidneys with vesicoureteral reflux.[16]

A second essential gene for conversion of the metanephric mesenchyme to epithelia is *Eya1,* a vertebrate homologue of the *Drosophila eyes absent* gene. In humans, mutations in the *Eya1* gene are associated with branchio-oto-renal syndrome, a complex multifaceted phenotype.[17] In mice homozygous for an *Eya1* mutation, kidney development is arrested at E11 because ureteric bud growth is inhibited and the mesenchyme remains uninduced, although Pax2 and WT1 expression appears normal.[18] However, two other markers of the metanephric mesenchyme, Six2 and GDNF expression, are lost in the eya1 mutants. The loss of GDNF expression most probably underlies the failure of ureteric bud growth. However, it is not clear if the mesenchyme is competent to respond to inductive signals if a wild-type inducer were to be used *in vitro.* The eyes absent gene family is part of a conserved network that underlies cell specification in several other developing tissues. Eya proteins share a conserved domain but lack DNA binding activity. The Eya proteins interact directly with the Six family of DNA-binding proteins. Mammalian Six genes are homologues of the *Drosophila sina oculis* homeobox gene. This cooperative interaction between Six and Eya proteins is necessary for nuclear translocation and transcriptional activation of Six target genes.[19]

The Wilms tumor suppressor gene, *WT1,* is another early markers of the metanephric mesenchyme and is essential for its survival. Wilms tumor is an embryonic kidney neoplasia that consists of undifferentiated mesenchymal cells, poorly organized epithelium, and surrounding stromal cells. Expression of WT1 is regulated spatially and temporally in a variety of tissues and is further complicated by the presence of at least four isoforms, generated by alternative splicing. In the developing kidney, WT1 can be found in the uninduced metanephric mesenchyme and in differentiating epithelium after induction.[20,21] Early expression of WT1 may be mediated by Pax2.[22] Initial expression levels are low in the metanephric mesenchyme, but become up-regulated at the S-shaped body stage in the precursor cells of the glomerular epithelium, the

podocytes. High WT1 levels persists in the adult podocytes. In the moue, *WT1* null mutants have complete renal agenesis,[23] because the metanephric mesenchyme undergoes apoptosis and the ureteric bud fails to grow out of the nephric duct. The arrest of ureteric bud growth is most probably due to lack of signaling by the *WT1* mutant mesenchyme. As in *Pax2* mutants, the mesenchyme is unable to respond to inductive signals even if a heterologous inducer is used *in vitro*. Thus, it appears that *WT1* is required early in the mesenchyme to promote cell survival, enabling cells to respond to inductive signals and express ureteric bud growth promoting factors.

The Establishment of Additional Cell Lineages

At the time of ureteric bud invasion, there appear to be at least two cell lineages established, the metanephric mesenchyme and the ureteric bud epithelia. As branching morphogenesis and induction of the mesenchyme progresses, additional cell lineages are evident. The early E11.5 mouse metanephros contains precursors for most all cell types, including endothelial, stromal, epithelial, and mesangial cells. However, it is far from clear if these cell types share a common precursor or if the metanephric mesenchyme is a mixed population of precursors. The latter point may well be true for the endothelial lineage. Although transplantation studies with lineage markers indicate that the vasculature can be derived from E11.5 metanephric kidneys, the Flk1 positive endothelial precursors have been observed closely associated with the ureteric bud epithelium, shortly after invasion, and are probably not derived from the metanephric mesenchyme. The lineages most likely to share a common origin within the metanephric mesenchyme are the stromal and epithelial lineages. The maintenance of these two lineages is essential for renal development, because the ratio of stroma to epithelia is a critical factor for the renewal of mesenchyme and the continued induction of new nephrons.

EPITHELIA VERSUS STROMA

What are the early events in the induced mesenchyme that separates the stromal lineage from the epithelial lineage? In response to inductive signals, Pax2 positive cells aggregate at the tips of the ureteric bud. Activation of the *Wnt4* gene in these early aggregates appears critical to promote polarization. *Wnt* genes encode a family of secreted peptides that are known to function in the development of a many tissues. Mice homozygous for a *wnt-4* mutation exhibit renal agenesis resulting from growth arrest shortly after branching of the ureteric bud.[24] Although some mesenchymal aggregation has occurred, there is no evidence of cell differentiation into a polarized epithelial vesicle. Expression of *Pax2* is maintained but reduced. Thus, wnt-4 may be a secondary inductive signal in the mesenchyme that propagates or maintains the primary induction response in the epithelial lineage. The transcription factor FoxD1/BF-2 is expressed in uninduced mesenchyme and becomes restricted to those cells not undergoing epithelial conversion after induction.[25] FoxD1 expression is found along the periphery of the kidney and in the interstitial mesenchyme, or stroma. After induction, there is little overlap between FoxD1 and the Pax2 expression domain, prominent in the condensing pretubular aggregates. Clear lineage analysis is still lacking, although the expression patterns are consistent with the interpretation that mesenchyme cells may already partitioned into a FoxD1 positive stromal precursor and a Pax2 positive epithelial precursor before or shortly after induction. Mouse mutants in FoxD1 exhibit severe developmental defects in the kidney that point to an essential role for FoxD1 in maintaining growth and structure.[25] Early ureteric bud growth and branching are unaffected, as is the formation of the first mesenchymal aggregates. However, at later stages (E13–14) these mesenchymal aggregates fail to differentiate into comma- and S-shaped bodies at a rate similar to wild-type. Branching of the ureteric bud is greatly reduced at this stage, resulting in fewer new mesenchymal aggregates forming. The fate of the initial aggregates is not fixed, because some are able to form epithelium and most all express the appropriate early markers, such as Pax2, wnt4, and WT1. Nevertheless, it appears that the FoxD1 expressing stromal lineage is necessary to maintain growth of both ureteric bud epithelium and mesenchymal aggregates. Perhaps factors secreted from the stroma provide survival or proliferation cues for the epithelial precursors, in the absence of which the non–self-renewing population of mesenchyme is exhausted.

Some survival factors that act on the mesenchyme have already been identified. The secreted transforming growth factor beta (TGFβ) family member BMP7 and the fibroblast growth factor-2 (FGF2) in combination dramatically promote survival of uninduced metanephric mesenchyme in vitro.[26] FGF2 is necessary to maintain the ability of the mesenchyme to respond to inductive signals in vitro. BMP7 alone inhibits apoptosis but is not sufficient to enable mesenchyme to undergo tubulogenesis at some later time. After induction, exogenously added FGF2 and BMP7 reduce the proportion of mesenchyme that undergoes tubulogenesis while increasing the population of FoxD1 positive stromal cells.[26] At least after induction occurs, there is a delicate balance between a self-renewing population of stromal and epithelial progenitor cells, the proportion of which must be well regulated by both autocrine and paracrine factors. Whether this lineage decision has already been made in the uninduced mesenchyme remains to be determined.

The role of stroma in regulating renal development is further underscored by studies with retinoic acid receptors. It is well documented that vitamin A deficiency results in severe renal defects.[27] In organ culture, retinoic acid stimulates expression of RET to dramatically increase the number of ureteric bud branch points, increasing the number of nephrons.[28] However, it is the stromal cell population that express the retinoic acid receptors (RARs), specifically RARα and RARβ2. Genetic studies with RARα and RARβ2 homozygous mutant mice indicate no significant renal defects when either gene is deleted. However, double homozygotes mutant for both RARα and RARβ2 exhibit severe growth retardation in the kidney.[29] These defects are primarily due to decreased expression of the RET protein in the ureteric bud epithelia and limited branching morphogenesis. Surprisingly, overexpression of RET with a HoxB7/RET transgene can completely rescue the double RAR mutants.[30] These studies suggest that stromal cells provide paracrine signals for maintaining RET expression in the ureteric bud epithelia and that retinoids are required for stromal proliferation. Reduced expression of stromal cell marker FoxD1, particularly in the interstitium of RAR double mutants, supports this hypothesis.

CELLS OF THE GLOMERULAR TUFT

The unique structure of the glomerulus is intricately linked to its ability to retain large macromolecules within the circulating bloodstream while allowing for rapid diffusion of ions and small molecules into the urinary space. The glomerulus consists of four major cell types: the endothelial cells of the microvasculature, the mesangial cells, the podocyte cells of the visceral epithelium, and the parietal epithelium. The development of the glomerular architecture and the origin of the individual cell types are just beginning to be understood.

The podocyte is a highly specialized epithelial cell whose function is integral to maintaining the filtration barrier in the glomerulus. The glomerular basement membrane separates the endothelial cells of the capillary tufts from the urinary space. The outside of the glomerular basement membrane, which faces the urinary space, is covered with podocyte cells and their interdigitated foot processes. At the basement membrane, these interdigitations meet to form a highly specialized cell–cell junction, called the slit diaphragm. The slit diaphragm has a specific pore size to enable small molecules to cross the filtration barrier into the urinary space, while retaining larger proteins in the blood stream. The podocytes are derived from condensing metanephric mesenchyme and can be visualized with specific markers at the S-shaped body stage. Although there are a number of genes expressed in the podocytes, there are only a few factors known to regulate podocyte differentiation. These include the WT1 gene, which is required early for metanephric mesenchyme survival but whose levels increase in podocyte precursors at the S-shaped body stage. In the mouse, complete WT1 null animals lack kidneys but reduced gene dosage and expression of WT1 results in specific podocyte defects.[31] Thus, the high levels of WT1 expression in podocytes appear to be required and make these precursor cells more sensitive to gene dosage. The basic helix-loop-helix protein Pod1 is expressed in epithelial precursor cells and in more mature interstitial mesenchyme. At later developmental stages, Pod1 is restricted to the podocytes. In mice homozygous for a Pod1 null allele, podocyte development appears arrested.[32] Normal podocytes flatten and wrap their foot processes around the glomerular basement membrane. Pod1 mutant podocytes remain more columnar and fail to fully develop foot processes. Because Pod1 is expressed in epithelial precursors and in the interstitium, it is unclear whether these podocyte effects are due to a general developmental arrest because of the stromal environment or a cell autonomous defect within the Pod1 mutant podocyte precursor cells.

341

Within the glomerular tuft, the origin of the endothelium and the mesangium is less clear. At the S-shaped body stage, the glomerular cleft forms at the most proximal part of the S-shaped body, furthest from the ureteric bud epithelium. Vascularization of the developing kidney is first evident within this developing tuft. The origin of these invading endothelial cells has been studied in some detail. Under normal growth conditions, kidneys excised at the time of induction and cultured *in vitro* do not exhibit signs of vascularization, leading to the presumption that endothelial cells migrate to the kidney some time after induction. However, hypoxygenation or treatment with vascular endothelial growth factor (VEGF) promotes survival or differentiation of endothelial precursors in these same cultures, suggesting that endothelial precursors are already present and require growth differentiation stimuli.[33,34] *In vivo* transplantation experiments using lacZ expressing donors or hosts also demonstrate that the E11.5 kidney rudiment has the potential to generate endothelial cells, although recruitment of endothelium is also observed from exogenous tissue depending on the environment.[35–37] The data are consistent with the idea that cells within the E11.5 kidney have the ability to differentiate along the endothelial lineage. Are these endothelial cells generated from the metanephric mesenchyme? Using a lacZ knockin allele for the endothelial specific receptor Flk-1, Robert *et al.*[37] showed presumptive angioblasts are dispersed along the periphery of the E12 kidney mesenchyme, with some positive cells invading the mesenchyme along the aspect of the growing ureteric bud. At later stages, Flk-1 positive angioblasts were localized to the nephrogenic zone, the developing glomerular cleft of the S-shaped bodies, and the more mature capillary loops, whereas VEGF localizes to the parietal and visceral glomerular epithelium. Injection of neutralizing VEGF antibodies into newborn mice, at a time when nephrogenesis is still ongoing, disturbs vascular growth and glomerular architecture.[38] The data suggest that endothelial cells originate independent of the metanephric mesenchyme and invade the growing kidney from the periphery and along the ureteric bud.

The mesangial cells are located between the capillary loops of the glomerular tuft and have been referred to as specialized pericytes. The pericytes are found within the capillary basement membranes and have contractile abilities, much like a smooth muscle cell. Whether the mesangial cell is derived from the endothelial or epithelial lineage remains unclear. However, genetic and chimeric analyses in the mouse have revealed a clear role for the platelet-derived growth factor receptor (PDGFR) and its ligand platelet-derived growth factor (PDGF). In mice deficient for either PDGF or PDGFR,[39,40] a complete absence of mesangial cells results in glomerular defects, including the lack of microvasculature in the tuft. PDGF is expressed in the developing endothelial cells of the glomerular tuft, whereas the receptor is found in the presumptive mesangial cell precursors. Using ES cell chimeras of *Pdgfr*[−/−] and [+/+] genotypes, only the wild-type cells could contribute to the mesangial lineage.[41] This cell autonomous effect indicates that signaling from the developing vasculature promotes proliferation and/or migration of the

mesangial precursor cells. Also, expression of PDGFR and smooth muscle actin supports a model in which mesangial cells are derived from smooth muscle of the afferent and efferent arterioles during glomerular maturation.[41]

What Constitutes a Renal Stem Cell?

The issue of renal stem cells is beginning to draw more attention as new information regarding development and lineage specification is unraveled.[42] A prospective renal stem cell should be self-renewing and able to generate all of the cell types in the kidney. Whether such a cell exists remains to be demonstrated *in vivo*, although the *in vitro* data of Oliver *et al.*[43] appear promising. In simplest terms, all of the cells in the kidney could be generated by a single stem cell population as outlined in Fig. 32–5. Despite the potential, there are several issues outstanding. Even at the earliest stage of kidney development there are already two identifiable cell types. The presence of early endothelial precursors at the time of induction would make a third distinct cell type. If the three earliest cell types can indeed be derived from the metanephric mesenchyme, a single stem cell may indeed exist and continue to proliferate as development progresses. At present, the data suggest that stroma and epithelia may share a common origin,

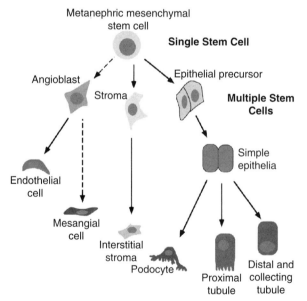

Figure 32–5. *The major cell lineages of the kidney.* Whether the kidney arises from a single renal stem cell or from multiple independent lineages remains to be determined. However, the basic differentiation scheme is becoming clearer. The cell lineage relationships are outlined schematically, with dotted lines reflecting ambiguity in terms of direct lineages. The metanephric mesenchyme contains angioblasts and stromal and epithelial precursors. Whether angioblast arise from mesenchymal cells or are a separate lineage that surround the mesenchyme is not entirely clear. Similarly, the origin of the mesangial cell is not well defined. Stromal and epithelial cells may share a common precursor, the metanephric mesenchyme, but segregate at the time of induction. The epithelial cell precursors, found in the aggregates at the ureteric bud tips, generate most all of the epithelial cell types in the nephron. (Please see CD-ROM for color version of this figure.)

whereas endothelial cells and their potential smooth muscle derivatives constitute a second lineage. However, even if there are three separate lineages already demarcated within the metanephric mesenchyme, the most relevant with respect to the repair of renal tissue is the epithelial lineage. Thus, if we consider the possibility of an epithelial stem cell, the following points would be among the criteria for selection: (1) the cells would most likely be a derivative of the intermediate mesoderm, (2) the cells would express a combination of markers specific for the metanephric mesenchyme, and (3) the cells should be able to contribute to all epithelial components of the nephron, *in vitro* and *in vivo*.

Unlike ES cells, it seems improbable that cells from the intermediate mesoderm can be cultured indefinitely without additional transformation or immortalization taking place. Embryonic fibroblasts can be cultured from the mouse, but, in most every case, a limited number of cell divisions occurs. The problem is apparent even *in vivo,* because the E11 metanephric mesenchyme is essentially quiescent and does not proliferate in the absence of induction. However, growth conditions that mimic induction might be able to allow for the mesenchyme cells to proliferate while suppressing their differentiation into epithelium. Alternatively, it may be possible to differentiate ES cells into intermediate mesodermal cells using combinations of growth and patterning factors, as has been done for motor neuron differentiation.

If metanephric mesenchymal cells were able to proliferate *in vitro,* the markers they might express should include the following: Pax2, lim1, WT1, GDNF, Six2, and FoxD1. Expression of these markers would indicate a mesenchymal cell that had not decided between the stromal and epithelial lineage. If cells express Pax2, WT1, and Wnt4, but not FoxD1, they could be epithelial stem cells. Such epithelial stem cells when injected into, or recombined with, an *in vitro* cultured metanephric kidney should be able to make all of the epithelial cells along the proximal-distal axis of the nephron. Such epithelial stem cells could prove significant in regenerating damaged tubules in acute and chronic renal injury.

At present, the complexity of the kidney still impedes progress in the area of tissue and cell-based therapies. Not only must the right cells be made but they must be able to organize into a specialized three-dimensional tubular structure capable of fulfilling all of the physiologic demands put on the nephrons. Developmental biology can provide a framework for understanding how these cells arise and what factors promote their differentiation and growth. Although we may not be able to make a kidney from scratch, it seems within the realm of possibility to provide the injured adult kidney with cells or factors to facilitate its own regeneration. Given the high incidence and severity of acute and chronic renal insufficiency, such therapies would be most welcome indeed.

ACKNOWLEDGMENTS

I thank the members of my laboratory for valuable discussion regarding this topic, particularly Pat Brophy, Yi Cai, and Sanj Patel. G.R.D. is supported by NIH grants DK54740 and DK39255 and a grant from the Polycystic Kidney Research Foundation.

REFERENCES

1. Dressler, G.R. (2002). Development of the excretory system. *In* "Mouse Development: patterning, Morphogenesis, and Organogenesis" (Ja.T.P.T. Rossant, ed.), pp. 395–420. Academic Press, San Diego, CA.
2. Kuure, S., Vuolteenaho, R., and Vainio, S. (2000). Kidney morphogenesis: cellular and molecular regulation. *Mech. Dev.* **92,** 31–45.
3. Drummond, I.A., Majumdar, A., Hentschel, H., Elger, M., Solnica-Krezel, L., Schier, A.F., Neuhauss, S.C., Stemple, D.L., Zwartkruis, F., Rangini, Z., Driever, W., and Fishman, M.C. (1998). Early development of the zebrafish pronephros and analysis of mutations affecting pronephric function. *Development* **125,** 4655–4667.
4. Vize, P.D., Seufert, D.W., Carroll, T.J., and Wallingford, J.B. (1997). Model systems for the study of kidney development: use of the pronephros in the analysis of organ induction and patterning. *Dev. Biol.* **188,** 189–204.
5. Qiao, J., Cohen, D., and Herzlinger, D. (1995). The metanephric blastema differentiates into collecting system and nephron epithelia in vitro. *Development* **121,** 3207–3214.
6. Bouchard, M., Souabni, A., Mandler, M., Neubuser, A., and Busslinger, M. (2002). Nephric lineage specification by Pax2 and Pax8. *Genes Dev.* **16,** 2958–2970.
7. Tsang, T.E., Shawlot, W., Kinder, S.J., Kobayashi, A., Kwan, K.M., Schughart, K., Kania, A., Jessell, T.M., Behringer, R.R., and Tam, P.P. (2000). Lim1 activity is required for intermediate mesoderm differentiation in the mouse embryo. *Dev. Biol.* **223,** 77–90.
8. Torres, M., Gomez-Pardo, E., Dressler, G.R., and Gruss, P. (1995). Pax-2 controls multiple steps of urogenital development. *Development* **121,** 4057–4065.
9. Mauch, T.J., Yang, G., Wright, M., Smith, D., and Schoenwolf, G.C. (2000). Signals from trunk paraxial mesoderm induce pronephros formation in chick intermediate mesoderm. *Dev. Biol.* **220,** 62–75.
10. Chan, T.C., Takahashi, S., and Asashima, M. (2000). A role for Xlim-1 in pronephros development in Xenopus laevis. *Dev. Biol.* **228,** 256–269.
11. Osafune, K., Nishinakamura, R., Komazaki, S., and Asashima, M. (2002). In vitro induction of the pronephric duct in Xenopus explants. *Dev. Growth Differ.* **44,** 161–167.
12. Obara-Ishihara, T., Kuhlman, J., Niswander, L., and Herzlinger, D. (1999). The surface ectoderm is essential for nephric duct formation in intermediate mesoderm. *Development* **126,** 1103–1108.
13. Wellik, D.M., Hawkes, P.J., and Capecchi, M.R. (2002). Hox11 paralogous genes are essential for metanephric kidney induction. *Genes Dev.* **16,** 1423–1432.
14. Kume, T., Deng, K., and Hogan, B.L. (2000). Murine forkhead/winged helix genes Foxc1 (Mf1) and Foxc2 (Mfh1) are required for the early organogenesis of the kidney and urinary tract. *Development* **127,** 1387–1395.
15. Brophy, P.D., Ostrom, L., Lang, K.M., and Dressler, G.R. (2001). Regulation of ureteric bud outgrowth by Pax2-dependent activation of the glial derived neurotrophic factor gene. *Development* **128,** 4747–4756.
16. Sanyanusin, P., Schimmenti, L.A., McNoe, L.A., Ward, T.A., Pierpont, M.E.M., Sullivan, M.J., Dobyns, W.B., and Eccles, M.R.

(1995). Mutation of the *Pax2* gene in a family with optic nerve colobomas, renal anomalies and vesicoureteral reflux. *Nat. Genet.* **9**, 358–364.

17. Abdelhak, S., Kalatzis, V., Heilig, R., Compain, S., Samson, D., Vincent, C., Weil, D., Cruaud, C., Sahly, I., Leibovici, M., Bitner-Glindzicz, M., Francis, M., Lacombe, D., Vigneron, J., Charachon, R., Boven, K., Bedbeder, P., Van Regemorter, N., Weissenbach, J., and Petit, C. (1997). A human homologue of the Drosophila eyes absent gene underlies branchio-oto-renal (BOR) syndrome and identifies a novel gene family. *Nat. Genet.* **15**, 157–164.

18. Xu, P.X., Adams, J., Peters, H., Brown, M.C., Heaney, S., and Maas, R. (1999). Eya1-deficient mice lack ears and kidneys and show abnormal apoptosis of organ primordia. *Nat. Genet.* **23**, 113–117.

19. Ohto, H., Kamada, S., Tago, K., Tominaga, S.I., Ozaki, H., Sato, S., and Kawakami, K. (1999). Cooperation of six and eya in activation of their target genes through nuclear translocation of Eya. *Mol. Cell Biol.* **19**, 6815–6824.

20. Pritchard-Jones, K., Fleming, S., Davidson, D., Bickmore, W., Porteous, D., Gosden, C., Bard, J., Buckler, A., Pelletier, J., Housman, D., van Heyningen, V., and Hastie, N. (1990). The candidate Wilms' tumor gene is involved in genitourinary development. *Nature* **346**, 194–197.

21. Armstrong, J.F., Pritchard-Jones, K., Bickmore, W.A., Hastie, N.D., and Bard, J.B.L. (1992). The expression of the Wilms' tumor gene, *WT1*, in the developing mammalian embryo. *Mech. Dev.* **40**, 85–97.

22. Dehbi, M., Ghahremani, M., Lechner, M., Dressler, G., and Pelletier, J. (1996). The paired-box transcription factor, PAX2, positively modulates expression of the Wilms' tumor suppressor gene (WT1). *Oncogene* **13**, 447–453.

23. Kreidberg, J.A., Sariola, H., Loring, J.M., Maeda, M., Pelletier, J., Housman, D., and Jaenisch, R. (1993). *WT1* is required for early kidney development. *Cell* **74**, 679–691.

24. Stark, K., Vainio, S., Vassileva, G., and McMahon, A.P. (1994). Epithelial transformation of metanephric mesenchyme in the developing kidney regulated by Wnt-4. *Nature* **372**, 679–683.

25. Hatini, V., Huh, S.O., Herzlinger, D., Soares, V.C., and Lai, E. (1996). Essential role of stromal mesenchyme in kidney morphogenesis revealed by targeted disruption of Winged Helix transcription factor BF-2. *Genes Dev.* **10**, 1467–1478.

26. Dudley, A.T., Godin, R.E., and Robertson, E.J. (1999). Interaction between FGF and BMP signaling pathways regulates development of metanephric mesenchyme. *Genes Dev.* **13**, 1601–1613.

27. Lelievre-Pegorier, M., Vilar, J., Ferrier, M.L., Moreau, E., Freund, N., Gilbert, T., and Merlet-Benichou, C. (1998). Mild vitamin A deficiency leads to inborn nephron deficit in the rat. *Kidney Int.* **54**, 1455–1462.

28. Vilar, J., Gilbert, T., Moreau, E., and Merlet-Benichou, C. (1996). Metanephros organogenesis is highly stimulated by vitamin A derivatives in organ culture. *Kidney Int.* **49**, 1478–1487.

29. Mendelsohn, C., Batourina, E., Fung, S., Gilbert, T., and Dodd, J. (1999). Stromal cells mediate retinoid-dependent functions essential for renal development. *Development* **126**, 1139–1148.

30. Batourina, E., Gim, S., Bello, N., Shy, M., Clagett-Dame, M., Srinivas, S., Costantini, F., and Mendelsohn, C. (2001). Vitamin A controls epithelial/mesenchymal interactions through Ret expression. *Nat. Genet.* **27**, 74–78.

31. Guo, J.K., Menke, A.L., Gubler, M.C., Clarke, A.R., Harrison, D., Hammes, A., Hastie, N.D., and Schedl, A. (2002). WT1 is a key regulator of podocyte function: reduced expression levels cause crescentic glomerulonephritis and mesangial sclerosis. *Hum. Mol. Genet.* **11**, 651–659.

32. Quaggin, S.E., Schwartz, L., Cui, S., Igarashi, P., Deimling, J., Post, M., and Rossant, J. (1999). The basic-helix-loop-helix protein pod1 is critically important for kidney and lung organogenesis. *Development* **126**, 5771–5783.

33. Tufro, A., Norwood, V.F., Carey, R.M., and Gomez, R.A. (1999). Vascular endothelial growth factor induces nephrogenesis and vasculogenesis. *J. Am. Soc. Nephrol.* **10**, 2125–2134.

34. Tufro-McReddie, A., Norwood, V.F., Aylor, K.W., Botkin, S.J., Carey, R.M., and Gomez, R.A. (1997). Oxygen regulates vascular endothelial growth factor-mediated vasculogenesis and tubulogenesis. *Dev. Biol.* **183**, 139–149.

35. Hyink, D.P., Tucker, D.C., St John, P.L., Leardkamolkarn, V., Accavitti, M.A., Abrass, C.K., and Abrahamson, D.R. (1996). Endogenous origin of glomerular endothelial and mesangial cells in grafts of embryonic kidneys. *Am. J. Physiol.* **270**, F886–899.

36. Robert, B., St. John, P.L., Hyink, D.P., and Abrahamson, D.R. (1996). Evidence that embryonic kidney cells expressing flk-1 are intrinsic, vasculogenic angioblasts. *Am. J. Physiol.* **271**, F744–753.

37. Robert, B., St. John, P.L., and Abrahamson, D.R. (1998). Direct visualization of renal vascular morphogenesis in Flk1 heterozygous mutant mice. *Am. J. Physiol.* **275**, F164–172.

38. Kitamoto, Y., Tokunaga, H., and Tomita, K. (1997). Vascular endothelial growth factor is an essential molecule for mouse kidney development: Glomerulogenesis and nephrogenesis. *J. Clin. Invest.* **99**, 2351–2357.

39. Leveen, P., Pekny, M., Gebre-Medhin, S., Swolin, B., Larsson, E., and Betsholtz, C. (1994). Mice deficient for PDGFD B show renal, cardiovascular, and hematological abnormalities. *Genes Dev.* **8**, 1876–1887.

40. Soriano, P. (1994). Abnormal kidney development and hematological disorders in PDGF beta- receptor mutant mice. *Genes Dev.* **8**, 1888–1896.

41. Lindahl, P., Hellstrom, M., Kalen, M., Karlsson, L., Pekny, M., Pekna, M., Soriano, P., and Betsholtz, C. (1998). Paracrine PDGF-B/PDGF-Rbeta signaling controls mesangial cell development in kidney glomeruli. *Development* **125**, 3313–3322.

42. Al-Awqati, Q., and Oliver, J.A. (2002). Stem cells in the kidney. *Kidney Int.* **61**, 387–395.

43. Oliver, J.A., Barasch, J., Yang, J., Herzlinger, D., and Al-Awqati, Q. (2002). Metanephric mesenchyme contains embryonic renal stem cells. *Am. J. Physiol. Renal Physiol.* **283**, F799–809.

44. Dudley, A.T., Lyons, K.M., and Robertson, E.J. (1995). A requirement for bone morphogenetic protein-7 during development of the mammalian kidney and eye. *Genes Dev.* **9**, 2795–2807.

Gonads–Müllerian Ducts

Josephine Bowles and Peter Koopman

Introduction

The embryonic gonad has unique value in terms of the study of cell-type specification because it has the capacity to develop into one of two very different organs, the testis or the ovary. For this reason, it is known, before the point of sex determination, as the "indifferent" or "bipotential" gonad. Experimentally, the system is useful because both gain-of-function and loss-of-function studies can be carried out without concomitant loss of the organ. Classical embryological experiments led to the conclusion that female development occurs as a "default" pathway in the absence of appropriate signals for male development. As detailed in this chapter, each cell type in the indifferent gonad has two distinct cell fates depending on whether the gonad, as a whole, undertakes the testicular or the ovarian program of development. We are just beginning to understand how the different cell types work together to ensure a single developmental fate for the organ.

Because most study in this field has been performed in the mouse, this chapter focuses on that model system. We describe the origin of the urogenital ridge and the morphological and cellular changes that occur once a sexual fate has been determined. We then review the various cell types in the indifferent gonad, their likely origins, and the means by which they are induced to adopt male- or female-appropriate fates. In addition, we describe the cell types known to migrate into the male gonad. We aim to condense our current knowledge regarding the cell-autonomous actions of transcription factors and the cell–cell actions of growth factors and other signalling molecules in the complicated orchestration of testicular and ovarian development (Fig. 33–1).

Origin of the Gonadal Primordium and Mesonephros

The urogenital ridge as a whole arises from the intermediate lateral plate mesoderm. At approximately 9 days post coitum (dpc), this mesoderm forms two elongated mounds on the coelomic surface of the dorsal side of the embryo. These lie to either side of the neural tube and extend almost the length of the body cavity. These mounds of mesoderm develop into the pronephros (anterior, including adrenal primordium), mesonephros (middle, primitive kidney), and metanephros (posterior, primordium of the definitive kidney). The genital ridges arise on the ventromedial surface of the mesonephroi, being first visible between 10.0–10.5 dpc. By 11.5 dpc, the gonadal primordium is 4–12 cells thick and no sex-specific structural differences can be observed.[1] It is believed that several types of bipotential somatic cells are present in this indifferent gonad. In addition, primordial germ cells (PGCs) migrate in and colonise the developing gonad from about 10.5 dpc.

Adjacent to the genital ridge, in the mesonephros, two duct systems form in a sex-independent fashion. The mesonephric duct, also known as the Wolffian duct, has the capacity to develop into the epididymis, *vas deferens,* and seminal vesicles of the male reproductive tract. The Müllerian duct forms later, beginning at the anterior of the mesonephros at approximately 11.5 dpc and running parallel to the mesonephric duct. This duct is formed by an infolding of the coelomic epithelium and is the anlage of the oviduct, uterus, and upper part of the vagina of the female system. In addition, by 11.5 dpc, a complex of tubules has formed in the mesonephros, connecting the mesonephric duct with the developing gonad. Mesonephric tubules regress in the female but are retained in the male, where they form the efferent ducts.

Several genes are known to be crucial for early gonadal development. Mice deficient of *Wt1, Sf1, Emx2,* or *Lhx9* have differing overall phenotypes but all lack gonads.[2–5] *M33*, the mouse homologue of a *Drosophila* Polycomb group gene also appears to be important for early growth of the gonad in both sexes.[6] *GATA-4* and its interaction partner, *FOG-2*, are required for normal gonadal development, downstream of the expression of *SF1* and *WT1*.[7] The transcription factor *PAX2* is required for development of both duct systems as well as for the mesonephric tubules, but it has no essential role in gonad formation.[8]

SRY and Sex-Specific Differentiation of the Gonad

The sex of the mammalian individual is ultimately determined by whether or not the Y-chromosome, and hence the *SRY* gene, is present.[9,10] We do not know how the expression of *SRY* is initiated, and it is possible that this varies among species. *SRY,* presumed to be a transcription factor, acts as a developmental switch to convert gonadal development from the ovarian default pathway to the testicular pathway. Transgenic experiments demonstrated that expression of

Handbook of Stem Cells
Volume 1
Copyright © 2004 by Academic Press

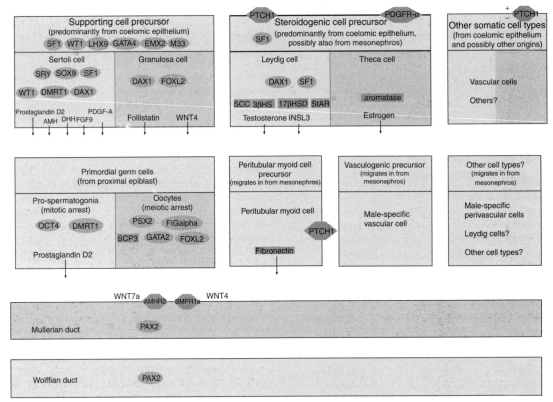

Figure 33–1. *Cell types of the mouse gonad and ducts of the mesonephros. Cell types of the indifferent gonad and precursor cells resident in the mesonephros are shown the upper sections of each box. Bipotential precursor cells give rise to differentiated cell types characteristic of the testis and ovary, and these are shown the lower sections, to the left and right respectively. Transcription factors are named in ovals, and enzymes or structural proteins are shown in rectangles. Cell surface receptors are depicted as hexagons. Secreted substances are shown with arrows. Müllerian and Wolffian ducts are represented as elongated rectangles at the bottom of the figure, with important known transcription factors and receptors indicated. See the text for additional details.*

mouse *Sry* can completely sex-reverse XX embryos, inducing them to develop as phenotypic males.[11] Based on our knowledge of human sex reversal cases, it has been postulated that *SRY* represses a negative regulator of male development.[12] The actual mechanism of action of *SRY* and its direct downstream target or targets are not yet known.

The expression of *Sry* is first detectable about 10.5 dpc in the centre of the genital ridge of XY embryos.[13–17] XX and XY mouse gonads are morphologically identical until approximately 12.5 dpc. By that time, XY gonads are larger than their XX counterparts and have a characteristic blood vessel on the surface farthest from the mesonephros. Moreover, epithelialised testis cords form in the XY gonad, with aggregates of large, round germ cells enclosed by polarized elongated Sertoli cells held together by tight junctions and abutting a basal lamina. On the outer side of the basal lamina is a layer of flattened peritubular myoid cells. The interstitial space, outside the testis cords, is composed of steroid-producing Leydig cells, a testis-specific vasculature, and other cell types that are not well defined. The basement membrane under the coelomic epithelium thickens to form a capsule of fibrous connective tissue, the tunica albuginea.

In contrast to the situation in the developing testis, little structural change is apparent in the developing ovary until approximately 16 dpc. At that time, supporting cells start to cluster around oocytes, the first overt sign of differentiation of ovarian structure. Steroidogenic theca cells surround the granulosa cells, but there is no production of a basal lamina or specialised extracellular matrix. There appears to be no equivalent in the female of the peritubular myoid cells found surrounding testis cords in the male. Vasculature is present, but branching is less extensive and no coelomic vessel forms.

Generally, it seems that all cells of the gonad cooperate to ensure that the entire population is recruited to either testicular or ovarian development. Occasionally, however, there is a breakdown in cellular cooperation, and a single organismal fate is not achieved. In such a situation, an ovotestis is formed, with both testicular and ovarian tissue present. An experimental example of this is when the Y-chromosome from the *Mus domesticus poshavinus* strain, considered to have a "weak" *Sry* allele, is present on a C57BL/6 background.[18] Even when an ovotestis does form, sex-specific clusters of cells are generally seen. Usually, the testicular compartment is found in the middle with ovarian tissue at either pole of the gonad.

Over the course of gestation, the ovarian portions may regress so that a relatively normal testis is present by birth.[19–22] Based on these observations, it has been proposed that *Sry* has a narrow window of time in which to act to overcome the ovarian pathway. It is thought that weak alleles of *Sry*, expressed later or at a lower level than normal, are mismatched with the ovarian program of development. The arrangement of testicular and ovarian tissue commonly seen in ovotestes is in accordance with the observation that *Sry* is expressed first in the centre and then in the poles of the developing gonad.[16,17]

Cellular Events Downstream of *Sry*

Several distinct, though interrelated, cellular responses have been described downstream of the expression of *Sry*. These result in rapid changes in the topological arrangement of the various cell types of the XY gonad; we explain them briefly as a prelude to our review of the origin and differentiation of the various cell types.

PROLIFERATION OF CELLS OF THE COELOMIC EPITHELIUM

Prior to *Sry* expression, cells of the superficial coelomic epithelium of the genital ridge proliferate and move into the underlying loose mesenchymal tissue in a sex-independent manner.[23] After *Sry* expression, the rate of proliferation at the coelomic epithelium of the male gonad increases substantially. Two rounds of male-specific proliferation have been observed.[23] Using bromodeoxyuridine (BrdU) staining and confocal microscopy, an initial burst of somatic cell proliferation was demonstrated in the SF1+ cell population at the coelomic epithelium between 11.3–11.5 dpc. The proliferating cells move into the genital ridge and are fated to become Sertoli cells. A second wave of male-specific proliferation is observed between 11.5–12.0 dpc, but in this case, it occurs in the SF1– cell population. BrdU pulse-chase experiments showed that these cells include precursors of endothelial and Leydig cells as well as uncharacterised somatic cells of the testis. Both waves of proliferation are dependent on *Sry* expression, but since *Sry* is not expressed in coelomic epithelial cells,[16,17,24] this proliferation has to be induced through a non–cell-autonomous mechanism. It is possible that *Sry*-expressing pre-Sertoli cells in the interior of the primordial gonad are able to recruit migrating "first round" coelomic epithelial cells to the Sertoli cell fate.[16] Cells of the coelomic epithelium may act as a stem cell population since several somatic cell types of the gonad arise from progenitors originally residing in the coelomic epithelium.[23] It is possible that some or all cell divisions are asymmetric, generating two cells with different fates.

MIGRATION OF MESONEPHRIC CELLS

It is established that mesonephric cells migrate in and colonise the XY gonad; no such cell migration occurs into the XX gonad.[25–31] Migrating cells produce peritubular myoid, endothelial, endothelial-associated, and possibly Leydig cells.[28–32] In ovotestes, regions of migration correlate with regions of testicular development.[22] It is believed that migration is induced by a diffusible (or cell-to-cell relay) male-specific signal or signals produced by the differentiating XY gonad and that it is capable of acting over at least 100 μm.[29,30] Migration of mesonephric cells into the gonad is essential for cord formation and the establishment of the male-specific vasculature, but it is not essential for male-specific cell proliferation. Mesonephric-to-gonad cell migration is often studied by grafting a labelled mesonephros and an unlabelled gonad.[25,29] In a variation of this, a mesonephros–XX gonad–XY gonad "sandwich" assay is set up.[30] The XY gonad is able to induce cell migration into the XX gonad, proving that the male-specific signal is a positive force. The alternative possibility, that the XX gonad is inhibitory to mesonephric cell migration, seems unlikely given this result. However, it remains possible that the XX gonad possesses some inhibitory mechanism.

FORMATION OF THE TESTIS CORDS

Testis cord organization is apparent in the male developing gonad from about 12.5 dpc, two days after *Sry* is first expressed. The formation of these cords is a complex event requiring Sertoli cell differentiation, germ cell aggregation, immigration of mesonephric cells, direct interaction between Sertoli and peritubular myoid cells, and deposition of a basement membrane between those two cell types.[33–35] Although mesonephric cells continue to migrate into an XY gonad until at least 16.5 dpc,[29] migration essential for cord formation must occur at least 2 to 4 hours before 11.5 dpc.[30] When a "sandwich" culture is assembled and mesonephric cells migrate into the XX gonad, cord formation is induced.[30] No cords form if the XY gonad used is 12.5 dpc or older, suggesting that the necessary initiating signal is no longer produced. In these "sandwich" culture assays, the sex of the donor mesonephros is irrelevant in the sense that cells will respond to a male signal from the gonad whether the mesonephros is XX or XY. However, at 12.5 dpc, XX mesonephroi are more capable of supplying cord-inducing migratory cells than are XY mesonephroi.[30] Presumably, this reflects that XY mesonephroi dissected away from an XY gonad at 12.5 dpc have already been largely depleted of an essential cell type or types. Because of the important contribution peritubular myoid cells make to cord formation, it is likely that precursors of these cells are depleted in 12.5-dpc XY mesonephroi. Although an XY gonad can induce immigration of cells from mesenchymal sources other than the mesonephros, such as the limb bud, the ingressing cells are unable to elicit testis cord formation.[25,30] It may be that precursors of peritubular myoid cells are lacking in non-mesonephric sources.

FORMATION OF THE COELOMIC VESSEL AND MALE-SPECIFIC VASCULATURE

Between 11.5 and 12.5 dpc, vascular organization of the gonadal primordia does not appear to be sex-specific and includes substantial proliferation of vascular cells.[36] Later, however, male-specific vascular patterning is observed.

Endothelial cells migrate into the gonad in a male-specific and *Sry*-dependent manner and contribute to the characteristic male pattern of vasculature.[29,31,36] In particular, a large coelomic blood vessel forms and runs in an anterior–posterior direction underneath the coelomic epithelium farthest from the gonad–mesonephros junction. In addition, abundant vascular branching is apparent between the testis cords.[36]

Bipotential Cell Types of the Gonad

SUPPORTING CELLS

Origin of the Supporting Cells

Supporting cells are so called because, in a functional gonad, they support the development of the germ cells. It is now confirmed that supporting cells of the XY and XX gonads—Sertoli cells and granulosa cells, respectively—have a common precursor.[17,24] Supporting cells derive from SF1+ cells of the coelomic epithelium that migrate in and colonise the gonad in a sex-independent fashion.[37,38] When coelomic epithelium cells of male gonads are labelled between 11.2 and 11.5 dpc, they can become Sertoli cells.[23,38] If labelled later, between 11.5 and 12.0 dpc, labelled cells are not found in cords but are localised in the interstitium. This suggests that there is a specific window of time during which cells of the coelomic epithelium must commit to the supporting cell lineage. In the XX gonad, cells of the coelomic epithelium also migrate in at this early point, but at least by 12.5 dpc, no fate restriction is obvious.[38] LHX9 may mark the coelomic epithelium cells that participate in early gonad colonisation. This LIM-homeodomain transcription factor is expressed in the coelomic epithelium but later turns off in presupporting cells as they differentiate, whether that be into Sertoli cells or granulosa cells.[5,39]

Specification of the Sertoli Cell Lineage by Sry

In XX–XY chimaeric mouse testes, most Sertoli cells are of XY-chromosomal constitution, and other somatic cell types are XY or XX in approximately equal proportions.[40–42] This observation led to the hypothesis that the Y-chromosomal male-determining factor must act solely in the presupporting cell lineage to induce Sertoli cell differentiation. In addition, it was predicted that its action is cell autonomous, although recruitment of some presupporting cells must be possible through a paracrine mechanism.[41,43] As predicted, the major means of Sertoli cell differentiation seems to be through the appropriate expression and cell-autonomous action of SRY. It appears that *Sry* is expressed only after coelomic epithelium cells have moved into the interior of the gonad and made the cell fate decision to become presupporting cells (see the section "Proliferation of Cells in the Coelomic Epithelium"). Presumably Sertoli cells, once specified, signal back to remaining cells of the coelomic epithelium to initiate *Sry*-dependent male-specific proliferation.

Sry is expressed transiently in these interior presupporting cells, at least in the mouse gonad.[13–16] Hence, SRY can only be responsible for the initiation, not for the maintenance, of Sertoli cell identity. The earliest gene known to lie in the genetic cascade downstream of SRY encodes the related transcription factor, SOX9. *Sox9* is expressed at low levels in XY and XX gonads prior to *Sry* expression, but it is up-regulated in XY gonads shortly after *Sry* is first detectable.[24,44,45] Male-specific nuclear localisation of the SOX9 has been observed.[45–48] Although it is not certain that SRY directly regulates *Sox9*,[49] it appears that expression of *Sox9* can elicit the same effect as expression of *Sry*. This is shown by a report describing a duplication of the chromosomal region containing *SOX9* that is able to induce male development in an XX human.[50] In mice, overexpression of *Sox9* is also able to sex-reverse XX mice.[51] Furthermore, the accidental mutation (a product of a transgenic experiment) of a site more than 1 megabase upstream of the *Sox9* gene has produced a line of mice known as *Odsex*. This mutation, a deletion of 134 kilobases, causes the up-regulation of SOX9 expression in XX gonads. These XX embryos are phenotypically indistinguishable from XX embryos sex reversed using the *Sry* transgene.[52] The critical experiment proving that SOX9 is essential for testis determination is to delete *Sox9* specifically in the gonad. We are still awaiting an analysis of the phenotype of such a mouse. Although *Sry* expression is gone by 12.5 dpc, *Sox9* remains expressed and may positively regulate its own expression and thereby maintain Sertoli cell identity.[53] SOX9 is more highly conserved than *SRY* and appears to be involved in Sertoli cell differentiation throughout the vertebrates.[54]

Specification of the Sertoli Cell Lineage in the Absence of SRY

Sertoli cell differentiation, as marked by *Sox9* expression, can be brought about in the absence of SRY by the experimental induction of mesonephric cell migration.[30] This indicates that some aspect of cell migration assists presupporting cells to differentiate into Sertoli cells. It is thought that immigrant peritubular myoid cell precursors directly interact with presupporting cells and thereby induce them to differentiate along the male-specific pathway. This type of SRY-independent Sertoli cell differentiation is accompanied by adoption of characteristic Sertoli cell morphology suggesting that presupporting cell–myoid cell interaction may induce polarization of the supporting cell precursors as well as *Sox9* expression. However, immigration of mesonephric cells does not appear to be essential for Sertoli cell specification. If the gonad and mesonephros are separated prior to mesonephric cell migration, Sertoli cells (as marked by expression of the gene encoding anti-Müllerian hormone, or AMH, also known as Müllerian inhibiting substance, or MIS) are still detected. These cells, however, do not adopt a polarized morphology.[25,26] Similarly, if testis cord formation is prevented by use of Desert hedgehog (DHH) inhibitors—cyclopamine or forskolin—Sertoli cells still differentiate and express the typical markers *Sox9* and *Amh*.[55] Clearly Sertoli-like cells that express male-specific marker genes are able to differentiate from presupporting cells even if they are not situated in a testicular cord environment.

Chimaera studies show that, once some Sertoli cells are specified, they are able to induce XX presupporting cells to differentiate into Sertoli cells.[41] At least some of this recruitment could result from interaction between XX presupporting cells and migrating myoid cells as described previously, but a recent report suggests another possible mechanism for XX Sertoli cell specification. The signalling molecule prostaglandin D_2 is synthesised in a male-specific manner, by both Sertoli and germ cells, downstream of *Sry* expression.[56] Prostaglandin D_2 can induce XX gonadal somatic cells to differentiate into Sertoli-like cells in that they express *Amh,* although they do not have a polarized morphology. It is hypothesised that, once some Sertoli cells are specified, other supporting cells could be recruited to the Sertoli cell lineage by the action of this molecule. When all presupporting cells are XY and express *Sry,* this mechanism would be redundant; however, when *Sry* is "weak" or in XX–XY chimaeras, such a feedback mechanism would help reinforce the decision to develop as a testis. In XX–XY gonad cocultures (with no mesonephros present) some Sertoli cell marker expression is reported in the XX gonad near the boundary.[30] This expression could be induced by the action of prostaglandin D_2 or some other paracrine factor produced in XY gonads.

Downstream of Sertoli Cell Specification

It is believed that expression of *Sry* in XY gonads induces a cascade of molecular and cellular events that leads to production of a testis. In particular, differentiated Sertoli cells are presumed to affect differentiation and migration of other cell types by either cell–cell signalling or cell contact. It is not at all clear how SRY or SOX9 mediate the genetic and cellular changes occurring immediately after the initiation of Sertoli cell differentiation. It is known that SOX9, working in a complex with SF1, WT1, GATA4, and DAX1, is responsible for the up-regulation of *Amh* once Sertoli cells are specified.[57–59] Recent results suggest that SOX8 may substitute for or assist SOX9 in this role.[60] No other direct downstream targets of SOX9 have been identified.

Secreted products fibroblast growth factor 9 (FGF9),[61] platelet-derived growth factor A (PDGF-A)[62] and DHH[63] are produced by differentiated Sertoli cells. Results of *Fgf9* knockout studies suggest that this growth factor induces proliferation of cells of the coelomic epithelium, thus expanding one or more of the somatic precursor populations.[61] The number of Sertoli and interstitial cells are dramatically reduced in these gonads. FGF9 also appears to induce mesonephric cell migration, but there is no evidence that FGF9 has a role in specification of Sertoli or other cell types of the male gonad.[61]

Knockout studies indicate that signalling through PDGFR-α is necessary for mesonephric cell migration.[62] PDGF-A is the likely ligand since *Pdgf-A* is male-specifically expressed by Sertoli cells at 12.5 dpc.[62] In PDGFR-α-null mice, Sertoli cells differentiate, but cords are not clearly defined and testis cord and interstitial compartments mingle. PDGF-A probably also contributes to promotion of the second (SF1−) wave of proliferation and migration.[62] The likely roles of PDGF-A signalling in fetal Leydig cell specification and male-pattern vascular organization will be described later in this chapter.

Although DHH is not required for the induction of mesonephric cell migration, intact testicular cords will not form in its absence.[64] It appears that both mesonephric myoid cell ingression (induced by other factors) and DHH signalling from Sertoli cells to peritubular myoid cell precursors are necessary for normal cord establishment. In *Dhh*-null mice, cells migrate in yet Sertoli cells remain apolar.[64] Along with PDGF-A, DHH is involved in fetal Leydig cell specification; this role will be explained in the section "Specification of the Leydig Cell Lineage."

Other growth factors, such as hepatocyte growth factor (HGF), can induce mesonephric cell migration and reorganisation of dissociated cells into cord-like structures when tested *in vitro,*[65,66] but it is not yet clear that HGF can do this *in vivo*. Mesonephric cell migration can be blocked by inhibition of matrix-degrading proteinases (MMPs), and it is possible that SRY inhibits expression of *Timp-3,* which encodes an endogenous inhibitor of the MMPs.[32]

Downstream of Sertoli cell specification, there are also changes in expression of transcription factors. Of note is *DMRT1,* male-specifically expressed during early gonadogenesis in all vertebrates tested thus far.[67–70] In mice, transcripts are detected in Sertoli and germ cells, although protein is detected only in Sertoli cells prenatally.[71] *Dmrt1* is related to *doublesex* and *mab-3 (DM)* genes in *Drosophila* and *Caenorhabditis elegans,* respectively, that act as sex regulators.[72] Its human orthologue maps to a chromosomal location associated with gonadal dysgenesis and sex reversal.[73] Knockout studies show that *Dmrt1* is essential for postnatal testis differentiation, but testis determination and embryonic testis development appears to proceed relatively normally and no sex reversal or gonadal dysgenesis is seen.[74] It is possible that other members of the family compensate for the lack of DMRT1 in these mice. *Dmrt1* is not necessary for normal ovarian development,[75] but other *DM* domain genes, especially *Dmrt3, -4,* and *-7,* may be involved in both testis and ovarian development in mammals.[76]

Several other genes expressed by newly differentiated Sertoli cells have been identified. These include *Vanin-1,* which encodes a glycosylphosphatidylinositol-anchored cell surface molecule that may be involved in the induction of migration,[56,75,76] and *Testatin,* which encodes a cysteine protease inhibitor.[77–79] Because of the fruitfulness of expression screening strategies, this list of genes is growing rapidly.[75,76,79–81]

Specification of the Granulosa Cell Lineage

Unlike Sertoli cells, granulosa cells can only differentiate and organize if germ cells are present. If an XX gonad has no germ cells, the presupporting cells either take on Sertoli cell-like characteristics or are lost altogether.[82] Further evidence for the interconvertability of the supporting cell lineages comes from studies of XX–XY chimaeras in which XY supporting cells can be recruited to form granulosa cells.[83,84] It seems that if SRY is not produced at levels above a certain threshold—for example, if the gene is expressed in a subthreshold number of presupporting cells—an ovary-determining signal can preempt Sertoli cell differentiation.[85] Similarly, if *Sry* is not expressed sufficiently early, supporting cell precursors eventually differentiate into granulosa cells and an ovary forms.[20,86] Despite the lack of obvious morphological change in the developing ovary until follicle formation, several genes are female-specifically expressed prior to that time. These include *Dax1*,[87] *Wnt4*,[88] *FoxL2*,[89] *caveolin-1*,[90] *follistatin,* and *Adamts19*.[79]

Dax1 is up-regulated in the female gonad shortly after the initiation of *Sry* expression.[87] Duplication of the region of the human genome encoding DAX1 leads to male-to-female sex reversal,[91–93] and this also happens to some extent when *Dax1* is overexpressed in XY mice.[86] These results suggested that *Dax1* acts antagonistically to *Sry* or some element of the male sex-determining pathway or acts as an ovarian-determining gene.[86,87,94] Given these results, it is surprising that deletion of *Dax1* does not affect ovarian development[95] but that testis structure and function is adversely affected. In XY *Dax1*-null mice, Sertoli cells differentiate and cord formation is attempted, but the resulting basal lamina is discontinuous.[96] If those XY mice also carry the "weak" *Sry* allele of *Mus domesticus poschiavinus,* they are fully sex reversed, indicating that DAX1 is required for testis differentiation.[97]

Like *Dax1*, *Wnt4* is expressed in supporting cell precursors of both sexes and then up-regulated in the female.[88] With SF1 and β-catenin, WNT4 acts to increase expression of *Dax1*,[98] suggesting a possible paracrine-recruiting role for this signalling molecule. Its other roles, to direct the female pattern of duct development, to maintain postmeiotic oocytes, and possibly to repress Leydig cell development, will be explained later in this review. In *Drosophila*, WNT4 is also required for ovarian morphogenesis, specifically in the regulation of cell movement.[99]

Recent results suggest that the forkhead transcription factor FOXL2 may be a genuine ovarian determinant. *FoxL2* is expressed in the female gonad from 12.5 dpc,[89] is associated in goat with a deletion that results in female-to-male sex reversal,[100] and underlies the human syndrome blepharophimosis–ptosis–epicanthus inversus syndrome, characterised by premature ovarian failure.[101] In the mouse, transcripts are detectable in both granulosa and germ cells, although FOXL2 may not be translated in germ cells.[102] It is highly conserved among vertebrates, including chicken and turtle.[89]

STEROIDOGENIC CELLS

Origin of the Steroidogenic Cells

Appropriate development of the steroidogenic cells of the gonad is essential for sexual development of the embryo as a whole, since the hormones secreted by these cells promote all secondary sexual characteristics. The origin of steroidogenic precursor cells has been controversial. It has been suggested that they arise from the coelomic epithelium[23,38] or the mesonephros[28,32] or that they share a common progenitor with adrenal steroid cells.[103,104] It remains possible that fetal Leydig cell precursors have more than one origin.

Specification of the Leydig Cell Lineage

Bipotential steroidogenic precursor cells differentiate into Leydig cells in the fetal testis and theca cells in the fetal ovary.

In *Dhh*-null embryos, fetal Leydig cells are rare or absent,[63,105] and recent studies suggest that DHH is necessary for Leydig cell specification.[106] The role of DHH appears to be to up-regulate SF1 and the biosynthetic enzyme p450 side chain cleavage (SCC) in steroidogenic cell precursors, thus determining the fate of these as Leydig cells. *Dhh* is not required for the proliferation or survival of fetal Leydig cells.[106] The gene encoding the DHH receptor, Patched1 *(PTCH1)*, is expressed on some gonadal somatic cells, presumably including steroidogenic precursor cells, from approximately 11.5 dpc and is up-regulated by the presence of DHH.[106]

The necessity for DHH signalling is variable to the point that fetal Leydig cells differentiate in *Dhh*-null embryos on some genetic backgrounds.[63] This implies that at least one other signalling pathway also plays a significant role. This is supported by the fact that although all fetal Leydig cells express *Ptch1*, not all *Ptch1*-expressing cells of the gonad become Leydig cells.[106] We now know that signalling through PDGFR-α is also necessary for Leydig cell differentiation.[62] In *Pdgfr-α*-null mice, the proliferation of Leydig cells appears to be deficient. It is proposed that Sertoli cells release PDGF-A, which signals SF1+ and PDGFR-α+ cells at the coelomic epithelium; they proliferate, express *Ptch1,* move into the gonad, and are able to respond to DHH released by the Sertoli cells. These SF1+ and PDGFR-α+ cells subsequently differentiate into Leydig cells.[62] Hence, the DHH and PDGF signalling pathways run in parallel with PDGF signalling acting to expand the DHH-responsive population of cells.

Based on the phenotype of the *Wnt4*-null XX mice, it has been proposed that WNT4 acts as a negative regulator of Leydig cell differentiation.[88] Although Sertoli cells do not differentiate and testis cords do not form, Leydig cells are present and ectopic steroidogenesis is initiated. In normal mice, *Wnt-4* is expressed in a female-specific manner after 11.5 dpc and is presumably negatively regulated by some element of the male-specific pathway.[88] This theory, that WNT4 can inhibit Leydig cell differentiation, has yet to be verified by *Wnt4* overexpression studies in XY mice. Recent results suggest that ectopic steroidogenesis in *Wnt4*-deleted mice might reflect ectopic migration of steroidogenic cells from the adjacent adrenal gland rather than a failure to inhibit Leydig cell differentiation.[107] In *Dax1*-null XY mice, Leydig cells are present but are restricted to the coelomic edge of the gonad. The significance of this finding and the possible contribution of DAX1 to differentiation or development of Leydig cells are not known.[96]

Downstream of Leydig Cell Specification

Once Leydig cells are specified, they start producing steroid-synthesising enzymes including SCC, 3β-hydroxysteroid dehydrogenase (3β-HSD), 17β-HSD, and steroidogenic acute regulatory protein (StAR). Testosterone is secreted by 12.5 dpc and induces the Wolffian ducts of the mesonephros to develop into the epididymis and vas deferens. Leydig cells also produce insulin-like factor-3, which is responsible for the transabdominal phase of testicular descent.[108,109] We do not know if Leydig cells influence the differentiation of any other cell types of the male gonad.

350

Specification of the Theca Cell Lineage

Presumably, in the absence of signalling from the Sertoli cells (DHH, PDGF-A, and possibly others), steroidogenic cells differentiate into theca cells. This cell type produces cytochrome P450 aromatase (the specific element of the aromatase complex), which catalyses the irreversible transformation of androgens into estrogens.

VASCULAR CELLS

Some of the cells that migrate from the coelomic epithelium after the second round of proliferation (11.5–12.0 dpc) differentiate into vascular cells.[23] Presumably, vascular precursors are derived from the coelomic epithelium in both sexes, although proliferation would ensure that the number of such resulting cells is much larger in the testis, at least early on. Vascular precursors also migrate into the gonad from the mesonephros in a male-specific manner (see the section "Vascular Endothelial Cells").

OTHER SOMATIC CELL TYPES

Besides presupporting, presteroidogenic, and prevascular cells, other somatic cell types are in the indifferent and developing gonad. We know this because, in proliferation studies, many of the BrdU+ cells do not label with markers of Sertoli, Leydig, endothelial, or germ cells.[23] One such uncharacterised somatic cell population is marked by expression of *Mgfe8* and localises to the peripheral stromal region of the gonad, particularly the gonad–mesonephros border.[110] This cell type is probably derived from the coelomic epithelium and, since *Mgfe8* encodes a soluble integrin-binding protein, may mediate cell-to-cell interactions. No sex-specific differences are obvious for this cell type.

GERM CELLS

Specification of PGCs and Colonisation of the Indifferent Gonad

PGCs are specified in the extraembryonic mesoderm about 7.2 dpc, being set aside from surrounding somatic cells by the expression of *Bmp4, fragilis,* and *stella.*[111,112] They migrate to the gonad through the hindgut, dorsal mesentery, and mesonephros and colonise the genital ridge by 11.5 dpc.[113]

Germ Cells in the Ovary

Approximately 13.5 dpc, PGCs in XX gonads enter meiosis and arrest in prophase I.[114] This change is marked by downregulation of the pluripotency marker *Oct4* and up-regulation of the synaptonemal complex protein gene *Scp3.*[115,116] It is believed that entry into meiosis occurs in an intrinsic clocklike fashion, for example, after a certain number of mitotic divisions. This postulate is based on observations that germ cells in nontestis ectopic locations, whether they arrive there by natural or experimental means, enter meiosis at the same time as those in the XX gonad.[114,117,118]

In the female gonad the presence of PGCs is required for granulosa cell differentiation, follicle organization, and maintenance.[82,119] The nature of this female-specific influence of the germ cells on the surrounding soma is not understood.

If PGCs are present, pregranulosa cells invade germ cell clusters, and each oocyte comes to be surrounded by a single layer of flattened granulosa cells, forming the primordial follicle.[120] In the absence of PGCs, pregranulosa cells are seen; they aggregate into mesenchymal condensations as is normal, but granulosa cells do not differentiate, the follicular structure of the ovary never forms, and a streak gonad results. It has been proposed that the "default" pathway, ovarian development, depends on the presence of meiotic cells in the gonad and that meiosis not only initiates the ovarian pathway but also antagonises the testicular pathway.[121,122] In support of this, we know that in ovotestes in which testis cords contain some oocytes, Sertoli cells can transdifferentiate into granulosa cells.[123] In ectopic migration studies, XX gonads can no longer be induced to form cords after 12.5 dpc[30] unless they are devoid of germ cells, in which case cords can still be induced at 13.5 dpc.[122] These results suggest that XX germ cells, or meiotic germ cells, may inhibit migration that leads to cord formation and testicular development.[122]

At least three transcription factors are expressed in a female-specific manner by PGCs. The gene-encoding FIGα, a transcription factor required for ovarian follicle formation, is expressed in female germ cells from 13 dpc.[124] The homeobox gene *Psx2* or *Gpbox* is initially expressed in both sexes and then up-regulated in the germ cells of the female, peaking at 12.5 dpc and remaining until 15.5 dpc.[125] Expression of *Gata2* is never detected in the male gonad, but it is female-specifically expressed in the germ cells from 11.5 to 15.5 dpc.[126] The roles of PSX2 and GATA2 are not known at this stage. It appears that one of the many roles of the signalling molecule WNT4, expressed by granulosa cells, is the postmeiotic maintenance of oocytes.[88] In *Wnt4*-null females, a marked reduction in oocyte development is observed, although germ cell migration and proliferation are unaffected.

Germ Cells in the Testis

In an XY gonad, PGCs undergo mitotic arrest around 12.5 dpc irrespective of their chromosomal constitution.[127] It is hypothesised that, in the environment of the developing testis, a male-specific signalling factor is secreted approximately 12.0 dpc and inhibits the entry of germ cells into meiosis or promotes the development of PGCs as prospermatogonia.[114,128] If PGCs are removed from an XY gonad before 12.5 dpc and allowed to develop in host nontestis tissue, they will enter meiosis and develop as oocytes. Sequestration of germ cells inside testis cords is probably not critical for meiotic inhibition since germ cells trapped in the interstitial tissue of the testis also avoid entry into meiosis and, of germ cells trapped in the mesonephros, some are prevented from entering meiosis.[129] Recent studies, in which testis cord formation is disrupted by treatment with the DHH inhibitor cyclopamine, confirm that the testis cord environment is not necessary for inhibition of the meiotic programme.[55] The identity of the male-specific signal is not known, but it is not DHH.[55,105]

The presence of PGCs is not necessary for Sertoli cell differentiation, testis cord formation or for the elaboration of the testis.[121] We now know that, downstream of *Sry* expression, the signalling molecule prostaglandin D_2 is released by both Sertoli and germ cells of the XY gonad.[56] It is thought that this generates a male-inducing feedback that reinforces male development. It is possible that the slight cord formation delays observed in germ cell-less testes[122] reflect the absence of PGC production of prostaglandin D_2.

Male-Specific Cell Types That Migrate into the Male Gonad

In addition to the bipotential cell types already residing in the indifferent gonad, several cell types migrate from the adjacent mesonephros once commitment has been made to the male-specific pathway of development (see the section "Migration of Mesonephric Cells").

PERITUBULAR MYOID CELLS

It is generally agreed that peritubular myoid cells originate in the mesonephros.[25,26,29,30,32] These myoepithelial cells synthesise fibronectin and cooperate with Sertoli cells to produce the basement membrane that surrounds the testis cords and separates them from the peritubular space.[35,130] As might be expected, since peritubular myoid cells arise from migrating cells responding to a male-specific signal, no analogous ovarian cell type has been found.

Peritubular myoid cells are depleted in *Fgf9*-null mice; this probably is the result of a lack of FGF9-induced migration of myoid precursors.[61] It has been demonstrated that DHH signalling between Sertoli cells and myoid precursors underlies their cooperative arrangement.[55] Since adult *Dhh* knockout mice have abnormal peritubular myoid cells and no basal lamina, it is likely that this DHH/PTCH1 signalling is important for some aspect of peritubular myoid cell development or maintenance.[64,105] BrdU studies show that proliferation of peritubular myoid cells is deficient in male gonads devoid of *Dax1*.[96] Testis cords do not organize normally in these mice, presumably because peritubular myoid cell numbers are low.

VASCULAR ENDOTHELIAL CELLS

Formation of male-specific vasculature is dependent on recruitment of endothelial cells from the mesonephros.[25,26,29] Recent studies have shown that recruited cells set up a male-specific blood flow network, which includes the coelomic vessel, and that these vessels are arterial rather than venous.[36] This network is superimposed on existing gonadal vasculature, rather than replacing it. After 12.0 dpc, blood flow is rerouted through the coelomic vessel in the XY gonad, and the new vessels enter the gonad through this outer surface. The Notch signalling pathway may be involved in the formation of the male-specific arterial system.[36] It is not known whether elements of the male-specific vasculature play some inductive role or roles in other events of testis formation.

When various PDGFs are used in culture to induce ectopic migration into an XX gonad, all of the cells that migrate in are endothelial. Since only *Pdgf-A* is male-specifically expressed in the gonad, it is likely that the PDGF-AA homodimer promotes this effect *in vivo*. In *Pdgfr*-α-null XY gonads, the coelomic vessel and vascular organization are abnormal.[62] Migration studies show that ingression of cells from the mesonephros does not occur in these animals and that PDGFR-α is required on interstitial cells of the gonad, rather than on the migrating cells.[62] These results suggest that PDGF signalling induces endothelial cell migration, but that the effect is indirect. PDGF-AA binding to PDGFR-α on gonadal interstitial cells must elicit a secondary signal received by cells of the mesonephros.[62] It is possible that abnormal vascular organization contributes to the abnormal cord formation seen in these receptor-null animals rather than that PDGF signalling has a primary role in myoid cell migration or cord formation.

Sex-Specific Differentiation of the Ducts of the Mesonephros

Under normal circumstances, only one of the two duct systems that develop in the mesonephros is retained and allowed to develop into a reproductive tract appropriate to the sex of the embryo. The two ducts must comprise different cell types since they respond very differently to sex hormones.[131] In males, AMH, a TGF-β family member produced by Sertoli cells, causes regression of the Müllerian duct, suppressing development of the female reproductive tract.[132,133] This hormone works through binding to the type I receptor, BMPR1a (ALK3), and the type II receptor, AMHR2,[134] both expressed in the mesenchyme that underlies the duct epithelium. The exact mechanism by which the duct is induced to degenerate is not known, though presumably Sma- and Mad-related (SMAD) proteins and downstream transcriptional regulation are involved. In females, no Sertoli cells differentiate; hence, no AMH is produced, and the duct remains and develops into female reproductive structures. Testosterone, produced by the fetal Leydig cells of the male gonad, promotes further development of the Wolffian duct in males. In the absence of testosterone, for example in normal females, the Wolffian duct degenerates.

The secreted signalling molecule, WNT4, is essential for formation of the Müllerian duct in both sexes.[88] It is expressed in the coelomic epithelium that infolds during Müllerian duct formation and subsequently in mesenchyme underlying the duct. *Wnt4* knockout females lack Müllerian duct derivatives and retain Wolffian duct derivatives.[88] No abnormal duct development is observed in *Wnt4*-null males since the Müllerian duct normally regresses in males in any case under the influence of AMH. Wnt4 is not expressed in the tissue surrounding Wolffian ducts and the retention of this duct system in *Wnt4* knockout females is a secondary effect likely resulting from the ectopic production and secretion of testosterone by the gonad.[88]

Once the Müllerian duct is formed, a second WNT factor, WNT7a, is expressed along its length; this factor directly or indirectly regulates the expression of *Amhr2* in the adjacent mesenchyme.[135] In addition to this role in making the surrounding mesenchyme responsive to AMH, *Wnt7a* is necessary for subsequent differentiation of Müllerian duct derivatives.[135,136]

Summary

The indifferent gonad is made up of several distinct bipotential cell types, which generally cooperate to bring about a single organismal fate: the development of either a testis or an ovary. After the expression of the male sex-determining gene, *Sry*, additional cell types migrate in and colonise the male gonad. Because of the lack of markers of cell types of the ovary, most research has focussed on testis development, but fortunately, this imbalance is now being addressed in several laboratories.

We are beginning to understand the molecular basis of cell fate decisions that bias towards the elaboration of one or other organ. The gathering evidence supports the idea that mechanisms exist for reinforcement or consolidation of the initial fate decision. It is becoming clear that transcription factors and signalling factors are, more often than not, called upon to carry out more than one role. Redundancy, or the sharing or supporting of a particular molecular role, is also emerging as a recurring theme. Despite both conceptual and specific advances, many questions remain. Among these is the problem of how the initiation and timing of *Sry* expression is regulated. Further work will be required to identify the downstream target or targets of SRY and the downstream targets of SOX9 other than *Amh*. The male-specific factor that prevents germ cells from entering meiosis, or forces them into a prospermatogenic fate, remains at large. Although some important signalling factors have been identified, it is likely that many others remain to be discovered.

Finally, 12 years after the role of *Sry* was convincingly demonstrated, we have attained some comprehension of the molecular events brought about by its expression in the formerly indifferent gonad. Slowly, we are building a framework that describes the cellular and molecular interactions between the cell populations necessary for the appropriate coordinated differentiation of the organ and therefore for reproductive success.

ACKNOWLEDGEMENTS

We are grateful to the Australian Research Council and the National Health and Medical Research Council of Australia for support. We thank Dagmar Wilhelm and Annemiek Beverdam for critical reading of the manuscript.

REFERENCES

1. Karl, J., and Capel, B. (1995). Three-dimensional structure of the developing mouse genital ridge. *Philos. Trans. R. Soc. Lond. Biol.* **350**, 235–242.

2. Kreidberg, J.A., Sariola, H., Loring, J.M., Maeda, M., Pelletier, J., Housman, D., and Jaenisch, R. (1993). WT-1 is required for early kidney development. *Cell* **74**, 679–691.

3. Luo, X., Ikeda, Y., and Parker, K.L. (1994). A cell-specific nuclear receptor is essential for adrenal and gonadal development and sexual differentiation. *Cell* **77**, 481–490.

4. Miyamoto, N., Yoshida, M., Kuratani, S., Matsuo, I., and Aizawa, S. (1997). Defects of urogenital development in mice lacking *Emx2*. *Development* **124**, 1653–1664.

5. Birk, O.S., Casiano, D.E., Wassif, C.A., Cogliati, T., Zhao, L., Zhao, Y., Grinberg, A., Huang, S., Kreidberg, J.A., Parker, K.L., Porter, F.D., and Westphal, H. (2000). The LIM homeobox gene *Lhx9* is essential for mouse gonad formation. *Nature* **403**, 909–913.

6. Katoh-Fukui, Y., Tsuchiya, R., Shiroishi, T., Nakahara, Y., Hashimoto, N., Noguchi, K., and Higashinakagawa, T. (1998). Male-to-female sex reversal in M33 mutant mice. *Nature* **393**, 688–692.

7. Tevosian, S., Albrecht, K., Crispiono, J., Fujiwara, Y., Eicher, E., and Orkin, S. (2002). Gonadal differentiation, sex determination, and normal Sry expression in mice require direct interaction between transcription partners GATA4 and FOG2. *Development* **129**, 4627–4634.

8. Torres, M., Gómez-Pardo, E., Dressler, G.R., and Gruss, P. (1995). *Pax-2* controls multiple steps of urogenital development. *Development* **121**, 4057–4065.

9. Gubbay, J., Collignon, J., Koopman, P., Capel, B., Economou, A., Münsterberg, A., Vivian, N., Goodfellow, P., and Lovell-Badge, R. (1990). A gene mapping to the sex-determining region of the mouse Y-chromosome is a member of a novel family of embryonically expressed genes. *Nature* **346**, 245–250.

10. Sinclair, A.H., Berta, P., Palmer, M.S., Hawkins, J.R., Griffiths, B.L., Smith, M.J., Foster, J.W., Frischauf, A.M., Lovell-Badge, R., and Goodfellow, P.N. (1990). A gene from the human sex-determining region encodes a protein with homology to a conserved DNA-binding motif. *Nature* **346**, 240–244.

11. Koopman, P., Gubbay, J., Vivian, N., Goodfellow, P., and Lovell-Badge, R. (1991). Male development of chromosomally female mice transgenic for *Sry*. *Nature* **351**, 117–121.

12. McElreavey, K., Vilain, E., Herskowitz, I., and Fellous, M. (1993). A regulatory cascade hypothesis for mammalian sex determination: SRY represses a negative regulator of male development. *Proc. Natl. Acad. Sci. USA* **90**, 3368–3372.

13. Koopman, P., Münsterberg, A., Capel, B., Vivian, N., and Lovell-Badge, R. (1990). Expression of a candidate sex-determining gene during mouse testis differentiation. *Nature* **348**, 450–452.

14. Hacker, A., Capel, B., Goodfellow, P., and Lovell-Badge, R. (1995). Expression of *Sry*, the mouse sex-determining gene. *Development* **121**, 1603–1614.

15. Jeske, Y.W.A., Bowles, J., Greenfield, A., and Koopman, P. (1995). Expression of a linear *Sry* transcript in the mouse genital ridge. *Nat. Genet.* **10**, 480–482.

16. Bullejos, M., and Koopman, P. (2001). Spatially dynamic expression of *Sry* in mouse genital ridges. *Dev. Dyn.* **221**, 201–205.

17. Albrecht, K., and Eicher, E. (2001). Evidence that *Sry* is expressed in pre-Sertoli cells and Sertoli and granulosa cells have a common precursor. *Dev. Biol.* **240**, 92–107.

18. Eicher, E.M., Washburn, L.L., Whitney, J.B., and Morrow, K.E. (1982). *Mus poschiavinus* Y-chromosome in the *C57BL/6J* murine genome causes sex reversal. *Science* **217**, 535–537.

19. Bradbury, M. (1987). Testes of XX in equilibrium with XY chimaeric mice develop from fetal ovotestes. *Dev. Genetics* **8**, 207–218.

20. Eicher, E.M., Shown, E.P., and Washburn, L.L. (1995). Sex reversal in C57BL/6J-Y^{POS} mice corrected by a *Sry* transgene. *Philos. Trans. R. Soc. Lond. Biol.* **350**, 263–269.

21. Nagamine, C., Capehart, J., Carlisle, C., and Chang, D. (1998). Ovotestes in B6-XXSxr sex-reversed mice. *Dev. Biol.* **196**, 24–32.

22. Albrecht, K., Capel, B., Washburn, L., and Eicher, E. (2000). Defective mesonephric cell migration is associated with abnormal testis cord development in C57BL/6J XY^Mus domesticus mice. *Dev. Biol.* **225**, 26–36.

23. Schmahl, J., Eicher, E., Washburn, L., and Capel, B. (2000). *Sry* induces cell proliferation in the mouse gonad. *Development* **127**, 65–73.

24. Lovell-Badge, R., Canning, C., and Sekido, R. (2002). Sex-determining genes in mice: Building pathways. *In* "Novartis Foundation Symposium: The Genetics and Biology of Sex Determination," Vol. 244, pp. 4–22. John Wiley & Sons, Chichester, U.K.

25. Buehr, M., Gu, S., and McLaren, A. (1993). Mesonephric contribution to testis differentiation in the fetal mouse. *Development* **117**, 273–281.

26. Merchant-Larios, H., Moreno-Mendoza, N., and Buehr, M. (1993). The role of the mesonephros in cell differentiation and morphogenesis of the mouse fetal testis. *Int. J. Dev. Biol.* **37**, 407–415.

27. Moreno-Mendoza, N., Herrera-Munoz, J., and Merchant-Larios, H. (1995). Limb bud mesenchyme permits seminiferous cord formation in the mouse fetal testis, but subsequent testosterone output is markedly affected by the sex of the donor stromal tissue. *Dev. Biol.* **169**, 51–56.

28. Merchant-Larios, H., and Moreno-Mendoza, N. (1998). Mesonephric stromal cells differentiate into Leydig cells in the mouse fetal testis. *Exp. Cell Res.* **244**, 230–238.

29. Martineau, J., Nordqvist, K., Tilmann, C., Lovell-Badge, R., and Capel, B. (1997). Male-specific cell migration into the developing gonad. *Curr. Biol.* **7**, 958–968.

30. Tilmann, C., and Capel, B. (1999). Mesonephric cell migration induces testis cord formation and Sertoli cell differentiation in the mammalian gonad. *Development* **126**, 2883–2890.

31. Capel, B., Albrecht, K.H., Washburn, L.L., and Eicher, E.M. (1999). Migration of mesonephric cells into the mammalian gonad depends on *Sry. Mech. Dev.* **84**, 127–131.

32. Nishino, K., Yamanouchi, K., Naito, K., and Tojo, H. (2001). Characterization of mesonephric cells that migrate into the XY gonad during testis differentiation. *Exp. Cell Res.* **267**, 225–232.

33. Tung, P., and Fritz, I. (1980). Interactions of Sertoli cells with myoid cells *in vitro. Biol. Reprod.* **23**, 207–217.

34. Skinner, M., Tung, P., and Fritz, I. (1985). Cooperativity between Sertoli cells and testicular peritubular cells in the production and deposition of extracellular matrix components. *J. Cell Biol.* **100**, 1941–1947.

35. Tung, P., and Fritz, I. (1987). Morphogenetic restructuring and formation of basement membranes by Sertoli cells and testis peritubular cells in coculture: inhibition of the morphogenetic cascade by cyclic AMP derivatives and by blocking direct cell contact. *Dev. Biol.* **120**, 139–153.

36. Brennan, J., Karl, J., and Capel, B. (2002). Divergent vascular mechanisms downstream of Sry establish the arterial system in the XY gonad. *Dev. Biol.* **244**, 418–428.

37. Paranko, J. (1987). Expression of type I and III collagen during morphogenesis of fetal rat testis and ovary. *Anat. Record* **219**, 91–101.

38. Karl, J., and Capel, B. (1998). Sertoli cells of the mouse testis originate from the coelomic epithelium. *Dev. Biol.* **203**, 323–333.

39. Mazaud, S., Oreal, E., Guigon, C., Carre-Eusebe, D., and Magre, S. (2002). Lhx9 expression during gonadal morphogenesis as related to the state of cell differentiation. *Gene Exp. Patterns* **2**, 373–377.

40. Burgoyne, P.S., Buehr, M., Koopman, P., Rossant, J., and McLaren, A. (1988). Cell-autonomous action of the testis-determining gene: Sertoli cells are exclusively XY in XX–XY chimaeric mouse testes. *Development* **102**, 443–450.

41. Palmer, S., and Burgoyne, P. (1991). *In situ* analysis of fetal, prepuberal, and adult XX–XY chimaeric mouse testes: Sertoli cells are predominantly, but not exclusively, XY. *Development* **112**, 265–268.

42. Patek, C.E., Kerr, J.B., Gosden, R.G., Jones, K.W., Hardy, K., Muggleton-Harris, A.L., Handyside, A.H., Whittingham, D.G., and Hooper, M.L. (1991). Sex chimaerism, fertility, and sex determination in the mouse. *Development* **113**, 311–325.

43. Patek, C., Kerr, J., Gosden, R., Jones, K., Hardy, K., Muggleton-Harris, A., Handyside, A., Whittingham, D., and ML, H. (1991). Sex chimaerism, fertility, and sex determination in the mouse. *Development* **113**, 311–325.

44. Kent, J., Wheatley, S.C., Andrews, J.E., Sinclair, A.H., and Koopman, P. (1996). A male-specific role for SOX9 in vertebrate sex determination. *Development* **122**, 2813–2822.

45. Morais da Silva, S., Hacker, A., Harley, V., Goodfellow, P., Swain, A., and Lovell-Badge, R. (1996). *Sox9* expression during gonadal development implies a conserved role for the gene in testis differentiation in mammals and birds. *Nat. Genet.* **14**, 62–68.

46. De Santa Barbara, P., Moniot, B., Poulat, F., and Berta, P. (2000). Expression and subcellular localization of SF-1, SOX9, WT1, and AMH proteins during early human testicular development. *Dev. Dyn.* **217**, 293–298.

47. Preiss, S., Argentaro, A., Clayton, A., John, A., Jans, D., Ogata, T., Nagai, T., Barroso, I., Schafer, A., and Harley, V. (2001). Compound effects of point mutations causing campomelic dysplasia–autosomal sex reversal upon SOX9 structure, nuclear transport, DNA binding, and transcriptional activation. *J. Biol. Chem.* **276**, 27,864–27,872.

48. Gasca, S., Canizares, J., de Santa Barbara, P., Mejean, C., Poulat, F., Berta, P., and Boizet-Bonhoure, B. (2002). A nuclear export signal within the high mobility group domain regulates the nucleocytoplasmic translocation of SOX9 during sexual determination. *Proc. Natl. Acad. Sci. USA* **99**, 11,199–11,204.

49. Kanai, Y., and Koopman, P. (1999). Structural and functional characterization of the mouse *Sox9* promoter: Implications for campomelic dysplasia. *Human Mol. Genet.* **8**, 691–696.

50. Huang, B., Wang, S., Ning, Y., Lamb, A., and Bartley, J. (1999). Autosomal XX sex reversal caused by duplication of *Sox9. Am. J. Med. Genet.* **87**, 349–353.

51. Vidal, V., Chaboissier, M., de Rooij, D., and Schedl, A. (2001). *Sox9* induces testis development in XX transgenic mice. *Nat. Genet.* **28**, 216–217.

52. Bishop, C.E., Whitworth, D.J., Qin, Y., Agoulnik, A.I., Agoulnik, I.U., Harrison, W.R., Behringer, R.R., and Overbeek, P.A. (2000). A transgenic insertion upstream of *Sox9* is associated with dominant XX sex reversal in the mouse. *Nat. Genet.* **26**, 490–494.

53. Koopman, P., Bullejos, M., and Bowles, J. (2001). Regulation of male sexual development by *Sry* and *Sox9. J. Exp. Zool.* **290**, 463–474.

54. Sinclair, A., Smith, C., Western, P., and McClive, P. (2002). A comparative analysis of vertebrate sex determination. *In* "Novartis Foundation Symposia: The Genetics and Biology of Sex Determination," Vol. 244, pp. 102–111. John Wiley & Sons, Chichester, U.K.

55. Yao, H., and Capel, B. (2002). Disruption of testis cords by cyclopamine or forskolin reveals independent cellular pathways in testis organogenesis. *Dev. Biol.* **246**, 356–365.

56. Adams, I., and McLaren, A. (2002). Sexually dimorphic development of mouse primordial germ cells: switching from oogenesis to spermatogenesis. *Development* **129**, 1155–1164.

57. De Santa Barbara, P., Bonneaud, N., Boizet, B., Desclozeaux, M., Moniot, B., Südbeck, P., Scherer, G., Poulat, F., and Berta, P. (1998). Direct interaction of SRY-related protein SOX9 and steroidogenic factor 1 regulates transcription of the human anti-Mullerian hormone gene. *Mol. Cell. Biol.* **18**, 6653–6665.

58. Arango, N., Lovell-Badge, R., and Behringer, R. (1999). Targeted mutagenesis of the endogenous mouse *Mis* gene promoter: *in vivo* definition of genetic pathways of vertebrate sexual development. *Cell* **99**, 409–419.

59. Tremblay, A., and Viger, R. (2001). Nuclear receptor Dax-1 represses the transcriptional cooperation between GATA-4 and SF-1 in Sertoli cells. *Biol. Reprod.* **64**, 1191–1199.

60. Schepers, G., Wilson, M., Wilhelm, D., and Koopman, P. (2003). SOX8 is expressed during testis differentiation in mice and synergises with SF1 to activate the Amh promoter *in vitro*. *J. Biol. Chem.* **278**, 28101–28108.

61. Colvin, J., Green, R., Schmahl, J., Capel, B., and Ornitz, D. (2001). Male-to-female sex reversal in mice lacking fibroblast growth factor 9. *Cell* **104**, 875–889.

62. Brennan, J., Tilmann, C., and Capel, B. (2003). Pdgfr-α mediates testis cord organization and fetal Leydig cell development in the XY gonad. *Genes Dev.* **17**, 800–810.

63. Bitgood, M.J., Shen, L., and McMahon, A.P. (1996). Sertoli cell signalling by desert hedgehog regulates the male germ line. *Curr. Biol.* **6**, 298–304.

64. Pierucci-Alves, F., Clark, A., and Russell, L. (2001). A developmental study of the *Desert hedgehog*-null mouse testis. *Biol. Reprod.* **65**, 1392–1402.

65. Ricci, G., Catizone, A., Innocenzi, A., and Galdieri, M. (1999). Hepatocyte growth factor (HGF) receptor expression and role of HGF during embryonic mouse testis development. *Dev. Biol.* **216**, 340–347.

66. Ricci, G., Catizone, A., and Galdieri, M. (2002). Pleiotropic activity of hepatocyte growth factor during embryonic mouse testis development. *Mech. Dev.* **118**, 19–28.

67. Raymond, C., Kettlewell, J., Hirsch, B., Bardwell, V., and Zarkower, D. (1999). Expression of *Dmrt1* in the genital ridge of mouse and chicken embryos suggests a role in vertebrate sexual development. *Dev. Biol.* **215**, 208–220.

68. Moniot, B., Berta, P., Scherer, G., Sudbeck, P., and Poulat, F. (2000). Male specific expression suggests role of DMRT1 in human sex determination. *Mech. Dev.* **91**, 323–325.

69. Smith, C., McClive, P., Western, P., Reed, K., and Sinclair, A. (1999). Conservation of a sex-determining gene. *Nature* **402**, 601–602.

70. Kettlewell, J., Raymond, C., and Zarkower, D. (2000). Temperature-dependent expression of turtle *Dmrt1* prior to sexual differentiation. *Genesis* **26**, 174–178.

71. Raymond, C., Murphy, M., O'Sullivan, M., Bardwell, V., and Zarkower, D. (2000). *Dmrt1*, a gene related to worm and fly sexual regulators, is required for mammalian testis differentiation. *Genes Dev.* **14**, 2587–2595.

72. Raymond, C., Shamu, C., Shen, M., Seifert, K., Hirsch, B., Hodgkin, J., and Zarkower, D. (1998). Evidence for evolutionary conservation of sex-determining genes. *Nature* **391**, 691–695.

73. Raymond, C., Parker, E., Kettlewell, J., Brown, L., Page, D., Kusz, K., Jaruzelska, J., Reinberg, Y., Flejter, W., Bardwell, V., Hirsch, B., and Zarkower, D. (1999). A region of human chromosome 9p required for testis development contains two genes related to known sexual regulators. *Human Mol. Genet.* **8**, 989–996.

74. Kim, S., Kettlewell, J., Anderson, R., Bardwell, V., and Zarkower, D. (2003). Sexually dimorphic expression of multiple doublesex-related genes in the embryonic mouse gonad. *Gene Expr. Patterns* **3**, 77–82.

75. Bowles, J., Bullejos, M., and Koopman, P. (2000). A subtractive gene expression screen suggests a role for *vanin-1* in testis development in mice. *Genesis* **27**, 124–135.

76. Grimmond, S., Van Hateren, N., Siggers, P., Arkell, R., Larder, R., Soares, M., Bonaldo, M., Smith, L., Tymowska-Lalanne, Z., Wells, C., and Greenfield, A. (2000). Sexually dimorphic expression of protease nexin-1 and vanin-1 in the developing mouse gonad prior to overt differentiation suggests a role in mammalian sexual development. *Human Mol. Genet.* **9**, 1553–1560.

77. Tohonen, V., Osterlund, C., and Nordqvist, K. (1998). Testatin: a cystatin-related gene expressed during early testis development. *Proc. Natl. Acad. Sci. USA* **95**, 14,208–14,213.

78. Kanno, Y., Tamura, M., Chuma, S., Sakura, T., Machida, T., and Nakatsuji, N. (1999). A cystatin-related gene, *testatin–cresp*, shows male-specific expression in germ and somatic cells from the initial stage of murine gonadal sex-differentiation. *Int. J. Dev. Biol.* **43**, 777–784.

79. Mencke, D., and Page, D. (2002). Sexually dimorphic gene expression in the developing mouse gonad. *Gene Expr. Patterns* **2**, 359–367.

80. Wertz, K., and Herrmann, B. (2000). Large-scale screen for genes involved in gonad development. *Mech. Dev.* **98**, 51–70.

81. McClive, P., and Sinclair, A. (2003). Type II and type ix collagen transcript isoforms are expressed during mouse testis development. *Biol. Reprod.* **68**, 1742–1747.

82. McLaren, A. (1991). Development of the mammalian gonad: the fate of the supporting cell lineage. *Bioessays* **13**, 151–156.

83. Burgoyne, P.S., Buehr, M., and McLaren, A. (1988). XY follicle cells in ovaries of XX–XY female mouse chimaeras. *Development* **104**, 683–688.

84. Palmer, S.J., and Burgoyne, P.S. (1991). XY follicle cells in the ovaries of XO–XY and XO–XY–XXY mosaic mice. *Development* **111**, 1017–1019.

85. Nagamine, C., Morohashi, K., Carlisle, C., and Chang, D. (1999). Sex reversal caused by *Mus musculus domesticus* Y-chromosomes linked to variant expression of the testis-determining gene *Sry*. *Dev. Biol.* **216**, 182–194.

86. Swain, A., Narvaez, V., Burgoyne, P.S., Camerino, G., and Lovell-Badge, R. (1998). *Dax1* antagonizes *Sry* action in mammalian sex determination. *Nature* **391**, 761–767.

87. Swain, A., Zanaria, E., Hacker, A., Lovell-Badge, R., and Camerino, G. (1996). Mouse *Dax1* expression is consistent with a role in sex determination as well as adrenal and hypothalamus function. *Nat. Genet.* **12**, 404–409.

88. Vainio, S., Heikkila, M., Kispert, A., Chin, N., and McMahon, A.P. (1999). Female development in mammals is regulated by Wnt-4 signalling. *Nature* **397**, 405–409.

89. Loffler, K., Zarkower, D., and Koopman, P. (2003). Etiology of ovarian failure in blepharophimosis–ptosis–epicanthus inversus syndrome (BPES): *FOXL2* is a conserved, early-acting gene in vertebrate ovarian development. *Endocrinology* **144**, 3237–3243.

90. Bullejos, M., Bowles, J., and Koopman, P. (2002). Extensive vascularization of developing mouse ovaries revealed by caveolin-1 expression. *Dev. Dyn.* **225**, 95–99.

91. Bardoni, B., Zanaria, E., Guioli, S., Floridia, G., Worley, K.C., Tonini, G., Ferrante, E., Chiumello, G., McCabe, E.R.B.,

Fraccaro, M., Zuffardi, O., and Camerino, G. (1994). A dosage sensitive locus at chromosome Xp21 is involved in male to female sex reversal. *Nat. Genet.* **7,** 497–501.

92. Muscatelli, F., Strom, T., Walker, A., Zanaria, E., Recan, D., Meindl, A., Bardoni, B., Guioli, S., Zehetner, G., Rabl, W., Schwarz, H., Kaplan, J., Camerino, G., Meitinger, T., and Monaco, A. (1994). Mutations in the DAX-1 gene give rise to both X-linked adrenal hypoplasia congenita and hypogonadotropic hypogonadism. *Nature* **372,** 672–676.

93. Zanaria, E., Muscatelli, F., Bardoni, B., Strom, T.M., Guioli, S., Guo, W., Lalli, E., Moser, C., Walker, A.P., McCabe, E.R.B., Meltinger, T., Monaco, A.P., Sassone-Corsi, P., and Camerino, G. (1994). An unusual member of the nuclear hormone receptor superfamily responsible for X-linked adrenal hypoplasia congenita. *Nature* **372,** 635–641.

94. Goodfellow, P., and Camerino, G. (1999). *DAX-1,* an "antitestis" gene. *Cell. Mol. Life Sci.* **55,** 857–863.

95. Yu, R.N., Ito, M., Saunders, T.L., Camper, S.A., and Jameson, J.L. (1998). Role of *Ahch* in gonadal development and gametogenesis. *Nat. Genet.* **20,** 353–357.

96. Meeks, J., Crawford, S., Russell, T., Morohashi, K., Weiss, J., and Jameson, J. (2003). Dax1 regulates testis cord organization during gonadal differentiation. *Development* **130,** 1029–1036.

97. Meeks, J., Weiss, J., and Jameson, J. (2003). Dax1 is required for testis determination. *Nat. Genet.* **34,** 32–33.

98. Mizusaki, H., Kawabe, K., Mukai, T., Ariyoshi, E., Kasahara, M., Yoshioka, H., Swain, A., and Morohashi, K. (2003). *Dax-1* (dosage-sensitive sex reversal-adrenal hypoplasia congenita critical region on the X-chromosome, gene 1) gene transcription is regulated by Wnt4 in the female developing gonad. *Mol. Endocrinol.* **17,** 507–519.

99. Cohen, E., Mariol, M.C., Wallace, R., Weyers, J., Kamberov, Y., Pradel, J., and Wilder, E. (2002). Wnt4 regulates cell movement and focal adhesion kinase during *Drosophila* ovarian morphogenesis. *Dev. Cell* **2,** 437–448.

100. Pailhoux, E., Vigier, B., Chaffaux, S., Servel, N., Taourit, S., Furet, J., Fellous, M., Grosclaude, F., Cribiu, E., Cotinot, C., and Vaiman, D. (2001). A 11.7-kb deletion triggers intersexuality and polledness in goats. *Nat. Genet.* **29,** 453–458.

101. Crisponi, L., Deiana, M., Loi, A., Chiappe, F., Uda, M., Amati, P., Bisceglia, L., Zelante, L., Nagaraja, R., Porcu, S., Ristaldi, M., Marzella, R., Rocchi, M., Nicolino, M., Leinhardt-Roussie, A., Nivelon, A., Verloes, A., Schlessinger, D., Gasparini, P., Bonneau, D., Cao, A., and Pilia, G. (2001). The putative forkhead transcription factor *FOXL2* is mutated in blepharophimosis–ptosis–epicanthus inversus syndrome. *Nat. Genet.* **27,** 159–166.

102. Cocquet, J., Pailhoux, E., Jaubert, F., Servel, N., Xia, X., Pannetier, M., De Baere, E., Messiaen, L., Cotinot, C., Fellous, M., and Veitia, R. (2002). Evolution and expression of FOXL2. *J. Med. Genet.* **39,** 916–921.

103. Hatano, O., Takakusu, A., Nomura, M., and Morohashi, K. (1996). Identical origin of adrenal cortex and gonad revealed by expression profiles of Ad4BP/SF-1. *Genes Cells* **1,** 663–671.

104. Morohashi, K.I. (1997). The ontogenesis of the steroidogenic tissues. *Genes Cells* **2,** 95–106.

105. Clark, A., Garland, K., and Russell, L. (2000). Desert hedgehog *(Dhh)* gene is required in the mouse testis for formation of adult-type Leydig cells and normal development of peritubular cells and seminiferous tubules. *Biol. Reprod.* **63,** 1825–1838.

106. Yao, H., Whoriskey, W., and Capel, B. (2002). Desert hedgehog–Patched 1 signalling specifies fetal Leydig cell fate in testis organogenesis. *Genes Dev.* **16,** 1433–1440.

107. Heikkila, M., Peltoketo, H., Leppaluoto, J., Ilves, M., Vuolteenaho, O., and Vainio, S. (2002). Wnt-4 deficiency alters mouse adrenal cortex function, reducing aldosterone production. *Endocrinology* **143,** 4358–4365.

108. Nef, S., and Parada, L. (1999). Cryptorchidism in mice mutant for *Insl3. Nat. Genet.* **22,** 295–299.

109. Zimmermann, S., Steding, G., Emmen, J.M.A., Brinkmann, A.O., Nayernia, K., Holstein, A.F., Engel, W., and Adham, I.M. (1999). Targeted disruption of the *Insl3* gene causes bilateral cryptorchidism. *Mol. Endocrinol.* **13,** 681–691.

110. Kanai, Y., Kanai-Azuma, M., Tajima, Y., Birk, O., Hayashi, Y., and Sanai, Y. (2000). Identification of a stromal cell type characterized by the secretion of a soluble integrin-binding protein, MFG-E8, in mouse early gonadogenesis. *Mech. Dev.* **96,** 223–227.

111. Lawson, K., Dunn, N., Roelen, B., Zeinstra, L., Davis, A., Wright, C., Korving, J., and Hogan, B. (1999). Bmp4 is required for the generation of primordial germ cells in the mouse embryo. *Genes Dev.* **13,** 424–436.

112. Saitou, M., Barton, S., and Surani, M. (2002). A molecular program for the specification of germ cell fate in mice. *Nature* **418,** 293–300.

113. Gomperts, M., Wylie, C., and Heasman, J. (1994). Primordial germ cell migration. *Ciba. Found. Symp.* **182,** 121–134.

114. McLaren, A., and Southee, D. (1997). Entry of mouse embryonic germ cells into meiosis. *Dev. Biol.* **187,** 107–113.

115. Scholer, H., Hatzopoulos, A., Balling, R., Suzuki, N., and Gruss, P. (1989). A family of octamer-specific proteins present during mouse embryogenesis: Evidence for germ line-specific expression of an Oct factor. *EMBO J.* **8,** 2543–2550.

116. Di Carlo, A., Travia, G., and De Felici, M. (2000). The meiotic specific synaptonemal complex protein SCP3 is expressed by female and male primordial germ cells of the mouse embryo. *Int. J. Dev. Biol.* **44,** 241–244.

117. Zamboni, L., and Upadhyay, S. (1983). Germ cell differentiation in mouse adrenal glands. *J. Exp. Zool.* **228,** 173–193.

118. Chuma, S., and Nakatsuji, N. (2001). Autonomous transition into meiosis of mouse fetal germ cells *in vitro* and its inhibition by gp130-mediated signalling. *Dev. Biol.* **229,** 468–479.

119. McLaren, A. (1988). Somatic and germ cell sex in mammals. *Philos. Trans. R. Soc. Lond. Biol.* **322,** 3–9.

120. Byskov, A.G. (1986). Differentiation of the mammalian embryonic gonad. *Physiol. Rev.* **66,** 71–117.

121. Burgoyne, P.S., and Palmer, S.J. (1991). The genetics of XY sex reversal in the mouse and other mammals. *Semin. Dev. Biol.* **2,** 277–284.

122. Yao, H., Tilmann, C., Zhao, G.Q., and Capel, B. (2002). The battle of the sexes: Opposing pathways in sex determination. *In* "Novartis Foundation Symposia: The Genetics and Biology of Sex Determination," Vol. 244, pp. 187–198. John Wiley & Sons, Chichester, U.K.

123. Ward, H., McLaren, A., and Baker, T. (1987). Gonadal development in T16H/XSxr hermaphrodite mice. *J. Reprod. Fertil.* **81,** 295–300.

124. Soyal, S., Amleh, A., and Dean, J. (2000). FIG-α, a germ cell-specific transcription factor required for ovarian follicle formation. *Development* **127,** 4645–4654.

125. Takasaki, N., McIsaac, R., and Dean, J. (2000). *Gpbox (Psx2),* a homeobox gene preferentially expressed in female germ cells at the onset of sexual dimorphism in mice. *Dev. Biol.* **223,** 181–193.

126. Siggers, P., Smith, L., and Greenfield, A. (2002). Sexually dimorphic expression of Gata-2 during mouse gonad development. *Mech. Dev.* **111,** 159–162.

127. McLaren, A. (1984). Meiosis and differentiation of mouse germ cells. *In* "Controlling Events in Meiosis: 38th Symposium of the Society for Experimental Biology," (C. Evans *et al.,* eds.), pp. 7–23. Company of Biologists, Cambridge.

128. Dolci, S., and De Felici, M. (1990). A study of meiosis in chimaeric mouse fetal gonads. *Development* **109,** 37–40.

129. McLaren, A., and Buehr, M. (1990). Development of mouse germ cells in cultures of fetal gonads. *Cell Diff. Dev.* **31,** 185–195.

130. Skinner, M.K., Stallard, B., Anthony, C.T., and Griswold, M.D. (1989). Cellular localization of fibronectin gene expression in the seminiferous tubule. *Mol. Cell. Endocrinol.* **66,** 45–52.

131. Jost, A., and Magre, S. (1984). Testicular development phases and dual hormonal control of sexual organogenesis. *In* "Sexual Differentiation: Basic and Clinical Aspects," (M. Serio, ed.). Raven Press, New York.

132. Cate, R.L., Mattaliano, R.J., Hession, C., Tizard, R., Farber, N.M., Cheung, A., Ninfa, E.G., Frey, A.Z., Gash, D.J., Chow, E.P., Fisher, R.A., Bertonis, J.M., Torres, G., Wallner, B.P., Ramachandran, K.L., Ragin, R.C., Manganaro, T.F., MacLaughlin, D.T., and Donahoe, P.K. (1986). Isolation of the bovine and human genes for Mullerian-inhibiting substance and expression of the human gene in animal cells. *Cell* **45,** 685–698.

133. Behringer, R.R., Finegold, M.J., and Cate, R.L. (1994). Mullerian-inhibiting substance function during mammalian sexual development. *Cell* **79,** 415–425.

134. Jamin, S., Arango, N., Mishina, Y., Hanks, M., and Behringer, R. (2002). Requirement of Bmpr1a for Mullerian duct regression during male sexual development. *Nat. Genet.* **32,** 408–410.

135. Parr, B., and McMahon, A. (1998). Sexually dimorphic development of the mammalian reproductive tract requires Wnt-7a. *Nature* **395,** 707–710.

136. Miller, C., and Sassoon, D. (1998). Wnt-7a maintains appropriate uterine patterning during the development of the mouse female reproductive tract. *Development* **125,** 3201–3211.

34

Liver

Elizabeth A. Jones, David Tosh, and Lesley M. Forrester

Introduction

The liver has a multitude of functions, including the regulation of carbohydrate, protein, and fat metabolism; the detoxification of endo- and xenobiotics; and the synthesis and secretion of plasma proteins, and bile. Liver disorders have been estimated to affect 17.5% of the population,[1] and the most severe cases can be treated by orthotopic transplantation. Liver transplantation, first performed by Thomas Starzl in 1963, has become an almost routine procedure with 1-year survival rates exceeding 80%,[2] but the shortage of donor organs greatly limits the use of this treatment. Liver cell therapies, including hepatocyte transplantation and the use of bioartificial liver systems, are being developed as alternative therapies to whole-liver transplantation for patients with hereditary liver disease and fulminant hepatic failure.

Hepatocyte transplantation has been used to reestablish liver function without organ transplantation and to act as a bridge until whole-organ liver transplantation becomes feasible.[3,4] Hepatocyte transplantation has several advantages over orthotopic liver transplantation:

1. Cell transplantation is a nonsurgical procedure with much less morbidity.
2. The liver has a high regenerative potential, so it may be possible to use transplanted hepatocytes to provide temporary liver function until the patient's own liver has time to regenerate.
3. Cells from a single donor could be used for many recipients.

Human trials have shown that hepatocyte transplantation is a promising alternative therapy for liver failure and some metabolic diseases of the liver. Intrasplenic transplantation of differentiated adult hepatocytes into human patients with severe encephalopathy and multisystem organ failure has been shown to control hyperammonemia and ensure short-term survival until orthotopic liver transplantation can be performed.[5] In 1998, a child with Crigler-Najjar type I, suffering from hyperbilirubinaemia, was given allogeneic hepatocytes by infusion through a portal vein catheter.[6] The procedure resulted in a reduction but not in a normalisation of serum bilirubin levels.

Hepatocyte transplantation has also been proposed as a liver-directed gene therapy for several inherited hepatic disorders. Liver-directed gene therapy may involve replacement of a nonfunctioning gene, overexpression of a normal gene, expression of a pharmacological gene product, or interference with gene expression (reviewed by Ghosh *et al.*[7]). The first long-term gene therapy for a hepatic metabolic disease used the *ex vivo* gene transfer approach.[8] Hepatocytes were isolated from a resected segment of the liver of a low-density lipoprotein receptor-deficient, Watanabe-heritable, hyperlipidaemic rabbit. The cultured cells were transduced with a therapeutic virus, and then the phenotypically corrected hepatocytes were transplanted back to the donor. This resulted in a long-term but modest reduction of serum low-density lipoprotein levels. This approach was then used in a clinical trial of gene therapy for patients with inherited low-density lipoprotein receptor deficiency (familial hypercholesterolaemia). Although *in vivo* expression of the transgene was demonstrated, the clinical effect was minimal and did not reach a therapeutically beneficial level.[9]

Another application of liver-directed gene therapy could be the exogenous expression of a protein to compensate for a deficiency in another organ. For example, transplanted hepatocytes could be engineered to produce insulin for the treatment of insulin-requiring diabetes mellitus.[10–12] In this case it would be highly desirable to have physiological regulation of the expression of the transgene by plasma glucose concentration. Inclusion of the natural regulatory regions of genes to drive transgene expression may provide such physiological control in the future.[10,13–15]

Bioartificial liver systems are being developed to replace normal liver function. To be used successfully, several prerequisites have to be fulfilled. First, the origin of the hepatocytes should be as close to human as possible because human hepatocytes do not always perform the same types of biotransformations as other animal species.[16,17] Second, the tissue mass required to replace the normal functioning of the liver is critical.[18] Third, the hepatocytes must express the full complement of liver functions and maintain their differentiated properties long term.

Hepatocyte transplantation therapies and bioartificial liver systems are also limited by the availability of donor tissue, as hepatocytes cannot be expanded sufficiently *in vitro* and they rapidly lose their hepatocyte-specific functions in culture.[19,20] Conventional approaches to maintaining the differentiated properties of isolated hepatocytes in culture include supplementation of the medium with hormones, cofactors such as nicotinamide,

Handbook of Stem Cells
Volume 1

pyruvate, dimethyl sulfoxide, and phenobarbital, the application of extracellular matrix components and co-culture with non-parenchymal epithelial cell types.[19] Alternative sources of cells for transplantation have been proposed including reversibly immortalised hepatocytes, bone marrow stem cells, hepatic progenitors, and embryonic stem (ES) cells. However, these alternatives pose their own problems. For example, the well-defined human hepatoma cell line HepG2 lacks the urea cycle enzymes[21] and has little capacity for either gluconeogenesis or ketogenesis.[22] The ideal cells for use in such liver cell therapies would expand extensively *in vitro,* differentiate into all mature liver cells, have minimal immunogenicity, be cryopreservable, and reconstitute liver tissue when transplanted.[23] ES cells fulfil many of these criteria and therefore may be an ideal source of cells in the treatment of hepatic disorders. However, the major challenge in the use of ES cells in any cell therapy is the difficulty in controlling the differentiation process to generate significant numbers of the desired cell type. Here, we summarise the research to date on the differentiation of ES cells into hepatocytes and speculate on the factors that might be involved in that process.

Summary of Liver Development

Molecular events that occur during normal liver development *in vivo* are likely to provide clues to understanding the differentiation of pluripotent stem cells, such as ES cells, into mature hepatocytes or bile duct cells *in vitro.* A brief outline of liver development is given here; in addition, there are several excellent reviews.[24–28]

The liver develops from the ventral endoderm of the foregut at the 14–20 somite stage.[29] A hepatic bud is formed first; it then expands and proliferates into the septum transversum to form the embryonic liver. Much of our understanding of the molecular control of early liver development has come from a series of elegant experiments from the Zaret laboratory. It has been shown that the ventral endoderm must express *Gata-4* and *Foxa2* (previously known as *Hnf-3β*) to be competent to undergo hepatic differentiation.[30] Specification of the liver depends on the concerted action of fibroblast growth factor (FGF) signalling from the adjacent cardiac mesoderm[31] and bone morphogenetic protein (BMP) signalling from the adjacent septum transversum[32] (Fig. 34–1). In the absence of these signals, the endoderm assumes a pancreatic fate.[32] Hepatic differentiation is evidenced by the synthesis of alpha-fetoprotein (Afp) and albumin (Alb) in the nascent hepatoblasts and by the more recently described liver-specific isoform of the *Ankrd17* gene (previously known as *Gtar*).[33]

Hepatoblasts proliferate from the endoderm to form a tissue bud and then proliferate further into the adjacent septum transversum, intermingling with endothelial cells. Although it is known that liver morphogenesis requires an interaction between hepatoblasts and blood vessel endothelium[34] (reviewed by Lammert *et al.*[35]), the specific mechanisms that mediate interaction have yet to be fully elucidated.

Hepatoblasts are thought to be bipotential and generate both hepatocytes and biliary epithelial cells.[36] The septum

transversum is essential for this process,[29,37] and several transcription factors—including *Hex,*[38,39] *Hlx-1,*[40] and *Prox-1*[41]—are implicated in the differentiation of hepatoblast to hepatocyte. In addition, the composition of the extracellular matrix has a significant effect on the genes expressed by cultured hepatocytes,[42,43] so it is possible that the extracellular matrix may also have a role in regulating hepatic differentiation.

The intrahepatic biliary ducts are thought to develop from hepatoblasts that differentiate first to form a ring of biliary precursor cells around the portal mesenchyme (the ductal plate), which is subsequently remodelled to form the bile ducts.[28,44,45] Several molecules are known to be involved in this process, including Hnf-6[46] and the Notch signalling pathway.[47]

Markers of the Hepatocyte Lineage *in Vivo*

ES cells generate a range of cell types when induced to differentiate *in vitro*. Therefore, it is important to be able to unequivocally identify the cell of interest. This is usually done by detecting expression of a tissue-specific protein or by observing a specific morphological feature. Cell-type identification has proven problematic when assessing the hepatic differentiation of ES cells, as many of the classical genes (such as *Afp* and *Alb*) that have been used as early liver markers *in vivo* are also expressed in visceral endoderm.[48] In the context of an intact embryo[49] and in explant studies,[31,32,50,51] this does not pose a problem, as expression of one of these proteins in combination with its spatial position is sufficient to identify a cell as a primitive hepatocyte. The identification of a novel liver-specific gene would greatly facilitate lineage analyses as well as permit detailed studies on the molecular and cellular basis of hepatic differentiation from pluripotent cell types. In this part of the chapter, we examine the merits of the different markers used to date in the characterisation of hepatic differentiation of ES cells.

EMBRYONIC MARKERS

Alpha-Fetoprotein

One of the earliest genes to be expressed in murine liver development is *Afp*. The function of this 70-kD protein is not yet fully understood, but it has been proposed to have a role in growth control, steroid binding, immune modulation, and osmotic pressure maintenance.[52] *Afp* is first detected at the onset of liver development.[50] Expression is high in the embryonic liver[49,53] and is down-regulated shortly after birth.[54] However, *Afp* is also expressed in the yolk sac endoderm *in vivo*.[49,53] As ES cells readily differentiate into cells of the primitive endoderm lineage, expression of *Afp* in differentiating ES cells cannot distinguish between primitive endoderm cells and cells that have committed to a hepatic fate.

Albumin

Alb is a soluble monomeric protein, which makes up about half of all serum protein in an adult. Alb functions primarily as a carrier protein for steroids, fatty acids, and thyroid hormones, and it plays a role in stabilising extracellular fluid volumes by

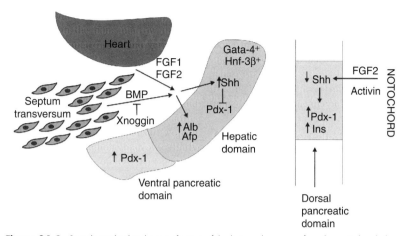

Figure 34–1. *Signals involved in the specification of the liver and pancreas from the ventral endoderm.*

contributing to the colloid osmotic pressure of the blood.[55] Shortly after the presumptive hepatic endoderm starts to produce *Afp*, *Alb* mRNA is synthesised. This occurs in the 7–8 somite stage in the mouse (embryonic day 8.5).[50] Although *Alb* has a more restricted pattern of expression than *Afp*, it is expressed in the yolk sac as well as the liver.[48,56] Like *Afp*, because *Alb* is expressed by extraembryonic endoderm, expression of *Alb* by cells in differentiating ES cell cultures cannot be taken as definitive evidence of hepatic differentiation. In addition, it has been shown that some cells take up Alb from the media, so the presence of Alb when detected by immunofluorescence may be artifactual.[57]

Ankyrin Repeat Domain 17

Gene trapping in ES cells is a random insertional mutagenesis approach that has been used to identify and characterise the function of novel genes.[58] We previously generated a gene trap vector insertion into *Ankrd17*, a gene that encodes an ankyrin repeat-containing protein of unknown function.[33] One splice isoform of this gene is expressed exclusively in the developing liver but, importantly, not in the extraembryonic endoderm. Ankrd17 is first expressed in embryonic day 8.5 mouse embryos in the cells of the ventral endoderm that have been specified to a hepatic fate. It therefore provides the earliest specific marker of a hepatic phenotype. However, its expression is down-regulated in hepatocytes as development proceeds, and it is not expressed in most adult hepatocytes, which limits its use as a hepatic marker.

MATURE HEPATOCYTE MARKERS

As hepatocytes mature, they begin to express several other proteins, such as α-1 antitrypsin (Aat),[48] glutamine synthetase (Gs),[59] and transthyretin (Ttr).[60] Although these proteins are enriched in the liver, none of them exhibit liver-specific expression. For example, murine Gs mRNA is found in pericentral hepatocytes and at a lower level in glial cells and the proximal tubular epithelium of the kidney.[61] However, the combined expression of these genes in a single cell can be

useful in defining the hepatic phenotype. The gluconeogenic enzyme glucose-6-phosphatase (G6P) is expressed in embryonic liver and kidney.[62] Tyrosine aminotransferase (Tat) is expressed in hepatocytes but not until the neonatal period.[63] These two enzymes are often used as markers of hepatic maturation as they are not expressed early in hepatic development.

ULTRASTRUCTURE OF HEPATOCYTES

In vivo, adult hepatocytes have a characteristic ultrastructural appearance:[64] The normal polyhedral hepatocyte has numerous subcellular organelles, such as well-developed and numerous mitochondria, peroxisomes, lysosomes, and complex rough and smooth endoplasmic reticulum. The normal hepatocyte stores glycogen and sometimes lipid droplets, and it secretes bile through the bile canaliculi between adjacent liver cells. In contrast, cells within the embryonic liver do not display such a distinctive profile and cannot be identified morphologically until they are relatively mature. At embryonic day 10.5 in mice, the liver primordium can be recognized as cords of primitive hepatocytes penetrating the septum transversum.[65] These primitive hepatocytes begin to acquire the organelles required for protein synthesis between days 10 and 11; by day 12, they have dilated Golgi complexes with associated vesicles and many mitochondria. Between days 12 and 17 of gestation, the embryonic hepatocytes become less stellate and eventually form cuboidal cells possessing both smooth and villous surfaces as well as many lipid vesicles. Glycogenesis first occurs during late fetal development, and both perinatal and more differentiated hepatocytes store a large reserve of glycogen.[66,67]

Endodermal Differentiation of ES Cells

Although much work has been done on the differentiation of ES cells into derivatives of ectoderm and mesoderm lineages (as demonstrated in parts 3 and 4 of this volume), less work has been done on the derivatives of endodermal cell types. Doetschman *et al.*[68] first demonstrated that the complex three-dimensional embryoid body (EB) structures that form when

ES cells differentiate in suspension culture had an outer layer of endoderm bordered by a basal lamina. The presence of the endoderm markers, Afp and Tfn, was confirmed by immunoprecipitation. Immunofluorescence using antibodies to TROMA1, expressed in both visceral and parietal endoderm, and TROMA3, specific for parietal endoderm, suggested that this endoderm layer consisted predominately of visceral yolk sac endoderm and not embryonic endoderm.

The pattern of endodermal gene expression in differentiating EBs was studied by Northern blot analysis and reverse transcription-polymerase chain reaction (RT-PCR).[69] The serum protein genes *Ttr, Afp,* and *Alb* were activated on day 3, 5, and 13, respectively; the *Ttr* expression was shown to be localised to the outer layer of endodermal cells by *in situ* hybridisation. The hepatic nuclear factors, *Hnf-1, -3* and *-4,* are expressed early in endoderm differentiation *in vivo*[70] and are also activated during ES cell differentiation *in vitro*.[69] Interestingly, when *Foxa2* is overexpressed in differentiating ES cells, the expression of genes associated with endodermal lineage, namely *Alb* and the cystic fibrosis transmembrane-conductance regulator, are induced.[71] However, expression of genes involved in late endoderm differentiation, such as *Aat,* are not subsequently induced.[71]

Gata-4 is expressed in both parietal and visceral endoderm of the early mouse embryo,[72] and targeted mutagenesis of the *Gata-4* gene results in a block to visceral endoderm generation *in vitro*.[73] However, *Gata-4*-deficient EBs can develop an external layer of visceral or parietal endoderm when grown in the presence of retinoic acid (RA) or RA/dbcAMP, respectively.[74] Forced expression of either *Gata-4* or *Gata-6* in ES cells is sufficient to induce differentiation toward extraembryonic endoderm.[75]

Recently it has been shown that endoderm can be induced in EBs either by limited exposure to serum or by culturing in the presence of Activin A under serum-free conditions.[76] Using an ES cell line with green fluorescent protein (GFP) targeted to the brachyury locus it was shown that definitive endoderm develops from a brachyury+ cell population.

Hepatic Differentiation of Murine ES Cells

Several groups have demonstrated that ES cells are able to differentiate into cells of the hepatocyte lineage *in vitro* (summarised in Table 34–1) and *in vivo*.[77,78]

Hamazaki *et al.*[79] showed by RT-PCR that differentiating murine ES cells, in the absence of additional growth factors, expressed endoderm-specific genes such as *Afp, Ttr,* and *Alb.* However, as they correctly state, these data do not distinguish hepatic differentiation from yolk sac lineage differentiation. Markers of more mature hepatocytes such as *Tat* and *G6P* were only observed when ES cells were differentiated in the presence of acidic fibroblast growth factor (aFGF), hepatocyte growth factor (HGF), and oncostatin M (OSM). aFGF is involved in the specification of hepatogenesis from the ventral endoderm,[31] and HGF and OSM have been shown to induce hepatocyte maturation *in vitro*.[80,81] In addition, Hamazaki *et al.*[79] observed that expression of the mature hepatocyte markers was further

induced when the differentiation was performed on a matrix of type 1 collagen. They concluded that addition of exogenous growth factors was necessary for the differentiation of mature hepatocytes from ES cells *in vitro*.

Miyashita *et al.*[82] used quantitative PCR analysis to demonstrate hepatic gene expression relating to both early and late stage liver development after 26 days of ES cell differentiation. In particular, G6P expression was detected although no exogenous growth factors had been added during differentiation.

Jones *et al.*[83] identified individual ES cell-derived hepatocytes within EBs in the absence of additional growth factors. They used an ES cell line carrying a gene trap integration into the *Ankrd17* gene that confers embryonic liver-specific expression of β-galactosidase (β-gal) *in vivo*.[33] The phenotype of the β-gal+ cells was confirmed by showing that they coexpress Afp, Tfn, and Alb using dual immunohistochemistry. In addition, transmission electron microscopy (TEM) showed that β-gal+ cells had an ultrastructure consistent with embryonic hepatocytes.

ES cell–derived hepatocytes have also been identified using the cellular uptake of indocyanine green (ICG).[84] No additional growth factors were required for hepatic differentiation to occur. ICG is an organic anion used clinically as a test substance to evaluate liver function, as it is nontoxic and is taken up and eliminated exclusively by hepatocytes. However, ICG can also be taken up by human trophoblasts,[85] so ICG uptake cannot be regarded as liver specific in the context of differentiating ES cells as some extraembryonic cells will be present in the milieu of differentiating cells.

The ICG+ cells identified by Yamada *et al.*[84] in differentiating cultures also expressed hepatocyte markers *(Alb, Afp, CPSase 1, LST-1, and PEPCK)* and were ultrastructurally similar to hepatocytes. The expression of *LST-1* may be significant, as it has been proposed that this organic anion transporter is liver specific. However, the expression of *LST-1* has not been examined in murine extraembryonic structures.[86] No glycogen granules were demonstrated in the ICG+ cells, and cells surrounding the ICG+ cells also expressed Alb. However, given the number of similarities between the ICG+ cells and hepatocytes, it is likely that these cells represent a population of mature hepatocytes; as they do express genes expressed in mature hepatocytes. Interestingly, the ICG+ cells were observed as clusters with a three-dimensional structure, most of which were adjacent to the cardiac beating areas. This is in contrast to our results, as we found no relationship between cardiac beating areas of the culture and β-gal+ hepatic cells.[87] Cell-cell interactions between embryonic cardiac mesoderm and definitive endoderm are essential for liver development *in vivo*.[29,31] Fair *et al.*[88] co-cultured murine ES cells with chick embryonic mesoderm and demonstrated an increase in mRNA for *Afp* and *Alb.*

Functionality of ES cell–derived hepatocytes was demonstrated by Chinzei *et al.*[89] ES cell–derived hepatocytes were identified by detecting *Alb* and *Afp* mRNA in EBs. ES cell–derived hepatocytes, within these EBs, were capable of synthesising urea by day 12, indicating that these cells had acquired at least partial function of mature hepatocytes.

TABLE 34-1

Strategies Used to Derive Hepatocytes from Murine ES Cells

Ref	Method of Differentiation	Differentiation Factors	Cell Identification	Functional Data	Transplantation Data
79	EB formed by hanging drop then cultured in suspension. Plated day 5 onto collagen type 1- or gelatin-coated dishes.	100 ng/ml aFGF—day 9–12 20 ng/ml HGF—day 12–18 10 ng/ml OSM—day 15–18 10^{-7} M Dex+ITS—day 15–18	Detection of *Afp, Ttr, Aat, Alb, Tat, G6P* mRNA by RTPCR.	None	None
83	EB formed by free aggregation then cultured in suspension. Plated day 5 onto gelatin-coated dishes.	None in addition to FCS	Expression of liver-specific isoform of *Ankrd17*. Detection of Alb, Afp, Ttr, Gs, and Aat by immunohistochemistry. Ultrastructure shown by TEM.	None	None
82	ES cells cultured without LIF for 2 days and then EB formed by free aggregation and cultured in suspension. Plated day 8 onto cell-culture dishes.	None in addition to FCS	Detection of *Foxa2, Hnf-3α, Hnf-3γ, Ttr, Afp, Alb, Aat, G6P, Gst,* and *Asgr1* mRNA by RT-PCR. Detection of Alb by immunohistochemistry.	None	None
84	EB formed in hanging drops. Plated onto gelatin-coated plastic after 5 days.	None in addition to FCS	Cellular uptake of ICG. Detection of *Alb, Afp,Ttr, Foxa2, Aat, Tdo, CPSase1, PEPCK,* and *Lst-1* mRNA by RT-PCR. Alb detected by immunohistochemistry. Ultrastructure shown by TEM.	None	EGFP–ES cell–derived ICG+ cells were isolated by microdissection and transplanted into male mice via the portal vein. Distribution of engrafted cells detected by EGFP fluorescence.
89	EB formed in hanging drops. Plated onto gelatin-coated plastic after 2 days.	None in addition to FCS or 20 ng/ml aFGF—day 6 10 ng/ml bFGF—day 6 10 ng/ml HGF—day 10 10 ng/ml OSM—day 16 10^{-7} M Dex+ITS—day 16	Detection of *Alb, Afp,* and *Tat* mRNA by RTPCR. Detection of Alb by Western blot and immunohistochemistry.	Urea synthesis measured by the manual diacetyl monoxime method.	Unfractionated cells of 9 day EB transplanted. Cells detected by Y-chromosome FISH; they expressed Alb.
99	*Foxa2*-transfected ES cell line cultured in 96-well, round-bottomed, Sumilon cell-tight spheroid plates for 1 month. Spheroid cells then grown in flasks containing chitin fibres.	50 ng/ml FGF2—for 1 month 10^{-7} M Dex 0.2 mM L-ascorbic -2-phosphate 10 mM nicotinamide	Alb and CK18 detected by immunocytochemistry. Glycogen detected by PAS staining and TEM Ultrastructure determined by TEM.	Synthesis of urea and triacylglycerol.	None

Continued

TABLE 34-1

Strategies Used to Derive Hepatocytes from Murine ES Cells—cont'd

Ref	Method of Differentiation	Differentiation Factors	Cell Identification	Functional Data	Transplantation Data
106	EB formed by trypsinising ES cells into aggregates and plating into bacteriological Petri dishes, or ES cells cultured in methylcellulose-based media for 6 days, dissociated into single cells, and replated in methylcellulose-based media for a further 6 days.	None in addition to FCS or Hepa cell-conditioned media.	GFP-inserted inframe with the translation start codon of Afp gene. GFP+ cells also express Alb (RTPCR).	Synthesis of haptoglobin and ApoE posttransplant.	GFP+ cells isolated by FACS and transplanted into the spleen of ROSA mice that had undergone partial hepatectomy. ES cell derivatives integrated into hepatic cords. Haptoglobin and ApoE produced when GFP+ cells transplanted into the corresponding deficient mouse.
94	EB formed by free aggregation then cultured in suspension. Plated day 5 onto gelatin-coated dishes.	HGF 20ng/mL β-NGF 50 ng/mL	Detection of Alb, Ttr, G6P, Hnf4, Sek1 mRNA by RT-PCR. Afp and Aat detected by immunohistochemistry.	None	None
76	EB formed by free aggregation in differentiation media, harvested day 2.5 and cultured in suspension in serum-free media. Plated day 6 or 10 onto matrigel-coated dishes.	FCS and 10⁻⁷M Dex or 5 ng/mL bfGf and no FCS.	Detection of Alb, Afp, Ttr, Aat, Tat, and CPS1 mRNA by RT-PCR.	None	GFP-Brachyury⁺ cells were isolated from day 5 EBs that had been induced with activin. These cells were cultured for a further 12 days then transplanted under the kidney capsules of SCID-beige mice. Hepatocytes were not detected in the grafts after 3 weeks.
103	EB formed by hanging drop then cultured in suspension. Plated day 4 onto gelatin-coated dishes and cultured to select nestin-positive cells. Dissociated and replated onto collagen-1-coated dishes on day 12.	Hydrocortisone Tfn EGF Insulin	Detection of Alb, Aat, Afp, and Foxa2 mRNA by RT-PCR. Detection of Afp, dipeptidyl peptidase IV, Alb, Aat, and cytokeratins 14, 18, and 19 by immunohistochemistry.	Alb synthesis estimated using the quantitative enzyme-linked immunoassay.	None

However, even when urea synthesis was at its maximum after 18 days of ES cell differentiation, it was 40-fold lower than that of mouse primary hepatocytes.

ENHANCING HEPATIC DIFFERENTIATION

If hepatocytes are to be generated in sufficient numbers to be useful for cell therapy, then it is important to define the culture conditions necessary to obtain a high yield of ES cell–derived hepatocytes. Protocols have been derived for the efficient derivation of dopaminergic and serotonergic neurons[90] and haematopoietic cells,[91,92] but to date, there has only been limited success in defining protocols for hepatocyte differentiation.

Adding Growth Factors

Hamazaki et al.[79] used a defined cocktail of growth factors to induce mature hepatic differentiation. In this experimental system, aFGF was added between days 9 and 12; HGF was added between days 12 and 18; and OSM, dexamethasone, and an insulin–transferrin–selenious acid (ITS) mixture were added between days 15 and 18. When ES cells were cultured without these additional growth factors, late differentiation markers (Tat and G6P) were not expressed during the study period (18 days). No data was presented to indicate the proportion of cells that had assumed a hepatic-like phenotype, but Alb expression was reported to increase seven- to nine-fold when cells were plated on collagen.[79] Using an ES cell line in which GFP has been inserted under the control of the Afp promoter, Hamazaki and Terada[93] have subsequently shown that the population of GFP positive cells increases from 1.2% to 2.4 % using this experimental protocol.

Kuai et al.[94] demonstrated the presence of hepatocyte-like cells when ES cells were allowed to differentiate in the presence of HGF and/or β-nerve growth factor (β-NGF). We observed cells expressing G6P when ES cells were differentiated in the absence of purified growth factors,[95] and HGF, β-NGF, aFGF, OSM, and dexamethasone added separately or in combination failed to have any significant effect on the amount of hepatic differentiation.[96] Similar results were obtained by Chinzei et al.[89] They used the same growth factor cocktail as Hamazaki et al., and no effect on the expression of the hepatic differentiation markers was observed. These conflicting results from different laboratories are possibly because of differences in ES cell lines; the precise combination, timing, and concentration of growth factors used; or the batch of fetal calf serum (FCS).

Manipulating Gene Expression

Overexpression of key transcription factors has been successful in driving differentiation of some cell types from ES cells. For example, forced expression of either Gata-4 or Gata-6 in ES cells is sufficient to induce differentiation toward extraembryonic endoderm.[75] Expression of HoxB4 from retroviral vectors[97] and from an elegant tetracycline-inducible expression system[98] have been shown to increase the differentiation of ES cells into haematopoietic lineages. Overexpression of Foxa2 in ES cells induces the expression of genes associated with the endodermal lineage.[71]

Ishizaka et al.[99] increased their yield of ES cell-derived hepatocytes by transfecting ES cells with the rat Foxa2 gene and then culturing them in a hepatocyte culture medium with FGF2 in a three-dimensional culture system to form spheroids. Cell culture media was supplemented with nicotinamide, dexamethasone, and L-ascorbic-2-phosphate. The use of nicotinamide supplements may be effective for hepatocyte differentiation[100] and for enhanced survival of hepatocytes.[101] When the spheroids were cultured in flasks containing chitin fibres, their numbers increased and were maintained for up to 4 months. The expression of mRNA of Alb, complement C3, cytochrome P450, phosphoenolpyruvate carboxykinase, and peroxisomal membrane protein 1–like protein (differentiated hepatocyte-enriched proteins) were detected by RT-PCR in these spheroids 1 and 4 months after the initial culture of the Foxa2 transfected ES cells. The cells on the surface of the spheroids maintained metabolic functions such as Alb production, expressed CK18, and had an ultrastructure consistent with hepatocytes (including the presence of glycogen granules).[99]

Functionality of the differentiated cells was shown by urea and triacylglycerol synthesis.[99] Insulin was added to the cultures to stimulate hepatic lipogenesis, and subsequent triacylglycerol secretion was measured. The concentration of secreted triacylglycerol was 70 times higher than that of primary rat hepatocytes. Urea and triacylglycerol synthesis rates remained constant over the 4-month culture period. These findings suggest that ES cell–derived hepatocytes can maintain at least some of their liver-specific metabolic functions in long-term culture. This technique increases the yield of hepatocyte-like cells. However, overexpression of Foxa2 in mouse hepatocytes influences the expression of genes involved in bile acid and glucose homeostasis,[102] so it may not be possible to use this method in a therapeutic setting.

Kania et al.[103] have described a method to derive hepatocytes from ES cells via the generation of nestin+ cells. These nestin+ cells were cultured in hepatocyte culture medium, which contained hydrocortisone, Tfn, insulin, and human epithelial growth factor (EGF). Expression of Afp, Alb, and Aat were significantly upregulated in comparison to undifferentiated ES cells. Alb was produced in up to 45% of Hoechst-33342–labeled cells. Additional use of a three dimensional histotypic culture system showed a significant accumulation of Alb in spheroids. Jochheim et al.[104] used a similar culture system to demonstrate that the gene expression pattern in their ES cell–derived hepatocytes is similar to that in early fetal liver. The maturation state of ES cell–derived hepatocytes has important consequences as immature cells may lack the metabolic competence required for cell transplantation or bioartificial liver systems.

Further delineation of the molecular mechanisms controlling hepatic development will hopefully enable the development of protocols for the more efficient derivation of ES cell–derived hepatocytes.

GENETIC MARKING OF HEPATOCYTES

Given the complexity of ES cell differentiation, it is unlikely that culture conditions will be discerned that will direct differentiation into a single cell type. Therefore, to obtain a uniform population of differentiated cells, a purification step is required. There are several potential methods of cell-type purification. An antibiotic resistance gene can be placed under the control of a tissue-specific promoter, and the cell type of interest can be subsequently selected by adding the appropriate antibiotic to differentiated ES cells. Li et al.[105] developed this lineage selection system for the purification of neural precursors.

An alternative strategy for purifying ES cell–derived hepatocytes from other cell types would be to insert a marker gene under the control of a liver-specific promoter and to sort the cells by flow cytometry based on the expression of the marker. Yin et al.[106] inserted green fluorescent protein (GFP) into the Afp locus by homologous recombination, and expression of GFP was used as a measure of hepatic differentiation. ES cells containing the transgene were grown in methylcellulose-based media to form EBs. After six days, less than 10% of the cells in these EBs were GFP+. To increase the yield of these cells, the EBs were disaggregated into single cells and replated in methylcellulose-based media. After six more days, GFP+ cells constituted 30–50% of the cells, which could then be purified by fluorescence-activated cell sorting (FACS). Although a promising strategy, it is limited by its inability to distinguish between hepatocytes and extraembryonic endodermal cells.

TRANSPLANTATION OF ES CELL–DERIVED HEPATOCYTES

Chinzei et al.[89] addressed the in vivo potential of differentiated hepatic cells by injecting dissociated, day 9 EBs into the portal vein of female mice that had been treated with 2-acetylaminofluorene and had also undergone partial hepatectomy. Subsequent analysis of these mice detected Alb-producing cells carrying an ES cell–derived Y-chromosome within the hepatic parenchyma. However, as the transplanted cells were not a purified population of a single differentiated, mature cell type, it is not possible to conclusively say that the hepatic cells within the EB directly produced these cells. As predicted from classical studies,[68,107] teratomas were found in mice that were transplanted with ES cells and with EBs up to day 6 of differentiation. The incidence of teratomas decreased with the culture duration, and no teratomas were observed in the livers of mice transplanted with day 9 EBs when they were analysed 4 weeks after transplantation. These data highlight one of the critical issues involved in the ES-derived cell therapy debate. The elimination of tumour-forming cells, the selective isolation of pure populations of cells committed to a desired lineage, or both could potentially overcome this problem.

Yamada et al.[84] attempted to identify and purify functional ES cell-derived hepatocytes prior to transplantation. To identify the ICG+ cells after transplantation, Yamada et al. used a derivative of EB3 ES cells, which carry the enhanced green fluorescent protein (EGFP) under the control of the cytosine-adenine-guanine expression cassette. EGFP-marked, ES cell–derived ICG+ cells were transplanted via the portal vein into normal mice in which liver damage had not been induced. Transplanted cells were detectable by EGFP fluorescence four

weeks after transplantation and appeared to have been incorporated into the liver parenchyma. No teratomas were observed. Double fluorescence staining for Alb and EGFP was not performed, but comparison of adjacent sections suggested that the transplanted ICG+ cells retained an Alb-producing ability because their immunoreactivity for Alb was similar to that seen in native hepatocytes.

Yin et al.[106] used ES cells that express GFP under the control of the Afp promotor to obtain a pure population of Afp-expressing cells by FACS.[106] They transplanted these cells into lacZ+ F1 hybrid ROSA26×129/Sv mice that had undergone a partial hepatectomy. No teratomas were observed in more than 100 mice 3 weeks after they were injected. Transplanted, β-gal− cells integrated into the architecture of the recipient liver in clusters and were shown to express Alb (by immunocytochemistry). It was estimated that 0.01% of the cells in the liver were derived from transplanted GFP+ cells. Interestingly, GFP− transplanted cells also generated β-gal− hepatocytes, suggesting that other cell types in the differentiating ES cell culture that do not express Afp are capable of differentiating into hepatocytes in vivo. Functionality of the GFP+ cells was confirmed by transplanting cells into partially hepatectomised ApoE- or haptoglobin- deficient mice. Three weeks after transplantation, ApoE and haptoglobin mRNAs were detected in the respective recipient livers and the proteins in serum. Thus, although the level of engraftment was low, this is the first example of ES-derived cells partially correcting a hepatic deficiency in an animal model.[106]

An alternative approach has been to transplant ES cells (24 hours after removal of leukaemia inhibitory factor) into mouse livers 24 hours after carbon tetrachloride injection and then purify the ES cell–derived hepatocytes from the resulting teratoma.[78] In this case, the Alb promotor was used to drive expression of an EGFP transgene, enabling the isolation of Alb-expressing cells. After transplantation into a secondary carbon tetrachloride–injected mouse, these cells were incorporated into liver tissue, rescuing mice from hepatic injury. This provides proof that ES cell–derived hepatocytes can form the basis of cellular therapies, but such a teratoma-based differentiation strategy would obviously not be appropriate for use in humans.

Hepatic Differentiation of Human ES Cells

Human ES cells have been shown to differentiate into cells that express ALB, AAT, and AFP.[108] Addition of β-NGF or HGF to the cultures allowed differentiation into all three embryonic lineages, including the expression of endodermal markers. Human ES cells have been shown to differentiate into hepatocyte-like cells after treating cultures with sodium butyrate.[109] This not only induced hepatic differentiation but also resulted in significant cell death. The remaining cells (10-15%) have morphological features similar to that of primary hepatocytes, and 70–80% of the cells express liver-associated proteins (ALB, AAT, and cytokeratin 8 and 18), accumulate glycogen, and have inducible cytochrome P450 activity. The cells did not express AFP. Sodium butyrate does not appear to have the same effect on murine ES cells,[110] emphasising the differences between human and murine ES cells and the difficulties translating research into clinical therapies.

Levenberg et al.[111] utilized biodegradable polymer scaffolds to promote human ES cell growth and differentiation. EBs were grown in the presence of activin A and insulin-like growth factor 1 (IGF). EB day 8 cells were seeded onto the scaffolds with matrigel or onto scaffolds coated in fibronectin. Compared with unconditioned controls, activin A–treated constructs produced high levels of AFP and ALB throughout the sample. IGF induced high levels of AFP and ALB in more defined areas. Two-week-old human ES cell–derived polymer scaffold constructs were implanted into the subcutaneous tissue of SCID mice. After 2 weeks, cells in the construct were still immunoreactive for AFP. Also, the implants appeared to recruit and anastomose with host vasculature.

Summary

Hepatocyte-like cells have been derived from murine and human ES cells in culture. Protocols for the efficient derivation of these cells are under development. However, several issues remain to be addressed before the transplantation of ES cell–derived hepatocytes can be used in a clinical setting. A reliable liver-specific marker must be identified, and the cells expressing this marker must be separated from other differentiated cell types. It remains to be determined if the transplanted cells home to the liver—and if not, what the effect is of engraftment in nonhepatic tissues. As with all types of transplantation, the difficulty of immune rejection must be addressed. ES cells have been described as the ultimate stem cell for generating cells required for tissue replacement and engineering. However, their differentiation is complex, and separation of mature cell types derived by this approach can be difficult. This, coupled with the danger of teratoma formation, means that we are still a long way from the clinical application of ES cell–based therapies. However, we hope that the progress that has been made towards this goal will continue at its rapid pace.

ACKNOWLEDGMENTS

Original investigations were supported by grants from The Wellcome Trust and the Leukemia Research Fund.

REFERENCES

1. Bellentani, S., and Tiribelli, C. (2001). The spectrum of liver disease in the general population: lesson from the Dionysos study. *J. Hepatol.* **35,** 531–537.
2. Neuberger, J. (2000). Liver transplantation. *J. Hepatol.* **32,** 198–207.
3. Strom, S.C., Chowdhury, J.R., and Fox, I.J. (1999). Hepatocyte transplantation for the treatment of human disease. *Semin. Liver Dis.* **19,** 39–48.
4. Ohashi, K., Park, F., and Kay, M.A. (2001). Hepatocyte transplantation: clinical and experimental application. *J. Mol. Med.* **79,** 617–630.
5. Schumacher, I.K., Okamoto, T., Kim, B.H., Chowdhury, N.R., Chowdhury, J.R., and Fox, I.J. (1996). Transplantation of conditionally immortalized hepatocytes to treat hepatic encephalopathy. *Hepatology* **24,** 337–343.
6. Fox, I.J., Chowdhury, J.R., Kaufman, S.S., Goertzen, T.C., Chowdhury, N.R., Warkentin, P.I., Dorko, K., Sauter, B.V., and Strom, S.C. (1998). Treatment of the Crigler-Najjar syndrome type I with hepatocyte transplantation. *N. Engl. J. Med.* **338,** 1422–1426.
7. Ghosh, S.S., Takahashi, M., Thummala, N.R., Parashar, B., Chowdhury, N.R., and Chowdhury, J.R. (2000). Liver-directed gene therapy: promises, problems, and prospects at the turn of the century. *J. Hepatol.* **32,** 238–252.
8. Chowdhury, J.R., Grossman, M., Gupta, S., Chowdhury, N.R., Baker, J.R., Jr., and Wilson, J.M. (1991). Long-term improvement of hypercholesterolemia after *ex vivo* gene therapy in LDLR-deficient rabbits. *Science* **254,** 1802–1805.
9. Grossman, M., Raper, S.E., Kozarsky, K., Stein, E.A., Engelhardt, J.F., Muller, D., Lupien, P.J., and Wilson, J.M. (1994). Successful *ex vivo* gene therapy directed to liver in a patient with familial hypercholesterolaemia. *Nat. Genet.* **6,** 335–341.
10. Ferber, S., Halkin, A., Cohen, H., Ber, I., Einav, Y., Goldberg, I., Barshack, I., Seijffers, R., Kopolovic, J., Kaiser, N., and Karasik, A. (2000). Pancreatic and duodenal homeobox gene 1 induces expression of insulin genes in liver and ameliorates streptozotocin-induced hyperglycaemia. *Nat. Med.* **6,** 568–572.
11. Horb, M.E., Shen, C.N., Tosh, D., and Slack, J.M. (2003). Experimental conversion of liver to pancreas. *Curr. Biol.* **13,** 105–115.
12. Yang, L., Li, S., Hatch, H., Ahrens, K., Cornelius, J.G., Petersen, B.E., and Peck, A.B. (2002). *In vitro* transdifferentiation of adult hepatic stem cells into pancreatic endocrine hormone-producing cells. *Proc. Natl. Acad. Sci. U. S. A.* **99,** 8078–8083.
13. Muzzin, P., Eisensmith, R.C., Copeland, K.C., and Woo, S.L. (1997). Hepatic insulin gene expression as treatment for type 1 diabetes mellitus in rats. *Mol. Endocrinol.* **11,** 833–837.
14. Thule, P.M., and Liu, J.M. (2000). Regulated hepatic insulin gene therapy of STZ-diabetic rats. *Gene Ther.* **7,** 1744–1752.
15. Alam, T., and Sollinger, H.W. (2002). Glucose-regulated insulin production in hepatocytes. *Transplantation* **74,** 1781–1787.
16. Zuber, R., Anzenbacherova, E., and Anzenbacher, P. (2002). Cytochromes P450 and experimental models of drug metabolism. *J. Cell Mol. Med.* **6,** 189–198.
17. Guengerich, F.P. (1997). Comparisons of catalytic selectivity of cytochrome P450 subfamily enzymes from different species. *Chem. Biol. Interact.* **106,** 161–182.
18. Morsiani, E., Brogli, M., Galavotti, D., Pazzi, P., Puviani, A.C., and Azzena, G.F. (2002). Biologic liver support: optimal cell source and mass. *Int. J. Artif. Organs* **25,** 985–993.
19. Guguen-Guillouzo, C., and Guillouzo, A. (1983). Modulation of functional activities in cultured rat hepatocytes. *Mol. Cell Biochem.* **54,** 35–56.
20. Padgham, C.R., and Paine, A.J. (1993). Altered expression of cytochrome P-450 mRNAs, and potentially of other transcripts encoding key hepatic functions, are triggered during the isolation of rat hepatocytes. *Biochem. J.* **289,** 621–624.
21. Hou, J., Hoshi, H., and Mckeehan, W. (1986). Arginine is an essential amino acid for human hepatoma cells (HEPG2). *In Vitro Cell Dev. Biol.* **22,** A35.

22. Agius, L. (1987). Human liver *in vitro* techniques for metabolic studies. *Baillieres Clin. Endocrinol. Metab.* **1**, 999–1021.

23. Susick, R., Moss, N., Kubota, H., Lecluyse, E., Hamilton, G., Luntz, T., Ludlow, J., Fair, J., Gerber, D., Bergstrand, K., White, J., Bruce, A., Drury, O., Gupta, S., and Reid, L.M. (2001). Hepatic progenitors and strategies for liver cell therapies. *Ann. N. Y. Acad. Sci.* **944**, 398–419.

24. Zaret, K.S. (2000). Liver specification and early morphogenesis. *Mech. Dev.* **92**, 83–88.

25. Darlington, G.J. (1999). Molecular mechanisms of liver development and differentiation. *Curr. Opin. Cell Biol.* **11**, 678–682.

26. Duncan, S.A. (2003). Mechanisms controlling early development of the liver. *Mech. Dev.* **120**, 19–33.

27. Zaret, K.S. (2001). Hepatocyte differentiation: from the endoderm and beyond. *Curr. Opin. Genet. Dev.* **11**, 568–574.

28. Lemaigre, F.P. (2003). Development of the biliary tract. *Mech. Dev.* **120**, 81–87.

29. Douarin, N.M. (1975). An experimental analysis of liver development. *Med. Biol.* **53**, 427–455.

30. Bossard, P., and Zaret, K.S. (1998). GATA transcription factors as potentiators of gut endoderm differentiation. *Development* **125**, 4909–4917.

31. Jung, J., Zheng, M., Goldfarb, M., and Zaret, K.S. (1999). Initiation of mammalian liver development from endoderm by fibroblast growth factors. *Science* **284**, 1998–2003.

32. Rossi, J.M., Dunn, N.R., Hogan, B.L., and Zaret, K.S. (2001). Distinct mesodermal signals, including BMPs from the septum transversum mesenchyme, are required in combination for hepatogenesis from the endoderm. *Genes Dev.* **15**, 1998–2009.

33. Watt, A.J., Jones, E.A., Ure, J.M., Peddie, D., Wilson, D.I., and Forrester, L.M. (2001). A gene trap integration provides an early *in situ* marker for hepatic specification of the foregut endoderm. *Mech. Dev.* **100**, 205–215.

34. Matsumoto, K., Yoshitomi, H., Rossant, J., and Zaret, K.S. (2001). Liver organogenesis promoted by endothelial cells prior to vascular function. *Science* **294**, 559–563.

35. Lammert, E., Cleaver, O., and Melton, D. (2003). Role of endothelial cells in early pancreas and liver development. *Mech. Dev.* **120**, 59–64.

36. Rogler, L.E. (1997). Selective bipotential differentiation of mouse embryonic hepatoblasts *in vitro*. *Am. J. Pathol.* **150**, 591–602.

37. Houssaint, E. (1980). Differentiation of the mouse hepatic primordium: I. An analysis of tissue interactions in hepatocyte differentiation. *Cell Differ.* **9**, 269–279.

38. Keng, V.W., Yagi, H., Ikawa, M., Nagano, T., Myint, Z., Yamada, K., Tanaka, T., Sato, A., Muramatsu, I., Okabe, M., Sato, M., and Noguchi, T. (2000). Homeobox gene *Hex* is essential for onset of mouse embryonic liver development and differentiation of the monocyte lineage. *Biochem. Biophys. Res. Commun.* **276**, 1155–1161.

39. Martinez Barbera, J.P., Clements, M., Thomas, P., Rodriguez, T., Meloy, D., Kioussis, D., and Beddington, R.S. (2000). The homeobox gene *Hex* is required in definitive endodermal tissues for normal forebrain, liver and thyroid formation. *Development* **127**, 2433–2445.

40. Hentsch, B., Lyons, I., Li, R., Hartley, L., Lints, T.J., Adams, J.M., and Harvey, R.P. (1996). *Hlx* homeobox gene is essential for an inductive tissue interaction that drives expansion of embryonic liver and gut. *Genes Dev.* **10**, 70–79.

41. Sosa-Pineda, B., Wigle, J.T., and Oliver, G. (2000). Hepatocyte migration during liver development requires Prox1. *Nat. Genet.* **25**, 254–255.

42. Ben-Ze'ev, A., Robinson, G.S., Bucher, N.L., and Farmer, S.R. (1988). Cell–cell and cell–matrix interactions differentially regulate the expression of hepatic and cytoskeletal genes in primary cultures of rat hepatocytes. *Proc. Natl. Acad. Sci. U. S. A.* **85**, 2161–2165.

43. Sanchez, A., Alvarez, A.M., Pagan, R., Roncero, C., Vilaro, S., Benito, M., and Fabregat, I. (2000). Fibronectin regulates morphology, cell organization, and gene expression of rat fetal hepatocytes in primary culture. *J. Hepatol.* **32**, 242–250.

44. Shiojiri, N. (1984). The origin of intrahepatic bile duct cells in the mouse. *J. Embryol. Exp. Morphol.* **79**, 25–39.

45. Shiojiri, N. (1997). Development and differentiation of bile ducts in the mammalian liver. *Microsci. Res. Tech.* **39**, 328–335.

46. Clotman, F., Lannoy, V.J., Reber, M., Cereghini, S., Cassiman, D., Jacquemin, P., Roskams, T., Rousseau, G.G., and Lemaigre, F.P. (2002). The onecut transcription factor HNF-6 is required for normal development of the biliary tract. *Development* **129**, 1819–1828.

47. McCright, B., Lozier, J., and Gridley, T. (2002). A mouse model of Alagille syndrome: Notch2 as a genetic modifier of Jag1 haploinsufficiency. *Development* **129**, 1075–1082.

48. Meehan, R.R., Barlow, D.P., Hill, R.E., Hogan, B.L., and Hastie, N.D. (1984). Pattern of serum protein gene expression in mouse visceral yolk sac and foetal liver. *EMBO J.* **3**, 1881–1885.

49. Jones, E.A., Clement-Jones, M., James, O.F., and Wilson, D.I. (2001). Differences between human and mouse alpha-fetoprotein expression during early development. *J. Anat.* **198**, 555–559.

50. Gualdi, R., Bossard, P., Zheng, M., Hamada, Y., Coleman, J.R., and Zaret, K.S. (1996). Hepatic specification of the gut endoderm *in vitro:* cell signalling and transcriptional control. *Genes Dev.* **10**, 1670–1682.

51. Bossard, P., and Zaret, K.S. (2000). Repressive and restrictive mesodermal interactions with gut endoderm: possible relation to Meckel's diverticulum. *Development* **127**, 4915–4923.

52. Chen, H., Egan, J.O., and Chiu, J.F. (1997). Regulation and activities of alpha-fetoprotein. *Crit. Rev. Eukaryot. Gene Expr.* **7**, 11–41.

53. Tyner, A.L., Godbout, R., Compton, R.S., and Tilghman, S.M. (1990). The ontogeny of alpha-fetoprotein gene expression in the mouse gastrointestinal tract. *J. Cell Biol.* **110**, 915–927.

54. Spear, B.T. (1999). Alpha-fetoprotein gene regulation: lessons from transgenic mice. *Semin. Cancer Biol.* **9**, 109–116.

55. Putnam, F.W. (1975). "The Plasma Proteins: Structure, Function, and Genetic Control." Academic Press, New York.

56. Cascio, S., and Zaret, K.S. (1991). Hepatocyte differentiation initiates during endodermal–mesenchymal interactions prior to liver formation. *Development* **113**, 217–225.

57. Rajagopal, J., Anderson, W.J., Kume, S., Martinez, O.I., and Melton, D.A. (2003). Insulin staining of ES cell progeny from insulin uptake. *Science* **299**, 363.

58. Stanford, W.L., Cohn, J.B., and Cordes, S.P. (2001). Mouse genomic technologies gene-trap mutagenesis: past, present, and beyond. *Nat. Rev. Genet.* **2**, 756–768.

59. Kuo, C.F., Paulson, K.E., and Darnell, J.E., Jr. (1988). Positional and developmental regulation of glutamine synthetase expression in mouse liver. *Mol. Cell Biol.* **8**, 4966–4971.

60. Makover, A., Soprano, D.R., Wyatt, M.L., and Goodman, D.S. (1989). An *in situ* hybridization study of the localization of retinol-binding protein and transthyretin messenger RNAs during fetal development in the rat. *Differentiation* **40**, 17–25.

61. Kuo, C.F., and Darnell, J.E., Jr. (1989). Mouse glutamine synthetase is encoded by a single gene that can be expressed in a localized fashion. *J. Mol. Biol.* **208**, 45–56.

62. Pan, C.J., Lei, K.J., Chen, H., Ward, J.M., and Chou, J.Y. (1998). Ontogeny of the murine glucose-6-phosphatase system. *Arch. Biochem. Biophys.* **358**, 17–24.

63. Greengard, O. (1969). The hormonal regulation of enzymes in prenatal and postnatal rat liver: effects of adenosine 3′,5′-(cyclic)-monophosphate. *Biochem. J.* **115**, 19–24.

64. Goldblatt, P.J., and Gunning, W.T., 3rd (1984). Ultrastructure of the liver and biliary tract in health and disease. *Ann. Clin. Lab. Sci.* **14**, 159–167.

65. Medlock, E.S., and Haar, J.L. (1983). The liver hemopoietic environment: I. Developing hepatocytes and their role in fetal hemopoiesis. *Anat. Rec.* **207**, 31–41.

66. Philippidis, H., and Ballard, F.J. (1969). The development of gluconeogenesis in rat liver: experiments *in vivo*. *Biochem. J.* **113**, 651–657.

67. Yeung, D., and Oliver, I.T. (1967). Gluconeogenesis from amino acids in neonatal rat liver. *Biochem. J.* **103**, 744–748.

68. Doetschman, T.C., Eistetter, H., Katz, M., Schmidt, W., and Kemler, R. (1985). The in vitro development of blastocyst-derived embryonic stem cell lines: formation of visceral yolk sac, blood islands, and myocardium. *J. Embryol. Exp. Morphol.* **87**, 27–45.

69. Abe, K., Niwa, H., Iwase, K., Takiguchi, M., Mori, M., Abe, S.I., and Yamamura, K.I. (1996). Endoderm-specific gene expression in embryonic stem cells differentiated to embryoid bodies. *Exp. Cell Res.* **229**, 27–34.

70. Schrem, H., Klempnauer, J., and Borlak, J. (2002). Liver-enriched transcription factors in liver function and development. Part I: the hepatocyte nuclear factor network and liver-specific gene expression. *Pharmacol. Rev.* **54**, 129–158.

71. Levinson-Dushnik, M., and Benvenisty, N. (1997). Involvement of hepatocyte nuclear factor 3 in endoderm differentiation of embryonic stem cells. *Mol. Cell Biol.* **17**, 3817–3822.

72. Arceci, R.J., King, A.A., Simon, M.C., Orkin, S.H., and Wilson, D.B. (1993). Mouse GATA-4: A retinoic acid-inducible GATA-binding transcription factor expressed in endodermally derived tissues and heart. *Mol. Cell Biol.* **13**, 2235–2246.

73. Soudais, C., Bielinska, M., Heikinheimo, M., MacArthur, C.A., Narita, N., Saffitz, J.E., Simon, M.C., Leiden, J.M., and Wilson, D.B. (1995). Targeted mutagenesis of the transcription factor *GATA-4* gene in mouse embryonic stem cells disrupts visceral endoderm differentiation *in vitro*. *Development* **121**, 3877–3888.

74. Bielinska, M., and Wilson, D.B. (1997). Induction of yolk sac endoderm in GATA-4-deficient embryoid bodies by retinoic acid. *Mech. Dev.* **65**, 43–54.

75. Fujikura, J., Yamato, E., Yonemura, S., Hosoda, K., Masui, S., Nakao, K., Miyazaki Ji, J., and Niwa, H. (2002). Differentiation of embryonic stem cells is induced by GATA factors. *Genes Dev.* **16**, 784–789.

76. Kubo, A., Shinozaki, K., Shannon, J.M., Kouskoff, V., Kennedy, M.. Woo, S., Fehling, H.J., and Keller, G. (2004). Development of definitive endoderm from embryonic stem cells in culture. *Development* **131**, 1651-1662.

77. Choi, D., Oh, H.J., Chang, U.J., Koo, S.K., Jiang, J.X., Hwang, S.Y., Lee, J.D., Yeoh, G.C., Shin, H.S., Lee, J.S., and Oh, B. (2002). *In vivo* differentiation of mouse embryonic stem cells into hepatocytes. *Cell Transplant.* **11**, 359–368.

78. Yamamoto, H., Quinn, G., Asari, A., Yamanokuchi, H., Teratani, T., Terada, M., and Ochiya, T. (2003). Differentiation of embryonic stem cells into hepatocytes: biological functions and therapeutic application. *Hepatology* **37**, 983–993.

79. Hamazaki, T., Iiboshi, Y., Oka, M., Papst, P.J., Meacham, A.M., Zon, L.I., and Terada, N. (2001). Hepatic maturation in differentiating embryonic stem cells in vitro. *FEBS Lett.* **497**, 15–19.

80. Kamiya, A., Kinoshita, T., Ito, Y., Matsui, T., Morikawa, Y., Senba, E., Nakashima, K., Taga, T., Yoshida, K., Kishimoto, T., and Miyajima, A. (1999). Fetal liver development requires a paracrine action of oncostatin M through the gp130 signal transducer. *EMBO J.* **18**, 2127–2136.

81. Kamiya, A., Kinoshita, T., and Miyajima, A. (2001). Oncostatin M and hepatocyte growth factor induce hepatic maturation via distinct signalling pathways. *FEBS Lett.* **492**, 90–94.

82. Miyashita, H., Suzuki, A., Fukao, K., Nakauchi, H., and Taniguchi, H. (2002). Evidence for hepatocyte differentiation from embryonic stem cells in vitro. Cell Transplantation. **11**, 429-434.

83. Jones, E.A., Tosh, D., Wilson, D.I., Lindsay, S., and Forrester, L.M. (2002). Hepatic differentiation of murine embryonic stem cells. *Exp. Cell Res.* **272**, 15–22.

84. Yamada, T., Yoshikawa, M., Kanda, S., Kato, Y., Nakajima, Y., Ishizaka, S., and Tsunoda, Y. (2002). *In vitro* differentiation of embryonic stem cells into hepatocyte-like cells identified by cellular uptake of indocyanine green. *Stem Cells* **20**, 146–154.

85. Bravo, P., el-Mir, M.Y., Serrano, M.A., Boyd, R., and Marin, J.J. (1993). Interaction between cholephilic anions and bile acid transport across basal membrane of human trophoblast. *Am. J. Physiol.* **265**, G242–G250.

86. Ogura, K., Choudhuri, S., and Klaassen, C.D. (2000). Full-length cDNA cloning and genomic organization of the mouse liver-specific organic anion transporter-1 (lst-1). *Biochem. Biophys. Res. Commun.* **272**, 563–570.

87. Jones, E.A., Tosh, D., and Forrester, L.M. (Unpublished data).

88. Fair, J.H., Cairns, B.A., Lapaglia, M., Wang, J., Meyer, A.A., Kim, H., Hatada, S., Smithies, O., and Pevny, L. (2003). Induction of hepatic differentiation in co-culture with embryonic cardiac mesoderm. *Surgery* **134**, 189-196

89. Chinzei, R., Tanaka, Y., Shimizu-Saito, K., Hara, Y., Kakinuma, S., Watanabe, M., Teramoto, K., Arii, S., Takase, K., Sato, C., Terada, N., and Teraoka, H. (2002). Embryoid body cells derived from a mouse embryonic stem cell line show differentiation into functional hepatocytes. *Hepatology* **36**, 22–29.

90. Lee, S.H., Lumelsky, N., Studer, L., Auerbach, J.M., and McKay, R.D. (2000). Efficient generation of midbrain and hindbrain neurons from mouse embryonic stem cells. *Nat. Biotechnol.* **18**, 675–679.

91. Wiles, M.V., and Keller, G. (1991). Multiple hematopoietic lineages develop from embryonic stem (ES) cells in culture. *Development* **111**, 259–267.

92. Nakano, T., Kodama, H., and Honjo, T. (1994). Generation of lymphohematopoietic cells from embryonic stem cells in culture. *Science* **265**, 1098–1101.

93. Hamazaki, T. and Terada, N. (2003). *In vitro* differentiation of embryonic stem cells into hepatocytes. M*ethods Enzymol.* **365**, 277-287.

94. Kuai, X.L., Cong, X.Q., Li, X.L., and Xiao, S.D. (2003). Generation of hepatocytes from cultured mouse embryonic stem cells. *Liver Transplant.* **9**, 1094-1099.

95. Jones, E.A., Tosh, D., and Forrester, L.M. (Unpublished data).

96. Jones, E.A., Tosh, D., and Forrester, L.M. (Unpublished data).

97. Helgason, C.D., Sauvageau, G., Lawrence, H.J., Largman, C., and Humphries, R.K. (1996). Overexpression of HOXB4 enhances the hematopoietic potential of embryonic stem cells differentiated *in vitro*. *Blood* **87**, 2740–2749.

98. Kyba, M., Perlingeiro, R.C., and Daley, G.Q. (2002). HoxB4 confers definitive lymphoid–myeloid engraftment potential on embryonic stem cell and yolk sac hematopoietic progenitors. *Cell* **109,** 29–37.

99. Ishizaka, S., Shiroi, A., Kanda, S., Yoshikawa, M., Tsujinoue, H., Kuriyama, S., Hasuma, T., Nakatani, K., and Takahashi, K. (2002). Development of hepatocytes from ES cells after transfection with the *HNF-3*β gene. *FASEB J.* **16,** 1444–1446.

100. Rosenberg, M.R., Strom, S.C., and Michalopoulos, G. (1982). Effect of hydrocortisone and nicotinamide on γ-glutamyltransferase in primary cultures of rat hepatocytes. *In Vitro* **18,** 775–782.

101. Inoue, C., Yamamoto, H., Nakamura, T., Ichihara, A., and Okamoto, H. (1989). Nicotinamide prolongs survival of primary cultured hepatocytes without involving loss of hepatocyte-specific functions. *J. Biol. Chem.* **264,** 4747–4750.

102. Rausa, F.M., Tan, Y., Zhou, H., Yoo, K.W., Stolz, D.B., Watkins, S.C., Franks, R.R., Unterman, T.G., and Costa, R.H. (2002). Elevated levels of hepatocyte nuclear factor 3beta in mouse hepatocytes influence expression of genes involved in bile acid and glucose homeostasis. *Mol. Cell. Biol.* **20,** 8264-8282.

103. Kania, G., Blyszczuk, P., Czyz, J., Navarrete-Santos, A., and Wobus, A.M. (2003). Differentiation of mouse embryonic stem cells into pancreatic and hepatic cells. *Methods Enzymol.* **365,** 287-303.

104. Jochheim, A., Hillemann, T., Kania, G., Scharf, J., Attaran, M., Manns, M.P., Wobus, A.M., and Ott, M. (2004). Quantitative gene expression profiling reveals a fetal hepatic phenotype of murine ES-derived hepatocytes. *Int. J. Dev. Biol.* **48,** 23-29.

105. Li, M., Pevny, L., Lovell-Badge, R., and Smith, A. (1998). Generation of purified neural precursors from embryonic stem cells by lineage selection. *Curr. Biol.* **8,** 971–974.

106. Yin, Y., Lim, Y.K., Salto-Tellez, M., Ng, S.C., Lin, C.S., and Lim, S.K. (2002). AFP(+), ESC-derived cells engraft and differentiate into hepatocytes *in vivo. Stem Cells* **20,** 338–346.

107. Martin, G.R. (1981). Isolation of a pluripotent cell line from early mouse embryos cultured in medium conditioned by teratocarcinoma stem cells. *Proc. Natl. Acad. Sci. U. S. A.* **78,** 7634–7638.

108. Schuldiner, M., Yanuka, O., Itskovitz-Eldor, J., Melton, D.A., and Benvenisty, N. (2000). From the cover: effects of eight growth factors on the differentiation of cells derived from human embryonic stem cells. *Proc. Natl. Acad. Sci. U. S. A.* **97,** 11,307–11,312.

109. Rambhatla, L., Chiu, C.P., Kundu, P., Peng, Y., and Carpenter, M.K. (2003). Generation of hepatocyte-like cells from human embryonic stem cells. *Cell Transplant.* **12,** 1–11.

110. Jones, E.A., Tosh, D., and Forrester, L.M. (Unpublished observations).

111. Levenberg, S., Huang, N.F., Lavik, E., Rogers, A.B., Itskovitz-Eldor, J., and Langer, R. (2003). Differentiation of human embryonic stem cells on three-dimensional polymer scaffolds. *Proc. Natl. Acad. Sci. U. S. A.* **100,** 12,741-12,746.

Gastrointestinal Tract

Frederick Charles Campbell

Embryonic Gastrointestinal Stem Cell Biology and the Postnatal Gut

How can an understanding of embryonic stem cell dynamics provide insight into the complexity of gastrointestinal physiology and disease? Essential stem cell properties, including longevity, self-renewal, and pluripotency,[1] are central to gut development; they also have an important role in postnatal homeostasis. Application of postgenomic methods to model systems has identified key regulatory pathways conserved across evolution. Molecular profiling of stem cell populations has provided insight into the biology of "stemness." These advances have provided a rational basis for morphogenetic events of gut ontogeny and greater understanding of the birth defects arising from inborn errors of these processes. Embryonic regulatory pathways mature into adult life and play an important role in maintenance of essential alimentary tract functions of digestion, absorption, excretion, detoxification, and fluid balance within a complex nutritional environment. Dysregulation of stem cell functions by acquired gastrointestinal diseases can manifest in abnormalities of epithelial nutrient absorption, acid or alkali secretion, barrier function, or regenerative healing. Gastrointestinal oncogenesis involves a series of mutations or epigenetic events that result in disordered cell proliferation, differentiation, or cell confinement by tissue boundaries. The clonal character of gastrointestinal tumours points to a stem cell origin and pattern of evolution,[2–4] governed partly by a hardwired stem cell regulatory apparatus. Analysis of molecular profiles that govern the conserved dynamics of embryonic gastrointestinal stem cell behaviour may yield new data that translate to advances in diagnosis, treatment, and outlook for gastrointestinal disease.

Hierarchy of Stem Cell Regulation

The regulatory apparatus that directs stem cell behaviour during development ultimately derives from genomic DNA. Networks of signalling events link to organized arrays of *cis*-regulatory elements in target genes. These networks determine the gene activation or repression in the appropriate cells and the time or spatial region in the developing organism. A particularly important class of signalling interrelations affects gene expression in response to identity or activity of neighbouring cells. This sophisticated system regulates the controlled expression of multiple genes that endow stem cells with appropriate growth potential, motility, self-renewal, and cell fate. By such means, the flow of temporal and spatial regulatory information from the genome defines stem cell morphogenetic competence to provide structure and function of the developing gut as well as homeostasis of the adult organ.

Stem Cell Predominance in the Developing Intestine

The gastrointestinal tract develops from a core of cells with multipotent, stem-like properties, called the definitive embryonic endoderm. This chapter briefly reviews vertebrate embryonic endoderm ontogeny and highlights known signal transduction pathways that regulate key stem cell activities involved in pattern formation, commitment, and differentiation.

EMBRYONIC COMMITMENT OF THE MAMMALIAN ENDODERM

Cells of the early embryo are partitioned into three groups during a process called gastrulation, whereby totipotent cells rearrange into three distinct germ layers: the ectoderm, which forms skin and the central nervous system; the mesoderm, which forms blood, bone, and muscle; and the endoderm, which forms the respiratory and digestive tracts. Although the morphogenetic events of endoderm formation are well recognised, our knowledge of regulatory mechanisms is less comprehensive. Formation of the endoderm commences with formation of the primitive streak in the posterior region of the embryo.[5] Most definitive (embryonic) endoderm cells originate from the anterior primitive streak.[6] Studies have revealed a high degree of conservation of some transcriptional regulators of endoderm development, such as GATA and forkhead families, between the species.[7,8] In vertebrates, signalling by Nodal (a transforming growth factor-beta, or TGFβ, family member), GATA, and forkhead transcription families are all implicated in endoderm formation.[9,10] Binding by the factor Nodal to its receptor complex leads to the phosphorylation of Smad2 (and possibly Smad3), which translocates to the nucleus and, with other proteins, activates transcription.[11] Smad2 partners include the forkhead protein FoxH1/Fast, which functions to specify the anterior primitive streak in the mouse.[12] In *Caenorhabditis elegans,* segregation of mesoderm and endoderm is regulated by a Wnt signalling pathway[13] involving WRM-1, a β-catenin homolog,[14] and MOM-4, a MAP3 kinase implicated in endoderm formation.[15,16]

PATTERNING AND GUT TUBE FORMATION

The process by which major body components arise begins with the regional expression of signalling factors in the morphogenetic field of the future structure.[17–19] These spatially confined signals direct expression of transcription factors essential to the generation of a pattern within subdivisions of a germ layer or early structure. Interactions among germ layers provide soluble or region-specific inductive signals. For example, the factor Nodal is secreted by the anterior endoderm to provide anterior patterning information.[20–23] After segregation, the embryonic endoderm migrates from the primitive streak to form the anterior and posterior endoderm. Although they appear morphologically homogeneous, differences exist in these endoderm components. Posterior endoderm has a higher cell division rate and expresses intestinal fatty acid-binding protein[24] and *Cdx2.*[25] Anterior ectoderm expresses a variety of signalling molecules.[26–34] In vertebrates, β-catenin has been shown to play a key role in the patterning of the early embryo.[35]

MORPHOGENESIS OF GUT REGIONS

The metamorphosis of endoderm from a two-dimensional sheet into a three-dimensional tube occurs after gastrulation and may be evolutionarily conserved in many vertebrates (Fig. 35–1). A fundamental change occurs in endoderm between gastrulation and early somite formation. At this stage, patterning instructions render the endoderm more determined, with a more restricted capacity for expression of tissue-specific markers.[36] Specific morphogenetic movements form the gut tube by folding or looping distinct endoderm regions. The dorsal foregut endoderm contributes to formation of oesophagus, stomach, dorsal pancreas, and duodenum; midgut–trunk endoderm forms the small intestine; and the posterior trunk endoderm forms the large intestine. Coincident with gut tube morphogenesis is the change of endoderm cells from flat, squamous cells to a thickened columnar epithelium, although they still need instruction to express organ-specific genes. The result of these patterning events is a gut tube now loosely divided into organ domains that can be defined by regions. Tube evaginations bud, grow, and eventually form differentiated organs. Ultimately, distinct regions of the tube express different sets of genes.

TRANSCRIPTIONAL DETERMINANTS OF REGIONAL SPECIFICITY

Differential anteroposterior and dorsoventral expression of the *Hox* and nuclear receptor gene cluster suggests a role in the determination of gut regional specificity in vertebrates. For example, the anterior gut tube, which generates the oesophagus, expresses several *Hoxb* genes:[37] *Nkx2.6,*[21,38] *Nkx 2.1,*[39,40] *Pax 8,*[41] and *Pax 9.*[42] Key transcription factors are also expressed in the domain of the gut that produces the stomach, pancreas, and duodenum, including *Pdx1,*[43,44] *Pax 4* and *6,*[45,46]

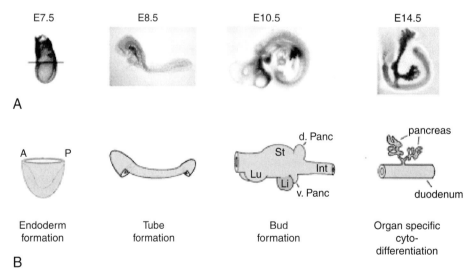

Figure 35–1. *Stages of endoderm development.* (A) Four stages of development of the gastrointestinal tract in mouse embryos (E7.5–14.5). These stages of gut morphogenesis are illustrated in panel B. The line dividing the E7.5 embryo separates the lower part of the conceptus, which forms the embryo proper, from the upper part, which derives extraembryonic structures such as the yolk sac. The later-stage embryos do not show the extraembryonic structures. At the end of gastrulation (E7.5), the endoderm is a one cell-layer thick cup of approximately 500 cells, which covers the mesoderm and ectoderm of the embryo. Within 24 hours (E8.5), a series of morphogenetic processes transforms the cup into a tube. The forming gut tube of the E8.5 embryo and the formation of organ buds in an E10.5 embryo are shown. (B) The schematized E10.5 gut tube shows the relative positions of organ buds. E14.5 in panel A shows a dissected stomach, pancreas, and duodenum that have been stained for Pdx1 expression. Significant branching and differentiation of organ cell types has occurred (Lu, lung; Li, liver; St, stomach; d. Panc., dorsal pancreatic bud; v. Panc., ventral pancreatic bud; and Int, duodenum–intestine). Reprinted with permission from *Wells et al.*[95] (Please see CD-ROM for color version of this figure.)

Nkx 2.2,[47] *Isl-1,*[48] and *NeuroD.*[49] The posterior gut tube, which generates the small intestine, large intestine, and colon, expresses *Cdx1, Cdx2,* and various genes in the *Hoxd* cluster[50] (Fig. 35–2). Mice that lack the *Pdx1, Pax4, Pax6, Neuro D,* or *Nkx2.2* fore- and midgut transcription factors show a range of abnormal phenotypes in the stomach, pancreas, and duodenum. Loss of *Pdx1* results in mice that lack a pancreas and certain endocrine cell types in the stomach and duodenum.[43,44,51] In contrast, absence of *Pax4, Pax6,* or *Nkx2.2* results in the loss of specific populations of hormone-producing cell types in the pancreas and duodenum. These transcription factors may regulate cell fate through the activation of specific target genes.[37,52–54] Expansion of cellular populations in the developing gut is orchestrated by several mesenchymal signals, such as Hlx (liver and intestinal epithelium), Pdx1 (pancreas), Cdx1 (intestinal crypts,) and NKx2.3 (midgut epithelium). Terminal differentiation results from signalling interaction between the mesenchyme (genes of the Notch/Delta pathway)[55] and the epithelium (Sonic hedgehog).[56,57]

Expression domains of specific transcription factors arranged in a spatial manner along the embryo axis may be essential to refine organ-specific regions (Fig. 35–2). Such axial expression domains may involve endoderm or mesoderm, either alone or in combination. In the chick hindgut, for example, reciprocal endoderm–mesoderm interaction results in spatially restricted *hox* gene expression and the establishment of posterior identity in the endoderm. Specifically, hindgut endoderm expresses Sonic hedgehog *(Shh),* which induces *bmp4* and *Hoxd-13* expression in the adjacent posterior mesoderm but not in the more anterior mesoderm. If *Hoxd-13* is misexpressed in the more anterior mesoderm, the adjacent stomach endoderm is transformed into an intestinal-type morphology.[50,58] In the developing foregut, it has been shown that epithelial cell proliferation in the stomach and duodenum is increased in mice that lack the mesenchymal-specific, forkhead transcription factor *Fkh6.*[59] Furthermore, these mice have structural abnormalities of the stomach, duodenum, and jejunum. Organ-region budding and morphogenesis may occur simultaneously with expression of region-specific genes. For example, expression of secretin, serotonin, and somatostatin is evident in the duodenal and intestinal domains during organ budding.[60] These studies provide insight into the biological roles of specific genes and outline the cascade of soluble and tissue-specific regulatory transcription factors that guide embryonic gastrointestinal stem cell function during gut development.

TRANSITION OF INTESTINAL ENDODERM TO INTESTINAL EPITHELIUM

Intestinal organogenesis proceeds as a proximal-to-distal wave of morphogenetic events.[61] First, the pseudostratified endoderm differentiates into a single-layered epithelium. Second, the epithelium folds to form intestinal villi and becomes compartmentalized into differentiating villus and proliferating intervillous epithelium. Basal crypts subsequently form by reshaping of the intervillous epithelium.[62] In parallel, the gastrointestinal tract mesenchyme differentiates into mucosal and submucosal connective tissue and the outer muscle layers. Reciprocal signalling between the epithelium and the mesenchyme directs the structure and function of the lining mucosa, submucosa, and muscle layers[63,64] (Fig. 35–3).

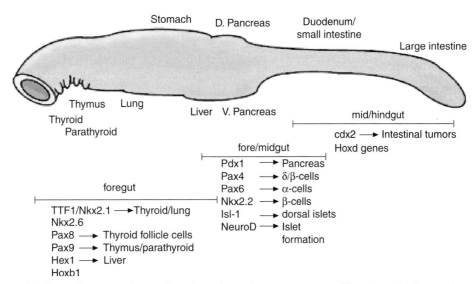

Figure 35–2. *Axial distribution of transcription factors in the early gut tube. A schematic representation of the E9.5 gut tube shows axial expression of several transcription factors that contribute to specific organs. Transcription factors expressed in overlapping domains along the foregut, midgut, or hindgut are listed. The transcription factors that have been genetically disrupted in mice show a corresponding phenotype, indicated by the arrows. For example, mice that lack the gene encoding the transcription factor Pdx1 have no pancreas. Reprinted with permission from Wells et al.*[95] *(Please see CD-ROM for color version of this figure.)*

Figure 35-3. *Model of villus formation in a normal intestine.* Stage 1: PDGF-A secreted from the epithelium (I) stimulates proliferation of PDGFR-α+ mesenchymal cells. Stage 2: An inducing signal (II) promotes clustering of PDGFR-α+ mesenchymal cells. A cluster-derived signal (III, BMP-2 and BMP-4?) triggers mitogenic arrest in the adjacent epithelium. Stage 3: PDGF-A secreted from the proliferating intervillous epithelium (I) promotes renewal of PDGFR-α+ mesenchymal cells. PDGFR-α+ cells detach from the villus cluster (IV) during villus elongation. Stage 4: In full-length villi, all cells have detached from the cluster. In the expanding intervillous region, new cluster induction and initiation of villus formation occurs. Reprinted with permission from Karlsson et al.[75] (Please see CD-ROM for color version of this figure.)

Gene targeting experiments have implicated various signalling molecules and transcription factors in these processes, including members of the epidermal growth factor,[65,66] *TGF-β,*[67] insulin-like growth factors *(IGF-1 and 2),*[68] hepatocyte growth factor,[69–72] Sonic and Indian hedgehog,[73,74] *Wnt,* and bone morphogenetic protein *(bmp)* families.[58,73]

Villus formation starts in the anterior portion of the small intestine and is first seen as a condensation of the mesenchyme. The generation of the villus epithelial folds coincides with the formation of mesenchymal clusters that express platelet-derived growth factor receptor-alpha (PDGFR-α), *bmp-2,* and *bmp-4.* These clusters remain beneath the villus tip during its invagination into the gut lumen.[75] Homeobox genes encode DNA-binding proteins that play crucial roles to define the body plan.[76] In *Drosophila,* the *caudal* gene participates in the definition of the anteroposterior axis during early embryogenesis, and its expression is maintained in the gut as well as in other organs.[77] *Cdx1* is one of the three *caudal* homologues identified in mammals. From day 14, *Cdx1* is selectively expressed in the endoderm of the developing mouse intestine and becomes restricted to and maintained in the proliferative crypt compartment during epithelium differentiation. *Cdx1* is a direct transcriptional target of the Wnt/β-catenin/T-cell factor (Tcf) signalling pathway.[78] This pathway plays a crucial role in the development and maintenance of the intestinal stem cell compartment. Disruption of Tcf-4 in mice does not disturb temporal transition of intestinal endoderm into epithelium but is associated with loss of proliferative compartments in intervillous regions and postnatal lethality. Hence, the Wnt/β-catenin/Tcf signalling pathway has a crucial role in the maintenance of the crypt stem fraction of the small intestine.[79]

Stem Cell Signatures: Transcriptional Profiling Studies

Although signals from adjacent cells or germ layers within a given "niche" influence essential stem cell features,[80] transcriptional profiling of isolated stem cell populations may provide some insight into the hardwired regulators of stemness. In a recent study, transcriptional profiles of mouse embryonic, neural, and hematopoietic stem cells were compared with each other and the corresponding differentiated cell populations. Each stem cell category was enriched for several unique genes, which may confer a degree of specificity. However, more than 200 other genes were enriched in all stem cell populations. This common set of stem cell genes could potentially underlie the essential stem cell properties of self-renewal and the ability to generate differentiated progeny. The authors suggested that essential attributes of stemness could involve (1) active Janus kinase/signal transducers and activators of transcription (JAK/STAT), including TGFβ, Yamaguchi sarcoma kinase, and Notch signalling; (2) genes conferring the capacity to sense growth hormone and thrombin; (3) genes conferring the capacity to sense signalling interactions with the extracellular matrix through integrin $α_6/β_1$, Adam 9, and bystin; (4) genes implicated in engagement in the cell cycle either arrested in G_1 or cycling; (5) genes that confer high resistance to stress, with up-regulated DNA repair, protein folding, ubiquitin, and detoxifier systems; (6) chromatin remodelling genes including DNA helicases, DNA methylases, and histone deacetylases; and (7) translation regulators including RNA helicases of the Vasa type.[81] As yet, the relevance of such molecular profiling studies to gastrointestinal stem cells remains to be determined.

Postnatal Maturation of Stem Cell Regulation

Considerable scientific effort has investigated embryonic gastrointestinal stem cell function both to elucidate gut development and to provide a template for postnatal stem cell function. Developmental signalling networks mature to regulate ontogeny of the mammalian intestine in postnatal life.[82] Although much remains to be learned, recent advances have highlighted the role of key signalling pathways in the maintenance of homeostasis and have shown effects of signalling dysregulation upon the pathobiology of gastrointestinal disease.

DEVELOPMENTAL STEM CELL REGULATORY GENES AND POSTNATAL DISEASE

As outlined previously, the Wnt signalling cascade is highly conserved throughout evolution and plays an important role in embryonic stem cell fate and pattern formation during development. Wnt signalling initiates a cascade that results in the translocation of β-catenin to the nucleus, where it interacts with Tcf to generate a transcriptionally active complex. In the absence of Wnt signals, β-catenin is degraded in the cytoplasm by the ubiquitin–proteasome pathway. Several proteins, including adenomatous polyposis coli (APC),[83] are instrumental in achieving this tight regulation of β-catenin levels within the cell. Wnt pathway mutations associated with the transactivation of Tcf target genes influence key events of colorectal carcinogenesis. Mutation of APC deregulates Wnt signalling, resulting in elevated β-catenin levels and

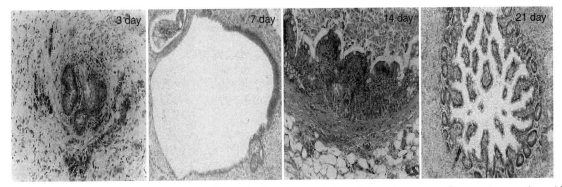

Figure 35–4. *Model of intestinal epithelial regeneration from grafts of crypt stem cell isolates.* Isolates of crypt stem cell aggregates were obtained from postnatal, 6-day rat intestine then grafted subcutaneously to inbred Albino Oxford rat recipients. Grafts retrieved 3, 7, 14, and 21 days after transplant show sequential stages of regeneration. At 3 days, simple tubular structures lined by a single layer of epithelium are shown. At 7 days, early crypt formation is shown. By 10 days, stunted villi and some evidence of differentiation with goblet cells can be seen. By 14 days, a well-established crypt villus architecture has developed. (Please see CD-ROM for color version of this figure.)

constitutively active β-catenin–Tcf complexes in the nucleus. The β-catenin–Tcf-4 complex constitutes the master switch that controls proliferation versus differentiation in healthy and malignant intestinal epithelial cells. Disruption of β-catenin–Tcf-4 activity results in decreased *c-Myc* and increased *p21(CIP1/WAF1)* transcription, resulting in G_1 arrest and differentiation.[84] APC mutation is associated with constitutive Tcf-4 signalling, maintenance of stem-like characteristics,[79] and increased crypt fission[85] central to the development of colorectal adenomas.[86] Stem cell self-renewal is an essential component of crypt fission[1] and may thus be influenced by the β-catenin–Tcf-4 complex.

These and other developmental pathways, which maintain the crypt stem cell fraction or regulate the stem cell functions of self-renewal and differentiation, may hold the key to postnatal intestinal diseases involving crypt depletion, such as in atrophic gastritis, impairment of mucosal healing, or epithelial transdifferentiation in intestinal metaplasia or dysplasia.

MODELS OF STEM CELL FUNCTION DURING REGENERATION

Although stem cell plasticity is the subject of intense research activity,[87–89] restricted lineage multipotent stem cells from intestinal crypts have a primary role in the regeneration of site-specific intestinal tissue. Regeneration recapitulates many processes of embryonic development, is central to healing to the gastrointestinal mucosa in inflammatory states, and may be implicated in gastrointestinal neoplasia. Useful models that induce discrete temporal stages of regeneration have been developed by grafting human fetal or postnatal murine or rodent stem cell preparations to ectopic sites in inbred or immunodeficient hosts (Fig. 35–4).[90–93] Preservation of epithelial–mesenchymal interactions is essential for successful regeneration.[91] These methods have been used to demonstrate differential metabolic competence,[92] expression of growth regulatory genes,[93] and stem cell governance of clonality[94] that may be relevant to tumourigenesis.

Summary

The application of new technologies to the study of embryonic stem cell characteristics and regulatory networks during development has already yielded unimagined advances in our understanding of postnatal gastrointestinal physiology and pathobiology of intestinal diseases. This chapter has considered mechanisms of information flow from the genome through differential expression of transcription or signalling factors linked to appropriate *cis*-regulatory sequences within gene promoters to provide temporal or spatial regulation of stem cell behaviour. Hierarchical developmental signalling pathways, preserved across evolution, are evident in the postnatal intestine and provide some of the key molecular signatures that underline common gastrointestinal disease. Recent signs show an accelerated pace of discovery in this area, anticipating future translation of knowledge into new diagnostics, new drugs, and newly emergent fields such as stem cell therapy and tissue engineering as well as greater insight into molecular controls of gastrointestinal cancers.

REFERENCES

1. Potten, C.S., and Loeffler, M. (1990). Stem cells: attributes, cycles, spirals, pitfalls, and uncertainties: lessons for and from the crypt. *Development* **110**, 1001–1020.
2. Peng, H., Lakhani, S., Lee, C., Zheng, Q., Chaggar, R.K., Wright, N.A., Pan, L., and Isaacson, P.G. (2000). Clonality analysis of defined cell populations in paraffin-embedded tissue sections by RT-PCR amplification of X-linked *G6PD* gene. *J. Pathol.* **191**, 313–317.
3. Garcia, S.B., Novelli, M., and Wright, N.A. (2000). The clonal origin and clonal evolution of epithelial tumours. *Int. J. Exp. Pathol.* **81**, 89–116.
4. Garcia, S.B., Park, H.S., Novelli, M., and Wright, N.A. (1999). Field cancerization, clonality, and epithelial stem cells: the spread of mutated clones in epithelial sheets. *J. Pathol.* **187**, 61–81.

5. Lawson, K.A., Meneses, J.J., and Pedersen, R.A. (1991). Clonal analysis of epiblast fate during germ layer formation in the mouse embryo. *Development* **113**, 891–911.

6. Rosenquist, G.C. (1971). The location of the pregut endoderm in the chick embryo at the primitive streak stage as determined by radioautographic mapping. *Dev. Biol.* **26**, 323–335.

7. Stainier, D.Y. (2002). A glimpse into the molecular entrails of endoderm formation. *Genes Dev.* **16**, 893–907.

8. Warga, R.M., and Stainier, D.Y. (2002). The guts of endoderm formation. *Results Probl. Cell Differ.* **40**, 28–47.

9. Iannaccone, P.M., Zhou, X., Khokha, M., Boucher, D., and Kuehn, M.R. (1992). Insertional mutation of a gene involved in growth regulation of the early mouse embryo. *Dev. Dyn.* **194**, 198–208.

10. Lowe, L.A., Yamada, S., and Kuehn, M.R. (2001). Genetic dissection of nodal function in patterning the mouse embryo. *Development* **128**, 1831–1843.

11. Waldrip, W.R., Bikoff, E.K., Hoodless, P.A., Wrana, J.L., and Robertson, E.J. (1998). Smad2 signalling in extraembryonic tissues determines anterior–posterior polarity of the early mouse embryo. *Cell* **92**, 797–808.

12. Hoodless, P.A., *et al.* (2001). FoxH1 (Fast) functions to specify the anterior primitive streak in the mouse. *Genes Dev.* **15**, 1257–1271.

13. Thorpe, C.J., Schlesinger, A., and Bowerman, B. (2000). Wnt signalling in *Caenorhabditis elegans:* regulating repressors and polarizing the cytoskeleton. *Trends Cell Biol.* **10**, 10–17.

14. Rocheleau, C.E., *et al.* (1999). WRM-1 activates the LIT-1 protein kinase to transduce anterior–posterior polarity signals in *C. elegans. Cell* **97**, 717–726.

15. Meneghini, M.D., *et al.* (1999). MAP kinase and Wnt pathways converge to down-regulate an HMG-domain repressor in *Caenorhabditis elegans. Nature* **399**, 793–797.

16. Shin, T.H., *et al.* (1999). MOM-4, a MAP kinase-related protein, activates WRM-1/LIT-1 kinase to transduce anterior–posterior polarity signals in *C. elegans. Mol. Cell* **4**, 275–280.

17. Davidson, E.H. (1993). Later embryogenesis: regulatory circuitry in morphogenetic fields. *Development* **118**, 665–690.

18. Davidson, E.H. (1994). Molecular biology of embryonic development: how far have we come in the last 10 years? *Bioessays* **16**, 603–615.

19. Davidson, E.H., Peterson, K.J., and Cameron, R.A. (1995). Origin of bilaterian body plans: evolution of developmental regulatory mechanisms. *Science* **270**, 1319–1325.

20. Ang, S.L., and Rossant, J. (1993). Anterior mesendoderm induces mouse *Engrailed* genes in explant cultures. *Development* **118**, 139–149.

21. Biben, C., Hatzistavrou, T., and Harvey, R.P. (1998). Expression of NK-2 class homeobox gene *Nkx2-6* in foregut endoderm and heart. *Mech. Dev.* **73**, 125–127.

22. Thomas, P., and Beddington, R. (1996). Anterior primitive endoderm may be responsible for patterning the anterior neural plate in the mouse embryo. *Curr. Biol.* **6**, 1487–1496.

23. Varlet, I., Collignon, J., and Robertson, E.J. (1997). Nodal expression in the primitive endoderm is required for specification of the anterior axis during mouse gastrulation. *Development* **124**, 1033–1044.

24. Green, R.P., Cohn, S.M., Sacchettini, J.C., Jackson, K.E., and Gordon, J.I. (1992). The mouse intestinal fatty acid-binding protein gene: nucleotide sequence, pattern of developmental and regional expression, and proposed structure of its protein product. *DNA Cell Biol.* **11**, 31–41.

25. Beck, F., Erler, T., Russell, A., and James, R. (1995). Expression of Cdx-2 in the mouse embryo and placenta: possible role in patterning of the extraembryonic membranes. *Dev. Dyn.* **204**, 219–227.

26. Beddington, R.S., and Smith, J.C. (1993). Control of vertebrate gastrulation: inducing signals and responding genes. *Curr. Opin. Genet. Dev.* **3**, 655–661.

27. Burdsal, C.A., Flannery, M.L., and Pedersen, R.A. (1998). FGF-2 alters the fate of mouse epiblast from ectoderm to mesoderm *in vitro. Dev. Biol.* **198**, 231–244.

28. Conlon, F.L., *et al.* (1994). A primary requirement for nodal in the formation and maintenance of the primitive streak in the mouse. *Development* **120**, 1919–1928.

29. Feldman, B., Poueymirou, W., Papaioannou, V.E., DeChiara, T.M., and Goldfarb, M. (1995). Requirement of FGF-4 for postimplantation mouse development. *Science* **267**, 246–249.

30. Niswander, L., and Martin, G.R. (1992). Fgf-4 expression during gastrulation, myogenesis, and limb and tooth development in the mouse. *Development* **114**, 755–768.

31. Stepp, M.A., Urry, L.A., and Hynes, R.O. (1994). Expression of α4-integrin mRNA and protein and fibronectin in the early chicken embryo. *Cell Adhes. Commun.* **2**, 359–375.

32. Winnier, G., Blessing, M., Labosky, P.A., and Hogan, B.L. (1995). Bone morphogenetic protein-4 is required for mesoderm formation and patterning in the mouse. *Genes Dev.* **9**, 2105–2116.

33. Yamaguchi, T.P., and Rossant, J. (1995). Fibroblast growth factors in mammalian development. *Curr. Opin. Genet. Dev.* **5**, 485–491.

34. Zhao, J., Lee, M., Smith, S., and Warburton, D. (1998). Abrogation of *Smad3* and *Smad2* or of *Smad4* gene expression positively regulates murine embryonic lung branching morphogenesis in culture. *Dev. Biol.* **194**, 182–195.

35. Heasman, J., Kofron, M., and Wylie, C. (2000). β-Catenin signalling activity dissected in the early *Xenopus* embryo: a novel antisense approach. *Dev. Biol.* **222**, 124–134.

36. Kim, S.K., Hebrok, M., and Melton, D.A. (1997). Notochord to endoderm signalling is required for pancreas development. *Development* **124**, 4243–4252.

37. Huang, D., Chen, S.W., Langston, A.W., and Gudas, L.J. (1998). A conserved retinoic acid responsive element in the murine *Hoxb-1* gene is required for expression in the developing gut. *Development* **125**, 3235–3246.

38. Nikolova, M., Chen, X., and Lufkin, T. (1997). Nkx2.6 expression is transiently and specifically restricted to the branchial region of pharyngeal-stage mouse embryos. *Mech. Dev.* **69**, 215–218.

39. Kimura, S., *et al.* (1996). The T/ebp null mouse: Thyroid-specific enhancer-binding protein is essential for the organogenesis of the thyroid, lung, ventral forebrain, and pituitary. *Genes Dev.* **10**, 60–69.

40. Rossi, D.L., Acebron, A., and Santisteban, P. (1995). Function of the homeo- and paired-domain proteins TTF-1 and Pax-8 in thyroid cell proliferation. *J. Biol. Chem.* **270**, 23,139–23,142.

41. Mansouri, A., Chowdhury, K., and Gruss, P. (1998). Follicular cells of the thyroid gland require *Pax8* gene function. *Nat. Genet.* **19**, 87–90.

42. Peters, H., Neubuser, A., Kratochwil, K., and Balling, R. (1998). *Pax9*-deficient mice lack pharyngeal pouch derivatives and teeth and exhibit craniofacial and limb abnormalities. *Genes Dev.* **12**, 2735–2747.

43. Ahlgren, U., Jonsson, J., and Edlund, H. (1996). The morphogenesis of the pancreatic mesenchyme is uncoupled from that of the pancreatic epithelium in IPF1/PDX1-deficient mice. *Development* **122**, 1409–1416.

44. Jonsson, J., Carlsson, L., Edlund, T., and Edlund, H. (1994). Insulin-promoter-factor 1 is required for pancreas development in mice. *Nature* **371**, 606–609.

45. Sosa-Pineda, B., Chowdhury, K., Torres, M., Oliver, G., and Gruss, P. (1997). The *Pax4* gene is essential for differentiation of insulin-producing β-cells in the mammalian pancreas. *Nature* **386,** 399–402.

46. St. Onge, L., Sosa-Pineda, B., Chowdhury, K., Mansouri, A., and Gruss, P. (1997). *Pax6* is required for differentiation of glucagon-producing α-cells in mouse pancreas. *Nature* **387,** 406–409.

47. Sussel, L., *et al.* (1998). Mice lacking the homeodomain transcription factor Nkx2.2 have diabetes due to arrested differentiation of pancreatic β-cells. *Development* **125,** 2213–2221.

48. Ahlgren, U., Pfaff, S.L., Jessell, T.M., Edlund, T., and Edlund, H. (1997). Independent requirement for ISL1 in formation of pancreatic mesenchyme and islet cells. *Nature* **385,** 257–260.

49. Naya, F.J., *et al.* (1997). Diabetes, defective pancreatic morphogenesis, and abnormal enteroendocrine differentiation in β2/neuroD-deficient mice. *Genes Dev.* **11,** 2323–2334.

50. Roberts, D.J., Smith, D.M., Goff, D.J., and Tabin, C.J. (1998). Epithelial–mesenchymal signalling during the regionalization of the chick gut. *Development* **125,** 2791–2801.

51. Larsson, L.I., Madsen, O.D., Serup, P., Jonsson, J., and Edlund, H. (1996). Pancreatic-duodenal homeobox 1 role in gastric endocrine patterning. *Mech. Dev.* **60,** 175–184.

52. Bossard, P., and Zaret, K.S. (1998). GATA transcription factors as potentiators of gut endoderm differentiation. *Development* **125,** 4909–4917.

53. Drummond, F., Sowden, J., Morrison, K., and Edwards, Y.H. (1996). The caudal-type homeobox protein Cdx-2 binds to the colon promoter of the carbonic anhydrase 1 gene. *Eur. J. Biochem.* **236,** 670–681.

54. Jin, T., and Drucker, D.J. (1996). Activation of proglucagon gene transcription through a novel promoter element by the caudal-related homeodomain protein cdx-2/3. *Mol. Cell Biol.* **16,** 19–28.

55. Jensen, J., *et al.* (2000). Control of endodermal endocrine development by Hes-1. *Nat. Genet.* **24,** 36–44.

56. Litingtung, Y., Lei, L., Westphal, H., and Chiang, C. (1998). Sonic hedgehog is essential to foregut development. *Nat. Genet.* **20,** 58–61.

57. Ramalho-Santos, M., Melton, D.A., and McMahon, A.P. (2000). Hedgehog signals regulate multiple aspects of gastrointestinal development. *Development* **127,** 2763–2772.

58. Roberts, D.J., *et al.* (1995). Sonic hedgehog is an endodermal signal inducing *Bmp-4* and *Hox* genes during induction and regionalization of the chick hindgut. *Development* **121,** 3163–3174.

59. Kaestner, K.H., Silberg, D.G., Traber, P.G., and Schutz, G. (1997). The mesenchymal winged helix transcription factor Fkh6 is required for the control of gastrointestinal proliferation and differentiation. *Genes Dev.* **11,** 1583–1595.

60. Gittes, G.K., Galante, P.E., Hanahan, D., Rutter, W.J., and Debase, H.T. (1996). Lineage-specific morphogenesis in the developing pancreas: role of mesenchymal factors. *Development* **122,** 439–447.

61. Kaufman, M.H., and Bard, J.B.L. (1999). *In* "The Anatomical Basis of Mouse Development," pp. 129–152. Academic Press, London.

62. Gordon, J.I., and Hermiston, M.L. (1994). Differentiation and self-renewal in mouse gastrointestinal epithelium. *Curr. Opin. Cell Biol.* **6,** 795–803

63. Kedinger, M., Simon, P.M., Grenier, J.F., and Haffen, K. (1981). Role of epithelial–mesenchymal interactions in the onto-genesis of intestinal brush-border enzymes. *Dev. Biol.* **86,** 339–347.

64. Duluc, I., Freund, J.N., Leberquier, C., and Kedinger, M. (1994). Fetal endoderm primarily holds the temporal and positional information required for mammalian intestinal development. *J. Cell Biol.* **126,** 211–221.

65. Luetteke, N.C., *et al.* (1994). The mouse waved-2 phenotype results from a point mutation in the EGF receptor tyrosine kinase. *Genes Dev.* **8,** 399–413.

66. Miettinen, P.J., *et al.* (1995). Epithelial immaturity and multi-organ failure in mice lacking epidermal growth factor receptor. *Nature* **376,** 337–341.

67. Kaartinen, V., *et al.* (1995). Abnormal lung development and cleft palate in mice lacking TGF-β3 indicates defects of epithelial–mesenchymal interaction. *Nat. Genet.* **11,** 415–421.

68. Liu, J.P., Baker, J., Perkins, A.S., Robertson, E.J., and Efstratiadis, A. (1993). Mice carrying null mutations of the genes encoding insulin-like growth factor I (Igf-1) and type 1 IGF receptor (Igf1r). *Cell* **75,** 59–72.

69. Sonnenberg, E., Meyer, D., Weidner, K.M., and Birchmeier, C. (1993). Scatter factor–hepatocyte growth factor and its receptor, the c-met tyrosine kinase, can mediate a signal exchange between mesenchyme and epithelia during mouse development. *J. Cell Biol.* **123,** 223–235.

70. Schmidt, C., *et al.* (1995). Scatter factor–hepatocyte growth factor is essential for liver development. *Nature* **373,** 699–702.

71. Uehara, Y., *et al.* (1995). Placental defect and embryonic lethality in mice lacking hepatocyte growth factor–scatter factor. *Nature* **373,** 702–705.

72. Kermorgant, S., *et al.* (1997). Developmental expression and functionality of hepatocyte growth factor and c-Met in human fetal digestive tissues. *Gastroenterology* **112,** 1635–1647.

73. Bitgood, M.J., and McMahon, A.P. (1995). *Hedgehog* and *Bmp* genes are coexpressed at many diverse sites of cell–cell interaction in the mouse embryo. *Dev. Biol.* **172,** 126–138.

74. Apelqvist, A., Ahlgren, U., and Edlund, H. (1997). Sonic hedgehog directs specialised mesoderm differentiation in the intestine and pancreas. *Curr. Biol.* **7,** 801–804.

75. Karlsson, L., Lindahl, P., Heath, J.K., and Betsholtz, C. (2000). Abnormal gastrointestinal development in PDGF-A- and PDGFR-α-deficient mice implicates a novel mesenchymal structure with putative instructive properties in villus morphogenesis. *Development* **127,** 3457–3466.

76. Krumlauf, R. (1994). *Hox* genes in vertebrate development. *Cell* **78,** 191–201.

77. Macdonald, P.M., and Struhl, G. (1986). A molecular gradient in early *Drosophila* embryos and its role in specifying the body pattern. *Nature* **324,** 537–545.

78. Lickert, H., *et al.* (2000). Wnt/β-catenin signalling regulates the expression of the homeobox gene *Cdx1* in embryonic intestine. *Development* **127,** 3805–3813.

79. Korinek, V., *et al.* (1998). Depletion of epithelial stem cell compartments in the small intestine of mice lacking Tcf-4. *Nat. Genet.* **19,** 379–383.

80. Mills, J.C., and Gordon, J.I. (2001). The intestinal stem cell niche: There grows the neighbourhood. *Proc. Natl. Acad. Sci. U. S. A.* **98,** 12,334–12,336.

81. Ramalho-Santos, M., Yoon, S., Matsuzaki, Y., Mulligan, R.C., and Melton, D.A. (2002). "Stemness": transcriptional profiling of embryonic and adult stem cells. *Science* **298,** 597–600.

82. Oesterreicher, T.J., Nanthakumar, N.N., Winston, J.H., and Henning, S.J. (1998). Rat trehalase: cDNA cloning and mRNA expression in adult rat tissues and during intestinal ontogeny. *Am. J. Physiol.* **274,** R1220–R1227.

83. Brantjes, H., Barker, N., van Es, J., and Clevers, H. (2002). TCF: Lady Justice casting the final verdict on the outcome of Wnt signalling. *Biol. Chem.* **383,** 255–261.

84. Van de Wetering, M., *et al.* (2002). The β-catenin/TCF-4 complex imposes a crypt progenitor phenotype on colorectal cancer cells. *Cell* **111,** 241–250.

85. Wasan, H.S., *et al.* (1998). APC in the regulation of intestinal crypt fission. *J. Pathol.* **185,** 246–255.

86. Wong, W.M., *et al.* (2002). Histogenesis of human colorectal adenomas and hyperplastic polyps: the role of cell proliferation and crypt fission. *Gut* **50,** 212–217.

87. Alison, M.R., *et al.* (2003). Plastic adult stem cells: will they graduate from the school of hard knocks? *J. Cell Sci.* **116,** 599–603.

88. Preston, S.L., *et al.* (2003). The new stem cell biology: something for everyone. *Mol. Pathol.* **56,** 86–96.

89. Holden, C., and Vogel, G. (2002). Stem cells: plasticity—time for a reappraisal? *Science* **296,** 2126–2129.

90. Tait, I.S., Flint, N., Campbell, F.C., and Evans, G.S. (1994). Generation of neomucosa *in vivo* by transplantation of dissociated rat postnatal small intestinal epithelium. *Differentiation* **56,** 91–100.

91. Patel, H.R., Tait, I.S., Evans, G.S., and Campbell, F.C. (1996). Influence of cell interactions in a novel model of postnatal mucosal regeneration. *Gut* **38,** 679–686.

92. Patel, H.R., Hewer, A., Phillips, D.H., Hayes, J.D., Wolf, C.R., and Campbell, F.C. (1997). Metabolic competence and susceptibility of intestinal epithelium to genotoxic injury during regeneration. *Carcinogenesis* **18,** 2171–2177.

93. Sattar, A., Robson, S.C., Patel, H.R., Angus, B., and Campbell, F.C. (1999). Expression of growth regulatory genes in a SCID mouse–human model of intestinal epithelial regeneration. *J. Pathol.* **187,** 229–236.

94. Slorach, E.M., Campbell, F.C., and Dorin, J.R. (1999). A mouse model of intestinal stem cell function and regeneration. *J. Cell Sci.* **112 (Pt. 18),** 3029–3038.

95. Wells, J.M., and Melton, D.A. (1999). Vertebrate endoderm development. *Annu. Rev. Cell Dev. Biol.* **15,** 393–410.

Trachea, Bronchi, and Lungs

Jeffrey A. Whitsett, Susan E. Wert, and Ravindhra Elluru

The formation of the lung provides a unique solution to the problem of adaptation of vertebrates to terrestrial life, facilitating oxygen and carbon dioxide exchange between inhaled gases in the alveoli and blood in the vascular system. The organ consists of the trachea, the main stem and lobar bronchi, and the conducting airways, conduits to the peripheral lung where an extensive epithelial-lined surface comes into contact with an equally extensive capillary bed. Primordial lung tubules are formed from foregut endodermal precursors that invade the splanchnic mesenchyme, proliferate, and branch to form conducting and peripheral airspaces. At maturity, the human lung consists of an estimated 40 distinct cell types, many of which are precisely organized along cephalocaudal, dorsal–ventral, and left–right axes. Presently, knowledge regarding the identity and fates of progenitor cells involved in lung morphogenesis, repair following lung injury, regeneration after resection, and oncogenesis is relatively limited. Alterations in lung structure and function accompany acute and chronic disorders that contribute to the pathogenesis of morbidity and mortality from lung disease, whether caused by genetic or environmental factors. The lung responds in pleiotropic ways to acute and chronic injury, resulting in resolution and repair, remodeling and fibrosis, and/or loss of lung parenchyma, with resultant emphysema. Therapeutic interventions in these processes may offer solutions to diseases affecting pulmonary function. This chapter summarizes knowledge regarding epithelial progenitor cells and "stem" cells contributing to (1) lung morphogenesis, (2) repair of the lung following injury or resection, and (3) potential utility of marrow-derived or adult multipotent progenitor cells for cell or gene replacement in the lung.

Lung Morphogenesis

The processes involved in organogenesis of the lung likely share principles with more thoroughly studied processes in other organs. Stepwise models of organogenesis provide a model wherein pluripotent stem cells in the blastocyst give rise to all cell types, generating multiple cell types through the production of multipotent progenitors, committed precursors, and mature cells, some of which may be terminally

differentiated and nonmitotic. Mechanisms underlying cell fate decisions and potential cell plasticity after specification are of considerable interest in the study of both organogenesis and the application of stem cells–multipotent progenitor cells, which may be useful for organ repair or gene transfer.

Trachea, Bronchi, and Peripheral Lung are Formed from Foregut Endodermal Precursors

EARLY PATTERNING OF THE FOREGUT ENDODERM

Patterning of the blastocyst is determined by maternally derived mRNAs that establish the dorsal–ventral axis of the embryo, creating ectoderm and mesoderm. Shortly thereafter, anterior–posterior axes of the embryo are established with formation of the definitive endoderm. The anterior region of the foregut endoderm contains the cells that will form trachea, thyroid, parathyroid, esophagus, lung, and stomach, each being derived from outpouching of cells along the gut tube.[1,2] The lung buds form between the thyroid and the hepatic buds. Cell microinjection experiments demonstrated that progenitors of the anterior foregut endoderm contribute cells to lung, foregut, and pancreas and can be labeled as early as embryonic day (E) 7.5, indicating that specification of subsets of endodermally derived cells occurs early in foregut development.[3]

In the mouse, formation of the lung begins as an outpouching or evagination of endodermally derived epithelial cells from the lateral–tracheal–esophageal groove of the common esophageal–tracheal tube. This formation is marked by expression of thyroid transcription factor-1 (TTF-1), a homeodomain containing the transcription factor of the Nkx2 family of proteins, an early marker of lung and thyroid specification.[4] The pharynx is initially connected to the common tracheal–esophageal tube at its cephalic end. Our current understanding of the embryology of the larynx and trachea is derived from sections of staged vertebrate and human embryos and rests primarily upon anatomic descriptions.[5–7] Formation of the respiratory tract is initiated as an epithelial thickening along the ventral aspect of the foregut, forming the respiratory primordium (see Fig. 36–1). The respiratory primordium consists of a group of mesenchymal cells that will form cartilaginous and supporting structures of the conducting airways, which are separated from the hepatic primordium by the septum transversum, a structure that will eventually

Handbook of Stem Cells
Volume 1

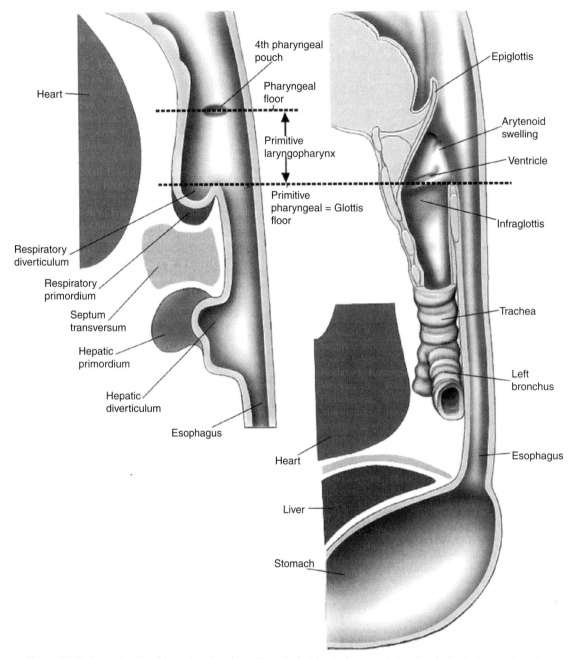

Figure 36–1. *Structural origins of the trachea, bronchi, and lung. On the left is the foregut endoderm from the fourth pharyngeal pouch to the esophagus and its relationship to the heart and the respiratory and hepatic primordia. The lung buds are formed from E9–9.5 as the endoderm evaginates into the mesenchyme of the respiratory primordium. On the right, the pharynx, trachea, and main bronchi are shown in relationship to the esophagus and heart in the mature lung. The lung contains numerous cell types contributing unique functions to maintain host defense and gas exchange.*

develop into the central tendon of the diaphragm. A medial slit in the pharyngeal floor gives rise to the larynx. The respiratory diverticulum is lined by both esophageal- and respiratory-like epithelial cells of mixed differentiation. The cephalic end of the respiratory diverticulum, the primitive pharyngeal floor, is located at the level of the fourth pharyngeal pouch.

The bronchopulmonary buds appear from the lateral aspect of the respiratory diverticulum and contain progenitors that will eventually form both the upper and lower respiratory tract. At the same time, extensive proliferation of the cardiac and hepatic primordium occurs on the opposite side of the septum transversum. The foregut lengthens, increasing the distance between respiratory and hepatic buds. The bronchopulmonary buds are drawn caudally and ventrally, and their elongation leads to the formation of two primary bronchi. The carina, the location of the bifurcation of the main (or primary) bronchi, originates from the caudal aspect of the respiratory diverticulum. Cells surrounding the proximal end of the tube, the pharyngeal arches, provide the mesodermal precursors that will form laryngeal cartilage and musculature. Epithelial cells in peripheral regions of the bronchial tubules proliferate, and the tubes undergo dichotomous branching to form the four lobar bronchi of the right lung and the single lobar bronchus of the left, which define the lobes of the mouse lung. Numbers of lobes and right–left symmetry vary greatly among mammalian species. Epithelial-lined, endodermally derived tubules invade the splanchnic mesenchyme, elongate, branch, and proliferate to form bronchial tubules. Continued branching and budding result in the formation of saccules until birth, after which the saccules expand and are further subdivided during septation to form alveoli, a process completed 3 to 4 weeks of postnatal age in the mouse and approximately 7 to 10 years in humans.[8–12] This general progression of anatomical changes is conserved among mammals and used to stage the processes characterizing lung morphogenesis (Table 36–1).

Establishment of Extrapulmonary and Intrapulmonary Precursors Occurs Before Lung Formation

Cell-tracing experiments, using dye microinjection of endodermal precursors at E6.5, demonstrated common progenitor cells in foregut structures that contributed to the formation of lung, pancreas, and liver in the mouse.[3] Using conditional expression of cre recombinase to label lung progenitor cells with a visible reporter protein (alkaline phosphatase or green fluorescent protein) demonstrated that the restriction of peripheral lung cells to specific epithelial cell lineages occurred prior to the formation of the primordial lung buds and that extrapulmonary structures (i.e., the trachea and bronchi) were lined primarily by a subset of cells distinct from those forming the lung periphery.[13] Peripheral lung epithelial precursors were distinguished from those of the gastrointestinal tract, liver, and pancreas before organ-bud formation and were labeled early in lung morphogenesis. Progenitors forming the peripheral lung comprised a small number of cells at the sites of secondary buds and branches. Outgrowth of epithelial cells from this peripheral lineage formed nearly all of the cells contributing to the intrapulmonary respiratory epithelium, including nonciliated and ciliated bronchiolar epithelial cells as well as type I and type II alveolar cells in the peripheral saccules and alveoli (Fig. 36–2). The only peripheral epithelial cells excluded from this lung lineage were neuroepithelial cells (NECs) in neuroepithelial bodies (NEBs). In the mouse, trachea, bronchi, tracheal–bronchial glands, and NEBs were derived from a proximal cell lineage that did not overlap with those of the peripheral lung. These lineages were established before the formation of the definitive lung buds. Thus, the respiratory epithelial cells lining intraparenchymal lung structures share common labeled progenitors distinct from most of the cells lining upper trachea–bronchi and NEBs. These two subsets of progenitors generate various differentiated cell types in the

TABLE 36–1
Pulmonary Epithelial Morphogenesis and Differentiation in the Mouse

Period[a]	Structural Events	Epithelial Cell Type	Markers
Embryonic E9.5 to E12.5	Lung buds Formation bronchi	Primitive columnar	TTF-1, FOXa2, GATA-6, FOXa1
Pseudoglandular E12.5 to E16.5	Airway branching Acinar multiplication or development of acinar tubules and buds	Basal Columnar Cuboidal NEBs	FOXj1 FOXa1, FOXa2 SP-C, SP-B CGRP
Canalicular E16.5 to E17.5	Saccule development initiated (with dilation of acinar tubules–buds)	Basal Columnar Clara Ciliated NEBs Cuboidal Squamous	FOXj1 CCSP, SP-B FOXa1, FOXa2 FOXj1, β-tubulin CGRP SP-B, SP-C T1α, RCA-1
Saccular E17 to P5 Alveolar P5 to P20–30	Growth–dilation of Saccules Alveolar growth–septation	Clara Ciliated Basal Type II (cuboidal) Type I (squamous) Goblet	CCSP, SP-A, SP-B, SP-D β-Tubulin, FOXj1 FOXj1 SP-A, SP-B, SP-C, SP-D Aquaporin-5, T1α, RCA-1 Mucin (Muc5A/C)

[a]Time periods adapted from Ten Have-Opbroek[92] and Wert.[93]

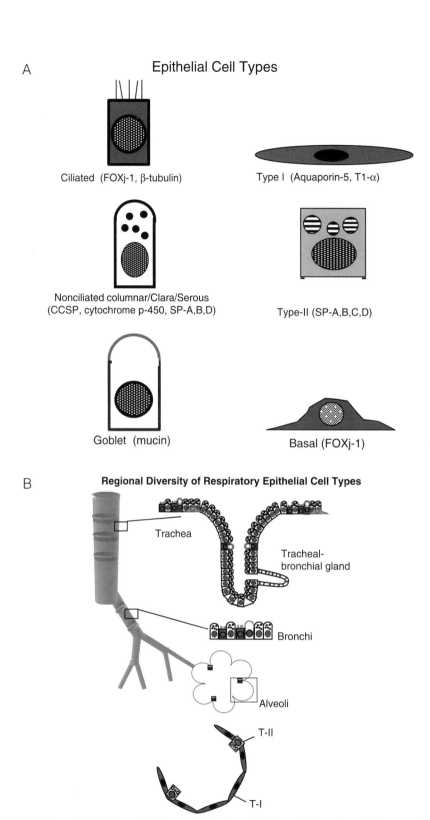

Figure 36–2. *Respiratory epithelial cell types.* (A) Diverse epithelial cell types line the conducting and peripheral airways. In the mouse, trachea and bronchi are lined primarily by ciliated, nonciliated columnar (Clara, serous, and intermediate cells), basal, and goblet cells. Numbers of each cell type are influenced developmentally, spatially, and in response to environmental challenge. Cell types are identified by characteristic morphology, by biochemical and immunohistochemical markers, and by patterns of gene expression. Some characteristic markers are shown in parentheses. The alveolar region is lined by cuboidal type II cells and squamous type I cells. Not shown are NECs, a relatively rare epithelial cell subtype expressing serotonin, bombesin, and *calcitonin* gene-related peptide (CGRP). (B) Shown are regions of trachea and tracheal glands, bronchi, and alveoli. Proximal conducting airways are lined by a pseudostratified epithelium. Smaller airways are lined by a simple columnar epithelium of diverse cell types. The alveoli are lined by cuboidal type II cells that are mitotically active following injury and by squamous type I cells that come into contact with the alveolar–capillary bed (not shown), facilitating gas exchange.

mature lung, including basal, ciliated, nonciliated-serous, and goblet cells in conducting airways and type I and type II epithelial cells in the alveoli of the mature mouse lung (Fig. 36–2).

Cell Plasticity During Lung Morphogenesis

Although the cephalocaudal axis of the lung is established prior to lung-bud formation *in vivo*, epithelial–mesenchymal interactions play a critical role in cell specification. Proliferation and branching of lung tubules requires inductive interaction with the mesenchyme. Microdissection of mesenchyme from surrounding lung tubules of the fetal lung inhibits growth and branching of the tubules in organ cultures *in vitro*.[14] Until E12.5, epithelial cells of the trachea can be induced to form cells typical of the peripheral lung by transplantation of the peripheral lung mesenchyme to the trachea or bronchi.[15] Thus, progenitor cells lining the respiratory tract maintain plasticity, can be reprogrammed by mesenchyme, and are influenced by several autocrine, paracrine, and juxtacrine signals. Likewise, tracheal–bronchial mesenchyme supports tracheal formation and cartilage development but does not support the growth and branching of peripheral lung buds when transplanted to the lung periphery. A precise reciprocal relationship exists between the epithelial cells of the developing lung buds and the underlying mesenchyme that changes along the cephalocaudal axis. For example, factors that interfere with growth of the peripheral lung mesenchyme and the formation of the pulmonary vasculature system cause reciprocal abnormalities in branching morphogenesis and alveolarization.

Growth and Differentiation of Cells Lining Respiratory Tubules

During formation of the mouse lung, endodermally derived epithelial cells are relatively undifferentiated, the early lung being lined predominantly by a simple, columnar, epithelial sheet covering the surfaces of trachea, bronchi, and forming lung tubules. These tubules undergo a process of branching morphogenesis with stereotypic budding and branching, producing the lobar and subsegmental bronchi and the intrapulmonary bronchioles. Epithelial cells proliferate most rapidly at the tips of lung buds. Cell division and shape are controlled to allow for lateral and dichotomous branching as the lung buds invade the splanchnic mesenchyme. Proliferation, migration, cell shape, and differentiation are modulated by several growth factors, signaling molecules, and cell matrix interactions to determine the cell type along the cephalocaudal axis.[16–21] Epithelial cell differentiation in the mouse becomes increasingly apparent after E13 or E14. The cells lining proximal airways become increasingly columnar, and a complex pseudostratified epithelium lines the larger conducting airways.[22–24] Differentiation of basal cells and nonciliated and ciliated columnar epithelial cells occurs during this time. Cells containing neuroendocrine granules are found in NEB

clusters at branch points and are associated with nerves; solitary cells, or NECs, are also observed along the conducting airways. The numbers and the extent of differentiation of epithelial cell types vary with development among species and after exposure to environmental factors. Epithelial cell differentiation generally proceeds from proximal to peripheral regions of conducting airways.[22–24] The various respiratory epithelial cell types are identified by morphological and biochemical criteria (Fig. 36–2 and Table 36–1).

Transcriptional Control of Epithelial Cell Diversity

The heterogeneity of cell types is marked and determined by the expression of several transcription factors that control epithelial cell differentiation. Epithelial cells lining the embryonic lung tubules express the transcription factors TTF-1, FOXa1, FOXa2, FOXj1, and GATA-6.[4,25–31] FOXj1, required for the formation of ciliated cells, is first expressed in basal cells and in ciliated cell precursors between E14–15.[29,30] β-Tubulin IV, a marker of ciliated cells, is detected shortly thereafter.[30] FOXa2 and GATA-6 are required for the formation of the early endoderm and are expressed in subsets of respiratory epithelial cells throughout prenatal lung morphogenesis.[25,27,28,31] Expression of TTF-1 marks the epithelial cells found in the primordial lung buds.[4] Thereafter, TTF-1 is expressed in bronchiolar cells and in subsets of epithelial cells in the lung periphery (i.e., in type II alveolar epithelial cells).[25,26] Expression of TTF-1, GATA-6, and FOXa2 decreases or is absent as cells undergo terminal differentiation (i.e., in type I cells). Thus, expression of TTF-1 is the first known marker of cells committed to respiratory epithelial cell phenotype and is accompanied thereafter by expression of lung cell-specific markers surfactant protein B and C (SP-B and SP-C) in both mouse and human.[25,32] Although trachea and main (or primary) bronchi are formed in TTF-1-null mutant mice, TTF-1 is required for the formation of the peripheral lung.[33] Thus, the concerted actions of various transcription factors are critical for commitment of endodermal precursors that form the lung tubules during morphogenesis. The increasing complexity of epithelial cell differentiation is accompanied by changes in the levels of TTF-1, GATA-6, and FOXa2 as well as other transcription factors (FOXa1, FOXj1, SOX family members, CEBPs, RARs, NF1, and TCF family markers, to name a few) along the cephalocaudal axis.[16–21] Although knowledge regarding each of their functions is limited, it is likely that the stoichiometry, interactions, and posttranslational modifications of these factors contribute to the transcriptional signals generating the diverse cell types lining the mature lung.

Postnatal Alveolarization

In the mouse, lobulation and formation of the conducting airways are completed around E14.5–15. Thereafter, the peripheral lung tubules grow rapidly, forming acinar tubules and buds at the periphery. The pulmonary vasculature becomes extensive, the mesenchyme thins, and the pulmonary capillaries come into apposition to the distal pulmonary capillaries. During the canalicular and saccular stages of morphogenesis, the peripheral lung tubules dilate (E16.5–P5) to form alveolar saccules, which then begin to septate to form true alveoli lined by type II and type I epithelial cells (P5–P14). Septation continues to generate increasing numbers of alveolar gas exchange units until lung morphogenesis is completed (approximately P20–25 in the mouse) and adolescence in the human.[9–12] Type II cells are actively mitotic during alveologenesis and also provide cells capable of renewing the alveolar epithelium after injury in the adult. Type II cells are precursors from which terminally differentiated, squamous type I epithelial cells arise.[34,35] Unlike many organs in which proliferation remains highly active throughout life (e.g., skin and intestine), cell proliferation and turnover is relatively slow in the mature lung, with an estimated half-life of 2–3 months in the rodent.[36–38]

Cell Diversity Supports Organ Function

The diversity of epithelial cell types contributes to unique physiological functions in the lung. Although the lung is not necessary for fetal survival, respiration after birth depends on lung function. Since external gases, accompanied by particles and pathogens, are continuously exchanged with the environment, the respiratory epithelium must maintain sterility, appropriate hydration, and patency of gas exchange surfaces at all times. Epithelial cells are required for maintenance of alveolar integrity and must be replaced by processes that do not interfere with ventilation. The distinct epithelial cell types lining various regions of the trachea, bronchi, and lung mediate host defense, mucociliary clearance, hydration of epithelial cell surfaces, neurosensory signaling, and surfactant homeostasis, the latter reducing surface tension at the air–liquid interface. Thus after birth, appropriate numbers of differentiated cells capable of meeting various physiologic functions are required. Furthermore, the lung responds to diverse environmental conditions. Changes in altitude, FiO_2, starvation, toxicants, particles, and infectious agents influence growth, cell differentiation, and function in the respiratory tract. Such adaptive responses are critical for survival under varied conditions; however, cellular changes accompanying the responses to the environment may have untoward physiological or medical consequences.

Teleological Arguments for Multipotent Progenitors or Lung Stem Cells

The respiratory tract is chronically exposed to environmental particles and pathogens but may be especially challenged by catastrophic exposures, for example, to heat, smoke, drowning, and certain infectious agents. Survival from such injuries requires rapid repair capable of supporting lung function in the face of repopulating the epithelial lining of the lung. Since failure to maintain respiration is tolerated only briefly, repair systems must be robust and capable of responding rapidly to

severe physiological challenge. Therefore, cellular systems of initiating a rapid and widespread repair process following extensive lung cell injury are required for survival. Failure to maintain epithelial–vascular integrity results in an alveolar–capillary leak and acute respiratory distress syndrome, often fatal in both infants and adults. Sublethal but catastrophic injuries are often accompanied by the induction of cytoprotective and reparative processes capable of protecting and/or regenerating extensive surface areas while maintaining gas exchange. Since many pathogens are cleared by the immune cell-mediated destruction of infected cells, the ongoing clearance of respiratory epithelial cells following infection may be a considerable challenge to stem cell or amplifying cell populations. In some organ systems, rare, nonproliferating, mitotically inactive cells (which retain DNA labeling for long periods during resting states, termed label-retaining cells, or LRCs) are thought to provide pools of stem cells that proliferate and differentiate during repair.[39–41] Since pulmonary epithelial cells must respond rapidly to injury, it is not surprising that many epithelial cell types enter the cell cycle, proliferate, migrate, and differentiate to repair the lung. Type I cells and ciliated cells are considered terminally differentiated and nonmitotic following injury.[34,35] Since respiration also depends on the pulmonary vascular system, proliferation and migration of endothelial and vascular cells are required for repair of the lung following injury. Precise reciprocal relationships exist between the alveolar epithelial and the vascular bed; therefore, repair of both compartments is required for maintenance and restoration of lung function.

Knowledge regarding the repair of pulmonary epithelial cells relies primarily upon studies in which the lung is exposed to toxicants, infectious agents, or immune challenges. Exposure to hyperoxia (90–100%) causes acute cell injury and initiates proliferation in subsets of respiratory epithelial cells.[42,43] In the alveoli, type I cells are most susceptible to oxidant injury. Two to three days following injury, type II alveolar cells are labeled by ^{3}H-thymidine.[34] Subsets of these cells differentiate into type I cells within 3–5 days. Therefore, type II cells provide a large pool of rapidly amplifying cells that divide and differentiate during repair of the alveolus. Similar experiments with other toxicants (e.g., naphthalene, exposure to detergent, and inhalation of NO_2, O_3, and SO_2) demonstrated that basal cells and nonciliated respiratory epithelial cells provide progenitors for replacement of the cells in conducting airways.[44–50] These experiments support the concept that basal cells and nonciliated–ciliated epithelial cells are capable of rapid amplification and differentiation following epithelial cell injury. Basal cells produce a complex, pseudostratified epithelia containing ciliated, goblet, nonciliated, and basal cells when grown at an air–liquid interface or on denuded tracheal grafts.[51,52] Therefore, both basal and nonciliated columnar epithelial cells represent a large pool of rapidly amplifying cells capable of restoring the integrity of the respiratory epithelium. Cell-labeling experiments, in which retrovirus expressing β-galactosidase was used to mark purified airway epithelial cells, demonstrated that nonciliated tracheal epithelial cells regenerated a complex pseudostratified or columnar epithelium in tracheal xenografts. Tracheal–bronchial glands lined by diverse cell types formed in this model.[52] Clusters of retrovirally labeled cells proliferated and formed clusters of goblet, ciliated, and columnar epithelial cells, indicating that varied cell types were derived from a common epithelial precursor. Together, the lung responds by robust proliferative activity following injury; however, the existence, requirement, or both for unique stem cells capable of self renewal and regeneration of differentiated respiratory epithelium remains unproven.

Evidence for Stem Cell Niches in the Lung

Stem cells capable of continued self-renewal are often located in unique cellular environments, where they are protected or strategically located to facilitate rapid restoration of organ structure and function.[53,54] Stem cells (e.g., in the intestinal crypts, cornea, and skin) are generally identified as a rare subset of nonproliferative cells that remain in an undifferentiated state. Tissue stem cells are self-renewing but are also able to generate progenitor cells that proliferate and differentiate into diverse cell types. Tissue stem cells are often defined by their low mitotic activities and slow turnover under normal conditions, and they are generally identified by the prolonged length of time that they retain DNA labels. LRCs have been identified in the lungs of mice exposed to naphthalene, to genetically engineered cellular toxicants, and to repeated detergent or SO_2 exposures.[44–48] These studies support the concept that a unique and rare set of pulmonary LRCs may be stem cells that play a role in lung repair. Pulmonary epithelial LRCs were identified in distinct sites along the conducting airways (Fig. 36–3). Following exposure to SO_2 or detergent, mitotic responses were observed in many cell types (basal and nonciliated respiratory epithelial cells), indicating activation of a pool of rapidly amplifying cells. However, after repeated exposure to toxicants, LRCs were identified in the necks of tracheal–bronchial glands and in folds of the respiratory epithelium, usually located in noncartilaginous regions of conducting airways.[48] These sites may be protected from exposure to toxicants, providing a pool of cells strategically located to replace injured surface cells. The presence of stem cell niches in the lung was further supported by studies in which expression of thymidine kinase in nonciliated respiratory epithelial cells was used to deplete subsets of epithelial cells following exposure to gancyclovir.[47] Likewise, exposure to naphthalene, metabolized by p450 cytochrome-dependent enzymes enriched in nonciliated respiratory epithelial cells (Clara), was used to cause selective cell death in the conducting airways. In both experiments, epithelial cells within NEBs, often located near branch points of conducting airways, were identified as a source of cells undergoing migration and mitosis after injury. These investigators proposed that a microenvironment formed near the NECs provided factors that were cytoprotective or that sustained progenitor, stem, or both types of cells required for repair of the lung (Fig. 36–3). Alternatively, distinct cells with stem and progenitor cell characteristics may populate these regions during lung morphogenesis.

Stem Cell Niches in Lung

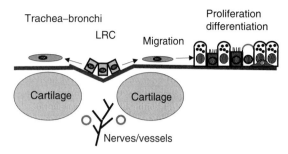

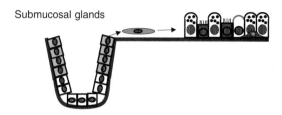

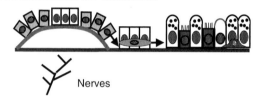

Figure 36–3. *Proposed stem cell niches.* Label-retaining cells (LRCs) are located in selective sites in intercartilaginous regions of the epithelial lining of conducting airways, the necks of tracheal–bronchial glands, and in clusters surrounding neuroepithelial cells. After injury, these cells migrate, proliferate, and differentiate to repair the lung surface.

Lung Growth after Pneumonectomy, Removal of Chest Masses, and Transplantation

Surgical resection of abnormal lung tissues and chest masses are common occurrences in clinical medicine. Compensatory lung growth is commonly observed in pediatric patients following lung transplantation, pneumonectomy, and removal of chest masses.[55,56] Several experimental models demonstrate the ability of the lung to undergo compensatory growth following resection.[57–60] In the sheep fetus, increasing airway pressure by tracheal occlusion is followed by cell proliferation and increased lung growth. On the contrary, loss of distention following removal of tracheal pressure gradients, as in ruptured amniotic membranes, oligohydramnios, and chest masses, results in lung hypoplasia.[61] Unilateral resection of the lung in rodents induces cell proliferation 3–4 days thereafter and is followed by continued growth of the lung parenchyma, resulting in increased lung tissue density derived by reinitiation of cell proliferation and septation or true alveolar–capillary growth.[57–60] Although lung regrowth is generally more robust in young animals, compensatory growth occurs even in adult rodents. It is unclear whether the regrowth is mediated by proliferation and differentiation of stem cells, by transient amplifying cells, or by both processes. After resection, many alveolar type II cells enter into the cell cycle, enhancing alveolar–capillary proliferation of alveolar surface area and lung volumes. Compensatory growth following lung resection or injury is influenced by many factors, including EGF, eNOS, VEGF-A, IGF, HGF, FGFs, and retinoic acid receptors.[62–67]

Lessons from Emphysema: Selective Loss of Stem Cells

A remaining enigma in lung biology rests with the remarkable variability of repair following distinct lung injuries. Extensive lung injury induced by oxygen exposure, viral infection, or allograft rejection may be followed by rapid and complete repair in spite of widespread cell loss. In contrast, other forms of lung injury (e.g., following exposure to elastase or bleomycin and α1-antitrypsin deficiency) are accompanied by failure to repair with resultant loss of lung tissues, resulting in emphysema, fibrosis, or both. Likewise, activation of epithelial apoptosis causes permanent emphysema in adult mice.[68] Therefore, not all forms of lung injury are identical, perhaps indicating that responses of lung cells to specific injuries or conditions influence distinct cell types, processes, or both. Some forms of injury may deplete or injure stem cells or exhaust amplifying cells, leading to failure to repair the lung. For example, even brief exposure of a transgene-blocking FGF signaling from E16–18 in the fetal lung caused permanent loss of alveoli in mice.[69] Likewise, oligohydramnios caused by amniotic fluid leak between 16–20 weeks gestation often leads to permanent lung hypoplasia and respiratory failure in human infants. In contrast, prolonged ruptured membranes later in gestation (after 22–24 weeks) are often associated with normal lung growth and function (for a review, see Geary and Whitsett[70]). Thus, survival or growth of subsets of progenitor cells, upon which subsequent lung growth is dependent, may be differentially influenced at distinct developmental times. Administration of dexamethasone during lung morphogenesis decreased lung growth and caused permanent airspace enlargement; coadministration of retinoic acid enhanced septation and lung growth, restoring alveolar size in this model.[71] Thus in some species, the lung is capable of considerable regeneration following resection or injury. On the contrary, some pulmonary injuries result in the permanent loss of parenchyma, contributing to acute or chronic pulmonary dysfunction. The pathobiology contributing to such diverse outcomes remains enigmatic.

Multipotent Adult Progenitor Cells Contribute to the Lung

Several decades of clinical work supports the utility of bone marrow transplantation for replacement of hematopoietic cells for therapy of genetic, neoplastic, and acquired diseases.

Likewise, the identity and characteristics of pluripotent stem cells and their ability to contribute to organogenesis in the embryo is well established in studies of the blastocyst. Embryonic stem cells differentiate into all cell types, including respiratory epithelial cells.[72] Recently, multipotent progenitor cells have been identified in various tissues during development and in the adult. Multipotent cells isolated from bone marrow, muscles, central nervous system, and other tissues in the adult can engraft at various sites where they contribute to vascular, epithelial, and stromal components of the organs.[73–83] The characteristics of these cells, conditions for mobilization, trafficking, engraftment, survival, differentiation, and proliferation remain important scientific issues. The ability to genetically modify such multipotent cells, and their ability to engraft in tissue sites that support their participation in organ function, provide previously unanticipated opportunities for future therapies of many diseases, including those of the lung. Allograft rejection associated with organ transplantation could be avoided if autologous tissue–derived stem cells could be isolated, cultured, modified, and transplanted, providing an opportunity for novel therapies for human diseases.

The ability of multipotent adult progenitor cells (MAPCs) to engraft in many tissues, including the lung, has been repeatedly demonstrated.[73–84] Following transplantation of bone marrow, purified human bone marrow–derived cells, or single-cell isolates, the injected cells or their derivatives were identified within organs where they acquired specific differentiated characteristics. Injection of whole bone marrow into lethally irradiated mice resulted in the targeting of cells to the lung and the persistence of cells in both bronchiolar and alveolar respiratory epithelium. In the studies of Kotton et al., engraftment was only seen after severe lung injury induced with bleomycin.[84] Marrow-derived cells were detected after 30 days and identified as type I epithelial cells, a cell type considered terminally differentiated. Mitosis of the engrafted cells was not observed, suggesting that the cells were trapped and persisted in the lung but did not provide a self-renewing cell population of biological significance. In contrast, relatively extensive engraftment of bone marrow–derived stem cells was observed after injection of isolated single cells into lethally irradiated mice.[83,85] In those studies, multipotent bone marrow–derived stem cells contributed to the bronchiolar and alveolar epithelium, colocalizing with the expression of SP-B, a cell-specific marker for peripheral respiratory epithelial cells. Since SP-B is expressed in both type II cells and non-ciliated bronchiolar cells, cell types that proliferate and differentiate following injury, these cells have potential to serve as airway progenitor cells for the delivery of therapeutic genes to the lung. Consistent with these observations, MAPCs engrafted and differentiated into liver, lung, endothelial, and the gastrointestinal tract.[86–88] Single cells isolated from MAPCs contributed substantially to numerous organs, including liver, gut, and lung, when injected into the blastocysts as well as into the adult mice.[86] Together, these studies support the concept that multipotent stem cells can engraft in distinct organ sites where they undergo organ-specific changes in differentiation, potentially providing multipotent cells that contribute to organogenesis. Such cells may be able to provide precursor cells for organ repair following injury or disease.

Although bone marrow–derived cells were observed in various respiratory epithelial cell types after transplantation in mice, the clinical applicability of the phenomenon remain unclear.[83–85] Rates of engraftment are relatively modest. Long-term survival of engrafted cells and their ability to serve as progenitors able to substantially replace lung cells for repair or to genetically replace diseased cells remain inadequately validated. In a recent study, analysis of respiratory tissues following gender-mismatched bone marrow transplantation demonstrated that donor-derived cells were detected in stromal or hematopoietic cells but not in epithelial cells.[89] Several recent studies strongly support the concept that cell fusion accounts for at least some of the observed tissue engraftment.[90,91] Multipotent progenitor cells have been isolated from various adult tissues, including bone marrow, muscle, and brain. Therefore, it may be possible to obtain MAPCs from an individual's tissues for reengraftment. The potential of MAPCs to differentiate into various cell types suggests that exploitation of plasticity may someday provide cells useful for genetic therapy. However, these potentials must be tempered by recent studies supporting the concept that the cells may engraft by cell fusion, acquiring characteristics of differentiated cells by generating somatic cell hybrids, and may not be able to provide a source of self-renewing progenitor cells.[90,91] Nevertheless, these experiments demonstrate the capability of marrow- or other tissue-derived MAPCs to contribute differentiated cells to many organs, including the lung.

Pulmonary Diseases Amenable to Cell and Gene Therapies

Engraftment of marrow- and tissue-derived stem cells offers potential therapies for the correction of several lethal genetic disorders of the lung. For example cystic fibrosis, α1-antitrypsin deficiency, hereditary SP-B deficiency, lymphangiomyomatosis, and mutations in the *SP-C* gene represent lethal pulmonary disorders without effective therapies. Conventional bone marrow transplantation results in the engraftment of hematopoietic cells in the lung. Donor-derived alveolar macrophages, lymphocytes, dendritic cells, and leukocytes are readily detected in the lung. Since bone marrow–derived cells enter the lung and acquire differentiated phenotypes, such cells can be used for genetic and cell therapies requiring modification of activities in hematopoietic cells affecting the lung. Diseases primarily affecting the lung parenchyma remain important clinical targets for cell and gene therapy. For example, cystic fibrosis, caused by mutations in the transmembrane-conductance regulator, affects ion transport and host defense in the airways and tracheal–bronchial glands. Likewise, in hereditary SP-B deficiency, a lethal lung disorder affecting newborns, SP-B must be expressed in type II cells for restoration of surfactant homeostasis and respiratory function. If these genes could be introduced into self-renewing progenitor cells, substantially replacing endogenous pulmonary epithelial cells, these lethal pulmonary disorders may be correctable. Since the bone marrow contributes its precursors to alveolar macrophages, disorders related to abnormalities in alveolar macrophage function, including many storage diseases and pulmonary alveolar proteinosis, may be amenable to cellular and genetic therapy.

REFERENCES

1. Wells, J.M., and Melton, D.A. (1999). Vertebrate endoderm development. *Annu. Rev. Cell. Dev. Biol.* **15,** 393–410.
2. Wells, J.M., and Melton, D.A. (2000). Early mouse endoderm is patterned by soluble factors from adjacent germ layers. *Development* **127,** 1563–1572.
3. Lawson, K.A., Meneses, J.J., and Pedersen, R.A. (1986). Cell fate and cell lineage in the endoderm of the presomite mouse embryo, studied with an intracellular tracer. *Dev. Biol.* **115,** 325–339.
4. Lazzaro, D., Price, M., de Felice, M., and Di Lauro, R. (1991). The transcription factor TTF-1 is expressed at the onset of thyroid and lung morphogenesis and in restricted regions of the fetal brain. *Development* **113,** 1093–1104.
5. Tucker, J.A., and O'Rahilly, R. (1972). Observations on the embryology of the human larynx. *Annu. Otol. Rhinol. Laryngol.* **81,** 520–523.
6. Tucker, G.F., Tucker, J.A., and Vidic, B. (1977). Anatomy and development of the cricoid: serial-section whole-organ study of perinatal larynges. *Annu. Otol. Rhinol. Laryngol.* **86,** 766–769.
7. Zaw-Tun, H.A. (1982). The tracheoesophageal septum—fact or fantasy? Origin and development of the respiratory primordium and esophagus. *Acta. Anat. (Basel)* **114,** 1–21.
8. Burri, P.H. (1997). Structural aspects of prenatal and postnatal development and growth of the lung. *In* "Lung Growth and Development" (J.A. MacDonald, ed.), 1st ed. Mercel Dekker, New York.
9. Ten Have-Opbroek, A.A. (1981). The development of the lung in mammals: an analysis of concepts and findings. *Am. J. Anat.* **162,** 201–219.
10. Langston, C., Kida, K., Reed, M., and Thurlbeck, W.M. (1984). Human lung growth in late gestation and in the neonate. *Am. Rev. Respir. Dis.* **129,** 607–613.
11. Hislop, A.A., Wigglesworth, J.S., and Desai, R. (1986). Alveolar development in the human fetus and infant. *Early Hum. Dev.* **13,** 1–11.
12. Zeltner, T.B., Caduff, J.H., Gehr, P., Pfenninger, J., and Burri, P.H. (1987). The postnatal development and growth of the human lung: I—Morphometry. *Respir. Physiol.* **67,** 247–267.
13. Perl, A.K., Wert, S.E., Nagy, A., Lobe, C.G., and Whitsett, J.A. (2002). Early restriction of peripheral and proximal cell lineages during formation of the lung. *Proc. Natl. Acad. Sci. USA* **99,** 10,482–10,487.
14. Spooner, B.S., and Wessells, N.K. (1970). Mammalian lung development: interactions in primordium formation and bronchial morphogenesis. *J. Exp. Zool.* **175,** 445–454.
15. Shannon, J.M., and Deterding, R.R. (1997). Epithelial–mesenchymal interactions in lung development. *In* "Lung Growth and Development" (J.A. MacDonald, ed.), p. 81. Marcel Dekker, New York.
16. Perl, A.K.T., and Whitsett, J.A. (1999). Molecular mechanisms controlling lung morphogenesis. *Clin. Genet.* **56,** 14–27.

17. Warburton, D., Schwarz, M., Tefft, D., Flores-Delgado, G., Anderson, K.D., and Cardoso, W.V. (2000). The molecular basis of lung morphogenesis. *Mech. Dev.* **92**, 55–81.

18. Hogan, B.L. (1999). Morphogenesis. *Cell* **96**, 225–233.

19. Costa, R.H., Kalinichenko, V.V., and Lim, L. (2001). Transcription factors in mouse lung development and function. *Am. J. Physiol.* **280**, L823–L838.

20. Cardoso, W.V. (2001). Molecular regulation of lung development. *Annu. Rev. Physiol.* **63**, 471–494.

21. Kaplan, F. (2000). Molecular determinants of fetal lung organogenesis. *Mol. Genet. Metab.* **71**, 321–341.

22. Amy, R.W., Bowes, D., Burri, P.H., Haines, J., and Thurlbeck, W.M. (1977). Postnatal growth of the mouse lung. *J. Anat.* **124**, 131–151.

23. Plopper, C.G, Alley, J.L., and Weir, A.J. (1986). Differentiation of tracheal epithelium during fetal lung maturation in the rhesus monkey *Macaca mulatta*. *Am. J. Anat.* **175**, 59–71.

24. Kawamata, S., and Fujita, H. (1983). Fine structural aspects of the development and aging of the tracheal epithelium of mice. *Arch. Histol. Japan* **46**, 355–372.

25. Zhou, L., Lim, L., Costa, R.H., and Whitsett, J.A. (1996). Thyroid transcription factor-1, hepatocyte nuclear factor-3β, surfactant protein B, C, and Clara cell secretory protein in developing mouse lung. *J. Histochem. Cytochem.* **44**, 1183–1193.

26. Stahlman, M.T., Gray, M.E., and Whitsett, J.A. (1996). Expression of thyroid transcription factor-1 (TTF-1) in fetal and neonatal human lung. *J. Histochem. Cytochem.* **44**, 673–678.

27. Yang, H., Lu, M.M., Zhang, L., Whitsett, J.A., and Morrisey, E.E. (2002). GATA-6 regulates differentiation of distal lung epithelium. *Development* **129**, 2233–2246.

28. Monaghan, A.P., Kaestner, K.H., Grau, E., and Schutz, G. (1993). Postimplantation expression patterns indicate a role for the mouse *forkhead–HNF-3α*, *-β*, and *-γ* genes in determination of the definitive endoderm, chordamesoderm, and neuroectoderm. *Development* **119**, 567–578.

29. Chen, J., Knowles, H.J., Hebert, J.L., and Hackett, B.P. (1998). Mutation of the mouse hepatocyte nuclear factor–forkhead homologue 4 gene results in an absence of cilia and random left–right asymmetry. *J. Clin. Invest.* **102**, 1077–1082.

30. Tichelaar, J.W., Wert, S.E., Costa, R.H., Kimura, S., and Whitsett, J.A. (1999). HNF-3–forkhead homolog-4 (HFH-4) is expressed in ciliated epithelial cells in the developing mouse lung. *J. Histochem. Cytochem.* **47**, 823–831.

31. Stahlman, M.T., Gray, M.E., and Whitsett, J.A. (1998). Temporal–spatial distribution of hepatocyte nuclear factor-3β in developing human lung and other foregut derivatives. *J. Histochem. Cytochem.* **46**, 955–962.

32. Khoor, A., Stahlman, M.T., Gray, M.E., and Whitsett, J.A. (1994). Temporal–spatial distribution of SP-B and SP-C proteins and mRNAs in the developing respiratory epithelium of human lung. *J. Histochem. Cytochem.* **42**, 1187–1199.

33. Kimura, S., Hara, Y., Pineau, T., Fernandez-Salguero, P., Fox, C.H., Ward, J.M., and Gonzalez, F.J. (1996). The T/ebp-null mouse: thyroid-specific enhancer-binding protein is essential for the organogenesis of the thyroid, lung, ventral forebrain, and pituitary. *Genes Dev.* **10**, 60–69.

34. Tryka, A.F., Witschi, H., Gosslee, D.G., McArthur, A.H., and Clapp, N.K. (1986). Patterns of cell proliferation during recovery from oxygen injury: species differences. *Am. Rev. Respir. Dis.* **133**, 1055–1059.

35. Adamson, I.Y., and Bowden, D.H. (1974). The type 2 cell as progenitor of alveolar epithelial regeneration: a cytodynamic study in mice after exposure to oxygen. *Lab. Invest.* **30**, 35–42.

36. Donnelly, G.M., Haack, D.G., and Heird, C.S. (1982). Tracheal epithelium: cell kinetics and differentiation in normal rat tissue. *Cell. Tissue Kinet.* **15**, 119–130.

37. Kauffman, S.L. (1980). Cell proliferation in mammalian lung. *Int. Rev. Exp. Path.* **22**, 131–191.

38. Breuer, R., Zajicek, G., Christensen, T.G., Lucey, E.C., and Snider, G.L. (1990). Cell kinetics of normal adult hamster bronchial epithelium in the steady state. *Am. J. Respir. Cell. Mol. Biol.* **2**, 51–58.

39. Cotsarelis, G., Cheng, S.Z., Dong, G., Sun, T.T., and Lavker, R.M. (1989). Existence of slow-cycling limbal epithelial basal cells that can be preferentially stimulated to proliferate: implications on epithelial stem cells. *Cell* **57**, 201–209.

40. Slack, J.M. (2000). Stem cells in epithelial tissues. *Science* **287**, 1431–1433.

41. Mackenzie, I.C., and Bickenbach, J.R. (1985). Label-retaining keratinocytes and Langerhans cells in mouse epithelia. *Cell. Tissue Res.* **242**, 551–556.

42. Frank, L., and Massaro, D. (1980). Oxygen toxicity. *Am. J. Med.* **69**, 117–126.

43. Smith, L.J. (1985). Hyperoxic lung injury: biochemical, cellular, and morphologic characterization in the mouse. *J. Lab. Clin. Med.* **106**, 269–278.

44. Reynolds, S.D., Giangreco, A., Power, J.H., and Stripp, B.R. (2000). Neuroepithelial bodies of pulmonary airways serve as a reservoir of progenitor cells capable of epithelial regeneration. *Am. J. Pathol.* **156**, 269–278.

45. Reynolds, S.D., Hong, K.U., Giangreco, A., Mango, G.W., Guron, C., Morimoto, Y., and Stripp, B.R. (2000). Conditional Clara cell ablation reveals a self-renewing progenitor function of pulmonary neuroendocrine cells. *Am. J. Physiol.* **278**, L1256–L1263.

46. Giangreco, A., Reynolds, S.D., and Stripp, B.R. (2002). Terminal bronchioles harbor a unique airway stem cell population that localizes to the bronchoalveolar duct junction. *Am. J. Pathol.* **161**, 173–182.

47. Hong, K.U., Reynolds, S.D., Giangreco, A., Hurley, C.M., and Stripp, B.R. (2001). Clara cell secretory protein-expressing cells of the airway neuroepithelial body microenvironment include a label-retaining subset and are critical for epithelial renewal after progenitor cell depletion. *Am. J. Respir. Cell. Mol. Biol.* **24**, 671–681.

48. Borthwick, D.W., Shahbazian, M., Krantz, Q.T., Dorin, J.R., and Randell, S.H. (2001). Evidence for stem cell niches in the tracheal epithelium. *Am. J. Respir. Cell. Mol. Biol.* **24**, 662–670.

49. Evans, M.J., Johnson, L.V., Stephens, R.J., and Freeman, G. (1976). Renewal of the terminal bronchiolar epithelium in the rat following exposure to NO_2 or O_3. *Lab. Invest.* **35**, 246–257.

50. Evans, M.J., Cabral, L.J., Stephens, R.J., and Freeman, G. (1975). Transformation of alveolar type 2 cells to type 1 cells following exposure to NO_2. *Exp. Mol. Pathol.* **22**, 142–150.

51. Ford, J.R., and Terzaghi-Howe, M. (1992). Basal cells are the progenitors of primary tracheal epithelial cell cultures. *Exp. Cell. Res.* **198**, 69–77.

52. Engelhardt, J.F., Schlossberg, H., Yankaskas, J.R., and Dudus, L. (1995). Progenitor cells of the adult human airway involved in submucosal gland development. *Development* **121**, 2031–2046.

53. Watt, F.M., and Hogan, B.L. (2000). Out of Eden: stem cells and their niches. *Science* **287**, 1427–1430.

54. Engelhardt, J.F. (2001). Stem cell niches in the mouse airway. *Am. J. Respir. Cell. Mol. Biol.* **24,** 649–652.

55. Nakajima, C., Kijimoto, C., Yokoyama, Y., Miyakawa, T., Tsuchiya, Y., Kuroda, T., Nakano, M., and Saeki, M. (1998). Longitudinal follow-up of pulmonary function after lobectomy in childhood: factors affecting lung growth. *Pediatr. Surg. Int.* **13,** 341–345.

56. Laros, C.D., and Westermann, C.J. (1987). Dilatation, compensatory growth, or both after pneumonectomy during childhood and adolescence: a 30-year follow-up study. *J. Thorac. Cardiovasc. Surg.* **93,** 570–576.

57. Buhain, W.J., and Brody, J.S. (1973). Compensatory growth of the lung following pneumonectomy. *J. Appl. Physiol.* **35,** 898–902.

58. Rannels, D.E., White, D.M., and Watkins, C.A. (1976). Rapidity of compensatory lung growth following pneumonectomy in adult rats. *J. Appl. Physiol.* **46,** 326–333.

59. Brody, J.S. (1975). Time course of and stimuli to compensatory growth of the lung after pneumonectomy. *J. Clin. Invest.* **56,** 897–904.

60. Cagle, P.T., and Thurlbeck, W.M. (1988). Postpneumonectomy compensatory lung growth. *Am. Rev. Respir. Dis.* **138,** 1314–1326.

61. Alcorn, D., Adamson, T.M., Lambert, T.F., Maloney, J.E., Ritchie, B.C., and Robinson, P.M. (1977). Morphological effects of chronic tracheal ligation and drainage in the fetal lamb lung. *J. Anat.* **123,** 649–660.

62. Kaza, A.K., Kron, I.L., Long, S.M., Fiser, S.M., Stevens, P.M., Kern, J.A., Tribble, C.G., and Laubach, V.E. (2001). Epidermal growth factor receptor up-regulation is associated with lung growth after lobectomy. *Annu. Thorac. Surg.* **72,** 380–385.

63. Kaza, A.K., Kron, I.L., Kern, J.A., Long, S.M., Fiser, S.M., Nguyen, R.P., Tribble, C.G., and Laubach, V.E. (2001). Retinoic acid enhances lung growth after pneumonectomy. *Annu. Thorac. Surg.* **71,** 1645–1650.

64. Kaza, A.K., Kron, I.L., Leuwerke, S.M., Tribble, C.G., and Laubach, V.E. (2002). Keratinocyte growth factor enhances postpneumonectomy lung growth by alveolar proliferation. *Circulation* **106,** I120–I124.

65. Nabeyrat, E., Besnard, V., Corroyer, S., Cazals, V., and Clement, A. (1998). Retinoic acid-induced proliferation of lung alveolar epithelial cells: relation with the IGF system. *Am. J. Physiol.* **275,** L71–L79.

66. Massaro, G.D., and Massaro, D. (1997). Retinoic acid treatment abrogates elastase-induced pulmonary emphysema in rats. *Nat. Med.* **3,** 675–677.

67. Leuwerke, S.M., Kaza, A.K., Tribble, C.G., Kron, I.L., and Laubach, V.E. (2002). Inhibition of compensatory lung growth in endothelial nitric oxide synthase-deficient mice. *Am. J. Physiol.* **282,** L1272–L1278.

68. Aoshiba, K., Yokohori, N., and Nagai, A. (2003). Alveolar wall apoptosis causes lung destruction and emphysematous changes. *Am. J. Respir. Cell Mol. Biol.* **28,** 555–562.

69. Hokuto, I., Perl, A.K.T., and Whitsett, J.A. (2003). Prenatal, but not postnatal, inhibition of fibroblast growth factor receptor signaling causes emphysema. *J. Biol. Chem.* **278,** 415–421.

70. Geary, C., and Whitsett, J. (2002). Inhaled nitric oxide for oligohydramnios-induced pulmonary hypoplasia: a report of two cases and review of the literature. *J. Perinatol.* **22,** 82–85.

71. Massaro, G.D., and Massaro, D. (2000). Retinoic acid treatment partially rescues failed septation in rats and mice. *Am. J. Physiol.* **278,** L955–L960.

72. Ali, N.N., Edgar, A.J., Samadikuchaksaraei, A., Timson, C.M., Romanska, H.M., Polak, J.M., and Bishop, A.E. (2002). Derivation of type II alveolar epithelial cells from murine embryonic stem cells. *Tissue Eng.* **8,** 541–550.

73. Pittenger, M.F., Mackay, A.M., Beck, S.C., Jaiswal, R.K., Douglas, R., Mosca, J.D., Moorman, M.A., Simonetti, D.W., Craig, S., Marshak, D.R. (1999). Multilineage potential of adult human mesenchymal stem cells. *Science* **284,** 143–147.

74. Ferrari, G., Cusella-De Angelis, G., Coletta, M., Paolucci, E., Stornaiuolo, A., Cossu, G., and Mavilio, F. (1998). Muscle regeneration by bone marrow-derived myogenic progenitors. *Science* **279,** 1528–1530.

75. Gussoni, E., Soneoka, Y., Strickland, C.D., Buzney, E.A., Khan, M.K., Flint, A.F., Kunkel, L.M., and Mulligan, R.C. (1999). Dystrophin expression in the mdx mouse restored by stem cell transplantation. *Nature* **401,** 390–394.

76. Orlic, D., Kajstura, J., Chimenti, S., Jakoniuk, I., Anderson, S.M., Li, B., Pickel, J., McKay, R., Nadal-Ginard, B., Bodine, D.M., Leri, A., and Anversa, P. (2001). Bone marrow cells regenerate infarcted myocardium. *Nature* **410,** 701–705.

77. Jackson, K.A., Majka, S.M., Wang, H., Pocius, J., Hartley, C.J., Mark, W., Majesky, M.W., Entman, M.L., Michael, L.H., Hirschi, K.K., and Goodell, M.A. (2001). Regeneration of ischemic cardiac muscle and vascular endothelium by adult stem cells. *J. Clin. Invest.* **107,** 1395–1402.

78. Lin, Y., Weisdorf, D.J., Solovey, A., and Hebbel, R.P. (2000). Origins of circulating endothelial cells and endothelial outgrowth from blood. *J. Clin. Invest.* **105,** 71–77.

79. Asahara, T., Masuda, H., Takahashi, T., Kalka, C., Pastore, C., Silver, M., Kearne, M., Magner, M., and Isner, J.M. (1999). Bone marrow origin of endothelial progenitor cells responsible for postnatal vasculogenesis in physiological and pathological neovascularization. *Circ. Res.* **85,** 221–228.

80. Petersen, B.E., Bowen, W.C., Patrene, K.D., Mars, W.M., Sullivan, A.K., Murase, N., Boggs, S.S., Greenberger, J.S., and Goff, J.P. (1999). Bone marrow as a potential source of hepatic oval cells. *Science* **284,** 1168–1170.

81. Theise, N.D., Badve, S., Saxena, R., Henegariu, O., Sell, S., Crawford, J.M., and Krause, D.S. (2000). Derivation of hepatocytes from bone marrow cells in mice after radiation-induced myeloablation. *Hepatology* **31,** 235–240.

82. Lagasse, E., Connors, H., Al-Dhalimy, M., Reitsma, M., Dohse, M., Osborne, L., Wang, X., Finegold, M., Weissman, I.L., and Grompe, M. (2000). Purified hematopoietic stem cells can differentiate into hepatocytes *in vivo*. *Nat. Med.* **6,** 1229–1234.

83. Krause, D.S., Theise, N.D., Collector, M.I., Henegariu, O., Hwang, S., Gardner, R., Neutzel, S., and Sharkis, S.J. (2001). Multiorgan, multilineage engraftment by a single bone marrow-derived stem cell. *Cell* **105,** 369–377.

84. Kotton, D.N., Ma, B.Y., Cardoso, W.V., Sanderson, E.A., Summer, R.S., Williams, M.C., and Fine, A. (2001). Bone marrow-derived cells as progenitors of lung alveolar epithelium. *Development* **128,** 5181–5188.

85. Grove, J.E., Lutzko, C., Priller, J., Henegariu, O., Theise, N.D., Kohn, D.B., and Krause, D.S. (2002). Marrow-derived cells as vehicles for delivery of gene therapy to pulmonary epithelium. *Am. J. Respir. Cell Mol. Biol.* **27,** 645–651.

86. Jiang, Y., Jahagirdar, B.N., Reinhardt, R.L., Schwartz, R.E., Keene, C.D., Ortiz-Gonzalez, X.R., Reyes, M., Lenvik, T., Lund, T., Blackstad, M., Du, J., Aldrich, S., Lisberg, A., Low, W.C., Largaespada, D.A., and Verfaillie, C.M. (2002). Pluripotency of

mesenchymal stem cells derived from adult marrow. *Nature* **418,** 41–49.

87. Schwartz, R.E., Reyes, M., Koodie, L., Jiang, Y., Blackstad, M., Lund, T., Lenvik, T., Johnson, S., Hu, W.S., and Verfaillie, C.M. (2002). Multipotent adult progenitor cells from bone marrow differentiate into functional hepatocyte-like cells. *J. Clin. Invest.* **109,** 1291–1302.

88. Reyes, M., Dudek, A., Jahagirdar, B., Koodie, L., Marker, P.H., and Verfaillie, C.M. (2002). Origin of endothelial progenitors in human postnatal bone marrow. *J. Clin. Invest.* **109,** 337–346.

89. Davies, J.C., Potter, M., Bush, A., Rosenthal, M., Geddes, D.M., and Alton, E.W. (2002). Bone marrow stem cells do not repopulate the healthy upper respiratory tract. *Pediatr. Pulmonol.* **34,** 251–256.

90. Ying, Q.L., Nichols, J., Evans, E.P., and Smith, A.G. (2002). Changing potency by spontaneous fusion. *Nature* **416,** 545–548.

91. Terada, N., Hamazaki, T., Oka, M., Hoki, M., Mastalerz, D.M., Nakano, Y., Meyer, E.M., Morel, L., Petersen, B.E., and Scott, E.W. (2002). Bone marrow cells adopt the phenotype of other cells by spontaneous cell fusion. *Nature* **416,** 542–545.

92. Ten Have-Opbroek, A.A. (1991). Lung development in the mouse embryo. *Exp. Lung Res.* **17,** 111–130.

93. Wert S.E., Glasser, S.W., Korfhagen, T.R., and Whitsett, J.A. (1993). Transcriptional elements from the human SP-C gene direct expression in the primordial respiratory epithelium of transgenic mice. *Dev. Biol.* **156,** 426–443.

Thymus and Parathyroid Organogenesis

Nancy R. Manley and C. Clare Blackburn

The vertebrate pharyngeal region is the source of the endoderm-derived glandular organs, the thyroid, ultimobranchial bodies, thymus, and parathyroids. These organs play a variety of essential physiological roles, from the regulation of calcium homeostasis to the generation of T-cells required for adaptive immunity. All of these organs originate from outpocketings of the pharyngeal endoderm and require interactions between the endoderm and the surrounding mesenchyme for their development. In this chapter, we focus on two of these organs that have diverse physiological roles but a common embryonic origin: the parathyroid and thymus glands. We begin by reviewing the initial patterning and early development of these organs and the molecular mechanisms controlling these processes. We also explain potential mechanisms for the evolution of these organs, which may have involved the same molecular pathways. Finally, we describe possible models for the differentiation of embryonic and fetal parathyroid and thymic epithelial progenitor or stem cells.

Overview

The thymus and parathyroids originate from shared organ primordia that develop from the third pharyngeal pouches, which begin to form at day 9.5 of embryonic development (E9.5) in the mouse. The pharyngeal pouches are transient, bilateral outpocketings of the pharyngeal endoderm that form in an anterior to posterior order beginning about E8.5. Each of the pouches contacts the surface ectoderm about one day after formation, through ectodermal invaginations called pharyngeal clefts. The pharyngeal pouches are directly surrounded by pharyngeal arch mesenchyme, which is primarily composed of neural crest cells (NCCs), although there is also a mesodermal component in the center of each arch.[1] Experimental and genetic evidence indicates that endoderm, ectoderm, and NCC mesenchyme are directly involved in some aspect of thymus and parathyroid organogenesis. In the model supported by current evidence (Fig. 37–1), the thymus and parathyroids are formed from bilateral endodermal primordia, each surrounded (at least during fetal stages) by a neural crest–derived capsule. These endodermal primordia separate from the pharyngeal endoderm and surface ectoderm soon after formation and begin to migrate toward their final

positions in the embryo. The thymus and parathyroid domains resolve into separate organs during this migration; indeed, they have spatially separate final locations.

Analysis of the molecular mechanisms directing these processes has lagged that of other endodermal organs, such as the lung, pancreas, and liver. Many of the same molecules are expressed in both the pharyngeal region and the more posterior endoderm, including *Hox* genes and Sonic hedgehog (Shh). Because global paradigms of endodermal organogenesis may exist, such as early regionalization of the endoderm and regionally restricted expression of organ-specific transcription factors prior to organ formation,[2] the mechanisms known to direct the development of other endodermal organs may provide clues about the pathways that could be acting in pharyngeal organogenesis.

Early Patterning (E8–10.5): Formation and Patterning of the Third Pharyngeal Pouch

How are the organ-specific domains within the third pouch established? This process may involve two separate steps: specifying third pouch identity and setting up positional information within the pouch along the proximal–distal (P–D), dorsal–ventral (D–V), and anterior–posterior (A–P) axes. Although these are separable processes, they may be controlled by overlapping sets of transcription factors and signaling molecules (Fig. 37–2).

IS POUCH FORMATION REQUIRED FOR ORGANOGENESIS?

Like other endodermal organs, the thymus and parathyroid initiate formation by budding off of the main endodermal tube—in this case, the foregut. However, this organ budding occurs at a unique and transient endodermal structure: the pharyngeal pouches, which predate the pharyngeal organs in evolution (see the section "Evolutionary Considerations: Gills vs Thymus—Shared and Distinct Genetic Programs"). The pharyngeal pouches are a series of bilateral outpocketings of lateral pharyngeal endoderm. The thymus and parathyroids arise from the third pair of pouches in mice. Although the mechanisms controlling pharyngeal pouch formation are not well understood, some genetic data suggests that pharyngeal pouch formation may be required for thymus and parathyroid organogenesis.

All of the known mouse mutants in which third pouch formation is defective are athymic and aparathyroid.

Handbook of Stem Cells
Volume 1
Copyright © 2004 by Academic Press
All rights of reproduction in any form reserved.

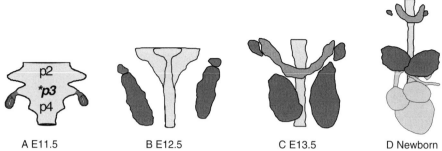

Figure 37-1. *Developmental progression of thymus and parathyroid organogenesis in the mouse.* (A) At E11.5, The common thymus–parathyroid rudiments are budding from the distal aspect of the third pharyngeal pouches. (B) By E12.5, the common primordia have been released from the pharynx and the surface ectoderm (not shown), have begun to migrate ventrally and medially, and are in the process of dividing into separate parathyroid and thymus lobes. (C) At E13.5, the organs are separated, and the parathyroids have begun to associate with the thyroid gland. The thymic lobes are approaching the midline. (D) In the newborn and adult animals, the thymus is seated in the anterior mediastinum above the heart, and the parathyroids are in variable locations, usually closely associated with the thyroid. (Please see CD-ROM for color version of this figure.)

Mutation of *Tbx1*, a candidate gene for DiGeorge syndrome expressed in the pharyngeal pouch endoderm and pharyngeal arch mesoderm, deletes the second, third, and fourth pharyngeal pouches; not surprisingly, these mice are both athymic and aparathyroid.[3] Fibroblast growth factor (Fgf8) is expressed in the pharyngeal endoderm and ectoderm at the time of pouch formation and is down-regulated in the third pouch in *Tbx1* mutants.[3] In *Fgf8* hypomorphic mutants, variable loss of or reduction in third pouch formation is correlated with athymia or thymic hypoplasia.[4,5] Analysis of *chordin* knockout mice also revealed a failure of both caudal pouch formation and thymus and parathyroid organogenesis, and it suggested that *chordin* expression in the pharyngeal endoderm is required for correct regulation of both *Tbx1* and *Fgf8* expression.[6] Collectively, these results suggest that pouch formation is required for thymus and parathyroid organogenesis.

Evidence from transplants of pharyngeal endoderm in both chick and mouse systems, however, indicates that the pharyngeal endoderm is specified at least to a thymus fate prior to or at initial pouch evagination.[1,7] In these experiments, prospective third pouch pharyngeal endoderm was transplanted to an ectopic location, either near the embryonic gut of the chick[1] or under the kidney capsule of adult nude mice.[7] In both studies, the transplanted endoderm developed into a histologically complete thymus; in the mouse study, T-cells were detected in the lymph nodes. Parathyroids were also detected in the transplants in the chick–quail grafts.[1]

These experiments provide strong evidence for an early specification of endoderm at least to a thymus fate. Thus, it seems likely that separate pouch formation and cell fate determination pathways exist and that both are required for thymus and parathyroid organogenesis to proceed normally. This would be consistent with the facts that the pharyngeal pouches predate the thymus and parathyroids in evolution and that the A–P and D–V patterns required to generate the pharyngeal organs are acquired later and imposed on existing

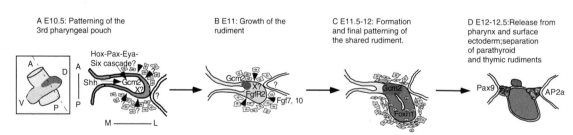

Figure 37-2. *Molecular control of thymus and parathyroid organogenesis.* (A) The box inset shows a lateral view of one third-pharyngeal pouch, with the prospective parathyroid and thymus domains. The coronal plane of section is indicated by a dashed line. At E10.5, the third pouch expresses the *Hoxa3–Pax1/9–Eya1–Six1* pathway but does not express *Shh* RNA. Both of these pathways are required for *Gcm2* expression. It is not known whether a thymus-specific factor (X) is also expressed or whether thymus fate is the default identity. It is also not known whether mesenchyme and ectoderm play a role in patterning. (B) At E11, the shared thymus–parathyroid rudiment begins to form by proliferation of the endoderm. Continued growth of the epithelial rudiment requires Fgf7 and Fgf10 signals from the mesenchyme and FgfR2IIIb in the endoderm, although initial formation of the rudiment is FGF independent. The exact location of the *Gcm2* domain relative to the thymus domain is not well defined at this stage, nor is it known whether a thymus-specific determinant (X) is expressed. (C) By E11.5–12, the *Gcm2* and *Foxn1* domains are well established. The rudiment still contacts both endoderm and ectoderm, and the mesenchymal capsule is beginning to condense. Lymphocyte progenitor cells are beginning to enter the thymic but not the parathyroid rudiment. (D) At E12–12.5, the connections to the pharynx and surface ectoderm undergo apoptosis, releasing the primordia, which begin to migrate. The parathyroids are beginning to separate from the thymic lobes (A: anterior, P: posterior, D: dorsal, V: ventral, M: medial, and L: lateral). (Please see CD-ROM for color version of this figure.)

structures (see the section "Evolutionary Considerations: Gills vs Thymus—Shared and Distinct Genetic Programs"). However, an alternative possibility is that the athymia caused by disruption of the Tbx1–FGF pathway reflects a direct effect on early patterning of the endoderm rather than an effect secondary to the loss of pouch formation. Investigation of the effects of the loss of Tbx1 and Fgf8 function in the absence of a pouch formation defect would be required to distinguish between these possibilities.

EARLY PATTERNING OF THE THIRD POUCH INTO ORGAN-SPECIFIC DOMAINS

Evidence from gene expression, ectopic transplantation, and mutant studies indicates that the third pouch is patterned into discrete parathyroid- and thymus-specific domains soon after formation, although overt development of the organ primordia does not begin until around E11 (Fig. 37–2). The earliest parathyroid-specific marker is a transcription factor, *Gcm2*, required for parathyroid organogenesis.[8] *Gcm2* is one of two mammalian orthologs of the *Drosophila* gene glial cells missing *(gcm)*, which defines a novel class of transcription factors.[9,10] *Gcm2* expression is initiated around E9.5 in the caudal pharyngeal endoderm, encompassing pouches 3 and 4.[11] By E10.5, it marks a discrete domain of the anterior third pouch endoderm and is subsequently restricted to the most dorsal and anterior part of the shared thymus and parathyroid primordium. *Gcm2* therefore appears to create a domain of parathyroid identity within the endoderm, similar to the role of Pdx1[12–14] and Ptf1a[15] in pancreas organogenesis or Nkx2.1[16] and TTF2[17] in the thyroid. Intriguingly, expression of the *gcm* gene in *Drosophila* acts as a cell fate switch between glial and neural cell identity in the developing central nervous system.[18,19] This expression pattern and implied function collectively suggest that *Gcm2* expression confers a parathyroid fate on cells of the developing third pharyngeal pouch.

It is tempting to speculate that there should be a thymus-specific counterpart to *Gcm2* with a complementary expression pattern. Currently, the earliest thymus-specific gene for which there is both expression and functional data is *Foxn1*. *Foxn1* is a forkhead-class transcription factor that is mutated in the classical mouse mutant *nude*[20] and in the human *nude* syndrome.[21] *Foxn1* is required cell-autonomously for the development of mature thymic epithelial cells (TECs)[22] and is strongly expressed in a complementary pattern to *Gcm2* in the shared primordium at E11.5.[11] However, although detectable between E9.5–11 by reverse transcription-polymerase chain reaction,[23,24] *Foxn1* is not required for primordium formation,[25] and no phenotype has been detected in *Foxn1*-null mutants prior to E12. Recent data has also shown that *IL-7* is specifically expressed in the thymic rudiment as early as E11.5 and that this expression is initiated in the *nude* thymus, suggesting that cells in the thymic remnant of *Foxn1*-mutant mice have been specified to a thymic fate.[26] Thus, although *Foxn1* is required for development of mature TECs, it is unlikely to specify thymic identity in the third pouch.

How then is thymus identity specified? There are currently two candidates for this function. One possibility is that the homeobox transcription factor Hoxa3 may fulfill this role. In this model, Hoxa3 specifies third pharyngeal pouch identity, such that the default fate of the third pharyngeal pouch is thymus. Parathyroid identity would then be imposed on this default state by the expression of *Gcm2*. The role of Hoxa3 is explained in detail in section "Transcription Factor Regulation of A–P Identity and Patterning."

Another candidate is *Ehox*, a distant member of the paired box family of homeodomain transcription factors[27] that has a strikingly restricted expression pattern consistent with a role in early thymus organogenesis, specification of the thymic epithelial lineage, or both. *Ehox* is expressed throughout the prospective foregut endoderm at E8.5, but by E9.5 it is limited to a ventral domain within the second and third pharyngeal pouches.[28] At E10.5, it is largely restricted to a domain apparently complementary to the *Gcm2*-expressing, prospective parathyroid domain of the third pharyngeal pouch. Strikingly, it is not expressed in the pharyngeal pouches at E11.5; by this stage, the domain previously marked by *Ehox* strongly expresses *Foxn1*. *Ehox* is therefore a candidate for defining a region competent to form thymus; however, functional analysis is required to test this possibility.

The division of the third pouch into discrete organ-specific domains is maintained in the developing organ primordia. Each thymus–parathyroid primordium initially contains the precursors to one thymus lobe and one parathyroid gland.[29] These domains, however, are not morphologically distinguishable at the earliest stages of primordium development, and a mechanism for boundary formation in the establishment of the thymus and parathyroid domains within the shared primordium must therefore exist. Since the *Gcm2* domain is established before primordium formation, it may define the thymus–parathyroid boundary. *Foxn1* expression initiates later, after primordium formation, at the most ventral tip of the third pouch, after which it spreads dorsally throughout the entire thymus-specific portion of the rudiment to the *Gcm2* expression domain.[11] The upstream signals establishing this *Foxn1* expression pattern have not been identified, although there is some evidence that Wnt signaling may be involved.[23] These expression patterns suggest that the thymus–parathyroid boundary may be maintained by *Gcm2*, repressing *Foxn1* expression within the parathyroid domain (Fig. 37–3). Given this model, it will be of interest to determine the fate of presumptive parathyroid cells in the absence of *Gcm2* expression.

TRANSCRIPTION FACTOR REGULATION OF A–P IDENTITY AND PATTERNING

Hox genes encode a highly conserved family of transcription factors that specify axial positional information in the developing embryos of many, if not all, animals.[30,31] *Hox* genes generally have their greatest effect at the most anterior boundary of their expression patterns. The *Hox* group 3 paralogous genes *(Hoxa3, Hoxb3, and Hoxd3)* have their anterior expression boundary in the pharyngeal region at the level of the third arch[32,33] and have been shown by mutational studies to be required for various aspects of thymus and parathyroid organogenesis.[34–37] The most important of these is *Hoxa3*.

Figure 37–3. *Formation of the thymus–parathyroid boundary in the shared primordium. The parathyroid domain is established first in the dorsal part of the primordia by expression of Gcm2. Foxn1 expression begins about E11.25 in the most ventral part of the primordia then spreads toward the Gcm2 domain. In this model, Gcm2 expression acts to repress Foxn1 expression within the parathyroid domain, effectively generating the thymus–parathyroid boundary at the interface between these two expression domains. (Please see CD-ROM for color version of this figure.)*

In *Hoxa3* mutants, pouch formation is normal, but the shared primordium never forms.[34,35,38] Furthermore, *Gcm2* expression is absent from the third pouch endoderm in *Hoxa3* mutants.[39] These results place *Hoxa3* as the earliest gene to specifically affect thymus and parathyroid organogenesis without affecting pouch formation.

At least part of the role of *Hoxa3* in thymus development is its regulation of *Pax1* and *Pax9* in the third pouch endoderm. *Pax1* and *Pax9* are closely related members of the paired-box transcription factor family that plays critical roles in the development of multiple organs.[40–42] Mutation of *Pax9* results in defects in both thymus and parathyroid organogenesis,[43] but *Pax1* mutants have less severe defects in thymus and parathyroid development and function.[37,44,45] *Pax1* and *Pax9* are specifically down-regulated in the third pharyngeal pouch in *Hoxa3^{−/−}* embryos at E10.5.[35,46] Furthermore, *Hoxa3^{+/−}Pax1^{−/−}* compound mutants have defects including thymic ectopia and hypoplasia and delayed separation of the thymic primordia from the pharynx, as well as increased severity of parathyroid defects.[37] These studies provided the initial evidence for a transcription factor cascade directing the early events in thymus and parathyroid organogenesis.

Recent evidence suggests that a *Hox–Pax–Eya–Six* regulatory network is likely to pattern the endoderm to establish third pouch identity (Fig. 37–2). This endodermal transcription factor regulatory network was proposed by Xu *et al.*[47] and is primarily based on the gene expression patterns and phenotypes in *Hoxa3-* and *Eya1-*mutant mice. Like *Hoxa3* mutants, both *Eya1* and *Six1* mutants are athymic and aparathyroid,[47,48] and *Eya1* mutants fail to express the parathyroid marker *Gcm2*.[47] The *Pax1* and *Pax9* single-mutant phenotypes are

less severe, possibly reflecting redundancy between these two genes.[37,43–45,49,50] In *Eya1* embryos, *Hoxa3* and *Pax1/9* expression is normal, but *Six1* is reduced in the third pouch endoderm.[47] *Gcm2* is also reduced in the *Pax1* single mutants and is initiated but not maintained in *Hoxa3^{+/−}Pax1^{−/−}* embryos.[37] Although *Hoxa3, Eya1,* and *Six1* are also expressed in both NCCs and ectoderm, since *Pax1/9* are restricted to endoderm, it is likely that any effects of this pathway are restricted to the endoderm.

This pathway is remarkably similar to the highly conserved *Pax–Eya–Six* pathway originally described in *Drosophila* eye development.[51] However, the position of *Hox* genes upstream of this pathway is not strictly conserved from *Drosophila*, consistent with the fact that *Pax1/9* gene expression in the pharyngeal pouches predates *Hox* gene endodermal expression in evolution (see "Evolutionary Considerations: Gills vs Thymus—Shared and Distinct Genetic Programs"). This "new" role for *Hoxa3* upstream of a *Pax–Eya–Six* network in vertebrates is also consistent with the fact that initiation of *Pax1* expression in the endoderm is *Hoxa3*-independent and maintenance requires *Hoxa3*.[35]

It is less clear what the relationships between *Hoxa3* and *Eya1* might be in NCCs, or what their functions might be in that cell type. As both of these mutants also have defects in the pharyngeal cartilages, which are NCC derived, it is possible that their NCC expression is not related to thymus–parathyroid organogenesis. Dissection of the roles of these genes in these different cell types will require tissue-specific knockout or transgenic approaches.

SIGNALING: ENDODERMAL INTRINSIC VERSUS NCC–ENDODERMAL PATTERNING

Although we have begun to make significant progress in identifying the transcription factors required for thymus–parathyroid organogenesis, little is known about the intercellular signaling pathways acting at the site of thymus–parathyroid induction and regulating early organogenesis. Signaling events important to organogenesis may be either epithelial–mesenchymal or intraepithelial. It is well established that NCCs are required to promote the growth and development of the thymic epithelial rudiment (see the section "Initiation, Outgrowth, and Formation of the Primordium (E11–12)"); however, a role for NCCs in initial patterning of the developing pouch has not yet been demonstrated. Fgf7 and Fgf10 signaling from the mesenchyme to the endoderm has been directly implicated in thymus development by mutational studies in mice (see the section "Separation of the Primordia from the Endoderm and Ectoderm"); however, the initial stages of organogenesis and epithelial cell differentiation until about E12.5 appear relatively normal in these mutants,[52] indicating that these FGF signals are not required for the earliest patterning and initiation events. Indeed, the endodermal transplantation experiments described previously suggest that acquisition of thymus identity may be endoderm-intrinsic.

Loss of NCC migration resulting from ectopic expression of noggin under the Hoxa2 promoter has been reported to result in loss of Pax1 in the third pouch endoderm.[53] Since initiation rather than maintenance of Pax1 is affected and Pax9 is normal in these transgenics, this is probably not because of loss of Hoxa3 in the NCCs. This study concluded that initial expression of Pax1 in the third pouch might depend on a signal from NCC mesenchyme. However, pharyngeal pouch formation is itself abnormal in these transgenics, raising the alternative possibility that loss of Pax1 could be secondary to a transgene-associated morphological defect. This seems likely, since both initial pouch formation and initiation of Pax1 expression in wild-type embryos precede NCC migration. Also, since Pax1/9 expression in the pouches predates the neural crest in evolution,[54] and Pax9 has a more critical role in thymus organogenesis than Pax1, the implications of this result for the role of mesenchyme in patterning of the third pouch are unclear.

By analogy with its role in other endoderm-derived organs, Shh is a good candidate for being involved in epithelial-intrinsic patterning of the pharyngeal endoderm. Down-regulation of *Shh* expression in the endoderm is necessary for organogenesis of the pancreas, intestine, and pituitary gland.[55–57] *Shh* is expressed throughout the gut endoderm both anterior and posterior to the pancreatic bud, but it is noticeably absent from the pancreatic endoderm. Ectopic expression of *Shh* in the pancreatic endoderm prevents expression of the pancreas-specific transcription factor Pdx1 and blocks pancreas development.[58] Conversely, inhibition of Hedgehog signaling with the sterol alkaloid cyclopamine induces pancreas formation from stomach endoderm.[58] Recent data from the Manley lab has suggested that the Shh pathway may be playing a similar role in patterning of the third pouch.[59] Although Shh is expressed throughout the ventral pharynx and in the first and second pouches, Shh RNA is absent from third pouch (Fig. 37–2). Even though Hoxa3 and Pax1 expression in the third pouch is normal in Shh mutants, Gcm2 is never expressed, and Foxn1 is initiated normally. Consistent with these expression patterns, the parathyroids are absent but the thymus forms, although later organogenesis and TEC differentiation are abnormal. These results suggest a model in which Gcm2 expression and parathyroid formation require Shh, perhaps in a gradient-dependent manner, and absence of Shh is required for thymus formation, similar to its role in pancreas.

Initiation, Outgrowth, and Formation of the Primordium (E11–12)

Once the endoderm is correctly patterned, the organ primordia form. Because of their origin in shared primordia, early thymus and parathyroid organogenesis share many aspects. However, this common origin necessitates mechanisms for segregating the two organs. By the end of early organogenesis, about E12–12.5, the thymus and parathyroid primordia have formed, separated from each other, and begun to terminally differentiate. The molecular mechanisms driving these processes are beginning to be identified (Fig. 37–2). However, major questions remain to be answered.

INDUCTION AND GROWTH OF THE THYMUS–PARATHYROID ORGAN RUDIMENT: INTRINSIC PATTERNING VERSUS EXTRINSIC SIGNALING

Overt thymus and parathyroid organogenesis begins about E11 by proliferation of the third pouch endoderm to form a primordium attached to the pharyngeal endoderm and contacts the surface ectoderm. Based on what is known from other organs, it is likely that epithelial–mesenchymal interactions may play an important role in initial organ outgrowth (reviewed by Grapin-Botton and Melton[2]). However, no mutants have been identified so far that have normal endodermal patterning but are defective in the initial formation of the thymus–parathyroid rudiment (see the section "Early Patterning (E8–10.5): Formation and Patterning of the Third Pharyngeal Pouch"). Some genetic evidence suggests that signals from the NCC mesenchyme are important. Splotch mutant mice and PDGFRα knockouts, both of which have severe reductions in NCCs, have been reported to have thymic agenesis, but patterning and initial organ formation have not been examined in these mutants.[60–63] Therefore, it is still not clear what the precise role of epithelial–mesenchymal interactions is in initial primordium formation.

The heterotopic transplant experiments described previously suggest that ectoderm and NCC are not the source of an inducing signal for initial organ outgrowth, since the endodermal explants were taken at or before pouch formation and therefore prior to contact between the endoderm and the ectoderm. The chick explants were also taken prior to NCC migration. It is possible that a signal at both transplant sites was able to substitute for a signal normally produced by surface ectoderm, NCCs, or both. Certainly, local mesenchyme is recruited to the ectopic organ site, and these cells likely provide at least some of the required growth signals for the epithelial rudiment, although the resulting thymi are always smaller than normal.

Recent evidence has shown that the initial induction of other endodermal organs, specifically the liver and the pancreas, requires signals from endothelial cells.[64,65] It is therefore possible that this mechanism may affect outgrowth and patterning of the thymus–parathyroid primordium. Although direct tests of this possibility have not yet been reported, the phenotypes of mutants in which pharyngeal arch vasculature is defective suggest that this pathway may be involved. The closest blood vessels to the third pouch are the third and fourth pharyngeal arch arteries. In *Hoxa3* mutants, which do not initiate thymus or parathyroid organogenesis, the third arch artery forms then degenerates between E10.5–11 near the normal time of initial thymus outgrowth.[66,67] In retinaldehyde dehydrogenase (RALDH2)-mutant mice, the third arch artery never forms. In these mice, the thymus is either deleted or ectopic, but the parathyroid never forms.[68] Furthermore, mice expressing only the 120 or 188 isoforms of vascular endothelial growth factor (VEGF) have a variety of partially penetrant defects in arch artery development and maintenance, primarily in the more caudal fourth and sixth arteries.[69] These defects were associated with various thymic and parathyroid defects, including aplasia. Together, these results suggest that pharyngeal organogenesis may require an endothelial signal, possibly VEGF, and that parathyroid formation may be more sensitive to this signal. Direct tests of the possible role of endothelium in early organogenesis are needed to fully investigate this possibility.

The role of mesenchyme in promoting growth of the epithelial rudiment was demonstrated by Auerbach in 1960 using tissue recombination experiments (see Table 37–1 and Auerbach, Hoffman et al., and Vainio et al.[70–72]). Strong evidence indicates that FGF signaling from the NCC is required to promote growth of the developing epithelial rudiment, specifically through FgfR2IIIb, the receptor for Fgf1, -3, -7, and -10. Isoform-specific mutation of the FGFR2-IIIb receptor results in severe thymic hypoplasia and suggests that the primary signal required from mesenchymal cells to support epithelial cell growth is Fgf7, Fgf10, or both.[52] Consistent with this, Fgf7 and Fgf10 are expressed by the perithymic mesenchyme at E12.5,[52,73] and FgfR2IIIb is expressed in both the thymic mesenchyme and the thymic epithelium.[73,74] Furthermore, Fgf10$^{-/-}$ mice have small thymi with low proliferation of TECs,[52] and Fgf10 in the mesenchyme is dependent on Fgf8 expression in the endoderm, ectoderm, or both,[5] similar to the developing limb bud, where epithelial Fgf8 regulation of Fgf10 in the underlying mesenchyme is required for outgrowth.[75,76] A recent study showed that Fgf7 and Fgf10 can replace mesenchyme in organ cultures to support TEC proliferation and concluded that mesenchymal signals are

dispensable for TEC differentiation, at least after E12.5.[73] However, as a small number of presumptive medullary TECs are present by E12.5,[77–79] an earlier role of mesenchyme in epithelial patterning cannot be excluded. Nonetheless, the primary role for mesenchyme, at least during early stages, appears to be to provide growth signals in the form of FGFs to the developing epithelial rudiment (Fig. 37–2).

SEPARATION OF THE PRIMORDIA FROM THE ENDODERM AND THE ECTODERM

About E11.5–E12, the shared primordia become detached from both the pharynx and the surface ectoderm. This release is associated with a brief, coordinated burst of apoptosis at both the endoderm and the ectoderm contact points, occurring over about a 6-hour period around E11.75.[7] This cell death could be either intrinsically programmed within the epithelium or induced by surrounding mesenchyme. Interestingly, two mutants have been identified that appear to have defects in separation of the rudiment. Pax9 is expressed in both the pharyngeal endoderm and the developing thymic rudiment. Pax9 mutants have small thymic lobes that remain attached to the pharynx.[49] Although early organogenesis has not been examined in detail in these mutants, separation from the ectoderm is likely normal. On the other hand, in mutants for the transcription factor AP2α, the thymic lobes remain attached to the surface ectoderm, and release from the endoderm appears normal.[79a] Although AP2α is expressed in both

TABLE 37–1
Thought Experiment: Revisiting Auerbach's Recombination Experiments

One of the first studies that showed a role for mesenchyme in promoting TEC growth was published by Auerbach in 1960.[70] In this study, he performed recombination experiments in which an isolated E12 thymic epithelium was cultured with heterologous mesenchyme and other cell types, and the epithelial lobes were scored for growth and lobulation. Although thymic mesenchyme supported epithelial growth the best, other sources of mesenchyme could also support growth, although usually with different lobulation morphologies. As we now know the growth factors produced by each of the tissue used in these experiments, we can ask the following question: Did the ability of mesenchyme to support thymic epithelium in Auerbach's explants correlate with expression of specific growth factors and signaling molecules?

Supported growth and lobulation	Signaling molecules expressed
E12 lung mesenchyme	Fgf10
E13 submandibular mesenchyme	Fgf2, -3, -7, and -10; BMP1, -2, -3, -4, and -7
E11 metanophrogenic mesenchyme	Fgf1 and Fgf10; BMP2, -4, and -7

Did not support growth and lobulation	Signaling molecules expressed
E12 limb bud mesenchyme	Shh; BMP2, -4, and -7
E12 lung epithelium	Shh; BMP4
Spinal cord	Shh; BMP4

These results suggest that the ability of different mesenchymal tissues to promote growth of the thymic epithelium observed by Auerbach was caused by FGF expression, possibly specifically Fgf10. In all three cases of rescue (lung, submandibular gland, and kidney), the corresponding epithelial bud expresses FgfR2IIIb. Furthermore, expression of Shh could be an inhibitory signal for thymic epithelial growth. Different FGFs and BMPs added to the submandibular epithelium also had different effects on submandibular morphology,[71] suggesting that this could be the basis for the different lobulation patterns reported by Auerbach for the different mesenchymal sources. However, E11.5 lung mesenchyme can also reprogram kidney epithelium to a lung fate and branching pattern.[72] Therefore, without molecular markers, we cannot distinguish whether the delay and morphological differences Auerbach reported were a reflection of reprogramming of the epithelium or delayed support of TECs by heterologous mesenchyme.

the surface ectoderm and the NCCs, this function for *AP2α* appears to be caused by its expression in the surface ectoderm, as NCC-specific deletion of AP2α results in normal thymus development.[80]

The fact that endodermal and ectodermal release are apparently controlled independently is consistent with the fact that in some organisms, such as fish, the thymus remains connected to the endoderm but is not associated with the ectoderm. Both Pax9 and AP2α encode transcription factors, suggesting that these are cell-autonomous processes within the endoderm and ectoderm. However, it is possible that both *AP2α* and *Pax9* are responding to a signal from the mesenchyme. In some of the *noggin* transgenic embryos with reduced NCCs, the thymic lobes failed to separate from the pharynx but had normal *Pax9* expression.[53] This result suggests that *Pax9* expression in the endoderm is necessary but not sufficient for separation and that perhaps some signal from NCCs is also required.

SEPARATION OF THE PARATHYROID AND THYMUS RUDIMENTS

So far, no mutants have been identified that affect this process. In the absence of molecular or genetic data or obvious morphological clues, we are left to speculate about the mechanisms controlling this process. The three most obvious possibilities are apoptosis at the junction, a mesenchymal invasion of the rudiment at the parathyroid–thymus junction, or differential cell adhesion. Although there is no direct evidence for or against any of these possibilities, the most attractive hypothesis of these three may be differential cell adhesion, because the physical division is anticipated by differential gene expression of *Gcm2* and *Foxn1*. This type of mechanism could be controlled by pathways downstream of these transcription factors. Distinguishing between these or other possible mechanisms will await genetic or molecular evidence.

MIGRATION OF THE RUDIMENTS

The thymus and parathyroids begin migration caudally and ventrally immediately after release from the pharynx. This is a process specific to mammals; it does not occur in birds, fish, or marsupials. Additionally, once separated, the parathyroids and thymus migrate independently.[36] The mechanisms underlying this unique process are not understood, although both genetic evidence and logic are consistent with migration being an active process mediated by NCCs. Since NCCs are on the surface of the organ primordium, those are the cells that contact the environment through which the primordia move. Some mutants with a very hypoplastic thymus (such as *nude*) are not ectopic, so ectopic location is not simply a side effect of small size. Although ectopic organs in some mutants are caused by delayed or failed separation from the pharynx, such as those seen in *Hoxa3–Pax1*-compound[37] or *Pax9*-single mutants,[49] there are some mutants in which migration seems to be specifically affected. *Hox3*- and retinoic acid receptor *(RAR)*-multiple mutants are likely to have actual organ migration defects. The *Hox3* paralogous group, *Hoxa3, Hoxb3*, and

Hoxd3, are all expressed in the NCC mesenchyme of the third and fourth arches, and mutants in which all but one copy of *Hoxa3* have been deleted (*Hoxa3$^{+/-}$Hoxb3$^{-/-}$Hoxd3$^{-/-}$*) have relatively normal-sized thymic lobes located ectopically in the neck.[36] *RARα* and *RARβ* are also expressed in the NCC mesenchyme, and double mutants have ectopic hypoplastic thymic lobes.[81] Reduction in the amount of NCCs in *noggin*-transgenic embryos also results in variable ectopic thymi; the authors suggest that there is a threshold level of NCCs required to allow migration.[53]

Evolutionary Considerations: Gills Versus Thymus—Shared and Distinct Genetic Programs

Investigation of the evolutionary origins of vertebrate structures can often provide insights into the roles that different cell types play in a developmental process, as well as the molecular mechanisms involved. In the case of the pharyngeal region, this approach provides some interesting hypotheses regarding the molecular and cellular requirements for thymus and parathyroid organogenesis. Furthermore, the evolutionary origins of thymus organogenesis are an important part of understanding the origins of adaptive immunity in vertebrates. Adaptive immunity requires the development of both a thymus and a lymphoid progenitor, which have origins in different embryonic cell lineages. Investigation of the origins of these lineages may provide clues as to how this complex interacting system evolved.[82]

The thymus is apparently specific to gnathostomes (jawed vertebrates), including cartilaginous fishes and higher vertebrates.[83] One potentially important difference is the presence of NCCs in vertebrate but not invertebrate species. However, although NCCs are important for thymic organogenesis, the presence of NCCs per se does not strictly correlate with the development of a thymus, as agnathans such as the lamprey have NCCs but do not have a thymus.[84] Evidence is accumulating that pharyngeal endoderm has intrinsic patterning mechanisms that predate the neural crest.[54,85–90] Therefore, it is likely that the capacity to make a thymus originally evolved within the endoderm. This conclusion is consistent with the heterotopic chick:quail endoderm transplant experiments described previously, which suggest that the pharyngeal endoderm is specified to a thymus fate before NCC migration.[1]

The molecular pathways known to be involved in thymus organogenesis also provide potential insights into the evolution of the thymus and parathyroids. The group I *Pax* transcription factors (*Pax1* and *Pax9* in mice[37,42]) are expressed in the developing pharyngeal pouches in all chordates examined.[44,86,87,91–94] *Pax1/9* genes have been identified as molecular markers for gill formation, and their expression in hemichordate gills has been proposed to be molecular evidence for evolutionary homology of these structures between hemichordates and chordates.[86] In the cephalochordate amphioxus and the agnathan lamprey, which are both athymic, *Pax1/9* expression is down-regulated at the point of fusion between endoderm and ectoderm just prior to gill perforation.[86,95] Addition of retinoic acid in amphioxus is associated with maintenance of *Pax1/9* expression and failure of gill perforation.[95] Since mouse mutants for *Pax1* and *Pax9* have defects in thymus and parathyroid development,[43,45,49] differences in the regulation of *Pax1/9* gene expression in the pharyngeal endoderm are a potential molecular mechanism for the evolution of thymus and parathyroid organogenesis.

Although *Hox* gene expression in the ectoderm (neural tube), and to a lesser extent in the mesoderm, is highly conserved,[95–101] *Hox* gene expression in the pharyngeal endoderm has so far been identified only in species that form a thymus, providing circumstantial evidence that these events may be linked. The modulation of *Hox* gene expression patterns has been proposed to be a mechanism for the evolution of different body plans.[99,102,103] Since *Hoxa3* is specifically required for patterning the third pouch and formation of the pharyngeal organs, it is a good candidate for playing a role in the evolution of the thymus and parathyroids. The requirement for *Hoxa3* to maintain *Pax1* and *Pax9* gene expression in the third pharyngeal pouch in mouse embryos[35,38] thus takes on a new connotation. This result presents an interesting parallel with the retinoic acid experiments in amphioxus and suggests a scenario in which expression of *Hoxa3* in the endoderm of the third pharyngeal pouch in mice overrides an evolutionarily conserved pathway for gill formation through up-regulation of the *Pax1/9* genes. This suggests the hypothesis that the acquisition of *Hoxa3* expression in the pharyngeal pouch endoderm in higher vertebrates resulted in the development of new pharyngeal pouch–derived structures, such as the thymus and parathyroids, during vertebrate evolution (Fig. 37–4).

Interspecific comparison of organogenesis can provide further interesting insights into possible mechanisms of establishing organ-specific domains in the developing third pouch. In cartilaginous rays and some amphibians, the thymus derives from dorsal pouches and the parathyroids derive from the ventral side—in contrast to mammals and boney fishes, where the opposite is true.[104] Furthermore, in some animals, the thymus derives from multiple pouches, and in mammals and fish, it appears to be restricted to a single pouch. This suggests that the patterning to produce thymus and parathyroid organogenesis may be based on a common mechanism restricted differently in different species. Comparison of the molecular markers for thymus and parathyroid organogenesis in these different species could provide insight into the molecular mechanisms patterning pouch-derived organs.

Immigration of Lymphocyte Progenitor Cells

Since the role of the thymus is to mediate T-cell development but the lymphocyte progenitor cells (LPCs) are formed in the bone marrow, they have to locate and colonize the thymus. Thymic homing of LPCs is mediated by as yet unidentified chemokines produced by the thymic epithelium that selectively attract LPCs. Elegant work from Petrie's lab has demonstrated that LPCs enter the postnatal thymus through

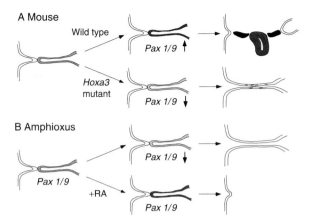

Figure 37–4. *Hoxa3-mutant phenotype resembles amphioxus gill development.* In both (A) wild-type mice and (B) amphioxus, *Pax1/9* gene expression is present in the pharyngeal pouches, which are initially in contact with surface ectoderm. (A) In wild-type mice, *Pax1/9* are up-regulated in the third pouch by *Hoxa3.* Soon after, the thymus–parathyroid primordium forms, and the remainder of the pouch degenerates (black). In *Hoxa3* mutants, *Pax1/9* expression is rapidly lost in the third pouch followed by failure of primordium formation and deterioration of the pouch. (B) In amphioxus, gills develop by fusion of the pharyngeal pouch endoderm and cleft ectoderm, associated with decreased *Amphipax1* expression. Addition of retinoic acid prevents *Amphipax1* down-regulation and causes failure of endoderm–ectoderm fusion. Therefore, in both amphioxus and mice, the maintenance or loss of *Pax1/9* gene expression in the pharyngeal pouches is correlated with similar morphological events. (Please see CD-ROM for color version of this figure.)

blood vessels at the corticomedullary interface.[105,106] Once inside, thymocytes take a stereotypical migration path out toward the capsule and then back to the medulla,[105,107] during which thymocytes are thought to encounter distinct microenvironments that promote specific stages of thymocyte differentiation (see the section "Thymus Differentiation: TECs—How Many Progenitors?"). Having returned to the medulla as "single positive" CD4+ or CD8+ thymocytes, they exit into the peripheral immune system via the vasculature. T-cell emigration, like LPC immigration, is likely a regulated process, although the mechanism is not understood in detail.

Neither process can happen the same way in the fetal thymus, particularly at early organogenesis stages, since the fetal thymus is (1) a moving target, (2) not fully vascularized at the earliest stages at which colonization occurs, and (3) still in the process of generating the full thymic architecture (reviewed by Petrie[108]). Immunohistochemical analysis suggests that LPCs enter the fetal thymus directly across the mesenchymal capsule. Therefore, at fetal stages, LPCs have to find the thymus, possibly by the same as yet unidentified chemoattractive mechanism operating in adults, and must traverse the mesenchymal capsule to enter the epithelial environment. In both chick and mouse, this fetal immigration occurs in waves rather than as a continuous process.[109,110] It is not clear at what point in development the mechanism of LPC immigration switches from the fetal to the adult mode or what triggers this change. However, as the thymic vasculature is established around E15.5, concomitant with elaboration of the medullary compartment, it is likely to be at or after this time.

LPCs within the fetal thymus do not encounter the same highly ordered microenvironments present in the mature organ. The elaboration of this mature architecture during fetal development depends on complex interactions between developing TECs and differentiating thymocytes, commonly referred to as cross talk.[111–113] The evidence supporting the role of these interactions has been extensively reviewed elsewhere and is not covered further in this chapter. However, the different mechanisms of LPC immigration in the fetal versus the adult thymus may have functional consequences for proper thymus development.

Terminal Differentiation (E12+)

How are all of the embryonic organogenesis pathways and mechanisms described previously relevant to the issue of organ-specific stem cells? The question of the tissue-of-origin of the thymic epithelium addresses how many progenitor or stem cells there might be and where they may come from; the early genetic pathways and cellular interactions may function to produce or regulate the self-renewal, proliferation, or differentiation of these cells.

PARATHYROID DIFFERENTIATION

Little is known about the mechanisms controlling parathyroid differentiation, and nothing is known about the existence or nature of parathyroid progenitor or "stem" cells. Differentiation of cells within the developing parathyroid gland begins quite early, with parathyroid hormone (PTH) expressed as early as E11.5.[8] *Gcm2* may be responsible for both parathyroid organogenesis and differentiation, as it is expressed throughout parathyroid development and in the adult parathyroid glands. Maintenance of *Gcm2* expression is under the regulation of *Hoxa3* and, at least in embryos, *Pax1*. *Hoxa3*$^{+/-}$*Pax1*$^{-/-}$ mutants initiate but do not maintain *Gcm2* expression, and parathyroids are very small or absent in theses mutants.[37] These data suggest that sustained expression of *Gcm2* may be required to maintain parathyroid development. Even more strikingly, *Hoxa3* newborn heterozygotes have 50% the normal serum levels of PTH.[114] This result suggests that the physiological calcium-sensing feedback loop in the parathyroid gland that regulates serum PTH levels may be directly or indirectly under the control of Hoxa3.

THYMUS DIFFERENTIATION: TECS — HOW MANY PROGENITORS?

The epithelial component of the mature thymus is highly heterogeneous. Several subtypes of the TEC exist and are organized into histologically defined cortical and medullary compartments.[115] Evidence supports roles for specific thymic epithelial subtypes in mediating different aspects of T-cell development. In particular, cortical epithelial cells mediate positive selection of the T-cell repertoire, and specific cortical epithelial subtypes are likely both to mediate T-cell lineage commitment and regulate proliferation–migration of specific thymocyte subsets (reviewed by Petrie[108]). Medullary epithelial cells are required for negative selection[116] and to drive the

final maturation stages of thymocyte development[117]; it is from the medulla that mature, naïve T-cells egress into the peripheral immune system.

The cellular origins of the different TEC types have recently been investigated through analysis of the differentiative capacity of defined epithelial cell populations in the E12.5 and E15.5 mouse thymus.[77,78] These studies have demonstrated that all epithelial progenitor cell activity in the fetal mouse thymus is contained in a population defined by monoclonal antibodies MTS20, MTS24, or both, which recognize determinants on the same epithelial cells in the embryonic thymus. This population can differentiate into all currently identified thymic epithelial subpopulations and, when grafted ectopically, is sufficient to generate a functional thymus. Phenotypic analysis has indicated that the E12.5 population cannot be subdivided on the basis of seven further markers of immature and differentiated TECs and that it expresses both Keratin 5 and Keratin 8,[77] coexpression of which was previously proposed to mark cortical thymic epithelial progenitor cells.[118] However, by E15.5, the population is heterogeneous with respect to the marker UEA1,[78] indicating that MTS24 now identifies both early progenitors and cells acquiring characteristics of terminally differentiated progeny. A further difference between these two MTS24$^+$ populations is in MHC Class II expression. Constitutive expression of MHC Class II, otherwise restricted to hematopoietic-lineage antigen-presenting cells, is one of the unique features of mature TECs and is of key functional significance because of its role in both positive and negative selection of the T-cell repertoire. At E12.5, MHC Class II expression is not detectable on MTS24$^+$ cells,[77] indicating their functional immaturity; however, by E15.5, most MTS24$^+$ cells express high levels of MHC Class II$^+$, again reflecting a high proportion of terminally differentiating cells in the population at this developmental stage.[78] Interestingly, at E12.5, the MTS24$^+$ population expresses *Hoxa3*, *Pax1*, and *Pax9*, and it also expresses *Foxn1*.[119] However, by E15.5, although *Hoxa3*, *Pax1*, and *Foxn1* are still expressed by the MTS24$^+$ progenitor population, MTS24$^+$ cells no longer express *Pax9*,[78] possibly indicating that in thymus organogenesis, *Pax9* is not required after development of the epithelial progenitor cell. That *Hoxa3* and *Pax1* are required for TEC differentiation has been demonstrated.[37,44]

At the time of writing, the differentiative capacity of the MTS24$^+$ population had yet to be analyzed at the clonal level. Since current evidence strongly indicates that all TECs are of endodermal origin (see the section "Early Patterning of the Third Pouch into Organ-Specific Domains"), at some level they must arise from a common progenitor in the foregut endoderm. As MTS20 and MTS24 are widely expressed throughout the foregut from E9.5 (the earliest stage examined), this common progenitor is likely to be MTS20$^+$24$^+$ (Fig. 37–5), and may therefore still be present in the population isolated from the E12.5 thymus. However, foregut endoderm may be specified either to a common thymic epithelial lineage, before divergence of the different TEC types, or independently to the (various) cortical and medullary thymic

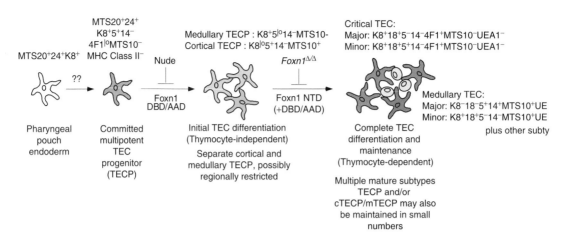

Figure 37–5. *Proposed model for TEC differentiation.* Marker phenotypes for each cell type are shown above the diagram. Cells in the third pharyngeal pouch endoderm (white) are patterned by an undetermined mechanism to a committed, multipotent TEC progenitor (TECP), which can form both cortical and medullary cell types. This multipotent TECs then differentiates into separate, regionally restricted cortical and medullary TECPs. This differentiation is independent of interactions with LPCs and is dependent on the Foxn1 DNA-binding (DBD) and acidic-activation domains (AAD). These intermediate, partially restricted progenitors then differentiate into the full range of cortical and medullary TEC subtypes, respectively. This differentiation depends on TEC–thymocyte cross talk and on the action of the Foxn1 N-terminal domain. Although it has not been conclusively demonstrated, some or all of these various progenitor cell types may be maintained in small numbers in the mature thymus. (Please see CD-ROM for color version of this figure.)

epithelial lineages. Either model would be consistent with current knowledge of the mechanisms controlling TEC differentiation, explained in the sections "Foxn1: A Multifunctional Regulator of TEC Differentiation" and "Possible Models of Thymic Medullary Differentiation." As neither MTS20 nor MTS24 are restricted to prospective TECs, it is also possible that these markers may identify other endodermal precursor cell types in the fore–midgut endoderm.

The question of whether a true epithelial stem cell exists in either the embryonic or postnatal thymus also remained unanswered at the time of writing. The postnatal thymic epithelium has some proliferative capacity, but it has not been demonstrated that this depends on an organ-specific stem cell activity. The strongest evidence for a postnatal thymic epithelial stem cell remains the observation that some human thymic epithelial tumors coexpress markers normally associated with mature cortical and medullary TECs and can differentiate into both cortical and medullary TEC types[120] (reviewed by Lampert *et al.*[104] and Blackburn *et al.*[121]). Conclusive identification of a postnatal thymic epithelial stem cell or cells will require assays designed to identify multipotent TECs that also retain self-renewing capacity. The observation that MTS20[+] and MTS24[+] cells are found as a rare subpopulation of the adult thymic medulla has lead to speculation that these cells may represent a residual thymic epithelial stem cell population. However, there is currently no evidence that the embryonic and adult MTS24 populations are lineally related.

Foxn1: A MULTIFUNCTIONAL REGULATOR OF TEC DIFFERENTIATION

It is well established that the generation of a complete thymic architecture requires interactions between developing thymocytes and TECs, termed cross talk[111–113] (see the section

"Immigration of Lymphocyte Progenitor Cells"). Recently, an incisive study demonstrated that initial TEC differentiation is independent of interactions with thymocytes but that cross talk is required for maturation and maintenance of both cortical and medullary TECs.[79] Furthermore, mesenchyme may not be required for TEC differentiation after E12.[73] Together, these data suggest that TEC differentiation may be controlled to some extent by an epithelial-intrinsic program, although the specific choice between cortical and medullary fates may be extrinsically influenced.

There is considerable genetic evidence to suggest that the transcription factor *Foxn1* plays a central role in controlling TEC differentiation. As described in the section "Early Patterning of the Third Pouch into Organ-Specific Domains," *Foxn1* is the gene mutated in the nude mouse. Homozygous null nude mice arrest TEC differentiation at a very early stage, generating a cystic thymic rudiment that cannot support T-cell development and that fails to express markers of mature TECs, including MHC Class II.[22,122] Null mutants for *Foxn1* also have a severe defect in LPC immigration,[123] possibly because of direct or indirect regulation of a chemokine signal.[124] *Foxn1* is expressed in TECs throughout fetal development and in the postnatal thymus,[25] but because of the very early phenotype in null mutants, it has been difficult to determine what, if any, role *Foxn1* plays after initial TEC differentiation.

Recent data from the Manley lab using a hypomorphic allele for *Foxn1*, denoted *Foxn1*[Δ], suggests that *Foxn1* regulates the progression of TEC differentiation from the cell-autonomous to the cross talk-dependent phases[125] (Fig. 37–5). The Foxn1 protein consists of three main domains: a central forkhead class DNA-binding domain, a C-terminal acidic activation domain, and an N-terminal domain of undetermined function.[126,127] The *Foxn1*[Δ] allele encodes a truncated protein in which the DNA-binding and activation domains are intact but most of the N-terminal domain is deleted.

In contrast to the early phenotype of nude mice, $Foxn1^{\Delta/\Delta}$ mice have later defects in thymus development and function, including 25-fold fewer thymocytes and partial blocks at both the earliest (TN1) and the double-positive thymocyte development stages. $Foxn1^{\Delta/\Delta}$-mutant thymi do not have organized cortical or medullary compartments. Most TECs in the adult $Foxn1^{\Delta/\Delta}$ mutants have a K5⁺K8⁺ phenotype, similar to that previously proposed to represent an immature TEC intermediate[77,79,118] and reminiscent of the phenotypes previously reported for the CD3ε26 transgenic and $Rag^{-/-}$, common γ-chain⁻/⁻ double mutants in which thymocyte development does not progress beyond the TN1 stage.[79,128] However, in those transgenics, exposure of the TECs to wild-type thymocytes resulted in significant rescue of normal TEC development,[118] and in the $Foxn1^{\Delta/\Delta}$ thymus, TECs appear unable to respond normally to cues from differentiating thymocytes, even in the presence of double-positive and single-positive cells.

Surprisingly, the $Foxn1^{\Delta/\Delta}$ phenotype is thymus specific, with normal skin and hair development. These results identify a previously unknown thymus-specific activity for the Foxn1 N-terminus. The $Foxn1^{\Delta}$ allele also reveals a vertebrate-specific function in the thymus for the N-terminal domain, which was previously proposed to be a site of functional changes in the Foxn1 protein during vertebrate evolution.[83,129]

POSSIBLE MODELS OF THYMIC MEDULLARY DIFFERENTIATION

The mechanisms controlling differentiation of the medullary and cortical compartments are largely unknown at the molecular level. Current ideas of the mechanisms by which the thymic cortex and thymic medulla develop are inferred from ontogenic marker analyses and functional analyses addressing medullary development in chimeric mice and in reaggregate fetal thymic organ culture (RFTOC).

In normal thymus ontogeny, differentiation toward cortical and medullary TEC phenotypes is first apparent at approximately E12.5; prospective cortical and medullary TECs cannot be distinguished within the E11.5 primordium on morphological or immunohistochemical grounds. By E12.5, a central cluster of K5ʰⁱMTS10⁺-prospective medullary TECs is apparent, and some cells adjacent to the capsule appear to be beginning to adopt a K5ˡᵒ/⁻K8⁺ phenotype, suggestive of differentiation to the cortical TEC lineage.[77] As described previously (section VI.C), it is clear that the initial development of these prospective medullary and cortical TECs is lymphocyte independent but that elaboration and maintenance of the mature cortical and medullary compartments depends on lymphoepithelial cross talk.[79]

Analysis of postnatal allophenic chimeric mice has indicated that the thymic medulla arises as a series of clonal islets, suggesting the existence of a medullary thymic epithelial progenitor–stem cell activity.[130] Grafting of chimeric RFTOC under the kidney capsule of recipient mice subsequently revealed the presence of medullary thymic epithelial progenitor cells until at least E16.5. The initially clonal medullary islets were shown to coalesce later in development,[130] the mature medulla being an apparently contiguous structure that closely follows the vascular tree.[131] The transcription factors RelB[132] and AIRE1[116] are both required for development of a fully functional medullary compartment and appear to function in the same pathway.[133–135] However, the mechanism or mechanisms controlling their expression remain unknown.

The grafted RFTOC assay also revealed an interesting and unexpected facet of TEC organization. Rodewald et al. demonstrated that although both medullary and cortical phenotype TECs develop in RFTOC maintained in culture, TECs in these cultures do not become properly compartmentalized. However, proper TEC organization occurred when RFTOC were subsequently grafted under the kidney capsule. In keeping with this observation, Bennett et al. demonstrated that many MTS20⁺24⁺ thymic epithelial progenitor cells differentiate into cells expressing markers of cortical and medullary TECs when cultured as RFTOC for 48 hours.[77] These prospective cortical and medullary epithelial cells, which remain MHC Class II⁻ and are therefore immature, are randomly distributed throughout the reaggregated cultures. However, on grafting under the kidney capsule, the same cultures generate functional thymi containing properly organized cortical and medullary compartments.[77] With the findings of Rodewald, these data suggest that a patterning mechanism may exist that can override initial, possibly stochastic, differentiation of TECs to cortical and medullary lineage cells in vitro. Since a key difference between in vitro and grafted RFTOC is the vascularization of the grafted tissue, it seems possible that the vasculature may provide direct or indirect signals required for organization of the thymic architecture. In vivo, it is likely that environmental constraints influence the initial differentiation of cortical and medullary TECs, as differentiation appears to occur in an ordered manner that reflects the mature architecture of the organ. However, the association of the medullary compartment with the vascular tree[131] implies that a vasculature-dependent mechanism may also operate in vivo.

In the context of a single endodermal origin for both the cortical and the medullary thymic epithelial compartment, the development of the medulla as a series of clonal islets could be consistent with the existence of separate cortical and medullary progenitor or stem cells and certainly suggests the existence of an intermediate "transit amplifying" cell type for medullary TECs (Fig. 37–5). However, it would also be consistent with commitment of a common thymic epithelial progenitor cell to medullary epithelial lineages, being controlled by mechanisms such as lateral inhibition, or regional commitment followed by migration such that single medullary progenitor cells proliferate as isolated clusters in response to appropriate stimuli. Elaboration of this initial medullary pattern may subsequently depend directly or indirectly on signals derived from the vasculature.[131] A recent report suggested that Fgf7 may specifically affect medullary epithelial cells.[74] However, a further study has indicated that Fgf7 and Fgf10 are mitogenic for both cortical and medullary TECs but have an apparently neutral effect on differentiation.[73] Further studies are required to determine the signals required for commitment to cortical and medullary lineages and for expansion and maintenance of these respective compartments.

Summary

Understanding of thymus and parathyroid development has progressed considerably in recent years, largely because of the use of molecular technologies for analyzing gene function in vertebrate models. As explained previously, the genetic hierarchies controlling development of both organs are beginning to be understood, and testable mechanistic models can be proposed for early patterning, organogenesis, and the differentiation of the major cell types within each organ. In addition, the issue of whether a residual progenitor–stem cell exists in the mature organ remains of central importance. All work performed so far to identify TEC progenitors has used fetal thymus as a source for cells. It is not known whether a comparable progenitor–stem cell population exists in the adult thymus. Such cells, if they exist, would likely be rare and thus difficult to isolate. Several minor adult thymic epithelial populations have been proposed as candidate progenitor–stem cells on the basis of phenotype and are variously located in the cortical or medullary compartments or at the corticomedullary junction. Determination of which, if any, of these candidates constitute adult thymic epithelial progenitor–stem cells will be an important next step that will require rigorous analysis of potency and self-renewal potential.

REFERENCES

1. LeLievre, C.S., and LeDouarin, N.M. (1975). Mesenchymal derivatives of the neural crest: analysis of chimaeric quail and chick embryos. *J. Embryol. Exp. Morph.* **34,** 125–154.
2. Grapin-Botton, A., and Melton, D.A. (2000). Endoderm development: from patterning to organogenesis. *Trends Genet.* **16,** 124–130.
3. Jerome, L.A., and Papaioannou, V.E. (2001). DiGeorge syndrome phenotype in mice mutant for the T-box gene, *Tbx1. Nat. Genet.* **27,** 286–291.
4. Abu-Issa, R., Smyth, G., Smoak, I., Yamamura, K., and Meyers, E.N. (2002). Fgf8 is required for pharyngeal arch and cardiovascular development in the mouse. *Development* **129,** 4613–4625.
5. Frank, D.U., Fotheringham, L.K., Brewer, J.A., Muglia, L.J., Tristani-Firouzi, M., Capecchi, M.R., and Moon, A.M. (2002). An Fgf8 mouse mutant phenocopies human 22q11 deletion syndrome. *Development* **129,** 4591–4603.
6. Bachiller, D., Klingensmith, J., Shneyder, N., Tran, U., Anderson, R., Rossant, J., and De Robertis, E.M. (2003). The role of chordin/Bmp signals in mammalian pharyngeal development and DiGeorge syndrome. *Development* **130,** 3567–3578.
7. Gordon, J., Wilson, V., Blair, N.F., Manley, N.R., and Blackburn, C.C. (2004). Functional evidence for a single endodermal origin for the thymic epithelium. *Nature Immunology* **5,** 546–553.
8. Gunther, T., Chen, Z.F., Kim, J., Priemel, M., Rueger, J.M., Amling, M., Moseley, J.M., Martin, T.J., Anderson, D.J., and Karsenty, G. (2000). Genetic ablation of parathyroid glands reveals another source of parathyroid hormone. *Nature* **406,** 199–203.
9. Akiyama, Y., Hosoya, T., Poole, A.M., and Hotta, Y. (1996). The gcm-motif: a novel DNA-binding motif conserved in *Drosophila* and mammals. *Proc. Natl. Acad. Sci. U. S. A.* **93,** 14, 912–14,916.
10. Kim, J., Jones, B.W., Zock, C., Chen, Z., Wang, H., Goodman, C.S., and Anderson, D.J. (1998). Isolation and characterization of mammalian homologs of the *Drosophila* gene glial cells missing. *Proc. Natl. Acad. Sci. U. S. A.* **95,** 12,364–12,369.
11. Gordon, J., Bennett, A.R., Blackburn, C.C., and Manley, N.R. (2001). Gcm2 and Foxn1 mark early parathyroid- and thymus-specific domains in the developing third pharyngeal pouch. *Mech. Dev.* **103,** 141–143.
12. Ahlgren, U., Jonsson, J., Jonsson, L., Simu, K., and Edlund, H. (1998). β-Cell-specific inactivation of the mouse *Ipf1/Pdx1* gene results in loss of the β-cell phenotype and maturity onset diabetes. *Genes Dev.* **12,** 1763–1768.
13. Jonsson, J., Carlsson, L., Edlund, T., and Edlund, H. (1994). Insulin- promoter factor 1 is required for pancreas development in mice. *Nature* **371,** 606–609.
14. Offield, M.F., Jetton, T.L., Labosky, P.A., Ray, M., Stein, R.W., Magnuson, M.A., Hogan, B.L., and Wright, C.V. (1996). PDX-1 is required for pancreatic outgrowth and differentiation of the rostral duodenum. *Development* **122,** 983–995.
15. Kawaguchi, Y., Cooper, B., Gannon, M., Ray, M., MacDonald, R.J., and Wright, C.V. (2002). The role of the transcriptional regulator Ptf1a in converting intestinal to pancreatic progenitors. *Nat. Genet.* **32,** 128–134.
16. Kimura, S., Hara, Y., Pineau, T., Fernandez-Salguero, P., Fox, C.H., Ward, J.M., and Gonzalez, F.J. (1996). The T/ebp-null mouse: Thyroid-specific enhancer-binding protein is essential for the organogenesis of the thyroid, lung, ventral forebrain, and pituitary. *Genes Dev.* **10,** 60–69.
17. Clifton-Bligh, R.J., Wentworth, J.M., Heinz, P., Crisp, M.S., John, R., Lazarus, J.H., Ludgate, M., and Chatterjee, V.K. (1998). Mutation of the gene encoding human TTF-2 associated with thyroid agenesis, cleft palate, and choanal atresia. *Nat. Genet.* **19,** 399–401.
18. Hosoya, T., Takizawa, K., Nitta, K., and Hotta, Y. (1995). Glial cells missing: a binary switch between neuronal and glial determination in *Drosophila. Cell* **82,** 1025–1036.
19. Jones, B.W., Fetter, R.D., Tear, G., and Goodman, C.S. (1995). Glial cells missing: a switch that controls glial versus neuronal fate. *Cell* **82,** 1013–1023.
20. Flanagan, S.P. (1966). *Nude,* a new hairless gene with pleiotropic effects in the mouse. *Genet. Res.* **8,** 295–309.
21. Frank, J., Pignata, C., Panteleyev, A.A., Prowse, D.M., Baden, H., Weiner, L., Gaetaniello, L., Ahmad, W., Pozzi, N., Cserhalmi-Friedman, P.B., Aita, V.M., Uyttendaele, H., Gordon, D., Ott, J., Brissette, J.L., and Christiano, A.M. (1999). Exposing the human nude phenotype [letter]. *Nature* **398,** 473–474.
22. Blackburn, C.C., Augustine, C.L., Li, R., Harvey, R.P., Malin, M.A., Boyd, R.L., Miller, J.F., and Morahan, G. (1996). The *nu* gene acts cell autonomously and is required for differentiation of thymic epithelial progenitors. *Proc. Natl. Acad. Sci. U. S. A.* **93,** 5742–5746.
23. Balciunaite, G., Keller, M.P., Balciunaite, E., Piali, L., Zuklys, S., Mathieu, Y.D., Gill, J., Boyd, R., Sussman, D.J., and Hollander, G.A. (2002). Wnt glycoproteins regulate the expression of *FoxN1,* the gene defective in nude mice. *Natl. Immunol.* **3,** 1102–1108.
24. Nehls, M., Pfeifer, D., Schorpp, M., Hedrich, H., and Boehm, T. (1994). New member of the winged-helix protein family disrupted in mouse and rat nude mutations. *Nature* **372,** 103–107.

25. Nehls, M., Kyewski, B., Messerle, M., Waldshütz, R., Schüddekopf, K., Smith, A.J., and Boehm, T. (1996). Two genetically separable steps in the differentiation of thymic epithelium. *Science* **272**, 886–889.

26. Zamisch, M., Moore-Scott, B., Su, D.M., Manley, N.R., and Richie, E. Ontogeny and regulation of IL-7 expressing thymic epithelial cells. (Submitted).

27. Jackson, M., Baird, J.W., Cambray, N., Ansell, J.D., Forrester, L.M., and Graham, G.J. (2002). Cloning and characterization of *Ehox,* a novel homeobox gene essential for embryonic stem cell differentiation. *J. Biol. Chem.* **277**, 38,683–38,692.

28. Morris, L., Gordon, J., Manley, N.R., and Blackburn C.C. (Unpublished).

29. Cordier, A.C., and Haumont, S.M. (1980). Development of thymus, parathyroids, and ultimobranchial bodies in NMRI and Nude mice. *Am. J. Anat.* **157**, 227–263.

30. Kenyon, C. (1994). If birds can fly, why can't we? Homeotic genes and evolution. *Cell* **78**, 175–180.

31. Krumlauf, R. (1994). *Hox* genes in vertebrate development. *Cell* **78**, 191–201.

32. Graham, A., Holland, P.W., Lumsden, A., Krumlauf, R., and Hogan, B.L. (1988). Expression of the homeobox genes *Hox 2.1* and *2.6* during mouse development. *Curr. Top. Microbiol. Immunol.* **137**, 87–93.

33. Hunt, P., Gulisano, M., Cook, M., Sham, M.H., Faiella, A., Wilkinson, D., Boncinelli, E., and Krumlauf, R. (1991). A distinct *Hox* code for the branchial region of the vertebrate head. *Nature* **353**, 861–864.

34. Chisaka, O., and Capecchi, M.R. (1991). Regionally restricted developmental defects resulting from targeted disruption of the mouse homeobox gene *hox-1.5*. *Nature* **350**, 473–479.

35. Manley, N.R., and Capecchi, M.R. (1995). The role of *Hoxa-3* in mouse thymus and thyroid development. *Development* **121**, 1989–2003.

36. Manley, N.R., and Capecchi, M.R. (1998). Hox group 3 paralogs regulate the development and migration of the thymus, thyroid, and parathyroid glands. *Dev. Biol.* **195**, 1–15.

37. Su, D., Ellis, S., Napier, A., Lee, K., and Manley, N.R. (2001). *Hoxa3* and *pax1* regulate epithelial cell death and proliferation during thymus and parathyroid organogenesis. *Dev. Biol.* **236**, 316–329.

38. Manley, N.R. (Unpublished data).

39. Ellis, S. and Manley, N.R. (Unpublished data).

40. Dahl, E., Koseki, H., and Balling, R. (1997). *Pax* genes and organogenesis. *Bioessays* **19**, 755–765.

41. Gruss, P., and Walther, C. (1992). *Pax* in development. *Cell* **69**, 719–722.

42. Strachan, T., and Read, A.P. (1994). *PAX* genes. *Curr. Opin. Gen. Dev.* **4**, 427–438.

43. Peters, H., Neubüser, A., Kratochwil, K., and Balling, R. (1998). *Pax9*-deficient mice lack pharyngeal pouch derivatives and teeth and exhibit craniofacial and limb abnormalities. *Genes Dev.* **12**, 2735–2747.

44. Su, D.M., and Manley, N.R. (2000). *Hoxa3* and *pax1* transcription factors regulate the ability of fetal thymic epithelial cells to promote thymocyte development. *J. Immunol.* **164**, 5753–5760.

45. Wallin, J., Eibel, H., Neubüser, A., Wilting, J., Koseki, H., and Balling, R. (1996). *Pax1* is expressed during development of the thymus epithelium and is required for normal T-cell maturation. *Development* **122**, 23–30.

46. Koushik, J., and Manley, N.R. (Unpublished).

47. Xu, P.X., Zheng, W., Laclef, C., Maire, P., Maas, R.L., Peters, H., and Xu, X. (2002). Eya1 is required for the morphogenesis of

mammalian thymus, parathyroid, and thyroid. *Development* **129**, 3033–3044.

48. Laclef, C., Souil, E., Demignon, J., and Maire, P. (2003). Thymus, kidney, and craniofacial abnormalities in Six1-deficient mice. *Mech. Dev.* **120**, 669–679.

49. Hetzer-Egger, C., Schorpp, M., Haas-Assenbaum, A., Balling, R., Peters, H., and Boehm, T. (2002). Thymopoiesis requires *Pax9* function in thymic epithelial cells. *Eur. J. Immunol.* **32**, 1175–1181.

50. Peters, H., Wilm, B., Sakai, N., Imai, K., Maas, R., and Balling, R. (1999). *Pax1* and *Pax9* synergistically regulate vertebral column development. *Development* **126**, 5399–5408.

51. Pignoni, F., Hu, B., Zavitz, K.H., Xiao, J., Garrity, P.A., and Zipursky, S.L. (1997). The eye-specification proteins So and Eya form a complex and regulate multiple steps in *Drosophila* eye development. *Cell* **91**, 881–891.

52. Revest, J.M., Suniara, R.K., Kerr, K., Owen, J.J., and Dickson, C. (2001). Development of the thymus requires signaling through the fibroblast growth factor receptor r2-iiib. *J. Immunol.* **167**, 1954–1961.

53. Ohnemus, S., Kanzler, B., Jerome-Majewska, L.A., Papaioannou, V.E., Boehm, T., and Mallo, M. (2002). Aortic arch and pharyngeal phenotype in the absence of BMP-dependent neural crest in the mouse. *Mech. Dev.* **119**, 127–135.

54. Ogasawara, M., Wada, H., Peters, H., and Satoh, N. (1999). Developmental expression of *Pax1/9* genes in urochordate and hemichordate gills: insight into function and evolution of the pharyngeal epithelium. *Development* **126**, 2539–2550.

55. Apelqvist, A., Ahlgren, U., and Edlund, H. (1997). Sonic hedgehog directs specialized mesoderm differentiation in the intestine and pancreas. *Curr. Biol.* **7**, 801–804.

56. Treier, M., Gleiberman, A.S., O'Connell, S.M., Szeto, D.P., McMahon, J.A., McMahon, A.P., and Rosenfeld, M.G. (1998). Multistep signaling requirements for pituitary organogenesis *in vivo*. *Genes Dev.* **12**, 1691–1704.

57. Zhang, J., Rosenthal, A., de Sauvage, F.J., and Shivdasani, R.A. (2001). Down-regulation of Hedgehog signaling is required for organogenesis of the small intestine in *Xenopus*. *Dev. Biol.* **229**, 188–202.

58. Hebrok, M., Kim, S.K., St. Jacques, B., McMahon, A.P., and Melton, D.A. (2000). Regulation of pancreas development by hedgehog signaling. *Development* **127**, 4905–4913.

59. Moore-Scott, B.A., and Manley, N.R. Differential expression of Sonic hedgehog along the anterior posterior axis regulates patterning of pharyngeal pouch endoderm and maintains arch morphology. (Submitted).

60. Franz, T. (1989). Persistent *truncus arteriosus* in the Splotch mutant mouse. *Anat. Embryol. (Berl.)* **180**, 457–464.

61. Soriano, P. (1997). The PDGF-α receptor is required for neural crest cell development and for normal patterning of the somites. *Development* **124**, 2691–2700.

62. Epstein, J.A., Li, J., Lang, D., Chen, F., Brown, C.B., Jin, F., Lu, M.M., Thomas, M., Liu, E., Wessels, A., and Lo, C.W. (2000). Migration of cardiac neural crest cells in Splotch embryos. *Development* **127**, 1869–1878.

63. Conway, S.J., Henderson, D.J., and Copp, A.J. (1997). *Pax3* is required for cardiac neural crest migration in the mouse: evidence from the splotch (Sp2H) mutant. *Development* **124**, 505–514.

64. Lammert, E., Cleaver, O., and Melton, D. (2001). Induction of pancreatic differentiation by signals from blood vessels. *Science* **294**, 564–567.

65. Matsumoto, K., Yoshitomi, H., Rossant, J., and Zaret, K.S. (2001). Liver organogenesis promoted by endothelial cells prior to vascular function. *Science* **294,** 559–563.

66. Kameda, Y., Nishimaki, T., Takeichi, M., and Chisaka, O. (2002). Homeobox gene *hoxa3* is essential for the formation of the carotid body in the mouse embryos. *Dev. Biol.* **247,** 197–209.

67. Kameda, Y., Watari-Goshima, N., Nishimaki, T., and Chisaka, O. (2003). Disruption of the *Hoxa3* homeobox gene results in anomalies of the carotid artery system and the arterial baroreceptors. *Cell Tissue Res.* **311,** 343–352.

68. Niederreither, K., Vermot, J., Le Roux, I., Schuhbaur, B., Chambon, P., and Dolle, P. (2003). The regional pattern of retinoic acid synthesis by RALDH2 is essential for the development of posterior pharyngeal arches and the enteric nervous system. *Development* **130,** 2525–2534.

69. Stalmans, I., Lambrechts, D., De Smet, F., Jansen, S., Wang, J., Maity, S., Kneer, P., von der Ohe, M., Swillen, A., Maes, C., Gewillig, M., Molin, D.G., Hellings, P., Boetel, T., Haardt, M., Compernolle, V., Dewerchin, M., Plaisance, B., Vlietinck, R., Emanuel, B., Gittenberger-de Groot, A.C., Scambler, P., Morrow, B., Driscol, D.A., Moons, L., Esguerra, C.V., Carmeliet, G., Behn-Krappa, A., Devriendt, K., Collen, D., Conway, S.J., and Carmeliet, P. (2003). VEGF: a modifier of the del22q11 (DiGeorge) syndrome? *Nat. Med.* **9,** 173–182.

70. Auerbach, R. (1960). Morphogenetic interactions in the development of the mouse thymus gland. *Dev. Biol.* **2,** 271–284.

71. Hoffman, M.P., Kidder, B.L., Steinberg, Z.L., Lakhani, S., Ho, S., Kleinman, H.K., and Larsen, M. (2002). Gene expression profiles of mouse submandibular gland development: FGFR1 regulates branching morphogenesis *in vitro* through BMP- and FGF-dependent mechanisms. *Development* **129,** 5767–5778.

72. Vainio, S., Lin, Y., and Pihlajaniemi, T. (2003). Induced repatterning of type XVIII collagen associates with ectopic Sonic hedgehog and lung surfactant C gene expression and changes in epithelial epigenesis in the ureteric bud. *J. Am. Soc. Nephrol.* **14,** S3–S8.

73. Jenkinson, W.E., Jenkinson, E.J., and Anderson, G. (2003). Differential requirement for mesenchyme in the proliferation and maturation of thymic epithelial progenitors. *J. Exp. Med.* **198,** 325–332.

74. Erickson, M., Morkowski, S., Lehar, S., Gillard, G., Beers, C., Dooley, J., Rubin, J.S., Rudensky, A., and Farr, A.G. (2002). Regulation of thymic epithelium by keratinocyte growth factor. *Blood* **100,** 3269–3278.

75. Moon, A.M., and Capecchi, M.R. (2000). Fgf8 is required for outgrowth and patterning of the limbs. *Nat. Genet.* **26,** 455–459.

76. Crossley, P.H., Minowada, G., MacArther, C.A., and Martin, G.R. (1996). Roles for FGF8 in the induction, initiation, and maintenance of chick limb development. *Cell* **84,** 127–136.

77. Bennett, A.R., Farley, A., Blair, N.F., Gordon, J., Sharp, L., and Blackburn, C.C. (2002). Identification and characterization of thymic epithelial progenitor cells. *Immunity* **16,** 803–814.

78. Gill, J., Malin, M., Hollander, G.A., and Boyd, R. (2002). Generation of a complete thymic microenvironment by MTS24(+) thymic epithelial cells. *Nat. Immunol.* **3,** 635–642.

79. Klug, D.B., Carter, C., Gimenez-Conti, I.B., and Richie, E.R. (2002). Cutting edge: thymocyte-independent and thymocyte-dependent phases of epithelial patterning in the fetal thymus. *J. Immunol.* **169,** 2842–2845.

79a. Gordan, J., Sullivan, S., Brewer, S., Ji, Y., Perkins, A., Williams, T., and Maniey, N.R. (unpublished data).

80. Brewer, S., Feng, W., Huang, J., Sullivan, S., and Williams, T. (2004). Cre-mediated deletion of AP-2α causes multiple neural crest-related defects. *Dev. Biol.* **267,** 135–152.

81. Mendelsohn, C., Lohnes, D., Decimo, D., Lufkin, T., LeMeur, M., Chambon, P., and Mark, M. (1994). Function of the retinoic acid receptors (RARs) during development: II—Multiple abnormalities at various stages of organogenesis in RAR double mutants. *Development* **120,** 2749–2771.

82. Anderson, M.K., and Rothenberg, E.V. (2000). Transcription factor expression in lymphocyte development: clues to the evolutionary origins of lymphoid cell lineages? *Curr. Top. Microbiol. Immunol.* **248,** 137–155.

83. Schlake, T., Schorpp, M., Nehls, M., and Boehm, T. (1997). The *nude* gene encodes a sequence-specific DNA-binding protein with homologs in organisms that lack an anticipatory immune system. *Proc. Natl. Acad. Sci. U. S. A.* **94,** 3842–3847.

84. Horigome, N., Myojin, M., Ueki, T., Hirano, S., Aizawa, S., and Kuratani, S. (1999). Development of cephalic neural crest cells in embryos of *Lampetra japonica,* with special reference to the evolution of the jaw. *Dev. Biol.* **207,** 287–308.

85. Graham, A., and Smith, A. (2001). Patterning the pharyngeal arches. *Bioessays* **23,** 54–61.

86. Ogasawara, M., Shigetani, Y., Hirano, S., Satoh, N., and Kuratani, S. (2000). *Pax1/Pax9*-related genes in an agnathan vertebrate, *Lampetra japonica:* expression pattern of LjPax9 implies sequential evolutionary events toward the gnathostome body plan. *Dev. Biol.* **223,** 399–410.

87. Müller, T.S., Ebsensperger, C., Neubüser, A., Koseki, H., Balling, R., Christ, B., and Wilting, J. (1996). Expression of avian *Pax1* and *Pax9* is intrinsically regulated in the pharyngeal endoderm but depends on environmental influences in the paraxial mesoderm. *Dev. Biol.* **178,** 403–417.

88. Piotrowski, T., and Nusslein-Volhard, C. (2000). The endoderm plays an important role in patterning the segmented pharyngeal region in zebra fish *(Danio rerio). Dev. Biol.* **225,** 339–356.

89. Veitch, E., Begbie, J., Schilling, T.F., Smith, M.M., and Graham, A. (1999). Pharyngeal arch patterning in the absence of neural crest. *Curr. Biol.* **9,** 1481–1484.

90. Wendling, O., Dennefeld, C., Chambon, P., and Mark, M. (2000). Retinoid signaling is essential for patterning the endoderm of the third and fourth pharyngeal arches. *Development* **127,** 1553–1562.

91. Okai, N., Tagawa, K., Humphreys, T., Satoh, N., and Osagawara, M. (2000). Characterization of gill-specific genes of the acorn worm *Ptychodera flava. Dev. Dyn.* **217,** 309–319.

92. Holland, N.D., Holland, L.Z., and Kozmik, Z. (1995). An amphioxus *Pax* gene, *AmphiPax-1,* expressed in embryonic endoderm but not in mesoderm: implications for the evolution of class I paired-box genes. *Mol. Marine Biol. Biotech.* **4,** 206–214.

93. Nornes, S., Mikkola, I., Krauss, S., Delghandi, M., Perander, M., and Johansen, T. (1996). Zebra fish *Pax9* encodes two proteins with distinct C-terminal transactivating domains of different potency negatively regulated by adjacent N-terminal sequences. *J. Biol. Chem.* **271,** 26,914–26,923.

94. Neubüser, A., Koseki, H., and Balling, R. (1995). Characterization and developmental expression of *Pax9,* a paired-box-containing gene related to *Pax1. Dev. Biol.* **170,** 701–716.

95. Holland, L.Z., and Holland, N.D. (1996). Expression of *AmphiHox-1* and *AmphiPax-1* in amphioxus embryos treated with retinoic acid: insights into evolution and patterning of the chordate nerve cord and pharynx. *Development* **122,** 1829–1838.

96. Holland, P. (1992). Homeobox genes in vertebrate evolution. *Bioessays* **14,** 267–273.

97. Irvine, S.Q., and Martindale, M.Q. (2000). Expression patterns of anterior *Hox* genes in the polychaete *Chaetopterus:* correlation with morphological boundaries. *Dev. Biol.* **217,** 333–351.

98. Locascio, A., Aniello, F., Amoroso, A., Manzanares, M., Krumlauf, R., and Branno, M. (1999). Patterning the ascidian nervous system: structure, expression, and transgenic analysis of the *CiHox3* gene. *Development* **126**, 4737–4748.

99. Manzanares, M., Wada, H., Itasaki, N., Trainor, P.A., Krumlauf, R., and Holland, P.W. (2000). Conservation and elaboration of *Hox* gene regulation during evolution of the vertebrate head. *Nature* **408**, 854–857.

100. Peterson, K.J., Irvine, S.Q., Cameron, R.A., and Davidson, E.H. (2000). Quantitative assessment of *Hox* complex expression in the indirect development of the polychaete annelid *Chaetopterus sp. Proc. Natl. Acad. Sci. U. S. A.* **97**, 4487–4492.

101. Carr, J.L., Shashikant, C.S., Bailey, W.J., and Ruddle, F.H. (1998). Molecular evolution of *Hox* gene regulation: cloning and transgenic analysis of the lamprey *HoxQ8* gene. *J. Exp. Zool.* **280**, 73–85.

102. Gellon, G., and McGinnis, W. (1998). Shaping animal body plans in development and evolution by modulation of *Hox* expression patterns. *Bioessays* **20**, 116–125.

103. Holland, P.W.H., and Garcia-Fernandez, J. (1996). *Hox* genes and chordate evolution. *Dev. Biol.* **173**, 382–395.

104. Lampert, I., and Ritter, M. (1988). The origin of the diverse epithelial cells of the thymus: Is there a common stem cell? *In* "Thymus Update," (M.D. Kendall *et al.*, eds.) pp. 5–25. Harwood Academic, London.

105. Lind, E.F., Prockop, S.E., Porritt, H.E., and Petrie, H.T. (2001). Mapping precursor movement through the postnatal thymus reveals specific microenvironments supporting defined stages of early lymphoid development. *J. Exp. Med.* **194**, 127–134.

106. Prockop, S., and Petrie, H.T. (2000). Cell migration and the anatomic control of thymocyte precursor differentiation. *Semin. Immunol.* **12**, 435–444.

107. Prockop, S.E., Palencia, S., Ryan, C.M., Gordon, K., Gray, D., and Petrie, H.T. (2002). Stromal cells provide the matrix for migration of early lymphoid progenitors through the thymic cortex. *J. Immunol.* **169**, 4354–4261.

108. Petrie, H.T. (2002). Role of thymic organ structure and stromal composition in steady-state postnatal T-cell production. *Immunol. Rev.* **189**, 8–19.

109. Manley, N. (2000). Thymus organogenesis and molecular mechanisms of thymic epithelial cell differentiation. *Semin. Immunol.* **12**, 421–428.

110. Dunon, D., and Imhof, B.A. (2000). The role of cell traffic in the emergence of the T-lymphoid system. *Semin. Immunol.* **12**, 429–433.

111. Ritter, M.A., and Boyd, R.L. (1993). Development in the thymus: it takes two to tango. *Immunol. Today* **14**, 462–469.

112. Van Ewijk, W., Shores, E.W., and Singer, A. (1994). Cross talk in the mouse thymus. *Immunol. Today* **15**, 214–217.

113. Van Ewijk, W., Kawamoto, H., Germeraad, W.T., and Katsura, Y. (2000). Developing thymocytes organize thymic microenvironments. *Curr. Top. Microbiol. Immunol.* **251**, 125–132.

114. Kovacs, C.S., Manley, N.R., Moseley, J.M., Martin, T.J., and Kronenberg, H.M. (2001). Fetal parathyroids are not required to maintain placental calcium transport. *J. Clin. Invest.* **107**, 1007–1015.

115. Boyd, R.L., Tucek, C.L., Godfrey, D.I., Izon, D.J., Wilson, T.J., Davidson, N.J., Bean, A.G., Ladyman, H.M., Ritter, M.A., and Hugo, P. (1993). The thymic microenvironment. *Immunol. Today* **14**, 445–459.

116. Anderson, M.S., Venanzi, E.S., Klein, L., Chen, Z., Berzins, S.P., Turley, S.J., von Boehmer, H., Bronson, R., Dierich, A., Benoist, C., and Mathis, D. (2002). Projection of an immunological self shadow within the thymus by the aire protein. *Science* **298**, 1395–1401.

117. Ge, Q., and Chen, W.F. (2000). Effect of murine thymic epithelial cell line (MTEC1) on the functional expression of CD4(+)CD8(−) thymocyte subgroups. *Int. Immunol.* **12**, 1127–1133.

118. Klug, D.B., Carter, C., Crouch, E., Roop, D., Conti, C.J., and Richie, E.R. (1998). Interdependence of cortical thymic epithelial cell differentiation and T-lineage commitment. *Proc. Natl. Acad. Sci. U. S. A.* **95**, 11,822–11,827.

119. Blackburn, C.C. (Unpublished data).

120. Schluep, M., Willcox, N., Ritter, M.A., Newsom-Davis, J., Larche, M., and Brown, A.N. (1988). *Myasthenia gravis* thymus: clinical, histological, and culture correlations. *J. Autoimmun.* **1**, 445–467.

121. Blackburn, C.C., Manley, N.R., Palmer, D.B., Boyd, R.L., Anderson, G., and Ritter, M.A. (2002). One for all and all for one: thymic epithelial stem cells and regeneration. *Trends Immunol.* **23**, 391–395.

122. Anderson, G., Jenkinson, E.J., Moore, N.C., and Owen, J.J. (1993). MHC class II-positive epithelium and mesenchyme cells are both required for T-cell development in the thymus. *Nature* **362**, 70–73.

123. Itoi, M., Kawamoto, H., Katsura, Y., and Amagai, T. (2001). Two distinct steps of immigration of hematopoietic progenitors into the early thymus anlage. *Int. Immunol.* **13**, 1203–1211.

124. Bleul, C.C., and Boehm, T. (2000). Chemokines define distinct microenvironments in the developing thymus. *Eur. J. Immunol.* **30**, 3371–3379.

125. Su, D.M., Navarre, S., Oh, W., Condie, B.G., and Manley, N.R. (2003). A domain of Foxn1 required for crosstalk-dependent thymic epithelial cell differentiation. *Nature Immunology* **4**, 1128–1135.

126. Schuddekopf, K., Schorpp, M., and Boehm, T. (1996). The whn transcription factor encoded by the nude locus contains an evolutionarily conserved and functionally indispensable activation domain. *Proc. Natl. Acad. Sci. U. S. A.* **93**, 9661–9664.

127. Brissette, J.L., Li, J., Kamimura, J., Lee, D., and Dotto, G.P. (1996). The product of the mouse nude locus, Whn, regulates the balance between epithelial cell growth and differentiation. *Genes Dev.* **10**, 2212–2221.

128. Holländer, G.A., Wang, B., Nichogiannopoulou, A., Platenberg, P.P., van Ewijk, W., Burakoff, S.J., Gutierrez-Ramos, J.C., and Terhorst, C. (1995). Developmental control point in induction of thymic cortex regulated by a subpopulation of prothymocytes. *Nature* **373**, 350–353.

129. Schlake, T., Schorpp, M., and Boehm, T. (2000). Formation of regulator–target gene relationships during evolution. *Gene* **256**, 29–34.

130. Rodewald, H.R., Paul, S., Haller, C., Bluethmann, H., and Blum, C. (2001). Thymus medulla consisting of epithelial islets each derived from a single progenitor. *Nature* **414**, 763–768.

131. Anderson, M., Anderson, S.K., and Farr, A.G. (2000). Thymic vasculature: organizer of the medullary epithelial compartment? *Int. Immunol.* **12**, 1105–1110.

132. Burkly, L., Hession, C., Ogata, L., Reilly, C., Marconi, L.A., Olson, D., Tizard, R., Cate, R., and Lo, D. (1995). Expression of *relB* is required for the development of thymic medulla and dendritic cells. *Nature* **373**, 531–536.

133. Pitkanen, J. and Peterson, P. (2003). Autoimmune regulator: from loss of function to autoimmunity. *Genes Immunol.* **4**, 12–21.

134. Heino, M., Peterson, P., Sillanpaa, N., Guerin, S., Wu, L., Anderson, G., Scott, H.S., Antonarakis, S.E., Kudoh, J., Shimizu, N., Jenkinson, E.J., Naquet, P., and Krohn, K.J. (2000). RNA and protein expression of the murine autoimmune regulator gene (Aire) in normal, RelB-deficient and in NOD mouse. *Eur. J. Immunol.* **30,** 1884–1893.

135. Zuklys, S., Balciunaite, G., Agarwal, A., Fasler-Kan, E., Palmer, E., and Hollander, G.A. (2000). Normal thymic architecture and negative selection are associated with *Aire* expression, the gene defective in the autoimmune polyendocrinopathy-candidiasis-ectodermal dystrophy (APECED). *J. Immunol.* **165,** 1976–1983.

Characterization of Human Embryonic Stem Cells

Melissa K. Carpenter and Mickie Bhatia

Pluripotent embryonic stem (ES) cells have indefinite replicative potential and the ability to differentiate into derivatives of all three germ layers. Initially, ES cells were isolated from the inner cell mass (ICM) of the mouse preimplantation embryo.[1,2] These cell lines were generated by removing the ICM from preimplantation blastocysts and serially passaging these cells on irradiated mouse feeder layers. The resulting cell lines showed unrestricted proliferative potential and were pluripotent. The mouse ES cells differentiated into derivatives of all three germ layers; upon injection into blastocysts, they contributed to all the tissue types in the resulting chimera. These cell lines have been largely used for the generation of genetically modified mice, but they also provide a unique tool for studying development of the embryo.

Human ES (hES) cell lines have been derived in multiple laboratories throughout the world[3–6] (see NIH registry Web site at http://escr.nih.gov). These cell populations grow as tightly compacted colonies of undifferentiated cells on mouse[5,6] or human[3] feeders or as colonies in feeder-free conditions using matrix and conditioned medium.[7] Although mouse ES cells can be maintained in culture conditions in which the feeder layer is replaced by leukemia inhibitory factor (LIF), the human cells do not appear to have this response to LIF,[5,6] indicating that mouse ES cells and hES cells require different signals to maintain pluripotency.

Two studies have directly compared the expression patterns of hES and mouse ES cells. Sato *et al.*[8] compared the transcriptional profile of one hES cell line (H1) to the published profiles for mouse ES cells.[9,10] This study identified a set of 918 genes enriched in undifferentiated hES cells compared to hES cells that had undergone differentiation. This set of genes included ligand–receptor pairs for the FGF, TGF-β–BMP, and Wnt signaling pathways. Some of these components corresponded to genes identified in previous studies[9,10] as "stemness" genes, indicating that a "core molecular program" may exist. In contrast, Ginis *et al.*[11] compared expression profiles of mouse ES cells (D3) with three hES cell lines (H1, H9, and I6) using immunocytochemistry, reverse

transcription-polymerase chain reaction (RT-PCR), and microarray analysis. As summarized in Table 38–1, ES cells from both species expressed transcription factors associated with pluripotent cells, such as Oct-4, Sox2, Tert, Utf1, and Rex-1. Using RT-PCR and immunocytochemistry, significant differences were found in expression of vimentin, ß-tubulin, α-fetoprotein, eomesodermin, ARNT, Foxd3, and the LIF receptor. Focused microarrays revealed profound differences in cell cycle regulation, control of apoptosis, and cytokine expression. These findings confirm that there are many differences between mouse and hES cells and demonstrate the need to use multiple methodologies to characterize these differences.

hES cells are maintained in media containing 20% fetal bovine serum or serum replacement media supplemented with basic fibroblast growth factor[12] and require the presence of feeder cells or conditioned medium from feeders. This culture system results in a heterogeneous population of cells that has been difficult to consistently characterize. In addition, the existing hES cell lines were derived in different laboratories using different procedures, which may result in cell lines with different qualities. Although some of the lines have been characterized extensively, most cell lines have not been available long enough to allow full characterization; therefore, further study will be required to definitively determine the differences and similarities of the different cell lines.

To date, hES cell lines have been characterized using surface markers and molecular markers used to characterize human embryonal carcinoma (EC) cells, mouse ES cells, and hematopoietic stem cells. Similar to mouse ES cells, the hES cells express alkaline phosphatase-related antigens.[5–7] In addition, the undifferentiated hES cells express the globoseries glycolipid antigens designated stage-specific embryonic antigen (SSEA-3 and SSEA-4), which are also expressed by human EC cells. In contrast to the mouse ES cells, the undifferentiated hES cells lack expression of a lactoseries oligosaccharide antigen SSEA-1.[13] In addition, the keratin sulfate-related antigens Tra1-60 and Tra1-81[14] expressed by human EC cells are also expressed by hES cells. Remarkably, all of the hES cell lines derived to date show similar expression of these markers (Table 38–2).

In our lab, we compared the expression of these markers in four different cell lines derived in a single laboratory (H1, H7, H9, and H14) maintained in feeder-free conditions using

Melissa K. Carpenter and Mickie Bhatia

TABLE 38–1
Comparison of Mouse and Human ES Cells

	Mouse ES	Human ES
Alkaline phosphatase	+	+
SSEA-1	+	−
SSEA-3	−	+
SSEA-4	−	+
Tra1-60	−	+
Tra1-81	−	+
Oct-3/4	+	+
Sox2	+	+
Rex-1	+	+
Tert	+	+
Fgf4	+	+
Utf1	+	+
Foxd3	+	−
Cx45	+	+
Cx43	+	+
BCRP-1	+	+
LIFR	+	−
gp130	+	+
Stat3	+	+
Nanog	+	+

quantitative analyses.[15] An average of 80–95%, 91–94%, and 88–93% of the cells in cultures from four cell lines expressed SSEA-4, Tra1-60, and Tra1-81, respectively. Therefore, the overall expression of surface markers was similar, although with extensive analysis, we found some small but statistically significant differences in the expression of markers among cell lines. As mentioned previously, hES cells have unlimited proliferative capacity. Therefore, we also performed quantitative analyses of marker expression in several hES cell lines over long-term culture in feeder-free conditions.[16] The hES cell cultures maintained high levels of expression (>80% of the cells) even after one year in continuous culture. Although the cultures appeared more similar than different, it is important to recognize that hES cell cultures represent mixed populations of cells, and it may be extremely difficult to determine differences among cell lines. Therefore, further analysis will be required to determine if these differences will correlate with other characteristics of the cells, such as the capacity to differentiate.

In addition to glycolipids and glycoproteins, hES cells also express integrins. Laminin is the first extracellular matrix protein expressed in the two- and four-cell stage mouse embryo,[17,18] and the laminin receptor is highly expressed in murine ES and EC cells.[19,20] This information, and the finding that hES cells appear to require matrix for the maintenance of the undifferentiated phenotype, led us to evaluate the expression of integrins in hES cells maintained on feeders or in feeder-free conditions. Cells in both conditions express high levels of $\alpha6$ and $\beta1$, moderate levels of $\alpha2$, and low levels of $\alpha1$, $\alpha2$, $\alpha3$, and $\beta4$.

TABLE 38–2

Cell Line		Karyotype	SSEA-1	SSEA-3	SSEA-4	Tra1-60	Tra1-81	Alkaline Phosphatase	CD90	AC133	Oct-4	hTert
H1	WA01	XY	−	+	+	+	+	+	+	+	+	+
H7	WA07	XX	−	+	+	+	+	+	+	+	+	+
H9	WA09	XX	−	+	+	+	+	+		+	+	+
HES-1	ES01	XX	−	+	+	+	+	+			+	
HES-2	ES02	XX	−	+	+	+	+	+			+	
HES-3	ES03	XX	−	+	+	+	+	+			+	
HES-4	ES04	XY	−	+	+	+	+	+			+	
HES-6	ES06	XY	−		+	+		+			+	
HSF-6	UC06	XX	−	+	+							
hESBGN.01	BG01	XY	−	+	+	+	+	+			+	+
hESBGN.02	BG02	XY	−	+	+	+	+	+			+	+
Miz-hES-1	MI01	XY	+/−	+	+	+	+	+			+	

This is consistent with the finding that the cells grow well on laminin and matrigel.[7] In addition to integrins, the undifferentiated hES cells within the colonies also express connexin 43, indicating the presence of gap junctions. This was confirmed using dye transfer studies demonstrating functional gap junctions between the hES cells.[15]

Expression of transcription factors has also been used to characterize the hES cells. The POU transcription factor, Oct-4, is expressed in pluripotent cell populations such as early embryo cells, blastomeres, and germ cells. *In vitro,* Oct-4 is expressed in pluripotent cells such as EC, ES, and embryonic germ cells.[21–23] Furthermore, it has been demonstrated that Oct-4 is necessary to retain pluripotency in murine embryonic cells[24] and that the level of expression can influence the status of pluripotency and direct the cells toward specific phenotypes.[25] In hES cells derived in different laboratories, Oct-4 is expressed[6,7] and is down-regulated upon differentiation.[26] Quantitative comparison using Taqman analysis of the transcription factors Oct-4, hTert, and cripto showed similar expression among the H1, H7, H9, and H14 cell lines. The level of expression of these factors was maintained for more than one year in continuous culture.[16] Furthermore, transcription factors such as Rex-1 and Sox2 were expressed by early and late passage cells, indicating that quantitation of these markers may be useful tools.

Cytogenetic analysis of hES cell lines show stable XX and XY karyotypes from multiple labs. Our lab has used G-banding to show that the cells retain a normal karyotype after one year in culture. We found that as many as 20% of the cultures contained some aneuploid cells.[16] However, it is unclear whether the presence of aneuploid cells in the hES cell cultures will alter the fundamental characteristics of the cells. Surprisingly, mouse ES cells exhibiting 38% or more normal karyotype can generate germ line chimeras.[27] It is unknown whether the types of aneuploidy seen in the hES cultures will affect growth rate, cell cycle regulation, or capacity to differentiate. However, the occasional identification of atypical cells, albeit at a low frequency, highlights the importance of careful monitoring.

In addition to flow cytometry and PCR analysis, several studies have used microarrays to compare expression of markers among cell lines. In our lab, the H1, H7, and H9 lines were analyzed by microarray and showed no consistent differences. These cultures were all at relatively low passage (p28–p37) and contained undifferentiated colonies surrounded by stroma-like cells. When later passage cultures are analyzed, some small differences are detected.[16] This most likely results directly or indirectly from a loss of stroma-like cells in later passage cultures. Further analysis using microarrays has been performed, comparing six hES cell lines derived in different labs. All lines showed significant homology in gene expression, including expression of Sox2, Nanog, GTCM-1, connexin 43, Oct-4, and cripto.[28] These data indicate that hES cell lines obtained from different sources and maintained in similar culture conditions share similar expression profiles. However, it should be noted that differences in culture conditions, such as maintaining the cells on feeders, may alter the signature profile of any cell line. A detailed analysis must be considered to profile all existing lines. In addition, hES cell

Cripto	GCTM-2	TG343	Genesis	GDF3	Feeder-Free Culture	Cryopreservation	Sox2	Rex-1	Utf1	Nanog	Teratoma Formation
+					+	+	+	+	+		+
+					+	+					+
+					+	+	+	+	+		+
+	+	+	+	+		+					+
+	+	+	+	+		+					+
+	+	+	+	+		+					+
+	+	+	+	+		+					+
+	+	+	+	+		+					+
							+	+	+		
							+	+	+		
											+

Factors for Consideration	Experimental Variations
I Removal and isolation of intracellular mass (ICM)	–Immunosurgery of trophoectoderm –Laser ablation of trophoectoderm –Direct "hatching" of ICM
II Stage of quality of embryo	–Fresh vs frozen embryo –Clinical "grade" of embryo –Developmental stage (e.g., 8-cell vs blastocyst)
III Culture conditions for establishment and expansion	–Direct coculture on MEF –Direct coculture on human feeders –Use of MEF-CM and matrix –Serum-free conditions with defined factors

cultures represent a heterogeneous population of cells, containing undifferentiated cells as well as some spontaneously differentiated cells. Further, these cells are in different states of cell cycle and may therefore be expressing different markers at different levels.

Considerations for the Derivation of New Human Embryonic Stem Cell Lines

As summarized previously, our knowledge of appropriate phenotypic and molecular markers and of functional criteria to evaluate and compare various hES cell lines is becoming more advanced. However, although most well-characterized cell lines share fundamental expression patterns, these lines also demonstrate distinct differentiation and growth patterns which have yet to be quantified. This raises the possibility that the differing approaches used to derive these cell lines may account for some of these unique properties. Unlike mouse ES cell lines, variations in stage and quality of embryos and in genetic background of the donors used to derived hES cells is not as tightly controlled and may contribute to differences in hES cell lines. To date, the derivation methods and culture conditions for the establishment and expansion of hES cell lines have not been tightly controlled, nor has any single methodology for derivation led to the number of hES cell lines needed for meaningful comparisons among the hES cell lines available. The available information on the behavior of established hES cell lines is important to consider when moving toward derivation of new cell lines and understanding the molecular basis that may account for different hES cell properties. It is likely that establishing and expanding newly

derived hES cell cultures is a complex *in vitro* selection process; therefore, the conditions used to derive hES cell lines may define properties such as cell cycle status, growth factor responsiveness, and differentiation capacity. Based on the available information, we have listed some of the experimental parameters that may affect the nature of hES cell lines in Table 38–3. As new cell lines are derived, it will be important to determine which (if any) of these parameters affects the status of the hES cells.

Summary

Overall, there are several useful markers available for the assessment of hES cells. However, it is unclear whether these markers will be predictive of the differentiative capacity of the hES cells. It is clear that continued characterization of the existing and newly created hES cells will be required to understand the mechanisms involved in retaining the undifferentiated state of the hES cells as well as the mechanisms involved in differentiation.

REFERENCES

1. Evans, M.J., and Kaufman, M.H. (1981). Establishment in culture of pluripotential cells from mouse embryos. *Nature* **292**, 154–156.
2. Martin, G.R. (1981). Isolation of a pluripotent cell line from early mouse embryos cultured in medium conditioned by teratocarcinoma stem cells. *Proc. Nat. Acad. Sci. USA* **78**, 7634–7638.
3. Richards, M., Fong, C.Y., Chan, W.K., Wong, P.C., and Bongso, A. (2002). Human feeders support prolonged undifferentiated growth of human inner cell masses and embryonic stem cells. *Nature Biotechnology* **20**, 933–936.
4. Amit, M., and Itskovitz-Eldor, J. (2002). Derivation and spontaneous differentiation of human embryonic stem cells. *J. Anat.* **200**, 225–232.
5. Thomson, J.A., Itskovitz-Eldor, J., Shapiro, S.S., Waknitz, M.A., Swiergiel, J.J., Marshall, V.S., and Jones, J.M. (1998). Embryonic stem cell lines derived from human blastocysts. *Science* **282**, 1145–1147.
6. Reubinoff, B., Pera, M.F., Fong, C.Y., Trounson, A., and Bongso, A. (2000). Embryonic stem cell lines from human blastocysts: Somatic differentiation *in vitro*. *Nature Biotechnology* **18**, 399–404.
7. Xu, C., Inokuma, M.S., Denham, J., Golds, K., Kundu, P., Gold, J.D., and Carpenter, M.K. (2001). Feeder-free growth of undifferentiated human embryonic stem cells on defined matrices with conditioned medium. *Nature Biotechnology* **19**, 971–974.
8. Sato, N., Sanjuan, I.M., Heke, M., Uchida, M., Naef, F., and Brivanlou, A.H. (2003). Molecular signature of human embryonic stem cells and its comparison with the mouse. *Dev. Biol.* **260**, 404–413.
9. Ivanova, N.B., Dimos, J.T., Schaniel, C., Hackney, J.A., Moore, K.A., and Lemischka, I.R. (2002). A stem cell molecular signature. *Science* **298**, 601–604.
10. Ramalho-Santos, M., Yoon, S., Matsuzaki, Y., Mulligan, R.C., and Melton, D.A. (2002). "Stemness": Transcriptional profiling of embryonic and adult stem cells. *Science* **298**, 597–600.
11. Ginis, I., Luo, Y., Miura, T., Thies, R., Brandenburg, R., Gerecht-Nir, S., Amit, M., Hoke, A., Carpenter, M., Itskovitz-Eldor, J., and

Rao, M., (2004). Differences between human and mouse embryonic stem cells. *Dev. Bio.* **269**, 360-380.

12. Amit, M., Carpenter, M.K., Inokuma, M.S., Chiu, C.P., Harris, C.P., Waknitz, M.A., Itskovitz-Eldor, J., and Thomson, J.A. (2000). Clonally derived human embryonic stem cell lines maintain pluripotency and proliferative potential for prolonged periods of culture. *Dev. Biol.* **227**, 271–278.

13. Kannagi, R., Cochran, N.A., Ishigami, F., Hakamori, S., Andrews, P.W., Knowles, B.B., and Solter, D. (1983). Stage-specific embryonic antigens (SSEA-3 and -4) are epitopes of a unique globo-series ganglioside isolated from human teratocarcinoma cells. *EMBO J.* **2**, 2355–2361.

14. Andrews, P.W., Banting, G., Damjanov, I., Arnaud, D., and Avner, P. (1984). Three monoclonal antibodies defining distinct differentiation antigens associated with different high molecular weight polypeptides on the surface of human embryonal carcinoma cells. *Hybridoma* **3**, 347–361.

15. Carpenter, M., Rosier, E., Fisk, G., Brandenberger, R., Ares, X., Miura, T., Lucero, M., and Rao, M.S. (2004). Properties of four human ES cell lines maintained in a feeder free culture system. *Dev. Dyn.* **229**, 243-258.

16. Rosler, E., Fisk, G., Ares, X., Irving, J., Miura, T., Rao, M., and Carpenter, M. (2004). Long term culture of human embryonic stem cells in feeder-free conditions. *Dev. Dyn.* **228**, 259-274.

17. Cooper, A.R., and MacQueen, H.A. (1983). Subunits of laminin are differentially synthesized in mouse eggs and early embryos. *Dev. Biol.* **96**, 467–471.

18. Ekblom, P., Vestweber, D., and Kemler, R. (1986). Cell-matrix interactions and cell adhesion during development. *Annu. Rev. Cell Biol.* **2**, 27–47.

19. Copper, H.M., Tamura, R.N., and V.Q. Copper (1991). The major laminin receptor of mouse embryonic stem cells is a novel isoform of the a6b1 integrin. *J. Cell Biol.* **115**, 843–850.

20. Hierck, B.P., Thorsteinsdottir, S., Niessen, C.M., Freund, E., Iperen, L.V., Hogervorst, F., Poelmann, R.E., Mummery, C.L., and Sonnenberg, A. (1993). Variants of the a6b1 laminin receptor in early murine development–distribution, molecular cloning, and chromosomal localization of the mouse integrin a6 subunit. *Cell Adhesion and Communication* **1**, 33–53.

21. Okamoto, K., Okazawa, H., Okuda, A., Sakai, M., Muramatsu, M., and Hamada, H. (1990). A novel octamer-binding transcription factor is differentially expressed in mouse embryonic stem cells. *Cell* **60**, 461–472.

22. Yeom, Y.I., Fuhrmann, G., Ovitt, C.E., Brehm, A., Ohbo, K., Gross, M., Hübner, K., and Schöler, H.R. (1996). Germ line regulatory element of Oct-4 specific for the totipotent cycle of embryonal cells. *Development* **122**, 881–894.

23. Rosner, M.H., Vigano, M.A., Ozato, K., Timmons, P.M., Poirier, F., Rigby, P., and Staudt, L.M. (1990). A POU-domain transcription factir in early stem cells and germ cells of the mammalian embryo. *Nature* **345**, 686–692.

24. Nichols, J., Zevnik, B., Anastassiadis, K., Niwa, H., Klewe-Nebenius, D., Chambers, I., Scholer, H., and Smith, A. (1998). Formation of pluripotent stem cells in the mammalian embryo depends on the POU transcription factor Oct-4. *Cell* **95**, 379–391.

25. Niwa, H., Miyazaki, J., and Smith, A.G. (2000). Quantitative expression of Oct-3–4 defines differentiation, dedifferentiation, or self-renewal of ES cells. *Nat. Genet.* **24**, 372–376.

26. Lebkowski, J.S., Gold, J., Xu, C., Funk, W., Chiu, C.P., and Carpenter, M.K. (2001). Human embryonic stem cells: Culture, differentiation, and genetic modification for regenerative medicine applications. *Cancer J.* **7 (Suppl. 2)**, S83–93.

27. Suzuki, H., Kamada, N., Ueda, O., Jishage, K., Kurihara, Y., Kurihara, H., Terauchi, Y., Azuma, S., Kadowaki, T., Kodama, T., Yazaki, Y., and Toyda, Y. (1997). Germ-line contribution of embryonic stem cells in chimeric mice: influence of karyotype and *in vitro* differentiation ability. *Exp Anim* **46**, 17–23.

28. Bhattacharya, B., Miura, T., Brandenberger, R., Mejido, J., Luo, Y., Yang, A., Joshi, B., Ginis, I., Thies, R., Amit, M., Lyons, I., Condie, B., Itskovitz-Eldor, J., Rao, M.S., and Puri, R. (2004). Gene expression in human embryonic stem cell lines: unique molecular signature. *Blood* **103**, 2956-2964.

Isolation and Maintenance of Murine Embryonic Stem Cells

Sir Martin Evans

Mouse embryonic stem (ES) cells were first isolated more than 20 years ago. Their isolation and the conditions for their growth and maintenance are well described both in the original references and in numerous reviews and methods texts, so this chapter is written more as a commentary than a cookbook.

I first discuss the growth and maintenance of cultures of mouse ES cells because their isolation depends upon the secure ability to maintain them. I would recommend that an established ES cell line be used to optimise growth conditions before attempts are made to isolate new ones.

ES cells grow well in culture and are not particularly fastidious about the media, but it must be remembered that ES cell cultures are essentially primary cultures. Therefore, it is necessary to use conditions of tissue culture that maintain their primary properties and do not select variants. Any growth in nonoptimal conditions will lead to selective pressure and the appearance of better-growing but worse-differentiating strains. In some cases these may be recognised as chromosomal variants, but in others there is no gross karyotypic change identifying the altered cell strain. They will certainly, however, be less able to differentiate and will produce abnormal chimaeras.

Maintenance of ES Cells

There are major requirements for ES cell culture in the context of maintaining their totipotency necessary for genetic engineering and gene targeting projects:

- The cells are maintained in their undifferentiated state
- They maintain their normal capability and range of differentiation
- The cells retain a normal karyotype, a prerequisite for germ line transmission

To maintain the stem cell state (suppression of differentiation), the cells need to be cultured with mitotically inactivated feeder cells or in the presence of leukaemia inhibitory factor (LIF).[1, 2] Each method has advantages and disadvantages. Feeders provide a more robust approach, as the supplementation of media by growth factors will lead to a more pulsatile addition of the

factors and will depend more on meticulous attention. Conversely, sufficient provision of feeders requires setting them up and inactivating at each passage. Growth in the presence of LIF may seem less troublesome and makes certain types of experiments much easier, but it can have its disadvantages. Some ES cell lines seemingly grow better on feeders than in the presence of LIF, whereas others can be switched between the two conditions with little trouble.

By far, the best practical method for maintaining totipotent cells in tissue culture remains the use of fibroblast feeders (STO or primary embryo fibroblast). For any serious long-term investment in ES cells, it is wise to expand and freeze ES cells over several passages, checking the karyotype (and germ line transmission) at each passage. Only use ES cells with proven karyotype and germ line transmission properties for critical experiments.

ES cell cultures are essentially primary cultures, and it is necessary therefore to use conditions of tissue culture that maintain their primary properties and do not select variants. It appears that extremes of growth conditions, either by plating the cells too sparsely or by allowing the cultures to become too dense and exhausting their medium, will encourage loss of the desired normal characteristics of ES cells. Either situation sets up conditions in which selection for abnormal (fast-growing, aneuploid) cells can occur. Healthy cultures of ES cells grow with a population doubling time of 15 to 20 hours. In practice, therefore, it is necessary to subculture ES cells about every three days and to renew the medium regularly.

Having said that ES cells are not particularly fastidious about the medium in which they are grown, the optimum formulation I have used is Dulbecco's modified Eagles medium (DMEM) high-glucose, low-pyruvate formulation mixed 1:1 with Ham's F12M medium. This peculiar mix is a compromise between the high-yielding DMEM, originally designed for maximal growth of tissue-culture cell lines for virus production, and the finely balanced Ham's F12, originally developed for the clonal growth of cells. I originally supplemented the DMEM with nonessential amino acids (NEAA) and a mixture of nucleosides (adenosine, guanosine, cytidine, and uridine) to a final concentration of 30 μM and thymidine to a final concentration of 10 μM. This supplement has not been tested properly when used in a DMEM/F12 mix, but it nevertheless may have an advantageous effect upon the primary cell isolation. ES cells grow happily in DMEM alone, but they

Handbook of Stem Cells
Volume 1
Copyright © 2004 by Academic Press
All rights of reproduction in any form reserved.

grow better in DMEM+NEAA and better still in DMEM/F12. The only snag with the latter is that it becomes acidified faster and the medium needs to be changed more frequently. These media may be prepared conveniently "in house" from pre-mixed powder. Alternatively 10× concentrates may be used or a medium may be bought ready to use at 1× concentration. The water used must be of the highest purity, and glassware cleanliness is critical. These latter points have proved to be the most important in establishment of new ES cell lines. I suspect that the most damaging contaminants are detergent residues and that the effects of these are not necessarily seen in bulk passage cultures. The most useful tool for optimization of media, sera, and other conditions is the cloning efficiency test (explained later in this chapter), which should also be used for any troubleshooting.

Media

The medium recommended for ES cells is as follows:

- DMEM/F12 (or DMEM)
- Glutamine (stored frozen as 100× concentrate of 200 mM)
- β-mercaptoethanol to a final concentration of 10^{-4} M either 4-μl neat in 500 ml or from a 10^{-2}M (100×) concentrate (prepared by adding 72-μl to 100-ml PBS)
- 10% calf serum and 10% foetal calf serum
- NEAA from 100× concentrate
- Nucleosides from 100× concentrate (if required)
- Antibiotics (if desired)—use only penicillin, streptomycin, kanamycin, or gentamicin, do not use antimycotics

Sera

Both foetal calf serum and newborn calf serum are used. It is a mistake to imagine that the higher price of foetal calf serum makes it better. Some newborn sera are excellent, and some foetal calf sera are extremely toxic to ES cells. Empirical selection is imperative. All serum should be carefully batch tested using a cloning efficiency test (explained later in this chapter) and ordered in a sufficient lot for the experiments planned. Look both for lack of toxicity (aim for a cloning efficiency of 20% or more) and growth promotion (the size of colonies). Aim to buy new serum batches that equal or exceed the quality of the presently used (control) sera. Be cautious with sera that show toxicity at high (e.g., 40%) concentrations; they can be excellent at lower levels, but other sera can be just as good without extra toxicity.

Colony-Forming Assay for Testing Culture Conditions

The colony-forming assay described should be used to test all the components of the media and also some culture procedures (e.g., viability of cells after different regimens of dissociation):

- Set up experimental media in six-well cluster dishes (2 ml/well) at twice the intended final concentration of

additives, and equilibrate in the incubator at 37°C, 5% CO_2 in air before use. If you are using feeder cells, these need either to be added at this stage or with the sample cells. Use duplicate wells for each condition and appropriate controls (e.g., a known "good" serum batch). For FCS batch testing, use growth media supplemented with the FCS batch at 5%, 10%, and 20%. All other components (e.g., mercaptoethanol concentrations and batches of media) may be tested in the same way.

- Disaggregate ES cell stock culture on day 2 after plating (i.e., semiconfluent), ensuring as close to a single cell suspension as possible. In a test of sera, remember if using trypsin to inactivate by a wash in serum containing medium before redispensing into serum-free medium. Count and resuspend in growth medium at a density of 10^3 cells/ml.
- Add 2-ml cell suspension to each well (making 4-ml total volume 1× concentration of additives), and return to the incubator.
- Incubate 6–8 days at 37°C, 5% CO_2 in air.
- Fix and then stain plates with Giemsa. ES cell colonies can be identified by characteristic morphology and dark staining properties. Differentiated colonies are paler in colour. (It is useful to check sample colony appearance before fixing and staining by inverted phase contrast.) Count the total number of colonies (the plating index) and the proportion of ES cell colonies. In tests of LIF or feeders, the maintenance of undifferentiated colonies is important.

I still recommend the use of inactivated feeder layers for the maintenance of ES cells. I have found that the attraction and convenience of feeder-free methods is outweighed by the frequency with which stocks deteriorate under these conditions and would therefore prefer that an important seed stock be maintained with feeders. It is possible to use a belt-and-braces policy—to use feeders and added LIF. For feeders, use either STO cells or primary mouse embryo fibroblasts.

STO cells are routinely grown in DMEM supplemented with 10% newborn calf serum. Remember that STO cells are effectively 3T3 cells and should be passaged promptly when they reach confluence to prevent the accumulation of non–contact-inhibited cells in the population. Passage STOs at 5×10^3 cells per cm^2 and expect a harvest of up to 20 times this. If a confluent 10 cm Petri dish yields $>10^7$ cells, then the cells are losing their contact inhibition and will no longer produce a good feeder layer. Either replace them with a new batch or (and effectively) clone them out be seeding at ~100 cells per dish and select a flat clone to establish a new stock. Some workers prefer to use primary embryo fibroblasts to prepare feeder layers rather than STO cells, as they feel that better ES cell growth can be obtained. This may, however, reflect abused STO cells rather than an intrinsic superiority of primary embryo fibroblasts.

Feeders are prepared in the following manner:

- Remove the medium from a confluent 10-cm dish of STO cells, and replace it with DMEM/10% NCS plus 10 μg/ml of mitomycin C. (Stock mitomycin C is made at 2 mg/ml with PBS and can be stored at 4°C for 2 weeks.)

- Incubate plates for 2 to 3 hours. Avoid longer exposure to mitomycin C.
- Remove mitomycin C from the STO cells, and wash each plate three times with 10-ml PBS.
- Trypsinize, resuspend, and pellet the cells by centrifugation. This is an important washing step.
- These cells may be resuspended in growth medium and seeded onto gelatinized tissue culture plates at 5×10^4 cells per square centimetre. These can be kept for later use (up to a week), or the inactivated cells can be stored for later use in suspension in a serum-containing medium at 4°C for a similar time.

ES Cell Passage Culture

Passage and maintenance of the ES cells is straightforward, bearing in mind the following:

The cells should not be allowed to become so confluent that the medium becomes excessively acidified. Given the chance, they will continue dividing until they start to kill themselves by overcrowding and exhaustion of the medium; avoid this. Expect to harvest about 3×10^5 cells per square centimetre and plate at $2 \times 10^5/cm^2$. Feed regularly and passage every 3 days. It is important that you seed the cells as a suspension of single cells with few if any aggregates. Such aggregates will initiate differentiation and can severely complicate the ES culture for many purposes. Cells are best disaggregated by careful washing with PBS (remember, you have 20% serum in the medium, and this needs to be fully removed) followed by trypsin/EGTA (0.125% trypsin with 10^{-4} M EGTA in PBS—an improvement on trypsin/EDTA). Incubation at room temperature is sufficient. (It is also possible to disaggregate ES cells by a prolonged incubation in PBS/EGTA, but their viability is reduced.) Immediately after the trypsin incubation, add growth medium and pipette up and down a few times to generate single cells. As it is important that the cells are well disaggregated, it is good to check by counting in a haemocytometer. You should see a mainly single-cell suspension with round, phase-bright cells. Dead cells or clumps are obvious; ragged and larger cells are feeders.

Isolation of New ES Cell Lines

Contrary to some well-expressed opinions, it is clear that it is possible to isolate ES cells from a variety of mouse strains and not just from strain 129. I append a prescriptive description of ES cell isolation (given later in this chapter), but first it is useful to consider the background and to point out that isolation is possible from stages of embryo from cleavage to early postimplantation and using different procedures.

Clearly, embryonic development starting from a single zygote proceeds through extensive cell proliferation and progressive cellular differentiation. At early stages there are cells with wide prospective fates, but these are not necessarily self-renewing populations. Pluripotential stem cells were first experimentally identified in the mouse as the stem cell of teratocarcinomas by Kleinsmith and Pierce, who were able to

passage the tumour by transferring single cells isolated from embryoid bodies.[3] These testicular teratocarcinomas in mice arise spontaneously in specific genetic strains and were extensively studied by Stevens.[4] The stem cells of these tumours arise from the primordial germ cells during gonad formation, and one question is whether this represents a parthenogenetic activation. This idea, that the teratocarcinoma stem cells might be embryo related rather than germ cell related was tested directly by transplanting early embryos to adult testes or kidneys.[5] Passageable, progressively growing teratocarcinomas were formed after transplantation of 1 to 3.5 day preimplantation embryos. From some of these tumours, clonal in vitro differentiating embryonal carcinoma cell lines were isolated and characterised; these were the direct forerunners of ES cells and their isolation. These demonstrated their pluripotentiality by forming well-differentiated teratocarcinomas upon reinjection into mice.[6] These also differentiated extremely well in vitro via an embryo-like route.[7, 8] A series of observations of the properties of these and similar embryonal carcinoma (EC) cells started to provide convincing evidence of their homology with the pluripotential cells in the normal embryo, which were able to generate teratocarcinomas under conditions of ectopic transplantation. There seemed to be every reason to suppose that direct isolation into tissue culture should be possible.[9]

Teratocarcinomas can also be formed from postimplantation mouse embryos. The embryonic part of the postimplantation mouse embryo undergoes gastrulation and forms an embryonic mesoderm by invagination from the ectoderm; this lies between the ectoderm and an embryonic endoderm. Skreb et al. isolated these three layers of the rat embryo by microdissection and tested their developmental potency by ectopic transplantation.[10] Only the embryonic ectoderm produced teratomas with multiple tissue types and was hence pluripotential, but these were not progressively growing teratocarcinomas. When these experiments were repeated with gastrulating mouse embryos, it was discovered that in contrast to the rat, transplantable teratocarcinomas were formed. At least, therefore, in the mouse, pluripotential stem cells could be recovered until about the end of gastrulation.[11] Direct isolation of ES cells, however, from such a late stage has not been reported.

Taking these comparisons and molecular data into consideration, we[12] have argued that mouse ES cells are—regardless of the route of isolation—homologous to the early postimplantational epiblast rather than the inner cell mass (ICM), as is often erroneously stated.

The culture conditions—feeder cells and media—had been refined by culturing both mouse and human teratocarcinoma EC cells. Evans and Kaufman, by using implantationally delayed blastocysts as the embryo source, succeeded in establishing cultures of pluripotential cells directly without an in vivo tumour step.[13] Subsequent studies showed isolation of such cell lines from both inbred and outbred strains, from normal 3.5-day blastocysts, and those that had been implantationally delayed. Martin in an independent work showed that isolated 3.5-day ICMs may also be used.[14] These cells, which have become known as ES cells, share the properties of indefinite proliferative capacity, embryonic phenotype, and differentiative capacity with their forerunners—the EC cells; in addition, being primarily derived, they may be kept entirely karyotypically normal.

Eistetter[15] reported that ES cell cultures may be established from disaggregated 16–21 cell morulae with an apparent immediate growth of the colonies from some of the explanted single cells. Up to four separate ES cell colonies were founded from a single embryo.

The latest stage of isolation into culture of ES cells from embryos has been reported by Brook and Gardner, who used 4.5-day-old hatched, peri-implantational embryos flushed from the uterus.[16] They microdissected the epiblast cells from both the primary endoderm and the trophectoderm. Both whole epiblasts and those that had been disaggregated into single cells readily generated ES cultures—if they were not left in contact with the endoderm. They also reconfirmed the benefit of using delayed blastocysts, showing that the isolated epiblasts of these were the most efficient source of ES cell cultures.

Method for Derivation of ES Cells

I would still recommend the original method of explantation of implantationally delayed blastocysts as the most effective method. It works well and involves no microdissection or immunosurgery.

First, it is essential to pay attention to the optimisation of the culture conditions, as described previously. If things don't work, suspect the purity of the media and particularly any possible contamination by detergent residues. Seemingly stupid problems such as aliquoting the medium into small batches and using untested vessels (e.g., bijou bottles) can arise. Suspect specific items that have not been tested in the ES cell cultures—for instance, the cleanliness of the glass Pasteur pipettes from which micropipettes are pulled for manipulation of the embryos and growth of ES cell colonies.

Delayed blastocysts:

- Mate mice by caging together overnight and observing mating plugs in the morning. Separate the plugged females.
- On day 2 (counting the day of plug as day 0), it is necessary to remove oestrogen activity but preserve progesterone. This was originally done by ovariectomy followed by injection of Depo-Provera, but we have introduced the less invasive, simpler, and considerably improved option of using the antiestrogenic effects of tamoxifen.[17] The mice are treated with 10-μg tamoxifen and 1-mg Depo-Provera. Dissolve the tamoxifen in ethanol to make a 100× stock, and dilute this in sesame oil before injecting a dose of 10 μg intraperitoneally. At the same time, administer a dose of 1-mg Depo-Provera subcutaneously. Kill the animals, and recover the delayed blastocysts by flushing from the uterus between day 6 and day 8.
- Prepare feeder layers preincubated in an ES cell medium. (Although it is routine to pretreat plastic Petri dishes with gelatine as an aid to ES cell culture, it is probably more important here than elsewhere.) I find that

1.6-cm four-well cluster dishes are convenient, but possibly better are 3-cm Petri dishes, each enclosed in a 10-cm plastic Petri dish (this aids handling and helps to minimise evaporation from the small volumes of medium).

- The embryos will enter diapause and may be recovered by flushing from the uterus 6 to 12 days later. They will be large, slightly ragged, hatched blastocysts, usually with a visible ICM.
- Using a drawn-out Pasteur pipette, recover the blastocysts and place them on preincubated feeder layers in full ES cell medium.
- Incubate for about four days, observing daily.
- When the blastocyst has attached and spread out with a visibly growing ICM derivative (but before this becomes encapsulated in a thick endodermal layer—if you see this happening, you've left it too long), carefully remove the medium and carefully wash twice in PBS with 10^{-4}-M EGTA.
- Wash with PBS/EGTA containing 0.125% trypsin and aspirate, leaving a thin wetting layer of the trypsin solution. Very briefly incubate at 37°C.
- Have a drawn-out Pasteur pipette with a tip aperture of 20 to 50 microns ready and filled with full ES cell medium. Observe under a dissecting microscope; when the cells are loosening but before everything swims off the dish, carefully flood the medium over the ICM area from the drawn-out pipette and then suck it up.
- This should neatly disaggregate it into single cells and small (2- to 4-cell) clumps—do not aim to make a complete single-cell suspension at this stage. Blow these cells out beneath the surface of the medium of a preincubated feeder dish or well in the ES cell medium.
- Incubate this dish for 7 to 10 days, observing carefully. Do not be tempted to feed daily, but if it seems necessary, replace about half the medium after 5 days. If many small ES cell colonies are becoming established, let them grow to a reasonable size before passaging 1:1 onto new feeders; thereafter, you should be able to grow it in the normal manner. (The size of the colonies depends upon the size of the cell aggregate that founded them—if they have come from a single cell, they can be left for 10 days before passage.) If few ES cell colonies appear, it is useful to repeat the trypsinisation and passage by drawn-out Pasteur pipette on each one before trusting a bulk passage.

With 129 mice and similar strains, and if all is going well, you should be able to establish new ES cell lines from up to half of the explanted blastocysts. It is useful to make a freeze stock at the earliest possibility. There are usually plentiful cells by passage 4–6.

Summary

Although it is relatively easy to create new cell lines, their full validation—stability in culture, karyotype, chimaera-forming ability, and germ line potential—takes a lot of time and work.

It is, therefore, important to have sufficient characterised stocks of particular passage and to freeze batches to allow useful repeatable studies to be undertaken.

REFERENCES

1. Williams, R.L., Hilton, D.J., Pease, S., Willson, T.A., Stewart, C.L., Gearing, D.P., Wagner, E.F., Metcalf, D., Nicola, N.A., and Gough, N.M. (1988). Myeloid leukaemia inhibitory factor maintains the developmental potential of embryonic stem cells. *Nature* **336,** 684–687.

2. Smith, A.G., Heath, J.K., Donaldson, D.D., Wong, G.G., Moreau, J., Stahl, M., and Rogers, D. (1988). Inhibition of pluripotential embryonic stem cell differentiation by purified polypeptides. *Nature* **336,** 688–690.

3. Kleinsmith, L.J., and Pierce, G.B. (1964). Multipotentiality of single embryonal carcinoma cells. *Cancer Research* **24,** 1544–1551.

4. Stevens, L.C. (1967). Origin of testicular tumours from primordial germ cells in mice. *J. Natl. Cancer Inst.* **38,** 549–552.

5. Stevens, L.C. (1970). The development of transplantable teratocarcinomas from intratesticular grafts of pre- and postfertilization mouse embryos. *Dev. Biol.* **21,** 364–382.

6. Evans, M.J. (1972). The isolation and properties of a clonal tissue culture strain of pluripotent mouse teratocarcinoma cells. *J. Embryol. Exp. Morphol.* **28,** 163–196.

7. Martin, G.R., and Evans, M.J. (1975). Differentiation of clonal lines of teratocarcinoma cells: formation of embryoid bodies *in vitro*. *Proc. Natl. Acad. Sci. USA* **72,** 1441–1445.

8. Martin, G.R., and Evans, M.J. (1975). Multiple differentiation of clonal teratoma stem cells following embryoid body formation *in vitro*. *Cell* **6,** 467–474.

9. Evans, M.J. (1981). Origin of mouse embryonal carcinoma cells and the possibility of their direct isolation into tissue culture. *J. Reprod. Fertil.* **62,** 625–631.

10. Levak-Svajger, B., Svajger, A., and Skreb, N. (1969). Separation of germ layers in presomite rat embryos. *Experientia* **25,** 1311–1312.

11. Damjanov, I., Solter, D., Belicza, M., and Skreb, N. (1971). Teratomas observed through extrauterine growth of seven-day mouse embryos. *J. Natl. Cancer Inst.* **46,** 471–480.

12. Evans, M.J., and Hunter, S.M. (2002). Source and nature of embryonic stem cells. *C. R. Biol.* **325,** 1003–1007.

13. Evans, M.J., and Kaufman, M.H. (1981). Establishment in culture of pluripotential cells from mouse embryos. *Nature* **292,** 154–156.

14. Martin, G.R. (1981). Isolation of a pluripotent cell line from early mouse embryos cultured in medium conditioned by teratocarcinoma cells. *Proc. Natl. Acad. Sci. USA* **78,** 7634–7638.

15. Eistetter, H.R. (1989). Pluripotent embryonal stem cell lines can be established from disaggregated mouse morulae. *Develop. Growth and Differ.* **31,** 275–282.

16. Brook, F.A., and Gardner, R.L. (1997). The origin and efficient derivation of embryonic stem cells in the mouse. *Proc. Natl. Acad. Sci. USA* **94,** 5709–5712.

17. Hunter, S.M., and Evans, M.J. (1999). Nonsurgical method for the induction of delayed implantation and recovery of viable blastocysts in rats and mice by the use of tamoxifen and Depo-Provera. *Mol. Reprod. Dev.* **52,** 29–32.

Isolation and Maintenance of Primate ES Cells

Michal Amit and Joseph Itskovitz-Eldor

Introduction

During the 1970s, multipotent cell lines were isolated from the stem cells of mouse teratocarcinomas.[1] Some of these embryonal carcinoma (EC) cell lines were shown to differentiate *in vitro* into a variety of cell types, including muscle and nerve cells.[2] When grown in suspension, EC cells tend to aggregate into cell clusters known as embryoid bodies (EBs) in which part of the cells differentiate spontaneously. They also had been shown to differentiate *in vivo,* forming teratocarcinomas following their injection into recipient mice.[3] EC cells served for years as models for research on development, establishing all the methodological know-how needed for the isolation and maintenance of embryonic stem (ES) cells.

The first mammalian ES cell lines were derived in 1981 from mouse blastocysts.[4,5] Since then, mouse ES (mES) cells have played a key role in developmental studies. Unlike EC cells, ES cells are regarded as pluripotent, thus possessing the ability to differentiate into each cell type of the adult body. Following their injection into blastocysts, mES cells were reported to integrate into all fetal germ layers, including the germ line;[6] in some cases, they were reported to develop into mature chimeric animals. Furthermore, several mES cell lines had been shown to form entire viable newborns when injected into tetraploid embryos or heat-treated blastocysts.[7,8]

Because of the unique features of mES cells and their proven differentiative abilities, much effort has been invested in the derivation of ES cell lines from additional animal species. ES cell lines and ES cell-like lines have been successfully isolated from rodents such as golden hamsters,[9] rats,[10] rabbits,[11,12] domestic animals,[13–18] and three nonhuman primates.[19–21] None of the ES cell lines cited here have been shown to demonstrate all features of mES cells; the bovine ES cell lines were not shown to create teratomas following injection into severe-combined immunodeficiency (SCID) mice. The ability of nonhuman primate ES cell lines to integrate into all three germ layers during embryonic development using the blastocyst injection model have not been tested. Therefore, the mES cell model is still the most potent research model among all existing ES cell lines.

The first successful derivation of human ES cell (hES) lines was reported in 1998.[22] The availability of hES cell lines provides a unique new research tool with widespread potential clinical applications (Fig. 40–1). Human ES cells may be used for various study areas, such as early human development, differentiation processes, lineage commitment, mechanisms of self-maintenance, gene or protein functions, drug testing, and drug toxicity. The availability of differentiation models of hES cells to specific lineages, similar to the existing ones for mES cells, may lead to future uses of these cells in cell-based therapy.

From the first report on hES cell isolation to date, additional groups have reported on the derivation of hES cell lines.[23–25] The increasing numbers of available hES cell lines indicate that the derivation of these lines is a reproducible procedure with reasonable success rates.

This chapter focuses on techniques for the derivation, characterization, maintenance, and differentiation of primate ES cells.

WHAT ARE PRIMATE ES CELLS?

Based on the well-characterized mES cells, a list of ES cells features was created, which includes the following criteria: (1) can be isolated from the inner cell mass (ICM) of the blastocyst; (2) are capable of prolonged undifferentiated proliferation in culture; (3) exhibit and maintain normal diploid karyotypes; (4) are pluripotent, that is, are able to differentiate into derivatives of the three embryonic germ layers; (5) are able to integrate into all fetal tissues during embryonic development following injection into the blastocyst, including the germ layer; (6) are clonogenic, that is, single ES cells have the ability to form a homogeneous line harboring all parental ES cell line features; (7) express high levels of *OCT 4,* a transcription factor known to be involved in their process self-maintenance; (8) can be induced to differentiate after continuous culture at the undifferentiated state; (9) remain in the S phase of the cell cycle for most of their life span; and (10) do not show X-chromosome inactivation.[26]

According to accumulating knowledge, primate ES cells meet most of these criteria. Both human and nonhuman primate ES cell lines were derived from embryos at the blastocyst stage.[19,20,22,23] All primate ES cell lines were shown to be capable of continuous culture at an undifferentiated state, but expression of high levels of *OCT 4* had been demonstrated only for hES cells.[19,20,22,23] The morphology of primate ES cells resembles that of mES cells. They create small and round colonies, although primate ES cell colonies seem somewhat less dense (Fig. 40–2). On the single-cell level, there is no notable difference: Like mES cells, primate ES cells are small and round, exhibiting a high nucleus-to-cytoplasm ratio with

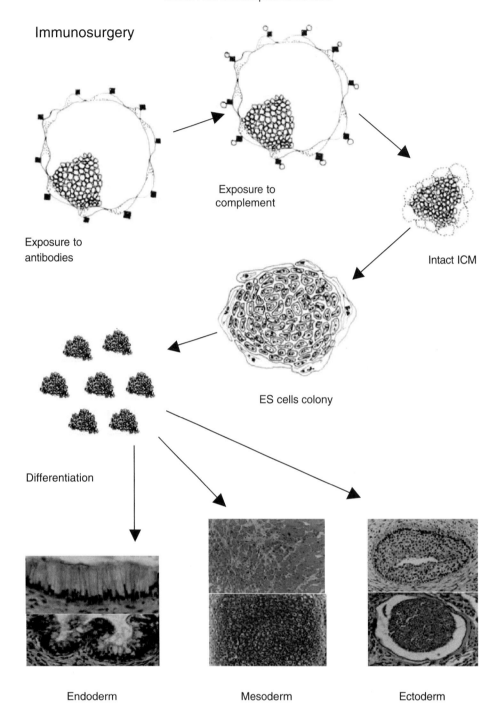

Immunosurgery

Exposure to
antibodies

Exposure to
complement

Intact ICM

ES cells colony

Differentiation

Endoderm

Mesoderm

Ectoderm

Figure 40–1. *Derivation, Differentiation, and Possible Applications of hES Cells.* To isolate hES cell lines, the ICM of the blastocyst is selectively removed and further cultured on mitotically inactivated MEF. When removed from the MEF feeder layer, the resulting hES cells may differentiate into representative tissues of the three embryonic germ layers both *in vitro* and *in vivo*. Because of their pluripotency, hES cells may be used for research such as early human development, lineage commitment, functionality of genes and proteins, drug testing, and drug toxicity. Further studies on lineage-specific differentiation may lead to the use of hES cells for cell-based therapy and clinical application. (Please see CD-ROM for color version of this figure.)

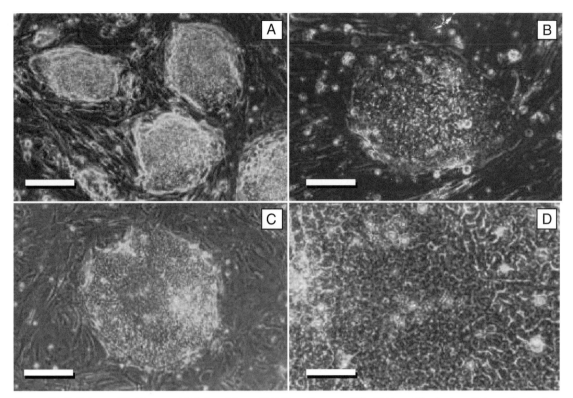

Figure 40–2. *Colonies of Undifferentiated Cells from Different ES Cell Lines Grown on MEFs.* (A) Mouse ES cell colony, (B) rhesus ES cell colony, and (C) human cell colony. (D) High magnification photograph of hES cells; note the high nucleus-to-cytoplasm ratio, the presence of one or more nucleoli, and the typical spacing between the cells.

a one or more prominent nucleoli and typical spacing between the cells (Fig. 40–2). Their pluripotency had been demonstrated both *in vitro* by the formation of EBs[20,27] and *in vivo* in teratomas[19,20,22,23] in which the cells differentiated into all three primary germ-layer derivatives. The karyotypes of primate ES cell lines were found to be normal diploid karyotypes even after prolonged culture.[28] Cases of karyotype instability are scarce,[28,29] suggesting that they represent random changes, which often occur in cell culture. Primate ES cells have also been shown to be clonogenic with resultant single-cell clones demonstrating all ES cell features.[19,28]

For ethical reasons, the ability of hES cells to integrate into fetal tissues during embryonic development cannot be tested. The specific stage of the cell cycle in which primate ES cells spend most of their time has not been reported so far, nor has the status of the X-chromosome inactivation, although the availability of normal 46 XX primate ES cell lines at the same ratio as XY lines may indicate that these lines demonstrate normal X-chromosome inactivation. The features of primate ES cells are summarized in Table 40–1.

The potential of primate ES cells in the research on early primate embryonic development, and the development of research models for chronic diseases and for transplantation medicine, encourage scientists to invest great efforts in the isolation of nonhuman primate ES cells.[19–21] The list and features of the reported nonhuman primate ES cell lines are summarized in Table 40–2. To date, there are more than two dozen established and well-characterized hES cell lines in several laboratories worldwide. The characteristics of the existing hES cell lines are summarized in Table 40–3.

Techniques for the Derivation of hES Cell Lines

The derivation of hES cell lines is a relatively simple procedure with success rates of up to 30% and 50% for mice

TABLE 40–1
Characteristics of Primate ES Cells

(1) Isolated from the ICM of the blastocyst

(2) Capable of prolonged undifferentiated proliferation in culture

(3) Exhibit and maintain normal diploid karyotype

(4) Pluripotent (i.e., able to differentiate into derivatives of the three embryonic germ layers, even after being cultured continuously at the undifferentiated stage)

(5) Clonogenic (i.e., each single ES cell has the ability to form a homogeneous line harboring all parental ES cell line features)

(6) Express high levels of *OCT 4*, a transcription factor known to be involved in the self-maintenance process of ES cells

TABLE 40–2
Characteristics of the Existing Nonhuman Primate ES Cell Lines

Line	Karyotype	EBs formation	Formation of teratomas	Continuous culture	Staining with undifferentiated markers	Reference
R278 rhesus ES cells	42, XY	Not available	+	>12 months	+	Thomson et al. 1995[19] and Thomson and Marshall 1998[46]
R366 rhesus ES cells	42, XY	+	+	>3 months	+	Thomson et al. 1995[19] and Thomson and Marshall 1998[46]
R367 rhesus ES cells	42, XY	Not available	+	>3 months	+	Thomson et al. 1995[19] and Thomson and Marshall 1998[46]
R394 rhesus ES cells	42, XX	Not available	+	Not available	Not available	Thomson et al. 1998[22]
R420 rhesus ES cells	42, XX	Not available	+	Not available	Not available	Thomson et al. 1998[22]
R456 rhesus ES cells	42, XX	Not available	Not available	Not available	Not available	Thomson et al. 1998[22]
R460 rhesus ES cells	42, XY	Not available	Not available	Not available	Not available	Thomson et al. 1998[22]
Cj11 marmoset ES cells	46, XX	+	Not available	>12 months	+	Thomson et al. 1996[20]
Cj25 marmoset ES cells	46, XX	+	Not available	>3 months	Not available	Thomson et al 1996.[20]
Cj28 marmoset ES cells	46, XY	+	Not available	>3 months	Not available	Thomson et al. 1996[20]
Cj33 marmoset ES cells	46, XX	+	Not available	>3 months	Not available	Thomson et al. 1996[20]
Cj35 marmoset ES cells	46, XX	+	Not available	>3 months	Not available	Thomson et al. 1996[20]
Cj36 marmoset ES cells	46, XX	+	Not available	>3 months	Not available	Thomson et al. 1996[20]
Cj39 marmoset ES cells	46, XX	+	Not available	>3 months	Not available	Thomson et al. 1996[20]
Cj62 marmoset ES cells	46, XX	+	Not available	>12 months	+	Thomson et al. 1996[20]
CMK5 cynomolgus monkey	40, XY	+	+	>3 months	+	Suemori et al.[21]
CMK6 cynomolgus monkey	40, XY	+	+	>6 months	+	Suemori et al.[21]
CMK7 cynomolgus monkey	40, XX	+	Not available	>1 month	+	Suemori et al.[21]
CMK9 cynomolgus monkey	40, XX	+	Not available	>3 months	+	Suemori et al.[21]

TABLE 40–3
Main Features of the Existing Human ES Cell Lines

Line	Karyotype	EBs formation	Formation of teratomas	Continuous culture	Staining with undifferentiated markers	Reference
H1	46, XY	+	+	> 6 months	+	Thomson et al. 1998[22]
H7	46, XX	+	+	> 6 months	+	Thomson et al., 1998[22]
H9	46, XX	+	+	> 8 months	+	Thomson et al., 1998[22]
H13	46, XY	+	+	> 6 months	+	Thomson et al., 1998[22]
H14	46, XY	+	+	> 6 months	+	Thomson et al., 1998[22]
hES-1	46, XX	+	+	64 passages	+	Reubinoff et al.[23]
hES-2	46, XX	+	+	44 passages	+	Reubinoff et al.[23]
hES-3	46, XX	+	+	250 doubling	+	ES Cell International[72]
hES-4	46, XY	+	+	250 doubling	+	ES Cell International[72]
hES-5	46, XY	Not available	Not available	100 doubling	+	ES Cell International[72]
hES-6	46, XX	+	+	100 doubling	+	ES Cell International[72]
hES on human feeders	46, XY	Not available	+	>10 passages	+	Richards et al.[36]
BG01	Not available	Not available	Not available	Not available	+	BresaGen[73]
BG02	Not available	Not available	Not available	Not available	+	BresaGen[73]
BG03	Not available	Not available	Not available	Not available	+	BresaGen[73]
BG04	Not available	Not available	Not available	Not available	+	BresaGen[73]
HSF-1	Not available	Not available	Not available	Not available	Not available	University of California[74]
HSF-6	46, XX	Not available	Not available	Not available	+	University of California[74]
Miz-hES-1	Not available	Not available	Not available	125 passages	+	NIH Registry[75]
ES-76	Not available	Not available	Not available	20 passages	+	Lanzendorf et al.[24]
ES-78.1	Not available	Not available	Not available	6 passages	+/−	Lanzendorf et al.[24]
ES-78.2	Not available	Not available	Not available	6 passages	+/−	Lanzendorf et al.[24]
I3	46, XX	+	+	110 passages	+	Amit and Itskovitz-Eldor[25]
I4	46, XX	+	To be examined	66 passages	+	Amit and Itskovitz-Eldor[25]
I6	46, XY	+	+	120 passages	+	Amit and Itskovitz-Eldor[25]
I8	46, XX	+	+	> 6 months	+	Amit and Itskovitz-Eldor[70]
I9	46, XX	+	+	> 6 months	+	Suss-Toby et al.[71]
J3	46, XY	+	+	>12 months	+/−	Amit et al.[70]

and humans, respectively.[25,30] Embryonic cell lines are derived from embryos at the blastocyst stage. The isolation can be conducted using three methods: immunosurgical isolation, mechanical isolation, or the use of an intact embryo. The protocols for these procedures are detailed in the sections "Immunosurgical Isolation" and "Mechanical Isolation."

IMMUNOSURGICAL ISOLATION

In the 1970s, Solter and Knowles developed a procedure known as immunosurgery for the derivation of some of the existing EC cell lines and for the research on early embryonic

development.[31] This method of selectively isolating the ICM from the blastocyst laid the groundwork for the first ES cell line derivation in 1981 from mouse blastocysts.[4,5]

The process of immunosurgery includes several stages (see the section "Immunosurgical Isolation"). Initially, the glycoprotein outer layer of the zona pellucida (ZP) is dissolved by Tyrode's solution or pronase enzyme. The exposed embryo is then incubated for approximately 30 minutes in antihuman whole serum antibodies, which attach to any human cell. Penetration of the antibodies into the blastocyst is prevented because of cell–cell connections within the outer layer of the trophoblasts, leaving the ICM untouched. After rinsing off any antibody residue, the blastocyst is transferred into a guinea pig complement-containing medium and incubated once more until cell lysis is notable (see the schematic drawing of the procedure in Fig. 40–1 and pictures in Fig. 40–3A through 40–3C). Since the ZP allows the penetration of both antibodies and guinea pig complement, it may be alternatively removed postlysis by complement proteins. Following the selective removal of the trophectoderm, the intact ICM is further cultured on mitotically inactivated mouse embryonic fibroblasts (MEFs, see the section "Preparation of MEF-Covered Plates for hES Cells" and Fig. 40–3).

MECHANICAL ISOLATION

ES cell lines can be derived directly from cultured blastocysts either by the mechanical dissection and partial removal of the trophoblast layer with 27G needles (Fig. 40–3D) or by plating a zona-free whole embryo on mitotically inactivated MEFs. When trophoblasts are only partially or are not removed, embryos attach to the feeder layer and flatten, permitting continuous growth of the ICM with the remaining surrounding trophoblasts as a monolayer (see the section "Mechanical Isolation"). When the ICM reaches sufficient size, it is selectively removed and propagated (Fig. 40–3E).

"LATE STAGE" EMBRYOS

Early mammalian embryonic development *in vivo* requires the division of the blastocyst's ICM into two layers shortly after implantation: a layer of primitive endoderm, which generates the extraembryonic endoderm, and a layer of primitive ectoderm, which generates the embryo itself and some extraembryonic derivatives.[32] The mammalian embryo continues to develop; at day 14 postfertilization, gastrulation occurs, in which cells become progressively restricted to a specific lineage. Thus the pluripotency of these cells is lost. In other words, pluripotent or totipotent cells exist and proliferate in the mammalian embryo for a short window of time whose exact borders were never defined.

The pluripotency of human postimplantation embryonic cells, between the time of implantation and the gastrulation process, has never been examined previously. Following their plating in whole on MEFs, as mentioned earlier, embryos most often flatten, and a small ICM colony, surrounded by a monolayer of trophoblasts, can be observed (Fig. 40–3E). In some cases, however, intact embryos continue to grow and to develop small cysts. In these embryos, small and flat structures of pluripotent-resembling cells can be recognized. Once selectively removed, these cells are further cultured and propagated on fresh MEF plates. The resulting cell line (e.g., J-3) exhibited the main characteristics of hES cell lines: (1) prolonged undifferentiated proliferation; (2) pluripotency, that is, the creation of EBs when grown in suspension or teratomas after injection into SCID beige mice; (3) maintenance of normal karyotypes after being continuously cultured for several months; and (4) partial or full expression of typical surface markers. Thus, although the lines were derived from embryos resembling the "postimplantation" stage, they remained pluripotent and immortal. The key question arising, of whether pluripotent cells derived from "postimplantation" embryos are significantly different from hES cells isolated using the traditional methods, has no clear answer so far. Further research is needed to fully characterize these cell lines.

DERIVATION OF hES CELL LINES HARBORING SPECIFIC GENETIC DEFECTS

The ability of hES cells to differentiate into each cell type of the adult body may be used for research on the nature and course of specific diseases. Models established by the use of hES cell lines carrying specific genetic defects may be highly effective in the development of drug or gene therapy designed to treat these diseases.

Two methods of obtaining such lines are genetic manipulation of existing hES cell lines or derivation of hES cell lines from genetically compromised embryos. Since the chance that donated surplus embryos from the *in vitro* fertilization (IVF) program carry genetic diseases is relatively low, the preferred source of donated embryos would be nonretrieved embryos from the preimplantation genetic diagnosis (PGD) program. PGD is designed for couples that are carriers of genetic diseases to ensure the transfer of healthy embryos to the uterus by their examination prior to implantation. For this purpose, the embryos are grown *in vitro* to the 6–8-cell stage, at which point one or two cells are removed and analyzed either by polymerase chain reaction (PCR) or by fluorescence *in situ* hybridization (FISH).

In our experience, post-PGD embryos continue to develop *in vitro* to the blastocyst stage. Five hES cell lines that were isolated from donated post-PGD blastocysts were derived and found to possess hES cell features. One line was found to harbor the Van Waardenburg disease (deletion at the *PAX3* gene), and the other had myotonic dystrophy. The cell lines carrying genetic diseases could therefore be used for the development of *in vitro* models for these disorders, and nonretrieved post-PGD embryos could be used as an additional source for surplus embryos for the isolation of hES cell lines.

PROTOCOLS FOR THE DERIVATION OF HES CELL LINES

Immunosurgical Isolation

1. Donated surplus embryos are cultured according to standard IVF protocols to the blastocyst stage.
2. Incubate the embryo for 30–60 seconds in Tyrode's solution (Sigma, acidic, Cat. No. T-1788) under the scope. When the ZP starts to dissolve, remove the embryo and wash it three times in fresh ES medium (see the section "ES Medium"). For this procedure, 0.5% pronase may also be used.
3. Incubate the embryo in antihuman whole serum antibodies (Sigma, H-8765) for 30 minutes. Immediately afterward, wash it three times in fresh ES medium.
4. Incubate the embryo for up to 30 minutes in guinea pig complement (diluted 1/10, Gibco BRL, Cat. No.10723-013). It is recommended to monitor the procedure: If trophoblasts

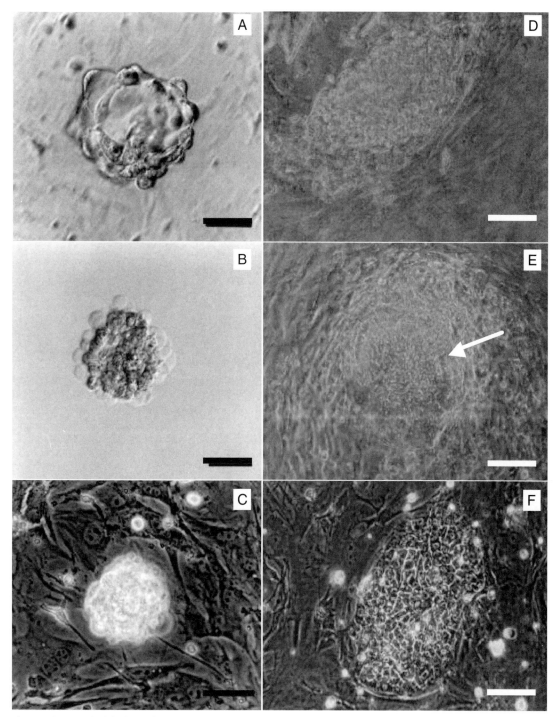

Figure 40–3. *Methods for hES Cell Lines Derivation.* (A) Human blastocyst after ZP removal by Tyrode's solution, during exposure to rabbit antihuman whole antiserum. (B) Embryo after exposure to guinea pig complement; the ICM is surrounded by cells after lysis. (C) The intact ICM on mitotically inactivated MEFs. (D) Growing the ICM after mechanical removal of the trophoblast. (E) Embryo placed in whole on MEFs after 6 days of culture. The growing ICM (white arrow) is surrounded by fibroblast-like cells. (F) Resulting hES cell colony cultured on MEFs. Bar = 50 μm. Pictures A–C are from Amit and Itskovitz-Eldor[25]

are lysed before the end of the incubation time, stop the incubation (an example is illustrated in Fig. 40–3).

5. Wash the intact ICM three times in fresh ES medium using pulled Pasteur pipette to remove the lyses trophoblasts.

6. Plate the intact ICM on a fresh MEF-covered culture dish.

Mechanical Isolation

1. Expose the embryo from ZP as described in the section "Immunosurgical Isolation."

2. If the ICM is clearly noticeable, remove as much trophoblast as possible using either 27-g syringe needles or blank pulled Pasteur pipette under stereoscope. If the ICM unrecognizable, plate the embryo in whole.

3. Plate the embryo on a fresh MEF-covered culture dish.

Methods for hES Cell Culture

For MEF production and culture, see Robertson.[30] After the ICM is plated on MEFs, the resultant ES cells are treated as described in the next section.

Preparation of MEF-Covered Plates for hES Cells

1. Add 8 ng/ml mitomycin C to a culture flask and incubate for 2 hours.

2. Wash four times with phosphate-buffered saline (PBS).

3. Add 2 ml of trypsin–EDTA (0.5% trypsin and 5.3 mM EDTA, Invitrogen Corporation, Cat. No. 15400-054) and cover the entire culture-flask surface.

4. Incubate for 6 minutes.

5. Tap the side of the flask to loosen the cells. Add 4 ml of ES medium (see the section "ES Medium") to neutralize the trypsin.

6. Remove cell suspension into conical tube.

7. Centrifuge for 5 minutes at 2000 rpm.

8. Remove suspension, resuspend in 10 ml of ES medium (see the section "ES Medium") and pipette to fracture the pellet.

9. Count the cells and resuspend them in the desired medium volume (see the section "ES Medium").

10. Add the cell suspension to the culture dishes. We recommend 4×10^5 cells per one well in six-well plates (40,000 cells/cm^2).

11. Let set for at least 2 hours before plating hES cells.

hES Cell Media

ES MEDIUM. Final concentrations:
- 80% DMEM or knockout DMEM (KO-DMEM, Invitrogen Corporation, Cat. No. 10829-018)
- 20% fetal bovine serum–defined (FBSd) (Hyclone, Cat. No. SH30070.03)
- 1% nonessential amino acid (Invitrogen Corporation, Cat. No. 11140-035)
- 1 mm of L-glutamine
- 0.1 mm of β-mercaptoethanol (Invitrogen Corporation, Cat. No. 31350-010)

Preparation: Pour all materials into a 22-μm filter unit and filter. Store at 4°C.

Note: Usable within 2 weeks.

SERUM-FREE MEDIUM. Final concentrations:
- 80% KO-DMEM
- 20% serum replacement (SR, Invitrogen Corporation, Cat. No. 10828-028)
- 1% nonessential amino acid
- 1 mm of L-glutamine
- 0.1 mm of β-mercaptoethanol
- 4 ng/ml basic fibroblast growth factor (bFGF, Invitrogen Corporation)

Preparation: Pour all materials into a 22-μm filter unit and filter. Store at 4°C.

Notes: Do not use this medium for MEF-covered plate preparation. Prepare MEF-covered plates using ES medium and change the medium before plating hES cells. This medium may be used within 2 weeks of preparation.

FREEZING MEDIUM. Final concentrations:
- 60% Dulbecco's Modified Eagle's Medium (DMEM)
- 20% Dimethyl sulfoxide (DMSO)
- 20% FBSd

Preparation: Pour all materials into a 22-μm filter, adding the DMSO last. Filter. Store between 2–8°C.

Note: May be used within 2 weeks of preparation.

hES Cell Splitting. Splitting medium:
- 1 mg/ml collagenase (Invitrogen Corporation, type IV, Cat. No. 17104-019)
- DMEM (Gibco BRL, Cat. No. 41965-039)

Note: May be used within 2 weeks of preparation.

Splitting protocol: During the first few passages, it is recommended to mechanically split the hES cell colonies using either syringes needles or pulled Pasteur pipettes. When the line consists of more than 10 colonies, it can be passaged using the following protocol:

1. Remove the medium from the well. Add 0.5 ml splitting medium, and incubate for at least 30 minutes.

2. Add 1 ml of culture medium (see the sections "ES Medium" and "Serum-Free Medium") and gently scrape cells with 5-ml pipette. The MEF feeder layer will remain on the plate.

3. Collect the cell suspension and put it into a conical tube.

4. Centrifuge for 3 minutes at 800 rpm at a recommended temperature of 4°C.

5. Resuspend the cells in the medium (see the sections "ES Medium" and "Serum-Free Medium") and plate onto a feeder-covered plate.

Note: For effective separation of hES cells from the feeder, longer collagenization is recommended.

hES Cell Freezing

1. Add a splitting medium (see the section "hES Cell Splitting") and incubate for at least 30 minutes.

2. Add 1 ml culture medium, gently scrape the cells using a 5-ml pipette, and transfer into conical tube.

3. Centrifuge for 3 minutes at 800 rpm at a recommended temperature of 4°C.
4. Resuspend the cells in the culture medium (see the sections "ES Medium" and "Serum-Free Medium").
5. Drop by drop, add an equivalent volume of freezing medium (see the section "Freezing Medium") and mix gently.
6. Put 0.5 ml into a 1-ml cryogenic vial.
7. Freeze overnight at –70°C (a Nalgene freezing box is recommended).
8. Transfer to liquid nitrogen on the following day.

Notes: Adding the freezing medium drop by drop is crucial for cell recovery. Do not fracture the cells into small clumps.

hES Cell Thawing
1. Remove the vial from liquid nitrogen.
2. Gently swirl the vial in a 37°C water bath.
3. When a small pellet of frozen cells remains, wash the vial in 70% ethanol.
4. Pipette the contents of the vial up and down once to mix.
5. Place the contents of the vial into a conical tube and add 2 ml of culture medium drop by drop.
6. Centrifuge for 3 minutes at 800 rpm at a recommended temperature of 4°C.
7. Remove supernatant and resuspend cells in 3-ml medium.
8. Place the cell suspension in one well of six-well plate or on a four-well plate.

Note: Adding the medium drop by drop is crucial for cell recovery.

Derivation of hES Cell Subclones

Human ES cell lines are derived from the ICM, which may not represent a homogenous cell population. To eliminate the possibility that the pluripotency of the lines reflects a collection of several distinct, committed multipotential cell types in the culture, parental lines have to be single-cell cloned (see cloning protocols in the section "Protocols for the Derivation of hES Cell Subclones"). The main aim of the first derivation of hES single-cell clones was to establish the parental lines' pluripotency, but as with mES cells, single-cell cloning has additional advantages.

METHOD FOR THE DERIVATION OF SINGLE-CELL CLONES

To derive single-cell clones, hES cells are trypsinized to single cells, and each cell is plated in a separate well of 96-well plates (for detailed protocols, see the section "Cloning hES Cells"). Alternatively, single cells may be plated in separate culture cylinders. After approximately 2 weeks of growth, the resulting colonies are passaged and propagated (see the section "Recovering Clones from Plates"). When cloning is conducted on hES cells, the rates of success highly depend on the culture medium. Several culture media were tested to clone the first parental hES cell

lines: medium supplemented with either FBS or serum replacement and either with or without human recombinant bFGF.[28] The highest cloning rates were obtained when serum-free growth conditions supplemented with bFGF were used (for integrations and concentrations, see the serum-free medium in the section "Serum-Free Medium"). Although success rates were relatively low (up to 1%), they have been found to be the most suitable conditions for the clonal derivation of hES single-cell lines. Human ES single-cell lines, H-9.1 and H-9.2, derived in these conditions maintained ES cells features:[28] They proliferated continuously as undifferentiated cells for prolonged periods (8 months), maintained stable and normal karyotypes, differentiated into advanced derivatives of all three embryonic germ layers *in vitro* in EBs and *in vivo* in teratomas, and expressed high levels of telomerase activity. Thus, the pluripotency of single hES cells has been established.

To date, many single-cell clones from seven parental ES cell lines—H1, H9, H13,[22] I3, I6,[25] and J3—have been derived. Interestingly, in the same culture conditions, most parental lines had the same cloning efficiency of 0.5%, with two exceptions: Line H-1 had a lower cloning efficiency of 0.16%, and the cloning of line I-4 proved unsuccessful.[25] The variation among the existing parental cell lines in respect to their cloning efficiency remains to be determined.

ADVANTAGES OF SINGLE-CELL CLONES

In addition to proving the pluripotency of single hES cells, single-cell clones may have further features. First, they are easier to grow and manipulate than the parental lines. Second, they form homogeneous cell populations, which may be instrumental for the development of research models based on gene knockout or targeted recombination. The transfected or knockout cells could be cloned and analyzed individually; clones that express the desired genotype could be further cultured and used for research. The main disadvantage of this strategy is the relatively low cloning efficiency (0.5–1%), which results in a rather difficult model to obtain when coupled with reduced successful recombination rates.[33] The advantage of this strategy, though, lies in the prolonged culture abilities, which make possible extended periods of research use once a satisfactorily manipulated single-cell clone is created.

Any future application of hES cells for scientific or therapeutic purposes will depend on their karyotypic stability. The first reports on hES cell line derivation specifically state that like mES cells, their karyotypes remain normal after continuous culture.[22,23] Although in some culture conditions hES cell lines retain normal karyotypes even after prolonged culture of over 107 passages, random karyotypic instability may still occur.[34] The karyotype of one culture of line I-6, for instance, became abnormal after 150 passages (30 months) of continuous culture on MEFs.[35] Since the first reports on hES cell line derivations, reports on karyotypic instability have accumulated. Amit *et al.* examined the karyotype of parental line H-9 after 7, 8, 10, and 13 months of continuous culture and found that only once, after 7 months of continuous culture, 4 of the 20 cells examined demonstrated abnormal karyotypes.[28] Eiges *et al.* reported on two cells with 17-chromosome trisomy in a stably transfected clone.[29] Based on the growing data on hES cells and the experience with mES cells, it is reasonable to assume that a subpopulation with an abnormal karyotype will acquire a selective growth advantage and take over the culture. Therefore, the periodical cloning of cultured hES cells for the purpose of maintaining a homogenous euploid population may be needed but will be infrequent.

PROTOCOLS FOR THE DERIVATION OF HES CELL SUBCLONES

Cloning hES Cells

1. Add 1 ml of trypsin–EDTA (0.5% trypsin and 5.3 mm EDTA, Invitrogen, Cat. No. 15400-054) to one well of a six-well plate.
2. Incubate for 5 minutes.
3. Add 2 ml of SR medium and collect the cells into a conical tube.
4. Centrifuge for 5 minutes at 1200 rpm.
5. Remove suspension, resuspend in 1 ml of serum-free medium, and pipette using a 1000-g pipette tip to fracture the pellet into single cells. Add 2 ml of serum-free medium.
6. Leave for 2 minutes to let small clumps sink.
7. Collect only the upper 2.5 ml and transfer into a clean tube. Dilute the cells at least 15-fold in a 58-mm Petri dish. Observe microscopically to ensure each cell is a sufficient distance from its neighboring cell so that individual cell collection is possible.
8. Collect single cells using a pulled Pasteur pipette, and plate each cell in a separate well of a 96-well plate. Cover the plates with 40,000 MEFs per square centimeter. Use serum-free medium as the culture medium for cloning the hES cells.

Recovering Clones from Plates

1. Collect the medium from the well, add 100 μl of type IV collagenase (1 mg/ml, Invitrogen Corporation, Cat. No.17104-019), and incubate for 30 minutes.
2. If the colony does not detach, add 100 μl dispase (10 mg/ml, Gibco BRL, Cat. No. 17105-041) and incubate for 5 minutes.
3. If the colony is still partly attached, incubate for an additional 5 minutes. Afterward, collect the colony and place it on a fresh culture plate.
4. Wash three times and plate in a fresh MEF-covered well.

From this stage, handle cells similarly to hES cells (see the section "Methods for hES Cell Culture").

Methods for hES Cell Culture

The traditional methods used for culturing hES cells have not changed dramatically since their development for the derivation and culture of ECs and mES cells.[30] Unlike mES cells, which can be cultured on gelatin with the addition of leukemia inhibitory factor (LIF) to the culture medium, until recently, hES cells could be cultured on mitotically inactivated MEFs only.[22,23] The feeder layer has a dual role: First, as the term implies, the MEFs support ES cell growth; second, the MEFs prevent spontaneous differentiation of ES cells during culture. Although hES cells require meticulous care, they can be cultured in large numbers and frozen and thawed with reasonable survival rates.[22,23] Since their first derivation in 1998, the culture systems of hES cells has enjoyed three major advantages in the basic culture conditions: (1) the ability to grow these cells under serum-free conditions;[28] (2) the use of human feeder layers as substitutes to MEFs,[34,36] and (3) the maintenance of the cells in an undifferentiated state in feeder-free conditions.[37] The protocols for hES cell culture with MEFs are described in the section "Methods for hES Cell Culture."

HUMAN FEEDERS

In the future, hES cells may be directly applied in cell-based therapies. Any clinical use of these cells will require compliance with FDA guidelines. During hES cell culture on MEFs with medium supplemented with FBS, there is a risk of exposing the cells to retroviruses or other pathogens. One of the solutions to this problem is the isolation and culture of hES cells in an entirely animal-free environment.

Recently, Richards *et al.* presented an animal-free system for the production and growth of hES cell lines.[36] In the culture medium proposed, FBS was replaced with a supplement of 20% human serum, and a human feeder layer replaced the MEFs. Coculture with human embryo-derived feeder layers or Fallopian tube epithelial feeder layers was found to support hES cell growth and isolation of an hES cell line.

Another animal-free culture system for hES cells consists of foreskin feeder layers and a medium supplemented with serum replacement.[34] The protocols of hES cell culture with foreskin fibroblast (FF) are described in the section "Protocols for Human Feeder Culture System." After more than 105 passages (more than 300 doublings), the three hES cell lines grown in these conditions—I3, I6, and H9—exhibited all hES cells features, including expression of typical surface markers and transcription factor *Oct 4,* differentiation into representative tissues of the three embryonic germ layers both in EBs and in teratomas, high telomerase activity after 46 passages of culture, and maintenance of normal karyotypes. The morphology of the hES cell colony grown on foreskin feeder layers is slightly different than that grown on MEFs in terms of its long and elliptic organization (Fig. 40–4A). No difference was found among the 12 FF lines tested for their ability to support prolonged and undifferentiated proliferation of hES cells.[35] A recent publication demonstrated the derivation of new hES cell lines using FFs as feeders and a medium supplemented with FCS.[38]

There are several advantages to the use of FFs as feeder layers.[34] The serum replacement enables better-defined

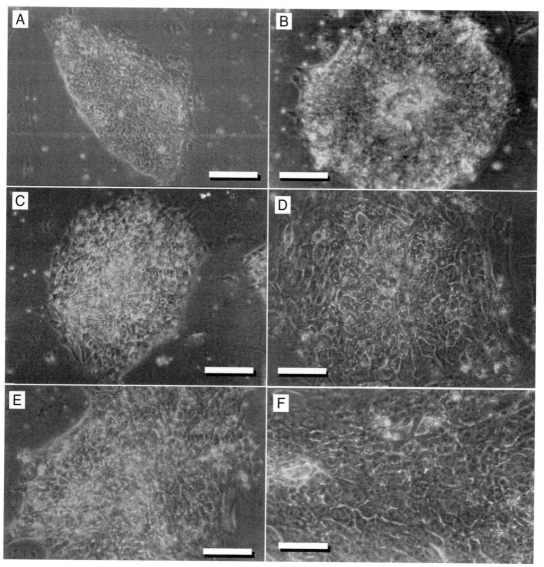

Figure 40–4. *Human ES Cell Colonies Grown in Different Culture Conditions.* (A) Human ES cell colony from line I-6 after several passages on foreskin matrix. Bar = 75 μm. (B) Example of the morphology of an undifferentiated ES cell colony from clone I-3.2, grown for 12 passages on matrigel matrix using MEF conditioned medium. Bar = 50 μm. (C) Human ES cell colony from line I-6 after several passages on MEF matrix. Bar = 75 μm. (D) Colony I-3 grown in feeder free conditions for 21 passages. Bar = 50 μm (E) Human ES cell colony from line I-6 after several passages on matrigel. Bar = 75 μm. No condition medium added. (F) Cells from cell line I-3 grown in feeder-free conditions for 20 passages. Bar = 38 μm.

culture conditions.[28] Furthermore, unlike embryo-derived or Fallopian tube epithelial human feeder layers,[36] which can grow to a certain limited passage, FFs can grow to 42 passages.[34] While exploring different FF lines, no difference was found between the ability of high-passage human foreskin feeders and the ability of low-passage ones to support the growth of hES cells, even after several cycles of freezing and thawing.[34] These feeders may therefore have an advantage when large-scale growth of hES cells is required and pathogens screening is essential.

PROTOCOLS FOR HUMAN FEEDER CULTURE SYSTEM

FF Medium
Final concentrations:

- 80% DMEM
- 20% FBSd
- 2 mm of L-glutamine
- 1% nonessential amino acid
- 0.1 mm of β-mercaptoethanol

Preparation: Pour all materials into a 22-μm filter unit and filter. Store between 2–8°C.

Notes: If desired, human serum or SR may replace FBSd. This medium may be used within 2 weeks of preparation.

Derivation of FF

For FF derivation, use FF medium (see the section "Human Feeders") with the addition of penicillin–streptomycin (Sigma P-3539) and kanamycin (Amresco, Ohio, Cat. No. 0408-106).

Preparation

1. Place foreskins in PBS supplemented with penicillin–streptomycin within 48 hours after circumcision.
2. Unfold the foreskins and wash three times with PBS.
3. Cut into small pieces using sharp Iris scissors (approximately eight pieces per foreskin).
4. Transfer the clean pieces into a new Petri dish and mince thoroughly using sharp Iris scissors.
5. Add 6 ml of trypsin–EDTA (0.5% trypsin and 5.3 mm EDTA, Invitrogen, Cat. No. 15400-054) and incubate for at least 30 minutes.
6. Neutralize the trypsin using at least 6 ml of FF culture medium (see the section "Human Feeders"). Transfer the FF into conical tubes. Use the FF culture medium to wash the plate.
7. Divide evenly into a T25 culture flask at a recommended ratio of two pieces per flask.
8. Add 6 ml of FF culture medium (see the section "Human Feeders").
9. Grow the hFF until the culture is confluent. Change the medium as needed (do not vacuum the lumps).
10. Freeze the resulting FF (see the section "FF Freezing").

FF Splitting

1. Add 2 ml of trypsin–EDTA (0.5% trypsin and 5.3 mm EDTA, Invitrogen Corporation, Cat. No. 15400-054) and cover the entire culture-flask surface.
2. Incubate for 6 minutes.
3. Tap the side of the flask to loosen the cells. Add 4 ml of culture medium (see the section "Human Feeders") to neutralize the trypsin.
4. Remove the cell suspension into a conical tube and centrifuge for 5 minutes at 1200 rpm.
5. Resuspend in culture medium (see the section "Human Feeders"), and pipette to fracture the pellet.
6. Distribute the cell suspension to a desired number of culture flasks.
7. Add 6 ml of FF culture medium (see the section "Human Feeders").

FF Freezing

1. Remove all lumps as much as possible.
2. Add 2 ml of trypsin–EDTA and cover the entire culture-flask surface.
3. Incubate for 6 minutes.

4. Tap the side of the flask to loosen the cells. Add 4 ml of culture medium (see the section "Human Feeders") to neutralize the trypsin.
5. Remove the cell suspension into a conical tube. Let the remaining lumps sink and remove the cell suspension into a clean conical tube.
6. Centrifuge for 5 minutes at 1200 rpm.
7. Add the culture medium (see the section "Human Feeders") and pipette up and down to break the pellet.
8. Drop by drop, add an equivalent volume of freezing medium (see the section "hES Cells Freezing") and mix gently.
9. Place 1 ml into 2-ml cryogenic vials (we place 1–2 vials per one confluent flask).
10. Freeze the vials overnight at −70°C in a Nalgene freezing box.
11. Transfer the vials into a liquid nitrogen container.

Notes: Adding the freezing medium drop by drop is crucial for cell recovery. If needed, the FF can be frozen using a freezing solution consisting of human serum (20%) or SR (30%) instead of FBS.

FF Thawing

1. Remove the vial from the liquid nitrogen and quickly thaw it in 37°C water bath.
2. When a small pellet of frozen cells remains, clean the vial using 70% ethanol.
3. Pipette the contents of the vial up and down once, and transfer the cells into a conical tube.
4. Drop by drop, add 2 ml of culture medium (see the section "Human Feeders").
5. Centrifuge for 5 minutes at 1500 rpm.
6. Resuspend the pellet in culture medium (see the section "Human Feeders").
7. Remove the cell suspension into a culture flask and add 6 ml of culture medium (see the section "Human Feeders").

Notes: Adding the medium drop by drop is crucial for cell recovery. Thaw one vial into one T25 culture flask. Do not thaw more than four vials at once.

Preparation of FF-Covered Plates

1. Add 8 ng/ml of mitomycin C into a culture flask and incubate for 2 hours.
2. Wash four times with PBS.
3. Add 2 ml of trypsin–EDTA (0.5% trypsin and 5.3 mm EDTA, Invitrogen Corporation, Cat. No. 15400-054) and cover the entire culture-flask surface.
4. Incubate for 6 minutes.
5. Tap the side of the flask to loosen cells. Add 4 ml of culture medium (see the section "Human Feeders") to neutralize the trypsin.
6. Remove the cell suspension into a conical tube.
7. Centrifuge for 5 minutes at 1200 rpm.
8. Add 10 ml of culture medium (see the section "Human Feeders") and pipette up and down to break the cell pellets.
9. Count the cells and resuspend them in a desired medium volume (see the section "Human Feeders").

10. Add the cell suspension to culture dishes. We recommend 4×10^5 cells per well on six-well plates.
11. Let set for at least 5 hours before plating the hES cells.

Notes: The FF number can be calculated as 3×10^4 cells per square centimeter. If possible, set the plate overnight before plating the hES cells.

hES Cell Culture with FF

All protocols are identical to culturing hES cells with MEFs; see the section "Methods for hES Cell Culture."

FEEDER-FREE CULTURE OF HES CELLS

For their large-scale growth and therapeutic applications, the ideal culture method for hES cells would be to grow them on an animal-free matrix using a serum-free medium. The first step toward this solution was reported by Xu *et al.,* who demonstrated a culture system in which hES cells were grown on matrigel, laminin, or fibronectin using 100% MEF-conditioned medium, supplemented with serum replacement.[37] The major shortcomings of this system are the possible exposure of the cells to mouse pathogens through the condition medium, the absence of a well-defined condition medium, and the need for simultaneous growth of MEFs. Richards *et al.* also tested the ability of human feeder-conditioned medium (embryo-derived, Fallopian tube epithelial, or FF feeder layers) to sustain a continuous undifferentiated proliferation of hES cells grown on collagen I, human extracellular matrix, or laminin.[36] These conditions were found inferior to the use of human feeder cells.

Another advancement is the ability to culture hES cells for prolonged periods without the use of both feeder cells and conditioned media. With the combination of human recombinant growth factors, serum replacement, and adhesion matrices like fibronectin, hES cells can be grown for more than 35 passages, maintaining all ES cells features.[35] Examples of undifferentiated hES cell colonies grown on the different matrices in these conditions are illustrated in Fig. 40–4, and resultant cell types after differentiation in teratomas are shown in Fig. 40–5.

The combination of serum replacement, human fibronectin, and human recombinant growth factors comprises a well-defined culture system for hES cells, which facilitates future uses of these cells in research practices and provides a safer alternative for future clinical applications.

Primate Versus mES Cells

Although primate and mES cells share most of the features of ES cells, there are some differences among them. The most distinct difference is the colonies' morphology. Unlike mES cells, which form compact and piled colonies, all primate ES cells were reported to form a "flat" morphology[19–22] (Fig. 40–2). On the single-cell level, however, there is no difference: both mouse and primate ES cells demonstrate typical spaces between the cells, a high nucleus-to-cytoplasm ratio, and the presence of one or more nucleoli (Fig. 40–2).

Several surface markers were shown to be related to the undifferentiated stage of cells.[38,40] Primate ES cells have been found to express different surface markers than mES cells. Although mES cells highly express surface marker stage-specific embryonic antigen-1 (SSEA-1), nonhuman primate ES cells and hES cells do not express this marker.[19–22] In addition, hES cells and nonhuman primate ES cells strongly express SSEA-4, tumor recognition antigen (TRA)-1-60, and TRA-1-81, and they weakly express SSEA-3, with the exception of cynomolgus ES cells, which do not express SSEA-3;[21] mES cells never express these markers.[30] Examples of the surface antigen expression are demonstrated in Fig. 40–6.

It had been reported that most mES cell lines are 40, XY.[41] The reduced numbers of XX mES cell lines were related to the lack of X-chromosome inactivation and X-chromosome deletions in mES cells.[42] Interestingly, no difference was found in the XX-to-XY ratio among primate ES cells lines. This finding may be linked to different timing of the X-chromosome inactivation during the early embryonic development of the mouse and primate.

LIF was found to maintain undifferentiated proliferation of mES cells with the absence of a MEF feeder layer.[43] Both hES and nonhuman primate ES cell lines failed to maintain undifferentiated morphology without an MEF feeder layer and with LIF.[19–23] This finding may indicate that different pathways govern the self-maintenance procedures of ES cells isolated from different species.

Another remarkable difference between mES cells and primate ES cells is the latter's ability to differentiate into trophoblasts *in vitro,* a characteristic that rarely appears in mES cells. Mouse trophoblasts do not secrete chorionic gonadotropin (CG), a hormone that was shown to be a crucial signal for maternal recognition of pregnancy secreted by the trophoectoderm.[44] Both rhesus and marmoset ES cells were shown to secrete increasing levels of CG when allowed to differentiate,[45] but cynomolgus ES cells did not.[21] Human ES cells were reported to differentiate into hCG-secreting trophoblasts *in vitro.*[46,47]

The differences between mouse and primate ES cells may reflect the differences in the embryonic development of these different species. Therefore, mES cells may be found less suitable for research on early primate embryonic development. One of the advantages of using nonhuman primate ES cells is their potential contribution to the creation of transgenic monkeys, which may serve as models for chronic illnesses.

PRIMATE ES CELL DIFFERENTIATION SYSTEMS

During their two decades of existence, many *in vitro* differentiation models were developed for mES cells. Similar models are gradually being created for primate ES cells. Most existing methods for directing mES cells differentiation include the formation of EBs as one of the initial steps, as is the case with the differentiation of mES cells into hematopoietic cells,[48] neurons,[49] and cardiomyocytes.[50] Apparently, this step encourages ES cells to differentiate and consequently

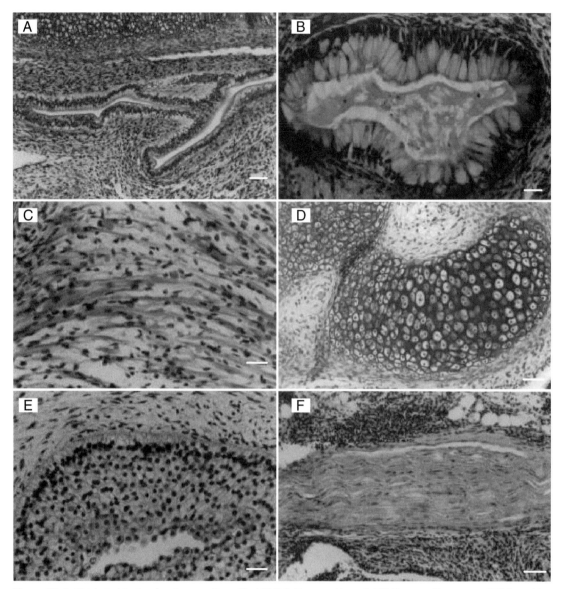

Figure 40–5. *Histological Sections from Teratomas Formed by hES Cells Grown on Matrigel, MEF Matrix, or Fibronectin in SCID Beige Mice.* (A) Columnar epithelium. (B) Mucus-secreting surface epithelium resembling the stratified epithelium found in the stomach. (C) Embryonal myotubes. (D) Cartilage. (E) Stratified epithelium. (F) Myelinated nerve (hematoxylin and eosin dye). Bar = 50 μm (A, E, D, and F). Bar = 25 μm (B and C). (Please see CD-ROM for color version of this figure.)

increases the rate and efficiency of differentiation. Human ES cells, like mES cells, spontaneously create EBs when cultured in suspension, including cystic EBs, which contain derivatives of the three embryonic germ layers.[27] All nonhuman primate ES cell lines were also reported to create EBs *in vitro,* although some of them seemed less organized than mouse derived EBs.[21,45] The procedure of preparing EBs from primate ES cells is described in the section "Formation of EBs."

Primate ES cells can also differentiate *in vivo.* Following their injection into the hind muscle of SCID mice, they spontaneously create teratomas in which they differentiate into representative tissues of the three embryonic germ layers. They have been shown to differentiate into bone and cartilage tissue, striated muscles, gut-like structures, structures resembling fetal glomeruli, neural rosettes, etc.[19–22] In EBs, ES cells differentiate as groups of cells or into simple structures; in teratomas, primate ES cells can create more complex and well-organized organ-like structures such as hair follicles, salivary gland, and teeth buds.[25,45] The development of organ-like structures in teratomas requires cooperation among cells and tissues derived from different germ layers. The protocol for teratoma formation is detailed in the section "Formation of Teratomas."

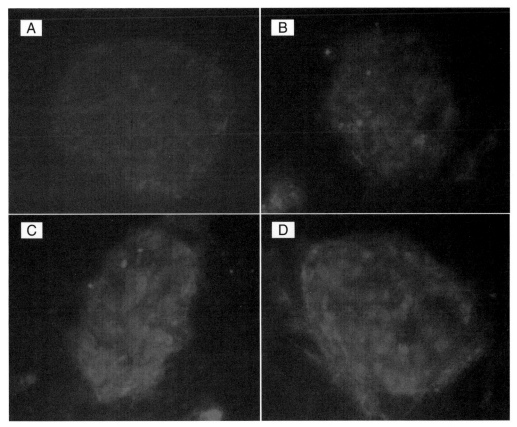

Figure 40–6. *Immunostaining of ES Cells with Typical Surface Markers.* (A) Mouse ES cell colony stained with SSEA-1. (B) Rhesus ES cells stained with SSEA4 and (C) TRA-1-60. (D). I-8 hES cell colony stained with TRA-81. (Please see CD-ROM for color version of this figure.)

One of the milestones in creating directed-differentiation systems for mES cells was to genetically manipulate these cells. The efficient and stable transfection models can be used both for creating pure populations of cells and for inducing directed differentiation. Additional uses may be to "flag" the cells to permit their recognition in histological sections and for research models aimed at examining the role of specific genes during specific differentiation or embryonic development.

Stable transfection protocols were already developed for hES cells. In some, various transfection agents were used;[25,29] others used lentivirus vectors.[51,52] Similar models were developed for nonhuman primate ES cells.[53,54]

To date, several studies have been published on lineage-specific differentiation of nonhuman primate ES cells in both spontaneous and directed-differentiation models. These include induced differentiation into hematopoietic cells using bone morphogenic protein 4,[55,56] spontaneous differentiation into endoderm derivatives,[57] and spontaneous[45] and induced differentiation into neural cells.[58,59]

Human ES cells had been shown to spontaneously differentiate into cardiomyocytes,[60] endothelial cells,[61] and insulin-secreting cells.[62] Directed differentiation models for hES cells include neural precursors,[23,63,64] hematopoietic

cells,[65,66] cardiomyocytes,[67,68] trophoblasts,[47] and hepatocyts.[69] The data presented here demonstrate the feasibility of developing differentiation models for primate ES cells similar to those of mES cells.

PROTOCOLS FOR PRIMATE ES CELL DIFFERENTIATION SYSTEMS

Formation of EBs

1. Remove the medium from the well. Add 0.5 ml splitting medium (see the section "hES Cell Splitting"), and incubate for at least 30 minutes.
2. Add 1 ml of culture medium (see the sections "ES Medium" and "Serum-Free Medium") and gently scrape cells with a 5-ml pipette.
3. Collect the cell suspension and place it into a conical tube.
4. Centrifuge for 3 minutes at 800 rpm at a recommended temperature of 4°C.
5. Resuspend the cells in the medium (see the sections "ES Medium" and "Serum-Free Medium") using a Gilson 1000-μm tip and plate on a 58-mm Petri dish.
6. Add 6 ml of medium.

Note: If EBs attach to the dish, scrape them off gently.

Formation of Teratomas

1. Scrap hES cells drawn from three confluent wells (of a six-well plate) using a policeman rubber scraper.
2. Centrifuge the cells for 5 minutes at 1200 rpm.
3. Leave as little medium as possible.
4. Inject the cells into the rear leg muscle of 4-week-old male, SCID, beige mice using an 18- or 21-g needle.
5. Teratomas will appear 6 weeks after the injection and can be harvested for analysis a fortnight later (8 weeks after the injection).

Notes: Greater amounts of cells will ensure teratoma formation but will reduce the mice's capability to carry it. Injection into one leg of each mouse is advisable to avoid unnecessary suffering. Human ES cells may be collected using collagenase splitting.

ACKNOWLEDGMENTS

The authors thank Mrs. Hadas O'Neill for editing the manuscript.

The research conducted was supported partly by the Technion Research and Development Foundation and partly by *NIH* grant 5R24RR18405.

REFERENCES

1. Kahan, B.W., and Ephrussi, B. (1970). Developmental potentialities of clonal *in vitro* cultures of mouse testicular teratoma. *J. Natl. Cancer Inst.* **44**, 1015–1036.
2. Martin, G.R., and Evans, M.J. (1974). The morphology and growth of a pluripotent teratocarcinoma cell line and its derivatives in tissue culture. *Cell* **2**, 163–172.
3. Evans, M.J. (1972). The isolation and properties of a clonal tissue culture strain of pluripotent mouse teratoma cells. *J. Embryol. Exp. Morphol.* **28**, 163–176.
4. Evans, M.J., and Kaufman, M.H. (1981). Establishment in culture of pluripotential cells from mouse embryos. *Nature* **292**, 154–156.
5. Martin, G.R. (1981). Isolation of a pluripotent cell line from early mouse embryos cultured in medium conditioned by teratocarcinoma stem cells. *Proc. Natl. Acad. Sci. USA* **78**, 7634–7638.
6. Bradley, A., Evans, M., Kaufman, M.H., and Robertson, E. (1984). Formation of germ line chimaeras from embryo-derived teratocarcinoma cell lines. *Nature* **309**, 255–256.
7. Nagy, A., Rossant, J., Nagy, R., Abramow-Newerly, W., and Roder, J.C. (1993). Derivation of completely cell culture-derived mice from early passage embryonic stem cells. *Proc. Natl. Acad. Sci. USA* **90**, 8424–8428.
8. Amano, T., Nakamura, K., Tani, T., Kato, Y., and Tsunoda, Y. (2000). Production of mice derived entirely from embryonic stem cells after injecting the cells into heat treated blastocysts. *Theriogenology* **53**, 1449–1458.
9. Doetschman, T., Williams, P., and Maeda, N. (1988). Establishment of hamster blastocyst-derived embryonic stem (ES) cells. *Dev. Biol.* **127**, 224–227.
10. Iannaccone, P.M., Taborn, G.U., Garton, R.L., Caplice, M.D., and Brenin, D.R. (1994). Pluripotent embryonic stem cells from the rat are capable of producing chimeras. *Dev. Biol.* **163**, 288–292 [erratum in *Dev. Biol.* (1997). **185**, 124–125].
11. Giles, J.R., Yang, X., Mark, W., and Foote, R.H. (1993). Pluripotency of cultured rabbit inner cell mass cells detected by isozyme analysis and eye pigmentation of fetuses following injection into blastocysts or morulae. *Mol. Reprod. Dev.* **36**, 130–138.
12. Graves, K.H., and Moreadith, R.W. (1993). Derivation and characterization of putative pluripotential embryonic stem cells from preimplantation rabbit embryos. *Mol. Reprod. Dev.* **36**, 424–433.
13. Notarianni, E., Galli, C., Laurie, S., Moor, R.M., and Evans, M.J. (1991). Derivation of pluripotent, embryonic cell lines from the pig and sheep. *J. Reprod. Fertil. Suppl.* **43**, 255–260.
14. Sims, M., and First, N.L. (1994). Production of calves by transfer of nuclei from cultured inner cell mass cells. *Proc. Natl. Acad. Sci. USA* **91**, 6143–6147.
15. Wheeler, M.B. (1994). Development and validation of swine embryonic stem cells: a review. *Reprod. Fertil. Dev.* **6**, 563–568.
16. Mitalipova, M., Beyhan, Z., and First, N.L. (2001). Pluripotency of bovine embryonic stem cell line derived from precompacting embryos. *Cloning* **3**, 59–67.
17. Li, M., Zhang, D., Hou, Y., Jiao, L., Zheng, X., and Wang, W.H. (2003). Isolation and culture of embryonic stem cells from porcine blastocysts. *Mol. Reprod. Dev.* **65**, 429–434.
18. Chen, L.R., Shiue, Y.L., Bertolini, L., Medrano, J.F., BonDurant, R.H., and Anderson, G.B. (1999). Establishment of pluripotent cell lines from porcine preimplantation embryos. *Theriogenology* **52**, 195–212.
19. Thomson, J.A., Kalishman, J., Golos, T.G., Durning, M., Harris, C.P., Becker, R.A., and Hearn, J.P. (1995). Isolation of a primate embryonic stem cell line. *Proc. Natl. Acad. Sci. USA* **92**, 7844–7848.
20. Thomson, J.A., Kalishman, J., Golos, T.G., Durning, M., Harris, C.P., and Hearn, J.P. (1996). Pluripotent cell lines derived from common marmoset *(Callithrix jacchus)* blastocysts. *Biol. Reprod.* **55**, 254–259.
21. Suemori, H., Tada, T., Torii, R., Hosoi, Y., Kobayashi, K. Imahie, H., Kondo, Y., Iritani, A., and Nakatsuji, N. (2001). Establishment of embryonic stem cell lines from cynomolgus monkey blastocysts produced by IVF or ICSI. *Dev. Dyn.* **222**, 273–279.
22. Thomson, J.A., Itskovitz-Eldor, J., Shapiro, S.S., Waknitz, M.A., Swiergiel, J.J., Marshall, V.S., and Jones, J.M. (1998). Embryonic stem cell lines derived from human blastocysts. *Science* **282**, 1145–1147 [erratum in *Science* (1998). **282**, 1827].
23. Reubinoff, B.E., Pera, M.F., Fong, C. Trounson, A., and Bongso, A. (2000). Embryonic stem cell lines from human blastocysts: somatic differentiation *in vitro*. *Natl. Biotechnol.* **18**, 399–404.
24. Lanzendorf, S.E., Boyd, C.A., Wright, D.L., Muasher, S., Oehninger, S., and Hodgen, G.D. (2001). Use of human gametes obtained from anonymous donors for the production of human embryonic stem cell lines. *Fertil. Steril.* **76**, 132–137.
25. Amit, M., and Itskovitz-Eldor, J. (2002). Derivation and spontaneous differentiation of human embryonic stem cells. *J. Anat.* **200**, 225–232.
26. Kirschstein, R., and Skirboll, L.R. (2000). Stem cells: scientific progress and future research directions. (available at http://www.nih.gov).
27. Itskovitz-Eldor, J., Schuldiner, M., Karsenti, D., Eden, A., Yanuka, O., Amit, M., Soreq, H., and Benvenisty, N. (2000). Differentiation of human embryonic stem cells into embryoid bodies comprising the three embryonic germ layers. *Mol. Med.* **6**, 88–95.

28. Amit, M., Carpenter, M.K., Inokuma, M.S., Chiu, C.P., Harris, C.P., Waknitz, M.A., Itskovitz-Eldor, J., and Thomson, J.A. (2000). Clonally derived human embryonic stem cell lines maintain pluripotency and proliferative potential for prolonged periods of culture. *Dev. Biol.* **227**, 271–278.

29. Eiges, R., Schuldiner, M., Drukker, M., Yanuka, O., Itskovitz-Eldor, J., and Benvenisty, N. (2001). Establishment of human embryonic stem cell-transfected clones carrying a marker for undifferentiated cells. *Curr. Biol.* **11**, 514–518.

30. Robertson, E.J. (1987). Embryo-derived stem cell lines. *In* "Teratocarcinomas and Embryonic Stem Cells: A Practical Approach," (E.J. Robertson, ed.), pp. 71–112. IRL Press, Oxford.

31. Solter, D., and Knowles, B.B. (1975). Immunosurgery of mouse blastocyst. *Proc. Natl. Acad. Sci. USA* **72**, 5099–5102.

32. Gardner, R.L. (1982). Investigation of cell lineage and differentiation in the extraembryonic endoderm of the mouse embryo. *J. Embryo. Exp. Morphol.* **68**, 175–198.

33. Zwaka, T.P., and Thomson, J.A. (2003). Homologous recombination in human embryonic stem cells. *Natl. Biotechnol.* **21**, 319–321.

34. Amit, M., Margulets, V., Segev, H., Shariki, C., Laevsky, I., Coleman, R., and Itskovitz-Eldor, J. (2003). Human feeder layers for human embryonic stem cells. *Biol. Reprod.* **68**, 2150–2156.

35. Amit, M. (Unpublished).

36. Richards, M., Fong, C.Y., Chan, W.K., Wong, P.C., and Bongso, A. (2002). Human feeders support prolonged undifferentiated growth of human inner cell masses and embryonic stem cells. *Natl. Biotechnol.* **20**, 933–936.

37. Xu, C., Inokuma, M.S., Denham, J., Golds, K., Kundu, P., Gold, J.D., and Carpenter, M.K. (2001). Feeder-free growth of undifferentiated human embryonic stem cells. *Natl. Biotechnol.* **19**, 971–974.

38. Hovatta, O., Mikkola, M., Gertow, K., Stromberg, A.M., Inzunza, J., Hreinsson, J., Rozell, B., Blennow, E., Andang, M., and Ahrlund-Richter, L. (2003). A culture system using human foreskin fibroblasts as feeder cells allows production of human embryonic stem cells. *Hum. Reprod.* **18**, 1404–1409.

39. Andrews, P.W., Goodfellow, P.N., Shevinsky, L., Bronson, D.L., and Knowles, B.B. (1982). Cell surface antigen of a clonal human embryonal carcinoma cell line: morphological and antigenic differentiation in culture. *Int. J. Cancer* **29**, 523–531.

40. Andrews, P.W., Banting, G.S., Damjanov, I., Arnaud, D., and Avner, P. (1984). Three monoclonal antibodies defining distinct differentiation antigen associated with different high molecular weight polypeptide on the surface of human embryonal carcinoma cells. *Hybridoma* **3**, 347–361.

41. Smith, A.G. (2000). Chapter 10: Embryonic stem cells. *In* "Stem cell biology," D.R. Marshak, *et al.*, eds.), pp. 205–230. Cold Spring Harbor Laboratory Press, Cold Spring Harbor, NY.

42. Rastan, S., and Robertson, E.J. (1985). X-chromosome deletions in embryo-derived (EK) cell lines associated with lack of X-chromosome inactivation. *J. Embryol. Exp. Morphol.* **90**, 379–388.

43. Williams, R., Hilton, D., Pease, S., Wilson, T., Stewart, C., Gearing, D., Wagner, E., Metcalf, D., Nicola, N., and Gough, N. (1988). Myeloid leukemia inhibitory factor maintains the developmental potential of embryonic stem cells. *Nature* **336**, 684–687.

44. Flint, A.P.F., Hearn, J.P., and Michael, A.E. (1990). The maternal recognition of pregnancy in mammals. *J. Zool. Lond.* **221**, 327–341.

45. Thomson, J.A., Marshall, V.S., and Trojanowski, J.Q. (1998). Neural differentiation of rhesus embryonic stem cells. *APMIS* **106**, 149–157.

46. Thomson, J.A., and Marshall, V.S. (1998). Primate embryonic stem cells. *Curr. Top. Dev. Biol.* **38**, 133–165.

47. Xu, R.H., Chen, X., Li, D.S., Li, R., Addicks, G.C., Glennon, C., Zwaka, T.P., and Thomson, J.A. (2002). BMP4 initiates human embryonic stem cell differentiation to trophoblast. *Natl. Biotechnol.* **20**, 1261–1264.

48. Keller, G.M. (1995). *In vitro* differentiation of embryonic stem cells. *Curr. Opin. Cell Biol.* **7**, 862–869.

49. Brüstle, O., Spiro, A.C., Karram, K., Choudhary, K., Okabe, S., and McKay, R.D.G. (1997). *In vitro*-generated neural precursors participate in mammalian brain development. *Proc. Natl. Acad. Sci. USA* **94**, 14,809–14,814.

50. Klug, M.G., Soonpaa, M.H., Koh, G.Y., and Field, L.J. (1996). Genetically selected cardiomyocytes from differentiating embryonic stem cells form stable intracardiac grafts. *J. Clin. Invest.* **98**, 216–224.

51. Ma, Y., Ramezani, A., Lewis, R., Hawley, R.G., and Thomson, J.A. (2003). High-level sustained transgene expression in human embryonic stem cells using lentiviral vectors. *Stem Cells* **21**, 111–117.

52. Gropp, M., Itsykson, P., Singer, O., Ben-Hur, T., Reinhartz, E., Galun, E., and Reubinoff, B.E. (2003). Stable genetic modification of human embryonic stem cells by lentiviral vectors. *Mol. Ther.* **7**, 281–287.

53. Asano, T., Hanazono, Y., Ueda, Y., Muramatsu, S., Kume, A., Suemori, H. Suzuki, Y., Kondo, Y., Harii, K., Hasegawa, M. Nakatsuji, N., and Ozawa, K. (2002). Highly efficient gene transfer into primate embryonic stem cells with a simian lentivirus vector. *Mol. Ther.* **6**, 162–168.

54. Hanazono, Y., Asano, T., Ueda, Y., and Ozawa, K. (2003). Genetic manipulation of primate embryonic and hematopoietic stem cells with simian lentivirus vectors. *Trends. Cardiovasc. Med.* **13**, 106–110.

55. Li, F., Lu, S., Vida, L., Thomson, J.A., and Honig, G.R. (2001). Bone morphogenetic protein 4 induces efficient hematopoietic differentiation of rhesus monkey embryonic stem cells *in vitro*. *Blood* **98**, 335–342.

56. Lu, S.J., Quan, C., Li, F., Vida, L., and Honig, G.R. (2002). Hematopoietic progenitor cells derived from embryonic stem cells: analysis of gene expression. *Stem Cells* **20**, 428–437.

57. Jacobson, L., Kahan, B., Djamali, A., Thomson, J., and Odorico, J.S. (2001). Differentiation of endoderm derivatives, pancreas, and intestine from rhesus embryonic stem cells. *Transplant Proc.* **33**, 674.

58. Kawasaki, H., Suemori, H., Mizuseki, K., Watanabe, K., Urano, F., Ichinose, H., Haruta, M., Takahashi, M., Yoshikawa, K., Nishikawa, S., Nakatsuji, N., and Sasai, Y. (2002). Generation of dopaminergic neurons and pigmented epithelia from primate ES cells by stromal cell-derived inducing activity. *Proc. Natl. Acad. Sci. USA* **99**, 1580–1585.

59. Mizuseki, K., Sakamoto, T., Watanabe, K., Muguruma, K., Ikeya, M., Nishiyama, A., Arakawa, A., Suemori, H., Nakatsuji, N., Kawasaki, H., Murakami, F., and Sasai, Y. (2003). Generation of neural crest-derived peripheral neurons and floor plate cells from mouse and primate embryonic stem cells. *Proc. Natl. Acad. Sci. USA* **100**, 5828–5833.

60. Kehat, I., Kenyagin-Karsenti, D., Snir, M., Segev, H., Amit, M., Gepstein, A., Livne, E., Binah, O., Itskovitz-Eldor, J., and Gepstein, L. (2001). Human embryonic stem cells can differentiate into myocytes with structural and functional properties of cardiomyocytes. *J. Clin. Invest.* **108**, 407–414.

61. Levenberg, S., Golub, J.S., Amit, M., Itskovitz-Eldor, J., and Langer, R. (2002). Endothelial cells derived from human embryonic stem cells. *Proc. Natl. Acad. Sci. USA* **99**, 4391–4396.

62. Assady, S., Maor, G., Amit, M., Itskovitz-Eldor, J., Skorecki, K.L., and Tzukerman, M. (2001). Insulin production by human embryonic stem cells. *Diabetes* **50**, 1691–1697.

63. Zhang, S.C., Wernig, M., Duncan, I.D., Brüstle, O., and Thomson, J.A. (2001). *In vitro* differentiation of transplantable neural precursors from human embryonic stem cells. *Natl. Biotechnol.* **19,** 1129–1133.

64. Reubinoff, B.E., Itsykson, P., Turetsky, T., Pera, M.F., Reinhartz, E., Itzik, A., and Ben-Hur, T. (2001). Neural progenitors from human embryonic stem cells. *Natl. Biotechnol.* **19,** 1134–1140.

65. Kaufman, D.S., Hanson, E.T., Lewis, R.L., Auerbach, R., and Thomson, J.A. (2001). Hematopoietic colony-forming cells derived from human embryonic stem cells. *Proc. Natl. Acad. Sci. USA* **98,** 10,716–10,721.

66. Chadwick, K., Wang, L., Li, L., Menendez, P. Murdoch, B., Rouleau, A., and Bhatia, M. (2003). Cytokines and BMP-4 promote hematopoietic differentiation of human embryonic stem cells. *Blood* **102,** 906–915.

67. Xu, C., Police, S., Rao, N., and Carpenter, M.K. (2002). Characterization and enrichment of cardiomyocytes derived from human embryonic stem cells. *Circ. Res.* **91,** 501–508.

68. Mummery, C., Ward, D., van den Brink, C.E., Bird, S.D., Doevendans, P.A,, Opthof, T., Brutel de la Riviere, A., Tertoolen, L., van der Heyden, M., and Pera M. (2002). Cardiomyocyte differentiation of mouse and human embryonic stem cells. *J. Anat.* **200,** 233–242.

69. Rambhatla, L., Chiu, C.P., Kundu, P., Peng, Y., and Carpenter, M.K. (2003). Generation of hepatocyte-like cells from human embryonic stem cells. *Cell Transplant.* **12,** 1–11.

70. Amit, M., and Itskovitz-Eldor, J. (Unpublished).

71. Suss-Toby, E., Gerecht-Nir, S., Amit, M., Manor, D., and Itskovitz-Eldor, J. (2004). Derivation of a diploid human embryonic stem cell line from a mononuclear zygote. *Hum. Reprod.* **19,** 670–675.

WEB SITES

72. ES Cell International. http://www.escellinternational. com/.

73. BresaGen. http://bresagen.com.au/.

74. University of California, San Francisco's Human Embryonic Stem Cell Lines. http://escells.ucsf.edu/.

75. NIH Human Embryonic Stem Cell Registry. http://stemcells. nih.gov/registry/index.asp.

Approaches for Derivation and Maintenance of Human ES Cells: Detailed Procedures and Alternatives

Irina Klimanskaya and Jill McMahon

Derivation of human embryonic stem (hES) cells is a challenging endeavor. Although derivation of mouse ES cell lines has become a common procedure, the limited number of currently available hES cell lines is testament to the difficulties encountered at various stages of their derivation and maintenance. The common techniques for the maintenance of hES cells are often complicated, involving mechanical passaging of the cells using collagenase or dispase. Distributors of the available hES cell lines frequently recommend attending special training courses before working with the hES cell lines they provide.

In our lab, we recently established and characterized 17 hES cell lines.[1] These lines have been adapted to trypsinization, which simplifies the passaging of the cells and generates cells in sufficient numbers to permit experimentation. All of these lines can be successfully frozen and thawed using very simple procedures with a recovery rate of 10% or higher.

Techniques for deriving and maintaining pluripotent human and mouse ES cells in culture have been described by a variety of labs, and there are notable similarities and differences. For the derivation and maintenance of hES cell lines in our lab, we adapted previously published methods[2–10] and developed an approach that consistently produced new cell lines and that proved to be easily taught to other investigators.

This chapter describes the aspects of derivation and maintenance of hES cells that we found to be helpful in generating hES cell lines. We respond to questions received from other researchers about equipment, preparation and quality control of media and reagents, cell passaging techniques, and other aspects of hES cells morphology and behavior.

Setting Up the Lab

EQUIPMENT

Initial steps in the derivation process are conducted under a dissecting microscope. We make an effort to keep embryos

and dishes containing the early mechanically passaged dispersions at 37°C. Dishes brought out of the incubators are set on 37°C slide warmers or viewed using microscopes fitted with heated stages. The mechanical dispersions necessitate having the dishes open for extended periods; since the cultures are vulnerable to contamination during this time, we have the dissecting microscope within a bench-top laminar flow hood. A high-quality stereo microscope with a wide-range zoom is essential for the mechanical dispersion of colonies, including the inner cell mass (ICM) outgrowth; it permits an overall assessment of each plate and evaluation of the morphology of each colony when doing the mechanical passaging.

The equipment used in our lab is as follows:

Stereomicroscope for microdissection: A Nikon SMZ-1500 with the magnification range 7.5–125× works well with its easy zoom and the positioning mirror that regulates the depth and contrast of the image. A whole 35-mm dish can be scanned for colony morphology, and the zoom permits selection with precision of the parts of the colony that are the best for dissection.

Inverted microscope: A Nikon TE 300, an inverted cell culture microscope is setup with phase and Hoffman modulation contrast (HMC) optics with phase objectives of 4×, 10×, 20×, and HMC 20× and 40×; HMC is recommended for viewing ES cells and required for embryo evaluation.

Heated microscope stage for both stereo and inverted microscope: A (Nikon) slide warmer keeps extra PMEF plates at 37°C during mechanical dispersions.

Bench-top laminar flow hood with a HEPA filter: Vertical hoods by Terra Universal (Anaheim, CA). Horizontal models sometimes produce too much vibration. We found that these vertical hoods were tall enough to accommodate a dissecting microscope and were very convenient and reliable.

Tissue culture incubator: All parameters (CO_2 concentration, humidity, and temperature) need to be checked daily with external monitoring equipment.

External monitoring equipment:

- Surface thermometer
- Mercury liquid-immersed thermometer
- Hygrometer
- CO_2 monitor and gas calibration kit (GD 444 SR-B by CEA Instruments, Emerson, NJ), calibrated regularly

QUALITY ASSURANCE OF EQUIPMENT

Consistency in growth conditions is very important for the development of the embryos and the growth of the hES cells. The checklist of parameters monitored daily includes the percentage of CO_2 (5.0), temperature (37°C), and humidity of the incubators (>90%). A checklist with daily readings is very helpful for timely recalibration if an undesirable trend is noticed. Warming rings and platforms are constantly monitored with surface thermometers.

Two incubators are set aside for derivations and expansion of new lines. The incubators are checked prior to any new derivation round by growing mouse embryos from the two-cell stage to blastocyst; a passing score requires 80% to go to blastocyst. Cultures at early stages, prior to being frozen, are split between the two incubators as a protection against incubator failure. The incubators are not opened frequently, thereby maintaining steady growth parameters.

STERILITY

There are some aspects of the derivation of hES cell lines that put the associated work under more stringent sterility requirements than those of any typical cell culture lab. These include the limited availability of frozen human embryos, the labor-intensive nature of derivation and expansion, the team effort involved, and the long periods in culture until the newly established lines can be expanded and safely frozen. In addition, because hES cells are prone to spontaneous differentiation under unfavorable conditions, many labs prefer not to use antibiotics in cell culture media.

The reagents should either be purchased sterile from the manufacturer or be filter-sterilized in the lab. Most of the cell culture supplies can be bought sterile. However, everything that is sterilized in-house by autoclaving or by dry heat needs to be quality controlled with biological indicators (spore strips from Steris, Mentor, OH).

If it comes to the worst, the triple-action drug Normocin (see media components) appears to be tolerated by hES cells without significant changes in their pluripotency or growth rate and permits the rescue of contaminated cultures.

Preparing and Screening Reagents

The hES cell lines in our facility were derived and continue to be grown on primary mouse embryo fibroblast (PMEF) monolayers. We derived the lines in media containing serum replacement and Plasmanate, a component of the medium used in the IVF field for thawing human embryos and fetal bovine serum (FBS) at early stages of derivation.

MEDIA COMPONENTS

- KO-DMEM (Invitrogen, Cat. No. 10829)
- DMEM high glucose (Invitrogen, Cat. No. 11960-044)
- Serum Replacement (Invitrogen, Cat. No. 10828-028): Each lot needs to be tested, but as a guide, we found that the lots with osmolarity higher than 470 mOsm/kg and endotoxicity lower than 0.9 EU/ml were the best. Upon thawing, make single-use aliquots and freeze.

- Plasmanate (Bayer, Cat. No. 613-25): Each lot needs to be tested.
- FBS (Hyclone, Cat. No. SH30070.02): Each lot needs to be tested. Heat inactivate, if desired, and freeze in aliquots.
- β-Mercaptoethanol, 55 mM (1000×) solution (Invitrogen, Cat. No. 21985-023)
- Non-essential amino acids (NEAA), 100× solution (Invitrogen, Cat. No. 11140-050)
- Penicillin–streptomycin, 100× solution (Invitrogen, Cat. No. 15070-063)
- Glutamax-I, 100× solution, a stable dipeptide of L-glutamine and L-alanyl, a glutamine substitute (Invitrogen, Cat. No. 35050-061)

Penicillin–streptomycin and Glutamax-I are kept in frozen single-use aliquots.

- Basic fibroblast growth factor (bFGF) (Invitrogen, Cat. No. #13256-029): Add 1.25 ml of hES cell growth media without leukemia inhibitory factor (LIF) or bFGF to a vial containing 10 μg of bFGF. This makes an 8 μg/ml stock solution. Increasing final bFGF concentration to 8–20 ng/ml can be beneficial for the cells, especially at early stages of derivation, after thawing or when the cells are grown at low density. Make 120-μl aliquots and freeze.
- Human LIF (Chemicon International, Cat. No. LIF1010)
- 0.05% trypsin–0.53 mM EDTA (Invitrogen, Cat. No. 25300-054)
- Gelatin from porcine skin (Sigma, Cat. No. G1880)
- Phosphate-buffered saline (PBS), Ca^{2+}, Mg^{2+}-free (Invitrogen, Cat. No. 14190-144)
- Normocin, an antibiotic active against gram +/– bacteria that also has antimycoplasma and antifungi activity (Invivogen, San Diego, CA; Cat. No. ant-nr-2; comes as a 500× solution)

MEDIA RECIPES

Bottles of media that are opened frequently become alkali rapidly; we suggest making smaller quantities that would last approximately a week.

PMEF Growth Medium

To a 500-ml bottle of high-glucose DMEM, add:

- 6 ml penicillin–streptomycin
- 6 ml Glutamax-I
- 50 ml FBS

hES Cell Basal Medium

To a 500-ml bottle of KO-DMEM, add:

- 6 ml penicillin–streptomycin
- 6 ml Glutamax-I
- 6 ml NEAA
- 0.6 ml β-mercaptoethanol

hES Cell Derivation Medium

Use this medium at early stages of ICM outgrowth. It has higher LIF and bFGF concentration and contains FBS.

You can switch to hES cell growth medium when a steady growth of colonies has been reached (usually passage 2–4).

To 100 ml of basal medium, add:

- 6.5 ml Plasmanate
- 6.5 ml Serum Replacement
- 6.5 ml heat inactivated FBS
- 240 µl of human LIF (final concentration 20 ng/ml)
- 120 µl of bFGF stock solution (final concentration 8 ng/ml), or more (up to 20 ng/ml)
- Sterilize by 0.22-µm filtration

hES Cell Growth Medium

To 200 ml of basal medium, add:

- 20 ml Plasmanate
- 20 ml serum replacement
- 240 µl of human LIF for 10 ng/ml, or 480 µl for 20 ng/ml
- 120 µl of bFGF stock solution (final concentration 4 ng/ml) for 1× bFGF, or more if a higher concentration is desired
- Sterilize by 0.22-µm filtration

Gelatin

Dissolve 0.5 g of gelatin in 500 ml of warm (50–60°C) Milli-Q water. Cool to room temperature, and sterilize by 0.22-µm filtration. This makes 0.1% solution.

Mitomycin C

Add 2 ml of sterile Milli-Q water to a vial (2 mg) of lyophilized mitomycin C (Sigma, Cat. No. M 0503); this makes 1 mg/ml stock solution. The solution is light sensitive and is good for two weeks at 4°C.

SCREENING MEDIA COMPONENTS

It is important to be consistent with screening, aliquoting, and storage of the media components. Various lots of Serum Replacement, Plasmanate, and FBS should be screened, preferably on hES cells. The screening of Serum Replacement lots should be done prior to the first lot running out so that an evaluation of its qualities can be compared side by side to the previous lot. Some newly derived hES cells will die out with a change in lots at the initial stages.

Screening of FBS, Plasmanate, or Serum Replacement

This test is based on a published procedure for screening FBS lots for mouse ES cell work.[11] This approach can be used for screening any combination of reagents or for finding the best concentrations for media supplements. The quality of the reagents is assessed by counting the number of colonies, evaluating the morphology of the hES cells, and staining for alkaline phosphatase activity as detected with Vector Red Kit (Vector Laboratories, Burlingame, CA).

1. Prepare 12-well plates with PMEFs. For each lot tested, you will need at least 12 wells to vary the concentration of the component being tested from the working concentration to high enough concentrations to evaluate toxicity: 8%, 10%, 20%, and 30%. Each concentration is done in triplicate and compared to media components at working concentrations known to support hES cell growth.

2. Split hES cells onto 12-well plates with a ratio of 1:6–1:10. The difference in reagents will be more noticeable when the cells are started at low density; however, some cell lines grow very slowly and differentiate when they are kept at a low density. Therefore, adjust the splitting ratio to the specific hES cell line. Resuspend the cells in a small volume of basal medium and add equal volumes of cell suspension to each well of the test plate; pipette up and down in each well or slowly move the plate in perpendicular directions for even distribution of the cells. Do not rotate, as doing so will move most of the freshly added cells to center.

3. Change the medium daily and evaluate colony morphology under the microscope. Human ES cells grow in flat, tightly packed colonies with sharp refractory borders. The colonies appear deep red when stained for alkaline phosphatase activity. In differentiating colonies, the cells are more loosely packed, with diffuse borders, and are pinker. Usually, the difference in the conditions being tested becomes more obvious as colonies grow bigger; however, as the colonies grow larger, they can begin to touch each other and they tend to differentiate. Staining one of the triplicate wells for alkaline phosphatase activity prior to seeing signs of differentiation is advisable. Continue with the other wells in each set for another day or two before staining (see Fig. 41–1 for a sample test).

Adequate record keeping for all commercial and in-house prepared lots of reagents are helpful for troubleshooting should the hES cells begin to exhibit differentiated morphology.

Preparing PMEF Feeders

We grow our hES cells on PMEF feeders that have been mitomycin C treated to generate stable monolayers. The PMEFs are made by standard procedures using 12.5 days post-coitus (dpc) (ICR) mouse embryos.[12] The 12.5 dpc embryos are eviscerated, but the heads are left on during tissue disruption in trypsin; plating density is 1.5 embryos per 150-mm plate. PMEFs are expanded once after the initial plating (1:5 split) and then frozen (P1). The growth rate of PMEFs and their performance as feeders decreases as they go through multiple passages; therefore, thawed PMEFs are only passaged once (P2) for expansion purposes prior to mitomycin C treatment, at which point a new vial of PMEFs would be thawed.

MITOMYCIN C TREATMENT AND PLATING

Mitomycin C is added to the media of a confluent plate of PMEFs at a concentration of 10 µg/ml and incubated at 37°C for 3 hours. The cells are harvested by trypsinization and plated on gelatinized plates in PMEF growth medium. In serum-free hES cell growth media, the PMEFs may appear less confluent because of the spindle-like form the cells take on. To ensure a confluent monolayer, we recommend a plating density of 50,000–60,000 cells/cm². We prefer to use

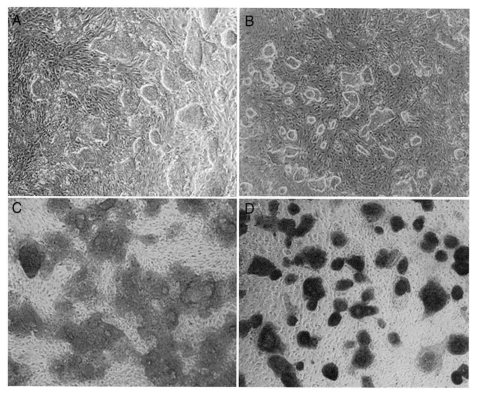

Figure 41-1. *Media testing.* (A and C) Comparison of 16% Serum Replacement with (B and D) 8% Serum Replacement and 8% Plasmanate. The quality of the media supplements is assessed by (A and B) evaluating the morphology of the colonies under phase contrast, as described in the text, followed by (C and D) staining for alkaline phosphatase activity. Note that although the morphology of the colonies in panels A and B is comparable, the activity of alkaline phosphatase is higher in (D) the medium with both Serum Replacement and Plasmanate. Magnification 40x.

plates of PMEFs no longer than 3–4 days after mitomycin C treatment.

Mechanical Passaging of hES Cell Colonies

Many established hES cell lines are passaged with collagenase or dispase in conjunction with mechanical dispersion. Mechanical dispersion can provide colonies of "perfect" morphology, as it permits one to selectively pick undifferentiated colonies or even undifferentiated parts from differentiated and overgrown colonies, but it is time-consuming and doesn't yield large numbers of cells, thus limiting expansion of the hES cell lines. Nevertheless, this procedure is invaluable at early stages of derivation or as a means of producing more homogeneously undifferentiated plates of cells for expansion or for adaptation to trypsin. It is also a tool for a "rescue operation" in critical situations when the success of salvaging a few colonies means saving an hES cell line.

MATERIALS NEEDED

Flame-Pulled Thin Capillaries

We use an alcohol or gas burner to pull presterilized glass Pasteur pipettes into finely drawn capillaries. The capillaries

are broken by hand into angled tips, the shape of a hypodermic needle. The diameter of the capillaries may vary, but the best results are achieved when they are 10–100 ES cells in diameter; this is how large the colony pieces are going to be. The choice of diameter depends on the operation: For instance, to do initial dispersion of an ICM outgrowth or to target undifferentiated parts of a colony, a diameter of 10–30 cells would be used.

Mouth-Controlled Suction Device

Similar to a mouth pipette used for embryo transfer, this device consists of a mouth piece (Meditech International, Cat. No. 15601 P), rubber tubing, and a 0.22-μm syringe filter with a rubber tubing adapter for the Pasteur pipette. It provides precision in all manipulations for colony dispersions.

MECHANICAL DISPERSION

The procedure is similar to vacuuming. Gentle dispersion of the colony is achieved by simultaneously cutting off the pieces with the angled end of the capillary, very lightly moving them off, and sucking them in. With the opening of the capillary positioned nearly horizontal to the bottom of the dish, begin moving from the sides toward the colony center, chopping off and gently sucking in each piece. The light suction helps to detach colony pieces and is applied at all times as you move from the periphery of the colony, collecting the colony parts. If the whole colony is detaching from the monolayer in one piece, it is probably differentiated and should be discarded.

When the desired number of colonies is dispersed, blow out the pieces into the same plate for ICM outgrowth dispersion or into a freshly prepared plate (see later sections of this chapter for details about preparing the receiving plate). To avoid having all the colonies stick to each other in the center of the plate, move the plate gently from side to side; do not swirl. (Fig. 41–2 shows examples of mechanically passaged cultures, pointing out parts of colonies that have differentiated and should be avoided when passaging the culture.)

Derivation of hES Cells

It is clear that many factors are not fully understood that influence whether an isolated ICM will produce an hES cell line. Some of the factors to consider are: at what stage the embryo was frozen and by what procedure, the length of time the embryo must be in culture to generate a blastocyst, the culture conditions, and the quality of both the ICM and the trophectoderm. When an embryo is ready for immunosurgery must be determined empirically, usually occurring between

day 5 and day 7. Any embryo that has undergone cavitation and has a relatively intact trophectoderm is a candidate for immunosurgery.

IMMUNOSURGERY

The process of immunosurgery is performed essentially as described by Solter and Knowles.[13] It involves removing the zona pellucida with acid Tyrode's solution, incubating the embryo in an antibody that binds to the trophectoderm and preferably not to the ICM cells (especially important for the embryos with nonintact trophectoderm), and then lysing the trophectoderm cells with complement. The dead cells that surround the ICM are removed by sucking the ICM through a narrow capillary. The isolated ICM is put on a prepared PMEF for further growth and dispersion.

Materials needed:

- Acid Tyrode's (Specialty Media, Cat. No. MR-004.D)
- Rabbit anti-human RBC antibody (purified IgG fraction, Inter-Cell Technologies, Hopewell, NJ, Cat. No. AG 28840): Aliquoted and stored at −80°C; freshly diluted 1:10 in hES cell derivation medium
- Complement (Sigma, Cat. No. S1639): Aliquoted and stored at −80°C; freshly diluted 1:10 in derivation medium

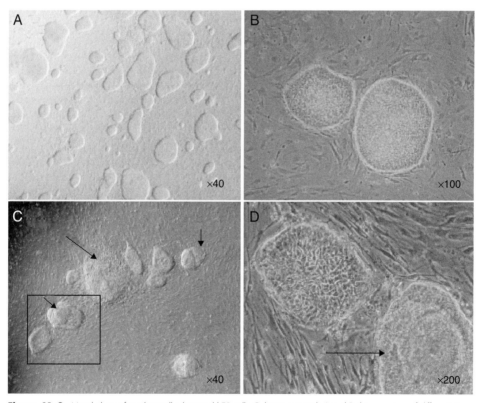

Figure 41–2. *Morphology of mechanically dispersed hES cells.* Colonies in panels A and B show no signs of differentiation. Note that the cells are small and tightly packed and that the colonies have sharp borders. In panel C, long arrow points to a differentiated colony that should not be dispersed; short arrows show partially differentiated colonies that can be dispersed and may produce undifferentiated colonies at the next passage. Panel D shows higher magnification of the framed colonies in panel C, shifted 90 degrees. The arrow points to a partially differentiated colony, which has become multilayered in the middle. The other colony is undifferentiated and is similar to the colonies shown in panels A and B.

- Capillaries for embryo transfer: Thinly drawn capillaries (approximately the diameter of the ICM) for the trophectoderm removal

Prepared Mitomycin C–Treated PMEF Plates

For the initial ICM outgrowth, change the medium on a four-well plate of mitomycin C-treated PMEFs to hES cell derivation medium the night before the immunosurgery to let it get conditioned by the PMEFs, final volume of 250 µl.

Instead of conditioning it overnight, the derivation medium can be supplemented with 30% of an hES cell-conditioned medium. To collect an hES cell-conditioned medium, add medium to a near-confluent culture of hES cells with good morphology (see Fig. 41–2A for an example of colony density and morphology), leave for 24 hours, collect the medium, filter.

IMMUNOSURGERY PROCEDURE

1. Each embryo is processed separately. A dish is prepared with a series of 30-µl microdrops, three for each step: acid Tyrode's, anti-human RBC antibody, complement, and three drops of derivation medium for each wash. The drops are covered with embryo-tested mineral oil and are equilibrated in the CO_2 incubator for 60 minutes.
2. Under the dissecting microscope, transfer the embryo into the first acid Tyrode's drop for a quick (1–2 seconds) wash, then move into the second drop. Watch the embryo closely; as soon as the zona pellucida thins and is nearly digested, move the embryo into the next series of hES cell medium drops. Move the embryos through the first antibody drop into the second and third drops, then put the dish into the incubator for 30 minutes.
3. Transfer the embryos through three drops of derivation medium and through three drops of the complement solution as described previously; incubate in the last drop of complement in the CO_2 incubator for 15 minutes and check for any "bubbling" trophoblast cells. If no cells show signs of lysis, or if only a few cells are bubbling, continue the incubation and recheck in 5 minutes. The embryo should be transferred to the drop of derivation medium as soon as all trophoblast cells are lysed or if no new bubbling cells appear after rechecking; the total incubation in complements should not exceed 30 minutes.
4. Gently pass the embryo through the opening of a thinly drawn capillary (about the diameter of the ICM); the lysed trophectoderm cells should detach after 1–2 passes.
5. Wash the ICM in the drops with derivation medium and place into the prepared well of a 4-well plate. The ICM should attach within 24 hours.

ICM DISPERSION

At early stages of derivation, we recommend doing the first dispersion as soon as at least two to three colony pieces can be obtained from the initial outgrowth (Fig. 41–3). The dispersed colonies may be left in the same well or moved to a new well. If there are only a few colony pieces (one to five), they should be placed close to each other but with enough space to permit growth. It is better to disperse colonies before they grow into contact with each other and prior to signs of differentiation, such as becoming multilayered.

When the colony growth is slow, change 2/3 of the medium every 2–3 days to keep it conditioned at all times. As more colonies appear, change 2/3 of the medium daily and increase volume to 500 µl/well of a 4-well plate.

Even if an original colony looks differentiated or comes off as a single piece, when replated, it usually gives an outgrowth of hES cells. When doing the initial dispersion, a part of the original colony should be left untouched as a backup, especially if the picked pieces are transferred into a new well. Expect it to grow back in 1–2 days; the new outgrowth can be picked and recombined with previously dispersed colonies. Multiple harvests can be obtained from the initial outgrowth. It is critical at this stage to expand the number of colonies slowly and steadily. See Fig. 41–4 as an example of the length of time between dispersions and appearance of the cultures during the process of derivation. In this case, no immunosurgery was done because the trophectoderm was not sufficiently intact.

Maintenance of Established hES Cell Cultures

Usually, once a steady growth of colonies is reached, the use of the hES cell derivation medium is discontinued and the cultures are maintained in hES cell growth medium. For established cultures, remove 1/3 of the medium from growing culture, put it on a new PMEF dish, and add 2/3 volume of fresh medium. Change 2/3 of the medium daily; the medium should not turn yellow. Cultures should be expanded gradually by the progression from relatively sparsely populated 4-well dishes to confluent 4-well dishes to 35-mm dishes. Throughout the process, the cultures should be observed daily, differentiated colonies can be removed, and undifferentiated colonies should be dispersed as necessary (see Fig. 41–5 for approaches to be used for dispersion of colonies with different morphologies).

By the time the cells are growing on a 35-mm dish or a 6-well plate, it is usually sufficient to disperse 50–100 average-sized colonies to populate a new well. In 1–2 days, it may be necessary to disperse some of the larger colonies, leaving the pieces in the same well. Usually, mechanical passaging needs to be done every 5–6 days, but several larger colonies may need to be dispersed daily.

ADAPTATION OF hES CELLS TO TRYPSIN

Our experience with trypsinization of 17 hES cell lines, established in our laboratory, as well as of H9 cells[2] demonstrates that after the initial adaptation of the lines to trypsin, this procedure can be robust and yield large quantities of hES cells that exhibit all the properties of pluripotential cells. Trypsinized cells retain undifferentiated colony morphology, express characteristic molecular markers (i.e., *Oct-4*, alkaline phosphatase, SSEA-3, SSEA-4, TRA-1-60, and TRA-1-81), differentiate into three germ layers *in vitro* and in teratomas, and maintain normal karyotypes.

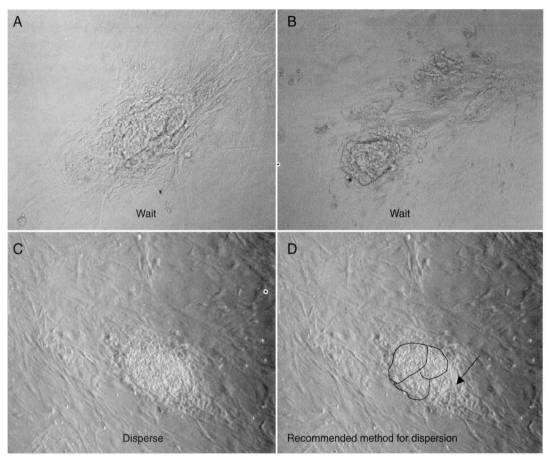

Figure 41-3. *Initial ICM outgrowth.* The initial outgrowth of the ICM rarely shows typical ES colony morphology and often includes many differentiated-looking cells. When no obvious ES cell-like colonies large enough for dispersion can be located, more time is required before the first colony dispersion can be done. (A and B) The initial ICM outgrowth of two future hES lines. At this stage, when the dispersion is attempted, the outgrowth and the PMEF monolayer come up together, so it is better to wait before dispersing. (C) The ICM is ready for dispersion when a colony of ES-like cells is large enough to be dispersed into several pieces, leaving 20-50% of the outgrowth on the original plate for future regrowth. (D) Lines transcribe the number of pieces recommended for the dispersion of this colony. A narrow capillary is used, and a small part of colony is left untouched for regrowth (arrow). Magnification 100x.

Newly derived hES cells may be successfully passaged with trypsin as early as passage 2–3 from a 4-well plate. However, trypsinization is not always successful, and several attempts may be necessary before the cells are adapted to trypsin; always keep a backup well of mechanically passaged cells.

The safest approach is to begin with a subconfluent 35-mm well of a 6-well plate of colonies with good morphology. Mechanically pick 50–100 colonies and transfer them into a new well as a backup. Differentiated colonies may be removed mechanically prior to trypsinization. Trypsinize the remaining colonies in the original well and plate into the same diameter well. The cells should be ready for the next split in 5–7 days (Fig. 41–6). For the second trypsinization, split 1:3. After this step, the cells can usually be trypsinized routinely without problems, but a mechanical backup always should be maintained until the cells are frozen and the test vials are successfully thawed.

Trypsinization

Generally, hES cells recover from trypsinization better when they are not dispersed to single cells but remain as small clumps of approximately 2–20 cells. The procedure works best when hES cell colonies are dispersed by a combination of enzymatic digestion and pipetting; we do the pipetting before the PMEF monolayer and the colonies turn into a single-cell suspension. The time in trypsin required for the cells to detach varies depending on the hES cell density, degree of differentiation, age of the culture, temperature of trypsin, etc. Therefore, instead of providing a fixed incubation time in trypsin, we recommend checking the appearance of the hES culture under the microscope and empirically working out the best incubation time for each plate (Fig. 41–7).

1. Warm the trypsin in a 37°C water bath; keep it warm until ready for the procedure.
2. Rinse the cells with PBS two times (1–2 ml per 35-mm dish).

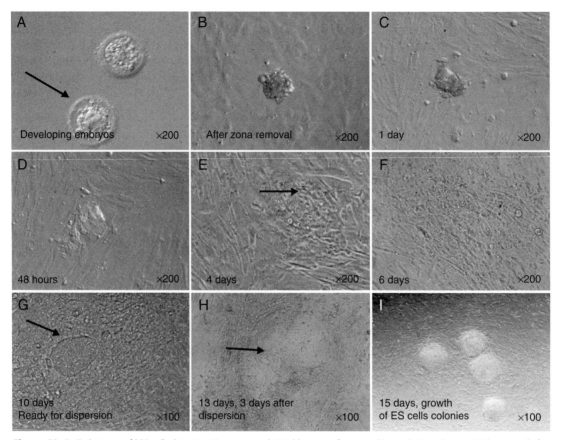

Figure 41–4. *Early stages of hES cells derivation.* (Arrow in panel A) A blastocyst of poor quality, grade 3, underwent (B) the removal of the zona pellucida. (C) The next day, after being plated on the PMEF monolayer, it has attached. (D) Forty-eight hours after plating, the ICM appears smaller, possibly because of some cell death. (E) Four days after plating, an outgrowing group of cells is visible with some small cells in the middle (arrow), (F) which become less visible 2 days later. (G) Ten days after plating, a small colony of ES-like cells (arrow) has formed within the large group of differentiated-looking cells and is now large enough for dispersion. (H) Original ICM outgrowth 3 days after it was dispersed; note regrowth of small ES-like cells in the cleared area (arrow), which are ready for another dispersion. (I) Formation of ES cell colonies from the recombined first and second dispersion.

3. Add 1 ml of trypsin to each 35-mm dish. Incubate in the hood at room temperature for several minutes, usually 2–5 minutes, frequently checking the cells under the microscope. The cells are ready for mechanical dispersion when the PMEFs begin to shrink; the colonies should round up but remain attached. Some cells may begin to detach and float (Fig. 41–7A and 41–7B).

4. Prepare a centrifuge tube with 10 ml of warm PMEF medium.

Note: It is necessary to use PMEF medium to inactivate the trypsin because our hES cell medium is serum free.
Tilt the plate and begin to gently pipette the trypsin solution up and down with an automatic 1-ml pipetteman (Gilson type), pouring it over the cell monolayer at an angle. Properly digested cells should detach easily, leaving visible clear gaps in the monolayer where the trypsin solution was poured. If no such gaps appear, leave it for another 1–2 minutes and test again. Expect the monolayer to detach

after several repetitions. On cell cultures less than 5 days old, you should be able to completely disperse the monolayer, but if the culture is older or very dense, there may be some undigested material that can be discarded. Usually, it takes 5–10 pipetting strokes to break the colonies into small clumps of cells (see Fig. 41–7C for the approximate clump size). Extensive pipetting should be avoided.

5. Transfer the trypsinized cell suspension into the prepared centrifuge tube; centrifuge for 5 minutes at 160 g.

6. Aspirate the medium, and resuspend the pellet in hES cell medium, again avoiding extensive pipetting to preserve small cell aggregates and to replate at the desired ratio. The colonies should become visible in 1–2 days, depending on the splitting ratio and the clump size (Fig. 41–7D).

Human ES cultures passaged with trypsin can be maintained in an undifferentiated state. However, if conditions are unfavorable because of changes in media quality, a splitting

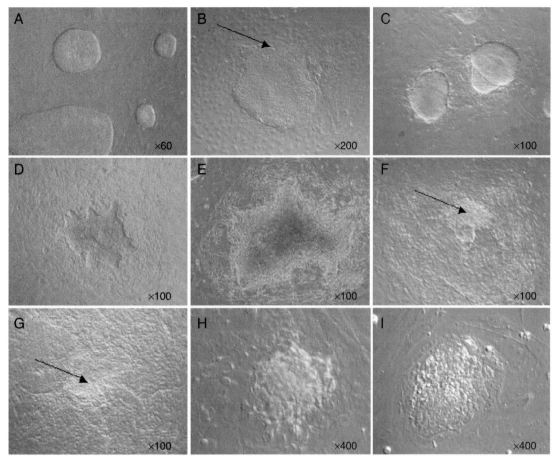

Figure 41–5. *Approaches for dispersion of colonies with different morphologies.* Various morphologies of hES cell colonies encountered at early stages of derivation when mechanical dispersion can be the tool of choice used to selectively pick undifferentiated colony parts. (A) All colonies are undifferentiated and can be mechanically passaged. (B) The colony that has few signs of differentiation (arrow) and is surrounded by differentiated cells; the undifferentiated part is easily separated from surrounding differentiated cells. (C) Partially differentiated, multilayered colonies (the centers are thickened and yellowish in color) can be mechanically dispersed into several small pieces but may result in both differentiated and undifferentiated colonies. (D–F) All these colonies are more extensively differentiated; a thin layer of differentiated cells covers them like a veil. They can be cut into pieces through the top cell layer and passaged, and they may yield undifferentiated colonies. (G–I) These colonies are badly differentiated; the arrow on panel G shows A group of undifferentiated cells within the large differentiated area. If this one must be saved, wait a few days for this group to increase in size.

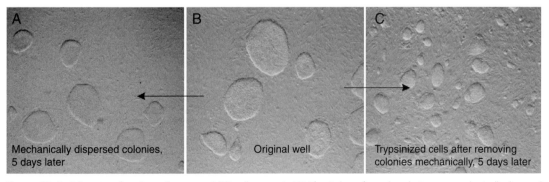

Figure 41–6. *Adaptation of mechanically passaged hES cells to trypsin.* (A) After 5 days of growth, colonies were mechanically dispersed and transferred to a fresh plate of PMEFs. (B) Morphologically, they are similar to the original plate. (C) The remaining colonies in the original plate, which were passaged with trypsin and plated onto a plate of the same growth area, show actively growing colonies and will probably be ready for passaging in 1–2 days.

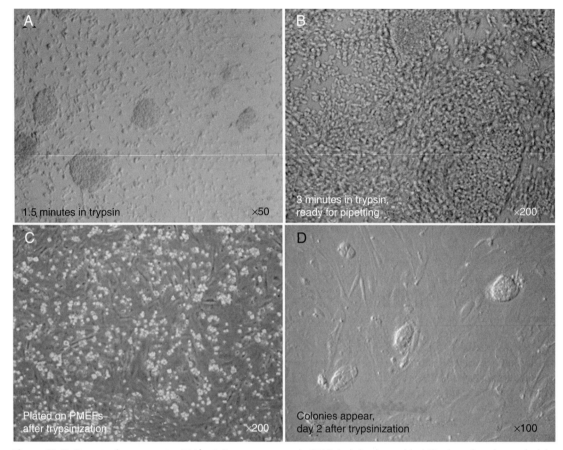

Figure 41–7. *Passaging by trypsinization.* (A) After 1.5 minutes in trypsin, the PMEFs look shrunken and the hES colonies have loosened a little. (B) After 3 minutes in trypsin at higher magnification, the colonies are less compact; this is a good time to begin pipetting. Please note that depending on the density of the colonies, the days after passaging, and the degree of differentiation, the time required to reach this stage may vary and needs to be worked out empirically. (C) Suspension of hES cells after replating onto fresh PMEFs. Note that most cells are in small cell aggregates. (D) Small colonies begin to appear on day 2 after plating (at a 1:3 ratio). The time at which the first colonies are seen may vary depending on the splitting ratio and the size of the cell aggregates.

ratio that is too high or low, or problems with PMEF quality, the cultures can have a degree of differentiation that should be evaluated prior to the next trypsinization (Fig. 41–8).

Freezing hES Cells

Many of the established hES cells have low recovery rates upon thawing, as low as 0.1–1%. This may be because of the method of passaging the cells. Mechanical picking or using collagenase dispersion usually results in large cell aggregates, which presumably do not get cryopreserved as efficiently as smaller clumps. Trypsinized cells in our lab have a recovery rate of about 10–20% or higher and do not require more complicated procedures like vitrification (Fig. 41–9).

FREEZING MEDIUM

The best recovery rate was observed in freezing medium consisting of 90% FBS–10% DMSO. However, *Oct-4*

expression in the thawed cells was lower than in cells frozen in hES cell growth medium with 10% DMSO. Nevertheless, by the next passage, the expression and distribution of Oct-4 and other markers of undifferentiated cells were indistinguishable between these two freezing conditions. We routinely use the 90% FBS–10% DMSO medium.

FREEZING PROTOCOL

Select a high-quality confluent culture with good morphology for freezing. We also recommend taking a picture of a sample field and staining for molecular markers characteristic of undifferentiated hES cells for future reference.

Materials needed:

- Chilled freezing medium: 90% FBS, 10% DMSO
- Cryovials, labeled with the line, passage number, and date
- Cryovial rack (rack with ice reservoir by Corning)
- Styrofoam rack from packaging for 15-ml centrifuge tubes
- −80°C freezer

446

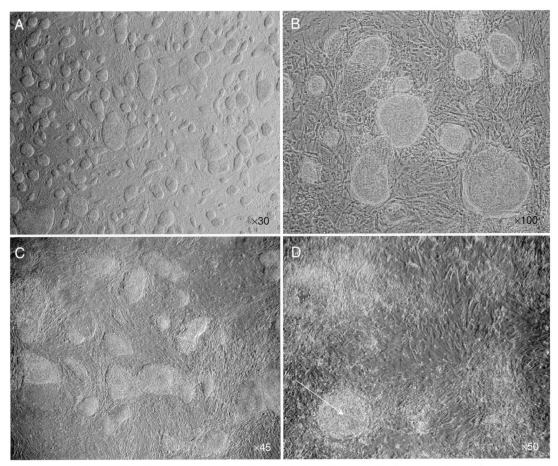

Figure 41-8. *Evaluation of the culture prior to trypsinization. (A and B) Mostly undifferentiated hES cells are ready for trypsinization. (C) The colonies are a little overgrown and show signs of differentiation but still can be safely passaged with trypsin. (D) Badly differentiated hES cells (an arrow points to a colony) can still be rescued by mechanically picking colony pieces and passaging.*

1. Trypsinize the cells; centrifuge in PMEF medium (see earlier explanation).
2. Resuspend the pellet in the cold freezing medium. We recommend freezing one confluent 35-mm plate per vial in 0.5 ml of freezing medium. Work quickly and keep the cells on ice after the addition of the freezing medium.
3. Aliquot cell suspension into prechilled freezing vials and sandwich the vials between two Styrofoam racks; tape to prevent the two racks from separating and transfer to a −80°C freezer overnight. Transfer the cryovials to liquid nitrogen for long-term storage.

Thawing hES Cells

Thawing hES cells is a relatively simple procedure. The main rule to follow is to do everything quickly.

PREPARATION

1. Prepare mitomycin C–treated PMEFs a day before thawing.
2. Make thawing medium. We use 70% hES cell growth medium supplemented with 2× hLIF and 8 ng/ml bFGF with 30% hES cell- or PMEF-conditioned medium.

3. Change the medium on the PMEF plate to the thawing medium; equilibrate in the CO_2 incubator for 1 hour. For 35-mm plates, use 1.5 ml medium; for four-well plates, use 0.5 ml medium per well.
4. Prepare a 50-ml conical tube with 10–15 ml of warm hES cell growth medium.

THAWING

1. Thaw the vial in a 37°C water bath, constantly agitating while ensuring that the neck of the vial is above the water level. Check the contents of the vial after about 40 seconds and at 10-second intervals until only a small piece of ice remains.
2. Quickly spray the vial with 70% isopropanol, then using a 1-ml pipetteman, add warm hES cell medium to the contents of the vial dropwise with gentle agitation. Do it quickly but very gently. Immediately transfer the contents into the prepared 50-ml tube with warm hES cell medium; centrifuge at 160 g for 5 minutes.
3. Remove the medium completely without touching the pellet.
4. Add 0.5 ml of hES cell thawing medium, gently resuspend the cells using a 1-ml pipetteman (2–4 repetitions), and

447

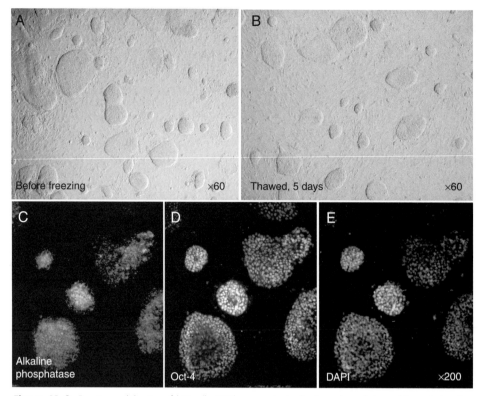

Figure 41–9. *Freezing and thawing of hES cells.* (A) The approximate density and morphology of the colonies of hES cells at freezing. (B) When thawed onto the same diameter plate, the colonies should be ready for the next split in 5–7 days. (C and D) Thawed hES cells show high expression of *Oct-4* and alkaline phosphatase. (E) same field as C and D, DAPI-stained.

transfer to prepared PMEF plates with equilibrated hES cell thawing medium. Spread the cells evenly throughout the well by moving the plate several times in two directions at 90 degrees to each other; avoid swirling.

5. Check the cells the next day; if there are many dead cells or the medium has changed color, change ⅔ of the medium; otherwise, do not change it for another day.

6. The colonies usually begin to appear in 3–4 days and can be ready for splitting in 5–10 days (Fig. 41–9).

hES Cell Quality Control

Although morphology of hES cells is often used for evaluating the quality of the culture and its readiness for passaging or freezing, this criteria alone cannot be used for an assessment of ES cell pluripotency. Staining for the expression of *Oct-4* or alkaline phosphatase even in colonies of "perfect" morphology can result in one or both of these markers appearing in the cells only at the periphery of the colony. It is important, therefore, to regularly assess the cells by analyzing the expression of markers of pluripotent cells. We look at *Oct-4,* SSEA-3, SSEA-4, TRA 1-60, and TRA 1-81 by immunostaining, or we perform an enzyme assay for alkaline phosphatase. The procedures for such assays and available antibodies are described elsewhere.

ACKNOWLEDGMENTS

We gratefully acknowledge the financial support of the Howard Hughes Medical Institution and the guidance and encouragement of Dr. Douglas Melton, the recipient of this HHMI grant, without whom this work could not have been accomplished. We would also like to thank our collaborators at Boston IVF, especially Dr. Jeannine Witmyer, for contributing their invaluable experience in the culture and evaluation of early embryos. A special thank you to Jocelyn Atienza and Chad Cowan for their ongoing work in developing and characterizing the hES cell lines reported on in this chapter. We are grateful to Drs. Martin Pera and Susan Lanzendorf for sharing helpful tips on derivation and maintenance of hES cells. Lastly, we would like to thank Dr. Andy McMahon for his generous support throughout this project. Jill would like to say a special thank you to Andy for his patience and understanding of the time-consuming process involved in the development of these techniques.

REFERENCES

1. Cowan, C.A., Klimanskaya, I., McMahon, J., Atienza, J., Witmyer, J., Zucker, J.P., Wang, S., Morton, C.C., McMahon, A.P., Powers, D., and Melton, D.A. (2004). Derivation of embryonic stem cell lines from human blastocysts. *New Engl. J. Med.* **350,** 1353–1356.

2. Robertson, E.J. (ed.) (1987). "Teratocarcinomas and Embryonic Stem Cells: A Practical Approach." IRL Press, Oxford.

3. Thomson, J.A., Itskovitz-Eldor, J., Shapiro, S.S., Waknitz, M.A., Swiergiel, J.J., Marshall, V.S., and Jones, J.M. (1998). Embryonic stem cell lines derived from human blastocysts. *Science* **282,** 1145–1147. [erratum in *Science* (1998). **282(5395),** 1827].

4. Amit, M., Carpenter, M.K., Inokuma, M.S., Chiu, C.P., Harris, C.P., Waknitz, M.A., Itskovitz-Eldor, J., and Thomson, J.A. (2000). Clonally derived human embryonic stem cell lines maintain pluripotency and proliferative potential for prolonged periods of culture. *Dev. Biol.* **227,** 271–278.

5. Thomson, J.A., Kalishman, J., Golos, T.G., Durning, M., Harris, C.P., Becker, R.A., Hearn, J.P. (1995). Isolation of a primate embryonic stem cell line. *Proc. Natl. Acad. Sci. USA* **92,** 7844–7848.

6. Reubinoff, B.E., Pera, M.F., Fong, C.Y., Trounson, A., and Bongso, A. (2000). Embryonic stem cell lines from human blastocysts: somatic differentiation *in vitro. Nat. Biotechnol.* **18,** 399–404. [erratum in *Natl. Biotechnol.* (2000). **18(5),** 559].

7. Richards, M., Fong, C.Y., Chan, W.K., Wong, P.C., and Bongso, A. (2002). Human feeders support prolonged undifferentiated growth of human inner cell masses and embryonic stem cells. *Nat. Biotechnol.* **20,** 933–936.

8. Lanzendorf, S.E., Boyd, C.A., Wright, D.L., Muasher, S., Oehninger, S., and Hodgen, G.D. (2001). Use of human gametes obtained from anonymous donors for the production of human embryonic stem cell lines. *Fertil. Steril.* **76,** 132–137.

9. Xu, C., Inokuma, M.S., Denham, J., Golds, K., Kundu, P., Gold, J.D., and Carpenter, M.K. (2001). Feeder-free growth of undifferentiated human embryonic stem cells. *Nat. Biotechnol.* **19,** 971–974.

10. Lebkowski, J.S., Gold, J., Xu, C., Funk, W., Chiu, C.P., and Carpenter, M.K. (2001). Human embryonic stem cells: culture, differentiation, and genetic modification for regenerative medicine applications. *Cancer J.* **7(Suppl. 2),** S83–S93.

11. Robertson, E.J. (ed.) (1987). "Teratocarcinomas and Embryonic Stem Cells: A Practical Approach," pp. 74. IRL Press, Oxford.

12. Robertson, E.J. (ed.) (1987). "Teratocarcinomas and Embryonic Stem Cells: A Practical Approach," pp. 77. IRL Press, Oxford.

13. Solter, D., and Knowles, B.B. (1975). Immunosurgery of mouse blastocyst. *PNAS* **72,** 5099–5102.

Isolation and Maintenance of Murine Embryonic Germ Cell Lines

Gabriela Durcova-Hills and Dame Anne McLaren

Historical Introduction

Primordial germ cells (PGCs) are embryonic precursors of gametes (sperm in males, eggs in females). Early attempts to culture isolated mouse PGCs were performed under simple conditions on a plastic or glass substrate in standard culture media. Female PGCs that had already entered meiosis survived for a week or more and made some progress through meiotic prophase, but earlier stages failed to survive.[1] When mouse fibroblast feeder cells were used as substrate, migratory and early postmigratory PGCs survived and proliferated for a few days.[2] Many factors have been shown to increase the proliferation of PGCs *in vitro,* such as leukaemia inhibitory factor (LIF), oncostatin M, interleukin-6, and ciliary neurotrophic factor (reviewed by Buehr[3]). Stem cell factor (SCF) is important for the survival of PGCs.[4] PGCs cocultured with mouse feeder cells that express SCF (Sl[4]-m220 or STO) in medium supplemented with LIF and fibroblast growth factor-2 (FGF-2) proliferated indefinitely and generated pluripotent cell lines[5,6] that resembled embryonic stem (ES) cell lines (see Chapter 39 of this volume). These "immortalized" pluripotent cells, termed embryonic germ (EG) cells, contributed to all cell lineages in chimeras, including the germ line.[7,8] EG cell lines have been derived from PGCs isolated from embryos at 8.0 and 8.5 days postcoitum (dpc) shortly after the establishment of the germ line, at 9.5 dpc during migration in the wall of the hindgut, and after entering the genital ridges between 11.5 and 12.5 dpc.[5–10] PGCs isolated from older embryos failed to generate EG cell lines when cultured under similar conditions. EG cell lines have been derived from different mouse strains, including 129Sv, C57BL/6, and strains of mixed background.

The first marker used for PGC identification *in vivo* and *in vitro* was tissue nonspecific alkaline phosphatase (AP).[11] Later cell-surface markers such as SSEA1,[12] 4C9,[13] EMA1,[14] and c-kit[15] were used to identify PGCs in mouse embryos as well as intracellular proteins including mouse vasa homolog,[16] germ cell nuclear antigen 1,[17] and OCT 3/4.[18] PGCs have been partially purified from the surrounding somatic cells by pricking the genital ridges,[19] by using antibodies for immunoaffinity purification,[20] or by magnetic or FACS cell sorting.[21,22]

The methods described in this chapter are those that have been used successfully in our laboratory for several years. Other laboratories use slightly different procedures that also work well.

Derivation of EG Cell Lines from PGCs

The culture conditions for deriving EG cell lines are the same for PGCs from embryos of different ages. However, the efficiency of derivation of new EG cell lines is considerably lower with 12.5- than with 8.5- or 11.5-dpc PGCs. Derivation of EG cells involves the following steps:

1. Isolation of tissue containing PGCs.
2. Purification of PGCs from somatic cells by magnetic cell sorting (optional).
3. Culture of PGCs leading to the derivation of new EG cell lines.
4. Maintenance of derived EG cell lines.
5. Characterisation of derived EG cell lines.

ISOLATION OF TISSUES CONTAINING PGCS

Reagents–Equipment

- *Plastics:* 10-cm tissue culture dishes (Nunc) are used for dissection of foetuses, and 1.5-ml Eppendorf tubes are used for collecting tissue containing PGCs. Sterile tips.
- *Dissecting medium:* Ca^{2+}/Mg^{2+}-free phosphate-buffered saline (PBS, Invitrogen Corporation, Cat. No. 20012-019) containing 10% foetal calf serum (FCS, Sigma).
- *Trypsin–EDTA:* Use 0.25% trypsin, 1-mM EDTA·4Na (Invitrogen Corporation, Cat. No. 25200-056).
- *Equipment:* Stereomicroscope (Zeiss), forceps with sharp tips for dissection (sterilized prior to use by autoclaving or wiping with 70% alcohol), and a bench-top centrifuge.

Isolation of Tissue Containing PGCs from 8.5 dpc Foetuses

1. Using forceps, dissect the embryo from decidua and extraembryonic membranes in the dissecting medium.
2. Remove the posterior part of the embryo, starting from the end of the primitive streak and continuing to the base of the

allantois, using sharp forceps. PGCs are located at the base of the allantois.

3. Collect PGC-containing fragments with a blue tip into a 1.5-ml Eppendorf tube containing dissecting medium. The whole dissection procedure should not exceed 1 hour. If longer times are required, the Eppendorf tube containing samples should be kept on ice.

Isolation of Genital Ridges from 11.5 or 12.5 dpc Foetuses

1. Dissect the embryos from their extraembryonic membranes. Cut the head off each embryo in the dissecting medium by using sharp forceps. Make a cut along the ventral midline of embryos. Remove the internal organs.

2. The urogenital ridges (genital ridges with mesonephros) lie on the dorsal wall of the embryo fragment by the dorsal aorta. Remove them, for example by holding the dorsal aorta at the anterior part of the embryo and peeling off both the aorta and the urogenital ridges. Collect the urogenital ridges in a 5-cm tissue culture dish filled with dissecting medium.

3. Separate the genital ridges from the mesonephros by using a needle or sharp forceps.

4. Collect the genital ridges in a 1.5-ml Eppendorf tube containing dissecting medium. By 12.5 dpc, female and male genital ridges can be distinguished by their morphology. Male 12.5 dpc genital ridges have "stripes" (i.e., testicular cords), whereas female genital ridges are "spotted."

MAGNETIC CELL SORTING OF PGCS

Reagents–Equipment

- *MiniMACS Starting Kit:* The kit (Miltenyi Biotec, Cat. No.130-042-101) contains 1 MiniMACS separating unit, 1 MACS multistand, 25 MS columns, one 1-ml unit of MACS microbeads (rat–antimouse IgM). We use as primary antibody TG1 (given to us by Dr. Peter Beverly), which recognises cell surface antigen SSEA1. Antibody against SSEA1 is available commercially from the Developmental Studies Hybridoma Bank, University of Iowa.
- *Sorting Medium:* Cell sorting is done in cold Dulbecco's Modified Eagle Medium (DMEM, Invitrogen Corporation, Cat. No. 41965-039) supplemented with 2% FCS, Penicillin G/Streptomycin (Invitrogen Corporation, Cat. No. 15140-122), L-glutamine (200 mM, Invitrogen Corporation, Cat. no. 25030-024).
- *Equipment:* Laminar flow hood, pipette aid or equivalent, and a cold room.

This method is adapted from that published by Pesce and De Felici.[21]

1. Collect 11.5 dpc genital ridges as described previously. Wash them twice with PBS to remove the traces of FCS (FCS inhibits the activity of trypsin).

2. Incubate the genital ridges in trypsin–EDTA for 5–10 minutes at 37°C in a water bath and then pipette with a yellow tip to obtain a single-cell suspension.

3. Add 500-µl cold sorting medium. Centrifuge at 1000 rpm for 5 minutes.

4. Resuspend the pellet in 500-µl cold sorting medium to obtain a single cell suspension. Remove small clumps if present in the cell suspension.

5. Add 50 µl of TG 1 antibody (the amount of primary antibody must be checked with each new lot of antibody) and incubate on a plate shaker for 45 minutes at 4°C.

6. Centrifuge at 700 rpm for 3 minutes. Resuspend the pellet in 500-µl cold sorting medium.

7. Add 20 µl of magnetically coated secondary antibody (microbeads conjugated with rat–antimouse IgM) and incubate on a plate shaker for 25 minutes at 4°C.

8. Under sterile conditions (e.g., in a laminar flow hood), pipette the magnetically coated cell suspension on top of the prewashed column. The column is washed with 1000 µl of the cold sorting medium. Do not allow the column to dry off.

9. Collect the negative fraction (i.e., cells that were not magnetically stained).

10. Wash the column with 500–1000 µl of the cold sorting medium. Then remove the column from the magnet and flush magnetically stained cells into a 1.5-ml Eppendorf tube with 1 ml of the cold sorting medium by using the plunger. Collect as a positive fraction.

11. Determine the purity of the positive fraction. Stain 50 µl from the positive fraction with AP solution (See the section "AP Staining" and Fig. 42–1). Count the number of AP+ cells with a haemocytometer. Seed cells from the positive fraction onto Sl⁴-m220 or STO cells in medium used for derivation of EG cell lines.

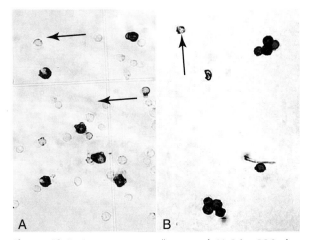

Figure 42–1. *Immunomagnetic cell sorting of 11.5-dpc PGCs from surrounding somatic cells. (A) Cell suspension of PGCs and somatic cells before cell sorting. PGCs are identified by AP activity (in black). Somatic cells (arrows) are negative for AP activity. (B) PGCs were sorted by magnetic beads. The purity of sorted PGCs is checked by AP activity. One somatic cell (arrow) was observed. (Please see CD-ROM for color version of this figure.)*

CULTURE OF PGCs LEADING TO THE DERIVATION OF NEW EG CELL LINES

Reagents–Equipment

- *PGC growth medium:* This culture medium is supplemented with LIF and FGF-2 (termed also bFGF) (see Table 42–1).
- *EG cell growth medium:* This culture medium is supplemented only with LIF.
- *FCS:* FCS is tested to support the growth of normal ES cells and EG cells.
- *Growth factors:* LIF (Chemicon International) used at concentration of 1000–1200 units in 1 ml of culture medium. FGF-2 (Invitrogen) is dissolved in PBS at the concentration of 10 μg in 1 ml of PBS. Aliquots are stored at −20°C.
- *Mitomycin C:* Make a stock solution of mitomycin C (Sigma, Cat. No. M 4287) by dissolving 2 mg in 1 ml of tissue culture water by vortexing for 30 minutes. Aliquots are stored at −20°C.
- *Gelatin:* Make 0.1% gelatin (Swine Skin type II, Sigma, G 2500) solution in water.
- *Plastics:* Four-well culture dishes (Nunc) are used for primary culture of PGCs, and 10-cm culture dishes are used for culturing feeder cells. Also used are 15-ml Falcon tubes.
- *Feeder cells:* Two cell lines used as feeder cells support the EG cell-like colonies arising during primary culture. Sl^4-m220 is a bone-marrow stromal cell line that stably expresses only the membrane-bound form of stem cell factor. STO cells express both the membrane and the soluble form of stem cell factor. Primary mouse embryonic fibroblasts (MEFs) derived from 12.5 dpc foetuses are also used as feeder cells (see Chapter 39) for secondary and subsequent subcultures.
- *Equipment:* Standard humidified tissue culture incubator (37°C, 5%CO$_2$ in air), laminar flow, liquid nitrogen storage, finely drawn Pasteur pipettes, and forceps.

TABLE 42–1
EG Cell Growth Medium

Component	Volume added for 40 ml
DMEM	32 ml
FCS	6 ml
L-glutamine 200 mM	0.4 ml
NEAA 100 mM	0.4 ml
Penicillin G + streptomycin	0.4 ml
Sodium pyruvate 100 mM	0.4 ml
β-Mercaptoethanol	0.4 ml
LIF	1200 units/ml
FGF-2^a	25 ng/ml

^{a}FGF-2 is added to this medium during the primary culture of PGCs.

Primary Culture

1. Seventy-two hours before starting the culture of PGCs, Sl^4-m220 cells are plated into five pregelatinised 10-cm culture dishes.
2. Treat subconfluent Sl^4-m220 cells with 12.5 μl of mitomycin C from the stock solution in 5 ml of feeder culture medium for 2 hours in the incubator.
3. Wash the feeder cells three times with PBS to remove the traces of mitomycin C.
4. Incubate cells with trypsin for 5 minutes at room temperature and pipette with blue tip to harvest a single-cell suspension.
5. Collect trypsinized cells in a 15-ml conical tube containing 9 ml of the feeder growth medium to inactivate and dilute the trypsin solution.
6. Centrifuge at 1000 rpm for 5 minutes, then remove solution.
7. Resuspend Sl^4-m220 cells in fresh feeder culture medium and plate at the density of 5 × in pregelatinised wells of four-well culture dishes.
8. The next day, first wash Sl^4-m220 cells with PBS then replace with the PGC growth medium supplemented with both LIF and FGF-2.
9. Collect tissues containing PGCs in a sterile 1.5-ml Eppendorf tube containing PBS supplemented with 10% FCS. When the isolation is completed, wash tissues twice with PBS.
10. Add 100–200 μl of trypsin (the volume depends on the amount of tissue) and incubate in a water bath at 37°C for 5–10 minutes. Cell suspension is obtained by pipetting tissues with a blue and then with a yellow tip. Add 800 μl of culture medium to trypsinized cell suspension.
11. Centrifuge as described previously. Resuspend the pellet in 500–1000 μl of the PGC growth medium. Plate cell suspension into Sl^4-m220-containing wells of four-well culture dishes. Plate approximately 0.5 of 8.5-dpc embryo or 0.2–0.25 of one 11.5-dpc genital ridge into one well of a four-well dish. Two genital ridges from 12.5 dpc may be cultured in a 35-mm culture dish.
12. Culture at 37°C, 5% CO$_2$ in air. After 2 days, change the PGC growth medium for medium freshly supplemented with both LIF and FGF-2. Then change the culture medium every day.
13. By 8 to 10 days of primary culture, small colonies with EG cell-like morphology are observed (Fig. 42–2). Mitotically inactive primary mouse feeder cells are prepared. After 2 more days of culture, colonies with EG cell like morphology are ready to be transferred into a new well of a 4-well dish.

Secondary and Following Sub-Cultures

14. Pick EG cell-like colonies from culture dishes with a pulled glass mouth pipette and wash twice in PBS.
15. Incubate the colony in trypsin for 5–10 minutes at 37°C. Transfer the colony into a well of a 4-well dish containing both the mitotically inactive MEF and the

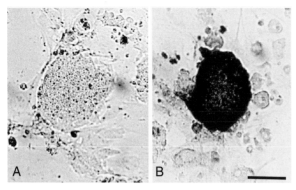

Figure 42–2. *PGCs cultured with LIF and FGF-2 on feeder cells formed multicellular colony. (A) A colony resembling an EG cell colony in appearance. (B) An EG cell-like colony expressing high AP activity. Scale bar 60 μm. (Please see CD-ROM for color version of this figure.)*

EG cell growth medium supplemented only with LIF. The colony is gently disaggregated into small clumps by pulling and pushing the colony up and down in the glass mouth pipette.

16. Culture in an incubator at 37°C, 5% CO_2 in air for a few days. After 1–2 days, the colonies with EG cell-like morphology will start growing on MEF feeders.

17. After two additional days, transfer colonies by glass mouth pipette onto fresh mitotically inactive MEF feeders in the EG cell growth medium in one well of a four-well dish.

18. After 3–4 days of culture, trypsinize the well and transfer the cell suspension into a 35-mm dish on mitotically inactive MEF feeders. If only a few EG cell-like colonies are observed, transfer them into a new well in a four-well dish. After 3–4 days, many EG cell-like colonies will be growing in the culture dish. Subculture them into a 35-mm culture dish as described previously. The transfer of EG cells into a 35-mm culture dish is counted as the first passage. Passage cells one or two more times to get enough EG cells to freeze in a few cryotubes in a liquid nitrogen storage tank (See the section "Freezing of EG Cells"). Record it in cell-line recording book.

MAINTENANCE OF DERIVED EG CELL LINE

This comprises maintenance, subculture, freezing, and thawing EG cell lines.

Equipment–Reagents

- *Medium:* Culture EG cells in the same medium used for derivation of EG cell-like colonies, but omit FGF2.
- *Plastics:* 35-mm culture dishes for growing EG cells on feeder cells prepared from primary MEFs. For some assays (i.e., Southern or an immunoblotting analysis) EG cells are grown on 10-cm gelatin-coated tissue culture dishes with a double amount of LIF (2400 U/ml).

- *FCS:* Use batch-tested FCS, tested both for supporting the growth of derived pluripotent cell lines (ES cells and EG cells) and for the ability to support derivation EG cell-like colonies from cultured PGCs.
- *Trypsin–EDTA:* Use 0.25% solution (Invitrogen).
- *Freezing solution:* Add 4-ml DMSO to 6-ml DMEM and mix. Then transfer into 30-ml FCS and mix well. Keep the freezing solution in a −20°C freezer.

Maintenance of Newly Derived EG Lines

1. EG cells are cultured on mitotically inactive MEF cells in the EG cell growth medium (see Table 42–1) supplemented only with LIF. The medium is changed every day. After 2–3 days, cells are ready to be subcultured or frozen.

2. Do not allow the culture medium during the culture of EG cells to turn yellowish because it might induce differentiation of EG cells. EG cell colonies during this period enlarge but keep the undifferentiated morphology. The undifferentiated EG cell colony usually has a round or oval shape with a distinct border around the colony in which individual cells are tightly compacted (Fig. 42–1). Signs of differentiation can be observed by the changing morphology of colonies and markers down-regulated during the differentiation (AP, Oct 3/4, and SSEA1). Signs of differentiation observed by changed morphology of EG colonies are as follows: (1) Colonies are surrounded by differentiated cells with flattened morphology. (2) Individual cells within the colony are recognised rather than a single clump. (3) Colonies adopt a more rounded shape, and some free-floating embryoid bodies are formed. When a culture starts spontaneously differentiating, it should be thrown away. If the culture is very important, subculture using a mouth pipette only those colonies that have "proper" EG cell phenotype. After 3–4 days, only EG cell-like colonies should be observed in the culture. Expand the cells and freeze.

Subculture of EG Cells

1. EG cell colonies grown on 35-mm culture dishes are usually ready to be subcultured 2–3 days after plating.

2. Wash cells with 1 ml of PBS. Harvest a single-cell suspension by treatment with trypsin (3–5 minutes at room temperature) and then pipetting with a blue tip.

3. Neutralise trypsin by adding 1 ml of EG cell growth medium. Transfer the cell suspension into a 15-ml tube containing 8 ml of culture medium.

4. Centrifuge at 1000 rpm for 5 minutes.

5. Resuspend the pellet in 6–8 ml of EG cell growth medium.

6. Plate 2 ml of EG cell suspension into one 35-mm culture dish. Culture at 37°C in an incubator.

Freezing of EG Cells

1. Remove the EG cell growth medium and wash cultures with PBS when EG cells are in a lag phase (growing phase).

2. Make a single-cell suspension by trypsin treatment, then pellet the cells as described previously.

3. Resuspend the pellet in a cold freezing solution. Use 1 ml of freezing solution for EG cells from one 35-mm culture dish. Transfer cells in freezing solution to cryotubes and label with cell name, passage number, and date.

4. Place cryotubes overnight into a $-80°C$ freezer. The next day, transfer the cryotubes into LN_2 and record their position in cell database file.

Thawing of EG Cells

1. Thaw frozen EG cells quickly by placing the cryotube into a water bath at 37°C.

2. Transfer the cell suspension into a 15-ml tube containing 9 ml of DMEM.

3. Centrifuge at 1000 rpm for 5 minutes.

4. Resuspend the cell pellet in the EG cell growth medium and seed onto mitotically inactive MEF cells in a 35-mm culture dish.

5. Place the culture into the CO_2 incubator. The next day, small colonies of growing EG cells are observed. Change the EG cell growth medium to remove dead, floating cells.

CHARACTERISATION OF DERIVED EG CELL LINES

Sexing by PCR

This technique is adapted from that previously published by Chuma and Nakatsuji.[23]

Equipment–Reagent

- Thermal cycler (e.g., PTC-100, MJ Research), electrophoresis equipment, tips, and tubes
- *PCR reagents:* dNTPs (10mM stocks), reaction buffer ($10 \times$ PCR buffer), Taq polymerase, and autoclaved distilled water
- *Primers:* Ube1XA: TGGTCTGGACCCAAACGCTGTC-CACA and Ube1XB: GGCAGCAGCCATCACATAATCC-AGATG
- *DNA size ladder:* 1-kb DNA ladder (Invitrogen)
- Agarose, TBA buffer (1X)

1. Isolate genomic DNA from derived EG cells (the EG cells were grown without feeder cells).

2. Set up a PCR reaction in 0.2-ml thin wall tubes kept on ice:

   - 15.5-μl distilled water
   - 2.5-μl $10 \times$ PCR buffer (15-mM $MgCl_2$)
   - 1-μl 10-mM dNTPs
   - 2.5-μl 10 pmol/μl Ube1XA primer
   - 2.5-μl 10 pmol/μl Ube1XB primer
   - 0.5-μl template DNA (genomic DNA from EG cells)
   - 0.25-μl Taq polymerase (5 U/μl)
   - Total volume is 25 μl

3. Transfer the tubes to a PCR block and run the PCR (Table 42–2).

4. After the amplification, add a loading buffer to 10 μl of the PCR products and run out on 2% agarose gel along with the 1-kb DNA marker. The size of PCR products are as

follows: The male has two bands, 217 and 198 basepair (bp), the female has just the 217-bp band.

AP Staining

Equipment–Reagents

- *Staining solution:* A kit is available from Sigma (Cat. No. 86-R). Add 50 μl of sodium nitrite solution to 2.25 ml of autoclaved water and mix. Then add 50 μl of FRV-alkaline solution and 50 μl of naphthol AS-BI alkaline solution. The staining solution must be used immediately. PGCs (from 8.5 to 12.5 dpc) and EG cells express a high level of tissue nonspecific AP.

1. PGCs or EG cells are grown on feeder cells in a four-well culture dish.

2. Aspirate the medium and rinse wells twice with 0.5 ml of PBS.

3. Fix cells by air drying for 15–20 minutes at room temperature.

4. Make the AP staining solution.

5. Add 200 μl of the staining solution to each well of the 4-well dish. Keep in the dark for 10–15 minutes.

6. Identify PGCs or EG cells by their dark-red staining.

Immunofluorescence Staining for SSEA1 and Oct 3/4

Equipment–Reagents

- *Plastic–glass:* Use Lab-tek chambers (Nunc) for staining of cultured EG cells or PGCs. For freshly prepared cell suspensions, use multiwell microscope glass slides (C.A. Hendley, Cat. No. PH-136) precoated with poly-L-lysine to enhance the adherence of cells. Coverslips.

- *Antibodies:* SSEA1 antibody is available from the Developmental Studies Hybridoma Bank, University of Iowa. TG 1(1:2) also recognizes SSEA1 antigen. Anti-Oct 3/4 (1:200) from Chemicon Int. Antimouse IgM-FITC (1:50, Sigma) and antimouse IgG-Texas Red (1:100, Santa Cruz). Toto3 is a fluorescent DNA stain, detecting the nucleus in interphase cells and the chromosomes in mitotic cells (1:500, Molecular Probe).

TABLE 42–2
Steps for Running the PCR

PCR step	Temperature (°C)	Time
1. Denaturing	94	1 min
2. Denaturing	94	30 sec
3. Annealing	66	30 sec
4. Extension	72	1 min
5. Cycle 29 times to step 2		
6. Extension	72	5 min
7. Hold	4	

- *Fixative solution:* Paraformaldehyde (PFA) fixation preserves structure as well as retaining antigen recognition. Use 4% PFA in PBS, 2-g PFA to 35-ml water, and warm to 60°C in the oven. Then add 20 µl of 10% NaOH (to dissolve PFA) and put back into the oven. After 10 minutes, when PFA is dissolved, fill with water to 40 ml, cool to room temperature, and add 5 ml of 10 × PBS. Titrate to pH 7.4 with 1N HCl. Fill to 50 ml with water. Filter using a 0.22-µm filter.
- *PBS-TX:* This solution is used for both blocking and permeabilization. Dissolve BSA (10 mg/1ml) in PBS. Add Triton X-100 so that the final concentration is 0.1%. BSA is a blocking agent that reduces nonspecific antibody binding. Triton X-100 is a detergent used to permeabilize plasma and nuclear membranes.
- *Equipment:* Fluorescence microscope and a humidified dark chamber.

1. Make a cell suspension of PGCs or EG cells by trypsin treatment.
2. Wash cells twice with PBS. Dilute the pellet in PBS to obtain appropriate cell density.
3. Apply cell suspension to poly-L-lysine-treated wells of a multiwell slide. Wait 10–15 minutes until cells stick to wells at room temperature. Keep samples in a humidified chamber. If cells have been grown in Lab-tek chambers, wash twice with PBS. In either case, remove the excess PBS and add the fixative solution (4% PFA) for 15 minutes at room temperature.
4. Remove the fixative solution and wash wells twice with PBS for 5 minutes each.
5. Permeabilize and block cells with PBS-TX for 20 minutes at room temperature.
6. Add TG-1 or Oct3/4 antibody diluted in PBS-TX. Incubate overnight at 4°C in a humidified chamber.
7. The next day, wash samples twice with PBS for 5 minutes each. Add secondary antibody coupled with fluorescence diluted in PBS-TX. Incubate in a humidified dark chamber for 60 minutes at room temperature.
8. Wash twice with PBS for 5 minutes each.
9. Counterstain nuclei with Toto3 for 15 minutes at room temperature. Place a drop of appropriate commercial fluorescent mounting medium on a slide and place a coverslip on top.
10. Examine samples under a fluorescence microscope (Fig. 42–3) with the appropriate filters as soon as possible because the signal diminishes over time. Store slides at 4°C (short-storage) or in a freezer at −20°C (for a few days) for subsequent observation.

Questions for Future Study

Highly purified PGCs, with negligible contamination from neighbouring somatic cells, can generate EG cell colonies and eventually EG cell lines, suggesting that somatic cells are not required for derivation of EG lines. However, PGCs convert into EG cells only when cocultured with feeder cells (Sl⁴-m220 or STO). When PGCs are cultured without feeder cells—even

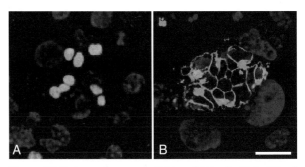

Figure 42-3. *Immunofluorescence Staining of EG cells.* (A) An EG cell colony expresses Oct3/4 antigen localised in the nucleus of EG cells. (B) SSEA1 is expressed on the cell surface of EG cells. Nuclei are counterstained with Toto3 (light gray). Oct3/4 and SSEA1 are identified by FITC. Scale bar 50 µm. (Please see CD-ROM for color version of this figure.)

in conditioned medium from feeder cells or supplemented with LIF, SCF, and FGF-2—EG cell-like colonies are not observed. This implies that feeder cells must provide other unidentified factors important for the conversion of PGCs into EG cells. For future studies, factors and signalling pathways involved in the process of conversion of PGCs into the new cell status of EG cells should be investigated. Such studies could throw light on the molecular basis of pluripotency.

Other questions arise from a comparison of EG cells and ES cells. PGCs at any particular embryonic stage may be considered a more defined cell type than inner cell mass or epiblast cells. Is this related to the finding that the efficiency of derivation (the number of colonies containing pluripotent cells, as a proportion of number of starting cells) is higher for ES cells than for EG cells? And higher for 8.5 dpc than for 11.5 dpc PGCs, lower still at 12.5 dpc, and zero at 13.5 dpc and later? Is the efficiency the same for PGCs from male and female embryos? And why does EG cell derivation require the presence of factors such as SCF and FGF-2, but ES cell derivation does not? Why has it proved possible to make pluripotent porcine EG cell lines,[24] when attempts to derive ES cells from farm animal species appear to have been tantalizingly unsuccessful?

ACKNOWLEDGMENT

We thank the Leverhulme Trust for financial support.

REFERENCES

1. De Felici, M., and McLaren, A. (1983). *In vitro* culture of mouse primordial germ cells. *Exp. Cell Res.* **144,** 417–427.
2. Donovan, P.J., Stott, D., Cairns, L.A., Heasman, J., and Wylie, C.C. (1986). Migratory and postmigratory mouse primordial germ cells behave differently in culture. *Cell* **44,** 831–838.
3. Buehr, M. (1997). The primordial germ cells of mammals: some current perspectives. *Exp. Cell Res.* **232,** 194–207.

4. Dolci, S., Williams, D.E., Ernst, M.K., Resnick, J.L., Brannan, C.I., Lock, L.F., Lyman, S.D., Boswell, H.S., and Donovan, P.J. (1991). Requirement for mast cell growth factor for primordial germ cells survival in culture. *Nature* **352**, 809–811.

5. Matsui, Y., Zsebo, K., and Hogan, B.L.M. (1992). Derivation of pluripotential embryonic stem cells from murine primordial germ cells in culture. *Cell* **70**, 841–847.

6. Resnick, J.L., Bixler, L.S., Cheng, L., and Donovan, P.J. (1992). Long-term proliferation of mouse primordial germ cells in culture. *Nature* **359**, 550–551.

7. Stewart, C.L., Gadi, I., and Bhatt, H. (1994). Stem cells from primordial germ cells can reenter the germ line. *Dev. Biol.* **161**, 626–628.

8. Labosky, P.A., Barlow, D.P., and Hogan, B.L.M. (1994). Mouse embryonic germ (EG) cell lines: transmission through the germ line and differences in the methylation imprint of insulin-like growth factor 2 receptor *(Igf2r)* gene compared with embryonic stem (ES) cell lines. *Development* **120**, 3197–3204.

9. Durcova-Hills, G., Ainscough, J.F.X., and McLaren, A. (2001). Pluripotent stem cells derived from migrating primordial germ cells. *Differentiation* **68**, 220–226.

10. Tada, T., Tada, M., Hilton, K., Barton, S.C., Sado, T., Takagi, N., and Surani, M.A. (1998). Epigenotype switching of imprintable loci in embryonic germ cells. *Dev. Genes Evol.* **207**, 551–561.

11. Chiquoine, A.D. (1954). The identification, origin, and migration of the primordial germ cells in the mouse embryo. *Anat. Rec.* **118**, 135–146.

12. Fox, M., Damjanov, I., Martinez-Hernandez, A., Knowles, B.B., and Solter, D. (1981). Immunohistochemical localization of the early embryonic antigen (SSEA1) in postimplantation mouse embryos and foetal and adult tissues. *Dev. Biol.* **83**, 391–398.

13. Yoshinaga, K., Muramatsu, H., and Muramatsu, T. (1991). Immunohistochemical localization of the carbohydrate antigen 4C9 in the mouse embryo: a reliable marker of mouse primordial germ cells. *Differentiation* **48**, 75–82.

14. Hahnel, A.L., and Eddy, E.M. (1986). Cell surface markers of mouse primordial germ cells defined by two monoclonal antibodies. *Gamete Res.* **15**, 25–34.

15. Orr-Urtreger, A., Avivi, A., Zimmer, Y., Givol, D., Yarden, Y., and Lonai, P. (1990). Developmental expression of c-kit, a protooncogene at the W locus of the mouse. *Development* **109**, 911–923.

16. Fujiwara, Y., Komiya, T., Kawabata, H., Sato, M., Fujimoto, H., Furusawa, M., and Noce, T. (1994). Isolation of a DEAD-family protein gene that encodes a murine homolog of *Drosophila vasa* and its specific expression in germ cell lineage. *Proc. Natl. Acad. Sci. USA* **91**, 12,258–12,262.

17. Enders, G.C., and May, J.J., II. (1994). Developmentally regulated expression of a mouse germ cell nuclear antigen examined from embryonic day 11 to adult in male and female mice. *Dev. Biol.* **163**, 331–340.

18. Schöler, H.R., Dressler, G.R., Balling, R., Rohdewohld, H., and Gruss, P. (1990). Oct-4: A germ line-specific transcription factor mapping to the mouse T-complex. *EMBO J.* **9**, 2185–2195.

19. De Felici, M., and McLaren, A. (1982). Isolation of mouse primordial germ cells. *Exp. Cell Res.* **142**, 476–482.

20. De Felici, M., and Pesce, M. (1995). Immunoaffinity purification of migratory mouse primordial germ cells. *Exp. Cell Res.* **216**, 277–279.

21. Pesce, M., and De Felici, M. (1995). Purification of mouse primordial germ cells by MiniMACS magnetic separation system. *Dev. Biol.* **170**, 722–725.

22. Abe, K., Hashiyama, M., MacGregor, G., Yamamura, K., and Abe, K. (1996). Purification of primordial germ cells from TNAP$^{\beta\text{-geo}}$ mouse embryos using FACS-gal. *Dev. Biol.* **180**, 468–472.

23. Chuma, S., and Nakatsuji, N. (2001). Autonomous transition into meiosis of mouse fetal germ cells *in vitro* and its inhibition by gp130-mediated signalling. *Dev. Biol.* **229**, 468–479.

24. Shim, H., Gutiérrez-Adán, A., Chen, L.R., BonDurant, R.H., Behboodi, E., and Anderson, G.B. (1997). Isolation of pluripotent stem cells from cultured porcine primordial germ cells. *Biol. Reprod.* **57**, 1089–1095.

Derivation and Differentiation of Human Embryonic Germ Cells

Michael J. Shamblott, Candace L. Kerr, Joyce Axelman, John W. Littlefield, Gregory O. Clark, Ethan S. Patterson, Russell C. Addis, Jennifer N. Kraszewski, Kathleen C. Kent, and John D. Gearhart

Embryonic germ (EG) cells are pluripotent stem cells derived from primordial germ cells (PGCs) that arise in the late embryonic and early fetal period of development. EG cells have been derived from several species, including mouse, pig, chicken, and human. Mouse, pig, and chicken EG cells have been demonstrated to contribute to experimentally produced chimeric animals, including germ line transmission in the latter two species. Furthermore, germ line transmission of mouse and chicken EG cell-derivatives have been demonstrated. Mouse and human EG cells can be differentiated *in vitro* to form embryoid bodies (EBs). Like EBs generated from embryonic stem (ES) cells, EG-derived EBs contain differentiated cells representing all three germ layers as well as mixed-cell populations of less differentiated progenitors and precursors. These human EB-derived (EBD) cells are capable of considerable cell proliferation and express a variety of lineage-specific markers. Human EBD cell cultures have a normal and stable karyotype and normal patterns of genomic imprinting, including X-inactivation. Transplantation studies have demonstrated that human EBD cells can engraft into a variety of rodent tissues and can participate in the recovery of rats following motor neuron injury.

Introduction

Pluripotent stem cells have been derived from two embryonic sources. ES cells were first derived from the inner cell mass of mouse preimplantation embryos,[1,2] and EG cells were initially derived from mouse PGCs.[3,4] Subsequently, EG cells have been derived from chicken,[5] pig,[6,7] and human PGCs.[8] Pig, chicken, and mouse EG cells have been demonstrated to contribute to experimentally produced chimeric animals, including germ line transmission in the latter two species.[9,10]

PRIMORDIAL GERM CELLS

PGCs are the sole means of genetic transmission between parent and offspring, as they generate eggs and sperm. In many species, such as *C. elegans,* germ cells are segregated very early in development, during the first embryonic cleavages[11,12] and are marked by deposition of ribonucleoprotein P-granules.[13,14] In mammals, the process occurs later in development and seems to be directed more by extrinsic factors than by preprogrammed intrinsic differences. For example, in mice, cells that generate PGCs are located close to extraembryonic ectoderm during gastrulation. Rather than having a previously determined fate, cells in this location receive external signals to further differentiate into PGCs, as demonstrated by the observation that transplantation of cells from other parts of the epiblast to this region can take on a PGC fate.[15] Several components of this signaling process have been identified. Initially, bone morphogenetic protein 4 (Bmp4) and Bmp8b produced by extraembryonic ectoderm program cells from the epiblast to become extraembryonic mesoderm precursors or PGCs.[16] Cells destined to become PGCs express higher levels of membrane protein fragilis than nuclear protein stella.[17]

In the mouse, PGCs are visible as alkaline phosphatase (AP) positive cells at the base of the allantois at 7.5 to 8.0 days postcoitus (dpc). They begin to associate with the endoderm that is invaginating to form the hindgut at 8.5 dpc. By 10.5 dpc, PGCs are associated with dorsal mesenteries and are translocated to the genital ridges.[18–20] The migration of PGCs is caused by both cellular migration and association with moving tissues. Throughout this migration, PGCs expand from approximately 130 cells at 8.5 dpc to more than 25,000 at 13.5 dpc.[21,22] Once they arrive at the genital ridge, PGCs continue proliferating until they enter prophase of the first meiotic division. In males, entry into meiosis is inhibited by signals from the developing testis, blocking PGCs at G_0 until after birth. In the absence of inhibitory signals, female PGCs undergo oogenesis.

Although not as thoroughly studied, much is known regarding the migratory path of human PGCs, including their association with gut endoderm and migration into developing genital ridges.[23,24]

PGCs do not survive well under standard tissue culture conditions and are not pluripotent stem cells *in vivo* or *in vitro*. Early attempts to use various growth factors and feeder layers succeeded in prolonging their survival, but proliferation was limited. The combination of leukemia inhibitory factor (LIF), basic fibroblast growth factor (bFGF), and c-kit ligand (KL, also known as stem cell factor, mast cell factor, or steel factor) proved to result in an immortal cell population, especially if the KL was presented in the transmembrane form by a layer of "feeder" cells[3,4,25] (see the section "Feeder Layer"). Instead of simply encouraging PGC proliferation, these factors cause the normally solitary PGCs to congregate and proliferate as multicellular colonies known as EG cells and to gain pluripotency. Mouse EG cell lines have been derived from PGCs prior to migration around 8.0–8.5 dpc, during migration at 9.5 dpc,[26] and after entry into the genital ridges between 11.5–12.5 dpc.[27,28]

The roles played by KL and the tyrosine kinase receptor for KL, c-Kit, in the *in vitro* derivation of EG cells from PGCs have parallels *in vivo*. c-Kit is expressed in PGCs, and KL is expressed along the PGC migratory pathway and in the genital ridges.[29,30] The roles of KL and c-Kit in PGC survival were originally characterized through several mutations at their respective loci, *Sl* and *W*, which resulted in subfertile or sterile mice.[31-33] PGCs are formed in homozygous mutant embryos of *W* and *Sl*, but mitosis is severely impaired, and the few PGCs that reach the gonad do not survive. KL is produced as a membrane-bound growth factor that can undergo proteolytic cleavage to generate a soluble form.[34] Mice lacking the membrane-bound KL but not the soluble form maintain low PGC numbers and are sterile, suggesting that the membrane-bound form but not the soluble form is essential for PGC survival.[35,36] The mechanism involved in KL-induced PGC survival has been shown to involve suppression of apoptosis.[37] The c-kit receptor has also been shown to be involved in the adhesion of mouse PGCs to somatic cells *in vitro*.[37] Other recent studies attempting to identify signaling pathways activated by KL binding to its receptor in mouse PGCs have shown activation of AKT kinase[38] and telomerase.[39]

In contrast to the embryologically early and relatively undifferentiated epiblast, PGCs arise late and have a specialized role during normal development. In this regard, it is somewhat surprising that exposure to three cytokines can convert PGCs to pluripotent stem cells *in vitro*. It is possible that the flexibility provided by extrinsic signaling during PGC specification, rather than intrinsic preprogramming, allows for this conversion.

COMPARISON TO ES CELLS

Both mouse ES and EG cells are pluripotent and demonstrate germ line transmission in experimentally produced chimeras.[10,28] Mouse ES and EG cells share several characteristics such as high levels of intracellular AP and presentation of specific cell-surface glycolipids[40,41] and glycoproteins.[42] These properties are characteristic of, but not specific for, pluripotent stem cells. Other important characteristics include growth as multicellular colonies, normal and stable karyotypes, the ability to be continuously passaged, and the capability to differentiate into cells derived from all three germ layers: endoderm, ectoderm, and mesoderm.

Human EG Cell Derivation

Although many combinations of cytokines and feeder layers have been evaluated, the standard practice for derivation of human EG cells remains similar to techniques developed for the mouse. As of 2003, approximately 140 human EG cultures have been derived in our laboratory using this general technique.

INITIAL DISAGGREGATION AND PLATING

Gonadal ridges and mesenteries of week 5–9 postfertilization human embryos (obtained as a result of therapeutic termination of pregnancies using a protocol approved by the Joint Committee on Clinical Investigation of the Johns Hopkins University School of Medicine) are collected in 1-ml ice-cold PGC growth media (see the section "PGC Growth Media Components") and rapidly transported to a sterile work space. The tissues are then soaked in calcium–magnesium-free Dulbecco's phosphate-buffered saline (DPBS) for 5 minutes in a three-well glass depression slide. The tissue is then transferred to 0.1-ml trypsin–EDTA solution in the depression slide. The concentration of trypsin and EDTA is varied such that at the earliest developmental stages, a gentler 0.05% trypsin–0.5-mM EDTA is used, and at later developmental stages, a stronger 0.25% trypsin–0.5-mM EDTA solution is used. In all cases, it is important to use fresh trypsin that has been aliquoted from frozen stock and thawed immediately prior to use. Prolonged warming of trypsin at 37°C is also avoided. The tissue is mechanically disaggregated thoroughly using a fine forceps and iris scissors. This process is carried out for 5–10 minutes at room temperature. The contents of the depression slide are then triturated briefly by using a 200-μl pipetman and tip, transferred to a 1.5-ml microfuge tube, and incubated at 37°C for 5–10 minutes. This disaggregation process often results in a single-cell suspension and large pieces of undigested tissue. To stop the digestion, PGC growth media is added to the microfuge tube. The volume added is based on the size and developmental stage of the initial tissue. When small fragments of tissue are available, approximately 0.4- to 0.6-ml PGC growth media is added, whereas larger tissues usually require 0.6 to 1.0 ml. After the PGC growth media is added, the tissue is further triturated with 30–50 gentle pumps using a 200-μl pipetman and tip. After trituration, the large tissue fragments are allowed to settle for approximately 30 seconds with visual inspection. Then, 0.1 ml of the digested tissue is transferred to each well of a 96-well tissue culture plate that has been previously prepared with a feeder layer (see the sections "Plating a STO Feeder Layer Prior to Inactivation" and "Plating a STO Feeder Layer After Inactivation,") and 0.1-ml PGC growth media per well. Usually the initial plating occupies 4 to 10 wells of the 96-well plate. The plate is incubated at 37°C in 5% CO_2 with 95% humidity for 7 days. Approximately 90% of the growth media is removed each day, and the plate is replenished with fresh PGC growth media.

SUBSEQUENT PASSAGE OF EG CULTURES

In the first 7 days of derivation (passage 0), most human EG cultures do not produce visible EG colonies. Staining for AP activity demonstrates the presence of solitary PGCs with either stationary or migratory[43] morphology (Fig.43–1A and

43–1B). Often, colonies of cells that do not stain AP⁺ are seen (Fig. 43–1D and 43–1E), as are small clumps of tissue remaining from the initial disaggregation (Fig. 43–1C). After 7 days, the media is removed and the wells are rinsed twice with calcium–magnesium-free DPBS for a total of 5 minutes. Then, 40 μl of freshly thawed trypsin solution is added to each well, and the plate is incubated on a heated platform or in a tissue culture incubator for 5 minutes at 37°C. As previously described, the trypsin solution is 0.05% trypsin–0.5-mM EDTA, 0.25% trypsin–0.5-mM EDTA, or a mixture of these two solutions. The important point at this stage is to facilitate the complete disaggregation of the STO cell feeder layer (see the section "Feeder Layer"), which can be a significant challenge. After the incubation in trypsin, the edge of the 96-well culture plate is hit firmly against a solid surface until the STO cells have completely lifted off of the growth surface. This process can be aided by scraping the well and gently triturating with a 200-μl pipetman and tip; it should not be carried out longer than 5 minutes. After the STO cells have been loosened, 0.16 ml of fresh PGC growth media is added to each well, and the contents are triturated

with 20–30 pumps of the pipetman and tip. This phase is critical to successful disaggregation of the STO feeder layer and EG cells. Once completed, 0.1 ml of disaggregated cell mixture is added to each of 2 wells of a 96-well plate that have been freshly prepared with mitotically inactivated STO cells and 0.1 ml of fresh PGC growth media (see the section "PGC Growth Media Components").

All subsequent passages are done as described. After 14–21 days (during passage 1 or 2), large and recognizable EG colonies will arise in some of the wells (Fig. 43–2). At this point, wells that do not have EG colonies are discarded.

Several common problems occur during the passage of human EG cells. One observation is that the STO feeder layer will sometimes not fully disaggregate. This can be observed by the presence of large cell aggregates immediately following disaggregation. If this occurs with regularity, it is a sign that the trypsinization method is insufficient or that the STO cells have become less contact inhibited (see the section "Evaluation of STO Cells") and have overgrown during the 7 days of culture. Another common occurrence is that the EG colonies do not fully disaggregate. The consequences of poor

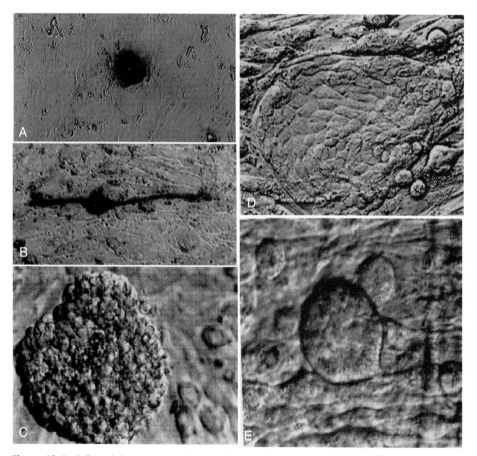

Figure 43–1. *Cell morphologies seen in early passage human embryonic germ culture. (A and B) Alkaline phosphatase-positive (AP⁺) stationary and migrating primordial germ cells. (C) Multicellular piece of undisaggregated gonadal tissue. (D and E) Flat and round cell colonies that do not lead to human EG cells.*

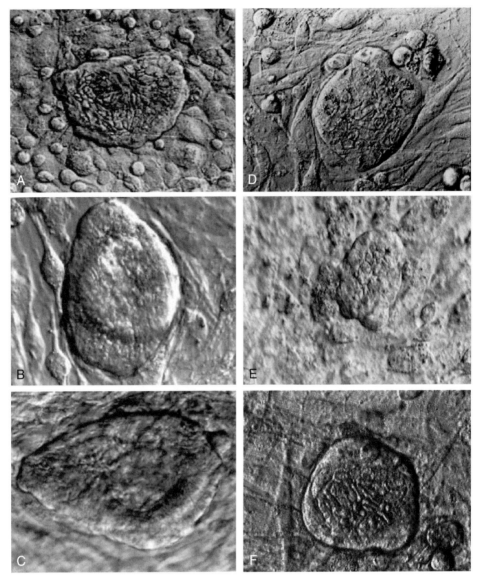

Figure 43-2. *Human EG colonies growing on a STO cell feeder layer.*

disaggregation are that the large pieces differentiate or die and fewer EG cells are available for continued culture expansion. Although much effort has been expended to find a solution to this problem, it remains the most difficult aspect and challenging hurdle to human EG cell biology.

To gain some insight into this problem, a series of electron microscopic images were taken to compare the cell–cell interactions found in mouse ES, mouse EG, and human EG cell colonies. It is evident from these images that cells within the human EG colonies adhere more completely to each other than cells within mouse ES and EG colonies (Fig. 43–3). It is possible that this tight association within the colony limits the access of disaggregation reagents. At this time, neither the nature of the cell–cell interactions nor an effective solution to this problem is evident.

Because of incomplete disaggregation and other intrinsic or extrinsic signals, many human EG colonies (10–30% per passage) differentiate to form three-dimensional structures termed EBs (see the section "Embryoid Body Formation and Analysis") or flatten into structures that are AP– and do not continue to proliferate (Fig. 43–4). EG colonies that are more fully disaggregated go on to produce new EG colonies, and under the best circumstances, EG cultures can be expanded continuously for many months and have routinely exceeded 20 passages. Inevitably, as large EG colonies are removed from the culture as a result of EB formation, the cultures become sparse and are discontinued for practical considerations. Efforts employing standard dimethyl sulfoxide (DMSO) cryopreservation techniques have so far been unsuccessful.

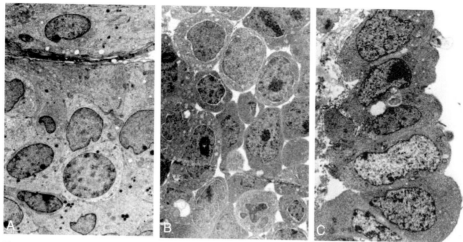

Figure 43–3. *Electron micrograph of EG and ES colonies.* (A) Human EG colony, (B) mouse EG colony, and (C) mouse ES colony.

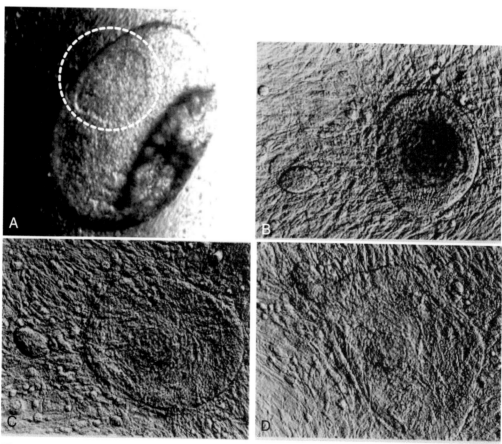

Figure 43–4. *Differentiating human EG colonies.* (A) Stereomicrograph of an EG colony with attached embryoid body (EB). The EG colony is circled. The diameter of the EB is approximately 0.5 mm. (B–D) Time lapse study of EG cell flattening: (B) Four days after disaggregation, the small EG colony on the left results from more complete disaggregation. The large colony on the right is composed of a dark residual colony surrounded by new EG cell growth. (C) Five days after disaggregation, the large EG colony has begun to flatten. (D) Seven days later, the large EG colony has completely flattened and did not survive as a recognizable EG cell colony after disaggregation and replating. In a separate experiment, EBs and these flattened structures are shown to be largely AP⁻.

FEEDER LAYER

Unlike ES cells, EG cell derivation is highly dependent on a specific type of feeder layer. Mouse STO fibroblasts are a spontaneously transformed cell line from the Sandoz inbred mouse. They are Thioguanine- and Ouabain-resistant, features of historical interest but not used in this context.[44] STO cells have been used to derive mouse embryonal carcinoma (EC), ES, and EG cells, and to date, they are the only cell type capable of generating human EG cells. The factor or factors provided exclusively by this cell type are not fully understood. However, the transmembrane form of KL is present on STO fibroblasts but not on most other cell types evaluated in our lab.

Although STO is a clonal cell line, individual isolates vary greatly in their ability to support human EG derivation. This is further complicated by the known phenotypic variation of STO cells in continuous culture. Given the very limited supply of human tissue, it is prudent to screen STO cells for suitability prior to use. The most reliable screening method is to produce a number of clonal STO lines (by limiting dilution or cloning cylinder) and to evaluate them for their ability to support the *derivation* of mouse EG cells. The growth of existing mouse EG lines is not a sufficient method, as most mouse EG lines become feeder layer independent after derivation. Derivation of mouse EG cells is not a simple undertaking. In an effort to more rapidly screen STO cells and to investigate the role of transmembrane KL, we have begun to screen STO cell lines by using an immunocytochemical method to detect KL (see the section "Evaluation of STO Cells"). Once a supportive STO fibroblast line is identified, it should be immediately cryopreserved in several low passage aliquots. One of these aliquots can then be expanded to provide many medium passage aliquots, which are thawed and used with limited further expansion. Continuous passage of STO fibroblasts without frequent screening should be avoided.

Plating a STO Feeder Layer Prior to Inactivation

There are two different methods used to prepare a STO feeder layer: plate-then-irradiate and irradiate-then-plate. Most human EG cultures are derived using the former method. This is practical when a large γ-irradiator is available. STO cells are passaged for short periods (not continuously) in PGC growth media without LIF, bFGF, or forskolin and are disaggregated using 0.05% trypsin–EDTA solution. One day prior to use, a 96-well culture dish is coated with 0.1% gelatin for 30 minutes. The gelatin is withdrawn, and 5×10^4 STO cells are plated per well in PGC growth media without LIF, bFGF, or forskolin. Similar cell densities ($\sim 1.5 \times 10^5$ cells/cm^2) can be achieved in other well configurations. The cells are grown overnight and then exposed to 5000 rads (1 rad = 0.01 Gy) of γ-radiation or X-ray. The cells are then returned to the tissue culture incubator until required. Prior to use, the growth media is removed, 0.1-ml PGC growth medium with added factors is added to each well (or half of the required well volume), and the dish is returned to the tissue culture incubator.

Plating a STO Feeder Layer After Inactivation

This method of STO cell preparation is used when a large γ-radiation unit is not available, when large amounts of cells are required, or if better control of STO cell density is required. STO cells are grown as described previously, trypsinized, counted, and resuspended in PGC growth media without added factors. The cells are placed into one or more 50-ml conical tubes and placed into the γ-irradiator or X-ray device. Cells are exposed to 5000 rads of γ-radiation or X-ray. Following exposure, cells are adjusted to a convenient concentration with PGC growth media without added factors, counted, and plated onto tissue culture dishes that have been previously coated with 0.1% gelatin for 30 minutes. Cells are allowed to adhere overnight, then the media is replaced with half the final volume of PGC growth media including factors prior to use.

Evaluation of STO Cells

The efficacy of mitotic inactivation must be evaluated occasionally to ensure that the STO cells are not capable of significant proliferation. STO cells that are unusually resistant to inactivation, have reduced cell-contact inhibition, or both must be avoided. To evaluate an inactivation, simply treat STO cells as described in the sections "Plating a STO Feeder Layer Prior to Inactivation" and "Plating a STO Feeder Layer After Inactivation," and then plate a known number of cells at low density. Effectively inactivated STO cells will not form clonal foci and will not increase significantly in number after 1 week in culture. Overexposure to of γ-radiation or to X-ray will cause STO cells to die or to deteriorate in less than 7 days after plating.

To evaluate STO cell clonal lines and to better understand the role of membrane-bound KL in EG cell derivation, we compared the relative amounts of KL mRNA transcripts using real-time reverse transcription-polymerase chain reaction (RTPCR) as well as the level of membrane-bound KL protein expression using immunocytochemistry. For this comparison, we examined parent STO lines from two independent sources and several clones derived from the parent lines. Up to 100-fold differences were observed in the expression levels of both KL mRNA and protein. To study the effect of these differences, the numbers of both mouse and human PGCs were compared after the first week in culture on these feeder layers. In some cases, twice as many PGCs were propagated on feeder layers expressing 100-fold higher levels of KL than lines expressing the lowest levels of KL. In approximately 25% of the clonal populations tested, neither RTPCR nor antibody staining could detect KL expression, suggesting that a significant number of the cells in the parent STO lines do not express detectable levels of KL. Moreover, within populations that showed high levels of KL mRNA expression, significant numbers of cells did not immunostain for KL. However, all cells from a mouse null *Sl/Sl*[4] mutant (no expression of KL) transfected with a human membrane-bound KL expression construct (*Sl/Sl*[4] hSCF[220])[45] showed uniform staining. Heterogeneity of KL expression in STO cell cultures and recently cloned lines may explain the variability observed when STO cells are used to derive both mouse and human EG cultures, and it further argues for vigilance in testing STO cells.

PGC GROWTH MEDIA COMPONENTS

Human EG cells are derived and maintained in Dulbecco's modified Eagle's medium (Gibco BRL) supplemented with 15% fetal bovine serum (FBS, Hyclone), 0.1-mM nonessential amino acids (Gibco BRL), 0.1-mM 2-mercaptoethanol (Sigma), 2-mM glutamine (Gibco BRL), 1-mM sodium pyruvate (Gibco BRL), 100 U/ml penicillin (Gibco BRL), 100 µg/ml streptomycin (Gibco BRL), 1000 U/ml human recombinant LIF (hrLIF, Chemicon), 1–2 ng/ml human recombinant bFGF (hrbFGF, R&D systems) and 10-µM forskolin (Sigma) prepared in DMSO.

EVALUATION OF EG CULTURES

Of 150 human PGC cultures initiated, 142 (~95%) demonstrated morphological, biochemical, and/or immunocytochemical characteristics consistent with previously characterized pluripotent stem cell lines. The easiest and most consistent method for evaluating EG cultures is to note the presence of tightly compacted multicellular colonies resembling early passage mouse ES and EG cell colonies (Fig. 43–2) rather than the flattened and more loosely associated colonies seen in human EC[46] and rhesus ES cells.[47] Under the best circumstances, the number of colonies should double or triple over a 1-week passage. The trend is usually to start with small colonies and to end with larger colonies that result from incomplete colony disaggregation (see the section "Subsequent Passage of EG Cultures").

High levels of AP activity are associated with human EG cells. Under standard culture conditions, human EG colonies are >70–90% AP+.[8] As colonies differentiate, one can observe a lower staining percentage and weaker staining, sometimes restricted to the periphery of the colony.

Human EG cells have been further characterized by TRA-1-60, and TRA-1-81 antibodies and to antibodies reactive to the SSEA1, SSEA3, and SSEA4 antigens.[40,41] Colonies stain strongly for four of the five antibodies.[8] The antibody recognizing SSEA-3 antigen stains the cells inconsistently and weakly. As with the results of AP staining, the percentage of cells within a colony that stain positive is variable.

The histological profile of human EG cells (AP+, SSEA-1+, SSEA-3+, SSEA-4+, TRA-1-60+, and TRA-1-81+) differs from undifferentiated human EC and rhesus ES cells, which are SSEA-1 negative.[47,48] The fact that differentiation of the human EC line NTERA2 leads to increased expression of SSEA-1 may suggest that this is indicative of differentiation in the human EG cultures. However, NTERA2 differentiation is accompanied by the loss of the other markers,[49,50] which are not observed in these cultures.

Karyotypic analyses carried out at passage 8–10 (60–70 days in culture) indicated apparently normal human chromosomes at the 300-band level of resolution.[51] Both XX and XY cultures have been derived.

Other markers of pluripotency, such as mRNA expression of the human ortholog of mouse Oct3/4 and telomerase enzyme activity, have been examined. Results differ greatly depending on the status of the EG colony, culture, or both. In general, relatively undifferentiated EG colonies are OCT4 mRNA+ as detected by RTPCR and have detectable levels of telomerase.

AP and Immunocytochemical Staining

Cells are fixed for detection of AP activity in 66% acetone–3% formaldehyde and then stained with naphthol/FRV-alkaline AP substrate (Sigma). For immunocytochemistry, cells are fixed in 3% paraformaldehyde in DPBS. Cell surface glycolipid- and glycoprotein-specific monoclonal antibodies are used at 1:15 to 1:50 dilution. MC480 (SSEA-1), MC631 (SSEA-3), and MC813-70 (SSEA-4) antibodies were supplied by the Developmental Studies Hybridoma Bank (University of Iowa). TRA-1-60 and TRA-1-81 were a gift from Dr. Peter Andrews (University of Sheffield, U.K.). Antibodies are detected by using biotinylated anti-mouse secondary antibody, streptavidin-conjugated horseradish peroxidase, and AEC chromogen (BioGenex).

Cytogenetic Analysis

Cells prepared for cytogenetic analyses are incubated in growth media with 0.1 µg/ml Colcemid for 3–4 hours, trypsinized, resuspended in 0.75-M KCl, incubated for 35 minutes at 37°C, then fixed in 3:1 methanol acetic acid. Cytogenetic analyses are usually carried out at passage 8–10 and 20.

EB Formation and Analysis

EBs form spontaneously in human EG cultures. Although this represents a loss of pluripotent EG cells from the culture, EBs provide evidence for the pluripotent status of the culture and provide cellular material for subsequent culture and experimentation (see the section "EBD Cells"). Initially, EBs provided the only direct evidence that human EG cultures were pluripotent, as all attempts to form teratomas in mice from human EG cells failed. To this day, there is no evidence of teratoma formation from human EG cells or their derivatives.

EB Embedding and Immunohistochemistry. The constituent cells of EBs can be identified most reliably by embedding them in paraffin and staining sections with a bank of well-characterized antibodies. This process avoids the significant problem of antibody trapping that complicates analyses of large three-dimensional structures when direct staining is attempted. EBs are collected from cultures and placed into a small drop of molten 2% low melting point agarose (FMC), prepared in DPBS, and cooled to 42°C. Solidified agarose containing EBs are then fixed in 3% paraformaldehyde in DPBS and embedded in paraffin. Individual 6-µm sections are placed on microscope slides (ProbeOn Plus, Fisher Scientific). Routinely, immunohistochemical analysis is carried out by using a BioTek-Tech Mate

1000 automated stainer (Ventana-BioTek Solutions). Manual staining is also carried out using standard immunohistochemical methods; however, antigen retrieval is required for some of the antibodies employed. Cryosections of EBs generally produce less satisfactory cell morphology and have not been used extensively. Antibodies used on paraffin sections include HHF35 (muscle specific actin, Dako), M 760 (desmin, Dako), CD34 (Immunotech), Z311, (S-100, Dako), sm311 (panneurofilament , Sternberger Monoclonals), A008 (α-1-fetoprotein), CKERAE1/AE3 (pancytokeratin, Boehringer Mannheim), OV-TL 12/30 (cytokeratin 7, Dako), and $K_s20.8$ (cytokeratin 20, Dako). Primary antibodies are detected by using biotinylated anti-rabbit or anti-mouse secondary antibody, streptavidin-conjugated horseradish peroxidase, and DAB chromogen (Ventana-BioTek Solutions). Slides are counter-stained with hematoxylin. Using these and other antibodies, it can be demonstrated that when human EG cells differentiate, they form EBs comprised of endodermal, ectodermal, and mesodermal derivatives.[8]

EBD Cells

Although a compelling demonstration of the potential of human EG cells, the limited growth characteristics of differentiated cells within EBs and difficulties associated with their isolation make extensive experimental manipulation difficult and limit their use in future cellular transplantation therapies. At least two possibilities exist to explain the presence of the observed differentiated cell types. These cells could be generated directly from the pluripotent EG cell, or they could proceed through a series of precursor or progenitor cell types prior to the acquisition of a mature phenotype. It seems unlikely that cells within EBs would bypass normal pathways of differentiation, so efforts have been made to isolate and expand these populations. The hypothesis was that progenitor–precursor cells would have desirable proliferation characteristics and could be recognized by the expression of molecules known to mark progenitor–precursor populations, as well as by the simultaneous expression of markers normally considered part of a mature cellular expression repertoire. Simultaneous expression of neuronal and glial markers by neural progenitors[52,53] and the expression of a variety of lineage-affiliated transcription factors and cytokine receptors[54] by multipotent hematopoietic progenitors provide some basis for this hypothesis. In this model of differentiation, multilineage gene expression by precursor or progenitor cells defines a ground state from which cell-extrinsic and -intrinsic signals work to continuously define a differentiated expression pattern and phenotype,[55] resulting in the developmental plasticity observed after the differentiation of bone marrow[56] and central nervous system stem cells.[57]

The method used to isolate cell populations from EBs is conceptually similar to microbiological selective media experiments. EBs are disaggregated and plated into several different cellular growth environments. These environments consist of combinations of a growth media and a matrix. Although many combinations were evaluated, most EBD cell cultures have been derived one of six environments formed by combinations of two growth media and three plating surfaces. The growth media are an RPMI 1640 media supplemented with 15% FBS and a low (5%) FBS media supplemented with bFGF, epidermal growth factor (EGF), insulin-like growth factor 1 (IGF1), and vascular endothelial growth factor (VEGF). The plating surfaces are bovine type I collagen, human extracellular matrix extract, and tissue culture-treated plastic. These are not intended to be highly selective environments; instead, they favor several basic themes: cells thriving in high serum and elevated glucose (10 mM) conditions versus cells proliferating in low glucose (5 mM) under the control of four mitogens. Binding surfaces included type I collagen, a biomatrix often thought to favor undifferentiated proliferation versus human extracellular matrix, a more complex mixture of laminin, collagen, and fibronectin. The initial assay is to determine conditions that favor extensive cell proliferation, with the hypothesis that this condition will favor undifferentiated cell populations or at least provide numerical disadvantage to the terminally differentiated constituents of the EB.

EBD GROWTH AND EXPRESSION CHARACTERISTICS

Cell populations capable of long-term and robust proliferation can be isolated as described previously from human EG-derived EBs.[58] Embryoid body-derived is the generic term used to describe cells derived in this way that are capable of extensive further proliferation. In general, the type I collagen and human extracellular matrices combined with the low serum media provide the most rapid and extensive cell proliferation.[58] EBD cell lines and cultures are routinely maintained in the environment in which they were derived. The EBD naming convention aids this process. The first two letters of the name refer to the EG culture from which it was derived. The second letter indicates the growth media (E for EGM2MV and R for RPMI1640), and the last letter indicates the matrix (C for collagen, E for human extracellular matrix extract, and P for plastic). For example, the EBD culture SDEC was derived from EG culture SD in EGM2MV medium on type I collagen.

To distinguish EBD cells from a simple population of cells rapidly proliferating but presumably uninteresting in terms of molecules expressed, it is important to establish a robust expression profile assay. The assay should use redundant measures when possible and must combine breadth, sensitivity, specificity, and speed. A series of 24 RTPCRs detecting products from five cell lineages (neuronal, glial, muscle, hematopoietic –vascular endothelia, and endoderm) combined with immunocytochemical staining provides a rapid measure of cell expression. Inevitably, molecular markers are not as definitively specific as desired, so multiple markers for each lineage are advisable.

Using this assay system (see the section "EBD Expression Profiling"), it can be demonstrated that most rapidly proliferating EBD cell cultures simultaneously express a wide array of mRNA and protein markers normally associated with distinct developmental lineages. This is not a surprising property considering that EBD cells are, at least during the derivation stage, a mixed-cell population. More remarkable is the finding that most (11 of 13) EBD cell *lines* isolated by dilution cloning also exhibit a broad multilineage gene expression profile. It can also be demonstrated that the expression profile for a given EBD culture remains stable throughout the life span of the culture. This normally exceeds 70 population doublings but is not unlimited since EBD cells are not immortal.[58]

More than 100 EBD cell cultures and clonally isolated cell lines have been derived and characterized as described here. Most of these cultures share the properties of rapid and robust proliferation and broad multilineage gene expression. Less than 10% of the EBD cultures derived have a narrow expression profile, with one extreme case expressing only nestin, vimentin, and α-1-fetoprotein mRNA. Other general trends in EBD expression are that many cultures appear to be neurally biased, with strong expression of neuronal, glial, and neural progenitor markers, and relatively weak in expression of muscle markers.[58]

Other general characteristics of EBD cells are the relative ease with which they can be genetically manipulated using lipofection and electroporation as well as with retroviral, adenoviral, and lentiviral vectors. Adenoviral and lentiviral vectors are capable of nearly 100% transduction efficiency. These techniques have been used to generate EBD lines that constitutively and tissue-specifically express enhanced GFP and contain many different genetic selection vectors. EBD cells can be immortalized by retroviral-based expression of the telomerase RNA subunit (pBABE).[59] Interestingly, after several hundred population doublings, these lines often become genetically unstable, generating at least two rearrangements: [47,XX,−1,+del (1)(q12),+i (1)(q10)] and [46,XX, del(4)(p14)]. Additionally, these EBD lines tend to have narrow expression profiles.

The imprinting pattern of several EBD cultures has been examined. In one study, expression levels of four imprinted genes (TSSC5, H19, SNRPN, and IGF2) were determined in five EBD cultures. Three of these genes (TSSC5, H19, and SNRPN) had normal monoallelic expression levels, and IGF2 had a partially relaxed imprinting pattern comparable to levels found in normal somatic cells. This study also determined that the imprinting control region that regulates H19 and IGF2 imprinting had a normal pattern of DNA methylation.[60] A second study determined that two XX EBD cultures had a normal pattern of X-inactivation.[61]

The proliferation and expression characteristics of EBD cells suggest they may be useful in the study of human cell differentiation and as a resource for cellular transplantation therapies. One important property in this regard is that no tumor of human origin has arisen in any animal receiving EBD cells, although hundreds of mice, rats, and African green monkeys have received EBD transplants in a variety of anatomical locations, often consisting of more than 1 million cells injected. This is in contrast to the infrequent yet significant number of teratocarcinomas that have arisen following transplantation of cells produced through neural and hematopoietic differentiation of mouse ES cells.

EBD TRANSPLANTATION

Transplantation of EBD cells into animal models of human disease constitutes an active and promising research avenue. Studies with EBD cells and many other cell types have suggested that tissue injury can be highly instructive to transplanted cells. This provides a powerful method to test the potential of cells to differentiate without an initial understanding of the underlying mechanisms. Importantly, these studies also suggest possibilities for the eventual treatment of patients suffering from these diseases.

One example of EBD cell transplantation is the use of an EBD culture named SDEC. This culture was initially selected for further study because of its strong neural expression bias. SDEC cells were introduced into the cerebrospinal fluid of normal rats, and rats exposed to the neuroadapted Sindbis virus. This virus specifically targets spinal cord motor neurons, and infection results in permanent hind limb paralysis. SDEC cells transplanted into virally injured rats engrafted extensively the length of spinal cord and migrated into the cord parenchyma. Substantial engraftment was not observed in uninjured animals receiving SDEC cells. Engrafted SDEC cells took on expression characteristics of mature neurons and astrocytes. Remarkably, albeit at low frequency, engrafted SDEC cells became immunoreactive to choline acetyltransferase and sent axons into the sciatic nerve. Even more remarkably, after 12 and 24 weeks, paralyzed animals receiving SDEC cells partially recovered hind limb function. In this experiment, the frequency and total number of neurons generated from SDEC cells was not sufficient to easily explain the significant recovery of function, which is not surprising since the transplanted SDEC cells are a mixed-cell population rather than a line or culture grown or differentiated to promote neural outcome. The mechanism proposed to explain the functional recovery involves EBD cells protecting host motor neurons from death and facilitating host motor neuron reafferentation, possibly through the secretion of transforming growth factor-α and brain-derived neurotrophic factor.[62]

This example illustrates several important points. The engraftment (and possibly one or more steps in cellular differentiation) of SDEC cells was promoted by an injury signal following viral infection. Once engrafted, cells within the SDEC population were capable of differentiation *in vivo* into mature astrocytes and neurons, some of which sent processes along the correct pathway to the sciatic nerve and were then capable of retrograde transport. It is difficult to see how this elaborate and spatially precise differentiation could be carried out *ex vivo* then introduced into an animal or patient. The use of a mixed-cell population may have allowed the variety of cellular responses that ultimately resulted in functional recovery. Some cells within the population were capable of forming new neural cells, and others took on supportive and protective roles. Although in this experimental model the multiple roles carried out by use of a mixed-cell population may have resulted in functional recovery, future experiments will need to focus on isolation of subpopulations to increase the efficiency of differentiation into required cell types and to address issues of safety. Lastly, the rats in all treatment groups

467

received immunosuppressive drugs to prevent rejection of the human EBD cells. In the near term, this will likely be a feature of all EBD-based cellular transplantation experiments and therapies.

EBD DERIVATION, GROWTH, AND CRYOPRESERVATION METHODS

EBs formed in the presence of PGC growth media are harvested in groups of 10 or more and are dissociated by digestion in 1-mg/ml Collagenase/Dispase (Roche) for 30 minutes to 1 hour at 37°C. Cells are then spun at 1000 rpm for 5 minutes and resuspended in various growth media–matrix environments. These include RPMI growth media [RPMI 1640 (LTI), 15% FCS, 0.1-mM nonessential amino acids, 2-mM L-glutamine, 100 U/ml penicillin, and 100 µg/ml streptomycin] and EGM2MV media (Clonetics) [5% FCS, hydrocortisone, hbFGF, hVEGF, R^3-IGF1, ascorbic acid, hEGF, heparin, gentamycin, and amphotericin B]. Matrices are bovine collagen I (Collaborative Biomedical, 10 µg/cm^2), human extracellular matrix (Collaborative Biomedical, 5 µg/cm^2), and tissue culture plastic. EBD cells are cultured at 37°C, 5% CO_2, 95% humidity and are routinely passaged 1:10 to 1:40 using 0.025% trypsin–0.01% EDTA (Clonetics) for 5 minutes at 37°C. Low serum cultures are treated with trypsin inhibitor (Clonetics) and then spun down and resuspended in growth media. EBD cells are cryopreserved in the presence of 50% FCS, 10% DMSO in a controlled rate freezing vessel and stored in liquid nitrogen.

EBD EXPRESSION PROFILING

Immunocytochemistry

Approximately 1×10^5 cells are plated in each well of an eight-well glass bottom chamber slide. Cells are fixed in either 4% paraformaldehyde in phosphate-buffered saline (PBS) or a 1:1 mixture of methanol–acetone for 10 minutes as recommended by the antibody manufacturer. Cells are permeablized in 0.1% Triton X-100, 1 × PBS for 10 minutes if required, then blocked in either Powerblock (BioGenex), 5% FBS, or 1–5% goat serum supplemented with 0.5% bovine serum albumin for 10–60 minutes as recommended by the antibody manufacturer. Primary antibodies and dilutions are as follows: neurofilament 68 kDA (Roche, 1:4), neuron-specific enolase (Pharmingen, 1:100), tau (Pharmingen, 5 µg/ml), vimentin (Roche, 1:10), nestin (NIH, 1:250), galactocerebroside (Sigma, 1:500), 2′,3′-cyclic nucleotide 3′-phosphodiesterase (Sigma, 1:500), O4 (Roche, 10 µg/ml), and SMI32 (Sternberger monoclonal, 1:5000). Detection was carried out by secondary antibodies conjugated to biotin, streptavidin-conjugated horseradish peroxidase, and 3-amino-9-ethylcarbazole chromogen (BioGenex).

mRNA Expression Profiles

RNA is prepared from cells growing on 60 or 100 mm tissue culture plates by using the Qiagen RNeasy kit. RNA preparations are digested with RNAse-free DNAse (Roche) 30 minutes at 37°C, then inactivated at 75°C for 5 minutes. Synthesis of cDNA is performed on 5-µg RNA by using oligo (dT)

primers and a standard MMLV (Invitrogen) reaction carried out at 42°C. Thirty cycles of PCR are carried out in the presence of 1.5-mM $MgCl_2$ with an annealing temperature of 55°C and incubation times of 30 seconds. PCRs are resolved on a 1.8% agarose gel. The efficacy of each PCR is established using appropriate commercially available human tissue RNA (Clontech). All amplimers are validated by Southern blot analysis by using oligonucleotide probes end-labeled with ^{32}P-ATP, hybridized in 6 × SSC, 5 × Denhardt's Solution, 0.1% SDS, 0.05% sodium pyrophosphate, 100 µg/ml of sheared and denatured salmon sperm DNA at 45°C. cDNA synthesis and genomic DNA contamination are monitored by primers specific to human phosphoglycerate kinase-1, which give products of ~250 basepair (bp) and ~500 bp when amplifying cDNA and genomic DNA, respectively.

Summary

Human EG cells can be derived from PGCs by using methods similar to those used to derive mouse EG cultures. Like mouse ES and EG cells, human EG cells require LIF for proliferation as undifferentiated stem cells. Unlike mouse EG cells, however, human EG cells do not readily lose their dependence on exogenous cytokines and factors supplied by the feeder layer, and they have a higher frequency of spontaneous differentiation into EBs. Although EBs are a loss to the pluripotent stem cell population, they are a source of cells expressing markers of mature cellular phenotypes as well as their presumed progenitors and precursors. Cells that retain a high capacity for cell proliferation and express markers of multiple lineages can be isolated from EBs and can be used in a variety of in vitro and in vivo differentiation paradigms. The current challenges are to match individual EBD cultures to desired endpoints and to enrich or purify populations of cells within EBD cultures to more specifically address biological requirements.

REFERENCES

1. Evans, M.J., and Kaufman, M.H. (1981). Establishment in culture of pluripotential cells from mouse embryos. Nature **292**, 154–156.
2. Martin, G.R. (1981). Isolation of a pluripotent cell line from early mouse embryos cultured in media conditioned by teratocarcinoma stem cells. Proc. Natl. Acad. Sci. USA **78**, 7634–7638.
3. Matsui, Y., Toksoz, D., Nishikawa, S., Nishikawa, S., Williams, D., Zsebo, K., and Hogan, B.L. (1991). Effect of steel factor and leukemia inhibitory factor on murine primordial germ cells in culture. Nature **353**, 750–752.
4. Resnick, J.L., Bixler, L.S., Cheng, L., and Donovan, P.J. (1992). Long-term proliferation of mouse primordial germ cells in culture. Nature **359**, 550–551.
5. Park, T.S., and Han, J.Y. (2000). Derivation and characterization of pluripotent embryonic germ cells in chicken. Mol. Reprod. Dev. **56**, 475–482.
6. Mueller, S., Prelle, K., Rieger, N., Petznek, H., Lassnig, C., Luksch, U., Aigner, B., Baetscher, M., Wolf, E., Mueller, M., and Brem, G. (1999). Chimeric pigs following blastocyst injection of transgenic porcine primordial germ cells. Mol. Reprod. Dev. **54**, 244–254.

7. Piedrahita, J.A., Moore, K., Oetama, B., Lee, C.K., Scales, N., Ramsoondar, J., Bazer, F.W., and Ott, T. (1998). Generation of transgenic porcine chimeras using primordial germ cell-derived colonies. *Biol. Reprod.* **58**, 1321–1329.

8. Shamblott, M.J., Axelman, J., Wang, S., Bugg, E.M., Littlefield, J.W., Donovan, P.J., Blumenthal, P.D., Huggins, G.R., and Gearhart, J.D. (1998). Derivation of pluripotent stem cells from cultured human primordial germ cells. *Proc. Natl. Acad. Sci. USA* **95**, 13,726–13,731.

9. Park, T.S., Hong, Y.H., Kwon, S.C., Lim, J.M., and Han, J.Y. (2003). Birth of germ line chimeras by transfer of chicken embryonic germ (EG). cells into recipient embryos. *Mol. Reprod. Dev.* **65**, 389–395.

10. Stewart, C., Gadi, I., and Bhatt, H. (1994). Stem cells from primordial germ cells can reenter the germ line. *Dev. Biol.* **161**, 626–628.

11. Deppe, U. (1978). Cell lineages of the embryo of the nematode *Caenorhabditis elegans. Proc. Natl. Acad. Sci. USA* **75**, 376–380.

12. Seydoux, G., and Fire, A. (1994). Soma–germ line asymmetry in the distributions of embryonic RNAs in *Caenorhabditis elegans. Development* **120**, 2823–2834.

13. Strome, S., and Wood, W.B. (1982). Immunofluorescence visualization of germ line-specific cytoplasmic granules in embryos, larvae, and adults of *Caenorhabditis elegans. Proc. Natl. Acad. Sci. USA* **79**, 1558–1562.

14. Hird, S.N., Paulsen, J.E., and Strome, S. (1996). Segregation of germ granules in living *Caenorhabditis elegans* embryos: cell type-specific mechanisms for cytoplasmic localization. *Development* **122**, 1303–1312.

15. McLaren, A. (2000). Establishment of the germ cell lineage in mammals. *J. Cell Physiol.* **182**, 141–143.

16. Ying, Y., Qi, X., and Zhao G.Q. (2001). Induction of primordial germ cells from murine epiblasts by synergistic action of bmp4 and bmp8b signaling pathways. *Proc. Natl. Acad. Sci. USA* **98**, 7858–7862.

17. Saitou, M., Barton, S.C., and Surani, M.A. (2002). A molecular program for the specification of germ cell fate in mice. *Nature* **418**, 293–300.

18. Chiquoine, A.D. (1954). The identification, origin, and migration of the primordial germ cells of the mouse embryo. *Anat. Rec.* **118**, 135–146.

19. Ginsburg, M., Snow, M.H., and McLaren, A. (1990). Primordial germ cells in the mouse embryo during gastrulation. *Development* **110**, 521–528.

20. Lawson, K., and Hage, W. (1994). Clonal analysis of the origin of primordial germ cells in the mouse. *In* "Germ Line Development," pp. 68–91. John Wiley & Sons, New York.

21. Mintz, B., and Russell, E.S. (1957). Gene-induced embryological modifications of primordial germ cells in the mouse. *J. Exp. Zool.* **134**, 207–237.

22. Tam, P.P., and Snow, M.H. (1981). Proliferation and migration of primordial germ cells during compensatory growth in mouse embryos. *J. Embryol. Exp. Morphol.* **64**, 133–147.

23. Fuss, A. (1911). Ueber extraregionare geschlechtszellen bei einem menshlichen embryo von 4 wochen. *Anat. Anz.* **39**, 407–409.

24. Witschi, E. (1948). Migration of the germ cells of human embryos from the yolk sac to the primitive gonadal folds. *In* "Contributions to embryology," pp. 76–79. Carnegie Institution of Washington.

25. Matsui, Y., Zsebo, K., and Hogan, B.L. (1992). Derivation of pluripotential embryonic stem cells from murine primordial germ cells in culture. *Cell* **70**, 841–847.

26. Durcova-Hills, G., Ainscough, J., and McLaren, A. (2001). Pluripotential stem cells derived from migrating primordial germ cells. *Differentiation*, **68**, 220–226.

27. Labosky, P.A., Barlow, D.P., and Hogan, B.L. (1994). Embryonic germ cell lines and their derivation from mouse primordial germ cells. *Ciba. Found. Symp.* **182**, 157–168; discussion 168–178.

28. Labosky, P., Barlow, D., and Hogan, B. (1994). Mouse embryonic germ (EG). cell lines: transmission through the germ line and differences in the methylation imprint of insulin-like growth factor 2 receptor (*igf2r*). gene compared with embryonic stem (ES) cell lines. *Development* **120**, 3197–3204.

29. Matsui, Y., Zsebo, K.M., and Hogan, B.L. (1990). Embryonic expression of a hematopoietic growth factor encoded by the Sl locus and the ligand for c-kit. *Nature* **347**, 667–669.

30. Keshet, E., Lyman, S.D., Williams, D.E., Anderson, D.M., Jenkins, N.A., Copeland, N.G., and Parada, J.F. (1991). Embryonic RNA expression patterns of the c-kit receptor and its cognate ligand suggest multiple functional roles in mouse development. *EMBO J.* **10**, 2425–2435.

31. Copeland, N.G., Gilbert, D.J., Cho, B.C., Donovan, P.J., Jenkins, N.A., Cosman, D., Anderson, D., Lyman, S.D., and Williams, D.E. (1990). Mast cell growth factor maps near the steel locus on mouse chromosome 10 and is deleted in a number of steel alleles. *Cell*, **63**, 175–183.

32. Flanagan, J.G., and Leder, P. (1990). The kit ligand: a cell surface molecule altered in steel mutant fibroblasts. *Cell* **63**, 185–194.

33. Zsebo, K.M., Williams, D.A., Geissler, E.N., Broudy, V.C., Martin, F.H., Atkins, H.L., Hsu, R.Y., Birkett, N.C., Okino, K.H., Murdock, D.C., *et al.* (1990). Stem cell factor is encoded at the Sl locus of the mouse and is the ligand for the c-kit tyrosine kinase receptor. *Cell* **63**, 213–224.

34. Flanagan, J.G., Chan, D.C., and Leder, P. (1991). Transmembrane form of the kit ligand growth factor is determined by alternative splicing and is missing in the Sld mutant. *Cell* **64**, 1025–1035.

35. Besmer, P., Manova, K., Duttlinger, R., Huang, E.J., Packer, A., Gyssler, C., and Bachvarova, R.F. (1993). The kit-ligand (steel factor). and its receptor c-kit/w: Pleiotropic roles in gametogenesis and melanogenesis. *Dev Suppl*, 125–137.

36. Lev, S., Blechman, J.M., Givol, D., and Yarden, Y. (1994). Steel factor and c-kit protooncogene: genetic lessons in signal transduction. *Crit. Rev. Oncog.* **5**, 141–168.

37. Pesce, M., Di Carlo, A., and De Felici, M. (1997). The c-kit receptor is involved in the adhesion of mouse primordial germ cells to somatic cells in culture. *Mech. Dev.* **68**, 37–44.

38. De Miguel, M.P., Cheng, L., Holland, E.C., Federspiel, M.J., and Donovan, P.J. (2002). Dissection of the c-kit signaling pathway in mouse primordial germ cells by retroviral-mediated gene transfer. *Proc. Natl. Acad. Sci. USA* **99**, 10,458–10,463.

39. Dolci, S., Levati, L., Pellegrini, M., Faraoni, I., Graziani, G., Di Carlo, A., and Geremia, R. (2002). Stem cell factor activates telomerase in mouse mitotic spermatogonia and in primordial germ cells. *J. Cell Sci.* **115**, 1643–1649.

40. Solter, D., and B. Knowles (1978). Monoclonal antibody defining a stage-specific mouse embryonic antigen (ssea-1). *Proc. Natl. Acad. Sci. USA* **75**, 5565–5569.

41. Kannagi, R., Cochran, N., Ishigami, F., Hakomori, S., Andrews, P., Knowles, B., and Solter, D. (1983). Stage-specific embryonic antigens (ssea-3 and -4) are epitopes of a unique globo-series ganglioside isolated from human teratocarcinoma cells. *EMBO J.* **2**, 2355–2361.

42. Andrews, P., Banting, G., Damjanov, I., Arnaud, D., and Avner, P. (1984). Three monoclonal antibodies defining distinct differentiation antigens associated with different high molecular

weight polypeptides on the surface of human embryonal carcinoma cells. *Hybridoma* **3,** 347–361.

43. Donovan, P.J., Stott, D., Cairns, L.A., Heasman, J., and Wylie, C.C. (1986). Migratory and postmigratory mouse primordial germ cells behave differently in culture. *Cell* **44,** 831–838.

44. Martin, G.R., and Evans, M.J. (1975). Differentiation of clonal lines of teratocarcinoma cells: formation of embryoid bodies *in vitro. Proc. Natl. Acad. Sci. USA* **72,** 1441–1444.

45. Toksoz, D., Zsebo, K.M., Smith, K.A., Hu, S., Brankow, D., Suggs, S.V., Martin, F.H., and Williams, D.A. (1992). Support of human hematopoiesis in long-term bone marrow cultures by murine stromal cells selectively expressing the membrane-bound and secreted forms of the human homolog of the steel gene product, stem cell factor. *Proc. Natl. Acad. Sci. USA* **89,** 7350–7354.

46. Andrews, P.W., Bronson, D.L., Benham, F., Strickland, S., and Knowles, B.B. (1980). A comparative study of eight cell lines derived from human testicular teratocarcinoma. *Int. J. Cancer* **26,** 269–280.

47. Thomson, J.A., Kalishman, J., Golos, T.G., Durning, M., Harris, C.P., Becker, R.A., and Hearn, J.P. (1995). Isolation of a primate embryonic stem cell line. *Proc. Natl. Acad. Sci. USA* **92,** 7844–7848.

48. Wenk, J., Andrews, P.W., Casper, J., Hata, J., Pera, M.F., von Keitz, A., Damjanov, I., and Fenderson, B.A. (1994). Glycolipids of germ cell tumors: extended globo-series glycolipids are a hallmark of human embryonal carcinoma cells. *Int. J. Cancer* **58,** 108–115.

49. Andrews, P.W., Goodfellow, P.N., Shevinsky, L.H., Bronson, D.L., and Knowles, B.B. (1982). Cell-surface antigens of a clonal human embryonal carcinoma cell line: morphological and antigenic differentiation in culture. *Int. J. Cancer* **29,** 523–531.

50. Damjanov, I., Fox, N., Knowles, B.B., Solter, D., Lange, P.H., and Fraley, E.E. (1982). Immunohistochemical localization of murine stage-specific embryonic antigens in human testicular germ cell tumors. *Am. J. Pathol.* **108,** 225–230.

51. Mitelman, F. (ed.). (1995). "An International System for Human Cytogenetic Nomenclature." S. Karger, Basel.

52. Colucci-D'Amato, G.L., Tino, A., Pernas-Alonso, R., ffrench-Mullen, J.M, and di Porzio, U. (1999). Neuronal and glial properties coexist in a novel mouse CNS immortalized cell line. (In process.). *Exp. Cell Res.* **252,** 383–391.

53. Piper, D.R., Mujtaba, T., Rao, M.S., and Lucero, M.T. (2000). Immunocytochemical and physiological characterization of a population of cultured human neural precursors. *J. Neurophysiol.* **84,** 534–548.

54. Hu, M., Krause, D., Greaves, M., Sharkis, S., Dexter, M., Heyworth, C., and Enver, T. (1997). Multilineage gene expression precedes commitment in the hemopoietic system. *Genes Dev.* **11,** 774–785.

55. Enver, T., Heyworth, C.M., and Dexter, T.M. (1998). Do stem cells play dice? *Blood* **92,** 348–351; discussion 352.

56. Petersen, B.E., Bowen, W.C., Patrene, K.D., Mars, W.M., Sullivan, A.K., Murase, N., Boggs, S.S., Greenberger, J.S., and Goff, J.P. (1999). Bone marrow as a potential source of hepatic oval cells. *Science* **284,** 1168–1170.

57. Bjornson, C.R., Rietze, R.L., Reynolds, B.A., Magli, M.C., and Vescovi, A.L. (1999). Turning brain into blood: A hematopoietic fate adopted by adult neural stem cells *in vivo. Science* **283,** 534–537.

58. Shamblott, M., Axelman, J., Littlefield, J., Blumenthal, P., Huggins, G., Cui, Y., Cheng, L., and Gearhart, J. (2001). Human embryonic germ cell derivatives express a broad range of developmentally distinct markers and proliferate extensively *in vitro. Proc. Natl. Acad. Sci. USA* **98,** 113–118.

59. Counter, C.M., Hahn, W.C., Wei, W., Caddle, S.D., Beijersbergen, R.L., Lansdorp, P.M., Sedivy, J.M., and Weinberg, R.A. (1998). Dissociation among *in vitro* telomerase activity, telomere maintenance, and cellular immortalization. *Proc. Natl. Acad. Sci. USA* **95,** 14,723–14,728.

60. Onyango, P. (2002). Monoallelic expression and methylation of imprinted genes in human and mouse embryonic germ cell lineages. *Proc. Natl. Acad. Sci. USA* **99,** 10,599–10,604.

61. Migeon, B.R., Lee, C.H., Chowdhury, A.K., and Carpenter, H. (2002). Species differences in TSIX/Tsix reveal the roles of these genes in X-chromosome inactivation. *Am. J. Hum. Genet.* **71,** 286–293.

62. Kerr, D.A., Llado, J., Shamblott, M.J., Maragakis, N.J., Irani, D.N., Crawford, T.O., Krishan, C., Dike, S., Gearhart, J.D., and Rothstein, J.D. (2003). Human embryonic germ cell derivatives facilitate motor recovery of rats with diffuse motor neuron injury. *J. Neurosci.* **23,** 5131–5140.

Isolation and Maintenance of Avian ES Cells

James N. Petitte

Introduction

Since the first reports of the isolation and characterization of pluripotent cell lines derived from mouse blastocysts, avian biologists have watched the application of murine embryonic stem (ES) cells in experimental biology with some envy, particularly when ES cells have been used to generate targeted changes to the mouse genome. Hence, the main impetus for the isolation and culture of avian ES cells has been the hope that such cells could be used to generate transgenic birds with specific modifications to the avian genome. To date, this has not been accomplished. However, before that goal could be attempted without futility, it was necessary to adapt the various technical strategies used with mice to the avian system. For example, methods to produce avian germ line chimeras needed to be developed so that chimeras with reasonable rates of germ line transmission could be produced from ES cells.[1,2] In addition, the survival to hatch of windowed and manipulated eggs needed to become more routine to improve the efficiency of producing chimeras.[3–5] Given the current limitations associated with the production of transgenic chickens through the microinjection of DNA or the use of retroviral vectors,[6] the culture of pluripotent avian ES cells would be a valuable tool for a variety of applications in the laboratory and the industrial arena.

Nevertheless, over the last decade or so, work on the isolation and culture of avian ES cells has proceeded with significant progress. In general, two experimental strategies have been employed with varying degrees of success. Both strategies are based upon similar approaches used to isolate mammalian ES cells from early embryos but with specific modifications for the distinctiveness of the avian embryo. Specifically, blastodermal cells are isolated from the unincubated embryo,[7] or primordial germ cells (PGCs) are isolated from the indifferent embryonic gonad.[8] Both sources of cells are usually cultured on a feeder layer system much like that for mammalian ES cells. What follows are procedures for the isolation and culture of chick ES cells. The outlined procedures are general but detailed enough for any laboratory to gain initial experience in avian ES cell culture.

Tissue Culture Materials

GENERAL CONSIDERATIONS

A basic cell culture facility is required. Essential pieces of equipment include a laminar flow biosafety cabinet, a CO_2 incubator, an inverted microscope with phase contrast, and a clinical centrifuge. The use of disposable glassware is highly recommended if not a requirement. High-quality water is important, and a good reverse-osmosis water system or double glass-distilled water is recommended when making solutions, media, or tissue culture supplements. Alternatively, liquid media and reagents can be purchased.

Whenever possible, all procedures should be carried out using sterile techniques. In some cases, this is not strictly possible—for example, during early embryo isolation. In those circumstances, it is possible to work at the laboratory bench and avoid contamination if care is taken.

CULTURE MEDIA AND SOLUTIONS

Medium

All procedures use Dulbecco's modified Eagle's medium (DMEM) without pyruvate and with high glucose. It is recommended that tissue culture media be purchased in liquid form to maintain consistency (e.g., Invitrogen). If using powdered medium, it is important to insure that the media is made properly. It should be dissolved in distilled water, buffered with the recommended amount of sodium bicarbonate, adjusted to pH 7.2 using hydrogen chloride, and diluted to the final volume before sterilization through a 0.2-μm filter. It is also recommended to incubate a sample of the medium in the CO_2 incubator to assess the sterility and the proper adjustment of pH. Disposable, sterile plastic bottles are recommended over sterile glass bottles to avoid traces of cleaning detergents, etc. All media, whether prepared from powder or bought in liquid form, should be stored at 4°C. Media stored longer than 14 days should be supplemented with 1 mM glutamine.

Trypsin–EDTA

This is routinely used for the dissociation of cells and can be purchased as 10X stocks. Unless otherwise noted, trypsin–EDTA solutions contain 0.25% trypsin and 0.04% EDTA × 4Na in Hank's balanced salt solution without magnesium or calcium.

Handbook of Stem Cells
Volume 1

Phosphate-Buffered Saline

The recommended phosphate-buffered saline (PBS, pH 7.4) is the calcium- and magnesium-free formulation unless otherwise noted.

Antibiotics

Media are always supplemented with antibiotics, e.g., penicillin, and streptomycin. This is necessary, particularly with the initiation of cultures since blastodermal cells are not isolated in sterile environments. It is also recommended to add antibiotics to PBS during the isolation of blastodermal cells. Antimycotics should only be considered if yeast or fungal contamination becomes a problem.

Serum

Fetal bovine serum (FBS) is used as supplement to culture ES cells and in the preparation of feeder layers and conditioned media. Sera prequalified for mouse ES cell culture is recommended. Alternatively, serum that has been hybridoma qualified can be used, but it still should be tested in-house for the culture of murine or avian ES cells. This can be done using an established murine ES cell line such as ES-D3 (ATCC No. CRL-1934). In addition, heat-treating serum at 56°C for 30 minutes can inactivate the complement.

Preparation of Feeder Layers and BRL-Conditioned Media

Feeder layers and buffalo rat liver (BRL)-conditioned media provide the best culture conditions for the isolation and maintenance of avian ES cells. Mitotically inactivated primary chicken fibroblasts have not been successful for the culture of chicken ES cells even though they have been used for the culture of mouse ES cells.[9] Other published procedures use a combination of feeder layers, a cocktail of cytokines, and even an antibody against retinoic acid to avoid retinoic acid-induced differentiation.[7] However, the combination of a fibroblast feeder layer and BRL-conditioned media has been relatively reliable and is recommended here for those who wish to begin avian ES cell culture. The feeder layer of choice is made of STO fibroblasts or from SNL 76/7 cells, which were derived from STO cells.

ROUTINE CULTURE OF STO CELLS

STO cells (ATCC No. CRL-1503) can be cultured in 100-mm dishes or in tissue culture flasks. Typical media is DMEM with 10% FBS supplemented with antibiotics. Media should be changed every 2 days. When confluent, the cells are passaged as follows:

1. Remove the medium and wash the surface with 5–10 ml of PBS.
2. Add 2–5 ml of trypsin–EDTA media (0.05–0.02%) to the dish or flask and incubate for 5–10 minutes at 37°C. Periodically examine the cells under an inverted microscope until the cells detach from the bottom.
3. Inhibit the trypsin by adding 2–5 ml of DMEM with 10% FB. Pipette the cells to generate a single cell suspension.
4. Add 50 ml of DMEM with 10% FB, mix well, and distribute to 5–10 plates or flasks.
5. After 4–5 days, the cells will grow to 90% confluence and should be subcultured or frozen.

PREPARATION OF FEEDER LAYERS STOCKS

1. Expand the cultures of STO cells to T-150 flasks, as outlined previously, to near confluency.
2. Aspirate the medium, and rinse with 10-ml PBS.
3. Remove the PBS, add 7 ml trypsin–EDTA, and incubate for 10 minutes at 37°C. Check the cells during incubation until they lift off the bottom.
4. Add 10 ml of media with serum and pipette the cells up and down several times. Pool the dispersed cells into a 50-ml conical centrifuge tube.
5. Pellet the cells at $200 \times g$ for 10 minutes, remove the supernatant, add DMEM with 20% FBS, and place on ice.
6. Irradiate the tubes with 3000 rads from a gamma source to mitotically inactivate the STO cells.
7. Count the cells using a hemacytometer and dilute, if needed, to about 1×10^7 cells/ml.
8. Add an equal volume of 20% FBS and 20% DMSO in DMEM; add dropwise on ice while swirling the tube.
9. Aliquot 1 ml to cryovials, label, and place in a precooled freezing container.
10. Place the container in a −70°C freezer overnight; the next day, place in liquid nitrogen.

PREPARATION OF FEEDER LAYERS FROM FROZEN STOCKS

1. Rapidly thaw cryovials of irradiated STO cells in a 37°C water bath.
2. Mix the cells in a cryovial by inversion and swab with 70% ethanol.
3. Open the vial and remove a 20-μl aliquot; mix 1:1 with trypan blue solution.
4. Count the viable and nonviable cells.
5. Dilute the irradiated cells in a complete medium at a concentration required to yield a confluent monolayer of cells, about 3×10^5 cells/ml.
6. Seed the cells onto gelatinized dishes, about 5×10^4 cells/cm².
7. The cells should attach and give a monolayer overnight. Observe the dishes the next day. If the cells are too sparse, new cells can be added. Otherwise, replace the media and use the cells in a few days.

PREPARATION OF BRL-CONDITIONED MEDIA

A BRL-conditioned medium is used as a supplement for the culture of chicken ES cells. Media conditioned by BRL cells have also been used to culture mouse ES cells.[10]

BRL Culture Medium

- High glucose DMEM (-pyruvate, -glutamine)
- 20% Heat-inactivated FBS (ES cell-qualified recommended)

- Penicillin-Streptomycin-Glutamine (100X) (Invitrogen Cat. No. 10378016)
- Nonessential amino acids solution, 10 mM (100X) (Invitrogen Cat. No. 11140050)
- Nucleosides (100X) (Specialty Media #ES-008-D)
- 1/100 volume of β-mercaptoethanol stock (stock is 7 μl β-ME in 10 ml DMEM)

CULTURE OF BRL CELLS

1. Seed the culture flasks with BRL 3A cells (ATCC No. CRL-1442) and grow the cells to confluency.
2. Incubate the cells with fresh media for 3 days at 37°C.
3. After the third day, removed the media, filter, and store between −20°C and −70°C. Replace the flasks with fresh media.
4. Repeat the procedure for up to 2 weeks to generate stocks of BRL-conditioned medium.

Collection of Stage X Embryos

Reproduction in birds is characterized by the oviposition of a calcified egg containing a large yolk-filled ovum surrounded by layers of albumen. Fertilization takes place in the infundibulum of the oviduct and is polyspermic; many sperm nuclei can be found after penetration of the vitelline membrane.[11] Nevertheless, only one sperm nucleus will fuse with the nucleus of the ovum. Subsequently, the fertilized egg enters the magnum, where a firm albumen capsule encases the ovum. As it passes through the isthmus, the outer and inner shell membranes are laid down in preparation for deposition of the eggshell. At this point, the fertilized ovum has spent 3.5–4 hours in the oviduct. The first cleavage divisions occur upon entry of the ovum into the shell gland or uterus. The egg spends the longest time in the shell gland, taking an additional 20–22 hours to complete formation of the eggshell. A considerable amount of cell division occurs during eggshell formation. When the egg is laid, the disk-shaped embryo or blastoderm contains 50,000–60,000 cells lying on the surface of the yolk. Generally, the blastoderm can be divided into a peripheral ring of cells attached to the yolk, called the area opaca, and a central, more translucent region, the area pellucida. The area pellucida is suspended above a nonyolky fluid deposited by the embryo. In general, the area opaca will contribute only to extraembryonic structures. Upon incubation, the area pellucida differentiates into two layers, an upper epiblast and a lower hypoblast. Only the epiblast will generate the embryo proper; the hypoblast contributes to some extraembryonic tissues. This period of development (i.e., fertilization through hypoblast formation) has been classified into a series of 14 stages for the domestic hen using Roman numerals.[12] Subsequent stages are classified using the staging system of Hamburger and Hamilton, which uses Arabic numerals.[13,14] Chicken ES cells are derived from cells of the area pellucida in the stage X embryo. To use cells from the stage X embryo to initiate ES cell culture, it is necessary to have a ready source of freshly laid chicken eggs. This is best accomplished with a flock of hens and roosters in either a natural mating or a battery cage system with artificial insemination. In either case, only freshly laid eggs yield enough embryos at stage X. Therefore, all eggs should be collected at the end of the day so that on the next day, only newly laid eggs are used to collect stage X embryos.

EQUIPMENT

- Standard dissection microscope with 6–40× magnification.
- Fiber-optic light source with a portable dark field–bright field stage (Chiu Technical Corporation, DKR-24 Base) (Fig. 44–1)
- Fine forceps and iris scissors
- Filter paper rings made from Whatman No. 1 filter paper cut with a paper punch
- Wooden applicator sticks, parafilm, fine human hair, cactus needles
- Sterile PBS and sterile glass Pasteur pipettes
- Sterile 100-mm Petri dishes
- Sterile microtubes (0.5 ml)
- Freshly laid chicken eggs

EMBRYO STAGING AND ISOLATION

1. Collect the freshly laid eggs and swab the eggs with 70% ethanol. Place a Petri dish with 15 ml of PBS on the dark field stage under the dissection microscope.
2. Crack the egg on its side and separate the albumen from the yolk. Place the yolk with the embryo side up in a Petri dish.
3. Place a filter paper ring over the embryo, visible as a pale white ring in a fertile egg. The germinal disk of an infertile egg is visible as a prominent, small (2-mm) white spot.
4. Allow the filter paper to absorb to the surface of the yolk and vitelline membrane, then cut the membrane around the filter paper with the iris scissors.

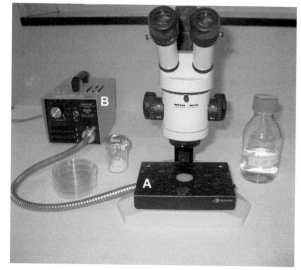

Figure 44–1. *Typical setup for the isolation and staging of unincubated chicken embryos. The equipment includes (A) a fiber-optic light source with (B) a portable dark field stage under a dissection microscope. Other items include Petri dishes, PBS, fine forceps, and fine scissors.*

5. After the ring is partially cut, hold the ring with fine forceps and finish cutting the embryo from the yolk.

6. Slowly peel the ring from the yolk with an upward motion until the ring is held vertically by the forceps. Some yolk will adhere to the ring–embryo.

7. Slowly immerse the edge of the ring into the Petri dish containing about 15 ml of PBS. As the ring–embryo is submerged, some yolk may float on the PBS.

8. When the ring reaches the bottom of the dish, orient the ring so that the ventral side of the embryo is the uppermost portion (Fig. 44–2A and 44–2B). At this point, the embryo needs to be cleaned of yolk. Hold the filter paper during cleaning with one tine of the fine forceps.

9. While looking through the dissection scope, slowly remove the yolk from the embryo using a hair loop half the size of the diameter of the embryo, about 3 mm. Hair loops can be made using a small strip of parafilm wound around a wooden applicator stick. Simply attach one end of the hair to the stick, loop the other end, then wrap that end with parafilm. If needed, a fine needle can be made using a cactus needle.

10. Remove the yolk from the center of the embryo to the periphery.

11. Once most of the yolk is removed, final cleanup and staging can be done using a Pasteur pipette. Using a blue pipette bulb, gently pulse PBS over the embryo to remove the remaining yolk.

12. Examine the embryo carefully to determine the stage. Stage X embryos are recommended for ES cell culture.

13. Using the hair loop, cut a circle in the central ⅓ of the embryo (Fig. 44–2C).

14. Once a cut is made, use the hair loop–cactus needle to remove the outer portion of the cut embryo, leaving only the central area (Fig. 44–2D).

15. While holding the filter paper ring with one tine of the forceps, use the hair loop to tease the disk off the vitelline membrane. This is best done by slipping the hair loop under the disk.

16. Hold the disk above the filter paper with the hair loop, then slide the filter paper ring out from under the disk. Then place the isolated disk back on the bottom of the dish.

17. Transfer the disk to a microtube containing about 200 µl of calcium- and magnesium-free PBS.

18. Collect about 10 central disks to initiate a culture. Alternatively, place one disk–tube to initiate a culture from a single embryo.

Practice is the key to getting proficient at embryo isolation. Expect only half of the eggs to provide useful embryos. Most are lost because of yolk breakage, infertility, or early embryonic death. Staging of the embryos should become second nature. On occasions, embryos are incorrectly staged because rough handling can removed the hypoblast of a stage XIII embryo, making it look like a stage X one.

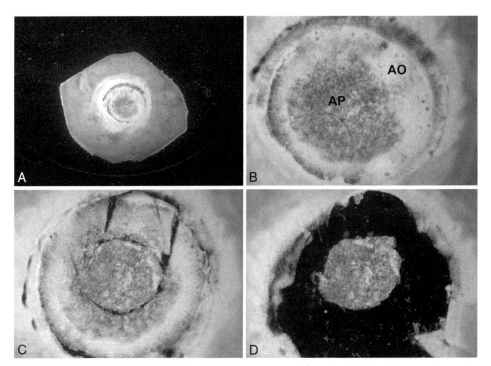

Figure 44–2. *Isolation of stage X central disk for ES cell culture.* (A) Embryos are removed from the yolk using a filter paper ring and are placed ventral side up in PBS. (B) A high magnification of a stage X embryo. The area pellucida (AP) and area opaca (AO) are indicated. (C) Using a hair loop, the central disk of the AP is cut. (D) An isolated central disk. Cells from the central disk are used to initiate ES cell culture.

Initiation of ES Cell Cultures

PREPARATION OF CULTURE MEDIA

To prepare 100 ml of CES-80 media, add the following:

- 80 ml BRL-conditioned media (pH 7.5)
- 10 ml FBS
- 8.8 ml DMEM
- 0.2 ml 55 mM β-mercaptoethanol
- 1 ml 100 mM sodium pyruvate

CHICKEN ES CELL CULTURE

1. The day before embryo isolation, prepare gamma-irradiated STO feeders in gelatinized 6- or 12-well tissue culture plates. Immediately before embryo isolation, replace the feeder media with CES-80 media.
2. Isolate the blastodermal cells from the area pellucida of stage X embryos as described in the section "Embryo Staging and Isolation."
3. Once enough disks are collected (10–40, depending on the well size), gently disperse the cells 4–5 times with a 1000 μl pipette.
4. Centrifuge at $300 \times g$ in a variable-speed microcentrifuge for 5 minutes.
5. Remove the supernatant and discard. Add 300–600 μl of CES-80 to the pellet and resuspend.
6. Count the cells on a hemacytometer and seed onto the previously prepared feeders. For a 12-well plate, seed 100,000–140,000 cells for each well; for a 6-well plate, seed 230,000–300,000 cells.

7. Incubate the cells at 37°C/5% CO_2 and replace media each day (2.5 ml for a 12-well plate and 6 ml for a 6-well plate). Sometimes it is necessary to change the media twice a day, morning and evening, if the cells are growing rapidly.
8. Passage the cells when ES-like colonies are prominent and the feeder layer begins to deteriorate.
9. A new STO feeder must be seeded one day prior to passaging.

Identification of ES Cells

Colonies of cells with an ES cell phenotype become apparent after about 1 week of culture (Fig. 44–3A). The blastodermal cells attached to the feeder layer lose their obvious lipid droplets, and take on characteristics typical of mammalian ES cells, i.e., a large nucleus with a prominent single nucleolus (Fig. 44–3A and 44–3B). Unlike mammalian ES cells, the chicken stem cells do not form raised colonies but tend to invade the feeder later and attach directly to the plastic culture dish. Avoid overgrown cultures to prevent differentiation (Fig. 44–3C and 44–3D). Many of the markers associated with mammalian ES cells are also expressed on chicken ES cells. These include SSEA-1 and EMA-1, but chicken ES cells do not express Oct-4. At the same time, alkaline phosphatase is not a distinguishing marker of chicken ES cells since all cells are positive for alkaline phosphatase in the early embryo.

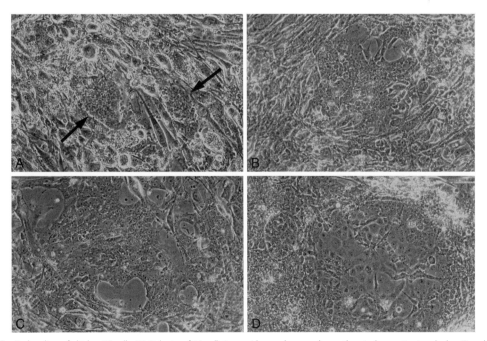

Figure 44–3. *Early culture of chicken ES cells.* (A) Colonies of ES cells (arrows) have a large nucleus with a single prominent nucleolus. (B and C) Expansion of the ES cells. (B) The cells are ready for passage. (D) The large colony is overgrown and has begun differentiate. Ideally, the ES cells expand without losing the typical stem cell phenotype.

Expansion and Subculture of ES Cells

In early cultures, it may be necessary to passage the entire plate onto a new plate since the number of colonies remains small. This approach is useful until the number of ES cells increases. Picking individual colonies and placing them onto a new feeder layer is possible, but only a fraction of the colonies would be expected to survive. It is likely that passaging the entire plate onto a new plate simply selects the most robust cells.

PASSAGE

1. For passage, remove the media and wash the cells twice with PBS. Add cold 0.05% trypsin–0.53-mM EDTA to the well (100 μl for a 12-well plate and 250 μl for a 6-well plate). Immediately observe under a microscope.
2. When the ES cells begin to detach (30 seconds–2 minutes), add CES-80 (1 ml for a 12-well plate and 2.5 ml for a 6-well plate) and aspirate the cells off the dish bottom.
3. Split the cell suspension to two new feeders layers prepared the day before.

Freezing and Thawing ES Cells

Stem cell cultures can be frozen for banking and thawed to recover early passages. This is done by pooling the contents of six-well plates. The stem cells are frozen with the associated feeder cells.

1. Add 0.25 ml of cold 0.05% trypsin–0.53-mM EDTA to each well of a six-well plate. Immediately observe under a microscope when the colonies begin to detach.
2. Add 2 ml of CES-80 and with a 5-ml pipette, gently pipette all cells from the plate.
3. Pool the cell suspension from several plates to a 15-ml centrifuge tube and centrifuge 5 minutes at $300 \times g$.
4. Carefully resuspend pellet in 0.25-ml DMEM with 20% FBS for each original well.
5. Dropwise, add 0.25 ml of cryopreservation medium containing DMEM, 20% FBS, and 20% DMSO.
6. In each cryovial, add 0.5–1.0 ml of cells.
7. Transfer the cells to a Nalgene freezing container (Fisher Cat. No. 15-350-50) and place at −70°C overnight.
8. Transfer the cells to liquid nitrogen.
9. To recover frozen cells, prepare fresh STO feeder layers the day before.
10. Thaw each cryovial in a 37°C water bath.
11. Swab the cryovial in 95% ethanol. Allow the vial to air dry before opening it.
12. Pipette cells from the vial into a 15-ml conical centrifuge tube.
13. Slowly, add 9.5 ml of CES-80 media dropwise, gently mix, and pellet at $150 \times g$ for 5 minutes.
14. Resuspend in 2.0 ml of CES-80 to seed into one well of a six-well plate.
15. Change the medium the next morning.

Other Approaches

Many of the approaches toward the culture of avian ES cells have taken a cue from procedures for the mouse with varying degrees of success. The procedures outlined previously are based upon the work of one laboratory.[15] Although the number of groups actively developing avian ES cells is small, it is worth reviewing other approaches.

Etches et al.[16] tested the culture of intact blastoderms and dispersed blastodermal cells cultured in a monolayer or with a confluent layer of mouse fibroblasts. After 48 hours of culture, the cells were injected into stage X embryos to generate somatic and germ line chimeras. More somatic chimeras were generated when the blastodermal cells were cultured on the feeder layer, but contributions to the germ line did not differ based upon the culture treatment. Immortal cell lines from the unincubated chicken blastoderm have been derived without a feeder layer, but the ability of this to form functional chimeras has not been documented.[17] Pain et al.[7] reported on the long-term culture of ES cells from stage X chicken embryos using a combination of growth factors and an antibody to retinoic acid. The cells were capable of differentiation into various cell types in vitro and could be used to produce somatic chimeras. To generate cultures of transgenic cells, it may be possible to enrich the starting cultures with cells that express the gene of interest[18] or to transfect established blastoderm-derived stem cells.[19]

In addition to blastodermal cells, the culture of ES cells from PGCs has been tested, usually for short-term culture. Allioli et al.[20] cultured gonadal PGCs harvested from day 5 embryos for four days. Initially, some cell death was observed; this was followed by a period of proliferation. The embryos could be infected with a retroviral vector that expressed lacZ. Chang et al.[21] isolated blood PGCs and cultured them on a feeder layer of stromal cells obtained from day 5 gonadal ridges. They noted an increase in the number of germ cells over 4 days. The cultures were supplemented with leukemia inhibitory factor (LIF), insulin-like growth factor-I (IGF-I), and basic fibroblast growth factor (bFGF). Similarly, Chang et al.[22] cultured PGCs from stage 27 germinal ridges for 5 days and proliferated on the stromal cells that arose from the germinal ridge. In this case, the PGCs were shown to retain their ability to migrate back to the gonad when injected into the blood stream of day 2.5 embryos. In a subsequent study, it was demonstrated that gonadal PGCs cultured for 5 days and injected into recipient embryos produce chickens that transmitted the donor genotype to about 3% of the offspring.[23] Recently, Park et al.[8] described the establishment of ES cells from gonadal PGCs that could be cultured for several months. Interestingly, the ES cells could only be established using chicken feeder layers that were not mitotically inactivated and did not attach to the feeder layer like other ES cell cultures. The reasons for this remain unknown, but the cultures were supplemented with stem cell factor, interleukin-11, LIF, bFGF, and IGF-I. Subsequently, it was reported that these cells could be used to make germ line chimeras.[24] Unfortunately, no one to date has used avian ES cells to produce a line of transgenic chicken. However, given the success of mammalian ES cells as a tool for experimental biology, it is likely only a matter of time before it will be possible to develop transgenic chickens using cultured cells from either source.

REFERENCES

1. Petitte, J.N., Clark, M.E., Liu, G., Verrinder Gibbins, A.M., and Etches, R.J. (1990). Production of somatic and germ line chimeras in the chicken by transfer of early blastodermal cells. *Development* **108**, 185–189.
2. Carsience, R.S., Clark, M.E., Verrinder Gibbins, A.M., and Etches, R.J. (1993). Germ line chimeric chickens from dispersed donor blastodermal cells and compromised recipient embryos. *Development* **117**, 669–675.
3. Perry, M.M. (1988). A complete culture system for the chick embryo. *Nature* **331**, 70–72.
4. Speksnijder, G., and Ivarie, R. (2000). A modified method of shell windowing for producing somatic or germ line chimeras in fertilized chicken eggs. *Poult. Sci.* **79**, 1430–1433.
5. Borwornpinyo, S. (2000). "Optimal Hatchability of Cultured Chicken Embryos from Freshly Laid Eggs in Surrogate Eggshells." M.S. thesis, North Carolina State University.
6. Mozdziak, P.E., Borwornpinyo, S., McCoy, D.W., and Petitte, J.N. (2003). Development of transgenic chickens expressing bacterial β-galactosidase. *Dev. Dyn.* **226**, 439–445.
7. Pain, B., Clark, M.E., Shen, M., Nakazawa, H., Sakurai, M., Samarut, J., and Etches, R.J. (1996). Long-term *in vitro* culture and characterization of avian embryonic stem cells with multiple morphogenetic potentialities. *Development* **122**, 2339–2348.
8. Park, T.S., and Han, J.Y. (2000). Derivation and characterization of pluripotent embryonic germ cells in chicken. *Mol. Reprod. Dev.* **56**, 475–482.
9. Yang, Z., and Petitte, J.N. (1994). Use of avian cytokines in mammalian embryonic stem cell culture. *Poult. Sci.* **73**, 965–974.
10. Hooper, M., Hardy, K., Handyside, A., Hunter, S., and Monk, M. (1987). HPRT-deficient (Lesch-Nyhan) mouse embryos derived from germ line colonization by cultured cells. *Nature* **326**, 292–295.
11. Perry, M.M. (1987). Nuclear events from fertilization to the early cleavage stages in the domestic fowl *(Gallus domesticus). J. Anat.* **150**, 99–109.
12. Eyal-Giladi, H., and Kochav, S. (1976). From cleavage to primitive streak formation: A complementary normal table and a new look at the first stages of the development of the chick—I. General morphology. *Dev. Biol.* **49**, 321–337.
13. Hamburger, V., and Hamilton, H.L. (1951). A series of normal stages in the development of the chick embryo. *J. Morphol.* **88**, 49–92.
14. Hamburger, V., and Hamilton, H.L. (1992). A series of normal stages in the development of the chick embryo. (First printed in 1951.) *Dev. Dyn.* **195**, 231–272.
15. Petitte, J.N., and Yang, Z. (1994). Method of producing an avian embryonic stem cell culture, and the avian embryonic stem cell culture produced by the process. U.S. Patent No. 5340740.
16. Etches, R.J., Clark, M.E., Toner, A., Liu, G., and Gibbins, A.M. (1996). Contributions to somatic and germ line lineages of chicken blastodermal cells maintained in culture. *Mol. Reprod. Dev.* **45**, 291–298.
17. Tsai, H. (1995). "Blastodermal Cells: The Way to the Germ Line." Ph.D. thesis, University of Wisconsin-Madison.
18. Wei, Q., Croy, B.A., and Etches, R.J. (2001). Selection of genetically modified chicken blastodermal cells by magnetic-activated cell sorting. *Poult. Sci.* **80**, 1671–1678.
19. Pain, B., Chenevier, P., and Samarut, J. (1999). Chicken embryonic stem cells and transgenic strategies. *Cells Tiss. Organs* **165**, 212–219.
20. Allioli, N., Thomas, J.L., Chebloune, Y., Nigon, V.M., Verdier, G., and Legras, C. (1994). Use of retroviral vectors to introduce and express the β-galactosidase marker gene in cultured chicken primordial germ cells. *Dev. Biol.* **165**, 30–37.
21. Chang, I.K., Tajima, A., Chikamune, T., and Ohno, T. (1995). Proliferation of chick primordial germ cells cultured on stroma cells from the germinal ridge. *Cell Biol. Int.* **19**, 143–149.
22. Chang, I.K., Yoshiki, A., Kusakabe, M., Tajima, A., Chikamune, T., Naito, M., and Ohno, T. (1995). Germ line chimera produced by transfer of cultured chick primordial germ cells. *Cell Biol. Int.* **19**, 569–576.
23. Chang, I.K., Jeong, D.K., Hong, Y.H., Park, T.S., Moon, Y.K., Ohno, T., and Han, J.Y. (1997). Production of germ line chimeric chickens by transfer of cultured primordial germ cells. *Cell Biol. Int.* **21**, 495–499.
24. Park, T.S., Hong, Y.H., Kwon, S.C., Lim, J.M., and Han, J.Y. (2003). Birth of germ line chimeras by transfer of chicken embryonic germ (EG) cells into recipient embryos. *Mol. Reprod. Dev.* **65**, 389–395.

Isolation and Maintenance of Trophoblast Stem Cells

Tilo Kunath and Janet Rossant

Introduction

Trophoblast stem (TS) cell lines can be derived from mouse blastocysts and early trophoblast tissue. The protocols and reagents described here are for the maintenance and derivation of TS cell lines.[1] Slight variations from the procedures or the suppliers of reagents are probably acceptable.

Reagents

The following reagents should be prepared before attempting to derive or culture TS cell lines.

FIBROBLAST GROWTH FACTOR 4 AND HEPARIN STOCKS

Stock solutions of 1000X FGF4 (25 μg/ml) and 1000X heparin (1.0 mg/ml) are prepared and stored at −80°C. Human recombinant fibroblast growth factor 4 (FGF4) (Sigma, Cat. No. F8424, or R&D Systems, Cat. No. 235-F4, 25 μg) is used, but other FGF ligands work as well. We found that aFGF (Sigma, Cat. No. F5542) and bFGF (Sigma, Cat. No. F0291) also maintained TS cells in culture at 25 ng/ml. However, derivation of TS cell lines with these other FGFs has not been attempted.

1. Prepare phosphate-buffered saline (PBS)/0.1% weight per volume (w/v) bovine serum albumin (BSA, 10 ml) by dissolving BSA, fraction V (10 mg, Sigma, Cat. No. A3311) in PBS without Ca^{2+}/Mg^{2+} (10 ml). Filter (0.45 μm) and aliquot (1.05–1.10 ml) to 9- or 1.5-ml microphuge tubes. Store at −80°C until needed.
2. Resuspend lyophilized FGF4 (or aFGF or bFGF) in its vial with 1.0 ml of PBS/0.1% (w/v) BSA (fraction V). Mix well with a P200 set at 100 μl, make 10 aliquots (10 × 100 μl) into 1.5-ml microphuge tubes, and freeze at −80°C. Thaw each aliquot as needed and store it at 4°C. The ligand is stable for 2 weeks at 4°C; do not refreeze.

3. Resuspend heparin (Sigma, Cat. No. H3149, 10,000 units) in PBS to a final concentration of 1.0 mg/ml (1000X) and store at −80°C in 1-ml aliquots. Thaw each aliquot as needed and store it at 4°C. This has a long shelf life at 4°C.

TS CELL MEDIA

TS cell medium (TSC medium, 650 ml) is prepared by adding reagents to RPMI 1640 + antibiotics (500 ml), as shown in Table 45–1.

EMBRYONIC FIBROBLAST-CONDITIONED MEDIUM

Embryonic fibroblast-conditioned medium (EMFI-CM) is used to culture TS cells in the absence of EMFIs. Plate mitomycin C–treated EMFIs in 100-mm dishes (2×10^6 cells; 2×10^5 cells/ml) and culture in TSC medium (10.0–10.5 ml/dish) for at least 72 hours (3 days). Collect the medium, spin to remove floating cells and debris, filter (0.45 μm), and store at −20°C in 10-ml aliquots. Thaw each aliquot as needed and store at 4°C; do not refreeze. Use the EMFIs to prepare two more batches of EMFI-CM, and then discard the cells. EMFIs are only used up to 10 days after the mitomycin C treatment.

OTHER MEDIUMS

The amounts of other media are shown in Table 45–2.

Derivation of TS Cell Lines from Blastocysts

The derivation of TS cell lines from embryonic day 3.5 (E3.5) mouse blastocysts is similar to the derivation of embryonic stem (ES) cell lines.[2,3] However, the success rate is considerably higher and less expertise is required to recognize pluripotent TS cell colonies. Instead of leukemia inhibitory factor as the pluripotent factor, FGF4 is used.

1. Set up matings (natural or superovulated) between the mice of interest.
2. Prepare four-well plates of mitomycin C–treated EMFIs (5×10^4 cells; 500 μl of 1×10^5 cells/ml/well) in TSC medium the day of or the day before flushing the blastocysts.
3. Replace the TSC medium with TSC + F4H medium (500 μl per well) prior to collecting blastocysts (day 1).

TABLE 45-1
TSC Medium

	Volume	Final Concentration	Stock Concentration	Supplier
RPMI 1640 + antibiotics[a]	500 ml			
Fetal bovine serum	130 ml	20%	100%	Gibco
Sodium pyruvate	6.5 ml	1 mM	100 mM	Gibco
β-Mercaptoethanol	6.5 ml	100 μM	10 mM	Sigma
L-Glutamine	6.5 ml	2 mM	200 mM	Gibco

[a]Antibiotics = penicillin and streptomycin at 50 mg/ml each.

4. Flush and collect E3.5 blastocysts.[2] In sterile conditions, place one blastocyst per well in the four-well plates containing TSC + F4H medium and culture at 37°C/5% CO_2.

5. The blastocysts should hatch from the zona pellucida and attach to the wells in 24–36 hours (day 2).

6. On day 3, a small outgrowth is formed from each embryo. Aspirate and feed each culture with TSC + F4H medium (500 μl). If an outgrowth has not formed yet, just feed with TSC + F4H medium (200 μl).

7. On day 4, the outgrowth is usually disaggregated. However, this will depend on its size; it is smaller than the size of the outgrowth disaggregated for ES cell line derivation. Larger outgrowths will work but with less efficiency.

8. Once suitable outgrowths have been chosen, they may be disaggregated by different means. The microdrop technique may be used.[3] However, we perform the disaggregation directly in the wells they were cultured in. Aspirate the medium and wash the cells with PBS (500 μl). Aspirate the PBS, add 0.1% trypsin–EDTA (100 μl), and incubate for 5 minutes at 37°C/5% CO_2. Using a P2 pipetteman or a drawn Pasteur pipette disaggregate the clump by pipetting up and down vigorously until the outgrowth is reduced to small clumps of cells. Immediately stop the trypsinization by adding 70cond + 1.5X F4H (400 μl) and return to the incubator.

9. Change the medium 24 hours after the disaggregation (70cond + 1.5X F4H, 500 μl).

TABLE 45-2
Other Media

TSC + F4H medium (e.g., 10 ml)		70cond + F4H medium (e.g., 10 ml)	
TSC medium	10 ml	EMFI-CM	7 ml
1000X FGF4	10 μl	TSC medium	3 ml
1000X heparin	10 μl	1000X FGF4	10 μl
		1000X heparin	10 μl

10. Two days later (day 7), aspirate and feed each culture (70cond + F4H, 500 μl). Continue to refeed every 2 to 3 days.

11. Between day 7 and day 11 (highly variable), TS cell colonies will begin to appear. They look like flat, epithelial sheets with a distinctive colony boundary.[1] They have been previously described as "epithelioid cells."[3]

12. Continue to feed the cultures until the TS cell colonies become sufficiently large to cover about 50% of the well or until the colonies start to appear overgrown. Some differentiation will be observed at the edges of the colonies. This is normal; they are most often giant cells and other intermediate trophoblast cell types.

13. Passage the half-confluent well of TS cells to a 6-well plate or a 35-mm dish of preplated EMFIs (1×10^5 cells/ml) (day 15 to day 20). If the number of colonies is low, the cells may be passaged to another 4-well plate or to a 12-well plate. Aspirate the medium and wash TS cells with PBS (500 μl). Aspirate the PBS, add trypsin–EDTA (100 μl), and incubate for 5 minutes at 37°C/5% CO_2. Stop the trypsinization by adding TSC + 1.5X F4H medium (400 μl) and pipetting up and down to get a near-single cell suspension. Transfer the cells to a 6-well plate or a 35-mm dish of TSC + 1.5X F4H medium (2 ml) on EMFIs. This first passage is crucial; this is the most likely time for the culture to differentiate.

14. Change the medium 24 hours after passage (TSC + 1.5X F4H medium, 2.5 ml).

15. Feed the cells every 2–3 days (TSC + F4H medium, 2.5 ml). There is often a large amount of giant cell differentiation for the first four to six passages. Even if the entire plate appears to have transformed into giant cells, TS cell colonies will still appear after 7–10 days. Follow the "Culturing TS Cell Lines" guidelines. After 6–7 more passages on EMFIs, TS cells may be cultured without them in 70cond + F4H medium.

Culturing TS Cell Lines

TS cells may be grown on EMFIs or regular tissue culture plastic (gelatin coating is not required). Newly derived lines should be passaged at least seven times before removing them from EMFIs.

CULTURING TS CELLS ON EMFIS

Plate mitomycin C-treated EMFIs at half the density (i.e., 1×10^5 cells/ml) used to culture ES cells and to prepare EMFI-CM. TS cells may be either plated on the EMFIs after they have adhered or coplated with the EMFIs. Prepare fresh TSC + F4H medium and culture TS cells in a standard tissue culture incubator ($37°C/5\%$ CO_2). The medium is normally changed every 2 days, and the cells are passaged (1 in 15 to 1 in 20) every fourth day or when the culture has reached approximately 80% confluency. Passaging TS cells at higher densities (i.e., 1 in 3 or 1 in 5) may lead to precocious differentiation. The cells are trypsinized to small clumps with some single cells. A complete single-cell suspension is not required, and it may even be detrimental to the culture. Trypsinizing for 3–4 minutes at $37°C$ with some pipetting up and down is usually sufficient.

CULTURING TS CELLS ON TISSUE CULTURE PLASTIC

TS cells grow well on standard tissue culture dishes if the medium is supplemented with EMFI-CM. The dishes do **not** need to be gelatin coated as mentioned by Tanaka *et al.*[1] The percentage of EMFI-CM used is 70%, and the rest is TSC medium (30%). Culture the TS cells in the 70cond + F4H; feed and passage the cells as described previously.

FREEZING TS CELLS

Prepare the following 2X freezing medium and cool to $4°C$:

- 50% FBS
- 30% TSC medium
- 20% DMSO

Lift and pellet TS cells. Resuspend the cells in TSC medium and add an equal volume of 2X freezing medium. Freeze the cells slowly at $-80°C$ overnight; transfer to liquid nitrogen after 48–72 hours. A confluent 100-mm dish has enough cells for about five vials.

THAWING TS CELLS

Hand-thaw a vial, put the contents over TSC medium (1 ml), and pellet. Resuspend the cells in TSC + F4H medium (5 ml) and plate over EMFIs (half-density) in a 60-mm plate.

Change the medium after 12–16 hours to get rid of the non-adherent cells. Feed 2 days later.

REMOVING EMFIS FROM TS CELL CULTURES

When switching from EMFIs to EMFI-CM, it may be desirable to get rid of the EMFIs immediately. The different adherence rates of EMFIs (fast) and TS cells (slow) can be used to obtain a pure TS cell population. Passage the cells to a new plate and incubate the culture for 1 hour at $37°C/5\%$ CO_2. Remove the supernatant and plate onto another tissue culture dish. This population of cells should consist almost entirely of TS cells. Since some TS cells do adhere with the EMFIs, the desired passage density may be increased a bit (e.g., 1 in 15 instead of 1 in 20). The originally plated TS cells may also be kept since some TS cells will have adhered with the EMFIs.

DNA TRANSDUCTION OF TS CELLS

Transfection of TS cells can be accomplished with Lipofectamine Plus (Gibco, Cat. No. 10964-013), following the manufacturer's instruction. Subconfluent TS cells (one day after passage) in six-well plates work well. For electroporation, collect near-confluent TS cells (5×10^6), resuspend in PBS (0.8 ml), and transfer to a Gene Pulser cuvette (0.4-cm electrode, BioRad Cat. No. 165-2088). Add linearized DNA (20 μg or less) and electroporate at 0.25 V and a capacitance of 500 μF. Incubate the cells on ice (20 minutes) and then plate in 70cond + F4H (10 ml) in a 100-mm plate. If necessary, drug selection (G418, 200 μg/ml) can begin 1 day later, and colonies can be picked as ES cell colonies are picked.[2,3]

REFERENCES

1. Tanaka, S., Kunath, T., Hadjantonakis, A.K., Nagy, A., and Rossant, J. (1998). Promotion of trophoblast stem cell proliferation by FGF4. *Science* **282,** 2072–2075.
2. Nagy, A., Gertsenstein, M., Vintersten, K., and Behringer, R. (2003). "Manipulating the Mouse Embryo: A Laboratory Manual," 3rd ed. Cold Spring Harbor Laboratory Press, Cold Spring Harbor, NY.
3. Robertson, E.J. (1987). "Teratocarcinomas and Embryonic Stem Cells: A Practical Approach," pp. 86–94. IRL Press, Oxford.

46

Isolation of Pluripotential Stem Cells from *Xenopus* Embryos

Miho Furue and Makoto Asashima

The blastocoelic roof (animal cap) of *Xenopus* eggs at the blastula stage is composed of a few layers of ectodermal cells fated to develop into epidermis and neural tissues during normal development. However, isolated animal caps from blastulae show pluripotency until the early gastrula stage. The isolated animal caps are cultured in a saline solution containing the inducing factor to be investigated, and the induced tissues are analyzed (animal cap assay). Without the inducing factor, the animal caps develop into atypical epidermis. Activin A, a member of the TGF-β family is a potent factor that can induce nearly all types of mesodermal and endodermal tissues, such as blood, muscle, brain, notochord, cartilage, and heart, in animal caps. Different concentrations of activin A trigger different gene cascades to initiate the differentiation of animal cap cells into different organ stem cells. Activin A, with retinoic acid (RA) treatment, also induces pronephros, pancreas, and liver. It is therefore theoretically possible to reproduce embryonic induction and design a fundamental embryonic form *in vitro*. The *Xenopus* animal cap is a useful tool, as the *Xenopus* pluripotential stem cells can be used to study embryonic development and differentiation and to further the field of tissue engineering.

Early Development of *Xenopus*

The cleaving *Xenopus* egg first forms a morula; this is followed by the blastula stage (Fig. 46–1). Signals from the vegetal hemisphere cells act on the overlying equatorial cells to induce the formation of mesoderm.[1–3] Following this, there is a marked change in gene expression causing maternal and paternal information to be generated. A cavity called the blastocoel develops inside the animal hemisphere. The roof of the blastocoel is known as the animal cap. The mesoderm on the leading edge of the dorsal marginal zone invaginates under the animal cap. The invaginating cells induce the central nervous system anlagen by secreting factors to the overlaying layer of ectodermal cells. This inductive phenomenon is called neural induction. The fundamental body patterning of the embryo is

established as a result of these inductive interactions during the process of *Xenopus* embryonic development.

Pluripotency of Animal Cap Cells

The blastocoelic roof (animal cap) is composed of a few layers of ectodermal cells fated to develop into epidermis and neural tissues during normal development. However, isolated animal caps from blastulae show pluripotency until the early gastrula stage. The isolated animal caps are cultured in a saline solution containing the inducing factor to be investigated, and the induced tissues are analyzed[4] (Fig. 46–2). Without the inducing factor, the animal caps develop into atypical epidermis. During the past decade, several members of the fibroblast growth factor and the transforming growth factor-β (TGF-β) families have been identified as factors that can induce various mesodermal tissues in the isolated animal caps.[5,6] Asashima found that activin A, a member of the TGF-β family, is a potent factor that can induce nearly all types of mesodermal and endodermal tissues in animal caps.[7–10]

ACTIVIN A

Activin A can convert the presumptive ectoderm cells that constitute *Xenopus* animal caps into mesoderm and endoderm. When animal cap cells are placed in saline solution containing activin A, different fates are initiated at different concentrations.[5,6,11–20] The effect of activin A on animal caps is therefore distinctly dose dependent, with increasing concentrations inducing more dorsal mesoderm (Fig. 46–3). Concentrations of 0.3–1 ng/ml of activin A induce ventral mesoderm such as blood cells, coelomic epithelium, and mesenchyme.[21,22] After treatment with 5–10 ng/ml of activin A, animal caps begin to elongate and differentiate into muscle.[23] This elongation is considered to mimic the convergent extension of dorsal mesoderm during gastrulation. At 50 ng/ml of activin A, notochord, the most dorsal mesoderm, is often induced with yolk-laden endoderm.[24] Cotreatment with 10 ng/ml of activin A and RA induces pronephros,[25–28] and cotreatment with 100 ng/ml of activin A and RA induces the differentiation of anterior endoderm such as liver, pancreas, and intestine.[29] Activin A can also convert newt animal caps into mesoderm and endoderm in a dose-dependent manner.[13,30] Treatment of newt animal caps with a high concentration of activin induces beating hearts along with anterior endoderm.[31]

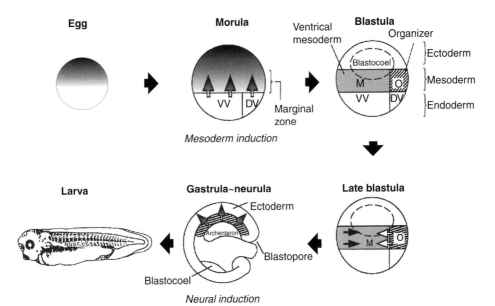

Figure 46–1. *Early events in xenopus development.* The unfertilized egg is radially symmetrical about the animal (darkly pigmented hemisphere)–vegetal (lightly pigmented hemisphere) axis. As cleavage progresses, the animal region becomes packed with numerous small cells, and the vegetal region contains only a relatively small number of large, yolk-laden macromeres (morula). The blastocoel becomes apparent, and mesoderm induction occurs during early cleavage stages (blastula). Presumptive dorsal and ventral mesoderm regions are determined by the late blastula stage (late blastula). Neural induction and dorsalization occur progressively during gastrulation (gastrula~neurula). Following early inductions, cell differentiation establishes the regional feature of the larva. (Please see CD-ROM for color version of this figure.)

In *Xenopus,* the beating heart, which can function *in vivo,* is also induced from animal caps treated with 100 ng/ml.[32] These phenomena suggest that differences in the concentration gradient of activin A in the embryo may direct the differentiation of undifferentiated cells into the range of organ stem cells. Furthermore, activin A can elicit the organizer in the animal cap. In summary, activin A may regulate the fate of the pluripotency of the animal cap.

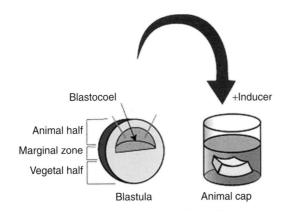

Figure 46–2. *Animal cap assay.* The most widely used bioassay in current research employs a piece of presumptive ectoderm tissue excised from the animal cap of a blastula stage embryo. The animal cap is cultured in saline solution containing the inducer for histological differentiation features. (Please see CD-ROM for color version of this figure.)

Protocol

1. Both males and females are injected with 600 IU of gonadotropin (Gestron; Denka Seiyaku Co., Kawasaki, Japan), and fertilized *Xenopus laevis* eggs are obtained.
2. The jelly coat of the egg is removed with Steinberg's solution (SS). (SS: 58 mM NaCl, 0.67 mM KCl, 0.34 mM Ca(NO$_3$)$_2$, 0.83 mM MgSO$_4$, 3.0 mM HEPES, 100 mg/L kanamycin sulfate, adjusted with 1 N NaOH to pH 7.4. Phenol red at 2 mg/L can be added if needed.) SS contains 4.5% cysteine hydrochloride (pH 7.8). The eggs are washed three times in SS.
3. The eggs are grown in SS until the late blastula stage (stage 9),[33] and the vitelline membranes are manually removed from stage 9 embryos with forceps. Animal caps (0.4 mm × 0.4 mm) are then dissected from the embryos.
4. After twice washing in SS containing 0.1% bovine serum albumin (SS-BSA, Fraction V, Sigma Chemical Co., St. Louis, MO), the animal caps are treated with activin A at the concentrations of 0, 0.1, 1, 10, 50, and 100 ng/ml in SS-BSA for 1 hour with the inner blastocoelic surface facing up.
5. After twice washing in SS-BSA, the animal caps are transferred in SS-BSA to 96-well plates (the plate floor is round), and cultured for 4 days at 20°C.
6. The animal cap explants are fixed with Bouin's fluid for 3 hours or in 10% formalin in 40% Dulbecco's phosphate-buffered saline (PBS) for more than 16 hours (the explants can be preserved for approximately 2 weeks in this

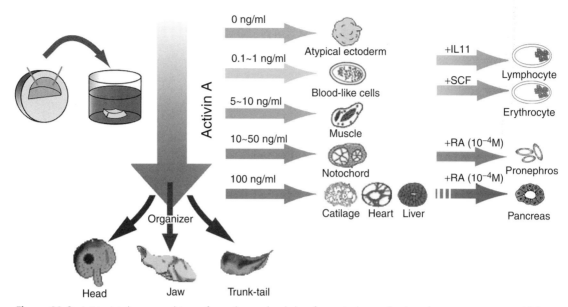

Figure 46–3. *Activin A induces several types of mesoderm and endoderm from animal cap cells, depending on its concentration. Without activin A, animal caps develop to atypical epidermis. With activin A and IL11, lymphocytes are induced. With activin and RA, pronephros or pancreas is induced. Furthermore, the activin-treated animal cap can function as an organizer, leading the induction of regional tissues (IL11, interleukin-11; SCF, stem cell factor; and RA, retinoic acid). (Please see CD-ROM for color version of this figure.)*

fixative solution). Then they are dehydrated, embedded in paraffin, and serially sectioned (6 μM). The sections are stained with hematoxylin and eosin for light microscopy.

SYNERGISTIC EFFECT OF RETINOIC ACID AND ACTIVIN A ON TISSUE DIFFERENTIATION

In vertebrates, RA has a posteriorization–lateralization activity on the central nervous system and mesodermal tissue.[34] Endogenous RA has been detected in early *Xenopus* embryos in a concentration gradient along the anterior–posterior axis.[35] Phased truncation of the head structures is observed following the addition of RA to *Xenopus* blastula-stage embryos.[34] RA has no inducing activity in the *Xenopus* animal cap assay, but it can modify the action of mesoderm inducers on mesoderm pattern formation.[36–38]

Kidney Induction

Xenopus provides an attractive system for studying kidney organogenesis because the *Xenopus* kidney forms the pronephros, the first stage of the functional embryonic kidney in vertebrates. The *Xenopus* pronephros is a simple paired organ that consists of a single large glomus, one set of tubules, and a single duct. This kidney structure can be induced *in vitro* from animal caps at a high frequency (100%) when the animal caps are treated with 10 ng/ml of activin and 10^{-4}-M RA (Fig. 46–4).[25–27] The *in vitro*-induced kidney forms pronephric ducts, tubules, and glomus as found in normal larvae[28] (Fig. 46–5). It also expresses several genes found in kidney rudiments of normal embryos at the same developmental stages. Using this *in vitro* kidney induction system, several genes expressed *in vivo* in embryos were

identified,[39,40] such as *XCIRP* (the *Xenopus* homolog of cold-inducible RNA-binding protein)[41,42] and *Xsal-3*.[43] This *in vitro* system is a valuable tool for the study of the development and differentiation of the kidney.

Pancreas Induction

As is the case in most vertebrates, *Xenopus* has a common pancreas. Dorsal and ventral pancreatic buds arise from the anterior endoderm during development then fuse to become the pancreas.[44] Developing endodermal organs require signals from mesoderm close to the endoderm, and mesenchymal signals play an important role in pancreas organogenesis.[45]

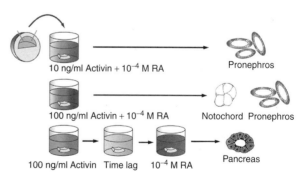

Figure 46–4. *Treatment with activin A plus retinoic acid.* Treatment of animal caps in a mixture of 10 ng/ml activin and 10^{-4} M RA induces the pronephros. Treatment in a mixture of 100 ng/ml activin and 10^{-4} M RA induces notochord or pronephros. When the animal caps treated with 100 ng/ml activin are cultured for 3–5 hours and then treated with 10^{-4} M RA, pancreas is induced. Adapted from Moriya et al.[29] with permission. (Please see CD-ROM for color version of this figure.)

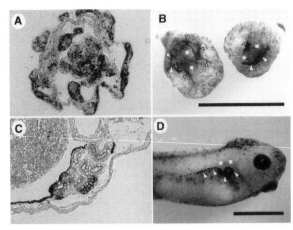

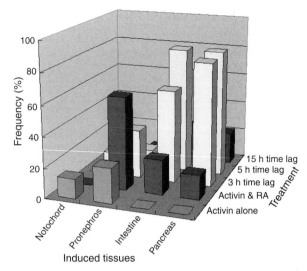

Figure 46–5. *Pronephros is induced in animal caps treated with activin A and RA. Staining of the pronephric tubules using the 3G8 antibody and the pronephric ducts using the 4A6 antibody in the induced pronephros of animal cap appeared as in vivo. (A) Section of animal cap stained by 3G8 antibody and 4A6 antibody. (B) Whole-mount immunostaining of the animal cap. (C) Section of pronephros in stage 40 larvae. (D) Whole-mount immunostaining of larvae. Bar = 1 mm. From Osafune et al. (Fig. 1, p. 162), with permission.[28] (Please see CD-ROM for color version of this figure.)*

Figure 46–6. *Difference in the tissues induced in animal caps treated with activin A and RA by various protocols. Treatment with activin A alone induces pronephros and notochord. When animal caps are treated with a mixture of activin A and RA, pronephros is mainly induced. When animal caps are treated with activin A, cultured for 3–5 hours in SS-BSA, and treated with RA, pancreas is mainly induced. When the time lag is more than 5 hours, the frequency of pancreas induction decreases.[29] (Please see CD-ROM for color version of this figure.)*

When animal caps are treated with 100 ng/ml of activin A for 1 hour, anterior endoderm, such as notochord, muscle, and pharynx, are induced. When animal caps are treated with a mixture of 100 ng/ml of activin A and RA at various concentrations for 1 hour, there is a dose-dependent effect on the patterning of mesodermal tissue formation. As the RA concentration is increased, the rate of notochord formation decreases. Pronephric tubule formation is gradually increased with further concentration increases. When animal caps are treated with 100 ng/ml of activin for 1 hour, washed twice with SS-BSA, cultured in SS-BSA for 3–5 hours, and then treated with RA at 10^{-4} M for 3–5 hours, pancreatic tissues are induced with high frequency (Fig. 46–6) along with an intestinal epithelium-like structure[29] (Fig. 46–7). Beyond 3–5 hours of treatment, RA has little effect, leading to the development of axial mesoderm. The induced pancreatic tissue expresses specific markers also expressed *in vivo,* such as insulin, glucagons, and the *XlHbox8* gene. This assay system will help determine the mechanisms of pancreas development.

Notochord Is Induced from Dissociated Cells of Animal Caps by Activin A

Animal cap cells can be dissociated in calcium- and magnesium-free (CMF) buffers. When treated with activin A, the dissociated cells reaggregate, and various tissues are induced in the reaggregates (Fig. 46–8A). Dissociated cells are more sensitive to the effects of activin A than animal caps.[46–48] Activin A induces the animal cap to differentiate into ventral mesoderm between 0.1–1 ng/ml, neural tissue and muscle between 5–10 ng/ml, dorsal mesoderm between 50 ng/ml, and endoderm between 100 ng/ml. On the other hand, activin A induces the dissociated cells of animal cap to differentiate into notochord between 0.5–7.5 ng/ml and endoderm tissues at

more than 7.5 ng/ml. In particular, activin A at 1 ng/ml induces notochord only (Fig. 46–9A). When cells treated with activin A are mixed with untreated cells, the cells treated with activin A at 1 ng/ml were concentrated in a central mass of the reaggregates and formed notochord (Figs. 46–8B and 46–9B). According to the thermodynamic model of cell–cell interaction,[49] the adhesion-binding activity of cells treated with 1 ng/ml of activin A is very strong because these cells move into the central region of a reaggregate. In contrast, the adhesion-binding activity of cells treated with 10 ng/ml of activin A may be weak because the reaggregates ultimately disintegrate. Activin A changes the adhesive properties of undifferentiated cells, thereby affecting the sorting events during early chordate development.

Protocol

1. The 0.4-mm × 0.4-mm animal cap sheet is cut from stage 8.5 embryos.
2. The animal caps are transferred in 40% of CMF-PBS. The outer layer of the animal cap sheet is discarded. The inner layer is dissociated into a single-cell suspension by gentle pipetting.
3. Cells from 10 caps are incubated for 1 hour in 5-ml SS-BSA containing activin A between 0.5–7.5 ng/ml.
4. The cells are swirled into the center of the dish and washed three times in fresh SS-BSA.
5. The cells are reaggregated in 1.5-ml tubes by gentle centrifugation at 100 × g for 5 minutes, and cultured for at least 5 hours at 20°C. The reaggregates are transferred into 96-well plastic plates, and cultured for 3 days.

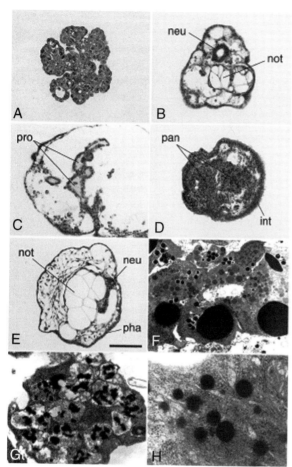

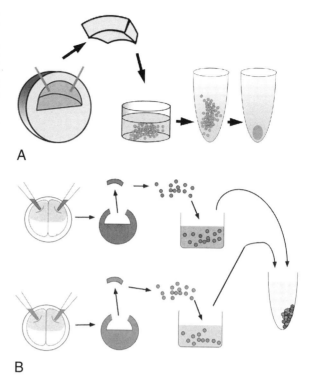

Figure 46–8. *Reaggregation assay.* (A) Schematic diagram of reaggregation assay. (B) Schematic diagram of the procedure for labeling Texas red-dextran-amine (TRDA), or with fluorescein-dextran-amine (FDA) on animal cap cells. *Xenopus* embryos at the two-cell stage are injected with TRDA or FDA. The embryos are grown to stage 8.5, and animal caps are then cut from the embryos. The inner cells of the animal caps are dissociated in CMF-PBS and treated with activin A at 0, 1, or 10 ng/ml for 1 hour. After that, the cells are mixed and reaggregated by centrifugation.[48] (Please see CD-ROM for color version of this figure.)

Figure 46–7. *Pancreas is induced in animal caps.* (A) Without inducers, the animal cap develops to atypical ectoderm. (B) Notochord and neural tissues are induced in the animal caps treated with 100 ng/ml activin A. (C) Pronephros is induced in the animal caps treated with a mixture of 100 ng/ml activin A and 10^{-4} M RA. (D) Pancreas is induced at high frequency when animal caps are treated with 100 ng/ml activin A, cultured for 3–5 hours in SS-BSA, then treated with 10^{-4} M RA. (E) When the animal cap is treated with 100 ng/ml-activin A, cultured for more than 5 hours, and treated with 10^{-4} M RA, notochord and pharynx are mainly induced. (F) An acinous structure in the animal cap explant. (G) Pancreatic-like A cells containing small granules with a round, dense core. (H) B cell–like cells containing small granules (not, notochord; neu, neural tissues; pro, pronephros; pan, pancreas; int, intestine; and pha, pharynx). Adapted from Moriya *et al.* (Fig. 2.3, pp. 595, 598), with permission.[29] (Please see CD-ROM for color version of this figure.)

Induction of Organizer in Animal Caps

The dorsal lip region of gastrulae, known as the organizer, plays a major role in establishing the fundamental body plan in embryos.[50] The dorsal lip is placed between two pieces of untreated animal cap and can interact with them from the inside of a vesicle.[51] The well-organized trunk and tails are induced when the early dorsal lip is sandwiched as an inducer; head structures are induced when the early dorsal lip is incubated in saline for the period required for gastrulation of embryos.[52–54] Activin A can elicit organizer activity in animal

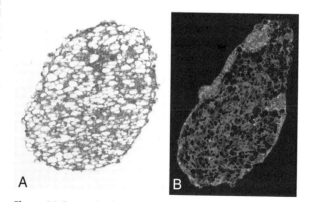

Figure 46–9. *Notochord is induced from the dissociated cells.* (A) Notochord is induced from the dissociated animal cap cells treated with 1 ng/ml activin A. (B) Reaggregates, composed of the TRDA-labeled cells treated with activin A at 1 ng/ml and the FDA-labeled cells treated with 0 ng/ml, showed that the TRDA-labeled cells were located in a central mass surrounded by FDA-labeled cells. Bars = 100 μm. Adapted from Kuroda *et al.* (Fig. 2.4, pp. 285–286), with permission.[48] (Please see CD-ROM for color version of this figure.)

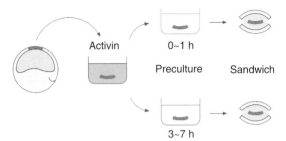

Figure 46–10. *Schematic diagram of the procedure for the sandwich culture method. Animal caps are treated with activin A and precultured in SS for various periods before sandwiching. (Please see CD-ROM for color version of this figure.)*

caps. When an activin A-treated animal cap is transplanted into the ventral side of early gastrulae, a well-organized, secondary embryo is induced.[55] By combining these systems, we have developed a method that reproduces the fundamental embryonic body *in vitro*[56] (Fig. 46–10). Animal caps are treated with 10–100 ng/ml of activin A and incubated for 0–7 hours in SS-BSA (preculture). They are then sandwiched between two animal caps. Animal caps precultured for a short

time induced trunk–tail structures, whereas those precultured for a long time induced head structures in addition to trunk–tail structures (Fig. 46–11). These time-dependent changes in inducing properties occurred more rapidly when the concentration of activin A was higher. These results demonstrated that the activin-treated animal caps functioned as a head organizer or a trunk–tail organizer depending upon the concentration of activin A and the duration of preculture. Furthermore, the intermediate preculture term initiates a gene expression cascade inducing the intermediate region between the head and trunk–tail structures, the maxillofacial region (see the section "Long-Term Culture to Induce Well-Differentiated Tissues").

PROTOCOL

1. Animal caps (0.4 mm × 0.4 mm) are cut from the late blastulae (stage 9). The animal cap sheets are treated with 10–100 ng/ml of activin A for 1 hour.
2. The treated animal caps are precultured in SS-BSA for 0–7 hours.
3. Animal cap sheets (0.8 mm × 0.8 mm) are cut from other late blastulae. The treated animal caps are sandwiched between the two untreated animal caps. The sandwiched

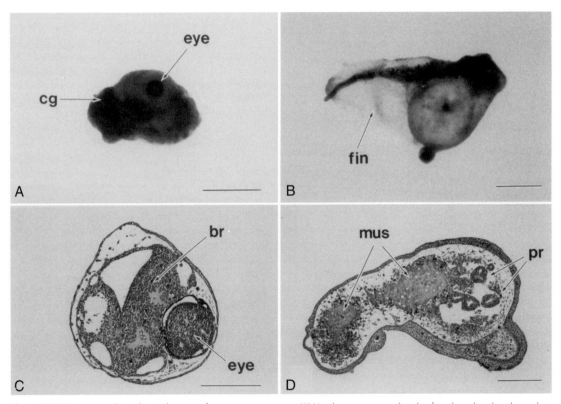

Figure 46–11. *Activin A-Treated animal cap can function as an organizer.* (A) Head structure was induced in four day-cultured explants when the animal cap treated with 100 ng/ml activin A for 10 minutes and precultured for 5 hours was sandwiched between the untreated animal caps. (B) Trunk–tail structure was induced in 4 day–cultured explants when the animal cap treated with 10 ng/ml activin A and precultured for 1 hour was sandwiched between the untreated animal caps. (C) Histological section of panel A. (D) Histological section of panel B (cg, cement gland; fin, caudal fin; br, brain ventricles; mus, muscle; and pro, pronephros). Adapted from Ariizumi *et al.* (Fig. 2, p. 501), with permission.[56] (Please see CD-ROM for color version of this figure.)

animal caps are incubated for approximately 10 minutes until the animal caps attach thoroughly to each other.

4. The sandwiched animal cap explants are transferred to 96-well plates and cultured in SS-BSA for 4 days at 20°C.

Long-Term Culture to Induce Well-Differentiated Tissues

To observe that the well-differentiated tissues are induced from animal caps, a long-term culture is needed. Maxillofacial cartilage is a well-differentiated tissue, and a long-term culture is needed for the undifferentiated cells to develop into cartilage tissue. We have described previously the sandwich culture method, showing that activin-treated animal caps can function as a head or a trunk–tail organizer depending on the activin A concentration and the preculture period following the activin treatment.[30,56] Activin A triggers several gene expression cascades in the presumptive ectoderm with a time course that mimics the sequence in normal embryonal development.[16,19] It is therefore theoretically possible to reproduce embryonic induction using activin A and undifferentiated presumptive ectoderm and to design a fundamental embryonic form *in vitro*. If the gene cascades are initiated by activin A to induce neural crest tissue fated to migrate into mandibular and branchial arches, the cartilage tissue in the maxillofacial and branchial region should be induced in animal caps cultured for a long time. From these suggestions, we succeeded in inducing jaw cartilage from animal cap.[57]

The animal cap treated with 100 ng/ml of activin A is sandwiched between two untreated animal caps and then cultured in SS-BSA. The Alcian blue-positive, undifferentiated mesenchymal cell condensation was found in the explants on day 4 of culture (Fig. 46–12A and 46–12B). However, chondrocytes were not identified. Chondrocyte-like cells and cartilaginous tissue were apparent in the mesenchymal cell condensation on day 7 of culture (Fig. 46–12C). Some of these chondrocytes appeared mature, and the amount of cartilaginous tissues increased by day 10 of culture (Fig. 46–12D). Perichondrium was noted surrounding the cartilaginous tissues, and the cartilage appeared hypertrophic on day 14 (Fig. 46–12E and 46–12F). *Xenopus distalless 4 (X-dll4)* mRNA was expressed throughout the explants

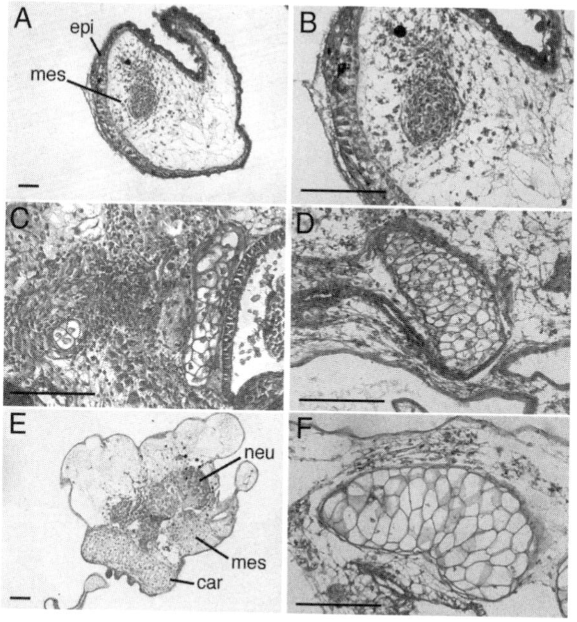

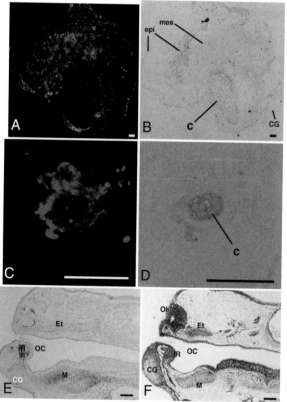

Figure 46–12. *Chondrocytes are apparent in animal cap explants cultured more than 7 days.* (A) Cell condensation, but not chondrocytes, were observed in 4 day–cultured explants. (B) Higher magnification of panel A. (C) Chondrocytes were observed in 7 day–cultured explants. (D) Some mature chondrocytes were seen in 10 day–cultured explants. (E) Perichondrium was noted surrounding the cartilaginous tissues, and the cartilage appeared hypertrophic in 14 day–cultured explants. (F) Higher magnification of panel E. epi, epidermis; mes, mesenchyme; car, cartilage; neu, neural tissue. (Bars = 50 μm).From Furue *et al.* (Fig. 2, p.15,476).[57] (Please see CD-ROM for color version of this figure.)

Figure 46–13. *Jaw cartilage is induced in the animal cap.* The animal cap explant expresses *X-dll4* and *gsc* mRNA, just as the maxillofacial region expresses *X-dll4* and the lower jaw expresses *gsc* mRNA in the embryo. (A) *X-dll4* mRNA expression in a section of a 7 day–cultured animal cap explant. (B) Alcian blue-staining of panel A. (C) *Gsc* mRNA in the serial section of panel A. (D) Alcian blue staining of panel C. (E) *Gsc* mRNA in the embryo. (F) *X-dll4* mRNA expression in the embryo. (cg, cement gland; et, ethmoid trabecular cartilage; ir, infrarostral cartilage; m, Meckel's cartilage; oc, oral cavity; ol, olfactory organ). Bars = 10 μm. Adapted from Furue *et al.* (Fig. 5, pp. 15,478).[57] (Please see CD-ROM for color version of this figure.)

(Fig. 46–13A), and goosecoid *(gsc)* mRNA was prominently expressed only in the cartilage (Fig. 46–13C). In *Xenopus* embryos, *gsc* expression is restricted to the cartilage of the lower jaw, and *X-dll4* is widely expressed in the ventral head region including the maxillofacial cartilage (Fig. 46–13E and 46–13F). These findings demonstrate that jaw cartilage was induced in the activin-treated, sandwiched explants. In addition, a normal developmental pattern was recapitulated in animal caps at the histological and genetic levels. The developmental cascade can be induced in animal caps treated with activin A. The induced tissues interact with each other, and various organ stem cells are also induced. Therefore, a long-term culture may induce well-differentiated organs in the animal cap explants, teeth, and limbs.

PROTOCOL

1. All tools are sterilized. Beakers, forceps, and razor blades are sterilized in dry open ovens. Cysteine hydrochloride solution is filtered through a 0.2-μm filter membrane. One liter of SS is sterilized using a high-pressure steam sterilizer.
2. The jelly coat is removed with SS containing 4.5% cysteine hydrochloride (pH 7.8), followed by three washes in sterile SS. Following this, all procedures are carried out under the clean bench.
3. The vitelline membranes of the late blastulae are manually removed with fine forceps, then animal caps (0.4 mm ×

0.4 mm) are cut. The animal caps are treated with 100 ng/ml of activin A solution for one hour with the inner blastocoelic surface facing up.
4. The animal caps (0.8 mm × 0.8 mm) are cut from other late blastulae. The activin A-treated animal caps are sandwiched between the two untreated animal caps.
5. Explants are put in 96-well plates and cultured in either SS-BSA or a nutrient-supplemented culture medium, RDX medium[58] containing 0.1% fatty acid-free BSA for 4 days at 20°C. After 4 days, the explants are transferred to 24-well plates.
6. Culture solutions are exchanged every 4 days. For cultures of more than 2 weeks, explants are cultured in RDX medium in a humidified atmosphere of 5% CO_2 at 20°C.[58]

Application for Biotechnology: Transplantation

The organ rudiments induced from activin A-treated animal caps can function *in vivo* when transplanted into a host embryo. Pronephros rudiment is induced in the animal cap treated with 10 ng/ml activin A plus 10^{-4} M RA. We removed the pronephric tubule primordial, located under somites, from *Xenopus* stage 20–25 embryos and transplanted into that site the animal caps treated with activin A and RA (Fig. 46–14).[26] Severe edema occurred with the bilateral removal of the pronephros primordial, and most of the embryos died within

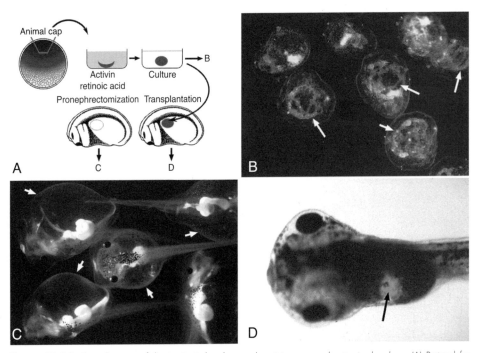

Figure 46–14. *Transplantation of the in vitro-induced pronephros into a pronephrectomized embryo. (A) Protocol for transplantation of in vitro-induced kidney. Blastula animal cap is treated with a mixture of activin and RA for 3 hours and cultured in saline solution for more than 17 hours. This animal cap is transplanted where the pronephros rudiment has been removed. (B) External views of the induced pronephros in animal caps. (C) Bilaterally pronephrectomized embryos develop severe edema. (D) The FDA-labeled transplant has developed normally in the pronephrectomized embryo. Adapted from Chan et al. (Fig. 1, p. 226), with permission.[26] (Please see CD-ROM for color version of this figure.)*

9 days. However, the embryos that underwent transplantation developed normally. These results demonstrate that the *in vitro*-induced kidney rudiment can function *in vivo,* and this model system will help to develop applications for tissue engineering and new therapies.

PROTOCOL

1. Animal caps (0.4 mm × 0.4 mm) are cut from late blastulae (stage 9). The animal cap sheets are treated with a mixture of 10 ng/ml of activin A and 10^{-4} M RA for 3 hours.
2. The treated animal caps are precultured in SS-BSA for 17 hours.
3. The pronephros rudiments are bilaterally removed from the host neurulae.
4. The treated animal cap is transplanted into the site from which the pronephros rudiment was removed.

Summary

Animal cap cells are fated to develop into epidermis and neural tissues in normal development. However, isolated animal cap cells possess pluripotency, and various tissues are induced when animal caps are treated with activin A. Different concentrations of activin A trigger different gene cascades to initiate the differentiation of animal cap cells into different organ stem cells. It is therefore theoretically possible to reproduce embryonic induction and design a fundamental embryonic form *in vitro.* This system is a useful tool in the study of embryonic development and differentiation and will help to further the field of tissue engineering.

REFERENCES

1. Nieuw: koop, P.D. (1969). The formation of the mesoderm in urodelean amphibians: I—Induction by the endoderm. *W. Roux's Arch. Ent. Mech. Org.* **162,** 341–373.
2. Nakamura, O., Takasaki, H., and Ishihara, M. (1971). Formation of the organizer from combination of presumptive ectoderm. *Proc. Jpn. Acad.* **47,** 313–318.
3. Asashima, M. (1975). Inducing effect of the presumptive endoderm of successive stages in *Triturus alpestris. Roux's Arch. Dev. Biol.* **177,** 301–308.
4. Yamada, T., and Takata, K. (1961). A technique for testing macromolecular samples in solution for morphogenetic effects on the isolated ectoderm of the amphibian gastrula. *Dev. Biol.* **3,** 411–423.
5. Asashima, M., Kinoshita, K., Ariizumi, T., and Malacinski, G.M. (1999). Role of activin and other peptide growth factors in body patterning in the early amphibian embryo. *Int. Rev. Cytol.* **191,** 1–52.
6. Asashima, M., Yokota, C., Takahashi, S., Lau, C.L., and Malacinski, G.M. (1999). Peptide growth factors in amphibian embryogenesis: intersection of modern molecular approaches with traditional inductive interaction paradigms. *Int. J. Dev. Biol.* **43,** 1–10.
7. Asashima, M., Nakano, H., Uchiyama, H., Davids, M., Plessow, S., Loppnow-Blinde, B., Hoppe, P., Dau, H., and Tiedemann, H. (1990). The vegetalizing factor belongs to a family of mesoderm-inducing proteins related to erythroid differentiation factor, *Naturwissenschaften* **77,** 389–391.

8. Asashima, M., Nakano, H., Shimada, K., Kinoshita, K., Ishii, K., Shibai, H., and Ueno, N. (1990). Mesodermal induction in early amphibian embryos by activin (erythroid differentiation factor). *Roux's Arch. Dev. Biol.* **198,** 330–335.
9. Asashima, M., Nakano, H., Uchiyama, H., Sugino, H., Nakamura, T., Eto, Y., Ejima, D., Nishimatsu, S., Ueno, N., and Kinoshita, K. (1991). Presence of activin (erythroid differentiation factor) in unfertilized eggs and blastulae of *Xenopus laevis. Proc. Natl. Acad. Sci. USA* **88,** 6511–6514.
10. Asashima, M., Uchiyama, H., Nakano, H., Eto, Y., Ejima, D., Sugino, H., Davids, M., Plessow, S., Born, J., Hoppe, P., Tiedemann, H., and Tiedemann, H. (1991). The vegetalizing factor from chicken embryos: its EDF (activin A)-like activity. *Mech. Dev.* **34,** 135–141.
11. Ariizumi, T., Moriya, N., Uchiyama, H., and Asashima, M. (1991). Concentration-dependent inducing activity of activin A. *Roux's Arch. Dev. Biol.* **200,** 230–233.
12. Ariizumi, T., Sawamura, K., Uchiyama, H., and Asashima, M. (1991). Dose- and time-dependent mesoderm induction and outgrowth formation by activin A in *Xenopus laevis. Int. J. Dev. Biol.* **35,** 407–414.
13. Ariizumi, T., and Asashima, M. (1995). Control of the embryonic body plan by activin during amphibian development. *Zool. Sci.* **12,** 509–521.
14. Asashima, M., and Kinoshita, K. (1996). Embryonic induction and role of activins during early amphibian development. *Hum. Cell* **9,** 277–282.
15. Asashima, M., and Mizuno, T. (2000). Kidney formation. *Tanpakushitsu Kakusan Koso.* **45,** 2221–2227.
16. Asashima, M., Ariizumi, T., and Malacinski, G.M. (2000). *In vitro* control of organogenesis and body patterning by activin during early amphibian development. *Comp. Biochem. Physiol. B. Biochem. Mol. Biol.* **126,** 169–178.
17. Asashima, M., Ariizumi, T., Takahashi, S., and Malacinski, G.M. (2000). Bioassays for studying the role of the peptide growth factor activin in early amphibian embryogenesis. *Methods Mol. Biol.* **136,** 15–26.
18. Ariizumi, T., Takano, K., Asashima, M., and Malacinski, G.M. (2000). Bioassays of inductive interactions in amphibian development. *Methods Mol. Biol.* **135,** 89–112.
19. Ariizumi, T., and Asashima, M. (2001). *In vitro* induction systems for analyses of amphibian organogenesis and body patterning. *Int. J. Dev. Biol.* **45,** 273–279.
20. Asashima, M., and Okabayashi, K. (2003). Current state of and outlook for organogenesis from undifferentiated cells. *Cornea* **22(Suppl. 1),** 2–12.
21. Miyanaga, Y., Shiurba, R., Nagata, S., Pfeiffer, C.J., and Asashima, M. (1998). Induction of blood cells in *Xenopus* embryo explants. *Dev. Genes Evol.* **207,** 417–426.
22. Miyanaga, Y., Shiurba, R., and Asashima, M. (1999). Blood cell induction in *Xenopus* animal cap explants: effects of fibroblast growth factor, bone morphogenetic proteins, and activin. *Dev. Genes Evol.* **209,** 69–76.
23. Tamai, K., Yokota, C., Ariizumi, T., and Asashima, M. (1999). Cytochalasin B inhibits morphogenetic movement and muscle differentiation of activin-treated ectoderm in *Xenopus. Dev. Growth Differ.* **41,** 41–49.
24. Ninomiya, H., Takahashi, S., Tanegashima, K., Yokota, C., and Asashima, M. (1999). Endoderm differentiation and inductive effect of activin-treated ectoderm in *Xenopus. Dev. Growth Differ.* **41,** 391–400.
25. Moriya, N., Uchiyama, H., and Asashima, M. (1993). Induction of pronephric tubules by activin and retinoic acid in

presumptive ectoderm of *Xenopus laevis*. *Dev. Growth Differ.* **35**, 123–128.

26. Chan, T.C., Ariizumi, T., and Asashima, M. (1999). A model system for organ engineering: Transplantation of *in vitro*-induced embryonic kidney. *Naturwissenschaften* **86**, 224–227.

27. Chan, T.C., Takahashi, S., and Asashima, M. (2000). A role for Xlim-1 in pronephros development in *Xenopus laevis*. *Dev. Biol.* **228**, 256–269.

28. Osafune, K., Nishinakamura, R., Komazaki, S., and Asashima, M. (2002). *In vitro* induction of the pronephric duct in *Xenopus* explants. *Dev. Growth Differ.* **44**, 161–167.

29. Moriya, N., Komazaki, S., Takahashi, S., Yokota, C., and Asashima, M. (2000). *In vitro* pancreas formation from *Xenopus* ectoderm treated with activin and retinoic acid. *Dev. Growth Differ.* **42**, 593–602.

30. Ariizumi, T., and Asashima, M. (1995). Head and trunk–tail organizing effects of the gastrula ectoderm of *Cynops pyrrhogaster* after treatment with activin A. *Roux's Arch. Dev. Biol.* **204**, 427–435.

31. Ariizumi, T., Komazaki, S., Asashima, M., and Malacinski, G.M. (1996). Activin treated urodele ectoderm: a model experimental system for cardiogenesis. *Int. J. Dev. Biol.* **40**, 715–718.

32. Ariizumi, T., Kinoshita, M., Yokota, C., Takano, K., Fukuda, K., Moriya, N., Malacinski, G.M., and Asashima, M. (2003). Amphibian *in vitro* heart induction: a simple and reliable model for the study of vertebrate cardiac development. *Int. J. Dev. Biol.* **47**, 405–410.

33. Nieuwkoop, P.D., and Faber, J. (1956). "Normal Table of *Xenopus laevis* (Daudin)." North-Holland Publishing Co., Amsterdam.

34. Durston, A.J., Timmermans, J.P., Hage, W.J., Hendriks, H.F., de Vries, N.J., Heideveld, M., and Nieuwkoop, P.D. (1989). Retinoic acid causes an anteroposterior transformation in the developing central nervous system. *Nature* **340**, 140–144.

35. Chen, Y., Huang, L., and Solursh, M. (1994). A concentration gradient of retinoids in the early *Xenopus laevis* embryo. *Dev. Biol.* **161**, 70–76.

36. Hashimoto, M., Kondo, S., Sakurai, T., Etoh, Y., Shibai, H., and Muramatsu, M. (1990). Activin/EDF as an inhibitor of neural differentiation. *Biochem. Biophys. Res. Commun.* **173**, 193–200.

37. Uchiyama, H., and Asashima, M. (1992). Specific erythroid differentiation of mouse erythroleukemia cells by activins and its enhancement by retinoic acids. *Biochem. Biophys. Res. Commun.* **187**, 347–352.

38. Taira, M., Otani, H., Saint-Jeannet, J.P., and Dawid, I.B. (1994). Role of the LIM class homeodomain protein Xlim-1 in neural and muscle induction by the Spemann organizer in *Xenopus*. *Nature* **372**, 677–679.

39. Sato, A., Asashima, M., Yokota, T., and Nishinakamura, R. (2000). Cloning and expression pattern of a *Xenopus* pronephros-specific gene, *XSMP-30*. *Mech. Dev.* **92**, 273–275.

40. Seville, R.A., Nijjar, S., Barnett, M.W., Masse, K., and Jones, E.A. (2002). Annexin IV (Xanx-4) has a functional role in the formation of pronephric tubules. *Development* **129**, 1693–1704.

41. Uochi, T., Takahashi, S., Ninomiya, H., Fukui, A., and Asashima, M. (1997). The Na+,K+-ATPase α-subunit requires gastrulation in the *Xenopus* embryo. *Dev. Growth Differ.* **39**, 571–580.

42. Uochi, T., and Asashima, M. (1998). XCIRP (*Xenopus* homolog of cold-inducible RNA-binding protein) is expressed transiently in developing pronephros and neural tissue. *Gene* **211**, 245–250.

43. Onuma, Y., Nishinakamura, R., Takahashi, S., Yokota, T., and Asashima, M. (1999). Molecular cloning of a novel *Xenopus spalt* gene (*Xsal-3*). *Biochem. Biophys. Res. Commun.* **264**, 151–156.

44. Slack, J.M. (1995). Developmental biology of the pancreas. *Development* **121**, 1569–1580.

45. Moriya, N., Komazaki, S., and Asashima, M. (2000). *In vitro* organogenesis of pancreas in *Xenopus laevis* dorsal lips treated with retinoic acid. *Dev. Growth Differ.* **42**, 175–185.

46. Green, J.B., and Smith, J.C. (1990). Graded changes in dose of a *Xenopus* activin A homologue elicit stepwise transitions in embryonic cell fate. *Nature* **347**, 391–394.

47. Green, J.B., Smith, J.C., and Gerhart, J.C. (1994). Slow emergence of a multithreshold response to activin requires cell contact-dependent sharpening but not prepattern. *Development* **120**, 2271–2278.

48. Kuroda, H., Sakumoto, H., Kinoshita, K., and Asashima, M. (1999). Changes in the adhesive properties of dissociated and reaggregated *Xenopus laevis* embryo cells. *Dev. Growth Differ.* **41**, 283–291.

49. Steinberg, M.S. (1964). "The Problem of Adhesive Selectivity in Cellular Interactions." Academic Press, New York.

50. Spemann, H., and Mangold, H. (1924). Über induktion von embryonalangen durch implantation artfremder organisatoren. *Arch. Mikrisk. Anat. Entwicklungsmech.* **100**, 599–638.

51. Holtfreter, J. (1933). Organisierungsstufen nach regional kombination von entomesoderm mit ektoderm. *Biol. Zbl.* **53**, 404–431.

52. Okada, Y.K., and Takaya, H. (1942). Further studies upon the regional differentiation of the inductive capacity of the organizer. *Proc. Imp. Acad. (Tokyo)* **18**, 514–519.

53. Okada, Y.K., and Hama, T. (1943). Examination of regional differences in the inductive activity of the organizer by means of transplantation into ectoderm vesicles. *Proc. Imp. Acad. (Tokyo)* **19**, 48–53.

54. Hama, T., Tsujimura, H., Kaneda, T., Takata, K., and Ohara, A. (1985). Inductive capacities on the dorsal mesoderm of the dorsal marginal zone and pharyngeal endoderm in the very early gastrula of the newt, and presumptive pharyngeal endoderm as an initiator of the organization center. *Dev. Growth Differ.* **27**, 419–433.

55. Ninomiya, H., Ariizumi, T., and Asashima, M. (1998). Activin-treated ectoderm has complete organizing center activity in *Cynops* embryos. *Dev. Growth Differ.* **40**, 199–208.

56. Ariizumi, T., and Asashima, M. (1994). *In vitro* control of the embryonic form of *Xenopus laevis* by activin A: time- and dose-dependent inducing properties of activin A-treated ectoderm. *Dev. Growth Differ.* **36**, 499–507.

57. Furue, M., Myoishi, Y., Fukui, Y., Ariizumi, T., Okamoto, T., and Asashima, M. (2002). Activin A induces craniofacial cartilage from undifferentiated *Xenopus* ectoderm *in vitro*. *Proc. Natl. Acad. Sci. USA* **99**, 15,474–15,479.

58. Fukui, Y., Furue, M., Myoishi, Y., Sato, J.D., Okamoto, T., and Asashima, M. (2003). Long-term culture of *Xenopus* presumptive ectoderm in a nutrient-supplemented culture medium. *Dev. Growth Differ.* **45**, 499–506.

Isolation and Culture of Zebra Fish ES Cells

Lianchun Fan and Paul Collodi

This chapter describes methods for the derivation, maintenance, and genetic manipulation of zebra fish embryonic stem (ES) cell cultures. A key component of the cell culture system is the use of feeder layers derived from the rainbow trout spleen cell line RTS34st. Zebra fish ES cells, cultured on growth-arrested RTS34st feeder layers, remain pluripotent and germ-line competent for several weeks and multiple passages. The ES cells are able to incorporate plasmid DNA in a targeted fashion by homologous recombination. Methods are described for the introduction of a targeting vector by electroporation along with procedures for the efficient selection of homologous recombinants using a visual marker screen. Also, a protocol is presented for the introduction of the ES cells into host embryos by microinjection to generate zebra fish germ-line chimeras.

Introduction

The zebra fish possesses several favorable characteristics that make it an ideal model for studies of vertebrate development and disease.[1–4] Forward genetic screens using chemical,[5,6] radiation,[7] transposon,[8] and viral[9] derived mutagens have been applied to zebra fish to generate thousands of mutations that perturb normal development. Using the extensive linkage map available and the nearly complete zebra fish genomic sequence,[10–12] some of the altered genes have been isolated by candidate and positional cloning methods[13–15] or by using inserted viral sequence as a genetic tag.[16,17] Reverse genetic methods have also been used to study zebra fish gene function. Transient inhibition of gene expression is routinely accomplished in zebra fish using morpholino-modified oligonucleotides,[18,19] and a target selected mutagenesis approach has been developed to isolate randomly introduced mutations that occur at a specific locus.[20]

Although these genetic strategies have been valuable, one deficiency of the zebra fish model is the absence of methods to target the inactivation of specific genes to generate knockouts. In mice, knockouts have been available for more than a decade and have provided a powerful approach to the study of gene function.[21,22] To generate the knockout, a mutation is introduced into a specific gene in mouse ES cell cultures by targeted insertion of vector DNA by homologous recombination.[22] Colonies of ES cells that harbor the targeted mutation are selected and expanded in culture and the cells are introduced into a host embryo, where they participate in development and contribute to the germ cell lineage. The resulting germ–line chimera carrying the targeted mutation is used to establish the knockout line. Although successful in mice, the ES cell–based gene targeting strategy has not been successfully applied to other species. The lack of success with nonmurine species is due to the absence of ES cell lines that are capable of contributing to the germ cell lineage of a host embryo.

To address this problem, our laboratory has been working to develop zebra fish ES cell lines that are suitable for use in the production of knockouts.[23–29] Methods have been developed to derive zebra fish ES cell lines that remain germ-line competent for a sufficient length of time in culture to introduce a targeting vector and select colonies of cells that have incorporated the vector by homologous recombination.[28] ES cells maintained in culture for several weeks and multiple passages have been used to produce zebra fish germ-line chimeras.[28,29] A key component of the ES cell culture system is the use of a feeder layer derived from the rainbow trout spleen cell line RTS34st.[30] The spleen cells produce factors that maintain the zebra fish cultures in a germ-line competent condition.[26,29] This embryo cell culture system will form the basis of a gene targeting strategy that will enhance the utility of the zebra fish model for studies of gene function. In this chapter, we describe methods for the derivation, maintenance, and genetic manipulation of zebra fish pluripotent ES cell cultures along with a protocol for using the cells to generate germ-line chimeras.

Derivation of Zebra Fish Embryonic Stem Cell Cultures

INITIATION OF PRIMARY CULTURES

Zebra fish ES cell cultures have been derived from both blastula- and gastrula-stage embryos[29] (Fig. 47–1). The zebra fish blastula comprises nondifferentiated cells and is, therefore, the most convenient stage to use for the derivation of pluripotent cultures. Suitable cultures can also be derived from the zebra fish gastrula; however, because cell differentiation has begun to occur at this stage of development, individual colonies that possess an ES like morphology must be identified and manually selected from the high

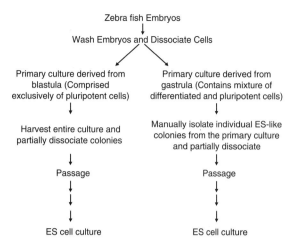

Figure 47–1. General protocol for the derivation of embryonic stem (ES) cell cultures initiated from zebra fish blastula- and gastrula-stage embryos.

percentage of differentiated cells present in the primary culture. The selected colonies are removed with a drawn-out Pasteur pipette, dissociated, and seeded into individual wells to establish the gastrula-derived cell line (Fig. 47–1). To avoid this additional procedure of removing individual colonies from the primary culture, we routinely use blastula-stage embryos to initiate pluripotent cultures. The cultures are maintained on feeder layers of growth-arrested RTS34st cells.[30]

To initiate the cultures,[25] groups of approximately 50 mid-blastula–stage embryos (1000 cell)[31] contained in a 35-mm Petri dish are rinsed three to five times in culture medium and soaked 2 minutes in bleach solution (0.5% Chlorox bleach in water) followed by three additional rinses with medium. The bleach treatment and rinses are repeated and the embryos are dechorionated in pronase solution (30 minutes in 0.5 mg/ml pronase [Sigma, St. Louis] in Hank's solution). The dechorionated embryos are rinsed three times in culture medium, suspended in trypsin/EDTA solution (0.2% trypsin, 1 mM EDTA in PBS, Sigma), and transferred into a 15-ml conical centrifuge tube. After 1 minute, the embryos are gently pipetted to dissociate the cells and fetal bovine serum (FBS) (10% final volume, Harlan, Indianapolis) is added to stop the action of the trypsin. The cells are collected by centrifugation (500 × g, 5 minute) and the pellet obtained from approximately 50 embryos is resuspended in 1.2 ml LDF culture medium (50% Leibowitz's L-15, 35% Dulbecco's Modified Eagle's, 15% Ham's F12 media [GIBCO-BRL, Grand Island, NY] supplemented with 0.18g/L sodium bicarbonate, 10^{-8} M sodium selenite)[32] and added to a single well of a six-well plate (Falcon) containing a confluent monolayer of growth-arrested RTS34st cells (see the section on preparation of growth-arrested RTS34st feeder layers). The plate is left undisturbed for 30 minutes to allow the embryo cells to attach to the feeder layer and then the following supplements are added at the final concentrations indicated: FBS (5%), zebra fish embryo extract (40 µg protein/ml, as discussed in the section on preparation of

growth-arrested RTS34st feeder layers), trout serum (1%, East Coast Biologics, North Berwick, ME), bovine insulin (10 µg/ml, Sigma), human epidermal growth factor (EGF) (50 ng/ml, Invitrogen, Carlsbad, CA), human basic fibroblast growth factor (bFGF) (30 ng/ml, GIBCO-BRL), and RTS34st cell-conditioned medium (630 µl, as discussed in the section on preparation of growth-arrested RTS34st feeder layers). The final volume in the well is adjusted to 2 ml and the plate is incubated (22° C) in ambient air for 3 to 5 days. Within 6 hours of plating, the cells aggregate to form dense clusters that continue to increase in size as the cells proliferate (Fig. 47–2A).

PASSAGING THE PRIMARY CULTURES

After 3 to 5 days, the cells contained in the primary culture are harvested by adding trypsin/EDTA solution and gently pipetting for 30 seconds to partially dissociate the cell aggregates. The cells are collected by centrifugation, resuspended in 2.4 ml LDF, and added to two wells of a six-well dish (1.2 ml/well), each well containing a confluent monolayer of growth-arrested RTS34st cells (see the section on preparation of growth-arrested RTS34st feeder layers). Because trypsin treatment of the primary culture results in partial dissociation of the cell aggregates, after the first passage, each of the wells contains a mixture of small cell aggregates with a few single cells. The supplements listed in the previous section for the primary culture are added to each well and the cultures are incubated (22° C) in ambient air for 3 to 5 days. To passage the cultures, the cells contained in two wells of the six-well plate are harvested, combined, and partially dissociated in trypsin/EDTA solution. The cells are collected by centrifugation (500 × g, 5 minute), resuspended in 3.6 ml LDF, and added to a 25-cm² flask containing a confluent layer of growth-arrested RTS34st cells (see the section on preparation of growth-arrested RTS34st feeder layers). The flask is allowed to sit undisturbed for approximately 2 hours so that the embryo cells can attach to the feeder layer and then the following supplements are added: FBS (5%), trout serum (1%), bovine insulin (10 µg/ml), EGF (50 ng/ml), bFGF (30 ng/ml), zebra fish embryo extract (40 µg protein/ml, see next section), and RTS34st cell-conditioned medium (1.890 ml, see next section), and the final volume is adjusted to 6 ml. The culture is incubated (22° C) in ambient air for 5 to 7 days. To passage the culture, the cells are harvested in trypsin/EDTA solution, resuspended in LDF, and divided equally between two 25-cm² flasks, each containing a confluent monolayer of RTS34st cells. With each passage the embryo cells become easier to dissociate and fewer aggregates are present in the culture. By passage 4 the embryo cells grow as a monolayer (Fig. 47–2B) and the cultures can be passaged approximately every 7 days.

PREPARATION OF GROWTH-ARRESTED RTS34ST FEEDER LAYERS, RTS34ST CELL-CONDITIONED MEDIUM, AND ZEBRA FISH EMBRYO EXTRACT

Stock cultures of RTS34st cells are grown in 25-cm² flasks containing Leibowitz's L-15 medium supplemented with FBS (30%).[30] To prepare the feeder layers, the RTS34st cells are

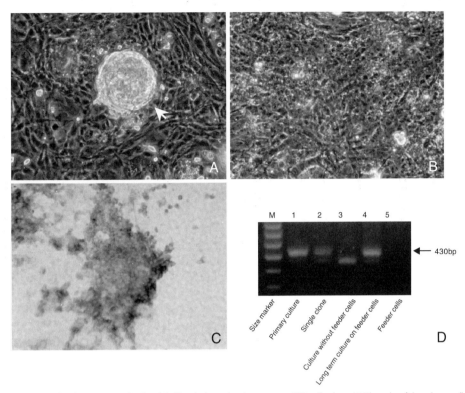

Figure 47–2. *Characteristics of zebra fish blastula-derived embryonic stem (ES) cell culture. (A) The zebra fish embryo cells aggregate to form dense homogeneous clusters that are present throughout the primary culture. A single-cell aggregate present in a 3-day-old primary culture is shown on a monolayer of growth-arrested RTS34st cells. (B) After several passages the ES cells proliferate as a monolayer. A passage 15 (3 month old) culture is shown. (C) The ES cells maintained on an RTS34st feeder layer express Pou-2 detected by in situ hybridization. (D) Pou-2 expression is lost when the ES cells are removed from the feeder layer. The cultures were analyzed by reverse transcriptase polymerase chain reaction (RT-PCR) to detect a 430-bp region of the Pou-2 cDNA.*

growth-arrested by irradiation (3000 rads), harvested by trypsinization, and added to individual wells of six-well plates (10^5 cells/well) or 25 cm² flasks (10^4 cells/cm²) 24 hours before use. Vials of the growth-arrested cells are stored frozen in liquid nitrogen until needed. RTS34st cell-conditioned medium is prepared by adding L-15 containing 30% FBS to a nearly confluent culture of proliferating RTS34st cells. After 3 days the medium is collected, filtered to remove any cells, and stored frozen (–20° C) until use. Once an aliquot of conditioned medium is thawed, it is stored at 4° C for up to 1 week.

Zebra fish embryo extract[33] is prepared by homogenizing a group of approximately 1000 embryos in 1 ml LDF medium and centrifuging (20,000 × g, 30 minutes) to remove the debris. The supernatant is collected, leaving behind the top layer of lipid material, filter sterilized, and the protein measured. The extract is stored frozen (–20° C) in 0.2 ml aliquots.

Production of Zebra fish Germ-line Chimeras

Zebra fish ES cell cultures remain pluripotent and germ-line competent when initiated and maintained on the RTS34st feeder layers.[28,29] In the presence of the feeder cells, the ES cell cultures continue to express the Pou-2 transcription factor, a marker of pluripotency[34] (Fig. 47–2C). Pou-2 expression is lost when the ES cells are passaged in the absence of the feeder cells or RTS34st cell-conditioned medium (Fig. 47–2D). Importantly, for gene targeting studies, zebra fish ES cells that are cultured for multiple passages on the feeder layers maintain the capacity to contribute to the germ cell lineage of a host embryo.[28,29] Germ-line chimeras have been generated from 6-week-old (passage 6) blastula- and gastrula-derived ES cell cultures[29] (Fig. 47–3A–C). The chimeras are produced by introducing the cultured ES cells into blastula-stage host embryos by microinjection[26] (Fig. 47–3D). Once in the embryo, the pluripotent ES cells participate in normal development and contribute to multiple tissues including the germ line of the host.[27] Using the microinjection technique, ES cells can be rapidly introduced into a large number of zebra fish embryos (300 embryos/hr), achieving a postinjection embryo survival rate of approximately 50%. Germ-line contribution of the ES cells is confirmed by demonstrating that F1 individuals, produced by the sexually mature chimeras, possess a pigmentation pattern and marker gene donated by the ES cells (Fig. 47–3A–C). Using ES cells and host embryos that are derived from different strains of zebra fish, germ-line chimeras are generated at

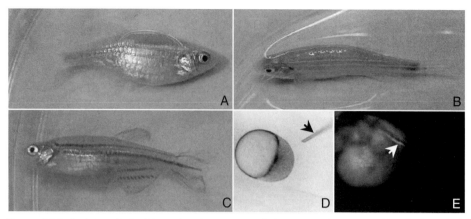

Figure 47–3. *Production of zebra fish germ-line chimeras using multiple passage embryonic stem (ES) cell cultures. The fish shown in (B) is a germ-line chimera that was produced by injecting cultured zebra fish ES cells (passage 6) derived from a wild-type fish into a host embryo obtained from a nonpigmented strain of fish (GASSI). The chimera was bred with the noninjected GASSI mate shown in (A) to produce an F1 individual (C) possessing wild-type pigmentation derived from the cultured ES cells. (D) To generate the chimera the ES cells were microinjected into blastula-stage host embryos using a needle (arrow) formed from a drawn-out glass Pasteur pipette. (E) ES cells expressing green fluorescent protein (GFP) can be used to facilitate the identification of germ-line chimeras. The photograph shows a potential germ-line chimeric larva that was identified a few days after injection by the presence of GFP+ cells in the region of the gonad (arrow).*

a frequency of approximately 2–4% (29). Work is in progress to determine if higher frequencies are obtained when the ES cells and host embryos are derived from the same strain.

Despite the low frequency of germ-line chimera formation, the capacity to inject large numbers of zebra fish embryos with ES cells makes it feasible to generate a sufficient number of germ-line chimeras to establish transgenic and knockout lines of fish. To screen the large numbers of potential germ-line chimeras, it is necessary to have available a rapid and convenient assay method to detect germ-line contribution of the ES cells. To address this problem, ES cell cultures were derived from a transgenic line of fish that carries a gene encoding the green fluorescent protein (GFP) under the control of the fish β-actin promoter.[28,29,35] The ES cell cultures constitutively express GFP making it possible to identify potential germ-line chimeras by the presence of GFP+ cells in the developing gonad a few days after injection (Fig. 47–3E). Approximately, 40% of the injected embryos that were identified in this manner were later confirmed to be germ-line chimeras by transmission of GFP to the F1 generation.[29] The efficiency of germ-line chimera identification was increased further by the production of a transgenic line of zebra fish that expresses the red fluorescent protein (RFP) under the control of the primordial germ cell (PGC)-specific promoter *vasa*. When ES cells are derived from this transgenic line of fish and injected into host embryos, the cells express RFP only when they differentiate into PGCs, making it possible to identify germ-line chimeras with 100% efficiency.

MICROINJECTION OF EMBRYONIC STEM CELLS INTO HOST EMBRYOS

To generate germ-line chimeras, host embryos obtained from the GASSI strain of zebra fish[36] are injected with ES cells. Although host embryos from other strains have been used to

successfully produce germ-line chimeras, the GASSI fish lack pigmentation on their body making it possible to use melanocyte formation as a visual marker of germ-line contribution.[26] The GASSI embryos are collected and incubated at 28° C until they reach the mid-blastula stage of development[31] when they are dechorionated in pronase (see the section on initiation of primary cultures) and rinsed with tank water. Approximately 50 of the dechorionated embryos are placed in a shallow trough made in agarose (1.2%) contained in a 60-mm Petri dish and covered with water. The trough will immobilize the embryos during the ES cell injections. Zebra fish ES cells derived from wild-type embryos (see the section on derivation of zebra fish ES cell cultures) and growing in a single well of a six-well plate are harvested in trypsin/EDTA solution (see the section on passaging the primary cultures) and suspended in LDF medium at a density of $2–3 \times 10^6$ cells/ml. Approximately 1 µl of the cell suspension is drawn into an injection needle formed from a glass Pasteur pipette connected to a Pipette-Aid pipetter (VWR) with Tygon tubing. To form the needle, the Pasteur pipette is heated over a flame and drawn-out and the end is broken off to produce an opening with a diameter of approximately 20 to 30 µm. Embryo injections are performed by inserting the end of the needle into the cell mass of each blastula immobilized on the agarose and releasing approximately 50 to 100 cells (Fig. 47–3D). After injection, the embryos are allowed to sit undisturbed on the agarose for approximately 24 hours before being transferred to a Petri dish containing water. The embryos are incubated (28° C) for 7 days and approximately 50% of the water is changed each day. The embryos are then transferred to a finger bowl (14 cm diameter × 6 cm deep) and incubated (28° C) for 7 days before being transferred to a 2.5 gallon tank and reared to sexual maturity (approximately 3 months).

When ES cells that express GFP or RFP are used, potential germ-line chimeras can be identified by screening the host embryos for the presence of fluorescent cells in the region of the gonad 3 days after injection (Fig. 47–3E). The potential germ-line chimeras that are identified in this manner are placed in a separate tank and raised to sexual maturity. Confirmation of germ-line chimerism is obtained by breeding the fish individually with a GASSI mate and screening the F1 generation of embryos for individuals that express the fluorescent marker gene throughout the body or by the formation of melanocytes. In situations in which GFP or RFP expression is not used to identify potential germ-line chimeras and it is, therefore, necessary to screen a large number of fish by breeding, the initial screen can be conducted by breeding groups of 25 to 30 injected fish. The F1 embryos are examined visually for melanocyte formation or DNA is isolated from batches of the F1 embryos and analyzed by polymerase chain reaction (PCR) to identify the presence of a marker gene carried by the ES cells. Once a group of fish containing a germ-line chimera is identified, each member of that group can be examined by pair-wise breeding.

Targeted Insertion of Vector DNA by Homologous Recombination in the Embryonic Stem Cells

Development of an ES cell–based gene targeting system in zebra fish will require that the cells are able to incorporate vector DNA in a targeted fashion by homologous recombination and that methods are available to identify and select the colonies of homologous recombinants.[22] Using a targeting vector that contained sequences that were homologous to a region of the zebra fish gonadotropin releasing hormone gene (gnrh3), we demonstrated that zebra fish ES cells are able to undergo homologous recombination and incorporate the vector DNA in a targeted fashion.[28] Individual colonies of homologous recombinants were identified and isolated using a PCR screen. Although successful, the PCR screen was laborious and required several months to obtain individual colonies.

To improve the efficiency of colony isolation, we have developed a visual screening method that makes it possible to rapidly identify, isolate, and expand individual colonies of homologous recombinants, obtaining a sufficient number of cells to perform embryo injections approximately 6 weeks after electroporation. The screening method involves the use of a targeting vector that contains the bacterial selectable marker gene neo located within the homologous region and the RFP gene located outside of the region (Fig. 47–4A). The targeting vector is introduced into the ES cell cultures by electroporation, and cells that have incorporated the plasmid are selected in G418. The resulting colonies that have incorporated the vector randomly are RFP+ and those that have undergone homologous recombination and targeted insertion of the plasmid are RFP− (Fig. 47–4B and C). Approximately 5 weeks after initiating G418 selection, the cultures are

examined by fluorescence microscopy and the colonies that completely lack RFP expression are manually selected from the dish using a micropipette and individually transferred to a single well of a 24-well plate. After 1 week, the cells contained in each well are harvested, and one third of the cell suspension is used for PCR analysis to confirm targeted insertion of the vector (Fig. 47–4D). One third of the cells are transferred into a new well to maintain the culture and the final third of the cell suspension is used for embryo injections. Colonies of cells that have undergone homologous recombination, determined by PCR, are passaged every 7 days and embryos are injected at each passage.

ELECTROPORATION OF ZEBRA FISH EMBRYONIC STEM CELLS AND SELECTION OF HOMOLOGOUS RECOMBINANTS

To introduce a targeting vector by electroporation, the zebra fish ES cells are harvested in trypsin/EDTA solution (see the section on passaging the primary cultures), washed two times, and suspended in PBS (7.5×10^6 cells/ml). A 0.75-ml aliquot of the cell suspension is added to a 0.4-cm electroporation cuvette and 50 µg of sterile, linearized, plasmid DNA dissolved in 50 µl TE buffer is added. The electroporation is performed using the following conditions: 950 µF, 300 V with a time constant of 11.6 ms. Cell mortality measured by trypan blue staining should be approximately 50%. Immediately after electroporation the cells are seeded into two culture dishes (100-mm diameter) each containing a monolayer of growth-arrested neo+ RTS34st cells. The RTS34st feeder cells were previously electroporated with a plasmid containing neo under the control of a constitutively active promoter and selected in G418. LDF medium containing the supplements described in the section on derivation of zebra fish ES cell cultures is added to the ES cell culture and G418 (500 µg/ml, Geneticin, Sigma) is added 24 hours after electroporation. The cultures are maintained at 22° C in ambient air and the medium is changed every 2 days. The nontransformed cells begin to die after 3 days in G418 and colonies begin to appear in approximately 2 weeks.

If the visual selection method using RFP (Fig. 47–4) is used to detect homologous recombinants, the RFP− colonies will be large enough to manually remove from the plate 4 to 5 weeks after selection is initiated. Individual colonies are picked from the plate using a Pipetman pipetter (10–50 µl, Rainin), transferred into a drop of trypsin/EDTA solution, and dissociated with gentle pipetting (30 seconds). Aliquots of the cell suspension can be removed for PCR analysis and embryo injections. The remaining cells are transferred to a single well of a 24-well dish containing a monolayer of neo+ RTS34st cells and the minimum amount of medium required to cover the bottom of the well. After the embryo cells have attached to the feeder layer (30 minutes), additional medium containing the supplements listed in the section on derivation of zebra fish ES cell cultures and G418 are added. The FBS present in the medium will inhibit the action of the trypsin. The medium is changed the next day to remove the residual trypsin and then every 5 days until the culture

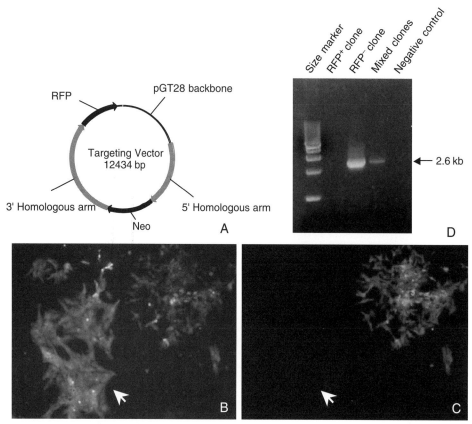

Figure 47–4. Targeted insertion of plasmid DNA by homologous recombination in zebra fish embryonic stem (ES) cell cultures. (A) Diagram of a targeting vector that incorporates a visual marker to detect homologous recombinants. The *neo* selectable marker is located within the region of the vector that is homologous to the gene being targeted and red fluorescent protein (RFP) is located outside of this region. After G418 selection, colonies that incorporate the vector by homologous recombination are RFP⁻ and those that undergo random insertion are RFP⁺. (B) A plasmid designed to target the inactivation of the zebra fish no tail gene *(ntl)* was introduced into ES cells that constitutively express green fluorescent protein (GFP). After G418 selection, two GFP⁺ colonies are shown by fluorescence microscopy. (C) The same two colonies shown in (B) are visualized using a rhodamine filter to detect RFP expression. The colony on the left (arrow) is RFP⁻ indicating that it is a homologous recombinant. (D) Polymerase chain reaction (PCR) analysis to detect homologous recombination using primers that amplify a unique 2.6-kb junction formed between the targeting vector and the endogenous *ntl*. DNA was isolated from the individual RFP⁻ and RFP⁺ colonies shown in (B) and (C) and from a mixture of colonies obtained from a plate that contained at least one homologous recombinant.

is ready to passage. After the cells have proliferated to form a nearly confluent (80%) monolayer the culture is expanded into a single well of a 12 well plate on growth-arrested *neo⁺* RTS34st feeder cells. A portion of the ES cells may be used for embryo injections at each passage. When a sufficient number of cells are obtained, DNA is isolated and homologous recombination is confirmed by Southern blot analysis.[28]

ACKNOWLEDGMENTS

This work was supported by grants from the USDA (2002-35205-11547), NIH (R01 GM69384), and Illinois-Indiana SeaGrant (02-340-1).

REFERENCES

1. Fishman, M.C. (2001). Zebrafish the canonical vertebrate. *Science* **294,** 1290–1291.
2. Eisen, J.S. (1996). Zebrafish make a big splash. *Cell* **87,** 969–977.
3. Nusslein-Volhard, C. (1994). Of flies and fishes. *Science* **266,** 572–574.
4. Streisinger, G., Walker, C., Dower, N., Knauber, D., and Singer, F. (1986). Production of clones of homozygous diploid zebrafish *(Brachydanio rerio). Nature* **291,** 293–296.
5. Currie, P.D. (1996). Zebrafish genetics: mutant cornucopia. *Curr. Biol.* **6,** 1548–1552.
6. Mullins, M.C., Hammerschmidt, M., Hafter, P., and Nusslein-Volhard, C. (1994). Large-scale mutagenesis in the zebrafish: in search of genes controlling development in a vertebrate. *Curr. Biol.* **4,** 189–202.

7. Walker, C. (1999). Haploid screens and gamma-ray mutagenesis. *In* " Methods in Cell Biology" (H.W. Detrich, M. Westerfield, and L.I. Zon, eds.), Vol. 60, pp. 43–70. Academic Press, San Diego, CA.

8. Ivics, Z., Izsvak, Z., and Hackett, P.B. (1999). Genetic applications of transposons and other repetitive elements in zebrafish. *In* "Methods in Cell Biology" (H.W. Detrich, M. Westerfield, and L.I. Zon, eds.), Vol. 60, pp. 99–131. Academic Press, San Diego, CA.

9. Amsterdam, A., Burgess, S., Golling, G., Chen, W., Sun, Z., Townsend, K., Farrington, S., Haldi, M., and Hopkins, N. (1999). A large-scale insertional mutagenesis screen in zebrafish. *Genes Dev.* **13**, 2713–2724.

10. Geisler, R., Rauch, G.J., Baier, H., van Bebber, F., Brobeta, L., Dekens, M.P., Finger, K., Fricke, C., Gates, M.A., Geiger, H., Geiger-Rudolph, S., Gilmour, D., Glaser, S., Gnugge, L., Habeck, H., Hingst, K., Holley, S., Keenan, J., Kirn, A., Knaut, H., Lashkari, D., Maderspacher, F., Martyn, U., Neuhauss, S., Neumann, C., Nicolson, T., Pelegri, F., Ray, R., Rick, J.M., Roehl, H., Roeser, T., Schauerte, H.E., Schier, A.F., Schönberger, U., Schönthaler, H.B., Schulte-Merker, S., Seydler, C., Talbot, W.S., Weiler, C., Nüsslein-Volhard, C., and Haffter, P., et al. (1999). A radiation hybrid map of the zebrafish genome. *Nat. Genet.* **23**, 86–89.

11. Hukriede, N., Fisher, D., Epstein, J., Joly, L., Tellis, P., Zhou, Y., Barbazuk, B., Cox, K., Fenton-Noriega, L., Hersey, C., Miles, J., Sheng, X., Song, A., Waterman, R., Johnson, S.L., Dawid, I.B., Chevrette, M., Zon, L.I., McPherson, J., and Ekker, M. (2001). The LN54 radiation hybrid map of zebrafish expressed sequences. *Genome Res.* **11**, 2127–2132.

12. Woods, I.G., Kelly, P.D., Chu, F., Ngo-Hazelett, P., Yan, Y.L., Huang, H., Postlethwait, J.H., and Talbot, W.S. (2000). A comparative map of the zebrafish genome. *Genome Res.* **10**, 1903–1914.

13. Kishimoto, Y., Lee, K.H., Zon, L., Hammerschmidt, M., and Schulte-Merker, S. (1997). The molecular nature of zebrafish *swirl*: BMP2 function is essential during early dorsoventral patterning. *Development* **124**, 4457–4466.

14. Schulte-Merker, S., van Eeden, F.J.M., Halpern, M.E., Kimmer, C.B., and Nusslein-Volhard, C. (1994). *no tail (ntl)* is the zebrafish homologue of the mouse T *(Brachyury)* gene. *Development* **120**, 1009–1015.

15. Zhang, J., Talbot, W.S., and Schier, A.F. (1998). Positional cloning identifies zebrafish *one-eyed pinhead* as a permissive EGF-related ligand required during gastrulation. *Cell* **92**, 241–251.

16. Gaiano, N., Amsterdam, A., Kawakami, K., Allende, M., Becker, T., and Hopkins, N. (1996), Insertional mutagenesis and rapid cloning of essential genes in zebrafish. *Nature* **383**, 829–832.

17. Golling, G., Amsterdam, A., Zhaoxia,, S., Antonelli, M., Maldonado, E., Chen, W., Burgess, S., Haldi, M., Artzt, K., Farrington, S., Lin, S-Y., Nissen, R.M., and Hopkins N. (2002). Insertional mutagenesis in zebrafish rapidly identifies genes essential for early vertebrate development. *Nat. Genet.* **31**, 135–140.

18. Nasevicius, A., and Ekker, S.C. (2000). Effective targeted gene "knockdown" in zebrafish. *Nat. Genet.* **26**, 216–220.

19. Ekker, S., and Larson, J. (2001). Morphant technology in model developmental systems. *Genesis* **30**, 89–93.

20. Wienholds, E., Schulte-Merker, S., Walderich, B., and Plasterk, R.H.A. (2002). Target-selected inactivation of the zebrafish *rag1* gene. *Science* **297**, 99–102.

21. Doetschman, T., Gregg, R.G., Maeda, N., Hooper, M.L., Melton, D.W., Thompson, S., and Smithies, O. (1987). Targeted correction of a mutant HPRT gene in mouse embryonic stem cells. *Nature* **330**, 576–578.

22. Capecchi, M. (1989). Altering the genome by homologous recombination. *Science* **244**, 1288–1292.

23. Collodi, P., Kamei, Y., Sharps, A., Weber, D., and Barnes, D. (1992). Fish embryo cell cultures for derivation of stem cells and transgenic chimeras. *Mol. Mar. Biol. Biotech.* **1**, 257–265.

24. Ghosh, C., and Collodi, P. (1994). Culture of cells from zebrafish blastula-stage embryos. *Cytotechnology* **14**, 21–26.

25. Sun, L., Bradford, S., Ghosh, C., Collodi, P., and Barnes, D.W. (1995). ES-like cell cultures derived from early zebrafish embryos. *Mol. Mar. Biol. Biotech.* **4**, 193–199.

26. Ma, C., Fan, L., Ganassin, R., Bols, N., and Collodi, P. (2001). Production of zebrafish germ-line chimeras from embryo cell cultures. *Proc. Natl. Acad. Sci. U. S. A.* **98**, 2461–2466.

27. Fan, L., and Collodi, P. (2002). Progress towards cell-mediated gene transfer in zebrafish. *Brief. Functional Genom. Proteom.* **1**, 131–138.

28. Fan, L., Alestrom, A., Alestrom, P., and Collodi, P. (2004). Development of cell cultures with competency for contributing to the zebrafish germ line. *Crit. Rev. Euk. Gene Exp.* **14**, 43–51.

29. Fan, L., Crodian, J., Alestrom, A., Alestrom, P., and Collodi, P. (2004). Zebrafish embryo cells remain pluripotent and germ-line competent for several weeks and multiple passages in culture. *Zebrafish* **1**, 21–26.

30. Ganassin, R., and Bols, N.C. (1999). A stromal cell line from rainbow trout spleen, RTS34st, that supports the growth of rainbow trout macrophages and produces conditioned medium with mitogenic effects on leukocytes. *In Vitro Cell Dev. Biol. Animal* **35**, 80– 86.

31. Kimmel, C.B., Ballard, W.W., Kimmel, S.R., Ullmann, B., and Schilling, T.F. (1995). Stages of embryonic development of the zebrafish. *Dev. Dyn.* **203**, 253–310.

32. Collodi, P., Kamei, Y., Ernst, T., Miranda, C., Buhler, D.R., and Barnes, D.W. (1992). Culture of cells from zebrafish *(Brachydanio rerio)* embryo and adult tissues. *Cell Biol. Toxicol.* **8**, 43–61.

33. Collodi, P., and Barnes, D. (1990). Mitogenic activity from fish embryos, *Proc. Natl. Acad. Sci. U. S. A.* **87**, 3498–3502.

34. Burgess, S., Reim, G., Chen, W., Hopkins, N., and Brand, M. (2002). The zebrafish *spiel-ohne- grenzen (spg)* gene encodes the POU domain protein Pou2 related to mammalian *Oct4* and is essential for formation of the midbrain and hindbrain, and for pre-gastrula morphogenesis. *Development* **129**, 905–916.

35. Higashijima, S., Okamoto, H., Ueno, N., Hotta, Y., and Eguchi, G. (1997). High-frequency generation of transgenic zebrafish which reliably express GFP in whole muscles or the whole body by using promoters of zebrafish origin. *Dev. Biol.* **192**, 289–299.

36. Gibbs, P.D., and Schmale, M.C. (2000). GFP as a genetic marker scorable throughout the life cycle of transgenic zebrafish. *Mar. Biotech.* **2**, 107–125.

48

Identification and Maintenance of Cell Lineage Progenitors Derived from Human ES Cells

Susan M. Hawes and Martin F. Pera

Introduction

Human embryonic stem (ES) cells, derived from inner cell mass (ICM) cells of human blastocysts are karyotypically normal and can be maintained indefinitely in culture while sustaining their ability to differentiate into somatic cell types indicative of all three embryonal germ layers.[1,2] Thus, human ES cells could be used as a renewable source of a wide range of embryonic or adult cells for the study of early human development, for screening of new pharmaceuticals, or for cellular replacement of damaged and diseased tissue following transplantation. Full exploitation of human ES cells in research and therapy will require an understanding of the molecular signals that induce early human embryonic cell fates, knowledge of what cell-specific markers identify early progenitor cell types, and development of methods to enrich and maintain these early cells in culture.

There are several possible models for differentiation pathways of ES cells. An ES cell might differentiate directly into a mature end cell with little proliferative potential. Alternatively, the ES cell might give rise to a lineage-restricted progenitor cell, a cell committed to a more restricted fate with some capacity for self renewal; these progenitors might resemble either lineage-restricted cells in the embryo or stem cells in adult tissues, but in either case they represent intermediates between the ES cell and a terminally differentiated mature cell.

Differentiation of mouse or human ES cells toward progenitor or somatic-cell types is commonly assessed by morphology, by marker expression, or by their developmental potential following transplantation into animal models, but often the factors that control lineage-specific differentiation are unknown. The identification of markers for stem or progenitor cells from differentiating human ES cells is in its infancy. This is in part due to the limitations in the current methodology for maintenance of human ES cells *in vitro* but also to our lack of understanding of these early cell populations within the developing mouse embryo and even more so

during human embryogenesis. Thus, although lineage specific markers known to be involved in mouse embryo development or representative of particular cell lineages have been defined, whether similar genes or markers identify similar cell populations during human ES cell differentiation remains to be seen. Moreover, whether a human ES cell-derived cell that expresses characteristic cell specific markers *in vitro* behaves functionally as its *in vivo* counterpart must be determined. Expansion and long-term cultivation of progenitor cells may, in itself, result in aberrant expression of cell lineage specific markers, making repeated testing of the multidevelopmental potential of progenitor cells essential.[3]

Another limitation to current methodologies is that the signals required to maintain and to expand progenitor cells in culture are not known. Limited expansion of hematopoietic stem cells (HSCs), one of the most studied adult stem cell populations, has been achieved using a number of cytokines. Long-term proliferation and maintenance of HSCs has not been reported,[4,5] although recently sonic hedgehog[6,7] and members of the Wnt gene family have been implicated[7] as factors that might help achieve this goal. The successful purification of Wnt-3a enables the demonstration that long-term expansion of HSCs in vitro may be possible.[8,9] Thus, our understanding of maintenance and expansion of stem, progenitor, and intermediate cell types from ES cells is limited.

Transplantation of neural precursors, isolated from differentiating human ES cells, into the brains of newborn mice, verified their potential to integrate and differentiate into adult neural cell types.[10] Such transplantation studies using normal or diseased animals will be important to assess the functional capability of human ES-derived cells.

Characteristics of Human Embryonic Stem Cells

Similar to ICM cells from which they are derived, human ES cells are pluripotent and are able, theoretically, to develop into all adult cell types. Certainly, following transplantation into immunocompromised mice, human ES cells form teratomas containing random differentiated cell types such as cartilage epithelia, squamous epithelia, neural cells, muscle cells, and glandular epithelia.[2] Human ES cells seem to have the ability to self-renew indefinitely. The HES2 cell line derived in 1998 by Reubinoff *et al.*[2] has been maintained in culture for up to 168

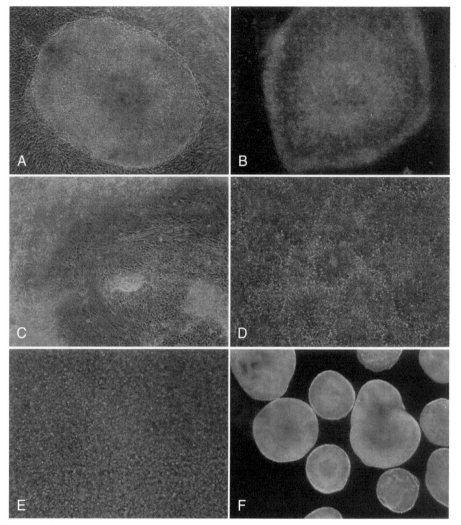

Figure 48–1. Human embryonic stem (ES) cell colonies of approximately 50,000 cells grown on mouse embryonic fibroblast (MEF) cells (A) and imaged by phase (B). Areas of morphologically distinct cells types within spontaneously differentiating human ES cells, 2 weeks following plating (C). Rosette-like cell clusters within 2 week spontaneously differentiating human ES cells (D). Human ES cells following 10 days of treatment with soluble noggin (E). Neurospheres formed following transfer of human ES cell-derived rosette cells into neural stem cell culture conditions (F). (Please see CD-ROM for color version of this figure.)

passages at the present time.[2a] Whether long-term cultivation of human ES cells under present culture conditions may result in subtle genetic or epigenetic changes affecting their underlying characteristics remains to be seen.

As the blastocyst implants and a proportion of ICM cells form the epiblast, pluripotent cells respond to extracellular signals and differentiate into committed cell types, losing their ability for self-renewal. Human ICM cells removed before exposure to such differentiative signals can be maintained and expanded in culture as ES cells. However, it is not as yet known what molecular signals mediate their self-renewal.

Unlike mouse ES cells, human ES cells are not apparently responsive to leukemia inhibitory factor[2] (LIF). Human ES cell maintenance requires co-culture with mouse embryonic fibroblast (MEF) cells. Routine passage of human ES cell colonies involves discarding cells that show morphologic changes indicative of early differentiation or by excluding larger differentiated cellular clumps by filtration following dissociation. Using these methods, progressive differentiation of the culture can be avoided, as assessed by morphology (Fig. 48–1A and B) and immunofluorescence using antibody markers specific for undifferentiated embryonic cells. When human ES cell colonies are grown on a low density of MEF cells without serum, addition of basic fibroblast growth factor (bFGF) enables stem cell maintenance.[11] However, if human ES cells are not passaged as they reach confluency, they spontaneously differentiate in vitro, with or without the presence of bFGF, generating many morphologically distinct cell types (Fig. 48–1C). Unlike the coordinated establishment of germ cell lineages during embryogenesis, differentiation of ES cells in culture is apparently disorganized resulting in colonies made up of progenitor cells of various cell types.

Differentiation of Human Embryonic Stem Cells

Strategies to promote differentiation of human ES cells into particular cell types have been adapted from studies undertaken using mouse ES cells. Two methods have been applied. In many studies, mouse ES cells are transferred as small clumps into a suspension culture where they develop into aggregates called embryoid bodies[12,13] (EBs). EB formation is assumed to, in some ways, recapitulate the three-dimensional complexity of the embryo, resulting in formation of progenitor cells representative of the three embryonal germ layers. Following disaggregation of EB, their constituent cells can be further cultivated to yield a variety of differentiated somatic cell types. The second method allows mouse ES cells to differentiate in vitro as an adherent cell layer without EB formation and has been utilized for derivation of neural[13–15] and hematopoietic progenitors.[16,17] Use of both of these protocols results in final cultures containing mixed cell populations. Both prior aggregation of human ES cells into EB[18,19] and spontaneous differentiation of human ES cells as an adherent cell layer[2,10,20] result in cultures of mixed populations of cells as evidenced by morphology and the expression of lineage-specific markers as assessed by reverse transcriptase polymerase chain reaction (RT-PCR) and immunostaining.

Clearly, to study the biology of human ES cell derivatives and to generate cells for cellular based transplantation therapies, pure populations of progenitor or somatic cell types need to be derived. Different strategies can be used to achieve this. First, the addition of soluble inducing factors to human ES cells may direct their differentiation or facilitate survival and growth of particular lineages. Second, using markers expressed by lineage-committed progenitors during embryogenesis, isolation or depletion of particular cells from mixed cell populations can be achieved using antibodies raised against cell surface markers and subsequent fluorescence-activated cell sorting (FACS) or immunomagnetic bead separation. Third, through genetic selection using selectable markers under the control of lineage-specific promoters, specific cell types can be isolated, generating pure cell populations. Thus, for example, using homologous recombination, mouse ES cells have been genetically modified to express antibiotic resistance under the control of the promoter for Sox2.[21] Subsequent culture of the mouse ES cells in the appropriate antibiotic resulted in higher proportions of

Sox2-positive cells with a neural identity evidenced by expression of markers expressed by the developing mouse neural tube.

Presence of Early Precursors Within Human Embryonic Stem Cell Colonies/Human Embryonic Stem Cells Express Markers of Early Germ Layer Lineages

Heterogeneity within human ES cell colonies[22] may indicate early progenitor cells with potential to develop into more differentiated cell types. Because present conditions to maintain human ES cells are probably suboptimal for stem cell maintenance, cells begin to differentiate under basal culture conditions. That human ES cell colonies may contain trophoblast cells is suggested by their secretion of human chorionic gonadotrophin (hCG) into the medium[2] and trophoblast differentiation is enhanced following treatment of ES cells with BMP-4.[23] A subpopulation of human ES cells isolated using the mouse ES cell surface marker SSEA1 expressed hCG, suggesting enrichment for trophoblast cells.[22] Subsequent analysis confirmed that in contrast to the mouse embryo, SSEA1 is localized to trophectoderm but not ICM cells of human blastocysts.

Whether all or only subpopulations of the cells within human ES cell colonies contribute to teratoma formation following transplantation into immunocompromised mice, used as assessment of human ES cell pluripotency, is uncertain. Clearly, clonal derivation of human ES cell colonies will be crucial for truly ascertaining a human ES cell ability for pluripotency. Clonal derivation of a human ES cell line by dissociation into single cells resulted in the establishment of two cell lines, propagated for 8 months and capable of teratoma formation in vivo.[11] However, in general, survival of human ES cells following dissociation into single cells is poor, making derivation of clonal cell lines difficult.[2a]

Mouse ES cells, like their embryonic precursors, readily differentiate into primitive endoderm.[24] Following implantation, mouse ICM cells differentiate into progenitors of the epiblast and of extraembryonic tissues. Establishment of the extraembryonic lineages including the visceral endoderm (VE) is critical for subsequent specification of the three germ layers, because the extraembryonic tissues produce spatially and temporally regulated signals that direct commitment of epiblast cells into specific fates.[25] Thus, the presence of primitive endoderm cells within human ES cell colonies may contribute to early differentiation events and produce signals that direct formation early progenitor cell types.

Published studies of human ES cell phenotype have observed not only expression of genes known to be expressed by pluripotent cells but also markers most commonly associated with specification of early cell lineages.[26,26a] One study reported that human ES cells were immunoreactive to neuronal marker βIII-tubulin.[27] Other workers have reported that human ES cells express hematopoietic markers, AC133, vascular endothelial growth factor receptor-1 (VEGFR –2, Flk-1), AC133, and c-kit,[26,28,29] as well as CD34 at apparently low frequency.[29] However, there are a number of explanations for the observed expression of differentiation lineage-specific markers in ES cell cultures. First, some markers of committed progenitors are also found on pluripotent stem cells. AC133 and c-kit are also expressed by ES cells and germ cells, respectively, and c-kit has recently been used as a marker to isolate putative oocyte-like cells from mouse ES cell cultures transfected with a germ cell specific Oct4 loci associated with a detectable marker green fluorescent protein.[30] Alternatively, expression of these markers at a low level may reflect promiscuity in transcription of differentiation markers in ES cells or low frequency spontaneous differentiation into particular lineages.

Lineage-specific Progenitor Cells Derived From Human Embryonic Stem Cells

BLOOD

The most extensively characterized adult stem cell population with respect to knowledge of multipotentiality, differentiation stage-specific marker expression, and the factors that govern growth and differentiation is the HSC.[4,5] HSCs are rare cell populations that reside within bone marrow or fetal (not adult) liver and can form all major blood cell lineages. Two types of HSCs have been described, characterized by their long-term (lifetime) or short-term (8–10 weeks) differentiative and/or reconstitutive abilities and are identified by antibodies that recognize cell surface proteins.[3,31] Two studies have developed methods to derive human hematopoietic progenitor cells from human ES cells.[26,29] Critical to both these studies is the use of cell surface markers previously shown to be expressed by subpopulations of HSCs. One study derived early hematopoietic precursors that were CD34+ but showed no immunoreactivity to CD45.[26] CD45 is a panleukocytic marker that along with CD34 identifies definitive hematopoietic cells within 3–5 week human embryos.[32,33] Using a CD34 antibody these workers enriched for a hematopoietic precursor population. The other study used CD45 as a marker to develop suitable differentiation conditions for blood precursors.[29]

The CD34 antigen is expressed by most human hematopoietic stem and progenitor cell populations (reviewed, reference 5). Following co-culture of human ES cells on mouse bone marrow or yolk sac stromal lines, hematopoietic stem and precursor cells were isolated by immunobeads conjugated with the CD34 antibody.[26] Using this co-culture method, it was found that human ES cell colonies differentiated into many morphologically distinct cell types after 3–5 days, 1–2% of which were immunoreactive for the CD34 antibody (CD34+) but not an antibody raised against CD38 (a marker for myeloid cells). Further analysis of the CD34+ cells revealed that 50% were also immunoreactive to a CD31 antibody (CD31+) suggesting that they may be endothelial cell progenitors. Evidence that the isolated CD34+ were hematopoietic progenitors was obtained following transfer of cells into

agar or methyl-cellulose containing cytokines. Colony forming units (CFU) were generated from the CD34+ cells at an average of 270 colonies per 10^5 cells in comparison to 10 colonies derived from CD34− cells. The CD34+ cells developed into colonies containing mature erythroid (red blood), myeloid (white blood), and megakaryocyte (platelet progenitor) cells upon subsequent differentiation. Interestingly, RT-PCR analysis of the differentiated CFU colonies for erythroid gene expression showed adult globin expression.

The second study used the formation of EBs from human ES cells before addition of growth factors and cytokines that enhanced blood progenitor development.[29] These authors used antibodies against CD34 andCD38, markers used previously to isolate human HSCs from umbilical cord blood, fetal liver, fetal bone marrow, and adult bone marrow.[34] Use of CD45 expression verified the presence of mature hematopoietic cells following 10 days of directed differentiation. Thus, using CD45 expression to monitor affects of altering differentiation protocols, the authors showed that by addition of BMP-4 to human ES-derived EB cultures they could increase the proportion of cells immunoreactive to CD45 (CD45+). Addition of cytokines with BMP-4 increases the proportion of CD45+ cells that co-express CD34. Of the CD45+ cells derived from the differentiated human ES cells all (100%) formed CFU colonies, in comparison to none of the CD45− cells. These CFU colonies formed secondary CFU, following disaggregation and replating.

Identification and isolation of endothelial cells from differentiating human ES cells was achieved using the cell surface marker platelet endothelial cell adhesion molecule (PECAM) or CD31.[28] Four days following formation of EB from human ES cells, CD31+ cells appeared. These CD31+ cells increased in proportion by day 13, when the EB were dissociated, and cells FACS sorted using the CD31 antibody. When these CD31+ cells were cultured on Matrigel, cord-like structures formed. Other vascular endothelial markers were also expressed by EB following 13 days in culture, including AC133 and vascular endothelial-cadherin (VE-cadherin). Verification of the identity of the CD31+ cells was confirmed by transplantation of cells into subcutaneous tissue of immunodeficient mice following seeding onto a biodegradable polymer scaffold. Immunoreactivity to human specific antibodies against CD31 and CD34 confirmed that the human ES cell-derived CD31+ cell population formed microvessels, some of which contained mouse blood cells. The authors did not use other human specific markers to show whether these cells were committed within the endothelial cell lineage or are able to produce other cell types *in vivo*.

NEURAL CELLS

Mouse

There are several well-established protocols for deriving neural cells from mouse ES cells; most but not all involve EB formation.[35–37] Protocols that first differentiate mouse ES cells into EB, allowing for formation of progenitor cells of the three primary germ layers, subsequently selectively enrich for neural cells by removal of serum. Following this, addition of bFGF and/or epidermal growth factor (EGF)[38] results in proliferation of neural stem and progenitor cells. The subsequent addition of FGF8, sonic hedgehog (SHH), and ascorbic acid results in derivation of midbrain neurons.[14,39] Neural progenitors and their derivatives have also been generated from mouse ES cells without prior formation of EB.[14,15] These data suggest that, similar to neural induction in the *Xenopus laevis* embryo, ES cells become neural cells as long as they are not acted on by signaling molecules (discussed in reference 37).

Human

A number of cell-specific markers have been used to identify neural stem and progenitor cell populations derived from human ES cells, including the intermediate filament protein nestin,[40] musashi-1,[41] and the neural-cell adhesion molecule (N-CAM). None of these markers are specific for neural stem or progenitor cells. Nestin, a marker characteristic for neural stem cells is localized to the neural tube and cerebral cortex of rat embryos becoming restricted to a subpopulation of ependymal cells in the adult. Nestin, likely present in all dividing neural populations, has also reported to be temporally expressed in muscle and pancreas[42–44] (discussed in reference 45). Musashi-1, more indicative of neural progenitors rather than stem cells[46] has also been shown to be present in stem cells of non-neural cell lineages.[47,48]

Putative neural stem or progenitor cells have been identified morphologically within differentiating human ES cell colonies by virtue of their formation of distinct rosette-like clusters, similar to structures within mouse and human neural tubes (Fig. 48–1D). The appearance of these cells occur within spontaneously differentiating human ES cell colonies, about 2 weeks after plating[2,10] or following culture of EB in the presence of FGF2.[49] Interestingly, when EB were cultured without FGF2, formation of rosette-like structures was not observed, possibly indicating differences between spontaneous differentiation of human ES cells as EB compared with monolayer cultures. The rosette cells stain positively for nestin, musashi, and N-CAM.

Further characterization of the human ES cell-derived rosette cells was achieved by propagating these cells as neurospheres. Propagation of neural stem cells derived from fetal or adult brain has been achieved by their transfer into nonattachment conditions using a defined medium with the addition of FGF and/or EGF (discussed in reference 45). Most neurospheres in culture comprise a heterogenous population of cells, containing few (<5%) with the ability for self-renewal.

Within the human ES cell-derived neurospheres, a high proportion of cells express neural markers nestin (97%), N-CAM (99%), and the neuronal and glial progenitor marker A2B5 (90%).[10] The developmental potential of these neural stem and progenitor cells was revealed following dissociation of the neurospheres and attachment onto adhesive substrate in the presence of serum. Further differentiation into the neuronal lineage was demonstrated by cellular staining with antibodies against βIII-tubulin, MAP2ab, neurofilament light chain protein (NF-L), glutamate, synaptophysin, and glutamic acid decarboxylase (GABA). The appearance of cells that

stain positively for A2B5 and glial fibrillary acidic protein (GFAP) was indicative of astrocytes and a small proportion of O1, O4, and myelin binding protein (MBP) positive cells suggestive of oligodendrocyte formation.[10,49] Reubinoff and colleagues observed that 57% of cells were immunoreactive to βIII-tubulin and 26% to GFAP. A low proportion of oligodendrocytes within these cultures may reflect limitations in the induction protocols toward this lineage.

Multilineage gene expression in the human neurospheres was assessed by RT-PCR analysis for non-neural genes.[10] Neurospheres expressed genes indicative of endoderm (alpha-fetoprotein [AFP], alpha-1 antitrypsin [AAT], transferrin, and amylase), hematopoietic (CD34, AC133, Flk-1), and epidermal (keratin) progenitors. It is unclear whether the RT-PCR results reflect the presence of low proportions of progenitors of other lineages within the spheres or promiscuous gene expression by the neural progenitors.

Maintenance of a progenitor population within the neurospheres was evidenced by serial cultivation of the spheres through approximately 20 to 25 population doublings.[10,49] To assess differentiation in vivo, both studies transplanted the human neurospheres into lateral ventricles of newborn mice. The human neural stem and progenitor cells successfully engrafted into the host brain and differentiated into neuronal and glial cells, thus showing that cell derivatives from human ES cells can migrate, integrate, and differentiate *in vivo* in response to regionally specific environmental cues.

Other studies used addition of soluble factors to human ES cell cultures to direct differentiation toward enhancement for neural lineages. Retinoic acid (RA), a critical regulator of mouse embryogenesis, directs differentiation of neural cell types in culture and neural differentiation of mouse ES cells and human ES cells (discussed in reference 36). Addition of RA to mouse ES cell-derived EB cultures increased the proportion of neural cell types from 15–30% to 100%. The mechanism by which RA potently induces neural cell populations from ES cells is not fully understood, but it involves upregulation of genes involved in embryonic neural pathways, such as SHH, Pax6, mash-1, and neuroD. Downregulation of the expression of brachyury, cardiac actin, and ξ globin suggests that RA inhibits mesoderm induction while promoting neural differentiation.[36]

Addition of RA and nerve growth-β (NGF) increases the proportion of neuronal cells that form within human ES cell-derived EB as assessed by detection of NF-L (neural progenitors) by *in situ* hybridization.[19] When either RA or NGF was added to EB cultures the number of NF-L positive cells within EB increased from 54% to 74%. Carpenter and colleagues reported an increased proportion of A2B5 and polysialylated neural cell adhesion molecule (PS-NCAM) positive cells following addition of RA to EB and subsequent disaggregation onto an adhesive substrate.[27] Subpopulations of nestin positive cells expressed PS-NCAM and A2B5. To a lesser proportion astrocyte cells were detected within the cultures by expression of GFAP and GalC. Further differentiation of these progenitors resulted in mature neuronal cell types that stained with antibodies against MAP-2, β-tubulin III, and GABA as well as being capable of responding to neuro-transmitters, GABA, acetylcholine, and ATP. About 3% of the neurons expressed tyrosine hydroxylase (TH) indicative of dopaminergic (DA) neurons.

The presence of cells expressing muscle actin and AFP showed that the induction protocol resulted in a heterogenous cell population. Purification of the mixed cell population using magnetic bead sorting with antibodies against cell surface proteins A2B5 and PS-NCAM resulted in an enriched neural progenitor cell population with 86% of cells immunoreactive to PS-NCAM and 91% to A2B5.

Based on the effect of the BMP family and their antagonists on embryonic neuralization, Pera and colleagues antagonized BMP-2 by adding soluble noggin to human ES cell cultures.[50] Between 5 to 10 days after noggin treatment of human ES cells, an apparently homogenous, morphologically distinct cell population formed. These noggin-treated human cells form neurospheres at a 10-fold greater frequency to cells isolated from spontaneously differentiating human ES cells, and with prolonged treatment, the entire culture could be converted into neurosphere precursors.[50a] Expression of Sox2, musashi1, nestin, and Pax6 but not brachyury or endoderm markers, GATA-4, and AFP suggests that these distinct cells are neural stem or progenitor cells. Their ability to differentiate into both neurons and astroglial cells confirmed this.

ENDODERMAL CELL TYPES

Compared with our understanding of neural and hematopoietic development, less is known about the factors that establish endodermal development in the mouse embryo and the signals that direct endoderm into different cellular fates such as hepatic and pancreatic differentiation.[51] Use of specific markers for the identification and isolation of endodermal cell types from human ES cells, with the ability to form hepatocytes, pancreatic β-islet cells, or lung all indicative of definitive endoderm is confounded by the similarity in molecular profiles between extraembryonic cells, VE, and embryonic or fetal liver.[52] The lack of temporal and spatial organization of ES cell differentiation makes identification of definitive endoderm (as opposed to extraembryonic endodermal cells) problematic. Detailed characterization of endoderm-specific gene expression during EB formation from mouse ES cells showed that cells immunoreactive to AFP and transthyretin (TTR) are present within yolk-sac-like structures. These cells are restricted to the outer layer of the EB and appear subsequent to expression of HNF1 and HNF3β; thus, they appear to be visceral and not embryonic endoderm.[53]

To distinguish hepatocytes derived from ES cells from extraembryonic cells, Jones and colleagues used an ES cell line in which a gene trapping event resulted in expression of β-galactosidase (β-gal) by embryonic liver cells.[54] Using this ES cell line to generate a transgenic mouse, the authors established that β-gal expression was restricted to early liver with no apparent detection in the yolk sac endoderm Thus, β-gal expression was used to identify cells *in vitro* that were expressing the target of the gene trap (a liver-specific ankyrin

repeat containing protein) and that had, therefore, differentiated into hepatocytes. EBs were disaggregated 5 days following formation and plated onto gelatin for further differentiation. Following 9 days, up to 90% of EB that had been disaggregated were positive for β-gal, compared with 27% of EB in suspension. Immunocytochemistry showed that the β-gal positive cells were positive for liver markers TTR, AFP, and albumin.

LIVER

Hepatocytes have been derived following EB formation from mouse ES cells.[54,55] After 5–9 days, on removal of LIF and EB formation, mouse ES cells differentiate into cells that express genes characteristic of early hepatic development, including HNF4-α, TTR, AFP, and albumin but no markers of mature hepatocytes. However, following attachment of the EB to an adhesive substrate and sequential addition of dexamethasone, oncostatin M, acidic FGF, and hepatocyte growth factor (HGF), expression of glucose-6-phosphate (G-6-P) and tyrosine aminotransferase (TAT) was observed, indicating differentiation toward mature hepatocytes.

Adding sodium butyrate to either human ES cells or to day 4 EBs produces an apparent homogenous population of cells with a distinctive epithelial morphology.[56] This directed differentiation protocol results in about 60–90% of cells being immunoreactive to hepatocyte markers, albumin, AAT, glycogen, cytokeratin (CK)-8, CK-18, CK-19 but not to AFP. Cells staining positively to CK-19 may suggest presence of biliary epithelial cells. Functional capacity of the differentiated hepatocyte-like cells was assessed by measurement of cytochrome P450 enzymes, characteristic of hepatocytes. The mechanism by which sodium butyrate induced human ES cells to develop into hepatocytes is not understood. Sodium butyrate inhibits histone deacetylase activity regulating chromatin and is known to induce differentiation of many different cell types. Whether the appearance of hepatocyte-like cells was due to directed differentiation by sodium butyrate or due to the high proportion of cell death (about 80%) and selective survival of hepatocyte progenitor cells remains to be determined.

PANCREAS

Successful derivation of pancreatic β-islet cells from human ES cells has not yet been reported. To date, it has been shown that differentiating human ES cells express genes characteristic of the establishment of the mouse embryonic pancreas following EB formation, but cell populations that produce insulin in culture have not been successfully isolated. Expression of genes indicative of pancreas development, such as Pdx1, neurogenin3, glucose transporter (GLUT)-1, GLUT2, and glucokinase was shown by RT-PCR analysis following 15 days in culture after EB formation.[57] Immunoreactivity to insulin was detected within EB after 19 days in culture with insulin secretion into the medium increasing from 21 to 31 days. However, only 2% of the total cells stained positively for insulin.

More controversial have been attempts to obtain pancreatic islet cells from mouse ES-derived neural progenitors.

Expansion of nestin-positive cells using a protocol for generation of neural precursors, and their further differentiation via pancreatic cell culture conditions, results in cellular clusters that secrete insulin *in vitro* albeit at low levels[58] although other workers found that insulin uptake from the culture medium accounted for this phenomena.[59] Although other pancreatic markers were detected (glucagon and somatostatin) within these mouse ES cell-derived nestin-positive cells, Pdx1, critical for pancreatic formation was not expressed. The cell cultures contain mixed cell populations of neuronal cells, evidenced by their immunoreactivity to β_{III}-tubulin. The relationship between nestin-positive cells and islet cells has been the subject of a number of experimental studies and considerable discussion. Nestin expression has been detected in both embryonic and adult pancreas.[44] Nestin-positive cells were isolated from rat and human pancreatic islets and expanded with addition of bFGF and EGF to the cultures, conditions adapted from proliferation of nestin-positive neural cell-types.[60] Further differentiation results in cells that expressed markers suggestive of hepatic lineages and pancreatic exocrine and endocrine cells, including insulin-secreting cells, suggesting a multipotent progenitor cell. However, examination of human embryonic pancreas revealed that, in contrast to adult cells, embryonic pancreatic epithelial cells do not stain positively for a nestin antibody,[61,62] and culture of these cells in conditions used to differentiate pancreatic cells failed to direct them into insulin-producing cells.[62] In the developing mouse embryo, mesenchymal cells surrounding the pancreatic bud are immunoreactive to nestin.[63] These studies suggest that, during embryo development, islet precursor cells are not demarcated by nestin expression. Whether the developmental potential of ES-derived cells that are immunoreactive to nestin is different than the potential of those cells from the embryo must be clarified.

Other strategies to direct mouse ES cells toward a pancreatic fate involve forced expression of Pax4 and Pdx1, genes that regulate endocrine pancreas development.[64] Detection of genes expressed during pancreatic formation using RT-PCR analysis, namely *islet-1, neurogenin-3, insulin, islet amyloid polypeptide (IAPP),* and *GLUT-2,* confirmed direction toward pancreatic cell types. In these experiments, the resulting cell populations were able to normalize blood glucose levels after transplantation into streptozotocin-diabetic mice. Finally, genetic selection for mouse ES cells expressing a selectable marker driven by the insulin promoter resulted in the isolation of a purified population of insulin-producing cells that temporarily restores blood glucose homeostasis following transplantation into a streptozotocin-diabetic mouse.[65]

Conclusions

Establishment of clinical therapies for the replacement of damaged or diseased cells involves derivation of pure populations of progenitor or somatic cell types from human ES cells. This objective is greatly aided by development of protocols to expand and maintain these early human cell populations in culture for long periods. Critical to this work is the use of

markers to identify and characterize the cells, as well as a means to select and isolate subpopulations. Application of markers and genes whose expression is characteristic of progenitor cells in the early mouse embryo or adult stem cells can facilitate this approach.

The appearance of ES cell-derived lineage-specific progenitor cells in vitro may reflect the regulation and timing of their development in the embryo *in vivo*.[38,66,67] This has been suggested by observations for mouse neural cell derivation. Differences between mouse and human embryo development may become apparent as we accrue more knowledge about the differentiation pathways for human ES cells. Observed differences between the effects of SHH and BMP-4 on mouse and nonhuman primate ES cells in their acquisition of dorsal or ventral fates have been reported.[67] Use of similar co-culture conditions to those applied for directing mouse ES cells into both dorsal and ventral fates results in primate ES-cell-derived ventral but not dorsal neural cells. This may reflect species differences in embryonic regulation or in expression of cell-specific markers.

Mouse and human embryogenesis develop on a different time scale.[68] Establishment of the mouse embryonic germ layers, gastrulation, and organogenesis occur over 8–9 days. Similar developmental processes within the human embryo occurs between 2 to 5 weeks after fertilization.[68] This difference in timing may influence how human ES cells differentiate *in vitro*. The timing of mouse ES cell neural induction

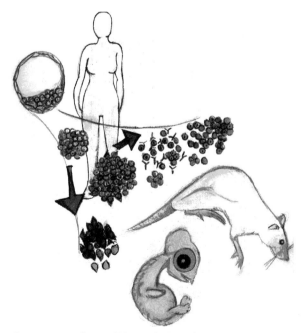

Figure 48-2. Before establishment of cell lines for use in clinical therapies, pure populations of progenitor cells from human embryonic stem (ES) cells derived from human blastocysts will be generated following directed differentiation or by isolation using cell-surface-specific markers. Before clinical use, their full biologic potential can be assessed by transplantation into embryonic and diseased or damaged animal models. (Please see CD-ROM for color version of this figure.)

in vitro corresponds to neurulation of the mouse embryo (3.5 days).[67] Differentiation of mouse ES-cell-derived oligodendrocyte progenitor cells into oligodendrocytes was similar to differentiation of relative cells within the mouse spinal cord. Interestingly, the appearance of equivalent neural cell types from nonhuman primate ES cells was later in comparison to the mouse (10 days) although significantly faster than in the embryo (5 weeks).[69]

Use of animal models to fully characterize human ES cell-derived progenitor cells will be critical before their adoption for clinical use (Fig. 48–2). Grafting of human ES cells into the somites of 1.5- to 2-day-old chick embryos shows that they integrate and differentiate within the host animal.[70] Transplantation of human ES cell-derived progenitor cells into different sites of the developing chick embryo or recombination with mouse embryonic explants will be a means to ascertain their developmental potential. This will verify and complement the use of cell-specific markers as *in vitro* functional assays, such as insulin secretion to identify β-cells of the pancreas and urea uptake by putative liver cells. Finally, transplantation into either diseased or damaged animal models will investigate the functional ability of progenitor cells.

REFERENCES

1. Thomson, J.A., Itskovitz-Eldor, J., Shapiro, S., Waknitz, M.A., and Swiergiel, J.J., Marshall, V.S., and Jones, J.M. (1998). Embryonic stem cell lines derived from human blastocysts. *Science* **282**, 1145–1147.

2. Reubinoff, B.E., Pera, M.F., Fong, C.Y., Trounson, A., and Bongso, A. (2000). Embryonic stem cell lines from human blastocysts: Somatic differentiation in vitro. *Nat. Biotechnol.* **18**, 399–404.

2a. Pera, unpublished observation.

3. Anderson, D.J. (2001). Stem cells and pattern formation in the nervous system: The possible versus the actual. *Neuron* **30**, 19–35.

4. Wagers, A.J., Christensen, J.L., and Weissman, I.L. (2002). Cell fate determination from stem cells. *Gene Ther.* **9**, 606–612.

5. Kondo, M., Wagers, A.J., Manz, M.G., Prohaska, S.S., Scherer, D.C., Beilhack, G.F., Shizuru, J.A., and Weissman, I.L. (2003). Biology of hematopoietic stem cells and progenitors: Implications for clinical application. *Annu. Rev. Immunol.* **21**, 759–806.

6. Bhardwaj G.M.B., Wu, D., Baker, D.P., Williams, K.P., Chadwick, K., Ling, L.E., Karanu, F.N., and Bhatia, M. (2001). Sonic hedgehog induces the proliferation of primitive human hematopoietic cells via BMP regulation. *Nat. Immunol.* **2**, 172–180.

7. Austin, T.W., Solar, G.P., Ziegler, F.C., Liem, L., and Matthews, W. (1997). A role for the Wnt gene family in hematopoiesis: Expansion of multilineage progenitor cells. *Blood* **89**, 3624–3635.

8. Reya, T., Duncan, A.W., Ailles, L., Domen, J., Scherer, D.C., Willert, K., Hintz, L., Nusse, R., and Weissman, I.L. (2003). A role for Wnt signalling in self-renewal of haematopoietic stem cells. *Nature* **423**, 409–414.

9. Willert, K., Brown, J.D., Danenberg, E., Duncan, A.W., Weissman, I.L., Reya, T., Yates, J.R., 3rd, and Nusse, R. (2003). Wnt proteins are lipid-modified and can act as stem cell growth factors. *Nature* **423**, 448–452.

10. Reubinoff, B.E., Itsykson, P., Turetsky, T., Pera, M.F., Reinhartz, E., Itzik, A., and Ben-Hur, T. (2001). Neural progenitors from human embryonic stem cells. *Nat. Biotechnol.* **19**, 1134–1140.

11. Amit, M., Carpenter, M.K., Inokuma, M.S., Chiu, C.P., Harris, C.P., Waknitz, M.A., Itskovitz-Eldor, J., and Thomson, J.A. (2000). Clonally derived human embryonic stem cell lines maintain pluripotency and proliferative potential for prolonged periods of culture. *Dev. Biol.* **227**, 271–278.

12. Doetschman, T.C., Eistetter, H., Katz, M., Schmidt, W., and Kemler, R. (1985). The in vitro development of blastocyst-derived embryonic stem cell lines: formation of visceral yolk sac, blood islands and myocardium. *J. Embryol. Exp. Morphol.* **87**, 27–45.

13. Kawasaki, H., Mizuseki, K., Nishikawa, S., Kaneko, S., Kuwana, Y., Nakanishi, S., Nishikawa, S.I., and Sasai, Y. (2000). Induction of midbrain dopaminergic neurons from ES cells by stromal cell-derived inducing activity. *Neuron* **28**, 31–40.

14. Tropepe, V., Hitoshi, S., Sirard, C., Mak, T.W., Rossant, J., and van der Kooy, D. (2001). Direct neural fate specification from embryonic stem cells: a primitive mammalian neural stem cell stage acquired through a default mechanism. *Neuron* **30**, 65–78.

15. Ying, Q.L.S.M., Griffiths, D., Li, M., and Smith, A. (2003). Conversion of embryonic stem cells into neuroectodermal precursors in adherent monoculture. *Nat. Biotechnol.* **21**, 183–186.

16. Nishikawa, S.I., Nishikawa, S., Hirashima, M., Matsuyoshi, N., and Kodama, H. (1998). Progressive lineage analysis by cell sorting and culture identifies FLK1+VE-cadherin+ cells at a diverging point of endothelial and hemopoietic lineages. *Development* **125**, 1747–1757.

17. Yamashita, J., Itoh, H., Hirashima, M., Ogawa, M., Nishikawa, S., Yurugi, T., Naito, M., and Nakao, T. (2000). Flk1-positive cells derived from embryonic stem cells serve as vascular progenitors. *Nature* **408**, 92–96.

18. Itskovitz-Eldor, J., Schuldiner, M., Karsenti, D., Eden, A., Yanuka, O., Amit, M., Soreq, H., and Benvenisty, N. (2000). Differentiation of human embryonic stem cells into embryoid bodies compromising the three embryonic germ layers. *Mol. Med.* **6**, 88–95.

19. Schuldiner, M., Yanuka, O., Itskovitz-Eldor, J., Melton, D.A., and Benvenisty, N. (2000). Effects of eight growth factors on the differentiation of cells derived from human embryonic stem cells. *Proc. Natl. Acad. Sci. USA* **97**, 11307–11312.

20. Pera, M.F. (2001). Human pluripotent stem cells: a progress report. *Curr. Opin. Genet. Dev.* **11**, 595–599.

21. Li, M., Pevny, R., Lovell-Badge, R., and Smith, A. (1998). Generation of purified neural precursors from embryonic stem cells by lineage selection. *Curr. Biol.* **8**, 971–974.

22. Henderson, J.K., Draper, J.S., Baillie, H.S., Fishel, S., Thomson, J.A., Moore, H., and Andrews, P.W. (2002). Preimplantation human embryos and embryonic stem cells show comparable expression of stage-specific embryonic antigens. *Stem Cells* **20**, 329–337.

23. Xu, R.H., Chen, X., Li, D.S., Li, R., Addicks, G.C., Glennon, C., Zwaka, T.P., and Thomson, J.A. (2002). BMP4 initiates human embryonic stem cell differentiation to trophoblast. *Nat. Biotechnol.* **20**, 1261–1264.

24. Gardner, R.L., and Brook, F.A. (1997). Reflections on the biology of embryonic stem (ES) cells. *Int. J. Dev. Biol.* **41**, 235–243.

25. Beddington, R.S., and Robertson, E.J. (1999). Axis development and early asymmetry in mammals. *Cell* **96**, 195–209.

26. Kaufman, D.S., Hanson, E.T., Lewis, R.L., Auerbach, R., and Thomson, J.A. (2001). Hematopoietic colony-forming cells derived from human embryonic stem cells. *Proc. Natl. Acad. Sci. USA* **98**, 10716–10721.

26a. Houssami and Pera, personal communication.

27. Carpenter, M.K., Inokuma, M.S., Denham, J., Mujtaba, T., Chiu, C.P., and Rao, M.S. (2001). Enrichment of neurons and neural precursors from human embryonic stem cells. *Exp. Neurol.* **172**, 383–397.

28. Levenberg, S., Golub, J.S., Amit, M., Itskovitz-Eldor, J., and Langer, R. (2002). Endothelial cells derived from human embryonic stem cells. Proc. *Natl. Acad. Sci. USA* **99**, 4391–4396.

29. Chadwick, K., Wang, L., Li, L., Menendez, P., Murdoch, B., Rouleau, A., and Bhatia, M. (2003). Cytokines and BMP-4 promote hematopoietic differentiation of human embryonic stem cells. *Blood* **102**, 906–915.

30. Hubner, K., Fuhrmann, G., Christenson, L.K., Kehler, J., Reinbold, R., De La Fuente, R., Wood, J., Strauss, J.F., 3rd, Boiani, M., and Scholer, H.R. (2003). Derivation of oocytes from mouse embryonic stem cells. *Science* **300**, 1251–1256.

31. Morrison, S.J., and Weissman, I.L. (1994). The long-term repopulating subset of hematopoietic stem cells is deterministic and isolatable by phenotype. *Immunity* **1**, 661–673.

32. Labastie, M.C., Cortes, F., Romeo, P.H., Dulac, C., and Peault, B. (1998). Molecular identity of hematopoietic precursor cells emerging in the human embryo. *Blood* **92**, 3624–3635.

33. Oberlin, E., Tavian, M., Blazsek, I., and Peault, B. (2002). Blood-forming potential of vascular endothelium in the human embryo. *Development* **129**, 4147–4157.

34. Baum, C.M., Weissman, I.L., Tsukamoto, S., Buckle, A.M., and Peault, B. (1992). Isolation of a candidate human hematopoietic stem-cell population. *Proc. Natl. Acad. Sci. USA* **89**, 2804–2808.

35. Hynes, M., and Rosenthal, A. (2000). Embryonic stem cells go dopaminergic. *Neuron* **28**, 11–14.

36. Guan, K., Chang, H., Rolletschek, A., and Wobus, A.M. (2001). Embryonic stem cell-derived neurogenesis. Retinoic acid induction and lineage selection of neuronal cells. *Cell Tissue Res.* **305**, 171–176.

37. Xian, H.Q., and Gottlieb, D.I. (2001). Peering into early neurogenesis with embryonic stem cells. *Trends Neurosci.* **24**, 685–686.

38. Okabe, S., Forsberg-Nilsson, K., Spiro, A.C., Segal, M., and McKay, R.D. (1996). Development of neuronal precursor cells and functional postmitotic neurons from embryonic stem cells in vitro. *Mech. Dev.* **59**, 89–102.

39. Lee, S.H., Lumelsky, N., Studer, L., Auerbach, J.M., and McKay, R.D. (2000). Efficient generation of midbrain and hindbrain neurons from mouse embryonic stem cells. *Nat. Biotechnol.* **18**, 675–679.

40. Lendahl, U., Zimmerman, L.B., and McKay, R.D. (1990). CNS stem cells express a new class of intermediate filament protein. *Cell* **60**, 585–595.

41. Sakakibara, S., Imai, T., Hamaguchi, K., Okabe, M., Aruga, J., Nakajima, K., Yasutomi, D., Nagata, T., Kurihara, Y., Uesugi, S., Miyata, T., Ogawa, M., Mikoshiba, K., and Okano, H. (1996). Mouse-Musashi-1, a neural RNA-binding protein highly enriched in the mammalian CNS stem cell. *Dev. Biol.* **176**, 230–242.

42. Wroblewski, J., Engstrom, M., Edwall-Arvidsson, C., Sjoberg, G., Sejerson, T., and Lendahl, U. (1997). Distribution of nestin in the developing mouse limb bud in vivo and in micro-mass cultures of cells isolated from limb buds. *Differentiation* **61**, 151–159.

43. Messam, C.A., Hou, J., and Major, E.O. (2000). Coexpression of nestin in neural and glial cells in the developing human CNS defined by a human-specific anti-nestin antibody. *Exp. Neurol.* **161**, 585–596.

44. Edlund, H. (2002). Pancreatic organogenesis—developmental mechanisms and implications for therapy. *Nat. Rev. Genet.* **3**, 524–532.

45. Pevny, L., and Rao, M.S. (2003). The stem-cell menagerie. *Trends Neurosci.* **26**, 351–359.

46. Good, P., Yoda, A., Sakakibara, S., Yamamoto, A., Imai, T., Sawa, H., Ikeuchi, T., Tsuji, S., Satoh, H., and Okano, H. (1998). The human Musashi homolog 1 (MSI1) gene encoding the homologue of Musashi/Nrp-1, a neural RNA-binding protein putatively expressed in CNS stem cells and neural progenitor cells. *Genomics* **52**, 382–384.

47. Potten, C.S., Booth, C., Tudor, G.L., Booth, D., Brady, G., Hurley, P., Ashton, G., Clarke, R., Sakakibara, S., and Okano, H. (2003). Identification of a putative intestinal stem cell and early lineage marker; musashi-1. *Differentiation* **71**, 28–41.

48. Saunders, P.T., Maguire, S.M., Macpherson, S., Fenelon, M.C., Sakakibara, S., and Okano, H. (2002). RNA binding protein Musashi1 is expressed in Sertoli cells in the rat testis from fetal life to adulthood. *Biol. Reprod.* **66**, 500–507.

49. Zhang, S.C., Wernig, M., Duncan, I.D., Brustle, O., and Thomson, J.A. (2001). In vitro differentiation of transplantable neural precursors from human embryonic stem cells. *Nat. Biotechnol.* **19**, 1129–1133.

50. Pera, M.F., Andrade, J., Houssami, S., Reubinoff, B.E., Trounson, A., Stanley, E.G., van Oostwaard, W., and Mummery, C. Regulation of human embryonic stem cell differentiation by BMP-2 and its antagonist noggin. *J. Cell Sci.* (submitted).

50a. Peh, Haues, Pera, unpublished.

51. Wells, J.M. (2003). Genes expressed in the developing endocrine pancreas and their importance for stem cell and diabetes research. *Diabetes Metab. Res. Rev.* **19**, 191–201.

52. Meehan, R.R., Barlow, D.P., Hill, R.E., Hogan, B.L., and Hastie, N.D. (1984). Pattern of serum protein gene expression in mouse visceral yolk sac and foetal liver. *EMBO J.* **3**, 1881–1885.

53. Abe, K., Niwa, H., Iwase, K., Takiguchi, M., Mori, M., Abe, I., and Yamamura, K.I. (1996). Endoderm-specific gene expression in embryonic stem cells differentiated to embryoid bodies. *Exp. Cell Res.* **229**, 27–34.

54. Jones, E.A., Tosh, D., Wilson, D.I., Lindsay, S., and Forrester, L.M. (2002). Hepatic differentiation of murine embryonic stem cells. *Exp. Cell Res.* **272**, 15–22.

55. Hamazaki, T., Iiboshi, Y., Oka, M., Papst, P.J., Meacham, A.M., Zon, L.I., and Terada, N. (2001). Hepatic maturation in differentiating embryonic stem cells in vitro. *FEBS Lett.* **497**, 15–19.

56. Rambhatla, L., Chiu, C.P., Kundu, P., Peng, Y., and Carpenter, M.K. (2003). Generation of hepatocyte-like cells from human embryonic stem cells. *Cell Transplant.* **12**, 1–11.

57. Assady, S., Maor, G., Amit, M., Itskovitz-Eldor, J., Skorecki, K.L., and Tzukerman, M. (2001). Insulin production by human embryonic stem cells. *Diabetes* **50**, 1691–1697.

58. Lumelsky, N., Blondel, O., Laeng, P., Velasco, I., Ravin, R., and McKay, R. (2001). Differentiation of embryonic stem cells to insulin-secreting structures similar to pancreatic islets. *Science* **292**, 1389–1394.

59. Rajagopal, J., Anderson, W.J., Kume, S., Martinez, O.I., and Melton, D.A. (2003). Insulin staining of ES cell progeny from insulin uptake. *Science* **299**, 363.

60. Zulewski, H., Abraham, E.J., Gerlach, M.J., Daniel, P.B., Moritz, W., Muller, B., Vallejo, M., Thomas, M.K., and Habener, J.F. (2001). Multipotential nestin-positive stem cells isolated from adult pancreatic islets differentiate ex vivo into pancreatic endocrine, exocrine, and hepatic phenotypes. *Diabetes* **50**, 521–533.

61. Piper, K., Ball, S.G., Turnpenny, L.W., Brickwood, S., Wilson, D.I., and Hanley, N.A. (2002). Beta-cell differentiation during human development does not rely on nestin-positive precursors: implications for stem cell-derived replacement therapy. *Diabetologia* **45**, 1045–1047.

62. Humphrey, R.K., Bucay, N., Beattie, G.M., Lopez, A., Messam, C.A., Cirulli, V., and Hayek, A. (2003). Characterization and isolation of promoter-defined nestin-positive cells from the human fetal pancreas. *Diabetes* **52,** 2519–2525.

63. Selander, L., and Edlund, H. (2002). Nestin is expressed in mesenchymal and not epithelial cells of the developing mouse pancreas. *Mech. Dev.* **113,** 189–192.

64. Blyszczuk, P., Czyz, J., Kania, G., Wagner, M., Roll, U., St. Onge, L., and Wobus, A.M. (2003). Expression of Pax4 in embryonic stem cells promotes differentiation of nestin-positive progenitor and insulin-producing cells. *Proc. Natl. Acad. Sci. USA* **100,** 998–1003.

65. Soria, B., Roche, E., Berna, G., Leon-Quinto, T., Reig, J.A., and Martin, F. (2000). Insulin-secreting cells derived from embryonic stem cells normalize glycemia in streptozotocin-induced diabetic mice. *Diabetes* **49,** 157–162.

66. Billon, N., Jolicoeur, C., Ying, Q.L., Smith, A., and Raff, M. (2002). Normal timing of oligodendrocyte development from genetically engineered, lineage-selectable mouse ES cells. *J. Cell Sci.* **115,** 3657–3665.

67. Mizuseki, K.S.T., Watanabe, K., Muguruma, K., Ikeya, M., Nishiyama, A., Arakawa, A., Suemori, H., Nakatsuji, N., Kawasaki, H., Murakami, F., and Sasai, Y. (2003). Generation of neural crest-derived peripheral neurons and floor plate cells from mouse and primate embryonic stem cells. *Proc. Natl. Acad. Sci. USA* **100,** 5823–5833.

68. Smith, A.G. (2001). Embryo-derived stem cells: of mice and men. *Annu. Rev. Cell Dev. Biol.* **17,** 435–462.

69. Kawasaki, H., Suemori, H., Mizuseki, K., Watanabe, K., Urano, F., Ichinose, H., Haruta, M., Takahashi, M., Yoshikawa, K., Nishikawa, S., Nakatsuji, N., and Sasai, Y. (2002). Generation of dopaminergic neurons and pigmented epithelia from primate ES cells by stromal cell-derived inducing activity. *Proc. Natl. Acad. Sci. USA* **99,** 1580–1585.

70. Goldstein, R.S., Drukker, M., Reubinoff, B.E., and Benvenisty, N. (2002). Integration and differentiation of human embryonic stem cells transplanted to the chick embryo. *Dev. Dyn.* **225,** 80–86.

Identification and Maintenance of Neural Precursors from Human Embryonic Stem Cells

Benjamin Reubinoff and Hanita Khaner

Highly enriched cultures of neural precursors may be derived from human embryonic stem (hES) cells. The neural precursors can proliferate in culture for prolonged periods of time, and can differentiate *in vitro* into mature neurons, astrocytes, and oligodendrocytes. The neurons that are generated respond to neurotransmitter application, their cell membranes contain voltage-dependent channels, and they generate action potentials in response to depolarizing stimuli. After transplantation to the brain ventricles of newborn mice, the neural precursors migrate extensively into the host brain parenchyma. The precursors respond to host brain signal, as suggested by their migration along established host brain migratory tracks and their differentiation in a regional specific manner to progeny of the three neural lineages. The establishment of neuroectodermal precursors from hES cells allows the study of human neurogenesis *in vitro* and the discovery of new drugs. In addition, the neural precursors may potentially serve as a platform for the development of specific functional neural cells for transplantation and gene therapy of neurologic disorders. In this chapter, we review the scientific background of the development of neural precursors from hES cells and describe methods for the isolation, propagation, and characterization of hES cell–derived neural precursors.

Introduction

hES cells attract considerable attention because of the possible far-reaching applications of these cells in regenerative medicine, drug discovery, and the study of human embryogenesis. Derivation of neural precursors from hES cells may be invaluable for the study of early human neurogenesis and for the use of hES cells as an unlimited source of neural cells for transplantation in neurodegenerative disorders. Neural cells may be generated from hES cells following spontaneous differentiation *in vitro* either in high density cultures[1] or through embryoid body (EB) formation.[2,3] However, the neural cells that are generated are within a mixture of other types of differentiated cells.[1,2] Various growth and differentiation-inducing factors such as retinoic acid can enhance the differentiation

toward the neural lineage in multicellular aggregates of hES cells.[3,4] However, the neural-inducing effect of retinoic acid is pleiotropic,[5] and it appears that the neural precursors produced in response to retinoic acid induction are developmentally restricted and can give rise to a limited range of neural cell types.[6] In addition, although differentiation-inducing factors can promote enrichment of the differentiated cells toward the neural lineage, these factors cannot exclusively direct the differentiation into the neural lineage. Controlled differentiation of hES cells into a purified neural precursors cell population is required for the experimental dissection of the events during early development of the human nervous system. Moreover, the generation of pure populations of hES cell–derived neural progeny, rather than mixed populations of differentiated cells, is required for transplantation therapy.[7,8]

DIRECTED NEURAL DIFFERENTIATION OF MOUSE EMBRYONIC STEM CELLS

It seems likely that during spontaneous early differentiation within EBs or high-density cultures, interactions between various cells mimic, in an unstructured fashion, the inductive processes occurring during axis formation in the embryo.[9] Identification of the factors involved in these interactions may facilitate directed differentiation of the stem cells into the neural lineage.

Several studies in the mouse ES cell system have examined the mechanisms of neural induction and the generation of neural precursors from undifferentiated ES cells. In line with a default mechanism of neural specification[10] it was shown that when ES cells are cultured at low density, under defined serum-free culture conditions, they acquire a neural identity and give rise to primitive neural stem cells (NSCs).[11] However, the efficiency of this approach is relatively low because only about 0.2% of the undifferentiated ES cells generate NSCs under these culture conditions.

Co-culture of undifferentiated mouse ES cells with the bone marrow–derived stromal cell line PA6, under serum-free conditions, induces neural differentiation in a high percentage of colonies.[12] However, the neural-inducing activity of PA6 stromal cells on primate nonhuman ES cells is less profound,[13] and the factor that exerts the stromal cell line activity was not purified or cloned.

Controlled differentiation of mouse ES cells into homogenous population equivalent to embryonic neuroectoderm

Handbook of Stem Cells
Volume 1
Copyright © 2004 by Academic Press
All rights of reproduction in any form reserved.

without the formation of EBs, extraembryonic cell populations, or other germ lineages has been reported. ES cells cultured in suspension in medium conditioned by the human hepatocellular carcinoma cell line HepG2 differentiated in an orderly and synchronous manner into primitive ectoderm, neural plate, and neural tube equivalent populations.[14] It remains to be determined whether this novel system will give rise to similar results in the hES cell system.

Interestingly, it was recently demonstrated that inductive exocrine signals, such as those resulting from co-culture or conditioned medium, are not required for mouse ES cells to commit efficiently to the neural fate.[5] Multicellular aggregates[15] or adherent monocultures of ES cells[5] readily differentiated into neural cells when inductive signals for nonneural fates were eliminated. In the latter case, it was shown that this process was not a simple default pathway but was dependent on autocrine fibroblast growth factor signaling. However, although this specific culture system could induce neural differentiation in about 60% of the ES cells, it could not give rise to a highly enriched preparation of neural precursors.

ENRICHMENT FOR NEURAL PRECURSORS

Given the current limitations of most approaches to direct the differentiation of ES cells into a homogeneous pure population of neural precursors, complementary strategies to select neural cells from a heterogeneous population of differentiated cells have been developed.[5,7,16–18] Enrichment for neural precursors may be accomplished in the mouse ES cell system by incorporating selective culture conditions.[16,19] In this approach, ES cells are first cultured as aggregates to initiate spontaneous differentiation, and then they are plated in a specific serum-free medium that favors the survival of ES cell–derived neural precursors. Further modification of the culture conditions and supplementation with mitogens (fibroblast growth factor-2 [FGF2]) establishes a highly enriched population of proliferating developmentally competent neuroepithelial precursors.[16,19]

Alternatively, neural cells have been sorted from heterogeneous populations of differentiated cells based on the expression of lineage-specific cell surface markers[17,18] or by genetic selection. In the latter approach, a selectable marker was inserted into the open reading frame of genes encoding lineage-specific transcription factors allowing genetic selection of neural precursors either by fluorescence-activated cell sorting (FACS) or drug selection.[5,7]

DEVELOPMENT OF NEURAL PRECURSORS FROM HUMAN EMBRYONIC STEM CELLS

Various approaches have been developed for the derivation of enriched cultures of proliferating developmentally competent neural precursors from hES cells. In most approaches, spontaneous differentiation was initially induced by the formation of EBs or by prolonged culture of hES cell colonies at high density. This initial differentiation-inducing step was then followed by the combination of neural precursors cell selection and culture under conditions that promoted the proliferation of NSCs.[18,20,22]

Two research groups induced initial uncontrolled spontaneous differentiation of hES cells through the formation of EBs and subsequently plated the cells onto appropriate substrates in defined medium-containing mitogens.[18,22] Neural precursors were then selected either by selective enzymatic digestion of neural tube-like structures followed by purification on the basis of differential adhesion[22] or by immunosorting of cells that expressed surface markers of neural progenitors.[18]

We have reported an alternative simple approach in which spontaneous differentiation is induced by prolonged culture without replenishment of the feeders.[20] Large colonies that include a variety of differentiated cells are formed under these culture conditions. Within about 54% of these colonies, distinct areas composed of small, piled, tightly packed early progenitor cells that are destined to give rise to neural precursors, when transferred to serum-free media, may be identified (Fig. 49–1B). The progenitor cells within these areas do not express markers of undifferentiated hES cells or the early neuroectodermal marker neural-cell adhesion molecule (N-CAM)[20] (see later discussion). Patches containing about 150 cells each are mechanically dissected from these distinct areas under dark-field stereomicroscopy and are replated in serum-free defined medium supplemented with mitogens (FGF2 and epidermal growth factor [EGF]). The aggregates gradually turn into round spheres that are highly enriched for proliferating developmentally competent neural precursors.[20]

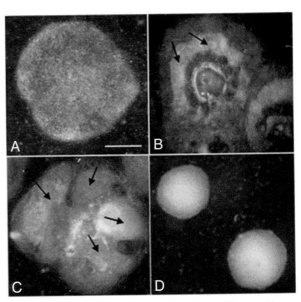

Figure 49–1. The derivation of neural spheres from undifferentiated human embryonic stem (hES) cells. Dark-field stereomicroscopic images of (A) undifferentiated hES cell colony 1 week after plating and (B) spontaneously differentiating hES cell colony, 3 weeks after plating, with a large gray opaque area (arrows) of early progenitor cells that are destined to give rise to neural progenitors. (C) Noggin treated differentiating colony, 2 weeks after plating, with abundant gray opaque areas (arrows) of the early progenitors. (D) hES cell–derived neural spheres 4 weeks after derivation and propagation in defined medium. Scale bars = 100 μm for A and C; 50 μm for B and 200 μm for D.

Controlled differentiation of the hES cells into the early progenitor cells that are destined to give rise to neural precursors when transferred to defined serum-free medium may be accomplished with the aid of the bone morphogenetic protein (BMP) antagonist noggin. When the hES cell colonies are cultured for prolonged periods on feeders in the presence of noggin, in most of the colonies the hES cells differentiate almost uniformly into the tightly packed small progenitor cells. A detailed characterization of these progenitor cells and the effect of noggin on the differentiation of hES cells have been recently described.[21]

Human ES cell–derived neural precursors proliferate in culture in the presence of mitogens (FGF2 with or without EGF) for prolonged periods of time and may be expanded into a large number of cells.[20,22] On withdrawal of mitogens and plating on appropriate substrate the precursors differentiate into mature neurons, astrocytes, and occasionally also into oligodendroglia progenitors. The neurons that are generated respond to neurotransmitter application, their cell membranes contain voltage-dependent channels, and they generate action potentials in response to depolarizing stimuli.[18]

Glutamatergic neurons and γ-aminobutyric acid (GABA)-producing neurons are most commonly generated following spontaneous differentiation of the neural precursors in vitro.[20,22] Tyrosine hydroxylase and serotonin producing neurons are observed at a low frequency, whereas differentiation into cholinergic neurons was not reported.[18,20,22] Methods that will allow the generation of a significant number of cells that are required for cell therapy of the common neurodegenerative disorders (e.g., oligodendrocytes, dopaminergic and cholinergic neurons) should be further developed.

The developmental potential of hES cell–derived neural precursors was also studied in vivo. Following transplantation into the neonatal mouse brain ventricles, hES cell–derived neural precursors incorporated in large numbers into the host brain parenchyma demonstrated widespread distribution and differentiated into neurons, astrocytes,[20,22] and oligodendrocyte.[20] The transplanted cells migrated along established host brain migratory tracks and differentiated in a region-specific manner indicating their capability to respond to local cues and participate in the processes of host brain development.[20] The morphology of graft-derived cells was indistinguishable from host cells; however, retrograde tracing, electrophysiologic studies, and transplantation experiments into animal models of diseases are required to prove the functional integration of transplanted cells. Teratoma formation was not observed in the recipient animals, and there was no evidence of undifferentiated ES cells within the transplanted cell population.[20,22] However, intraventricular clusters composed of mature and immature neuroepithelial cells were reported.[22]

Long-term studies are required to determine the safety of hES cell–derived neural progeny transplantation and to rule out potential hazards such as tumor formation or the development of cells from other lineages. These pioneer transplantation studies highlight the potential of hES cells to serve in the future as an unlimited donor source of neural cells for transplantation.

OTHER POTENTIAL RENEWABLE SOURCES OF HUMAN NEURAL PRECURSORS

In addition to hES cells, other renewable sources of human neural cells may be considered as a potential donor of cells for transplantation. Human neurons may be generated from teratocarcinoma cell lines[23] or from immortalized neural precursor cells.[24] However, the tumorigenic origin of the former cells or the incorporation and expression of an oncogene by the latter may hamper clinical use. Recent reports have described the derivation of self-renewing multipotent NSCs from human fetal and adult brain. These clonally derived NSCs are capable of continuous growth, give rise to all fundamental neural lineages in vitro, successfully survive transplantation into animals, and are capable of expressing foreign genes.[25–30]

Although NSCs show great promise, it is possible that neural progeny derived from ES cells may represent a more primitive precursor population with greater regenerative potential than fetal or adult-derived cells. The potential of both cell types to survive transplantation and reconstruct tissues in various central nervous system (CNS) disorders will have to be compared and studied. Although both cell types will facilitate the study of human neurogenesis, the establishment of neural precursors from hES cells will allow an earlier and more complete dissection of the neural lineage development. It may be that the frequency of homologous recombination in hES cells[31] is much higher than that in NSCs and, therefore, that the only practical route for introducing targeted genetic modifications into human neural tissue—either for generation of disease models in vitro or for types of gene therapy—lies in the reproducible generation and isolation of neural precursors from genetically modified hES cells. Finally, the derivation of neural precursors from hES cells offers the possibility to overcome any risk of graft rejection by production of stem cells from the patient's own tissue via somatic cell nuclear transfer.[32] Moreover, the use of nuclear transfer to yield hES cells from individuals with specific genetic predispositions to certain diseases of the CNS could provide a powerful tool for the generation of in vitro models for disease pathogenesis.

Adult stem cells from nonneural tissues may give rise to neurons and potentially may also serve as a source of neural cells.[33,34] Most notable are the multipotent adult progenitor cells (MAPCs) that are co-purified with bone marrow mesenchymal stem cells and are almost as versatile as ES cells.[35] MAPCs can give rise to cultures enriched for neural cells. The advantages of MAPCs over ES cells are that they probably do not form teratomas, and because they are derived from the patient's own bone marrow, the potential problem of rejection can be overcome. At present, it is unclear whether it will be possible to expand adult stem cells to bulk quantities sufficient enough to meet the requirements for cell therapy. It remains to be seen whether adult stem cell–derived neurons will function similar to ES cells in animal models of diseases.[36] More research on the various types of stem cells is required, and it is too early to predict which type of cells will ultimately prevail in regenerative medicine.

POTENTIAL APPLICATIONS OF HUMAN EMBRYONIC STEM CELL DERIVED NEURAL PRECURSORS

The establishment of neuroectodermal precursors from hES cells provides real advantages for basic and applied studies of human CNS development and disease. Directing hES cells to differentiate to the neural lineage, the establishment of neural precursors, and their differentiated progeny will enable a complete *in vitro* study of human neurogenesis. It will allow access to hitherto unexplored territories of gene expression for modern genomics data mining and will provide a platform for the discovery of polypeptide growth and differentiation factors that might find application in neural tissue regeneration. *In vitro* human models of degenerative diseases may be created for basic research and drug discovery. New assays for toxicology and high-throughput screens for neuroprotective compounds may be developed.

Generation of neural precursors from hES cells *in vitro* may serve as a platform for further manipulations with growth and differentiating factors that may eventually enable the derivation of specific functional neural cells for transplantation therapy. This approach was tested in the mouse ES cell system. Dopaminergic neurons were developed *in vitro* from ES cell–derived neural precursors and were implanted into parkinsonian rats. The engrafted cells led to the recovery from parkinsonism, and teratoma tumor formation was not observed.[36] Mouse ES cell–derived neural precursors were also directed to establish more committed oligodendroglia progenitors that were transplanted into a rat model of a human myelin disease. The engrafted cells efficiently myelinated axons in the host brain and spinal cord.[37] These encouraging results from the mouse model suggest that hES cell–derived neural precursors may eventually be applicable to cell and gene therapy of human neurologic disorders.

In the next section, we describe methods for the development of neural precursors from undifferentiated hES cell colonies.

Protocols for the Selection and Maintenance of Neural Precursors from Human Embryonic Stem Cells

The two main current approaches for the development of neural precursors from undifferentiated hES cells have been described briefly in the section on the development of neural precursors from hES. The major difference between the two approaches is the method of induction of differentiation using either EBs formation[18,22] or prolonged culture of hES cell colonies in the presence of serum without replenishment of feeders. Here we describe in detail the protocols for the generation and maintenance of hES cell–derived neural progenitors using the latter approach.

The protocol is composed of two major steps:

1. Induction of spontaneous or controlled differentiation of hES cells into early progenitor cells that are destined to give rise to neural precursors. In the spontaneous differentiation approach, colonies of hES cells are cultured for prolonged periods on mouse embryonic fibroblast feeders to induce uncontrolled differentiation into a mixture of cells that include the desired early progenitor cells. In the controlled differentiation approach, the differentiating colonies are treated with the BMP antagonist noggin to direct their differentiation toward the early progenitor cells.[21]

2. Isolation and propagation of the early progenitors in defined culture conditions in which they give rise to enriched cultures of neural precursors. Clumps of the early progenitor cells that are destined to give rise to neural progenitors are mechanically dissected and replated in defined serum-free media supplemented with mitogens, in which they form free-floating spheres. These spheres may be propagated for prolonged periods of time and they are mainly composed of proliferating developmentally competent neural precursors.[20] A schematic presentation of our protocol is presented in Fig. 49–2.

SPONTANEOUS DIFFERENTIATION PROTOCOL

Undifferentiated hES cell colonies (Fig. 49–1A) are cultured in serum-containing medium (see the following section) on mitotically inactivated (mitomycin C) mouse embryonic fibroblast feeder layers in gelatin-coated tissue culture dishes and are passaged weekly as previously described.[1] To induce spontaneous differentiation, the colonies are cultured for

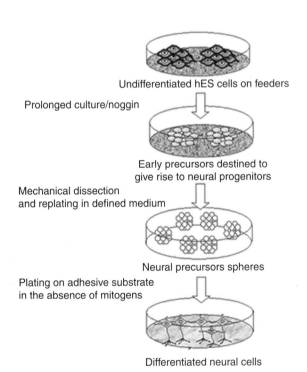

Figure 49–2. Schematic presentation of the protocol for the derivation of human embryonic stem (hES) cell–derived neural cells. (Please see CD-ROM for color version of this figure.)

514

prolonged periods of time (between 3 to 4 weeks) without replenishment of the feeders. The medium (see the following section) is replaced daily. One to 2 weeks after passage, changes in cell morphology can be identified mainly in the center of the colonies, indicating the initiation of early differentiation. During subsequent weeks, the process of spontaneous differentiation is markedly accelerated. Distinct areas that are comprised of small, piled, tightly packed early progenitor cells with a uniform gray opaque appearance under dark-field stereomicroscopy are identified in 40–50% of the colonies (Fig. 49–1B). These progenitors are destined to give rise to neural precursors on transfer and culture in defined serum-free culture conditions (see later). The major disadvantage of the spontaneous differentiation approach is that the process of differentiation is not controlled and the desired early progenitors develop only in about a half of the colonies.

Human Embryonic Stem Cell Culture Medium

The serum-containing medium used for the maintenance of undifferentiated hES cells and during prolonged culture for the induction of spontaneous differentiation is composed of Dulbecco's modified Eagle's medium (DMEM), with glucose 4500 mg/L without sodium pyruvate supplemented with 20% defined fetal calf serum (FCS, Hyclone, Logan, Utah), 1 mM L-glutamine, 50 U/ml penicillin, 50 µg/ml streptomycin, 1% nonessential amino acids, 0.1 mM β-mercaptoethanol, and 1% insulin transferrin selenium (ITS) (all from Gibco-invitrogen Corporation, Grand Island, NY).

CONTROLLED DIFFERENTIATION PROTOCOL

Undifferentiated hES cell colonies (Fig. 49–1A) are propagated in serum-containing medium on feeders as previously described.[1,20] To induce differentiation, at the usual passage, clumps of undifferentiated hES cells are plated on fresh feeders and cultured in a modified hES cell medium (see the following section), supplemented with a reduced serum concentration and with the BMP antagonist noggin. Noggin belongs to a class of polypeptides that bind to BMPs and consequently inhibit their activity (reviewed in reference 38). The medium is supplemented with noggin during the initial 6–8 day period after passage, being replaced every other day. Then, the hES cell colonies are further cultured in the modified hES cell medium for an additional 4–6 days in the absence of noggin. The medium is replaced every day during this culture period. Under these culture conditions, the hES cells in most of the colonies (70–90% of the colonies) differentiate almost uniformly into tightly packed piled small early progenitor cells. In parallel, the colonies acquire a nearly uniform gray opaque appearance under dark-field stereomicroscopy (Fig. 49–1C). A detailed characterization of these early progenitors and the effect of noggin on the differentiation of hES cells have been recently described.[21] The major advantage of this approach is that it allows controlled differentiation of hES cells into a nearly uniform population of early precursors that are destined to give rise to neural progenitors on culture under appropriate conditions.

Modified Human Embryonic Stem Cell Medium

The medium is composed as described in the section on hES cell culture medium, although it is supplemented with a reduced serum concentration—10% defined FCS (Hyclone) and 500 ng/ml of noggin (R&D Systems).

DERIVATION AND EXPANSION OF NEURAL SPHERES

When the early progenitors described previously are transferred into defined culture conditions that support the propagation of neural precursors,[39] they form free-floating expandable cell aggregates (spheres) that are highly enriched for neural precursors. Patches of about 150 cells are mechanically dissected, under dark-field stereomicroscopy, from the gray opaque areas within the colonies by means of the razor-sharp edge of a micro glass pipette or by a razor blade (no. 15 surgical blades, Swann-Morton, Sheffield, UK). These progenitor cell clumps are transferred to plastic tissue culture dishes (60 × 15 mm Petri dishes, Falcon, Franklin Lakes, NJ) and cultured in neural precursors medium supplemented with mitogens (NPM, as detailed in the following section on neural precursors medium). Under these culture conditions, the clumps form free-floating spherical structures within 2–3 days. Once a week, the culture dish is replaced when the spheres are subcultured by dissection into small clumps using a surgical razor blade.[39] The medium is replaced twice a week. During the initial 1–3 weeks of sphere culture, some cell death is observed and the spheres gradually acquire a uniform round morphology[20] (Fig. 49–1D).

Neural Precursors Medium (NPM)

DMEM/F12 (1:1), B27 supplementation (1:50), glutamine 2 mM, penicillin 50 µ/ml, and streptomycin 50 µg/ml (all from Gibco-invitrogen Corporation) supplemented with 20 ng/ml human recombinant EGF and 20 ng/ml human recombinant fibroblast growth factor 2 (FGF2) (both from R&D Systems, Inc., Minneapolis, MN).

CHARACTERIZATION OF THE NEURAL SPHERES

The phenotype of the precursors within the spheres may be characterized at various time points during propagation. Marker expression may be analyzed at the RNA level by various methods such as real time reverse transcriptase polymerase chain reaction (RT-PCR), in situ hybridization, and microarrays or at the protein level by immunocytochemistry. Characterization at the RNA level may be useful for the confirmation of immunocytochemical results or when antibodies for specific markers are not available. In the following section, we mainly focus on immunophenotyping of the neural precursors.

Markers of Neural Precursors

Various markers may be used to identify and determine the percentage of neural precursors within the spheres. It should be noted that some of the markers are not specific to the neural lineage. Therefore, characterization with multiple neural markers is recommended to confirm the neural identity of the precursors. In this section, we briefly review the various markers that are most commonly used to identify neural precursors.

The intermediate filament protein nestin is a major cytoskeletal protein expressed by neuronal precursors in the mammalian CNS.[40] Before neurogenesis, most cells in the neuroepithelium are nestin-positive, but, as cells differentiate into neurons, nestin is down-regulated.[41] In addition, in vitro studies confirmed that nestin-positive cells are neural precursor cells that will further differentiate into mature neurons and glia cells.[42] Although nestin is widely used as a marker of neural precursors, it is not specific to the neural lineage and is also expressed by mesenchymal cells.[43]

Two additional, commonly used markers of neural precursors are N-CAM and its polysialylated form PSA-NCAM; both have a role in cell migration and cell–cell interactions. It has been demonstrated that neural precursors derived from the rodent's neonatal and adult brains express both molecules (reviewed in reference 44). Furthermore, neural precursor cells from different brain regions were isolated on the basis of the expression of these two molecules.[45,46] As for nestin, N-CAM is not a specific marker of the neural lineage, and it may also be expressed by fetal muscle and kidney.[47]

Neural precursors may also be identified by the monoclonal antibody A2B5, which recognizes a membrane epitope characteristically expressed in glial progenitors.[37] Historically, the A2B5 antibody was found to distinguish between two types of astrocytes (types 1 and 2) that were found in cultures of the developing rat optic nerve.[48,49] However, although the A2B5 antibody has been most commonly used to mark the glial lineage, hES cell–derived neural precursors that are immunoreactive with A2B5 give rise to both neurons and glia cells.[18]

The expression of the highly conserved lineage-specific neuroectodermal transcriptional factors Sox1 and Sox2 may also be used to identify neural precursors.[7,50] The transcription factor Sox1 is the earliest known specific marker of neuroectoderm in the mouse embryo. Sox1 is first expressed in the neural plate, and although its expression is subsequently maintained in the neuroepithelial cells, it is down-regulated during neuronal and glial differentiation.[51,52] Sox2 is expressed in an overlapping pattern that also encompasses floor plate and early neural crest cells.[7] Antibodies against Sox1 and Sox2 have been successfully used to identify differentiation of mouse ES cells into neuroectodermal progenitors.[7,50] It remains to be seen whether these markers will be also useful in the hES cell system.

The gene Musashi-1 (Msi-1), which was first described in the fruit fly Drosophila, encodes an RNA-binding protein associated with asymmetrical divisions in neural progenitor cells. The protein, Msi-1, was shown to be expressed in neural precursor cells during the development of the external sensory organ of Drosophila.[53] Recently, the mammalian homologue product mouse-Msi-1 was found to be highly expressed in stem cells of the mouse CNS. Similar to other neural precursor markers, m-Msi-1 is down-regulated during neural differentiation.[54] It has recently been demonstrated that Msi-1 is also expressed by hES cell–derived neural precursors.[22]

Indirect Immunofluorescence Characterization of the Precursors Within the Spheres

For the immunophenotyping of the precursors, the spheres are mechanically disaggregated with a razor blade into small clumps (diameter of 20–50 μm), under dark-field stereomicroscopy. These small clumps are transferred to a centrifuge tube containing a small volume (100–500 μl) of NPM in the absence of mitogens (see the section on neural progenitor medium). Pipetting the clumps gently up and down several times further disaggregates the clumps into smaller clusters and single cells. The cell clusters are then plated on laminin precoated cover slips (see the following section) in NPM in the absence of mitogens, for overnight incubation. Fixation is performed with 4% paraformaldehyde for 20–30 minutes at room temperature, followed by three washes with phosphate-buffered saline (PBS). The samples are blocked with 5% heat inactivated goat serum (Dako, Carpinteria, CA) and permeabilized with 0.2% Triton X (Sigma) in PBS with or without 0.1% borine serum albumin (BSA) for 30–60 minutes at room temperature. It should be noted that Triton X is omitted from all solutions when surface markers are stained. Samples are then incubated with the primary antibodies at room temperature for 1 hour, followed by three washes with PBS. Incubation with the secondary antibodies usually conjugated to a fluorescence dye is for 30–60 minutes at room temperature, followed by PBS washing. Cover slips are counterstained and mounted with a Vectashield mounting solution with or without DAPI (Vector Laboratories, Burlingame, CA). Proper control stainings for the primary and secondary antibodies are conducted to rule out nonspecific staining or antibody cross reactivity. The source of primary antibodies and working dilutions are listed in Table 49–1.

Cover Slips Coating

The coating of cover slips is performed in a tissue culture hood under sterile conditions. Sterile cover slips (MARIENFELD laboratory glassware—16 mm, Germany) are placed in tissue culture dishes (12-well plates, Corning Costar #3513, Corning, NY). The cover slips are incubated for 1 hour at room temperature in poly-D-lysine solution (30–70 kD, Sigma, 10 μg/ml in PBS). Laminin (Sigma) is diluted to a final concentration of 4 μg/ml in cold PBS and is kept on ice. The cover slips are then washed three times with PBS and incubated overnight in the laminin solution at 4°C. It is possible to extend the incubation for several weeks at the same temperature. To keep the cover slips sterile during this period, the tissue culture dish is wrapped up with paraffin paper. The cells should be plated on the cover slips immediately after the removal of the laminin solution before the cover slips get dry. Fibronectin (Sigma, 20 μg/ml in water) can be used as an alternative to laminin. Cover slips that are coated with poly-D-lysine (as described previously) are incubated in the fibronectin solution for a minimum of 4 hours at room temperature.[18]

TABLE 49-1
Source of Primary Antibodies and Working Dilutions

	Antigen/Antibody	Species and Type	Clonality	Dilution	Source	Reference
Neural progenitors	N-CAM	Mouse IgG	Monoclonal	1:10	Dako, Carpinteria, CA	20
	PSA-NCAM	Mouse IgM	Monoclonal	1:100–200	Chemicon, Temecula, CA	20
	A2B5	Mouse IgM	Hybridoma	1:20	ATCC, Manassas, VA	20
	Nestin	Rabbit	Polyclonal	1:100–200	Chemicon	20
	Musashi	Rabbit	Polyclonal	1:200–1000	Chemicon	22
Neurons	β-Tubulin III	Mouse IgG	Hybridoma	1:1000–3000	Sigma, St. Louis, MO	18, 20
	MAP2ab	Mouse IgG	Hybridoma	1:100	Neomarkers, Fremont, CA	20
	Neurofilament (NF) 70 kD	Mouse IgG	Monoclonal	1:100	Chemicon	20
	NF 160 kD	Mouse IgG	Monoclonal	1:50	Chemicon	20
	NF 200 kD	Rabbit	Polyclonal	1:5000	Sigma	22
	Synaptophysin	Mouse IgG	Monoclonal	1:50	Dako	20
	GABA	Rabbit	Polyclonal	1:1000–10000	Sigma	20, 22
	Glutamate	Rabbit	Polyclonal	1:1000	Sigma	20
	Serotonin	Rabbit	Polyclonal	1:1000–4000	Sigma	20
	Tyrosine hydroxylase	Mouse IgG	Hybridoma	1:500–1000	Sigma	20
Glia	Vimentin	Mouse IgG	Monoclonal	1:10–20	Dako	20
	GFAP	Rabbit	Polyclonal	1:500–1000	Dako	18, 20, 22
	O4	Mouse IgM	Monoclonal	1:10–50	Chemicon	20

GABA, γ-aminobutyric acid; GFAP, glial fibrillary acid protein; MAP, microtubule-associated protein; N-CAM, neural-cell adhesion molecule; PSA-NCAM. polysialylated form of N-CAM.

Characterization of the Developmental Potential of the Neural Precursors

The characterization of the neural precursors should include an analysis of their potential to give rise to mature neurons and glia cells. The development of the neural precursors to progeny of all three neural lineages may be tested both following differentiation *in vitro* and after transplantation to the developing brain.[20,22] Transplantation studies are useful for the analysis of the capability of the neural precursors to migrate and differentiate in response to host parenchymal cues and to participate in the processes of host brain development.[20] Characterization of the electrophysiologic properties of the neurons that develop from the neural precursors, both *in vitro* and *in vivo,* as well as retrograde tracing studies, are required to determine their maturity and capability of functional integration in a host brain. A detailed description of the methods that are used for transplantation experiments and electrophysiologic studies is beyond the scope of this chapter. Here we briefly describe the methodology for induction of differentiation *in vitro* and for the immunophenotyping of differentiated progeny.

Markers of Differentiated Progeny

A large number of antibodies are commercially available for the immunophenotyping of neural cells. Here we describe some of the most commonly used markers.

β-tubulin type III is a characteristic marker of neurons and its expression is considered one of the earliest events in cells that are destined to neuronal differentiation. The monoclonal antibody against β-tubulin III, which is also termed TuJ1, is widely used to study the distribution and morphology of immature neurons *in vivo* and *in vitro*.[55–57] Light-chain (70 kD) neurofilament is also expressed in immature neurons.[20,22] Markers of more mature neurons include MAP2ab, which is usually expressed in the dendritic tree[16,18,20,21]; medium (160 kD) and heavy chain (200 kD) neurofilament proteins[16,20,22]; and NeuN-neuronal nuclear antigen Flax.[27] The generation of synaptic vesicles and synapses may be identified with the aid of anti-synaptophysin[18,20] and anti-synapsin I, Wu.[58]

Demonstrating the synthesis of neurotransmitters (e.g., glutamate, GABA, and serotonin) or key enzymes in the metabolism of neurotransmitters (e.g., tyrosine hydroxylase and choline acetyltransferase [ChAT])[58,59] may also indicate maturity and allows the characterization of the subtype of neurons that are generated by the neural precursors.

The glial fibrillary acidic protein (GFAP) is an intermediate-filament protein that is highly specific for cells of astroglial lineage.[60]Astrocyte progenitors of the CNS usually express vimentin as the major intermediate filament. A switch between vimentin and GFAP expression follows astrocyte maturation. Thus, GFAP is considered an astrocyte maturation marker and is widely used to identify astroglial lineage cells.[61] A variety of markers of the oligodendroglial lineage have been identified.[62] So far, in the hES cell system, only with the oligodendroglial progenitor marker O4 has immunoreactivity been demonstrated following differentiation of neural precursors *in vitro*.[20,22]

Indirect Immunofluorescence Characterization of Differentiated Neural Cells

The hES cell–derived neural spheres are disaggregated to small clusters of cells (as detailed previously) and plated on laminin-precoated cover slips in NPM medium without mitogens. In the absence of mitogens, the precursors readily differentiate during an incubation period of 7–21 days. The medium is replaced twice a week. To promote the survival of neurons, the medium may be supplemented with various survival factors such as brain-derived neurotrophic factor (BDNF), neurotrophin-3 (NT-3), and neurotrophin-4 (NT-4) (10–20 ng/ml, R&D Systems).[18,63] The methods for fixation and immunostaining are described in the section on indirect immunofluorescence characterization of the precursors within the spheres and the information on antibodies is listed in Table 49–1.

REFERENCES

1. Reubinoff, B.E., Pera, M.F., Fong, C.Y., Trounson, A., and Bongso, A. (2000). Embryonic stem cell lines from human blastocysts: somatic differentiation *in vitro*. *Nat. Biotechnol.* **18**, 399–405.
2. Itskovitz-Eldor, J., Schuldiner, M., Karsenti, D., Eden, A., Yanuka, O., Amit, M., Soreq, H., and Benvenisty, N. (2000). Differentiation of human embryonic stem cells into embryoid bodies comprising the three embryonic germ layers. *Mol. Med.* **6**, 88–95.
3. Schuldiner, M., Yanuka, O., Itskovitz-Eldor, J., Melton, D.A., and Benvenisty, N. (2000). Effects of eight growth factors on the differentiation of cells derived from human embryonic stem cells. *Proc. Natl. Acad. Sci. U. S. A.* **97**, 11,307–11,312.
4. Schuldiner, M., Eiges, R., Eden, A., Yanuka, O., Itskovitz-Eldor, J., Goldstein, R.S., and Benvenisty, N. (2001). Induced neuronal differentiation of human embryonic stem cells. *Brain Res.* **913**, 201–205.
5. Ying, Q.L., Stavridis, M., Griffiths, D., Li, M., and Smith, A. (2003). Conversion of embryonic stem cells into neuroectodermal precursors in adherent monoculture. *Nat. Biotechnol.* **21**, 183–186.
6. Renoncourt, Y., Carroll, P., Filippi, P., Arce, V., and Alonso, S. (1998). Neurons derived in vitro from ES cells express homeoproteins characteristic of motoneurons and interneurons. *Mech. Dev.* **79**, 185–197.
7. Li, M., Pevny, L., Lovell-Badge, R., and Smith, A. (1998). Generation of purified neural precursors from embryonic stem cells by lineage selection. *Curr. Biol.* **8**, 971–974.
8. Stavridis, M.P., and Smith, A.G. (2003). Neural differentiation of mouse embryonic stem cells. *Biochem. Soc. Trans.* **31**, 45–49.
9. Beddington, R.S., and Robertson, E.J. (1999). Axis development and early asymmetry in mammals. *Cell* **96**, 195–209.
10. Munoz-Sanjuan, I., and Brivanlou, A.H. (2002). Neural induction, the default model and embryonic stem cells. *Nat. Rev. Neurosci.* **3**, 271–280.
11. Tropepe, V., Hitoshi, S., Sirard, C., Mak, T.W., Rossant, J., and van der Kooy, D. (2001). Direct neural fate specification from embryonic stem cells: a primitive mammalian neural stem cell stage acquired through a default mechanism. *Neuron* **30**, 65–78.
12. Kawasaki, H., Mizuseki, K., Nishikawa, S., Kaneko, S., Kuwana, Y., Nakanishi, S., Nishikawa, S.I., and Sasai, Y. (2000). Induction of midbrain dopaminergic neurons from ES cells by stromal cell-derived inducing activity. *Neuron* **28**, 31–40.
13. Kawasaki, H., Suemori, H., Mizuseki, K., Watanabe, K., Urano, F., Ichinose, H., Haruta, M., Takahashi, M., Yoshikawa, K., Nishikawa, S., Nakatsuji, N., and Sasai, Y. (2002). Generation of dopaminergic neurons and pigmented epithelia from primate ES cells by stromal cell-derived inducing activity. *Proc. Natl. Acad. Sci. U. S. A.* **99**, 1580–1585.
14. Rathjen. J., Haines, B.P., Hudson, K.M., Nesci, A., Dunn, S., and Rathjen, P.D. (2002). Directed differentiation of pluripotent cells to neural lineages: homogeneous formation and differentiation of a neurectoderm population. *Development* **129**, 2649–2661.
15. Wiles, M.V., and Johansson, B.M. (1999). Embryonic stem cell development in a chemically defined medium. *Exp. Cell. Res.* **247**, 241–248.
16. Okabe, S., Forsberg-Nilsson, K., Spiro, A.C., Segal, M., and McKay, R.D.G. (1996). Development of neuronal precursor cells and functional postmitotic neurons from embryonic stem cells in vitro. *Mech. Dev.* **59**, 89–102.
17. Mujtaba, T., Piper, D.R., Kalyani, A., Groves, A.K., Lucero, M.T., and Rao, M.S. (1999). Lineage-restricted neural precursors can be isolated from both the mouse neural tube and cultured ES cells. *Dev. Biol.* **214**, 113–127.
18. Carpenter, M.K., Inokuma, M.S., Denham, J., Mujtaba, T., Chiu, C.P., and Rao, M.S., (2001). Enrichment of neurons and neural precursors from human embryonic stem cells. *Exp. Neurol.* **172**, 383–397.
19. Brustle, O., Spiro, A.C., Karram, K., Choudhary, K., Okabe, S., and McKay, R.D. (1997). In vitro-generated neural precursors participate in mammalian brain development. *Proc. Natl. Acad. Sci. U. S. A.* **94**, 14,809–14,814.
20. Reubinoff, B.E., Itsykson, P., Turetsky, T., Pera, M.F., Reinhartz, E., Itzik, A., and Ben-Hur, T. (2001). Neural progenitors from human embryonic stem cells. *Nat. Biotechnol.* **19**, 1134–1140.
21. Pera, M.F., Andrade, J., Houssami, S., Reubinoff, B., Trounson, A., Stanley, E.G., Ward-van Oostwaard, D., and Mummery, C. (2004). Regulation of human embryonic stem cell differentiation by BMP-2 and its antagonist noggin. *J. Cell. Sci.* **117**, 1269–1280.
22. Zhang, S.C., Wernig, M., Duncan, I.D., Brustle, O., and Thomson, J.A. (2001). In vitro differentiation of transplantable neural precursors from human embryonic stem cells. *Nat. Biotechnol.* **19**, 1129–1133.
23. Trojanowski, J.Q., Kleppner, S.R., Hartley, R.S., Miyazono, M., Fraser, N.W., Kesari, S., and Lee, V.M. (1997). Transfectable and transplantable postmitotic human neurons: a potential "platform" for gene therapy of nervous system diseases. *Exp. Neurol.* **144**, 92–97.

24. Sah, D.W.Y., Ray, J., and Gage, F.H. (1997). Bipotent progenitor cell lines from the human CNS. *Nat. Biotechnol.* **15**, 574–580.

25. Vescovi, A.L., Parati, E.A., Gritti, A., Poulin, P., Ferrario, M., Wanke, E., Frolichsthal-Schoeller, P., Cova, L., Arcellana-Panlilio, M., Colombo, A., and Galli, R. (1999). Isolation and cloning of multipotential stem cells from the embryonic human CNS and establishment of transplantable human neural stem cell lines by epigenetic stimulation. *Exp. Neurol.* **156**, 71–83.

26. Vescovi, A.L., and Snyder, E.Y. (1999). Establishment and properties of neural stem cell clones: plasticity in vitro and in vivo. *Brain Pathol.* **9**, 569–598.

27. Flax, J.D., Aurora, S., Yang, C., Simonin, C., Wills, A.M., Billinghurst, L.L., Jendoubi, M., Sidman, R.L., Wolfe, J.H., Kim, S.U., and Snyder, E.Y. (1998). Engraftable human neural stem cells respond to developmental cues, replace neurons, and express foreign genes. *Nat. Biotechnol.* **16**, 1033–1039.

28. Kukekov, V.G., Laywell, E.D., Suslov, O., Davies, K., Scheffler, B., Thomas, L.B., O'Brien, T.F., Kusakabe, M., and Steindler, D.A. (1999). Multipotent stem/progenitor cells with similar properties arise from two neurogenic regions of adult human brain. *Exp. Neurol.* **156**, 333–344.

29. Uchida, N., Buck, D.W., He, D., Reitsma, M.J., Masek, M., Phan, T.V., Tsukamoto, A.S., Gage, F.H., and Weissman IL. (2000). Direct isolation of human central nervous system stem cells. *Proc. Natl. Acad. Sci. U. S. A.* **97**, 14,720–14,725.

30. Nunes, M.C., Roy, N.S., Keyoung, H.M., Goodman, R.R., McKhann, G 2nd., Jiang, L., Kang, J., Nedergaard, M., and Goldman, S.A. (2003). Identification and isolation of multipotential neural progenitor cells from the subcortical white matter of the adult human brain. *Nat. Med.* **9**, 439–447.

31. Zwaka, T.P., and Thomson, J.A. (2003). Homologous recombination in human embryonic stem cells. *Nat. Biotechnol.* **21**, 319–321.

32. Rideout, W.M 3rd., Hochedlinger, K., Kyba, M., Daley, G.Q., and Jaenisch, R. (2002). Correction of a genetic defect by nuclear transplantation and combined cell and gene therapy. *Cell* **109**, 17–27.

33. Black, I.B., and Woodbury, D. (2001). Adult rat and human bone marrow stromal stem cells differentiate into neurons. *Blood. Cells. Mol. Dis.* **27**, 632–636.

34. Brazelton, T.R., Rossi, F.M., Keshet, G.I., and Blau, H.M. (2000). From marrow to brain: expression of neuronal phenotypes in adult mice. *Science* **290**, 1775–1779.

35. Jiang, Y., Jahagirdar, B.N., Reinhardt, R.L., Schwartz, R.E., Keene, C.D., Ortiz-Gonzalez, X.R., Reyes, M., Lenvik, T., Lund, T., Blackstad, M., Du, J., Aldrich, S., Lisberg, A., Low, W.C., Largaespada, D.A., and Verfaillie, C.M. (2002). Pluripotency of mesenchymal stem cells derived from adult marrow. *Nature* **418**, 41–49.

36. Kim, J.H., Auerbach, J.M., Rodriguez-Gomez, J.A., Velasco, I., Gavin, D., Lumelsky, N., Lee, S.H., Nguyen, J., Sanchez-Pernaute, R., Bankiewicz, K., and McKay, R. (2002). Dopamine neurons derived from embryonic stem cells function in an animal model of Parkinson's disease. *Nature* **418**, 50–56.

37. Brustle, O., Jones, K.N., Learish, R.D., Karram, K., Choudhary, K., Wiestler, O.D., Duncan, I.D., and McKay, R.D. (1999). Embryonic stem cell-derived glial precursors: a source of myelinating transplants. *Science* **285**, 754–756.

38. Wilson, P.A., and Hemmati-Brivanlou, A. (1997). Vertebrate neural induction: inducers, inhibitors, and a new synthesis. *Neuron* **18**, 699–710.

39. Svendsen, C.N., ter Borg, M.G., Armstrong, R.J., Rosser, A.E., Chandran, S., Ostenfeld, T., and Caldwell, M.A. (1998). A new method for the rapid and long term growth of human neural precursor cells. *J. Neurosci. Methods* **85**, 141–152.

40. Lendahl, U., Zimmerman, L.B., and McKay, R.D. (1990). CNS stem cells express a new class of intermediate filament protein. *Cell* **60**, 585–595.

41. Frederiksen, K., and McKay, R.D. (1988). Proliferation and differentiation of rat neuroepithelial precursor cells in vivo. *J. Neurosci.* **8**, 1144–1151.

42. McKay, R.D., and Brustle, O. (1997). Stem cells in the central nervous system. *Science* **276**, 66–71.

43. Sejersen, T., and Lendahl, U. (1993). Transient expression of nestin during skeletal muscle development. *J. Cell. Sci.* **106**, 1291–1300.

44. Ronn, L.C., Hartz, B.P., and Bock, E. (1998). The neural cell adhesion molecule (NCAM) in development and plasticity of the nervous system. *Exp. Gerontol.* **33**, 853–64.

45. Mayer-Proschel, M., Kalyani, A.J., Mujtaba, T., and Rao, M.S. (1997). Isolation of lineage-restricted neuronal precursors from multipotent neuroepithelial stem cells. *Neuron* **19**, 773–785.

46. Alonso, G. (1999). Neuronal progenitor-like cells expressing polysialylated neural cell adhesion molecule are present on the ventricular surface of the adult rat brain and spinal cord. *J. Comp. Neurol.* **414**, 149–166.

47. Cifuentes-Diaz, C., Nicolet, M., Goudou, D., Rieger, F., Mege, R.M. (1993). N-cadherin and N-CAM-mediated adhesion in development and regeneration of skeletal muscle. *Neuromusc. Disord.* **3**, 361–365.

48. Raff, M.C., Abney, E.R., Cohen, J., Lindsay, R., and Noble, M. (1983). Two types of astrocytes in cultures of developing rat white matter: differences in morphology, surface gangliosides, and growth characteristics. *J. Neurosci.* **3**, 1289–1300.

49. Miller, R.H., David, S., Patel, R., Abney, E.R., and Raff, M.C. (1985). A quantitative immunohistochemical study of macroglial cell development in the rat optic nerve: in vivo evidence for two distinct astrocyte lineages. *Dev. Biol.* **111**, 35–41.

50. Wichterle, H., Lieberam, I., Porter, J.A., and Jessell, T.M. (2002). Directed differentiation of embryonic stem cells into motor neurons. *Cell* **110**, 385–397.

51. Pevny, L.H., Sockanathan, S., Placzek, M., and Lovell-Badge, R. (1998). A role for SOX1 in neural determination. *Development* **125**, 1967–1978.

52. Wood, H.B., and Episkopou, V. (1999). Comparative expression of the mouse Sox1, Sox2 and Sox3 genes from pre-gastrulation to early somite stages. *Mech Dev.* **86**, 197–201.

53. Nakamura, M., Okano, H., Blendy, J.A., and Montell, C. (1994). Musashi, a neural RNA-binding protein required for Drosophila adult external sensory organ development. *Neuron* **13**, 67–81.

54. Sakakibara, S., Imai, T., Hamaguchi, K., Okabe, M., Aruga, J., Nakajima, K., Yasutomi, D., Nagata, T., Kurihara, Y., Uesugi, S., Miyata, T., Ogawa, M., Mikoshiba, K., and Okano, H. (1996). Mouse-Musashi-1, a neural RNA-binding protein highly enriched in the mammalian CNS stem cell. *Dev. Biol.* **176**, 230–242.

55. Lee, M.K., Rebhun, L.I., and Frankfurter, A. (1990). Posttranslational modification of class III beta-tubulin. *Proc. Natl. Acad. Sci. U. S. A.* **87**, 7195–7199.

56. Menezes, J.R., and Luskin, M.B. (1994). Expression of neuron-specific tubulin defines a novel population in the proliferative layers of the developing telencephalon. *J. Neurosci.* **14**, 5399–5416.

57. Ferreira, A., and Caceres, A. (1992). Expression of the class III beta-tubulin isotype in developing neurons in culture. *J. Neurosci. Res.* **32**, 516–529.

58. Wu, P., Tarasenko, Y.I., Gu, Y., Huang, L.Y., Coggeshall, R.E., and Yu, Y. (2002). Region-specific generation of cholinergic neurons from fetal human neural stem cells grafted in adult rat. *Nat. Neurosci.* **5,** 1271–1278.

59. Lee, S.H., Lumelsky, N., Studer, L., Auerbach, J.M., and McKay, R.D. (2000). Efficient generation of midbrain and hindbrain neurons from mouse embryonic stem cells. *Nat. Biotechnol.* **18,** 675–679.

60. Reeves, S.A., Helman, L.J., Allison, A., and Israel, M.A. (1989). Molecular cloning and primary structure of human glial fibrillary acidic protein. *Proc. Natl. Acad. Sci. U. S. A.* **86,** 5178–5182.

61. Gomes, F.C., Paulin, D., and Moura Neto, V. (1999). Glial fibrillary acidic protein (GFAP): modulation by growth factors and its implication in astrocyte differentiation. *Braz. J. Med. Biol. Res.* **32,** 619–631.

62. Stangel, M., and Hartung, H.P. (2002) Remyelinating strategies for the treatment of multiple sclerosis. *Prog. Neurobiol.* **68,** 361–376.

63. Caldwell, M.A., He, X., Wilkie, N., Pollack, S., Marshall, G., Wafford, K.A., and Svendsen, C.N. (2001). Growth factors regulate the survival and fate of cells derived from human neurospheres. *Nat. Biotechnol.* **19,** 475–479.

Generation of Precursors and Primitive Human Hematopoietic Cells from Human ESC Lines

Mickie Bhatia

Establishment of pluripotent human embryonic stem cell (hESC) lines has given rise to new opportunities for regenerative-based medicine.[1] Use of hESC lines is further complicated by the now recognized differences in murine embryonic stem cells (mESCs) versus hESCs (see Table 38-1). Although it is difficult to accept based on the developmental similarities between the species, hESCs, unlike mESCs, possess distinct growth and differentiation requirements.[2] Accordingly, not all previous work from mESC studies is directly applicable to understanding hESCs. This is especially important in regard to differences in methodologies used to proliferate or differentiate hESCs or to assay pluripotency by chimera formation.[3] Accordingly, applicability of ESCs to stem cell therapies requires the fundamental study of hESCs.

Although there are several target organs and tissues considered for hESC-based cell-replacement therapies, the generation of hematopoietic cells has been argued to have the broadest applicability. Reconstitution of cellular components of the hematopoietic system has immense utility in several areas of clinical medicine and describes the functional property of mammalian hematopoietic stem cells (HSCs). These include replacing cells responsible for innate and acquired immunity, providing red cells for oxygen transport, and ultimately recovering hematopoietic function by repopulating all lineages that make up the entire blood system. The latter property can be envisioned to apply to patients undergoing cancer therapy and individuals with blood-borne infectious disease and to include approaches to induce tolerance in whole-organ allogeneic transplant recipients. In cases in which the number or compatibility of human HSCs is insufficient, hESCs have been suggested as a viable source of transplantable hematopoietic cells. Although the number of hESCs is virtually unlimited, the ability to efficiently differentiate adequate numbers of cells that possess hematopoietic repopulating ability remains to be determined. Achieving this goal is confounded by the difficulty of experimentally generating murine hematopoietic cell types capable of *in vivo* reconstitution from mESCs, suggesting that similar limitations may

arise using human counterparts. In this chapter we outline some potential approaches and efforts to differentiate and assay primitive hematopoietic cells derived from ESCs.

Functional Criteria and Assays for Hematopoietic Stem Cells

Most of our current understanding and indeed the conceptual foundation of mammalian HSC biology has arisen from seminal work using mouse bone marrow (BM)-derived cells.[4,5] In the mouse, candidate HSC transplantation has evolved to allow the purification of single cells from the adult BM of donors that replace the entire recipient hematopoietic system in myeloablated hosts.[6,7] This *in vivo* repopulation ability of HSCs provides the functional criteria used to formulate the "gold standard" assay used to operationally define mammalian HSCs.[8] For obvious ethical reasons, similar assays are not available for detecting human HSCs.[9] However, evidence from human clinical marking studies using retroviral tagging of transplanted human hematopoietic cells indicates that cells with similar multilineage hematopoietic repopulating function exist in the human,[10,11] but they have yet to be prospectively purified to homogeneity or effectively tracked retrospectively by retroviral tagging strategies *in vivo*. Enrichment methods have shown that specific cell surface phenotypes are sufficient for isolating a heterogeneous cell population containing putative human HSCs[12,13] but have not provided the precise definition of the human HSC cell surface phenotype.

The hematopoietic system consists of a heterogeneous array of cells ranging from large numbers of differentiated cells with defined function to rare pluripotent stem cells with extensive developmental and proliferative potential.[4,14–16] Although the differentiation program of mature blood cells is reasonably well defined, much less is known about the HSC hierarchy and the cells that compose the human hematopoietic progenitor compartment.[4] *In vitro*, detection of primitive human hematopoietic cells is accomplished by a variety of assay systems.[17] Clonogenic hematopoietic assays detect progenitor cells committed to a specific lineage by seeding candidate populations into semisolid media such as methylcellulose together with cytokines and hematopoietic growth factors to stimulate clonal proliferation into myeloid restricted lineages that include granulocytes, macrophages, and erythroid cells. Progenitors identified by this assay are retrospectively classified as colony-forming units (CFUs) and can be quantitatively subdivided into lineage-restricted subtypes by examining the composition of the resulting progeny (e.g., CFU-GM = granulocytes and macrophages). Cells that are capable of survival and proliferation during extended co-culture with BM-derived stromal cells and thereby give rise to expanded numbers of cells with CFC capacity are termed long-term culture initiating cells (LTC-ICs). Because LTC-IC are capable of initiating long-term cultures and give rise to numerous CFUs, LTC-ICs represent CFU precursors and are considered the most primitive hematopoietic progenitor detectable *in vitro*.

Although *in vitro* detectable progenitors provide critical insight into the cellular arrangement of cells comprising the primitive hematopoietic compartment, these assays do not detect cells that meet the criteria for pluripotent HSCs. *In vitro* detectable cells are unable to support development of all blood lineages, are only active for a limited time, and are not challenged to reconstitute the blood system *in vivo*.[9] The only conclusive way to assay HSCs is by repopulation of the entire hematopoietic system in conditioned recipients.[18] Therefore, information regarding human stem cells using surrogate *in vitro* assays such as CFU and LTC-IC detection is limited. More recently, experimental hematologists have relied on a wide range of human–mouse xenotransplantation models that allow detection of candidate human hematopoietic cells capable of *in vivo* reconstitution.[19] Although these transplantation assay systems differ by delivery method and specific background strains of immune-deficient recipient mice, the nonobese-diabetic-severe combined immunodeficiency (NOD-SCID) mouse that engrafts intravenously transplanted human cells has been the most used.[9] The underlying rationale of the NOD-SCID repopulation assay was to develop a transplantation system that mimicked current methods of human BM transplantation and reconstituting function of candidate human HSCs.[20] NOD-SCID mice transplanted via tail vein injection with human hematopoietic cells from adult BM or cord blood (CB) are able to repopulate the mouse BM with human cells.[21] A large body of evidence from several studies indicates that this human repopulating cell is more primitive and distinct from most human CFUs and LTC-ICs.[22–24] This primitive human engrafting cell is operationally defined as a SCID-repopulating cell (SRC). Using cell purification and retroviral gene marking, SRCs that are capable of engrafting NOD-SCID mice have been shown to be biologically distinct from CFUs and most LTC-ICs.[23,25] CFUs and LTC-ICs can be transduced at very high efficiencies with retrovirus; however, transduction of SRCs is extremely rare.[23,26] This differential susceptibility to infection supports their biologic distinctiveness from cells detected by *in vitro* assays and correlates to the inability to infect stem cells in human clinical trials. Purification studies using a stringent two-step strategy involving depletion of lineage-positive cells (Lin+ fraction) followed by fluorescence-activated cell sorting of the Lin− fraction facilitates the purification of a cell population from CB and BM that is highly enriched for cells capable of multilineage repopulation in NOD/SCID recipients.[25]

These somatic human SRCs are enriched by 1500-fold in the Lin− cell fraction that expresses high levels of cell surface CD34 and no CD38 antigens. Fractions of primitive Lin−CD34+ cells that express CD38 are not capable of engraftment at any cell dose but are highly enriched for more mature LTC-ICs and CFCs. Through limiting dilution analysis using Poisson statistics, the frequency of 1 SRC in 617 Lin−CD34+CD38− cells was determined.[25] One SRC transplanted at limiting cell doses into NOD-SCID mice is able to produce approximately 400,000 progeny cells 6–12 weeks posttransplantation. Detailed flow cytometric analysis of the BM of highly engrafted NOD-SCID mice demonstrated both lymphoid and myeloid differentiation and the retention of a significant fraction of primitive CD34+ subpopulations.[25,27] These studies demonstrate that NOD-SCID transplantation of human SRCs derived from adult BM or CB provides a functional assay to define the nature of purified human HSCs and to examine and optimize human HSC expansion and gene transfer.[28] Using these functional criteria to define primitive human hematopoietic cells, the hierarchical organization of the hematopoietic system can be assembled.[29]

In addition to allowing a functional definition of human hematopoietic stem and progenitor cells, these assays and definitions provide a critical tool to examine alternative sources of hematopoietic stem/progenitor cells, such as those generated from hESC lines.

Lesson Learned: Primitive Hematopoietic Cells Derived from Mouse Embryonic Stem Cells

Based on the length of study and rigorous methodologies used, the characterization of mammalian HSCs has mainly been predicated on research in the murine system. These accumulative studies have provided a conceptual basis that can be applied to the behavior of other stem cells and has formed the starting point for approaches to derive HSCs from mESCs and to evaluate the functionality of these putative HSCs using *in vivo* reconstitution assays.

Previous studies using different methods of mESC differentiation have shown a limited capacity to engraft adults.[30] However, there have been several reports that demonstrate the ability to generate primitive hematopoietic cell types from mESCs *in vitro*. Research into mouse HSCs derived from ESCs is more advanced than its human counterpart, and several methodologies have been designed to differentiate ESCs into the hematopoietic lineage *in vitro*. Primitive hematopoietic cells can be derived through the formation of embryoid bodies (EBs),[31] by co-culturing ESC with stromal cell lines,[32] and through the culture of ESCs on collagen-coated plates.[33] Murine ESCs have been shown to retain CFU potential past 30 days *in vitro*,[30] and primitive erythroid lineages are detectable as early as 4 days into culture.[31] In serum-free cultures, the addition of bone morphogenetic protein-4 (BMP-4) was shown to induce the hematopoietic lineage from pluripotent mESCs, indicating that these cells mimic the embryonic character of ventral mesoderm and subsequent hematopoietic cell fate progression.[34] Murine ESC hematopoietic differentiation seems to be more effective when exogenous cytokine cocktails are added, including combinations of stem cell factor (SCF), interleukin (IL)-3, IL-6, IL-11, granulocyte-cell stimulating factor (G-SCF), and FLT3 ligand.[32,33,35,36]

However, in the context of the most rigorous assays and definitions of HSCs, these approaches have not been shown to give rise to cells with multilineage repopulating ability *in vivo* and are, therefore, considered to generate only hematopoietic progenitors and not HSCs. *In vitro* derivation of HSCs capable of long-term engraftment from mESCs has proven to be technically challenging. Because aggregation of mESCs into the inner cell mass of blastocyst recipients routinely results in an ESC-derived contribution to definitive hematopoiesis and in HSCs capable of hematopoietic repopulation,[37] it is known that mESCs retain the developmental capacity to differentiate into HSCs. However, there have been few reports that describe *in vivo* hematopoietic function of transplanted hematopoietic cells derived from mESCs. After 22 days of EB formation and differentiation, limited lymphoid engraftment using adoptive transfer has been demonstrated *in vivo*.[38] Direct injection of EBs that have undergone limited short-term culture has been shown to give rise to transient levels of B-lymphoid engraftment; however, these results are compromised by the frequency of teratoma formation arising from intravenous introduction of undifferentiated ESCs remaining within mouse EBs.[39] In addition to these reports that demonstrate limited hematopoietic repopulation, there are at least three recent publications that are noteworthy in the context of this review that have evaluated HSC function derived from mESCs.

Using aggregation to tetraploid embryos, Forrester *et al.*[40] demonstrated the ability of mESCs to generate cells in day 14–15 fetal liver that can be transplanted into adult hosts and give rise to long-term hematopoietic repopulation. Hematopoietic progeny were of multiple lineages and included T-cells, macrophages, and erythroid cells. The extent and magnitude of hematopoietic reconstitution that was achieved and whether these cells give rise to all eight hematopoietic lineages in recipient hosts are unclear from this study. Nevertheless, this study represented the first demonstration that mESC lines are capable of differentiating into hematopoietic cells with *in vivo* repopulating capacity after prolonged passage in culture.[40] However, this repopulation was dependent on forming tetraploid–ESC chimeras, suggesting that critical signals present during embryonic development are essential in the generation of transplantable HSCs.

More recently, introduction of a chimeric oncoprotein BCR-ABL, which has been associated with myeloid leukemias, allowed repopulation by mESC-derived cells on transplantation into adult recipients.[30] Hematopoietic cells derived from EBs transduced with BCR-ABL maintained a primitive blast phenotype and were restricted to CFU progenitor potential within the erythroid lineage. In contrast, clonal propagation and injection of expanded cells into irradiated

hosts allowed for differentiation into multiple lineages including T- and B-cells and myeloid progenitors.[30] The repopulation included clones that expressed both embryonic and adult globins, suggesting that mESC differentiation into the hematopoietic lineage arises from a common progenitor that possessing embryonic erythroid and definitive lymphoid-myeloid hematopoietic potential.

Aside from growth factors extrinsically capable of regulating hematopoietic cell fate during embryonic development, insights into transcription factors that potentially govern mammalian HSC self-renewal have recently been reported, indicating the central role for HoxB4. Ectopic HoxB4 expression in murine embryonic stem cells (mESCs) is able to confer HSC properties onto undefined mESC progeny.[41] Murine ESC progeny expressing HoxB4 were able to engraft lethally irradiated adult recipients and contribute to long-term, multilineage hematopoiesis in primary and secondary recipients. Interestingly, HoxB4 was previously implicated in the self-renewal of mouse BM-derived HSCs.[41] Expression of HoxB4 is tightly regulated by other transcription factors. Recently, Giannola and co-workers reported that combinations of early-acting cytokines increased HoxB4 promoter activity in adult primitive hematopoietic cells,[41] suggesting the HoxB4 can be controlled by extrinsic factors as opposed to gene transduction into target cells. Taken together, these studies suggest that the key regulatory factors that are capable of modulating adult HSCs are also able to confer HSC properties on differentiating mammalian ESCs, implying that similar paradigms are applicable to hESCs but remain to be tested. However, as evidenced by the low gene transfer efficiency into human HSCs in most clinical trials,[10,11] progress in developing efficient transduction procedures for human BM-derived HSCs has been difficult, suggesting that testing the role of HoxB4 in hESCs by transduction-overexpression may be limited by the inability to transduce hematopoietic-derived hESCs.

Efforts to Generate Primitive Hematopoietic Cells Derived from Human Embryonic Stem Cell Lines

Although the majority of our current understanding of HSCs comes from the murine system, information regarding the phenotype, *ex vivo* culture conditions, and gene transfer protocols for murine HSCs have not proven to be applicable to cells with similar properties in the human. In addition to the inability to apply information and technology devised from murine HSC work, progress has been hindered in understanding the nature of human HSCs by the reliance on heterogeneous samples from individual donors that differ in quality and responsiveness to cytokines and growth factors used in *ex vivo* culture. Isolation procedures of putative human HSC have been optimized to allow substantive enrichment of primitive cell populations, but definitive cell surface markers capable of purifying the adult human HSCs are yet to be defined.

In vitro surrogate assays (CFU and LTC-IC) and human xenotransplantation models for primitive hematopoietic reconstituting cells provide the only means to develop, measure, and understand the fundamental mechanisms by which established hESC lines may generate candidate hematopoietic stem/progenitor cells.[17] In contrast to the mouse, *in vivo* hematopoietic reconstitution of hESC-derived cells has yet to be demonstrated,[41,42] illustrating our limited knowledge of the optimal *in vitro* requirements for the differentiation of hESCs.

Our ability to obtain human hematopoietic progenitors, let alone to achieve effective repopulating ability from hESC-derived cells, is currently in its infancy in comparison to previous mESC studies. Given unexpected differences that control the undifferentiated proliferation of mESCs and hESCs,[43] it can be expected that significant differences will exist in the specific factors that direct hESC differentiation into the hematopoietic fate. Kaufman *et al.*[44] were the first to demonstrate that hESCs can be differentiated to the hematopoietic fate Using three different hESC lines maintained by co-culture on mouse embryonic fibroblasts (MEFs), co-culture of hESCs with either irradiated mouse BM stromal cell line S17 or the mouse yolk sac endothelial cell line C166 permitted differentiation of hESCs into a variety of hematopoietic cell types within 3–5 days. Hematopoietic progenitors were detected by *in vitro* CFU assays and included multiple myeloid lineages that were similar to CFUs obtainable from adult human BM. At 14 days of co-culture on S17 or C166 support lines, it was observed that most CFUs generated were of the erythroid lineage; however, between 14 and 21 days primarily myeloid CFUs were observed, until eventual loss of CFU generation after 21 days. It was shown that, although treatment with exogenous cytokines was not required, differentiation did not occur in the absence of fetal calf serum. Terminally differentiated hematopoietic cells also expressed surface antigens characteristic of primitive cells in primary human hematopoietic tissue such as the CD34 antigen and vascular endothelial growth factor (VEGF) receptor Flk-1, both typical of murine and human HSCs.[32,33,44] LMO-2, TAL-1, and GATA-2, which are known to be expressed at early stages of hematopoietic development, were expressed in differentiating ESCs cultured on either S17 or C166 support cultures. Most surprisingly, was the complete absence of cell surface CD45, the hematopoietic panleukocyte marker. CD45 is expressed on all known sources of human hematopoietic cells, it is used as a diagnostic index for quality of hematopoietic products transplanted clinically, and its murine homologue Ly5 has been observed to have a similar correlation to hematopoietic potential in both adult and mESCs. Nevertheless, this study indicates that hESC lines possess hematopoietic potential that can be augmented by co-culture on stromal or endothelial microenvironments known to support growth of adult hematopoietic cells.[44]

Our laboratory has developed alternative methods to differentiate hESCs into the hematopoietic lineage using similar hematopoietic cytokine combinations known to support survival and expansion of somatic human hematopoietic cells capable of multilineage repopulation in NOD-SCID mice.[22] In the absence of co-culture, these hematopoietic cytokines are able to provide large number of CFUs that are found exclusively in differentiated cells expressing CD45. Under these conditions, cells devoid of CD45 cell surface expression possessed no hematopoietic potential.[45] Unlike mESCs that respond to BMP-4 treatment to induce ventral mesoderm programs and augment hematopoietic lineage commitment,[46] BMP-4 had little effect on differentiation toward the production of hematopoietic progenitors but was capable of supporting secondary replating of CFU, suggestive of a role for BMP-4 in ESC-derived hematopoietic progenitor self-renewal, analogous to its role in CB SRC expansion.[29] This technology has formulated the basis for our continued efforts to generate hematopoietic progenitors to be tested for repopulating ability using the NOD-SCID assay or other comparable human–xenotransplantation assays for human HSC function.

Limitations Toward Deriving Human Hematopoietic Stem Cells from Human Embryonic Stem Cell Precursors

It is possible that self-renewal does not contribute to heterogeneity of the adult HSC compartment but instead that all HSC clones follow a predetermined fate. This suggests that the self-renewal and differentiation behavior of HSCs in adult BM is predetermined, suggesting that attempts to recapitulate complex embryonic conditions *in vitro* that allow the emergence of bona fide HSCs during embryonic patterning may be unattainable,[47] notwithstanding introduction of genes such as *HOXB4*.[41] In addition, the narrow combinations of cytokines used to differentiate hESCs toward the hematopoietic lineage *in vitro* may result in defects in the engraftment potential of the resulting progeny. This is exemplified by the inability of adult mouse or human repopulating cells to compete against unmanipulated cells for *in vivo* reconstitution,[48] suggesting that cytokines as the sole stimulus do not allow cell divisions without loss of hematopoietic repopulating ability.[49]

Repopulating activity is dependent on compatible microenvironments of transplanted recipients.[50] Therefore, irradiated adult hosts may be ontogenically unsuitable for putative HSCs derived from hESCs. This may include the inability for embryonic-derived HSCs to home to the adult BM hematopoietic microenvironment on transplantation or the inability of the adult BM to provide appropriate signals required to maintain the embryonic-derived HSCs. This is supported by studies in the murine system in which purified subsets of putative HSCs derived from E9.0 yolk sac are able to provide long-term repopulation when transplanted into conditioned newborn mice but fail to repopulate in adult recipients.[51]

Fundamental Study of Hematopoietic Lineage Progression from Human Embryonic Stem Cells

The study of hESC differentiation into the hematopoietic lineage provides a novel tool to better understand the fundamental

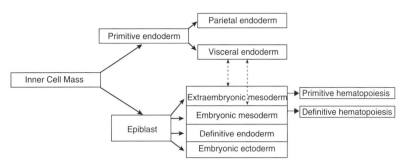

Figure 50–1. Schematic illustration of developmental principles of images of lineage specification toward hematopoietic cell fate.

basis of embryonic hematopoietic commitment and development that cannot be examined in other human systems.[42] Differentiation of ESCs *in vitro* provides a powerful model system for addressing questions of lineage commitment, and the generation of mature lineages from ESCs in culture provides access to populations of early precursors that are difficult, if not impossible, to access *in vivo*. The developmental potential of ESCs carrying targeted mutations of genes essential for embryonic development can be determined in culture, whereas analysis of these mutations *in vivo* is often complicated by early death of the embryo *in utero*.[31] As with studies characterizing lineage relationships and precursor developmental potentials, most of our knowledge of growth regulation within the human hematopoietic system comes from experiments with adult BM. Isolation of early embryonic precursors could provide a means of identifying novel regulators that act at early stages of hematopoietic development that could not otherwise be examined, and sequential steps that program precursors to develop appropriately into hematopoietic tissue (similar cellular patterning during mammalian embryogenesis) from hESCs may be a necessity to generate functional human HSCs.

MAMMALIAN EMBRYOGENESIS TO MODEL HUMAN EMBRYONIC STEM CELL DIFFERENTIATION TOWARD HEMATOPOIETIC CELL FATE

The blood system in mammals originates during gastrulation from the patterning epiblast that gives rise to mesoderm and subsequent committed blood cells. Epiblast patterning is governed by inductive signals of adjacent visceral endoderm (VE), with the anterior and posterior regions of the epiblast specified to ectodermal and mesodermal fates, respectively. Explant cultures in *Xenopus,* avian, and murine embryos have suggested that the VE plays an instructive role in mesoderm differentiation[52] based on the ability of VE to respecify tissue that are not normally endowed with endothelial and hematopoietic cell fate potential.[53,54] The VE expresses numerous signaling factors required for the specification of the mouse epiblast,[55] most of which specify ectodermal fates. Mesodermal specification, however, seems to be positively controlled by VE secretion of the transforming growth factor β (TGFβ) and fibroblast growth factor (FGF) superfamilies of

growth factors, and include Activin A, bFGF, and BMP-4.[56–58] BMP-4, however, is minimally expressed by the VE, suggesting that different VE-derived morphogens are involved in inductive interactions and/or signaling between the VE and prospective ventroposterior mesoderm. According to *Xenopus* and avian models,[57,59–61] production of BMP-2 and BMP-6 from the VE represents the most potent candidates for induction to mesoderm fate. In addition, studies using mouse models have reported that Indian hedgehog, specifically expressed in the VE, is a key mediator of VE-induced hematopoietic differentiation of the epiblast.[62,63] A schematic representation of lineage relationships during embryonic hematopoiesis is illustrated in Fig. 50–1.

It has been assumed that specification of the epiblast is determined by a localized concentration gradient of both agonistic and antagonistic factors secreted by the VE[64] that establishes the ectodermal specification, thereby opposing mesodermal fate. Antagonistic factors of mesodermal specification are products of specific VE regions that express TGFβ/BMP antagonists such as Chordin, Cerberus, Follistatin, Lefty, and Gremlin.[55,65] The higher expression of these antagonists in undifferentiated hESCs as compared with spontaneously differentiated cells[3] is suggestive of negative regulation of this differentiation process by these pathways. Taken together, these observations describe the complex interplay between signaling pathways required for appropriate cell fate specification and subsequent mesodermal lineage development that may be necessary to mimic *in vitro* generation of functional HSCs from hESCs.

PRECURSOR ORIGINS OF MAMMALIAN HEMATOPOIETIC STEM CELLS

Invertebrates possess a vascular system that is open to the interstitial space and, therefore, is permissive to the entry of developing hematopoietic cells into the circulation. In the mammal, a more efficient closed circulatory system has evolved, necessitating the formation of endothelial vasculature that itself gives rise to hematopoietic cells, thereby allowing incorporation of blood cells into this closed system. Among vertebrates analyzed to date, initiation of embryonic hematopoiesis has been observed in the yolk sac and along the vitelline, umbilical arteries, and the ventral wall of the dorsal aorta, suggesting a close association of hematopoietic emergence with the major vasculature. Studies using mESC lines[66–68] following cellular Flk-1 expression

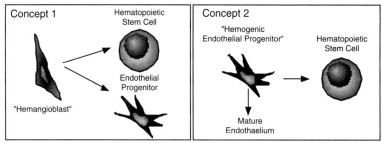

Figure 50–2. Concepts to define the nature of hematopoietic precursors.

have suggested that there is an intermediate stage of embryonic development, which represents precursors with hematopoietic and endothelial potentials,[66,69] that originates from the lateral mesoderm. Studies in *Drosophila* and *Xenopus* support the notion that the origin of hematopoiesis may arise from a developmental transition of endothelial cells capable of blood formation. However, the exact nature of cells representing immediate precursors of HSCs remains unclear, and at least two views have been proposed as shown in Fig. 50–2.

Concept 1 suggests that a distinct uncommitted parent "hemangioblast" that possesses both endothelial and hematopoietic capacity is derived from mesoderm. Although this concept was introduced more that 100 years ago, hemangioblasts with these properties have yet to be identified *in vivo*, and formal proof for the existence of hemangioblast cells awaits the use of clonal assays. Concept 2, an alternative to hemangioblastic origin of hematopoiesis, is the idea that hematopoietic fate arises from specialized endothelial cells termed hemogenic endothelial progenitors (HEPs) that are triggered to form blood in response to local environmental cues. *In vivo*, attempts to characterize cells that represent precursors of the HSCs have been difficult, but insights into endothelial and hematopoietic differentiation have recently benefited from mESC models that allowed the resolution of intermediate cellular stages of mesoderm development.[70] However, because most data that have lead to the current concepts of the cellular origin of hematopoiesis were generated from mouse models, application of these paradigms to understanding lineage relationships between endothelial and hematopoietic cells in the human remains to be determined.

In the human, studies of hematopoietic and endothelial development have been hampered by difficulties associated with obtaining early human embryos and lack of conditions capable of reproducing human embryonic developmental processes *in vitro*. Accordingly, the processes and signals that govern the complex relationship between the emergence of hematopoietic and endothelial cell fate remain elusive, and further investigation is limited by the inability to identify and isolate primitive human hematopoietic and endothelial precursors. However, because hESCs show significant differences from their mESC counterparts, it is unclear whether the use of hESCs will recapitulate hematopoietic and endothelial development described in the mouse or whether the mouse even provides a representative model of human embryo development for these lineages.

Recently we have demonstrated hemogenic competency of differentiating hESCs originating from a unique population of endothelial-like precursors (unpublished results). During human EB development, colonization of platelet endothelial cell adhesion molecule (PECAM)-1+ and VE-cadherin+ cells preceded emergence of committed CD45-expressing hematopoietic cells. Before hematopoietic commitment, cells expressing Flk-1 or PECAM-1 were isolated from human EBs and were shown to possess properties of the endothelium. PECAM-1+/Flk-1+/VE-cadherin+ cells could be differentiated toward the hematopoietic lineage on cytokine stimulation or matured toward the endothelial lineage in response to VEGF and pituitary hormones. Derivation of these precursors from hESCs was augmented by addition of exogenous BMP-4 during human EB formation. Based on these findings, we believe we have now identified a novel population of human BMP-responsive hemogenic endothelial precursors that gives rise to both hematopoietic and endothelial cell fate. Based on cell surface phenotype, we have termed these precursors as hESC-derived CD45⁻ PFV cells. These findings have direct implications not only to our understanding of human development but also to potential clinical applications postinjury that require regeneration of both the human blood system and vasculature. In addition, our report represents the first demonstration that precursors of a specific tissue lineage can be prospectively isolated from human EBs, indicating the hESC differentiation progresses as development of discrete cell types that become more restricted, thereby describing a hierarchical organization of developmental events of cell fate commitment from hESCs.

Future Work: Human Embryonic Stem Cell–Derived Hematopoietic Stem Cells?

Fundamental investigations into lineage relationship among hESC progeny will most likely lead to insights by which procedures and technology can be developed that will allow the generation of transplantable human HSCs from ESCs. Initially, these experimental studies may be restricted to human xenotransplantation models to develop a fundamental understanding of human HSC induction, but this work will hopefully lead to therapeutic protocols for the generation of expandable and transplantable human HSCs derived from hESCs for the purposes of regenerative therapies.

ACKNOWLEDGEMENTS

The author would like to thank Drs. Chantal Cerdan, Lisheng Wang, and Pablo Menendez for their input, insights, and guidance toward the final preparation of this chapter. Supported by: a Canada Research Chair in Stem Cell Biology and Regenerative Medicine to M.B.; and the Canadian Institutes of Health Research (CIHR), National Cancer Institute of Canada (NCIC), and the National Centres of Excellence (NCE)—StemNet.

REFERENCES

1. Thomson, J.A., Itskovitz-Eldor, J., Shapiro, S.S., Waknitz, M.A., Swiergiel, J.J., Marshall, V.S., and Jones, J.M. (1998). Embryonic stem cell lines derived from human blastocysts. *Science* 282, 1145–1147.

2. Bhatia, M. (2003). The ultimate source of human hematopoietic stem cells: thinking outside the marrow. *Cloning Stem Cells* 5, 89–97.

3. Sato, N., Sanjuan, I.M., Heke, M., Uchida, M., Naef, F., and Brivanlou, A.H. (2003). Molecular signature of human embryonic stem cells and its comparison with the mouse. *Dev. Biol.* 260, 404–413.

4. Ogawa, M. (1994). Hematopoiesis. *J. Allergy Clin. Immunol.* 94, 645–650.

5. Domen, J., and Weissman, I.L. (1999). Self-renewal, differentiation or death: regulation and manipulation of hematopoietic stem cell fate. *Mol. Med. Today* 5, 201–208.

6. Osawa, M., Hanada, K., Hamada, H., and Nakauchi, H. (1996). Long-term lymphohematopoietic reconstitution by a single CD34-low/negative hematopoietic stem cell. *Science* 273, 242–245.

7. Iscove, N.N., and Nawa, K. Hematopoietic stem cells expand during serial transplantation in vivo without apparent exhaustion. *Curr. Biol.* 7, 805–808.

8. Lagasse, E., Connors, H., Al-Dhalimy, M., Reitsma, M., Dohse, M., Osborne, L., Wang, X., Finegold, M., Weissman, I.L., and Grompe, M. (2000). Purified hematopoietic stem cells can differentiate into hepatocytes in vivo. *Nat. Med.* 6, 1229–1234.

9. Dick, J.E., Bhatia, M., Gan, O., Kapp, U., and Wang, J.C. (1997). Assay of human stem cells by repopulation of NOD/SCID mice. *Stem Cells* 15 (Suppl 1), 199–203; discussion 204–207.

10. Brenner, M.K., Rill, D.R., Holladay, M.S., Heslop, H.E., Moen, R.C., Buschle, M., Krance, R.A., Santana, V.M., Anderson, W.F., and Ihle, J.N. (1993). Gene marking to determine whether autologous marrow infusion restores long-term haemopoiesis in cancer patients. *Lancet* 342, 1134–1137.

11. Brenner, M.K. (1996). Gene transfer to hematopoietic cells. *N. Engl. J. Med.* 335, 337–339.

12. Gallacher, L., Murdoch, B., Wu, D.M., Karanu, F.N., Keeney, M., and Bhatia, M. (2000). Isolation and characterization of human CD34(-)Lin(−) and CD34(+)Lin(−) hematopoietic stem cells using cell surface markers AC133 and CD7. *Blood* 95, 2813–2820.

13. Huang, S., Law, P., Young, D., and Ho, A.D. (1998). Candidate hematopoietic stem cells from fetal tissues, umbilical cord blood vs. adult bone marrow and mobilized peripheral blood. *Exp. Hematol.* 26, 1162–1171.

14. Ogawa, M., Porter, P.N., and Nakahata, T. (1983). Renewal and commitment to differentiation of hemopoietic stem cells (an interpretive review). *Blood* 61, 823–829.

15. Till, J.E., and McCulloch, E.A. (1980). Hemopoietic stem cell differentiation. *Biochim. Biophys. Acta* 605, 431–459.

16. Ogawa, M. (1993). Differentiation and proliferation of hematopoietic stem cells. *Blood* 81, 2844–2853.

17. Eaves, C. et al. (1999). Introduction to stem cell biology in vitro. Threshold to the future. *Ann. N. Y. Acad. Sci.* 872, 1–8.

18. Morrison, S.J., Shah, N.M., and Anderson, D.J. (1997). Regulatory mechanisms in stem cell biology. *Cell* 88, 287–298.

19. Greiner, D.L., Hesselton, R.A., Shultz, L.D., Moore, M.A., and Rafii, S. (1998). SCID mouse models of human stem cell engraftment. *Stem Cells* 16, 166–177.

20. Lapidot, T., Pflumino, F., Doedens, M., Murdoch, B., Williams, D.E., and Dick, J.E. (1992). Cytokine stimulation of multilineage hematopoiesis from immature human cells engrafted in SCID mice. *Science* 255, 1137–1141.

21. Cashman, J.D., Lapidot, T., Wang, J.C., Doedens, M., Schultz, L.D., Lansdorp, P., Dick, J.E., and Eaves, C.J. (1997). Kinetic evidence of the regeneration of multilineage hematopoiesis from primitive cells in normal human bone marrow transplanted into immunodeficient mice. *Blood* 89, 4307–4316.

22. Bhatia, M., Bonnet, D., Kapp, U., Wang, J.C., Murdoch, B., and Dick, J.E. (1997). Quantitative analysis reveals expansion of human hematopoietic repopulating cells after short-term ex vivo culture. *J. Exp. Med.* 186, 619–624.

23. Larochelle, A., Vormoor, J., Hanenberg, H., Wang, J.C., Bhatia, M., Lapidot, T., Moritz, T., Murdoch, B., Xiao, X.L., Kato, I., Williams, D.A., and Dick, J.E. (1996). Identification of primitive human hematopoietic cells capable of repopulating NOD/SCID mouse bone marrow: implications for gene therapy. *Nat. Med.* 2, 1329–1337.

24. Bhatia, M. (2001). AC133 expression in human stem cells. *Leukemia* 15, 1685–1688.

25. Bhatia, M., Wang, J.C.Y., Kapp, U., Bonnet, D., and Dick, J.E. (1997). Purification of primitive human hematopoietic cells capable of repopulating immune-deficient mice. *Proc. Natl. Acad. Sci. U. S. A.* 94, 5320–5325.

26. Guenechea, G., Gan, O.I., Dorrell, C., and Dick, J.E. (2001). Distinct classes of human stem cells that differ in proliferative and self-renewal potential. *Nat. Immunol.* 2, 75–82.

27. Karanu, F.N., Murdoch, B., Miyabayashi, T., Ohno, M., Koremoto, M., Gallacher, L., Wu, D., Itoh, A, Sakano, S., and Bhatia, M. (2001). Human homologues of Delta-1 and Delta-4 function as mitogenic regulators of primitive human hematopoietic cells. *Blood* 97, 1960–1967.

28. Dick, J.E. (2000). Gene therapy turns the corner. *Nat. Med.* 6, 624–626.

29. Bhardwaj, G., Murdoch, B., Wu, D., Baker, D.P., Williams, K.P., Chadwick, K., Ling, L.E., Karanu, F.N., and Bhatia, M. (2001). Sonic hedgehog induces the proliferation of primitive human hematopoietic cells via BMP regulation. *Nat. Immunol.* 2, 172–180.

30. Perlingeiro, R.C., Kyba, M., and Daley, G.Q. (2001). Clonal analysis of differentiating embryonic stem cells reveals a hematopoietic progenitor with primitive erythroid and adult lymphoid-myeloid potential. *Development* 128, 4597–4604.

31. Keller, G.M. (1995). In vitro differentiation of embryonic stem cells. *Curr. Opin. Cell Biol.* 7, 862–869.

32. Palacios, R., Golunski, E., and Samaridis, J. (1995). In vitro generation of hematopoietic stem cells from an embryonic stem cell line. *Proc. Natl. Acad. Sci. U. S. A.* 92, 7530–7534.

33. Ogawa, M., Kizumoto, M., Nishikawa, S., Fujimoto, T., Kodama, H., and Nishikawa, S.I. (1999). Expression of alpha4-integrin defines the earliest precursor of hematopoietic cell lineage diverged from endothelial cells. *Blood* 93, 1168–1177.

34. Johansson, B.M., and Wiles, M.V. (1995). Evidence for involvement of activin A and bone morphogenetic protein 4 in mammalian

mesoderm and hematopoietic development. *Mol. Cell Biol.* **15**, 141–151.

35. Uzan, G., Prandini, M.H., Rosa, J.P., and Berthier, R. (1996). Hematopoietic differentiation of embryonic stem cells: an in vitro model to study gene regulation during megakaryocytopoiesis. *Stem Cells* **14**, 194–199.

36. McClanahan, T., Dalrymple, S., Barkett, M., and Lee, F. (1993). Hematopoietic growth factor receptor genes as markers of lineage commitment during in vitro development of hematopoietic cells. *Blood* **81**, 2903–2915.

37. Beddington, R.S., Robertson, E.J., Greiner, D.L., Hesselton, R.A., Shultz, L.D., Moore, M.A., and Rafii, S. (1989). An assessment of the developmental potential of embryonic stem cells in the midgestation mouse embryo. *Development* **105**, 733–737.

38. Muller, A.M., and Dzierzak, E.A. (1993). ES cells have only a limited lymphopoietic potential after adoptive transfer into mouse recipients. *Development* **118**, 1343–1351.

39. Mead, P.E., Brivanlou, I.H., Kelley, C.M., and Zon, L.I. (1996). BMP-4-responsive regulation of dorsal-ventral patterning by the homeobox protein Mix.1. *Nature* **382**, 357–60.

40. Forrester, L.M., Bernstein, A., Rossant, J., and Nagy, A. (1991). Long-term reconstitution of the mouse hematopoietic system by embryonic stem cell-derived fetal liver. *Proc. Natl. Acad. Sci. U. S. A.* **88**, 7514–7517.

41. Kyba, M., Perlingeiro, R.C., and Daley, G.Q. (2002). HoxB4 confers definitive lymphoid-myeloid engraftment potential on embryonic stem cell and yolk sac hematopoietic progenitors. *Cell* **109**, 29–37.

42. Kaufman, D.S., and Thomson, J.A. (2002). Human ES cells: haematopoiesis and transplantation strategies. *J. Anat.* **200**, 243–248.

43. Lebkowski, J.S., Gold, J., Xu, C., Funk, W., Chiu, C.P., and Carpenter, M.K. (2001). Human embryonic stem cells: culture, differentiation, and genetic modification for regenerative medicine applications. *Cancer J.* **7** (Suppl 2), S83–93.

44. Kaufman, D.S., Hanson, E.T., Lewis, R.L., Auerbach, R., and Thomson, J.A. (2001). Hematopoietic colony-forming cells derived from human embryonic stem cells. *Proc. Natl. Acad. Sci. U. S. A.* **98**, 10716–10721.

45. Chadwick, K., Wang, L., Li, L., Menendez, P., Murdoch, B., Rouleau, A., and Bhatia, M. (2003). Cytokines and BMP-4 promote hematopoietic differentiation of human embryonic stem cells. *Blood* **102**, 906–915.

46. Hemmati-Brivanlou, A., and Thomsen, G.H. (1995). Ventral mesodermal patterning in Xenopus embryos: expression patterns and activities of BMP-2 and BMP-4. *Dev. Genet.* **17**, 78–89.

47. Muller-Sieburg, C.E., Cho, R.H., Thoman, M., Adkins, B., and Sieburg, H.B. (2002). Deterministic regulation of hematopoietic stem cell self-renewal and differentiation. *Blood* **100**, 1302–1309.

48. Yoder, M.C., Papaioannou, V.E., Breitfeld, P.P., and Williams, D.A. (1994). Murine yolk sac endoderm- and mesoderm-derived cell lines support in vitro growth and differentiation of hematopoietic cells. *Blood* **83**, 2436–2443.

49. Verfaillie, C.M. (2002). Hematopoietic stem cells for transplantation. *Nat. Immunol.* **3**, 314–317.

50. Flake, A.W., and Zanjani, E.D. (1999). In utero hematopoietic stem cell transplantation: ontogenic opportunities and biologic barriers. *Blood* **94**, 2179–2191.

51. Yoder, M.C. et al. (1997). Characterization of definitive lympho-hematopoietic stem cells in the day 9 murine yolk sac. *Immunity* **7**, 335–344.

52. Downs, K.M., Gifford, S., Blahnik, M., and Gardner, R.L. (1998). Vascularization in the murine allantois occurs by vasculogenesis

53. Miura, Y., and Wilt, F.H. (1969). Tissue interaction and the formation of the first erythroblasts of the chick embryo. *Dev. Biol.* **19**, 201–211.

54. Kikkawa, M., Yamazaki, M., Izutsu, Y., and Maeno, M. (2001). Two-step induction of primitive erythrocytes in Xenopus laevis embryos: signals from the vegetal endoderm and the overlying ectoderm. *Int. J. Dev. Biol.* **45**, 387–396.

55. Bielinska, M., Narita, N., and Wilson, D.B. (1999). Distinct roles for visceral endoderm during embryonic mouse development. *Int. J. Dev. Biol.* **43**, 183–205.

56. Smith, J.C. (1989). Mesoderm induction and mesoderm-inducing factors in early amphibian development. *Development* **105**, 665–677.

57. Miyanaga, Y., Shiurba, R., and Asashima, M. (1999). Blood cell induction in Xenopus animal cap explants: effects of fibroblast growth factor, bone morphogenetic proteins, and activin. *Dev. Genes Evol.* **209**, 69–76.

58. Faloon, P., Arentson, E., Kazarov, A., Deng, C.X., Porcher, C., Orkin, S., and Choi, K. (2000). Basic fibroblast growth factor positively regulates hematopoietic development. *Development* **127**, 1931–1941.

59. Clement, J.H., Fettes, P., Knochel, S., Lef, J., and Knochel, W. (1995). Bone morphogenetic protein 2 in the early development of *Xenopus laevis*. *Mech. Dev.* **52**, 357–370.

60. Suzuki, A., Kaneko, E., Maeda, J., and Ueno, N. (1997). Mesoderm induction by BMP-4 and -7 heterodimers. *Biochem. Biophys. Res. Commun.* **232**, 153–156.

61. Nishimatsu, S., and Thomsen, G.H. (1998). Ventral mesoderm induction and patterning by bone morphogenetic protein heterodimers in Xenopus embryos. *Mech. Dev.* **74**, 75–88.

62. Maye, P., Becker, S., Kasameyer, E., Byrd, N., and Grabel, L. (2000). Indian hedgehog signaling in extraembryonic endoderm and ectoderm differentiation in ES embryoid bodies. *Mech. Dev.* **94**, 117–132.

63. Dyer, M.A., Farrington, S.M., Mohn, D., Munday, J.R., and Baron, M.H. (2001). Indian hedgehog activates hematopoiesis and vasculogenesis and can respecify prospective neurectodermal cell fate in the mouse embryo. *Development* **128**, 1717–1730.

64. Hogan, B.L. (1996). Bone morphogenetic proteins: Multifunctional regulators of vertebrate development. *Genes Dev.* **10**, 1580–1594.

65. Perea-Gomez, A., Rhinn, M., and Ang, S.L. (2001). Role of the anterior visceral endoderm in restricting posterior signals in the mouse embryo. *Int. J. Dev. Biol.* **45**, 311–320.

66. Nishikawa, S.I., Nishikawa, S., Hirashima, M., Matsuyoshi, N., and Kodama, H. (1998). Progressive lineage analysis by cell sorting and culture identifies FLK1+VE-cadherin+ cells at a diverging point of endothelial and hemopoietic lineages. *Development* **125**, 1747–1757.

67. Becker-Hapak, M., McAllister, S.S., and Dowdy, S.F. (2001). TAT-mediated protein transduction into mammalian cells. *Methods* **24**, 247–256.

68. Chung, Y.S., Zhang, W.J., Arentson, E., Kingsley, P.D., Palis, J., and Choi, K. (2002). Lineage analysis of the hemangioblast as defined by FLK1 and SCL expression. *Development* **129**, 5511–5520.

69. Lacaud, G., Robertson, S., Palis, J., Kennedy, M., and Keller, G. (2001). Regulation of hemangioblast development. *Ann. N. Y. Acad. Sci.* **938**, 96–107; discussion 108.

70. Fehling, H.J., Lacaud, G., Kubo, A., Kennedy, M., Robertson, S., Keller, G., and Kouskoff, V. (2003). Tracking mesoderm induction and its specification to the hemangioblast during embryonic stem cell differentiation. *Development* **130**, 4217–4227.

without accompanying erythropoiesis. *Development* **125**, 4507–4520.

51

Growth Factors and the Serum-free Culture of Human Pluripotent Stem Cells

Alice Pébay and Martin F. Pera

Introduction

The development of human embryonic stem (ES) cells in 1998,[1] presaged by work on stem cell lines from human embryonal carcinoma (EC) and monkey ES cells (review in reference 2), led to a great surge of interest in the biology and potential therapeutic applications of pluripotent stem cells. The early reports of derivation of both monkey and human ES cells used serum-containing medium in combination with mouse embryo feeder cell support to maintain stem cell renewal, methodology that did not differ very much from those used previously to establish and propagate mouse ES cells or human EC cells. However, several critical differences in growth properties of mouse and human ES cells soon emerged. The human cells display very low cloning efficiency when dissociated to single cells, and the addition of leukemia inhibitory factor (LIF) is without effect on the growth of human stem cells in the absence of a feeder cell layer.[3] Both of these properties of human pluripotent stem cells were first noted in early efforts to characterize human EC cells, and the findings meant that techniques that had been developed for efficient propagation and manipulation of mouse ES cells would find limited application in the human system.

The original methods for cultivation of human ES cells had several drawbacks. The use of fetal calf serum and mouse feeder cells potentially exposes the human cells to unknown pathogens, in particular viruses or prions, that might be transmitted between species. Although the use of culture components derived from animal products does not preclude the clinical use of cells derived from human ES cultures in transplantation, most regulatory agencies will regard such cell products in the same category as xenotransplants, a factor that will complicate their use considerably. Both serum and feeder cell layers also contain many undefined components that may have profound and undesirable effects on ES cell differentiation. The poor growth of human ES cells following dissociation to single cells means that cloning at low densities, key to many experimental manipulations, is problematic. Moreover, because single cells survive poorly, and

large aggregates of cells usually differentiate, the resulting requirement to subculture the cells as clusters of an appropriate size can limit the ability to scale up the culture while maintaining cells in an undifferentiated state. Careful examination of ES cell cultures grown under conditions presently regarded as optimal, using appropriate panels of markers, reveals considerable heterogeneity in the expression of stem cell antigens in cells throughout the culture a phenomenon that likely results from a continuous process of spontaneous differentiation.[3a]

Thus, the major challenges to the development of human ES cell culture systems are as follows: to eliminate the use of serum in the medium, to eliminate the use of feeder cells, to improve the cloning efficiency, and to enable scale-up of the cultures. Since the first reports of the development of human ES cells, there have been several advances in our ability to grow these cells *in vitro,* but not all of these goals have been achieved to date. This chapter reviews the current status of development of culture systems for human ES cells in the context of previous work on mouse ES cells and human EC cells.

Mouse Embryonal Carcinoma and Embryonic Stem Cells

The growth requirements of pluripotent stem cells have been studied in most detail in the mouse. Although the intent of this chapter is not to capture all of this work, there are some important lessons from these studies. The origins of this research trace back to the cultivation of mouse EC cells from teratocarcinomas that develop experimentally following ectopic transplantation of embryos or from gonadal neoplasms that occur spontaneously with relatively high frequency in certain inbred strains.[4] Although many workers described EC cell lines that could be grown independently of feeder cells, other mouse EC cell lines clearly retained feeder cell dependence. Through the 1980s, the burgeoning of interest in growth factors and autocrine models of growth regulation were accompanied by the development of serum-free systems for the cultivation of mouse EC cells[5] and by efforts to examine potential autocrine regulators of EC cell growth.[6] This work, which focused on mouse EC cell lines with minimal growth requirements, tended to overlook the importance of interactions with the feeder cell layer for maintenance of stem cell pluripotentiality.

Handbook of Stem Cells
Volume 1

The original reports of mouse ES cell derivation used embryonic fibroblast feeder cells and serum-containing medium. A key advance was the discovery of LIF, or differentiation inhibitory activity, as a critical component for maintenance of the pluripotent state.[7,8] LIF and other members of this cytokine family that act through engagement of their particular receptors and the gp130 receptor maintain mouse ES cells in the pluripotent state through activation of JAK/STAT signalling.[9] Production of LIF is one of the factors that accounts for the requirement of feeder cells to support mouse ES cell growth.[10] Although many workers maintain mouse ES cells on a feeder layer in the presence of LIF, there are certainly a number of examples of germ-line competent mouse ES cell lines that can be maintained without a feeder cell layer in the presence of LIF (e.g., reference 11). Notwithstanding the evidence that LIF is important for mouse ES cell renewal, it is important to recognize that mice deficient in the gp130 receptor can still undergo normal development through mid-gestation,[12] that mouse ES cell lines lacking the LIF receptor can still form colonies on a feeder cell layer,[13] and that there is evidence that factors other than LIF can maintain mouse and human EC cells in the pluripotent state.[14,15] These factors remain to be identified, but the important message for human ES cell work is that extrinsic pathways independent of gp130 signaling may have a role in pluripotent stem cell maintenance.

Whether or not a feeder cell layer is used, mouse ES cells cultured in the presence of LIF are often grown in the presence of serum. This requirement for serum can be replaced by the use of a proprietary formulation known as Knockout Serum Replacer, discussed later. In addition to effects on stem cell renewal, components of serum can activate or inhibit signaling pathways critical to differentiation into particular lineages. Thus, growth of mouse ES cells in chemically defined medium has enabled direction of differentiation into specific lineages and provided evidence for a default pathway of neural differentiation.[16,17]

Human Embryonal Carcinoma Cells

Human EC cell lines have been isolated by a number of investigators from different pathologic subclasses of these human tumors using different methodologies. Thus, although the stem cells of these cultures have certain common characteristics including marker expression, the lines do vary in their ability to differentiate and in their growth requirements *in vitro*.[18] One general observation is that many human EC cells, like human ES cells, are difficult to passage as single cells at low density. Although some human EC cell lines do not require feeder cell support, other pluripotent cell lines show a strong feeder cell dependence that is not met by addition of LIF to the culture medium.[19] There is a spectrum of growth requirements among human EC cell lines that ranges from cell lines displaying a feeder cell requirement similar to that of human ES cells to those EC lines that may be grown at clonal density at high efficiency in the absence of a feeder cell layer. In general, the more robust the human EC cell line in

minimalist culture conditions, the more limited its capacity for differentiation.

Early efforts to analyze the growth requirements of human EC cells led to identification of several factors critical for their growth. One important attachment factor identified was the serum protein vitronectin, which on its own was able to support adhesion and subsequent growth of feeder independent EC cell lines in the presence of insulin, transferrin, and albumin.[20] Studies by Graham and co-workers on feeder cell-independent clones of the cell line Tera-2 revealed a key role for insulin-like growth factors in maintaining survival of pluripotent stem cells in the absence of serum.[21] In addition to insulin-like growth factors, which are antiapoptotic for human EC cells, several factors active through tyrosine kinase surface receptors were identified with effect on human EC cells. Several groups reported a mitogenic effect of fibroblast growth factor-2 (FGF-2) on clones of the Tera-2 cell line grown under serum-free conditions[22,23]; FGF-1 and FGF-4 were also active. At high doses, FGF-2 stimulated cell motility. Further studies by Mummery and her co-workers[24] pointed to a potential role for platelet derived growth factor (PDGF) signaling in promoting growth of pluripotent human EC cells. The presence of receptors for this molecule was surprising because, in the mouse, expression of PDGF receptors occurs only after commitment of cells to mesoderm differentiation. There was indirect evidence for a potential autocrine role of this molecule in driving EC cell proliferation.

These observations on feeder independent human EC lines can be contrasted to work with pluripotent, feeder-dependent human EC cell lines. These cells cannot be maintained without a feeder cell layer even in the presence of serum; insulin, PDGF, FGF-2, and LIF, along with many other known factors, fail to replace the requirement of a feeder layer for stem cell maintenance, at least in the presence of serum.[15,19] Supernatants produced by a feeder-independent yolk sac carcinoma cell line capable of growth in the absence of serum could substitute for a feeder cell layer, but the active principle in these supernatants remains unknown.

In addition to the identification of factors that drive human EC stem cell renewal, bone morphogenetic proteins (BMPs) have been identified by several groups as inducers of human EC cell differentiation.[25,26] In both reports, the cell type induced by BMP treatment is an epithelial cell, and one group reported patterns of gene expression characteristic of extraembryonic differentiation in these cells.

Several candidate autocrine growth factor regulators were identified through studies of human EC cells. TDGF-1, also known as cripto, is an epidermal growth factor Cripto/FRL-1/Cryptic (EGF-CFC) superfamily member that is expressed in human EC cells and a few other cell types.[27] Transcripts for a smaller, truncated form of this growth factor are more widely expressed in transformed cells and in normal human tissues.[28] In a clone of the cell line Tera-2, recombinant TDGF-1 was found to be mitogenic. The transforming growth factor beta (TGFβ) superfamily member GDF-3 (also known as Vgr-1)[29] is expressed in mouse and human EC cells[30] and mouse ES cells, but there is no evidence for its expression in the peri-implantation phase of mouse embryonic development, and distribution of its transcripts in adult tissues is fairly limited. *GDF-3* is, therefore, a gene whose expression might represent adaptation of stem cells to a condition of permanent self-renewal *in vitro*. However, this member of the TGFβ superfamily is unusual, because it lacks a key cysteine residue involved in dimerization of most superfamily members and because no biologic activity of GDF-3 either *in vitro* or *in vivo* has been described thus far.[31] Finally, human EC cell lines and ES cell lines express receptors for the Wnt family of secreted regulators,[32] and recent evidence implicates these molecules in the control of differentiation of mouse ES cells.[33,34]

Human Embryonic Stem Cells

CRITICAL COMPONENTS OF THE ORIGINAL CULTURE SYSTEMS

To date, there are eight published reports of the derivation of human ES cell lines, and most of these have used very similar culture conditions.[1,3,35-40] As noted previously, unlike mouse ES cells, human ES cells do not respond to LIF. Nonetheless, the first successful derivations[1,3] of human ES cells used LIF in combination with a feeder layer of early passage mouse embryonic fibroblasts in a media optimized for the propagation of mouse ES cells, supplemented with 20% fetal calf serum. This media used by Thomson *et al.*,[1] similar to that used to support monkey ES cells and mouse ES cells, consisted of 80% Dulbecco's modified Eagle's medium (no pyruvate, high glucose formulation), 20% fetal calf serum, 1 mM glutamine, 0.1 mM β-mercaptoethanol and 1% nonessential amino acids. There have been few reports of the use of alternative basal media, and no groups have reported systematic studies of the role of low-molecular-weight components of the basal media in the support of human ES cell growth. Optimization of the basal media can markedly affect the growth factor requirements of particular cell types *in vitro,* and more work in this area is certainly merited. In the original cell culture system used to establish human ES cells, omission of either feeder cells or serum leads to rapid differentiation of the ES cells. Individual lots of serum or feeder cells can vary significantly in their ability to promote human ES cell growth, and the extent and range of ES cell differentiation *in vitro* is also strongly influenced by the batch of serum or feeder cells used for growth.

Because of potential concerns over biosafety in the clinical application of cell transplants derived from ES cells grown in the presence of animal feeder cell layers, Bongso and co-workers[40] developed ES cell lines in the presence of human feeder cells. Several groups have now described the growth of human ES cells on various types of human feeder cells, including fibroblasts, marrow stromal cells, and other cell types, and a recent report described derivation of human ES cell lines on STO cells,[39] a permanent line of mouse embryo fibroblasts. Both human feeder cell layers and STO cells are much easier to maintain than primary mouse embryo fibroblasts, and the properties of the ES cells grown on these cells appear similar to those grown on early passage embryo fibroblasts.

Elimination of the use of a feeder cell layer will require some understanding of the molecular basis of the support of stem cell renewal. In an effort to identify proteins produced by feeder cells that might be responsible for stem cell maintenance, Lim and Bodnar[41] carried out proteomic analysis of secreted products found in conditioned medium of STO feeder cells. One secreted protein identified of interest was the insulin-like growth factor binding protein (IGFBP)-4, which may play a role in presenting insulin-like growth factors to the cell; insulin or insulin-like growth factors are components of most serum substitutes and will enhance human ES cell colony growth even in the presence of serum.[41a] Other factors found in the STO conditioned medium included pigment epithelium derived factor; a range of extracellular matrix components including SPARC, nidogen, and collagen alpha 1 and 2 chains; and several antioxidant proteins. This proteomic analysis probably was most likely to detect relatively abundant components of conditioned medium and may well have missed critical membrane-bound regulators of stem cell growth and differentiation. One example of this latter class of protein is the BMP antagonist gremlin, a protein produced by fibroblasts that is mainly cell associated; gremlin transcripts are found in mouse embryonic fibroblast feeder cells used to support human ES cell growth, and BMPs, which are produced by human ES cells, have a profound differentiation effect on human ES cells.[42] It is likely, although unproven, that feeder cell layers have multiple roles in the support of human ES cell growth and that multiple proteins (cytokines, survival factors, antidifferentiative proteins, and extracellular matrix components) in either secreted or membrane-associated forms are involved in the interactions between feeder cells and stem cells.

Another approach to definition of ES cell growth requirements is to ask what receptors the stem cells themselves express. A recent microarray analysis showed that human ES cells express transcripts of all four FGF receptors, BMPR1A, and Frzd5, indicating possible roles for FGF, BMP, and Wnt family members in stem cell regulation.[43]

BASIC FIBROBLAST GROWTH FACTOR (FGF-2) AND KNOCKOUT SERUM REPLACER

In 2000, Amit *et al.*[44] examined the use of different media to increase the cloning efficiency of human ES cells. One of the results of this study was the description of conditions allowing the use of a serum-free medium for the propagation of human ES cells. Basal media comprised of 80% Dulbecco's modified Eagle's medium (no pyruvate, high glucose formulation), 1 mM glutamine, 0.1 mM β-mercaptoethanol, and 1% nonessential amino acids. These media were then supplemented with either 20% fetal calf serum, or 20% Knockout Serum Replacer, with or without 4 ng/ml FGF-2. Knockout Serum Replacer[45] is a proprietary serum replacement consisting of amino acids, vitamins, transferrin or substitutes, insulin or insulin substitutes, trace elements, collagen precursors, and albumin preloaded with lipid. The composition of this serum replacement is not precisely specified by the manufacturer, and the description provides for the use of albumin substitutes, including other sources of animal protein such as embryo extracts.

In this study, the cells were passaged every week. The authors showed that FGF-2 was without effect in presence of serum but increased the cloning efficiency of human ES cells when added to basal medium supplemented with serum replacer in the presence of a feeder cell layer. Under conditions of routine maintenance, FGF-2 blocked stem cell differentiation, as judged by cell morphology; in presence of serum replacer and FGF-2, human ES cells appeared smaller and colonies were more compacted. The use of this system enabled long-term maintenance of diploid pluripotent cells expressing markers characteristic of human ES cells. The system has since been modified to incorporate DMEM:Nutrient Mixture F12 as the basal media and a reduced feeder cell layer density. As noted previously, FGF-2 and other members of this growth factor family were shown to be mitogenic for human EC cells under serum-free conditions, but in the EC cell studies there was no indication that these factors inhibited differentiation. Recent work indicates that the primary action of FGF-2 on human ES cells is indeed inhibition of differentiation rather than promotion of stem cell proliferation.[46]

The system described previously is now widely used, but the cloning efficiency of human ES cells in the system remains low, and feeder cells are still required. Xu et al.[47] described a further modification of this system that replaced the feeder cell layer with a combination of conditioned medium from mouse embryonic fibroblasts and Matrigel, a commercially available basement membrane extract. Laminin functioned well as a substrate for ES cell growth and may be an alternative to Matrigel in this system. This system also enabled long-term maintenance of the ES cells. However, both this system and the feeder cell based culture method using FGF-2 supplemented media still incorporate an undefined mixture of animal products.

SPHINGOSINE-1-PHOSPHATE (S1P) AND PLATELET DERIVED GROWTH FACTOR

One goal for the development of an ES cell culture system for use in potential clinical applications is the elimination of serum and feeder layers and their replacement with defined components consisting of no animal products. Our laboratory has, therefore, studied the components of serum likely to be critical to ES cell growth. Thus, another approach to the propagation of human ES cells in absence of serum is the use of S1P (10 μM) and PDGF (20 ng/ml), two bioactive molecules present in serum. S1P, which is a lysophospholipid, and PDGF have pleiotropic effects on numerous cell types, such as proliferation, differentiation, and migration.[48,49] Most of S1P's effects are mediated by five specific lysophospholipid G-protein receptors: $S1P_1$, $S1P_2$, $S1P_3$, $S1P_4$, and $S1P_5$.[50] Moreover, S1P also acts as an intracellular second messenger with as yet undefined intracellular targets.[51] The different isoforms of PDGF bind two tyrosine kinase receptors, PDGFR- and PDGFR-with different affinities. Among other signaling pathways, PDGF can stimulate the sphingosine kinases (SPKs), leading to a transient increase in intracellular S1P

concentration, which is held to be responsible for PDGF-induced cell proliferation or survival in different cell types.[52]

When added to serum-free medium in the presence of a feeder cell layer, these molecules are able to maintain the human ES cells in the undifferentiated state, probably through the activation of the extracellular signal-regulated kinases (ERKs) and through the activation of the SPKs. The serum-free culture medium consisted of Dulbecco's modified Eagle's medium (without sodium pyruvate, high glucose formulation) supplemented with 1% insulin/transferrin/selenium (ITS), 0.1 mM β-mercaptoethanol, 1% nonessential amino acids, 2 mM glutamine, 25 mM Hepes, penicillin (50 U/ml), streptomycin (50 mg/ml), 10 μM S1P, and 20 ng/ml PDGF-AB (both extemporaneously prepared). Cells were passaged every 7 days. The cells remain diploid, retain markers of human ES cells, and are pluripotent as evidenced by differentiation in vitro and by formation of teratomas when grafted into immunodeprived animals. Although this technique presents the advantage of using a totally defined serum-free medium, a feeder cell layer is still required, clonal growth is very poor, and stem cell phenotype is more labile than in serum-based culture systems.

Future Prospects

To date, two different protocols are available to cultivate human ES cells in serum-free conditions. Although these developments represent important steps toward the development of robust culture methodologies for propagation of human ES cells and eventual therapeutic use, some challenges remain. Both techniques require the use of feeder cells. Neither technique allows for clonal growth at high efficiency. Neither technique has been shown to be adaptable to scale-up methodologies such as bioreactor cell production. Many experimental laboratory protocols often require large numbers of homogenous populations of stem cells; thus, even before clinical application of this technology there is an urgent need to optimize the culture conditions of human ES cells.

Such a challenge might be achieved by identifying the factors synthesized and released by the feeder cells and by the stem cells themselves and by identifying molecules produced by cells at early stages of differentiation that might influence stem cell fate. Also critical to our understanding will be dissecting the signaling pathways involved in the maintenance and self-renewal of human ES cells. The findings to date suggest that tyrosine kinase receptors and G-protein coupled receptors, probably acting through MEK and SPK, act to maintain pluripotentiality, in contrast to the role of the MEK pathway in mouse ES cells. However, there is much to be learned about how extrinsic factors regulate networks of transcriptional factors that are thought to be critical to the maintenance of the pluripotent state, such as Oct-4, nanog, and FoxD3.

A further challenge will be to understand how modifications in the culture system might affect the properties of different ES cell isolates over the long term. Although we know that the systems developed to date can support long-term cultivation of pluripotent cells with normal karyotypes, no studies have examined potential effects various culture conditions on long-term genetic stability of ES cells at a higher resolution level of analysis (microdeletion, amplification, or point mutations). We also know nothing of how culture conditions affect epigenetic stability of ES cells, and how epigenetic changes might alter the potential for a given cell line to respond to extracellular or intracellular triggers for differentiation into particular lineages. The answers to these important questions will require systematic comparison of different ES cell lines propagated under defined conditions over long periods, using appropriate assays for genetic and epigenetic stability and differentiation capacity.

REFERENCES

1. Thomson, J.A., Itskovitz-Eldor, J., Shapiro, S.S., Waknitz, M.A., Swiergiel, J.J., Marshall, V.S., and Jones, J.M. (1998). Embryonic stem cell lines derived from human blastocysts. *Science* **282**, 1145–1147.

2. Pera, M.F., Reubinoff, B., and Trounson, A. (2000). Human embryonic stem cells. *J. Cell Sci.* **113 (Pt 1)**, 5–10.

3. Reubinoff, B.E., Pera, M.F., Fong, C.Y., Trounson, A., and Bongso, A. (2000). Embryonic stem cell lines from human blastocysts: Somatic differentiation in vitro. *Nat. Biotechnol.* **18**, 399–404.

3a. Laslett et al., unpublished.

4. Robertson, E., and Bradley, A. (1986). Production of permanent cell lines from early embryos and their use in studying developmental problems. *In* "Experimental Approaches to Mammalian Embryonic Development" (J. Rossant, and R. Pedersen, Eds.), pp. 475–508. Cambridge University Press, Cambridge, UK.

5. Rizzino, A., and Sato, G. (1978). Growth of embryonal carcinoma cells in serum-free medium. *Proc. Natl. Acad. Sci. USA* **75**, 1844–1848.

6. Heath, J.K., and Rees, A.R. (1985). Growth factors in mammalian embryogenesis. *Ciba Found. Symp.* **116**, 3–22.

7. Smith, A.G., Heath, J.K., Donaldson, D.D., Wong, G.G., Moreau, J., Stahl, M., and Rogers, D. (1988). Inhibition of pluripotential embryonic stem cell differentiation by purified polypeptides. *Nature* **336**, 688–690.

8. Williams, R.L., Hilton, D.J., Pease, S., Willson, T.A., Stewart, C.L., Gearing, D.P., Wagner, E.F., Metcalf, D., Nicola, N.A., and Gough, N.M. (1988). Myeloid leukaemia inhibitory factor maintains the developmental potential of embryonic stem cells. *Nature* **336**, 684–687.

9. Burdon, T., Smith, A., and Savatier, P. (2002). Signalling, cell cycle and pluripotency in embryonic stem cells. *Trends Cell Biol.* **12**, 432–438.

10. Stewart, C.L., Kaspar, P., Brunet, L.J., Bhatt, H., Gadi, I., Kontgen, F., and Abbondanzo, S.J. (1992). Blastocyst implantation depends on maternal expression of leukaemia inhibitory factor. *Nature* **359**, 76–79.

11. Ward, C.M., Stern, P., Willington, M.A., and Flenniken, A.M. (2002). Efficient germline transmission of mouse embryonic stem cells grown in synthetic serum in the absence of a fibroblast feeder layer. *Lab. Invest.* **82**, 1765–1767.

12. Yoshida, K., Taga, T., Saito, M., Suematsu, S., Kumanogoh, A., Tanaka, T., Fujiwara, H., Hirata, M., Yamagami, T., Nakahata, T., Hirabayashi, T., Yoneda, Y., Tanaka, K., Wang, W.Z., Mori, C., Shiota, K., Yoshida, N., and Kishimoto, T. (1996). Targeted disruption of gp130, a common signal transducer for the interleukin 6 family of cytokines, leads to myocardial and hematological disorders. *Proc. Natl. Acad. Sci. USA* **93**, 407–411.

13. Chambers, I., Colby, D., Robertson, M., Nichols, J., Lee, S., Tweedie, S., and Smith, A. (2003). Functional expression cloning of Nanog, a pluripotency sustaining factor in embryonic stem cells. *Cell* **113**, 643–655.

14. Dani, C., Chambers, I., Johnstone, S., Robertson, M., Ebrahimi, B., Saito, M., Taga, T., Li, M., Burdon, T., Nichols, J., and Smith, A. (1998). Paracrine induction of stem cell renewal by LIF-deficient cells: a new ES cell regulatory pathway. *Dev. Biol.* **203**, 149–162.

15. Roach, S., Cooper, S., Bennett, W., and Pera, M.F. (1993). Cultured cell lines from human teratomas: windows into tumour growth and differentiation and early human development. *Eur. Urol.* **23**, 82–87, discussion 87–88.

16. Wiles, M.V., and Johansson, B.M. (1999). Embryonic stem cell development in a chemically defined medium. *Exp. Cell Res.* **247**, 241–248.

17. Tropepe, V., Hitoshi, S., Sirard, C., Mak, T.W., Rossant, J., and van der Kooy, D. (2001). Direct neural fate specification from embryonic stem cells: a primitive mammalian neural stem cell stage acquired through a default mechanism. *Neuron* **30**, 65–78.

18. Andrews, P.W. (1988). Human teratocarcinomas. *Biochim. Biophys. Acta* **948**, 17–36.

19. Pera, M.F., Cooper, S., Mills, J., and Parrington, J.M. (1989). Isolation and characterization of a multipotent clone of human embryonal carcinoma cells. *Differentiation* **42**, 10–23.

20. Cooper, S., and Pera, M.F. (1988). Vitronectin production by human yolk sac carcinoma cells resembling parietal endoderm. *Development* **104**, 565–574.

21. Biddle, C., Li, C.H., Schofield, P.N., Tate, V.E., Hopkins, B., Engstrom, W., Huskisson, N.S., and Graham, C.F. (1988). Insulin-like growth factors and the multiplication of Tera-2, a human teratoma-derived cell line. *J. Cell Sci.* **90 (Pt 3)**, 475–484.

22. Schofield, P.N., Granerus, M., Lee, A., Ektrom, T.J., and Engstrom, W. (1992). Concentration-dependent modulation of basic fibroblast growth factor action on multiplication and locomotion of human teratocarcinoma cells. *FEBS Lett.* **298**, 154–158.

23. Mummery, C.L., van Rooyen, M., Bracke, M., van den Eijnden-van Raaij, J., van Zoelen, E.J., and Alitalo, K. (1993). Fibroblast growth factor-mediated growth regulation and receptor expression in embryonal carcinoma and embryonic stem cells and human germ cell tumours. *Biochem. Biophys. Res. Commun.* **191**, 188–195.

24. Weima, S.M., van Rooijen, M.A., Mummery, C.L., Feyen, A., de Laat, S.W., and van Zoelen, E.J. (1990). Identification of the type-B receptor for platelet-derived growth factor in human embryonal carcinoma cells. *Exp. Cell Res.* **186**, 324–331.

25. Pera, M.F., and Herszfeld, D. (1998). Differentiation of human pluripotent teratocarcinoma stem cells induced by bone morphogenetic protein-2. *Reprod. Fertil. Dev.* **10**, 551–555.

26. Caricasole, A., Ward-van Oostwaard, D., Zeinstra, L., van den Eijnden-van Raaij, A., and Mummery, C. (2000). Bone morphogenetic proteins (BMPs) induce epithelial differentiation of NT2D1 human embryonal carcinoma cells. *Int. J. Dev. Biol.* **44**, 443–450.

27. Baldassarre, G., Romano, A., Armenante, F., Rambaldi, M., Paoletti, I., Sandomenico, C., Pepe, S., Staibano, S., Salvatore, G., De Rosa, G., Persico, M.G., and Viglietto, G. (1997). Expression of teratocarcinoma-derived growth factor-1 (TDGF-1) in testis germ cell tumors and its effects on growth and differentiation of embryonal carcinoma cell line NTERA2/D1. *Oncogene* **15**, 927–936.

28. Baldassarre, G., Tucci, M., Lembo, G., Pacifico, F.M., Dono, R., Lago, C.T., Barra, A., Bianco, C., Viglietto, G., Salomon, D., Persico, M.G. (2001). A truncated form of teratocarcinoma-derived growth factor-1 (cripto-1) mRNA expressed in human colon carcinoma cell lines and tumors. *Tumour Biol.* **22**, 286–293.

29. Lyons, K., Graycar, J.L., Lee, A., Hashmi, S., Lindquist, P.B., Chen, E.Y., Hogan, B.L., and Derynck, R. (1989). Vgr-1, a mammalian gene related to Xenopus Vg-1, is a member of the transforming growth factor beta gene superfamily. *Proc. Natl. Acad. Sci. USA* **86**, 4554–4558.

30. Caricasole, A.A., van Schaik, R.H., Zeinstra, L.M., Wierikx, C.D., van Gurp, R.J., van den Pol, M., Looijenga, L.H., Oosterhuis, J.W., Pera, M.F., Ward, A., de Bruijn, D., Kramer, P., de Jong, F.H., and van den Eijnden-van Raaij, A.J. (1998). Human growth-differentiation factor 3 (hGDF3): developmental regulation in human teratocarcinoma cell lines and expression in primary testicular germ cell tumours. *Oncogene* **16**, 95–103.

31. McPherron, A.C., and Lee, S.J. (1993). GDF-3 and GDF-9: Two new members of the transforming growth factor-beta superfamily containing a novel pattern of cysteines. *J. Biol. Chem.* **268**, 3444–3449.

32. Walsh, J., and Andrews, P.W. (2003). Expression of Wnt and Notch pathway genes in a pluripotent human embryonal carcinoma cell line and embryonic stem cell. *APMIS.* **111**, 197–210; discussion 210–211.

33. Kielman, M.F., Rindapaa, M., Gaspar, C., van Poppel, N., Breukel, C., van Leeuwen, S., Taketo, M.M., Roberts, S., Smits, R., and Fodde, R. (2002). Apc modulates embryonic stem-cell differentiation by controlling the dosage of beta-catenin signaling. *Nat. Genet.* **32**, 594–605.

34. Aubert, J., Dunstan, H., Chambers, I., and Smith, A. (2002). Functional gene screening in embryonic stem cells implicates Wnt antagonism in neural differentiation. *Nat. Biotechnol.* **20**, 1240–1245.

35. Amit, M., Margulets, V., Segev, H., Shariki, K., Laevsky, I., Coleman, R., and Itskovitz-Eldor, J. (2003). Human feeder layers for human embryonic stem cells. *Biol. Reprod.* **68**, 2150–2156.

36. Cheng, L., Hammond, H., Ye, Z., Zhan, X., and Dravid, G. (2003). Human adult marrow cells support prolonged expansion of human embryonic stem cells in culture. *Stem Cells* **21**, 131–142.

37. Hovatta, O., Mikkola, M., Gertow, K., Stromberg, A.M., Inzunza, J., Hreinsson, J., Rozell, B., Blennow, E., Andang, M., and Ahrlund-Richter, L. (2003). A culture system using human foreskin fibroblasts as feeder cells allows production of human embryonic stem cells. *Hum. Reprod.* **18**, 1404–1409.

38. Mitalipova, M., Calhoun, J., Shin, S., Wininger, D., Schulz, T., Noggle, S., Venable, A., Lyons, I., Robins, A., and Stice, S. (2003). Human embryonic stem cell lines derived from discarded embryos. *Stem Cells* **21**, 521–526.

39. Park, J.H., Kim, S.J., Oh, E.J., Moon, S.Y., Roh, S.I., Kim, C.G., and Yoon, H.S. (2003). Establishment and maintenance of human embryonic stem cells on STO, a permanently growing cell line. *Biol. Reprod.* **69**, 2007–2014.

40. Richards, M., Fong, C.Y., Chan, W.K., Wong, P.C., and Bongso, A. (2002). Human feeders support prolonged undifferentiated growth of human inner cell masses and embryonic stem cells. *Nat. Biotechnol.* **20**, 933–936.

41. Lim, J.W., and Bodnar, A. (2002). Proteome analysis of conditioned medium from mouse embryonic fibroblast feeder layers which support the growth of human embryonic stem cells. *Proteomics* **2**, 1187–1203.

41a. Pera, unpublished.

42. Pera, M.F., Andrade, J., Houssami, S., Reubinoff, B., Trounson, A., Stanley, E.G., Ward-van Oostwaard, D., and Mummery, C. (2004). Regulation of human embryonic stem cell differen-tiation by BMP-2 and its antagonist noggin. *J. Cell Sci.* **117**, 1269–1280.

43. Sato, N., Sanjuan, I.M., Heke, M., Uchida, M., Naef, F., and Brivanlou, A.H. (2003). Molecular signature of human embryonic stem cells and its comparison with the mouse. *Dev. Biol.* **260**, 404–413.

44. Amit, M., Carpenter, M.K., Inokuma, M.S., Chiu, C.P., Harris, C.P., Waknitz, M.A., Itskovitz-Eldor, J., and Thomson, J.A. (2000). Clonally derived human embryonic stem cell lines maintain pluripotency and proliferative potential for prolonged periods of culture. *Dev. Biol.* **227**, 271–278.

45. Price, P., Goldsborough, M.D., and Tilkins, M.L. (2002). Method for expanding embryonic stem cells in serum-free culture, U S Patent Application 20020076747. US Patent and Trademark Office.

46. Filipczyk, *et al.* (Unpublished).

47. Xu, C., Inokuma, M.S., Denham, J., Golds, K., Kundu, P., Gold, J.D., and Carpenter, M.K. (2001). Feeder-free growth of undifferentiated human embryonic stem cells. *Nat. Biotechnol.* **19**, 971–974.

48. Takuwa, Y., Takuwa, N., and Sugimoto, N. (2002). The edg family g protein-coupled receptors for lysophospholipids: Their signaling properties and biological activities. *J. Biochem. (Tokyo)* **131**, 767–771.

49. Heldin, C.H., and Westermark, B. (1999). Mechanism of action and in vivo role of platelet-derived growth factor. *Physiol. Rev.* **79**, 1283-1316.

50. Chun, J., Goetzl, E.J., Hla, T., Igarashi, Y., Lynch, K.R., Moolenaar, W., Pyne, S., and Tigyi, G. (2002). International Union of Pharmacology. XXXIV. Lysophospholipid receptor nomenclature. *Pharmacol. Rev.* **54**, 265–269.

51. Payne, S.G., Milstien, S., and Spiegel, S. (2002). Sphingosine-1-phosphate: dual messenger functions. *FEBS Lett.* **531**, 54–57.

52. Olivera, A., and Spiegel, S. (1993). Sphingosine-1-phosphate as second messenger in cell proliferation induced by PDGF and FCS mitogens. *Nature* **365**, 557–560.

52

Feeder-free Culture

Chunhui Xu and Melissa K. Carpenter

Introduction

Because of their remarkable proliferative capacity and differentiation potential, human embryonic stem (hES) cells may provide a source of cells for cell therapies, drug screening, and functional genomics applications. Derivation of hES cell lines has been accomplished in several laboratories by culturing cells from the inner cell mass of preimplantation embryos on mouse or human embryonic feeder cells.[1-4] In these conditions, the cells are maintained in the undifferentiated state and show stability in long-term culture.[5,6] hES cells have been maintained on feeders in media containing serum or serum replacement supplemented with basic fibroblast growth factor (bFGF). In addition, we have found that hES cells maintained on or off feeders express integrins $\alpha 6$ and $\beta 1$, which may form a laminin-specific receptor, suggesting that the cells may interact with matrix components.[7] These findings indicate that hES cells require both soluble factors and matrix proteins.

In our laboratory, we have developed methods for maintaining the hES cells in feeder-free conditions. In this culture system, hES cells can be maintained on Matrigel or laminin-coated plates in serum-free medium conditioned by mouse embryonic fibroblast (MEF) feeders,[7] as shown in Fig. 52–1. Cells maintained using these feeder-free conditions retain a normal karyotype and a stable proliferation rate; express SSEA-4, TRA-1-60, TRA-1-80, alkaline phosphatase, hTERT, and OCT-4; and have the capacity to differentiate into cell types representing the three germ layers both *in vitro* and *in vivo*.[7] Furthermore, the cells maintain these features even after long-term culture for up to 700 population-doublings.[8] The cells maintained in feeder-free conditions can be induced to differentiate using specific culture conditions into neural progenitors,[9] cardiomyocytes,[10] trophoblast,[11] hepatocyte-like cells,[12] oligodendrocytes,[13] and hematopoietic progenitors.[14] In addition, feeder-free hES cells can be genetically modified by transfection with plasmids[15,16] or infection with lentiviral vectors.[17] In this chapter, we present in the first three sections detailed protocols for the maintenance of hES cells in feeder-free conditions and then briefly describe in the fourth section methods for the characterization of hES cells.

Handbook of Stem Cells
Volume 1

Materials for Feeder-free hES Cell Culture

SOLUTIONS AND MEDIA

Stock Solutions

1. *Collagenase IV solution (200 U/ml).* Dissolve 20,000 units of collagenase IV (Gibco/Invitrogen, Cat. No. 17104-019) in 100 ml knockout Dulbecco's modified Eagle's medium (DMEM). Add all components to a 250 ml filter unit (0.22 μM, Corning, cellulose acetate, low protein-binding) and filter. Aliquot and store at −20°C until use. Note: In our hands, 200 units/ml is usually 1 mg/ml.
2. DMEM, high-glucose, without glutamine (Gibco/Invitrogen, Cat. No. 11965-092).
3. Dimethyl sulfoxide (DMSO, Sigma, Cat. No. D2650).
4. Fetal bovine serum (FBS, Hyclone, Cat. No. SH30071-03).
5. *Gelatin (0.5%).* Add 100 ml of 2% gelatin (Sigma, Cat. No. G1393) and 300 ml of water for embryo transfer (Sigma, Cat. No. W1503) into a 500-ml filter unit (0.22 μM, Corning, cellulose acetate, low protein-binding) and filter. Store at 4°C.
6. L-glutamine solution (200 mM, Gibco/Invitrogen, Cat. No. 25030-081). Make aliquots of 10 ml and store at −20°C.
7. *Human basic fibroblast growth factor, recombinant (hbFGF, 10 μg/ml).* Dissolve 10 μg hbFGF (Gibco/Invitrogen, Cat. No. 13256-029) in 1 ml PBS with 0.2% BSA (Fraction V, Sigma, Cat. No. A9576). Filter the solution using a 0.22-μM, Corning, cellulose acetate, low protein-binding filter. When handling hbFGF, prewet all pipette tips, tubes, and the filter with PBS + 0.2% BSA. hbFGF is very sticky, and this will prevent some loss of the bFGF. Store stock at −20°C or −80°C (for long-term storage, keep stocks at −80°C). Store thawed aliquots at 4°C for up to 1 month.
8. Knockout DMEM (Gibco/Invitrogen, Cat. No. 10829-018).
9. Knockout serum replacement (Gibco/Invitrogen, Cat. No. 10828-028).
10. Laminin (Sigma, Cat. No. L-6274).
11. *Matrigel.* Either growth factor-reduced Matrigel (Becton Dickinson, Cat. No. 356231) or regular Matrigel (Becton Dickinson, Cat. No. 354234) can be used for coating plates. To prepare Matrigel aliquots, slowly thaw Matrigel at 4°C overnight to avoid the formation of a gel. Add 10 ml of cold knockout DMEM to the bottle containing 10 ml Matrigel. Keep the mixture on ice, mix well with a pipette, aliquot 1–2 ml into each prechilled tube, and store at −20°C.

12. *β-mercaptoethanol (1.43 M).* 14.3 M β-mercaptoethanol (Sigma, Cat. No. M 7522) is diluted 1:10 in PBS and stored at −20°C or −80°C in 40-μl aliquots. Aliquots are thawed and used immediately; do not reuse.

13. Nonessential amino acids (10 mM) (Gibco/Invitrogen, Cat. No. 11140-050).

14. Sterile PBS without Ca²⁺Mg²⁺ (Gibco/Invitrogen, Cat. No. 14190-144).

15. Trypsin–EDTA (0.05% trypsin–0.53-mM EDTA) (Gibco/Invitrogen, Cat. No. 25300-054).

Media

1. *MEF medium.* Add all medium components listed here to a 500-ml filter unit (0.22 μM, Corning, cellulose acetate,

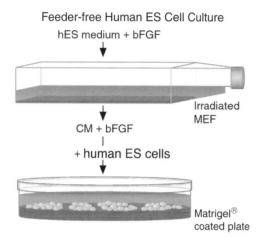

Feeder-free Human ES Cell Culture

hES medium + bFGF

Irradiated MEF

CM + bFGF

+ human ES cells

Matrigel® coated plate

Characterization of Human ES Cells

Morphology
Markers
  • OCT4 and hTERT
  • Surface markers
Telomerase activity
Karyotyping
Proliferation
Differentiation
  • *In vitro* differentiation
  • Teratoma formation

Figure 52–1. *Feeder-free hES culture. MEF cells are irradiated to 40 Gy and seeded into a flask for preparation of conditioned medium (CM). After at least five hours, the medium is exchanged with hES medium. CM is collected daily and supplemented with an additional 4–8 ng/ml of hbFGF before addition to the hES cells on Matrigel or laminin. These cultures can then be assessed for the assays suggested in the table.*

low protein-binding) and filter. Store at 4°C and use within 1 month.
  a. 450 ml DMEM
  b. 50 ml FBS (final concentration 10%, heat inactivated)
  c. 5 ml 200 mM L-glutamine (final concentration 2 mM)

2. *hES serum-free medium.* Add all medium components listed here to a 500-ml filter unit (0.22 μM, Corning, cellulose acetate, low protein-binding) and filter. Store at 4°C for no longer than 2 weeks.
  a. 400 ml knockout DMEM
  b. 100 ml knockout serum replacement
  c. 5 ml nonessential amino acids (final concentration 1%)
  d. 2.5 ml 200 mM L-glutamine (final concentration of 1 mM)
  e. 35 μl 0.14 M β-mercaptoethanol (final concentration of 0.1 mM)

3. *Differentiation medium.* The differentiation medium is made by replacing knockout serum replacement with 20% FBS (not heat inactivated) in the hES serum-free medium described previously.

4. *Cryopreservation medium.* Filter the components listed here using a 100-ml filter unit (0.22 μM, Corning, cellulose acetate, low protein-binding), then add 20 ml of DMSO.
  a. 40 ml knockout DMEM (for ES cells) or 60 ml DMEM (for MEFs)
  b. 40 ml knockout serum replacement (for ES cells) or 20 ml FBS (for MEFs)

TISSUE CULTURE PLATES AND FLASKS

We use six-well plates (Falcon, Cat. No. 3046) for ES culture; a T75 flask (Corning, Cat. No. 430641), T150 flask (Corning, Cat. No. 430825), and T225 flask (Corning, Cat. No. 431082) for MEF culture; six-well low-attachment plates (Corning, Cat. No. 29443-030) for embryoid bodies (EBs); and four-well plates for thawing hES cells (Nunc, Cat. No. 176740).

INCUBATORS

All cells are maintained under sterile conditions in a humidified incubator in a 5% CO_2–95% air atmosphere at 37°C.

Preparation of Conditioned Medium from MEFs

HARVESTING MEFS

This protocol is modified from "Teratocarcinomas and Embryonic Stem Cells: A Practical Approach."[18] In our laboratory, we do not add antibiotics to any of our culture media.

1. Anesthetize a 13-day pregnant mouse (we use CF-1 mice) using isoflurane or halothane. When the mouse is anesthetized, perform a cervical dislocation.

2. Saturate the abdomen with 70% ethanol and pull back the skin to expose the peritoneum. With sterile tools, cut open the peritoneal wall to expose the uterine horns. Remove the uterine horns and place them in a 10-cm dish. Wash three times in 10 ml sterile PBS without Ca²⁺Mg²⁺.

3. Cut open each embryonic sac with scissors and release the embryos into the dish.

4. Using two pairs of watchmaker's forceps, remove the placenta and membranes from the embryo. Once they have been removed, dissect out the viscera. Place the embryos in a clean Petri dish and wash three times with 10 ml sterile PBS.

5. Transfer two embryos to a 35-mm culture dish. With curved iris scissors or a sterile razor blade, **finely** mince the tissue.

6. Add 2 ml trypsin–EDTA to the minced tissue and incubate the tissue for 5–10 minutes at 37°C.

7. Inactivate trypsin–EDTA by adding 5 ml MEF medium and transfer the contents to a 15-ml tube.

8. Dissociate cells by trituration. Allow larger clumps to settle to bottom of the tube, and remove and plate the supernatant in a 15 ml MEF medium. We plate approximately two embryos in each T150 flask. Rock the flask back and forth to ensure an even distribution of the cells and place in the incubator.

9. Split at 1:2 when cells are 80–85% confluent. This is usually the next day in our laboratory.

10. When cells reach 80–85% confluence at this passage (passage 1), they can be maintained by splitting 1:2 every other day (see the section "Thawing and Maintaining MEFs") and used for feeders or can be frozen (see the section "Cryopreservation of MEFs").

11. As with any new cell in the laboratory, a representative sample should be tested for mycoplasma and sterility.

CRYOPRESERVING MEFs

1. Prelabel all cryovials with the following information: cell line, passage number, number or surface area of cells frozen, date, and initials.

2. Aspirate the MEF medium from the flask.

3. Wash the cells once in PBS without $Ca^{2+}Mg^{2+}$ (2–3 ml/T75 and 5–10 ml/T150).

4. Add trypsin–EDTA to the cells (1.0 ml/T75 and 1.5–2.0 ml/T150), and rock the flask back and forth to evenly distribute the solution. Incubate for approximately 5 minutes at 37°C.

5. Detach the cells from the plate by pipetting or tapping the flask against the heel of your hand.

6. Neutralize the trypsin–EDTA by adding MEF medium (5 ml/T75 and 10 ml/T150).

7. Gently pipette the cell mixture to break up clumps of cells. If clumps remain, transfer the suspension to a 50 ml tube and allow the chunks to settle out.

8. Perform a cell count of the cell suspension to determine the number of vials needed. We usually freeze 10 million –20 million cells per milliliter in each vial.

9. Pellet the cells by centrifugation for five minutes at $300 \times g$.

10. Resuspend the pellet in 0.5 ml of MEF medium containing 20% FBS per vial—that is, one half the final volume required for freezing.

11. Dropwise, add an equivalent volume (0.5 ml per vial) of cryopreservation medium and mix. The resulting DMSO concentration should be 10%.

12. Place 1 ml of cell mixture into each freezing vial.

13. Rapidly transfer the cells to a Nalgene freezing container (Fisher, Cat. No. 15-350-50) and place at −70°C overnight. Transfer the cells to liquid nitrogen the next day for long-term storage. Alternatively, cells can be frozen using a controlled-rate freezer and transferred to liquid nitrogen at the completion of the freeze cycle.

THAWING AND MAINTAINING MEFs

1. Remove a vial of MEF from the liquid nitrogen storage bank.

2. Do a quick thaw in a 37°C water bath. Carefully swirl the vial in a 37°C water bath. To avoid potential contamination, do not immerse the vial above the level of the cap.

3. When just a small crystal of ice remains in the tube, sterilize the outside of the vial with 70% ethanol.

4. Remove the contents of the vial by gently pipetting the cell suspension up and down once, and transfer them to a 15 ml conical tube.

5. Slowly add 10 ml warm MEF medium to the tube dropwise (this will reduce osmotic shock).

6. Centrifuge the cell suspension at $300 \times g$ for 5 minutes.

7. Remove the supernatant.

8. Resuspend the cell pellet in 10 ml (T75) or 20 ml (T150) of culture medium, and transfer to a flask. The plating density will need to be determined for each lot of MEF. We plate ~5×10^4 to 1.5×10^5 cells/cm^2.

9. Place in a 37°C incubator.

10. Replace the medium the next day and split the MEFs 2 to 3 days after thawing, when they become 80–85% confluent.

11. The MEFs are expanded by splitting 1:2 every other day with trypsin. It is important to keep cells subconfluent so that they will not "contact inhibit." In our laboratory, MEFs are only used through passage 5.

IRRADIATING AND PLATING MEFs

1. Coat the flasks or plates with gelatin by adding the appropriate volume of 0.5% gelatin (15 ml/T225, 10 ml/T150, 5 ml/T75, and 1 ml/well of six-well plates) and by incubating at 37°C for at least 1 hour. Use the flasks or plates 1 hour to 1 day after coating. Remove the gelatin solution immediately before use.

2. Prepare MEFs for irradiation by aspirating the medium from MEF culture.

3. Wash the cells once in PBS without Ca^{2+}/Mg^{2+} (2–3 ml/T75 and 5–10 ml/T150).

4. Add trypsin–EDTA (1.0 ml/T75 and 1.5 ml/T150), and incubate at 37°C until cells are rounded up (usually 3–10 minutes). To loosen cells, either tap the flask against the heel of your hand or pipette them off.

5. Add 9 ml of MEF medium for T150, transfer the cell suspension into a 15-ml conical tube, and gently triturate several times to dissociate the cells.

6. Perform a cell count using a hemacytometer.

7. Irradiate the cell suspension at 40–80 Gy. This number is variable among fibroblast sources. The goal is to stop proliferation without damaging the cells.

8. Spin down cells at $300 \times g$ for 5 minutes and discard the supernatant.

9. Resuspend the cells in 10–30 ml of MEF medium. Plate at 56,000 cells/cm² for cultures to be used for conditioned medium (CM). The final volumes should be 3 ml/well for a six-well plate, 10 ml/T75, 20 ml/T150, and 50 ml/T225.

10. When placing the plate or flask in the incubator, gently shake the plate left to right and back to front to obtain an even distribution of cells. Do not swirl the plate or flask, as all cells will accumulate in the center of the dish.

11. Irradiated MEFs can be used 5 hours to 7 days after plating for CM production.

PREPARING CM

1. Plate irradiated MEFs at 56,000 cells/cm² in MEF medium as described previously. The final volumes should be 3 ml/well for a six-well plate, 10 ml/T75, 20 ml/T150, and 50 ml/T225.

2. To condition the medium, replace the MEF medium with hES medium (0.5 ml/cm²) supplemented with 4 ng/ml hbFGF (0.4 ml/cm²) 1 day before use.

3. Collect CM from feeder flasks or plates after overnight incubation, and add an additional 8 ng/ml hbFGF. (When using unfiltered hbFGF, add 4 ng/ml.)

4. Add fresh hES serum replacement medium containing 4 ng/ml hbFGF (0.4 ml/cm²) to the feeders.

5. The MEFs can be used for 1 week, with CM collection once every day.

STORING CM

For convenience, CM can be generated and stored prior to use.

1. Collect CM daily as described previously and store at 4°C from day 1 to 7.

2. Pool CM and filter through a 500 ml filter unit (0.22 μM, Corning, cellulose acetate, low protein-binding).

3. Stored pooled CM at −20°C for up to 5 months.

4. Thaw CM at 37°C before using. Store CM at 4°C and use within 1 week after thaw. Note: Do not allow CM to sit at 37°C for prolonged periods.

Culture of hES Cells on Matrigel or Laminin in CM

PREPARATION OF MATRIGEL-COATED PLATES

1. Slowly thaw Matrigel aliquots at 4°C for at least 2 hours to avoid the formation of a gel.

2. Dilute the Matrigel aliquots 1:15 in cold knockout DMEM (for a final dilution of 1:30).

3. Add 1 ml of Matrigel solution to coat each well of a six-well plate.

4. Incubate the plates for 1 hour at RT or at least overnight at 4°C. The plates with Matrigel solution can be stored at 4°C for 1 week.

5. Remove Matrigel solution immediately before use.

PREPARATION OF LAMININ-COATED PLATES

1. Slowly thaw the laminin at 4°C to avoid the formation of a gel.

2. Dilute in PBS to a final concentration of 20 μg/ml.

3. Add 1 ml laminin solution to each well to coat six-well plates.

4. Incubate the plate for 1 hour at RT or at least overnight at 4°C. The plates with laminin solution can be stored at 4°C for 1 week.

5. Wash the plate with knockout DMEM before introducing cells.

PASSAGE OF hES CELLS ON MATRIGEL OR LAMININ

1. Aspirate the medium from hES cells, and add 1 ml of 200 units/ml collagenase IV per well of a six-well plate.

2. Incubate cells for 5–10 minutes at 37°C. Incubation time will vary among batches of collagenase; therefore, determine the appropriate incubation time by examining the colonies. Stop incubation when the edges of the colonies start to pull from the plate.

3. Aspirate the collagenase, and gently wash once with 2-ml PBS.

4. Add 2 ml of CM into each well.

5. Gently scrape the cells with a cell scraper or a 10-ml pipette to collect most of the cells from the well, and transfer cells into a 15-ml tube.

6. Dissociate the cells into small clusters (50–500 cells) by gently pipetting. Do not triturate the cells to a single-cell suspension.

7. Remove the Matrigel or laminin-containing solution from the previously prepared plates.

8. Seed the cells into each well of the Matrigel or laminin-coated plates. The final volume of medium should be 4 ml per well. In this system, the hES cells are maintained at high density. At confluence (usually 1 week in culture) the cells will be 300,000–500,000 cells/cm². We find that the optimal split ratio is 1:3 to 1:6. Using these ratios, the seeding density is 50,000–150,000 cells/cm².

9. Return the plate to the incubator. Be sure to gently shake the plate left to right and back to front to obtain even distribution of cells (do not swirl the dish, as the cells will collect in the middle of the dish).

10. The day after seeding, undifferentiated cells are visible as small colonies. Single cells between the colonies will begin to differentiate. As the cells proliferate, the colonies will become large and compact, taking most of the surface area of the culture dish (Fig. 52–2).

DAILY MAINTENANCE OF FEEDER-FREE CULTURE

1. Collect CM from the feeders and filter using a 0.22-μm filter. Alternatively, frozen CM can be thawed and used within a week.

2. When feeding cells, only prepare the amount of medium needed each time. Place this aliquot in a 37°C water bath until warm. Use immediately. Do not heat the entire bottle of medium, as the knockout DMEM and knockout serum replacement do not tolerate repeated warming and cooling.

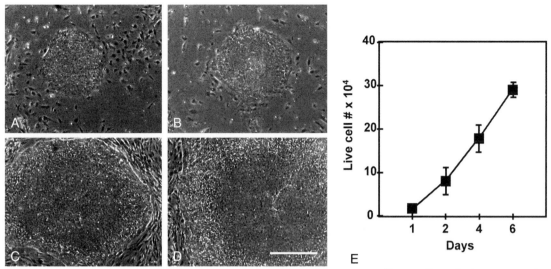

Figure 52-2. *Growth of hES cells in feeder-free conditions.* phase images of H7 (passage 31) undifferentiated hES cell colonies maintained in feeder-free conditions were taken (A and B) 2 days and (C and D) 5 days after seeding. Bar = 200 μm. (E) Proliferation of H7 cells (passage 24) was measured by counting live cells at various days after seeding. H7 hES cells were dissociated with collagenase IV, resuspended in CM, and plated into Matrigel-coated 24-well plates. Cells were harvested with trypsin and counted at days 2, 4, and 6 after seeding. Each point on the graph represents the mean ± standard deviation of cell counts for 3 separate wells.

3. Add hbFGF to CM at a final concentration of 8 ng/ml (4 ng/ml if using unfiltered hbFGF).

4. Feed the hES cells with 4 ml CM supplemented with hbFGF per well of a six-well plate daily. We find that one feeding can be skipped at day 2 or 3 after splitting.

5. Passage when cells are 100% confluent. At this time, the undifferentiated cells should cover ~80% of the surface area. The cells between the colonies of undifferentiated cells appear to be stroma-like cells (Fig. 52-2). The colonies (but not the stroma-like cells) show positive immunoreactivity for SSEA-4, Tra-1-60, Tra-1-81, and alkaline phosphatase.

FREEZING hES CELLS

1. Treat the cells with 200 U/ml collagenase IV for 5–10 minutes at 37°C (until the edges of the colonies curl). Remove the collagenase and add 2 ml hES medium per well.

2. With a 5-ml pipette, gently pipette and scrape colonies from the plate. Add the cell suspension to a 15 ml centrifuge tube and **gently** break up the colonies. It is important to be gentle in this step, as larger clusters seem to result in a better yield upon thaw. Ideally, colonies meant for freezing are left slightly larger than they would be for splitting.

3. Centrifuge for 5 minutes at $300 \times g$.

4. Resuspend pellet (gently) at 1×10^6 in 0.5-ml hES serum-free medium containing 20% knockout serum replacement per vial. (This is half the final volume required for freezing.)

5. Dropwise, add an equivalent volume (0.5 ml per vial) of cryopreservation medium and mix. The final DMSO concentration is 10%.

6. Place 1.0 ml of cell mixture in each freezing vial.

7. Rapidly transfer the cells to a Nalgene freezing container

(Fisher, Cat. No. 15-350-50), and place immediately at −70°C overnight (do not leave cells in DMSO at room temperature for long periods of time). Transfer cells to liquid nitrogen the next day for long-term storage. Alternatively, cells can be frozen using a controlled-rate freezer and transferred to liquid nitrogen at the end of the freeze cycle.

THAWING hES CELLS

1. Remove a vial of hES cells from the liquid nitrogen storage tank.

2. Thaw a cryovial by gently swirling it in a 37°C water bath until only a small ice-crystal pellet remains in the tube, being careful not to submerge the cryovial.

3. Sterilize the outside of the cryovial in 70% ethanol.

4. Remove the contents of the vial very gently and transfer the cells into a 15 ml conical centrifuge tube.

5. Slowly, add 10 ml of warm CM or hES cell medium dropwise (to reduce osmotic shock). While adding the medium, mix the cells in the tube by gently tapping the tube with a finger.

6. Centrifuge at $150 \times g$ for 5 minutes.

7. Resuspend in 0.5–1.0 ml of CM, and add 0.5 ml per well of a four-well plate precoated with Matrigel.

8. Change the medium daily with CM. It may take 2 weeks before the cells are ready to be expanded.

Characterization of Feeder-free hES Cell Cultures

hES cells express several glycoproteins and glycolipids initially identified on human embryonic carcinoma cells.[1–4,6,7,15,19] In addition, hES cells express OCT-4, a POU transcription factor expressed by early embryos, ES and embryonic germ cells,[2,6,7,15] and hTERT, the catalytic component of telomerase.[7,15] Together, these are a panel of markers that have been associated with pluripotent cells and specifically with hES cells.[6] We have assessed expression of these markers in feeder-free cultures and have found similar expression patterns to hES cells maintained on feeders.[7] In addition, we have compared the properties of four separate hES cell lines[20] and have evaluated these cells maintained in long-term cultures.[8] In our laboratory, we typically evaluate (1) expression of undifferentiated cell markers such as OCT-4, hTERT, SSEA-4, TRA-1-60, TRA-1-81, and alkaline phosphatase; (2) telomerase activity; (3) karyotype; (4) proliferation rate; (5) *in vitro* differentiation capacity; and (6) teratoma formation.

QUANTITATIVE RT-PCR ANALYSIS OF OCT-4 AND hTERT

1. Harvest cells by adding 350–700 µl of lysis buffer to each well of the six-well plate (Qiagen, Valencia, CA), and isolate RNA using the Qiagen RNeasy (Qiagen, Valencia, CA) kit, following the tissue isolation procedure with the QiaShredder (Qiagen, Valencia, CA).
2. Prior to reverse transcription-polymerase chain reaction (RT-PCR) analysis, treat the RNA samples with DNase I to remove contaminating genomic DNA.
3. Set up TaqMan one-step RT-PCR using a master mix (Applied Biosystems, Foster City, CA) and specific primers and probes for OCT-4 (forward GAAACCCACACT-GCAGCAGA, reverse CACATCCTTCTCGAGCCCA, and probe FAM-CAGCCACATCGCCCAGCAGC-TAM) and hTERT (purchase from Applied Biosystems Part No. 4319447F). The reaction mixture contains 1X RT-Master Mix, 300 nM for each primer, 80 nM of probe, and approximately 50 ng of total RNA in nuclease-free water.
4. Perform real-time RT-PCR on the ABI Prism 7700 Sequence Detection System (Applied Biosystems, Foster City, CA). The reaction was conducted under the following conditions: reverse transcription at 48°C for 30 minutes, denaturation and AmpliTaq gold activation at 95°C for 10 minutes, and amplification for 40 cycles at 95°C for 15 seconds and 60°C for 1 minute.
5. Set up and run RT-PCR for the 18S ribosomal RNA as a control using a kit for TaqMan ribosomal RNA control reagents (Applied Biosystems, Foster City, CA) according to the manufacturer's instructions.
6. Analyze reactions using the ABI Prism 7700 Sequence Detection System. Relative quantitation of gene expression among multiple samples can be achieved by normalization against endogenous 18S ribosomal RNA using the $\Delta\Delta C_T$ method described in ABI User Bulletin #2, Relative Quantitation of Gene Expression, 1997.

FLOW CYTOMETRY ANALYSIS OF SURFACE MARKERS

1. When hES cell cultures reach confluence, remove the culture medium and wash with PBS.
2. Dissociate the cells by incubating with 0.5 mM EDTA in PBS at 37°C for 5–10 minutes.

3. Resuspend the cells to about 5×10^5 cells in 50 µl diluent containing 0.1% BSA in PBS for each test.
4. Add 50 µl/test of primary antibodies—IgG isotype control (0.5 µl/test) for SSEA-1 and SSEA-4; IgM isotype control (1:20) for TRA-1-60 and TRA-1-81; and SSEA-1 (1:20), SSEA-4 (1:40), TRA-1-60 (1:80), and TRA-1-81 (1:160) diluted in the diluent—at 37°C for 30 minutes. In our laboratory, the antibodies against SSEA-1 and SSEA-4 were obtained from the Developmental Studies Hybridoma Bank (University of Iowa, Iowa City). TRA-1-60 and TRA-1-81 were a gift from Dr. Peter Andrews (University of Sheffield, U.K.). All of these antibodies are now available from Chemicon.
5. After washing with the diluent, incubate the cells with rat antimouse κ-chain antibodies conjugated with phycoerythrin (Becton Dickinson, San Jose, CA) at 4°C for 30 minutes.
6. Wash the cells and analyze on FACScalibur Flow Cytometer (Becton Dickinson, San Jose, CA) using CellQuest software.

IMMUNOCYTOCHEMISTRY OF SURFACE MARKERS

1. Passage the hES cells into Matrigel or laminin-coated chamber slides and maintain the cells in CM for 2–7 days.
2. Remove the medium and incubate the cells with primary antibodies—SSEA-1 (1:10), SSEA-4 (1:20), TRA-1-60 (1:40), and TRA-1-81 (1:80)—diluted in warm knockout DMEM at 37°C for 30 minutes.
3. Wash the cells with warm knockout DMEM.
4. Fix the cells in 2% paraformaldehyde in PBS for 15 minutes.
5. Wash the cells with PBS (twice, 5 minutes each).
6. Block the cells by incubation in 5% normal goat serum (NGS) in PBS at RT for 30 minutes
7. Incubate with the fluorescein isothiocyanate (FITC)-conjugated goat antimouse IgG (Sigma) diluted 1:125 in PBS containing 1% NGS at RT for 30 minutes.
8. Wash the cells with PBS (three times, 5 minutes each), stain with 4′,6-diamidino-2-phenylindole (DAPI), and mount the slides.

DETECTION OF ALKALINE PHOSPHATASE

1. Passage the hES cells into Matrigel or laminin-coated chamber slides and maintain the cells in CM for 2–7 days.
2. Remove the culture medium, wash with PBS, fix the cells with 4% paraformaldehyde for 15 minutes, and wash with PBS.
3. Incubate the cells with an alkaline phosphatase substrate (Vector Laboratories, Inc., Burlingame, CA) at RT in the dark for 1 hour.
4. Rinse the slides gently once for 2–5 minutes in 100% ethanol before mounting.

FORMATION OF TERATOMAS

1. When cells reach confluence, harvest the cells by incubating them in 200 units/ml of collagenase IV at 37°C for 10 minutes. Be careful not to dissociate to single cells.
2. Wash the cells in PBS, resuspend them at 1×10^8/ml, and store the cells in PBS.

3. Inject the cells intramuscularly into severe-combined immunodeficiency, beige mice (~5 × 10⁶ cells in 50 μl per site).

4. Monitor teratoma formation. After teratomas become visible (usually 70–90 days in our hands), they are excised and processed for histological analysis.

FORMATION OF EBS

In vitro differentiation can be induced by culturing the hES cells in suspension to form EBs. We have evaluated the differentiation of hES cells into neurons, cardiomyocytes, and hepatocyte-like cells by using EBs generated with the following procedure:

1. Aspirate the medium from the hES cells, add 1 ml/well of collagenase IV (200 U/ml) into six-well plates, and incubate at 37°C for 5 minutes.

2. Aspirate the collagenase IV and wash once with 2 ml PBS.

3. Add 2 ml of differentiation medium into each well.

4. Scrape the cells with a cell scraper or pipette and transfer them to one well of a low-attachment plate (1:1 split). Cells should be collected in clumps. Add 2 ml of differentiation medium to each well for total volume of 4 ml per well. Depending on the density of the hES cells, the split ratio for this procedure can vary.

5. After overnight culture in suspension, ES cells form floating aggregates known as EBs.

6. To change the medium, transfer the EBs into a 15 ml tube and let the aggregates settle for 5 minutes. Aspirate the supernatant, replace with fresh differentiation medium (4 ml/well), and transfer the EBs to low-attachment six-well plates for further culture.

7. Change the medium every 2–3 days. During the first few days, the EBs are small with irregular outlines; they increase in size by day 4 in suspension. The EBs can be maintained in suspension for more than 10 days. Alternatively, EBs at different stages can be transferred to adherent tissue culture plates for further induction of differentiation.

IMMUNOCYTOCHE1MICAL ANALYSIS OF DIFFERENTIATED CULTURES

To identify specific cell types in the differentiated culture, immunocytochemical or RT-PCR analysis can be used to detect cell type-specific markers. Here are a few examples of immunocytochemical analysis of β-tubulin III for neurons, alpha fetoprotein (AFP) for endoderm cells, and cardiac troponin I (cTnI) for cardiomyocytes:

1. For β-tubulin III or AFP analysis, fix EB outgrowth cultures in 4% paraformaldehyde at RT for 20 minutes followed by permeabilization for 2 minutes in 100% ethanol. For cTnI staining, fix cells in methanol:acetone (3:1) for 20 minutes at −20°C.

2. After fixation, wash the cells twice with PBS (5 minutes each).

3. Block with 10% NGS in PBS at RT for 2 hours or at 4°C overnight.

4. Incubate the cells at RT for 2 hours with a monoclonal antibody against β-tubulin III, AFP (Sigma) diluted 1:500,

or cTnI (Spectral Diagnostic INC, Toronto, Ontario, Canada) diluted 1:450 in 1% NGS in PBS.

5. Wash the cells three times with PBS on a shaker, 5–10 minutes/washing.

6. Incubate the cells with FITC-conjugated goat antimouse IgG (Sigma) diluted 1:128 in PBS containing 1% NGS at RT for 30 minutes.

7. Wash the cells three times with PBS on a shaker, 5–10 minutes/washing.

8. Mount slides with Vectashield mounting media for fluorescence with DAPI.

ACKNOWLEDGMENTS

We appreciate the members of the stem cell team at Geron Corporation for providing technical details and critical review. We thank Drs. Jane Lebkowski and Calvin Harley for insightful discussions and review of the manuscript.

REFERENCES

1. Thomson, J.A., Itskovitz-Eldor, J., Shapiro, S.S., Waknitz, M.A., Swiergiel, J.J., Marshall, V.S., and Jones, J.M. (1998). Embryonic stem cell lines derived from human blastocysts. *Science* **282,** 1145–1147.

2. Reubinoff, B.E., Pera, M.F., Fong, C.Y., Trounson, A., and Bongso, A. (2000). Embryonic stem cell lines from human blastocysts: somatic differentiation *in vitro*. *Nat. Biotechnol.* **18,** 399–404.

3. Amit, M., and Itskovitz-Eldor, J. (2002). Derivation and spontaneous differentiation of human embryonic stem cells. *J. Anat.* **200,** 225–232.

4. Richards, M., Fong, C.Y., Chan, W.K., Wong, P.C., and Bongso, A. (2002). Human feeders support prolonged undifferentiated growth of human inner cell masses and embryonic stem cells. *Nat. Biotechnol.* **20,** 933–936.

5. Amit, M., Carpenter, M.K., Inokuma, M.S., Chiu, C.P., Harris, C.P., Waknitz, M.A., Itskovitz-Eldor, J., and Thomson, J.A. (2000). Clonally derived human embryonic stem cell lines maintain pluripotency and proliferative potential for prolonged periods of culture. *Dev. Biol.* **227,** 271–278.

6. Carpenter, M.K., Rosler, E., and Rao, M.S. (2003). Characterization and differentiation of human embryonic stem cells. *Clon. Stem Cells* **5,** 79–88.

7. Xu, C., Inokuma, M.S., Denham, J., Golds, K., Kundu, P., Gold, J.D., and Carpenter, M.K. (2001). Feeder-free growth of undifferentiated human embryonic stem cells. *Nat. Biotechnol.* **19,** 971–974.

8. Rosler, E.S., Fisk, G.J., Ares, X., Irving, J., Miura, T., Rao, M.S., and Carpenter, M.K. (2004). Long-term culture of human embryonic stem cells in feeder-free culture. *Devel Dyn.* **229,** 259-274.

9. Carpenter, M.K., Inokuma, M.S., Denham, J., Mujtaba, T., Chiu, C.P., and Rao, M.S. (2001). Enrichment of neurons and neural precursors from human embryonic stem cells. *Exp. Neurol.* **172,** 383–397.

10. Xu, C., Police, S., Rao, N., and Carpenter, M.K. (2002). Characterization and enrichment of cardiomyocytes derived from human embryonic stem cells. *Circ. Res.* **91,** 501–508.

11. Xu, R.H., Chen, X., Li, D.S., Li, R., Addicks, G.C., Glennon, C., Zwaka, T.P., and Thomson, J.A. (2002). BMP4 initiates human embryonic stem cell differentiation to trophoblast. *Nat. Biotechnol.* **20,** 1261–1264.

12. Rambhatla L., Chiu, C.P., Kundu, P., Peng, Y., and Carpenter, M.K. (2003). Generation of hepatocyte-like cells from human embryonic stem cells. *Cell Transplant.* **12,** 1-11.

13. Nistor, I.G., Totoiu, M.O., Haque, N., Carpenter, M.K., and Keirstead, H.S. (Submitted). Generation of high-purity oligodendrocyte cultures from human embryonic stem cells.

14. Chadwick, K., Wang, D., Li, L., Menendez, P., Murdoch, B., Rouleau, A., and Bhatia, M. (2003). Human embryonic stem cell differentiation toward the hematopoietic lineage in response to cytokines and BMP-4. *Blood* **102,** 906–915.

15. Lebkowski, J.S., Gold, J., Xu, C., Funk, W., Chiu, C.P., and Carpenter, M.K. (2001). Human embryonic stem cells: culture, differentiation, and genetic modification for regenerative medicine applications. *Cancer J.* **7(Suppl. 2),** S83–S93.

16. Zwaka, T.P., and Thomson, J.A. (2003). Homologous recombination in human embryonic stem cells. *Nat. Biotechnol.* **21,** 319–321.

17. Ma, Y., Ramezani, A., Lewis, R., Hawley, R.G., and Thomson, J.A. (2003). High-level sustained transgene expression in human embryonic stem cells using lentiviral vectors. *Stem Cells* **21,** 111–117.

18. Robertson, E.J. (ed.) (1987). "Teratocarcinomas and Embryonic Stem Cells: A Practical Approach." IRL Press, Washington, DC.

19. Henderson, J.K., Draper, J.S., Baillie, H.S., Fishel, S., Thomson, J.A., Moore, H., and Andrews, P.W. (2002). Preimplantation human embryos and embryonic stem cells show comparable expression of stage-specific embryonic antigens. *Stem Cells* **20,** 329–337.

20. Carpenter, M.K., Rosler, E.S., Fisk, G.J., Brandenberger, R., Ares, X., Miura, T., Lucero, M., and Rao, M.S. (2004). Properties of four human embryonic stem cell lines maintained in a feeder-free culture system. *Dev. Dyn.* **229,** 243-258.

21. Kim, N.Y., Piatyszek, M.A., Prowse, K.R., Harley, C.B., West, M.D., Ho, P.L., Coviello, G.M., Wright, W.E., Weinrich, S.L., and Shay, J.W. (1994). Specific association of human telomerase activity with immortal cell lines and cancer. *Science* **266,** 2011–2015.

22. Weinrich, S.L., Pruzan, R., Ma, L., Ouellette, M., Tesmer, V.M., Holt, S.E., Bodnar, A.G., Lichtsteiner, S., Kim, N.W., Trager, J.B., Taylor, R.D., Carlos, R., Andrews, W.H., Wright, W.E., Shay, J.W., Harley, C.B., and Morin, G.B. (1997). Reconstitution of human telomerase with the template RNA component hTR and the catalytic protein subunit hTRT. *Nat. Genet.* **17,** 498–502.

Genetic Manipulation of Human Embryonic Stem Cells

Yoav Mayshar and Nissim Benvenisty

Genetic manipulation, the process of inducing changes in gene expression and the expression of novel genes, has proved to be an indispensable tool in recent genetic research. The implementation of increasingly powerful genetic tools for mouse embryonic stem (ES) cells has led to an explosion of data concerning the specific properties of an enormous array of genes. Available techniques allow the elimination of target-gene expression, the tissue-specific induction of reporter-gene expression, the overexpression of cellular genes, and more. It is not surprising, therefore, that a short time after the derivation of human ES cells, several studies described the genetic manipulation of these cells using a variety of techniques. This chapter focuses on the recent advances in the genetic manipulation of human ES cells, the methods available, and their possible uses. A brief description of advanced genetic manipulation techniques not yet demonstrated in these cells is also presented.

Introduction

The new technology of establishing human ES cell lines has raised great hopes for breaking new ground in basic and clinical research. Clearly, genetic manipulation will play a pivotal role in applying this technology to biological research as well as to the specific needs of transplantation medicine.

Genetic manipulation has proved to be a key experimental procedure in the field of mouse ES cell research since the initial isolation of such cells more than 20 years ago.[1,2] Many effective techniques have since been developed for bringing about specific genetic modifications. Some of these methodologies have recently been adapted for the manipulation of human ES cells. These include both transfection and infection protocols as well as overexpression and homologous recombination procedures. The newly acquired availability of these techniques should make genetic engineering of human ES cells routine and enable great advances in the field of human ES cell research.

By introducing genetic modifications to mouse ES cells, numerous genetically modified animals have been produced, and these have proved to be an extremely valuable tool

Handbook of Stem Cells
Volume 1

for research. Obviously, no equivalent research can be conducted in humans. Thus, despite the great potential attributed to human ES cells, much of the basic developmental research using these cells may be limited to *in vitro* studies. Researchers of human ES cells are therefore forced to adopt developmental models such as embryoid bodies (EBs) for studying early embryogenesis. This chapter presents the principle aspects of *in vitro* genetic manipulation of human ES cells and the possible uses of the methods available.

Methods of Genetic Manipulation

A variety of methods are used for manipulating mammalian gene expression. Many of these have been used in mouse ES cell research. Of these, several gene delivery methods have been shown to be effective in human ES cells including: transfection by various chemical reagents,[3] electroporation,[4] and viral infection.[5–7] Transfection is probably the most commonly used method for genetic manipulation. The system is straightforward and relatively easy to calibrate. It provides sufficient numbers of cells for clonal expansion and allows the insertion of constructs of virtually unlimited size. Recently, long-term transgene expression in ES cells was demonstrated using infection by lentiviral vectors.[5] This technique has been shown to be highly effective and could therefore emerge as a popular tool in human ES cell genetic engineering.

TRANSFECTION

The method used for gene delivery is one of the major variables that directly effects the efficiency of genetic manipulation.[8] The choice of gene delivery method should be based on the nature of experiment to be performed. The duration of the genetic modification is one factor that will dictate this choice. For short-term induction, transient expression can be achieved through the introduction of supercoiled plasmid DNA, from which transcription has been shown to be more efficient than from the linear form.[9] Transcription from transiently introduced plasmids usually peaks around 48 hours after transfection. Usually, positive cells demonstrate relatively high expression levels as a result of a high copy number of plasmids being introduced into transfected cells. Stable transfection is accomplished by selecting for cells in which the vector DNA has integrated into the genome. In this type of experiment, it is important to linearize the vector, as this significantly raises integration and targeting efficiencies.[10]

A positive selection marker under regulation of a strong constitutive promoter is frequently included in the insert when the gene target is nonselectable. Selection should not be carried out immediately following transfection. Delaying the selection gives the cells time to recuperate and express the resistance marker. Given that the various selection reagents are toxic to all mammalian cells, the feeder layer supporting the cells must also be resistant to the selection drug. To this end, lines of transgenic mice, carrying various genes conferring resistance to selection drugs, are available for the derivation of resistant feeder cells.

Transfection Reagents

In the case of chemical-based transfection, carrier molecules bind the foreign nucleic acids and introduce them into the cells through the plasma membrane. In general, the cellular uptake of the exogenous nucleic acids is thought to occur either through endocytosis or, in the case of lipid-based reagents, through fusion of a lipidic vesicle to the plasma membrane. The first study to describe stable transfection in human ES cells also described a comparative study on the efficiency of a variety of reagents commonly used in other cell types.[3] The reagents tested were Lipofectamine Plus (Life Technologies), FuGene 6 (Roche), and ExGen 500 (Fermentas). Lipofectamine Plus is a cationic lipid-based reagent that forms small unilamellar liposomes whose positive charges bind both the DNA backbone and the negatively charged cellular membrane. This product produced low transfection efficiency. FuGene 6, a nonliposomal formulation of lipids, provided similarly low transfection efficiency. By far the best results were obtained by using ExGen 500, a linear polyethylenimine molecule with a high cationic charge density. This method routinely produces transient transfection rates of approximately 10% and stable transfection efficiency of 10^{-5}–10^{-6}. The main advantages of chemical transfection are, notably, the relative simplicity of the procedure and that it can be performed on an adherent cell culture.

Electroporation

Transfection by electroporation was adopted early as the method for gene targeting in mouse ES cells.[11] This process involves applying a brief high-voltage shock to cells in suspension in the presence of DNA molecules. The electric shock causes transient pores to open in the cell membrane, enabling DNA to enter. The application of mouse ES cell electroporation procedures to human ES cells produced very low transfection rates, both in transient[3] and stable[4] transfection. These low frequencies were probably caused by the low survival rates of human ES cells following the voltage shock. Recently, Zwaka and Thomson[4] increased the yield of electroporation 100-fold to achieve a stable integration rate of ~10^{-5}. This was performed by modifying the electroporation parameters and electroporating the cells in clumps rather than separately in normal culture medium rather than in phosphate-buffered saline. In this way, the mouse electroporation protocol was customized for human ES cells. Using electroporation, homologous recombination efficiencies were reported to be between 2–40%, subject to the properties of the vector employed. Numerous homologous recombination clones have thus been generated for a number of vector constructs, demonstrating the feasibility of achieving efficient gene targeting in human ES cells.

Infection

Unlike transfection methods, viral vectors can produce a large percentage of infected cells.[12] Viral vectors also allow easy determination of the vector copy number for both transient and stable expression. Several groups have recently reported transgene expression in human ES cells using lentiviral vectors.[5–7] Lentiviral infection provides a very high proportion of stable integrants, although integration cannot be targeted and vector size may be a limiting factor. Because of its efficiency, this method could prove useful in bypassing the need for selection and time-consuming clonal expansion as well as in experiments intended to induce random insertional mutagenesis or gene trap.

Genetic Modification Approaches

One major role of genetic engineering will be research into the early stages of human development and the genes involved in this process. The roles of many of these genes have been elucidated using genetic manipulation techniques, mostly with the aid of genetically modified animals. Several studies using EB models have shown that specific early embryonic developmental processes can to some extent be recapitulated *in vitro*.[13–18] Human ES cells thus provide researchers with a unique system for investigating the early stages of embryonic development through the implementation of genetic manipulation techniques. These techniques can also be used to determine gene function at the cellular level.

Several approaches can be used to discover the activity of specific genes in ES cells through genetic manipulation. These include overexpression of cellular or foreign genes, use of reporter genes, and gene silencing. In this section, we summarize the major techniques currently used in human ES cells and several other techniques likely to be implemented in human ES cell research in the near future (Fig. 53–1).

EXOGENOUS GENE EXPRESSION

The concept of directed differentiation is an example of the possible utility of introducing exogenous properties into human ES cells. Extensive studies are being carried out on directed differentiation in human ES cells. The addition of specific growth factors to EBs during the differentiation process has been shown to modify their differentiation potential.[19] The use of various enrichment protocols has made it possible to obtain several cell types, such as neurons,[20–23] hematopoietic cells,[24] and cardiomyocytes.[25–28] Although the creation of substantial amounts of certain cell types has been reported, the outcomes of some differentiation protocols are often inconsistent and are currently unable to yield the pure cell populations required for transplantation.

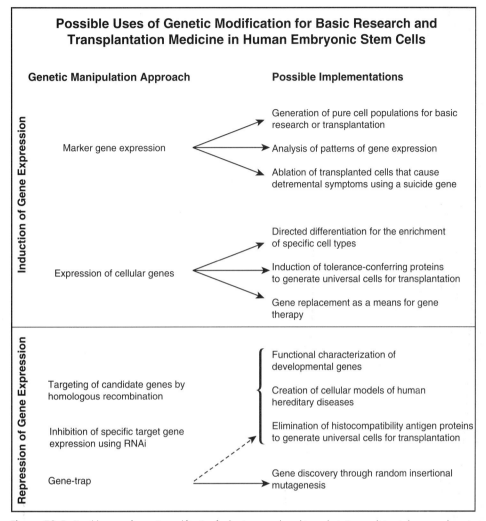

Figure 53-1. Possible uses of genetic modification for basic research and transplantation medicine in human embryonic stem cells.

Genetic manipulation could complement these methods and facilitate the practical application of human ES cells in transplantation medicine.

Genetic Labeling

The introduction of constitutively expressed reporter genes, such as the gene encoding for green fluorescent protein (GFP) into the cells, allows their detection in a mixed population. This method was applied in a transplantation experiment, where undifferentiated human ES cells were introduced into an early-stage chick embryo.[29] In another study, using the reporter gene regulated by a promoter of an ES cell-enriched gene *(Rex1)*, it was possible to follow undifferentiated cell populations during differentiation *in vitro*. Such labeling also enables direct selection of the specifically labeled or nonlabeled cells out of an entire heterogenous cell population using a fluorescence-activated cell sorter.[3] Accordingly, Zwaka and Thomson[4] created knockin cell lines using GFP or neomycin-resistance promoterless constructs. Through this method, in

the homologous recombination events selected, the reporter genes were regulated by the endogenous OCT4 promoter. By placing the reporter under the regulation of the native gene, the possible position effects that could confound the interpretation of the results are avoided, and the entire set of *cis*-acting elements is used.

Alternatively, the introduction of a conditional suicide gene could solve one of the principle concerns facing cellular transplantation. Adverse effects from transplants may occur as a result of malfunction or uncontrolled proliferation of grafted cells.[30] Selective ablation of human ES cells expressing herpes simplex virus thymidine kinase *(HSV-tk)* has been demonstrated in an animal model. Growth of teratomas formed by transplanting phosphoglycerate kinase–*HSV-tk* transfected cells was successfully arrested by oral administration of the pro-drug ganciclovir.[31] Using this technique, it will be possible to transplant "fail safe" cells into patients. These cells could then be eliminated upon the onset of harmful symptoms.

Probably the most direct way for the enrichment of a specific cell type using genetic manipulation is to isolate it using a tissue-specific promoter driving a reporter or resistance gene. This method has been demonstrated for the enrichment of undifferentiated human ES cells,[3] but it can also be applied to isolate specific populations of differentiated cells. In mouse ES cells, through expression of a neomycin-resistance gene regulated by the endogenous promoter of *sox2*, a neuronal progenitor specific gene, Li *et al.*[32] produced highly enriched neural precursors from a heterogeneous population following selection. Similarly, mouse cardiac cells were isolated by using a reporter gene driven by the cardiac α-actin promoter.[33] Of course, the efficiency of such direct selection methods could be improved under culture conditions that allow greater quantities of the desired cell type to be produced.

Overexpression of Cellular Genes as Dominant Effectors of Cell Fate

The overexpression of developmentally important genes is being used to achieve directed differentiation. Several regulatory genes have been introduced in various mouse experiments. Hepatocyte nuclear factor 3 transcription factors HNF3-α and HNF3-β induced differentiation of mouse ES cells toward the early endodermal lineage.[34] Ectopic expression of *HoxB4*, a homeotic selector gene, has enabled the use of mouse ES cells for the repopulation of myeloid and lymphoid lineages in immune-deficient mice.[35,36] Through the expression of the nuclear receptor related-1 (Nurr1) transcription factor, Kim *et al.*[37] generated a highly enriched population of midbrain neural stem cells shown to ameliorate the phenotype of a mouse model of Parkinson's disease.

As yet, no single key factor or gene has been found that could cause undifferentiated ES cells to differentiate *en masse* to a specific lineage or cell type. Therefore, a combination of genetic manipulation and selective culture conditions would probably be necessary to generate differentiated transplant-ready cells from undifferentiated ES cells.

GENE SILENCING

As opposed to the exogenous expression of various genes, gene silencing assesses the functionality of a particular gene through its elimination. The most common method for generating silencing is homologous recombination in which an exogenous sequence is inserted within the gene's coding region, thus disrupting it. Gene trap is an additional method through which many genomic sequences can be randomly mutated. Various other targeted modifications used to induce more subtle or controlled effects are available, and recently, an RNA-based silencing approach has been gaining recognition.

GENE TARGETING

Genetic modification has for many years been considered a cornerstone in mammalian biology research. Two major advances in genetic manipulation of the mammalian genome were the isolation of mouse ES cells and the development of targeting vectors.[38] Together, these two methods have enabled the relatively straightforward production of genetically modified mice, carrying predesigned alterations to their genome. The subsequent proliferation of data has shed light on the functional characteristics of many genes and has led to the creation of various models for human disease. Although several mouse models have been created, some have proved inadequate in recapitulating some or all aspects of the human phenotype. Research is often limited by the lack of an adequate mouse model, and working with primary cultures can often be problematic. In light of these difficulties, the creation of a cellular model of human disease, using human ES cells, will be valuable.

Mutation of the hypoxanthine guanine phosphoribosyl transferase *(HPRT)* gene in humans is the basis for Lesch-Nyhan syndrome, a severe genetic disease. This syndrome is manifested in a variety of problems related to high uric acid levels. These include gout-like arthritis and renal failure. There are also neurological disorders associated with this disease, but the exact causes are still unknown. Mouse models for *HPRT* deficiency failed to fully recapitulate the human disease,[39,40] possibly because uric acid metabolism is different in humans. Homologous recombination was recently used to disrupt *HPRT*[4,41] using positive–negative selection.[42] Analysis of mutant human ES cell metabolism showed that unlike their mouse counterparts, human cells mimic the Lesch-Nyhan phenotype.[41] The *HPRT* gene has long been used for the analysis of homologous recombination and has been extensively studied.

HPRT is ideal for analyzing homologous recombination, as it is X-linked. Thus, mutation of the single allele in male cells may produce a phenotype. Cells lacking *HPRT* activity can be selected with 6-thioguanine (6TG). By culturing these cells in HAT medium, they can be selectively eliminated. In many cases, the rate-limiting step toward obtaining targeted recombinants is the high number of nonhomologous integrations, making screening for homologous recombinants time consuming. The additional negative selection is useful for confirming successful homologous recombination events and eliminating false positives. Thus, by using an $HPRT^-$ cell line as a base for further genetic manipulation, an *HPRT* minigene can be used as an additional positive and negative selection by correcting the *HPRT* deficiency.[43] In cases other than *HPRT* targeting, a vector is usually constructed that contains a positive selection cassette (usually the neomycin-resistance gene) flanked by sequences homologous to the endogenous target gene. A negative selection marker, usually *HSV-tk*, is often placed in such a way that following linearization of the vector, it is located outside the region of homology. Thus, when homologous recombination has successfully occurred, the transfected cells will not contain the *HSV-tk* gene and will be resistant to the drug ganciclovir.

When targeting expressed genes, promoterless constructs can be employed to increase the efficiency of homologous recombination by reducing the selectability of most random integrations.[44–46] This method requires careful calibration of the concentration of the selection reagent subject to the strength of endogenous promoter.[47] Zwaka and Thomson[4] targeted the gene encoding OCT4 *(POU5F1)* using this approach and achieved homologous recombination rates of up to 40%.

As opposed to gene targeting, random gene disruption is being widely performed by gene trap (reviewed by Stanford et al.[48]). In this method, a reporter gene lacking an essential regulatory element is randomly inserted into the genome. Thus, when the reporter gene is expressed, this often is because of the use of an endogenous regulatory sequence. A large-scale disruption of genes is therefore made possible, allowing the discovery of new genes and the creation of banks for a variety of mutations.

Induction of Homozygosity in Mutant Alleles

Several methods have been developed to make mutated alleles homozygous in mouse ES cells. When mutating the mouse genome, there is often an option of generating homozygosity through breeding two heterozygotes. However, research with human models will require in vitro manipulation. Two strategies can be employed to this end: targeting the remaining allele by a second round of homologous recombination using distinct selection markers[49,50] and growing transfected cells in high concentrations of the selection reagent, thus selecting for spontaneous homozygotization of the mutated allele containing the resistance gene.[51]

Effect of the Extent and Nature of Homology on Targeting Efficiency

The length of the homologous regions has been shown to be a critical factor in determining the effectiveness of targeted recombination.[11,52,53] By increasing the length of homology from 2 kb to 10 kb, an exponential increase in targeting efficiency is achieved. A less dramatic rate of increase is observed with up to 14 kb of homology.[54] The length of the short arm of homology should not be less than approximately 0.5 kb.[52,53] The use of isogenic rather than nonisogenic DNA has also been shown to increase the rate of targeted recombination dramatically,[50,54] although the need for isogenic DNA for human somatic cell lines[55] and ES cells[41] has recently been disputed.

ADVANCED METHODS OF GENE TARGETING

It has been shown that the strategy of inserting a selection cassette to generate a knockout phenotype can confound the interpretation of these experiments, as the exogenous promoter may disrupt endogenous gene expression more than 100 kb from the point of insertion.[56] This disruption of the local regulatory elements can produce an artifact phenotype where none exists.[57] This is demonstrated by distinct phenotypic effects caused by different constructs used to target the same gene.[58] Removal of the selection cassette is therefore recommended. Clean mutations can be achieved either by the "hit-and-run" or "tag-and-exchange" methods or by the application of an exogenous recombinase.

Hit-and-Run and Tag-and-Exchange Methods

Several strategies have been demonstrated that can create specific substitutions. These strategies create subtle mutations in the gene as opposed to disrupting it with a large insert. The hit-and-run method[59,60] is based upon selection of intrachromosomal recombination events that excise the vector sequence. In another strategy, termed tag and exchange (double replacement),[43] a series of targeting procedures is performed. In the first stage, the gene is targeted with a vector that contains both positive and negative selections in the insert. In the second stage, a vector containing the mutation of choice is inserted by homologous recombination and selected by the loss of the negative selection marker.

Exogenous Recombinases

By introducing highly efficient and specific exogenous recombination systems, both efficiency and tight control over the recombination event are achieved. The system most widely used is the Cre recombinase from phage P1. Cre identifies a highly specific 34-bp target sequence (lox P) and promotes reciprocal recombination between two such sites.[61] The versatility of the system is such, that depending on the location of the lox P sequences, it can promote either reversible integration or excision while retaining the recombination sites' integrity. Thus the Cre-lox system has been used for a variety of ends. These include the induction of chromosomal rearrangements[62–64] and spatial or temporal inactivation of cellular genes by deletion[65] or activation[66–68] of reporter genes. They also include multiple insertions into the same genomic site[69] and the creation of clean mutations devoid of exogenous regulatory sequences.[70,71] For further information regarding the design of targeting constructs, see Muller.[72]

RNA INTERFERENCE

Although gene targeting remains the most powerful method for the silencing of endogenous gene expression, posttranscriptional gene silencing has lately been characterized as a potent method of down-regulating specific genes. Double-stranded RNA (dsRNA) molecules have been shown to initiate RNA interference (RNAi),[73] causing sequence specific mRNA degradation. The main advantage of RNAi is that it acts in trans. This means that RNAi-inducing molecules can be directly introduced by transfection[73–76] or synthesized within the cells using expression vectors, either transiently or by stable integration.[76–79] Because RNAi does not entail any modification of the targeted gene, it should be relatively simple to generate transient or conditional gene silencing using this method.

The evolutionarily conserved machinery that underlies the phenomenon of homology-dependent gene silencing involves endonuclease (DICER) processing of dsRNA into small interfering RNA (siRNA). siRNAs are 21- to 23-nt-long fragments that in turn are incorporated into RISC, a multicomponent nuclease that uses the siRNA as a guide for the degradation of mRNA substrate (for review, see Hannon[80]). Although the use of long dsRNA has been demonstrated to be effective, it is well established that dsRNA within mammalian cells may induce a cellular response by interferon, thus generating nonspecific effects.[81] Direct use of siRNA has been shown to circumvent this problem.[75] The use of RNAi technology has been demonstrated for both mouse ES and mouse embryonal carcinoma lines.[74,76] Most recently, RNAi has been shown to faithfully recapitulate the knockout phenotype in ES cell-derived mouse embryos.[82] In light of the aforementioned recent improvements in the field of RNAi, it seems that RNAi may quickly become a widely used method for rapid gene silencing in human ES cells.

Summary

One advantage of ES cells over other stem cell types under research is their accessibility for genetic manipulation. Progress so far indicates that genetic manipulation in human ES cells will closely resemble that of their veteran mouse counterparts. Thus, in addition to the methods used so far, the implementation of other advanced strategies for genetic manipulation can probably be expected in human ES cells. Possible uses for genetically modified human ES cells could be the creation of cellular models for disease, the study of various aspects of early human development, transplantation medicine, and more. Thus, many studies using genetic manipulation techniques in human ES cells are foreseeable.

REFERENCES

1. Evans, M.J., and Kaufman, M.H. (1981). Establishment in culture of pluripotential cells from mouse embryos. *Nature* **292**, 154–156.

2. Martin, G.R. (1981). Isolation of a pluripotent cell line from early mouse embryos cultured in medium conditioned by teratocarcinoma stem cells. *Proc. Natl. Acad. Sci. USA* **78**, 7634–7638.

3. Eiges, R., Schuldiner, M., Drukker, M., Yanuka, O., Itskovitz-Eldor, J., and Benvenisty, N. (2001). Establishment of human embryonic stem cell-transfected clones carrying a marker for undifferentiated cells. *Curr. Biol.* **11**, 514–518.

4. Zwaka, T.P., and Thomson, J.A. (2003). Homologous recombination in human embryonic stem cells. *Nat. Biotechnol.* **21**, 319–321.

5. Pfeifer, A., Ikawa, M., Dayn, Y., and Verma, I.M. (2002). Transgenesis by lentiviral vectors: lack of gene silencing in mammalian embryonic stem cells and preimplantation embryos. *Proc. Natl. Acad. Sci. USA* **99**, 2140–2145.

6. Ma, Y., Ramezani, A., Lewis, R., Hawley, R.G., and Thomson, J.A. (2003). High-level, sustained transgene expression in human embryonic stem cells using lentiviral vectors. *Stem Cells* **21**, 111–117.

7. Gropp, M., Itsykson, P., Singer, O., Ben-Hur, T., Reinhartz, E., Galun, E., and Reubinoff, B.E. (2003). Stable genetic modification of human embryonic stem cells by lentiviral vectors. *Mol. Ther.* **7**, 281–287.

8. Vasquez, K.M., Marburger, K., Intody, Z., and Wilson, J.H. (2001). Manipulating the mammalian genome by homologous recombination. *Proc. Natl. Acad. Sci. USA* **98**, 8403–8410.

9. Weintraub, H., Cheng, P.F., and Conrad, K. (1986). Expression of transfected DNA depends on DNA topology. *Cell* **46**, 115–122.

10. Thomas, K.R., Folger, K.R., and Capecchi, M.R. (1986). High-frequency targeting of genes to specific sites in the mammalian genome. *Cell* **44**, 419–428.

11. Thomas, K.R., and Capecchi, M.R. (1987). Site-directed mutagenesis by gene targeting in mouse embryo-derived stem cells. *Cell* **51**, 503–512.

12. Robertson, E., Bradley, A., Kuehn, M., and Evans, M. (1986). Germ line transmission of genes introduced into cultured pluripotential cells by retroviral vector. *Nature* **323**, 445–448.

13. Risau, W., Sariola, H., Zerwes, H.G., Sasse, J., Ekblom, P., Kemler, R., and Doetschman, T. (1988). Vasculogenesis and angiogenesis in embryonic stem cell-derived embryoid bodies. *Development* **102**, 471–478.

14. Keller, G., Kennedy, M., Papayannopoulou, T., and Wiles, M.V. (1993). Hematopoietic commitment during embryonic stem cell differentiation in culture. *Mol. Cell. Biol.* **13**, 473–486.

15. Yamada, G., Kioussi, C., Schubert, F.R., Eto, Y., Chowdhury, K., Pituello, F., and Gruss, P. (1994). Regulated expression of *Brachyury(T), Nkx1.1,* and *Pax* genes in embryoid bodies. *Biochem. Biophys. Res. Commun.* **199**, 552–563.

16. Coucouvanis, E., and Martin, G.R. (1995). Signals for death and survival: a two-step mechanism for cavitation in the vertebrate embryo. *Cell* **83**, 279–287.

17. Levinson-Dushnik, M., and Benvenisty, N. (1995). Embryogenesis *in vitro:* study of differentiation of embryonic stem cells. *Biol. Neonate* **67**, 77–83.

18. Itskovitz-Eldor, J., Schuldiner, M., Karsenti, D., Eden, A., Yanuka, O., Amit, M., Soreq, H., and Benvenisty, N. (2000). Differentiation of human embryonic stem cells into embryoid bodies comprising the three embryonic germ layers. *Mol. Med.* **6**, 88–95.

19. Schuldiner, M., Yanuka, O., Itskovitz-Eldor, J., Melton, D.A., and Benvenisty, N. (2000). Effects of eight growth factors on the differentiation of cells derived from human embryonic stem cells. *Proc. Natl. Acad. Sci. USA* **97**, 11,307–11,312.

20. Schuldiner, M., Eiges, R., Eden, A., Yanuka, O., Itskovitz-Eldor, J., Goldstein, R.S., and Benvenisty, N. (2001). Induced neuronal differentiation of human embryonic stem cells. *Brain Res.* **913**, 201–205.

21. Zhang, S.C., Wernig, M., Duncan, I.D., Brustle, O., and Thomson, J.A. (2001). *In vitro* differentiation of transplantable neural precursors from human embryonic stem cells. *Natl. Biotechnol.* **19**, 1129–1133.

22. Reubinoff, B.E., Itsykson, P., Turetsky, T., Pera, M.F., Reinhartz, E., Itzik, A., and Ben-Hur, T. (2001). Neural progenitors from human embryonic stem cells. *Nat. Biotechnol.* **19**, 1134–1140.

23. Carpenter, M.K., Inokuma, M.S., Denham, J., Mujtaba, T., Chiu, C.P., and Rao, M.S. (2001). Enrichment of neurons and neural precursors from human embryonic stem cells. *Exp. Neurol.* **172**, 383–397.

24. Kaufman, D.S., Hanson, E.T., Lewis, R.L., Auerbach, R., and Thomson, J.A. (2001). Hematopoietic colony-forming cells derived from human embryonic stem cells. *Proc. Natl. Acad. Sci. USA* **98**, 10,716–10,721.

25. Kehat, I., Kenyagin-Karsenti, D., Snir, M., Segev, H., Amit, M., Gepstein, A., Livne, E., Binah, O., Itskovitz-Eldor, J., and Gepstein, L. (2001). Human embryonic stem cells can differentiate into myocytes with structural and functional properties of cardiomyocytes. *J. Clin. Invest.* **108**, 407–414.

26. Xu, C., Police, S., Rao, N., and Carpenter, M.K. (2002). Characterization and enrichment of cardiomyocytes derived from human embryonic stem cells. *Circ. Res.* **91**, 501–508.

27. Mummery, C., Ward, D., van den Brink, C.E., Bird, S.D., Doevendans, P.A., Opthof, T., Brutel de la Riviere, A., Tertoolen, L., van der Heyden, M., and Pera, M. (2002). Cardiomyocyte differentiation of mouse and human embryonic stem cells. *J. Anat.* **200**, 233–242.

28. Kehat, I., Gepstein, A., Spira, A., Itskovitz-Eldor, J., and Gepstein, L. (2002). High-resolution electrophysiological assessment of human embryonic stem cell-derived cardiomyocytes: a novel *in vitro* model for the study of conduction. *Circ. Res.* **91,** 659–661.

29. Goldstein, R.S., Drukker, M., Reubinoff, B.E., and Benvenisty, N. (2002). Integration and differentiation of human embryonic stem cells transplanted to the chick embryo. *Dev. Dyn.* **225,** 80–86.

30. Freed, C.R., Greene, P.E., Breeze, R.E., Tsai, W.Y., DuMouchel, W., Kao, R., Dillon, S., Winfield, H., Culver, S., Trojanowski, J.Q., Eidelberg, D., and Fahn, S. (2001). Transplantation of embryonic dopamine neurons for severe Parkinson's disease. *N. Engl. J. Med.* **344,** 710–719.

31. Schuldiner, M., Itskovitz-Eldor, J., and Benvenisty, N. (2003). Selective ablation of human embryonic stem cells expressing a "suicide" gene. *Stem Cells* **21,** 257–265.

32. Li, M., Pevny, L., Lovell-Badge, R., and Smith, A. (1998). Generation of purified neural precursors from embryonic stem cells by lineage selection. *Curr. Biol.* **8,** 971–974.

33. Kolossov, E., Fleischmann, B.K., Liu, Q., Bloch, W., Viatchenko-Karpinski, S., Manzke, O., Ji, G.J., Bohlen, H., Addicks, K., and Hescheler, J. (1998). Functional characteristics of ES cell-derived cardiac precursor cells identified by tissue-specific expression of the green fluorescent protein. *J. Cell. Biol.* **143,** 2045–2056.

34. Levinson-Dushnik, M., and Benvenisty, N. (1997). Involvement of hepatocyte nuclear factor 3 in endoderm differentiation of embryonic stem cells. *Mol. Cell. Biol.* **17,** 3817–3822.

35. Kyba, M., Perlingeiro, R.C., and Daley, G.Q. (2002). HoxB4 confers definitive lymphoid-myeloid engraftment potential on embryonic stem cell and yolk sac hematopoietic progenitors. *Cell* **109,** 29–37.

36. Rideout, W.M., 3rd, Hochedlinger, K., Kyba, M., Daley, G.Q., and Jaenisch, R. (2002). Correction of a genetic defect by nuclear transplantation and combined cell and gene therapy. *Cell* **109,** 17–27.

37. Kim, J.H., Auerbach, J.M., Rodriguez-Gomez, J.A., Velasco, I., Gavin, D., Lumelsky, N., Lee, S.H., Nguyen, J., Sanchez-Pernaute, R., Bankiewicz, K., and McKay, R. (2002). Dopamine neurons derived from embryonic stem cells function in an animal model of Parkinson's disease. *Nature* **418,** 50–56.

38. Smithies, O., Gregg, R.G., Boggs, S.S., Koralewski, M.A., and Kucherlapati, R.S. (1985). Insertion of DNA sequences into the human chromosomal β-globin locus by homologous recombination. *Nature* **317,** 230–234.

39. Engle, S.J., Womer, D.E., Davies, P.M., Boivin, G., Sahota, A., Simmonds, H.A., Stambrook, P.J., and Tischfield, J.A. (1996). HPRT–APRT-deficient mice are not a model for Lesch-Nyhan syndrome. *Hum. Mol. Genet.* **5,** 1607–1610.

40. Bedell, M.A., Largaespada, D.A., Jenkins, N.A., and Copeland, N.G. (1997). Mouse models of human disease: Part II—Recent progress and future directions. *Genes Dev.* **11,** 11–43.

41. Urbach, A., Schuldiner, M., and Benvenisty, N. (in press).

42. Mansour, S.L., Thomas, K.R., and Capecchi, M.R. (1988). Disruption of the protooncogene *int-2* in mouse embryo-derived stem cells: a general strategy for targeting mutations to nonselectable genes. *Nature* **336,** 348–352.

43. Stacey, A., Schnieke, A., McWhir, J., Cooper, J., Colman, A., and Melton, D.W. (1994). Use of double-replacement gene targeting to replace the murine α-lactalbumin gene with its human counterpart in embryonic stem cells and mice. *Mol. Cell. Biol.* **14,** 1009–1016.

44. Doetschman, T., Maeda, N., and Smithies, O. (1988). Targeted mutation of the *Hprt* gene in mouse embryonic stem cells. *Proc. Natl. Acad. Sci. USA* **85,** 8583–8587.

45. Charron, J., Malynn, B.A., Robertson, E.J., Goff, S.P., and Alt, F.W. (1990). High-frequency disruption of the *N-myc* gene in embryonic stem and pre-B-cell lines by homologous recombination. *Mol. Cell. Biol.* **10,** 1799–1804.

46. Te Riele, H., Maandag, E.R., Clarke, A., Hooper, M., and Berns, A. (1990). Consecutive inactivation of both alleles of the *pim-1* protooncogene by homologous recombination in embryonic stem cells. *Nature* **348,** 649–651.

47. Hanson, K.D., and Sedivy, J.M. (1995). Analysis of biological selections for high-efficiency gene targeting. *Mol. Cell. Biol.* **15,** 45–51.

48. Stanford, W.L., Cohn, J.B., and Cordes, S.P. (2001). Gene-trap mutagenesis: past, present, and beyond. *Nat. Rev. Genet.* **2,** 756–768.

49. Mortensen, R.M., Zubiaur, M., Neer, E.J., and Seidman, J.G. (1991). Embryonic stem cells lacking a functional inhibitory G-protein subunit (α-i2) produced by gene targeting of both alleles. *Proc. Natl. Acad. Sci. USA* **88,** 7036–7040.

50. Te Riele, H., Maandag, E.R., and Berns, A. (1992). Highly efficient gene targeting in embryonic stem cells through homologous recombination with isogenic DNA constructs. *Proc. Natl. Acad. Sci. USA* **89,** 5128–5132.

51. Mortensen, R.M., Conner, D.A., Chao, S., Geisterfer-Lowrance, A.A., and Seidman, J.G. (1992). Production of homozygous mutant ES cells with a single targeting construct. *Mol. Cell. Biol.* **12,** 2391–2395.

52. Hasty, P., Rivera-Perez, J., and Bradley, A. (1991). The length of homology required for gene targeting in embryonic stem cells. *Mol. Cell. Biol.* **11,** 5586–5591.

53. Thomas, K.R., Deng, C., and Capecchi, M.R. (1992). High-fidelity gene targeting in embryonic stem cells by using sequence replacement vectors. *Mol. Cell. Biol.* **12,** 2919–2923.

54. Deng, C., and Capecchi, M.R. (1992). Reexamination of gene targeting frequency as a function of the extent of homology between the targeting vector and the target locus. *Mol. Cell. Biol.* **12,** 3365–3371.

55. Sedivy, J.M., Vogelstein, B., Liber, H.L., Hendrickson, E.A., and Rosmarin, A. (1999). Gene targeting in human cells without isogenic DNA. *Science* **283,** 9.

56. Pham, C.T., MacIvor, D.M., Hug, B.A., Heusel, J.W., and Ley, T.J. (1996). Long-range disruption of gene expression by a selectable marker cassette. *Proc. Natl. Acad. Sci. USA* **93,** 13,090–13,095.

57. Fiering, S., Epner, E., Robinson, K., Zhuang, Y., Telling, A., Hu, M., Martin, D.I., Enver, T., Ley, T.J., and Groudine, M. (1995). Targeted deletion of 5′HS2 of the murine β-globin LCR reveals that it is not essential for proper regulation of the β-globin locus. *Genes Dev.* **9,** 2203–2213.

58. Olson, E.N., Arnold, H.H., Rigby, P.W., and Wold, B.J. (1996). Know your neighbors: three phenotypes in null mutants of the myogenic bHLH gene *MRF4*. *Cell* **85,** 1–4.

59. Hasty, P., Ramirez-Solis, R., Krumlauf, R., and Bradley, A. (1991). Introduction of a subtle mutation into the Hox-2.6 locus in embryonic stem cells. *Nature* **350,** 243–246.

60. Ramirez-Solis, R., Zheng, H., Whiting, J., Krumlauf, R., and Bradley, A. (1993). Hoxb-4 (Hox-2.6) mutant mice show homeotic transformation of a cervical vertebra and defects in the closure of the sternal rudiments. *Cell* **73,** 279–294.

61. Sauer, B., and Henderson, N. (1988). Site-specific DNA recombination in mammalian cells by the Cre recombinase of bacteriophage P1. *Proc. Natl. Acad. Sci. USA* **85,** 5166–5170.

62. Ramirez-Solis, R., Liu, P., and Bradley, A. (1995). Chromosome engineering in mice. *Nature* **378,** 720–724.

63. Li, Z.W., Stark, G., Gotz, J., Rulicke, T., Gschwind, M., Huber, G., Muller, U., and Weissmann, C. (1996). Generation of mice with a 200-kb amyloid precursor protein gene deletion by Cre recombinase-mediated site-specific recombination in embryonic stem cells. *Proc. Natl. Acad. Sci. USA* **93,** 6158–6162.

64. Zheng, B., Sage, M., Sheppeard, E.A., Jurecic, V., and Bradley, A. (2000). Engineering mouse chromosomes with Cre–loxP: Range, efficiency, and somatic applications. *Mol. Cell. Biol.* **20,** 648–655.

65. Gu, H., Marth, J.D., Orban, P.C., Mossmann, H., and Rajewsky, K. (1994). Deletion of a DNA polymerase-β gene segment in T-cells using cell type-specific gene targeting. *Science* **265,** 103–106.

66. Orban, P.C., Chui, D., and Marth, J.D. (1992). Tissue- and site-specific DNA recombination in transgenic mice. *Proc. Natl. Acad. Sci. USA* **89,** 6861–6865.

67. Yamauchi, Y., Abe, K., Mantani, A., Hitoshi, Y., Suzuki, M., Osuzu, F., Kuratani, S., and Yamamura, K. (1999). A novel transgenic technique that allows specific marking of the neural crest cell lineage in mice. *Dev. Biol.* **212,** 191–203.

68. Gu, G., Dubauskaite, J., and Melton, D.A. (2002). Direct evidence for the pancreatic lineage: NGN3+ cells are islet progenitors and are distinct from duct progenitors. *Development* **129,** 2447–2457.

69. Fukushige, S., and Sauer, B. (1992). Genomic targeting with a positive-selection lox integration vector allows highly reproducible gene expression in mammalian cells. *Proc. Natl. Acad. Sci. USA* **89,** 7905–7909.

70. Gu, H., Zou, Y.R., and Rajewsky, K. (1993). Independent control of immunoglobulin switch recombination at individual switch regions evidenced through Cre–loxP-mediated gene targeting. *Cell* **73,** 1155–1164.

71. Pelanda, R., Schaal, S., Torres, R.M., and Rajewsky, K. (1996). A prematurely expressed *Ig*-κ transgene, but not a *V*-κ–*J*-κ gene segment targeted into the *Ig*-κ locus, can rescue B-cell development in lambda5-deficient mice. *Immunity* **5,** 229–239.

72. Muller, U. (1999). Ten years of gene targeting: Targeted mouse mutants, from vector design to phenotype analysis. *Mech. Dev.* **82,** 3–21.

73. Fire, A., Xu, S., Montgomery, M.K., Kostas, S.A., Driver, S.E., and Mello, C.C. (1998). Potent and specific genetic interference by double-stranded RNA in *Caenorhabditis elegans*. *Nature* **391,** 806–811.

74. Billy, E., Brondani, V., Zhang, H., Muller, U., and Filipowicz, W. (2001). Specific interference with gene expression induced by long, double-stranded RNA in mouse embryonal teratocarcinoma cell lines. *Proc. Natl. Acad. Sci. USA* **98,** 14,428–14,433.

75. Elbashir, S.M., Harborth, J., Lendeckel, W., Yalcin, A., Weber, K., and Tuschl, T. (2001). Duplexes of 21-nucleotide RNAs mediate RNA interference in cultured mammalian cells. *Nature* **411,** 494–498.

76. Yang, S., Tutton, S., Pierce, E., and Yoon, K. (2001). Specific double-stranded RNA interference in undifferentiated mouse embryonic stem cells. *Mol. Cell. Biol.* **21,** 7807–7816.

77. Brummelkamp, T.R., Bernards, R., and Agami, R. (2002). A system for stable expression of short interfering RNAs in mammalian cells. *Science* **296,** 550–553.

78. Brummelkamp, T.R., Bernards, R., and Agami, R. (2002). Stable suppression of tumorigenicity by virus-mediated RNA interference. *Cancer Cell* **2,** 243–247.

79. Barton, G.M., and Medzhitov, R. (2002). Retroviral delivery of small interfering RNA into primary cells. *Proc. Natl. Acad. Sci. USA* **99,** 14,943–14,945.

80. Hannon, G.J. (2002). RNA interference. *Nature* **418,** 244–251.

81. Williams, B.R. (1999). PKR: A sentinel kinase for cellular stress. *Oncogene* **18,** 6112–6120.

82. Kunath, T., Gish, G., Lickert, H., Jones, N., Pawson, T., and Rossant, J. (2003). Transgenic RNA interference in ES cell-derived embryos recapitulates a genetic null phenotype. *Nat. Biotechnol.* **21,** 559–561.

54

Homologous Recombination in Human Embryonic Stem Cells

Thomas P. Zwaka and James A. Thomson

Biologists have long attempted by chemical means to induce in higher organisms predictable and specific changes as hereditary characters.
Avery,[1] 1944

Introduction

Homologous recombination provides a precise mechanism for defined modifications of genomes in living cells[2] and has been used extensively with mouse embryonic stem (ES) cells to investigate gene function and to create mouse models of human diseases.[3–6] The ability to modify the mouse genome in the intact mouse in a predetermined manner has revolutionized biomedical research involving mice. Two breakthroughs have made this possible: the derivation of ES cells[7,8] and the identification of conditions for recombination between the incoming DNA and the homologous sequences in the mammalian chromosome.[3–6]

Recently, human ES cell lines have been derived from preimplantation embryos.[9,10] Human ES cells can be maintained for a prolonged period of culture and retain their ability to form extraembryonic tissues and advanced derivatives of all three embryonic germ layers.[11] Human ES cells provide a new model for understanding human development, a renewal source of human cells either for *in vitro* studies or for transplantation therapies, and new *in vitro* models for understanding human disease.

Differences between mouse and human ES cells delayed the development of homologous recombination techniques in human ES cells. First, high, stable transfection efficiencies in human ES cells have been difficult to achieve; in particular, electroporation protocols established for mouse ES cells do not work in human ES cells.[12] Second, in contrast to mouse ES cells, human ES cells clone inefficiently from single cells, making screening procedures to identify rare homologous recombination events difficult.[11] We recently developed protocols to overcome these problems.[12] Here we describe how these protocols allowed us to successfully target a ubiquitously

Handbook of Stem Cells
Volume 1
Copyright © 2004 by Academic Press
All rights of reproduction in any form reserved.

expressed gene *(HPRT1)*, an ES cell-specific gene *(POU5F1)*, and a tissue-specific gene (tyrosine hydroxylase, *TH*).

Targeted Ablation of the *HPRT1* Gene as a Tool to Optimize Homologous Recombination Efficiency

The *HPRT1* gene is located on the X-chromosome, so a single, homologous recombination event can lead to complete loss of function in XY cells. *HPRT1*-deficient cells can be selected based on their resistance to 2-amino-6-captopurine (6-TG); thus, the frequency of homologous recombination events is easy to estimate.[13] It was because of these properties that the *HPRT1* gene played such an important role in the initial development of homologous recombination in mouse ES cells.[4,5,14]

Therefore, we designed a gene-targeting vector that was able to ablate parts of the human *HPRT1* gene and used this system to optimize transfection protocols in human ES cells.[12] The gene-targeting vector was constructed by substitution of the last three exons (exons 7, 8, and 9) of the *HPRT1* gene by a neomycin-resistance *(neo)* cassette under the thymidine kinase *(tk)* promoter control (Fig. 54–1A). This cassette was flanked by a 10-kb homologous arm in the 5′ region and by a 1.9-kb homologous arm in the 3′ region. At the end of the 3′ homologous arm, the *tk* gene was added for negative selection.[15]

Previously described problems with nonisogenic genomic DNA in mouse experiments[16] encouraged us to use homologous DNA isogenic to the human ES cell line we wanted to target (H1 subclone 1). This DNA was obtained by long-distance, high-fidelity, genomic polymerase chain reaction (PCR) and was subcloned into a PCR-cloning vector.

For human ES cells, the best chemical reagents yield stable (drug-selectable) transfection rates of about 10^{-5}, and mouse ES cell electroporation procedures yield rates that are significantly lower.[17] Therefore, we started to test our *HPRT1* gene-targeting vector system using FuGene-6 and ExGen 500, two chemical transfection reagents commonly used in human ES cell work.

Two days before transfection, human ES cells (H1 subclone 1) were trypsinized and plated on Matrigel at a density of 200,000 cells per six-well plate. They were then cultured

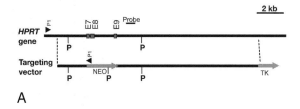

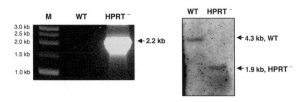

A

B

Figure 54–1. *Knockout of the HPRT1 gene.* (A) Genomic organization of the human *HPRT1* gene and the gene-targeting vector. The 3′ probe for Southern blot analysis is shown. (B) PCR analysis of ES cell lines with P1 (left) and Southern blot analysis with dedicated probe and PstI digest (right) (E: exon, P: PstI, P1: primer pair, TK: thymidine kinase, HPRT: knockout, WT: wild-type cells, and M: marker). (Please see CD-ROM for color version of this figure.)

TABLE 54–1
Numbers of Colonies Obtained by Positive and Negative Selection and Targeted Events in the *HPRT* Gene Locus[a]

Selection procedure	ExGen 500	FuGene 500	Electroporation
G418	130	261	350
G418 and ganciclovir	35	61	50
G418 and 6-TG	0	0	7

[a]From 1.5×10^7 electroporated human ES cells.

with fibroblast-conditioned medium in six-well platess.[18] Transfection, using FuGene-6 or ExGen 500, was performed according to manufacturers' recommendations. Briefly, the vector was coincubated with the plasmid (2-µg DNA and 6-µl FuGene-6 or 3-µg DNA and 10-µl ExGen 500) and added to the supernatant of each well of the six-well plate. In experiments using ExGen 500, we gently centrifuged the 6-well plate after adding the DNA–ExGen mixture (300 g for 5 minutes). The medium was changed 4 hours after transfection, and G418 selection was started 2 days after transfection. Two days later, selection with 6-TG (1 mM), GANC (1 µM), or both began.

Although G418 (130 versus 261) and ganciclovir-resistant (35 versus 61) clones were obtained for both transfection reagents, none of these were G418 and 6-TG resistant (*HPRT⁻*), indicating that none were the result of homologous recombination (Table 54–1). These results are consistent with the observations that transfection using lipid (FuGene-6) and cationic (ExGen 500) reagents results in inefficient homologous recombination in other mammalian cell types and that physical methods of introducing DNA, in general, are more effective.[19] A possible explanation is that physical transfection induces a cellular stress reaction and activates the recombination machinery to a greater extent than do chemical transfection reagents.[20]

Many parameters influence the transfection rate for electroporation, and usually, the procedure has to be optimized for each cell line.[21,22] This is critical for human ES cells, as they are sensitive and difficult to grow from individual cells.[11] Indeed, the difference in the diameter of human and mouse ES cells suggests that successful protocols will be

significantly different (Fig. 54–2). This was confirmed by an experiment, using a typical mouse ES cell protocol, that clearly showed the overall transfection rate to be too low in human ES cells to expect recovery of homologous-recombinant clones (Table 54–1). In our hands, electroporation using a typical mouse ES cell protocol[23]—220-V, 960-µF electroporation in phosphate-buffered saline (PBS)—yielded a stable transfection rate in human ES cells that was lower than 10^{-7}.

We adapted electroporation parameters for human ES cells. To increase plating efficiency, we removed ES cell colonies from the culture dish as intact, small clumps and plated them out at a high density following electroporation. Also, to increase survival, we used culture medium instead of PBS as an electroporation buffer and performed electroporation at room temperature. And finally, we changed the physical parameters of the electric field during electroporation. Applying this modified protocol, we were able to achieve stable, G418-resistant transfection rates that were 100-fold (or more) higher than standard mouse ES cell electroporation procedures.

To remove ES cells as clumps, we treated cultures with collagenase IV (1 mg/ml, Invitrogen) for 7 minutes, washed with media, and resuspended the cells in 0.5 ml of culture media ($1.5–3.0 \times 10^7$ cells). Just prior to electroporation, 0.3 ml of PBS (Invitrogen) containing 40 µg of linearized

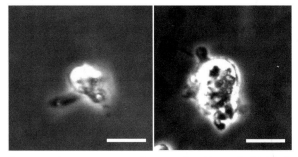

Figure 54–2. *Size comparison of mouse (Left) and human (Right) ES cells.* Bar = 10 µm.

targeting vector DNA was added. Cells were then exposed to a single, 320-V, 200-μF pulse at room temperature, using the BioRad Gene Pulser II (0.4-cm gap cuvette). Cells were incubated for 10 minutes at room temperature and were plated at high density (3.0 ×10⁷ cells per 10-cm culture dish) on matrigel.[18] G418 selection (50 μg/ml, Invitrogen) was started 48 hours after electroporation. After 1 week, G418 concentration was doubled, and 6-TG selection (1 mM, Sigma) was started. After 3 weeks, surviving colonies were picked, transferred into 48-well plates, and analyzed individually by PCR using primers specific for the *neo* cassette and for the *HPRT1* gene just upstream of the 5′ region of homology, respectively. PCR-positive clones were rescreened by Southern blot analysis using PstI-digested DNA and a probe 3′ of the *neo* cassette. After transfection of 1.5 × 10⁷ human ES cells, 350 G418-resistant clones were obtained. Among them, 50 were ganciclovir-resistant, and of those, 7 were also 6-TG-resistant, suggesting successful homologous recombination (Table 54–1). PCR and Southern blotting (Fig. 54–2B) confirmed that homologous recombination had occurred in all 6-TG-resistant clones. Electroporation of human ES cells by a DNA construct containing a *neo* resistance cassette, under the control of the *tk* promoter, yielded a stable transfection rate of 5.6 × 10⁻⁵.

Oct4 eGFP/*neo* Knockin

A useful application for "knockins" in human ES cells will be to generate cell lines with a selectable marker introduced into a locus with a tissue-specific expression pattern. Such knockins can be used, for example, to purify a specific ES cell-derived cell type from a mixed population.[24–27] To test this approach, we introduced two reporter genes into the Oct4 coding gene *POU5F1* by homologous recombination. Oct4 belongs to the POU (Pit, Oct, Unc) transcription factor family, is expressed exclusively in the pluripotent cells of the embryo, and is a central regulator of pluripotency.[28,29] We introduced two promoterless reporter–selection cassettes into the 3′ untranslated region (UTR) of the human *Oct4* gene[30] (Fig. 54–3A). The first cassette contained an internal ribosomal entry site (IRES) sequence of the encephalomyocarditis virus[31] and a gene encoding the enhanced green fluorescence protein (eGFP).[32] The second cassette included the same IRES sequence and a gene encoding *neo*. The cassettes were flanked by two homologous arms (6.3 kb in the 5′ direction and 1.6 kb in the 3′ direction). After electroporation of 1.5 × 10⁷ human ES cells with the linearized targeting vector, we obtained 103 G418-resistant clones. PCR and DNA Southern blotting demonstrated that 28 of these clones (27%) were positive for homologous recombination (Fig. 54–3B). Using a second targeting vector with a longer 3′ homologous arm, the rate of homologous recombination increased to almost 40% (22 homologous clones out of 56 G418-resistant clones). Similar transfection experiments, using FuGene-6 with the same *Oct4* gene-targeting vector, produced 11 G418-resistant clones, none of which resulted from homologous recombination.

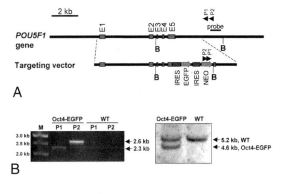

A

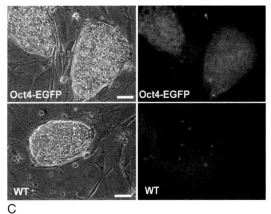

B

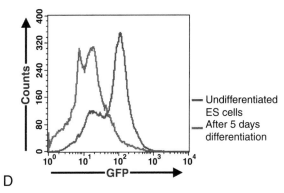

C

D

Figure 54–3. *Knockin of an IRES–eGFP–IRES–neo cassette into the 3′ UTR of the Oct4-Coding gene POU5F1. (A) Genomic structure of the human POU5F1 gene and the gene-targeting vector. The 3′ probe for Southern blot analysis is shown. (B) PCR analysis of ES cell lines (with P1 and P2 (left) and Southern blot analysis with dedicated probe and BamHI digest (right). (C) Fluorescence microscopy (right) and phase contrast (left) of Oct4 knockin and wild-type colonies. Bar = 25 μm. (D) Flow cytometry of Oct4 knockin, undifferentiated (eGFP+) ES cells and their differentiated derivates after five days of differentiation (E: exon, B: BamHI, P1 and P2: primer pairs 1 and 2, Oct4-eGFP: heterozygous knockin, WT: wild-type cells, and M: marker). (Please see CD-ROM for color version of this figure.)*

Human ES cells with the Oct4 knockin expressed eGFP. After induction of differentiation with various stimuli, eGFP expression was turned off, indicating a down-regulation of Oct4. Both drug selection and flow cytometry for eGFP expression allowed purification of undifferentiated ES cells

Thomas P. Zwaka and James A. Thomson

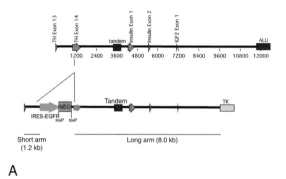

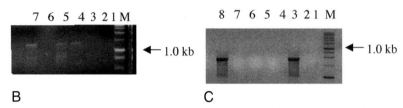

Figure 54–4. *Knockin of an IRES–eGFP cassette into the 3′ UTR of the TH gene. (A) Partial structure of the human TH gene and the gene-targeting vector. (B) Some of the G418/GANC resistant clones (clones 4, 5, and 7) are positive in the screening PCR, indicating successful homologous recombination. (C) After Cre transfection, two of the eight screened clones (clones 3 and 8) show the PCR product that indicates a positive recombination event. (Please see CD-ROM for color version of this figure.)*

from a mixed, partially differentiated cell population. These properties will make the knockin cell lines useful for studying Oct4 gene expression during differentiation, *in vitro,* and for optimizing culture conditions for human ES cells.

TH eGFP Knockin

As *Oct4* and *HPRT* are both expressed in human ES cells, we next asked if it is possible to target a gene not expressed in ES cells. *TH* is the rate-limiting enzyme in the synthesis of dopamine, and it is one of the most common markers used for dopaminergic neurons.[33] To achieve bicistronic expression of both *TH* and eGFP, we constructed a gene-targeting vector that introduces an IRES–eGFP reporter gene cassette into the 3′ UTR region in the last exon of the *TH* gene[34] (Fig. 54–4A). The cassette is flanked by a short homologous arm 5′ of this exon (1.4 kb) and a long homologous arm in the 3′ region of the last exon (8 kb). The long arm follows the gene for *tk* for negative selection of random-integrated, stable-transfected clones. Between the long homologous arm and the IRES–eGFP cassette, we cloned a PGK-driven *neo* resistance cassette flanked by two *loxP* sites. After transfection of 6.0×10^7 human ES cells (cell line H9) and double selection—for the positive selection marker *neo* with G418 and the negative selection marker TK with ganciclovir—we obtained five PCR-confirmed, homologous-recombinant clones (Fig. 54–4B).

The positive selection marker in this experiment was a *neo* cassette under the PGK promoter. As this cassette is still in the knockin cell line, it could interfere with the normal expression of the *TH* gene and the IRES–eGFP reporter gene. To delete the *neo* cassette, we transiently transfected two of the *TH*–eGFP knockin cell lines with a plasmid containing the phage recombinase Cre under the control of the EF1α promoter.[35] We transfected with FuGene-6 and used the protocols described previously. The cDNA of Cre was followed by an IRES–eGFP cassette. After transient transfection with this plasmid, Cre-overexpressing cells could be easily identified by eGFP expression. Those eGFP⁺ cells were purified by fluorescence-activated cell sorting. Individual clones were analyzed for successful recombination of the two *loxP* sites, and two clones were identified that have the *neo* cassette excised by PCR (Fig. 54–4C). The clones were confirmed to have a normal karyotype.

We performed the *TH* gene targeting on cell line H9 using a targeting construct homologous to genomic DNA from the cell line H1 (see Table 54–2), suggesting that isogenic DNA is not required to obtain homologous recombination in human ES cells.

Summary

The overall targeting frequencies for the three genes described here suggest that homologous recombination is a broadly applicable technique in human ES cells (Table 54–2). The homologous recombination frequencies are roughly comparable to those observed for mouse ES cells and suggest that although successful transfection strategies differ between human and mouse ES cells, homologous recombination

TABLE 54-2
Comparison of Gene-Targeting Frequencies in Different Experimental Settings in Human ES Cells[a]

Selection procedure	Old mouse ES cell protocol	HPRT1 in H1.1	Oct4 short vector in H1.1	Oct4 long vector in H1.1	Oct4 short vector in H9	TH in H9
G418	1.0	230	69	37	48	ND
G418 and ganciclovir	ND[b]	3.3	ND	ND	ND	3.8
Homologous[c] recombinants	ND	5	19	15	2	1.3

[a]Data normalized to 1.5×10^8 electroporated human ES cells.
[b]ND = not determined.
[c]Homologous DNA was isogenic to H1 genomic DNA.

may be similar. We also demonstrated that the Cre–lox system can be used to excise specific sequences from human ES cells.

Homologous recombination in human ES cells will be important for studying gene function *in vitro* and for lineage selection. It is a powerful approach for understanding the function of any human gene. For therapeutic applications in transplantation medicine, controlled modification of specific genes should be useful for purifying specific ES cell-derived, differentiated cell types from a mixed population[36] and for altering the antigenicity of ES cell derivatives. Additionally, it should be possible to give cells new properties (such as viral resistance) to combat specific diseases. Homologous recombination in human ES cells might also be used for recently described approaches combining therapeutic cloning with gene therapy.[37]

In vitro studies will be particularly useful for learning more about the pathogenesis of diseases where mouse models have proved inadequate. For example, *HPRT*-deficient mice fail to demonstrate a Lesch-Nyhan-like phenotype.[38] *In vitro* neural differentiation of *HPRT-* human ES cells or transplantation of ES cell-derived neural tissue to an animal model could help in understanding the pathogenesis of Lesch-Nyhan syndrome. Another example of where human ES cells and homologous recombination will be useful is in understanding the function of the human heart. Specific mutations and polymorphisms that predispose people to an increased risk for sudden death syndrome or severe arrhythmia at a young age have been identified. Mice generated from ES cells in which ion channel genes have been modified by homologous recombination often have a normal heart,[35,39] again reflecting basic, clinically significant species differences. With homologous recombination, one could generate human ES cell lines bearing mutations or polymorphisms in specific ion channels and could use ES cell-derived cardiomyocytes to better understand the effects of the mutations on the physiology of the heart. A panel of ion channel polymorphisms should be extremely useful for screening drugs for toxic side effects on the heart prior to clinical trials. Thus, homologous recombination in human ES cells would be useful for numerous *in vitro* models of human disease.

ACKNOWLEDGMENTS

We thank Henry Yuen and the Oscar Rennebohm Foundation for their gifts to the Wisconsin Foundation that supports this work. We thank S. Witowski, J. Antosiewicz, and K. Murphy for technical assistance. The double IRES cassette and the Cre–IRES–eGFP cassette were provided by O. Weber and H.J. Fehling (University of Ulm, Germany).

REFERENCES

1. Avery, O.T., MacLeod, C.M., and McCarty, M. (1944). Studies on the chemical nature of the substance inducing transformation of pneumococcal types: Induction of transformation by a deoxyribonucleic acid fraction isolated from Pneumococcus type III. *J. Exp. Med.* **79,** 137–158.
2. Smithies, O., Gregg, R.G., Boggs, S.S., Koralewski, M.A., and Kucherlapati, R.S. (1985). Insertion of DNA sequences into the human chromosomal β-globin locus by homologous recombination. *Nature* **317,** 230–234.
3. Thomas, K.R., Folger, K.R., and Capecchi, M.R. (1986). High-frequency targeting of genes to specific sites in the mammalian genome. *Cell* **44,** 419–428.
4. Thomas, K.R., and Capecchi, M.R. (1987). Site-directed mutagenesis by gene targeting in mouse embryo-derived stem cells. *Cell* **51,** 503–512.
5. Doetschman, T., Gregg, R.G., Maeda, N., Hooper, M.L., Melton, D.W., Thompson, S., and Smithies, O. (1987). Targeted correction of a mutant *HPRT* gene in mouse embryonic stem cells. *Nature* **330,** 576–578.
6. Smithies, O. (1993). Animal models of human genetic diseases. *Trends Genet.* **9,** 112–116.
7. Martin, G.R. (1981). Isolation of a pluripotent cell line from early mouse embryos cultured in medium conditioned by teratocarcinoma stem cells. *Proc. Natl. Acad. Sci. USA* **78,** 7634–7638.
8. Evans, M.J., and Kaufman, M.H. (1981). Establishment in culture of pluripotential cells from mouse embryos. *Nature* **292,** 154–156.
9. Thomson, J.A., Itskovitz-Eldor, J., Shapiro, S.S., Waknitz, M.A., Swiergiel, J.J., Marshall, V.S., and Jones, J.M. (1998). Embryonic stem cell lines derived from human blastocysts. *Science* **282,** 1145–1147.

10. Reubinoff, B.E., Pera, M.F., Fong, C.Y., Trounson, A., and Bongso, A. (2000). Embryonic stem cell lines from human blastocysts: somatic differentiation *in vitro. Nat. Biotechnol.* **18,** 399–404.

11. Amit, M., Carpenter, M.K., Inokuma, M.S., Chiu, C.P., Harris, C.P., Waknitz, M.A., Itskovitz-Eldor, J., and Thomson, J.A. (2000). Clonally derived human embryonic stem cell lines maintain pluripotency and proliferative potential for prolonged periods of culture. *Dev. Biol.* **227,** 271–278.

12. Zwaka, T.P., and Thomson, J.A. (2003). Homologous recombination in human embryonic stem cells. *Nat. Biotechnol.* **21,** 319–321.

13. Albertini, R.J. (2001). HPRT mutations in humans: biomarkers for mechanistic studies. *Mutat. Res.* **489,** 1–16.

14. Kuehn, M.R., Bradley, A., Robertson, E.J., and Evans, M.J. (1987). A potential animal model for Lesch-Nyhan syndrome through introduction of HPRT mutations into mice. *Nature* **326,** 295–298.

15. Mansour, S.L., Thomas, K.R., and Capecchi, M.R. (1988). Disruption of the protooncogene *int-2* in mouse embryo-derived stem cells: a general strategy for targeting mutations to nonselectable genes. *Nature* **336,** 348–352.

16. Deng, C., and Capecchi, M.R. (1992). Reexamination of gene targeting frequency as a function of the extent of homology between the targeting vector and the target locus. *Mol. Cell Biol.* **12,** 3365–3371.

17. Eiges, R., Schuldiner, M., Drukker, M., Yanuka, O., Itskovitz-Eldor, J., and Benvenisty, N. (2001). Establishment of human embryonic stem cell-transfected clones carrying a marker for undifferentiated cells. *Curr Biol.* **11,** 514–518.

18. Xu, C., Inokuma, M.S., Denham, J., Golds, K., Kundu, P., Gold, J.D., and Carpenter, M.K. (2001). Feeder-free growth of undifferentiated human embryonic stem cells. *Nat. Biotechnol.* **19,** 971–974.

19. Vasquez, K.M., Marburger, K., Intody, Z., and Wilson, J.H. (2001). Manipulating the mammalian genome by homologous recombination. *Proc. Natl. Acad. Sci. USA* **98,** 8403–8410.

20. Morrison, C., and Takeda, S. (2000). Genetic analysis of homologous DNA recombination in vertebrate somatic cells. *Int. J. Biochem. Cell Biol.* **32,** 817–831.

21. Potter, H., Weir, L., and Leder, P. (1984). Enhancer-dependent expression of human κ-immunoglobulin genes introduced into mouse pre-B lymphocytes by electroporation. *Proc. Natl. Acad. Sci. USA* **81,** 7161–7165.

22. Baum, C., Forster, P., Hegewisch-Becker, S., and Harbers, K. (1994). An optimized electroporation protocol applicable to a wide range of cell lines. *Biotechniques* **17,** 1058–1062.

23. Fehling, H.J., Swat, W., Laplace, C., Kuhn, R., Rajewsky, K., Muller, U., and von Boehmer, H. (1994). MHC class I expression in mice lacking the proteasome subunit LMP-7. *Science* **265,** 1234–1237.

24. Wernig, M., Tucker, K.L., Gornik, V., Schneiders, A., Buschwald, R., Wiestler, O.D., Barde, Y.A., and Brustle, O. (2002). τ-eGFP embryonic stem cells: an efficient tool for neuronal lineage selection and transplantation. *J. Neurosci. Res.* **69,** 918–924.

25. Xian, H.Q., McNichols, E., St Clair, A., and Gottlieb, D.I. (2003). A subset of ES cell-derived neural cells marked by gene targeting. *Stem Cells* **21,** 41–49.

26. Ying, Q.L., Stavridis, M., Griffiths, D., Li, M., and Smith, A. (2003). Conversion of embryonic stem cells into neuroectodermal precursors in adherent monoculture. *Nat. Biotechnol.* **21,** 183–186.

27. Mountford, P., Zevnik, B., Duwel, A., Nichols, J., Li, M., Dani, C., Robertson, M., Chambers, I., and Smith, A. (1994). Dicistronic targeting constructs: Reporters and modifiers of mammalian gene expression. *Proc. Natl. Acad. Sci. USA* **91,** 4303–4307.

28. Nichols, J., Zevnik, B., Anastassiadis, K., Niwa, H., Klewe-Nebenius, D., Chambers, I., Scholer, H., and Smith, A. (1998). Formation of pluripotent stem cells in the mammalian embryo depends on the POU transcription factor Oct4. *Cell* **95,** 379–391.

29. Niwa, H., Miyazaki, J., and Smith, A.G. (2000). Quantitative expression of Oct-3/4 defines differentiation, dedifferentiation, or self-renewal of ES cells. *Nat. Genet.* **24,** 372–376.

30. Takeda, J., Seino, S., and Bell, G.I. (1992). Human *Oct3* gene family: cDNA sequences, alternative splicing, gene organization, chromosomal location, and expression at low levels in adult tissues. *Nucleic Acids Res.* **20,** 4613–4620.

31. Jang, S.K., and Wimmer, E. (1990). Cap-independent translation of encephalomyocarditis virus RNA: structural elements of the internal ribosomal entry site and involvement of a cellular 57-kD RNA-binding protein. *Genes Dev.* **4,** 1560–1572.

32. Zhang, G., Gurtu, V., and Kain, S.R. (1996). An enhanced green fluorescent protein allows sensitive detection of gene transfer in mammalian cells. *Biochem. Biophys. Res. Commun.* **227,** 707–711.

33. Haavik, J., and Toska, K. (1998). Tyrosine hydroxylase and Parkinson's disease. *Mol. Neurobiol.* **16,** 285–309.

34. O'Malley, K.L., Anhalt, M.J., Martin, B.M., Kelsoe, J.R., Winfield, S.L., and Ginns, E.I. (1987). Isolation and characterization of the human tyrosine hydroxylase gene: identification of 5′ alternative splice sites responsible for multiple mRNAs. *Biochemistry* **26,** 6910–6914.

35. Kilby, N.J., Snaith, M.R., and Murray, J.A. (1993). Site-specific recombinases: tools for genome engineering. *Trends Genet.* **9,** 413–421.

36. Odorico, J.S., Kaufman, D.S., and Thomson, J.A. (2001). Multilineage differentiation from human embryonic stem cell lines. *Stem Cells* **19,** 193–204.

37. Rideout, W.M., 3rd, Hochedlinger, K., Kyba, M., Daley, G.Q., and Jaenisch, R. (2002). Correction of a genetic defect by nuclear transplantation and combined cell and gene therapy. *Cell* **109,** 17–27.

38. Finger, S., Heavens, R.P., Sirinathsinghji, D.J., Kuehn, M.R., and Dunnett, S.B. (1988). Behavioral and neurochemical evaluation of a transgenic mouse model of Lesch-Nyhan syndrome. *J. Neurol. Sci.* **86,** 203–213.

39. London, B. (2001). Cardiac arrhythmias: From (transgenic) mice to men. *J. Cardiovasc. Electrophysiol.* **12,** 1089–1091.

Transduction of Human ES Cells by Lentiviral Vectors

Michal Gropp and Benjamin Reubinoff

In this chapter, we focus on the use of vectors derived from lentiviruses for stable gene delivery into human embryonic stem (hES) cells. The lentiviruses are a subgroup of retroviruses associated with slow chronic diseases in humans and animals. Vectors derived from lentiviruses have been developed over the last few years and have been shown to efficiently transduce a variety of cell types, including primary cells. The key properties of lentiviral vectors include: (1) efficient infection of both dividing and nondividing cells; (2) integration into the host cell DNA, thus allowing a stable expression and germ line transmission of the transgene; and (3) lack of immunogenicity. The potential of modified lentiviral vectors pseudotyped with vesicular stomatitis virus glycoprotein (VSV-G) to promote efficient and stable gene delivery into hES cells was recently demonstrated. Transgene expression was stable during prolonged undifferentiated proliferation of transduced hES cells in culture as well as during differentiation into progeny representing all three germinal layers both *in vitro* and *in vivo*. Thus, the transduced cells remain pluripotent and retain their self-renewal potential. Genetic modifications of hES cells with lentiviral vectors may have far reaching applications for basic and applied research of hES cells.

Introduction

The strategies for gene transfer into ES cells are based on nonviral and viral delivery systems. Nonviral systems include electroporation, microinjection, and transfection. The gene transfer efficiency of these systems is relatively low, and they promote mostly transient transgene expression. However, they are considered safe.[1] In contrast, gene delivery systems based on viral vectors are highly efficient. The unique properties of each virus affect its suitability for specific gene delivery applications. Although some viruses remain extrachromosomal in the infected cell, allowing high transient activity of the transgene, other viruses integrate into the host DNA and thus enable a stable transgene expression.[2]

In this chapter, we focus on the use of vectors derived from lentiviruses for stable gene delivery into hES cells. To understand how wild-type (WT) lentiviruses were turned into vectors that mediate gene transfer, one must be familiar with their unique properties. We therefore describe briefly the viral genome organization and life cycle and the design of safe and efficient lentiviral vectors. A more detailed description of the biology of lentiviruses can be found in other reviews.[3–5]

GENETICS AND LIFE CYCLE OF LENTIVIRUSES

The lentiviruses are a subgroup of retroviruses associated with slow chronic diseases in humans and animals. The best-characterized lentivirus is the human immunodeficiency virus type 1 (HIV-1), which causes acquired immunodeficiency syndrome in humans. Like other retroviruses, lentiviruses are RNA viruses that replicate through a unique life cycle; upon entry into the host cells, the RNA genome of lentiviruses is reverse transcribed into a DNA that is integrated into the host cell chromosomal DNA.

The lentiviral genome is in two identical RNA molecules. The genome contains three genes, *gag, pol,* and *env,* encoding the viral core structural proteins, replicative proteins, envelope glycoprotein, and several additional regulatory and accessory genes critical for viral pathogenesis. After reverse transcription of the viral RNA, the proviral DNA genes are flanked by two identical long terminal repeats (LTRs) containing most of the viral regulatory elements (Fig. 55–1).

The life cycle of the lentivirus begins when the virus infects the host cell by binding to specific receptors on its surface and subsequently enters its cytoplasm. Following entry into the cytoplasm, the viral genome is uncoated, reverse transcribed into double-stranded proviral DNA, and permanently integrated into the genome of the host cell. The integrated provirus uses the host cell machinery for its replication and expression throughout the lifetime of the infected host cell.

DESIGN OF LENTIVIRAL VECTORS

Vectors based on HIV-1 were developed over the last several years, and were shown to be efficient gene delivery tools.[6–8] The HIV-1-derived vectors were designed to exploit the characteristics of all retroviruses: (1) efficient infection of host cells; (2) integration into the host DNA, thus allowing stable expression and germ line transmission of the transgene; (3) lack of immunogenicity; and (4) unique arrangement of the

Handbook of Stem Cells
Volume 1
Copyright © 2004 by Academic Press
All rights of reproduction in any form reserved.

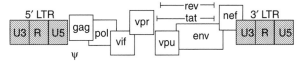

Figure 55–1. *Representation of the HIV-1 provirus.* The scheme depicts the structure of the HIV-1 provirus after reverse transcription of the viral RNA and integration into the host cell DNA. The HIV-1 genome contains three genes, *gag, pol,* and *env,* encoding the viral core structural proteins, replication proteins, and envelope glycoprotein. Six additional regulatory and accessory genes—*vif, vpr, vpu, rev, tat,* and *nef*—critical for viral pathogenesis are also present. The proviral DNA genes are flanked by two identical long terminal repeats (LTRs) comprising two unique regions (U3 and U5) and a repeat region (R), containing most of the viral regulatory elements. The packaging signal, ψ, is located within the coding region.

viral genome in which most of the regulatory *cis*-acting elements are located in the viral LTRs and the coding *trans*-acting elements are located in the center, allowing easy genetic manipulation of either the regulatory or the coding sequence (see Fig. 55–1). One significant advantage of lentiviruses in their use for gene transfer is that in contrast to "simple" retroviruses that can infect only dividing cells, lentiviruses are capable of replicating in both dividing and nondividing cells. Hence, HIV-1–derived vectors were able to efficiently transduce various types of cells, including stem cells, nondividing cells, and fully differentiated cells *in vivo* and *in vitro.*[7,9,10]

DEVELOPMENT OF SAFER LENTIVIRAL VECTORS

Since the parental HIV-1 causes a severe disease in humans, the issue of biosafety was one of the major concerns in the design of HIV-1–derived vectors. Consequently, steps were taken to increase their biosafety: First, all HIV-1 genes were deleted from the viral vector construct, generating a replication-defective transfer vector that contained, in addition to the transgene, only the regulatory elements of the virus (Fig. 55–2A). These viral elements are essential for its replication, integration, and encapsidation. Second, the proteins necessary for packaging and for envelope formation were provided *in trans* by the addition of two supplementary plasmids that lacked the packaging signal: a packaging plasmid encoding the structural and accessory proteins of HIV-1 except for the envelope (Fig. 55–2B) and an envelope plasmid encoding a heterologous envelope VSV-G (Fig. 55–2C). The use of VSV-G for pseudotyping the HIV-1–derived vectors prevented the generation of WT virus and was beneficial because it broadened the host range and increased the stability of the viral particles, allowing simple concentration of the virus.[11]

Transfer-vector viral particles were produced by transient cotransfection into highly transfectable cells of the three plasmids: (1) the replication-defective HIV-1 transfer vector expressing the transgene from the viral promoter in the 5′ LTR, which was the only construct containing the packaging signal and therefore was able to encapsidate and form a virion; (2) the packaging plasmid expressing all viral genes except the envelope; and (3) the envelope plasmid expressing VSV-G (see Fig. 55–2). The supernatant containing the recombinant virions was collected and used to infect the target cells.

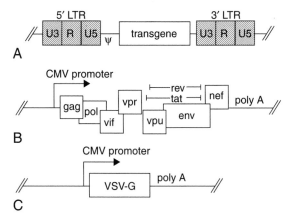

Figure 55–2. *First generation of HIV-1–derived vector system.* The scheme depicts the three plasmid components first used to generate the recombinant HIV-1 virions. (A) The replication-defective transfer vector, harboring the transgene, containing a deletion of the entire viral-coding region, and leaving only the regulatory elements of the virus essential for its replication, integration, and encapsidation. This plasmid is the only vector containing the packaging signal ψ. (B) A packaging plasmid encoding the structural and accessory proteins of HIV-1 except the envelope, lacking the packaging signal. (C) An envelope plasmid encoding a heterologous envelope, vesicular stomatitis virus glycoprotein (VSV-G).

Following infection, the replication-defective provirus integrated into the host cell genome, where it continuously expressed the transgene but was unable to form a replication-competent virus. Infection with the replication-defective virus, which is able to undergo only one cycle of replication and integration, is termed transduction.[8,12–14]

To further improve vector biosafety, self-inactivating (SIN) HIV-1 transfer vectors were constructed by introducing a large deletion in the U3 region of the viral LTR that abolished its promoter–enhancer activity.[15,16] In these SIN vectors, an internal heterologous promoter directed the expression of the transgene. The deletion of promoter–enhancer sequences in the viral LTR was not only another precaution against production of WT virions but also an improvement to the performance of the internal promoters.[16] The packaging vector was further improved by deleting most regulatory and accessory genes from the construct, leaving only the *gag, pol,* and *rev* genes (Fig. 55–3B).

IMPROVEMENT OF VECTOR PERFORMANCE

To improve the performance of the transfer vectors, additional viral elements were incorporated into the transfer vector (Fig. 55–3A). The posttranscriptional regulatory element from Woodchuck hepatitis virus (WPRE), shown to increase the expression levels of lentiviral vectors,[17] was added downstream of the transgene. The central polypurine tract (cPPT) sequence, present in all lentiviral *pol* genes, was reinserted upstream of the internal promoter. The insertion of cPPT, which is required in *cis* for the nuclear import of the HIV-1 genome into the nucleus of the host cell, greatly increased the transduction efficiency.[18,19] HIV-1–derived vectors containing both cPPT and WPRE were shown to promote enhanced transduction and transgene expression.[20]

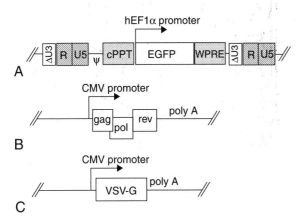

Figure 55–3. *Advanced HIV-1–derived vector system.* The scheme depicts the improved three plasmid components used to generate the recombinant HIV-1 virions. (A) The transfer vector is a modified SIN HIV-1 replication-defective vector, containing a large deletion in the U3 region of the LTR, which abolishes its promoter–enhancer activity. In this vector, the expression of the reporter gene, enhanced green fluorescence protein (EGFP), is driven by the constitutive human elongation factor 1α (hEF1α) promoter. The modified SIN vector contains additional regulatory elements that improve vector performance: the posttranscriptional regulatory element from Woodchuck hepatitis virus (WPRE), which increases transgene expression, and the central polypurine tract (cPPT) of HIV-1, which enhances transduction efficiencies. (B) The advanced packaging plasmid harbors only three viral genes necessary for packaging under the control of the cytomegalovirus (CMV) promoter. (C) The envelope plasmid harbors the vesicular stomatitis virus glycoprotein (VSV-G) under the control of the CMV promoter and is used for pseudotyping the virions.

To summarize the development of lentiviral vectors thus far, recombinant HIV-1 virions are produced by transient cotransfection into highly transfectable cells of (1) the replication-defective, modified SIN HIV-1 transfer vector expressing the transgene from an internal promoter, (2) the advanced packaging plasmid encoding only three necessary viral genes, and (3) the envelope plasmid expressing VSV-G (see Fig. 55–3).

TRANSDUCTION OF ES CELLS BY LENTIVIRAL VECTORS

Vectors based on "simple" retroviruses such as the Moloney murine leukemia virus (MoMLV) were used extensively for gene delivery into mammalian cells. However, when MoMLV-derived vectors were used for transduction of mouse ES and EC cells, it was found that even though the provirus had integrated into the host cell DNA, expression of the transgene was down-regulated over time.[21–24] The mechanism of this stem cell-specific gene silencing is still unclear, but data from various studies suggest the involvement of *de novo* methylation of the integrated provirus and *trans*-acting transcriptional repressors.[24]

The recent development of lentiviral-derived vectors and their ability to efficiently transduce a variety of cell types, including primary cells, promoted the study of these vectors as potential gene delivery tools for ES cells.

Hamaguchi *et al.*[25] was the first group to report that HIV-1–based vector pseudotyped with VSV-G could efficiently transduce mouse ES cells. They further showed that after differentiation *in vitro* of the transduced cells, they exhibited sustained although reduced expression of the transgene.[25] Pfeifer *et al.*[26] have further implored the use of improved SIN HIV-1–based vectors pseudotyped with VSV-G for transduction of mouse ES cells. Similar to the results of Hamaguchi *et al.*, the improved SIN HIV-1 vectors efficiently transduced mouse ES cells. Moreover, the transduced cells maintained transgene expression during undifferentiated proliferation of the ES cells as well as during differentiation *in vitro* and *in vivo*. Finally, the transduced mouse ES cells were used to generate transgenic mice. The chimeric mice that were formed and their progeny expressed the transgene in different tissues.[26] These results indicated that the use of lentiviral vectors for transduction of ES cells enables germ line transmission of the transgene and sustained transgene expression, which is not developmentally silenced.

Asano *et al.*[27] used for their study ES cells derived from the cynomolgus monkey, which exhibit similar features to hES cells. The vector employed in this study was based on another member of the lentiviruses, simian immunodeficiency virus (SIV), derived from the nonpathogenic African green monkey. The modified SIV vector pseudotyped with VSV-G efficiently transduced monkey ES cells, and high levels of green fluorescent protein (GFP) expression persisted for long periods of undifferentiated proliferation. Moreover, embryoid bodies generated from the transduced cells expressed the transgene, implying that transgene expression was sustained during *in vitro* differentiation of the cynomolgus ES cells.

Since the establishment of hES cell lines from human blastocytes.[28,29] a major effort was invested in the development of efficient strategies for gene delivery into these cells. Initial data highlighting the potential of lentiviral vectors to serve as tools for gene delivery into hES cells was reported by Pfeifer *et al.*[26] An advanced, SIN HIV-1–derived vector pseudotyped with VSV-G efficiently transduced hES cells. Sustained transgene expression was observed over several passages. We have developed a protocol for efficient delivery of transgenes into hES cells using a modified, SIN HIV-1–derived vector.[30] After efficient transduction of the hES cells, we observed sustained transgene expression during long-term (38 weeks) undifferentiated proliferation *in vitro*. Transgene expression was stable during differentiation *in vitro* and *in vivo* into derivatives of all three germ layers. Thus, the transduced hES cells retained their capability for self-renewal as well as their pluripotent potential. Ma *et al.*[31] additionally showed the ability of a different SIN HIV-1–based vector to efficiently transduce hES cells and confer stable transgene expression for 60 days in culture and throughout differentiation *in vitro* into the hematopoietic lineage.

Together, the data from all the studies carried out to date indicate that lentiviral-based vectors, and especially HIV-1–derived vectors, are powerful, efficient tools for gene delivery into ES cells. These vectors are significantly advantageous over "simple" retroviral vectors for transduction of both primate and nonprimate ES cells. First, they confer sustained transgene expression during prolonged proliferation of transduced ES cells. Second, the transduced cells retain their potential for self-renewal and continue to proliferate as undifferentiated cells in culture. Third, they promote stable transgene expression throughout differentiation *in vitro* and *in vivo*. Lastly, the transduced cells retain their pluripotency and are able to differentiate into cell types from all three germinal layers both *in vitro* and *in vivo*.

POTENTIAL APPLICATIONS OF GENETIC MODIFICATIONS OF hES CELLS BY LENTIVIRAL VECTORS

The studies performed until now established the use of HIV-1–derived vectors as efficient gene delivery tools into hES cells, which promote stable and high expression of the transgene. This technique could soon be used in various applications.

The lentiviral vectors could be designed to overexpress transcriptional factors that direct the differentiation of hES cells into a specific cell type.[32] Constructing vectors containing lineage- or cell type–specific promoters driving the expression of selectable markers (such as antibiotic resistance or GFP) could promote the selection of either undifferentiated stem cells or differentiated cells of specific lineages.[33] The ability to direct the differentiation of hES cells or to select a specific lineage may be highly valuable to the study of human embryogenesis and could provide an unlimited supply of a pure population of various cell types for transplantation therapy.

Lentiviral vectors may potentially be used to express specific genes in transplanted hES cells for the correction of genetic diseases.

Lentiviral vectors may be invaluable for the study of gene function in hES cells and of early human development. These vectors may be employed to silence genes of interest by designing vectors expressing specific short interfering RNA (siRNA) sequences. In this approach, the expression of a targeted gene is eliminated at the posttranscriptional level. SiRNAs delivered by lentiviral vectors have recently been shown to mediate specific, stable, and functional gene silencing in primary mammalian cells.[34] Moreover, knockout of genes at the DNA level can be achieved using a Cre–*loxP* system in which the Cre recombinase is transiently expressed from a lentiviral vector.[35]

Finally, screening for genes that induce specific phenotypes in hES cells can be performed by transducing hES cells with lentiviral vectors expressing various cDNA libraries.

In the next section, we describe the practical aspects of the generation of recombinant HIV-1 virions and the transduction of hES cells.

Recombinant Virus Production and Transduction of hES Cells

In general, recombinant virions are produced by transient cotransfection of the replication-defective, modified, SIN HIV-1 transfer vector carrying the transgene, the packaging plasmid, and the envelope plasmid expressing VSV-G in human 293T cells. The supernatant containing the recombinant virions is collected, concentrated, and then used to transduce hES cells.

TISSUE CULTURE AND MEDIA

Growth and Maintenance of hES Cells

Human ES cells may be cultured on mouse embryonic fibroblast (MEF) feeders with serum-containing medium[29] or on feeder-free Matrigel-coated plates.[36]

Media

Serum-free Medium. The serum-free medium used for the propagation of hES cells is composed of 80% knockout Dulbecco's modified Eagle's medium (DMEM, Gibco) supplemented with 20% serum replacement (SR, Gibco), 1 mM L-glutamine, 50 U/ml penicillin, 50 μg/ml streptomycin, 1% nonessential amino acids, 0.1 mM β-mercaptoethanol, and 4 ng/ml basic fibroblast growth factor (bFGF).

Serum-containing Medium. The serum-containing medium used for the propagation of hES cells is composed of 80% DMEM supplemented with 20% fetal calf serum (FCS, Hyclone), 1 mM L-glutamine, 50 U/ml penicillin, 50 μg/ml streptomycin, 1% nonessential amino acids, and 0.1 mM β-mercaptoethanol.

Growth of 293T Cells

293T human embryonic kidney cells are routinely grown in DMEM containing 10% FCS, 1-mM L-glutamine, 100-U/ml penicillin, and 0.01-mg/ml streptomycin.

PLASMID COMPONENTS

The transfer vectors used by most groups are SIN-modified HIV-1 vectors such as pSIN18.cPPT.hEF1α.EGFP.WPRE or SINF-EF1α-GFP-SAR.[30,31] These vectors express the transgene from an internal promoter and contain additional regulatory elements. The internal promoters reported to be active in hES cell are elongation factor 1α (EF1α), phosphoglycerate kinase (PGK), and the hybrid promoter CAG composed of CMV immediate early enhancer, chicken β-actin promoter, and a rabbit β-globin intran. However, other promoters may also be active in hES cells. The envelope plasmid expressing the heterologous envelope VSV-G is pMDG. The packaging plasmid expressing the *gag, pol,* and *rev* genes is pCMVΔR8.91. The three plasmids are depicted in Fig. 55–3. Plasmid DNA should be relatively pure and can be purified by commercially available kits.

GENERATION OF RECOMBINANT HIV-1 VIRIONS

This section describes the production of recombinant virions by transient cotransfection of three plasmids into 293T cells (third-generation packaging system). Note that some laboratories are using a fourth-generation packaging system in which the *rev* gene is expressed from a separate plasmid.[14] We routinely use FuGene-6 transfection reagent (Roche Molecular Biochemicals, Mannheim, Germany), but the calcium-phosphate transfection method (or any other efficient transfection technique) can be used for the production of recombinant virions.[14]

FuGene-6 Transfection Protocol

1. Twenty-four hours before transfection, seed $1.5–2 \times 10^6$ 293T cells on 10-cm tissue culture plates in 10 ml DMEM containing 10% FCS, 1 mM L-glutamine, 100 U/ml

penicillin, and 0.01 mg/ml streptomycin; incubate at 37°C. On the day of transfection, the confluence of the 293T cells should be approximately 60%.

2. In an Eppendorf tube, combine a total of 20 µg of plasmid DNA: 3.5 µg of the envelope plasmid pMDG, 6.5 µg of the packaging plasmid pCMVΔR8.91, and 10 µg of the transfer vector pSIN18.cPPT.hEF1α.EGFP.WPRE.

3. Place serum-free medium (Optimem, Gibco) in a second Eppendorf tube as diluent for the FuGene-6 transfection reagent. Note that the final volume of the transfection—including the three plasmids, the FuGene-6 reagent, and the Optimem medium—should be 600 µl. Add 55 µl FuGene-6 transfection reagent (a ratio of 2.7 FuGene reagent to 1 plasmid DNA) directly to the Optimem medium in a dropwise fashion. Flick the tube gently to mix. Incubate at room temperature for approximately 5 minutes.

4. Add the FuGene-6–Optimem solution to the tube containing the DNA drop by drop. Flick the tube gently. Incubate at room temperature for 15–45 minutes to allow complex formation.

5. Dropwise, add the complex mixture to the 293T cells, distributing it around the culture plate. Swirl the plate to ensure even distribution of the transfection complex. Incubate the plates at 37°C.

Collection of Recombinant Viruses

1. The day after transfection (16–20 hours after transfection), replace the medium with 10 ml fresh serum-free medium (see the section "Serum-free Medium"). An alternative medium is the serum-containing medium used for routine growth of hES cells[29] (see the section "Serum-containing Medium").

2. After further incubation of 24 hours at 37°C, collect the supernatant containing the viral particles. Store the supernatant in the dark at 4°C. Replace the supernatant in the culture plate with 10 ml fresh serum-free or serum-containing medium. Incubate the plate at 37°C for an additional 24 hours and collect the supernatant.

3. Combine the two collected supernatants (for a total of 20 ml per 10-cm tissue culture plate) and filter it through a 0.45-µm filter (Sartorius, Goettingen, Germany). Proceed to concentration of the virus. Save some virus (~0.1 ml) for measurement of viral titer.

Concentration of Recombinant Virions

1. Concentrate the virus by ultracentrifugation at $50,000 \times g$ at 4°C for 2 hours. We use a Sorvall model Discovery 100 centrifuge and a Surespin 630 swinging bucket rotor for this step.

2. After centrifugation, resuspend the pellet immediately in serum-free medium containing 20% SR at 0.1 of the volume of the original medium (10× concentration). For resuspension of the virus, gently pipette it several times.

3. Use the concentrated virus immediately for transduction or resuspend it in a minimal volume of phosphate-buffered saline (PBS) and store frozen at −80°C. Save some virus (~0.01 ml) for measurement of viral titer.

TRANSDUCTION OF hES CELLS

Several methods can be used for the transduction of hES cells, depending on their method of culturing. Two protocols will be described here: the transduction of hES cells cultured on MEF feeders with serum-containing medium[30] and the transduction of hES cells cultured without feeders on Matrigel-coated plates.[31]

Transduction of hES Cells Cultured in Serum-containing Medium[30]

1. Human ES cells are grown from cell clumps and are maintained on MEF feeders in serum-containing medium as described.[29]

2. At the time of routine passage, isolate clumps of undifferentiated cells from hES colonies by mechanical slicing followed by digestion with 10 mg/ml dispase (Gibco-BRL).

3. Incubate the hES cell clumps with the concentrated virus (1 ml) in the presence of 5 µg/ml Polybrene (Sigma) in 35-mm Petri dishes (Falcon), at 37°C for 2 hours.

4. Add fresh concentrated virus (1 ml) and continue the incubation for another 1.5–2 hours.

5. Collect the transduced stem cell clumps, wash them briefly in PBS, and replate them on MEF feeders.

6. Measure transduction efficiency using fluorescence-activated cell sorting (FACS) analysis seven days after transduction.

Transduction of hES Cells Cultured Without Feeders

These instructions have been adapted from Ma et al.[31]

1. Human ES cells are cultured without feeders in MEF-conditioned medium on Matrigel-coated plates, as described.[36]

2. At the time of routine passage, wash hES cells with PBS and dissociate them to single cells using 0.05% trypsin–0.53-mM EDTA.

3. Incubate the dissociated hES cells with the concentrated virus in the presence of 5-µg/ml Polybrene, and replate them on Matrigel-coated plates.

4. The following day, change the medium.

5. Measure transduction efficiency using FACS analysis 7 days after transduction.

FACS ANALYSIS

The measurement of transduction efficiency is based on the analysis of the percentage of GFP-expressing cells and is performed using a FACScalibur system (Becton-Dickenson) and CellQuest software. The level of spontaneous differentiation among the transduced hES cells can be determined by analysis of the percentage of cells immunoreactive with antibodies against stem cell–specific markers such as SSEA-4, TRA-1-60 (both commercially available), or the GCTM2 antibody.[37]

1. In the presence of serum, separate the transduced hES cell colonies from the MEF feeders with dispase (10 mg/ml). If the hES cells are grown on Matrigel, proceed directly to step 2.

2. Wash the cells with PBS and trypsinize them using 0.05% trypsin–0.5 mM EDTA to obtain a single-cell suspension.

3. Centrifuge the cells at 1500 rpm for 5 minutes.

4. Incubate the cells with the primary stem cell–specific antibody on ice for 30 minutes.
5. Wash the cells with cold PBS and centrifuge them at 1500 rpm for 5 minutes.
6. Incubate the pellet with a secondary antibody for 30 minutes on ice. As a control, incubate the cells with the secondary antibody only.
7. Wash the cells in cold PBS as in step 5, and resuspend the pellet in FACS buffer (PBS supplemented with 1% BSA and 0.1% sodium azide) containing 1 µg/ml propidium iodide (PI) for gating out dead cells.
8. Using FACS, analyze the percentage of GFP+ hES cells. The percentage of undifferentiated cells among the transduced hES cells is determined by analyzing the percentage of GFP-expressing cells immunoreactive with the stem cell-specific antibody.

MEASUREMENT OF VIRAL TITER

The method described here for determining viral titers is based on GFP expression. Other methods, which determine viral titers by measuring other viral parameters, are described elsewhere.[14]

1. Twenty-four hours before transduction, plate approximately 5×10^4 293T cells (or HeLa cells) per well in a 12-well tissue culture plate so that the following day there will be 10^5 cells per well. Incubate the cells at 37°C for 24 hours.
2. The following day, transduce the cells with serial dilutions of the nonconcentrated and concentrated virus. After incubation for 24 hours at 37°C, replace the medium.
3. Two or three days after transduction, trypsinize the cells using 0.25% trypsin–1 mM EDTA. Centrifuge the trypsinized cells at 1500 rpm for 5 minutes, and resuspend in FACS buffer containing PI.
4. Measure the percentage of GFP+ cells by FACS analysis. The viral titer (transducing units per milliliter, TU/ml) is calculated by multiplying the percentage of transduced cells by the total number of the cells on the day of transduction (1×10^5) and then dividing it by the volume of the viral supernatant used for transduction.

SELECTION FOR TRANSDUCED hES CELLS

Since transduction efficiencies vary, for certain applications, it may be necessary to enrich the percentage of transduced hES cells by selection for GFP-expressing cells. In general, selection can be performed by two methods: First, the transduced hES cells can be observed directly under the fluorescent microscope and regions can be selected mechanically from the hES cell colonies that express high levels of GFP. These regions can be further selectively passaged to increase the percentage of GFP-expressing cells.[30] Second, the transduced, GFP+ hES cells can be sorted by FACS.[31]

REFERENCES

1. Nishikawa, M., and Huang, L. (2001). Nonviral vectors in the new millennium: delivery barriers in gene transfer. *Hum. Gene. Ther.* **12**, 861–870.
2. Kay, M.A., Glorioso, J.C., and Naldini, L. (2001). Viral vectors for gene therapy: the art of turning infectious agents into vehicles of therapeutics. *Nat. Med.* **7**, 33–40.
3. Buchschacher, G.L., Jr. (2001). Introduction to retroviruses and retroviral vectors. *Somat. Cell. Mol. Genet.* **26**, 1–11.
4. Goff, S.P. (2001). Retroviridae: The retroviruses and their replication. *In* "Fields Virology," (D.M. Knipe *et al.*, eds.), Vol. 2, pp. 1871–1939. Lippincott Williams and Wilkins, Philadelphia.
5. Palu, G., Parolin, C., Takeuchi, Y., and Pizzato, M. (2000). Progress with retroviral gene vectors. *Rev. Med. Virol.* **10**, 185–202.
6. Naldini, L., Blomer, U., Gage, F.H., Trono, D., and Verma, I.M. (1996). Efficient transfer, integration, and sustained long-term expression of the transgene in adult rat brains injected with a lentiviral vector. *Proc. Natl. Acad. Sci. U. S. A.* **93**, 11,382–11,388.
7. Naldini, L., Blomer, U., Gallay, P., Ory, D., Mulligan, R., Gage, F.H., Verma, I.M., and Trono, D. (1996). *In vivo* gene delivery and stable transduction of nondividing cells by a lentiviral vector. *Science* **272**, 263–267.
8. Vigna, E., and Naldini, L. (2000). Lentiviral vectors: excellent tools for experimental gene transfer and promising candidates for gene therapy. *J. Gene Med.* **2**, 308–316.
9. Blomer, U., Naldini, L., Kafri, T., Trono, D., Verma, I.M., and Gage, F.H. (1997). Highly efficient and sustained gene transfer in adult neurons with a lentivirus vector. *J. Virol.* **71**, 6641–6649.
10. Kafri, T., Blomer, U., Peterson, D.A., Gage, F.H., and Verma, I.M. (1997). Sustained expression of genes delivered directly into liver and muscle by lentiviral vectors. *Nat. Genet.* **17**, 314–317.
11. Burns, J.C., Friedmann, T., Driever, W., Burrascano, M., and Yee, J.K. (1993). Vesicular stomatitis virus G glycoprotein pseudotyped retroviral vectors: concentration to very high titer and efficient gene transfer into mammalian and nonmammalian cells. *Proc. Natl. Acad. Sci. U. S. A.* **90**, 8033–8037.
12. Zufferey, R., Nagy, D., Mandel, R.J., Naldini, L., and Trono, D. (1997). Multiply attenuated lentiviral vector achieves efficient gene delivery *in vivo*. *Nat. Biotechnol.* **15**, 871–875.
13. Dull, T., Zufferey, R., Kelly, M., Mandel, R.J., Nguyen, M., Trono, D., and Naldini, L. (1998). A third-generation lentivirus vector with a conditional packaging system. *J. Virol.* **72**, 8463–8471.
14. Follenzi, A., and Naldini, L. (2002). HIV-based vectors: preparation and use. *Methods Mol. Med.* **69**, 259–274.
15. Miyoshi, H., Blomer, U., Takahashi, M., Gage, F.H., and Verma, I.M. (1998). Development of a self-inactivating lentivirus vector. *J. Virol.* **72**, 8150–8157.
16. Zufferey, R., Dull, T., Mandel, R.J., Bukovsky, A., Quiroz, D., Naldini, L., and Trono, D. (1998). Self-inactivating lentivirus vector for safe and efficient *in vivo* gene delivery. *J. Virol.* **72**, 9873–9880.
17. Zufferey, R., Donello, J.E., Trono, D., and Hope, T.J. (1999). Woodchuck hepatitis virus posttranscriptional regulatory element enhances expression of transgenes delivered by retroviral vectors. *J. Virol.* **73**, 2886–2892.
18. Zennou, V., Petit, C., Guetard, D., Nerhbass, U., Montagnier, L., and Charneau, P. (2000). HIV-1 genome nuclear import is mediated by a central DNA flap. *Cell* **101**, 173–185.
19. Follenzi, A., Ailles, L.E., Bakovic, S., Geuna, M., and Naldini, L. (2000). Gene transfer by lentiviral vectors is limited by nuclear translocation and rescued by HIV-1 *pol* sequences. *Nat. Genet.* **25**, 217–222.
20. Barry, S.C., Harder, B., Brzezinski, M., Flint, L.Y., Seppen, J., and Osborne, W.R. (2001). Lentivirus vectors encoding both central polypurine tract and posttranscriptional regulatory element provide enhanced transduction and transgene expression. *Hum. Gene Ther.* **12**, 1103–1108.

21. Jahner, D., Stuhlmann, H., Stewart, C.L., Harbers, K., Lohler, J., Simon, I., and Jaenisch, R. (1982). *De novo* methylation and expression of retroviral genomes during mouse embryogenesis. *Nature* **298,** 623–628.

22. Stewart, C.L., Stuhlmann, H., Jahner, D., and Jaenisch, R. (1982). *De novo* methylation, expression, and infectivity of retroviral genomes introduced into embryonal carcinoma cells. *Proc. Natl. Acad. Sci. U. S. A.* **79,** 4098–4102.

23. Niwa, O., Yokota, Y., Ishida, H., and Sugahara, T. (1983). Independent mechanisms involved in suppression of the Moloney leukemia virus genome during differentiation of murine teratocarcinoma cells. *Cell* **32,** 1105–1113.

24. Pannell, D., and Ellis, J. (2001). Silencing of gene expression: implications for design of retrovirus vectors. *Rev. Med. Virol.* **11,** 205–217.

25. Hamaguchi, I., Woods, N.B., Panagopoulos, I., Andersson, E., Mikkola, H., Fahlman, C., Zufferey, R., Carlsson, L., Trono, D., and Karlsson, S. (2000). Lentivirus vector gene expression during ES cell-derived hematopoietic development *in vitro. J. Virol.* **74,** 10,778–10,784.

26. Pfeifer, A., Ikawa, M., Dayn, Y., and Verma, I.M. (2002). Transgenesis by lentiviral vectors: lack of gene silencing in mammalian embryonic stem cells and preimplantation embryos. *Proc. Natl. Acad. Sci. U. S. A.* **99,** 2140–2145.

27. Asano, T., Hanazono, Y., Ueda, Y., Muramatsu, S., Kume, A., Suemori, H., Suzuki, Y., Kondo, Y., Harii, K., Hasegawa, M., Nakatsuji, N., and Ozawa, K. (2002). Highly efficient gene transfer into primate embryonic stem cells with a simian lentivirus vector. *Mol. Ther.* **6,** 162–168.

28. Thomson, J.A., Itskovitz-Eldor, J., Shapiro, S.S., Waknitz, M.A., Swiergiel, J.J., Marshall, V.S., and Jones, J.M. (1998). Embryonic stem cell lines derived from human blastocysts. *Science* **282,** 1145–1147.

29. Reubinoff, B.E., Pera, M.F., Fong, C.Y., Trounson, A., and Bongso, A. (2000). Embryonic stem cell lines from human blastocysts: somatic differentiation *in vitro. Nat. Biotechnol.* **18,** 399–404.

30. Gropp, M., Itsykson, P., Singer, O., Ben-Hur, T., Reinhartz, E., Galun, E., and Reubinoff, B.E. (2003). Stable genetic modification of human embryonic stem cells by lentiviral vectors. *Mol. Ther.* **7,** 281–287.

31. Ma, Y., Ramezani, A., Lewis, R., Hawley, R.G., and Thomson, J.A. (2003). High-level sustained transgene expression in human embryonic stem cells using lentiviral vectors. *Stem Cells* **21,** 111–117.

32. Klug, M.G., Soonpaa, M.H., Koh, G.Y., and Field, L.J. (1996). Genetically selected cardiomyocytes from differentiating embryonic stem cells form stable intracardiac grafts. *J. Clin. Invest.* **98,** 216–224.

33. Eiges, R., Schuldiner, M., Drukker, M., Yanuka, O., Itskovitz-Eldor, J., and Benvenisty, N. (2001). Establishment of human embryonic stem cell-transfected clones carrying a marker for undifferentiated cells. *Curr. Biol.* **11,** 514–518.

34. Rubinson, D.A., Dillon, C.P., Kwiatkowski, A.V., Sievers, C., Yang, L., Kopinja, J., Zhang, M., McManus, M.T., Gertler, F.B., Scott, M.L., and Van Parijs, L. (2003). A lentivirus-based system to functionally silence genes in primary mammalian cells, stem cells, and transgenic mice by RNA interference. *Nat. Genet.* **33,** 401–406.

35. Pfeifer, A., Brandon, E.P., Kootstra, N., Gage, F.H., and Verma, I.M. (2001). Delivery of the Cre recombinase by a self-deleting lentiviral vector: Efficient gene targeting *in vivo. Proc. Natl. Acad. Sci. U. S. A.* **98,** 11,450–11,455.

36. Xu, C., Inokuma, M.S., Denham, J., Golds, K., Kundu, P., Gold, J.D., and Carpenter, M.K. (2001). Feeder-free growth of undifferentiated human embryonic stem cells. *Nat. Biotechnol.* **19,** 971–974.

37. Pera, M.F., Blasco-Lafita, M.J., Cooper, S., Mason, M., Mills, J., and Monaghan, P. (1988). Analysis of cell differentiation lineage in human teratomas using new monoclonal antibodies to cytostructural antigens of embryonal carcinoma cells. *Differentiation* **39,** 139–149.

56

Surface Antigen Markers

Jonathan S. Draper and Peter W. Andrews

Introduction

The accessibility of molecules on the surface of cells makes them exceptionally convenient markers for characterizing cell types. Often recognized as antigens by specific antibodies, some such surface molecules are common to many cells, but some show highly restricted patterns of expression characteristic of particular cell types. Such antigens with restricted expression were called *differentiation antigens* by Boyse and Old,[1] and the patterns of expression of these markers, or *surface antigen phenotypes,* have been widely used for analyzing cell relationships in the hematopoietic and lymphoid systems. Initially, polyclonal sera, produced by cross-immunizing mice of different strains bearing alternate alleles of specific surface antigens, were used to define subsets of lymphocytes with different functional characteristics. With the subsequent development of monoclonal antibodies,[2] a wide array of so-called cluster determinant markers were characterized for defining cells of different lineages within the hematopoietic system of both mice and humans[3] and for identifying the pluripotent hematopoietic stem cells from bone marrow.[4]

However, although many surface antigens are informative in certain defined contexts, many are frequently reused at different temporal and special points during the life of an organism. An apposite example is the expression of stage-specific embryonic antigen-3 and -4 (SSEA3 and SSEA4) on cells of cleavage and blastocyst stage human embryos and separately as part of the P-blood group system on adult red blood cells.[5] Indeed, it can be difficult to establish whether expression of an antigen is restricted to a specific cell type. Thus, caution is required when interpreting the presence or absence of a particular antigen and extrapolating to the identification of the cell type or to the definition of lineage relationships between cell types. That two cell types express a common antigen is not evidence that they are related by a common lineage, though this erroneous argument is sometimes encountered. Nevertheless, surface antigens can provide powerful tools for analyzing and sorting cells that have particular characteristics within specific contexts. Added flexibility is provided by the ability to use antibodies directed to surface antigens for labeling and sorting live cells into discrete populations that retain viability.

Cell Surface Embryonic Antigens of the Laboratory Mouse

Building on the work of Boyse and Old with differentiation antigens of the adult hematopoietic system, Artzt *et al.*[6] proposed that immunization of inbred adult mice with syngeneic embryonic cells should yield an antiserum that would recognize those antigens that are only expressed in the embryo and not in the adult. They immunized 129 mice with F9 embryonal carcinoma (EC) cells derived from a teratocarcinoma of a 129 male mouse. The resulting antiserum did react specifically with EC cells and some early embryonic cells, notably those of cleavage-stage embryos and the inner cell mass (ICM) of the blastocyst, but not with postblastocyst-stage embryos, differentiated derivatives of EC cells, or various cells of adult origins. This pattern of reactivity supported the notion that embryo-specific surface antigens exist and contributed to the argument that EC cells from teratocarcinomas are malignant counterparts of ICM cells, the "stem cells" of the early embryo.[7,8]

Although some progress was made in characterizing the F9 antigen as a high-molecular-weight glycoprotein, the complexity and variability of such sera impeded detailed study. The development of monoclonal antibodies[2] provided a route to much better defined reagents. Of these, the best known is the monoclonal antibody MC480, produced from a BALB/c mouse immunized with EC cells from a 129 teratocarcinoma.[9] This antibody defines SSEA1, which shows a similar pattern of expression to the F9 antigen, and most likely, the epitope recognized by MC480 is a significant component of the F9 antigen. Other monoclonal antibody-defined antigens of mouse EC were identified (e.g., 3C4-10),[10] but these have not found wide use.

SSEA1 was identified as a glycosphingolipid, and the epitope was shown to be the Lewis-X (Le^x) hapten.[11,12] However, the epitope can also be carried by high-molecular-weight glycoproteins.[13,14] Like the F9 antigen, SSEA1 was found to be expressed by blastomeres of late cleavage- and morula-stage embryos, by cells of the ICM, and by trophectoderm. It is also characteristically expressed by mouse EC and embryonic stem (ES) cells and has become one of the hallmarks for identifying these undifferentiated stems cells; their differentiation is typically characterized by disappearance of this antigen.[15] Nevertheless, variant EC lines lacking expression of SSEA1

Handbook of Stem Cells
Volume 1

have been isolated,[16-18] so SSEA1 expression is not, in itself, a requirement for a pluripotent EC–ES phenotype.

Another embryonic antigen, SSEA3, was defined by a monoclonal antibody, MC631, raised by immunizing rats with four-cell stage mouse embryos.[19] This antigen was found to be expressed by cleavage embryos of most strains of mice but then disappears from the ICM of the blastocyst to reappear on the primitive endoderm. Its reactivity was thus the reciprocal of SSEA1 expression. It also proved to be a glycosphingolipid but with a globoseries core structure rather than with the lactoseries core of SSEA1 (Table 56–1). A further antigen in the series, SSEA4, defined by monoclonal antibody MC813-70, shows an expression pattern similar to that of SSEA3 and is a globoseries glycosphingolipid similar to the SSEA3-reactive lipid but with a terminal sialic acid.[20]

Although SSEA3 and SSEA4 are not expressed by murine EC cells and embryonic cells of the ICM, the Forssman antigen is expressed by these cells.[21,22] The Forssman antigen is also a globoseries glycolipid, but it has a terminal galactosamine residue that can be added to globoside in rodent but not in human cells.

Capitalizing on these studies of teratocarcinoma-derived EC cells, Evans and Kaufman and, independently, Martin demonstrated in 1981 that it is possible to derive cell lines by explanting the ICM of a blastocysts onto feeder cell layers *in vitro* under conditions used in some of the early derivations of EC cell lines.[23,24] Subsequently, embryonic germ cell lines closely resembling EC and ES cells were established.[25,26] These embryo-derived cells closely resembled EC cells morphologically and in developmental potential. They also expressed similar markers, including SSEA1.

Human EC and ES Cells

Initially, it was assumed that human EC cells would closely resemble mouse EC cells; in the first studies of cell lines derived from human testicular cancers, it was reported that human EC cells, like murine EC cells, were F9 antigen-positive.[27,28] However, on more detailed examination, it was established that although human EC cells closely resemble mouse EC cells in their general morphology and growth patterns, they do not express some of the markers characteristic of mouse EC cells; in particular, they lacked SSEA1.[29] By contrast, human EC cells *in vitro* and in tumors express SSEA3 and SSEA4.[19,20,30-32]

The functional significance of these glycolipid antigens, which provide excellent markers of the undifferentiated EC and ES cells in both mice and humans, remains obscure. They appear to be strongly developmentally regulated: SSEA1 expression is rapidly down-regulated on differentiation of mouse EC cells. In human EC and ES cells, not only is differentiation marked by down-regulation of the globoseries

TABLE 56–1
Glycolipid Antigens of Mouse and Human EC and ES Cells

Antigen globoseries glycolipids	Oligosaccharide structure
SSEA3	Galβ1→3GalNAcβ1→3Galα1→4Galβ1→4Glcβ1→Cer
SSEA3, SSEA4	NeuNAcα→3Galβ1→3GalNAcβ1→3Galα1→4Galβ1→4Glcβ1→Cer
Forssman	GalNAcα1→3GalNAcβ1→3Galα1→4Galβ1→4Glcβ1→Cer
Lactoseries glycolipids	
SSEA1	Galβ1→4GlcNAcβ1→4Galβ1→4Glcβ1→Cer 3 ↑ Fucα1
Ganglioseries glycolipids	
9-O-acetyl GD3 (ME311)	(9-O-acetyl)NeuNAcα2→8NeuNAcα2→3Galβ1→4Glcβ1→Cer
GT3 (A2B5)	NeuNAcα2→8NeuNAcα2→8NeuNAcα2→3Galβ1→4Glcβ1→Cer

All of these glycosphingolipid antigens are synthesized by extension from a common precursor, lactosylceramide. The likely parts of these structures comprising the epitopes recognized by the different antibodies are highlighted. The enzymes responsible for the addition of the third sugar residues (galactosyl, glucosaminyl-, and sialyltransferase) appear to regulate the rate-limiting step that controls which synthetic pathway predominates. Human EC and ES cells are characterized by expression of the glycolipid antigens SSEA3 and SSEA4, and not the lactoseries antigen SSEA1 (Leˣ). By contrast, mouse EC and ES cells are typically characterized by their expression of SSEA1. Mouse cells also express the globoseries Forssman antigen, which is not synthesized by human cells. Thus, despite the apparent distinction between mouse and human EC and ES cells in terms of their terminal sugars that comprise the different epitopes, the undifferentiated cells of both species do seem to share in common the expression of globoseries core structures.

antigens SSEA3, but at least on some derivative cells, these antigens are replaced by SSEA1 or by ganglioseries antigens, notably ganglioside GT3 recognized by antibody A2B5 (Table 56–1).[30,33] This change in expression seems to relate to switching expression of the glycosyl transferases responsible for synthesis of the globo-, lacto-, and ganglioseries core oligosaccharide structures.[34] It might be that the difference between mouse and human EC–ES cells is slighter than at first sight, since globoseries glycolipids are prominent in both species. The differences are in terminal modifications to yield Forssman in the mouse and SSEA3 and SSEA4 in humans (Table 56–1). SSEA1 mouse EC cells and SSEA3/4 human EC cells[35,36] have been reported, although at least in the case of the human cells, this is a consequence of changes to terminal modification rather than of expression of core glycolipid structures.[33] However, a small number of humans, those with the p^k and pp blood groups, are unable to synthesize the elongated globoseries structures and do not express SSEA3 or SSEA4.[5] So lack of these structures is evidently not detrimental to embryonic development. More tellingly, it is possible to eliminate all glycolipid synthesis with the inhibitor of glucosylceramide synthetase, PDMP: NTERA2 human EC cells still survive and differentiate in the presence of this inhibitor,[37] and embryos of medaka fish develop normally despite near-elimination of glycolipid synthesis.[38] Interestingly, however, p^k and pp women frequently have high rates of early spontaneous abortions, which might be caused by an immune response to embryonic antigens,[39] perhaps SSEA3, SSEA4, or both.

A different series of antigens of human EC and ES cells comprises the keratan sulfates, different epitopes of which are recognized by several antibodies, most notably TRA-1-60, TRA-1-81, GCTM2, K4, and K21.[40–44] Of these antigens, TRA-1-60 is dependent upon a terminal sialic acid,[41] and GCTM2 has been reported to recognize the internal protein structure.[43] Unlike SSEA3 and SSEA4, expression of these antigens is unaffected by PDMP.[38]

Human ES cells closely resemble human EC cells in expression of these antigens; they are generally SSEA3$^+$, SSEA4$^+$, TRA-1-60$^+$, TRA-1-81$^+$, GCTM2$^+$, and SSEA1$^-$.[45–47] Likewise, the ICM cells of human blastocyst stage embryos are SSEA3$^+$, SSEA4$^+$, TRA-1-60$^+$, and SSEA1$^-$,[48] so human EC and ES cells resemble human ICM cells as mouse EC and ES cells resemble mouse ICM cells, even though these cells differ between the two species.

Other surface antigens that appear characteristic of human EC and ES cells include Thy1[43,50] and the tissue-nonspecific form of alkaline phosphatase, which can be readily recognized by the monoclonal antibodies TRA-2-49 and TRA-2-54.[47,49]

The differentiation of human EC and ES cells is characterized by the loss of expression of all of these various markers of undifferentiated cells.[33,47,48,51,52] At the same time, various antigens appear. SSEA1, which seems to be absent from undifferentiated human EC and ES cells, frequently appears on differentiation.[30,33,47] At least some of the cells that express this antigen may belong to the trophoblastic lineage.[48] Ganglioside antigens, notably GT3, recognized by antibody

A2B5,[33,53] and GD2 and GD3, recognized by antibodies VIN2PB22 and VINIS56,[54] all appear on subsets of cells upon human EC and ES differentiation[47] and most likely identify cells of the neural lineages.[55]

One set of antigens that can cause confusion in comparisons of mouse and human EC and ES cells is the class 1 major histocompatibility antigens, H-2 in mice and HLA in humans. H-2 antigens are not expressed by murine EC cells, although they do appear on differentiation. HLA is generally expressed by human EC and ES cells and may show a transient down-regulation upon differentiation.[47,51,56] HLA class 1 antigen expression is also strongly induced in human EC and ES lines by interferon-γ, although an antiviral response does not occur.[47,57]

Summary

Several surface marker antigens that show developmental regulation are found on both mouse and human EC and ES cells, although there are significant species differences in the particular antigens expressed (Table 56–2) and a greater array of such markers is available for the human cells. These antigens can provide important tools both for identifying undifferentiated stem cells and for monitoring their differentiation. A workshop comparison of the antigens expressed by a large panel of human EC cells suggested that SSEA3, an antigen rapidly lost as human EC cells differentiate, may be one of the more sensitive indicators of the undifferentiated state.[58] However, a similar comparison of antigen expression by a panel of human ES lines remains to be undertaken. Furthermore, caution is warranted; some human EC cell sublines may lack SSEA3 expression but retain the expression of other markers of the undifferentiated state and display pluripotency as evidenced by an ability to differentiate in vivo and in vitro. Also, many of the key markers so far defined have oligosaccharide

TABLE 56–2
Differential Expression of Characteristic Surface Marker Antigens of Mouse and Human EC and ES Cells

Antigen	Mouse	Human	Comments
Forssman	Yes	No	Globoseries glycolipid
SSEA1 (Le^x)	Yes	No	Lactoseries glycolipid
SSEA3	No	Yes	Globoseries glycolipid
SSEA4	No	Yes	Globoseries glycolipid
TRA-1-60	No	Yes	Keratan sulfate
TRA-1-81	No	Yes	Keratan sulfate
GCTM2	No	Yes	Keratan sulfate
Liver-alkaline phosphatase (L-ALP)	Yes	Yes	No antibody is available for murine ALP, but human L-ALP is recognized by antibodies TRA-2-54 and TRA-2-49
MHC Class 1	No	Yes	H-2 in the mouse; HLA in humans

epitopes, the expression of which depend on a variety of complex interacting factors, not merely the expression or the lack of expression of specific glycosyl transferases. There remains, therefore, considerable scope for the identification of additional surface antigens for identifying and monitoring undifferentiated human ES cells.

Appendix: Methods

INDIRECT IMMUNOFLUORESCENCE AND FLOW CYTOMETRY

1. Harvest cells to obtain a single cell suspension. Use any standard protocol; typically 0.25% trypsin in 1-mM EDTA, in Ca^{++}/Mg^{++}–free Dulbecco's phosphate-buffered saline (PBS), is used. After pelleting, resuspend the cells in either HEPES-buffered medium or wash buffer (5% fetal calf serum in PBS plus 0.1% sodium azide) to 10^7 cells per milliliter. (If there are fewer cells, then 2×10^6/ml can be used conveniently).

2. Choose antibodies and dilute as appropriate in wash buffer.

3. Distribute the primary antibodies (Table 56–3), diluted appropriately after a preliminary titration, at 50 µl per well of a round-bottom 96-well plate, 1 well for each assay point. To prevent carryover from one well to another, it is good practice to use every other well of the plate. As a negative control, we use the antibody from the original parent myeloma of most hybridomas, namely P3X63Ag8. However, others may prefer a class-matched nonreactive antibody if one is available or no first antibody.

4. Add 50 µl of cell suspension (i.e., 10^5–5×10^5 cells) to each 50 µl of antibody.

5. Seal the plate by covering it with a sticky plastic cover, ensuring that each well is sealed, and incubate at 4°C, with gentle shaking, for 30–60 minutes.

6. Spin the plate at $280 \times g$ for 3 minutes using microtiter plate carriers in a tissue culture centrifuge. Check that the cells are pelleted, and remove the plastic seal using a sharp motion but holding the plate firmly to avoid disturbing the cell pellet. Dump the supernatant by inverting the plate with a rapid downward movement; blot the surface and turn the plate over. Provided that this is done in a single movement without hesitation, the cells remain as pellets at the bottom of the wells. If there are any concerns about pathogens, etc., contaminating a culture, supernatants can be removed by aspiration rather than dumping.

7. Wash the cells by adding 100 µl of wash buffer to each well, seal, and agitate to resuspend the cells. Spin down as described previously. After removing the supernatant, repeat with two more washes.

8. After the third wash, remove the supernatant, and add 50 µl of fluorescent-tagged antibody, previously titered and diluted in wash buffer to each well. We routinely use FITC-tagged goat–antimouse IgM or antimouse IgG as appropriate to the first antibody. Antimouse IgM, but not antimouse IgG, usually works satisfactorily with MC631 (a rat IgM). Affinity-purified and/or $F(ab')_2$ second antibodies may be used if required to eliminate background.

9. Seal the plate as described previously, and repeat the incubation and washings as before.

10. Resuspend the cells, about 5×10^5 per milliliter, in wash buffer and analyze in the flow cytometer. The precise final cell concentration will depend upon local operating conditions and protocols.

TABLE 56–3

Common Antibodies Used to Detect Antigens Expressed by Human EC and ES Cells

Antibody	Antigen	Antibody species and isotype	Remarks	Reference–supplier
MC631	SSEA3	Rat IgM	Undifferentiated hES–EC	19,30,47,48
MC480	SSEA1 (Le^x)	Mouse IgM	Differentiated hES–EC; including trophoblast	9,33,47,48
A2B5	GT3	Mouse IgM	Neural	33,47,53
ME311	9-0-acetylGD3	Mouse IgG	Neural	47,60
VINI556	GD3	Mouse IgM	Neural	47,54
VIN2PB22	GD2	Mouse IgM	Neural	47,54
MC813-70	SSEA4	Mouse IgG	Undifferentiated hES–EC	20,33,47,48
TRA-1-60	TRA-1-60	Mouse IgM	Undifferentiated hES–EC	40,41,47,48
TRA-1-81	TRA-1-81	Mouse IgM	Undifferentiated hES–EC	40,41,47,48
TRA-2-54	L-ALP	Mouse IgG	Undifferentiated hES–EC	47,48,49
TRA-2-49	L-ALP	Mouse IgG	Undifferentiated hES–EC	47,48,49
TRA-1-85	Ok[a]	Mouse IgG	Panhuman	47,48,59
BBM1	β_2-microglobulin	Mouse IgG	HLA	47,61
W6/32	HLA-A, -B, -C	Mouse IgG	HLA	47,62

Notes

All antibodies, both primary and secondary, should be pretitered on a standard cell line to determine optimal concentrations. For monoclonal antibodies, we typically find that the dilution for ascites is between 1:100 and 1:1000, and for hybridoma supernatants, it is between 2 × and 1:10.

A useful antibody is TRA-1-85 (Table 56–3).[59] This antibody recognizes an antigen, Ok[a], that appears to be expressed by all human cells but not by mouse cells. It is therefore valuable as a tool for distinguishing human ES cells from the mouse feeder cells on which they are commonly grown.

FACS

1. Harvest the hES cells using trypsin–EDTA as before for analysis. Note, however, that lower concentrations of trypsin (0.05%) greatly improve cell viability. The cells should be pelleted in aliquots—10^7 cells per aliquot is convenient.

2. Resuspend the cells in primary antibody, diluted in medium without added azide, as determined by prior titration (100 µl per 10^7 cells). The primary and secondary antibodies should be sterilized using a 0.2-micron cellulose acetate filter.

3. Incubate the cells, with occasional shaking, at 4°C for 20–30 minutes.

4. Wash the cells by adding 10-ml medium and pellet by centrifugation at 200 g for 5 minutes; repeat this wash step once.

5. Remove supernatant and gently flick to disperse the pellet. Add 100 µl of diluted secondary antibody per 10^7 cells and incubate, with occasional shaking, at 4°C for 20 minutes.

6. Wash the cells twice as described previously. After the final wash, resuspend the cells in medium at 10^7 cells per milliliter. Sort the cells using the flow cytometer according to local protocols. If the cells are to be cultured after sorting, sort into hES medium supplemented with antibiotics.

Notes

Our standard is 0.25% trypsin–1-mM EDTA in PBS. However, for human ES cells, it is necessary to use a lower trypsin concentrations (0.05% trypsin–1-mM EDTA) if cell viability is to be maintained for culturing after sorting.

IN SITU IMMUNOFLUORESCENCE FOR SURFACE ANTIGENS

1. Remove the medium from the cells and replace with primary antibody diluted as appropriate in hES medium. To maintain the cultures after staining, the antibody should be sterilized by filtration using a 0.2-micron cellulose acetate filter.

2. Place the cells in the incubator for 30 minutes at 37°C.

3. Remove the antibody–medium solution and wash three times with fresh medium.

4. Add the secondary antibody, diluted as appropriate in hES medium.

5. Place the cells in the incubator for 30 minutes at 37°C.

6. Remove the antibody–medium solution and wash three times with PBS (with Ca^{2+} and Mg^{2+}).

7. Visualize under PBS (with Mg^{2+} and Ca^{2+}). The cells are still alive at this point, so they can be recultured if necessary. Alternatively, the cells can be fixed by treatment with a 4% PFA solution for 20 minutes and then stored under a 50:50 solution of PBS:glycerol.

Solutions and Notes

The use of PBS, with Ca^{2+} and Mg^{2+}, or medium stops the cells from detaching from the tissue culture plastic.

4% PFA is 4% paraformaldehyde in PBS (without Ca^{2+} and Mg^{2+}). Heat to 65°C to dissolve, and then filter to remove particulates. This can be frozen at −20°C but should be used within 2 weeks. PFA is toxic, so take appropriate measures to protect yourself during preparation and usage (e.g., weigh out and make up in a fume cupboard).

ACKNOWLEDGMENTS

This work was supported partly by grants from the Wellcome Trust, Yorkshire Cancer Research, and the BBSRC.

REFERENCES

1. Boyse, E.A., and Old, L.J. (1969). Some aspects of normal and abnormal cell surface genetics. *Ann. Rev. Genet.* **3,** 269–290.

2. Kohler, G., and Milstein, C. (1975). Continuous cultures of fused cells secreting antibody of predefined specificity. *Nature* **256,** 495–497.

3. Mason, D.Y., Andre, P., Bensussan, A., Buckley, C., Civin, C., Clark, E., de Haas, M., Goyert, S., Hadam, M., Hart, D., Horejsi, V., Meuer, S., Morissey, J., Schwartz-Albiez, R., Shaw, S., Simmons, D., Uguccioni, M., van der Schoot, E., Viver, E., and Zola, H. (2001). CD antigens. *Tiss. Antigens* **58,** 425–430.

4. Weissman, I.L., Anderson, D.J., and Gage, F. (2001). Stem and progenitor cells: Origins, phenotypes, lineage commitments, and transdifferentiations. *Annu. Rev. Cell Dev. Biol.* **17,** 387–403.

5. Tippett, P., Andrews, P.W., Knowles, B.B., Solter, D., Goodfellow, P.N. (1986). Red cell antigens P (globoside) and Luke: Identification by monoclonal antibodies defining the murine stage-specific embryonic antigens 3 and 4 (SSEA-3 and -4). *Vox Sang.* **51,** 53–56.

6. Artzt, K., Dubois, P., Bennett, D., Condamine, H., Babinet, C., and Jacob, F. (1973). Surface antigens common to mouse cleavage embryos and primitive teratocarcinoma cells in culture. *Proc. Natl. Acad. Sci. USA* **70,** 2988–2992.

7. Jacob, F. (1978). Mouse teratocarcinoma and mouse embryo. *Proc. R. Soc. Lond. B.* **201,** 249–270.

8. Martin, G.R. (1980). Teratocarcinoma and mammalian embryogenesis. *Science* **209,** 768–776.

9. Solter, D., and Knowles, B.B. (1978). Monoclonal antibody defining a stage-specific mouse embryonic antigen SSEA1. *Proc. Natl. Acad. Sci. USA* **75,** 5565–5569.

10. Goodfellow, P.N., Levinson, J.R., Williams, V.E., and McDevitt, H.O. (1979). Monoclonal antibodies reacting with murine teratocarcinoma cells. *Proc. Natl. Acad. Sci. USA* **76,** 377–380.

11. Gooi, H. ., Thorpe, S.J., Hounsell, E.F., Rumpold, H., Kraft, D., Forster, O., and Feizi, T. (1983). Marker of peripheral blood granulocytes and monocytes of man recognized by two monoclonal antibodies VEP8 and VEP9 involves the trisaccharide 3-fucosyl-N-acetyllactosamine. *Eur. J. Immunol.* **13**, 306–312.

12. Kannagi, R., Nudelman, E., Levery, S.B., Hakomori, S. (1982). A series of human erythrocyte glycosphingolipids reacting to the monoclonal antibody directed to a developmentally regulated antigen, SSEA1. *J. Biol. Chem.* **257**, 14,865–14,874.

13. Andrews, P.W., Knowles, B.B., Cossu, G., and Solter, D. (1982). Teratocarcinoma and mouse embryo cell surface antigens: characterization of the molecules carrying the SSEA1 antigenic determinant. *In* "Teratocarcinoma and Embryonic Cell Interactions," (T. Murumatsu *et al.,* Eds.), pp. 103–119. Japan Scientific Societies Press, Tokyo.

14. Childs, R.A., Pennington, J., Uemura, K., Scudder, P., Goodfellow, P.N., Evans, M.J., and Feizi, T. (1983). High-molecular-weight glycoproteins are the major carriers of the carbohydrate differentiation antigens I, i, and SSEA1 of mouse teratocarcinoma cells. *Biochem. J.* **215**, 491–503.

15. Solter, D., Shevinsky, L., Knowles, B.B., and Strickland, S. (1979). The induction of antigenic changes in a teratocarcinoma stem cell line F9 by retinoic acid. *Dev. Biol.* **70**, 515–521.

16. Buckalew, J.J., Sterman, B., and Rosenstraus, M. (1985). Variant embryonal carcinoma cells lacking SSEA1 and Forssman antigens remain developmentally pluripotent. *Dev. Biol.* **107**, 134–141.

17. Gregorova, S., Loudova, M., Dohnal, K., Nosek, J., and Forejt, J. (1984). Establishment of a pluripotent embryonal carcinoma cell line not expressing SSEA1 and ECMA-7 phenotypes. *Cell Differ.* **15**, 87–92.

18. Rosenstraus, M.J. (1983). Isolation and characterization of an embryonal carcinoma cell line lacking SSEA1 antigen. *Dev. Biol.* **99**, 318–323.

19. Shevinsky, L.H., Knowles, B.B., Damjanov, I., and Solter, D. (1982). Monoclonal antibody to murine embryos defines a stage-specific embryonic antigen expressed on mouse embryos and human teratocarcinoma cells. *Cell* **30**, 697–705.

20. Kannagi, R., Cochran, N.A., Ishigami, F., Hakomori, S.I., Andrews, P.W., Knowles, B.B., Solter, D. (1983). Stage-specific embryonic antigens SSEA3 and -4 are epitopes of a unique globoseries ganglioside isolated from human teratocarcinoma cells. *EMBO J.* **2**, 2355–2361.

21. Stern, P.L., Willison, K.R., Lennox, E., Galfre, G., Milstein, C., Secher, D., and Ziegler, A. (1978). Monoclonal antibodies as probes for differentiation and tumor-associated antigens: a Forssman specificity on teratocarcinoma stem cells. *Cell* **14**, 775–783.

22. Willison, K.R., and Stern, P.L. (1978). Expression of a Forssman antigenic specificity in the preimplantation mouse embryo. *Cell* **14**, 785–793.

23. Evans, M.J., and Kaufman, M.H. (1981). Establishment in culture of pluripotential cells from mouse embryos. *Nature* **292**, 154–156.

24. Martin, G.R. (1981). Isolation of a pluripotent cell line from early mouse embryos cultured in medium conditioned by teratocarcinoma stem cells. *Proc. Natl. Acad. Sci. USA* **78**, 7634–7638.

25. Matsui, Y., Zsebo, K., and Hogan, B.L. (1992). Derivation of pluripotential embryonic stem cells from murine primordial germ cells in culture. *Cell* **70**, 841–847.

26. Labosky, P.A., Barlow, D.P., and Hogan, B.L. (1994). Mouse embryonic germ (EG) cell lines: transmission through the germ line and differences in the methylation imprint of insulin-like growth factor 2 receptor *(Igf2r)* gene compared with embryonic stem (ES) cell lines. *Development* **120**, 3197–3204.

27. Hogan, B., Fellows, M., Avner, P., and Jacob, F. (1977). Isolation of a human teratoma cell line, which expresses F9 antigen. *Nature* **270**, 515–518.

28. Holden, S., Bernard, O., Artzt, K., Whitmore, W.F., and Bennett, D. (1977). Human and mouse embryonal carcinoma cells in culture share an embryonic antigen F9. *Nature* **270**, 518–520.

29. Andrews, P.W., Bronson, D.L., Benham, F., Strickland, S., and Knowles, B.B. (1980). A comparative study of eight cell lines derived from human testicular teratocarcinoma. *Int. J. Cancer* **26**, 269–280.

30. Andrews, P.W., Goodfellow, P.N., Shevinsky, L.H., Bronson, D.L., and Knowles, B.B. (1982). Cell-surface antigens of a clonal human embryonal carcinoma cell line: morphological and antigenic differentiation in culture. *Int. J. Cancer* **29**, 523–531.

31. Damjanov, I., Fox, N., Knowles, B.B., Solter, D., Lange, P.H., and Fraley, E.E. (1982). Immunohistochemical localization of murine stage-specific embryonic antigens in human testicular germ cell tumors. *Am. J. Pathol.* **108**, 225–230.

32. Krupnick, J.G., Damjanov, I., Damjanov, A., Zhu, Z.M., and Fenderson, B.A. (1994). Globoseries carbohydrate antigens are expressed in different forms on human and murine teratocarcinoma-derived cells. *Int. J. Cancer* **59**, 692–698.

33. Fenderson, B.A., Andrews, P.W., Nudelman, E., Clausen, H., and Hakomori, S. (1987). Glycolipid core structure switching from globo- to lacto- and ganglioseries during retinoic acid-induced differentiation of TERA-2-derived human embryonal carcinoma cells. *Dev. Biol.* **122**, 21–34.

34. Chen, C., Fenderson, B.A., Andrews, P.W., and Hakomori, S.I. (1989). Glycolipid-glycosyltransferases in human embryonal carcinoma cells during retinoic acid-induced differentiation. *Biochemistry* **28**, 2229–2238.

35. Andrews, P.W., Damjanov, I., Simon, D., and Dignazio, M. (1985). A pluripotent human stem cell clone isolated from the TERA-2 teratocarcinoma line lacks antigens SSEA-3 and SSEA-4 *in vitro* but expresses these antigens when grown as a xenograft tumor. *Differentiation* **29**, 127–135.

36. Thompson, S., Stern, P.L., Webb., M., Walsh, F.S., Engström, W., Evans, E.P., Shi, W.K., Hopkins, B., and Graham, C.F. (1984). Cloned human teratoma cells differentiate into neuron-like cells and other cell types in retinoic acid. *J. Cell Sci.* **72**, 37–64.

37. Fenderson, B.A., Radin, N., and Andrews, P.W. (1993). Differentiation antigens of human germ cell tumors: distribution of carbohydrate epitopes on glycolipids and glycoproteins analyzed using PDMP, an inhibitor of glycolipid synthesis. *Eur. Urol.* **23**, 30–37.

38. Fenderson, B.A., Ostrander, G.K., Hausken, Z., Radin, N.S., and Hakomori, S. (1992). A ceramide analogue, PDMP, inhibits glycolipid synthesis in fish embryos. *Exp. Cell Res.* **198**, 362–366.

39. Race, R.R., and Sanger, R. (1975). "Blood Groups in Man," 6th ed., pp. 169–171. Blackwell Scientific Publications, Oxford.

40. Andrews, P.W., Banting, G., Damjanov, I., Arnaud, D., and Avner, P. (1984). Three monoclonal antibodies defining distinct differentiation antigens associated with different high-molecular-weight polypeptides on the surface of human embryonal carcinoma cells. *Hybridoma* **3**, 347–361.

41. Badcock, G., Pigott, C., Goepel, J., and Andrews, P.W. (1999). The human embryonal carcinoma marker antigen TRA-1-60 is a sialylated keratan sulfate proteoglycan. *Cancer Res.* **59**, 4715–4719.

42. Pera, M.F., Blasco-Lafita, M.J., Cooper, S., Mason, M., Mills, J., and Monaghan, P. (1988). Analysis of cell differentiation lineage in human teratomas using new monoclonal antibodies to cytostructural antigens of embryonal carcinoma cells. *Differentiation* **39,** 139–149.

43. Cooper, S., Bennett, W., Andrade, J., Reubinoff, B.E., Thomson, J., and Pera, M.F. (2002). Biochemical properties of a keratan sulfate–chondroitin sulfate proteoglycan expressed in primate pluripotent stem cells. *J. Anat.* **200,** 259–265.

44. Rettig, W.J., Cordon-Cardo, C., Ng, J.S., Oettgen, H.F., Old, L.J., and Lloyd, K.O. (1985). High-molecular-weight glycoproteins of human teratocarcinoma defined by monoclonal antibodies to carbohydrate determinants. *Cancer Res.* **45,** 815–821.

45. Thomson, J.A., Itskovitz-Eldor, J., Shapiro, S.S., Waknitz, M.A., Swiergiel, J.J., Marshall, V.S., and Jones, J.M. (1998). Embryonic stem cell lines derived from human blastocysts. *Science* **282,** 1145–1147.

46. Reubinoff, B.E., Pera, M.F., Fong, C.Y., Trounson, A., and Bongso, A. (2000). Embryonic stem cell lines from human blastocysts: somatic differentiation *in vitro. Nat. Biotechnol.* **18,** 399–404.

47. Draper, J.S., Pigott, C., Thomson, J.A., and Andrews, P.W. (2002). Surface antigens of human embryonic stem cells: changes upon differentiation in culture. *J. Anat.* **200,** 249–258.

48. Henderson, J.K., Draper, J.S., Baillie, H.S., Fishel, S., Thomson, J.A., Moore, H., and Andrews, P.W. (2002). Preimplantation human embryos and embryonic stem cells show comparable expression of stage-specific embryonic antigens. *Stem Cells* **20,** 329–337.

49. Andrews, P.W., Meyer, L.J., Bednarz, K.L., and Harris, H. (1984). Two monoclonal antibodies recognizing determinants on human embryonal carcinoma cells react specifically with the liver isozyme of human alkaline phosphatase. *Hybridoma* **3,** 33–39.

50. Andrews, P.W., Goodfellow, P.N., and Bronson, D.L. (1983). Cell-surface characteristics and other markers of differentiation of human teratocarcinoma cells in culture. *In* "Teratocarcinoma Stem Cells," (Silver *et al.,* Eds.), pp. 579–590, Cold Spring Harbor Press, Cold Spring Harbor, NY.

51. Andrews, P.W., Damjanov, I., Simon, D., Banting, G., Carlin, C., Dracopoli, N.C., and Fogh, J. (1984). Pluripotent embryonal carcinoma clones derived from the human teratocarcinoma cell line Tera-2: differentiation *in vivo* and *in vitro. Lab. Invest.* **50,** 147–162.

52. Andrews, P.W. (1984). Retinoic acid induces neuronal differentiation of a cloned human embryonal carcinoma cell line *in vitro. Dev. Biol.* **103,** 285–293.

53. Eisenbarth, G.S., Walsh, F.S., and Nirenberg, M. (1979). Monoclonal antibody to a plasma membrane antigen of neurons. *Proc. Natl. Acad. Sci. USA* **76,** 4913–4917.

54. Andrews, P.W., Nudelman, E., Hakomori, S., and Fenderson, B.A. (1990). Different patterns of glycolipid antigens are expressed following differentiation of TERA-2 human embryonal carcinoma cells induced by retinoic acid, hexamethylene bisacetamide (HMBA), or bromodeoxyuridine (BrdU). *Differentiation* **43,** 131–138.

55. Przyborski, S.A., Morton, I.E., Wood, A., and Andrews, P.W. (2000). Developmental regulation of neurogenesis in the pluripotent human embryonal carcinoma cell line NTERA-2. *Eur. J. Neurosci.* **12,** 3521–3528.

56. Andrews, P.W., Bronson, D.L., Wiles, M.V., and Goodfellow, P.N. (1981). The expression of major histocompatibility antigens by human teratocarcinoma-derived cells lines. *Tissue Antigens* **17,** 493–500.

57. Andrews, P.W., Trinchieri, G., Perussia, B., and Baglioni, C. (1987). Induction of class 1 major histocompatibility complex antigens in human teratocarcinoma cells by interferon without induction of differentiation, growth inhibition, or resistance to viral infection. *Cancer Res.* **47,** 740–746.

58. Andrews, P.W., Casper, J., Damjanov, I., Duggan-Keen, M., Giwercman, A., Hata, J.I., von Keitz, A., Looijenga, L.H.J., Millán, J.L., Oosterhuis, J.W., Pera, M., Sawada, M., Schmoll, H.J., Skakkebaek, N.E., van Putten, W., and Stern, P. (1996). Comparative analysis of cell surface antigens expressed by cell lines derived from human germ cell tumors. *Int. J. Cancer* **66,** 806–816.

59. Williams, B.P., Daniels, G.L., Pym, B., Sheer, D., Povey, S., Okubo, Y., Andrews, P.W., and Goodfellow, P.N. (1988). Biochemical and genetic analysis of the Ok[a] blood group antigen. *Immunogenetics* **27,** 322–329.

60. Thurin, J., Herlyn, M., Hindsgaul, O., Stromberg, N., Karlsson, K.A., Elder, D., Steplewski, Z., and Koprowski, H. (1985). Proton NMR and fast-atom bombardment mass spectrometry analysis of the melanoma-associated ganglioside 9-O-acetyl-GD3. *J. Biol. Chem.* **260,** 14,556–14,563.

61. Brodsky, F.M., Bodmer, W.F., and Parham, P. (1979). Characterization of a monoclonal anti-β 2-microglobulin antibody and its use in the genetic and biochemical analysis of major histocompatibility antigens. *Eur. J. Immunol.* **9,** 536–545.

62. Barnstable, C.J., Bodmer, W.F., Brown, G., Galfre, G., Milstein, C., Williams, A.F., and Ziegler, A. (1978). Production of monoclonal antibodies to group A erythrocytes, HLA, and other human cell surface antigens: new tools for genetic analysis. *Cell* **14,** 9–20.

Lineage Marking

Andras Nagy

Definitions

Mammalian development starts from a singe cell, the zygote, which is the ancestor to all the somatic and germ cells of the entire later organism. This type of developmental capacity is called *totipotency*. In the first few divisions of preimplantation development, the cells (blastomeres) retain this totipotency, but shortly before implantation, at the blastocyst stage, cells become committed to certain tissues of the later conceptus. Three cell types are clearly distinguishable at this stage: the *trophectoderm,* committed to the trophoblast cells of the placenta; the *primitive endoderm,* which derivatives remain extraembryonic and will form the parietal and visceral endoderm; and the *primitive ectoderm* responsible for all cells in the embryo proper and for some internal extraembryonic membranes, such as allantois, amnion, and yolk sac mesoderm (the inner layer of this membrane). A given cell of the blastocyst is only capable of differentiating into a subset of cells of the conceptus; therefore, these cells are no longer totipotent. Instead they are referred to as *pluripotent.* After implantation, further subdivisions of developmental commitments occur in the embryo proper, as the embryonic ectoderm, mesoderm, and definitive endoderm form. The following organogenesis produces the final cellular diversity of an individual by differentiating highly specialized cell types (*differentiated* cells) for organ functions. The cellular diversity consists of approximately 260 distinguishable cell types in mammals, which make up an estimated total cell number of 1 trillion (10^{12}) in an adult human or 10 billion (10^{10}) in a mouse.

The progress of cell commitment to an ever-decreasing range of cell types can be viewed from the opposite direction: Every cell among the 260 cell types has its own "history" that can be traced. This trace is often referred to as the *lineage* (Fig. 57–1). If the traces are looked at from a given *progenitor* or a *stem cell* (the origin) in the forward direction, the set of traces is the *fate* of the cell. If the fate remains within a single type of differentiated cells or results in two or more kinds, the origin is called *uni-, bi-,* or *multipotential,* respectively. With these definitions, cell lineage and fate are practically the same phenomenon, a set of developmental traces viewed either from the differentiated product or the origin. In Fig. 57–1,

therefore, the fate of p1 is d1 and d2, and the fate of p2 is d1. The progenitor cell, p1, is bipotential, and p2 is unipotential. For the differentiated cell, the lineage of d2 is simple: It goes back to p1 only. The d1 lineage could be trace back to either the p1 or the p2 progenitor.

The development of neurons and oligodendrocytes are good examples for the paths depicted in Fig. 57–1. Analyses of cerebral cortical cultures[1] and developing chicken spinal cord[2,3] indicate that these two cell types share a common precursor. On the other hand, oligodendrocytes originate from several cell types, such as the small foci of cells in the floor of the third ventricle that generated the oligodendrocytes for the optic nerve[4,5] and the oligodendrocyte precursors from the motor neuron pool.[6,7]

Questions to Ask

There are two basic questions to be asked about cell lineages or cell fates:

- The lineage question: What are the traces and progenitors that lead to a certain differentiated cell type, for example, d1?
- The fate question: What are the possible differentiated products of a certain progenitor cell, such as p1?

Markers and Lineage Marking

As cells go through the diversification process, they correspondingly change their *gene expression profile.* This profile determines the properties of the cells and therefore their *identities.* Cells of the same type express similar genes. Within this pool are some genes specific to one particular cell type. These genes are referred to as cell type-specific *markers.* For example, hepatocytes, astrocytes, neurons, and cardiac myocytes can be identified by the expression of albumin, GFAP, Neu-N, and α-myosin heavy chain, respectively.

To identify traces during development or adult regeneration–or renewal is not a simple task. There is often no specific marker identifying a lineage along its complete trace. Instead, there is a set of genes expressed at certain segments of the lineage. For example, oligodendrocytes go through several developmental stages, such as proliferative and differentiative phases. The immature oligodendrocytes can first be identified by a surface antigen expression recognized by an antibody, A2B5. As the cells mature, they acquire another specific surface marker recognized by the antibody called O4. Then, as they further differentiate, they start expressinzg myelin-specific

Handbook of Stem Cells
Volume 1

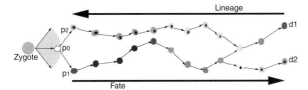

Figure 57-1. *Relationship between cell lineage and cell fate. See text.* (See color plate 6.)

genes such as MBP and PLP.[8] Typically, a temporal series of specific markers or the lack of certain gene expression represents a particular lineage. If these markers are known and easy to detect, they can be used to characterize the fate of a progenitor or a stem cell. However, to follow all the descendents of a given progenitor, there is a need for a unique identifier characteristic of the progenitor under study and retained in the derivatives. Providing this identifier is *lineage marking*, the subject of this chapter.

MARKING WITH ENDOGENOUS IDENTIFIERS

It was pointed out earlier that existence of a unique marker gene or genes covering an entire lineage is not common. Fortunately, though, there are useful genetic differences among individuals within or among species that can be used as identifiers in cell–tissue transplantation or chimera studies. These types of lineage marking were important in early studies of fate mapping. A great deal of knowledge was acquired using embryo transplantation chimeras between quail and chicken.[9] The nuclei of quail cells contain heterochromatin condensed into one (or sometimes two) large mass.[10] This easily recognizable phenomenon was used to distinguish quail from chicken cells. In the mouse, *in situ* hybridization for a specific genomic sequence of *Mus caroli* can also discriminate between these and *Mus musculus* cells in chimeric tissues.[11,12] Haplotype cell surface markers have been frequently used to study hematopoietic lineages.[13] *In situ* hybridization for the Y-chromosome can be used as an identifier when grafting male cells into female recipients (review by Jackson *et al.*).[14] The visualization is relatively straightforward with Y-chromosome-specific probes on histological section.[15,16]

The unique advantage of the endogenous identifiers is that they are "built-in"; therefore, they do not require genetic or other modifications of cells. Grafting, chimera-making, and frequent requirements for bridging between genders or even species, however, limits the use of such endogenous markers. Modern transgenic methods have in the recent years replaced these traditional approaches. Before detailing these, I should mention another historically important approach that provides a short-term, transient marking of a cell and its progenitors.

MARKING WITH DYES OR ENZYMES

Vital fluorescence dyes or an enzyme with a long half-life can mark cells in a temporary manner. Among these dyes, the most popular are DiI (a carbocyanine) and its derivatives because of their high photostability and low toxicity. These dyes label cell membranes by inserting two long hydrocarbon chains into the lipid bilayers, resulting in an orange-red (565 nm) fluorescence emission. DiI can be used with DiO, which gives a green fluorescent color. These dyes are usually applied to cells either from an ethanol solution or directly from the dye crystal. This simple labeling technique has frequently been used in nonmammalian model systems to successfully address lineage, potentiality, and fate questions.[17–19]

Horseradish peroxidase[20,21] and Rhodamine-conjugated dextran[22,23] has also extensively been used for cell marking; however, these techniques are more invasive, as they have to be microinjected into the cells.

The obvious limitations to all these methods are the temporary nature of marking and the need for free access to cells for labeling. In the mouse, the usefulness of these approaches is further limited by the requirement for *in vitro* culturing of postimplantation-stage embryos.

MARKING WITH EXOGENOUS GENETIC IDENTIFIERS

Rapidly evolving transgene-based approaches are currently the most versatile methods of lineage marking. This fact, however, does not mean that these approaches have replaced more traditional techniques. They all have their optimal applications, and they are still valid members of the arsenal of options. There are two categories of exogenous genetic identifiers: passive and active markers.

"Passive" Exogenous Genetic Markers

Passive exogenous markers are identified on the basis of genomic insertion of a known DNA sequence into the genome. Their detection requires techniques such as DNA *in situ* hybridization or Southern blotting. A typical example of this category is retroviral insertion. Probing with a retroviral sequence in a genomic Southern blot detects an integration site-specific band pattern. In the case of multiple integrations, the Southern blotting can serve as a fingerprint for a group of cells derived from a single precursor or stem cell. Such an identifier can be used as a tool to measure the turnover of active stem cells that generate an entire hematopoietic compartment.[24] Unfortunately, such an approach is not practical at a single-cell level, which restricts its application in lineage studies. A useful passive genetic identifier for many lineage studies and for fate mapping has been created by direct transgene insertion into the mouse genome.[25,26] In this transgenic mouse line, a β-globin transgene was inserted into chromosome 3 in a tandem repeat of approximately 1000 copies, which created a long enough unique and known sequence to visualize with DNA *in situ* hybridization on histological sections[27] (Fig. 57–2A).

"Active" Exogenous Genetic Markers

Active exogenous genetic markers are based on reporter gene expression from a transgene. There are several reporters available and proven to be useful in lineage studies and fate mapping. Depending on the application, one may be better than the other. The most common reporters fall into two groups: enzymes and fluorescent proteins.

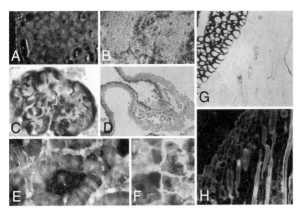

Figure 57-2. *Lineage marking at the cellular level.* (A) DNA *in situ* hybridization in trophoblast cells transgenic to the multicopy globin gene insertion.[26] (B) Chimeric tissue where one of the components is N-myc oncogene deficient and LacZ tagged with the Rosa-26 gene trap. (C) Immunohistochemical staining for podocyte-specific expression of green fluorescent protein (GFP). (D) LacZ staining of a chimeric yolk sac in which one of the components is expressing the reporter from the vascular endothelial growth factor locus.[30] (E and F) LacZ and human alkaline phosphatase double staining on mosaic intestine and pancreas.[41] (F and H) LacZ staining and GFP visualization of an adjacent section of skin of a Z/EG, K14-Cre recombinase double transgenic animal.[56] Part C provided by S. Quaggin. (See color plate 7.)

Enzyme Activity-Based Reporters. The β-*galactosidase* (*lacZ* gene of the E. coli) has had a very successful "career" as a reporter for all sorts of eukaryotic cells. The expression of the enzyme by a heterologous promoter seems to be neutral for the functioning of cells. A variety of substrates can be used for detecting β-galactosidase. The most common is an indole derivative, 5-bromo–4-chloro–3-indolyl–β-D–galactoside (X-gal[28]), which produces a blue color as it beaks down. This simple histochemical staining works on small tissues as whole mount and on histological cryostat sections. Many useful transgenic mouse lines have been made with different specificity for LacZ expression. Of those, the most known is a gene trap insertion of *lacZ* into an endogenous locus named Rosa-26.[29] This locus provides expression throughout the entire embryo and in most of the adult tissues. Fig. 57–2B shows an example for use of Rosa-26 transgenic and N-myc-deficient embryonic stem (ES) cells in a chimera study. The derivatives of these cells (LacZ stained blue) are not able to contribute to the chondrocyte lineage of the embryo. Since the aim of most gene trap programs is to generate *lacZ* insertions randomly in all the genes of the mouse, cell type-or lineage-specific LacZ tagging is now created in huge numbers. Fig. 57–2I shows an example of a LacZ-stained embryo in which the trap vector "landed" in the *Mef-2c* gene (see the Centre for Modeling Human Disease gene trap database at http://cmhd.mshri.on.ca/sub/genetrap.asp). In addition to gene trap lines, many targeted alleles contain a *lacZ* gene placed into the target vector in such a way that the enzyme is expressed under the regulation of the endogenous gene. Fig. 57–3B shows an example in which the *lacZ* gene was knocked in to the endothelial-specific *flk-1*

locus. Fig. 57–2D shows a yolk sac section from a chimeric embryo created by diploid–tetraploid embryo aggregation. In the diploid component, LacZ was expressed from both alleles of the vascular endothelial growth factor (VEGF) gene,[30] and the tetraploid cells were wild type for VEGF. In the resulting chimera, the yolk sac mesoderrm—derived completely from the diploid cells—shows a blue staining. The yolk sac endoderm, however, show a mosaic LacZ pattern since it is derived from both diploid and tetraploid cells. The LacZ protein is rather tolerant to N- and C-terminal modifications. Heterologous functional domains may be added, which changes the property of the enzyme, such as the intracellular localization. There are variants that translocate the protein to the nucleus or anchor it to the cell membrane.[31]

Alkaline phosphatase is an essential, constitutively expressed enzyme in cells. Similar to LacZ, a simple histochemical or whole-mount staining procedure can visualize enzyme activity in cells. Endogenous alkaline phosphatases can easily be inactivated by a brief heat treatment (at 70°C for 15 minutes). However, the alkaline phosphatase expressed by the human placenta (hPLAP) is unique alkaline phosphatases in that it is not affected by such a heat treatment.[32] This unique property has been utilized for detection of hPLAP activity when expressed from a transgene. Since heat treatment can be applied to both whole mount and cryostat sections, hPLAP has become a convenient histological marker, which allows simple detection–recognition of enzyme-containing cells. Since hPLAP is efficiently transported into axons, it is an ideal reporter if nerve visualization is required. Fig. 57–3C shows sporadic hPLAP+ cells in a 10.5 days postcoitus (dpc) embryo, and Fig. 57–2E and 57–2F show double staining for LacZ and hPLAP on a cryostat section of intestine and pancreas of a mosaic newborn (for more details, see the next sections of this chapter). However, compared to LacZ, hPLAP stain penetration to whole mount tissue is slightly more limited, and the quality of histological sections falls short of excellence because of the heat treatment of the tissue.

Green Fluorescent Proteins. The *green fluorescent protein* (GFP) isolated from the jellyfish *(Aequorea victoria)* has recently joined the group of reporters used to trace lineages and determine cell fate in mouse and other model organisms.[33–35] Several mutant derivatives have been developed providing different levels of stability and intensity and a spectrum of light emission.[36] The gene that encodes for GFP can be applied in heterologous-transient or -stable integrant transgenic expression settings or its mRNA for transient production of the protein. In the latter method, the mRNA is injected into the cells.[37] This reporter is definitely unique since its visualization does not require cell fixation. Instead, live specimens can be observed, and cells expressing GFP (or its derivatives) can be followed in their dynamic behavior. However, not even GFP could overcome the main obstacle in studying mammalian development, that the embryo needs an intra-*utero* environment. *Ex vivo* organ culture systems are gaining importance to overcome this limitation; however, the very early postimplantation time is not yet possible to follow *in vitro*.

Establishing Overall-Expressor Transgenic Lines in the Mouse. There are several considerations in expressing reporters for lineage marking from stable integrant transgenes. When cell grafting is the approach to studying cell fate, derivatives of the graft should be identifiable. For this purpose, the reporter has to be expressed ubiquitously in the donor. Interestingly, a reliable ubiquitous expression is a difficult to achieve. For more than 10 years, the Rosa-26 gene trap line has been the overall LacZ expressor reporter in the mouse.[17] Second on the "popularity list" is a LacZ line that has the transgene integration on the X-chromosome. This line has been used successfully in several studies[38–40] to address cell fate and lineage determination questions during gastrulation.

Establishing a new overall expressor, a ubiquitous reporter transgenic mouse line, is a challenging task. Even the most promising, endogenously ubiquitous promoter gives unstable, mosaic, or restricted expression from most insertion sites in the genome. Generally, a transgenic mouse line is produced by injecting the desired transgene into the pronucleus of a zygote. This approach requires far too many founder animals to be established and tested for expression. For this reason, ES cell-mediated transgenesis may be a better alternative. If the same constructs are introduced into ES cells, hundreds of transgenic clones can be isolated in a short time. These clones, which all represent a unique genomic integration site of the transgene, can be screened for overall expression of the reporter, first in undifferentiated ES cells and then in *in vitro*

differentiation assays. If only the best overall expressor ES cell line is used to generate mice, the chance of obtaining satisfying reporter expression is high.[41] ES cells may also provide control on transgene insertion. The most common method is targeted integration of a transgene (reporter) into a well-characterized loci, for example, Rosa-26.[42,43] Recombinase-mediated cassette exchange is an alternative that would eliminate the uncertainty of transgene expression because of random genomic insertion. Three recombinase–integrase systems are available for such an approach; the Cre, Flip (Flp), and PhiC31.[44–46] Using any of these, a "docking" site can to be prepared and characterized for expression permissiveness. The transgene is then equipped with a recognition site or sites of the recombinase and introduced into the cells with the enzyme. Site-specific genomic integration of the transgene can thus be achieved at a high efficiency.

Chimera—A Tool of Fate Mapping

The possibility of combining two or more embryos in one chimera contributed tremendously to the understanding of lineage determination and cell fate in mouse development (for a review, see Nagy and Rossant[47]). Identifiers described previously are essential to detecting and characterizing the contribution of a chimeric component to a lineage, cell type, or organ. Injection of cells isolated from the preimplantation embryo into a blastocyst and characterization of the allocation of derivatives of each compartment in later stages revealed the first specification events.[48] Chimeras (Fig. 57–3D) have also been very informative in addressing basic organization questions, for example, whether complex structures are derived from single progenitors (clonality in development).[49,50]

The use of ES cells and tetraploid embryos expanded the horizon of questions that could be addressed. ES cells are not able to contribute to the trophectoderm and primitive endoderm lineages of the developing chimeras.[26] On the other hand, cells derived from tetraploid embryos are excluded from the primitive ectoderm lineage when they have to compete with diploid embryo or ES cell derivatives.[26,51] For chimera production, one can choose any two of the following three sources as components: diploid embryo, tetraploid embryo, and ES cells. In addition, two diploid embryos can be chosen, increasing the number of possible combinations to four. Depending on the actual combination, different lineage allocation can be obtained for the selected components[47,52] (Fig. 57–4). The most extreme separation occurs when tetraploid embryos are aggregated with ES cells; practically no chimeric lineages are generated. The cells in the resulting embryo are either tetraploid derived (trophoblast lineage of the placenta, visceral, and parietal endoderm) or ES cell derived (amnion, allantois, embryonic mesoderm component of the placenta and yolk sac, umbilical cord, and embryo proper) (Fig. 57–3A). In a broader sense, the lineage restrictions in chimeras could be considered lineage marking.

Cell and Tissue Grafting

The classical chimera production restricts the components to the sources discussed in the previous paragraph and the timing

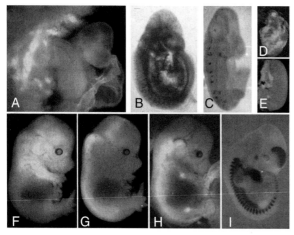

Figure 57–3. *Whole mount embryos and organs with lineage-marked cells. (A) ES cell-derived embryo in the uterus. The trophoblast of the placenta and the yolk sac endoderm is GFP transgenic tetraploid embryo-derived. (B) Whole mount LacZ stained embryo in which the* lacZ *gene is inserted into the flk-1, endothelial cell specifically expressed receptor kinase.[70] (C) Z/AP and Cre recombinase double transgenic embryo with sporadic human placental alkaline phosphatase activation.[41] (D) Heart of the chimeric embryo between Cyan Fluorescent Protein expressor ES cells and GFP transgenic embryo.[36] Z/EG and Cre recombinase double transgenic embryos with (E) GFP podocyte-specific,[71] (F) complete, (G) differentiated neuron-specific, and (H) chondrocyte-specific activation. (I) LacZ-stained embryo derived from a Mef-2c gene trap ES cell line. Part h provided by J. Haigh, and part i provided by K. Vintersten and B. Stanford. (See color plate 8.)*

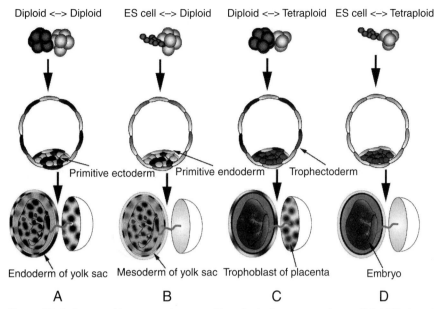

Figure 57–4. *Diagram of lineage contributions in different kinds of aggregation chimeras.*[52] Solid blacks and grays indicate nonchimeric tissues, and stripes indicate chimeric tissues.

to the preimplantation stages. Later stage cell mixing is also possible, but it is more demanding and the possible applications are more limited. Small tissue transplantation can be performed between two postimplantation stage embryos. If the graft is tagged with a unique identifier, the fate of these cells can be followed during development of the recipient. This technique has been in practice for almost 20 years. Developmental trajectories, as they are depicted in Fig. 57–1, are dynamic processes not only at the level of gene expression but also at the level of cell allocations in the developing embryo. These two levels interact: Allocation can induce gene expression changes, and gene expression changes can influence cell allocations. Knowing the complexity of mammalian gastrulation, one can easily imagine the heroic effort of creating the map of cell movements in the early postimplantation embryo using mostly LacZ-marked tissue grafting and still pictures showing the allocation of the graft derivatives.[53]

Further limitations associated with this approach come from our inability to successfully place the postimplantation-stage embryo back into the uterus environment where it could develop further. *In vitro* postimplantation embryo culture sets a limitation on the "developmental stage window" of isolation from 6.5 dpc to 10.5 dpc and on survival for a period of only 2–3 days.

Using Genetic Switches

Grafting identifier-tagged tissues from one embryo to another creates a small population of progenitor cells whose derivatives can be easily recognized at later stages. The experimental achievement of such a scenario is rather invasive, and it is full of limitations, as it was pointed out in the previous paragraph. State-of-art tools, however, can be used to achieve a

similar situation with much less invasiveness. The key element is the Cre site-specific recombinase, which recombines DNA between two consensus loxP sites. If two loxP sites are similarly oriented in the same DNA strand, the result of such a recombination is the excision of the intervening sequence. This property allows the design of the Cre excision-conditional reporter *Rosa26R*, a knockin transgenic mouse line that uses the wide spread expression from the Rosa26 locus, where now the LacZ expression is Cre excision conditional.[42,54] A similar reporter line has been developed for the other popular recombinase system: the Flp.[55] The features of a sophisticated "switch reporter," the *Z/EG* transgene,[56] are the following: A strong overall expressor promoter (CMV enhancer + Chicken β-actin promoter[57]) is driving a *lacZ-neomycin* resistance fusion gene (β*geo*) followed by three polyadenilation (pA) sites. The β*geo* and the 3xpAs are flanked by loxP sites, and a coding region of an enhanced green fluorescent protein (EGFP) with its own pA follows this flanked region. This transgene was inserted as a single copy into a single site of the mouse genome leading to the expression of the β*geo* only. However, EGFP expression can be activated by Cre recombinase; Cre activity removes β*geo*+3xpA and moves the EGFP coding region under the transcriptional control of the promoter (Fig. 57–3F). The EGFP activation is, therefore, dependent on the presence and action of the Cre recombinase. Z/AP, another reporter line,[41,42,54,56] can be used in the same way as Z/EG, except that the second reporter is hPLAP instead of EGFP.

Cre recombinase has had a great career in mouse genetics.[58] Dozens of transgenic mouse lines have been produced, expressing this phage enzyme with different spatial and temporal control (http://www.mshri.on.ca/nagy/Cre-pub.html).

Double transgenic combination of a Cre transgene and the Z/EG (or Z/AP) reporter turns on EGFP (hPLAP) expression not only in the actual Cre expressor cells but also in any cell that had an ancestor express the recombinase during the course of development. Therefore, the EGFP⁺ cells in these double transgenic embryos or animals are the union of all the cells expressing the recombinase and those that had a Cre recombinase expressor ancestor (Fig. 57–3E through 57–3H). It is easy to recognize that an efficient Cre recombinase excision is not always advantageous in this situation, since the resulting set of EGFP⁺ (hPLAP⁺) cells could be too large, obscuring the recognition of fates derived from a single Cre⁺ progenitor. A less efficient Cre recombinase is preferable here. If the excision (activation of the second reporter) only occurs sporadically, the allocation of the descendent cells may still reflect the clonality (Fig. 57–3C) and reveal the potential of the progenitor. Low-frequency activation of the Cre recombinase can be achieved by the use of either the tamoxifen-[59–61] or the tetracycline-inducible[62] Cre recombinase systems. Proper titering of the inducer could create the most informative excision–activation frequency of progenitors. In addition, withdrawal of the inducer may be used to create an upper developmental limit of the excision–activation of the reporter.[63,64]

The induction of low-frequency or controlled activation of the conditional reporter is also possible by direct injection of the recombinase[65,66] or its mRNA into cells of developing embryos.

Future Directions

It is difficult to predict what the distant future will bring into this exciting area. In the near future, however, efforts will certainly lead to novel features that will provide means to follow the behavior of cells. New imaging techniques will allow the recording of the dynamic property of cells, such as movements, speed, direction, interactions with other cells in *in vitro* cultures, or formation of specific embryonic structures in *ex vivo* cultures of early postimplantation embryos.[67] The study of later development may require slice cultures for filming cellular events, such as the birth of neurons from radial glia cells.[68] Another technical development, ultrasound-guided embryonic transplantation, is expected to have an effect on lineage studies and fate mapping. It is becoming possible to graft reporter-tagged cells into early postimplantation-stage embryos[72] while *in utero* and to recover the embryos at a later stage for studying the derivatives of the graft.

Remembering the enormous effort behind generating the complete map of lineage development in *C. elegans*—which consists of less than 1000 cells—the task of untangling the same system in the mammalian embryo may seem impossible. This conclusion comes not only from the dramatic increase in cell number but also from the increased plasticity of higher organisms. Plasticity creates a stochastic component in differentiation and cell determination processes. Therefore, the lineage studies and fate mapping have to take this uncertainty component into account.

Nevertheless, the increasing understanding of lineage determination and differentiation will place us in a good position to control these processes both *in vivo* and *in vitro*. ES cells have been playing an important role in this process. The acquired knowledge, in return, promotes the development of technologies aiming controlled *in vitro* differentiation of ES cells into therapeutically useful cell types.

ACKNOWLEDGMENTS

I am grateful to Patrick Tam for useful discussion and to Kristina Vintersten for very valuable comments and help to finalize this chapter.

REFERENCES

1. He, W., Ingraham, C., Rising, L., Goderie, S., and Temple, S. (2001). Multipotent stem cells from the mouse basal forebrain contribute GABAergic neurons and oligodendrocytes to the cerebral cortex during embryogenesis. *J. Neurosci.* **21,** 8854–8862.
2. Leber, S.M., and Sanes, J.R. (1991). Lineage analysis with a recombinant retrovirus: application to chick spinal motor neurons. *Adv. Neurol.* **56,** 27–36.
3. Leber, S.M., Breedlove, S.M., and Sanes, J.R. (1990). Lineage, arrangement, and death of clonally related motoneurons in chick spinal cord. *J. Neurosci.* **10,** 2451–2462.
4. Miller, R.H., and Ono, K. (1998). Morphological analysis of the early stages of oligodendrocyte development in the vertebrate central nervous system. *Microsci. Res. Tech.* **41,** 441–453.
5. Ono, K., Yasui, Y., Rutishauser, U., and Miller, R.H. (1997). Focal ventricular origin and migration of oligodendrocyte precursors into the chick optic nerve. *Neuron* **19,** 283–292.
6. Zhou, Q., Choi, G., and Anderson, D.J. (2001). The bHLH transcription factor Olig2 promotes oligodendrocyte differentiation in collaboration with Nkx2.2. *Neuron* **31,** 791–807.
7. Zhou, Q., and Anderson, D.J. (2002). The bHLH transcription factors OLIG2 and OLIG1 couple neuronal and glial subtype specification. *Cell* **109,** 61–73.
8. Miller, R.H. (2002). Regulation of oligodendrocyte development in the vertebrate CNS. *Prog. NeuroBiol.* **67,** 451–467.
9. Teillet, M.A., Ziller, C., and Le Douarin, N.M. (1999). Quail-chick chimeras. *Methods Mol. Biol.* **97,** 305–318.
10. Le Douarin, N., and Barq, G. (1969). Use of Japanese quail cells as "biological markers" in experimental embryology. *CR Acad. Sci. Hebd. Seances Acad. Sci. D.* **269,** 1543–1546.
11. Rossant, J., Croy, B.A., Clark, D.A., and Chapman, V.M. (1983). Interspecific hybrids and chimeras in mice. *J. Exp. Zool.* **228,** 223–233.
12. Rossant, J. (1985). Interspecific cell markers and lineage in mammals. *Philos. Trans. R. Soc. Lond. B. Biol. Sci.* **312,** 91–100.
13. Jackson, K.A., Mi, T., and Goodell, M.A. (1999). Hematopoietic potential of stem cells isolated from murine skeletal muscle. *Proc. Natl. Acad. Sci. USA* **96,** 14,482–14,486.
14. Jackson, K.A., Majka, S.M., Wulf, G.G., and Goodell, M.A. (2002). Stem cells: a minireview. *J. Cell Biochem. Suppl.* **38,** 1–6.
15. Hutchinson, R.M., Pringle, J.H., Potter, L., Patel, I., and Jeffreys, A.J. (1989). Rapid identification of donor and recipient cells after allogeneic bone marrow transplantation using specific genetic markers. *Br. J. Haematol.* **72,** 133–140.

16. Mezey, E., Chandross, K.J., Harta, G., Maki, R.A., and McKercher, S.R. (2000). Turning blood into brain: cells bearing neuronal antigens generated *in vivo* from bone marrow. *Science* **290,** 1779–1782.

17. Downs, K.M., Temkin, R., Gifford, S., and McHugh, J. (2001). Study of the murine allantois by allantoic explants. *Dev. Biol.* **233,** 347–364.

18. Selleck, M.A., and Stern, C.D. (1991). Fate mapping and cell lineage analysis of Hensen's node in the chick embryo. *Development* **112,** 615–626.

19. Collazo, A., Bronner-Fraser, M., and Fraser, S.E. (1993). Vital dye labeling of *Xenopus laevis* trunk neural crest reveals multipotency and novel pathways of migration. *Development* **118,** 363–376.

20. Lawson, K.A., and Pedersen, R.A. (1992). Clonal analysis of cell fate during gastrulation and early neurulation in the mouse. *Ciba. Found. Symp.* **165,** 3–21; discussion 21–26.

21. Kadokawa, Y., Kato, Y., and Eguchi, G. (1987). Cell lineage analysis of the primitive and visceral endoderm of mouse embryos cultured *in vitro*. *Cell Differ.* **21,** 69–76.

22. Cruz, Y.P., and Pedersen, R.A. (1985). Cell fate in the polar trophectoderm of mouse blastocysts as studied by microinjection of cell lineage tracers. *Dev. Biol.* **112,** 73–83.

23. Winkel, G.K., and Pedersen, R.A. (1988). Fate of the inner cell mass in mouse embryos as studied by microinjection of lineage tracers. *Dev. Biol.* **127,** 143–156.

24. Lemischka, I.R., Raulet, D.H., and Mulligan, R.C. (1986). Developmental potential and dynamic behavior of hematopoietic stem cells. *Cell* **45,** 917–927.

25. Clarke, H.J., Varmuza, S., Prideaux, V.R., and Rossant, J. (1988). The development potential of parthenogenetically derived cells in chimeric mouse embryos: implications for action of imprinted genes. *Development* **104,** 175–182.

26. Nagy, A., Gocza E., Diaz E.M., Prideaux V.R., Ivanyi E., Markkula M., and Rossant J. (1990). Embryonic stem cells alone are able to support fetal development in the mouse. *Development* **110,** 815–821.

27. Lo, C.W. (1986). Localization of low abundance DNA sequences in tissue sections by *in situ* hybridization. *J. Cell Sci.* **81,** 143–162.

28. Holt, S.J., and Sadler, P.W. (1958). Studies in enzyme cytochemistry III. Relationships between solubility, molecular association and structure in indigoid dyes. *Proc. Royal Soc.* **148B,** 495–505.

29. Friedrich, G., and Soriano, P. (1991). Promoter traps in embryonic stem cells: a genetic screen to identify and mutate developmental genes in mice. *Genes Dev.* **5,** 1513–1523.

30. Damert, A., Miquerol, L., Gertsenstein, M., Risau, W., and Nagy, A. (2002). Insufficient VEGFA activity in yolk sac endoderm compromises hematopoietic and endothelial differentiation. *Development* **129,** 1881–1892.

31. Skarnes, W.C., Moss, J.E., Hurtley, S.M., and Beddington, R.S. (1995). Capturing genes encoding membrane and secreted proteins important for mouse development. *Proc. Natl. Acad. Sci. USA* **92,** 6592–6596.

32. DePrimo, S.E., Stambrook, P.J., and Stringer, J.R. (1996). Human placental alkaline phosphatase as a histochemical marker of gene expression in transgenic mice. *Transgenic Res.* **5,** 459–466.

33. Hadjantonakis, A.K., Gertsenstein, M., Ikawa, M., Okabe, M., and Nagy, A. (1998). Generating green fluorescent mice by germ line transmission of green fluorescent ES cells. *Mech. Dev.* **76,** 79–90.

34. Okabe, M., Ikawa, M., Kominami, K., Nakanishi, T., and Nishimune, Y. (1997). "Green mice" as a source of ubiquitous green cells. *FEBS Lett.* **407,** 313–319.

35. Zernicka-Goetz, M., and Pines, J. (2001). Use of green fluorescent protein in mouse embryos. *Methods* **24,** 55–60.

36. Hadjantonakis, A.K., Macmaster, S., and Nagy, A. (2002). Embryonic stem cells and mice expressing different GFP variants for multiple noninvasive reporter usage within a single animal. *BMC Biotechnol.* **2,** 11.

37. Zernicka-Goetz, M., Pines, J., McLean Hunter, S., Dixon, J.P., Siemering, K.R., Haseloff, J., and Evans, M. J. (1997). Following cell fate in the living mouse embryo. *Development* **124,** 1133–1137.

38. Tam, P.P., Williams, E.A., and Tan, S.S. (1994). Expression of an X-linked *HMG-lacZ* transgene in mouse embryos: implication of chromosomal imprinting and lineage-specific X-chromosome activity. *Dev. Genet.* **15,** 491–503.

39. Stone, L.M., Tan, S.S., Tam, P.P., and Finger, T.E. (2002). Analysis of cell lineage relationships in taste buds. *J. Neurosci.* **22,** 4522–4529.

40. Kinder, S.J., Tsang, T.E., Wakamiya, M., Sasaki, H., Behringer, R.R., Nagy, A., and Tam, P.P. (2001). The organizer of the mouse gastrula is composed of a dynamic population of progenitor cells for the axial mesoderm. *Development* **128,** 3623–3634.

41. Lobe, C.G., Koop, K.E., Kreppner, W., Lomeli, H., Gertsenstein, M., and Nagy, A. (1999). Z/AP, a double reporter for cre-mediated recombination. *Dev. Biol.* **208,** 281–292.

42. Soriano, P. (1999). Generalized lacZ expression with the ROSA26 Cre reporter strain. *Nat. Genet.* **21,** 70–71.

43. Srinivas, S., Watanabe, T., Lin, C.S., William, C.M., Tanabe, Y., Jessell, T.M., and Costantini, F. (2001). Cre reporter strains produced by targeted insertion of EYFP and ECFP into the ROSA26 locus. *BMC Dev. Biol.* **1,** 4.

44. Kolb, A.F. (2001). Selection-marker-free modification of the murine β-casein gene using a lox2272 [correction of lox2722] site. *Anal. Biochem.* **290,** 260–271.

45. Araki, K., Imaizumi, T., Okuyama, K., Oike, Y., and Yamamura, K. (1997). Efficiency of recombination by Cre transient expression in embryonic stem cells: comparison of various promoters. *J. Biochem. (Tokyo)* **122,** 977–982.

46. Belteki, G., Gertsenstein, M., Ow, D.W., and Nagy, A. (2003). Site-specific cassette exchange and germ line transmission with mouse ES cells expressing phiC31 integrase. *Nat. Biotechnol.* **21,** 321–324.

47. Nagy, A., and Rossant, J. (2001). Chimaeras and mosaics for dissecting complex mutant phenotypes. *Int. J. Dev. Biol.* **45,** 577–582.

48. Gardner, R.L., and Rossant, J. (1979). Investigation of the fate of 4–5 day postcoitus mouse inner cell mass cells by blastocyst injection. *J. Embryol. Exp. Morphol.* **52,** 141–152.

49. Schmidt, G.H., Garbutt, D.J., Wilkinson, M.M., and Ponder, B.A. (1985). Clonal analysis of intestinal crypt populations in mouse aggregation chimaeras. *J. Embryol. Exp. Morphol.* **85,** 121–130.

50. Rossant, J., Vijh, K.M., Grossi, C.E., and Cooper, M.D. (1986). Clonal origin of hematopoietic colonies in the postnatal mouse liver. *Nature* **319,** 507–511.

51. Nagy, A., Rossant, J., Nagy, R., Abramow-Newerly, W., and Roder, J.C. (1993). Derivation of completely cell culture-derived mice from early passage embryonic stem cells. *Proc. Natl. Acad. Sci. USA* **90,** 8424–8428.

52. Nagy, A., and Rossant, J. (2000). Production and analysis of ES cell aggregation chimeras. *In* "Gene Targeting: A Practical Approach," (A.L. Joyner, Ed.), pp. 177–206. Oxford University Press, Oxford.

53. Davidson, B.P., Camus, A., and Tam, P.P.L. (1999). *In* "Cell Lineage and Fate Determination," (S.A. Moody, Ed.), pp. 491–504. Academic Press, San Diego.

54. Mao, X., Fujiwara, Y., and Orkin, S.H. (1999). Improved reporter strain for monitoring Cre recombinase-mediated DNA excisions in mice. *Proc. Natl. Acad. Sci. USA* **96,** 5037–5042.

55. Awatramani, R., Soriano, P., Mai, J.J., and Dymecki, S. (2001). An Flp indicator mouse expressing alkaline phosphatase from the ROSA26 locus. *Nat. Genet.* **29,** 257–259.

56. Novak, A., Guo, C., Yang, W., Nagy, A., and Lobe, C.G. (2000). Z/EG, a double reporter mouse line that expresses enhanced green fluorescent protein upon Cre-mediated excision. *Genesis* **28,** 147–155.

57. Niwa, H., Yamamura, K., and Miyazaki, J. (1991). Efficient selection for high-expression transfectants with a novel eukaryotic vector. *Gene* **108,** 193–199.

58. Nagy, A. (2000). Cre recombinase: the universal reagent for genome tailoring. *Genesis* **26,** 99–109.

59. Hayashi, S., and McMahon, A.P. (2002). Efficient recombination in diverse tissues by a tamoxifen-inducible form of Cre: a tool for temporally regulated gene activation–inactivation in the mouse. *Dev. Biol.* **244,** 305–318.

60. Metzger, D., and Chambon, P. (2001). Site- and time-specific gene targeting in the mouse. *Methods* **24,** 71–80.

61. Metzger, D., Clifford, J., Chiba, H., and Chambon, P. (1995). Conditional site-specific recombination in mammalian cells using a ligand-dependent chimeric Cre recombinase. *Proc. Natl. Acad. Sci. USA* **92,** 6991–6995.

62. St. Onge, L., Furth, P.A., and Gruss, P. (1996). Temporal control of the Cre recombinase in transgenic mice by a tetracycline responsive promoter. *Nucleic Acids Res.* **24,** 3875–3877.

63. Perl, A.K., Wert, S.E., Nagy, A., Lobe, C.G., and Whitsett, J.A. (2002). Early restriction of peripheral and proximal cell lineages during formation of the lung. *Proc. Natl. Acad. Sci. USA* **99,** 10,482–10,487.

64. Lindeberg, J., Mattsson, R., and Ebendal, T. (2002). Timing the doxycycline yields different patterns of genomic recombination in brain neurons with a new inducible *Cre* transgene. *J. Neurosci. Res.* **68,** 248–253.

65. Joshi, S.K., Hashimoto, K., and Koni, P.A. (2002). Induced DNA recombination by Cre recombinase protein transduction. *Genesis* **33,** 48–54.

66. Jo, D., Nashabi, A., Doxsee, C., Lin, Q., Unutmaz, D., Chen, J., and Ruley, H.E. (2001). Epigenetic regulation of gene structure and function with a cell-permeable Cre recombinase. *Nat. Biotechnol.* **19,** 929–933.

67. Jones, E.A., Crotty, D., Kulesa, P.M., Waters, C.W., Baron, M.H., Fraser, S.E., and Dickinson, M.E. (2002). Dynamic *in vivo* imaging of postimplantation mammalian embryos using whole embryo culture. *Genesis* **34,** 228–235.

68. Miyata, T., Kawaguchi, A., Okano, H., and Ogawa, M. (2001). Asymmetric inheritance of radial glial fibers by cortical neurons. *Neuron* **31,** 727–741.

69. Miquerol L., and Nagy, A. (Unpublished).

70. Shalaby, F., Ho, J., Stanford, W.L., Fischer, K.D., Schuh, A.C., Schwartz, L., Bernstein, A., and Rossant, J. (1997). A requirement for Flk1 in primitive and definitive hematopoiesis and vasculogenesis. *Cell* **89,** 981–990.

71. Eremina, V., Sood, M., Haigh, J., Nagy, A., Lajoie, G., Ferrara, N., Gerber, H.P., Kikkawa, Y., Miner, J.H., and Quaggin, S.E. (2003). Glomerular-specific alterations of VEGF-A expression lead to distinct congenital and acquired renal diseases. *J. Clin Invest* **111,** 707–716.

72. Liu A, Joyner AL, Turnbull DH. (1998). Alteration of limb and brain patterning in early mouse embryos by ultrasound-guided injection of Shh-expressing cells. *Mech Dev.* 75(1–2), 107-115.

58

Use of Gene Chips to Define Genetic Pathways

S. Steven Potter, Eric W. Brunskill, Bradley Huntsman, and Larry T. Patterson

Introduction

Much of the current work in developmental biology is devoted to the definition of genetic regulatory networks. What are the genetic programs that drive the formation of the heart, brain, lungs, kidneys, and so on? This is the key question of the day. Such genetic programs are often pyramidal in structure. A single growth factor or transcription factor can regulate multiple genes, some of which are additional gene regulators. Hence, a single genetic switch can sometimes initiate a genetic cascade that alters the expression patterns of large numbers of downstream genes. For example, the mutation of just one *Hox* gene in *Drosophila* can cause global changes in gene expression patterns that dramatically alter the developmental destinies of groups of cells, giving striking homeotic transformations of one structure into another.

The current work toward unraveling the genetic pathways of development and disease resembles the efforts of biochemists many decades ago in characterizing the biochemical pathways of intermediary metabolism. In each case, there is daunting complexity. Genetic pathways will likely be more complex, as they have a more neural network character. A single gene is often regulated by many upstream genes and can affect the expression of many downstream targets; biochemical pathways are typically more linear, with one substrate converted to one product. In each case, the end result, requiring enormous research effort by many laboratories, is a wall chart with hundreds, or thousands, of arrows connecting substrates or genes. Each chart is of fundamental importance in our understanding of how cells and organisms work.

The bulk of the work done to date to elaborate genetic programs has been extremely labor intensive. For example, one approach is to carry out a detailed dissection of the promoter of an interesting gene. This strategy can lead to a deep understanding of the upstream regulation of one gene, but it can require enormous effort. It is difficult to imagine using this method to unravel the many complexities of the genetic programs of organogenesis. An approach commonly used to identify downstream targets is to create mutant mice and to perform molecular marker analysis by *in situ* hybridizations to find genes with altered expression. This requires good guessing and the

slow process of checking candidate target genes individually. It has been effective but tedious.

The challenge is to make use of the global gene expression analysis tools now available to devise new approaches that rapidly reveal genetic pathways.

Strategy for Rapid Identification of Downstream Targets Using Appropriate Progenitor Cells and Microarrays

Downstream targets are operationally defined as those genes that show altered transcription levels in response to expression of the transcription factor gene of interest. Direct targets consist of those genes that the transcription factor directly interacts with, and indirect targets are genes further downstream in the resulting genetic cascade. It is useful to be able to identify both direct and indirect targets, but it is also important to be able to distinguish the two.

In an ideal experiment, one would examine the gene expression profile of a single embryonic cell prior to and then after the expression of the transcription factor gene of interest. Genes that are up- or down-regulated in response to expression of the transcription factor represent targets. In practice, however, this experiment is extremely difficult to execute. First, microarray analysis of the gene expression profiles of single cells is problematic. Current single cell microarray analysis protocols are mostly polymerase chain reaction (PCR) based, usually require more than 60 cycles of amplification, and do not provide desired representation of starting mRNA populations. Second, it is very difficult to identify the embryonic cell of the appropriate type preceding and following expression of the transcription factor of interest. Even homogeneous-appearing cells in a forming organ can be diverse in gene expression profile.[1] It is also impossible to analyze a single cell at two time points, since the first analysis destroys the cell.

As technologies improve, some of these difficulties will be overcome. Microarray target-amplification procedures are continually improving, allowing robust analysis of ever smaller amounts of starting RNA. And transgenic mice with appropriate promoter–reporter combinations might allow the FACS isolation of populations of embryonic cells before and after expression of the gene of interest. Such an experiment would offer the advantage of using progenitor cells isolated directly from the embryo, avoiding possible cell culture associated artifacts. One major uncertainty, however, would remain.

Handbook of Stem Cells
Volume 1

More than one transcription factor gene could be changing expression level between the two isolated developmental time points. Consequently, in attempting to identify targets of a specific transcription factor gene, one could also be selecting targets of an unrelated gene from a completely different genetic pathway. Although this sort of FACS–microarray analysis would provide a useful definition of changing gene expression profiles during development, it would, therefore, be difficult to identify downstream targets of a single transcription factor.

In an effort to re-create the ideal experiment in a cell culture system, we have proposed a strategy[2,3] (Fig. 58–1). First, a developmentally appropriate progenitor cell line is created. Second, a DNA construct allowing inducible expression of the transcription factor gene of interest is introduced into the cell line. Third, microarrays are used to define gene expression profiles of the cells with and without induced expression of the gene of interest. Genes altered in expression level in response to induction of the transcription factor represent downstream targets.

This strategy offers several important advantages in the search for downstream targets. First, it gives a global analysis of the genome for potential targets. Microarrays with essentially complete representation of the mouse and human genomes are now readily available. No guessing of possible targets is required. Some of the most interesting targets might be those that were not suspected. Second, it uses developmentally appropriate cells. Presumably cells with the correct milieu of cofactors are ideal for the identification of biologically relevant targets. Third, the use of a cell culture system allows generous amounts of starting material for microarray analysis. This in turn permits the use of amplification protocols that give robust microarray results. Fourth, this is a very

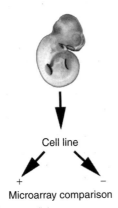

Cell line

+   −

Microarray comparison

Figure 58–1. *Progenitor cell line–microarray strategy for the study of genetic pathways. An embryo is used to make cell lines. The embryo carries an SV40-Tag transgene to facilitate immortalization and developmental arrest of the desired cells. This can be accomplished by connecting the promoter of the transcription factor of interest to SV40-Tag. Alternatively, the inducible temperature-sensitive SV40-Tag of the Immortomouse could be used. The embryo also can carry a mutation of the transcription factor gene to completely remove any expression. The resulting cell line is then manipulated to generate populations of cells with (+) and without (−) expression of the transcription factor of interest. Microarray comparisons of the gene expression profiles of the two populations of cells identify downstream target genes that respond to the transcription factor.*

clean system, comparing clonal cells that have or have not been induced to express the transcription factor of interest. There are no heterogeneous cell types, dissection differences, developmental timing differences, or other issues to complicate the results. Microarray comparisons of cell lines with induced versus uninduced transcription factor gene expression often give surprisingly few differences, which contrasts with the results commonly observed for tissue comparisons. And finally, the cell line strategy can be readily adapted to quickly distinguish direct from indirect targets.

Making Cell Lines

The expression of the Simian virus-40 large-T antigen gene *(SV40-Tag)* in transgenic mice can result in the immortalization and developmental arrest of desired cell types.[4,5] Mellon's group, for example, has generated cells locked at different stages of pituitary development using this approach.[6,7] They used a short version of the LH-β promoter to drive *SV40-Tag* expression and immortalize cells representing a relatively late stage of gonadotrope development, expressing α-subunit, GnRH receptor, and the LH-β subunit (but not the FSH-β subunit). They then used a longer fragment of the human α-subunit gene, activated earlier in development to immortalize a progenitor cell expressing only the α-subunit gene. The timed activation of *SV40-Tag* allowed the generation of pituitary cell lines representing distinct stages of differentiation. The use of a cell type-specific promoter drives immortalization of selected cells, with other cells being lost through senescence during passage in culture.

In another example, the MHP36 cells were derived from the hippocampal anlage of an *SV40-Tag* transgenic embryonic day (E) 14 embryo. In this case, a temperature-sensitive *SV40-Tag* was used, so the protein could be inactivated at body temperature, allowing further differentiation of the cells. When "implanted near the damaged CA1 field in 4VO-treated adult rats these cells (multipotential *in vitro*) migrated to the damaged area, reconstituted the gross morphology of the CA1 pyramidal layer, took up both neuronal and glial phenotypes, and gave rise to cognitive recovery."[8] Surprisingly, these cells could also restore cognitive function when implanted into brain-damaged marmosets.[8] In another example a quadripotential mesenchymal progenitor cell line was isolated from the bone marrow of a temperature sensitive *SV40-Tag* transgenic mouse. The BMC9 clone could be induced in culture to generate chondrocytes, adipocytes, osteoclasts, or osteoblasts under different conditions.[9] In addition, otocyst cell lines have been made that are stable and embryonic in character at 33°C but capable of differentiating when grown at 39°C with *SV40-Tag* inactivated.[10]

The mechanisms of action of *SV40-Tag* are not entirely understood, but it has been shown to bind and inactivate the p53 tumor suppressor protein.[11] Although it is likely true that no cell grown in culture will ever provide an exact replica of the cell *in vivo*, it is nevertheless also true, as illustrated in the examples of the preceding paragraph and many others, that cells grown in culture can sometimes retain the ability to differentiate *in vivo* or *in vitro* and can provide extremely useful models.

By making cell lines from homozygous null embryos, it is possible to create starting cells with no expression of the transcription factor gene being studied. The preferred strategy, therefore, is to make a transgenic mouse embryo homozygous for the transcription factor gene knockout with the same transcription factor gene promoter driving *SV40-Tag*. The promoter then drives *SV40-Tag* in the cells that would normally begin to express the transcription factor, thereby immortalizing them and developmentally freezing them. In essence, a switch is accomplished, with the cells of interest activating *SV40-Tag* expression in place of the transcription factor gene. Ideally the cells are in this manner developmentally locked at the point where they would normally express the transcription factor gene.

Alternatives to Making a New Cell Line

Significant effort is required to make a developmentally appropriate cell line carrying the homozygous null mutation. It is therefore useful to consider alternatives. In many cases, it is possible to use an existing cell line that approximates the cell type and developmental stage of interest. If the cells do not yet express the transcription factor gene of interest, then a strategy like the one previously described can be used by introducing an inducible version of the gene into the premade cells. If the cells represent a later developmental stage and already express the gene of interest, then one can down-regulate the gene to give the same end result: cells with and without its function. Inducible down-regulation can be achieved, for example, with a dominant negative construct that encodes the DNA-binding domain of the transcription factor connected to the powerful Engrailed repressor.[12–14] Induction of this construct would express a protein that binds to downstream targets and represses transcription. Another strategy would be to use RNA interference.

Inducible Expression of the Transcription Factor Gene

Several methods are available for achieving inducible expression of the transcription factor in cell lines. The Tet-On and Tet-Off systems, marketed by Clontech, allow effective regulation of gene expression with tetracycline or its derivative, doxycycline.[15] This strategy generally requires two sequential stable transfections, one to introduce constitutive expression of a Tet repressor converted into an activator by fusion to VP16 and the second to introduce the gene to be regulated, with Tet operator sequences inserted in the promoter. This approach can permit tight control of expression, with up to 1000-fold induction (although 10- to 100-fold is more common). The Tet system regulates expression at the level of gene transcription.

Another method for gene regulation uses a fusion of the transcription factor under study with the ligand-binding domain of a steroid hormone receptor.[16,17] This method operates at the posttranscription and posttranslation level, apparently regulating localization of the fusion protein within the cell. Treatment with a hormone triggers release from a cytoplasmic position, allowing entry into the nucleus and regulation of downstream targets. One complication is that this system requires fusion of the transcription factor with the steroid ligand-binding domain, which raises questions about the fidelity of the recognized targets. A second complication is that this system requires treatment with a hormone, which might alter gene expression patterns. This problem is at least partially overcome through the use of a mutated ER domain that responds to tamoxifen.

Another tool for the regulation of gene expression is RNA interference. It has been shown that short interfering RNA (siRNA) of 21–25 basepair (bp) can effectively inhibit gene expression in tissue culture cells.[18,19] With siRNA, it is possible to remove expression of interesting transcription factors for already established cell lines and to observe the resulting changes in gene expression. If new cell lines are made, then it is not necessary to begin with embryos homozygous mutant for the transcription factor being studied, since its function will be removed. With siRNA, it might also be possible to simultaneously remove the functions of all members of a given transcription factor family, rapidly addressing issues of functional redundancy of target gene regulation. In addition, siRNA simply removes function of an endogenously expressed gene, thereby avoiding the nonbiological, high expression levels associated with most gene induction systems. This in turn might remove some of the complications regarding tissue specificity and gene family member specificity described later.

Direct Versus Indirect Targets

Distinguishing direct from indirect targets can be difficult. The timing of the induction response provides one measure. Direct targets should show a rapid change in expression level. If alteration of the target gene expression occurs after a delay of more than a few hours, then it is unlikely to represent a direct target.

One can also study the promoter of the target gene. Will the promoter, when connected to a reporter gene, show a transcriptional response to the transcription factor of interest? Do gel shift assays show direct binding of the transcription factor to the promoter sequences? Can targeted mutation of the putative binding sites block this interaction? Such promoter analyses can provide important information helping to distinguish direct and indirect targets. The problem is that this strategy is quite labor intensive and cannot be rapidly applied to a large number of genes. In addition, these experiments are not guaranteed to succeed, since *cis*-regulatory elements can sometimes reside large distances from a gene and can, on occasion, be very difficult to find. So positive results can show with some certainty that a gene is a direct target, but negative results do not prove that it is indirect.

The preferred method for determining which targets are direct makes use of a posttranslational gene expression induction system. In this case, it is possible to induce transcription factor function in the presence of cycloheximide, which blocks protein synthesis. Tamoxifen induction using the transcription factor–steroid receptor ligand-binding domain fusion approach, for example, results in translocation of the transcription factor protein from the cytoplasm to the nucleus, where it can interact with *cis*-regulatory elements of target genes. In cycloheximide-treated cells, only direct targets show altered expression level in response to the induction. Cycloheximide blocks proteins synthesis by the direct targets, which in turn blocks regulation of further downstream indirect targets.

Examples Using the Progenitor Cell–Microarray Strategy

A few examples will be briefly reviewed to demonstrate how the progenitor cell–microarray approach can be used to work out genetic pathways and to illustrate some of the strengths as well as potential complications of the procedure.

Mice with homozygous mutation of the *Gsh-1* homeobox gene show severe growth retardation as a result of pituitary defects, which appear to be secondary to abnormalities in the hypothalamus, where *Gsh-1* is expressed. In an early application of the progenitor cell–microarray approach, hypothalamus cell lines were made from homozygous *Gsh-1* mutant mice carrying a *Gsh-1* promoter driving *SV40-Tag* expression.[2] Stable transfection introduced Tet-inducible *Gsh-1* expression, and Affymetrix microarrays were used to identify downstream targets, which were then confirmed to have altered expression in response to *Gsh-1* induction by Northern blot. Only approximately 1 in 1000 genes on the microarray showed reproducible altered expression following *Gsh-1* induction. In addition, most of the responsive genes showed relatively low (less than three-fold) change in expression, which is again common. This study demonstrated the feasibility of the progenitor cell–microarray approach.

Another study using this approach investigated the genetic pathway downstream of the *Hoxa11* and *Hoxd11* genes in kidney development.[20] The *Hoxa11* and *Hoxd11* genes show functional redundancy. Single mutants have relatively normal kidney development, but mice homozygous mutant for both *Hoxa11* and *Hoxd11* show striking defects in kidney-branching morphogenesis of the ureteric bud, resulting in a severe reduction in the number of nephrons.[21] *Hoxa11* and *Hoxd11* are expressed in the metanephric mesenchyme, not the ureteric bud, suggesting that the primary defect is a failure of the of the mesenchyme to properly signal the bud to branch.

Embryonic kidney cell lines were made from transgenic mice carrying the *Hoxa11* promoter connected to *SV40-Tag*. Cell lines made from mice with wild-type *Hoxa11/d11* maintained excellent embryonic character in tissue culture.[22] Microarray analysis showed that the cell lines expressed genes appropriate for the early metanephric mesenchyme. Furthermore, the mK3 cell line was capable of inducing branching morphogenesis of the ureteric bud in organ co-culture experiments, showing that these cells maintained this key embryonic function.[22] In subsequent experiments, embryonic kidney cell lines were made from mice homozygous mutant for *Hoxa11/d11* and gene expression profiles of cells with and without *Hoxa11* expression were compared. Again, relatively few genes, approximately 1 in 1000, showed altered expression.

Only one gene showed a dramatic (> 10-fold) change in expression in response to *Hoxa11*. This gene, *α8 integrin*, was of particular interest because it had previously been shown to be expressed in the mesenchymal cells that flank the ureteric bud, and the knockout of this gene resulted in a branching morphogenesis phenotype similar to that seen in the *Hoxa11/d11* mutants.[23] This suggested that *α8 integrin* might be a key downstream effector of *Hoxa11/d11* function in the developing kidney. Furthermore, *in vivo* confirmation was provided by *in situ* hybridizations showing greatly reduced *8 integrin* expression in the developing kidneys of the *Hoxa11/d11* mutants.[20]

We describe another example of the progenitor cell–microarray strategy to illustrate that care must be used in interpreting the results. As mentioned, the mK3 cells appeared to represent the early kidney metanephric mesenchyme and, indeed, were capable if inducing branching morphogenesis of the ureteric bud in organ coculture. Their developmental function and their microarray gene expression profiles indicated these cells were developmentally locked prior to expression of the paired box transcription factor Pax-2. Induction of the metanephric mesenchyme by the ureteric bud results in dramatic up-regulation of Pax-2 expression. Both organ culture and gene targeting studies have shown an essential role for Pax-2 in kidney development. It was therefore of interest to use the mK3 cells to search for the target genes regulated by Pax-2.

As shown in Fig. 58–2, the Tet system was used to allow inducible Pax-2 expression in a subclone of mK3 cells. In this case, the Tet-Off system gave greater than 10-fold induction of Pax-2 expression following Tet removal. This was confirmed by both Northern and Western blot. Affymetrix microarray comparison of the induced and uninduced gene expression profiles identified only one gene, encoding the protease granzyme B, showing dramatic, greater than 10-fold change in expression following *Pax-2* induction. This up-regulation of granzyme B in response to *Pax-2* expression in the mK3 cells was repeatedly confirmed by Northern analysis. The granzyme B gene plays a role in apoptosis, an important process during kidney development. Nevertheless, the

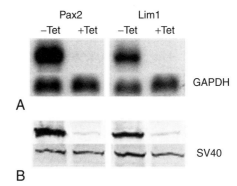

Figure 58–2. *Inducible expression of Pax-2 and Lim1 using the Tet-Off system.* (A) Northern blots showing levels of *Pax-2* and *Lim1* transcripts before and after the addition of tetracycline. Below is a GAPDH loading control. (B) Western blots showing Pax-2 and Lim1 protein levels before and after treatment with tetracycline. Below is an *SV40-Tag* loading control.

relationship between Pax-2 and granzyme B during kidney development appears uncertain. First, granzyme B has been reported to be expressed only in the hematopoietic system,[24] where it helps to drive a death response in the targets of T-cells. We considered that granzyme B expression in the developing kidney had been overlooked, but we failed to detect a granzyme B signal in developing kidneys using *in situ* hybridizations. This raised the possibility that a nonkidney target of Pax-2 had been found, even though embryonic kidney cells had been used. Other evidence, described later in this chapter, indicates that one cell type can be used to find targets for multiple tissues. The granzyme B gene did show reproducible, approximately 40-fold up-regulation in response to Pax-2 expression in the mK3 cells, showing that the *Pax-2* gene could definitely modulate granzyme B expression. But is this a biologically true transcription factor–target gene relationship? Probably not, at least for the kidney. It seems more likely that Pax-2, or a closely related member of the Pax family, regulates granzyme B expression in T-cells. This illustrates that the results of the search might be broader than expected. This offers some advantages, as a single experiment can find targets for multiple tissues and perhaps targets for other closely related members of the transcription factor family. But it also illustrates that great care must be taken in interpreting results.

The mK3 cells could also be used to search for the downstream targets of the *Lim1* gene, which encodes a transcription factor with a Lim domain and a homeodomain. The targeting of the *Lim1* gene gave a remarkable phenotype.[25] Those mice surviving to birth were missing heads as well as structures derived from the intermediate mesoderm, including kidneys and reproductive tracts. Clearly, the *Lim1* gene plays a key role in programming development of the nervous system and intermediate mesoderm. *Lim1* is expressed in the early intermediate mesoderm and again later in the development of the metanephric mesenchyme during the formation of nephrons. The mK3 cells do not express *Lim1* but represent precursors to cells that would later express this gene. To begin to identify *Lim1* targets, we again used the Tet-Off system to allow inducible expression in mK3 cells (Fig. 58–2). Affymetrix microarray comparison of RNA from *Lim1* induced and uninduced cells identified genes with altered expression levels. First, as is typical in these experiments, the gene showing the largest change in expression was the induced transcription factor gene itself. *Lim1* was called 34-fold increased in expression. In addition the microarray screen identified neuropeptide Y–Y1 receptor (d63818), vascular cell adhesion molecule-1 (VCAM-1, X67783), 3T3-L1 lipid-binding protein (W29562), nephroblastoma overexpressed (nov, Y09257), brain neuron cytoplasmic protein (W46015), neuraxin (AA795146), and a transcriptional regulatory protein (W75918) (GenBank numbers). For five of these genes, the differences in expression following *Lim1* induction were confirmed by real-time PCR, with nov (+4.9, +6.3, and +5.7), 3T3-L1 lipid-binding protein (+8.8 and +11.1), transcriptional regulatory protein (+2.1 and +2.1), and VCAM-1 (+2.8, +3.2, +2.5, and +2.6) induced; brain neuron cytoplasmic protein (−3.5) was repressed (results of separate real-time PCR experiments). It is interesting that the list of candidate targets includes both genes associated with the kidney, such as *nov*, and CNS genes, such as *neuraxin* and brain neuron cytoplasmic protein. Even though kidney cells were used for the screen, the results again appear to be broad in scope.

Related Instructive Examples

Although appropriate cell types offer a more correct collection of cofactors, and presumably optimize conditions for the identification of tissue-specific and developmental timing-specific downstream targets, the experiments described previously nevertheless illustrate a surprising flexibility, with CNS targets, for example, identified using kidney cells. Perhaps this reflects a high, nonbiological level of gene expression achieved with the Tet-inducible system, which reduces or removes the need for appropriate cofactors to activate targets. In any case, it suggests that useful results might be obtained using heterologous cell types, and indeed, this appears to be true. Lee *et al.*,[26] for example, were able to use osteosarcoma cells with inducible expression of the *WT-1* gene to find the downstream target amphiregulin, which appears to play a role in driving branching morphogenesis of the developing kidney. This group used the same strategy, inducible expression in osteosarcoma cells, to find the β-chain of the interleukin-2/15 receptor to be a target of the EWS-WT-1 isoform. This same group used inducible expression of *WT1* in rat embryonic kidney cells to find the downstream target Podocalyxin, the major structural membrane protein of kidney glomerular podocytes.[27]

A B-cell line and high-density oligonucleotide microarrays were used to identify a large number (74) of genes showing reproducible changes in expression 8 hours after Tet induction of *c-myc*.[28] Ten of these had been previously described as *c-myc* targets, providing a measure of validation of the procedure. This rapid screen therefore found 64 new candidate downstream targets of *c-myc*. Coller *et al.*[29] also searched for *c-myc* targets using microarrays. In this case, retroviral transduction was used to introduce a *c-myc*–estrogen receptor fusion gene into primary human fibroblasts (WI38). Microarray comparisons of before and after induction with 4-hydroxy tamoxifen treatment found about 36 downstream targets. Cycloheximide was used to distinguish direct from indirect targets. Of interest is that most of the targets (26 of 36) were direct. In addition, none of the 36 targets showed greater than 10-fold change in expression in response to *c-myc*. This rather low change in expression for most targets has been a consistent feature of such microarray studies.

Several interesting variations have been described. For example, Kannan *et al.*[30] used a temperature-sensitive p53. A temperature shift resulted in a conformational change and activation of the p53 protein. Microarray comparisons of gene expression profiles at the two temperatures allowed identification of p53 targets. By performing the shift in the presence or absence of cycloheximide, it was again possible to distinguish direct from indirect targets.

S. Steven Potter, Eric W. Brunskill, Bradley Huntsman, and Larry T. Patterson

Summary

The cell line–microarray strategy allows a rapid search of essentially the entire genome for downstream targets of a specific transcription factor. This is perhaps the most efficient method available for establishing transcription factor–target gene relationships. The global nature of the screen eliminates the need for accurate guessing. Furthermore, with some induction systems, cycloheximide can be used to quickly distinguish direct from indirect targets, making it unnecessary to dissect individual target gene promoters. As the use of this strategy becomes more widespread, it will greatly speed our understanding of the genetic regulatory pathways of development and disease.

ACKNOWLEDGMENTS

We thank Sheila Bell for the embryo photograph used in Fig. 58–1. This work was supported by NIH grants DK61916-01 (S.S.P.) and DK02702 (L.T.P.).

REFERENCES

1. Chiang, M.K., and Melton, D.A. (2003). Single-cell transcript analysis of pancreas development. *Dev. Cell* **4**, 383–393.
2. Li, H., Schrick, J.J., Fewell, G.D., MacFarland, K.L., Witte, D.P., Bodenmiller, D.M., Hsieh-Li, H.M., Su, C.Y., and Potter, S.S. (1999). Novel strategy yields candidate *Gsh-1* homeobox gene targets using hypothalamus progenitor cell lines. *Dev. Biol.* **211**, 64–76.
3. Potter, S.S., Valerius, M.T., and Brunskill, E.W. (2002). Using progenitor cells and gene chips to define genetic pathways. *Methods Mol. Biol.* **185**, 269–284.
4. Windle, J.J., Weiner, R.I., and Mellon, P.L. (1990). Cell lines of the pituitary gonadotrope lineage derived by targeted oncogenesis in transgenic mice. *Mol. Endocrinol.* **4**, 597–603.
5. Mellon, P.L., Windle, J.J., and Weiner, R.I. (1991). Immortalization of neuroendocrine cells by targeted oncogenesis. *Recent Prog. Horm. Res.* **47**, 69–93.
6. Alarid, E.T., Windle, J.J., Whyte, D.B., and Mellon, P.L. (1996). Immortalization of pituitary cells at discrete stages of development by directed oncogenesis in transgenic mice. *Development* **122**, 3319–3329.
7. Alarid, E.T., Holley, S., Hayakawa, M., and Mellon, P.L. (1998). Discrete stages of anterior pituitary differentiation recapitulated in immortalized cell lines. *Mol. Cell Endocrinol.* **140**, 25–30.
8. Gray, J.A., Grigoryan, G., Virley, D., Patel, S., Sinden, J.D., and Hodges, H. (2000). Conditionally immortalized, multipotential, and multifunctional neural stem cell lines as an approach to clinical transplantation. *Cell Transplant* **9**, 153–168.
9. Dennis, J.E., Merriam, A., Awadallah, A., Yoo, J.U., Johnstone, B., and Caplan, A.I. (1999). A quadripotential mesenchymal progenitor cell isolated from the marrow of an adult mouse. *J. Bone Miner. Res.* **14**, 700–709.
10. Barald, K.F., Lindberg, K.H., Hardimann, K., Kavka, A.I., Lewis, J.E., Victor, J.C., Gardner, C.A., and Poniatowski, A. (1997). Immortalized cell lines from embryonic avian and murine otocysts: tools for molecular studies of the developing inner ear. *Int. J. Dev. Neurosci* **15**, 523–540.
11. Carbone, M., Rizzo, P., Grimley, P.M., Procopio, A., Mew, D.J., Shridhar, V., de Bartolomeis, A., Esposito, V., Giuliano, M.T., Steinberg, S.M., Levine, A.S., Giordano, A., and Pass, H.I. (1997). Simian virus-40 large-T antigen binds p53 in human mesotheliomas. *Natl. Med.* **3**, 908–912.
12. Kessler, D.S. (1997). Siamois is required for formation of Spemann's organizer. *Proc. Nat. Acad. Sci. USA* **94**, 13,017–13,022.
13. Taylor, D., Badiani, P., and Weston, K. (1996). A dominant interfering Myb mutant causes apoptosis in T-cells. *Genes Dev.* **10**, 2732–2744.
14. Mariani, F.V., and Harland, R.M. (1998). XBF-2 is a transcriptional repressor that converts ectoderm into neural tissue. *Development* **125**, 5019–5031.
15. Bujard, H. (1999). Controlling genes with tetracyclines. *J. Gene Med.* **1**, 372–374.
16. Gammill, L.S., and Sive, H. (1997). Identification of *otx2* target genes and restrictions in ectodermal competence during *Xenopus* cement gland formation. *Development* **124**, 471–481.
17. Tada, M., Casey, E.S., Fairclough, L., and Smith, J.C. (1998). Bix1, a direct target of *Xenopus* T-box genes, causes formation of ventral mesoderm and endoderm. *Development* **125**, 3997–4006.
18. Elbashir, S.M., Harborth, J., Lendeckel, W., Yalcin, A., Weber, K., and Tuschl, T. (2001). Duplexes of 21-nucleotide RNAs mediate RNA interference in cultured mammalian cells. *Nature* **411**, 494–498.
19. Caplen, N.J., Parrish, S., Imani, F., Fire, A., and Morgan, R.A. (2001). Specific inhibition of gene expression by small double-stranded RNAs in invertebrate and vertebrate systems. *Proc. Natl. Acad. Sci. U. S. A.* **98**, 9742–9747.
20. Valerius, M.T., Patterson, L.T., Feng, Y., and Potter, S.S. (2002). *Hoxa11* is upstream of Integrin-α8 expression in the developing kidney. *Proc. Nat. Acad. Sci. U.S.A.* **99**, 8090–8095.
21. Patterson, L.T., Pembaur, M., and Potter, S.S. (2001). *Hoxa11* and *Hoxd11* regulate branching morphogenesis of the ureteric bud in the developing kidney. *Development* **128**, 2153–2161.
22. Valerius, M.T., Patterson, L.T., Witte, D.P., and Potter, S.S. (2002). Microarray analysis of novel cell lines representing two stages of metanephric mesenchyme differentiation. *Mech. Dev.* **112**, 219–232.
23. Muller, U., Wang, D., Denda, S., Meneses, J.J., Pedersen, R.A., and Reichardt, L.F. (1997). Integrin-α8/β1 is critically important for epithelial–mesenchymal interactions during kidney morphogenesis. *Cell* **88**, 603–613.
24. Hanson, R.D., Sclar, G.M., Kanagawa, O., and Ley, T.J. (1991). The 5′-flanking region of the human CGL-1/granzyme B gene targets expression of a reporter gene to activated T-lymphocytes in transgenic mice. *J. Biol. Chem.* **266**, 24,433–24,438.
25. Shawlot, W., and Behringer, R.R. (1995). Requirement for Lim1 in head-organizer function. *Nature* **374**, 425–430.
26. Lee, S.B., Huang, K., Palmer, R., Truong, V.B., Herzlinger, D., Kolquist, K.A., Wong, J., Paulding, C., Yoon, S.K., Gerald, W., Oliner, J.D., and Haber, D.A. (1999). The Wilms tumor suppressor WT1 encodes a transcriptional activator of amphiregulin. *Cell* **98**, 663–673.
27. Palmer, R.E., Kotsianti, A., Cadman, B., Boyd, T., Gerald, W., and Haber, D.A. (2001). WT1 regulates the expression of the major glomerular podocyte membrane protein Podocalyxin. *Curr. Biol.* **11**, 1805–1809.

28. Schuhmacher, M., Kohlhuber, F., Holzel, M., Kaiser, C., Burtscher, H., Jarsch, M., Bornkamm, G.W., Laux, G., Polack, A., Weidle, U.H., and Eick, D. (2001). The transcriptional program of a human B-cell line in response to Myc. *Nucleic Acids Res.* **29,** 397–406.

29. Coller, H.A., Grandori, C., Tamayo, P., Colbert, T., Lander, E.S., Eisenmann, R.N., and Golub, T.R. (2000). Expression analysis with oligonucleotide microarrays reveals that Myc regulates genes involved in growth, cell cycle, signaling, and adhesion. *Proc. Natl. Acad. Sci. U. S. A.* **97,** 3260–3265.

30. Kannan, K. *et al.* (2001). DNA microarrays identification of primary and secondary target genes regulated by p53. *Oncogene* **20,** 2225–2234.

Caveats of Gene-Targeted and Transgenic Mice

Klaus I. Matthaei

Introduction

A major breakthrough in medical research has been the ability to genetically modify the germ line of mice and to allow the study of gene function *in vivo*. This has occurred as a result of two major discoveries. The first was the ability to isolate from the inner cell mass of mouse blastocysts (day 3.5 after fertilization) totipotent embryonic stem (ES) cells. These ES cells, following culture *in vitro* and reinjection into a host blastocyst, could contribute to the germ line (sperm or ova) of the resultant chimera, enabling them to produce offspring that contain the genes of the injected stem cells (called germ line transmission).[1,2] The second discovery was the development of methods that allowed the modification of specific genes within the ES cells by homologous recombination in a process known as gene targeting.[3,4] The modification in the ES cells could thereby be transmitted through the germ line of the chimera to the cells' offspring. In most cases, the procedure was used to inactivate the function of a specific gene, resulting in "knockout" or "null mutant" mice. Together, these two methodological advances have allowed the study of thousands of genes *in vivo* and have led to a better understanding of the molecular function of a diverse range of genes. In particular, they have aided the understanding of several disease processes and hence the development of possible treatments that will benefit humankind. However, the observed phenotype of gene-targeted mice may be dependent on numerous other factors in addition to the specific genetic modification. Therefore, it could be questioned whether this procedure is sufficiently reliable to enable the prediction of the correct function of the deleted gene in every case. Although some phenotypic changes in behavior have been described as being caused by the (mixed) strain of mouse in which the mutation was analyzed (and not by the mutation),[5] it is possible that these effects may be more universal and more profound than expected. Factors that may influence the observed phenotype of gene-targeted mice (and possibly transgenic mice) are explained here.

Handbook of Stem Cells
Volume 1
Copyright © 2004 by Academic Press
All rights of reproduction in any form reserved.

Phenotype Differences Because of Strain Variation

IN $G_{\alpha}z$-DEFICIENT MICE

Our first indication that the strain of the genetically modified mouse could influence the observed phenotype came from the deletion of the α-subunit of the guanosine triphosphate-binding protein Gz ($G_{\alpha}z$) by gene targeting.[6] My colleagues and I introduced our mutation into C57BL/6 (B6) ES cells[7] and proceeded to inject the mutated clones into BALB/c (BALB) mouse blastocysts (Fig. 59–1). Since B6 ES cells do not contribute to the germ line of chimera efficiently, in the first three rounds of breeding, our first chimera did not produce black offspring (no germ line transmission of the ES cell coat color). To improve our ability to observe germ line transmission, we therefore bred the chimera with BALB females (since B6/BALB F1 mice have easily identifiable pigmented eyes at birth). Germ line transmission of the mutation was finally achieved at very low frequency with the BALB females. Interbreeding of the B6/BALB F1 $G_{\alpha}z$ heterozygous (+/−) mice produced our first $G_{\alpha}z$-deficient (−/−) and wild-type (+/+) mice for experimentation. It is noteworthy that the −/− and +/+ mice had a mixed genetic background (B6/BALB F2), which was clearly observed by the range of coat colors (white, agouti, and black) obtained within both genotypes (see Fig. 59–1 K).

$G_{\alpha}z$, like $G_{\alpha}q$, is highly expressed in blood platelets. Since it had been shown that the deletion of $G_{\alpha}q$ totally protected $G_{\alpha}q^{-/-}$ mice from adrenaline-induced thromboembolism and death,[8] my colleagues and I also wanted to investigate this possibility in the $G_{\alpha}z$ mice. However, since we had only just generated these mice, we had very small numbers of animals for experimentation. We therefore conducted a pilot study and injected three $G_{\alpha}z^{-/-}$ and three $G_{\alpha}z^{+/+}$ mice with adrenaline. Surprisingly, all three of the wild-type mice were killed by this treatment, whereas all of the $G_{\alpha}z$-deficient mice survived. It appeared that the deletion of $G_{\alpha}z$ function, like $G_{\alpha}q$, also protected these mice from thromboembolism and death. However, when we repeated the experiment and increased the number to nine for each group, we observed that some wild-type mice survived the treatment and some mutant mice were killed. There was no longer a difference between the two groups, since half of the mice in each group either survived or died.[9] The deletion of $G_{\alpha}z$, therefore, did not protect from

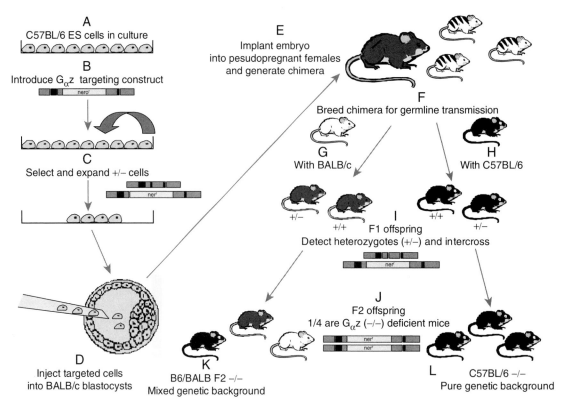

Figure 59-1. *Targeting the gene for* $G_{\alpha}z$. (A) ES cells from a B6 mouse were grown on tissue culture plates. (B) The cloned $G_{\alpha}z$ gene was disabled by the insertion of a neomycin resistance gene *(Neo^R)* at the start site of transcription, and this was introduced into the ES cells. One copy of the endogenous gene is replaced by homologous recombination and this makes the ES cells heterozygous for the $G_{\alpha}z$ mutation (described as +/− [normal/deleted]). (C) The $G_{\alpha}z^{+/-}$ ES cells were identified using molecular biology methods (D) and then injected into a host blastocyst of the BALB strain. (E) The injected embryos were implanted into pseudopregnant female mice. The injected stem cells then contributed to the formation of the resultant embryo, called a chimera, which consisted of both the injected cells and the cells of the (host) embryo. Since the ES cells were from mice with a black coat color (B6) and the host blastocyst was BALB (white), the chimera had a coat color of white and black. (F) It is possible to determine whether the injected ES cells contributed to testis formation by determining if the chimera produced sperm derived from the injected cells. This was done by breeding the chimera and examining the coat color of the offspring. (G) Since the coat color of the ES cells was black and the host blastocyst was white, it was possible to detect germ line transmission. BALB mice bred with other BALB mice produce white offspring, whereas B6 mice bred with BALB mice produce brown offspring. The production of brown mice by the chimera after mating with a BALB female therefore indicated that the sperm were derived from the ES cells, hence germ line transmission. (H) B6 mice bred with other B6 mice produced black offspring. The chimera also produced black offspring after mating with a B6 female. Note that in this case, the offspring were not of a mixed genetic background and were pure B6. (I) Since the ES cells were heterozygous (+/− for the mutation, the chimera produced sperm that were either wild-type (+) or that carried the $G_{\alpha}z$ mutation (−). The chimera therefore produced offspring in which 50% were +/− for the mutation. (J) To obtain the full effect of the gene deletion, both copies of the $G_{\alpha}z$ gene had to be mutated (−/−). This was achieved by the interbreeding of two $G_{\alpha}z^{+/-}$ mice (K) and resulted in offspring where one-quarter were −/−, half were +/−, and another quarter were +/+ for $G_{\alpha}z$. Since they were also obtained from an intercross of B6/BALB F1 mice, the resultant offspring are B6/BALB F2. It is noteworthy that the coat color of these mice does not indicate the gene deletion, since $G_{\alpha}z$ is not linked to the coat-color genes and therefore segregated independently. Mice of all three $G_{\alpha}z$ genotypes (−/−, +/−, and +/+) were therefore observed to have all three coat colors—white, brown, and black—clearly indicating the mixed genetic background. (L) After intercrossing two heterozygous mice obtained in part H, one-quarter of the offspring were also −/−, half were +/−, and another quarter were +/+ for $G_{\alpha}z$. However, in this case, all of the mice were black, indicating their pure B6 origin.

adrenaline-induced thromboembolism and death. Why did we have this discrepancy between the first and the second experiments? Since the $G_{\alpha}z$-deficient and wild-type mice were a mixture of two mouse strains, was it possible that the genetic background was responsible for this dramatic difference? We therefore challenged wild-type mice of both the B6 and the BALB strains with increasing amounts of adrenaline. It immediately became clear that there was a dramatic difference between the mortality rate of B6 and that of BALB mice to the adrenaline challenge.[9] The BALB mice were considerably more sensitive to all concentrations of adrenaline than the B6.

By chance, in our first experiment, we had analyzed three knockout animals that had a B6-like (less sensitive to adrenaline) genetic background, and the controls were more like the (more sensitive) BALB strain. After crossing the $G_{\alpha}z$ mutation to the BALB strain for 10 generations (N10 BALB), we could show that the there was no difference to adrenaline challenge between the N10 BALB $G_{\alpha}z^{+/+}$ and the N10 BALB $G_{\alpha}z^{-/-}$ mice, proving that the deletion of $G_{\alpha}z$ was not protective.[9] Our initial observation was therefore clearly the result of strain variation and not the deletion of $G_{\alpha}z$. The important point here is that if in the initial experiment we had injected five animals in each group and by chance all of the +/+ mice had died and all of the −/− animals survived, we would not have discovered this strain variation and would have attributed the protection to the deletion of $G_\alpha z$.

The chimera that produced germ line offspring with the BALB/c strain eventually transmitted the gene deletion to a B6 female (see Fig. 59–1H). We were therefore also able to produce $G_\alpha z^{-/-}$ mice in a pure B6 genetic background (see Fig. 59–1L). Surprisingly, offspring of matings in which both parents were of the B6 $G_\alpha z^{-/-}$ genotype died within 24 hours of birth. This was in contrast to matings between $G_\alpha z^{-/-}$ mice in the mixed genetic background (B6/BALB F2) or of the N10 BALB genetic constitution, which could raise their young normally.[6] Surprisingly, B6 $G_\alpha z^{-/-}$ mice also survived if their parents were heterozygous. This prompted us to examine whether the B6 $G_\alpha z^{-/-}$ females were deficient in some maternal function. When B6 $G_\alpha z^{-/-}$ mice from a homozygous cross were adopted by B6 $G_\alpha z^{+/+}$ females directly after birth, the $G_\alpha z^{-/-}$ pups survive.[10] Moreover, when B6 $G_\alpha z^{+/+}$ pups were adopted by B6 $G_\alpha z^{-/-}$ females, the B6 $G_\alpha z^{+/+}$ pups did not thrive. The B6 $G_\alpha z^{-/-}$ females, therefore, in contrast to N10 BALB or B6/BALB F2 $G_\alpha z^{-/-}$ females, could not raise their offspring in a normal manner. Thus, it appears that there is a modifier gene or genes that interact with $G_\alpha z$ and allows the offspring to survive after birth and that this gene is different in the B6 strain than in the BALB. More notably, it is clear that the same gene deletion can have a dramatically different phenotype in different strains of mice.

IN INTERLEUKIN-5 DEFICIENT MICE

The previous section has demonstrated that the genetic background in which a gene is deleted can have a dramatic effect on the observed phenotype. In the case of the $G_\alpha z^{-/-}$ mice, the difference was easily detected: life versus death. What if the change in phenotype had been subtle?

Interleukin (IL)-5 is a regulatory cytokine[11] that promotes the differentiation and proliferation of specific blood leukocytes called eosinophils.[12,13] Eosinophil recruitment is a characteristic feature of several pathological conditions—including asthma, where the number of eosinophils in the allergic lung directly correlate with the severity of the disease.[14,15] IL-5 may therefore be a potential therapeutic target for the treatment of asthma.

To examine the role of IL-5 and eosinophils in the pathogenesis of allergic lung disease, we deleted the function of IL-5 by gene targeting in B6 ES cells[7] and generated B6 IL-5–deficient mice.[16] These were challenged in a mouse model of allergic lung disease.[17] In response to aeroallergen challenge, sensitized wild-type B6 (IL-5+/+) mice developed the hallmark features of allergic lung disease, including a blood and lung eosinophilia as well as extensive lung damage. The mice also developed airway hyperreactivity (AHR) in response to the spasmogen β-methacholine. However, when IL-5–deficient mice were submitted to this regimen, the eosinophilia, lung damage, and AHR were absent. Moreover, reconstitution of IL-5 by infection with a recombinant vaccinia virus, engineered to produce IL-5, restored the

aeroallergen-induced eosinophilia and airways dysfunction in the IL-5−/− animals. We concluded, therefore, that IL-5 and eosinophils were the central mediators of pathogenesis in this model of allergic lung disease.[17] However, in a similar study, a different conclusion was made: Although eosinophilia and lung damage were dramatically attenuated, AHR was not abolished when an antibody to deplete the levels of IL-5 was used.[18] What was the reason for this discrepancy?

It could be argued that antibody administration to an animal might not be as efficient in inhibiting IL-5 function as ablating the gene. Gene targeting could therefore be argued to be more effective and give an unequivocal result. However, we found another difference in the experimental protocols used in the two studies: In our experiment,[17] we used B6 mice, whereas the antibody experiment used a different strain of mouse, the BALB.[18] Could the strains involved make this subtle but possibly critical difference? To investigate this possibility, we bred the IL-5 deletion from the pure B6 onto the BALB background for five generations and repeated the aeroallergen experiment using our protocol. To our surprise, AHR was present even though the eosinophilia was markedly attenuated and the lung damage abolished in the N5 BALB IL-5−/− mice.[19] Thus, the two strains of mice exhibited different phenotypes in spite of an identical genetic deletion. Again, it is clear that the genetic background can dramatically influence the observed phenotype associated with a gene deletion. Moreover, this difference may be subtle but extremely important in the analysis of gene function.

IN IL-13 DEFICIENT MICE

IL-13 was deleted in 129/J ES cells and introduced into B6 blastocysts. The resultant chimera then transmitted the mutation to a B6 female, and heterozygotes were intercrossed to generate the null-mutant mice.[20] The IL-13−/− mice were therefore of a mixed genetic background (129/B6 F2). This mutation was bred to the BALB strain, and the fifth generation BALB IL-13 heterozygotes (+/−) were interbred to produce N5 BALB IL-13–deficient mice.[20] The N5 BALB IL-13−/− mice were then shown to exhibit AHR in response to aeroallergen challenge.[21] Surprisingly, after breeding the mice to the BALB strain for two more generations, the N7 BALB IL-13-deficient mice no longer exhibited AHR in response to challenge.[22] What was the cause of this difference between the N5 and the N7 BALB IL-13–deficient mice?

The involvement of IL-4 and its receptor was suggested by the finding that AHR in the allergic N5 BALB IL-13–deficient mice was absent after administration of an anti-IL-4 antibody.[21] Interestingly, IL-13 and IL-4 both use the α-subunit of the IL-4 receptor (IL-4Rα) as the principle signaling receptor subunit.[23,24] Moreover, there is a polymorphism in the IL-4Rα receptor between B6 and BALB mice, and this has been shown to modulate the function of IL-4.[25] To test the possibility that there was a difference in the IL-4Rα in the two strains of mice, the receptor was analyzed. It was shown that the N5 BALB IL-13−/− mice have the B6 form of the receptor; in the N7 BALB IL-13−/− mice, it is the BALB form.[26] Although at this stage it is not clear how this difference may allow the induction of

AHR in the N5 animals and not in the N7 mice, it again points out that the genotype of the host animal can play a major role in the apparent phenotype associated with a gene deletion.

IN TRANSGENIC MICE

The genetic background can also influence the expression of a transgene, as shown by our observations on the transgenic expression of $G_{\alpha}z$ in the B6 and BALB genetic backgrounds. My colleagues and I wanted to reconstitute $G_{\alpha}z$ expression by generating transgenic mice that expressed $G_{\alpha}z$ and then crossing these to the $G_{\alpha}z$-deleted animals.[27] We generated a construct in which $G_{\alpha}z$ expression was under the control of the constitutive elongation factor 1α promoter.[28] To monitor expression, we added the enhanced green fluorescent protein (EGFP) gene after an internal ribosome entry site (IRES),[29] which allows the expression of $G_{\alpha}z$ as well as EGFP. This construct was electroporated into B6 ES cells, and transgenic ES colonies were identified by polymerase chain reaction and strong EGFP fluorescence. Strong $G_{\alpha}z$ and EGFP expression in the ES cells was confirmed by Western blotting. Several $G_{\alpha}z$-overexpressing colonies were injected into BALB blastocysts, and chimeras were generated. However, all chimeras from every clone died within the first week of birth. On autopsy, we discovered that the chimera all expressed high levels of EGFP (which implied high $G_{\alpha}z$ expression). In our experience, such lethality was most unusual. We therefore concluded that the overexpression of $G_{\alpha}z$ in the B6 background was detrimental to mouse survival. We also concluded that there might be an interaction with $G_{\alpha}z$ overexpression and the host genotype similar to that seen for the deletion of the $G_{\alpha}z$ gene.

As a consequence of these considerations, we electroporated the $G_{\alpha}z$.IRES.EGFP construct into BALB ES cells[30] and generated ES colonies expressing $G_{\alpha}z$ as well as EGFP. In contrast to the B6 ES cells, where only strong expression of $G_{\alpha}z$ and EGFP was seen, only weak expression was observed in all transgenic BALB ES colonies. No colonies with strong expression were found. Moreover, after injection into B6 blastocysts, all colonies generated germ line-competent chimera, and the construct was successfully transmitted to their offspring. However, none of the transgenic offspring expressed appreciable protein levels of EGFP or $G_{\alpha}z$.

The important point here is that when the $G_{\alpha}z$ construct was introduced into B6 ES cells, all colonies (>15) had strong expression of both $G_{\alpha}z$ and EGFP. On the other hand, when the identical construct was introduced into BALB ES cells, all colonies had weak $G_{\alpha}z$ and EGFP expression. I cannot explain these findings except to suggest that the transgenic expression of $G_{\alpha}z$ is influenced by a modifier gene or genes different in B6 and in BALB mice. I also suggest that strain variation may affect the expression of other transgenes as well as of $G_{\alpha}z$.

Phenotype Differences Because of the Hitchhiker Effect

A common practice in gene targeting experiments is to analyze the mutated mice in a 129/B6 F2 mixed genetic background. This occurs since the mutation is introduced into 129 ES cells, which have a very efficient rate of contribution to the germ line of chimera when injected into host blastocysts. Germ line transmission is therefore readily obtained. This is observed by the appearance of the dominant agouti (brown) coat color of 129 mice when 129/B6 chimeras are bred with B6 females. The germ line offspring carrying the mutation are therefore 129/B6 F1. Intercrossing the heterozygotes then produces gene-deficient animals on a 129/B6 F2 mixed genetic background. It has, however, been recognized for some time that strain variation can influence the behavior of mice.[5] Other phenotypes have also been subsequently attributed to the mixed genetic background, and this has resulted in retraction of the original conclusion (see, for example, Hagg[31]). Moreover, since the 129 strain also has a poor reproductive performance, it is becoming a common practice to cross the targeted mutation to a strain such as B6. After each generation of crossing to the new strain, the offspring are selected for the targeted locus. However, because the probability of genetic recombination on the targeted chromosome is inversely related to the distance from the loci of the genes, the alleles of the genes of the original strain whose loci are close to the targeted gene will remain together with the mutated allele,[5] the so-called hitchhiker effect.[32] Hence, the genes around the targeted locus will continue to be from the original strain. On the other hand, in the control animals, the wild-type alleles will invariably be of the new strain since there is no selection pressure for the retention of this region of the chromosome. Although statistics predict that after 10 generations of crossing into the new strain only 0.1% of the original strain remains, the actual amount of original DNA remaining is rarely determined and may be far more significant than expected. Indeed, it was found recently that after 11 crosses of the p53 deletion[33] from the 129 to the BALB/c strain, as much as 21 centimorgans (cM) of the 129 strain remained around the targeted locus.[34] Since this is approximately 1.5% of the total mouse genome, as many as 400 hitchhiker genes may have remained from the 129 strain in the p53 N12 BALB mice. Therefore, as many as 400 genes could be different between the p53-deleted animals and the wild-type controls.

Interestingly, targeting in the 129 strain and keeping the mutation congenic in this strain may not overcome the hitchhiker problem, since there is a high degree of genetic variation within the many 129 mouse substrains.[35] The 129 substrains are sufficiently different, so they often do not allow skin grafting to be successful between different members of the strain.[35] If a targeted mutation is made in one 129 substrain and then crossed to another, the same problems with mixed genetic background may arise.

An example of a possible hitchhiker effect can be seen from the targeted deletion of *IL-4*. BALB mice are highly susceptible and die after infection with the parasite *Leishmania major*, whereas B6 mice are resistant and survive. The difference was proposed to be because of the type of immune response that occurs in the two strains of mice. B6 mice respond with an interferon gamma–driven T-helper 1 (TH1) response, whereas BALB respond with a TH2 response controlled by *IL-4*.[36] The deletion of *IL-4* was therefore proposed to render BALB/c mice resistant to this parasite. To test this hypothesis, the *IL-4* gene was deleted in 129 ES cells, and the mutation was crossed to the BALB strain. These mice were then shown to be resistant to Leishmania infection, supporting the hypothesis that *IL-4* controlled the TH2 response.[37] However, when the identical targeting construct was used to delete *IL-4* directly in BALB ES cells, the resultant pure BALB *IL-4*[−/−] mice remained sensitive to Leishmania infection.[30] Although it could be argued that this difference was because of the precise substrain of Leishmania used, it could also be because of hitchhiker genes from the 129 strain of mouse that, like B6 mice, are resistant to Leishmania infection. In the case of *IL-4,* the hitchhiker genes include *IL-3, -5,* and *-13;* the granulocyte–macrophage colony-stimulating factor; as well as the conserved noncoding region 1 (CNS-1),[38] all of which have been shown to play a role in the immune response.

Phenotype Differences Because of the Design of the Targeting Construct

INTERRUPTION OF EXONS

The design of the targeting construct may also be of critical importance in the observed mutant phenotype. Genetically deficient animals have been made by simple insertions or by deletions of portions of the gene, usually with the insertion of a selectable marker like the neomycin resistance *(Neo[R])* gene. It is not within the scope of this chapter to fully detail the intricate modifications employed in different targeting strategies; however, it is noteworthy that caution should be exercised in the interpretation of all targeting experiments since little is known of the possible effects on neighboring genes. For example, three laboratories using different deletion strategies have targeted the myogenic basic helix–loop–helix (bHLH) gene *MRF4* (see Olson *et al.*[39]). The three attempts were designed to delete function by removing part of the coding sequence and inserting the same selection cassette. In all three cases, the deleted sequences were in a similar region of the gene, although they were not identical in size and, in one case, the inserted selection cassette had the opposite orientation. However, each type of *MRF4*-deficient mouse exhibited a different phenotype. Since there are few examples in which the same gene has been targeted more than once, it is difficult to assess whether this is a more general result. It is clear, however, that the method used to disrupt function can influence the observed phenotype of the deletion of a gene.

INTERRUPTION OF INTRONS

The interruption or deletion of intronic sequences may similarly produce a change in phenotype. In one of the *MRF4* mutants described in the previous section, it was found that the mRNA for a neighboring gene, *Myf5,* was also absent. This was attributed to a *cis* effect since intercrosses of *MRF4*[+/−] and *Myf5*[+/−] mice also induced the *Myf5*-null phenotype.[40] It is clear, therefore, that the mutation of one gene can influence the function of other genes.

Another example of intronic interruption was the insertion of a Neo cassette into intron 20 of the *N*-methyl-D-aspartate receptor 1 (NMDAR1).[41] This simple insertion reduced the expression of the receptor protein in the mice to about 5% of normal levels and induced a specific phenotype including infertility and schizophrenia.[41] It is possible that the insertion had simply interrupted the efficient splicing of the NMDAR1 mRNA. However, it is also possible that a noncoding sequence in the intron, which has regulatory function, had been affected. An example of such a sequence is CNS-1, known to be a coordinate regulator of the TH2 cytokines IL-4, -5, and -13.[42,43] It has been proposed that many intronic RNA transcripts may also have function.[44] Therefore, the common practice of random deletion of intronic as well as exonic sequences may have unknown and possibly severe consequences by influencing the expression of the target gene as well as of nearby genes. Moreover, since many genes can occur clustered in the genome, it is quite likely that other groups of genes may share regulatory regions, such as those described for CNS-1.

Additional complications may arise during gene targeting experiments since some genes have been shown to overlap in their DNA sequence. The disruption of one gene may thereby affect another (often unknown) gene. To delete the function of the mouse flightless *(Fliih)* gene,[45] my colleagues and I were careful not to delete any of the mouse *Fliih* 3′ coding region since we knew that this was shared with the 3′ noncoding sequence of another gene: lethal giant larvae *(Llglh)* located in the opposite orientation.[46] Moreover, since this shared region is conserved in mammals,[46,47] it may have some as yet unknown function. As a consequence, it is essential that all detail be given in the generation and analysis of null-mutant mice.

Phenotype Differences Because of Epigenetic Mechanisms

Most researchers have observed that in some experiments, there are one or more in a group of animals that do not respond to a treatment as well as the rest. This variation is usually attributed to experimental technique or some other environmental factor. However, the variation may also be caused by epigenetic mechanisms that are not simply the result of the presence or absence of particular genes. Such epigenetic mechanisms have been reported to control the expression of the agouti coat color gene in B6 *(A[vy])* mice.[48] These mice have been kept closely inbred for 30 generations by brother–sister mating and are therefore genetically identical. Surprisingly, however, these mice display a range of coat color phenotypes ranging from no expression of the agouti gene (yellow) to patchy to completely agouti (brown).[48] The expression of the coat color gene in these mice is regulated by the insertion of an intracisternal A particle (IAP) retrotransposon 100 kilobases (kb) upstream from the promoter for the agouti hair color. Retrotransposons, when active, have the ability to affect the transcription of neighboring genes and perturb their function. When the IAP is silent in the *A[vy]* mice, the agouti protein can be expressed in the hair follicles, and the mouse fur becomes brown. When the IAP is active, transcription of the agouti gene is inhibited; thus, the production of the agouti protein is suppressed, and the mice remain yellow. Intermediate forms are also found since the phenotype is variegated. Some mice therefore have patches of both colors since the IAP is switched off in some cells of the mouse but not in others. Interestingly, each mouse of whatever phenotype also has the capability of producing offspring with the complete range of coat colors. This is because the IAP particle expression is silenced in the germ line (sperm or ova) at each generation. After fertilization, however, the IAP expression reactivates randomly, allowing the full range of coat color expression in the offspring.[48] Since there may be tens of thousands of transcriptionally competent retrotransposons in the mammalian genome, many genes may be affected by this mechanism. Epigenetic mechanisms may therefore be a consideration in the analysis of the observed phenotype of null-mutant and transgenic mice.

Approaches to Control for Experimental Variation

GENETIC BACKGROUND MUST BE CAREFULLY DESCRIBED

It is not the intention here to undermine the use of gene targeting or transgenic overexpression of genes in medical research but rather to highlight the possible complications in the interpretation of the data. Some concepts described here are not new. Strain variation has been described previously as influencing the observed phenotype in null mutants,[5] and this was also the topic of the Banbury Conference.[49] However, I describe here additional and at times subtle interactions between the gene of interest and the host genotype that may influence the observed phenotype, including the possibility of previously unconsidered epigenetic mechanisms.

These very complications may shed new light on molecular mechanisms. There are now examples in which investigators have used strain variation to their advantage and have thereby been able to identify modifier genes that influence the phenotype of the null allele (see, for example, Mattes et al.[50]). However, in the literature there are still numerous publications in which there is little description of the genetic composition of the modified mice or the specific controls used. It is imperative that these are described in detail since there are now several genes that have been deleted in the ES cells of one strain and then crossed to another strain. As described previously, IL-4 was deleted in 129 ES cells and crossed to the BALB strain,[37] whereas another group targeted IL-4 directly in BALB ES cells.[30] Of interest here is that the mice crossed to the BALB strain from the 129 were also referred to as BALB, just as those directly targeted in the BALB/c strain. Since the two strains of mice with the same genetic deletion, but different genetic background, appeared to have a different phenotype, a complete description of the genetic composition of the mouse strain used is required to allow a better assessment of the data. Moreover, the overexpression of genes in transgenic mice could be similarly affected; therefore, the genetic background of these mice also requires complete description.

TISSUE-SPECIFIC CONTROL OF GENE EXPRESSION

Given the complications of the genetic approach described here, how will unequivocal answers for the complete function of every gene ever be found? A possible solution is to use inducible systems to control the gene deletions (or the overexpression of a transgene). In this way, the control is built into the same animal.

Various inducible systems have been designed in attempts to regulate tissue-specific gene expression. The earliest of these was the Cre–loxP system to specifically regulate immunoglobulin expression in B-cells.[51] LoxP sites were inserted into the immunoglobulin gene, and these did not affect normal gene expression. Expression of the gene was then deleted in B-cells by excision of a portion of the gene between the loxP sites using the tissue-specific expression of Cre recombinase. This was achieved by crossing the "loxP" immunoglobulin gene–marked mice with mice transgenically expressing the Cre recombinase under the control of a B-cell–specific promoter.[51] This system allowed the expression to be successfully switched off in most (but not all) B-cells.

TEMPORAL-SPECIFIC CONTROL OF GENE EXPRESSION

Attempts at temporal control of gene expression have also been made using different chemicals or hormones to regulate the function of the promoter of a transgene. These include ecdysone, estrogen, progesterone, and chemical inducers of dimerization or tetracycline (reviewed, for example, by Mills[52]). All of these systems function to varying degrees, but all often suffer from "leakiness" in that they allow a high basal expression of the gene when they are "off" or do not fully express in all target cells when they are "on." The transgenes are therefore not truly tissue or temporal specific since they can be expressed in the wrong tissue or at the wrong time. The observed phenotype may therefore not be representative of the function of the gene.

TISSUE- AND TEMPORAL-SPECIFIC CONTROL OF GENE EXPRESSION

Bacterial lac Operon

The lac operon in the bacterium Escherichia coli functions by a repression mechanism in which an inhibitor protein (lacI) binds to regulatory sites (lacO) in the promoter and turns off transcription (Fig. 59–2). On the addition of lactose, the lacI protein undergoes a conformational change, which changes its binding affinity for the lacO sequences. The lacI protein thereby comes off the lacO sites, and transcription can occur. E. coli uses this system to tightly control the genes required for the use of lactose, and it is completely reversible.

lac Operon in Mice

Recently, Cronin et al.[53] modified the bacterial lac operon system to control gene expression in mice (Fig. 59–3). The tyrosinase (Tyr) gene is responsible for one of the major

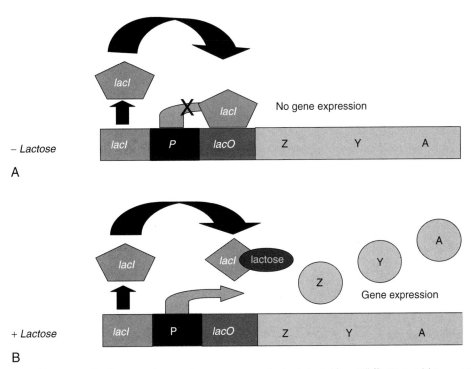

Figure 59–2. *Bacterial lac operon.* The *lac* operon functions by a repression mechanism (adapted from Mills[52]). (A) An inhibitor protein, lacI, binds to regulatory sites *lacO* in the promoter (P) and turns off transcription of the genes required for lactose metabolism. (B) On the addition of lactose, the lacI protein undergoes a conformational change, which changes its binding affinity for the *lacO* sequences. The lacI protein thereby comes off the *lacO* sites and transcription of the *lac* genes can occur. (A, transacetylase; Y, permease; and Z, β-galactosidase.)

coat colors in mice (refer to the A^{vy} mice previously considered). Indeed, wild-type albino mice can be made to express coat (and eye) color when made transgenic with a transgene expressing *Tyr* under the control of its own promoter[53] (see Fig. 59–3A and 59–3B). Moreover, the introduction of *lacO* sites into the tyrosinase promoter allowed the continued expression of coat color in the transgenic (Tyr^{lacO}) mice, indicating that the *lacO* sites did not inhibit the function of the promoter (see Fig. 59–3C). Cronin *et al.*[53] next generated a transgenic mouse that expressed a modified form of the lacI protein in all tissues (lacIR mice), which are also albino (see Fig. 59–3D). Crossing the lacIR mice (see Fig. 59–3E) with the Tyr^{lacO} mice inhibited the expression of coat color in the doubly transgenic mice (see Fig. 59–3F). Moreover, the administration of the lactose analogue, isopropyl β-D-thiogalactoside (IPTG) to the Tyr^{lacO}/lacIR mice in the drinking water restored coat color expression (see Fig. 59–3G). Indeed, the effect was fully reversible. In doubly transgenic adult mice, (and even in the embryo or nursing pup of a mother receiving IPTG in the drinking water), the expression could be switched on or off at will. Coat (and eye) color gene expression was therefore tightly controlled in these mice.[53]

Future Directions

The *lacO/lacI* system could have a much wider application by allowing temporal- and tissue-specific control of any gene in mice, thereby giving considerably more control to the

researcher to investigate gene function. The operator sites could be introduced into the promoter of any gene of interest using standard molecular techniques, and this construct could be inserted into the gene in ES cells by homologous recombination. The mutations would be introduced using a "knockin" strategy with a selection cassette flanked by *loxP* sites that are present in an intron but also carry the desired *lacO* sites in the promoter of the desired gene. The selection cassette would be removed by using Cre *in vitro* in the modified ES cells or *in vivo* with a Cre-expressing mouse after germ line transmission of the mutation (see, for example, Lomeli *et al.*[54]). Intercrossing the *lacO*-modified mouse with a *lacI*-expressing mouse such as *lacIR* will turn off gene expression in all cells. The gene can then be temporally regulated by the administration of IPTG in the drinking water (see Fig. 59–3). Tissue- and temporal-specific control of the gene could also be achieved by crossing the *lacO*-modified mouse with a mouse expressing *lacI* from a tissue-specific, rather than a generalized, promoter.

This system has several provisos. First, the remaining *loxP* site in the intron after Neo excision may have affects on the normal function of the target gene (or other genes nearby, as explained previously). Second, the introduction of the *lacO* sites into the promoter could have major effects on the function of the target gene (or, again, on neighboring genes). However, in the absence of the lacI protein, the mice should be completely normal. Any effects of the genetic manipulation

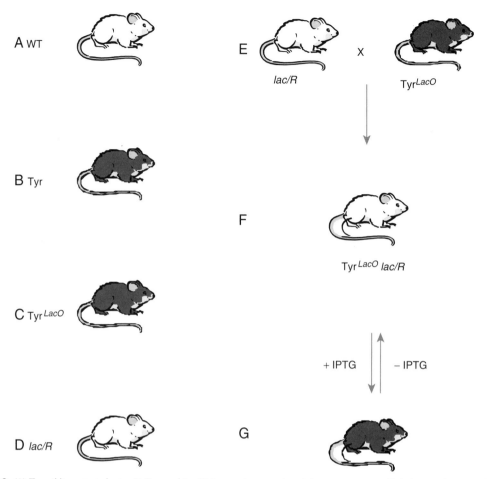

Figure 59–3. (A) The wild-type control mice (WT) are white. (B) Transgenic expression of the tyrosinase gene *(Tyr)* changes the coat color to brown. (C) Introduction of *lacO* sites into the tyrosinase promoter *(Tyr^lacO)* allows the continued expression of coat color. (D) *lacIR* mice that carry the inhibitor protein transgene *LacI* are also white. (E) Interbreeding the *lacIR* mice with the *Tyr^lacO* mice produces (F) doubly transgenic mice without coat color. (G) The addition of IPTG into the drinking water removes the lacI protein from the *lacO* sites to allow the reversible expression of coat color.

should therefore be observable if carefully compared to the wild-type of the exact same strain.

The "position effect" of the introduced *lacI* transgene could also be a problem. The position effect is where the same construct can have a different phenotype in different founders because of the random integration of the transgene near (usually unknown) regulatory elements (see, for example, Feng *et al.*[55]). This effect could be overcome by introducing the *lacI* transgene into a specific site such as the ROSA26 locus by homologous recombination.[56] Since this promoter has been shown to be constitutive and also expressed in all tissues,[57] *lacI* would also be expressed universally at all stages of development. Again, any effects of the introduction of the *lacI* transgene could be monitored in the animal when compared to wild-type mice. Crossing the *lacIR* mice with a gene-specific *lacO*-modified mouse would finally allow the target gene to be tightly regulated by the administration of IPTG. Tissue-specific regulation of the gene could also be achieved by the

expression of the lacI protein from a tissue-specific promoter rather than a generalized promoter. Similarly, transgenes could be controlled by incorporating the *lacO* sites into the transgene promoter and crossing with the constitutive lacIR mice, as was done for the Tyr^lacO mice described previously.

The *lacO/lacI* system has enormous potential for studying the function of any gene *in vivo,* since the administration of IPTG should allow complete control of the gene by the experimentalist. Moreover, since the gene can be switched on and off at will in the same animal, it should be possible to obtain a better understanding of gene function without referring to another mouse as control. The function of a particular gene may only relate to the specific strain of mouse in which it was studied since, as indicated previously, the function of many genes may be different in different strains of mice. Moreover, since it is not known which mouse strain has a genetic repertoire similar to the human, it is also not known which result will be directly applicable to the human. It could be argued, therefore, that gene targeting studies should be performed in an outbred strain of mouse. However, although it is feasible to isolate ES cells from outbred strains, it could also be argued that the outbred genetic background may not allow the identification of subtle functions of a gene. It may be simpler to target the genes in ES cells from the available inbred strains of mice. The genes could then be examined in a pure genetic background with the added advantage that these strains have been extensively studied. Moreover, if the –/– animals of the two inbred strains are now intercrossed, F1 mice will be produced that have the deleted gene and are genetically identical. Intercrossing the +/+ animals of the same strains will also give the appropriate control since these F1 animals will be genetically identical to each other as well as to the –/– mice, except for the gene deletion. Moreover, the F1 mice will be heterozygous for all genes that are different in the two strains and may therefore equate to a more "outbred" strain of mouse. Comparisons of gene function in the three genetic backgrounds should therefore give a clearer indication of gene function.

Summary

The aim of medical research is to clearly define the function of target genes and then to be able to translate that finding into a clinical setting and alleviate disease. It is clear from our current studies that many factors influence the resultant phenotype after the manipulation of a specific gene either by gene targeting or by overexpression. The ability to switch a gene function on and off at will in individual animals—in a temporal- and tissue-specific manner and in a variety of genetic (and epigenetic) backgrounds—should enable a more informative approach to the identification of gene function in health and disease.

ACKNOWLEDGMENTS

I am indebted to the many colleagues who have contributed over the years to the discussion of this topic and who are referenced through the publications herein; special thanks to Caryl Hill for also critically editing the manuscript. In addition, I am indebted to A.C. Blackburn, J. Holgate, I.A. Hendry, and K.J. Leck for allowing me to communicate unpublished data. My sincerest thanks to Wes Whitten, who alerted me to strain variation in 1991 and in particular that the 129 mouse was a "mongrel"strain.

REFERENCES

1. Evans, M.J., and Kaufman, M.H. (1981). Establishment in culture of pluripotential cells from mouse embryos. *Nature* **292**, 154–156.
2. Martin, G.R. (1981). Isolation of a pluripotent cell line from early mouse embryos cultured in medium conditioned by teratocarcinoma stem cells. *Proc. Natl. Acad. Sci. USA* **78**, 7634–7638.
3. Doetschman, T., Gregg, R.G., Maeda, N., Hooper, M.L., Melton, D.W., Thompson, S., and Smithies, O. (1987). Targeted correction of a mutant *HPRT* gene in mouse embryonic stem cells. *Nature* **330**, 576–578.
4. Thomas, K.R., and Capecchi, M.R. (1987). Site-directed mutagenesis by gene targeting in mouse embryo-derived stem cells. *Cell* **51**, 503–512.
5. Gerlai, R. (1996). Gene-targeting studies of mammalian behavior: is it the mutation or the background genotype? *Trends Neurosci.* **19**, 177–181.
6. Hendry, I.A., Kelleher, K.L., Bartlett, S.E., Leck, K.J., Reynolds, A.J., Heydon, K., Mellick, A., Megirian, D., and Matthaei, K.I. (2000). Hypertolerance to morphine in G(z α)-deficient mice. *Brain Res.* **870**, 10–19.
7. Ledermann, B., and Burki, K. (1991). Establishment of a germ line competent C57BL/6 embryonic stem cell line. *Exp. Cell Res.* **197**, 254–258.
8. Offermanns, S., Toombs, C.F., Hu, Y.H., and Simon, M.I. (1997). Defective platelet activation in G α (q)-deficient mice. *Nature* **389**, 183–186.
9. Kelleher, K.L., Matthaei, K.I., and Hendry, I.A. (2001). Targeted disruption of the mouse *Gz-α* gene: a role for *Gz* in platelet function? *Thromb. Haemost.* **85**, 529–532.
10. Holgate, J., and Hendry, I.A. (Personal communication).
11. Campbell, H.D., Sanderson, C.J., Wang, Y., Hort, Y., Martinson, M.E., Tucker, W.Q., Stellwagen, A., Strath, M., and Young, I.G. (1988). Isolation, structure, and expression of cDNA and genomic clones for murine eosinophil differentiation factor: Comparison with other eosinophilopoietic lymphokines and identity with interleukin-5. *Eur. J. Biochem.* **174**, 345–352.
12. Coffman, R.L., Seymour, B.W., Hudak, S., Jackson, J., and Rennick, D. (1989). Antibody to interleukin-5 inhibits helminth-induced eosinophilia in mice. *Science* **245**, 308–310.
13. Sanderson, C.J. (1992). Interleukin-5, eosinophils, and disease. *Blood* **79**, 3101–3109.
14. De Monchy, J.G., Kauffman, H.F., Venge, P., Koeter, G.H., Jansen, H.M., Sluiter, H.J., and De Vries, K. (1985). Bronchoalveolar eosinophilia during allergen-induced late asthmatic reactions. *Am. Rev. Respir. Dis.* **131**, 373–376.
15. Beasley, R., Roche, W.R., Roberts, J.A., and Holgate, S.T. (1989). Cellular events in the bronchi in mild asthma and after bronchial provocation. *Am. Rev. Respir. Dis.* **139**, 806–817.
16. Kopf, M., Brombacher, F., Hodgkin, P.D., Ramsay, A.J., Milbourne, E.A., Dai, W.J., Ovington, K.S., Behm, C.A., Kohler, G., Young, I.G., and Matthaei, K.I. (1996). IL-5-deficient mice have a developmental defect in CD5+ B-1 cells and lack eosinophilia but have normal antibody and cytotoxic T-cell responses. *Immunity* **4**, 15–24.
17. Foster, P.S., Hogan, S.P., Ramsay, A.J., Matthaei, K.I., and Young, I.G. (1996). Interleukin-5 deficiency abolishes eosinophilia, airways hyperreactivity, and lung damage in a mouse asthma model. *J. Exp. Med.* **183**, 195–201.
18. Corry, D.B., Folkesson, H.G., Warnock, M.L., Erle, D.J., Matthay, M.A., Wiener-Kronish, J.P., and Locksley, R.M. (1996). Interleukin-4, but not interleukin-5 or eosinophils, is required in a murine model of acute airway hyperreactivity. *J. Exp. Med.* **183**, 109–117.
19. Hogan, S.P., Matthaei, K.I., Young, J.M., Koskinen, A., Young, I.G., and Foster, P.S. (1998). A novel T-cell-regulated mechanism modulating allergen-induced airways hyperreactivity in BALB/c mice independently of IL-4 and IL-5. *J. Immunol.* **161**, 1501–1509.
20. McKenzie, G.J., Emson, C.L., Bell, S.E., Anderson, S., Fallon, P., Zurawski, G., Murray, R., Grencis, R., and McKenzie, A.N. (1998).

Impaired development of Th2 cells in IL-13-deficient mice. *Immunity* **9**, 423–432.

21. Webb, D.C., McKenzie, A.N., Koskinen, A.M., Yang, M., Mattes, J., and Foster, P.S. (2000). Integrated signals between IL-13, IL-4, and IL-5 regulate airways hyperreactivity. *J. Immunol.* **165**, 108–113.

22. Walter, D.M., McIntire, J.J., Berry, G., McKenzie, A.N., Donaldson, D.D., DeKruyff, R.H., and Umetsu, D.T. (2001). Critical role for IL-13 in the development of allergen-induced airway hyperreactivity. *J. Immunol.* **167**, 4668–4675.

23. Zurawski, S.M., Vega, F., Jr., Huyghe, B., and Zurawski, G. (1993). Receptors for interleukin-13 and interleukin-4 are complex and share a novel component that functions in signal transduction. *EMBO. J.* **12**, 2663–2670.

24. Smerz-Bertling, C., and Duschl, A. (1995). Both interleukin-4 and interleukin-13 induce tyrosine phosphorylation of the 140-kDa subunit of the interleukin-4 receptor. *J. Biol. Chem.* **270**, 966–970.

25. Schulte, T., Kurrle, R., Rollinghoff, M., and Gessner, A. (1997). Molecular characterization and functional analysis of murine interleukin-4 receptor allotypes. *J. Exp. Med.* **186**, 1419–1429.

26. Webb, D., Matthaei, K.I., Cai, Y., McKenzie, A.N.J., and Foster, P.S. (2004). Polymorphisms in IL-4Ralpha correlate with airways hyperactivity, eosinophila, and ym protein expression in allergic IL-13 –/– mice. *J. Immunol.* **172**, 1092–1098.

27. Leck, K.J., Hendry, I.A., and Matthaei, K.I. (Unpublished).

28. Goldman, L.A., Cutrone, E.C., Kotenko, S.V., Krause, C.D., and Langer, J.A. (1996). Modifications of vectors pEF-BOS, pcDNA1, and pcDNA3 result in improved convenience and expression. *Biotechniques* **21**, 1013–1015.

29. Jang, S.K., Pestova, T.V., Hellen, C.U., Witherell, G.W., and Wimmer, E. (1990). Cap-independent translation of picornavirus RNAs: structure and function of the internal ribosomal entry site. *Enzyme* **44**, 292–309.

30. Noben-Trauth, N., Kohler, G., Burki, K., and Ledermann, B. (1996). Efficient targeting of the *IL-4* gene in a BALB/c embryonic stem cell line. *Transgenic Res.* **5**, 487–491.

31. Hagg, T. (1999). Neuronal cell death: retraction. *Science* **285**, 340.

32. Crusio, W.E. (1996). Gene-targeting studies: new methods, old problems. *Trends Neurosci.* **19**, 186–187; discussion 188–189.

33. Jacks, T., Remington, L., Williams, B.O., Schmitt, E.M., Halachmi, S., Bronson, R.T., and Weinberg, R.A. (1994). Tumor spectrum analysis in p53-mutant mice. *Curr. Biol.* **4**, 1–7.

34. Blackburn, A.C. (Personal communication).

35. Simpson, E.M., Linder, C.C., Sargent, E.E., Davisson, M.T., Mobraaten, L.E., and Sharp, J.J. (1997). Genetic variation among 129 substrains and its importance for targeted mutagenesis in mice. *Natl. Genet.* **16**, 19–27.

36. Reiner, S.L., and Locksley, R.M. (1995). The regulation of immunity to *Leishmania major*. *Annu. Rev. Immunol.* **13**, 151–177.

37. Kopf, M., Brombacher, F., Kohler, G., Kienzle, G., Widmann, K.H., Lefrang, K., Humborg, C., Ledermann, B., and Solbach, W. (1996). IL-4-deficient Balb/c mice resist infection with *Leishmania major*. *J. Exp. Med.* **184**, 1127–1136.

38. Kelly, B.L., and Locksley, R.M. (2000). Coordinate regulation of the IL-4, IL-13, and IL-5 cytokine cluster in Th2 clones revealed by allelic expression patterns. *J. Immunol.* **165**, 2982–2986.

39. Olson, E.N., Arnold, H.H., Rigby, P.W., and Wold, B.J. (1996). Know your neighbors: three phenotypes in null mutants of the myogenic bHLH gene *MRF4*. *Cell* **85**, 1–4.

40. Floss, T., Arnold, H.H., and Braun, T. (1996). Myf-5(m1)/Myf-6(m1) compound heterozygous mouse mutants down-regulate Myf-5 expression and exert rib defects: evidence for long-range *cis* effects on Myf-5 transcription. *Dev. Biol.* **174**, 140–147.

41. Mohn, A.R., Gainetdinov, R.R., Caron, M.G., and Koller, B.H. (1999). Mice with reduced NMDA-receptor expression display behaviors related to schizophrenia. *Cell* **98**, 427–436.

42. Loots, G.G., Locksley, R.M., Blankespoor, C.M., Wang, Z.E., Miller, W., Rubin, E.M., and Frazer, K.A. (2000). Identification of a coordinate regulator of interleukin-4, -13, and -5 by cross-species sequence comparisons. *Science* **288**, 136–140.

43. Mohrs, M., Blankespoor, C.M., Wang, Z.E., Loots, G.G., Afzal, V., Hadeiba, H., Shinkai, K., Rubin, E.M., and Locksley, R.M. (2001). Deletion of a coordinate regulator of type 2 cytokine expression in mice. *Natl. Immunol.* **2**, 842–847.

44. Mattick, J.S. (2001). Noncoding RNAs: The architects of eukaryotic complexity. *EMBO Rep.* **2**, 986–991.

45. Campbell, H.D., Fountain, S., McLennan, I.S., Berven, L.A., Crouch, M.F., Davy, D.A., Hooper, J.A., Waterford, K., Chen, K.S., Lupski, J.R., Ledermann, B., Young, I.G., and Matthaei, K.I. (2002). Fliih, a gelsolin-related cytoskeletal regulator essential for early mammalian embryonic development. *Mol. Cell Biol.* **22**, 3518–3526.

46. Campbell, H.D., Fountain, S., Young, I.G., Weitz, S., Lichter, P., and Hoheisel, J.D. (2000). *Fliih*, the murine homologue of the *Drosophila melanogaster* flightless I gene: Nucleotide sequence, chromosomal mapping, and overlap with Llglh. *DNA Seq.* **11**, 29–40.

47. Campbell, H.D., Young, I.G., and Matthaei, K.I. (2000). Mammalian homologues of the *Drosophila melanogaster* flightless I gene involved in early development. *Curr. Genomics* **1**, 59–70.

48. Whitelaw, E., and Martin, D.I. (2001). Retrotransposons as epigenetic mediators of phenotypic variation in mammals. *Natl. Genet.* **27**, 361–365.

49. (1997). Mutant mice and neuroscience: recommendations concerning genetic background. (Banbury Conference on genetic background in mice). *Neuron* **19**, 755–759.

50. Mattes, J., Yang, M., Mahalingam, S., Kuehr, J., Webb, D.C., Simson, L., Hogan, S.P., Koskinen, A., McKenzie, A.N., Dent, L.A., Rothenberg, M.E., Matthaei, K.I., Young, I.G., and Foster, P.S. (2002). Intrinsic defect in T-cell production of interleukin (IL)-13 in the absence of both IL-5 and eotaxin precludes the development of eosinophilia and airways hyperreactivity in experimental asthma. *J. Exp. Med.* **195**, 1433–1444.

51. Gu, H., Zou, Y.R., and Rajewsky, K. (1993). Independent control of immunoglobulin switch recombination at individual switch regions evidenced through Cre–loxP-mediated gene targeting. *Cell* **73**, 1155–1164.

52. Mills, A.A. (2001). Changing colors in mice: an inducible system that delivers. *Genes Dev.* **15**, 1461–1467.

53. Cronin, C.A., Gluba, W., and Scrable, H. (2001). The lac operator–repressor system is functional in the mouse. *Genes Dev.* **15**, 1506–1517.

54. Lomeli, H., Ramos-Mejia, V., Gertsenstein, M., Lobe, C.G., and Nagy, A. (2000). Targeted insertion of Cre recombinase into the *TNAP* gene: excision in primordial germ cells. *Genesis* **26**, 116–117.

55. Feng, G., Mellor, R.H., Bernstein, M., Keller-Peck, C., Nguyen, Q.T., Wallace, M., Nerbonne, J.M., Lichtman, J.W., and Sanes, J.R. (2000). Imaging neuronal subsets in transgenic mice expressing multiple spectral variants of GFP. *Neuron* **28**, 41–51.

56. Srinivas, S., Watanabe, T., Lin, C.S., William, C.M., Tanabe, Y., Jessell, T.M., and Costantini, F. (2001). Cre reporter strains produced by targeted insertion of EYFP and ECFP into the ROSA26 locus. *BMC Dev. Biol.* **1**, 4.

57. Friedrich, G., and Soriano, P. (1991). Promoter traps in embryonic stem cells: a genetic screen to identify and mutate developmental genes in mice. *Genes Dev.* **5**, 1513–1523.

Gene-Based Screens of Chemically Mutagenized Mouse Embryonic Stem Cells

Jay L. Vivian, Yijing Chen, and Terry Magnuson

Introduction

Chemical mutagens are standard tools for mutagenesis in a variety of organisms, and they are a primary means of creating mutations in phenotype-based screens in most genetic systems. Although varied in the experimental design, all whole animal screens involve the generation of lines harboring mutated chromosomes followed by the examination of the resulting phenotypes in the heterozygous or homozygous state. In contrast, gene-based screens rely on the identification of lines that carry mutations in specific genes, prior to any phenotypic examination. The ability to perform gene-based screens has been made possible by recent technological advances in the high-throughput detection of subtle mutations.

Chemical mutagens have also been used successfully in the mutagenesis of mouse embryonic stem (ES) cells.[1,2] This approach holds a variety of advantages over mutagenesis in the whole animal. Cell culture–based mutagenesis is distinguished from whole animal mutagenesis in its ability to use a variety of mutagens, to monitor and modulate mutation load, and to screen a large number of lines. The possibility of generating and characterizing mutations in cell culture enables the rapid identification of many mutations in genes, which can be transmitted to a mouse line. In this chapter, we describe the merits and methods of gene-based screens to identify chemically induced mutations in ES cells. Several chemical mutagens have been successfully used to mutagenize mouse ES cells, and the potential exists for the use of almost any mutagen.

Nature of Chemically Induced Mutations

The genomic lesions generated by chemical mutagens are typically subtle; *N*-ethyl–*N*-nitrosourea (ENU) and ethyl methanesulfonate (EMS), for example, generate single-base substitutions in mouse spermatogonia and cell culture,[3,4] whereas the 6-chloro-9-[3-(2-chloroethylamino)propylamino]-2-methoxy-acridine (ICR191) often induces single-base insertions or deletions.[5] Although ENU can induce an array of

base substitutions in the mouse,[6] EMS generally induces transitions at guanine-cytosine base pairs, and ICR191 typically induces single-base additions or deletions within stretches of guanines or cytosines in cell culture. Such bias indicates that genes may differ in their frequency of mutagenesis with some mutagens, which is dependent partly on the size of the coding region and the sequence composition. The mutability and types of mutations are further influenced by the cell type being mutagenized in a screen, be it cultured cells, spermatogonia, or somatic cells. For example, EMS mainly induces point mutations in *Drosophila* and mammalian cell culture, whereas small deletions (~1.3 kb) can be generated in *Caenorhabditis elegans* at a low frequency (13%).[7] A given mutagen can thus display different efficacies and lesion profiles depending on the cell type or organism being mutagenized.

The subtle nature of chemically induced mutations provides genetic tools distinct from the mutations created by disruption from gene targeting or gene traps. Point mutations can produce null alleles through structural disruption of an important domain of the protein. Hypomorphic, neomorphic, and null alleles can also be generated from chemically induced mutations, allowing a spectrum of genetic tools for analysis of gene function. Hypomorphic alleles, for example, may allow the analysis of genes whose null state results in early embryonic lethality; the extended survival of such mutations provides insight to gene function in later development or during adult life. Subtle mutations can also remove a function of a specific domain of a protein, allowing the analysis of the importance of that particular region *in vivo*. These structure–function analyses, particularly when extended to numerous mutations, provide a wealth of detailed information on the domains and functionality of a protein in an *in vivo* context.

Although base substitutions are commonly thought to induce missense mutations, single-base alterations in consensus splice sequences can result in exon skipping, which often generates a frameshift. Mutations that alter splicing were observed in 7% of the ENU-induced mutations identified in our initial gene-based screen,[8] and 26% of hypoxanthine guanine phosphoribosyl transferase *(Hprt)* mutations were identified as loss-of-function.[1] ICR191 can also cause frameshifts by single-base additions or deletions within the coding region of a gene. An insertion in the 5′ end of the

Jay L. Vivian, Yijing Chen, and Terry Magnuson

coding region of a gene is likely to produce a null allele. A truncated protein with an out-of-frame carboxy terminus is often unstable and thus may result in a loss of function even if a portion of the amino terminus is translated. A null allele generated from subtle mutations such as these can provide advantages in some situations over other mutagenesis techniques, such as gene targeting or gene trap mutagenesis. For example, the gross disruption of a gene generated in a gene targeting event or gene trap may cause problems in the interpretation of resulting phenotypes. This phenomenon is well documented in the targeted disruption of the myogenic regulatory factor *Mrf4* gene. Three different targeted mutations of *Mrf4* are available,[9] each generating differing defects in rib formation. Analysis of these alleles demonstrated that the insertion into the *Mrf4* locus exerts subtle effects on the adjacent *Myf5* locus in *cis,* lying 10 kb away. The generation of subtle null alleles without the large insertions associated with gene targeting may be necessary to properly identify the function of some genes.

In contrast to gene targeting or gene trap techniques that aim to mutate a single locus, chemical mutagens create alterations in many genomic sites of a given cell. The ability of chemical mutagens to induce many changes in a single genome underlies the efficiency in using these mutagens in a large-scale screen. However, with this ability are concerns that potential linked mutations may arise. Given the mutation loads calculated from gene-based screens (Fig. 60–1), a closely linked mutation that would be difficult to eliminate using recombination is possible though uncommon. Using the well-characterized mutation rates with ENU in ES cells,[8] the likelihood of an intragenic mutation within 1 centimorgan (cM) of a mutation, outside of which crossover events can be quickly identified to eliminate linked mutations, is approximately 10%. Phenotypic analysis of mutations obtained in any chemical mutagenesis would be best analyzed using compound heterozygotes and possibly using alleles with similar phenotypic severity, requiring multiple mutant alleles of a gene. High-throughput mutation screens, such as the cell-based screens described in this chapter, allow the rapid development of allelic series of mutations, and they will help to obviate the concerns with mutation load inherent to any chemical mutagenesis.

Chemical Mutagenesis of Mouse ES Cells

Given the homogeneous and controlled conditions of cell culture, chemical mutagenesis of ES cells is highly reproducible. The ability to generate many mutagenized ES cell lines enables the researcher to characterize and alter new mutagenesis protocols in a straightforward fashion. Characterization and optimization of mutagenesis procedures in culture are aided by loss-of-function frequencies of selectable loci, such as the endogenous *Hprt* locus in male ES cells and transgenic herpesvirus thymidine kinase *(HSV-tk)* expression cassettes. These markers are initially used to define whether a mutagen will provide a suitable mutation frequency for the development of a library of muta1genized ES cells. *Hprt* is located on the X-chromosome, and thus it is hemizygous in male

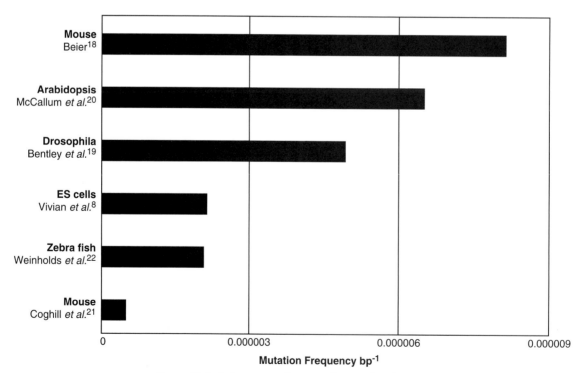

Figure 60–1. *Per-base mutation frequencies from gene-based screens.*

ES cell lines. However, the use of *HSV-tk* has several advantages over the use of *Hprt*. Selection of loss of function of *HSV-tk* can be initiated a few days after treatment of a mutagen. The coding region of *HSV-tk* (1.1 kb)[10] is significantly larger than *Hprt* (656 bp),[11] making a larger target for nondirected mutagenesis. The GC content of *HSV-tk* is higher than that of *Hprt*, thus making it more mutable with acridine mutagens such as ICR191. An *HSV-tk* expression cassette targeted using homologous recombination, such as the *Ncam-tk* used in our laboratory,[12] ensures single-copy integration in a defined region of the genome and allows direct comparison of mutation frequencies among different ES cell lines.

The concentration of a mutagen required to give a desired mutation frequency in ES cells will typically result in a high rate of lethality. Although we have not seen a large difference in how various wild-type ES cell lines respond to a particular mutagen, different mutagens have dramatically differing capacities for mutagenicity and toxicity. Both of these variables need to be properly defined prior to large-scale mutagenesis. For example, the concentration of ENU used in the development of published libraries consistently confers a survival rate of about 15%,[8,13] whereas the ICR191 survival rate is about 2%.[13] The key feature of successful chemical mutagenesis in ES cells is that mutagenized cells that harbor a mutation load maintain germ line transmission, allowing the transfer of the mutations from cell culture to a mouse line. A threshold concentration of any mutagen exists, beyond which the capacity for germ line transmission is compromised. We have observed an optimal ENU concentration of 0.2 mg/ml to be a good balance between significant mutation frequency and maintenance of germ line competence; higher concentrations of ENU clearly affect in a negative fashion the ability to maintain germ line competence.

A variety of chemical mutagens have been successfully employed to generate germ line-competent, mutagenized mouse ES cells from several genetic backgrounds, including ENU, EMS, and ICR191.[1,2] In contrast, large-scale, whole-animal mouse mutagenesis screens currently use only ENU because of its relative efficiency to mutate spermatogonia.[14] Additionally, careful consideration must be given to genetic background, as the mutagenicity of ENU is highly variable among mouse strains.[15] In contrast, several ES cell lines with differing genetic backgrounds have been successfully used in chemical mutageneses. At the concentrations used to generate germ line-competent ES cells, ENU and EMS induce a loss-of-function frequency at *Hprt* of 1/1750 and 1/2000, respectively.[2,13] Chemicals that interfere with the cellular DNA repair machinery, such as the alkylguanine transferase inhibitor O^6-benzylguanine (O^6-BG), can alter the mutation frequency of chemical mutagens in ES cell culture,[1] allowing more exotic mutagenesis procedures. Pretreatment of ES cells with O^6-BG prior to mutagenesis with alkylating mutagens such as ENU can increase the mutation frequency 3.5-fold.

Mutagenized ES cells have been used for several types of mutation screens. Although this chapter focuses on the use of ES cells for gene-based mutation screens, chemically treated ES cells have been successfully employed in phenotype-based

whole-animal screens.[2,16] In this procedure, ES cells are mutagenized with EMS and then randomly chosen for the generation of chimeras. After passage of the ES cells through the germ line, the animals are subjected to a whole-animal cross for the examination of dominant or recessive phenotypes. The initial report using this methodology examined eight founder lines for a detailed phenotypic analysis. Of the eight founder lines examined, five produced offspring with visible heritable defects, and three produced mice with heritable defects in fertility. Genetic mapping of two of these heritable phenotypes identified novel mutations in the mouse *Twist* and *fibrillin* loci. Shortened breeding methods are possible when using 100% germ line–competent chimera males generated from chemically mutagenized ES cells.[17] This is possible by backcrossing chimeras to their female offspring; the resulting offspring are subsequently examined for phenotypes. This breeding method is one generation shorter than the three-generation crosses performed in recessive screens used in whole-animal mutagenesis.

Gene-Based Screens for Subtle Mutations

Gene-based screens are performed to detect mutations in specific sequences of a mutagenized genome. In contrast to phenotype-based screens, the location of a mutation identified in a gene-based screen is immediately known, which allows the simple identification of homozygous individuals for phenotypic analysis and heterozygous carriers for stock maintenance. Gene-based screens for the chemically induced mutations have been performed in a variety of organisms (Fig. 60–1),[8,18–22] borne partly from technical advancements in the detection of subtle mutations. Although mutagenesis procedures have been established for many years in model organisms prior to the application of gene-based screening methods, precise calculations of mutation load were not commonly available. Data from gene-based screens provide an average per-base mutation frequency (Fig. 60–1), which offers a more accurate and generalized assessment of the genomewide mutation load than phenotypic tests such as the specific locus test. Furthermore, these calculations predict the number of mutations that would be obtained in a screen given the length of the sequences and the number of mutagenized genomes to be screened. Accurate assessment of a mutation load relies on a large sample size and a sensitive mutation-detection assay. The small sample sizes used in mouse whole-animal gene-based screens may explain the range of the mutation load reported in these screens.

The nondirected nature of any gene-based chemical mutagenesis screen distinguishes this technique both from phenotype-based screens in the whole animal and from other mutagenesis techniques such as gene targeting. Chemical mutagenesis, with gene trap screens, is distinct in that neither the site of mutagenesis nor the type of phenotypic alteration is directed or selected for. Although not truly random (because of the target sequence bias of some mutagens), chemically induced mutations are widely distributed and can potentially occur at any site within the coding region of a gene. A key feature of gene-based screens is the independence of phenotypic severity as a means of identification; therefore, a portion of mutations identified in a gene-based screen will result in no obvious phenotypic effect. The proportion of mutations that fall into this category is the subject of much debate, and it is certainly highly gene dependent. Half of the ENU-induced *Hprt* mutations identified in a gene-based screen in ES cells resulted in loss of function,[1] and 40% of the Smad mutations were observed to cause phenotypes in the mouse.[8] The unbiased nature of gene-based screens can be valuable in identifying subtle mutations that would be missed in a phenotype-based screen.

Chemical mutagens provide a convenient means for generating large numbers of subtle mutations without generating targeting constructs. Although point mutations can be generated using gene targeting, this approach can be time consuming. Each desired point mutation must be generated with a unique targeting vector, which then must be electroporated into ES cells. The nature of gene targeting in ES cells requires the use of selectable markers that must generally be removed from the targeted locus, typically through recombination using cre–lox technology[23] or "hit-and-run" techniques.[24] The use of chemical mutagens avoids the front-end process of construct generation and selection of targeting events.

Development of a Mutagenized ES Cell Library

The ability to cryopreserve mutagenized ES cells allows the generation of a permanent cryopreserved library for use in screening for mutations in many genes. A generalized procedure for gene-based screens of chemically mutagenized cells is shown in Fig. 60–2. Mutagens including ENU and ICR191 have been successfully employed using these procedures in ES cells[8]; this approach can conceivably be used with any mutagen.

CELLS ARE TREATED WITH MUTAGEN FOR A STATED TIME AND CONCENTRATION IN CELL CULTURE MEDIA

Cell lines derived from inbred strains are preferred for use in gene-based chemical mutagenesis to avoid polymorphisms that would complicate mutation detection. Several ES cell lines from different inbred genetic backgrounds have been successfully used for chemical mutagenesis.[1,2] The concentration and duration of treatment are defined from pilot experiments with selectable markers. Previous work has described a treatment regimen of ENU at a concentration of 0.2 mg/ml for 2 hours,[1] and EMS has been used at a concentration of 0.6 mg/ml for 16 to 20 hours.[2] Typically, the mutagenesis is performed on cells plated the previous day onto a tissue culture plate at a density of 2×10^6 per 10-cm dish. This density is sparse to ensure even treatment of all cells with mutagen.

CELLS ARE REPLATED, ALLOWED TO GROW TO COLONIES, AND PICKED INTO A MULTIWELL FORMAT

Cells are washed, trypsinized thoroughly to a single-cell suspension, and replated onto several (10–20) 10-cm dishes.

The plating density is dictated by the lethality of the mutagen at the concentration used; 200 surviving ES cells per 10-cm dish are a convenient plating. These cells are allowed to grow in normal growth media without selection for 8–10 days to form colonies. The resulting colonies can have differentiated morphologies not suitable for germ line transmission; thus, it is important to pick the best colonies under a stereomicroscope. The number of colonies to be picked in a single mutagenesis is determined by the ambitions, patience, and technical support of the investigator. Because of the subsequent splitting, handling numerous plates can be cumbersome; we usually pick no more than 1000 colonies per mutagenesis.

COLONIES ARE SPLIT IN DUPLICATE FOR CRYOPRESERVATION AND NUCLEIC ACID ISOLATION

Cells can be frozen using standard procedures in the multiwell format. Nucleic acids are isolated from one or more of the duplicate plates for mutation detection. If the gene is expressed in ES cells, then total RNA can be isolated for use in a reverse transcription reaction as a template for mutation detection. Genomic DNA is useful both for mutation detection of genes not expressed in ES cells and for mutation detection of nontranscribed regions of the genome, such as transcriptional regulatory elements. Nucleic acid isolation (total RNA or genomic DNA) is obtained using commercially available columns in a multiwell format (Qiagen). An inexpensive and effective means of crude preparation of genomic DNA can be attained using an overnight proteinase K digestion of ES cells. The cryopreserved cells and the representative nucleic acid constitute a cryopreserved library.

SEQUENCES ARE AMPLIFIED USING PCR AND SUBJECTED TO A SUITABLE MUTATION DETECTION METHOD

Several technologies are available for the detection of subtle mutations, including D-HPLC, TGCE, SSCP, and direct sequencing, all of which have been used successfully in gene-based screens of chemically induced mutations (Fig. 60–1). A comparison of the merits and limitations of these technologies is beyond the scope of this chapter. An ideal mutation detection method would be sensitive, high throughput, automated, and economical. If a mutation is detected, the polymerase chain reaction (PCR) product is sequenced to identify the resulting molecular lesion.

CELLS WITH A MUTATION ARE THAWED AND INJECTED FOR GENERATION OF CHIMERAS

Prior to injection, a subcloning step may be necessary to determine the clonality of a colony.[25] Mutagens such as alkylating agents initially generate a covalent modification of one of the bases of a given base pair. After DNA replication and cell division, only one daughter cell will carry the lesion. Thus, many ES cell colonies picked after a chemical mutagenesis are not clonal. Subcloning involves expanding a cryopreserved cell line, trypsinizing to isolate single cells, and spreading these diluted cells sparsely onto a tissue culture dish. We have had the best success using a mouth pipette to

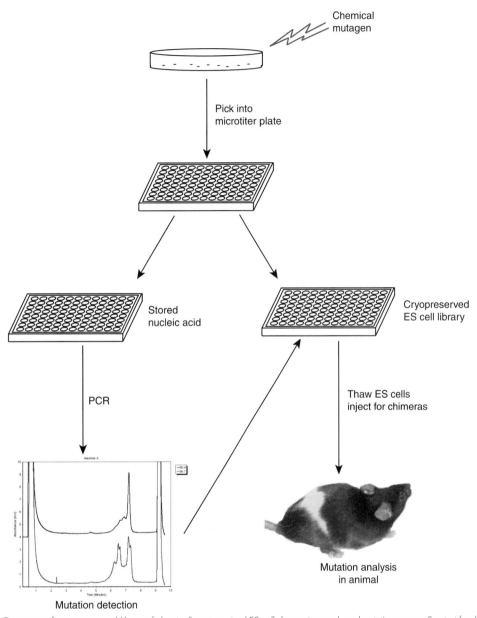

Figure 60–2. *Generation of a cryopreserved library of chemically mutagenized ES cells for use in gene-based mutation screens. See text for details. (Please see CD-ROM for color version of this figure.)*

select single trypsinized cells under a microscope and to thoroughly disperse them onto the dish. These cells are allowed to grow to colonies, which are then picked into a multiwell format. Colonies are then split in duplicate; one plate is used for cryopreservation, and the other is used for nucleic acid isolation. Mutation detection is performed in an identical fashion as in the primary screen. If all subclones are observed to harbor the mutation, then the nonsubcloned cells are used for injection; otherwise, one or more of the subcloned colonies are used. Many of the cryopreserved ES cell colonies (71%) from our ENU-treated library have been observed to be nonclonal. The use of chemically treated ES cells for the generation of

chimeric mice is identical to the procedures used in gene targeting techniques.

Gene-Based Screen for ENU-Induced Mutations in *Smad2* and *Smad4*

The first gene-based screen of a cryopreserved library of chemically mutagenized ES cells was performed to identify mutations in the coding regions of *Smad2* and *Smad4*.[8] The procedures described previously for the generation and screening of a mutagenized library were developed partly from this screen. The phenotypic analysis of the mutations

603

identified in this screen highlights the types of alleles that can be identified and the utility of novel subtle alleles to study gene function. *Smad2* and *Smad4* were chosen as candidates for mutagenesis for several reasons. Biochemical evidence demonstrated these factors to be critical intracellular components of TGFβ-superfamily signaling. SMAD4 is thought to be the central mediator of all Tgfβ-superfamily signaling, and SMAD2 is activated through phosphorylation only in response to a subset of TGFβ-superfamily ligands—specifically, ACTIVIN, TGFβ, and NODAL.[26] The activated Smad complex can then translocate to the nucleus to affect the transcription of target genes through interaction with many transcriptional regulators. The ability of these factors to respond to multiple ligands suggested many functions for these factors in a variety of biological contexts. Targeted disruption of either the murine *Smad2* or *Smad4* genes results in a perigastrulation lethality.[27] These phenotypes demonstrate functions of these factors in a variety of very early developmental processes, including epiblast proliferation, mesoderm formation, and extraembryonic tissue-mediated early embryonic patterning events. However, genetic models to study functions for these factors in later embryonic development and adult life were unavailable because of the early lethality of the null alleles. We were particularly interested in identifying hypomorphic alleles that bypass the early lethality of the null alleles to detail functions for *Smad2* and *Smad4* in later life. Additionally, the extensive literature describing protein structure of the Smads was available to aid in the identification of point mutations that disrupt protein interaction domains and posttranslational modification sites.

Using a heteroduplex-based mutation detection method,[28] we recovered 29 cell lines with mutations in *Smad2* or *Smad4*.[8] These results demonstrate that even a modest-sized library of ENU-mutagenized ES cells can be used to identify many mutations. All mutations were single-base alterations; two mutations altered consensus splice-site sequences, resulting in altered splicing. Most point mutations within the coding region resulted in single amino acid alterations distributed throughout the coding regions of these genes. An average per locus mutation frequency of 1 in 143 cell lines was observed in this screen, along with a per-base mutation frequency of 1 in 464 kb. Subsequent screening of this library has shown comparable per-base mutation frequencies for several other loci,[13] demonstrating the genomewide distribution of mutations within the library as well as the ability to screen a cryopreserved library repeatedly to identify numerous mutations in almost any gene. Five ENU-induced mutations in *Smad2* or *Smad4* were initially sent through the germ line and examined for phenotypes in the mouse.

One allele of *Smad2*, *Smad2^{m1Mag}*, resulted in a serine to leucine alteration within a conserved region of the Mad Homology 2 domain. When this allele was crossed to a *Smad2* knockout allele, the resulting embryos exhibited phenotypes closely resembling those observed in the embryos homozygous for the targeted allele. These results indicated a significant reduction of function associated with *Smad2^{m1Mag}*.

However, embryos homozygous for *Smad2^{m1Mag}* showed more advanced embryonic development, demonstrating this allele was hypomorphic in character. Homozygous embryos survived to embryonic day (E) 9.5, 2 days later than the embryos homozygous for the null alleles. The embryos displayed significant embryonic defects, including an expanded pericardial cavity and anterior truncations (Fig. 60–3B). Visualization of the early embryonic vasculature with an antibody against PECAM-1 showed morphological defects in the dorsal aorta (Fig. 60–3D), the likely cause of both the expanded pericardium and the embryonic lethality. This hypomorphic allele provided evidence for previously unknown functions for *Smad2* in the early morphogenesis of the embryonic vasculature.

Of the four ENU-induced *Smad4* alleles analyzed, three missense mutations surprisingly gave no obvious phenotype when crossed to homozygosity or against a targeted null allele. However, the fourth ENU-induced *Smad4* allele, *Smad4^{m4Mag}*, caused a dramatic exon-skipping event of exon 10, resulting in an out-of-frame translation near the carboxy terminus. Embryos homozygous for this mutation died by E7.5 and exhibited phenotypes similar those observed in embryos homozygous for a targeted null mutation of *Smad4*, indicating that this allele is nonfunctional (Fig. 60–3F). Consistent with tumor-derived nonsense mutations of *Smad4*, this altered protein was highly unstable[29] and was not detected in Western blots using cells heterozygous for the mutation. Interestingly, protein derived from the wild-type allele of *Smad4* was also significantly reduced in heterozygous cells (Fig. 60–3G), suggesting the mutant protein may confer instability to the wild-type protein. This allele thus demonstrated a molecular dominant-negative or neomorphic activity. The lowered level of SMAD4 protein in heterozygous mice, which are viable, may prove to be a useful sensitized background to study *Smad4* function.

Sequence-Based and *In Vitro* Mutation Analysis

As seen in the *Smad2/Smad4* screen, numerous mutations can be quickly identified using gene-based screens of chemically treated ES cells. A real challenge for the investigator is to predict the phenotypic severity and the utility of a given mutation. This filtering step is important given the time consuming and costly nature of chimera generation and germ line transmission. As gene-based screens are unbiased toward the types of mutations recovered, a proportion of the mutations detected within the coding region of a gene will be silent. We have observed that about 31% of ENU-induced mutations result in no alteration of the primary protein sequence.[8] Unless a silent mutation fulfills a need for a genetic marker, these mutations are generally not pursued further. Most of the remaining mutations from point mutagens result in single amino acid substitutions, and they can occur at any site in the protein. The ability to make such predictions is aided by structural information that may be available for the protein in question and is predicated by what the investigator deems

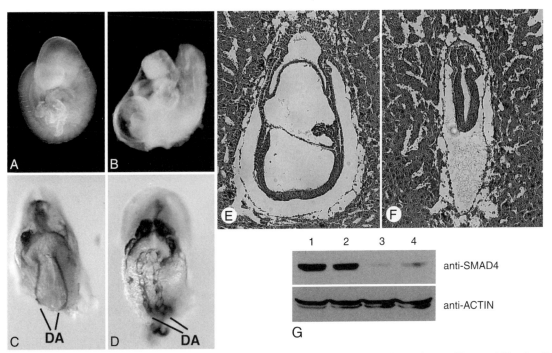

Figure 60–3. *Phenotypes of two ENU-induced alleles identified in a gene-based screen in ES cells. Lateral view of (A) a wild-type and (B) a Smad2^{m1Mag} homozygote at E9.5. Note the defects in the formation of the anterior neuroectoderm and the expanded pericardial cavity. Ventral view of (C) a wild-type and (D) a Smad2^{m1Mag} homozygote, using an anti-PECAM-1 antibody to visualize embryonic vasculature. Note that although PECAM-1+ endothelial cells are present in mutant embryos, the dorsal aorta (DA) fails to lumenize. Hematoxylin and eosin stain of sagittal sections of (E) wild-type and (F) Smad4^{m4Mag} homozygous embryos. Note the failure of mesoderm formation and the reduced size of the epiblast. (G) Western blot to detect SMAD4 protein in wild-type (lanes 1 and 2) and Smad4^{m4Ma} (lane 3 and 4) heterozygous fibroblasts. SMAD4 protein levels in the heterozygotes are significantly below the one-half level expected in wild-type tissue. (Adapted from Vivian et al.,[8] copyright 2002 National Academy of Sciences, USA). (Please see CD-ROM for color version of this figure.)*

interesting. If extensive structural knowledge is available for the protein, including crystal structure, protein–protein interactions, and posttranslational modification sites, hypothesis-based experiments can be developed to address how a given mutation can alter function.

The use of sequence alignments of homologous proteins remains a straightforward and generalizable means of identifying important domains of a protein to be examined in a mutagenesis screen. The underlying principle is that proteins with similar structural or functional motifs will share sequence similarity within these regions. The availability of genome sequences from an increasing number of organisms will add to the list of related proteins and enhance the power of sequence base–based homology mapping. Alignments are performed using any of the alignment tools available from the bioinformatics community. The SIFT program provides an automated extension of this analysis[30] and generates a score that predicts the phenotypic severity of an amino acid alteration. The use of sequence homology is not without limitations, however. One of the ENU-induced *Smad4* mutations identified in our preliminary screen was predicted to alter gene function using SIFT; subsequent analysis of this allele in the mouse demonstrated no obvious phenotypic alteration. As more sophisticated bioinformatics tools become available, the ability to predict how a mutation can alter gene function will become better.

In vitro testing of a particular mutation prior to, or in conjunction with, germ line transmission can also be performed to gain information on the effects of a mutation on protein function. These tests require knowledge of the putative functions for the protein and an experimental assay to measure that function. The availability of an antibody to a mutagenesis target is a valuable tool to examine protein stability of a mutant or for coimmunoprecipitation assays to examine perturbation of protein interactions. Antibodies that detect posttranslational modifications are becoming available, and they can be useful in examining the phosphorylation and methylation status of a mutant protein. Many mutant protein activities—for example, Smad mutations from tumor tissues—have been assayed with a *Xenopus* animal cap assay.[31] Mutagenesis becomes a more powerful tool for the investigator if these reagents and assays are available.

Future Directions in Chemical Mutagenesis in ES Cells

Several chemicals have been used to induce mutations in ES cells, and the potential for using virtually any mutagen exists. The procedures described in this chapter are potentially applicable for use with novel mutagens. Higher throughput and inexpensive mutation detection technologies to detect subtle

Jay L. Vivian, Yijing Chen, and Terry Magnuson

mutations are continuing to be developed. The use of novel mutagens with relatively low mutation frequencies would then be feasible given a sufficiently large library of mutagenized cells. The temperature-gradient capillary-electrophoresis mutation detection system combines capillary electrophoresis with a graded temperature block to resolve heteroduplexes, and it allows a throughput of 1200 samples per day.[32] The generation of even a very large mutagenized library is straightforward, and robotics-assisted ES cell-colony picking and ES cell culturing would aid throughput and expand the types of mutagens that can be used in gene-based mutation detection methods.

An intriguing extension of mutagenesis in ES cell culture is the selection of mutagenized ES cells with mutations in specific biochemical or genetic pathways. A screen of this sort can be conceived in several ways (Fig. 60–4). In one scenario, an ES cell line harboring a reporter responsive to a particular transcriptional regulatory element is mutagenized with a chemical mutagen. The resulting colonies are then assayed for an altered reporter readout profile; alteration of reporter gene activity may indicate the presence of a mutation in a trans-acting component of the regulatory element. In another scenario, altered subcellular localization of a protein can be monitored using cell sorting and a fluorescent antibody to identify cells with mutations in the target protein or in a protein involved in protein trafficking. As chemically mutagenized cells are heterozygous for the mutations they acquire, recessive phenotypes will not be recovered in these cell-based assays. A means of homozygosing mutations in culture would be required to identify recessive mutations. Techniques to generate homozygosed chromosomes are available, some of which allow chromosome-specific homozygosity testing of mutations.[33,34] One method relies on the presence of a neomycin-resistance cassette on a chromosome. High concentrations of G418 can select for rare mitotic recombination events that result in the homozygosing of the chromosome harboring the resistance cassette. Another method relies on the targeting of recombination sites such as loxP elements near the centromere of a chromosome. Expression of CRE and subsequent selection for mitotic recombination events then allow for the generation of ES cells homozygous for that chromosome. Combining chemical mutation strategies with subsequent phenotypic analysis in ES cell culture will further increase the ability to quickly identify genetic tools for the understanding of gene function and for the development of mouse models of disease.

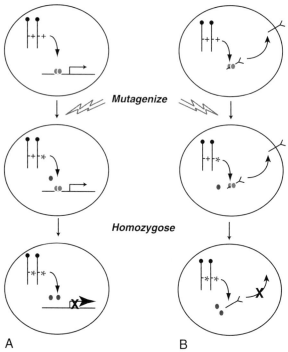

Figure 60–4. *Possible methods of identifying mutations in a specific biochemical pathway in ES cells.* An ES cell is represented by a circle. (A) Shown is an ES cell line harboring a reporter (thin arrow) whose expression requires the binding of a transcriptional factor (black dot) (arrow). A mutation (asterisk) is induced after treatment with a chemical mutagen, resulting production of an altered protein (gray dot) that no longer binds to the reporter element. Expression of the reporter is not altered in heterozygous cells, however, because of the protein from the wild-type allele. After homozygosing, all protein is derived from the mutant allele, resulting in altered expression of the reporter. (B) A protein (black dot) is required for the localization of a protein ("Y") to the membrane. After mutagenesis and homozygosing, the mutant protein (gray dot) can no longer function to localize the protein to the membrane, which can thus be identified by cell sorting. (Please see CD-ROM for color version of this figure.)

REFERENCES

1. Chen, Y., Yee, D., Dains, K., Chatterjee, A., Cavalcoli, J., Schneider, E., Om, J., Woychik, R.P., and Magnuson, T. (2000). Genotype-based screen for ENU-induced mutations in mouse embryonic stem cells. *Nat. Genet.* **24,** 314–317.

2. Munroe, R.J., Bergstrom, R.A., Zheng, Q.Y., Libby, B., Smith, R., John, S.W., Schimenti, K.J., Browning, V.L., and Schimenti, J.C. (2000). Mouse mutants from chemically mutagenized embryonic stem cells. *Nat. Genet.* **24,** 318–321.

3. Klungland, A., Laake, K., Hoff, E., and Seeberg, E. (1995). Spectrum of mutations induced by methyl and ethyl methanesulfonate at the *Hprt* locus of normal and tag-expressing Chinese hamster fibroblasts. *Carcinogenesis* **16,** 1281–1285.

4. Shibuya, T., and Morimoto, K. (1993). A review of the genotoxicity of 1-ethyl–1-nitrosourea. *Mutat. Res.* **297,** 3–38.

5. Taft, S.A., Liber, H.L., and Skopek, T.R. (1994). Mutational spectrum of ICR-191 at the *Hprt* locus in human lymphoblastoid cells. *Environ. Mol. Mutagen.* **23,** 96–100.

6. Skopek, T.R., Walker, V.E., Cochrane, J.E., Craft, T.R., and Cariello, N.F. (1992). Mutational spectrum at the *Hprt* locus in splenic T-cells of B6C3F1 mice exposed to N-ethyl–N-nitrosourea. *Proc. Natl. Acad. Sci. U.S.A.* **89,** 7866–7870.

7. Anderson, P. (1995). Mutagenesis. *Methods Cell Biol.* **48,** 31–58.

8. Vivian, J.L., Chen, Y., Yee, D., Schneider, E., and Magnuson, T. (2002). An allelic series of mutations in Smad2 and Smad4 identified in a genotype-based screen of N-ethyl–N-nitrosourea-mutagenized mouse embryonic stem cells. *Proc. Natl. Acad. Sci. U.S.A.* **99,** 15,542–15,547.

9. Yoon, J.K., Olson, E.N., Arnold, H.H., and Wold, B.J. (1997). Different MRF4 knockout alleles differentially disrupt Myf-5 expression: *cis*-regulatory interactions at the MRF4/Myf-5 locus. *Dev. Biol.* **188**, 349–362.

10. McKnight, S.L. (1980). The nucleotide sequence and transcript map of the herpes simplex virus thymidine kinase gene. *Nucleic Acids Res.* **8**, 5949–5964.

11. Konecki, D.S., Brennand, J., Fuscoe, J.C., Caskey, C.T., and Chinault, A.C. (1982). Hypoxanthine-guanine phosphoribosyl transferase genes of mouse and Chinese hamster: construction and sequence analysis of cDNA recombinants. *Nucleic Acids Res.* **10**, 6763–6775.

12. Thomas, J.W., LaMantia, C., and Magnuson, T. (1998). X-ray-induced mutations in mouse embryonic stem cells. *Proc. Natl. Acad. Sci. U.S.A.* **95**, 1114–1119.

13. Vivian, J.L., Chen, Y., and Magnuson, T. (Unpublished data).

14. Russell, W.L., Kelly, E.M., Hunsicker, P.R., Bangham, J.W., Maddux, S.C., and Phipps, E.L. (1979). Specific-locus test shows ethyl nitrosourea to be the most potent mutagen in the mouse. *Proc. Natl. Acad. Sci. U.S.A.* **76**, 5818–5819.

15. Justice, M.J., Carpenter, D.A., Favor, J., Neuhauser-Klaus, A., Hrabe de Angelis, M., Soewarto, D., Moser, A., Cordes, S., Miller, D., Chapman, V., Weber, J.S., Rinchik, E.M., Hunsicker, P.R., Russell, W.L., and Bode, V.C. (2000). Effects of ENU dosage on mouse strains. *Mamm. Genome* **11**, 484–488.

16. Browning, V.L., Chaudhry, S.S., Planchart, A., Dixon, M.J., and Schimenti, J.C. (2001). Mutations of the mouse *Twist* and *sy* (fibrillin 2) genes induced by chemical mutagenesis of ES cells. *Genomics* **73**, 291–298.

17. Chen, Y., Schimenti, J., and Magnuson, T. (2000). Toward the yeastification of mouse genetics: chemical mutagenesis of embryonic stem cells. *Mamm. Genome* **11**, 598–602.

18. Beier, D.R. (2000). Sequence-based analysis of mutagenized mice. *Mamm. Genome* **11**, 594–597.

19. Bentley, A., MacLennan, B., Calvo, J., and Dearolf, C.R. (2000). Targeted recovery of mutations in *Drosophila*. *Genetics* **156**, 1169–1173.

20. McCallum, C.M., Comai, L., Greene, E.A., and Henikoff, S. (2000). Targeted screening for induced mutations. *Nat. Biotechnol.* **18**, 455–457.

21. Coghill, E.L., Hugill, A., Parkinson, N., Davison, C., Glenister, P., Clements, S., Hunter, J., Cox, R.D., and Brown, S.D. (2002). A gene-driven approach to the identification of ENU mutants in the mouse. *Nat. Genet.* **30**, 255–256.

22. Wienholds, E., Schulte-Merker, S., Walderich, B., and Plasterk, R.H. (2002). Target-selected inactivation of the zebra fish *rag1* gene. *Science* **297**, 99–102.

23. Sauer, B., and Henderson, N. (1989). Cre-stimulated recombination at loxP-containing DNA sequences placed into the mammalian genome. *Nucleic Acids Res.* **17**, 147–161.

24. Hasty, P., Ramirez-Solis, R., Krumlauf, R., and Bradley, A. (1991). Introduction of a subtle mutation into the Hox-2.6 locus in embryonic stem cells. *Nature* **350**, 243–246.

25. Chen, Y., Vivian, J.L., and Magnuson, T. (2003). Gene-based chemical mutagenesis in mouse embryonic stem cells. *Methods Enzymology* **365**, 406–415.

26. Attisano, L., and Tuen Lee-Hoeflich, S. (2001). The Smads. *Genome Biol.* **2**, Reviews 3010.

27. Weinstein, M., Yang, X., and Deng, C. (2000). Functions of mammalian *Smad* genes as revealed by targeted gene disruption in mice. *Cytokine Growth Fact. Rev.* **11**, 49–58.

28. Xiao, W., and Oefner, P.J. (2001). Denaturing high-performance liquid chromatography: a review. *Hum. Mutat.* **17**, 439–474.

29. Maurice, D., Pierreux, C.E., Howell, M., Wilentz, R.E., Owen, M.J., and Hill, C.S. (2001). Loss of Smad4 function in pancreatic tumors: C-terminal truncation leads to decreased stability. *J. Biol. Chem.* **276**, 43,175–43,181.

30. Ng, P.C., and Henikoff, S. (2003). SIFT: Predicting amino acid changes that affect protein function. *Nucleic Acids Res.* **31**, 3812–3814.

31. Eppert, K., Scherer, S.W., Ozcelik, H., Pirone, R., Hoodless, P., Kim, H., Tsui, L.C., Bapat, B., Gallinger, S., Andrulis, I.L., Thomsen, G.H., Wrana, J.L., and Attisano, L. (1996). MADR2 maps to 18q21 and encodes a TGFβ-regulated MAD-related protein that is functionally mutated in colorectal carcinoma. *Cell* **86**, 543–552.

32. Li, Q., Liu, Z., Monroe, H., and Culiat, C.T. (2002). Integrated platform for detection of DNA sequence variants using capillary array electrophoresis. *Electrophoresis* **23**, 1499–1511.

33. Lefebvre, L., Dionne, N., Karaskova, J., Squire, J.A., and Nagy, A. (2001). Selection for transgene homozygosity in embryonic stem cells results in extensive loss of heterozygosity. *Nat. Genet.* **27**, 257–258.

34. Liu, P., Jenkins, N.A., and Copeland, N.G. (2002). Efficient Cre–loxP-induced mitotic recombination in mouse embryonic stem cells. *Nat. Genet.* **30**, 66–72.

61

Engineering of ES Cell Genomes with Recombinase Systems

Harald von Melchner and A. Francis Stewart

With the completion of the human and mouse genome sequences, the mutational analysis of the mouse genome has entered a new phase. The combined use of site-specific recombination with gene targeting or gene trapping in embryonic stem (ES) cells now permits a remarkable range of highly sophisticated mutagenic design.

In this chapter, we focus on the applied properties and uses of site-specific recombination. Because the applications of site-specific recombination in mammalian genomes have been driven by method development for the mouse, many of the examples cited and experience gained refers to mouse work.

Site-specific recombination systems mediate DNA rearrangements by breaking and joining DNA molecules at two specific sites, termed recombination targets (RTs). Site-specific recombinases (SSRs) have been found in diverse prokaryotes and lower eukaryotes. They fall into two main classes, termed tyrosine or serine recombinases, according to a fundamental difference in their enzymatic mechanisms. Among the large variety known, only three so far have been shown to work efficiently in ES cells. They are the tyrosine recombinases, Cre and FLPe, and the recently described large serine recombinase, φC31 integrase.

The product of recombination depends upon the nature and position of the RTs. In principle, DNA excision, DNA inversion, DNA integration, and chromosomal translocation are possible. For Cre and FLP, recombination is inherently reversible. For φC31, recombination is directional. These features impose different limitations on how the recombinases are applied and how their RTs are used to effect the desired recombination event.

Products of Site-Specific Recombination

Cre AND FLP

Both Cre and FLP recognize 34 base pair (bp) RTs comprised of a 13-bp inverted repeat flanking an 8-bp spacer. The RTs for Cre and FLP are called loxP and FRT, respectively.

Cre and FLP bind cooperatively to their respective 13-bp inverted repeat sequences; hence, they form dimers on one fully occupied RT.[1] Recombination is mediated between two dimer-bound RTs binding to form a tetrameric synaptic complex, within which the exchange of spacer strands occurs through a Holliday junction.[2,3] After recombination, the spacers are hybrids, with the upper strand coming from one parent and the lower strand coming from the other. Therefore, recombination requires perfect complementarity in the spacer and will not occur between two RTs that have sequence differences in the spacer. The need for complementarity in the spacer of the product also imposes directionality on the RT. Recombination will only occur when the two RTs are orientated so that the product has a complementary spacer. No recombination will occur from the opposite orientation.

Although Cre and FLP enzymatic mechanisms are similar, they differ in several details. The single-strand cleavages made by Cre in the loxP spacer are 6 bp apart, but they are 8 bp apart for FLP cleavage in the FRT. Cre makes specific contacts with its spacer DNA, but FLP does not. Hence, the Cre synaptic junction is tighter and more stable than the FLP junction,[1] which probably explains why Cre is a significantly better tool when applied to recombination exercises in mammalian genomes.

Both enzymatic mechanisms are inherently symmetrical. Thus, the reactions are inherently reversible. Reversibility imposes certain limitations on their performance in engineering approaches. There are three types of recombination reactions according to the disposition of the spacer, namely, excision–integration, inversion, and translocation (Fig. 61–1).

1. Excision occurs when two RTs are placed in a DNA molecule so that their spacers are arranged as direct repeats. Recombination results in the excision of the DNA interval between the RTs, which is released as a covalent circle (Fig. 61–1A). Since the reactions are reversible, the reverse of excision describes a way to integrate DNA circles site specifically. However, the excision–integration reaction has an asymmetry derived from the differences between the substrates and the products. For excision, recombination is an intramolecular reaction with the two RTs in the substrate tethered together. Integration is an intermolecular reaction in which the two RTs can potentially be an infinite distance apart. Hence, excision is favored over integration.[4]

Handbook of Stem Cells
Volume 1

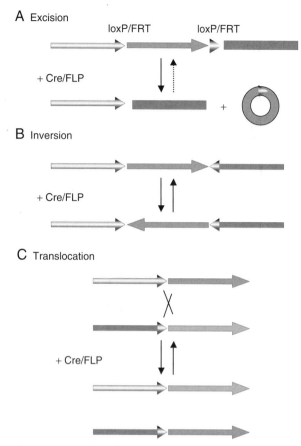

A Excision

loxP/FRT   loxP/FRT

+ Cre/FLP

+

B Inversion

+ Cre/FLP

C Translocation

+ Cre/FLP

Figure 61–1. *Products of site-specific recombination using Cre and FLP. (A) Cre or FLP excise a DNA region between two RTs (loxP or FRT for Cre or FLP, respectively) arranged as a direct repeat. The excised DNA is released as a covalent circle. The reverse of this reaction represents a way to site-specifically integrate a covalent circle. (B) An inversion is produced when the RTs are arranged as an indirect repeat. (C) Recombination between RTs on different molecules results in a reciprocal translocation, whose orientation is directed by the orientation of the RTs. Triangles indicate RTs and their orientation. (Please see CD-ROM for color version of this figure.)*

2. Inversion occurs when two RTs are placed in a DNA molecule so that their spacers are arranged as indirect repeats. Recombination results in the inversion of the DNA interval between the two RTs (Fig. 61–1B). Since the reaction is reversible, the end product of inversion will be 50% in one orientation and 50% in the other.

3. Translocation occurs when RTs are placed in two linear DNA molecules (Fig. 61–1C). The product of translocation is directed by the orientation of the spacer, and again, reversibility means that the end product of translocation will be a 50:50 mixture of the untranslocated and translocated molecules.

Although Cre and FLP are remarkable tools for genetic engineering, inherent reversibility has limited certain applications. Most successful applications involve excisions, since directionality is driven by the preference for intramolecular

(excision) recombination over intermolecular (integration). In contrast, integration, inversion,[5] and translocation[6] reactions have been limited to special circumstances. This limitation has driven the development of strategies for directional recombination based on either mutant variations of the RTs or combinatorial use of two or more different RTs.

Strategies for Directional Recombination Using Cre and FLP

Directional Recombination Between Two Mutated RTs. In Cre and FLP recombination with wild-type RTs, the RTs in the substrate and product are identical. Since dimeric binding of the inverted repeats in an RT is cooperative, it is possible that asymmetrically mutated inverted repeats can be used to impose directionality. The mutant loxP sites, lox66 and lox71, are the preeminent example of this strategy.[7] The logic is simple: One substrate loxP site is mutated in its left-hand inverted repeat (mutation, or mut–spacer–wild type, or wt), and the other in its right-hand inverted repeat (wt–spacer–mut). Before recombination, dimeric binding to the mutant inverted repeat is promoted by cooperation from the monomer that binds to the wt half site. After recombination, one RT is wt–spacer–wt; the other is mut–spacer–mut. Hence, the reverse reaction is compromised because the mut–spacer–mut RT is ineffective for binding the enzyme (Fig. 61–2A). However, directionality comes at the price of reduced recombination efficiency.[7] The strategy works superbly in smaller genomes (*E. coli* and yeasts), and success in ES cells and plants has been reported.[7–9]

Directional Recombination Using Four RTs. Since recombination between two RTs by Cre and FLP requires sequence identity in the spacer, two RTs with different spacers will not recombine with each other. The use of RTs with different spacers (heterotypic RTs) is central to two directional strategies, termed recombinase-mediated cassette exchange (RMCE) and flip-excision (FLEx).

RMCE. RMCE was first described by Bode and colleagues using FLP recombinase but has found wider use with Cre.[10,11] It relies on the placement of heterotypic RTs into the genome, usually flanking a selectable gene. The DNA interval containing the selectable gene is then replaced by an incoming cassette also flanked by the two RTs (Fig. 61–2B). Possibly because this strategy does not directly address the inherent reversibility problem, the most reliable applications include a counterselectable gene, usually herpesvirus thymidine kinase *(HSV-tk),* alongside the selectable gene between the heterotypic RTs.[12] Counterselection is applied to enhance the cassette replacement.

The spacer of the loxP site cannot be freely mutated.[13,14] This has limited the number of heterotypic lox sites available. The first site used with loxP, lox511, has a single point mutation in the spacer. Under certain circumstances, which appear to relate to excessive exposure to Cre enzyme either by long periods of exposure in culture or during development or by very high levels of Cre expression, loxP×lox511 recombination can occur.[15,16] This compromises certain applications, so use

A Recombination mutant lox sites

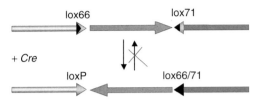

B RMCE

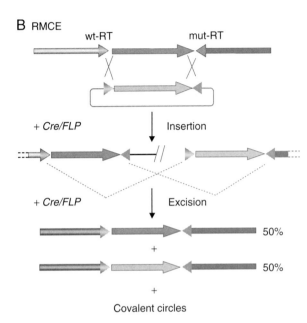

C FLEx

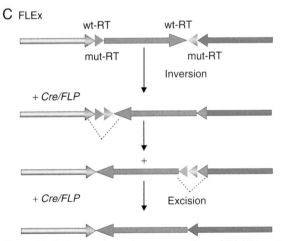

Figure 61-2. *Directional recombination using Cre and FLP.* (A) Inversion between mutant lox66 and lox71 generates a wild-type loxP site and a double mutant lox66/lox71 site that cannot recombine, hence imposing directionality. Similarly, locked directionality can be imposed on integration or translocation reactions (not shown, see Fig. 61-1A and 61-1C). (B) Recombinase-mediated cassette exchange (RMCE). Intermolecular recombination occurs between two different (heterotypic) RTs, here shown as wild type (wt, dark triangles) and mutant (mut, light triangles). Intramolecular recombination between heterotypic RTs is not possible. The RTs flank the exchange cassettes on a linear recipient molecule and on a circular donor molecule. The insertion of the donor cassette is followed by the excision of the recipient's cassette in 50% of cases. (C) Flip-excision (FLEx). Inversion of the RT-flanked fragment occurs either at wild-type or mutant RTs. After either inversion, pairs of homotypic RTs in direct orientation flank a heterotypic RT. Excision between the directly repeated homotypic RTs excises the heterotypic RT, locking the recombination product. The final product is flanked by heterotypic RTs, which cannot recombine. (Please see CD-ROM for color version of this figure.)

of doubly, or more, mutated spacers (e.g., lox 2272)[13] appears to be a better choice than lox511.

Two variations of RMCE that do not employ heterotypic RTs have also been reported. The first employs loxP sites arranged in inverted orientation. As described previously, Cre catalyzes intramolecular inversion of this arrangement to produce a 50:50 mixture of both orientations. In the presence of another cassette also flanked by inverted loxP sites, intermolecular recombination to insert the incoming cassette is possible.[17] Both orientations of the RMCE product will be found, which may be useful if the opposite orientation can serve as a control or useful variation.

The second variation employs the two recombinase systems, Cre and FLP, in parallel. Both genomic and incoming cassettes are flanked by loxP and FRT sites.[16] This strategy requires the coexpression of both recombinases.

A potential limitation of RMCE relates to the length of the regions that can be exchanged. Placement of the two genomic RTs at distances more than a few kilobases apart has until now required two rounds of targeting in ES cells. Consequently, the relationship of the distance between the genomic RTs to RMCE efficiency has not been systematically explored. Similarly, the relationship of the distance between RTs on the incoming construct to RMCE efficiency, which could achieve the insertion or exchange of long stretches of DNA, has not been published.

FLEX   Recently, a method to use heterotypic RTs to achieve directional inversion, termed FLEx, has been published.[18] In this strategy, pairs of heterotypic RTs flank a cassette in inverse orientations. Recombination between either pair of homotypic RTs inverts the cassette and places the other homotypic RT pair near each other in a direct orientation. Recombination between this pair of directly repeated RTs excises one of the other heterotypic RTs, "locking" the recombination product against reinversion to the original orientation (Fig. 61-2C). The FLEx principle, which could include the parallel usage of two recombinase systems rather than heterotypic RTs, opens several new options for inversion strategies to induce, ablate, or replace gene expression by design. Some applications of FLEx may be limited by undesired interference from DNA sequence cassettes in the orientation in which they should be neutral (i.e., either before or after inversion).

PRODUCTS OF SITE-SPECIFIC RECOMBINATION: φC31

Until recently, it was believed that serine recombinases were unsuitable for genetic engineering applications because the preeminent examples of this class—the resolvases γδ and Tn3, and the invertases, Hin and Gin—require specific substrate topologies, cofactors, or both for recombination.[19] This belief was challenged by the observation that the

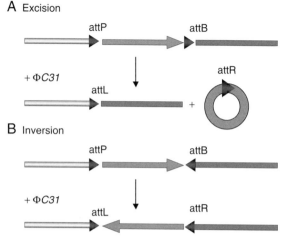

A Excision

attP   attB

+ ΦC31

attL   attR

B Inversion

attP   attB

+ ΦC31

attL   attR

Figure 61–3. *Products of fC31 recombination.* The φC31-specific RTs, attP and attB, are shown (A) in excision and (B) in inversion orientations. After recombination, the RTs are changed to attL and attR and cannot be recombined by φC31 in the reverse reaction. A directional translocation is also possible (not shown, see Fig. 61–1C). (Please see CD-ROM for color version of this figure.)

Streptomyces phage φC31 integrase, a member of a subgroup termed the large serine recombinases, could recombine linear DNA templates without cofactors *in vitro*.[20] Notably, φC31 catalyzes directional recombination and hence presents options for integration that are not straightforward to achieve with Cre and FLP.

φC31 mediates recombination between two RTs, attP and attB, to produce attL and attR (Fig. 61–3). Only attP and attB can be recombined by φC31 alone. The reverse reaction is believed to require an as yet unidentified cofactor.[19] The minimal attP and attB sites, 39 and 34 bp, respectively,[21] include imperfect inverted repeats and are probably each bound by a homodimer.[22] Many molecular details remain to be established, and no structures for large serine recombinases are available. However, applications of φC31 in mammalian cells are promising,[23] including site-directed integration into ES cells[24] and attB-directed integration into cryptic attP sites in the mouse and human genomes.[25–27] Possibly, these examples of cryptic genomic recombination with φC31 indicate a certain lack of stringent specificity, which could be a source of concern. If this proves not to be a major problem, then it is likely that φC31 will soon emerge as the tool of choice for integrations, hopefully applicable to insertions of large DNA molecules, and for other applications to complement or replace Cre and FLP.

OTHER SSRs

Although not exhaustive, several laboratories have searched without obvious success for other tyrosine recombinases useful for engineering mammalian genomes. Cre recombinase appears to be unusually good for genome engineering. The properties of wild-type FLP recombinase in mammalian

cells were poor, and the version currently employed, FLPe, was specifically selected for improvements by a molecular evolution strategy.[28,29] There is still a need to identify more of these useful enzymes. Current explorations are directed toward other members of the large serine recombinase family and toward molecular evolution strategies to improve or alter the properties of existing recombinases. Beyond the strategy to identify FLPe, other molecular evolution exercises have been applied to alter the sequence specificity of Cre,[30,31] FLPe,[32] and φC31.[33] None of these altered specificity recombinases have been applied in mice; however, with more work, molecular evolution presents the possibility of engineering "designer" recombinases that target specific sequences in complex genomes.[30]

Parameters That Affect Recombination Efficiency Between Two RTs

After integration into a genome, the rate at which two RTs recombine in a population of cells is influenced by several factors, of which we describe four. This description is limited to Cre and FLP since insufficient applied work has been done so far with φC31 or other large serine recombinases.

1. *The level of recombinase enzyme activity:* Although it has not been studied carefully, both *a priori* deduction and certain evidence suggest that recombination in a living cell is a threshold phenomenon, requiring intracellular recombinase enzyme activity above a certain limit. When studying Cre recombination in B-cells, Schwenk *et al.*[34] found that although 80% of B-cells expressed Cre recombinase, recombination between loxP sites could only be found in about 60%. Furthermore, this result was the same whether recombination was induced on a single allele or on both alleles of a loxP-flanked gene. Hence, it appears that in this experiment, only three-quarters of Cre-expressing cells were competent for recombination and that these cells recombined one or two alleles equally well. Although a threshold level of recombinase activity may be required, heavy overexpression provokes the problem of unwanted recombination with cryptic RTs in the genome.[35] Nevertheless, the numerous reported successes with Cre recombination in mice imply that the window between these two expression limits is wide.

2. *The physical distance between the two RTs:* At a fixed enzyme concentration, the initial rate of recombination *in vitro* is simply determined by the rate at which the two RTs randomly collide with each other. The rate at which two RTs in the same DNA molecule randomly collide is determined, at short distances (less than 400 bp), by the inherent stiffness of DNA and, at longer distances, by the volume of the maximum distance between them.[36] Notably, chromatin increases the flexibility of DNA at shorter distances.[36] Hence, in chromatin, optimum rates for recombination are achieved when RTs are placed 200 bp apart. As distances increase, recombination rates decrease. Therefore, the design of conditional alleles should aim not

only to decisively mutate the protein of interest but also to place the two RTs closely together.

3. *Chromatin position effects affecting recombination:* It is suspected that chromatin position effects can impair recombination efficiencies, and some evidence has been presented.[37] Although a careful study in flies demonstrates that chromatin can affect site-specific recombination,[38] the magnitude of these effects for conditional mutagenesis in the mouse remains to be determined. Potentially, overall recombination efficiencies are more dependent upon points 1 and 2 than upon position effects. Notably, Cre-mediated recombination appears to be very efficient during the substantial chromatin-remodeling events that occur during meiosis in spermatogenesis.[39]

4. *Site-specific recombination in the cell cycle:* No evidence that site-specific recombination is limited to certain phases of the cell cycle has been reported. Although, conceptually, there may be limits during M phase, it is clear that many Cre-mediated events occur between S and G_1 phases of the cell cycle in ES cells.[40]

Inducible Recombinase Systems

SSRs bring the ability to make a single, intentional, alteration in a living genome. In the context of a mouse, further controls to direct the recombination to a particular cell type (spatial control) or at a particular time (temporal control) have been developed. Spatial control relies on the use of gene regulatory elements, either in transgenes or through knockins, to deliver the desired expression patterns (see Chapters 59 and 63 for further details). Temporal control has been achieved by local delivery systems or by ligand-inducible systems.

LOCAL DELIVERY SYSTEMS

Local delivery systems rely on the use of either viral vectors or cell-permeable proteins. A range of viral vectors that express Cre or FLP have been described. Notable examples include the use of a retro- or lentivirus to deliver a transient burst of Cre expression because it deletes its own gene, thus describing a potential way to achieve transient spatial Cre expression,[41–43] and the use of adenoviral delivery of Cre.[44] Viral delivery of SSRs can be used to induce recombination in restricted regions of mice, usually near the application site; however, achieving uniform recombination in all cells of a given type is problematic. Nevertheless, this limitation is not restrictive for the induction of certain types of tumors in mouse models carrying RTs because partial recombination suffices to establish the tumorigenic change in gene expression. Notably, tumorigenesis in the lung in a conditional mouse model has been promoted by adenoviral delivery of Cre.[45]

The use of cell-permeable derivatives of Cre protein to induce recombination in cells in culture has been described.[46,47] Whether this method can be extended beyond cell culture to routine application in mice remains an unanswered question.

LIGAND REGULATION

Ligand regulation of Cre and FLP recombinases has been achieved at the transcriptional and posttranslational levels. The first description of ligand-inducible Cre expression in mice was achieved using a transgene carrying the interferon-inducible Mx promoter.[48] Because of the idiosyncrasies of induced Cre expression levels in different cell types, this mouse line shows good properties for induced recombination in liver and lymphocytes but only partial induction of recombination elsewhere. It is, therefore, of limited utility.

The leading eukaryotic ligand-inducible gene switch is based on the tetracycline repressor.[49,50] Its application to regulate Cre expression has presented challenges; however, notable successes have been reported.[51,52] This switch relies upon two components: a *trans*-acting effector based on one of several variations of the tetracycline repressor and a tetracycline-responsive transgene composed of an artificial promoter containing binding sites for the tetracycline repressor (tetOs) and the gene to be regulated (here, *Cre*). It is beyond the scope of this chapter to report the general properties and problems of the tet system except to note that a major problem appears to arise from the genomic site of integration of the tet-responsive transgene. Flanking chromatin effects (position effects) impinge on the tetO promoter so that only a few, rare integration sites appear to maintain the tetO promoter in a quiescent yet highly activatable state. Nevertheless, integrants into such sites are being identified,[52] so potentially, the application of this strategy for regulation of Cre recombinase may be available for more than just a few tissue-specific cases. Other ligand-regulated gene expression switches, for example, the use of the lac repressor,[53] may also be applicable to regulate recombinase expression.

Site-specific recombination can also be induced with ligands at the posttranslational level. This relies on the expression of the recombinase as a fusion protein with a ligand-binding domain (LBD) of a steroid receptor.[4] In the absence of a cognate ligand, the LBD represses the recombinase enzyme activity, and repression is released by binding of ligand. For application in mice and mammalian cells in culture, a mutant LBD needs to be employed to circumvent activation by endogenous ligands (hormones) that activate wild-type steroid LBDs. Several mutant LBDs have been tested. The mutated LBD known as ER(T2) has emerged as the leading mutant LBD for use in mice. It is induced with the synthetic antiestrogen, tamoxifen.[54]

Both strategies for ligand regulation of Cre recombination have certain advantages and disadvantages. The Cre–LBD ligand switch has the advantage of simplicity over the two-component tet switch, so it may be more readily applicable to a range of applications. However, tetracycline is a better inducing ligand than tamoxifen since it is largely neutral; tamoxifen blocks the endogenous estrogen receptor. This limits the applicability of Cre–ER(T2) recombination during development, since tamoxifen induces abortion at high doses before day 11 of gestation.[55] Emerging evidence also indicates that tamoxifen does not efficiently induce Cre–LBDs in the brain.[37] In both strategies, unwanted background recombination before ligand induction is a common problem, as is the need to achieve high levels of Cre recombinase protein expression for efficient recombination after induction.

Conditional Gene Targeting

As explained in Chapter 63, targeted mutagenesis in ES cells has been used extensively to inactivate genes for which cloned sequences are available. The ability of ES cells to pass mutations induced *in vitro* to the germ line of transgenic offspring *in vivo* provides a unique opportunity to analyze gene functions in the context of entire organisms. Consequently, more than 2500 unique genes have been functionally inactivated in mice (knockout mice) using this technology, and some mouse strains have proved useful as models for human disease.[56] However, for most of these mutant strains, the significance for human disease remains uncertain because germ line mutations can reveal only the earliest, nonredundant role of a gene. Moreover, between 15% and 30% of the genes targeted in ES cells are required for development and cause embryonic lethal phenotypes when passaged to the germ line. These factors preclude accurate functional analysis in the adult.

Because most human disorders are the result of a late-onset gene dysfunction, strategies of conditional mutagenesis employing Cre and FLP have been developed.[50,57] Although many variations are possible, a simple consensus for conditional strategies in mice has emerged.

To create a conditional allele, one or more exons of the target gene are flanked by insertion of two RTs into introns. Introns are the preferred sites for the insertion of RTs because in these positions, they are likely to have no mutagenic effect before recombination. Other potential neutral sites can be used; however, it is useful to place the RTs as close together as practically possible and so that recombination deletes an essential section of the encoded protein. An alternative to the deletion of an exon or exons that encode an essential part of the chosen protein is to delete an exon that results in a frameshift of the protein-reading frame.[58]

Fig. 61–4 illustrates a common strategy for generating conditional alleles. In the targeting vector, loxP sites flank one or more exons of the target gene, and FRT sites flank the expression cassette of a selectable marker gene. After selecting for homologous recombinants in ES cells, the selectable marker is removed from the genome by FLPe.[29,59] In this arrangement, Cre is reserved for conditional mutagenesis in the mouse, and FLPe is used for removal of the selectable marker gene. Although removal of the selectable marker gene is not essential, it is nevertheless advisable because its presence can interfere with gene expression in the mouse.[60] Alternatively, the mutagenic effect of the selectable marker can be gainfully employed as a hypomorphic mutant of the target gene.[61,62]

To induce mutations in mice with conditional alleles, Cre is usually delivered by one of the following methods:

1. *Spatial*: Crossing to a transgenic strain in which Cre is expressed from a tissue-specific promoter. Only tissues with Cre expression develop a target gene mutation in the double transgenic offspring and thus reveal its tissue-specific function.

2. *Temporal*: Crossing to a transgenic strain containing a ubiquitously expressed, ligand-inducible Cre. Recombination occurs in all cells of double transgenic offspring after ligand induction; thus, the cell types requiring the target gene at the time of induction can be identified. Because of the difficulties of obtaining ubiquitous expression from transgenes without mosaicism, this approach has remained elusive until recently.[63]

3. *Spatiotemporal*: Crossing to a transgenic strain containing a tissue-specific, ligand-regulated Cre transgene. In double transgenic offspring, recombination occurs only in cell types expressing the transgene and after ligand induction.

4. *Local delivery of Cre:* Notably by adenoviruses to specific cells and tissues (see previous sections of this chapter). Unlike the first three methods, this method does not require extensive breeding.

By permitting discrete conditional mutagenesis during development and in the adult, these strategies significantly extend the range and power of mutagenic analyses in the mouse.[57] A prominent example involves the insulin receptor gene that, when inactivated in the germ line, causes embryonic lethality. In contrast, when inactivation was restricted to skeletal muscle[64] or to pancreatic and hepatic tissues by a conditional approach,[65] the mice developed severe abnormalities of glucose metabolism, revealing the receptor's normal role in the adult.

Major limitations encountered with conditional mutagenesis are (1) a relatively low number of tissue-specific promoters available for exclusive recombinase expression in somatic cells, (2) the leakiness of most inducible SSR systems, and (3) chromatin position effects affecting recombination efficiency between RTs as well as the expression of the SSRs.

Overall, about 60 mouse strains with conditional alleles of specific genes have been produced, and more than 100 strains with tissue-specific or inducible Cre recombinase are available for breeding[57] (see http://www.mshri.on.ca/nagy/cre.htm). Compared to classical knockouts, these numbers are quite modest and reflect the overall complexity of the approach.

Conditional Gene Trapping

As described previously and in Chapter 63, targeted mutagenesis in ES cells requires detailed knowledge of gene structure and organization as well as its physical isolation in a targeting vector. Although the availability of the mouse genome sequence greatly assists targeted mutagenesis, the generation of mutant mouse strains by this procedure is still time consuming, labor intensive, expensive, and inefficient, as it can handle only one gene at a time. To address this problem, several types of vectors referred to as *gene traps* have been developed that insert a promoterless reporter gene and

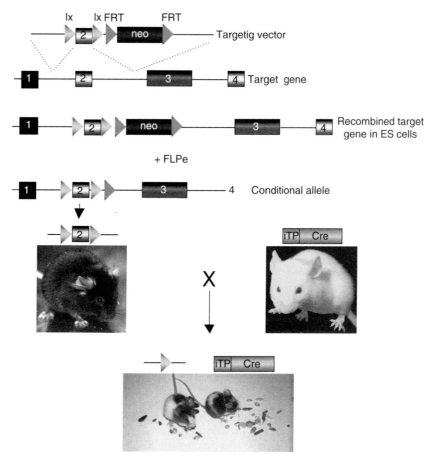

Figure 61–4. *Common strategy for creating conditional alleles in the mouse.* In the targeting vector, an exon (here, exon 2) of the target gene is flanked by loxP sites (1x) in direct (excision) orientation (light triangles). The targeting vector contains a selection cassette (here, neomycin, abbreviated as neo), flanked by FRT sites in direct orientation (dark triangles). After introducing the vector into ES cells and selecting for homologous recombinants, the neomycin cassette is removed using FLPe in ES cells, mice, or oocytes. Homozygous mice for the conditional allele are crossed to mice expressing Cre in a spatially and/or temporally restricted manner (;TP, inducible tissue-specific promoter). This deletes the loxP flanked exon 2 from the target gene and causes the designed mutation. (Please see CD-ROM for color version of this figure.)

sequences that interfere with gene expression (i.e., splice sites and polyadenylation signals) into mostly random chromosomal sites. Gene trap insertions inactivate cellular genes and insert molecular tags into the genome. This enables the rapid identification of any gene linked to a specific function. Thus, unlike gene targeting by homologous recombination, gene trapping is not restricted by regional determinants of homologous recombination efficiency and can be used to modify any gene of the mouse genome.[66] Since gene trap integrations are distributed mostly randomly across the genome, a large number of mutations can be induced in ES cells within a limited number of experiments. However, all currently employed gene trap vectors irreversibly modify their targets. Consequently, like a conventional knockout, a mouse mutant generated from an ES cell clone is similarly limited to reporting the earliest developmental function of the targeted gene.

To address this issue, gene trap vectors are being developed that can induce conditional mutations in any gene of the mouse genome. The vectors rely on two directional recombinase systems, which are activated in succession to invert gene trap sequence elements that interfere with gene expression (i.e., splice acceptor and polyadenylation sequences) from a mutagenic orientation on the coding strand to a nonmutagenic orientation on the noncoding strand. Hence, mutations can be repaired and reinduced by activating two directional SSR systems in succession.

For example, in the conditional FlipROSA retroviral gene trap vector, a gene selection and disruption cassette (GDSC) consisting of a selectable marker gene, a 5′-splice acceptor sequence, and a 3′-polyadenylation site[67] is flanked by attB and attP sites in inverse orientations (Fig. 61–5). In its original orientation, the GDSC disrupts the expression of a trapped gene but is itself expressed from the trapped gene's promoter.

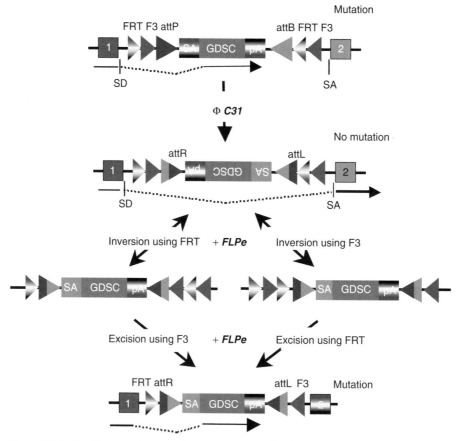

Figure 61–5. *Conditional gene inactivation by a gene trap vector.* The FlipROSA gene trap vector is illustrated after integration into an intron of an expressed gene. Transcripts (shown as a thin, black arrow) initiated at the endogenous promoter are spliced from the splice donor (SD) of an endogenous exon (here, exon 1) to the splice acceptor (SA) of the FlipROSA vector. The gene disruption and selection cassette (GDSC) is expressed, and the endogenous transcript is captured and prematurely terminated at the vector's polyadenylation sequence (pA) causing a mutation. The triangles represents FRT (light), F3 (dark), and the φC31 sites attP and attB. In the first step, φC31 inverts the cassette through the att sites to position the GDSC onto the minus strand. This reactivates normal splicing between the endogenous splice sites and deletes the gene trap vector from the mature transcript, repairing the mutation. FLPe-mediated inversion, using a FLEx application, repositions the GDSC back onto the coding strand and reinduces the mutation. (Please see CD-ROM for color version of this figure.)

This enables a positive selection of ES cells with gene trap insertions in expressed genes. By exposing these cells to φC31, the GDSC is inverted onto the noncoding strand. This reactivates normal splicing, eliminating the gene trap vector from the mature endogenous transcript (Fig. 61–5). As ES cells with the inverted gene trap version are unlikely to cause germ line mutations, they are essentially comparable to ES cells with conditional alleles generated by gene targeting. To reactivate the mutation in somatic cells, the gene trap must be repositioned onto the coding strand. For this, two additional RTs are used in an application of the FLEx strategy; for example, wild-type FRT and mutant F3 sites are inserted pairwise and in inverse orientation next to the attachment sites (Fig. 61–5). In the presence of FLPe, the GDSC inverts at either FRT or F3 sites, which places FRT or F3 sites near each other in a direct orientation. Recombination between the pairs of directly repeated FRT or

F3 sites excises the intervening heterotypic RT, thus "locking" the final recombination product against reinversion (Fig. 61–5).

Recombination systems are interchangeable in gene trap vectors as long as directionality is maintained. For some applications, particularly for those relying on the assembled collection of Cre *deleter* strains (Cre–Zoo) (see http://www.mshri.on.ca/nagy/cre.htm), the choice of a Cre-inducible gene trap vector is recommended (see http://www.genetrap.de).

Although powerful, gene traps rely on random integration. Consequently the mutagenic outcome is variable and knockout, hypomorphic, or dominant-negative alleles can be produced. Advanced gene trap vectors have been developed to improve the predictability of the mutagenic outcome. These improvements include vectors with better splice acceptors and vectors to trap functional classes of gene products, such as cell surface and secreted proteins (see http://www.genetrap.de).[68,69]

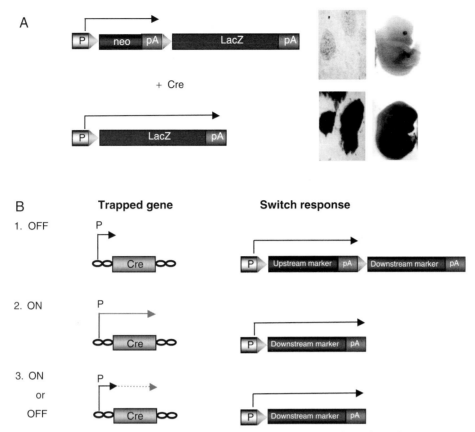

Figure 61–6. *Applying recombination as a one-way gene expression switch.* (A) A neomycin cassette (neo), flanked by loxP sites (light triangles) in direct orientations, is expressed from a constitutively active promoter (P) and simultaneously blocks the expression of a downstream gene (here, the β-galactosidase gene, *LacZ*) by polyadenylation (pA). ES cells or transgenic mice expressing the switch vector do not express *LacZ* (white). Cre deletes the neomycin cassette, which induces *LacZ* expression and stains blue with X-Gal. (B) Use of the one-way switch in a genetic screen for inducible genes. A switch cassette is integrated into ES cells by selection for the upstream selection marker, flanked by loxP sites. The downstream marker is not expressed because of premature polyadenylation. These cells are transduced with a Cre gene trap vector. Vector integrations into active genes express Cre so that these are eliminated by continued selection for the upstream marker. Hence, surviving cells do not express Cre, which must be integrated into silent genomic sites (OFF). Then, cells are treated with an inducer, which may be a cytokine, a hormone, or a differentiation protocol. If this change activates a gene trap insertion site to express Cre, then recombination ensues and selection applied for the activation of the downstream marker can be used to isolate these cells (ON). Regardless of whether Cre expression stays on or is subsequently turned off, the expression of the downstream marker continues (ON or OFF), facilitating the identification of transient sites of activation of Cre expression. (Please see CD-ROM for color version of this figure.)

Conditional Gene Activation

By exploiting recombinase-mediated DNA excision, one-time molecular switches can be assembled in conventional expression vectors to achieve permanent gene activation by transient exposure to an SSR activity.[70] The core element of a molecular switch is a DNA fragment of variable length flanked by RTs in direct orientations. The fragment, commonly referred to as the STOP sequence, is used to block gene expression; hence, it either disrupts the coding sequence of a gene or keeps the gene a distance from an active promoter (Fig. 61–6A). STOP sequences used for spacing are frequently selectable marker or reporter genes usually expressed before recombination. Recombination deletes the STOP sequence from the vector, which activates gene expression (Fig. 61–6A).

Because activation is irreversible, switch vectors are frequently used to trace recombinase activity in transgenic mice. In the context of conditional mutagenesis, several mouse reporter strains have been developed to pretest the ability of a *deleter* strain to induce tissue-specific mutations. Most mice available to date express lox-STOP–lox-*LacZ* switch vectors, where *LacZ* is a gene encoding an easily detectable histochemical marker. Several newer strains use enhanced green fluorescent protein instead of *LacZ* for detection in living cells and *in vivo* imaging.[71–73]

The best reporter quality is obtained with vectors knocked into ubiquitously transcribed chromosomal regions such as ROSA26.[74] From such locations, the expression of the reporter gene after recombination accurately reflects the expression of the *Cre* transgene. If the cells that originally express Cre in the *deleter* strain are known, expression patterns of the marker gene can potentially predict progenitor–progeny relationships (lineage tracing) and patterns of cell migration (fate mapping) during mouse development (see Chapter 59).[50]

Since switch vector activation requires only transient Cre expression, they have been used in combination with gene trapping to report transient gene activity in differentiating ES cells.[75] The core element is an ES cell line expressing a switch vector from a ubiquitously active chromosomal site (see previous sections of this chapter). The switch vector contains two selectable marker genes, of which the upstream one is flanked by loxP sites and blocks the expression of the downstream gene (Fig. 61–6B). When this cell line is treated with gene trap vectors that insert a *Cre* gene randomly throughout the genome, insertions into active genes will express *Cre,* leading to deletion of the upstream gene by recombination. Selection for it eliminates ES cells with expressed gene trap integrations. The surviving ES cells are enriched for insertions into "silent" genes and can be used to screen for genes activated by signals. Various signals can be employed, such as signal transduction pathways activated by differentiation, cytokines, or hormones. If the signal activates the site of *Cre* insertion, Cre is expressed, and the upstream gene is deleted. Selection for the downstream gene therefore identifies the signal-responsive genes (Fig. 61–6B).

As many developmentally regulated genes are only transiently expressed, the strategy is well suited for the molecular analysis of mouse development.

Chromosomal Engineering

The genome modifications explained previously (gene targeting, gene trapping, and gene activation) are approaches largely directed toward alterations of single-gene products. Chromosomal engineering encompasses applications of recombination to effect translocations or large alterations of the mouse genome in ES cells. The major goals for chromosomal engineering strategies are (1) to create a region of homozygosity; (2) to create a haploid region; (3) to delete large regions for analyses of gene complexes, chromatin domains, or gene linkages; (4) to invert chromosomal segments to create balancer chromosomes; (5) to replace mouse genes, chromatin, or both regions with functional counterparts from gene duplications or other species (usually human); (6) to create translocations; (7) to relocate a locus to a different nuclear compartment; and (8) to study structural components of the genome (telomeres, centromeres, and repeated sequences).

The induction of precise chromosomal rearrangements by Cre requires two consecutive gene targeting events in ES cells to insert loxP sites into prespecified chromosomal regions, referred to as *end points.* Recombination between end points located on the same chromosome yield deletions, inversions, and duplications; recombination between end points located on different chromosomes yield translocations. For the Cre/loxP system, the recombination frequency between loxP sites on the same chromosome *(in cis)*

decreases as the distance between loxP sites increases. Nonetheless, recombination can occur over vast distances.[76] With loxP sites on different chromosomes, the recombination frequency *(in trans)* decreases 2–3 orders of magnitude for homologous chromosomes and even further for heterologous chromosomes.

Strategies to isolate ES cells with chromosomal rearrangements rely on the combined use of positive and negative selectable marker genes in the targeting vectors. For example, a negative selectable marker gene such as the *HSV-tk* inserted between the loxP sites on the same chromosome enables the selection for deletions, as only ES cells that lose the negative marker gene survive counterselection. Conversely, the reconstitution of a positive selectable marker gene divided between two heterologous end points, such as *HPRT,* is used to isolate ES cells with chromosomal translocations.

The earliest descriptions of the use of Cre for chromosomal engineering include its use in direct translocations[77] and defined deletions, inversions, and duplications.[40] Recently, loss of heterozygosity for chromosomal arms driven by Cre/loxP recombination and drug selection has been described at frequencies high enough to complement functional genomic screens with randomly mutagenized ES cells.[78,79] Similarly, Cre-based strategies to precisely delete, invert, or duplicate genomic regions have been advanced.[80]

Although extremely powerful, the use of Cre/loxP to engineer the mouse chromosome in this way is impeded by the need to perform two rounds of homologous recombination to introduce the loxP sites.

Three alternative strategies present easier solutions for certain circumstances. First, increasing G418 drug selection on ES cells that express a weakened neomycin-resistance gene can induce a conversion, producing homozygosity of the allele (Fig. 61–7A).[81] Recently, it has been realized that the mechanism involves mitotic recombination so that the entire chromosomal arm distal from the neomycin-resistance gene is translocated.[82] This describes a simple, albeit inefficient, way to create homozygosity along chromosomal arms. Second, Su *et al.*[83] describe the use of retroviral integration to place a second loxP site randomly in the genome. Since Cre-mediated recombination *in cis* is much more efficient than *in trans,* the location of the second loxP site on the same chromosome as the first can be readily selected and a nested series of chromosomal deletions and inversions can be made. Third, very large targeting constructs based on bacterial artificial chromosomes (BACs) present new options for chromosomal engineering.[84] Although the upper size limit for BACs (approximately 400 kb) is modest compared to chromosomal dimensions, many small to moderate engineering tasks can be more easily accomplished by generating complex, modified alleles in BACs then recombining the entire set of changes into ES cells in one round of targeting.

Fig. 61–7B illustrates the type chromosomal rearrangements inducible by Cre between loxP sites on the same chromosome. If the loxP sites have the same orientation, and recombination proceeds during the G1 phase of the cell cycle, the resulting products are a chromosome with a deletion plus a reciprocal ring chromosome containing the excised segment.

A. Loss of heterozygosity

B. Deletion and duplication

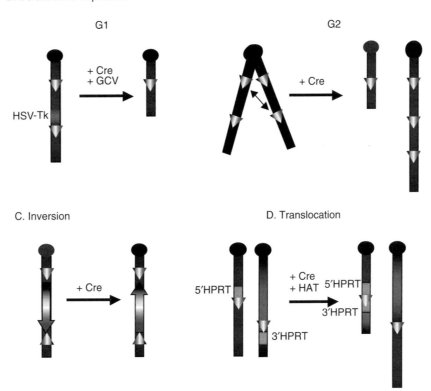

C. Inversion

D. Translocation

Figure 61-7. *Chromosomal engineering in ES cells and mice using selection, site-specific recombination, or both.* Mouse chromosomes are illustrated with centromeres as black circles at the top. (A) Loss of heterozygosity. In ES cells, a chromosomal arm carrying an integrated selection marker (light-colored mark, usually a weakened version of the neomycin-resistance gene *neo*) can be selected for homozygosity (or for loss of heterozygosity) by increasing G418 selection pressure. This conversion is relatively inefficient and can be increased at least 50-fold by Cre if loxP sites are integrated alongside the weakened neomycin gene and at the same chromosomal position on the homologous chromosome. (B) Deletions and duplications. Two loxP sites (light triangles), integrated in direct orientation on a single chromosome, can be used for deletions after Cre expression with or without selection, here illustrated as counterselection using deletion of the HSV-thymidine kinase *(HSV-tk)* gene and application of the drug ganciclovir (GCV). To the right is illustrated a further event possible in G2 of the cell cycle when the chromosome is duplicated and attached at the centromeres. Here, Cre recombination can also produce a duplication and a deletion product. (C) Inversions. Two loxP sites in inverted orientation on a single chromosome can be used for Cre-mediated inversions, again with or without a selection step. Possible G2 events as illustrated in panel B are lethal (not shown). (D) Translocations. Two loxP sites on different chromosomes can be used to mediate site-specific translocations, with or without selection (illustrated here using a reconstruction of the *HPRT* gene and selection in HAT medium). (Please see CD-ROM for color version of this figure.)

In principle, the ring chromosome could insert back *in trans* in a reverse reaction. However, in reality, it is rapidly lost during cellular replication. If recombination proceeds during the G_2 phase of the cell cycle, recombination can occur between any two of the four loxP sites present on sister chromatids. The most important possibility is the generation of a duplication and a deletion (Fig. 61–7B).

If the loxP sites are on the same chromosome in opposite orientations, Cre induces inversions that can involve regions larger than 30 centimorgans (cM) (Fig. 61–7C).[76] Regional inversions suppress recombination between homologous chromosomes. In combination with a homozygous mutant allele within the inversion, these inversions can be used as a balancer chromosome to facilitate the maintenance and identification of known and unknown mutations on the corresponding, uninverted chromosomal region.[80]

The most challenging application for site-specific recombination is the translocation of nonhomologous chromosomes in a mouse.[6] To model human oncogenic chromosomal translocations, loxP sites have been placed at known chromosomal breakpoints in specific genes located on heterologous chromosomes (Fig. 61–7D). Cre-mediated translocations and the expression of the oncogenic fusion proteins in the mouse have been reported.[85] However, chromosomal translocations induced by recombination between loxP sites on heterologous chromosomes are only viable if the loxP sites on the two chromosomes have the same orientation relative to their respective centromeres. If this is not the case, the recombined chromosomes will either lack a centromere (acentric) or have two centromeres (dicentric), both of which are incompatible with cell survival.

A notable exception from the remarkable successes of chromosomal engineering involves the integration or replacement of DNA regions larger than a few kilobases. RMCE is the current strategy for integrations and replacements; however, it is possible that this strategy is limited to relatively small pieces of DNA. Possibly, either the use of ϕC31[24] or large BAC-targeting vectors[84] will lift this limitation from a few kilobases to a few hundred or more kilobases.

Summary

The combined use of site-specific recombination and gene targeting or random integration in ES cells has resulted in (1) the emergence of technologies that enable the induction of mutations in a prespecified temporal and spatially restricted manner; (2) the activation of genes in specific cells and tissues; (3) enhanced analysis of cell fate and differentiation during development; (4) the precise modification of genomic loci; (5) and the deletion, inversion, duplication, or translocation of chromosomes, referred to as chromosomal engineering. Their prospective large-scale implementation by international mouse and ES cell mutagenesis screening programs will clearly further the annotation and functional dissection of mammalian genes. Collectively, the increasingly sophisticated technologies will greatly assist the establishment of mouse models for human disease as well as the intelligent identification of molecular targets for drug development.

REFERENCES

1. Ringrose, L. Chabanis, S., Angrand, P. O., Woodroofe, C., and Stewart, A.F. (1998). Comparative kinetic analysis of FLP and cre recombinases: Mathematical models for DNA binding and recombination. *J. Mol. Biol.* **284**, 363–384.

2. Van Duyne, G.D. (2001). A structural view of cre/loxp site-specific recombination. *Annu. Rev. Biophys. Biomol. Struct.* **30**, 87–104.

3. Chen, Y., and Rice, P.A. (2003). New insight into site-specific recombination from FLP recombinase–DNA structures. *Annu. Rev. Biophys. Biomol. Struct.* **32**, 135–159.

4. Logie, C., and Stewart, A.F. (1995). Ligand-regulated site-specific recombination. *Proc. Natl. Acad. Sci. U. S. A.* **92**, 5940–5944.

5. Lam, K.P., and Rajewsky, K. (1998). Rapid elimination of mature autoreactive B-cells demonstrated by Cre-induced change in B-cell antigen receptor specificity *in vivo. Proc. Natl. Acad. Sci. U. S. A.* **95**, 13,171–13,175.

6. Testa, G., and Stewart, A.F. (2000). Creating a transloxation: engineering interchromosomal translocations in the mouse. *EMBO Rep.* **1**, 120–121.

7. Albert, H., Dale, E.C., Lee, E., and Ow, D.W. (1995). Site-specific integration of DNA into wild-type and mutant lox sites placed in the plant genome. *Plant J.* **7**, 649–659.

8. Araki, K., Araki, M., and Yamamura, K. (1997). Targeted integration of DNA using mutant lox sites in embryonic stem cells. *Nucleic Acids Res.* **25**, 868–872.

9. Zhang, Z., and Lutz, B. (2002). Cre recombinase-mediated inversion using lox66 and lox71: method to introduce conditional point mutations into the CREB-binding protein. *Nucleic Acids Res.* **30**, e90.

10. Schlake, T., and Bode, J. (1994). Use of mutated FLP recognition target (FRT) sites for the exchange of expression cassettes at defined chromosomal loci. *Biochemistry* **33**, 12,746–12,751.

11. Baer, A., and Bode, J. (2001). Coping with kinetic and thermodynamic barriers: RMCE, an efficient strategy for the targeted integration of transgenes. *Curr. Opin. Biotechnol.* **12**, 473–480.

12. Seibler, J., Schubeler, D., Fiering, S., Groudine, M., and Bode, J. (1998). DNA cassette exchange in ES cells mediated by Flp recombinase: an efficient strategy for repeated modification of tagged loci by marker-free constructs. *Biochemistry* **37**, 6229–6234.

13. Lee, G., and Saito, I. (1998). Role of nucleotide sequences of loxP spacer region in Cre-mediated recombination. *Gene* **216**, 55–65.

14. Langer, S.J., Ghafoori, A.P., Byrd, M., and Leinwand, L. (2002). A genetic screen identifies novel noncompatible loxP sites. *Nucleic Acids Res.* **30**, 3067–3077.

15. Kolb, A.F. (2001). Selection marker-free modification of the murine β-casein gene using a lox2272 [correction of lox2722] site. *Anal. Biochem.* **290**, 260–271.

16. Lauth, M., Spreafico, F., Dethleffsen, K., and Meyer, M. (2002). Stable and efficient cassette exchange under nonselectable conditions by combined use of two site-specific recombinases. *Nucleic Acids Res.* **30**, e115.

17. Feng, Y.Q., Seibler, J.Alami, R., Eisen, A., Westerman, K.A., Leboulch, P., Fiering, S., and Bouhassira, E. E. (1999). Site-specific chromosomal integration in mammalian cells: highly efficient CRE recombinase-mediated cassette exchange. *J. Mol. Biol.* **292**, 779–785.

18. Schnutgen, F., Doerflinger, N., Calleja, C., Wendling, O., Chambon, P., and Ghyselinck, N. B. (2003). A directional strategy for monitoring Cre-mediated recombination at the cellular level in the mouse. *Nat. Biotechnol.* **21,** 562–565.

19. Smith, M.C., and Thorpe, H.M. (2002). Diversity in the serine recombinases. *Mol. Microbiol.* **44,** 299–307.

20. Thorpe, H.M., and Smith, M.C. (1998). *In vitro* site-specific integration of bacteriophage DNA catalyzed by a recombinase of the resolvase–invertase family. *Proc. Natl. Acad. Sci. U. S. A.* **95,** 5505–5510.

21. Groth, A.C., Olivares, E.C., Thyagarajan, B., and Calos, M.P. (2000). A phage integrase directs efficient site-specific integration in human cells. *Proc. Natl. Acad. Sci. U. S. A.* **97,** 5995–6000.

22. Thorpe, H.M., Wilson, S.E., and Smith, M.C. (2000). Control of directionality in the site-specific recombination system of the Streptomyces phage phiC31. *Mol. Microbiol.* **38,** 232–241.

23. Andreas, S., Schwenk, F., Kuter-Luks, B., Faust, N., and Kuhn, R. (2002). Enhanced efficiency through nuclear localization signal fusion on phage PhiC31-integrase: activity comparison with Cre and FLPe recombinase in mammalian cells. *Nucleic Acids Res.* **30,** 2299–2306.

24. Belteki, G., Gertsenstein, M., Ow, D.W., and Nagy, A. (2003). Site-specific cassette exchange and germ line transmission with mouse ES cells expressing phiC31 integrase. *Nat. Biotechnol.* **21,** 321–324.

25. Thyagarajan, B., Olivares, E.C., Hollis, R.P., Ginsburg, D.S., and Calos, M.P. (2001). Site-specific genomic integration in mammalian cells mediated by phage phiC31 integrase. *Mol. Cell Biol.* **21,** 3926–3934.

26. Olivares, E.C., Hollis, R. P., Chalberg, T. W., Meuse, L., Kay, M. A., and Calos, M. P. (2002). Site-specific genomic integration produces therapeutic factor IX levels in mice. *Nat. Biotechnol.* **20,** 1124–1128.

27. Ortiz-Urda, S., Thyagarajan, B., Keene, D. R., Lin, Q., Fang, M., Calos, M. P., and Khavari, P. A. (2002). Stable nonviral genetic correction of inherited human skin disease. *Nat. Med.* **8,** 1166–1170.

28. Buchholz, F., Angrand, P.O., and Stewart, A.F. (1998). Improved properties of FLP recombinase evolved by cycling mutagenesis. *Nat. Biotechnol.* **16,** 657–662.

29. Rodriguez, C.I., Buchholz, F., Galloway, J., Sequerra, R., Kasper, J., Ayala, R., Stewart, A. F., and Dymecki, S. M. (2000). High-efficiency deleter mice show that FLPe is an alternative to Cre/loxP. *Nat. Genet.* **25,** 139–140.

30. Buchholz, F., and Stewart, A.F. (2001). Alteration of Cre recombinase site specificity by substrate-linked protein evolution. *Nat. Biotechnol.* **19,** 1047–1052.

31. Santoro, S.W., and Schultz, P.G. (2002). Directed evolution of the site specificity of Cre recombinase. *Proc. Natl. Acad. Sci. U. S. A.* **99,** 4185–4190.

32. Voziyanov, Y., Konieczka, J.H., Stewart, A.F., and Jayaram, M. (2003). Stepwise manipulation of DNA specificity in Flp recombinase: progressively adapting Flp to individual and combinatorial mutations in its target site. *J. Mol. Biol.* **326,** 65–76.

33. Sclimenti, C.R., Thyagarajan, B., and Calos, M.P. (2001). Directed evolution of a recombinase for improved genomic integration at a native human sequence. *Nucleic Acids Res.* **29,** 5044–5051.

34. Schwenk, F., Kuhn, R., Angrand, P.O., Rajewsky, K., and Stewart, A.F. (1998). Temporally and spatially regulated somatic mutagenesis in mice. *Nucleic Acids Res.* **26,** 1427–1432.

35. Schmidt, E.E., Taylor, D.S., Prigge, J.R., Barnett, S., and Capecchi, M.R. (2000). Illegitimate Cre-dependent chromosome rearrangements in transgenic mouse spermatids. *Proc. Natl. Acad. Sci. U. S. A.* **97,** 13,702–13,707.

36. Ringrose, L., Chabanis, S., Angrand, P.O., Woodroofe, C., and Stewart, A.F. (1999). Quantitative comparison of DNA looping *in vitro* and *in vivo*: chromatin increases effective DNA flexibility at short distances. *EMBO J.* **18,** 6630–6641.

37. Vooijs, M., Jonkers, J., and Berns, A. (2001). A highly efficient ligand-regulated Cre recombinase mouse line shows that LoxP recombination is position dependent. *EMBO Rep.* **2,** 292–297.

38. Fitzgerald, D.P., and Bender, W. (2001). Polycomb group repression reduces DNA accessibility. *Mol. Cell Biol.* **21,** 6585–6597.

39. Herault, Y., Rassoulzadegan, M., Cuzin, F., and Duboule, D. (1998). Engineering chromosomes in mice through targeted meiotic recombination (TAMERE). *Nat. Genet.* **20,** 381–384.

40. Ramirez-Solis, R., Liu, P., and Bradley, A. (1995). Chromosome engineering in mice. *Nature* **378,** 720–724.

41. Choulika, A., Guyot, V., and Nicolas, J.F. (1996). Transfer of single gene-containing long terminal repeats into the genome of mammalian cells by a retroviral vector carrying the *cre* gene and the loxP site. *J. Virol.* **70,** 1792–1798.

42. Russ, A.P., Friedel, C., Grez, M., and von Melchner, H. (1996). Self-deleting retrovirus vectors for gene therapy. *J. Virol.* **70,** 4927–4932.

43. Pfeifer, A., Brandon, E.P., Kootstra, N., Gage, F.H., and Verma, I.M. (2001). Delivery of the Cre recombinase by a self-deleting lentiviral vector: Efficient gene targeting *in vivo*. *Proc. Natl. Acad. Sci. U. S. A.* **98,** 11,450–11,455.

44. Akagi, K., Sandig, V., Vooijs, M., Van der Valk, M., Giovannini, M., Strauss, M., and Berns, A. (1997). Cre-mediated somatic site-specific recombination in mice. *Nucleic Acids Res.* **25,** 1766–1773.

45. Meuwissen, R., Linn, S.C., van der Valk, M., Mooi, W.J., and Berns, A. (2001). Mouse model for lung tumorigenesis through Cre–lox-controlled sporadic activation of the *K-Ras* oncogene. *Oncogene* **20,** 6551–6558.

46. Jo, D., Nashabi, A., Doxsee, C., Lin, Q., Unutmaz, D., Chen, J., and Ruley, H. E. (2001). Epigenetic regulation of gene structure and function with a cell-permeable Cre recombinase. *Nat. Biotechnol.* **19,** 929–933.

47. Peitz, M., Pfannkuche, K., Rajewsky, K., and Edenhofer, F. (2002). Ability of the hydrophobic FGF and basic TAT peptides to promote cellular uptake of recombinant Cre recombinase: a tool for efficient genetic engineering of mammalian genomes. *Proc. Natl. Acad. Sci. U. S. A.* **99,** 4489–4494.

48. Kuhn, R., Schwenk, F., Aguet, M., and Rajewsky, K. (1995). Inducible gene targeting in mice. *Science* **269,** 1427–1429.

49. Schonig, K., and Bujard, H. (2003). Generating conditional mouse mutants via tetracycline-controlled gene expression. *Methods Mol. Biol.* **209,** 69–104.

50. Lewandoski, M. (2001). Conditional control of gene expression in the mouse. *Nat. Rev. Genet.* **2,** 743–755.

51. Utomo, A.R., Nikitin, A.Y., and Lee, W.H. (1999). Temporal, spatial, and cell type-specific control of Cre-mediated DNA recombination in transgenic mice. *Nat. Biotechnol.* **17,** 1091–1096.

52. Schonig, K., Schwenk, F., Rajewsky, K., and Bujard, H. (2002). Stringent doxycycline dependent control of CRE recombinase *in vivo*. *Nucleic Acids Res.* **30,** e134.

53. Cronin, C.A., Gluba, W., and Scrable, H. (2001). The lac operator–repressor system is functional in the mouse. *Genes Dev.* **15,** 1506–1517.

54. Metzger, D., and Feil, R. (1999). Engineering the mouse genome by site-specific recombination. *Curr. Opin. Biotechnol.* **10,** 470–476.

55. Danielian, P.S., Muccino, D., Rowitch, D.H., Michael, S.K., and McMahon, A.P. (1998). Modification of gene activity in mouse embryos *in utero* by a tamoxifen-inducible form of Cre recombinase. *Curr. Biol.* **8,** 1323–1326.

56. Zambrowicz, B.P., and Sands, A.T. (2003). Knockouts model the 100 best-selling drugs: will they model the next 100? *Nat. Rev. Drug Discov.* **2,** 38–51.

57. Kuhn, R., and Schwenk, F. (2003). Conditional knockout mice. *Methods Mol. Biol.* **209,** 159–185.

58. Shibata, H., Toyama, K.,Shioya, H., Ito, M., Hirota, M., Hasegawa, S., Matsumoto, H., Takano, H., Akiyama, T., Toyoshima, K., Kanamaru, R., Kanegae, Y., Saito, I., Nakamura, Y., Shiba, K., and Noda, T. (1997). Rapid colorectal adenoma formation initiated by conditional targeting of the *Apc* gene. *Science* **278,** 120–123.

59. Schaft, J., Ashery-Padan, R., van der Hoeven, F., Gruss, P., and Stewart, A.F. (2001). Efficient FLP recombination in mouse ES cells and oocytes. *Genesis* **31,** 6–10.

60. Kaul, A., Koster, M., Neuhaus, H., and Braun, T. (2000). Myf-5 revisited: loss of early myotome formation does not lead to a rib phenotype in homozygous Myf-5-mutant mice. *Cell* **102,** 17–19.

61. Nagy, A., Moens, C., Ivanyi, E., Pawling, J., Gertsenstein, M., Hadjantonakis, A.K., Pirity, M., and Rossant, J. (1998). Dissecting the role of N-myc in development using a single targeting vector to generate a series of alleles. *Curr. Biol.* **8,** 661–664.

62. Meyers, E.N., Lewandoski, M., and Martin, G.R. (1998). An Fgf8 mutant allelic series generated by Cre- and Flp-mediated recombination. *Nat. Genet.* **18,** 136–141.

63. Seibler, J., Zevnik, B., Kuter-Luks, B., Andreas, S., Kern, H., Hennek, T., Rode, A., Heimann, C., Faust, N., Kauselmann, G., Schoor, M., Jaenisch, R., Rajewsky, K., Kuhn, R., and Schwenk, F. (2003). Rapid generation of inducible mouse mutants. *Nucleic Acids Res.* **31,** e12.

64. Bruning, J.C., Michael, M.D., Winnay, J.N., Hayashi, T., Horsch, D., Accili, D., Goodyear, L.J., and Kahn, C.R. (1998). A muscle-specific insulin receptor knockout exhibits features of the metabolic syndrome of NIDDM without altering glucose tolerance. *Mol. Cell* **2,** 559–569.

65. Kulkarni, R.N., Bruning, J. C., Winnay, J. N., Postic, C., Magnuson, M.A., and Kahn, C.R. (1999). Tissue-specific knockout of the insulin receptor in pancreatic beta cells creates an insulin secretory defect similar to that in type 2 diabetes. *Cell* **96,** 329–339.

66. Stanford, W.L., Cohn, J.B., and Cordes, S.P. (2001). Gene trap mutagenesis: past, present, and beyond. *Nat. Rev. Genet.* **2,** 756–768.

67. Friedrich, G., and Soriano, P. (1991). Promoter traps in embryonic stem cells: A genetic screen to identify and mutate developmental genes in mice. *Genes Dev.* **5,** 1513–1523.

68. Mitchell, K.J., Pinson, K.I., Kelly, O.G., Brennan, J., Zupicich, J., Scherz, P., Leighton, P.A., Goodrich, L.V., Lu, X., Avery, B.J., Tate, P., Dill, K., Pangilinan, E., Wakenight, P., Tessier-Lavigne, M., and Skarnes, W.C. (2001). Functional analysis of secreted and transmembrane proteins critical to mouse development. *Nat. Genet.* **28,** 241–249.

69. Gebauer, M., von Melchner, H., and Beckers, T. (2001). Genomewide trapping of genes that encode secreted and transmembrane proteins repressed by oncogenic signaling. *Genome Res.* **11,** 1871–1877.

70. Angrand, P.O., Woodroofe, C.P., Buchholz, F., and Stewart, A.F. (1998). Inducible expression based on regulated recombination: a single vector strategy for stable expression in cultured cells. *Nucleic Acids Res.* **26,** 3263–3269.

71. Pasqualetti, M., Ren, S. Y., Poulet, M., LeMeur, M., Dierich, A., and Rijli, F.M. (2002). A Hoxa2 knockin allele that expresses EGFP upon conditional Cre-mediated recombination. *Genesis* **32,** 109–111.

72. Constien, R., Forde, A., Liliensiek, B., Grone, H.J., Nawroth, P., Hammerling, G., and Arnold, B. (2001). Characterization of a novel EGFP reporter mouse to monitor Cre recombination as demonstrated by a Tie2 Cre mouse line. *Genesis* **30,** 36–44.

73. Mao, X., Fujiwara, Y., Chapdelaine, A., Yang, H., and Orkin, S.H. (2001). Activation of EGFP expression by Cre-mediated excision in a new ROSA26 reporter mouse strain. *Blood* **97,** 324–326.

74. Soriano, P. (1999). Generalized lacZ expression with the ROSA26 Cre reporter strain. *Nat. Genet.* **21,** 70–71.

75. Thorey, I.S., Muth, K., Russ, A. P., Otte, J., Reffelmann, A., and von Melchner, H. (1998). Selective disruption of genes transiently induced in differentiating mouse embryonic stem cells by using gene trap mutagenesis and site-specific recombination. *Mol. Cell Biol.* **18,** 3081–3088.

76. Zheng, B., Sage, M., Sheppeard, E.A., Jurecic, V., and Bradley, A. (2000). Engineering mouse chromosomes with Cre/loxP: Range, efficiency, and somatic applications. *Mol. Cell Biol.* **20,** 648–655.

77. Smith, A.J., De Sousa, M.A., Kwabi-Addo, B., Heppell-Parton, A., Impey, H., and Rabbitts, P. (1995). A site-directed chromosomal translocation induced in embryonic stem cells by Cre/loxP recombination. *Nat. Genet.* **9,** 376–385.

78. Liu, P., Jenkins, N.A., and Copeland, N.G. (2002). Efficient Cre/loxP-induced mitotic recombination in mouse embryonic stem cells. *Nat. Genet.* **30,** 66–72.

79. Koike, H., Horie, K., Fukuyama, H., Kondoh, G., Nagata, S., and Takeda, J. (2002). Efficient biallelic mutagenesis with Cre/loxP-mediated interchromosomal recombination. *EMBO Rep.* **3,** 433–437.

80. Yu, Y., and Bradley, A. (2001). Engineering chromosomal rearrangements in mice. *Nat. Rev. Genet.* **2,** 780–790.

81. Mortensen, R.M., Conner, D.A., Chao, S., Geisterfer-Lowrance, A.A., and Seidman, J.G. (1992). Production of homozygous mutant ES cells with a single targeting construct. *Mol. Cell Biol.* **12,** 2391–2395.

82. Lefebvre, L., Dionne, N., Karaskova, J., Squire, J.A., and Nagy, A. (2001). Selection for transgene homozygosity in embryonic stem cells results in extensive loss of heterozygosity. *Nat. Genet.* **27,** 257–258.

83. Su, H., Wang, X., and Bradley, A. (2000). Nested chromosomal deletions induced with retroviral vectors in mice. *Nat. Genet.* **24,** 92–95.

84. Testa, G., Zhang, Y., Vintersten, K., Benes, V., Pijnappel, W.W., Chambers, I., Smith, A.J., Smith, A.G., and Stewart, A. F. (2003). Engineering the mouse genome with bacterial artificial chromosomes to create multipurpose alleles. *Nat. Biotechnol.* **21,** 443–447.

85. Collins, E.C., Pannell, R., Simpson, E.M., Forster, A., and Rabbitts, T.H. (2000). Interchromosomal recombination of *Mll* and *Af9* genes mediated by cre/loxP in mouse development. *EMBO Rep.* **1,** 127–132.

ES Cells and Nuclear Transfer Cloning

Anthony C.F. Perry and Lorenz Studer

Introduction

Aside from the developmental potency of embryonic stem (ES) cells, functional nuclear plasticity has perhaps never been more poignantly demonstrated than by the production of developmentally competent mouse embryos via somatic cell nuclear transfer (scnt).[1] The cloning of mammals by nuclear transfer (nt) has been applied to taxonomically varied species including mice,[1] sheep,[2] rhesus monkeys,[3] domestic cattle,[4] goats,[5] pigs,[6] rabbits,[7] domestic cats,[8] mules,[9] and horses.[10]

We here review nt cloning in the context of ES cells. In particular, we describe and compare scnt and ES cell nuclear transfer (esnt) cloning. Because the mouse has emerged as the preeminent model in both nt and ES cell research, our analysis focuses on the mouse. Although there are clearly significant interspecies differences, it is likely that many of the findings emerging from work on mouse nt will be applicable to other genera and should inform the debate on the clinical potential of nt for humans. We start by describing a general procedure for mouse nt cloning (which is shared by esnt and scnt) and then summarize the outcome of scnt and the features of ES cells and phenomena associated with esnt. Finally, scnt and esnt are compared with respect to their applications and places in nt research.

The Prevailing Method of Nuclear Transfer Mouse Cloning

With relatively few exceptions,[11–17] reports of mouse cloning describe a method of piezo-actuated microinjection to deliver a functional donor nucleus into a recipient, enucleated oocyte arrested at the second metaphase of meiosis.[1] This method of cloning is now outlined and has been applied to generate cloned mice from several somatic cell types and ES cells (see later). A key element of this success is the piezo-actuation of a flush- and cylindrical-ended micropipette. Piezo-actuation harnesses the piezo-electric effect to translate a crystal lattice distortion to a pipette tip, so that it rapidly (in the microsecond range) moves a short distance (approximately 0.5 μm). This is beneficial for at least two reasons. First, the injection of mouse oocytes via conventional pipettes large enough to deliver a sperm head (≥4.5 μm) usually results

in oocyte death. By contrast, piezo-actuation can be harnessed to propel a pipette tip through a zona pellucida or oolemma such that >90% of injected oocytes survive and are developmentally competent. This enhanced survival is likely because the force with which the needle tip is propelled through the plasma membrane leaves a neat wound that the oocyte is able to repair. The second advantage is that piezo-actuated microinjection is relatively quick; skilled operators are able to process more cells within a given time compared to conventional microinjection. This reduces micromanipulation time and hence cellular trauma. We now summarize some of the key steps of cloning by nuclear microinjection, which has also been described elsewhere.[18,19]

ENUCLEATION OF THE RECIPIENT OOCYTE

In mouse nt cloning by nuclear microinjection, metaphase II oocytes are typically used as nucleus recipients, with cloning efficacy dropping rapidly if the donor nucleus is transferred after activation (reviewed in reference 19). Oocytes from the F1 (C57BL/6 × DBA/2) hybrid strain B6D2F1 are a favored source for micromanipulation because they are relatively tolerant to mechanical and other environmental insults and have clearly visible metaphase plates (by phase contrast microscopy in the absence of fluorescent dyes) and they and their derivative embryos are relatively easy to culture *in vitro*. Mature metaphase II (mII) oocytes are typically obtained by superovulating 8–12-week-old mice by the administration of 5–7.5 IU of pregnant mare serum gonadotropin (PMSG) and approximately 48 hours later, human chorionic gonadotropin (HCG). Oocytes are collected 13–15 hours after HCG administration, incubated in HEPES-buffered CZB[20] containing 0.1% (w/v) bovine testis hyaluronidase until associated cumulus cells have dispersed, and then washed in CZB-H three to four times. Denuded oocytes (and embryos) are incubated in CZB or KSOM[21] under mineral oil (Squibb) at 37–38°C in a water-saturated mixture of 5% CO_2 (v/v) in air. When required, they are transferred, typically in batches of 10–20, to a microscope stage droplet of CZB-H medium containing an inhibitor of microfilament assembly such as cytochalasin B (5 μg/ml) before and during enucleation. Disruption of actin-containing microfilaments allows a portion of the oocyte enclosed within a membrane to be aspirated into a pipette with minimal damage to subcellular structures or loss of viability.

Enucleation of the mII oocyte is achieved by aspiration using a piezo electrically actuated micropipette. The oocyte is anchored by suction with a conventional holding micropipette so that the translucent metaphase plate is located opposite

Handbook of Stem Cells
Volume 1

the anchor. The metaphase plate becomes easier to see as temperatures approach 30°C; some workers perform enucleation on heated stages or in warm (25–28°C) micromanipulation rooms. The flat tip of a piezo electrically driven enucleation micropipette (with an internal diameter of approximately 7 μm) is brought into contact with the zona pellucida. Almost all mouse cloning by nuclear microinjection to date has reportedly used a piezo impact micromanipulator made by Prime Tech Ltd. (Japan). Most workers load the needle with elemental mercury introduced into the uncrafted end of the capillary to approximately 3 mm and moved to the needle tip when the pipette is mounted on the microscope stage. However, this is not essential and the mercury can be substituted for certain types of Fluorinert. Enucleation (and injection) needles contain a 12% (w/v) PVP (average M_r 360,000) solution in CZB-H. The PVP-CZB-H solution is introduced by back-filling. Collectively, the mercury/Fluorinert and PVP-CZB-H stabilize the pipette and increase its momentum during piezo-actuation, making the needle tip easier to control and its action more powerful.

While maintaining a small negative pressure within the micropipette, several piezo pulses (setting examples: intensity = 1–5, speed = 4–16) are applied to advance it through the zona pellucida into the perivitelline space. Next, without piezo and with a zero (or slightly positive) net pressure inside the pipette, the needle tip is gently advanced to a position adjacent to the mII plate. Oocyte cytoplasm containing the metaphase plate is then aspirated into the pipette in the minimal volume and the pipette (now containing the mII chromosomes) withdrawn. As the needle emerges through its entry site in the zona pellucida, the oocyte cytoplasm (ooplasm) containing the mII chromosomes conveniently pinches off. The microinjection pipette is then pulled clear of the zona pellucida and the chromosomes discharged into surrounding medium before removal of chromosomes from the next oocyte. After a recovery period of approximately 5 minutes, the oocytes are washed (prolonged exposure of oocytes to residual cytochalasin is detrimental) and placed in the incubator in fresh culture medium lacking microfilament disrupting agents. Batches of 10–20 oocytes may be enucleated in approximately 10 minutes and allowed to recover for between 30 minutes and several hours before nuclear microinjection.

NUCLEAR MICROINJECTION

Donor cells are typically prepared immediately before microinjection. Acutely isolated cells or cells just harvested from tissue culture are gently mixed with a droplet of 12% (w/v) PVP in CZB-H and placed in a droplet (approximately 10 μl) on the microscope stage. A nucleus donor cell is then drawn into the injection pipette. The pipette tip diameter should be slightly smaller than that of the cell but larger than that of the nucleus (e.g., 5 μm inner diameter for cumulus cells). By gently aspirating the cell in and out of the pipette two to five times, its plasma membrane breaks after which cytoplasm can be seen to disperse. Nuclear integrity should remain intact, allowing the nucleus to be drawn into the

pipette and another harvested. In this way, experienced workers can collect five to seven nuclei to form a line within the microinjection needle. The assembly is then moved to a drop of CZB-H into which a group of 10–20 enucleated oocytes are placed. One of the enucleated oocytes is selected and held in position, and the microinjection needle advanced so that its tip just touches the zona pellucida. The zona is penetrated by the needle tip with a few piezo pulses as described previously and the zona core expelled into the perivitelline space. Now, with gentle positive pressure inside the pipette, the nucleus nearest the end is moved to within a few microns of the tip and pushed forwards until it is almost touching the opposite face of the enucleated oocyte. This causes tension in the invaginated membrane at the needle tip, such that with the application of a single piezo pulse (at the lowest possible intensity, generally the lowest setting on the machine), the membrane breaks and clearly starts to relax back along the length of the (now) deeply inserted needle shaft. The needle is then gently withdrawn, dislodging any apparent plasma membrane adherences, and pulled free of the oocyte, which now contains a set of somatic cell chromosomes.

OOCYTE ACTIVATION AND EMBRYO CULTURE

When the entire batch has been injected, oocytes are allowed to recover for 5 minutes before being returned to the incubator, usually for 1 to 3 hours before activation. This is the enigmatic period of reprogramming, in which donor chromosomes have an opportunity to assume a pre-embryonic chromatin configuration able to potentiate embryonic development. Following this period, the oocytes are activated by incubating them in Ca^{2+}-free CZB containing 2.5 to 10 mM $SrCl_2$ and 5 μg/ml cytochalasin B for approximately 5 hours. The inclusion of cytochalasin is normal for most (diploid) cells to prevent cytokinesis (and hence chromosome loss), although in cases in which post-S-phase (i.e., 4C) ES cells are used as nucleus donors it is omitted.[22] Activation optimally produces embryos containing two or three pseudopronuclei. Embryos are washed and cultured in fresh CZB until their examination, and/or transfer into pseudopregnant recipient females.

We now summarize certain of the phenotypic outcomes of this procedure and their associated molecular phenomena, starting with an account of scnt.

Cloning by Somatic Cell Nuclear Transfer

SOMATIC CELL NUCLEAR TRANSFER CLONING AND ASSOCIATED PHENOTYPES

At its inception, mouse scnt donor nucleus delivery was by piezo-actuated microinjection.[1] Up to approximately 2% of starting embryos generated by scnt can develop to term.[1,23] Mice have now been cloned from males and females[24] of different strains[25] using cultured cells[22] and acutely isolated cells of the ovary, testis, tail tip, or cerebral cortex.[1,19,25–27] Although nuclear microinjection is the prevalent method in mouse cloning, the use of a cell fusion method to deliver the donor nucleus has produced mouse clones with a similar efficiency.[1,11] However, it is possible that the outcomes of the procedures are subtly different. Although difficult to gauge, the influence of methodology and technical competence are generally likely to be key determinants of experimental outcome in nt.[28] Approximately 30–60% of starting scnt embryos develop to the blastocyst stage *in vitro,* regardless of whether cumulus cells, Sertoli cells, or presumptive fibroblasts are used as nucleus donors.[1,24,29] In one study, some 50% of transferred scnt morulae/blastocysts failed to implant, and, of those that did, more than half of the resultant conceptuses failed to undergo chorionic plate formation.[29] Indeed, >90% of transferred embryos had undergone developmental catastrophe before embryonic day 11.5, implicating placental defects as a major cause of developmental restriction following scnt.[29]

Mouse scnt clone-associated placentas at term are typically two to three times larger than those of noncloned counterparts.[1,29,30] This placentomegaly correlates with an expanded spongiotrophoblast layer and, in some cases, disruption of the labyrinth layer.[29,31] Placental aberrations notwithstanding, most scnt clones (>92% in one study reporting the birth of 155 somatic cell–derived offspring[30]) are normal at birth when assessed using gross criteria, including birth weight and initiation of active movement.[1,29,30,32] Moreover, scnt-cloned offspring usually develop to become fertile.[29]

Although appearing normal at birth, mice cloned by scnt are subject to phenotypes that do not become apparent until adulthood. These phenotypes include obesity; the weight of B6C3F$_1$ scnt clones becomes increasingly greater than the norm from approximately 8–10 weeks of age.[33] This is not a consequence of lethargy or increased dietary intake, because feeding behavior and home cage activity do not differ significantly between clones and controls.[33,34] Serum leptin and insulin (but not corticosterone) levels were higher than those of noncloned controls, consistent with the involvement of a leptin-independent mechanism. However, the penetrance and extent of this late-onset, scnt-associated obesity is strain-dependent; although 77% of adults cloned from B6C3F$_1$ cumulus cell nuclei became markedly gross, the corresponding figure for B6D2F$_1$ is only 20%.[33,34]

Several additional phenotypic anomalies do not manifest themselves until adulthood—sometimes late adulthood—in scnt clones. In a study of 12 Sertoli cell–derived B6D2F$_1$ (scnt) clones, 10 died within 800 days, significantly earlier than controls[32] (see also reference 29). All of the clones underwent an idiopathic elevation in serum lactate dehydrogenase (LDH) and NH$_3$ indicating impaired hepatic function, and four of the six autopsied clones exhibited extensive necrosis of the liver. All six had perished of pneumonia and two had tumors, indicating immune impairment; analysis of a further 20 clones revealed a reduction in serum immunoglobulin production by 4 to 5 months of age.[32] Premature death in scnt clones is unlikely to be associated with telomere shortening, because the telomeres of scnt cloned mice are as long, if not longer, than those of nonclones.[23] In addition, clone life span is occasionally at least as long as that of controls: two of the 12 scnt clones studied in detail outlasted the experiment

(>800 days[32]), and Cumulina—the first cloned mouse reported—lived for approximately 940 days, with typical life expectancy of ~800 days for nonclones (e.g., reference 35).

In neither of the two scnt clone–associated phenotypes in which it has been examined, placental enlargement or obesity is the trait transmitted to offspring, whether the clones are mated with other clones or nonclones.[34,36] Thus, at least a subset of scnt cloning phenotypes is corrected during gametogenesis, indicating that such phenotypes are epigenetic rather than genetic phenomena.

THE GENETICS AND EPIGENETICS OF SOMATIC CELL–DERIVED CLONES

Descriptions of molecular profiles in scnt clones are scant and preliminary. The transcription factor Oct4 (see later) is expressed from the four-cell stage in control mouse embryos and is required in a dose-sensitive manner for maintenance of the inner cell mass (ICM).[37,38] Oct4 is expressed in most cumulus-derived scnt embryos (75–89%),[39,40] but its mRNA is aberrantly distributed between the ICM and trophectoderm (TE) in 54% of these.[39] Such ectopic Oct4 mRNA localization—assessed using an *Oct4-GFP* transgene—correlated strongly with the *in vitro* developmental potency of nt blastocysts in terms of their ability to form outgrowths and subsequently generate ES (ntES) cells.[39] A comparative scan of 10 genes exhibiting a pattern of expression similar to that of Oct4 in control, fertilization-derived embryos—including four PRAME-like *(pramel4-7)* and five developmental pluripotency associated *(Dppa1-5)* genes—revealed that one or more was present at altered levels in 38% of cumulus scnt blastocysts.[40] Three transcripts that are abundant in cumulus (donor) cells but absent in preimplantation embryos were not detected in cumulus scnt blastocysts.[40] These data broadly suggest that somatic cell chromatin undergoes many, perhaps most, of the reprogramming changes required to direct embryonic development following nt but that the remaining minority of these changes are incomplete and incompatible with preimplantation development.

Looked at another way, developmentally incompatible chromatin changes would produce epigenetically dysfunctional scnt embryos that tended to be "filtered out" during the preimplantation phase. Consistent with this, there is no compelling evidence for altered expression postimplantation of either imprinted (e.g., *Meg1/Grb10, Peg1/Mest, H19, Igf2*) or nonimprinted (e.g., *Igfbp2, Esx1*) genes in scnt fetuses or neonates.[29,30] Contrastingly, scnt clone–associated placentae exhibited a marked reduction in cellular mRNA levels for subsets of both imprinted (*Peg1/Mest, Meg1/Grb10, Meg3/Gtl2*) and nonimprinted (*Igfbp2, Igfbp6, Vegfr2/Flk1, Esx1*) genes.[30] DNA microarray analysis of two cumulus scnt clone–associated placentas indicated that approximately 4% of genes surveyed were expressed at levels that significantly differed from those of noncloned controls.[41]

Genomic analysis of scnt cloned fetuses suggests that both paternally (*Igf2* and *Peg1/Mest*) and maternally (*Igf2r, H19, Meg1/Grb10, Meg3/Gtl2,* and *p57^{Kip2}*) monoallelically expressed genes are expressed from the same allele as they normally would be in noncloned controls.[29,30] Aberrant monoallelic expression of the normally biallelically expressed gene *Ascl2* was reported in 71% of cumulus scnt preimplantation embryos; faithful biallelic expression of a second gene *Igf2r* was influenced by culture conditions.[42] It is unlikely that the *Igf2r* anomalies were among the altered genomic DNA methylation patterns in two scnt offspring as judged by restriction landmark genomic scanning (RLGS), because these corresponded to monoallelic ("haploid") signals.[43] RLGS patterns of scnt clones were altered compared with controls at four loci (out of 1490 analyzed = 0.27%) and in three cases corresponded to genes whose RLGS profiles varied between tissues in noncloned controls.[43]

Nuclear Transfer Cloning and Embryonic Stem Cells

EMBRYONIC STEM CELLS: PLURIPOTENT, CULTURED CELLS DERIVED FROM THE INNER CELL MASS OF BLASTOCYSTS

ES cells have been established from the ICMs of blastocysts derived by fertilization (i.e., the union of sperm and egg).[44,45] ES cells are amenable to long-term culture in an undifferentiated, euploid state and can either renew or differentiate *in vitro*. They can differentiate *in vivo* following transplantation, to produce cells of all lineages including those of the germ line. ES cells were first demonstrated in the mouse,[44,45] but cultured cell lines derived from preimplantation embryos have subsequently been reported for additional species including hamster, cattle, rhesus and cynomolgus monkeys, marmoset, and human.[46–51] These cells share with mouse ES cells the twin features of self-renewal and pluripotency, and, although it has yet to be shown that they are equivalent to mouse ES cells, they are also often referred to as ES cells. Work on mouse ES cells and ES cell nt is, therefore, likely to affect studies in other species.

The molecular correlates of ES cell self-renewal are still being elucidated and are discussed in detail elsewhere in the volume. Briefly, mouse ES cells are maintained in an undifferentiated, pluripotent state as a result of at least two distinct signaling pathways involving LIF, Stat3/Jak, Oct4, and Nanog.[37,52–58]

LIF signaling is mediated via a heterodimeric receptor comprised of gp130 and LIFR subunits expressed on the surface of undifferentiated ES cells. Stimulation of this receptor following LIF binding results in activation of the Jak/Stat3 network.[59–61] In addition to Stat3, expression of the POU domain transcription factor Oct4 (also known as Oct3 or Oct3/4) correlates with the maintenance of ES cells in an undifferentiated state.[37,54–56] Steady-state levels of Oct4 drop markedly when pluripotent mouse ES cells differentiate. Mouse ES cells are typically maintained in an undifferentiated state by co-culturing them with feeder cells such as fetal fibroblasts or STO cells, which provide LIF *in trans*.[53,62] Recently, it has been reported that a distinct, LIF (and feeder)

independent pathway operates for mouse ES cell self-renewal *in vitro*.[57,58] This pathway is mediated in the mouse via the transcription factor Nanog. Primate ES cells are insensitive to LIF,[63] raising the possibility that they retain their pluripotency via a functional orthologs of Nanog.

In addition to Oct4, alkaline phosphatase is also an apparent marker of undifferentiated presumptive ES cells in many, if not all species, and stage-specific embryonic antigen (SSEA)-1, SSEA-3, and SSEA-4 are present in the ES cells of some but not all.[63] Hence, research on the mouse is likely to provide insights into many facets of ES cells and ES cell manipulation, but it is unlikely that all will hold universally.

CLONING BY TRANSFER OF EMBRYONIC STEM CELL NUCLEI AND THE PHENOTYPES OF RESULTING CLONES

Although classical diploid ES cells can differentiate into all cell types within the embryo proper, they are not totipotent in that they cannot produce an entire individual; for one thing, they lack the ability to generate TE-derived, extraembryonic tissue.[64] The first demonstration that ES cell nuclei are indeed able to potentiate full development of an entire individual came with nt cloning using as nucleus donors ES cell lines derived from inbred and hybrid strains and containing both gene targeted and nontargeted alleles.[22] This was the first report of cloning using established cell lines as nucleus donors: one of the lines, E14, was derived from the inbred strain 129/Ola around 1985. This result was remarkable because during ES cell culture the normal selective checks and balances required for cellular survival *in vivo* had been absent for a prolonged period (at least 33 to 66 cell divisions[22]). Consistent with this, the culture of ES cells correlates with loss of developmental potency in chimeric embryos[65,66] (see also later discussion).

Several groups have now produced cloned offspring by esnt (Table 62–1). This process is marginally more efficient than scnt when expressed as a percentage of nt zygotes (activated eggs) that result in live offspring. Typical values for scnt are ~1 to 2%, whereas esnt commonly produces values of ~3 % (Table 62–1). Some laboratories that have not produced scnt offspring have reported term development via esnt, further attesting to the comparative ease of the latter.

Although still poorly characterized, developmental attenuation seemingly occurs at different stages in scnt and esnt embryos, with poor esnt embryo preimplantation development balanced by improved peri-implantation and postimplantation survival relative to the corresponding stages in scnt embryos.[22,29] Early attenuation of development may reflect difficulties intrinsic to nt using rapidly cycling cells such as ES cells as donors, although arrest of cultures in metaphase by treatment with nocodazole before nt does not markedly affect the developmental potency of the resulting esnt embryos.[13,15,22] Analysis of reciprocal chimeras produced from tetraploid TE and ICM suggests that both ICM- and TE-derived cell lineages contribute to the aberrance of esnt clone development.[16] Furthermore, the proportion of

TABLE 62-1
Comparative Summary of Nuclear Transfer Using Embryonic Stem (ES) or Somatic Cells as Nucleus Donors

ES Cell Line(s) or Somatic Cells	Inbred/Hybrid	Passage no.	Targeted?	% Term Offspring	Ave. Weight Offspring (g)	% Survivors	Ref.	Laboratory
ES								
E14	Inbred	≥22–33	No	0.4	1.7	20	22	Wakayama
E14	Inbred	≥22–33	Yes	0.4	N.R.	0	22	Wakayama
R1	Hybrid	≥32	No	3.0	1.7	50	22	Wakayama
V18.6, J1, V26.2	Inbred	8–12	No	N.R.	~1.8	0	71	Jaenisch
V18.6, J1, V26.2, V39.7	Inbred	N.R.	No	1.8	N.R. (~2.0)*	0	69	Jaenisch
V6.5, 129B6, V17.2, V8.1, F1.2-3	Hybrid	8–12	No	N.R.	~1.9	70	71	Jaenisch
V6.5, 129B6, V17.2, V8.1, F1.2-3, V30.30	Hybrid	N.R.	No	3.6	N.R. (~2.0)*	78	69	Jaenisch
V6.5, V6.5 sc84, rtTA2ΔSD-18	Hybrid	5–9	Yes/No	3.1	N.R.	100	70	Jaenisch
V18.6, J1, LJG-13	Inbred	5–11	Yes/No	2.5	N.R.	0	70	Jaenisch
J1	Inbred	35	No	0	–	–	70	Jaenisch
HM-1	Inbred	19	No	3.1	1.6	26	68	Wilmut
R1	Hybrid	19–25	No	0.1	1.9	33	68	Wilmut
NARA-5	Hybrid	<10	No	≤~0.7	1.5	0	13	Tsunoda
NARA-6-12	Hybrid	<10	No	≤~0.7	1.3	27	12	Tsunoda
R1	Inbred	17–23	No	N.R.	1.6	0	12	Tsunoda
NR2, GFP	Inbred	17–23	Yes/No	N.R.	1.6	33	12	Tsunoda
R1	Hybrid	15–19	No	1.5	N.R.	100	67	Renard
TT2	Hybrid	N.R.	Yes	3.5	N.R.	85	15	Kono
TT2	Hybrid	N.R.	Yes	3.5	N.R.	40	17	Kono
Somatic								
Somatic: cumulus	Hybrid	–	No	~2.2	N.R.	71	1	Wakayama
Somatic: tail tip	Hybrid	–	No	~0.6	1.3	33	24	Wakayama
Somatic: Sertoli	Hybrid	–	No	~1.2	1.6	100	26	Ogura

N.R., not reported.
*Average value for inbred- and hybrid-derived clones. †Percentage is of starting, one-cell embryos.

postblastocyst development is inversely correlated to the ES donor cell culture passage number.[67,68]

Improved implantation rates for esnt embryos imply that they readily produce extraembryonic lineages. Indeed, development exclusively of esnt placentas in the absence of discernible embryonic structures has been reported for a variety of ES nucleus donor cell lines.[12,22] This is paradoxic given that diploid ES cells make a limited or negligible contribution to placental development in chimeras, even when their contribution to the embryo proper is substantial.[64] The production of placentae with little or no embryonic material has also been observed following scnt with different donor cell types, although the phenomenon is extremely rare in fertilization-derived conceptuses.[29]

In addition to higher rates of implantation relative to scnt embryos, esnt fetal development to term also occurs at a higher rate.[22] Even so, this development is evidently less stable than it is in scnt; offspring produced by esnt exhibit a greater variety of abnormalities to a broader range of degrees. A high proportion of esnt clones die within a short time of delivery (Table 62–1). This phenomenon is influenced by strain, with clones produced from inbred ES donor cells perishing perinatally in at least 75% of cases and those from hybrid-derived lines usually surviving (Table 62–1). Perinatal death has been reportedly due to respiratory failure of unknown aetiology[68,69] or abdominal distension and subcutaneous hemorrhage.[12]

A range of sizes have been reported for neonatal esnt offspring, and when compared with fertilization-derived pups they can be small,[12] within the normal range,[12,22,68] or large.[12,68–71]

The genetic contribution to this predisposition and other esnt phenotypes is difficult to assess because no single cell line has been used by all of the groups reporting esnt cloning (Table 62–1). However, several groups have worked with the hybrid-derived line R1 for which they report offspring within the normal birth weight range (1.5–1.7g)[12,22,67] or enlarged (1.8–1.9g).[12,68] Survival varied from 0–100% (Table 62–1). Factors other than genetics are thus likely to contribute to esnt clone phenotypes, including donor cell culture passage number.[68] Indeed, it has previously been reported that changes in imprint marks occurred by passage 9–12 in hybrid-derived ES cell lines (SF1-3 and -8) and that these changes were present in fetuses completely derived from the cell lines by tetraploid chimera technology, where they were associated with phenotypes that included polyhydramnios, poor mandibular development, and interstitial bleeding.[68] Cultured ES cells are highly tolerant of altered methylation,[72,73] and even lines lacking the major maintenance methyltransferase Dnmt-1 are viable in an undifferentiated state.[74] Therefore, potential consequences of general methylation changes in ES cells do not necessarily manifest themselves during in vitro culture. With little or no selection against ES cell genome methylation (and, ipso facto, other) changes during culture in vitro, esnt likely provides a phenotypic read-out of epigenetic changes in ES cells on a developmental and occasionally organismal level.[66,69,71] These epigenetic changes are now discussed.

EPIGENETIC ALTERATIONS IN EMBRYONIC STEM CELLS ASSOCIATED WITH DYSREGULATION OF GENE EXPRESSION IN EMBRYONIC STEM CELL NUCLEAR TRANSFER OFFSPRING

Many irregularities in CpG methylation in undifferentiated ES cells[72,73] may be reparable, because a wave of de novo genomic DNA methylation occurs during gastrulation or ES cell differentiation in vitro.[75] However, imprinted gene loci require germ line passage for de novo methylation, with hypomethylation at these loci evidently being tolerated in pluripotent ES cells and their differentiated derivatives.[74] Imprinted gene loci are thus susceptible to aberrant DNA methylation in ES cells.[66,71] The attrition of allelic methylation patterns has been described during ES cell culture at both maternally expressed (Igfr2 and H19) and paternally expressed (Igf2 and U2af1-rs1) imprinted gene loci.[66]

Marked variations in DNA methylation within the differentially methylated region (DMR) of the paternally imprinted gene H19 have been reported even between ES cell subclones.[71] Altered H19 gene methylation was observed in the placentas of esnt cloned offspring and correlated with changes in H19 expression levels.[71] Levels of expression of H19 and to a lesser extent Igf2, Peg1/Mest, and Meg1/Grb10 varied markedly between esnt clone–associated placentas, and H19, Igf2, Cdkn1c (p57), and Sgce exhibited deviation from the norm in esnt clone–derived tissues.[41,71]

Genomic DNA from dnmt1 null ES cells rescued by a dnmt1 construct is globally methylated at all but imprinted gene loci.[74] Such rescued cells are pluripotent, suggesting that methylation marks at imprinted gene loci are not (all) required for normal development. This precedent for aberrant imprinting in developmentally viable cells in vivo is consistent with a limited role of imprinted gene expression—or at least of imprinting per se—in explaining esnt clone phenotypes. This could explain why no clear correlation has been reported between imprinted gene expression and phenotypes in esnt clones.[71]

The less relevant imprinted gene expression is to explaining esnt clone developmental outcome, the more relevant the expression of nonimprinted gene expression must presumably be. Microarray analysis suggests that expression of both imprinted and nonimprinted genes in esnt neonatal clone livers is abnormal, although to a lesser extent than in associated placentas, in which 4% of the 10,000 genes analyzed differed dramatically in expression levels compared with controls.[41]

NUCLEAR TRANSFER EMBRYONIC STEM (NTES) CELL LINES GENERATED VIA ADULT SOMATIC AND EMBRYONIC STEM CELL NUCLEAR TRANSFER

The production of developmentally potent blastocysts by nt cloning (nt blastocysts) has been extended to allow the derivation of ES cells from them, termed ntES cells.[76–78] Such ntES cells have been produced using nt blastocysts cloned from fetal cerebral cortex cells,[76] cumulus cells,[77,78] tail tip cells,[78,79] and mature B and T lymphocytes.[80]

The precise relationship between mouse ES and ntES cell lines is undefined, but they predictably share characteristics.

Like ES cells, ntES cells express SSEA-1, Oct4, and alkaline phosphatase, but unlike many ES cell lines, ntES cells are not dependent on LIF for culture in an undifferentiated state.[76,77] Like ES cells, ntES cells exhibit full pluripotency and can differentiate to produce cells of all three germ layers *in vitro* and *in vivo*.[78] They contribute extensively to the coats of chimeras following injection into fertilization-derived blastocysts and are able to differentiate into gametes.[78]

The efficiency with which ntES cell lines are generated from scnt embryos exceeds the rate of term development of clones. For example, although usually fewer than 3% of hybrid-derived cumulus scnt blastocysts develop to term,[1] more than 14% of hybrid-derived cumulus scnt blastocysts can produce ntES cell lines.[78] Tail tip scnt blastocysts yield ntES cell lines at a generally lower frequency (approximately 6%)[78] and nt from mature T and B lymphocytes produced nt blastocysts of which 5% (2/41) gave rise to ntES cell lines.[80] The efficiency of derivation of ntES cell lines does not depend on the sex of the nucleus donor.[78] These rates of ntES cell line generation are generally greater than rates of term development following scnt. This presumably correlates with the relative efficiencies of different levels of reprogramming as defined by chromatin changes that lead to gene expression permissive for development. Clearly, less information is required to produce an undifferentiated ICM (and consequently, ntES cells) compared with an advanced developmental stage such as offspring, and, therefore, less stringent conditions are likely be placed on reprogramming.

From these data, it follows that most ntES cell lines (11/14 = ~80% for cumulus scnt)[78] are derived from developmentally nonviable nt blastocysts, and in one model the data predict that ~80% of ntES cell lines would fail to support term development following nt. Indeed, where nucleus donors were ntES cells derived from the hybrid B6D2F$_1$, 1.2% of starting embryos (2.8% of nt blastocysts) developed to term compared with 3% of starting embryos following nt from the ES cell line R1, which is derived from a hybrid strain of embryo produced by fertilization.[22,78] This represents a drop in developmental potency of 60% (vs the predicted ~80%) where ntES cells were used as nucleus donors compared with ES cells.

THE PRESCRIPTIVE DIFFERENTIATION OF NUCLEAR TRANSFER EMBRYONIC STEM CELLS *IN VITRO*

Based in part on their similarity to ES cells, the derivation of ntES cells suggests manifold potential applications, including their use for autologous cell transplantation and as a potentially unlimited source of differentiated cells to elucidate the molecular mechanisms of diseases caused by (rare) genetic defects. Moreover, ntES cells could be used to derive autologous postmeiotic cells *in vitro* for assisted reproduction.[81]

The differentiation *in vitro* of ntES cells yields cells representative of all three germ layers[76,78] (Fig. 62–1). However, as of mid-2003, prescriptive *in vitro* differentiation has been restricted to neural and hematopoietic lineages described in two reports.[78,79] Neural differentiation of classical ES cells has been induced by several methods, including multistep embryoid body (EB) protocols.[82,83] The sole report of prescriptive

neural differentiation of ntES cells *in vitro* was based on one such multistep protocol.[78] This study demonstrated that ntES cell–derived neural precursors respond appropriately to patterning cues that determine regional subtype specification and allowed the highly efficient generation of midbrain dopaminergic neurons.[78] Moreover, the considerable variability in neural yield among various ntES cell lines observed with EB-based protocols can be reduced with a protocol that induces neural differentiation via co-culture on stromal feeder cells.[84]

The use of immunodeficient, *Rag2 null* mice demonstrated for the first time how ntES cells might be used therapeutically.[79] The nt of tail tip cells from immunodeficient mice produced nt blastocysts from which a single *Rag2*$^{−/−}$ ntES cell line was derived. Gene targeting of the line allowed rescue of the *Rag2* genotype and subsequent differentiation *in vitro* into hematopoietic cells (via EB formation) and retroviral overexpression of HoxB4.[79] On transplantation, these cells contributed to a limited yet significant extent to both myeloid and lymphoid lineages.

Several additional therapeutically valuable cell types have been efficaciously elicited from classical ES cell cultures, including pancreatic beta cells, cardiomyocytes, and skeletal muscle cells.[85,86] The application of these protocols to ntES cells, thus, promises a source of isogenic (in addition to allogenic) material for cell therapies in major pathologic conditions such as diabetes and myopathies.

Summary: The Merits and Demerits of Embryonic Stem Cell Nuclear Transfer

Cloning by esnt produces modestly more offspring per starting embryo than scnt cloning (Table 62–1) and has become a paradigm in nt biology. Yet to what extent is esnt justified and what are its relative merits and demerits compared with scnt?

The technology of gene targeting in ES cells has now been combined with nt,[15,17,22,70] and the use of genetically modified lines as donors for esnt promises to streamline gene targeting by guaranteeing germ line transmission, thereby reducing the number of breeding steps required to obtain mice homozygous for the mutated allele. Furthermore, ES cells can be derived *de novo* and subsequently gene targeted (or otherwise modified) before esnt cloning. In this way, genetic backgrounds of interest can be conserved in cloned offspring (with the exception of the introduced mutation) and could aid the study of polygenic traits. In addition, the use of cultured cells as nucleus donors (as in esnt) clearly facilitates their characterization and manipulation before nt compared with the acutely isolated cells typical of scnt. A major caveat to the use of esnt in the generation of targeted animals is that the procedure may of itself introduce cloning-associated phenotypes, complicating the interpretation of the targeting experiment. Cloning-associated phenotypes are not (all) transmitted via the germ line and may, therefore, be absent from progeny,[34,36] but the additional breeding required would remove one of the key advantages—a reduction of breeding time—promised by esnt in the generation of gene-targeted animals.

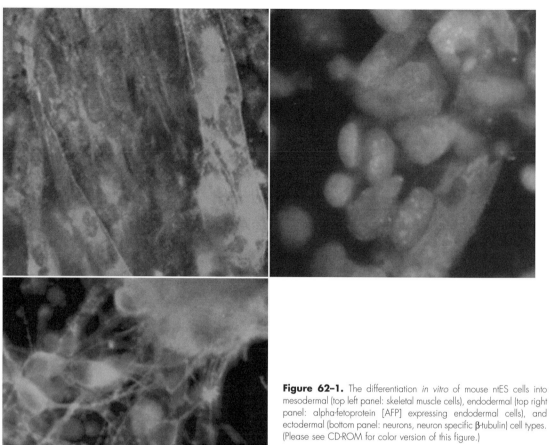

Figure 62–1. The differentiation *in vitro* of mouse ntES cells into mesodermal (top left panel: skeletal muscle cells), endodermal (top right panel: alpha-fetoprotein [AFP] expressing endodermal cells), and ectodermal (bottom panel: neurons, neuron specific β-tubulin) cell types. (Please see CD-ROM for color version of this figure.)

Moreover, the use of esnt as a research tool suffers from major drawbacks compared with scnt. Undifferentiated ES cells are not only remarkably tolerant of epigenetic changes but are subject to them at a high rate, at least at the level of genomic DNA methylation.[66,71–73] Such epigenetic instability is tolerated *in vitro* because in many cases it is not associated with a phenotype in undifferentiated cells.[74] However, this is not the case on differentiation; *dnmt1 null* ES cells are viable only until they differentiate. Moreover, initiation of the embryogenic program following esnt results in dysregulation of gene expression,[41,71] which is presumably responsible for blatant phenotypes such as perinatal death[22] and fetal overgrowth.[69] Such overgrowth is anomalous in scnt offspring[1,24,26,29,30] with few contradictory reports (two enlarged

cumulus scnt clones).[41] Accordingly, and in contrast to clones produced by esnt, there is no strong evidence for extensive dysregulation of gene expression in scnt clones.[29,30]

Cloning by esnt is thus a conflation of at least two complex unknowns: epigenetic dysregulation in ES cells and genomic reprogramming in nt. Moreover, viewed as a tool in research on reprogramming in nt, esnt suffers from the additional setback that any contribution made to this reprogramming during ES cell culture is not defined. In contrast, acutely isolated somatic cells exhibit a profile of gene expression that is constrained by the function of the cell before scnt.

Finally, with a few possible, contentious exceptions, it is highly unlikely that esnt cloning will be sanctioned clinically. This situation stands in stark contrast to scnt, which will enable the production of human ntES cells for therapeutic applications. Extrapolating from esnt as if its associated phenomena are superimposable on those of scnt is, therefore, not only incorrect but essentially irrelevant to the clinical debate.

ACKNOWLEDGMENTS

We are grateful to Doug Sipp, Atsuo Ogura, and Raj Ladher for their critiques of this manuscript during its preparation.

REFERENCES

1. Wakayama, T., Perry, A.C.F., Zuccotti, M., Johnson, K.R., and Yanagimachi, R. (1998). Full-term development of mice from enucleated oocytes injected with cumulus cell nuclei. *Nature* **394,** 369–374.
2. Willadsen, S.M. (1986). Nuclear transplantation in sheep embryos. *Nature* **320,** 63–65.
3. Meng, L., Ely, J.J., Stouffer, R.L., and Wolf, D.P. (1997). Rhesus monkeys produced by nuclear transfer. *Biol. Reprod.* **57,** 454–459.
4. Cibelli, J.B., Stice, S.L., Golueke, P.J., Kane, J.J., Jerry, J., Blackwell, C., Ponce de Leon, F.A., and Robl, J.M. (1998). Cloned transgenic calves produced from nonquiescent fetal fibroblasts. *Science* **280,** 1256–1258.
5. Baguisi, A., Behboodi, E., Melican, D.T., Pollock, J.S., Destrempes, M.M., Cammuso, C., Williams, J.L., Nims, S.D., Porter, C.A., Midura, P., Palacios, M.J., Ayres, S.L., Denniston, R.S., Hayes, M.L., Ziomek, C.A., Meade, H.M., Godke, R.A., Gavin, W.G., Overström, E.W., and Echelard, Y. (1999). Production of goats by somatic cell nuclear transfer. *Nat. Biotechnol.* **17,** 456–461.
6. Onishi, A., Iwamoto, M., Akita, T., Mikawa, S., Takeda, K., Awata, T., Hanada, H., and Perry, A.C.F. (2000). Pig cloning by microinjection of fetal fibroblast nuclei. *Science* **289,** 1188–1190.
7. Chesne, P., Adenot, P.G., Viglietta, C., Baratte, M., Boulanger, L., and Renard, J.P. (2002). Cloned rabbits produced by nuclear transfer from adult somatic cells. *Nat. Biotechnol.* **20,** 366–369.
8. Shin, T., Kraemer, D., Pryor, J., Liu, L., Rugila, J., Howe, L., Buck, S., Murphy, K., Lyons, L., and Westhusin, M. (2002). A cat cloned by nuclear transplantation. *Nature* **415,** 859.
9. Woods, G.L., White, K.L., Vanderwall, D.K., Li, G.-P., Aston, K.I., Bunch, T.D., Meerdo, L.N., and Pate, B.J. (2003). A mule cloned from fetal cells by nuclear transfer. *Science* **301,** 1063.
10. Galli, C., Lagutina, I., Crotti, G., Colleoni, S., Turini, P., Ponderato, N., Duchi, R., and Lazzari, G. (2003). Pregnancy: a cloned horse born to its dam twin. *Nature* **424,** 635.
11. Ogura, A., Inoue, K., Takano, K., Wakayama, T., and Yanagimachi, R. (2000). Birth of mice after nuclear transfer by electrofusion using tail tip cells. *Mol. Reprod. Dev.* **57,** 55–59.
12. Amano, T., Kato, Y., and Tsunoda, Y. (2001). Full-term development of enucleated mouse oocytes fused with embryonic stem cells from different cell lines. *Reproduction* **121,** 729–733.
13. Amano, T., Tani, T., Kato, Y., and Tsunoda, Y. (2001). Mouse cloned from embryonic stem (ES) cells synchronized in metaphase with nocodazole. *J. Exp. Zool.* **289,** 139–145.
14. Ono, Y., Shimozawa, N., Ito, M., and Kono, T. (2001). Cloned mice from fetal fibroblast cells arrested at metaphase by a serial nuclear transfer. *Biol. Reprod.* **64,** 44–50.
15. Ono, Y., Shimozawa, N., Muguruma, K., Kimoto, S., Hioki, K., Tachibana, M., Shinkai, Y., Ito, M., and Kono, T. (2001).

16. Amano, T., Kato, Y., and Tsunoda, Y. (2002). The developmental potential of the inner cell mass of blastocysts that were derived from mouse ES cells using nuclear transfer technology. *Cell Tissue Res.* **307,** 367–370.
17. Shimozawa, N., Ono, Y., Muguruma, K., Hioki, K., Araki, Y., Shinkai, Y., Kono, T., and Ito, M. (2002). Direct production of gene-targeted mice from ES cells by nuclear transfer and gene transmission to their progeny. *Exp. Anim.* **51,** 375–381.
18. Ogura, A., Ogonuki, K., Takano, K., and Inoue, K. (2001). Microinsemination, nuclear transfer and cytoplasmic transfer: The application of new reproductive engineering techniques to mouse genetics. *Mamm. Genome* **12,** 803–812.
19. Wakayama, T., and Perry, A.C.F. (2002). Cloning of mice. *In* "Principles of Cloning" (J.B. Cibelli, R.P. Lanza, K.H.S. Campbell, and M.D. West, eds.), pp. 301–341. Academic Press, San Diego.
20. Chatot, C.L., Ziomek, C.A., Bavister, B.D., Lewis, J.L., and Torres, I. (1989). An improved culture medium supports development of random-bred 1-cell mouse embryos in vitro. *J. Reprod. Fertil.* **86,** 679–688.
21. Lawitts, J.A., and Biggers, J.D. (1993). Culture of preimplantation embryos. *Methods Enzymol.* **225,** 153–164.
22. Wakayama, T., Rodriguez, I., Perry, A.C.F., Yanagimachi, R., and Mombaerts, P. (1999). Mice cloned from embryonic stem cells. *Proc. Natl. Acad. Sci. U. S. A.* **96,** 14984–14989.
23. Wakayama, T., Shinkai, Y., Tamashiro, K.L.K., Niida, H., Blanchard, D.C., Blanchard, R.J., Ogura, A., Tanemura, K., Tachibana, M., Perry, A.C.F., Colgan, D.F., Mombaerts, P., and Yanagimachi, R. (2000). Cloning of mice to six generations. *Nature* **407,** 318–319.
24. Wakayama, T., and Yanagimachi, R. (1999). Cloning of male mice from adult tail-tip cells. *Nat. Genet.* **22,** 127–128.
25. Wakayama, T., and Yanagimachi, R. (2001). Mouse cloning with nucleus donor cells of different age and type. *Mol. Reprod. Dev.* **58,** 376–383.
26. Ogura, A., Inoue, K., Ogonuki, N., Noguchi, A., Takano, K., Nagano, R., Suzuki, O., Lee, J., Ishino, F., and Matsuda, J. (2000). Production of male cloned mice from fresh, cultured, and cryopreserved immature Sertoli cells. *Biol. Reprod.* **62,** 1579–1584.
27. Yamazaki, Y., Makino, H., Hamaguchi-Hamada, K., Hamada, S., Sugino, H., Kawase, E., Miyata, T., Ogawa, M., Yanagimachi, R., and Yagi, T. (2001). Assessment of the developmental totipotency of neural cells in the cerebral cortex of mouse embryo by nuclear transfer. *Proc. Natl. Acad. Sci. U. S. A.* **98,** 14022–14026.
28. Perry, A.C.F., and Wakayama, T. (2002). Untimely ends and new beginnings in mouse cloning. *Nat. Genet.* **30,** 243–244.
29. Ogura, A., Inoue, K., Ogonuki, N., Lee, J., Kohda, T., and Ishino, F. (2002). Phenotypic effects of somatic cell cloning in the mouse. *Cloning Stem Cells* **4,** 397–405.
30. Inoue, K., Kohda, T., Lee, J., Ogonuki, N., Mochida, K., Noguchi, Y., Tanemura, K., Kaneko-Ishino, T., Ishino, F., and Ogura, A. (2002). Faithful expression of imprinted genes in cloned mice. *Science* **295,** 297.
31. Tanaka, S., Oda, M., Toyoshima, Y., Wakayama, T., Tanaka, M., Yoshida, N., Hattori, N., Ohgane, J., Yanagimachi, R., and Shiota, K. (2001). Placentomegaly in cloned mouse concepti caused by expansion of the spongiotrophoblast layer. *Biol. Reprod.* **65,** 1813–1821.
32. Ogonuki, N., Inoue, K., Yamamoto, Y., Noguchi, Y., Tanemura, K., Suzuki, O., Nakayama, H., Doi, K., Ohtomo, Y., Satoh, M., Nishida, A., and Ogura, A. (2002). Early death of mice cloned from somatic cells. *Nat. Genet.* **30,** 253–254.

33. Tamashiro, K.L.K., Wakayama, T., Blanchard, R.J., Blanchard, D.C., and Yanagimachi, R. (2000). Postnatal growth and behavioral development of mice cloned from adult cumulus cells. *Biol. Reprod.* **63,** 328–334.

34. Tamashiro, K.L.K., Wakayama, T., Akutsu, H., Yamazaki, Y., Lachey, J.L., Wortmsan, M.D., Seeley, R.J., D'Alessio, D.A., Woods, S.C., Yanagimachi, R., and Sakai, R.R. (2002). Cloned mice have an obese phenotype that is not transmitted to their offspring. *Nat. Med.* **63,** 328–334.

35. Lohrke, H., Hesse, B., and Goerttler, K. (1984). Spontaneous tumors and lifespan of female NMRI mice of the outbred stock Sut:NMRT during a lifetime study. *J. Cancer Res. Clin. Oncol.* **108,** 192–196.

36. Shimozawa, N., Ono, Y., Kimoto, S., Hioki, K., Araki, Y., Shinkai, Y., Kono, T., and Ito, M. (2002). Abnormalities in cloned mice are not transmitted to the progeny. *Genesis* **34,** 203–207.

37. Nichols, J., Zevnik, B., Anastassiadis, K., Niwa, H., Klewe-Nebenius, D., Chambers, I., Schöler, H., and Smith, A. (1998). Formation of pluripotent stem cells in the mammalian embryo depends on the POU transcription factor Oct4. *Cell* **95,** 379–391.

38. Niwa, H., Miyazaki, J., and Smith, A.G. (2000). Quantitative expression of Oct-3/4 defines differentiation, dedifferentiation or self-renewal of ES cells. *Nature Genet.* **24,** 372–376.

39. Boiani, M., Eckardt, S., Schöler, H.R., and McLaughlin, K.J. (2002). Oct4 distribution and level in mouse clones: consequences for pluripotency. *Genes Dev.* **16,** 1209–1219.

40. Bortvin, A., Eggan, K., Skaletsky, H., Akutsu, H., Berry, D.L., Yanagimachi, R., Page, D.C., and Jaenisch, R. (2003). Incomplete reactivation of *Oct4*-related genes in mouse embryos cloned from somatic nuclei. *Development* **130,** 1673–1680.

41. Humpherys, D., Eggan, K., Akutsu, H., Friedman, A., Hochedlinger, K., Yanagaimachi, R., Lander, E.S., Golub, T.R., and Jaenisch, R. (2002). Abnormal gene expression in cloned mice derived from embryonic stem cell and cumulus cell nuclei. *Proc. Natl. Acad. Sci. U. S. A.* **99,** 12889–12894.

42. Mann, M.R.W., Chung, Y.G., Nolen, L.D., Verona, R.I., Latham, K.E., and Bartolomei, M.S. (2003). Disruption of imprinted gene methylation and expression in cloned preimplantation stage mouse embryos. *Biol. Reprod.* **69,** 902–914.

43. Ohgane, J., Wakayama, T., Kogo, Y., Senda, S., Hattori, N., Tanaka, S., Yanagimachi, R., and Shiota, K. (2001). DNA methylation variation in cloned mice. *Genesis* **30,** 45–50.

44. Martin, G.R. (1981). Isolation of a pluripotent cell line from early mouse embryos cultured in medium conditioned by teratocarcinoma stem cells. *Proc. Natl. Acad. Sci. U. S. A.* **78,** 7634–7636.

45. Evans, M.J., and Kaufman, M.H. (1981). Establishment in culture of pluripotential cells from mouse embryos. *Nature* **292,** 154–156.

46. Doetschman, T., Williams, P., and Maeda N. (1988). Establishment of hamster blastocyst-derived embryonic stem (ES) cells. *Dev. Biol.* **127,** 224–227.

47. Thompson, J.A., Kalishman, J., Golos, T.G., Durning, M., Harris, C.P., Becker, R.A., and Hearn, J.P. (1995). Isolation of a primate embryonic stem cell line. *Proc. Natl. Acad. Sci. U. S. A.* **92,** 7844–7848.

48. Thompson, J.A., Kalishman, J., Golos, T.G., Durning, M., Harris, C.P., and Hearn, J.P. (1996). Pluripotent cell lines derived from common marmoset (*Callithrix jacchus*) blastocysts. *Biol. Reprod.* **55,** 254–259.

49. Thompson, J.A., Itskovitz-Eldor, J., Shapiro, S.S., Waknitz, M.A., Swiegiel, J.J., Marshall, V.S., and Jones, J.M. (1998). Embryonic stem cell lines derived from human blastocysts. *Science* **282,** 1145–1147.

50. Cibelli, J.B., Stice, S.L., Golueke, P.J., Kane, J.J., Jerry, J., Blackwell, C., Ponce de Leon, F.A., and Robl, J.M. (1998). Transgenic bovine chimeric offspring produced from somatic cell-derived stem-like cells. *Nat. Biotechnol.* **16,** 620–621.

51. Suemori, H., Tada, T., Torii, R., Hosoi, Y., Kobayashi, K., Imahie, H., Kondo, Y., Iritani, A., and Nakatsuji, N. (2001). Establishment of embryonic stem cell lines from cynomolgus monkey blastocysts produced by IVF or ICSI. *Dev. Dyn.* **222,** 273–279.

52. Smith, A.G., Heath, J.K., Donaldson, D.D., Wong G.G., Moreau, J., Stahl, M., and Rogers, D. (1988). Inhibition of pluripotential embryonic stem cell differentiation by purified polypeptides. *Nature* **336,** 688–690.

53. Williams, R.L., Hilton, D.J., Pease, S., Willson, T.A., Stewart, C.L., Gearing, D.P., Wagner, E.F., Metcalf, D., Nicola, N.A., and Gough, N.M. (1988). Myeloid leukemia inhibitory factor maintains the developmental potential of embryonic stem cells. *Nature* **336,** 372–375.

54. Okamoto, K., Okazawa, H., Okuda, A., Sakai, M., Muramatsu, M., and Hamada, H. (1990). A novel octamer binding transcription factor is differentially expressed in mouse embryonic cells. *Cell* **60,** 461–472.

55. Rosner, M.H., Vigano, M.A., Ozato, K., Timmons, P.M., Poirier, F., Rigby, P.W., and Staudt, L.M. (1990). A POU-domain transcription factor in early stem cells and germ cells of the mammalian embryo. *Nature* **345,** 686–692.

56. Schöler, H.R., Dressler, G.R., Balling, R., Rohdewohld, H., and Gruss, P. (1990). Oct-4: A germline-specific transcription factor mapping to the mouse t-complex. *EMBO J.* **9,** 2185–2195.

57. Chambers, I., Colby, D., Robertson, M., Nichols, J., Lee, S., Tweedie, S., and Smith, A. (2003). Functional expression cloning of Nanog, a pluripotency sustaining factor in embryonic stem cells. *Cell* **113,** 643–655.

58. Mitsui, K., Tokuzawa, Y., Itoh, H., Segawa, K., Murakami, M., Takahashi, K., Maruyama, M., Maeda, M., and Yamanaka, S. (2003). The homeoprotein Nanog is required for maintenance of pluripotency in mouse epiblast and ES cells. *Cell* **113,** 631–642.

59. Ernst, M., Oates, A., and Dunn, A.R. (1996). Gp130-mediated signal transduction in embryonic stem cells involves interaction of Jak and Ras/mitogen-activated protein kinase pathways. *J. Biol. Chem.* **271,** 30136–30143.

60. Niwa, H., Burdon, T., Chambers, I., and Smith, A. (1998). Self-renewal of pluripotent embryonic stem cells is mediated via activation of STAT3. *Genes Dev.* **12,** 2048–2060.

61. Matsuda, T., Nakamura, T., Nakao, K., Arai, T., Katsuki, M., Heike, T., and Yokota, T. (1999). STAT3 activation is sufficient to maintain an undifferentiated state of mouse embryonic stem cells. *EMBO J.* **18,** 4261–4269.

62. Martin, G.R., and Evans, M.J. (1975). Differentiation of clonal lines of teratocarcinoma cells: Formation of embryoid bodies in vitro. *Proc. Natl. Acad. Sci. U. S. A.* **72,** 1441–1445.

63. Nakatsuji, N., and Suemori, H. (2002). Embryonic stem cell lines of nonhuman primates. *Sci. World* **2,** 1762–1773.

64. Nagy, A., Gocza, E., Diaz, E.M., Prideaux, V.R., Ivanyi, E., Markkula, M., and Rossant, J. (1990). Embryonic stem cells alone are able to support fetal development in the mouse. *Development* **110,** 815–821.

65. Nagy, A., Rossant, J., Nagy, R., Abramow-Newerly, W., and Roder, J.C. (1993). Derivation of completely cell culture-derived mice from early-passage embryonic stem cells. *Proc. Natl. Acad. Sci. U. S. A.* **90,** 8424–8428.

66. Dean, W., Bowden, L., Aitchison, A., Klose, J., Moore, T., Meneses, J.J., Reik, W., and Feil, R. (1998). Altered imprinted gene methylation and expression in completely ES cell-derived

mouse fetuses: association with aberrant phenotypes. *Development* **125**, 2273–2282.

67. Zhou, Q., Jouneau, A., Brochard, V., Adenot, P., and Renard, J.P. (2001). Developmental potential of mouse embryos reconstructed from metaphase embryonic stem cell nuclei. *Biol. Reprod.* **65**, 412–419.

68. Gao, S., McGarry, M., Ferrier, T., Pallante, B., Gasparrini, B., Fletcher, J., Harkness, L., De Sousa, P., McWhir, J., and Wilmut, I. (2003). Effect of cell confluence on production of cloned mice using an inbred embryonic stem cell line. *Biol. Reprod.* **68**, 595–603.

69. Eggan, K., Akutsu, H., Loring, J., Jackson-Grusby, L., Klemm, M., Rideout, W.M. 3rd, Yanagimachi, R., and Jaenisch, R. (2001). Hybrid vigor, fetal overgrowth, and viability of mice derived by nuclear cloning and tetraploid embryo complementation. *Proc. Natl. Acad. Sci. U. S. A.* **98**, 6209–6214.

70. Rideout, W.M., 3rd., Wakayama, T., Wutz, A., Eggan, K., Jackson-Grusby, L., Dausman, J., Yanagimachi, R., and Jaenisch, R. (2000). Generation of mice from wild-type and targeted ES cells by nuclear cloning. *Nat. Genet.* **24**, 109–110.

71. Humpherys, D., Eggan, K., Akutsu, H., Hochedlinger, K., Rideout, W.M., Biniszkiewcz, D., Yanagaimachi, R., and Jaenisch, R. (2001). Epigenetic instability in ES cells and cloned mice. *Science* **293**, 95–97.

72. Antequera, F., Boyes, J., and Bird, A. (1990). High levels of de novo methylation and altered chromatin structure at CpG islands in cell lines. *Cell* **62**, 503–514.

73. Frank, D., Keshet, I., Shani, M., Levine, A., Razin, A., and Cedar, H. (1991). Demethylation of CpG islands in embryonic stem cells. *Nature* **351**, 239–241.

74. Tucker, K.L., Beard, C., Dausmann, J., Jackson-Grusby, L., Laird, P.W., Lei, H., Li, E., and Jaenisch, R. (1996). Germ-line passage is required for establishment of methylation and expression patterns of imprinted but not of nonimprinted genes. *Genes Dev.* **10**, 1008–1020.

75. Weng, A., Magnuson, T., and Storb, U. (1995). Strain-specific transgene methylation occurs early in mouse development and can be recapitulated in embryonic stem cells. *Development* **121**, 2853–2859.

76. Kawase, E., Yamazaki, Y., Yagi, T., Yanagimachi, R., and Pedersen, R.A. (2000). Mouse embryonic stem (ES) cell lines established from neuronal cell-derived cloned blastocysts. *Genesis* **28**, 156–163.

77. Munsie, M.J., Michalska, A.E., O'Brien, C.M., Trounson, A.O., Pera, M.F., and Mountford, P.S. (2000). Isolation of pluripotent embryonic stem cells from reprogrammed adult mouse somatic cell nuclei. *Curr. Biol.* **10**, 989–992.

78. Wakayama, T., Tabar, V., Rodriguez, I., Perry, A.C.F., Studer, L., and Mombaerts, P. (2001). Differentiation of embryonic stem cell lines generated from adult somatic cells by nuclear transfer. *Science* **292**, 740–743.

79. Rideout, W.M. 3rd, Hochedlinger, K., Kyba, M., Daley, G.Q., and Jaenisch, R. (2002). Correction of a genetic defect by nuclear transplantation and combined cell and gene therapy. *Cell* **109**, 17–27.

80. Hochedlinger, K., and Jaenisch, R. (2002). Monoclonal mice generated by nuclear transfer from mature B and T donor cells. *Nature* **415**, 1035–1038.

81. Hübner, K., Fuhrmann, G., Christenson, L.K., Kehler, J., Reinbold, R., De La, F.R., Wood, J., Strauss, J.F., III, Boiani, M., and Scholer, H.R. (2003). Derivation of oocytes from mouse embryonic stem cells. *Science* **300**, 1251–1256.

82. Okabe, S., Forsberg-Nilsson, K., Spiro, A.C., Segal, M., and McKay, R.D.G. (1996). Development of neuronal precursor cells and functional postmitotic neurons from embryonic stem cells in vitro. *Mech. Dev.* **59**, 89–102.

83. Lee, S.-H., Lumelsky, N., Studer, L., Auerbach, J.M., and McKay, R.D.G. (2000). Efficient generation of midbrain and hindbrain neurons from mouse embryonic stem cells. *Nat. Biotechnol.* **18**, 675–679.

84. Barberi, T., Klivenyi, P., Calingasan, N.Y., Lee, H., Kawamata, H., Loonam, K., Perrier, A.L., Bruses, J.L., Rubio, M.E., Topf, N., Tabar, V., Harrison, N.L., Beal, M.F., Moore, M.A.S., and Studer, L. (2003). Specification of neural subtypes from fertilization and nuclear transfer ES cells and therapeutic application in Parkinsonian mice. *Nat. Biotechnol.* **21**, 1200–1207.

85. Klug, M.G., Soonpaa, M.H., Koh, G.Y., and Field, L.J. (1996). Genetically selected cardiomyocytes from differentiating embryonic stem cells form stable intracardiac grafts. *J. Clin. Invest.* **98**, 216–224.

86. Lumelsky, N., Blondel, O., Laeng, P., Velasco, I., Ravin, R., and McKay, R. (2001). Differentiation of embryonic stem cells to insulin-secreting structures similar to pancreatic islets. *Science* **292**, 1389–1394.

63

Parthenogenetic Stem Cells

J. David Wininger

Introduction

Parthenogenesis is a form of reproduction in which an egg can develop into an embryo without being fertilized by a sperm. Parthenogenesis is derived from the Greek words for "virgin birth," and several insect species including aphids, bees, and ants are known to reproduce by parthenogenesis. Recently, parthenogenesis has received considerable attention as a tool for the production of stem cells. Human stem cells derived from embryos, fetal primordial germ cells, umbilical cord blood, and adult tissues provide potential cell based therapies for repair of degenerating or damaged tissues. Although establishment of stem cell lines via parthenogenesis was demonstrated by Kaufman et al.[1] Twenty years ago in the mouse model, the pluripotency of the cells and the efficacy of their derivatives were poorly explored. The possibility of deriving stem cells from parthenogenetic embryos could eliminate the requirement to produce and destroy viable embryos and may reduce the ethical concerns surrounding stem cell research. Because parthenogenetic stem cells contain only maternal genes, their use of may reduce the occurrence of immune-mediated rejection following graft transplantation. This chapter reviews recent advances in parthenogenesis research and discusses its potential impact on the stem cell debate.

Parthenogenesis Research

The phenomenon of parthenogenesis was discovered in the 18th century by Charles Bonnet. In 1899, Jacques Loeb accomplished the first clear case of artificial parthenogenesis when he pricked unfertilized frog eggs with a needle and found that normal embryonic development occurred is some cases. In 1936, Gregory Pincus parthenogenetically activated rabbit eggs by changes in temperature and using chemical agents. The molecular events that lead to oocyte activation have been studied extensively in invertebrates, amphibians, and mice. This research led to activation models involving increased intracellular calcium transients.

Susko-Parrish et al.[2] examined the response of in vitro matured bovine oocytes to parthenogenetic activation using compounds that increased intracellular calcium (ionomycin) or inhibit protein phosphorylation (6-dimethylaminopurine

[DMAP]). They showed that, after sequential induction of a Ca^{2+} transient and inhibition of protein phosphorylation, bovine oocytes enter into embryonic cell cycles without undergoing a second reductional division. In other words, they were able to produce diploid parthenotes that continued developing as if in mitosis. Bovine blastocysts that developed averaged 70–80 cells, which compared well with fertilized in vitro matured oocytes, and were able to cause extended cycles in 33.3% of recipient cattle after nonsurgical transfer to the uterus.

Mouse oocytes have been activated by exposure to Ca^{2+}- and Mg^{2+}-free medium; medium containing hyaluronidase; exposure to ethanol, Ca^{2+} ionophores, or chelators; inhibitors of protein synthesis; and electrical stimulation. A recent study by Lin et al.[3] reported the establishment of murine parthenogenetic stem cell lines that retained a normal karyotype, expressed stem cell markers SSEA-1 and Oct4, and were positive for alkaline phosphatase and telomerase. Teratomatous growth of these cells displayed the development of a variety of tissue types encompassing all three germ layers. In addition, their cells demonstrated the potential of in vitro differentiation of endoderm, neuronal, and hematopoietic lineages.

There have been only a few reports on parthenogenesis in primates. In 2002, Cibelli et al.[4] demonstrated broad differentiation capabilities of primate (Macaca fascicular) pluripotent stem cells derived by parthenogenesis. The in vitro differentiation of these cells to well-characterized dopaminergic neurons is very interesting because of their potential to replace lost neurons in Parkinson's disease. Rhoton-Vlasak et al.[5] have shown that brief incubations of human oocytes with calcium ionophore can induce pronuclear formation, and Nakagawa et al.[6] recently demonstrated that pronuclear formation and cleavage occurs following incubation with calcium ionophore and puromycin or DMAP.

Lin et al.[3] reported parthenogenetic activation of a small number of mature human oocytes using Ca^{2+} ionophore and DMAP. Five blastocysts developed from 25 oocytes and cells from one blastocyst proliferated and survived beyond two passages. Wininger et al.[7] reported an activation rate of 59% (40/68) following treatment of mature human oocytes with Ca^{2+} ionophore and DMAP (Fig. 63–1).

Following activation, 37% (15/40) of the parthenotes progressed to the blastocyst stage and 60% (9/15) of the treated blastocysts attached to feeder cells following immunosurgery (Fig. 63–2). Cell masses remained attached to the feeder cells for 3–5 days before their growth arrested. To date, no human parthenogenetic stem cells lines have been established.

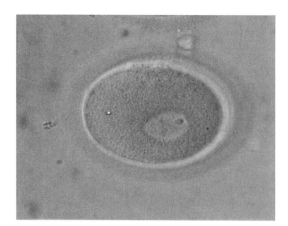

Figure 63-1. An activated human oocyte displaying one pronucleus following treatment with Ca²⁺ ionophore and 6-dimethylaminopurine (DMAP).

Homozygous Stem Cells

The discovery of the pluripotential characteristics of human stem cell lines from materials such as embryos, fetal primordial germ cells, umbilical cord blood, and adult tissues have made cell-based therapies a promising approach for tissue repair and regeneration. However, the issue of immune-mediated rejection of an allotransplant remains a major challenge. Immunogenicity of a stem cell derivative depends on the expression of the major histocompatibility complex (MHC) genes that are highly polymorphic for each antigen. This polymorphism is further amplified by heterozygosity. A transplant can be much less immunogenic when its two MHC haplotypes are identical (homozygous), resulting in a much higher probability for tissue matching. There are several potential ways to develop an MHC homozygous graft including the knockout of one MHC haplotype in a heterozygous stem cell or the fertilization of an oocyte with a sperm that has an MHC identical to the oocyte.

In contrast to the types of stem cells mentioned previously, stem cells derived through parthenogenetic activation of metaphase II oocytes are either uniformly homozygous for the MHC genes or include minimal crossover-associated heterozygosity. Without the contribution from a sperm, an oocyte has a unique advantage in homozygosity, which renders its derivatives less immunogenic and provides a broader match with different MHC phenotypes. Lin *et al.*[3] proposed that a graft derived from such homozygous stem cells, presenting as few as three or four antigens, would match a much wider range of phenotypes than a heterozygous graft. Because some HLA haplotypes have a higher distribution in the population, the use of homozygous stem cells renders the possibility of creating a bank of stem cells covering most phenotypes in the general population. It has been estimated that that stem cells from approximately 300 parthenotes could provide close matches for the majority of the U.S. population.[8]

Establishment of mouse stem cells lines from homozygous materials was accomplished by Kaufman *et al.*[1] in 1983 via parthenogenetic activation. Although some studies have implied partial differentiation defects following formation of parthenogenetic stem cells,[9] other studies demonstrated unrestricted lineage differentiation in chimeras.[10] The recent establishment of a homozygous stem cell line in nonhuman primates that differentiated to neuronal cells[4] and *in vitro* ectodermal, mesodermal, and endodermal differentiation in the murine model[3] demonstrate the possibilities of homozygous stem cells.

Imprinting

The term *imprinting* refers to the fact that some chromosomes, segments of chromosomes, or some genes are stamped with a "memory" of the parent from whom it came: In the cells of a child it is possible to tell which chromosome copy came from the mother (maternal chromosome) and which copy was inherited from the father (paternal chromosome). Genetic imprinting occurs in the ovary or testis early in the formation of the eggs and sperm. This is accomplished via DNA methylation, histone acetylation, and its chromatin structure. Some genes are imprinted to be switched off or inactive only if they are passed down through an egg cell; others will be inactivated only if they are passed down through a sperm cell. Imprinting will then occur again in the next generation when that person produces his or her own sperm or eggs.

In humans, it is currently estimated that less than 100 out of the estimated 30,000 genes may be subject to genetic imprinting. Although this is, therefore, not a common mechanism controlling gene expression in humans, it is nevertheless an important one and provides interesting new insights into the mechanisms of gene expression.

Genetic imprinting may play a major role in fetal development. It appears that the maternal and paternal genomes are epigenetically different, and that both sets are required for successful development.[11] In parthenotes, all their genetic material is of maternal origin and, therefore, lack paternal imprinting. Examination of triploid pregnancies that resulted in a miscarriage gave rise to the theory that the father's genes control the supply of nutrients to the developing fetus through the placenta, whereas the genes passed through the egg from the mother are important for fetal development. Fetuses that had received two copies of each chromosome from the father and one from the mother had large placentas, and the fetus was small. On the other hand, when the extra copy of the

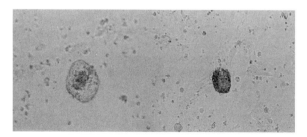

Figure 63-2. (left) Human blastocyst at 120 hours formed by parthenogenetic activation of a metaphase II oocyte. (right) Human inner cell mass attached to murine feeder cells 20 hours following immunosurgery.

chromosomes came from the mother, the fetus was larger and the placenta small. Recently, Kono *et al.*[12] verified that the maternal genome is responsible for the initial fetal development, whereas the paternal genome is responsible for the placental development.

Imprinting may be a mechanism to prevent placental mammalian parthenotes from implanting, ensuring that the developing fetus contains both male and female chromosomes. However, imprinting's role in parthenogenetic activation may not preclude the therapeutic use of parthenogenetic stem cells. It may be that many of the stringent effects of imprinting are overcome when the oocytes are artificially activated with chemicals. Imprinting appears to play a less significant role as a parthenogenetic stem cell differentiates, as confirmed by the diversity and functionality of tissue generated from these cells.

Conclusion

Parthenogenesis for stem cell derivation has been carried out for more than 20 years in a variety of species. Only recently has the technique been applied in the nonhuman primate and human models. Although a stem cell line was established in the nonhuman primate model, no human parthenogenetic stem cell lines have been established. Using unfertilized human eggs as a source for stem cell derivation is much less controversial than using embryos and may have the added advantage of homozygosity, which renders its derivatives less immunogenic and provides a broader match with different MHC phenotypes. Much more research is required to determine if this promising technique can be applied to human oocytes for the production of stem cell lines that will provide cell-based therapies for a variety of disorders including Parkinson's disease, Alzheimer's disease, and diabetes.

ACKNOWLEDGMENTS

I would like to thank Steve Huang and Art Mandell of Stemron Corp. and Jason Hipp of Wake Forest University Medical School for their assistance with this chapter.

REFERENCES

1. Kaufman, M.H., Robertson, E.J., Handyside, A.H., and Evans, M.J. (1983). Establishment of pluripotential cell lines from haploid mouse embryos. *J. Embryol. Exp. Morphol.* **73,** 249–261.
2. Susko-Parrish, J.L., Leibfried-Rutledge, M.L., Northey, D.L., Schutzkus, V., and First, N.L. (1994). Inhibition of protein kinases after an induced calcium transient causes transition of bovine oocytes to embryonic cycles without meiotic completion. *Dev. Biol.* **166,** 729–739.
3. Lin, H., Lei, J.L., Wininger, J.D., Hguyen, M.T., Khanna, R., Hartmann, C., Yan, W.L., and Huang, S.C. (2003). Multilineage potential of homozygous stem cells derived from metaphase II oocytes. *Stem Cells* **21,** 152–161.
4. Cibelli, J.B., Grant, K.A., Champman, K.B., Lanza, R.P., Vrana, K.E., Cunniff, K., Worst, T., Green, H., Walker, S., Gutin, P., Vilner, L., Tabar, V., Dominko, T., Kane, J., Wettstein, P., Studer, L., and West, M. (2002). Parthenogenetic stem cells in nonhuman primates. *Science* **295,** 819.
5. Rhoton-Vlasak, A., Lu, P.Y., Barud, K.M., Dewald, G.W., and Hammitt, D.G. (2001). Efficacy of calcium ionophore A23187 for oocyte activation for generating parthenotes for human embryo research. *J. Assist. Reprod. Genet.* **13,** 793–796.
6. Nakagawa, K., Yamano, S., Nakasaka, H., Hinokio, K., Yoshizawa, M., and Aono, T. (2001). A combination of calcium ionophore and puromycin effectively produces human parthenogenones with one haploid pronuclei. *Zygote* **9,** 83–88.
7. Wininger, J.D., Huang, S., Massey, J.B., Lei, J., and Lin, H. (2002). Assessment of parthenogenetic activation of human metaphase II oocytes for stem cell derivation. ASRM Annual Meeting; Seattle WA. *Fertil Steril* **78**(3 Suppl 1), S76–S77.
8. Mandell, A., Stemron Corp. (personal communication).
9. Newman-Smith, E.D., and Werb, Z. (1995). Stem cell defects in parthenogenetic peri-implantation embryos. *Development* **121,** 2069–2077.
10. Vortmeyer, A.O., Devouassoux-Shisheboran, M., Li, G., Mohr, V., Tavassoli, F., and Zhuang, Z. (1999). Microdissection-based analysis of mature ovarian teratoma. *Am. J. Pathol.* **154,** 987–991.
11. Surani, M.A.H., Barton, S.C., and Norris, M.L. (1984). Development of reconstituted mouse eggs suggests imprinting of the genome during gametogenesis. *Nature* **308,** 548–550.
12. Kono, T., Obata, Y., Yoshimzu, T., Nakahara, T., and Carroll, J. (1996). Epigenetic modifications during oocyte growth correlates with extended parthenogenetic development in the mouse. *Nat. Genet.* **13,** 91–94.

64

Pluripotency in Normal and Clone Mouse Embryos

Michele Boiani and Hans Schöler

Introduction

Fundamental processes in biology and medicine have often been elucidated using the mouse model for research. Embryonic stem (ES) cells, established so far only in mouse and certain primates[1] such as humans,[2] have been particularly useful. A recent article reported a significant advance, combining mouse cloning technology with repair of a genetic defect through genetic manipulations of ES cells.[3] In another recent report, clone-derived neurons have corrected the phenotype of Parkinsonian mice (therapeutic cloning).[4] Even though the ultimate goal of therapeutic cloning is to obtain pluripotent stem cells and to differentiate them into cell types cells that could replace cells or complement tissues and organs of the human body, reproductive cloning may be necessary as a gold standard to test procedures and techniques in animal species other than human.

To date, 10 mammalian species have been successfully cloned from somatic cell nuclei by independent groups using various procedures (sheep,[5] cattle,[6] mouse,[7] goat,[8] pig,[9,10] cat,[11] rabbit,[12] rat,[13] horse,[14] and deer[15]). However, cloning efficiencies are low in all these species because of embryonic lethality. This suggests that errors encountered during cloning are fundamental and systematic in nature. Because pluripotency is a fundamental feature of early mammalian embryos, it is plausible that different donor cell types have different degrees of permissibility in reinstating pluripotency-associated marks on their nuclei after transplantation in the ooplasm. Interestingly, overtly abnormal tissue of clone *Xenopus* embryos demonstrates an unsuspected broad developmental capacity in the context of a normal (i.e., nonclone) embryonic environment,[16] which suggests that non–cell-autonomous processes participate in the expression of pluripotency. Whether this is the case only in frogs or whether it is also true in mammals remains to be determined, and experimental assays like those described here are necessary.

The objective of this chapter is to describe three approaches used to evaluate pluripotency in nuclear transfer clone mouse embryos: (1) the rate of development to key stages *in vitro* and *in vivo*, (2) the profile of gene expression of the clone embryo at the stage of transfer *in vivo,* and (3) the ability to derive ES cells from clone embryos. These approaches are in use in our laboratory, and their experimental protocols are provided. Perhaps, there is no single protocol for cloning that works for all mammalian species, or for various cell types in one species, because of obvious differences between oocytes, nucleus donor cells, and embryos of different species. Protocols for genetic analysis of clones and for ES cell derivation are more consistent; however, readers should be aware that some technicalities must be worked out and adapted to the specific situation.

WHY PLURIPOTENCY

Several facts point to the importance of pluripotency in normal and clone mouse embryos.

In normal mouse embryos:

- *Oct4* (also known as *Oct3* and *Pou5f1*) is a paradigmatic gene that is associated with embryonic pluripotency, and its correct distribution and expression level at the blastocyst stage is the limiting factor in the derivation of ES cells.[17]
- After derivation, ES cells can differentiate in vitro into two distinct cell types based on *Oct4* expression levels.[18]
- The differentiation of mouse ES cells into germ cells, including mature oocytes,[19] never before documented *in vitro,* was demonstrated using Oct4 as a marker.

In clone mouse embryos:

- *Oct4*, which is silent in somatic cells, must be expressed after nuclear transfer into the oocyte; derivation of clones from differentiated cells and of ES cells from the clone blastocyst seems to vary, although not necessarily correlate with or depend on the type of cell used as the nucleus donor.
- Most clone mouse embryos express *Oct4* abnormally at the blastocyst stage[20,21] yet they resemble normal embryos in that the rate of ES cell formation is dependent on Oct4.[20]

WHY NUCLEAR TRANSPLANTATION

Totipotency, that is, the full range of developmental capabilities, requires that all the genetic information be in place in the cell nucleus. In the past, nuclear transplantation has been an effective tool to assess the general mode of cellular differentiation (i.e., whether cells become specialized through the physical loss of genetic material). Currently, nuclear transplantation

Handbook of Stem Cells
Volume 1

shows that epigenetic changes occurring in cells undergoing differentiation can be reversed, at least in a minority of the cells used as nucleus donors. Striking examples include those of olfactory neurons[22,23] and brain tumor cells.[24]

Nuclear Transfer Proves That Cell Differentiation Is an Epigenetic Process

The question of whether cells lose totipotency or pluripotency by discarding genetic information as they differentiate is one that was deeply rooted in nineteenth century biology. For vertebrates, the problem was solved by the nuclear transfer experiments of Briggs and King[25,26] and Gurdon[27] in *Rana* and *Xenopus* in the 1950s and 1960s. These researchers found that the efficiency of obtaining clones of normal development (expressed as the percentage of nuclear transfers) progressively decreased with use of cells that were more differentiated. When terminally differentiated cells were the source for nuclei, the resulting clone embryos arrested at metamorphosis, and no live frogs were obtained. Producing frogs of tadpole stages had answered, however, a long-standing and fundamental question of biology: No loss of genetic material had occurred during differentiation (the keratinocyte or erythrocyte nucleus was still able to express the program required to direct embryonic development and form complex structures). Similar experiments in mammals had to be postponed until culture techniques for oocytes and embryos—now routine—were pioneered by Brinster in the late 1960s[28,29] and until nuclear transplantation was pioneered in mammals by McGrath and Solter[30] in the early 1980s.

Nuclear Transfer Suggests That Nuclear (Epigenetic) Marks of Differentiation Are Reversible

Although the true identity and differentiation state of the donor cell that gave rise to surviving mammalian clones has not been determined in most successful nuclear transfers performed to date, it is accepted that most cells would contribute at least to the preimplantation stages of clone development (even tumor cells can do so[24]), facilitated by maternal support from the oocyte cytoplasm. In doing so, the different donor types, while bearing the same genetic information, have different cloning efficiencies. When the first clone mammal was obtained in cattle by transfer of embryonic nuclei,[31] it was apparent that even embryonic nuclei were not fully permissive to the reinstatement of pluripotency as measured by rate of development. After mice were cloned from somatic cells,[7] ES cells proved superior to cumulus cells as nucleus donors.[32] Comparison of various donor cells suggested that their degree of differentiation might be a factor in cloning;[33] nonetheless, the nuclei of adult somatic cells were compatible with the requirements of development, albeit inefficiently. Typically, fewer than 5% of reconstructed oocytes develop into clone adults regardless of which of the ten cloned species or which donor nuclei is used. In the mouse, the highest cloning rate from somatic cells reported to date approximates 6%.[34]

It is unclear whether the ability of certain somatic cells to support development reflects an epigenetic process of nuclear dedifferentiation or rather that those cells were already in a permissive state. The "stem cell hypothesis" envisions that cloning using adult somatic cells succeeds because the rare stem cells that reside within the adult tissues are the actual nucleus donors. Some adult stem cells express *Oct4*,[35] a marker of embryonic pluripotency, whereas others do not.[36] Consensus among researchers is that the proportion of stem cells in the adult tissues in which they reside is several orders of magnitude lower than 5%. This number would not be expected to become enriched during culture of nucleus donor cells because of the peculiar "niche" requirements of adult stem cells.[37,38] To resolve the dilemma and to identify which cells are the actual nucleus donors, we either need to experimentally isolate and purify adult stem cells or totally exclude them from the nucleus donor cell population. Recently, the success in generating clone mice from mature lymphocytes has provided unequivocal evidence that terminally differentiated cells, although phenotypically unipotent, remain genetically totipotent.[39] When fully differentiated cortical neurons from adult mice were tested by a different cloning procedure than the one used for lymphocytes, they totally lacked the ability to support postimplantation embryonic development.[40] Like lymphocytes, fully differentiated neurons in adult mammalian brains have genomic rearrangements, which may (lymphocytes) or may not (neurons) be compatible with developmental totipotency after nuclear transfer. Thus, the question of whether an oocyte could reprogram a donor nucleus from a terminal differentiation state back to a state equivalent to early embryonic pluripotency still remains to be answered. The recent report of mice cloned from terminally differentiated olfactory neurons[22,23] was based on the intermediate derivation of ES cells then used as nucleus for a second round of nuclear transfer or for blastocyst injection.

Practical Ways to Measure Pluripotency After Nucleus Transplantation

PLURIPOPTENCY IN RETROSPECT—RATE OF DEVELOPMENT TO KEY STAGES *IN VITRO* AND *IN VIVO*

Reprogramming of the potency of a donor nucleus after transplantation into an ooplasm can be measured at least in part by the subsequent development of the clone either *in vitro* or *in utero*. Under natural circumstances, development is a measure of how pluripotency is restricted as the totipotent zygote cleaves and the cell lineages emerge and keep on developing. However, when nuclear transfer is concerned, restriction is actually the second crucial issue; the first issue pertains to how pluripotency is re-established after nuclear transplantation into an oocyte. Failure to initiate the expression of pluripotency-associated genes[21] and failure to regulate *Oct4* in a lineage-specific manner[20] have been reported, indicating that both issues are concerned.

The highest cloning efficiency in mammals reported to date denotes that about 6% of total transfers yield live births,[34] arguing that a higher percentage of differentiated somatic cell nuclei is incapable of being "reprogrammed" to an embryonic pluripotent state capable of undergoing proper regulation and eliciting the formation of wholly unrelated cell types up to the entire organism (Fig. 64–1). It should be kept in mind, however, that if the goal of (reproductive) cloning were to produce healthy offspring, then cloning would be an almost total failure because most clone animals suffer illnesses (e.g., obesity) and premature death. It should be emphasized that most clone embryos die before and after implantation. It is hard to think of a flawed experiment as a desirable source of information about pluripotency. The recent implementation of clone–clone embryo aggregation as a means to increase developmental rates of clones may in part solve the problem. However, normality of clone animals obtained from aggregation remains to be assessed.[41]

There are two possible, but not mutually exclusive, approaches to draw this information from cloning experiments. The first is to use donor cells of different potency (e.g., terminal unipotent cell, oligopotent precursor cell, multipotent fetal cell, pluripotent ES cell) and determine whether they perform differently at cloning as far as they go. The second approach

is to use only one donor and measure the potency attained by the clone blastomeres, tissues, or organs at various stages of embryonic development. Different cell types do indeed exhibit different success rates in cloning, which could reflect several factors: (1) different degrees of compatibility between the somatic cell nucleus and the cytoplasm of the recipient oocyte or preimplantation-stage embryo, not necessarily related to the degree of reprogramming; (2) different degrees of similarity between the somatic genome and an ideal, pluripotent, and "not-so-in-need-of-reprogramming" situation; and (3) different ways that potency is restricted in different cells. As examples, consider the efficient preimplantation development of clones derived from primordial germ cells[20,42] (PGCs) that may be due to the compatibility of these germ cells with the ooplasm (itself a germ cell). Also, the superior postimplantation development of clones derived from ES cells may be due to the fact that these cells are already pluripotent. Finally, among somatic cells, Sertoli cells could support full development of mouse clones when they were recovered from

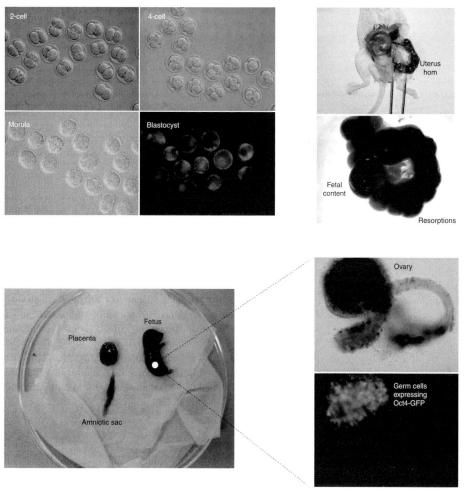

Figure 64–1. *Clone mouse embryos derived from cumulus cell nuclei.* Preimplantation development through two-cell, four-cell, morula, and blastocyst (Oct4-GFP) stages is shown (upper left panel). Following embryo transfer to the uterus, assessment at mid-gestation (day 10.5) confirms the widely reported incompetence of most clone embryos to develop at postimplantation (upper right panel). However, a scant number of clones develop to term (lower panel).

newborns but not from adults (described in the section on nuclear transfer from adult somatic cells); similarly, neurons were successful when derived from fetuses but not from adults (described in the section on nuclear transfer from fetal germ cells and the section on nuclear transfer from adult somatic cells). Despite the abundance of data available on development to key stages, pluripotency may be difficult to resolve by this approach, because of confounding factors that have no direct relationship to pluripotency. For instance, if there is faulty expression of a gene not related to pluripotency such as the integrin α4 gene, the clone embryo will die of heart and placental failure at mid-gestation even though all the lineages have been established, not to mention the ability of gastrulation mutants to give rise to ES cells.[43,44]

Embryo Splitting

Considering that the fertilized eocyte, or zygote, is a totipotent cell, a long-held view in biology has been that normal development of the embryo entails a progressive restriction of totipotency, then of pluripotency, and ultimately differentiation into various cell types. This can be measured by the ability of the early cleaving embryo to form a developmentally competent blastocyst after separating or splitting into blastomeres. Splitting embryos was in fact the first experimental way to clone mammals (e.g., sheep).[45] Mouse, rabbit, pig, and monkey embryos have also been cloned by splitting; however, this method gives rise to smaller blastocysts having limited ability to give rise to live offspring. For instance, in the mouse, separated blastomeres at the two-cell stage develop less efficiently into live offspring than whole two-cell embryos; the strong limitation of four-cell and the inability of eight-cell-stage blastomeres to accomplish this[46–48] suggested that either the restriction of totipotency had irreversibly occurred or that the cell number (1/4, 1/8) was not compensated after splitting. Although largely disregarded by scientists, size control plays an important part in animal development.[49] In this case, pluripotency translates in development if a sufficient number of cells are present. The nuclear transfer experiments were to address the issue of restriction (of pluripotency) versus size.

Nuclear Transfer from Embryonic and Embryonic Stem Cells

One may expect that all the nuclei in early embryos have developmental totipotency, and nuclear transfer experiments can be designed (in different ways) to test such expectation. When exchange of pronuclei (one possible way) is carried out in mouse zygotes, the reconstituted embryos are capable of full-term development. Similar experiments using nuclei from two-, four- and eight-cell embryos fused into enucleated zygotes result in lower (two-cell) or rare (four-cell, eight-cell) full-term development.[50] When oocytes at the second metaphase are used as recipients (another way), the reconstituted eggs develop into blastocysts only when an early two-cell nucleus is transplanted (36% of transplantations) but very rarely if the donor nucleus is derived from a late two-cell, eight-cell, or inner cell mass (ICM) of a blastocyst (0–3%).[42] Similar to ICM, nuclei injected from trophectoderm (TE) can form blastocysts, but to

obtain full-term development of the chimera the clone ICM must be transplanted from the clone into a host blastocyst.[51] The inability of cell nuclei from the later embryonic stages to support development was seen as evidence that the totipotency of the transferred nucleus was rapidly lost during cleavage. However, the same nuclei from two-, four- and eight-cell–stage blastomeres transferred not into second metaphase oocytes but into enucleated two-cell blastomeres resulted in significant amounts of full-term development.[52,53] By serial nuclear transfer (first into oocyte, with pronuclear formation on activation, and then into a zygote), even the genetic material of a four-cell embryo was capable of directing full-term development after transfer into an enucleated zygote.[51]

The previous results suggest that early difficulties at cloning from embryonic nuclei may be related to the (restricted) potency of donors and to the state of the recipient cell. Thus, the one-cell cytoplasm would be compatible only with pronuclei and early two-cell nuclei, whereas the ooplasm at the second metaphase would be compatible with most types of nuclei. Factor(s) necessary for successful development seem to be removed along with the pronuclei; however, interpretation of these results is difficult because of the different embryonic stages and methods used for nuclear transfer (i.e., nucleus injection, karyoplast fusion, serial nuclear transfer).

Embryonic cells of the blastocyst ICM are regarded as peculiar because they are the founder cell population of the fetus and precursors to ES cells available in mice and humans. Although ICM cells offer limited options to study pluripotency because of their transient nature and small number (10–30 per embryo), derivative ES cells can be expanded and propagated readily *in vitro*. Pluripotency is apparent from the fate of whole ES cells injected into blastocysts. When the host blastocysts are tetraploid, adult animals formed entirely of ES cell derivatives can be obtained.[55] However, when ES cells are injected into diploid blastocysts so as to give rise to chimeras, the ES cell potential to differentiate into extraembryonic (placental) lineages is low. The requirement for a supportive blastocyst raised doubts on the ability of ES cells to contribute to or form and to direct development of an entire individual (ES cell–derived embryoid bodies lack such ability). The question thus became whether a single ES cell could ever be totipotent. The answer came from the nuclear transfer of single ES cell nuclei into oocytes.[32] In this study, several mice were cloned from E14 and R1 ES cells that had been passaged at least 22–33 times, proving that an ES cell nucleus could direct full-term development of an individual. The study also established the feasibility of cloning mice from *in vitro* cell lines (amenable to genetic manipulation). Nevertheless, most reports of successful mouse cloning from ES cells by either nucleus transplantation into oocytes or tetraploid embryo complementation were based on 129- or sometimes B6-strain-derived ES cell lines.[3,32,39,56,57] Other investigators who did not use the conventional ES cell lines encountered more limited success.[58–60]

Nuclear Transfer from Fetal Somatic Cells

Until recently, it was believed that cells from earlier stages of development or from younger animals had less genetic damage than adult somatic cells, for which the success rate of cloning had been consistently very low. Wakayama and Yanagimachi[33] found that the success rates to term from the nuclear transfer of fetal versus adult cells were similar, as were those of germ versus somatic cells to blastocyst. This indicated to the investigators that the accumulation of mutational damage in adult somatic cells is not the main limiting factor in mouse cloning but that technical problems and/or problems of genomic reprogramming by oocytes were the contributing factors. Although the concept that adult mouse cells might be as good as younger cells for cloning purposes is technically supported, it is still theoretically premature. Reasons that call for caution are as follows: (1) the life span of a mouse (only 18–24 months on average) is too short for DNA mutations to accumulate and become phenotypically apparent compared with other species, such as humans (lifespan of 70 or more years) and (2) adult mutations are not as apparent if they occur in silent regions of the genome (facultative heterochromatin); however, these regions are to be expressed in early development. Thus, a phenotypically normal cell may reveal a full load of mutations (mostly epigenetic, but also genetic) that previously accumulated on heterochromatic DNA, when placed in a different context such as in the oocyte after nuclear transfer. As a consequence—provided that these mutations were compatible with life—clones would not be phenotypically identical with the original animal or might carry dormant cytopathologic problems ready to become overt at some point in life. Epigenetic problems in the clones seem to be erased as the cell nuclei go through the germline.[61] Whether genetic defects associated with cloning are also eliminated or "filtered" by the gonad remains to be determined.

Nuclear Transfer from Fetal Stem Cells

To date, overt fetal stem cells have not been available as nucleus donors for mouse cloning, and the issue of if, when, and how fetal stem cells were used as nucleus donors is controversial. Neuronal stem cells may have been used for cloning serendipitously. Yamazaki and colleagues[34] tested neural cells dissected from different regions of the fetal brain (15.5–17.5 days postcoitus [dpc]). Clone pups were consistently derived from immature neural stages (V cortical zone; 5.8% of the reconstructed oocytes developed to term) but not from postmitotic differentiated stages (P cortical zone; 0.5%). This suggested a large decline in the potency of neurons to support normal development after their migration from V to P zone, which is completed after birth and probably accounts for the initial[7] and confirmed[40] inability to successfully clone mice directly from brain cells. Interestingly, there were no significant differences in the rates of preimplantation development and development up to mid–gestation-stage clones derived from fetal versus adult brain cells.

Nuclear Transfer from Fetal Germ Cells

Germ cells offer a perfect opportunity to test how potentially imprint-free nuclei affect embryonic development, and this has indeed been investigated. However, collecting and manipulating germ cells has proved to be a difficult task. Germ cells arise by embryonic day 6.5 and can be recognized as alkaline phosphatase–positive PGCs by day 7.5 on their migratory route to the genital ridges.[62] During this time, they undergo erasure of the parental imprints, starting asynchronously from approximately day 10.5 or perhaps earlier (as may be inferred from the ability of embryonic germ (EG) cells to contribute to mouse chimeras).[63] One would expect germ cell nuclei taken before, but not during or after, erasure has occurred to support successful cloning by nuclear transfer, but evidence for this has proved very difficult to obtain. In females, after germ cells have reached the genital ridge they enter meiosis, further increasing the difficulty in using germ cells.[64] For this reason, only male germ cells have been consistently used as nucleus donors for cloning after colonizing the genital ridge and becoming arrested (embryonic day 13.5 to 16.5).

High ratios of enucleated eggs receiving male PGC nuclei developed to two-cell, four-cell, eight-cell and blastocyst stage (54–100%, 11–67%, 6–43%, and 6–20%, respectively).[42] However, live fetuses were not obtained after transfer of reconstituted eggs to recipients, although implantation sites were observed. Using a serial nuclear transplantation and complementation approach (aggregation with normal embryo), postimplantation survival of germ cell clones was still low, with no chimeric animals born. Glucose phosphate isomerase (GPI) analysis at mid-gestation revealed that some concepti had chimerism in the fetuses, trophoblast, and yolk sac at day 10.5 of pregnancy.[65] Other investigators showed that when germ cell nuclei were transplanted into enucleated oocytes, clones developed to day 9.5 of gestation. The concepti consisted of a small embryo, with characteristically abnormal placenta. When the clone ICM was "rescued" from the abnormal placenta by transfer into a tetraploid host blastocyst, the germ cell clones again did not develop past day 9.5 of gestation.[66] All male fetal germ cells were found to be diploid and reconstituted one-cell embryos exhibited ploidy of 4×, 6×, or 8× at metaphase of the first cell division,[67] but this was not the sole cause of early embryonic lethality. Instead, deregulation of several imprinted genes because of "intermediate states" of DNA methylation is regarded as the key factor in developmental failure of germ cell clones. Cloned embryos produced from 12.5–13.5 dpc PGCs showed growth retardation and early embryonic lethality at around day 9.5. Clone embryos from 11.5 dpc PGCs had significantly improved development, surviving until at least day 11.5 of the fetal stage.[64] Several intermediate states of genomic imprinting between somatic cell state and the erased state were seen in clone embryos derived from day 11.5–13.5 male and female germ cells; fewer states were noted when donor PGCs of earlier stages were used.

This suggested that the erasure process of genomic imprinting memory proceeds at day 10.5–11.5 of PGCs, with the precise timing for each imprinted gene possibly being under strict control. This implied that germ cell nuclei before day 10.5 (i.e., before colonization of the genital ridge) may be able to support normal embryonic development after cloning.

To date, there is only one report of full-term development of a mouse clone possibly derived from fetal germ cells,[33] but the investigators were uncertain as to whether the gonadal cells used for cloning were indeed germ cells or somatic (stromal) cells. Interestingly, as of yet PGC-derived EG have not been reported as nucleus donors to clone mice. This may be a promising undertaking as EG cells are known to contribute to chimeras, as opposed to native PGCs.

Nuclear Transfer from Adult Somatic Cells

Cumulus Cells. The making of Cumulina is a landmark in mammalian cloning. Unlike Dolly the sheep, who was cloned from a somatic cell that had been in culture for several days, Cumulina was derived from a fresh cumulus cell (i.e., from a terminally differentiated adult somatic cell taken fresh from a mouse and used immediately). Deriving live clones from cumulus cells is perhaps the most difficult approach to mouse cloning, and this has been attempted by a limited number of investigators in addition to Wakayama and Yanagimachi, and only a handful have been successful in obtaining full development independently by direct nucleus injection.[20,68] The recurring question is "Why is the success rate of cloning so low?,"[69] but a more pertinent question should be "Why is the number of scientists capable of cloning mice from cumulus cells so small in contrast to the number of reports?" Beyond a doubt, technical skill greatly attributes to the success rate of cloning. Although Wakayama and colleagues produced cloned mice (except that they tended to die earlier, suffering illnesses), others failed to do so. Kato and colleagues[70] could not obtain any fetuses from cumulus cells of growing follicles. The donor follicular cells used by Kato had been cultured, in contrast to Wakayama, who used fresh ones. Kato used a serial nuclear transfer approach (including karyoplast fusion) as opposed to direct injection, and when the serial nuclear transfer was not performed, most reconstituted oocytes stopped developing at the two-cell stage and no blastocysts were obtained. Genetic background differences between the donor cells and recipient cytoplasm may also have accounted for the different results obtained by Wakayama and Kato. It was demonstrated previously that the genetic background was critically important for later development in androgenetic embryos[71] and pronuclei replacement.[72] Kato and colleagues used the CD-1 strain as the donor cells, and F1(C57BLxC3H) mice were used as the recipient cytoplasm. Although this combination of mouse strains was appropriate to produce chimeric animals by nuclear transfer into one blastomere at the two-cell stage,[73] it was unclear whether the same combination was also suitable for nuclear transfer of somatic cell nuclei into oocytes. The role played by plasmic modifiers should be considered.[74]

In a comprehensive technical review, Wakayama and Yanagimachi[69] examined the following: (1) the effect of timing of oocyte and zygote activation and duration of *in vitro* culture of clone embryos on the success rate of cloning, (2) the effect of dimethylsulphoxide (DMSO) on embryo development (this reagent is routinely included in the activation medium as a carrier for cytochalasin B), and (3) the effect of cytochalasin B as an agent used to prevent pseudo polar body extrusion and ensure the correct ploidy of reconstituted embryos. Wakayama and Yanagimachi concluded that neither

the method or timing of oocyte activation nor the type of cytokinesis inhibition might account for the low success rate of mouse cloning. Because it is clear that technical skill is a determining factor in the success of cloning, trying to learn of pluripotency through comparison of developmental rates is something that belongs to art more than science. Based on our experience with 21 clone mice generated from 1430 reconstructed oocytes in 13 sets of embryo transfers, 10 of which are still alive as of April 2003, we conclude that the usefulness of developmental data in the analysis of pluripotency is overstated (see Fig. 64–1). A new approach holds promises for higher rates of success.[75]

Neurons. Cloning mice by using brain cells from adult cerebral cortex was not successful, with all clone embryos dying either before or shortly after implantation.[7] This has been confirmed recently by using adult cerebral cortical and cerebellar Purkinje cells.[40] Clone pups were derived consistently only when neurons from the developing fetal cortex were used as nucleus donors. It is possible that neural cells in advanced stages of differentiation have lost their developmental totipotency, or, in the adult, this feature may have become restricted to only a few cells (in contrast to the fetal brain). There is controversy regarding whether the aneuploidy described in terminally differentiated neurons (predisposing apoptosis) plays a role in their developmental inadequacy after nuclear transfer.[40] The ability of olfactory neuron-derived ES cells to support full development after nuclear transfer argues that neurons themselves have not so far been proved capable of undergoing complete reprogramming by a single event of nuclear transfer.[22,23]

Sertoli Cells. When Sertoli cells (the male counterparts of cumulus cells) were used for mouse cloning,[7] only one fetus (8.5 dpc) and no live offspring were obtained. Sertoli cells were collected from mature adult males and used fresh, but they appeared to be too large for micromanipulation and injection without incurring damage to either the donor cell or the recipient oocyte. Thus, technical difficulties in handling a relatively large nucleus, rather than the size of the donor nucleus itself, was proposed to account for the poor *in vitro* and *in vivo* development of oocytes reconstructed with Sertoli cell nuclei. When smaller Sertoli cells were collected from newborn mice and used to reconstruct oocytes, the clones resulted in live offspring.[76] Synchronization of actively cycling newborn Sertoli cells in culture raised some issues, however. The G_1/G_0 state, which was deemed to be important in the success of Cumulina, was induced here by culturing immature Sertoli cells in the absence of serum for 1 week. This artificial process may have introduced changes that have the potential to affect the cells' developmental capacity. It has been noted that consistent changes occur in fetal neuronal cells *in vitro* and may include genetic or epigenetic alterations that account at least in part for the observed developmental potency after nuclear transfer.[77] Thus, it is questionable to test the nucleus reprogramming ability of the oocyte using a donor cell that had been cultured *in vitro*.

Other Donor Cells. As the previous example of Sertoli cells shows, it is possible that the cells with which scientists cannot clone animals today may one day become the cells of choice. So far, we are still in the first phase. Czolowska and colleagues[78] were the first researchers to test the behavior of thymocyte nuclei after injection in metaphase II mouse oocytes, thereby generating tetraploid embryos. Kono and colleagues[79] later produced diploid clone embryos. Results showed that only a minimal percentage of the mouse oocytes transplanted with nuclei from thymocytes attained the morula or blastocyst stage (3.1% females, 0% males). None developed beyond implantation.[33]

Only a very limited number of mouse oocytes were injected with nuclei from female and male splenocytes, resulting in 22.4% and 21.1% of the activated oocytes developing to morula or blastocyst, respectively. Two fetuses were recovered at 8.5–12.5 dpc after embryo transfer of the female clones only.[33]

Similarly, macrophages were able to support development to blastocyst (22.9–31.0% for females and males) and beyond, producing four fetuses at mid-gestation from the female clones. In the same report, full-term development was achieved when fibroblasts were used as nucleus donor cells and more than 400 oocytes had undergone micromanipulation. This suggests that the inability of splenocyte- and macrophage-derived clones to yield pups was due to a mere limitation in number.

To date, overt adult stem cells have not been used successfully as nucleus donors in cloning procedures, because of the difficulty in isolating and obtaining sufficiently pure yields. Kato *et al.* have recently undertaken the study of adult stem cells as nucleus donors for bovine cloning.[33a]

Nuclear Transfer from Terminally Differentiated Adult Cells

When Hochedlinger and Jaenisch[39] obtained the so-called monoclonal mouse from nuclear transfer of mature T and B lymphocytes, they seemingly demonstrated nuclear reprogramming from perhaps one of the most differentiated states in the soma. Mature lymphocytes are terminal, unipotent cells; however, they were able to form pluripotent embryos and give rise to clone pups after nuclear transplantation into oocytes. Mice cloned from a B-cell nucleus were viable and carried fully rearranged immunoglobulin alleles in all tissues; similarly, a mouse cloned from a T-cell nucleus carried rearranged T-cell-receptor genes in all tissues. However, it is not clear as to what extent this study is a (conclusive) demonstration of nuclear reprogramming from a terminally differentiated state by means of an oocyte. Cloning was an extremely inefficient process (yielded up 4% blastocysts) that required ES cell derivation and tetraploid embryo complementation, indicating that the lymphocyte-derived clone embryos relied indeed on extensive *in vitro* and *in vivo* support, in contrast with their alleged totipotency. In another study, mouse oocytes receiving thymocyte nuclei never developed beyond implantation unlike oocytes receiving the nuclei of other cell types (spleen cells, macrophages, etc.).[33] Thus, it is unknown whether the monoclonal clone blastocysts generated by Hochedlinger and colleagues could have formed viable extraembryonic lineages (placenta). The experiment proved, however, that reprogramming of TE-specific genes to generate

a self-supportive adult clone animal was bypassed by a complementation strategy, regardless of whether it had occurred.

CURRENT PLURIPOTENCY—ANALYSIS OF GENE EXPRESSION

Transcriptional silencing and erasure of differentiated cellular memory, appropriate activation of the reconstructed one-cell embryo, and appropriate gene expression at later stages of development must be established in the transplanted nucleus within a short period of time after transplantation—about 24 hours in the mouse. Developmental rates indicate that these processes rarely result in the donor nucleus returning to a state equivalent to that of a zygote or early embryonic nucleus. Gene expression analysis is expected to provide more insight into these processes. Unlike development to key embryonic or fetal stages, which is a retrospective view of reprogramming up to those stages, analysis of gene expression applies to a specific stage and, therefore, has a provisional value. Blastocysts can be formed in the absence of essential genes or in embryos with abnormal imprinting, as is the case for several null mutants and tetraploid, androgenetic, and parthenogenetic embryos, all of which fail after implantation. Because of this, gene expression analysis is difficult to perform (given the amount of material) and difficult to interpret. Reporters such as Oct4-GFP are in part to solve this problem (Fig. 64–1).

Reprogramming can be measured by a chosen set of relevant genes that are expressed (or are not expressed) at specific stages, such as the stage of zygotic genome activation, the stage of inner versus outer cell polarization (morula), and the blastocyst stage when the first differentiated tissue of the embryo is formed (TE). To date, there has been only one report establishing a causal-effect relationship between the expression profile of a single gene *Oct4* in clone mouse blastocysts and their prospects for subsequent development as measured by ES cell formation.[20]

Genome-wide or Gene-targeted Analysis

Clones are known to present a wide range of gene expression defects. When the affected gene is not known, or it could be potentially any gene, global gene expression analysis by cDNA microarray technology may prove informative. This approach revealed that changes in gene expression levels occur at embryonic stages and in adult tissues of mouse clones compared with normal mice and that down-regulation of gene expression is more frequent than up-regulation.[80] Drawbacks to this approach include a finite number of genes present on the microarray and some of the RNAs in the sample may not be translated into proteins. Targeted studies showed that clone embryos exhibit some differences in gene expression by reverse transcriptase–polymerase chain reaction (RT-PCR) compared with their normal counterparts (see reference 20 and references therein), but they could not attribute the failure of most clones at the time of implantation to altered gene expression profiles. In a recent RT-PCR analysis, Bortvin and colleagues[21] showed that, although cumulus cell–derived mouse clones silence somatic genes, activation of the so-called developmental pluripotency associated (Dppa) genes was incomplete. Absence of passive demethylation and inappropriate early *de novo* methylation at the four- to eight-cell stage[81] or inappropriate translocation of DNA methyltransferase (Dnmt1) to the nucleus at the eight-cell stage[82] confirmed that inadequate nuclear reprogramming had occurred. Whether these abnormalities are consequential or not, it remains to be determined. As revealed by Byrne and colleagues[16] in clone *Xenopus* larvae, generalization and predictions are difficult to make. Gene expression defects did not prevent the tissues of abnormal clone blastulae from participating in normal development when grafted.

Oct4 and Developmental Pluripotency-Associated Genes

Oct4 is one of several pluripotency-associated genes, and the study of these genes in clones is a pristine field that has great potential, considering recent advances in the isolating and characterizing of other pluripotency-associated genes in non-clone embryos (e.g., Sox2,[83] Foxd3/Genesis[84]). Oct4 is a POU domain transcription factor encoded by the *Pou5f1* locus. It is expressed in the ICM, epiblast, and later in germ cells.[85] Oct4 is essential in establishing and maintaining pluripotency of the ICM, and in its absence, ICM differentiates into TE. *Oct4*-null embryos die around the time of implantation and fail to outgrow in culture. Although mouse embryos homozygous for a targeted deletion of *Oct4* can develop into structures resembling blastocysts,[86] they do not form a pluripotent ICM and die shortly after implantation because of an inability to differentiate into embryonic lineages. *In vitro*, variations in the level of *Oct4* expression, as little as 30% above or below the normal level, regulate the differentiation of ES cells into extraembryonic endoderm and mesoderm or TE, respectively.[18] Thus, subtle changes in *Oct4* expression may have predictable consequences for the early postimplantation embryo. It will be interesting to see whether the levels of *Oct4* gene expression matter *in vivo*.

Analysis of *Oct4* and 10 *Oct4*-related genes in clone mouse blastocysts showed incomplete inactivation of these genes in most cumulus cell–derived clones, as opposed to the situation of ES cell–derived clones in which these genes were already expressed before nuclear transfer.[21] Buehr and colleagues[17] tracked the pattern of *Oct4* expression in cultured rat and mouse embryos. Outgrowths containing Oct4-positive and Oct4-negative cells could not be distinguished from each other morphologically, with unexpected and rapid restriction of *Oct4* expression occurring before overt differentiation. Thus, it appears that if *Oct4* expression is not maintained in primary outgrowths, ES cell precursors are probably lost at this stage. This assumption may underlie difficulties commonly experienced in deriving ES cell lines from some strains; the high frequency and long duration of *Oct4* expression in mouse strain 129 outgrowths may contribute to the strain's permissiveness to ES cell derivation.[17] Transgenic reporters, such as the Oct4 ß-geo construct or the Oct4 GFP, are useful in evaluating Oct4 level and distribution in mouse clones.[20]

Although the connection between Oct4 and the Dppa genes is a new field for investigation, Oct4 has been demonstrated to interact with other transcription factors (e.g., Sox2,[83]

Foxd3/Genesis[84]). Interactions between these factors suggest an additional level of transcriptional regulation, and the molecular partners and networks involved are discussed in more detail in Chapter 3. For example, Oct4 and Sox2 cooperate to activate transcription of *Fgf4* in F9 embryonal carcinoma cells,[87] and Oct-4 physically interacts with the Foxd3 DNA-binding domain when these two factors bind to identical regulatory DNA sequences.[88] Like *Oct4, Sox2*, a member of the SRY-related HMG box gene family, marks the pluripotent lineage of the early mouse embryo and is expressed in the ICM, epiblast, and germ cells; however, unlike *Oct4, Sox2* is also expressed in multipotential cells of the extraembryonic ectoderm. *Sox2* expression is also associated with uncommitted dividing stem and precursor cells of the developing central nervous system (CNS) and can be used to isolate these cells.[89] Foxd3 is a member of the forkhead family of transcriptional regulators and is required for maintenance of embryonic cells of the early mouse embryo. *Foxd3*[−/−] embryos die after implantation at approximately 6.5 dpc with a loss of epiblast cells; expansion of proximal extraembryonic tissues; and a distal, mislocalized anterior organizing center. Moreover, it has not been possible to establish ES cell lines or to generate teratocarcinomas neither from *Foxd3*[−/−] nor from *Sox2*[−/−] blastocysts.

PLURIPOTENCY IN PROSPECT—DERIVATION OF PLURIPOTENT CELL LINES

Late preimplantation-stage clones have been obtained consistently in several "cloning laboratories" worldwide. However, most clones fail at postimplantation development (irrespective of the donor cell), leaving a limited and compromised material for analysis of pluripotency and its restriction during organogenesis. Cell lines derived from clones can be maintained and expanded according to well-established protocols, thereby providing a steady source of biologic material for investigation. The difficulty in analyzing development *in situ* may be circumvented by using ES cells, which are derived from late preimplantation stages and provide a renewable and expandable source of material. For about two decades, ES cells have been differentiated *in vitro* into all three EG layers (endoderm, mesoderm, and ectoderm); *in vivo*, competent ES cells also have contributed to the germ cell lineage (notably, the germ line has not been reported *in vitro*, until very recently[19]). Thus, comparison of clone and normal ES cells may reveal aspects of pluripotency regulation that may account for the subsequent peri-implantation and postimplantation failure of clones. Oct4 is essential for the pluripotent state of the mouse ICM and derivative ES cells.

Although Oct4 is important in embryonic pluripotency and ES cells, there may be different pathways to pluripotency depending on whether embryonic or adult stem cells are tested. Transcriptional profiling of embryonic, neuronal, and hematopoietic stem cells for more than 6000 gene probes has revealed that the expression of 216 genes is enriched in all three types of stem cells.[36] Interestingly, of the 216 genes, 60 have been mapped to a chromosomal location, and 12 of these have been found on chromosome 17. Thus, this chromosome contains almost four times the number of stem cell–enriched genes compared with random distribution of these genes on chromosomes. Chromosome 17 also harbors the t-complex, which contains genes involved in embryonic development and spermatogenesis. Of the 12 genes, 4 (including *Oct4*[90]) map to the t-complex.

Aspects of the Establishment of Embryonic Stem Cells in Normal Embryos

ES cells are *in vitro* derivatives of the ICM or epiblast of the blastocyst-stage embryo.[91,92] Intact blastocysts or isolated ICMs and epiblasts are cultured on a feeder layer or in a medium containing the cytokine leukemia inhibitory factor (LIF,[93] also known as differentiation inhibiting activity or DIA[94]), and allowed to attach to the substrate and outgrow for several days. The resulting cell clumps are then disaggregated and plated under the same conditions. Within a few days, colonies of ES cells may appear, which can be picked, dissociated, replated, and cultured further. Protocols for the derivation of ES cells from mouse strain 129 are well established.[95] Recently, mouse ES cells have been shown to maintain their cardinal features in the absence of LIF, provided the *Nanog* gene is continually expressed.[96]

Down-regulation of Oct4 appears to be a limiting factor in deriving pluripotent cell lines from preimplantation embryos in mice and rats.[17] Thus, comparison of clone and normal ES cells may reveal how pluripotency is regulated once it has been established; however, it may not reveal the basis for developmental failure and lack of pluripotency in clones at earlier stages (before the blastocyst).

Aspects of the Establishment of Embryonic Stem Cells in Clone Embryos

Derivation of ES cells from clone embryos demonstrates that reprogramming of the donor nucleus occurs at an earlier stage than would be apparent from clones of fetal stages, which are difficult obtain because of the low efficiency of cloning. Pluripotent cell lines have been derived from clone mouse blastocysts generated by transfer of somatic cell nuclei into oocytes. Munsie and colleagues[97] were the first to report XX "ES-like" cell lines that were derived from the ICM of clone blastocysts themselves derived from cumulus cells. Kawase and colleagues[98] then derived XY ES cells cloned from neurons. These reports reinforced the notion that 129 and its substrains are the most efficient for deriving mouse ES cells and that this background has proved efficient for producing clone mice. It is difficult to derive ES cell lines from strains such as CBA and almost impossible from FVB and NOD. It seems, however, quite likely that such strain restriction reflects peculiar aspects of the *in vitro* derivation process itself rather than biologic limitation of non-129 strains.[99]

The karyotype of the clone ES cells was found to be normal ($2n = 40$) and reflected the gender of the nucleus donor. Pluripotency was tested *in vitro* and *in vivo*. *In vitro*, clone ES cells displayed the characteristic morphology and marker expression of conventional ES cells (e.g., alkaline phosphatase, SSEA-1, Oct4, Fgf4). On the other hand, although the donor neuronal cells used by Kawase all express the neuronal marker MAP-2 and beta-tubulin class III, neither of these markers were detected in the clone ES cells. Embryoid bodies generated from clone ES cells differentiated into a variety of cell types, including neurons and contractile muscle. *In vivo*, the clone ES cells gave rise to teratocarcinomas (consisting of all three germ layers: endoderm, mesoderm, and ectoderm) after injection into the hind legs or the testis capsule of immunocompromised mice. After injection into blastocysts followed by embryo transfer, the cells were again able to contribute extensively to all three embryonic germ layers, giving rise to chimeric pups. Therefore, the clone-derived cell lines were described as de facto pluripotent ES cells. Furthermore, they were also able to contribute to the germ line *in vivo*.[100] Thus, it appears that once clone ES cells are established, their function is indistinguishable from that of normal ES cells.

It is also clear that the process of ES cell derivation from clone blastocysts has to take into account additional, peculiar factors (i.e., the reprogramming of genes responsible for the identity of ICM cells and the pluripotency and self-renewal capacity of their ES cell derivatives). Buehr and colleagues[17] examined the expression of one such gene during the derivation of ES cells from normal mouse and rat blastocysts. They chose Oct4 because its level of expression is critical in mouse ES cells.[18] Oct4-positive and Oct4-negative cells were observed in the same outgrowths, and, although morphologically indistinguishable, outgrowths with different ratios of Oct4-expressing cells correlated with the ability to derive ES cell lines.

To date, no published report could exclude donor cell type –specific restrictions on the developmental potential of clone-derived ES cells. Only one study has evaluated the developmental pluripotency of single ES cells injected in blastocysts, and these were normal ES cells.[101] Eggan and colleagues[56] showed that clone ES cells are epigenetically unstable. All this suggests that limitations in ES cell differentiation may become evident at later stages of development as a late consequence of epigenetic instability, and this may not become apparent unless clone ES cells are tested at the single cell level.

Protocols

CLONING MICE FROM OVARIAN CUMULUS CELL

Development to cleavage stages is a limited indicator for assessing the potency and viability of clones, because a large proportion of morula-stage clones do not form blastocysts. The blastocyst stage has more potential for further development, and, practically, it is the last stage that can be analyzed *in vitro* before transfer into the uterus. We herein describe the mouse cloning protocol that was established in our laboratory and used to derive clone blastocysts from cumulus cell nuclei (not expressing *Oct4*) and germ cell nuclei (already expressing *Oct4*). Using this method, a total of 952 blastocysts (28%) were derived from cumulus cells in 45 nuclear transfer experiments and used for gene expression analysis or derivation of ES cells; a total of 21 clone pups were born from the transfer of 1593 clones (blastocysts to 2.5 dpc uterus, two- and four-cell to 0.5 dpc oviduct) *in vivo* in 13 experiments spanning over a 1-year period.

Mice

For cloning we used 8- to 12-week-old B6C3F1 females (Taconic) as oocyte donors; and 6- to 24-week-old F1(B6OG2) females (OG2 mice provided by Dr. Jeffrey Mann) as nucleus donors. The OG2 mice carry an *Oct4*-GFP transgene that is expressed in the pluripotent cell lineages.[102] All mice were kept in a colony room under controlled temperature (20°C) and photoperiod (0800–2000 light hours) and fed with Harlan-Teklad chow (low phytosterol content).

Superovulation

Oocytes were recovered after gonadotropin stimulation with 10 units each of pregnant mare serum gonadotropin (PMSG) (Calbiochem cat. no. 367222) and human chorionic gonadotropin (HCG) (Calbiochem cat. no. 230734) injected intraperitoneal (i.p.) at 5 p.m. 48 hours apart.

Recovery of Superovulated Oocytes

Mice were sacrificed at 7 a.m. on the day after injection of HCG. The oviducts were dissected and the cumulus-oocyte masses were released in warm Hepes-buffered CZB medium[103] containing glucose 1 g/L, polyvinylpyrolidone 0.1% w/v (PVP 40 kDa, ICN cat. no.529504), without albumin and glutamine. This medium was prepared in 95% the standard volume (hence hypertonic). The cumulus masses were transferred into drops of hyaluronidase (Calbiochem cat. no. 38594) dissolved in HEPES-buffered CZB medium at a working concentration of 50 U/ml. After 20–30 minutes at 28°C, the cumulus-free oocytes were washed of the enzyme and incubated in culture medium in 5% CO_2 atmosphere at 37°C; the dispersed cumulus cells were stored at 4°C until use as nucleus donors. The culture medium was alpha MEM (Sigma M4526) supplemented with albumin (ICN cat. no. 103700) 0.4% w/v and prepared in 20-µl drops in 35-mm plastic dishes (Corning, cat.no. 430588) under silicon oil (Sigma, cat. no. DMPS-V).

Setup for Oocyte Micromanipulation

Our micromanipulation setup was operated at a room temperature (RT) of 28°C and consisted of an inverted microscope (Nikon Eclipse 2000U) fitted with differential interference contrast (DIC) extended long working distance (ELWD) optics. The microscope was equipped with a manual micromanipulator (Narishige MN-188NE) and a piezo unit (PrimeTech PMAS-CT150). Using such optics in combination with glass-bottomed vessels, the removal of metaphase chromosomes ("enucleation") from the oocytes became possible without need to stain chromosomes with a dye specific for DNA (e.g., Hoechst 33342).

Removal of the Oocyte Chromosomes

The oocytes were enucleated between 7:30 and 10 a.m. in batches of 20 in HEPES-buffered CZB medium added with cytochalasin B 1 µg/ml (ICN cat. no. 195119, from a stock solution 5-µg/µL in DMSO). Each single batch was processed in approximately 10 minutes, then immediately transferred back to culture medium and rinsed several times.

Nucleus Transplantation

The transplantation of nuclei into the oocytes took place 1 hour after the last batch of oocytes had undergone enucleation. Cumulus cells were retrieved from the cold; germ cells were isolated mechanically and used fresh from 13.5–16.5 dpc fetal male gonads. An 8–10 µm internal diameter (i.d.) microcapillary (injection needle), back-loaded with mercury (approximately 5 µl), was used for microinjection. Both the oocytes and the cumulus cells were processed into the same drop of HEPES-buffered CZB medium in the presence of 1% w/v PVP (Calbiochem, molecular weight 40 kDa). Approximately 30–40 donor cells were sucked into the injection needle while applying piezo pulses, and their nuclei rapidly injected one by one into the oocytes. The piezo parameters were set as follows: speed 2, intensity 3 to aspirate cumulus cells; speed 2, intensity 2–3 to drill the zona pellucida; speed 1, intensity 1 to penetrate the oolemma. The nuclear injection was conducted on batches of 30 oocytes in usually less than 15 minutes, and the last batch was completed between noon and 1 p.m. The injected oocytes were let to recover in the same dish for 10 minutes, before an intermediate passage in a 1:1 part mixture of alpha MEM and Hepes-CZB at RT for 30 minutes, followed by incubation in culture medium with albumin.

Culture of the Reconstructed Oocytes

Activation of the reconstructed oocytes started at least 1 hour after the last batch of oocytes had been injected with nuclei but not later than 3:00 p.m. Activation was induced by exposing the oocytes to 10 mM $SrCl_2$ (Sigma cat. no. 0390) in Ca-free M16 medium supplemented with vitamins (Sigma cat. no. R7256) and in the presence of 5-µg/ml cytochalasin B (dissolved in DMSO) required to prevent pseudo polar body extrusion. Particular care was paid to remove calcium through passages in preactivation drops of Ca-free M16 medium. Six hours after the activation had started, the oocytes were washed thoroughly in 3% albumin and incubated in culture medium. Cleavage was allowed in 20-µl droplets of culture medium, with no changes to the drop except adding an equal volume of culture medium to the same drop on day 2.

Embryo Transfer

The observation has been consistently made that the first or second day of plugs (0.5 dpc) was not as good as the third to provide the best support to the ensuing pregnancy after transfer of the blastocysts to the uterus 2 days later (2.5 dpc). Recipient females that had been plugged by vasectomized males were anesthetized using a mixture of xylazine (e.g., Rompun) and ketamine (e.g., Ketalar), administered at a dosage of 0.2 mg and 0.3 mg per 10 g body weight, respectively. Before transfer, embryos were rinsed in HEPES-buffered CZB medium containing PVP. The tip of a mouth-operated micropipette carrying the embryos was inserted through a hole made in the uterus wall by a 27-G needle.

Oct4 mRNA WHOLE-MOUNT *IN SITU* HYBRIDIZATION

Using the following experimental protocol, we determined whether the silent state of *Oct4* in the somatic nucleus could be converted to an active state after nuclear transfer. *Oct4* encodes a transcription factor expressed in pluripotent cells (e.g., ES cells) and is required for mouse embryo development past the blastocyst stage. Clone and control (fertilized) blastocysts were fixed and analyzed by *in situ* hybridization (Oct4 RNA probe, or riboprobe). Using this method, aberrant spatial distribution of Oct4 transcript was detected in a large proportion of clones.[20] Restriction of Oct4 transcript to the ICM was observed in only 34% of somatic cell clones; in the remaining clones, Oct4 mRNA was either absent or expressed in both ICM and TE (Fig. 64–2). *Oct4* expression in clones was also monitored using the *Oct4-GFP* transgene. The onset of *Oct4-GFP* expression in clones was at the four- to eight-cell stage, as observed in control *Oct4-GFP* transgenic embryos. However, 18% of somatic cell clones that developed to the blastocyst stage did not express *Oct4-GFP* at the four-cell or subsequent stages. Presence of the transgene in GFP-negative cloned blastocysts was ascertained by PCR, eliminating loss of genetic material (e.g., aneuploidy) as the culprit for absence of transgene expression.

Preparation of the Probe

Probes are prepared as digoxigenin-labeled RNA. Single-stranded RNA probes are synthesized *in vitro* by the transcription of linearized plasmid DNA templates, such that a DIG-labeled RNA that is complementary (antisense) to the mRNA (sense) is generated. This is achieved using the appropriate RNA polymerase (T3, T7, or SP6) in the presence of DIG-labeled uridine triphosphate (DIG-UTP) to transcribe sequences downstream the appropriate polymerase initiation site. In our case, DIG-labeled riboprobes (*Oct4* cDNA, sense and antisense) were

generated by T3 and T7 RNA polymerases from linearized pBluescript containing a full-length *Oct4* cDNA insert.[90]

SPECIFIC INSTRUCTIONS

1. Mix these reagents (Promega Riboprobe System T3/T7 cat. no. 1450) in a 200-μl tube at room temperature (RT) in the following order (to avoid subsequent precipitation):

5× transcription buffer	4 μl
100 mM DTT	2 μl
RNAse inhibitor (20 U/μl)	1 μl
rNTP mix (2.5 mM each)	4 μl
Linearized template (1.0 μg/μl)	1 μl
SP6, T7 or T3 polymerase (20 U/μl)	1 μl
H_2O	up to 20 μl

   - 2.5 mM rNTPs mix: mix equal parts of 10 mM ATP, 10 mM CTP, 10 mM GTP, 0.65 parts of 10 mM UTP, and 0.35 parts of DIG-UTP 10 mM.

2. Seal the tube and incubate at 37°C for 2 hours (an incubator can be used to ensure even heat; optional: add 1 μl polymerase after 1 hour).

3. Remove 1 μl aliquot and electrophorese on a 1% agarose–TBE gel. For synthesis of ~10 μg riboprobe, the RNA band should be ~10× more intense than the one corresponding to the linearized plasmid.

4. Add 2 μl RNAse-free DNAse I (provided in the Promega kit) and incubate for 20 minutes at 37°C.

5. Separate the RNA from unincorporated nucleotides and RNA–DNA–protein complexes on a G50 spin column (ProbeQuant, Amersham cat. no. 27-5335-01). Briefly, prepare the column and its matrix according to the manufacturer's instructions; load the riboprobe volume

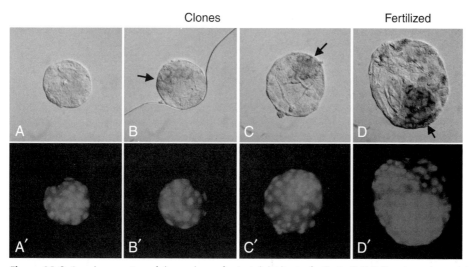

Clones   **Fertilized**

Figure 64–2. Squash preparations of clone embryos after *in situ* hybridization for Oct4 mRNA (A-D) and propidium iodide staining (E–H). Although ICM cells are defined largely by their position within the inside part of the blastocyst, this does not necessarily confirm that the inner cells in clones were pluripotent. Therefore, we verified the nature of the clone ICM cells using Oct4 as a genetic marker of pluripotency (arrow). Clone blastocysts do not express Oct4 (A), or have a lower level of expression (B,C) than observed in control blastocysts (D).

(max 50 μl) on the center of the filter; spin the column within a microcentrifuge support tube at 4°C at 735 g for 2 minutes; the purified sample is collected at the bottom of the support tube.

6. The probe should be stored at –80°C, or it can also be stored at –20°C in hybridization buffer (see later), which makes the probe completely resistant to RNase attack and stable indefinitely.

OPTIONAL TEST FOR RIBOPROBE LABELING

To assess the efficiency of DIG incorporation, we compare our probe to a prelabeled, commercially available reference probe.

1. Transfer an aliquot of purified riboprobe and several dilutions of the reference probe to a membrane (Nylon or nitrocellulose membrane), and let air-dry.

2. Cross-link the RNA to the membrane using a UV cross-linker.

3. Wash briefly (10 seconds) in maleate buffer w/Tween (MABT).

- 10× MAB:

	NaCl	8.7 g
	Maleic acid	11.6 g
	H$_2$O	up to 1000 ml
	pH	adjusted to 7.5 with 1M NaOH

- MABT: 1× MAB, 0.1% Tween-20

4. Incubate in 1% blocking reagent in MAB for 30 minutes at RT.

- Blocking reagent (BR) (Boehringer cat. no. 1096176): make 10% stocks in MAB; heat to dissolve, then autoclave, aliquot, and freeze.

5. Incubate the membrane with anti-DIG, alkaline phosphatase (AP)-tagged antibody: 1/5000 in 1% BR in MAB (w/o Tween) for 30 minutes at RT.

6. Wash 2 × 5 seconds with MAB.

7. Equilibrate for 2 minutes with NTMT.

- NTMT:

	5 M NaCl	1 ml
	2 M Tris-HCl; pH 9.5	2.5 ml
	2 M MgCl$_2$	1.25 ml
	10% Tween-20	500 μl
	H$_2$O	up to 50 ml

The pH at this step is critically important because the AP reaction only occurs at the proper pH (9.5) .

8. Incubate with AP substrate, keep dark, do not shake or mix; a brown or blue–purple color precipitate forms.

- AP substrate: Roche cat. no. 1-442-074 (formerly Boehringer); this substrate is not the classical NBT–BCIP or Fast Red.

9. When sufficient color intensity has been reached, stop the reaction by rinsing the membrane thoroughly in H$_2$O.

10. Estimate the yield of DIG labeling by comparing the intensities of the sample probe and the reference probe dilutions.

SAMPLES: FIXATION AND PRETREATMENTS

1. Collect the embryos (e.g., blastocysts at 72–96 hours) and wash in phosphate-buffered saline (PBS) containing 3 mg/ml bovine serum albumin (BSA) (add, dissolve, and filter).

2. Fix the embryos in 4% paraformaldehyde + 0.1% glutaraldehyde in PBS (30 min at RT, or O/N at 4°C) in 96-well round-bottom dish (e.g., Nunc, 150 μl per well). Optional: fix may contain 2–5 mM EGTA as a precaution against the effects of endogenous RNases.

- Paraformaldehyde: Sigma cat. no. P-6148: dissolve in one tenth of the final volume of PBS 10× at 65°C; the solution is cloudy; add NaOH by the drop until clear; bring to volume with water; filter; cool to 4°C and store aliquots in 50-ml tubes at –20°C.

3. Wash the embryos twice in PBT.

- PBT: 0.2% Triton-X-100 in PBS

4. Treat with 10 μg/ml proteinase K in PBT for 30 minutes at RT.

- NOTE: use PCR-grade proteinase K (e.g., Roche cat. no. 92643520) to ensure the highest quality and absence of contaminant activities; pretest each new enzyme batch for the optimal time; the embryos are sticky after this treatment; therefore, rinse carefully.

5. Fix the embryos again (4% paraformaldehyde + 0.1% glutaraldehyde in PBS) to block proteinase K and preserve the sample.

6. Wash with 1:1 PBT–hybridization mix.

- Hybridization mix:

Formamide	25 ml
20× SSC (pH 5, adjusted with citric acid)	12.5 ml
Boehringer blocking reagent	0.5 g
Heat to 65°C for about 1 hour.	
Once dissolved add:	
10% Tween-20	0.5 ml
Torula yeast RNA (stock ~10 mg/ml) (heat for 2 minutes at 65°C to clear)	0.5 ml
Heparin (50 mg/ml)	50 μg/ml
H$_2$O	up to 50 ml

Filter the solution. The hybridization solution can be prepared before, aliquoted, and stored at –20°C.

7. Treat the embryo samples with hybridization mix and incubate for 3 hours at 60–65°C (or the longer, the better). Prehybridization is crucial to prevent nonspecific binding of the probe and reduce the background.

8. Heat the RNA probe for 5 minutes at 95°C to relieve the RNA secondary structures that may have formed during storage. Add the probe to the hybridization mix. The final probe concentration should be about 200 ng/ml and has to be adjusted empirically.

9. Treat the embryo samples with the hybridization mix containing the DIG-labeled RNA probe and incubate O/N at 50–70°C. We hybridized the Oct4 riboprobe at 58°C.

POSTHYBRIDIZATION WASHES

1. Wash in 2 × SSC, 0.1% SDS for 5 minutes at RT.

   • 20× SSC: 3 M NaCl, 0.3 M trisodium citrate

2. Wash in 0.1 × SSC, 0.1% SDS for 30 minutes at 58°C.

3. Wash in maleate buffer (MAB) for 1 minute. NOTE: samples become very sticky in MAB.

INCUBATION WITH ANTIBODY

To inhibit the endogenous alkaline phosphatase, levamisole (Sigma cat. no. L-9756) 2 mM can be added to the following steps (200 µl 1M levamisole per 100 ml working solution).

1. Preincubate 1 hour at RT in MABT + 0.1–1% blocking reagent + 10% heat-inactivated sheep serum.

   • Sheep serum: Sigma cat. no. S-2263. Heat inactivation: 30 minutes at 65°C, cooled to RT and stored in aliquots at –20°C

2. Incubate O/N at 4°C in MABT + 0.1% blocking reagent + 10% sheep serum + 1/2000 dilution of anti-DIG antibody coupled to alkaline phosphatase.

   • Alkaline phosphatase conjugate (AP) anti-DIG antibody: Roche cat. no. 1 175 041 /1 093 274 (formerly Boehringer)

POSTANTIBODY WASHES AND HISTOCHEMISTRY

To inhibit the endogenous alkaline phosphatase, levamisole (Sigma cat. no. L-9756) 2 mM can be added to the following steps (200 µl 1 M levamisole per 100 ml working solution). NOTE: this will reduce the unspecific signal but will also affect the specific one.

1. Rinse 3 times with MABT.
2. Wash 3× 1 hour with 5 ml MABT.
3. Wash 2–3× 10 minutes with NTMT.
4. Incubate with AP substrate (or freshly made developing solution: 200 µl NBT–BCIP stock solution (Boehringer cat. no. 1681451) in 10 ml NTMT). Keep the tubes and the reaction in the dark as much as possible. NOTE: NTMT should be fresh made and checked for pH to be 9.5.
5. Incubate in the dark at RT until the appropriate color reaction is detected (usually it takes 30–60 minutes for blastocysts). When color has developed to the desired extent, transfer to 25 mM EDTA to stop the reaction. Wash 2× 10 minutes with PBT at RT.

6. Store at 4°C in PBT including 10 mM EDTA and 0.1% Sodium azide (optional: postfix O/N at 4°C in 4% paraformaldehyde before storing).

7. Embryos are photographed on a Nikon Eclipse TE 2000 inverted microscope using an Olympus C4000 digital camera.

EMBRYONIC STEM CELL DERIVATION FROM CLONE BLASTOCYSTS

The ability of clone ICMs to give rise to pluripotent cell lines was tested. To identify such cells, we took advantage of the *Oct4*-GFP transgene carried by the B6OG2F1 nucleus donor cells. Oct4 is a marker for pluripotent cell lineages in the embryo, fetus, and adult, where it is specifically expressed in the ICM and epiblast, germ cells, and oocytes and spermatogonia, respectively. To determine whether the Oct4-GFP signal within the blastocyst-stage clone related to subsequent development, Oct4-GFP was graded in blastocysts as being either absent, weak, or strong (on a relative scale of intensity). Using this method, the blastocysts were placed on a feeder layer and assessed for outgrowth formation. ICM colonies and ES cell lines were successfully derived from the outgrowth of cumulus cell clone blastocysts (Fig. 64–3). In most cases, a strong GFP signal in the blastocyst corresponded to a strong signal in the outgrowths.[20] ES cells could be derived only from outgrowths with strong GFP signal (3/13), but not from outgrowths with weak or absent GFP (0/15). These observations were confirmed by analysis of the endogenous Oct4. More than half (52%) of all clone outgrowths lacked Oct4 mRNA expressing cells. In clone outgrowths with Oct4-expressing cells, levels of Oct4 mRNA were generally lower than in controls. One of the clone ES cell lines was tested for germ line transmission and found to be competent.

Blastocyst Outgrowth Formation

STO (SNL) feeder cells, a murine embryonic fibroblast cell line expressing the recombinant LIF and G418 antibiotic resistance (neo), were used as feeder cells. Confluent SNL cells were mitotically inactivated by exposure to mitomycin C (10 µg/ml in DMEM) for 2–3 hours on the day before use. After careful washing, feeders were maintained in DMEM medium with supplements (14% fetal bovine serum, 5 g/L glucose, 0.1 mM nonessential amino acids, 2 mM L-glutamine, 0.1 mM β-mercaptoethanol, and 50 U/ml penicillin-streptomycin) before seeding the blastocysts. These were deprived of their zona pellucida by exposure to Tyrode solution and plated on feeder cells in four-well plates (Nunc), and their outgrowths examined 3–6 days later, a time point equivalent to developmental day 7–10. Optional: LIF may be added in culture (1000 U/ml), although SNL cells make it.

Embryonic Stem Cell Derivation

The DMEM was removed from the four-well plates, replaced with Trypsin 0.25%/EDTA, and incubated at RT. After 10 minutes, the trypsin was inactivated by addition of DMEM with serum. The ICM colonies were individually picked by a mouth-operated micropipette (flame-polished tip) and

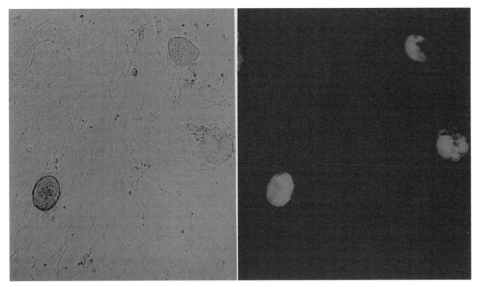

Figure 64–3. Appearance of mouse clone embryonic stem (ES) cell colonies at the first passage, obtained after plating clone blastocysts on feeder cells (day 4), splitting the inner cell mass (ICM) colonies on day 7, and plating the disaggregated ICMs onto fresh feeders. The somatic nucleus donor cells carried the *Oct4-GFP* transgene that is used to visualize the pluripotent state of ICM and incipient ES cells.

transferred into microdrops of DMEM with serum for disaggregation. After reducing the ICM colonies to small clumps (but not to a single-cell suspension), these were seeded on mitotically inactivated SNL cells in 96-well plates. This next passage was performed 6 days later under the same conditions as described, except that the ES cell colonies were not picked, but the entire layer of colonies on feeder cells was dissociated with trypsin and replated. As long as SNL cells are used as feeders, extra LIF is not strictly required; however, it may be added as an option. Unlike SNL cells, culture on regular mouse embryonic fibroblasts (MEFs) requires exogenous LIF.

ACKNOWLEDGMENTS

We would like to gratefully acknowledge all the doctors, staff, and students in Dr. Schöler's laboratory for their contribution to the study of the mouse germ line using Oct4 and Oct4/GFP. We are indebted to Drs. John McLaughlin and Sigrid Eckardt from the adjacent laboratory for their precious collaboration in the mouse cloning experiments. S.E. performed the *in situ* hybridization shown in Fig. 64–2. We thank Dr. Jeffrey Mann (Division of Biology, Beckman Research Institute of the City of Hope, Duarte, CA) for providing the OG2 mouse strain. We also thank Dr. Fatima Cavaleri for useful comments and Areti Malapetsa for editing the manuscript. This work was supported by the Marion Dilley and David George Jones Funds and the Commonwealth and General Assembly of Pennsylvania.

REFERENCES

1. Thomson, J.A., and Marshall, V.S. (1998). Primate embryonic stem cells. *Curr. Top. Dev. Biol.* **38,** 133–165.

2. Amit, M., Carpenter, M.K., Inokuma, M.S., Chiu, C.P., Harris, C.P., Waknitz, M.A., Itskovitz-Eldor, J., and Thomson, J.A. (2000). Clonally derived human embryonic stem cell lines maintain pluripotency and proliferative potential for prolonged periods of culture. *Dev. Biol.* **227,** 271–278.

3. Rideout, W.M., 3rd, Hochedlinger, K., Kyba, M., Daley, G.Q., and Jaenisch, R. (2002). Correction of a genetic defect by nuclear transplantation and combined cell and gene therapy. *Cell* **109,** 17–27.

4. Barberi, T., Klivenya, P., Calingasan, N.Y., Lee, H., Kawamata, H., Loonam, K., Perrier, A.L., Burses, J., Rubio, M.E., Topf, N., Tabar, V., Harrison, N.L., Beal, M.F., Moore, M.A., and Studer, L. (2003). Neural subtype specification of fertilization and nuclear transfer embryonic stem cells and application in parkinsonian mice. *Nat Biotechnol.* **21,** 1200-1207.

5. Wilmut, I., Schnieke, A.E., McWhir, J., Kind, A.J., and Campbell, K.H. (1997). Viable offspring derived from fetal and adult mammalian cells. *Nature* **385,** 810–813.

6. Cibelli, J.B., Stice, S.L., Golueke, P.J., Kane, J.J., Jerry, J., Blackwell, C., Ponce de Leon, F.A., and Robl, J.M. (1998). Cloned transgenic calves produced from nonquiescent fetal fibroblasts. *Science* **280,** 1256–1258.

7. Wakayama, T., Perry, A.C., Zuccotti, M., Johnson, K.R., and Yanagimachi, R. (1998). Full-term development of mice from enucleated oocytes injected with cumulus cell nuclei. *Nature* **394,** 369–374.

8. Baguisi, A., Behboodi, E., Melican, D.T., Pollock, J.S., Destrempes, M.M., Cammuso, C., Williams, J.L., Nims, S.D., Porter, C.A., Midura, P., Palacios, M.J., Ayres, S.L., Denniston, R.S., Hayes, M.L., Ziomek, C.A., Meade, H.M., Godke, R.A., Gavin, W.G., Overstrom, E.W., and Echelard, Y. (1999). Production of goats by somatic cell nuclear transfer. *Nat. Biotechnol.* **17,** 456–461.

9. Onishi, A., Iwamoto, M., Akita, T., Mikawa, S., Takeda, K., Awata, T., Hanada, H., and Perry, A.C. (2000). Pig cloning by microinjection of fetal fibroblast nuclei. *Science* **289,** 1188–1190.

10. Polejaeva, I.A., Chen, S.H., Vaught, T.D., Page, R.L., Mullins, J., Ball, S., Dai, Y., Boone, J., Walker, S., Ayares, D.L., Colman, A., and Campbell, K.H. (2000). Cloned pigs produced by nuclear transfer from adult somatic cells. *Nature* **407**, 86–90.

11. Shin, T., Kraemer, D., Pryor, J., Liu, L., Rugila, J., Howe, L., Buck, S., Murphy, K., Lyons, L., and Westhusin, M. (2002). A cat cloned by nuclear transplantation. *Nature* **415**, 859.

12. Chesne, P., Adenot, P.G., Viglietta, C., Baratte, M., Boulanger, L., and Renard, J.P. (2002). Cloned rabbits produced by nuclear transfer from adult somatic cells. *Nat. Biotechnol.* **20**, 366–369.

13. Zhou, Q., Renard, J.P., Le Friec, G., Brochard, V., Beaujean, N., Cherifi, Y., Fraichard, A., and Cozzi, J. (2003). Generation of fertile cloned rats by regulating oocyte activation. *Science* **302**, 1179.

14. Galli, C., Lagutina, I., Crotti, G., Colleoni, S., Turini, P., Ponderato, N., Duchi, R., and Lazzari, G. (2003). Pregnancy: a cloned horse born to its dam twin. *Nature* **424**, 635.

15. (Press release) "CVM Researchers First to Clone White-tailed Deer." Available at *http://www.cvm.tamu.edu/news/releases/deer_clone.shtml*. (Accessed May 1, 2004).

16. Byrne, J.A., Simonsson, S., and Gurdon, J.B. (2002). From intestine to muscle: nuclear reprogramming through defective cloned embryos. *Proc. Natl. Acad. Sci. U. S. A.* **99**, 6059–6063.

17. Buehr, M., Nichols, J., Stenhouse, F., Mountford, P., Greenhalgh, C.J., Kantachuvesiri, S., Brooker, G., Mullins, J., and Smith, A.G. (2003). Rapid loss of oct-4 and pluripotency in cultured rodent blastocysts and derivative cell lines. *Biol. Reprod.* **68**, 222–229.

18. Niwa, H., Miyazaki, J., and Smith, A.G. (2000). Quantitative expression of Oct-3/4 defines differentiation, dedifferentiation or self-renewal of ES cells. *Nat. Genet.* **24**, 372–376.

19. Hübner, K., Fuhrmann, G., Christenson, L.K., Kehler, J., Reinbold, R., De La Fuente, R., Wood, J., Strauss, J.F., 3rd, Boiani, M., and Schöler, H.R. (2003). Derivation of oocytes from mouse embryonic stem cells. *Science* **300**, 1251–1256.

20. Boiani, M., Eckardt, S., Schöler, H.R., and McLaughlin, K. J. (2002). Oct4 distribution and level in mouse clones: consequences for pluripotency. *Genes Dev.* **16**, 1209–1219.

21. Bortvin, A., Eggan, K., Skaletsky, H., Akutsu, H., Berry, D.L., Yanagimachi, R., Page, D.C., and Jaenisch, R. (2003). Incomplete reactivation of Oct4-related genes in mouse embryos cloned from somatic nuclei. *Development* **130**, 1673–1680.

22. Li, J., Ishii, T., Feinstein, P., and Mombaerts, P. (2004). Odorant receptor gene choice is reset by nuclear transfer from mouse olfactory sensory neurons. *Nature* **428**, 393–399.

23. Eggan, K., Baldwin, K., Tackett, M., Osborne, J., Gogos, J., Chess, A., Axel, R., Jaenisch, R. (2004). Mice cloned form olfactory sensory neurons. *Nature* **428**, 44–49.

24. Li, L., Connelly, M.C., Wetmore, C., Curran, T., and Morgan, J.I. (2003). Mouse embryos cloned from brain tumors. *Cancer Res.* **63**, 2733–2736.

25. Briggs, R., and King, T.J. (1952). Transplantation of living nuclei from blastula cells into enucleated frog eggs. *Proc. Natl. Acad. Sci. U. S. A.* **38**, 455–463.

26. Briggs, R., and King, T.J. (1957). Changes in the nuclei of differentiating endoderm cells as revealed by nuclear transplantation. *J. Morphol.* **100**. 269-312.

27. Gurdon, J.B. (1962). Developmental capacity of nuclei taken from intestinal epithelium cells of feeding tadpoles D. *J. Embryol. Exp. Morphol.* **10**, 622–640.

28. Brinster, R.L. (1965). Studies on the development of mouse embryos *in vitro*. IV. Interaction of energy sources. *J. Reprod. Fertil.* **10**, 227–240.

29. Cross, P.C., and Brinster, R.L. (1970). *In vitro* development of mouse oocytes. *Biol. Reprod.* **3**, 298–307.

30. McGrath, J., and Solter, D. (1983). Nuclear transplantation in mouse embryos. *J. Exp. Zool.* **228**, 355–362.

31. Willadsen, S.M. (1986). Nuclear transplantation in sheep embryos. *Nature* **320**, 63–65.

32. Wakayama, T., Rodriguez, I., Perry, A.C., Yanagimachi, R., and Mombaerts, P. (1999). Mice cloned from embryonic stem cells. *Proc. Natl. Acad. Sci. U.S.A.* **96**, 14984–14989.

33. Wakayama, T., and Yanagimachi, R. (2001). Mouse cloning with nucleus donor cells of different age and type. *Mol. Reprod. Dev.* **58**, 376–383.

33a. Kato, Y., Imabayashi, H., Mori, T., Tani, T., Taniguchi, M., Higashi, M., Matsumoto, M., Umezawa, A., Tsunoda, Y. (2004). Nuclear transfer of adult bone marrow mesenchymal stem cells: developmental totipotency of tissue-specific stem cells from an adult mammal. *Biol. Reprod.* **70**, 415–418.

34. Yamazaki, Y., Makino, H., Hamaguchi-Hamada, K., Hamada, S., Sugino, H., Kawase, E., Miyata, T., Ogawa, M., Yanagimachi, R., and Yagi, T. (2001). Assessment of the developmental totipotency of neural cells in the cerebral cortex of mouse embryo by nuclear transfer. *Proc. Natl. Acad. Sci. U. S. A.* **98**, 14022–14026.

35. Jiang, Y., Vaessen, B., Lenvik, T., Blackstad, M., Reyes, M., and Verfaillie, C.M. (2002). Multipotent progenitor cells can be isolated from postnatal murine bone marrow, muscle, and brain. *Exp. Hematol.* **30**, 896–904.

36. Ramalho-Santos, M., Yoon, S., Matsuzaki, Y., Mulligan, R.C., and Melton, D.A. (2002). "Stemness": transcriptional profiling of embryonic and adult stem cells. *Science* **298**, 597–600.

37. Watt, F.M., and Hogan, B.L. (2000). Out of Eden: stem cells and their niches. *Science* **287**, 1427–1430.

38. Spradling, A., Drummond-Barbosa, D., and Kai, T. (2001). Stem cells find their niche. *Nature* **414**, 98–104.

39. Hochedlinger, K., and Jaenisch, R. (2002). Monoclonal mice generated by nuclear transfer from mature B and T donor cells. *Nature* **415**, 1035–1038.

40. Osada, T., Kusakabe, H., Akutsu, H., Yagi, T., and Yanagimachi, R. (2002). Adult murine neurons: their chromatin and chromosome changes and failure to support embryonic development as revealed by nuclear transfer. *Cytogenet. Genome Res.* **97**, 7–12.

41. Boiani, M., Eckardt, S., Leu, N.A., Schöler, H.R., and McLaughlin, K.J. (2003). Pluripotency deficit in clones overcome by clone–clone aggregation: epigenetic complementation? *EMBO J.* **22**, 5304–5312.

42. Tsunoda, Y., Tokunaga, T., Imai, H., and Uchida, T. (1989). Nuclear transplantation of male primordial germ cells in the mouse. *Development* **107**, 407–411.

43. Yang, J.T., Rayburn, H., and Hynes, R.O. (1995). Cell adhesion events mediated by alpha 4 integrins are essential in placental and cardiac development. *Development* **121**, 549–560.

44. Morin-Kensicki, E.M., Faust, C., LaMantia, C., and Magnuson, T. (2001). Cell and tissue requirements for the gene *eed* during mouse gastrulation and organogenesis. *Genesis* **31**, 142–146.

45. Willadsen, S.M. (1979). A method for culture of micromanipulated sheep embryos and its use to produce monozygotic twins. *Nature* **277**, 298–300.

46. Rossant, J. (1976). Postimplantation development of blastomeres isolated from 4- and 8-cell mouse eggs. *J. Embryol. Exp. Morphol.* **36**, 283–290.

47. Kelly, S.J. (1977). Studies of the developmental potential of 4- and 8-cell stage mouse blastomeres. *J. Exp. Zool.* **200**, 365–376.

48. Tarkowski, A.K., Ozdzenski, W., and Czolowska, R. (2001). Mouse singletons and twins developed from isolated diploid blastomeres supported with tetraploid blastomeres. *Int. J. Dev. Biol.* **45,** 591–596.

49. Conlon, I., and Raff, M. (1999). Size control in animal development. *Cell* **96,** 235–244.

50. McGrath, J., and Solter, D. (1984). Inability of mouse blastomere nuclei transferred to enucleated zygotes to support development *in vitro. Science* **226,** 1317–1319.

51. Sotomaru, Y., Kato, Y., and Tsunoda, Y. (1999). Induction of pluripotency by injection of mouse trophectoderm cell nuclei into blastocysts following transplantation into enucleated oocytes. *Theriogenology* **52,** 213–220.

52. Kono, T., and Tsunoda, Y. (1989). Development of single blastomeres from four- and eight-cell mouse embryos fused into the enucleated half of a two-cell embryo. *Gamete Res.* **22,** 427–434.

53. Kono, T., Tsunoda, Y., Watanabe, T., and Nakahara, T. (1989). Development of chimaeric two-cell mouse embryos produced by allogenic exchange of single nucleus from two- and eight-cell embryos. *Gamete Res.* **24,** 375–384.

54. Kwon, O.Y., and Kono, T. (1996). Production of identical sextuplet mice by transferring metaphase nuclei from four-cell embryos. *Proc. Natl. Acad. Sci. U. S. A.* **93,** 13010–13013.

55. Nagy, A., Rossant, J., Nagy, R., Abramow-Newerly, W., and Roder, J.C. (1993). Derivation of completely cell culture-derived mice from early-passage embryonic stem cells. *Proc. Natl. Acad. Sci. U. S. A.* **90,** 8424–8428.

56. Eggan, K., Akutsu, H., Loring, J., Jackson-Grusby, L., Klemm, M., Rideout, W.M., 3rd, Yanagimachi, R., and Jaenisch, R. (2001). Hybrid vigor, fetal overgrowth, and viability of mice derived by nuclear cloning and tetraploid embryo complementation. *Proc. Natl. Acad. Sci. U. S. A.* **98,** 6209–6214.

57. Zhou, Q., Jouneau, A., Brochard, V., Adenot, P., and Renard, J.P. (2001). Developmental potential of mouse embryos reconstructed from metaphase embryonic stem cell nuclei. *Biol. Reprod.* **65,** 412–419.

58. Tsunoda, Y., and Kato, Y. (1993). Nuclear transplantation of embryonic stem cells in mice. *J. Reprod. Fertil.* **98,** 537–540.

59. Sato, K., Hosaka, K., Ohi, S., Uchiyama, H., Tokieda, Y., and Ishiwata, I. (2000). Mouse fetuses by nuclear transfer from embryonic stem cells. *Hum. Cell* **13,** 197–202.

60. Sato, K., Hosaka, K., Ohkawa, M., Tokieda, Y., and Ishiwata, I. (2001). Cloned transgenic mouse fetuses from embryonic stem cells. *Hum. Cell* **14,** 301–304.

61. Tamashiro, K.L., Wakayama, T., Akutsu, H., Yamazaki, Y., Lachey, J.L., Wortman, M.D., Seeley, R.J., D'Alessio, D.A., Woods, S.C., Yanagimachi, R., and Sakai, R.R. (2002). Cloned mice have an obese phenotype not transmitted to their offspring. *Nat. Med.* **8,** 262–267.

62. Ginsburg, M., Snow, M.H., and McLaren, A. (1990). Primordial germ cells in the mouse embryo during gastrulation. *Development* **110,** 521–528.

63. Labosky, P.A., Barlow, D.P., and Hogan, B.L. (1994). Embryonic germ cell lines and their derivation from mouse primordial germ cells. *Ciba Found. Symp.* **182,** 157–168; discussion 168–178.

64. Lee, J., Inoue, K., Ono, R., Ogonuki, N., Kohda, T., Kaneko-Ishino, T., Ogura, A., and Ishino, F. (2002). Erasing genomic imprinting memory in mouse clone embryos produced from day 11.5 primordial germ cells. *Development* **129,** 1807–1817.

65. Kato, Y., and Tsunoda, Y. (1995). Germ cell nuclei of male fetal mice can support development of chimeras to midgestation following serial transplantation. *Development* **121,** 779–783.

66. Kato, Y., Rideout, W.M., 3rd, Hilton, K., Barton, S.C., Tsunoda, Y., and Surani, M.A. (1999). Developmental potential of mouse primordial germ cells. *Development* **126,** 1823–1832.

67. Tsunoda, Y., Kato, Y., and O'Neill, G.T. (1992). Cytogenetic analysis of reconstituted one-cell mouse embryos derived from nuclear transfer of fetal male germ cells. *J. Reprod. Fertil.* **96,** 275–281.

68. Rybouchkin, A., Heindryckx, B., Van der Elst, J., and Dhont, M. (2002). Developmental potential of cloned mouse embryos reconstructed by a conventional technique of nuclear injection. *Reproduction* **124,** 197–207.

69. Wakayama, T., and Yanagimachi, R. (2001). Effect of cytokinesis inhibitors, DMSO and the timing of oocyte activation on mouse cloning using cumulus cell nuclei. *Reproduction* **122,** 49–60.

70. Kato, Y., Yabuuchi, A., Motosugi, N., Kato, J., and Tsunoda, Y. (1999). Developmental potential of mouse follicular epithelial cells and cumulus cells after nuclear transfer. *Biol. Reprod.* **61,** 1110–1114.

71. Latham, K.E., and Solter, D. (1991). Effect of egg composition on the developmental capacity of androgenetic mouse embryos. *Development* **113,** 561–568.

72. Reik, W., Romer, I., Barton, S.C., Surani, M.A., Howlett, S.K., and Klose, J. (1993). Adult phenotype in the mouse can be affected by epigenetic events in the early embryo. *Development* **119,** 933–942.

73. Nakamura, K., and Tsunoda, Y. (1987). Chimeras obtained by the nuclear transplantation technique in the mouse. *Jpn. J. Anim. Reprod.* **33,** 82–87.

74. Latham, K.E., and Sapienza, C. (1998). Localization of genes encoding egg modifiers of paternal genome function to mouse chromosomes one and two. *Development* **125,** 929–935.

75. Houdebine, L.M. (2003). Cloning by numbers. *Nat. Biotechnol.* **21,** 1451–1452.

76. Ogura, A., Inoue, K., Ogonuki, N., Noguchi, A., Takano, K., Nagano, R., Suzuki, O., Lee, J., Ishino, F., and Matsuda, J. (2000). Production of male cloned mice from fresh, cultured, and cryopreserved immature Sertoli cells. *Biol. Reprod.* **62,** 1579–1584.

77. Morshead, C.M., Benveniste, P., Iscove, N.N., and van der Kooy, D. (2002). Hematopoietic competence is a rare property of neural stem cells that may depend on genetic and epigenetic alterations. *Nat. Med.* **8,** 268–273.

78. Czolowska, R., Modlinski, J.A., and Tarkowski, A.K. (1984). Behaviour of thymocyte nuclei in non-activated and activated mouse oocytes. *J. Cell. Sci.* **69,** 19–34.

79. Kono, T., Ogawa, M., and Nakahara, T. (1993). Thymocyte transfer to enucleated mouse oocytes in the mouse. *J. Reprod. Dev.* **39,** 301–307.

80. Humpherys, D., Eggan, K., Akutsu, H., Friedman, A., Hochedlinger, K., Yanagimachi, R., Lander, E.S., Golub, T.R., and Jaenisch, R. (2002). Abnormal gene expression in cloned mice derived from embryonic stem cell and cumulus cell nuclei. *Proc. Natl. Acad. Sci. U. S. A.* **99,** 12889–12894.

81. Dean, W., Santos, F., Stojkovic, M., Zakhartchenko, V., Walter, J., Wolf, E., and Reik, W. (2001). Conservation of methylation reprogramming in mammalian development: Aberrant reprogramming in cloned embryos. *Proc. Natl. Acad. Sci. U. S. A.* **98,** 13734–13738.

82. Chung, Y.G., Ratnam, S., Chaillet, J.R., and Latham, K.E. (2003). Abnormal regulation of DNA methyltransferase expression in cloned mouse embryos. *Biol Reprod.* **59,** 146-153.

83. Avilion, A.A., Nicolis, S.K., Pevny, L.H., Perez, L., Vivian, N., and Lovell-Badge, R. (2003). Multipotent cell lineages in early mouse development depend on SOX2 function. *Genes Dev.* **17,** 126–140.

84. Hanna, L.A., Foreman, R.K., Tarasenko, I.A., Kessler, D.S., and Labosky, P.A. (2002). Requirement for Foxd3 in maintaining pluripotent cells of the early mouse embryo. *Genes Dev.* **16**, 2650–2661.

85. Pesce, M., and Schöler, H.R. (2000). Oct-4: Control of totipotency and germline determination. *Mol. Reprod. Dev.* **55**, 452–457.

86. Nichols, J., Zevnik, B., Anastassiadis, K., Niwa, H., Klewe-Nebenius, D., Chambers, I., Schöler, H., and Smith, A. (1998). Formation of pluripotent stem cells in the mammalian embryo depends on the POU transcription factor Oct4. *Cell* **95**, 379–391.

87. Ambrosetti, D.C., Schöler, H.R., Dailey, L., and Basilico, C. (2000). Modulation of the activity of multiple transcriptional activation domains by the DNA binding domains mediates the synergistic action of Sox2 and Oct-3 on the fibroblast growth factor-4 enhancer. *J. Biol. Chem.* **275**, 23387–23397.

88. Guo, Y., Costa, R., Ramsey, H., Starnes, T., Vance, G., Robertson, K., Kelley, M., Reinbold, R., Schöler, H., and Hromas, R. (2002). The embryonic stem cell transcription factors Oct-4 and FoxD3 interact to regulate endodermal-specific promoter expression. *Proc. Natl. Acad. Sci. U. S. A.* **99**, 3663–3667.

89. Zappone, M.V., Galli, R., Catena, R., Meani, N., De Biasi, S., Mattei, E., Tiveron, C., Vescovi, A.L., Lovell-Badge, R., Ottolenghi, S., and Nicolis, S.K. (2000). Sox2 regulatory sequences direct expression of a (beta)-geo transgene to telencephalic neural stem cells and precursors of the mouse embryo, revealing regionalization of gene expression in CNS stem cells. *Development* **127**, 2367–2382.

90. Schöler, H.R., Dressler, G.R., Balling, R., Rohdewohld, H., and Gruss, P. (1990). Oct-4: a germline-specific transcription factor mapping to the mouse t-complex. *EMBO J.* **9**, 2185–2195.

91. Brook, F.A., and Gardner, R.L. (1997). The origin and efficient derivation of embryonic stem cells in the mouse. *Proc. Natl. Acad. Sci. U.S.A.* **94**, 5709–5712.

92. Evans, M.J., and Kaufman, M.H. (1981). Establishment in culture of pluripotential cells from mouse embryos. *Nature* **292**, 154–156.

93. Williams, R.L., Hilton, D.J., Pease, S., Willson, T.A., Stewart, C.L., Gearing, D.P., Wagner, E.F., Metcalf, D., Nicola, N.A., and Gough, N.M. (1988). Myeloid leukaemia inhibitory factor maintains the developmental potential of embryonic stem cells. *Nature* **336**, 684–687.

94. Smith, A.G., Heath, J.K., Donaldson, D.D., Wong, G.G., Moreau, J., Stahl, M., and Rogers, D. (1988). Inhibition of pluripotential embryonic stem cell differentiation by purified polypeptides. *Nature* **336**, 688–690.

95. Robertson, E.J. (1987). Embryo-derived stem cell lines. *In* "Teratocarcinomas and Embryonic Stem Cells: A Practical Approach" (Robertson, E.G., Ed.). pp. 71–112. IRL Press, Oxford, United Kingdom.

96. Chambers, I., Colby, D., Robertson, M., Nichols, J., Lee, S., Tweedie, S., and Smith, A. (2003). Functional expression cloning of Nanog, a pluripotency sustaining factor in embryonic stem cells. *Cell* **113**, 643–655.

97. Munsie, M.J., Michalska, A.E., O'Brien, C.M., Trounson, A.O., Pera, M.F., and Mountford, P.S. (2000). Isolation of pluripotent embryonic stem cells from reprogrammed adult mouse somatic cell nuclei. *Curr. Biol.* **10**, 989–992.

98. Kawase, E., Yamazaki, Y., Yagi, T., Yanagimachi, R., and Pedersen, R.A. (2000). Mouse embryonic stem (ES) cell lines established from neuronal cell-derived cloned blastocysts. *Genesis* **28**, 156–163.

99. Schoonjans, L., Kreemers, V., Danloy, S., Moreadith, R.W., Laroche, Y., and Collen, D. (2003). Improved generation of germline-competent embryonic stem cell lines from inbred mouse strains. *Stem Cells* **21**, 90–97.

100. Wakayama, T., Tabar, V., Rodriguez, I., Perry, A.C., Studer, L., and Mombaerts, P. (2001). Differentiation of embryonic stem cell lines generated from adult somatic cells by nuclear transfer. *Science* **292**, 740–743.

101. Saburi, S., Azuma, S., Sato, E., Toyoda, Y., and Tachi, C. (1997). Developmental fate of single embryonic stem cells microinjected into 8-cell-stage mouse embryos. *Differentiation* **62**, 1–11.

102. Szabo, P.E., Hubner, K., Schöler, H., and Mann, J.R. (2002). Allele-specific expression of imprinted genes in mouse migratory primordial germ cells. *Mech. Dev.* **115**, 157–160.

103. Chatot, C.L., Ziomek, C.A., Bavister, B.D., Lewis, J.L., and Torres, I. (1989). An improved culture medium supports development of random-bred 1-cell mouse embryos *in vitro*. *J. Reprod. Fertil.* **86**, 679–688.

65

Genomic Reprogramming

Azim Surani

Introduction

Most cells contain the same set of genes and yet they are extremely diverse in appearance. They are all derived from a totipotent zygote generated after fertilization of an oocyte. William Harvey in 1651 was the first to propose that "everything comes from an egg," which also encapsulated the concept of epigenesis or the gradual emergence of the embryo and fetus from an egg. Nearly 300 years later, Waddington elaborated on epigenesis in his famous sketch depicting the "epigenetic landscape." Developmental biologists also began to consider whether all nuclei could be reprogrammed and become totipotent in nuclear transfer experiments beginning with Jacques Loeb and Hans Spemann.[1] From many subsequent experiments it became clear that the maternally inherited factors contained within the oocyte also have the extraordinary property to restore totipotency to a differentiated somatic nucleus when transplanted into it.[2] The components within the oocyte must have the property to alter the somatic nucleus so that it can recapitulate the entire developmental program and thus give rise to an exact genetic copy or clone of the individual who donated the transplanted nucleus. This transformation of differentiated cell to a totipotent state is probably the most widely understood meaning of genomic reprogramming. However, it is important to note that extensive epigenetic reprogramming of the genome also occurs in the germ line and during early development, which is essential for generating the totipotent zygote and for creating the pluripotent epiblast cells from which both germ cells and somatic cells are subsequently derived.[3]

Specification of diverse cell types from pluripotent cells is determined by the expression of precise set of genes while the rest are repressed. These newly acquired cell fates are propagated by heritable epigenetic mechanisms through modifications of chromatin[4] and by DNA methylation.[5] These epigenetic modifications, although heritable, are also reversible and can be erased, which is why it is possible to change the phenotypic characteristics of cells and restore totipotency to somatic nuclei under specific conditions (Fig. 65–1). To understand the mechanisms of reprogramming, it is important to know the nature of chromatin modifications and the mechanisms that can reverse or erase the existing modifications and

also how new modifications are imposed. These reprogramming factors normally play a significant role during early development; thus, it is important to determine their role in this context and how these factors act on somatic nuclei during restoration of totipotency or pluripotency.

Genomic Reprogramming in Germ Cells

Germ cells provide the enduring link between generations; thus, this lineage exhibits many unique properties including the extensive epigenetic reprogramming of the genome before gametogenesis. This reprogramming is crucial for generating viable and functional gametes, which in turn generate a totipotent zygote.[3] Primordial germ cells (PGCs) are amongst the first cells to undergo specification from pluripotent epiblast cells, when the distinction between germ cells and soma is established.[6] PGCs, as precursors of sperm and oocyte, are highly specialized cells and are the only cells that can undergo meiosis. However, PGCs retain expression of some markers of pluripotency such as *Oct4*. It is also possible to derive pluripotent embryonic germ (EG) cells from PGCs.[7] In this context it is interesting to determine both how PGC specification occurs and how these cells undergo dedifferentiation to pluripotent EG cells, which may provide some insights into genomic reprogramming.

STEM CELL MODEL FOR THE SPECIFICATION OF GERM CELLS IN MAMMALS

There are two key mechanisms for the specification of germ cells. The first involves inheritance of preformed germ plasm,

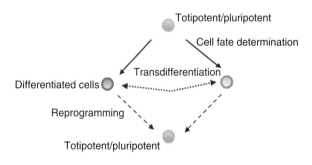

Figure 65–1. Genomic reprogramming involves heritable but reversible epigenetic modifications. (Please see CD-ROM for color version of this figure.)

which is found in *Drosophila* and *Caenorhabditis elegans.*[8] In mammals, germ cell specification occurs according to the stem cell model in which germ cells are derived from pluripotent epiblast cells in response to signaling molecules from the extraembryonic ectoderm.[6,9] Bone morphogenetic protein (BMP)-4 and BMP-8b are among the key signaling molecules in conferring germ cell competence on pluripotent epiblast cells in mice starting at E6.5 (Fig. 65–2), an event that is detected by the expression of *fragilis,* a transmembrane protein.[10,11] These germ cell competent cells are initially destined for a mesoderm somatic cell fate as they show expression of *Brachyury* and some region-specific *Hox* genes as they migrate toward the posterior proximal region.[10] However, at around E7.25, cells that ultimately acquire germ cell fate switch off the somatic program through repression of a number of genes, which continue to be expressed in the neighboring somatic cells. Cells that acquire germ cell fate continue to show expression of markers of pluripotency including *Oct4.* A unique marker of germ cells at this time is *stella,* which is first detected in the 45–50 founder germ cells at E7.5.[11] Thus, diversification between germ cell and somatic cell fate among neighboring cells occurs over approximately 6–10 hours between E7.25–E7.5; the repression of somatic cell program is one of the major events during germ cell specification.

From Stem Cells to Germ Cells

Recent studies show that it is also possible to derive PGCs and gametes from pluripotent stem cells. In one study, ES cells with *gcOct4-GFP* reporter that drives expression specifically in germ cells were generated. These ES cells with the reporter were allowed to undergo differentiation when cells with green fluorescent protein (GFP) were detected.[12] These cells showed expression of a variety of germ cell-specific markers. Further cultures following cell sorting eventually produced oocyte-like cells that underwent development to form blastocyst-like structures. The latter show that mouse ES cells can differentiate into oocyte and subsequently into blastocysts under these conditions. With further detailed characterization of germ cells and gametes, such an *in vitro* system may be useful for investigations concerning specific aspects of germ cell development.

Another study has similarly been carried out to generate spermatogenic cells from pluripotent ES cells. In this case, the endogenous mouse homologue of *Vasa, Mvh* was used to knockin the reporters *LacZ* and *GFP.*[13] In this study, germ cells were generated in embryoid bodies, which were detected through the expression of MVH-GFP. This process was greatly enhanced by the exposure of ES cells to BMP4. These MVH-GFP cells were aggregated with E12.5–13.5 male gonadal cells when germ cells within these aggregates developed into elongated spermatids. These studies shows that it may be possible generate an efficient *in vitro* system to derive germ cells from pluripotent ES cells. Such a system would be useful to study the mechanism of PGC specification *in vitro,* other aspects including the formation of gametes, and aspects of epigenetic reprogramming of the genome. Derivation of germ cells from human ES cells would be particularly useful for studies on this lineage. Furthermore, derivation of human oocytes from ES cells would greatly add to this scarce resource, thus providing opportunities for fundamental studies on somatic cell reprogramming and for the subsequent derivation of stem cell lines from human somatic cells for investigations of specific mutations and diseases.

From Germ Cells to Stem Cells

Embryonal carcinoma (EC) cells that are derived from PGCs *in vivo* were the first pluripotent stem cells to be identified, and several loci have been identified that have critical role in this process. At the same time, derivation of pluripotent cells from PGCs has also been achieved *in vitro.*[7] This conversion of germ cells into EG cells occurs in the presence of leukemia inhibitory factor (LIF), basic fibroblast growth factor (FGF-2), and the Kit ligand (KL). The precise mechanism for conversion of the highly specialized germ cells into pluripotent stem cells is largely unknown. Further investigations would provide insights into dedifferentiation of cells and on the mechanism of genomic reprogramming.

EPIGENETIC REPROGRAMMING IN GERM CELLS

One of the properties of germ cells of particular interest is the epigenetic reprogramming of the genome. This event occurs when PGCs enter into the developing gonads (Fig. 65–2), when there is extensive erasure of epigenetic modifications including erasure of genomic imprints and reactivation of the inactive X chromosome.[3,14,15] New parental imprints are initiated later during gametogenesis, particularly oogenesis, and these modifications that are heritable after fertilization dictate parent of origin dependent gene expression.[16]

As germ cells proliferate after the formation of founder population at E7.5, they start to migrate to the developing gonads. At this stage, germ cells and somatic cells contain epigenetic marks associated with imprinted genes. During their migration, female germ cells also show inactivation of one X chromosome. On the entry of germ cells into developing

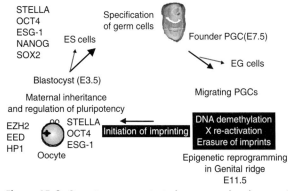

Figure 65–2. Genomic reprogramming in the oocyte, early embryos, and the germ line. The origin of pluripotent embryonic stem (ES) cells and embryonic germ (EG) cells are indicated. (Please see CD-ROM for color version of this figure.)

gonads at E10.5–E11.5, a major epigenetic reprogramming event occurs, which includes reactivation of the inactive X chromosome and the erasure of epigenetic marks associated with imprinted genes. Indeed, there appears to be genome-wide DNA demethylation of the genome at this time. This genomic reprogramming event occurs relatively rapidly and is completed by E12.5.[3,14,15]

The mechanism involved in the erasure of epigenetic modifications in the germ line may provide insights on the erasure of epigenetic modifications from somatic nuclei that occurs after transplantation into oocytes, which restores totipotency. If this is the case, similar factors may be transcribed during oocyte maturation at the germinal vesicle stage and translated to be stored in oocytes as maternally inherited factors. The onset of genomic reprogramming in PGCs in the gonad may be triggered by a signal from somatic cells or in response to a developmental timer such as the number of cell divisions in PGCs since the establishment of the founder population of PGCs.[14] Because the gonads at E11.5 are bipotential, it is possible that the signal from somatic cells, if it exists, should be the same in both male and female embryos. In this case, it would be of interest to discover the nature of the signal and determine how such an external cue can trigger extensive genomic reprogramming. However, there is also support for the alternative developmental timer model because EG cells show erasure of imprints even when they are derived from PGCs in which this process has not yet commenced.[17] It is possible that erasure is initiated when germ cells complete a critical number of cell cycles although, as these cells are cultured in a complex medium, a role for an environmental cue cannot be entirely discounted. Whatever the case may be, it is important to note that EG cells themselves have the property to induce erasure of epigenetic modifications from somatic nuclei (see later).

Genomic Reprogramming in Oocytes

Resumption of oocyte growth is accompanied by further epigenetic reprogramming events, particularly the initiation of genomic imprints. The majority of the epigenetic marks associated with imprinting are introduced during oocyte growth, although some genes acquire paternal-specific imprints in the male germ line.[18] These epigenetic marks are eventually detected as DNA methylation of specific *cis*-control elements. Some of the marks, for example in the *Igf2r* locus ensure that the gene will only be active when maternally inherited, whereas others such as *Peg3* will be silent in the female genome.[16] *Dnmt3l* is a key gene involved in the initiation of parental imprints, which acts together with the *de novo* DNA methylase enzyme Dnmt3a.[19,20] A mutation in the *Dnmt3l* gene does not disrupt development or maturation of the oocyte except that these oocytes do not carry appropriate maternal imprints or epigenetic marks. Following their fertilization, the resulting embryos are unable to develop normally and they die shortly after implantation. Other genes such as *H19* undergo DNA methylation in the paternal germ line, and this gene is repressed in the paternal genome. This topic is discussed comprehensively elsewhere.[16]

MATERNAL INHERITANCE AND REPROGRAMMING OF PARENTAL GENOMES

As in other organisms, mouse oocytes contain a number of maternally inherited proteins and message (Fig. 65–2). In mammals, there are maternally inherited factors that are essential for totipotency and pluripotency such as Oct4, Esg1, and Stella,[3] although there is no Nanog.[21,22] Maternal inheritance of Stella is apparently necessary for normal preimplantation development.[23] The oocytes also contain epigenetic modifiers, including the *Polycomb* group proteins Ezh2 and eed and the heterochromatin factor HP1.[24,25] These factors are essential for regulating early development and for generating the pluripotent epiblast and trophectoderm cells of blastocysts. The oocyte is also likely to inherit some key chromatin remodeling factors.

In mammals, the parental genomes exhibit epigenetic asymmetry in the zygote as a result of imprinting, which confers functional differences between parental genomes. At fertilization, the maternal genome apparently has high methylated lysine 9 histone H3 (H3meK9).[24,25] Immediately after fertilization the heterochromatin protein HP1β, binds preferentially to the maternal genome. The Polycomb proteins Ezh2 and eed also bind preferentially to the maternal genome. While this takes place, the paternal genome that has relatively low levels of H3meK9 shows genome-wide DNA demethylation, thus enhancing the epigenetic differences between the parental genomes. Ezh2 has the conserved SET domain with histone methylase activity for methylation of histone H3-lysine 27/lysine 9 (H3meK27/9). The maternal inheritance of Ezh2 per se is apparently important because depletion of this factor from oocytes results in development of very small neonates presumably because of an effect on placental development. This seems likely because the neonates eventually grow and acquire normal size indicating a placental functional deficiency during development.[25] Whether this is due to an effect on imprinted genes remains to be determined. These experiments show that factors present within the oocyte have the potential to exert a variety of epigenetic effects on development. Somatic nuclei transplanted into oocytes would be affected by the activities of these factors during reprogramming, but the variable expression of genes associated with totipotency and of imprinted genes argues that appropriate epigenetic reprogramming of the genome may not be accomplished in every case (see later).

Factors involved in chromatin remodeling are also likely to be important for early development and genomic reprogramming because they regulate accessibility to DNA.[26] The SWI/SNF-like complexes consist of at least two ATPase subunits BRG1 and BRM.[27,28] *Brg1* is important during preimplantation development because loss of function is lethal during preimplantation development.[28] It is also known that mutation in *ATRX,* a member of the SNF2 helicase/ATPase family has an effect on DNA methylation of highly repeated sequences.[29] Mutation in *Lsh* similarly results in substantial demethylation of the genome. Lsh is related to the SNF2 subfamily; most members of the SNF2 family of proteins appear to have the capacity to alter chromatin structure.[30] The activity of the nucleosome-dependent ATPase ISWI may be used in chromatin remodeling in nuclear reprogramming of somatic nuclei, and if so, it is likely to be present in the oocyte and would have a role in the zygote.[26,31] One of the earliest changes observed following fertilization (or indeed after transplantation of the somatic nucleus) is the apparent increase in the size of the nucleus. It is possible that that this morphologic change is in response to chromatin remodeling factors belonging to the ISWI complexes. This activity may be necessary for the initial unwinding of the chromosomes to facilitate epigenetic modifications of the chromatin.

REPROGRAMMING DURING EARLY DEVELOPMENT

Epigenetic reprogramming of the embryonic genome continues throughout preimplantation development as judged by the continual changes in histone modifications and a decline in the genomic levels of DNA methylation.[32] During preimplantation development, both pluripotent epiblast and differentiated trophectoderm cells are formed. There are differences in the epigenetic reprogramming in these two tissues. For example, there is preferential paternal X inactivation in the trophectoderm, a process in which the *Polycomb* group proteins, Ezh2/eed complex has a significant role.[25,33,34] The cells of the late morula that are positive for the expression of *Nanog* and destined to form the inner cell mass cease to show Ezh2/eed accumulation at Xi as seen with the paternal X chromosome in the trophectoderm. Ezh2 is also detected in the inner cell mass, which may account for the presence of the overall H3meK27 staining of epiblast cells, which are positive for Oct4 expression.[25]

It appears that histone modifications such as H3meK27 may have a role in the maintenance of epigenetic plasticity of the pluripotent epiblast cells because the loss of function of Ezh2 is early embryonic lethal, and it is not possible to derive pluripotent ES cells from blastocyst that are null for Ezh2.[35] These experiments show the importance of appropriate epigenetic reprogramming of the genome for early development and for generating pluripotent epiblast cells that are the precursors of both somatic and germ cell lineages.

As we learn more about nuclear reprogramming events that occur normally in germ cells, oocytes, and early development, these studies are likely to be used to identify key candidates for genomic reprogramming.

Reprogramming Somatic Nuclei

NUCLEAR TRANSPLANTATION

Epigenetic reprogramming of somatic nuclei transplanted into oocytes must require erasure and initiation of appropriate epigenetic modifications compatible for development. This subject has already been reviewed extensively elsewhere.[2] At least some of the key reprogramming events may be faulty to account for the very low success rate because somatic nuclei undergo variable reprogramming resulting in a wide variety of phenotypes. The effects of aberrant reprogramming are apparent particularly soon after implantation and during postimplantation development. Both the embryo and extraembryonic

tissue seem to be affected. Some epigenetic marks associated with imprinted genes are erased resulting in aberrant expression of these genes. It seems likely, therefore, that a large number of genes fail to show appropriate temporal and spatial patterns of expression. Further studies on the mechanisms of genomic reprogramming during normal development and following nuclear transplantation are necessary to assess the reasons for faulty reprogramming of somatic nuclei.

REPROGRAMMING IN EMBRYONIC STEM/ EMBRYONIC GERM—SOMATIC CELL HYBRIDS

Somatic nuclear reprogramming has also been demonstrated in hybrid cells between pluripotent ES/EG and somatic cells, which also restores pluripotency in somatic nuclei.[36,37] These studies indicate that not only the oocytes but also pluripotent ES/EG cells must contain appropriate factors to reprogram somatic nucleus. Reprogramming of somatic nuclei in ES/EG—somatic cell hybrids is, however, relatively less complex compared with its transplantation into oocytes. This is because the somatic nucleus in the oocyte has to be reprogramed to recapitulate the entire program of early development to the blastocyst stage. It is important to note that this donor somatic nucleus has to be reprogramed to generate both pluripotent epiblast cells and the highly differentiated trophectoderm cells. The latter should be viewed as a transdifferentiation event because somatic nuclei of diverse origin must direct differentiation of highly specialized trophectoderm cells after only a few cleavage divisions. Indeed, in some respects, this transdifferentiation event is more striking as a reprogramming event. Reprogramming of somatic nuclei in ES/EG—somatic cell hybrids by comparison is less complex because there is restoration of pluripotency without the necessity to recapitulate early events of development.

Although EG and ES cells on the whole have similar effects on somatic nuclei there is at least one critical difference between them. Using the EG—thymocyte hybrid cells, it was shown that the somatic nucleus underwent extensive reprogramming resulting in the erasure of DNA methylation associated with imprinted genes, and the inactive X chromosome was reactivated. The somatic nucleus also acquired pluripotency as judged by the activation of the *Oct4* gene, and the hybrid cells could differentiate into all three germ layers in chimeras.[36] This study shows that, EG cells apart from conferring pluripotency to somatic nucleus, retained a key property found only in germ cells, which is the ability to erase parental imprints, and induce genome-wide DNA demethylation. Experiments using ES—thymocyte hybrid cells gave similar results including the restoration of pluripotency to somatic nuclei as shown by the activation of Oct4-GFP reporter gene and for the ability of these cells to differentiate into a variety of cell types.[26] However, unlike EG cells, ES cell do not cause erasure of imprints from somatic nuclei. Furthermore, in ES—EG hybrids, EG cells can induce erasure of imprints from ES cells, which shows that EG cells have dominant activity for the erasure of imprints and DNA demethylation. However, from these studies, it is clear that DNA demethylation activity at least for the erasure of imprints present in EG cells is not essential for the restoring pluripotency to somatic cells. It is possible to use this system to design cell-based assays in search of key reprogramming factors.

The ability of ES/EG cells to restore pluripotency in somatic nuclei is significant because it also opens up possibilities to identify the molecules involved in reprogramming of somatic nuclei. Such studies are difficult with mammalian oocytes partly because they are small compared with amphibian oocytes,[38] and it is difficult to collect large numbers of them. More importantly, as discussed previously, oocytes are complex cells containing factors essential for pluripotency and for early development and differentiation of trophectoderm cells. By contrast, pluripotent ES/EG cells are relatively less complex, and, more importantly, they can be grown indefinitely *in vitro,* and, thus, they can provide a considerable source of material for analysis. For example, it is possible to use nuclear extracts from ES/EG cells to examine reprogramming of somatic nuclei as described in one experimental approach.[39] The availability of relatively large amounts of nuclear extracts from ES/EG cells also makes it possible to undertake biochemical studies to identify the key reprogramming factors.

Conclusions

The evidence from studies on early mammalian development shows that there is dynamic and extensive reprogramming of the genome in the oocyte, zygote, and germ cells. Pluripotent stem cells also appear to show considerable potential for genomic reprogramming, and, although there are differences between ES and EG cells, both of them can restore pluripotency to somatic nuclei. There is maternal inheritance of factors for pluripotency, epigenetic modifications, and chromatin remodeling in the oocyte. Reprogramming in the oocyte is relatively complex because the parental pronuclei exhibit epigenetic asymmetry in the zygote. The paternal genome becomes rapidly demethylated after fertilization, but the maternal genome does not, at least in part because of the differential histone modifications such as the preferential H3meK9 of the maternal genome but not of the paternal genome and the preferential binding of HP1β and Ezh2/eed proteins to it. It is possible that epigenetic reprogramming of somatic nuclei may be affected by their original epigenetic state.

The phenomenon of reprogramming of somatic nuclei is now well established in mammals by nuclear transplantation studies and in heterokaryons, but the mechanisms and the key molecules involved are yet unknown. It is reasonable to assume that some of the factors that are involved in reprogramming of the genome in the germ line are also present in the oocyte. It is also possible that some of the basic reprogramming factors present in pluripotent stem cells are also present in the oocyte.

A likely sequence of events for converting a somatic nucleus to a pluripotent nucleus may first require chromatin-remodeling activity. Many of these complexes are known to

exist in mammals, but at this stage it is not known precisely which are important for reprogramming of somatic nuclei. This may be followed by changes in histone modifications compatible with pluripotency. These complexes are not yet fully determined, and the histone modifiers also must be identified.

Because ES/EG cells apparently have the capacity for reprogramming somatic nuclei to pluripotency, they may be used for the identification of key molecules necessary for genomic reprogramming through cell-based assays combined with appropriate biochemical and cellular analyses.

REFERENCES

1. McLaren, A. (2000). Cloning: pathways to a pluripotent future. *Science* **288**, 1775–1780.
2. Rideout, W.M., 3rd, Eggan, K., and Jaenisch, R. (2001). Nuclear cloning and epigenetic reprogramming of the genome. *Science* **293**, 1093–1098.
3. Surani, M.A. (2001). Reprogramming of genome function through epigenetic inheritance. *Nature* **414**, 122–128.
4. Fischle, W., Wang, Y., and Allis, C.D. (2003). Histone and chromatin cross-talk. *Curr. Opin. Cell Biol.* **15**, 172–183.
5. Bird, A. (2002). DNA methylation patterns and epigenetic memory. *Genes Dev.* **16**, 6–21.
6. Lawson, K.A., and Hage, W.J. (1994). Clonal analysis of the origin of primordial germ cells in the mouse. *Ciba Found. Symp.* **182**, 68–84.
7. Donovan, P.J., and de Miguel, M.P. (2003). Turning germ cells into stem cells. *Curr. Opin. Genet. Dev.* **13**, 463–471.
8. Seydoux, G., and Strome, S. (1999). Launching the germline in *Caenorhabditis elegans:* regulation of gene expression in early germ cells. *Development* **126**, 3275–3283.
9. Lawson, K.A., Dunn, N.R., Roelen, B.A., Zeinstra, L.M., Davis, A.M., Wright, C.V., Korving, J.P., and Hogan, B.L. (1999). Bmp4 is required for the generation of primordial germ cells in the mouse embryo. *Genes Dev.* **13**, 424–436.
10. Saitou, M., Payer, B., Lange, U.C., Erhardt, S., Barton, S.C., and Surani, M.A. (2003). Specification of germ cell fate in mice. *Philos. Trans. R. Soc. Lond. Biol. Sci.* **358**, 1363–1370.
11. Saitou, M., Barton, S.C., and Surani, M.A. (2002). A molecular programme for the specification of germ cell fate in mice. *Nature* **418**, 293–300.
12. Hubner, K., Fuhrmann, G., Christenson, L.K., Kehler, J., Reinbold, R., De La Fuente, R., Wood, J., Strauss, J.F., 3rd, Boiani, M., and Scholer, H.R. (2003). Derivation of oocytes from mouse embryonic stem cells. *Science* **300**, 1251–1256.
13. Toyooka, Y., Tsunekawa, N., Akasu, R., and Noce, T. (2003). Embryonic stem cells can form germ cells in vitro. *Proc. Natl. Acad. Sci. USA* **100**, 11457–11462.
14. Hajkova, P., Erhardt, S., Lane, N., Haaf, T., El-Maarri, O., Reik, W., Walter, J., and Surani, M.A. (2002). Epigenetic reprogramming in mouse primordial germ cells. *Mech. Dev.* **117**, 15–23.
15. Lee, J., Inoue, K., Ono, R., Ogonuki, N., Kohda, T., Kaneko-Ishino, T., Ogura, A., and Ishino, F. (2002). Erasing genomic imprinting memory in mouse clone embryos produced from day 11.5 primordial germ cells. *Development* **129**, 1807–1817.
16. Ferguson-Smith, A.C., and Surani, M.A. (2001). Imprinting and the epigenetic asymmetry between parental genomes. *Science* **293**, 1086–1089.

17. Durcova-Hills, G., Ainscough, J., and McLaren, A. (2001). Pluripotential stem cells derived from migrating primordial germ cells. *Differentiation* **68,** 220–226.

18. Reik, W., and Walter, J. (2001). Evolution of imprinting mechanisms: the battle of the sexes begins in the zygote. *Nat. Genet.* **27,** 255–256.

19. Bourc'his, D., Xu, G.L., Lin, C.S., Bollman, B., and Bestor, T.H. (2001). Dnmt3L and the establishment of maternal genomic imprints. *Science* **294,** 2536–2539.

20. Hata, K., Okano, M., Lei, H., and Li, E. (2002). Dnmt3L cooperates with the Dnmt3 family of de novo DNA methyltransferases to establish maternal imprints in mice. *Development* **129,** 1983–1993.

21. Mitsui, K., Tokuzawa, Y., Itoh, H., Segawa, K., Murakami, M., Takahashi, K., Maruyama, M., Maeda, M., and Yamanaka, S. (2003). The homeoprotein Nanog is required for maintenance of pluripotency in mouse epiblast and ES cells. *Cell* **113,** 631–642.

22. Chambers, I., Colby, D., Robertson, M., Nichols, J., Lee, S., Tweedie, S., and Smith, A. (2003). Functional expression cloning of Nanog, a pluripotency sustaining factor in embryonic stem cells. *Cell* **113,** 643–655.

23. Payes, B., Saitou, M., Barton, S.C., Thresher, R., Dixon, J.P., Zahn, D., Colledge, W.H., Carlton, M.B., Nakano, T., and Surani, A. (2003). *stella* is a maternal effect gene required for normal early development in mice. *Curr. Biol.* **13,** 2110–2117.

24. Arney, K.L., Bao, S., Bannister, A.J., Kouzarides, T., and Surani, M.A. (2002). Histone methylation defines epigenetic asymmetry in the mouse zygote. *Int. J. Dev. Biol.* **46,** 317–320.

25. Erhardt, S., Su, I.H., Schneider, R., Barton, S., Bannister, A.J., Perez-Burgos, L., Jenuwein, T., Kouzarides, T., Tarakhovsky, A., and Surani, M.A. (2003). Consequences of the depletion of zygotic and embryonic enhancer of zeste 2 during preimplantation mouse development. *Development* **130,** 4235–4248.

26. Tada, T., and Tada, M. (2001). Toti-/pluripotential stem cells and epigenetic modifications. *Cell Struct. Funct.* **26,** 149–160.

27. Reyes, J.C., Barra, J., Muchardt, C., Camus, A., Babinet, C., and Yaniv, M. (1998). Altered control of cellular proliferation in the absence of mammalian brahma (SNF2alpha). *EMBO J.* **17,** 6979–6991.

28. Bultman, S., Gebuhr, T., Yee, D., La Mantia, C., Nicholson, J., Gilliam, A., Randazzo, F., Metzger, D., Chambon, P., Crabtree, G., and Magnuson, T. (2000). A Brg1 null mutation in the mouse reveals functional differences among mammalian SWI/SNF complexes. *Mol. Cell* **6,** 1287–1295.

29. Gibbons, R.J., McDowell, T.L., Raman, S., O'Rourke, D.M., Garrick, D., Ayyub, H., and Higgs, D.R. (2000). Mutations in ATRX, encoding a SWI/SNF-like protein, cause diverse changes in the pattern of DNA methylation. *Nat. Genet.* **24,** 368–371.

30. Meehan, R.R., Pennings, S., and Stancheva, I. (2001). Lashings of DNA methylation, forkfuls of chromatin remodeling. *Genes Dev.* **15,** 3231–3236.

31. Kikyo, N., Wade, P.A., Guschin, D., Ge, H., and Wolffe, A.P. (2000). Active remodeling of somatic nuclei in egg cytoplasm by the nucleosomal ATPase ISWI. *Science* **289,** 2360–2362.

32. Li, E. (2002). Chromatin modification and epigenetic reprogramming in mammalian development. *Nat. Rev. Genet.* **3,** 662–673.

33. Plath, K., Fang, J., Mlynarczyk-Evans, S.K., Cao, R., Worringer, K.A., Wang, H., de la Cruz, C.C., Otte, A.P., Panning, B., and Zhang, Y. (2003). Role of histone H3 lysine 27 methylation in X inactivation. *Science* **300,** 131–135.

34. Silva, J., Mak, W., Zvetkova, I., Appanah, R., Nesterova, T.B., Webster, Z., Peters, A.H., Jenuwein, T., Otte, A.P., and Brockdorff, N. (2003). Establishment of histone h3 methylation on the inactive X chromosome requires transient recruitment of Eed-Enx1 polycomb group complexes. *Dev. Cell* **4,** 481–495.

35. O'Carroll, D., Erhardt S., Pagani, M., Barton, S.C., Surani, M.A. and Jenuwein, T. (2001). The Polycomb group gene Ezh2 is required for early mouse development. *Mol. Cell Biol.* **21,** 4330–4336.

36. Tada, M., Tada, T., Lefebvre, L., Barton, S.C., and Surani, M.A. (1997). Embryonic germ cells induce epigenetic reprogramming of somatic nucleus in hybrid cells. *EMBO J.* **16,** 6510–6520.

37. Tada, M. (2001). Nuclear reprogramming of somatic cells by in vitro hybridisation with ES cells. *Curr. Biol.* **11,** 1553–1558.

38. Byrne, J.A., Simonsson, S., Western, P.S., and Gurdon, J.B. (2003). Nuclei of adult mammalian somatic cells are directly reprogrammed to oct-4 stem cell gene expression by amphibian oocytes. *Curr. Biol.* **13,** 1206–1213.

39. Collas, P. (2003). Nuclear reprogramming in cell-free extracts. *Philos. Trans. R. Soc. Lond. Biol. Sci.* **358,** 1389–1395.

66

Immunogenicity of Human Embryonic Stem Cells

Micha Drukker, Gil Katz, Ofer Mandelboim, and Nissim Benvenisty

The recent introduction of human embryonic stem (ES) cells into the emerging field of cellular transplantation therapeutics has boosted worldwide attention to the potential medical treatments that may be available using these cells. Harnessing their potential must meet with several safety prerequisites including the cells' capability to improve symptoms without generating hazardous side effects and the prevention of immune rejection processes by the patient. Examination of the expression profile of immunologic antigens in human ES cells suggests that these cells might be rejected upon transplantation; however, they may be better reagents than more conventional sources. Importantly, the capability to derive autologous ES cell lines specifically for each patient may serve to circumvent rejection. This review outlines the immunologic properties of human ES cells related to immune rejection processes. In addition, various methodologies to overcome rejection of human ES derived cells are discussed.

Introduction

Human ES cells were recently isolated and cultured *in vitro*.[1,2] Similar to their murine counterparts, they were derived from the inner cell mass (ICM) of blastocyst-stage embryos. The pluripotency of these cells is demonstrated by the cells' potential to spontaneously differentiate to various cell types of the three embryonic germ layers including ectoderm, mesoderm, and endoderm. This differentiation was observed *in vivo,* during teratoma formation following injection of the cells into severe combined immunodeficient (SCID) mice[1,2] and *in vitro* by their aggregation to spherical structures termed embryoid bodies (EBs).[3] Remarkably, *in vitro* differentiation can be directed toward specific cell lineages by addition of various growth factors,[4] and enrichment protocols were developed for specific cell types such as neurons,[5–8] trophoblasts,[9] endothelial cells,[10] and cardiomyocytes.[11–14] Similarly, manipulating culture conditions by combining specialized feeder cells and growth factors was shown to induce differentiation toward the hematopoietic lineage.[15] In addition, the differentiation pathway of transplanted human ES cells in the chick embryo was suggested to be directed to the neuronal lineage by positioning the cells next to the notochord and neuronal tube.[16] The application of genetic manipulation techniques to human ES cells may also be used to enrich cultures of specific cell types.

This principle was demonstrated by transfecting human ES cells with a transgene, containing the enhanced green fluorescent protein (eGFP) marker gene fused to the promoter sequence of the *Rex-1* gene, which is expressed in pluripotent cells.[17] Similarly, knockin of the eGFP gene into the *POU5F1* locus in human ES cells was shown to enable tracking of undifferentiated cells.[18] These studies demonstrated systems in which eGFP expression persist mainly in undifferentiated cultures, allowing the isolation of undifferentiated cells out of a heterogeneous population.

Human ES cells are capable of indefinitely propagating in culture while remaining undifferentiated, and their differentiation can be rapidly induced. Thus, it was suggested that they could serve as a primary source of transplantable cell types for therapy in a broad range of diseases and injuries. The use of human ES cells in the clinic has several advantages over other fetal-derived cells because the latter are only rarely available and are difficult to maintain in culture, and their genetic manipulation is technically difficult. Moreover, adult cells may be inferior to ES cells because of their immunologic properties which are discussed later.

There are still, however, several problems that should be considered before the transplantation of human ES-derived cells. These include, for example, the isolation of a desired cell type out of a mixed population before transplantation, because other cell types may cause deleterious effects. This problem may be overcome by introducing a marker protein into the cells that will be expressed only when differentiation to a specific cell type has taken place.[17] However, even after careful *in vitro* selection of the desired cells, transplantation may still result in dangerous side effects such as teratoma formation from remaining undifferentiated cells.[19] In this regard Schuldiner *et al.*[20] created stably transfected human ES cell clones with the suicide gene element HSV thymidine kinase (HSV-*tk*). After the injection of these cells into a mouse model, the suicide gene enabled the destruction of overproliferating human ES cells by drug administration.[20] Transplanted cells might also transmit infectious agents such as human pathogens or murine viruses that could pass from murine feeder cells to the human ES cells. Therefore, human ES cell lines growing in the presence of human feeder cells were recently derived.[21–23]

Finally, one major concern regarding transplantation of human ES cells is immune rejection by the patient. The aim of this review is to describe the status of human ES cell immunogenicity. In addition, we describe several unique strategies that may be used to tolerate the transplant. These include transplantation into immune-privileged sites, generating a data base of many cell lines derived from different donors,

Handbook of Stem Cells
Volume 1

establishment of autologous ES cell line following somatic nuclear transfer (NT) or egg parthenogenesis, and induction of donor specific hematopoietic chimerism. In addition, molecules involved in immunologic responses can be genetically manipulated. As each of these approaches has its own advantages and disadvantages, their potential use in therapy is discussed on the basis of experimental feasibility and potential use in the clinic.

Immunologic Considerations for Embryonic Stem Cell Transplantation

In most cases, the transplantation of tissues or organs between two genetically unrelated individuals without treatment by immunosuppressive drugs will result in the generation of an immune response toward the transplant and consequently to graft rejection. This process is aimed at alloantigens: which are antigens that vary between individuals and are, therefore, perceived as foreign by the recipient immune system. The probability of complete alloantigen matching between two individuals is the multiplication of allele frequency in all immunogenic loci. In human ES cell therapy, as in organ transplantation, the three most important classes of alloantigens that may cause rejection are the major histocompatibility complex (MHC) antigens, the minor histocompatibility complex (mHC) antigens, and the ABO blood group antigens. This section presents the mechanisms by which any of these classes of antigens can be perceived as foreign in the context of human ES cell–based therapy. In addition, we discuss the natural killer (NK) cells that may also be involved in graft rejection.

MAJOR HISTOCOMPATIBILITY COMPLEX ANTIGENS

The genes coding for the human MHC family of glycoproteins are located in a cluster at chromosome 6 that contains approximately 200 genes. In humans, the MHC proteins were named human leukocyte antigen (HLA). These genes encode for two classes of HLA molecules, the class I α-chain (HLA-I) and the class II α and β chains (HLA-II). There are three HLA-I genes, called HLA-A, HLA-B, and HLA-C (classical HLA-I). The products of these genes form complexes with the nonpolymorphic β_2-microglobulin molecule encoded on chromosome 15. Together with a short peptide generated in the cytosol and transported into the endoplasmic reticulum (ER), the complex translocates to the cell membrane, where it forms a functional MHC class I molecule (MHC-I) (Fig. 66–1A). MHC class II (MHC-II) molecules are formed by association of HLA-II α and β chains in addition to a peptide derived mostly from intracellular vesicles. There are three pairs of HLA-II genes, termed HLA-DP, HLA-DQ, and HLA-DR (Fig. 66–1B). In some individuals an additional DRβ-chain can pair with DRα chain, forming a fourth pair.

The pivotal role played by MHC molecules is to present small peptides derived from pathogens to T lymphocytes. In addition, the MHC-I proteins can serve as ligands for receptors expressed on another type of lymphocytes—the natural killer (NK) cells. MHC-I molecules are expressed in varying levels on most nucleated cells. The molecules function by

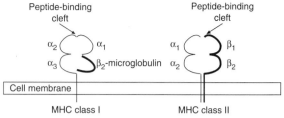

Figure 66–1. *Schematic illustration of major histocompatibility complex molecules. (A) The MHC-I molecules are heterodimers composed of highly variable transmembrane heavy chain HLA-A, -B, or -C bound noncovalently to the nonvariable β_2-microglobulin light chain. α_1 and α_2 domains create the peptide-binding cleft. (B) The MHC-II molecules are composed of two glycoprotein variable HLA-II chains. The α_1 and β_1 domains form the peptide-binding cleft.*

presenting their bound peptides to CD8 cytotoxic T-cells that kill pathogen infected cells upon recognition of nonself peptides. In contrast, MHC-II molecules are expressed mainly on specialized antigen-presenting cells (APCs) including dendritic cells (DCs), B lymphocytes, and macrophages. Interaction of these cells with CD4 T-cells activates macrophages and antibody production by B cells.

Polymorphism and polygenicity are the two properties of MHC molecules that prevent transfer of organs between individuals. The MHC genes are the most polymorphic in the human genome with some of the genes having a few hundred alleles.[24] Because up to seven different MHC molecules are expressed co-dominantly (i.e., from both paternal and maternal chromosomes) in every person, the number of possible MHC combinations in the population is striking. In some cases, difference in even a single amino acid at the MHC antigen can give rise to an alloreactive immune response, because the nonself MHC molecule is perceived as foreign, leading to graft destruction.[25] The cellular mechanisms that activate rejection are highly complex and can occur through several possible routes. We first discuss the expression of MHC molecules on human ES cells and then the possible mechanisms of rejection that may act on their differentiated derivatives.

The expression of MHC molecules on human ES cells was recently assayed in our laboratory using a panel of antibodies.[26] Undifferentiated cells were found to express only low levels of MHC-I molecules, whereas spontaneous differentiation of the cells *in vitro* into EBs caused a moderated elevation in MHC-I expression (2- to 4-fold increase). A higher elevation in expression was found following differentiation of the cells *in vivo* into teratomas (8- to 10-fold increase).[26] However, the absolute level of expression was still below other somatic cells tested, such as monocytes and HeLa cells (Fig. 66–2A). These results are in contrast with the reported expression of MHC-I on mouse ES cells, in which the undifferentiated cells are MHC-I negative and fully mature EB cells express only very low levels of MHC-I.[27] Potent inducers of MHC molecules are the cytokine family of interferons (IFNs) that are normally released during the activation of the

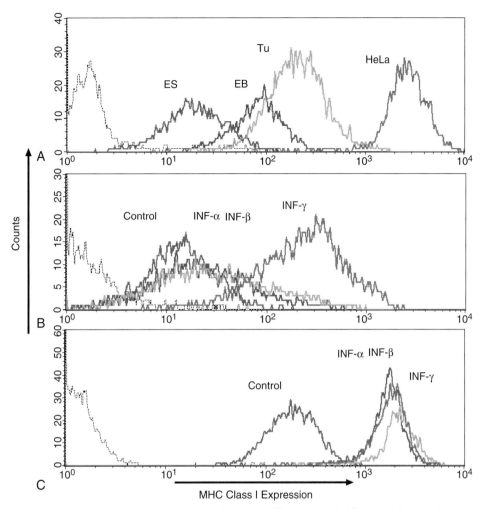

Figure 66–2. *Expression of major histocompatibility complex (MHC-I) in undifferentiated and differentiated human embryonic stem (ES) cells. (A) Fluorescence-activated cell sorting (FACS) analysis of HLA-I expression (assayed by the W6/32 Ab).*[26] *Influence of interferon IFN-α, β, or γ on undifferentiated human ES cells (B), and on in vivo differentiated human ES cells (C). EB, in vitro differentiated embryoid bodies (EBs) derived from human ES cells; ES, undifferentiated human ES cells; HeLa, cervix epithelial somatic cell line; Tu, an in vivo differentiated tumor derived from human ES cells.*

immune system. The addition of IFN-γ to human ES cells resulted in marked elevation of MHC-I expression, whereas neither IFN-α nor IFN-β had any effect (Fig. 66–2B). In agreement with these results, DNA microarray analysis revealed that mRNA levels of the receptor for IFN-γ but not for IFN-α and IFN-β are expressed in the cells. Interestingly, all IFNs had similar strong inductive effect on MHC-I expression when the human ES–derived teratoma cell line was used. In this case, the expression levels were similar to those observed in somatic cells (Fig. 66–2C).[26] In contrast, MHC-II molecules were virtually absent from both undifferentiated and differentiated human ES cells, even following IFN stimulation. We conclude that differentiated human ES cells are undoubtedly capable to express high levels of MHC-I molecules. As expected, these cells do not readily express MHC-II molecules; however, it is still possible that following hematopoietic differentiation the cells will express high levels of these molecules.

Direct Recognition of Nonself Major Histocompatibility Complex Molecules

During their maturation, T-cells undergo selection for those cells that can respond to foreign antigens bound to a particular self-MHC molecule but not to self-antigens, a process called positive and negative selection. The result is a huge repertoire of cells, each expressing a different, highly variable T-cell receptor (TCR). Normally, this molecule interacts with a bound antigen, within the self-MHC molecule. Interestingly, it was found that approximately 1–10% of T lymphocytes in every individual can also respond to nonself MHC molecules expressed on transplantable tissues originated from an unrelated person (reviewed in reference 28). This phenomenon is thought to reflect the cross-reactive nature of the TCR, which is normally specific for a certain self-MHC in a complex with nonself antigen but may react with nonself MHC molecules following transplantation. This may lead to

T-cell activation that targets the graft for destruction by cellular and humoral effector mechanisms.

Following transplantation alloreactive T-cells may mediate graft rejection by three direct routes. The first takes place when effector alloreactive CD8 T-cells recognize nonself MHC molecules, especially MHC-I molecules on the surface of the transplanted cells. As effector T-cells (also termed armed effector T-cells) do not require further differentiation or proliferation, their direct binding to allogeneic MHC-I molecules will cause rejection. However, the number and specificity of alloreactive effector T-cells rely on pre-exposure to pathogens, thus the extent of this reaction may vary greatly. In the second route, alloreactive memory CD8 T-cells may differentiate to effector cells upon interaction with donor cells harboring MHC-I in the presence of recipient CD4 T-cells. As the latter can provide help signals for restimulation of memory CD8 T-cells, CD4-dependent expansion of alloreactive CD8 T-cells after transplantation can contribute greatly to graft rejection (reviewed in reference 29). The third possible mechanism of direct rejection occurs through activation of naive circulating T-cells that following activation differentiate into effector T-cells. The most potent cells that activate naive T-cells are DCs that express on their surface not only MHC molecules but also co-stimulatory molecules such as B7.1 (CD80) and B7.2 (CD86) that are essential for T-cell activation and differentiation.

During conventional organ transplantation the transferred tissue carries some APCs called "passenger leukocytes" into the recipient. These cells play a pivotal role in activating the immune system to react against the graft. Following organ transfer these cells migrate to regional lymph nodes, where they encounter naive T-cells (reviewed in references 30 and 31). Encountering the foreign APCs, alloreactive T-cells are stimulated and become effector T-cells, resulting in the direct attack of the graft after their return to circulation (Fig. 66–3A). This route most probably will not cause rejection of differentiated human ES cells since these derivatives may contain DCs or other APCs, only if hematopoietic differentiation has taken place. In this regard, it is possible to ensure safety by depletion of DCs from the transplanted cells resulting in significantly reduced acute immune rejection.[32] Alternatively, it may be possible to track dendritic differentiation by transgene introduction into undifferentiated human ES cells that will express a marker protein upon DC differentiation.

Indirect Recognition of Nonself Major Histocompatibility Complex Molecules

Indirect recognition of nonself MHC molecules is initiated through uptake of foreign MHC proteins by recipient APCs and their presentation by self-MHC molecules to T cells, leading to their sensitization (Fig. 66–3B) (reviewed in reference 30). This pathway is analogous to pathogen presentation by DCs and, therefore, can activate immune response not only toward nonself MHC antigens by also to other polymorphic antigens (see next section). T cells activated in this route may initiate graft rejection by activating B cells to differentiate into plasma cells (terminally differentiated

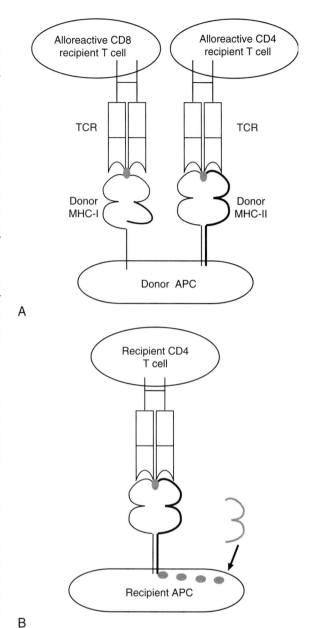

Figure 66–3. *Direct and indirect pathways of rejection. (A) Direct allorecognition—donor-derived antigen-presenting cells (APCs) stimulate alloreactive recipient T cells at the peripheral lymph nodes. Major histocompatibility complex (MHC-1) interacts with CD8-positive T-cells, whereas CD4-positive T-cells interact with MHC-II. (B) Indirect allorecognition—recipient APCs process MHC peptides derived from donor cells and present them to recipient allospecific T-cells, preferentially to CD4+ T-cells.*

B cells) that secrete alloantibodies. In this way, when human ES cell–derived antigens will serve to conjugate T and B cells, secreted antibodies would bind alloantigens on the surface of the transplanted cells. This will invariably lead to antibody-dependent destruction mechanisms such as the complement system (see reference in 33).

Another pathway of graft rejection is delayed-type hypersensitivity (DTH). This response may be initiated when local recipient APCs ingest graft proteins, process them, and present the resulting peptides to the T_H1 subset of T cells.[34] Following presentation to previously activated T_H1, cells, they release a battery of cytokines[35] that recruit phagocytes and plasma leading to tissue damage. Thus, if polymorphic peptides derived from transplanted differentiated human ES cells will activate local inflammatory response, due to their presentation to local T_H1 cells, the graft and its surrounding may suffer a profound damage.

Since these indirect pathways do not require direct recognition between alloantigens expressed on the transplant and cells of the recipient immune system, they are likely to play a major role in rejecting human ES differentiated derivatives. This is because differentiated human ES cells express MHC-I proteins that may act as stimulators and as targets for the indirect route of rejection. The methodologies that can be adopted to evade these effects may include the use of matching MHC isotypes, production of autologous cell lines, hematopoietic chimerism, and genetic manipulation techniques to lower MHC expression on the cells (see the section on minimizing rejection risks).

MINOR HISTOCOMPATIBILITY ALLOREACTIVITY

With the exception of organ transplantation between identical twins, transplantation between MHC-matched, genetically unrelated individuals may result in a slow rejection. This phenomenon reflects the genetic variation within the population that translates to differences in the bound peptides presented by the MHC molecules. As noted previously, T cells are highly discriminative in their capability to recognize only nonself peptides bound to self-MHC proteins but can become sensitized when even a single amino acid is substituted within a self-peptide.[36] Thus, cellular proteins that may lead to rejection, because of their natural variation, were named mHCs. The vigor at which this reaction takes place is dependent on the sum of genetic differences between individuals, meaning that a high variation in mHC antigens increases the proportion of alloreactive T cells leading to accelerated rejection.[37]

When considering differentiated human ES cells for transplantation, mHC alloantigens may be far less significant than MHC differences, which are the major cause of graft rejection. Moreover, keeping in mind that human ES cell derivatives do not contain APCs, the stimulation of direct allorecognition by recipient CD8 T cells to donor mHC antigens is likely to be limited. In this regard, the problem of mHC alloantigens can be partially circumvented using human ES cell lines derived from a female embryo for clinical applications. These cell lines will not contain chromosome Y specific antigens (H-Y antigens) that are an important group of mHCs.

THE ROLE OF ABO BLOOD GROUP ANTIGENS IN GRAFT REJECTION

The first histocompatibility alloantigens identified were the ABO blood group antigens. The difference between the A and B antigens lies in a single sugar unit addition (absent in O blood type) to the carbohydrate chain of a cell surface glycolipid that is expressed not only on erythrocytes but presumably on many cell types of the body.[38,39] Alloreactive antibodies that may recognize this polymorphism develop at early childhood in individuals that do not carry either A, B, or both antigens, as a result of exposure to polysaccharides of intestine bacteria.[40] Thus, transplantation of vascularized organs between ABO-incompatible individuals will invariably result in recognition of the organ by alloreactive antibodies, followed by activation of the complement system leading to organ destruction.

It is not known today whether human ES cells or their differentiated derivatives express ABO antigens. However, as many cell types of the body express these antigens[38,39] it is possible that they will be present on the surface of human ES cell derivatives. Therefore, matching these antigens before transplantation could be a prerequisite not only in conventional medicine but also in ES cell–based therapies. This is important since compatibility of ABO antigens is probably also essential for the survival of nonvascularized organs such as the pancreas.[41] One strategy that may be used to avoid ABO incompatibility is to derive new human ES cell lines from fertilized eggs that do not code for A or B antigens. These lines can serve as universal donors for every individual because they will not be recognized as foreign in the context of ABO antigens.

TRANSPLANT REJECTION BY NATURAL KILLER CELLS

Reduced expression of MHC proteins on graft cells is thought to increase the transplants' resistance to rejection. However, down-regulation of MHC-I can initiate cytotoxic response by recipient NK lymphocytes, caused by MHC-I proteins' inhibitory effect on NK cells.[42] It was recently demonstrated that transplanted mouse ES-derived hematopoietic progenitors, expressing low levels of MHC-I molecules, were susceptible to NK-mediated cytolysis following injection to immune-deficient mice.[43] In our own studies we examined the susceptibility of human ES cells to lysis by NK cells, in light of the very small amounts of MHC-I molecules expressed by human ES cells.[26] We found that irrespective of the cells state of differentiation and the expression level of MHC-I (induced by IFN-γ), in vitro, they were not recognized by NK cells. Moreover, the high incidence of human[2] and mouse[44] ES cell–derived teratomas in SCID mice, which have normal populations of NK cells,[45] implies that ES cells are not readily rejected by NK cells.

In another experiment, we tested the presence of NK inhibitory molecules on human ES cells. Among these are the nonclassical HLA-I molecules HLA-G and HLA-E that were found to inhibit the cytolytic activity of NK cells.[42] HLA-G is normally expressed on cytotrophoblasts at the fetomaternal interface[46] and was also found on trophectodermal cells of human blastocyst-stage embryos but not on the cells of the ICM.[47] Cytotrophoblasts express only low levels of MHC-I. Thus, HLA-G expression functions to protect the fetus from maternal NK cells. HLA-E is normally expressed on all MHC-I expressing cells, serving to present HLA-I leader peptides to

Micha Drukker, Gil Katz, Ofer Mandelboim, and Nissim Benvenisty

NK cells, thus contributing to their inhibition.[48] We found that HLA-G was absent from undifferentiated and differentiated human ES cells; therefore, the lack in NK cell killing could not be explained by HLA-G inhibition.[26] HLA-E on the other hand was clearly expressed on human ES–derived teratoma cells, and its expression was simultaneously induced together with MHC-I by IFNs. This indicates that antigen processing and presentation in these cells is normal and that inhibition of NK cells will probably occur *in vivo*.

Minimizing Rejection Risks of Human Embryonic Stem–Derived Cells

The isolation of human ES cells has created great interest in their capability to differentiate to various cell types that may be beneficial in transplantation medicine. We have speculated that transplanting human ES cells similarly to organ transplantation will induce rejection by the host immune system. A general strategy to avoid rejection is to transplant cells into one of the natural immune-privileged sites of the body where immune responses are limited, such as the brain, eye, and the testis. Alternatively, overcoming rejection can be dealt with by matching polymorphic differences, creating syngeneic (i.e., genetically identical) cell lines specifically for each patient, inducing hematopoietic chimerism, or by introducing genetic changes to human ES cell lines to create a universal donor cell line (Fig. 66–4).

ALLOGRAFT TRANSPLANTATION INTO IMMUNE-PRIVILEGED SITES

The rate at which allogeneic grafts are rejected depends not only on MHC mismatches but also on the site of transplantation. In various animals, the immune response to grafts placed in the anterior part of the eye, brain, or testis is considerably restricted in comparison to other locations of the body. Therefore, these sites were termed immunologically privileged sites. One of the notable examples in this regard is corneal eye transplantations, which do not require tissue

matching or immunosuppression. The mechanisms contributing to immune privilege are complex and include at least three lines of defense: (1) these sites have an atypical lymphatic drainage and are separated from the rest of the body by physical barriers such as the blood–brain barrier, (2) immune-privileged tissues produce local immunosuppressive cytokines such as transforming growth factor β (TGFβ) that restricts immune responses, and (3) they express Fas ligand (FasL) that induces apoptosis in Fas-bearing lymphocytes (reviewed in 49).

Can these sites be used to suppress immune response toward differentiated human ES cells? Accumulating data concerning transplantation of non-MHC matched dopaminergic neurons in Parkinson's patients suggests that such transplants survive for long periods of time and may improve symptoms even in absence of immunosuppression.[50] Therefore, it is reasonable that grafted human ES differentiated derivatives, in immune-privileged sites such as the brain, may have better survival than in other sites. However, rejection processes can still occur in the brain and in other immune-privileged sites and therefore some degree of immunosuppression may be necessary. It may be also possible to confer immunoresistance to transplanted cells by genetically manipulating the cells to express proteins, such as FasL, that limit immune responses in immune-privileged sites (see the section on genetic engineering).

MATCHING ALLOANTIGENIC INCOMPATIBILITY

ABO antigens are the simplest form of genetic variation that must be dealt with to ensure safe transplantation. Routinely, AB antigens are matched before transplantation, but, in the context of human ES cells, it may be ideal to create cell lines that would be of the O blood group. Thus, cells derived from these cell lines would be compatible to every individual, because the O antigen is not recognized by pre-existing antibodies.

Matching HLA differences between nonrelated individuals poses a far more difficult task than ABO antigens. As these antigens are the primary targets during graft rejection, huge efforts are made to match HLA haplotypes before transplantation of

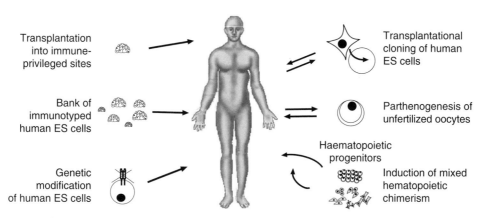

Figure 66–4. Strategies for reducing the immunogenicity of human embryonic stem (ES)-differentiated derivatives.

certain organs. In contrast, the transplantation of differentiated human ES cells has some advantages including the relatively low levels of MHC-I molecules expressed during both *in vivo* and *in vitro* differentiation and the absence of MHC-II molecules even following IFN induction (see the section MHC antigens). Moreover, as discussed previously, human ES cell differentiated derivatives will most probably not contain APCs, which in organ transplantation could directly stimulate alloreactive T-cells. Together, these characteristics may enable the use of less severe immunosuppression treatment and prolonged graft survival.

However, wide therapeutic use of human ES cells may require HLA matching. It has been proposed that many cell lines with a broad variety of haplotypes could be derived so that each patient will have a matching cell line. Theoretically, the number of allele combinations for the three genes of MHC-I alone is more than 10 million haplotypes, generating more than a billion diploid combinations.[51] These numbers make it virtually impossible to build a bank of human ES cell lines that will be compatible for the majority of the population. However, some allele mismatches have only a small contribution to graft rejection[52] and not all alleles are evenly distributed in the population. Thus, the size of such a cell line bank is difficult to predict but may require millions of cell lines to treat the majority of the population. Selecting cell lines that are homozygous to HLA alleles may help to reduce the banks' size, because these cell lines can be matched to more individuals than fully heterozygous cell lines. Even better, cell lines obtained by somatic NT or parthenogenesis can be derived from selected immunotyped individuals that are HLA-compatible to a relatively large proportion of the population (see the next section).

GENERATION OF AUTOLOGOUS HUMAN EMBRYONIC STEM CELL LINES

Generation of an autologous ES cell line for each patient will overcome the problem of rejection. This may be accomplished by somatic cell NT to enucleated oocytes, from which ES cells can be eventually derived after *in vitro* development to the blastocyst stage. Alternatively, it may be possible to generate parthenogenetic ES cell lines from *in vitro* activated human eggs that were allowed to develop to blastocysts. Although these options may be seen as excellent solutions to the problem of rejection, it is important to note that neither has been successfully implemented in humans.

Derivation of Autologous Embryonic Stem Cell Lines Using Somatic Cell Nuclear Transfer

The generation of an autologous ES cell line that carries the patient's genome may be the ideal reagent for transplantation, because these cells are almost completely genetically identical to the donor. This procedure involves the transfer of a patient's nucleus into an enucleated oocyte, and, if nuclear reprogramming has occurred, the embryos may mature normally. Embryos reaching the blastocyst stage are then disaggregated and ES cell lines can be derived. This procedure termed therapeutic cloning or genomic replacement gives rise

to cells genetically identical to the nucleus donor except for maternal mitochondrial DNA. To date, the isolation of ES cells from NT embryos was successful only in mice.[53–55] Although attempts to create ES cell lines from NT embryos were also carried out in humans, the reconstituted embryos did not reach to the blastocyst stage.[56] Assuming that these cell lines could be obtained despite the many technical difficulties, it is still not clear whether the mHC differences between the donor and the ES cell line, originating from mitochondrial polymorphism, would initiate rejection. A recently published work by Lanza *et al.*[57] examined this question in the bovine system. The authors examined the survival of cardiac, skeletal muscle, and renal mHC allografts obtained from NT embryos in the nuclear donor. Interestingly, although transplants expressed mitochondrial mHC antigenic alleles of the egg donor, they were not rejected acutely or by DTH response. Thus, it is possible that similar results will be obtained in humans, and, even if rejection processes are initiated, they are likely to be less severe than in transplantation over MHC differences. Overall NT-derived ES cells could be an ideal source of transplantable cells because they will probably not be rejected. However, the complicated experimental procedures involved and the high costs of NT and derivation of ES cell lines may be far too formidable for widespread application. Moreover, complex ethical issues may restrict the broad use of this procedure (discussed in reference 58).

Parthenogenetic Derivation of Embryonic Stem Cell Lines

Parthenogenesis is the process by which an unfertilized oocyte becomes activated and starts to divide. Although in some vertebrates this occurs normally as part of the life cycle, in humans and other primates this process is rare. The recent isolation of parthenogenetic pluripotent stem cells capable to differentiate to the three embryonic germ layers from primate eggs *(Macaca fascicularis)*[59] have raised hopes that this procedure will be also applicable to human eggs. However, human parthenotes have not yet been cultivated to the blastocyst stage, and no ES cell lines were isolated.[56] There are two main reasons to pursue the production of these special pluripotent stem cells from human oocytes: (1) from the ethical point of view, using parthenogenetic embryos may be much less problematic than normal embryos as they are clearly not viable and stop developing normally during pregnancy (see reference 59) and (2) because parthenogenetic embryos are derived from eggs, they are fully immunocompatible to the female from which they were taken. This means that if human parthenogenetic pluripotent stem cells are derived from female patients, the differentiated cells could be transplanted back without risk of rejection. Moreover, because these cells are homozygous at all loci they could serve as excellent donors for HLA banks accomplishing HLA matching in a greater proportion of patients than normal ES cell lines (see "Matching Alloantigenic Incompatibility"). These cell lines may also be advantageous for their transplantation to genetically related family members as the HLA genes are linked on a specific region in chromosome 6, which covers approximately 4 cM of DNA. Therefore, if recombination within the HLA region does not occur, half of the cell lines derived from a patient will be HLA matched to her offspring, although a 50% difference in the mHC loci will still remain. Importantly, these cell lines will not contain H-Y antigens that are derived only from male cell lines and potentially can activate graft rejection (see the section on mHC alloreactivity). In conclusion, it seems that derivation of human pluripotent stem cell lines by parthenogenesis may eventually be simpler and less costly than by NT owing to the low yield of reprogrammed embryos and other technical difficulties. The possibility of preparing HLA-compatible cell lines for genetically related patients may make parthenogenesis a primary route for derivation of autologous ES cells for transplantation.

THE USE OF HEMATOPOIETIC CHIMERISM FOR TOLERANCE INDUCTION

In contrast to the aforementioned strategies, in some circumstances MHC matching may be unnecessary if the host is conditioned to stably carry donor-specific multilineage hematopoiesis, a state called mixed hematopoietic chimerism (reviewed in reference 60). In this process donor-derived bone marrow cells are transplanted to another individual, leading to long-term hematopoietic coexistence of both host and donor cells. Donor APCs populate the thymus together with host APCs, causing negative selection of self-recognizing immature T-cells. Thus, alloreactive T-cells are depleted. In this case, an additional organ from the same donor can be transferred to the host with a limited risk of rejection, as has been demonstrated in 28 cases of human transplantations.[61]

The issue of mixed hematopoietic chimerism has a special relevance to the clinical use of human ES cells. Using these cells, it may be possible to generate hematopoietic cells[15] and other cell types from a single cell line, thus tolerance can be achieved allowing cellular transplantation of various differentiated cells. Ideally, if mixed chimerism persists, even when an HLA noncompatible human ES cell line is used, immunosuppression may be unnecessary. Induction of tolerance by hematopoietic progenitors derived from human ES cells may have an additional advantage over bone marrow cells. Because the latter contain mature T-cells, these must be depleted, otherwise graft-versus-host disease (GVHD), in which donor T-cells attack host tissues due to allorecognition, may develop (reviewed in reference 62). T-cells require multiple steps of activation in the thymus and other peripheral lymph nodes for their maturation. Human ES hematopoietic derivatives will, therefore, most probably not be able to cause GVHD.

Although mixed hematopoietic chimerism may induce tolerance to a second graft, current protocols require complete or partial myeloablation (elimination of the host hematopoietic system) by cytotoxic drugs or whole-body irradiation.[62] This requirement may severely restrict the broad use of this methodology in humans as it is highly hazardous to the patient. An alternative to irradiation is antibody-dependent depletion of CD4 and CD8 T cells in combination with local thymic irradiation.[63]

A recent work by Fandrich *et al.*[64] raised the possibility that ES cells similarly to bone marrow cells can act to induce donor-specific tolerance. The authors showed that rat ES–like cells (RESC), derived from preimplantation-stage embryos, express low levels of MHC-I and lack expression of MHC-II and co-stimulatory molecules. To test the immunogenicity and differentiation capacity, the cells were injected into the portal vein of fully MHC-mismatched rats without prior conditioning. Surprisingly, the cells not only survived but also exhibited differentiation to monocytes and B-cells. Moreover, a state of stable mixed chimerism was observed in the injected animals. Presumably, blood chimerism allowed acceptance of a second-set cardiac transplant from the same donor rat strain, but not from a third-party origin, demonstrating that immunocompetence is not hampered by RESC treatment. The authors suggest two mechanisms underlying RESC resistance to alloreactive T-cells. One explanation is that allogeneic RESC do not express co-stimulatory molecules prior to transplantation; therefore, alloreactive naive T-cells are not sensitized toward them. Another explanation is that the presence of FasL (CD95L) on the transplanted RESC may activate Fas on alloreactive T-cells, leading to their apoptosis. Do human ES cells share these characteristics as well? At this time it is clear that co-stimulatory molecules CD80 and CD86 are not expressed on undifferentiated cells (M.D. and N.B., unpublished), but it still is not clear whether FasL is expressed. Testing the capability to induce tolerance by injecting undifferentiated cells into humans could devastatingly lead to teratomas. Therefore, other *in vitro* means must be developed to test their capacity to confer tolerance such as those used in rodents.[65] Also, if injection of undifferentiated human ES cells eventually proves to be safe, there is no indication that *in vivo*, like RESC, they will differentiate and function as thymic APCs that are required for donor-specific tolerance induction.

If indeed human ES cells prove to induce donor-specific mixed chimerism, then this procedure may be highly advantageous to confer tolerance for second-set transplants. However, questions regarding the biologic mechanisms underlying tolerance induction and the need for host preconditioning in humans must be met before using this procedure in the clinic.

GENETIC ENGINEERING OF HUMAN EMBRYONIC STEM CELLS

An alternative method to those previously described is to genetically alter the immune properties of the cells. To generate such a "universal cell" that can be transplanted to every individual it will be necessary to either reduce expression of the polymorphic MHC and mHC molecules or prevent their killing, using natural immune-suppressive mechanisms such as those known to work in immune-privileged sites.

When homozygous β_2-microglobulin knockout mice were produced they were found to be almost totally negative for MHC-I expression, since β_2-microglobulin is required for assembly and translocation of MHC-I to the cell membrane.[66] Later MHC-II knockout mice were also prepared, and the two strains were crossed to produce mice lacking both MHC-I and

MHC-II (reviewed in reference 67). It was hoped that tissues from this strain could serve as a "universal donor" across MHC mismatches. Surprisingly, skin grafts from these mice were rejected across MHC, and even mHC disparities, most probably through a T-cell dependent mechanism.[68,69] Apparently, even in β_2-microglobulin knockout mice some residual HLA molecules were expressed on the cells' surface contributing to T-cell activation and rejection.[70] Lowering MHC expression could also function to increase the susceptibility to NK cell–mediated rejection.[71] Does this mean that human transplants derived from MHC-I knockout cells would also be rejected? Because differentiated human ES cells do not express lysis ligands to NK cells, they may prove to be resistant to this type of rejection.[26] However, it is still not clear whether residual MHC-I molecules will induce rejection by alloreactive T cells.

In addition to β_2-microglobulin, other genes may be targeted to lower MHC expression. In the case of MHC-I these include genes encoding for proteins important to assembly and translocation, such as the transporters associated with antigen processing-1 and -2 (TAP1 and TAP2) and tapasin that markedly lead to MHC-I down-regulation following deletion.[72,73] For MHC-II the ideal target may prove to be the invariant chain (il) that chaperones MHC-II molecules to the endosome and subsequently to the outer membrane.[74] Alternatively, factors that participate in transcriptional control of MHC genes, for instance the class II activator (CIITA) and regulatory factor X, 5 (RFX5), which are important to MHC-II expression (reviewed in reference 75), may be targeted for global intervention in MHC expression.

Although, it is not clear whether MHC down-regulation in human ES cells will reduce the possibility of rejection, this situation may be hazardous in some other circumstances. Malignant transformation and viral infection of such genetically modified human ES cells could go undetected as a result of the cells' loss of capacity to present peptides to T-cells. However, NK cells may act to kill cells that have lost MHC expression (see the section on transplant rejection by NK cells). This reaction is stimulated in response to an interplay between the MHC-I levels and recognition of cellular or viral ligands. Thus, in the case of reduction in MHC-I levels a killing reaction may be stimulated in response cell surface ligands. We may presume that nonmalignant differentiated human ES cells will not be readily rejected by NK cells because significant expression of lysis ligands was not recorded in these cells.[26] However, transformation or infection of MHC-I negative human ES cells may still lead to ligand expression and to rejection by NK cells, as an alternative to the reduced capacity of T-cell cytotoxicity.

Protecting transplants may be also achieved by expression of protective molecules. The best known example of such a molecule is FasL that was found to restrict immune responses in immune-privileged sites by inducing apoptosis of T-cells that express its receptor Fas.[76] Attempts to protect allotransplants from the devastating effects of alloreactive T-cells either by transplantation of FasL-expressing cells or by transgenic induction of FasL expression gave conflicting results.

For instance, transgenic expression of FasL in heart and pancreatic transplants resulted in tissue damage or accelerated rejection, supposedly due to of Fas expression within the vicinity of the graft. Nevertheless, in other cases, ectopic FasL expression associates with reduced immune response to allografts as demonstrated with liver, kidneys, lung, blood vessels, and thyroid transplants (reviewed in reference 49). Can this approach be used to protect differentiated human ES cells from rejection? Currently it is reasonable to speculate that it may work for human ES cells keeping in mind two possible complications. One could be the expression of Fas by differentiated human ES cells that would make the induction of FasL expression impossible. In addition, in tissues expressing Fas, transplanting of FasL-positive cells may induce massive cell death. It may be possible to create a universal donor cell line by combining MHC reduction with FasL expression, which will allow safe transplantation to all patients.

Conclusions

In contrast to conventional transplantation medicine that relies on rarely available donated organs and tissues, human ES cells offer to serve as an unlimited cell source for various cell types urgently required for transplantation therapeutics. To exploit this possibility, it is essential to explore the rejection processes that may be induced toward grafts following transplantation of noncompatible ES cell derivatives. The pivotal cellular molecules activating rejection are the MHC alloantigens, mHC antigens, and the ABO blood group antigens. It is known today that human ES cells and their differentiated derivatives can be induced to express high levels of MHC-I molecules, which may initiate rejection by either direct or indirect routes. To circumvent this problem it may be possible in the future to transplant the cells into immune-privileged sites or to build banks of cell lines that would match a high proportion of the population. Alternatively, it may be possible to derive isogeneic cell lines by NT or preferably by parthenogenesis. The latter may be superior because they will be easier to obtain, are fully compatible with to the donor, and may serve to treat genetically related individuals. Other possibilities include induction of hematopoietic chimerism by hematopoietic derivatives of human ES cells and the genetic manipulation of the cells to reduce their susceptibility to recognition by the recipient immune system. Recently, several studies describing the genetic manipulation of human ES cells have been published. Thus, this option may serve in the near future to explore the construction of a universal donor cell line, which ideally could be grafted to virtually all individuals without the need for strong immunosuppression.

REFERENCES

1. Thomson, J.A., Itskovitz-Eldor, J., Shapiro, S.S., Waknitz, M.A., Swiergiel, J.J., Marshall, V.S., and Jones, J.M. (1998). Embryonic stem cell lines derived from human blastocysts. *Science* **282,** 1145–1147.

2. Reubinoff, B.E., Pera, M.F., Fong, C.Y., Trounson, A., and Bongso, A. (2000). Embryonic stem cell lines from human blastocysts: somatic differentiation *in vitro*. *Nat. Biotechnol.* **18**, 399–404.

3. Itskovitz-Eldor, J., Schuldiner, M., Karsenti, D., Eden, A., Yanuka, O., Amit, M., Soreq, H., and Benvenisty, N. (2000). Differentiation of human embryonic stem cells into embryoid bodies comprising the three embryonic germ layers. *Mol. Med.* **6**, 88–95.

4. Schuldiner, M., Yanuka, O., Itskovitz-Eldor, J., Melton, D.A., and Benvenisty, N. (2000). Effects of eight growth factors on the differentiation of cells derived from human embryonic stem cells. *Proc. Natl. Acad. Sci. U. S. A.* **97**, 11307–11312.

5. Schuldiner, M., Eiges, R., Eden, A., Yanuka, O., Itskovitz-Eldor, J., Goldstein, R.S., and Benvenisty, N. (2001). Induced neuronal differentiation of human embryonic stem cells. *Brain. Res.* **913**, 201–205.

6. Zhang, S.C., Wernig, M., Duncan, I.D., Brustle, O., and Thomson, J.A. (2001). *In vitro* differentiation of transplantable neural precursors from human embryonic stem cells. *Nat. Biotechnol.* **19**, 1129–1133.

7. Reubinoff, B.E., Itsykson, P., Turetsky, T., Pera, M.F., Reinhartz, E., Itzik, A., and Ben-Hur, T. (2001). Neural progenitors from human embryonic stem cells. *Nat. Biotechnol.* **19**, 1134–1140.

8. Carpenter, M.K., Inokuma, M.S., Denham, J., Mujtaba, T., Chiu, C.P., and Rao, M.S. (2001). Enrichment of neurons and neural precursors from human embryonic stem cells. *Exp. Neurol.* **172**, 383–397.

9. Xu, R.H., Chen, X., Li, D.S., Li, R., Addicks, G.C., Glennon, C., Zwaka, T.P., and Thomson, J.A. (2002). BMP4 initiates human embryonic stem cell differentiation to trophoblast. *Nat. Biotechnol.* **20**, 1261–1264.

10. Levenberg, S., Golub, J.S., Amit, M., Itskovitz-Eldor, J., and Langer, R. (2002). Endothelial cells derived from human embryonic stem cells. *Proc. Natl. Acad. Sci. U. S. A.* **99**, 4391–4396.

11. Kehat, I., Kenyagin-Karsenti, D., Snir, M., Segev, H., Amit, M., Gepstein, A., Livne, E., Binah, O., Itskovitz-Eldor, J., and Gepstein, L. (2001). Human embryonic stem cells can differentiate into myocytes with structural and functional properties of cardiomyocytes. *J. Clin. Invest.* **108**, 407–414.

12. Xu, C., Police, S., Rao, N., and Carpenter, M.K. (2002). Characterization and enrichment of cardiomyocytes derived from human embryonic stem cells. *Circ. Res.* **91**, 501–508.

13. Mummery, C., Ward, D., van den Brink, C.E., Bird, S.D., Doevendans, P.A., Opthof, T., Brutel de la Riviere, A., Tertoolen, L., van der Heyden, M., and Pera, M. (2002). Cardiomyocyte differentiation of mouse and human embryonic stem cells. *J. Anat.* **200**, 233–242.

14. Kehat, I., Gepstein, A., Spira, A., Itskovitz-Eldor, J., and Gepstein, L. (2002). High-resolution electrophysiological assessment of human embryonic stem cell-derived cardiomyocytes: a novel *in vitro* model for the study of conduction. *Circ. Res.* **91**, 659–661.

15. Kaufman, D.S., Hanson, E.T., Lewis, R.L., Auerbach, R., and Thomson, J.A. (2001). Hematopoietic colony-forming cells derived from human embryonic stem cells. *Proc. Natl. Acad. Sci. U. S. A.* **98**, 10716–10721.

16. Goldstein, R.S., Drukker, M., Reubinoff, B.E., and Benvenisty, N. (2002). Integration and differentiation of human embryonic stem cells transplanted to the chick embryo. *Dev. Dyn.* **225**, 80–86.

17. Eiges, R., Schuldiner, M., Drukker, M., Yanuka, O., Itskovitz-Eldor, J., and Benvenisty, N. (2001). Establishment of human embryonic stem cell-transfected clones carrying a marker for undifferentiated cells. *Curr. Biol.* **11**, 514–518.

18. Zwaka, T.P., and Thomson, J.A. (2003). Homologous recombination in human embryonic stem cells. *Nat. Biotechnol.* **21**, 319–321.

19. Bjorklund, L.M., Sanchez-Pernaute, R., Chung, S., Andersson, T., Chen, I.Y., McNaught, K.S., Brownell, A.L., Jenkins, B.G., Wahlestedt, C., Kim, K.S., and Isacson, O. (2002). Embryonic stem cells develop into functional dopaminergic neurons after transplantation in a Parkinson rat model. *Proc. Natl. Acad. Sci. U. S. A.* **99**, 2344–2349.

20. Schuldiner, M., Itskovitz-Eldor, J., and Benvenisty, N. (2003). Selective ablation of human embryonic stem cells expressing a "suicide" gene. *Stem Cells* **21**, 257–265.

21. Richards, M., Fong, C.Y., Chan, W.K., Wong, P.C., and Bongso, A. (2002). Human feeders support prolonged undifferentiated growth of human inner cell masses and embryonic stem cells. *Nat. Biotechnol.* **20**, 933–936.

22. Amit, M., Margulets, V., Segev, H., Shariki, K., Laevsky, I., Coleman, R., and Itskovitz-Eldor, J. (2003). Human feeder layers for human embryonic stem cells. *Biol. Reprod.* **68**, 2150–2156.

23. Cheng, L., Hammond, H., Ye, Z., Zhan, X., and Dravid, G. (2003). Human adult marrow cells support prolonged expansion of human embryonic stem cells in culture. *Stem Cells* **21**, 131–142.

24. Schreuder, G.M., Hurley, C.K., Marsh, S.G., Lau, M., Maiers, M., Kollman, C., and Noreen, H.J. (2001). The HLA Dictionary 2001: a summary of HLA-A, -B, -C, -DRB1/3/4/5 and -DQB1 alleles and their association with serologically defined HLA-A, -B, -C, -DR and -DQ antigens. *Eur. J. Immunogenet.* **28**, 565–596.

25. Fleischhauer, K., Kernan, N.A., O'Reilly, R.J., Dupont, B., and Yang, S.Y. (1990). Bone marrow-allograft rejection by T lymphocytes recognizing a single amino acid difference in HLA-B44. *N. Engl. J. Med.* **323**, 1818–1822.

26. Drukker, M., Katz, G., Urbach, A., Schuldiner, M., Markel, G., Itskovitz-Eldor, J., Reubinoff, B., Mandelboim, O., and Benvenisty, N. (2002). Characterization of the expression of MHC proteins in human embryonic stem cells. *Proc. Natl. Acad. Sci. U. S. A.* **99**, 9864–9869.

27. Tian, L., Catt, J.W., O'Neill, C., and King, N.J. (1997). Expression of immunoglobulin superfamily cell adhesion molecules on murine embryonic stem cells. *Biol. Reprod.* **57**, 561–568.

28. Zavazava, N., and Kabelitz, D. (2000). Alloreactivity and apoptosis in graft rejection and transplantation tolerance. *J. Leukoc. Biol.* **68**, 167–174.

29. Kaech, S.M., and Ahmed, R. (2003). CD8 T cells remember with a little help. *Science* **300**, 263–265.

30. Gould, D.S., and Auchincloss, H., Jr. (1999). Direct and indirect recognition: the role of MHC antigens in graft rejection. *Immunol. Today* **20**, 77–82.

31. Rogers, N.J., and Lechler, R.I. (2001). Allorecognition. *Am. J. Transplant.* **1**, 97–102.

32. Iwai, H., Kuma, S., Inaba, M.M., Good, R.A., Yamashita, T., Kumazawa, T., and Ikehara, S. (1989). Acceptance of murine thyroid allografts by pretreatment of anti-Ia antibody or anti-dendritic cell antibody *in vitro*. *Transplantation* **47**, 45–49.

33. Boisgerault, F., Anosova, N.G., Tam, R.C., Illigens, B.M., Fedoseyeva, E.V., and Benichou, G. (2000). Induction of T-cell response to cryptic MHC determinants during allograft rejection. *Hum. Immunol.* **61**, 1352–1362.

34. Sirak, J., Orosz, C.G., Wakely, E., and VanBuskirk, A.M. (1997). Alloreactive delayed-type hypersensitivity in graft recipients: complexity of responses and divergence from acute rejection. *Transplantation* **63**, 1300–1307.

35. Liew, F.Y. (2002). T(H)1 and T(H)2 cells: a historical perspective. *Nat. Rev. Immunol.* **2**, 55–60.

36. den Haan, J.M., Meadows, L.M., Wang, W., Pool, J., Blokland, E., Bishop, T.L., Reinhardus, C., Shabanowitz, J., Offringa, R., Hunt, D.F., Engelhard, V.H., and Goulmy, E. (1998). The minor histocompatibility antigen HA-1: a diallelic gene with a single amino acid polymorphism. *Science* **279**, 1054–1057.

37. Simpson, E., Scott, D., James, E., Lombardi, G., Cwynarski, K., Dazzi, F., Millrain, J.M., and Dyson, P. J. (2001). Minor H antigens: genes and peptides. *Eur. J. Immunogenet.* **28**, 505–513.

38. Lill, P.H., Stejskal, R., and Mlsna, J. (1979). Distribution of H antigen in persons of blood groups A, B, and AB. *Vox. Sang.* **36**, 159–165.

39. Clausen, H., and Hakomori, S. (1989). ABH and related histo-blood group antigens: immunochemical differences in carrier isotypes and their distribution. *Vox. Sang.* **56**, 1–20.

40. Springer, G.F., and Horton, R.E. (1969). Blood group isoantibody stimulation in man by feeding blood group-active bacteria. *J. Clin. Invest.* **48**, 1280–1291.

41. Clayton, H.A., Swift, S.M., James, R.F., Horsburgh, T., and London, N.J. (1993). Human islet transplantation: is blood group compatibility important? *Transplantation* **56**, 1538–1540.

42. Moretta, L., Bottino, C., Cantoni, C., Mingari, M.C., and Moretta, A. (2001). Human natural killer cell function and receptors. *Curr. Opin. Pharmacol.* **1**, 387–391.

43. Rideout, W.M., 3rd, Hochedlinger, K., Kyba, M., Daley, G.Q., and Jaenisch, R. (2002). Correction of a genetic defect by nuclear transplantation and combined cell and gene therapy. *Cell* **109**, 17–27.

44. Damjanov, I., Damjanov, A., and Solter, D. (1987). Production of teratocarcinomas from embryos transplanted to extra-uterine sites. *In* "Teratocarcinomas and embryonic stem cells: A practical approach" (E. J. Robertson, Ed.), pp. 1–18. IRL Press Limited, Oxford, UK.

45. Dorshkind, K., Pollack, S.B., Bosma, M.J., and Phillips, R.A. (1985). Natural killer (NK) cells are present in mice with severe combined immunodeficiency (scid). *J. Immunol.* **134**, 3798–3801.

46. Kovats, S., Main, E.K., Librach, C., Stubblebine, M., Fisher, S.J., and DeMars, R. (1990). A class I antigen, HLA-G, expressed in human trophoblasts. *Science* **248**, 220–223.

47. Jurisicova, A., Casper, R.F., MacLusky, N.J., Mills, G.B., and Librach, C.L. (1996). HLA-G expression during preimplantation human embryo development. *Proc. Natl. Acad. Sci. U. S. A.* **93**, 161–165.

48. Lee, N., Goodlett, D.R., Ishitani, A., Marquardt, H., and Geraghty, D.E. (1998). HLA-E surface expression depends on binding of TAP-dependent peptides derived from certain HLA class I signal sequences. *J. Immunol.* **160**, 4951–4960.

49. Green, D.R., and Ferguson, T.A. (2001). The role of Fas ligand in immune privilege. *Nat. Rev. Mol. Cell. Biol.* **2**, 917–924.

50. Freed, C.R., Greene, P.E., Breeze, R.E., Tsai, W.Y., DuMouchel, W., Kao, R., Dillon, S., Winfield, H., Culver, S., Trojanowski, J.Q., Eidelberg, D., and Fahn, S. (2001). Transplantation of embryonic dopamine neurons for severe Parkinson's disease. *N. Engl. J. Med.* **344**, 710–719.

51. Rubinstein, P. (2001). HLA matching for bone marrow transplantation: how much is enough? *N. Engl. J. Med.* **345**, 1842–1844.

52. Petersdorf, E.W., Hansen, J.A., Martin, P.J., Woolfrey, A., Malkki, M., Gooley, T., Storer, B., Mickelson, E., Smith, A., and Anasetti, C. (2001). Major-histocompatibility-complex class I alleles and antigens in hematopoietic-cell transplantation. *N. Engl. J. Med.* **345**, 1794–1800.

53. Kawase, E., Yamazaki, Y., Yagi, T., Yanagimachi, R., and Pedersen, R.A. (2000). Mouse embryonic stem (ES) cell lines established from neuronal cell-derived cloned blastocysts. *Genesis* **28**, 156–163.

54. Munsie, M.J., Michalska, A.E., O'Brien, C.M., Trounson, A.O., Pera, M.F., and Mountford, P.S. (2000). Isolation of pluripotent embryonic stem cells from reprogrammed adult mouse somatic cell nuclei. *Curr. Biol.* **10**, 989–992.

55. Wakayama, T., Tabar, V., Rodriguez, I., Perry, A.C., Studer, L., and Mombaerts, P. (2001). Differentiation of embryonic stem cell lines generated from adult somatic cells by nuclear transfer. *Science* **292**, 740–743.

56. Cibelli, J.B., Kiessling, A.A., Cunniff, K., Richards, C., Lanza, R.P., and West, M.D. (2001). Somatic cell nuclear transfer in humans: Pronuclear and early embryonic development. *E-biomed. J. Regener. Med.* **2**, 25–31.

57. Lanza, R.P., Chung, H.Y., Yoo, J.J., Wettstein, P.J., Blackwell, C., Borson, N., Hofmeister, E., Schuch, G., Soker, S., Moraes, C.T., West, M.D., and Atala, A. (2002). Generation of histocompatible tissues using nuclear transplantation. *Nat. Biotechnol.* **20**, 689–696.

58. Lanza, R.P., Caplan, A.L., Silver, L.M., Cibelli, J.B., West, M.D., and Green, R.M. (2000). The ethical validity of using nuclear transfer in human transplantation. *JAMA* **284**, 3175–3179.

59. Cibelli, J.B., Grant, K.A., Chapman, K.B., Cunniff, K., Worst, T., Green, H.L., Walker, S.J., Gutin, P.H., Vilner, L., Tabar, V., Dominko, T., Kane, J., Wettstein, P.J., Lanza, R.P., Studer, L., Vrana, K.E., and West, M.D. (2002). Parthenogenetic stem cells in nonhuman primates. *Science* **295**, 819.

60. Sykes, M. (2001). Mixed chimerism and transplant tolerance. *Immunity* **14**, 417–424.

61. Dey, B., Sykes, M., and Spitzer, T.R. (1998). Outcomes of recipients of both bone marrow and solid organ transplants: a review. *Medicine (Baltimore)* **77**, 355–369.

62. van den Brink, M.R., and Burakoff, S.J. (2002). Cytolytic pathways in haematopoietic stem-cell transplantation. *Nat. Rev. Immunol.* **2**, 273–281.

63. Sykes, M., Szot, G.L., Swenson, K.A., and Pearson, D.A. (1997). Induction of high levels of allogeneic hematopoietic reconstitution and donor-specific tolerance without myelosuppressive conditioning. *Nat. Med.* **3**, 783–787.

64. Fandrich, F., Lin, X., Chai, G.X., Schulze, M., Ganten, D., Bader, M., Holle, J., Huang, D.S., Parwaresch, R., Zavazava, N., and Binas, B. (2002). Preimplantation-stage stem cells induce long-term allogeneic graft acceptance without supplementary host conditioning. *Nat. Med.* **8**, 171–178.

65. Reich-Zeliger, S., Zhao, Y., Krauthgamer, R., Bachar-Lustig, E., and Reisner, Y. (2000). Anti-third party CD8+ CTLs as potent veto cells: coexpression of CD8 and FasL is a prerequisite. *Immunity* **13**, 507–515.

66. Zijlstra, M., Bix, M., Simister, N.E., Loring, J.M., Raulet, D.H., and Jaenisch, R. (1990). Beta 2-microglobulin deficient mice lack CD4-8+ cytolytic T cells. *Nature* **344**, 742–746.

67. Mannon, R.B., and Coffman, T.M. (1999). Gene targeting: applications in transplantation research. *Kidney Int.* **56**, 18–27.

68. Grusby, M.J., Auchincloss, H., Jr., Lee, R., Johnson, R.S., Spencer, J.P., Zijlstra, M., Jaenisch, R., Papaioannou, V.E., and Glimcher, L.H. (1993). Mice lacking major histocompatibility complex class I and class II molecules. *Proc. Natl. Acad. Sci. U. S. A.* **90**, 3913–3917.

69. Dierich, A., Chan, S.H., Benoist, C., and Mathis, D. (1993). Graft rejection by T cells not restricted by conventional major histocompatibility complex molecules. *Eur. J. Immunol.* **23**, 2725–2728.

70. Lee, R.S., Grusby, M.J., Laufer, T.M., Colvin, R., Glimcher, L.H., and Auchincloss, H., Jr. (1997). CD8+ effector cells responding to residual class I antigens, with help from CD4+ cells stimulated indirectly, cause rejection of "major histocompatibility complex-deficient" skin grafts. *Transplantation* **63,** 1123–1133.

71. Bix, M., Liao, N.S., Zijlstra, M., Loring, J., Jaenisch, R., and Raulet, D. (1991). Rejection of class I MHC-deficient haemopoietic cells by irradiated MHC-matched mice. *Nature* **349,** 329–331.

72. Van Kaer, L., Ashton-Rickardt, P.G., Ploegh, H.L., and Tonegawa, S. (1992). TAP1 mutant mice are deficient in antigen presentation, surface class I molecules, and CD4-8+ T cells. *Cell* **71,** 1205–1214.

73. Garbi, N., Tan, P., Diehl, A.D., Chambers, B.J., Ljunggren, H.G., Momburg, F., and Hammerling, G.J. (2000). Impaired immune responses and altered peptide repertoire in tapasin-deficient mice. *Nat. Immunol.* **1,** 234–238.

74. Viville, S., Neefjes, J., Lotteau, V., Dierich, A., Lemeur, M., Ploegh, H., Benoist, C., and Mathis, D. (1993). Mice lacking the MHC class II-associated invariant chain. *Cell* **72,** 635–648.

75. Reith, W., and Mach, B. (2001). The bare lymphocyte syndrome and the regulation of MHC expression. *Annu. Rev. Immunol.* **19,** 331–373.

76. Griffith, T.S., Brunner, T., Fletcher, S.M., Green, D.R., and Ferguson, T.A. (1995). Fas ligand-induced apoptosis as a mechanism of immune privilege. *Science* **270,** 1189–1192.

67

Thymus and Tolerance in Transplantation

Daniel H.D. Gray, Jason W. Gill, Alan O. Trounson, and Richard L. Boyd

Stem cell–based research is a highly complex, rapidly evolving technology that offers the ultimate horizon in clinical therapy—the physical replacement of damaged or missing cells and tissues. Although such "cell based" therapies are of unquestionable potential importance, unless they are of autologous origin, any transplantation of such cells will meet the fate of immune rejection. Therefore, fundamental to successful translation of stem cell–based therapies to the clinic is the manipulation of either the host or the donor to facilitate engraftment and long-term acceptance. Depletion of major histocompatibility complex (MHC) "transplantation antigens" on the donor cells would prevent their recognition and subsequent rejection by the immune intervention; however, this would also potentiate pathological consequences should such cells become infected with microorganisms or undergo cancerous transformation. The only logical solution to long-term acceptance of transplanted foreign cells and tissues is to recapitulate the body's own mechanisms that ensure self-tolerance. This fundamentally involves an active thymus to generate T-cells and to purge the evolving pool of "self-reactive" cells. In the current context, thymic function would be manipulated such that the developing T-cells would also encounter "donor" cells, with the evolving repertoire of new T-cells entering the blood stream being equally purged of both "self-reactive" and "donor-reactive" T-cells. In principle, grafted tissue of the same donor type would be accepted like the patient's own tissues. However, the thymus undergoes severe age-related atrophy and is effectively nonfunctional from around 20 years of age. This review covers the basis of thymic function and development, its age-related degeneration, and the ways in which the latter can be overcome to facilitate tolerance to stem cell–based therapies.

Introduction

The immune system presents a formidable challenge to the potential therapeutic benefits of stem cell transplantation. The immunological barriers that currently preclude long-term acceptance of tissue and organ transplants also confront stem cell transfers. Despite recent advances in immunosuppression and tissue matching, transplants from unrelated donors

(allogeneic) are nearly always rejected. The rejection of allografts is a consequence of immune responses to a range of proteins that vary among individuals and are therefore perceived as foreign by the host, particularly those encoded by the MHC.

The transplantation of autologous stem cells (either adult stem cells or embryonic stem cells rendered genetically identical by nuclear transfer) could theoretically circumvent these problems. However, the necessity for customisation of each transplant may limit the clinical applicability of such approaches. Alternatively, transplantation of stem cells rendered MHC deficient may pose a threat to the host, since they will be unable to mount an immune response against these cells in the event of viral infection or malignancy. A broader solution to immune rejection of stem cells would be the induction of immune tolerance to alloantigens, which has become the Holy Grail of transplantation.

Tolerance is the failure of the immune system to react to antigen. Self-tolerance (unresponsiveness to self-antigens) is a crucial property of the immune system. This is predominantly established and maintained by the deletion or inactivation of self-reactive lymphocytes as they develop in the thymus (T-cells) or the bone marrow (B-cells). Given the central role of T-cells in all adaptive immune responses, particularly those involved in transplant rejection, thymic tolerance mechanisms are especially important. This chapter examines our understanding of how the thymus imposes tolerance and proposes novel ways it may be manipulated to achieve acceptance of stem cell transplants.

THYMUS AND CENTRAL TOLERANCE

The thymus is a bilobed, encapsulated organ situated in the upper thorax, anterior to the heart. Each lobe comprises numerous lobules bound by invaginations of the capsule, called trabeculae. The body of the thymus is divided into an outer region, the cortex, and an inner region, the medulla. As the exclusive site of mainstream T-cell development, thymic function is fundamental to the establishment and maintenance of the adaptive immune system. This unique capacity is imparted by thymic stromal cells, which include epithelium, dendritic cells (DCs), macrophages, and fibroblasts.

Developing T-cells (thymocytes), which comprise about 98% of thymic cellularity, are derived from bone marrow hemopoietic stem cells (HSCs) that enter the thymus via the bloodstream. Thymocytes undergo a sequence of proliferation and differentiation as they migrate from the outer subcapsule, through the cortex, and then through the medulla and are ultimately exported from the thymus as mature T-cells. The most important factor governing the developmental fate of thymocytes is the random rearrangement of genes encoding the T-cell receptor (TcR). It is through the TcR that T-cells recognise and are activated by foreign peptides in the context of polymorphic MHC molecules. Thus, the specificity of the TcR following α- and β-chain rearrangement is rigorously screened by self-MHC–peptide complexes expressed on thymic stromal cells during the processes of positive and negative selection. These selection processes cause the apoptosis of those thymocytes with "inappropriate" TcRs (approximately 98% of all thymocytes[1]), ensuring that only those T-cells of potential use to the host are exported.

The development of thymocytes can be tracked through the differential expression of CD3 and the CD4 and CD8 coreceptors. The most immature thymocytes are CD3−CD4− CD8− (triple-negative, TN), which develop into CD3loCD4+ CD8+ double-positive (DP) cells that in turn mature into CD3hiCD4+CD8− or CD3hiCD4−CD8+ single-positive (SP) T-cells[2] (Fig. 67–1). Thymic stromal cells provide discrete microenvironments within which the various thymocyte developmental steps occur.[3] These interactions give rise to mature CD4+ (helper) and CD8+ (cytotoxic) T-cells capable of responding to foreign pathogens while remaining tolerant of self-tissue. This section describes features of thymic ontogeny and the key aspects of thymocyte development pertaining to central tolerance.

THYMIC ONTOGENY

T-cell production commences soon after thymic organogenesis and continues throughout life. Thymic organogenesis is a complex series of developmental processes comprising input

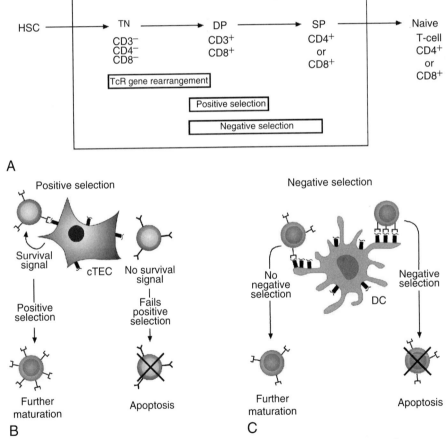

Figure 67-1. *Thymic T-Cell development.* (A) Blood-borne HSCs seed the thymus and undergo differentiative steps distinguished by their expression of CD3, CD4, and CD8. TcR gene rearrangement occurs early in thymocyte development. Productive rearrangements result in the expression of the new TcR that is then screened by positive and negative selection. Although DP thymocytes must be positively selected for further maturation, DP and immature SP thymocytes are eligible for negative selection. (B) cTECs deliver survival signals to DP thymocytes with TcRs capable of low avidity interactions with self-peptide–MHC. Those bearing TcRs that cannot recognise self-peptide–MHC die by apoptosis. (C) Negative selection occurs when TcR+ thymocytes interact with self-peptide–MHC with a high avidity (usually on DCs) and are deleted through apoptosis. (Please see CD-ROM for color version of this figure.)

from multiple embryonic germ layers under the control of discrete molecular cues. The primordial murine thymus forms around embryonic day 10.5 (E10.5) from an outpocketing of the third pharyngeal pouch endoderm with contributions from neural crest mesenchyme of the third and fourth pharyngeal arches. The physical contribution of neural crest–derived mesodermal cells to the thymic capsule and perivascular connective tissue has been established by cell lineage analyses.[4,5] Ablation of this contribution results in severe defects in thymus formation because of the lack of mesenchymal-derived fibroblast growth factors (FGF7 and -10), which drive thymic epithelial cell (TEC) proliferation.[6,7] Although there has been much controversy over the contribution of the ectoderm to the thymic rudiment, current theories exclude any direct incorporation.[8]

The bilateral thymic rudiments formed by these interactions bud off the pharynx and move medially, ventrally, and caudally to fuse at the midline above the heart by E12.5. This coincides with HSC colonisation of the thymic rudiments through the mesenchymal capsule, under the influence of chemoattractants produced by the thymic epithelium.[9] The subsequent development of thymocytes and the various subsets of TECs that support them rely upon reciprocal interactions in what is termed "thymic cross talk."[10,11] Thus, the presence of immature thymocytes (first seen around E14) leads to the development of cortical TECs (cTECs), and more mature SP thymocytes (arising around E18) are required for the differentiation of medullary TEC (mTEC).[12]

Although thymocytes are known to arise from HSCs, the developmental origins of epithelial cells are only beginning to be understood. Recently, evidence emerged for a common TEC precursor for both cortical and medullary epithelial cells.[13] Elegant experiments using chimeric mice formed by injecting embryonic stem cells into blastocysts of different MHC haplotypes demonstrated that mTEC islets arise from clonal progenitors.[14] These studies were extended when it was shown that a subset of embryonic TECs, recognised by the monoclonal antibody MTS-24, could reconstitute a complete thymic microenvironment.[15,16] This provided further evidence for a single population capable of generating all major TEC subsets. However, heterogeneity within the MTS-24+ TEC population necessitates the development of clonal differentiation assays to identify a putative TE stem cell. By birth, interactions among developing thymocytes and stromal cells have established the thymic microenvironments required for all steps of T-cell development.

EARLY THYMOCYTE DEVELOPMENT

HSC-derived thymocyte precursors enter the postnatal thymus through large blood vessels at the cortico–medullary junction.[17,18] How committed these cells are to the T-cell lineage has been a matter of controversy, partly because of conflicting data concerning the lineage potential of the most immature thymocytes. In particular, it seems difficult to distinguish rapid differentiation upon entry into the thymic microenvironment from extrathymic differentiation prior to immigration. Nevertheless, these cells reside and migrate through the thymic

cortex as they undergo further T-cell commitment and the early stages of thymocyte development.[19]

The immature TN thymocytes can be divided into four genetically and phenotypically distinct subsets (TN1–4) based on the expression of the surface molecules CD25 (IL-2Rα chain) and CD44 (adhesion molecule).[20] Progression through these subsets correlates with important control points in T-cell differentiation.[21] The most immature of these subsets are CD25−CD44+ (TN1) thymocytes, which bear TcR genes in germline configuration.[20] The proliferation and differentiation of these cells depends upon the provision of stromal-derived cytokines, in particular stem cell factor (the ligand for c-kit) and IL-7.[22,23] Under the influence of these and other cytokines, TN1 thymocytes differentiate into TN2 cells (CD44+CD25+), increasing in size and proliferating extensively.[24]

The TN2 subset also depends upon stromal cell support, with thymic epithelium and fibroblasts required for their differentiation into CD44−CD25+ TN3 thymocytes.[21] The transition from TN2 to TN3 thymocytes is accompanied by the initiation of TcRβ chain gene rearrangement, leading to irreversible commitment to the T-cell lineage.[21,25,26] Recent studies have revealed a role for the surface receptor Notch-1 in governing these processes.[27] Notch signalling is an evolutionarily conserved pathway controlling multiple cell-fate decisions, initiated by interactions between Notch receptors and their ligands on neighbouring cells.[28] Delta-like-1 interaction with Notch-1 receptors on thymocytes is critical for the earliest stages of T-cell commitment,[29,30] leading to TcRβ chain gene rearrangement, up-regulation of pTα (a component of the pre-TcR), and progression beyond the DN3 stage.[31,32]

Following successful gene rearrangement, the TcRβ chain is expressed in association with the invariable, surrogate pTα protein to form the pre-TcR complex.[33,34] Signalling through this constitutively activated complex halts further TcRβ chain rearrangement and drives TN3 thymocyte proliferation and differentiation.[25,35] This phase of pre-TcR–mediated proliferation has been postulated to expand the potentially useful thymocyte repertoire prior to TcRα chain rearrangement and other selection events.[36] TcRα chain gene rearrangement normally commences as the cells mature into the cycling CD44−CD25− TN4 thymocytes.[21] TN4 thymocytes rapidly differentiate into the CD4+CD8+ DP subset of thymocytes via an intermediate phenotype of CD4+CD8− or CD4−CD8+, termed immature SP.[37,38] These cell subsets undergo several rounds of proliferation[39] until reaching the DP stage, where the newly expressed TcRα chain protein replaces pTα.

The developmental fate of each thymocyte depends upon the specificity of the αβTcR or TcRβ it expresses. Thymic selection processes ensure that only those thymocytes capable of recognising self-MHC, without the potential to cause immune responses to self-tissues, develop to maturity.

POSITIVE SELECTION

Positive selection refers to the provision of survival signals to thymocytes interacting with self-peptide–MHC[1,40] (Fig. 67–1). Those thymocytes expressing TcRs that cannot recognise self-MHC molecules (and therefore cannot perform host immune responses) fail positive selection and die by programmed cell death (apoptosis) within 4 days.[41] Some DP thymocytes can escape this fate by continuing to rearrange their TcRα chain genes if the initial rearrangement was not productive, thereby increasing the yield of potentially useful thymocytes.[36,42]

Many of the features of positive selection have been elucidated using TcR transgenic mice, in which nearly all thymocytes express a TcR with the same, known specificity for MHC–peptide.[43–47] When TcR transgenic thymocytes were introduced into mice of different MHC genotypes, it was found that positive selection progressed only in mice bearing cognate MHC (i.e., the MHC that the TcR is "restricted" to).[43–47] Furthermore, the MHC specificity of the TcR defined the eventual effector functions of the developing thymocyte. Thus, those bearing TcRs that recognise MHC class I molecules develop into CD8+ cytotoxic T-cells (involved in viral and tumour immunity), and those recognising MHC class II molecules develop into CD4+ helper T-cells (involved in all adaptive immunity).[36]

More recent studies employing TcR transgenic mice investigated the nature of the TcR signal required for positive selection. Most experimental data suggests positive selection results from lower avidity (functional affinity) TcR interactions rather than those leading to negative selection or T-cell activation.[1] These studies also revealed a critical role for the self-peptides complexed with MHC molecules in influencing the thymocyte repertoire selected. In normal mice, MHC presentation of a variety of self-peptides leads to the positive selection of a broader range of TcR specificities (i.e., thymocytes) than observed if only an invariant peptide is presented.[48]

Although low-avidity TcR signalling is essential for positive selection, it is likely that some form of non-TcR interaction is also involved.[49] The finding that only the thymic cortical epithelium is capable of inducing positive selection suggests that these cells express a unique, or a unique combination, of cell surface costimulatory molecules.[50,51] The nature of the specialised signals delivered by cortical epithelium to mediate positive selection remains unknown.

Upon receiving the initial positive selection signal, DP thymocytes up-regulate the TcR and transiently express the activation marker CD69. These cells require continual TEC contact to complete the differentiation process initiated by positive selection[52,53] and migrate toward the medulla as they develop into mature CD4+CD8− or CD4−CD8+ SP thymocytes.

NEGATIVE SELECTION

Negative selection is the induction of apoptosis or inactivation of thymocytes expressing TcRs that bind self-peptide–MHC with a high avidity[36] (Fig. 67–1). While positive selection ensures that only those thymocytes capable of recognising self-MHC molecules continue to develop, negative selection censures those clones that might be activated by such self-stimulation in the periphery. In this way, T-cells with the

potential to cause autoimmunity are purged from the repertoire, establishing central tolerance.

How does the interaction between TcR and self-peptide–MHC lead to two opposing outcomes in positive and negative selection? It is thought that the major differentiating factor is the avidity of this interaction. TcR stimulation leading to negative selection is of a higher avidity than that inducing positive selection.[1] It also seems that other cell surface receptors, such as CD28, CD5, and CD43, can cause deletion in conjunction with TcR ligation.[54] In addition, positive and negative selection occur in different thymic microenvironments. Although positive selection is restricted to the cortex, negative selection occurs at the cortico–medullary junction and medulla proper.[55] Consistent with this, only the DP and semimature SP thymocytes are susceptible to negative selection.[56] Negative selection is predominantly mediated by thymic DCs and, to some extent, by medullary epithelial cells.[57,58] DCs are the most efficient mediators of negative selection, presumably because of high levels of MHC and costimulatory molecule expression.[59,60] However, a unique role for a subset of medullary epithelial cells is emerging in the induction of central tolerance.

A long-standing question regarding central tolerance has been how the thymus mediates the negative selection of thymocytes bearing TcRs specific for peripheral self-antigens (e.g., insulin or thyroglobulin). Recent studies have demonstrated that a subset of medullary epithelial cells express a range of "ectopic" tissue-specific antigens.[61] This ectopic expression has been linked to the *AIRE* gene, a lack of which causes a spectrum of autoimmune diseases in mice and humans.[62] *AIRE*-dependent central tolerance induction to peripheral antigens appears to be mediated by a deletional mechanism.[63]

Negative selection is estimated to induce the apoptosis of between 50 and 70% of the positively selected thymocyte repertoire.[59,64,65] In this way, negative selection induces central tolerance to self-antigens by removing autoreactive thymocytes from the repertoire prior to export. However, deletional tolerance (also called recessive tolerance) does not appear to be complete, as autoreactive T-cells have been detected in the periphery of mice and humans, presumably controlled by peripheral tolerance mechanisms.[66]

There are data that suggest the thymus also produces regulatory or suppressive T-cells that modulate immune responses of autoreactive T-cells that may escape negative selection. This function would extend a "dominant" tolerance into the peripheral immune system.

SELECTION OF IMMUNOREGULATORY T-CELLS

The first demonstration of a dominant form of thymic tolerance was shown by Le Douarin and colleagues in chick–quail chimeras. The engraftment of quail thymic epithelium into embryonic chicks induced tolerance to subsequent quail tissue grafts that was not mediated by negative selection.[67,68] Since these experiments, a large body of literature has emerged describing the development and function of several subsets of immunoregulatory or suppressor T-cells.

Perhaps the most well known of these are the CD4+CD25+ immunoregulatory T-cells. This subset seems to arise in the thymus and comprises 5–10% of the peripheral CD4+ T-cell pool. Their loss leads to the spontaneous development of various organ-specific autoimmune diseases[69] and enhances allograft rejection.[66] Although their precise mode of action remains unknown, it has been shown that they require antigen-specific TcR stimulation to mediate suppression and that this requires cell-to-cell contact with the T-cells they suppress.[66] This suppression to some extent seems to involve inhibition of IL-2–mediated proliferation of self-reactive T-cells.[70]

Studies in various transgenic mouse models have revealed much about the development of this subset in the thymus. The positive selection of thymocytes destined to become CD4+CD25+ T-cells occurs on cTECs through a relatively high-avidity TcR interaction with MHC class II compared to conventional thymocytes.[71,72] Whether their developmental requirements differ from conventional thymocytes in any other respects remains to be shown. However, recent studies have defined the transcription factor *Foxp3* as a critical regulator of CD4+CD25+ T-cell development.[73,74] These studies also found that retroviral gene transfer of *Foxp3* conferred suppressor function to normal naïve peripheral T-cells. Further studies into the regulatory targets of *Foxp3* activity should reveal more about the molecular mechanisms of CD4+ CD25+ suppressor activity and development.

Another T-cell subpopulation that may have immunoregulatory function is the natural killer T-cell (NKT-cell) identified in mice and humans. Initially defined by coexpression of the NK cell receptor NK1.1 and TcR, further studies have shown this to be a very heterogeneous population.[75] The most well-characterised NKT-cell subpopulation express an invariant TcRα chain comprising the Vα14 variable region and the Jα18 joining region.[76] These cells are restricted to the non-classical MHC class I molecule CD1d and exhibit strong responses to the glycolipid α-galactosyl ceramide. NKT-cell responses can influence immune responses to various pathogens, tumours, and autoantigens. A body of literature has demonstrated the ability of NKT-cells to prevent autoimmunity, particularly in models of diabetes and multiple sclerosis.[76] This effect is mediated by the provision of IL-4, which skews the autoimmune response from a destructive Th1-type response to a nondestructive Th2-type response (for examples, see Hammond et al.[77] and Singh et al.[78]). Although a direct role for these cells in the maintenance or induction of tolerance has yet to be established, their potent regulatory functions may influence immunity in a variety of settings.

It has been established that these cells arise in the thymus then mature further in the periphery.[79–81] Most evidence suggests that thymic NKT-cells arise from the positive selection of those DP thymocytes expressing the Vα14–Jα8 TcR rearrangement.[76] However, unlike conventional thymocytes, this selection is mediated by CD1d+ DP thymocytes rather than by cTECs.[82,83] A relatively high avidity TcR interaction with CD1d and an unknown self-ligand (likely to be a glycolipid) has been proposed to be important in NKT-cell selection.[84]

These thymocytes go on to develop as CD4+ or DN NKT-cells, up-regulating NK1.1 following export from the thymus.[80,81]

Although it has become clear that the thymus generates nonconventional T-cell subsets capable of suppressing or manipulating immune responses, the mechanisms by which this is achieved have yet to be determined. This highlights the importance of thymic function in establishing and maintaining not only deletional or anergic (recessive) tolerance but also dominant tolerance.

THYMIC INVOLUTION AND REGENERATION

A major anomaly of the immune system is the involution of the thymus with age. Despite its importance in maintaining a diverse, tolerant peripheral T-cell pool, the thymus is dramatically reduced in size and function in the elderly. In mice, it is a gradual process initiated following sexual maturity.[85] Involution is characterised by decreased thymic size, collapse of the cortex, infiltration of adipose tissue associated with large perivascular spaces, an indistinct cortico–medullary junction, decreased MHC class II expression, and reduction in thymic export.[86–89] Despite a decrease in thymocyte numbers of up to 100-fold in the atrophied thymus, the major developmental subsets are retained at similar proportions as for the young. Although the rate of mature T-cell export from the thymus remains the same (~1% per day), the overall decrease in thymic size reduces the numbers of recent thymic emigrants to fewer than 5% of that of the young adult.[90] This leads to expansion of peripheral memory T-cells to compensate for reduced naïve input.[91] This causes a narrowing of T-cell diversity associated with declined T-cell function, reduced capacity to resist disease, and increased likelihood of autoimmune disease.[92,93]

Current data suggests that although thymic atrophy is influenced by many factors, sex steroids are the main cause. Animals bearing defective androgen receptors did not exhibit age-related thymic atrophy.[94] Furthermore, normal mice deprived of androgens demonstrated thymic regeneration that could be inhibited by administration of synthetic sex steroids.[95–98] Thymic stromal cells appear to be the primary mediators of this effect. Olsen et al.[98] used bone marrow transfers between normal and androgen receptor-deficient mice to demonstrate that androgens modulate thymic size by acting on stromal cells. This study extended earlier findings showing that progesterone and estrogen receptors on the thymic stroma were necessary for thymic involution mediated by these sex steroids.[99,100]

A logical means of ameliorating the problems associated with age-related thymic atrophy would be to affect thymic regeneration to restore its full functional capacity. This could be particularly important for accelerating immune reconstitution following the lymphopenia that accompanies radiation and chemotherapy. One means of achieving thymic regeneration involves the ablation of sex steroids, removing their inhibitory effect upon the thymus.[90] Comprehensive studies by Sutherland et al.[101] examined the immune reconstitution of aged or immunodepleted mice following castration, finding the attending thymic regeneration induced a return to young levels of T-cell development, thymic export, peripheral naïve

Daniel H.D. Gray, Jason W. Gill, Alan O. Trounson, and Richard L. Boyd

T-cells, and immune responsiveness to viral challenge. Analysis of prostate cancer patients undergoing sex steroid blockade by luteinising hormone-releasing hormone-agonist (LHRH-A) treatment revealed a significant increase in naïve T-cells within 4 months of treatment, indicating that chemical castration enhanced thymus function in humans.[101] The direct effects of sex steroid withdrawal on thymic stromal cells are not known, nor is the mechanism by which these cells drive thymocyte proliferation and differentiation to affect thymic regeneration.

Other key factors shown to have a regenerative effect on the thymus include IL-7 and keratinocyte growth factor (KGF).[102,103] Importantly, KGF administration has been shown to specifically protect TECs from irradiation and chemotherapy regimens as well as from the damage caused during graft-versus-host disease.[103,104] The emerging central role of these factors and the thymic stroma in thymic regeneration emphasises the need for further research in this area.

Thymus as a Target for Stem Cell Tolerance

The central role of the thymus in the establishment and maintenance of immune tolerance makes it an obvious target for strategies aimed at inducing tolerance to foreign antigens. This section examines established experimental models of donor-specific tolerance and proposes novel ways the thymus may be manipulated in these scenarios to achieve lifelong acceptance of allogeneic stem cell transplants in adults.

CURRENT METHODS OF TRANSPLANT TOLERANCE INDUCTION

There are no clinical protocols for the induction of donor-specific tolerance to allografts. The survival of solid tissue grafts relies upon immunosuppressive regimes. Although these drugs suppress the host immune system enough to prevent acute rejection, they do not improve chronic rejection rates and cause significant side effects.[105] The induction of donor-specific tolerance may reduce acute and chronic allograft rejection and obviate the need for long-term immunosuppression. Although there are many experimental models for the induction of immune tolerance, we will focus here only on those with the most therapeutic promise, namely, costimulatory blockade and haematopoietic chimerism.

Costimulatory blockade prolongs allograft survival in many animal models.[106] This treatment acts by inhibiting the costimulatory signals T-cells require in addition to TcR ligation for full activation. Most work has focused on the inhibition of two major costimulatory signals: the CD28/CD80 or CD86 pathway (using a CTLA-Ig fusion protein or monoclonal antibodies) or the CD40/CD154 pathway (using monoclonal antibodies). Blocking both of these pathways synergistically prolongs allograft acceptance.[107] The mechanisms proposed to mediate this effect predominantly involve anergy but also include apoptosis, immune deviation, or regulation of alloreactive T-cells, depending upon the models examined.[106,108] However, these effects are not lifelong in the presence of a

functional thymus because of the development of new alloreactive T-cells.

By contrast, lifelong, donor-specific tolerance can be achieved by the induction of mixed haematopoietic chimerism in various rodent models.[105,109] Chimerism is a state in which both donor and host cells contribute to haematopoiesis. This occurs following the transplant of HSCs (from donor bone marrow or fetal liver) into partially immunodepleted hosts. The engraftment of donor HSCs in the host bone marrow allows their continual migration to the thymus and development into DCs to mediate deletion of alloreactive thymocytes.[110] (Fig. 67–2). It is also possible that donor-specific immunoregulatory cells are generated in the chimeric thymus and contribute to tolerance induction. The establishment of chimerism enables the long-term acceptance of allografts in most models and humans[109] (for an exception, see Gleit et al.[111]). However, a problem with this approach has been the toxicity of radiation and chemotherapy regimens required for the myeloablation of host cells. The morbidity associated with this preconditioning has precluded the clinical use of allogeneic bone marrow transplantation for diseases other than malignancies. In an effort to reduce the need for harsh preconditioning protocols, Wekerle et al.[112] found the combination of costimulatory blockade with administration of high doses of allogeneic bone marrow could achieve up to 15% haematopoietic chimerism. Many studies have since investigated and modified this protocol to establish long-term chimeras, demonstrating thymic deletion of alloreactive

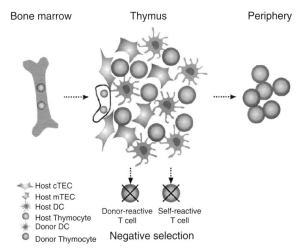

Host cTEC
Host mTEC
Host DC
Host Thymocyte
Donor DC
Donor Thymocyte

Bone marrow   Thymus   Periphery

Donor-reactive   Self-reactive
T cell   T cell

Negative selection

Figure 67–2. *Induction of central allograft tolerance by mixed haematopoietic chimerism. Adoptive transfer of donor bone marrow to a preconditioned recipient eliminates donor-reactive T-cells by negative selection following interaction with donor thymic antigen-presenting cells. T-cell progenitor cells from the bone marrow enter the thymus. During maturation in the thymus, recipient-derived and donor-derived thymocytes are exposed to recipient and donor antigens on thymic DCs and TECs. Thymocytes that react strongly with either are deleted as part of negative selection. Consequently, alloreactive T-cells that react with donor or recipient histocompatibility antigens are not exported from the thymus to the peripheral T-cell pool, where they may otherwise cause graft rejection or graft-versus-host disease. (Please see CD-ROM for color version of this figure.)*

thymocytes and tolerance to skin grafts.[109,113] The recent demonstration that these protocols can be combined with some immunosuppressive regimens should facilitate their transfer into the clinic.[114]

However, T-cell tolerance induction in mixed chimeras is dependent upon thymic function. A limitation to the efficacy of this approach is the reduced functional capacity of the adult involuted thymus. The reconstitution of thymic T-cell production in adults will be essential for chimerism-induced tolerance.

THYMIC GENERATION AND REGENERATION FOR DONOR-SPECIFIC TOLERANCE

As explained earlier, thymic involution can be reversed by sex steroid ablation to restore the functional capacity of the thymus. It has recently been demonstrated that treatment with LHRH-A to block sex steroids significantly increases naïve T-cell production in 50–60% of adult humans.[101] Thymic regeneration prior to or following donor HSC transplant may increase the rate and degree of chimerism achieved, leading to more efficient induction of long-term tolerance. LHRH-A treatment could easily be incorporated with nonmyeloablative preconditioning protocols and stem cells transplanted following confirmation of chimerism and tolerance (Fig. 67–3A).

However, such an approach would not be appropriate for the 40–50% of patients whose thymi may not be regenerated by this treatment. An alternative would be to induce or graft ectopic thymi (Fig. 67–3B). A viable ectopic thymus in a permissive environment (i.e., sex steroid blockade) could support efficient chimerism and tolerance induction. Support for such an approach in humans comes from the observation that allogeneic thymic grafts in athymic, DiGeorge syndrome patients are sufficient to establish T-cell immunity.[115,116] These and other findings[117] demonstrate that T-cells generated in allogeneic thymi are capable of recognising and reacting to host MHC determinants, even though they were selected on donor epithelial components. This suggests that *cis*-interactions with host haematopoietic elements in the thymus significantly contribute to selection or that T-cells are positively selected on donor MHC molecules can cross-react with host MHC.[65,118] These T-cells are also tolerant of mismatched alloantigens, as recently demonstrated in a large animal model.[117]

The ideal source of thymic tissue for engraftment into patients incapable of thymic regeneration would be from the same allogeneic donor embryonic stem cells that the therapeutic tissue was to be derived from. Recent studies describing a putative TEC stem cell[13] may enable research into the engineering of thymic tissue from embryonic stem cells. The grafting of such tissue into patients during the conditioning phase (which comprises peripheral T-cell depletion and immunosuppression) should enhance the acceptance of the thymic graft and ultimately the induction of chimerism. Alternatively, the identification of factors that induce TEC stem cell activity may allow the induction of ectopic thymus formation in the host without the need for thymic grafting.

The reestablishment of thymic function using these approaches would potentiate chimerism and donor-specific tolerance. The targeting of the thymus in this way enlists both

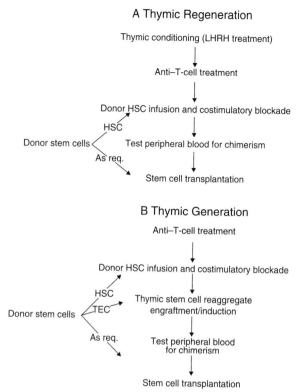

Figure 67–3. *Thymic regeneration and generation.* (A) Regeneration of the involuted adult thymus by LHRH treatment in conjunction with donor HSC infusion would establish chimerism. Peripheral blood could be analysed by flow cytometry and mixed lymphocyte reactions for chimerism and tolerance to alloantigens. Therapeutic stem cells could then be transplanted as required. (B) If regeneration was not possible, thymic stem cells could be grafted or induced to produce an ectopic thymus during the preconditioning phase (to avoid rejection of allogeneic thymus). Following donor HSC infusion, chimerism and tolerance could be tested prior to stem cell engraftment. In each case, transplanted tissues would be derived from appropriately differentiated donor embryonic stem cells.

recessive (e.g., deletion) and dominant (e.g., immunoregulation) mechanisms to impose long-term tolerance to stem cell alloantigens.

USE OF EMBRYONIC STEM CELL DERIVATIVES TO INDUCE TOLERANCE

It was recently reported[119] that rat embryonic stem cell-like cells capable of differentiation into ectodermal and endodermal lineages *in vitro*[120] can be used to induce transplantation tolerance in thymic-intact recipient rats. This was an interesting proof-of-concept report of the strategy for using embryonic stem cell derivatives to induce mixed hematopoietic chimerism with the essential involvement of thymic function and probable thymic cellular chimerism. In this study, rat embryonic stem cells of the WKY origin were generated by the methods generally reported for deriving mouse or human embryonic stem cells from the inner cell masses of developing 4- to 5-day-old embryos (blastocysts). These undifferentiated stem cell colonies remain stable during long-term

Daniel H.D. Gray, Jason W. Gill, Alan O. Trounson, and Richard L. Boyd

repeated passage on mouse embryonic fibroblast feeder cells. The embryonic stem cells expressed low MHC class I levels; no MHC class II or costimulatory antigens; and no B-cell, T-cell, NK cell, or macrophage markers.

When the embryonic stem cells ($1-10 \times 10^6$ cells) were injected into the portal vein of fully MHC-mismatched DA rats, partial mixed chimerism was observed (5–8% of white blood cells were of the donor WKY strain) with monocytes and B-cells in the spleen and thymus. The treated animals were transplanted with adult WKY heart tissue or third-party CAP heart tissue heterotopically into the abdomen a week after the cell transfer. Donor WKY allografts were accepted permanently (>150 days) in thymic-intact recipients. Third-party CAP allografts were acutely rejected, as were WKY allografts in rats thymectomized 1 week before embryonic stem cell treatment. However, this study did not formally show that tolerance was induced by thymic negative selection of alloreactive thymocytes. Indeed, it is unlikely that the thymic chimerism observed could induce such changes in the peripheral T-cell repertoire in the 7 days prior to the heart transplantation, given that adult T-cell development normally takes weeks.[121,122]

Nevertheless, these data are interesting because they suggest that early embryonic stem cell–derived progenitors are probably capable of colonising bone marrow and the thymus without inducing inflammatory reactions such as graft-versus-host disease. The clonal deletion of alloreactive T-cells because of antigens expressed in the chimeric thymus could then protect grafts of tissues formed by differentiation of the donor embryonic stem cells. This would suggest that patients treated with weakly immunogenic embryonic stem cell derivatives following activation of thymic regrowth could be efficiently transformed to tolerance for follow-up transplantation of heart, pancreatic, muscle, neurone, hepatic, etc., tissue derived from the embryonic stem cells. This would be a desirable alternative to nuclear transfer (therapeutic cloning) for compatibility of transplants of allogeneic stem cells.[123]

Summary

During the course of thymic T-cell development, selection processes impose recessive and dominant tolerance on cell-mediated immunity. The crucial role of the thymus in tolerance induction makes it an obvious target for the induction of transplantation tolerance. Although the establishment of donor–host haematopoietic chimerism can lead to lifelong tolerance to alloantigens, thymic involution in adults presents a technical problem to this approach. Regeneration of thymic function by sex steroid blockade or the establishment of ectopic thymi can restore T-cell development and could potentiate chimerism-induced tolerance to subsequent stem cell transplants. In all of these scenarios, the manipulation of embryonic stem cell lines will be critical. The ability to reproducibly direct the differentiation of cell lines towards immune stem cell lineages (such as haematopoietic and thymic), in addition to therapeutic tissues, will allow testing of such strategies for the induction of immune tolerance to stem cell transplants.

If this could be achieved with multiple stem cell lines, the institution of stem cell banking would allow a degree of tissue matching with patients to reduce HLA and minor histocompatibility differences. Together, such research and resources would allow the establishment of protocols inducing stem cell-specific tolerance for patients of various ages and genetic backgrounds.

REFERENCES

1. Sebzda, E., Mariathasan, S., Ohteki, T., Jones, R., Bachmann, M.F., and Ohashi, P.S. (1999). Selection of the T-cell repertoire. *Annu. Rev. Immunol.* **17,** 829–874.
2. Nikolic-Zugic, J. (1991). Phenotypic and functional stages in the intrathymic development of α–β T-cells. *Immunol. Today* **12,** 65–70.
3. Boyd, R.L., Tucek, C.L., Godfrey, D.I., Wilson, T.J., Davidson, N.J., Bean, A.G.D., Ladyman, H.M., Ritter, M.A., and Hugo, P. (1993). The thymic microenvironment. *Immunol. Today* **14,** 445–459.
4. Le Lievre, C.S., and Le Douarin, N.M. (1975). Mesenchymal derivatives of the neural crest: analysis of chimaeric quail and chick embryos. *J. Embryol. Exp. Morphol.* **34,** 125–154.
5. Jiang, X., Rowitch, D.H., Soriano, P., McMahon, A.P., and Sucov, H.M. (2000). Fate of the mammalian cardiac neural crest. *Development* **127,** 1607–1616.
6. Bockman, D.E., and Kirby, M.L. (1984). Dependence of thymus development on derivatives of the neural crest. *Science* **223,** 498–500.
7. Jenkinson, W.E., Jenkinson, E., and Anderson, G., (2003). Differential requirement for mesenchyme in the proliferation and maturation of thymic epithelial progenitors. *J. Exp. Med.* **198,** 325–332.
8. Manley, N.R., and Blackburn, C.C. (2003). A developmental look at thymus organogenesis: where do the nonhematopoietic cells in the thymus come from? *Curr. Opin. Immunol.* **15,** 225–232.
9. Wilkinson, B., Owen, J.J.T., and Jenkinson, E.J. (1999). Factors regulating stem cell recruitment to the fetal thymus. *J. Immunol.* **162,** 3873–3881.
10. Ritter, M.A., and Boyd, R.L. (1993). Development in the thymus: it takes two to tango. *Immunol. Today* **14,** 1993.
11. Van Ewijk, W., Shores, E.W., and Singer, A. (1994). Cross talk in the mouse thymus. *Immunol. Today* **15,** 214–217.
12. Van Ewijk, W., Wang, B., Hollander, G., Kawamoto, H., Spanopoulou, E., Itoi, M., Amagai, T., Jiang, Y.F., Germeraad, W.T., Chen, W.F., and Katsura, Y. (1999). Thymic microenvironments: 3-D versus 2-D? *Semin. Immunol.* **11,** 57–64.
13. Blackburn, C.C., Manley, N., Palmer, D.B., Boyd, R.L., Anderson, G., and Ritter, M.A. (2002). One for all and all for one: thymic epithelial stem cells and regeneration. *Trends Immunol.* **23,** 391–395.
14. Rodewald, H.R., Paul, S., Haller, C., Bluethmann, H., and Blum, C. (2001). Thymus medulla consisting of epithelial islets, each derived from a single progenitor. *Nature* **414,** 763–768.
15. Gill, J., Malin, M., Hollander, G.A., and Boyd, R. (2002). Generation of a complete thymic microenvironment by MTS24+ thymic epithelial cells. *Nat. Immunol.* **3,** 635–642.
16. Bennett, A.R., Farley, A., Blair, N.F., Gordon, J., Sharp, L., and Blackburn, C.C. (2002). Identification and characterization of thymic epithelial progenitor cells. *Immunity* **16,** 803–814.
17. Kyewski, B.A. (1987). Seeding of thymic microenvironments defined by distinct thymocyte–stromal cell interactions is developmentally controlled. *J. Exp. Med.* **166,** 520–538.

18. Penit, C., and Vasseur, F. (1988). Sequential events in thymocyte differentiation and thymus regeneration revealed by a combination of bromodeoxyuridine DNA labelling and antimitotic drug treatment. *J. Immunol.* **140**, 3315–3323.

19. Lind, E.F., Prockop, S.E., Porritt, H.E., and Petrie, H.T. (2001). Mapping precursor movement through the postnatal thymus reveals specific microenvironments supporting defined stages of early lymphoid development. *J. Exp. Med.* **194**, 127–134.

20. Godfrey, D.I., Kennedy, J., Suda, T., and Zlotnik, A. (1993). A developmental pathway involving four phenotypically and functionally distinct subsets of CD3⁻CD4⁻CD8⁻ triple-negative adult mouse thymocytes defined by CD44 and CD25 expression. *J. Immunol.* **150**, 4244–4252.

21. Godfrey, D.I., and Zlotnik, A. (1993). Control points in early T-cell development. *Immunol. Today* **14**, 547–553.

22. Oosterwegel, M.A., Haks, M.C., Jeffry, U., Murray, R., and Kruisbeek, A.M. (1997). Induction of *TCR* gene rearrangements in uncommitted stem cells by a subset of IL-7-producing, MHC class II-expressing thymic stromal cells. *Immunity* **6**, 351–360.

23. Di Santo, J.P., and Rodewald, H.R. (1998). *In vivo* roles of receptor tyrosine kinases and cytokine receptors in early thymocyte development. *Curr. Opin. Immunol.* **10**, 196–207.

24. Penit, C., Lucas, B., and Vasseur, F. (1995). Cell expansion and growth arrest phases during the transition from precursor (CD4⁻CD8⁻) to immature (CD4⁺CD8⁺) thymocytes in normal and genetically modified mice. *J. Immunol.* **154**, 5103–5113.

25. Dudley, E.C., Petrie, H.T., Shah, L.M., Owen, M.J., and Hayday, A.C. (1994). T-cell receptor-β chain gene rearrangement and selection during thymocyte development in adult mice. *Immunity* **1**, 83–93.

26. Godfrey, D.I., Kennedy, J., Mombaerts, P., Tonegawa, S., and Zlotnik, A. (1994). Onset of *TCR-β* gene rearrangement and role of *TCR-β* expression during CD3⁻CD4⁻CD8⁻ thymocyte differentiation. *J. Immunol.* **152**, 4783–4792.

27. MacDonald, H.R., Wilson, A., and Radtke, F. (2001). Notch1 and T-cell development: Insights from conditional knockout mice. *Trends Immunol.* **22**, 155–160.

28. Artavanis-Tsakonas, S., Rand, M.D., and Lake, R.J. (1999). Notch signalling: cell fate control and signal integration in development. *Science* **284**, 770–776.

29. Radtke, F., Wilson, A., Stark, G., Bauer, M., van Meerwijk, J.P., MacDonald, H.R., and Aguet, M. (1999). Deficient T-cell fate specification in mice with an induced inactivation of Notch1. *Immunity* **10**, 547–558.

30. Schmitt, T.M., and Zuniga-Pflucker, J.C. (2002). Induction of T-cell development from hematopoietic progenitor cells by Delta-like-1 *in vitro*. *Immunity* **17**, 749–756.

31. Wolfer, A., Wilson, A., Nemir, M., MacDonald, H.R., and Radtke, F. (2002). Inactivation of Notch1 impairs VDJβ rearrangement and allows pre-TCR⁻ independent survival of early α–β lineage thymocytes. *Immunity* **16**, 869–879.

32. Reizis, B., and Leder, P. (2002). Direct induction of T-lymphocyte-specific gene expression by the mammalian Notch signalling pathway. *Genes Dev.* **16**, 295–300.

33. Groettrup, M., Ungewiss, K., Azogui, O., Palacios, R., Owen, M.J., Hayday, A.C., and von Boehmer, H. (1993). A novel disulfide-linked heterodimer on pre-T-cells consists of the T-cell receptor-β chain and a 33-kd glycoprotein. *Cell* **75**, 283–294.

34. Saint-Ruf, C., Ungewiss, K., Groettrup, M., Bruno, L., Fehling, H.J., and von Boehmer, H. (1994). Analysis and expression of a cloned pre-T-cell receptor gene. *Science* **266**, 1208–1212.

35. Mallick, C.A., Dudley, E.C., Viney, J.L., Owen, M.J., and Hayday, A.C. (1993). Rearrangement and diversity of T-cell receptor-β chain genes in thymocytes: critical role for the β-chain in development. *Cell* **73**, 513–519.

36. Von Boehmer, H., Aifantis, I., Gounari, F., Azogui, O., Haughn, L., Apostolou, I., Jaeckel, E., Grassi, F., and Klein, L. (2003). Thymic selection revisited: how essential is it? *Immunol. Rev.* **191**, 62–78.

37. Tatsumi, Y., Kumanogoh, A., Saitoh, M., Mizushima, Y., Kimura, K., Suzuki, S., Yagi, H., Horiuchi, A., Ogata, M., Hamaoka, T., and Fujiwara, H. (1990). Differentiation of thymocytes from CD3⁻CD4⁻CD8⁻ through CD3⁻CD4⁻CD8⁺ into more mature stages induced by a thymic stromal cell clone. *Proc. Natl. Acad. Sci. U. S. A.* **87**, 2750–2754.

38. Hugo, P., Waanders, G.A., Scollay, R., Shortman, K., and Boyd, R.L. (1990). Ontogeny of a novel CD4⁺CD8⁻CD3⁻ thymocyte subpopulation: a comparison with CD4⁻CD8⁺CD3⁻ thymocytes. *Int. Immunol.* **2**, 209–218.

39. Penit, C., Vasseur, F., and Papiernik, M. (1988). *In vivo* dynamics of CD4⁻CD8⁻ thymocytes: proliferation, renewal, and differentiation of different cell subsets studied by DNA biosynthetic labelling and surface antigen detection. *Eur. J. Immunol.* **18**, 1343–1350.

40. Jameson, S.C., and Bevan, M.J. (1998). T-cell selection. *Curr. Opin. Immunol.* **10**, 214–219.

41. Huesmann, M., Scott, B., Kisielow, P., and von Boehmer, H. (1991). Kinetics and efficacy of positive selection in the thymus of normal and T-cell receptor transgenic mice. *Cell* **66**, 533–540.

42. Petrie, H.T., Livak, F., Schatz, D.G., Strasser, A., Crispe, I.N., and Shortman, K. (1993). Multiple rearrangements in T-cell receptor-α chain genes maximize the production of useful thymocytes. *J. Exp. Med.* **178**, 615–622.

43. Scott, B., Bluthmann, H., Teh, H.S., and von Boehmer, H. (1989). The generation of mature T-cells requires interaction of the α–β T-cell receptor with major histocompatibility antigens. *Nature* **338**, 591–593.

44. Kisielow, P., Teh, H.S., Bluthmann, H., and von Boehmer, H. (1988). Positive selection of antigen-specific T-cells in thymus by restricting MHC molecules. *Nature* **335**, 730–733.

45. Teh, H.S., Kisielow, P., Scott, B., Kishi, H., Uematsu, Y., Bluthmann, H., and von Boehmer, H. (1988). Thymic major histocompatibility complex antigens and the α–β T-cell receptor determine the CD4/CD8 phenotype of T-cells. *Nature* **335**, 229–233.

46. Sha, W.C., Nelson, C.A., Newberry, R.D., Kranz, D.M., Russell, J.H., and Loh, D.Y. (1988). Selective expression of an antigen receptor on CD8-bearing T-lymphocytes in transgenic mice. *Nature* **335**, 271–274.

47. Kaye, J., Hsu, M.L., Sauron, M.E., Jameson, S.C., Gascoigne, N.R., and Hedrick, S.M. (1989). Selective development of CD4+ T-cells in transgenic mice expressing a class II MHC-restricted antigen receptor. *Nature* **341**, 746–749.

48. Janeway, C.A., Jr., Travers, P., Walport, M., and Schlomchik, M. (2001). The development and survival of lymphocytes. *In* "Immunobiology: the Immune System in Health and Disease," (S. Gibbs, Ed.) Garland Publishing, New York.

49. Anderson, G., and Jenkinson, E.J. (2001). Lymphostromal interactions in thymic development and function. *Nat. Rev. Immunol.* **1**, 31–40.

50. Benoist, C., and Mathis, D. (1989). Positive selection of the T-cell repertoire: where and when does it occur? *Cell* **58**, 1027–1033.

51. Anderson, G., Owen, J.J., Moore, N.C., and Jenkinson, E.J. (1994). Thymic epithelial cell provide unique signals for positive selection of CD4+CD8+ thymocytes *in vitro*. *J. Exp. Med.* **179**, 2027–2031.

52. Wilkinson, R.W., Anderson, G., Owen, J.J., and Jenkinson, E.J. (1995). Positive selection of thymocytes involves sustained interactions with the thymic microenvironment. *J. Immunol.* **155,** 5234–5240.

53. Dyall, R., and Nikolic-Zugic, J. (1995). The majority of postselection CD4+ single-positive thymocytes requires the thymus to produce long-lived, functional T-cells. *J. Exp. Med.* **181,** 235–245.

54. Kishimoto, H., and Sprent, J. (2000). The thymus and central tolerance. *Clin. Immunol.* **95,** S3–S7.

55. Surh, C.D., and Sprent, J. (1994). T-cell apoptosis detected *in situ* during positive and negative selection in the thymus. *Nature* **372,** 100–103.

56. Kishimoto, H., and Sprent, J. (1997). Negative selection in the thymus includes semimature T-cells. *J. Exp. Med.* **185,** 263–271.

57. Sprent, J., and Webb, S.R. (1995). Intrathymic and extrathymic clonal deletion of T-cells. *Curr. Opin. Immunol.* **7,** 196–205.

58. Hoffmann, M.W., Heath, W.R., Ruschmeyer, D., and Miller, J.F. (1995). Deletion of high-avidity T-cells by thymic epithelium. *Proc. Natl. Acad. Sci. U. S. A.* **92,** 9851–9855.

59. van Meerwijk, J.P., Marguerat, S., Lees, R.K., Germain, R.N., Fowlkes, B.J., and MacDonald, H.R. (1997). Quantitative impact of thymic clonal deletion on the T-cell repertoire. *J. Exp. Med.* **185,** 377–383.

60. Anderson, G., Partington, K.M., and Jenkinson, E.J. (1998). Differential effects of peptide diversity and stromal cell type in positive and negative selection in the thymus. *J. Immunol.* **161,** 6599–6603.

61. Derbinski, J., Schulte, A., Kyewski, B., and Klein, L. (2001). Promiscuous gene expression in medullary thymic epithelial cells mirrors the peripheral self. *Nat. Immunol.* **2,** 1032–1039.

62. Anderson, M.S., Venanzi, E.S., Klein, L. Chen, Z., Berzins, S.P., Turley, S.J., von Boehmer, H., Bronson, R., Dierich, A., Benoist, C., and Mathis, D. (2002). Projection of an immunological self shadow within the thymus by the aire protein. *Science* **298,** 1395–1401.

63. Liston, A., Lesage, S., Wilson, J., Peltonen, L., and Goodnow, C.C. (2003). Aire regulates negative selection of organ-specific T-cells. *Nat. Immunol.* **4,** 350–354.

64. Ignatowicz, L., Kappler, J., and Marrack, P. (1996). The repertoire of T-cells shaped by a single MHC–peptide ligand. *Cell* **84,** 521–529.

65. Zerrahn, J., Held, W., and Raulet, D. (1997). The MHC reactivity of the T-cell repertoire prior to positive and negative selection. *Cell* **88,** 627–636.

66. Sakaguchi, S., Sakaguchi, N., Shimizu, J., Yamazaki, S., Sakihama, T., Itoh, M., Kuniyasu, Y., Nomura, T., Toda, M., and Takahashi, T. (2001). Immunologic tolerance maintained by CD25+CD4+ regulatory T-cells: their common role in controlling autoimmunity, tumour immunity, and transplantation tolerance. *Immunol. Rev.* **182,** 18–32.

67. Ohki, H., Martin, C., Corbel, C., Coltey, M., and Le Douarin, N.M. (1987). Tolerance induced by thymic epithelial grafts in birds. *Science* **237,** 1032–1035.

68. Ohki, H., Martin, C., Coltey, M., and Le Douarin, N.M. (1988). Implants of quail thymic epithelium generate permanent tolerance in embryologically constructed quail–chick chimeras. *Development* **104,** 619–630.

69. Shevach, E.M. (2000). Regulatory T-cells in autoimmunity. *Annu. Rev. Immunol.* **18,** 423–449.

70. Shevach, E.M. (2002). CD4+CD25+ suppressor T-cells: more questions than answers. *Nat. Rev. Immunol.* **2,** 389–400.

71. Jordan, M.S. (2001). Thymic selection of CD4+CD25+ regulatory T-cells induced by an agonist self-peptide. *Nat. Immunol.* **2,** 301–306.

72. Bensinger, S.J., Bandeira, A., Jordan, M.S., Caton, A.J., and Laufer, T.M. (2001). Major histocompatibility complex class II-positive cortical epithelium mediates the selection of CD4+CD25+ immunoregulatory T-cells. *J. Exp. Med.* **194,** 427–438.

73. Hori, S., Nomura, T., and Sakaguchi, S. (2003). Control of regulatory T-cell development by the transcription factor Foxp3. *Science* **299,** 1057–1061.

74. Fontenot, J.D., Gavin, M.A., and Rudensky, A. (2003). Foxp3 programs the development and function of CD4+CD25 regulatory T-cells. *Nat. Immunol.* **4,** 330–336.

75. Godfrey, D.I., Hammond, K.J., Poulton, L.D., Smyth, M.J., and Baxter, A.G. (2000). NKT-cells: facts, function, and fallacies. *Immunol. Today* **21,** 573–583.

76. Kronenberg, M., and Gapin, L. (2002). The unconventional lifestyle of NKT-cells. *Nat. Rev. Immunol.* **2,** 557–568.

77. Hammond, K.J., Poulton, L.D., Palmisano, L.J., Silveira, P.A., Godfrey, D.I., and Baxter, A.G. (1998). α–β T-cell receptor (TCR)+CD4−CD8− (NKT) thymocytes prevent insulin-dependent diabetes mellitus in nonobese diabetic (NOD)–Lt mice by the influence of interleukin (IL)-4 and/or IL-10. *J. Exp. Med.* **187,** 1047–1056.

78. Singh, A.K., Wilson, M.T., Hong, S., Olivares-Villagomez, D., Du, C., Stanic, A.K., Joyce, S., Sriram, S., Koezuka, Y., and Van Kaer, L. (2001). Natural killer T-cell activation protects mice against experimental autoimmune encephalomyelitis. *J. Exp. Med.* **194,** 1801–1811.

79. Gapin, L., Matsuda, J.L., Surh, C.D., and Kronenberg, M. (2001). NKT-cells derive from double-positive thymocytes that are positively selected by CD1d. *Nat. Immunol.* **2,** 971–978.

80. Benlagha, K., Kyin, T., Beavis, A., Teyton, L., and Bendelac, A. (2002). A thymic precursor to the NK T-cell lineage. *Science* **296,** 553–555.

81. Pellicci, D.G., Hammond, K.J., Uldrich, A.P., Baxter, A.G., Smyth, M.J., and Godfrey, D.I. (2002). A natural killer T (NKT) cell developmental pathway involving a thymus-dependent NK1.1(−)CD4(+) CD1d-dependent precursor stage. *J. Exp. Med.* **195,** 835–844.

82. Bendelac, A. (1995). Positive selection of mouse NKT-cells by CD1-expressing cortical thymocytes. *J. Exp. Med.* **182,** 2091–2096.

83. Coles, M.C., and Raulet, D.H. (2000). NK1.1+ T-cells in the liver arise in the thymus and are selected by interactions with class I molecules on CD4+CD8+ cells. *J. Immunol.* **164,** 2412–2418.

84. Chiu, Y.H., Park, S.H., Benlagha, K., Forestier, C., Jayawardena-Wolf, J., Savage, P.B., Teyton, L., and Bendelac, A. (2002). Multiple defects in antigen presentation and T-cell development by mice expressing cytoplasmic tail-truncated CD1d. *Nat. Immunol.* **1,** 55–60.

85. Hirokawa, K., Utsuyama, M., Kasai, M., and Kurashima, C. (1992). Aging and immunity. *Acta. Pathol. Jpn.* **42,** 537–548.

86. Ortman, C.L., Dittmar, K.A., Witte, P.L., and Le, P.T. (2002). Molecular characterization of the mouse-involuted thymus: Aberrations in expression of transcription regulators in thymocyte and epithelial compartments. *Int. Immunol.* **14,** 813–822.

87. Haynes, B.F., Sempowski, G.D., Wells, A.F., and Hale, L.P. (2000). The human thymus during aging. *Immunol. Res.* **22,** 253–261.

88. Takeoka, Y., Chen, S.Y., Yago, H., Boyd, R., Suehiro, S., Shultz, L.D., Ansari, A.A., and Gershwin, M.E. (1996). The murine thymic microenvironment: changes with age. *Int. Arch Allergy Immunol.* **111,** 5–12.

89. Farr, A.G., and Sidman, C.L. (1984). Reduced expression of Ia antigens by thymic epithelial cells of aged mice. *J. Immunol.* **133**, 98–103.

90. Berzins, S.P., Uldrich, A.P., Sutherland, J.S., Gill, J., Miller, J.F., Godfrey, D.I., and Boyd, R.L. (2002). Thymic regeneration: teaching an old immune system new tricks. *Trends Mol. Med.* **8**, 469–476.

91. Haynes, B.F., Markert, M.L., Sempowski, G.D., Patel, D.D., and Hale, L.P. (2000). The role of the thymus in immune reconstitution in aging, bone marrow transplantation, and HIV-1 infection. *Annu. Rev. Immunol.* **18**, 529–560.

92. Aspinall, R., and Andrew, D. (2000). Thymic involution in aging. *J. Clin. Immunol.* **20**, 250–256.

93. Mackall, C.L., and Gress, R.E. (1997). Thymic aging and T-cell regeneration. *Immunol. Rev.* **160**, 91–102.

94. Olsen, N.J., Watson, M.B., and Kovacs, W.J. (1991). Studies of immunological function in mice with defective androgen action: distinction between alterations in immune function due to hormonal insensitivity and alterations due to other genetic factors. *Immunology* **73**, 52–57.

95. Olsen, N.J., Watson, M.B., Henderson, G.S., and Kovacs, W.J. (1991). Androgen deprivation induces phenotypic and functional changes in the thymus of adult mice. *Endocrinology* **129**, 2471–2476.

96. Kendall, M.D., Fitzpatrick, F.T.A., Greenstein, B.D., Khoylou, F., Safieh, B., and Hamblin, A. (1990). Reversal of ageing changes in the thymus of rats by chemical or surgical castration. *Cell Tissue Res.* **261**, 555–564.

97. Windmill, K.F., Meade, B.J., and Lee, V.W.K. (1993). Effect of prepubertal gonadectomy and sex-steroid treatment on the growth and lymphocyte populations of the rat thymus. *Reprod. Fertil. Dev.* **5**, 73–81.

98. Olsen, N.J., Olson, G., Viselli, S.M., Gu, X., and Kovacs, W.J. (2001). Androgen receptors in thymic epithelium modulate thymus size and thymocyte development. *Endocrinology* **142**, 1278–1283.

99. Tibbetts, T.A., DeMayo, F., Rich, S., Conneely, O.M., and O'Malley, B.W. (1999). Progesterone receptors in the thymus are required for thymic involution during pregnancy and for normal fertility. *Proc. Natl. Acad. Sci. U. S. A.* **96**, 12,021–12,026.

100. Staples, J.E., Gasiewicz, T.A., Fiore, N.C., Lubahn, D.B., Korach, K.S., and Silverstone, A.E. (1999). Estrogen receptor-α is necessary in thymic development and estradiol-induced thymic alterations. *J. Immunol.* **163**, 4168–4174.

101. Sutherland, J.S., Goldberg, G.L., Berzins, S.P., Heng, T.S., Blazar, B.R., Millar, J.L., Malin, M.A., Chidgey, A.P., and Boyd, R.L. (2003). Activation of thymic regeneration in mice and humans following sex-steroid blockade. (Submitted).

102. Bolotin E., Smorgorzewska, M., Smith, S., Widmer, M., and Weinberg, K. (1996) Enhancement of thymopoiesis after bone marrow transplant by *in vivo* interleukin-7. *Blood* **88**, 1887-1894.

103. Min, D., Taylor, P.A., Panoskaltsis-Mortari, A.., Chung, B., Danilenko, D.M., Farrell, C., Lacey, D.L., Blazer, B.R., and Weinberg, K.I. (2002). Protection from thymic epithelial cell injury by keratinocyte growth factor: a new approach to improve thymic and peripheral T-cell reconstitution after bone marrow transplantation. *Blood.* **99**, 4592-6000.

104. Rossi, S., Blazer, B.R., Farrell, C.L., Danilenko, D.M., Lacey, D.L., Weinberg, K.I., Krenger, W., and Hollander, G.H. (2002). Keratinocyte growth factor preserves normal thymopoiesis and thymic microenvironment during experimental graft-versus-host disease. *Blood.* **100**, 682-691.

105. Nikolic, B., and Sykes, M. (1997). Bone marrow chimerism and transplantation tolerance. *Curr. Opin. Immunol.* **9**, 634–640.

106. Wekerle, T., Kurtz, J., Bigenzahn, S. Takeuchi, Y. and Sykes, M. (2002). Mechanisms of transplant tolerance induction using costimulatory blockade. *Curr. Opin. Immunol.* **14**, 592–600.

107. Larsen, C.P., Elwood, E.T., Alexander, D.Z., Ritchie, S.C., Hendrix, R., Tucker-Burden, C., Cho, H.R., Aruffo, A., Hollenbaugh, D., Lindsey, P.S., Winn, K.J., and Pearson, T.C. (1996). Long-term acceptance of skin and cardiac allografts after blocking CD40 and CD28 pathways. *Nature* **381**, 434–438.

108. Dai, Z., and Lakkis, F.G. (1999). The role of cytokines, CTLA-4, and costimulation in transplant tolerance and rejection. *Curr. Opin. Immunol.* **11**, 504–508.

109. Wekerle, T., and Sykes, M. (2001). Mixed chimerism and transplantation tolerance. *Annu. Rev. Med.* **52**, 353–370.

110. Sykes, M., and Sachs, D.H. (2001). Mixed chimerism. *Philos. Trans. R. Soc. Lond. B. Biol. Sci.* **356**, 707–726.

111. Gleit, Z.L., Fuchimoto, Y., Yamada, K., Melendy, E., Scheier-Dolberg, R., Monajati, L., Coburn, R.C., Neville, D.M., Jr., Sachs, D.H., and Huang, C.A. (2002). Variable relationship between chimerism and tolerance after haematopoietic cell transplantation without myelosuppressive conditioning. *Transplantation* **74**, 1535–1544.

112. Wekerle, T., Kurtz, J., Ito, H., Ronquillo, J.V., Dong, V., Zhao, G., Shaffer, J., Sayegh, M.H., and Sykes, M. (2000). Allogeneic bone marrow transplantation with costimulatory blockade induces macrochimaerism and tolerance without cytoreductive host treatment. *Nat. Med.* **6**, 464–469.

113. Rifle, G., and Mousson, C. (2003). Donor-derived hematopoietic cells in organ transplantation: a major step towards allograft tolerance? *Transplantation* **75**(9 Suppl.), 3S–7S.

114. Blaha, P., Bigenzahn, S., Koporc, Z., Schmid, M., Langer, F., Selzer, E., Bergmeister, H., Wrba, F., Kurtz, J., Kiss, C., Roth, E., Muehlbacher, F., Sykes, M., and Wekerle, T. (2003). The influence of immunosuppressive drugs on tolerance induction through bone marrow transplantation with costimulatory blockade. *Blood* **101**, 2886–2893.

115. Markert, M.L., Kostyu, D.D., Ward, F.E., McLaughlin, T.M., Watson, T.J., Buckley, R.H., Schiff, S.E., Ungerleider, R.M., Gaynor, J.W., Oldham, K.T., Mahaffey, S.M., Ballow, M., Driscoll, D.A., Hale, L.P., and Haynes, B.F. (1997). Successful formation of chimeric human thymus allograft following transplantation of cultured postnatal human thymus. *J. Immunol.* **158**, 998–1005.

116. Markert, M.L., Boeck, A., Hale, G., Kloster, A.L., McLaughlin, T.M., Batchvarova, M.N., Douek, D.C., Koup, R.A., Kostyu, D.D., Ward, F.E., Rice, H.E., Mahaffey, S.M., Schiff, R.I., Buckley, R.H., and Haynes, B.F. (1999). Transplantation of thymus tissue in complete DiGeorge syndrome. *N. Engl. J. Med.* **341**, 1180–1189.

117. Yamada, K., Vagefi, P.A., Utsugi, R., Kitamura, H., Barth, R.N., LaMattina, J.C., and Sachs, D.H. (2003). Thymic transplantation in miniature swine: III. Induction of tolerance by transplantation of composite thymokidneys across major histocompatibility complex-mismatched barriers. *Transplantation* **76**, 530–536.

118. Chidgey, A., and Boyd, R.L. (2001). Thymic stromal cells and positive selection. *APMIS* **109**, 481–492.

119. Ruhnke, M., Ungefroren, H., Zehle, G., Bader, M., Kremer, B., and Fandrich, F. (2003). Long-term culture and differentiation of rat embryonic stem cell-like cells into neuronal, glial, endothelial, and hepatic lineages. *Stem Cells* **21**, 428–436.

120. Fandrich, F., Lin, X., Chai, G.X., Schulze, M., Ganten, D., Bader, M., Holle, J., Huang, D.S., Parwaresch, R., Zavazava, N., Binas, B. (2002). Preimplantation-stage stem cells induce long-term allogeneic graft acceptance without supplementary host conditioning. *Nat. Med.* **8,** 171–178.

121. Scollay, R. and Godfrey, D.I. (1995). Thymic emigration: conveyor belt or lucky dips? *Immunol. Today* **16(6),** 268-273.

122. Porritt, H.E., Gordon, K., and Petrie, H.T. (2003). Kinetics of steady-state differentiation and mapping of intrathymic-signaling environments by stem cell transplantation in nonirradiated mice. *J. Exp. Med.* **198(6),** 957-962.

123. Trounson, A. (2002). Nuclear transfer for stem cells (NTSC). *In* "Principles of Cloning," (J.B. Cibelli *et al.,* Eds.), pp. 435–441. Cambridge University Press, Cambridge.

68

Neural Stem Cells: Therapeutic Applications in Neurodegenerative Diseases

Rodolfo Gonzalez, Yang D. Teng, Kook I. Park, Jean Pyo Lee, Jitka Ourednik, Vaclav Ourednik, Jaimie Imitola, Franz-Josef Mueller, Richard L. Sidman, and Evan Y. Snyder

Introduction

Despite the presence of endogenous neural stem cells (NSCs) in the mammalian brain, it is recognized that intrinsic "self-repair" activity for the most devastating of injuries is inadequate or ineffective. This poor "regenerative" ability, particularly in the adult central nervous system (CNS), may be because of the limited number and restricted location of native NSCs and/or limitations imposed by the surrounding microenvironment, which may not be supportive or instructive for neuronal differentiation. NSCs expanded *ex vivo* in culture and then implanted into regions needing repair may overcome those limitations related simply to inadequate numbers of NSCs near the defective region. Whether the environment may also inhibit exogenous NSCs from surviving or differentiating toward replacement cells is a possibility. However, several transplantation experiments have suggested that neurogenic cues are transiently elaborated during degenerative processes (perhaps recapitulating developmental cues) and that exogenous NSCs are able to sense, home in, and respond appropriately to those. In other words, NSCs appear to respond *in vivo* to neurogenic signals not only when they occur appropriately during development but even when induced at later stages by certain neurodegenerative processes.

In this chapter, we review some of the work that has been performed in animal models of CNS diseases, where transplanted NSCs have mediated a therapeutic effect. These disorders include rodent models of genetic and acquired (e.g., traumatic and ischemic) neurodegeneration, inheritable metabolic disorders, age-related degeneration, and neoplasms. These conditions often have widespread neural cell loss, dysfunction, or both. The disseminated nature of the pathology in these diseases is not readily treated by conventional transplantation approaches in which a solid tissue graft or a limited number of nonmotile cells are delivered to a restricted area. Similarly, most gene therapy approaches tend to fall short because of their limited "sphere of influence" following injection of the vector into the CNS parenchyma. The use of

bone marrow transplantation, even with hematopoietic stem cells, is typically inadequate because the cells do not efficiently broach the blood–brain barrier. Cells from nonneural organs, if they transdifferentiate into neural cells at all (a controversial prospect), do so far too inefficiently to be therapeutically reliable for cell replacement in these conditions.

NSCs, on the other hand, circumvent many of these obstacles. Because they differentiate robustly into neural cells, integrate seamlessly into neural parenchyma as multiple neural cell types (both neuronal and glial), respond to normal developmental and regeneration cues, and migrate (even long distances) to multiple, disseminated areas of neuropathology, NSCs appear to be ideally suited for the molecular and cellular therapies required by extensive, diffuse (even "global") degenerative processes. Examples of such widespread neurodegenerative conditions include myelin disorders, storage diseases, motor neuron degeneration, dementing conditions such as Alzheimer's disease, and ischemic and traumatic pathologies such as stroke. Some diseases appear to be restricted in their involvement—Parkinson's disease localized to the mesostriatum, Huntington's to the caudate, spinal cord contusion to a few spinal segments, and cerebellar degeneration to the hindbrain. However, even these disorders require that cell replacement be distributed evenly over relatively large terrain, that multiple neural cell types be replaced even in a given region, or both. Again, these needs are best accomplished by a migratory, responsive, multipotent neural progenitor even if transplantation is directed toward a more circumscribed CNS region.

Definition of Neural Stem Cells

NSCs are the most primordial cells of the nervous system. They generate the array of specialized cells throughout the CNS (and probably the peripheral, autonomic, and enteric nervous systems as well).[1–3] NSCs are operationally defined by their ability: (1) to differentiate into cells of all neural lineages (i.e., neurons, ideally of multiple subtypes; oligodendroglia, and astroglia) in multiple regional and developmental contexts; (2) to self-renew (i.e., to generate new NSCs with similar potential); and (3) to populate developing and/or degenerating CNS (and possibly other neural) regions. To affirm that a single cell possesses these capabilities, clonal populations (i.e., the affirmed progeny of a single cell) must

Handbook of Stem Cells
Volume 1

be examined. Although several antigenic markers have been proffered as distinguishing NSCs from other neural and non-neural progenitors—for example nestin (an intermediate filament consistent with an immature neuroectodermal lineage), musashi 1 (an RNA-binding protein), AC133 (a cell surface marker), Hoechst dye exclusion (the "side population" after flow cytometric analysis)—none has been sufficiently specific or sensitive to supplant the previously mentioned operational definitions. The presence of a panel of immunologic markers—not just one marker—will support but not cinch this assessment. Similarly, the ability of a cell to form a cytosphere (a floating cluster of cells *in vitro*) is a characteristic of any actively propagating cell of any lineage when maintained in serum-free medium without an adherent substrate. Hence, it cannot be used by itself to define an NSC; it simply affirms that the cell is mitotic. Several studies were recently performed to determine whether NSCs share with embryonic stem (ES) cells and/or stem cells from other somatic organs the expression of certain "universal stemness genes." Some studies find a degree of overlap, and others find none[4–6]—perhaps reflecting differences in the cellular populations being analyzed. Hence, the answer remains uncertain. It is likely that if any genes are held in common they will be those integral to self-renewal and hence involved in maintaining cells within the cell cycle.

Neural cells with stem cell properties have been isolated from the embryonic, neonatal, and adult rodent nervous system and propagated *in vitro* by a variety of equally effective and safe means—both epigenetic and genetic. When mitotic, a stem cell retains its greatest degree of multipotency. A rapid cascade of commitment steps and a progressive narrowing of potential, often under the instruction of pertinent external environmental cues, accompany its exit from the cell cycle. The extent to which the commitment of an NSC is preprogrammed within the cell (i.e., cell autonomous) versus the extent to which it is directed by external signals from the milieu (i.e., cell nonautonomous) remains to be determined and is controversial. Epigenetic means for inducing cells to enter and remain within the cell cycle have typically entailed adding mitogens—such as epidermal growth factor or basic fibroblast growth factor—to serum-free culture medium.[7,8] In addition, or as an alternative, certain cell cycle–associated genes—including those that help mediate the action of mitogens—can be transduced into a stem cell to maintain its ability to self-renew, for blunt senescence, to hold commitment in abeyance, to preserve multipotency, or all of these. One such gene is *myc,* the overexpression of which will maintain stem-like behavior in an NSC.[7,9] The gene does not preclude responsiveness of the NSC to normal environmental and growth control cues and is down-regulated following transplantation *in vivo.*

It remains to be determined whether prolonged passaging of NSCs *in vitro* (whether by mitogens or by other techniques) changes these cells so that they no longer reflect the capacities and potential of their *in vivo* predecessors and counterparts. However, it is clear that maintaining NSCs in a proliferative state in culture does *not* subvert their ability to respond to normal developmental cues *in vivo* following transplantation, including the ability to withdraw from the cell cycle, to interact faithfully with host cells, and to differentiate.[10–17]

With the earliest recognition that neural cells with stem cell properties, propagated in culture, could be reimplanted into the mammalian brain, where they could reintegrate appropriately and stably express foreign genes, translational neurobiologists began to speculate about how such a phenomenon might be harnessed for therapeutic advantage as well as for understanding developmental mechanisms. These, and the studies they spawned, provided hope that the use of NSCs might circumvent some limitations of available graft material and gene transfer vehicles and make feasible a variety of new therapeutic strategies.

Therapeutic Potential of Neural Stem Cells

The clinical potential of the NSC is rooted in its inherent biologic properties. The ability of NSCs and their progeny to develop into integral cytoarchitectural components of many regions throughout the host brain as neurons, oligodendrocytes, astrocytes, or even immature neural progenitors makes them capable of replacing a range of missing or dysfunctional neural cells. Although the field of neural repair has tended to place emphasis on the replacement of missing neurons in neurodegenerative diseases or oligodendrocytes in demyelinating diseases, it is becoming increasingly evident that simultaneously replacing a diseased cell's "neighboring cells"—typically astrocytes—may be of equal importance because of the indispensable trophic, guidance, and detoxification role such "chaperone" cells may play. Fortuitously, part of the biological repertoire of an NSC is to generate the variety of cells that constitute the "fabric" of a given neural region. NSCs in particular differentiation states will spontaneously produce a variety of neurotrophic factors that may serve trophic, protective, or both functions—for example, glial cell line-derived neurotrophic factor (GDNF), brain-derived neurotrophic factor (BDNF), nerve growth factor (NGF), and neurotrophin-3 (NT-3).[18] NSCs also inherently express most of the "housekeeping" enzymes and factors necessary for any cell to maintain normal metabolism.

NSCs may also be readily engineered *ex vivo* to express a variety of molecules that either are not produced by NSCs or are not produced in therapeutically adequate quantities. The NSCs are amenable to various types of viral vector transduction as well as to other gene transfer strategies, such as lipofection, electroporation, and calcium-phosphate precipitation. Following transplantation, such engrafted NSCs may then be used as cellular vectors for the *in vivo* expression of exogenous genes of developmental and/or therapeutic relevance.[14,19–21] Such gene products can be delivered either to circumscribed regions[21] or, if necessary, to more widely disseminated areas throughout the host CNS.[14,19,20] Because they display significant migratory capacity as well as an ability to integrate widely throughout the brain when implanted into germinal zones, NSCs may help to reconstitute enzyme and cellular deficiencies in a global fashion (Fig. 68–1).

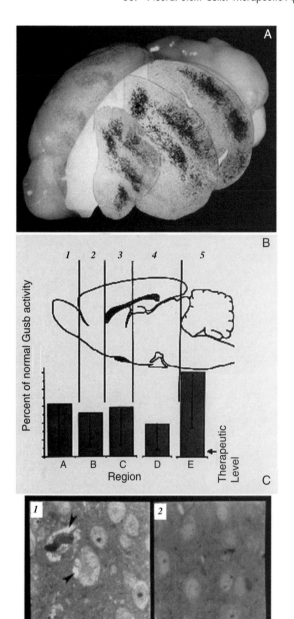

The ability of true NSCs to adjust to their regions of engraftment probably obviates the need for abstracting stem cells from specific CNS regions. Furthermore, NSCs appear to possess a tropism for degenerating CNS regions (Fig. 68–2). NSCs may be attracted—across long distances—to regions of neurodegeneration in brains of all ages, including old age. Under some circumstances, an environment in which a particular type of neural cell has degenerated creates a milieu that directs the differentiation of an NSC toward maintaining homeostasis, including replenishment of a specific deficient neural cell type. Through mechanisms yet to be determined, it appears that some neurodegenerative processes (e.g., those associated with apoptosis) elaborate neurogenic signals that recapitulate developmental cues to which NSCs can respond (Fig. 68–3).

It would seem that NSC-mediated cell replacement would only be feasible in "cell autonomous" disease states—that is, diseases in which the pathology is restricted to a particular cell whose life span is short-circuited but within an extracellular milieu otherwise normal. Conversely, a "cell nonautonomous" condition, where normal cells die because of an inhospitable microenvironment, would appear not to be amenable to NSC therapy given that "replacement" cells would presumably meet a similar fate. Surprisingly, however, NSCs may nevertheless be useful in such cell-extrinsic pathological conditions. It appears that NSCs, particularly in their immature, undifferentiated state, may be more resistant to certain stressors—various toxic metabolites, oxidizing agents—than more mature cells. Furthermore, if the NSCs are not inherently more resistant, they can be readily genetically engineered *ex vivo* to become more resistant.

Despite their extensive plasticity, NSCs never produce cell types inappropriate to the brain (e.g., muscle, bone, or teeth) or yield neoplasms. The use of NSCs as graft material in the CNS may be considered almost analogous to hematopoietic stem cell-mediated reconstitution of the bone marrow.

Therefore, the biological repertoire of the NSC, if harnessed, may provide multiple strategies for addressing CNS dysfunction. Some of these approaches have already shown promise experimentally in animal models of neurodegeneration.[14,19,20,22] Some illustrative examples are briefly described in the next sections of this chapter.

Figure 68–1. *Widespread engraftment of NSCs expressing GUSB throughout the brain of the MPS VII mouse. (A) Brain of a mature MPS VII mouse after receiving a neonatal intraventricular transplant of murine NSCs expressing GUSB. Donor NSC-derived cells, identified by their X-gal histochemical reaction for expression of the LacZ marker gene, have engrafted throughout the recipient mutant brain. Coronal sections—placed at their appropriate level by computer—show these cells to span the rostral–caudal expanse of the brain. (B) Distribution of GUSB enzymatic activity throughout brains of MPS VII NSC transplant recipients. Serial sections were collected from throughout the brains of transplant recipients and assayed for GUSB activity. Sections were pooled to reflect the activity within the demarcated regions. The regions were defined by anatomical landmarks in the anterior-to-posterior plane to permit comparison among animals. The mean levels of GUSB activity for each region (n = 17) are presented as the percentage of average normal levels for each region. Untreated MPS VII mice* show no GUSB activity biochemically or histochemically. Enzyme activity of 2% of normal is corrective based on data from liver and spleen. (C) Decreased lysosomal storage in a treated MPS VII mouse brain at 8 months. (1) Extensive vacuolation representing distended lysosomes (arrowheads) in both neurons and glia in the neocortex of an 8-month-old, untransplanted control MPS VII mouse. (2) Decrease in lysosomal storage in the cortex of an MPS VII mouse treated at birth from a region analogous to the untreated control section in panel 1. The other regions of this animal's brain showed a similar decrease in storage compared with untreated, age-matched mutants in regions where GUSB was expressed. Scale bars = 21 μm. Adapted from Snyder et al.[19] (Please see CD-ROM for color version of this figure.)

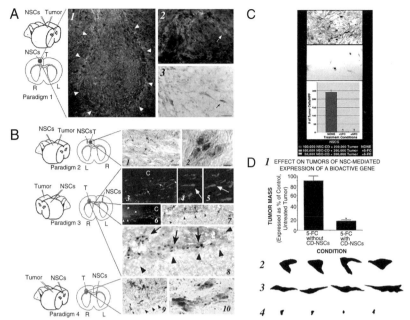

Figure 68–2. *Neural stem cells display extensive tropism for pathology in the adult brain and can express bioactive genes within such pathological situations: evidence from intracranial gliomas.* (A) NSCs migrate extensively throughout a brain tumor mass *in vivo* and "trail" advancing tumor cells. Paradigm *(1)*, in which NSCs are implanted directly into an established experimental intracranial glioblastoma, is illustrated schematically. *(1)* The virulent and aggressively invasive CNS-1 glioblastoma cell line, used to create the tumor, has been labeled *ex vivo* by transduction with GFP cDNA. The NSCs stably express *lacZ* and produce βgal. This panel, processed for double immunofluorescence using an anti-βgal antibody (NSCs) and an anti-GFP antibody (glioblastoma cells), shows a section of brain (under low power) from an adult nude mouse sacrificed 10 days after NSC injection into the glioblastoma; arrowheads mark where the tumor mass interfaces with normal tissue. Donor βgal+ NSCs can be seen extensively distributed throughout the mass, interspersed among the tumor cells. This degree of interspersion by NSCs after injection occurs within 48 hours. Interestingly, although NSCs have extensively migrated and distributed themselves within the mass, they largely stop at the junction between tumor and normal tissue except where a tumor cell is infiltrating normal tissue; then, NSCs appear to follow the invading tumor cell into surrounding tissue. *(1 and 2)* Detail of the trailing of individual glioblastoma cells migrating from the main tumor bed *(2)*. High-power view, under fluorescence microscopy, of single migrating infiltrating GFP+ tumor cells in apposition to βgal+ NSCs (white arrow). *(3)* Costaining with Xgal (the arrow points to the *lacZ*-expressing NSCs) and with neutral red (for the elongated glioblastoma cells). The NSC is in direct juxtaposition to a single migrating, invading the neutral red+, spindle-shaped tumor cell (arrow), with the NSC "piggybacking" the glioma cell. Scale bar = 60 µm. (B) NSCs implanted at various intracranial sites far from main tumor bed migrate through normal adult tissue toward glioblastoma cells. *(1 and 2)* Same hemisphere: A section through the tumor from an adult nude mouse 6 days following NSC implantation caudal to tumor. Panel *1* shows a tumor populated as pictured under low power in Fig. 68–1A. Note Xgal+ NSCs interspersed among neutral red+ tumor cells. *(2)* High-power view of NSCs in juxtaposition to islands of tumor cells. *(3–8)* Contralateral hemisphere. *(2–5)* Views through the corpus callosum (c), where βgal+ immunopositive NSCs (arrows) are migrating from their site of implantation on one side of the brain toward tumor on the other. Two NSCs indicated by arrows in panel *3* are viewed at higher magnification in panels *4* and *5* to show the classic elongated morphology and leading process of a migrating neural progenitor oriented toward its target. *(6)* βgal+ NSCs are "homing in" on the GFP+ tumor, having migrated from the other hemisphere. In panel *7*, and magnified further in panel *8*, the Xgal+ NSCs (arrows) have entered the neutral red+ tumor (arrowheads) from the opposite hemisphere. *(9 and 10)* Intraventricular: A section through the brain tumor of an adult nude mouse 6 days after NSC injection into the contralateral cerebral ventricle. *(9)* Xgal+ NSCs are distributed within the neutral red+ main tumor bed (edge delineated by arrowheads). *(10)* At higher power, the NSCs are in juxtaposition to migrating islands of glioblastoma cells. Fibroblast control cells never migrated from their injection site in any paradigm. All Xgal positivity was corroborated by anti-βgal immunoreactivity. Scale bars = 20 µm *(1; also applies to 3)* 8 µm *(2)*, 14 µm *(4 and 5)*, 30 µm *(6 and 7)*, 15 µm *(8)*, 20 µm *(9)*, and 15 µm *(10)*. (C) Bioactive transgene (cytosine deaminase, *CD*) remains functional (as assayed by *in vitro* oncolysis) when expressed within NSCs. CNS-1 glioblastoma cells were cocultured with murine CD-NSCs. *(1)* Cocultures unexposed to 5-FC grew healthily and confluent, *(2)* whereas plates exposed to 5-FC showed dramatic loss of tumor cells represented quantitatively by the histograms (* = *p* < 0.001). The oncolytic effect was identical whether 1×10^5 CD-NSCs or half that number were cocultured with a constant number of tumor cells. (Subconfluent NSCs were still mitotic at the time of 5-FC exposure and thus subject to self-elimination by the generated 5-FU and its toxic metabolites.) (D) Expression of *CD* delivered by NSCs *in vivo* as assayed by reduction in tumor mass. The size of an intracranial glioblastoma populated with CD-NSCs in an adult nude mouse treated with 5-FC was compared with that of tumor treated with 5-FC but lacking CD-NSCs. These data, standardized against and expressed as a percentage of a control tumor populated with CD-NSCs receiving no treatment, are in the histograms in panel *1*. These measurements were derived from measuring the surface area of tumors; camera lucidas of them are in panels *2–4*. Note the large areas of panel *2* a control non–5-2FC-treated, tumor-containing CD-NSCs and in panel *3* a control 5-FC-treated, tumor-lacking CD-NSCs as compared to panel *4* the dramatically smaller tumor areas of the 5-FC-treated animal, which also received CD-NSCs (~80% reduction, * = *p* < 0.001), suggesting both activity and specificity of the transgene. *(3)* The lack of effect of 5-FC on tumor mass when no CD-bearing NSCs were within the tumor was identical to panel *4* the effect of CD-NSCs in the tumor without the gene being employed. Modified from Aboody et al.[21] (Please see CD-ROM for color version of this figure.)

Gene Therapy Using Neural Stem Cells

As stated previously, the ability of NSCs to deliver therapeutic gene products in an immediate, direct, sustained, and perhaps regulated fashion as normal cytoarchitectural components throughout the CNS may overcome some of the limitations of standard viral and cellular vectors (reviewed by Park et al.[23]). The feasibility of this strategy was first demonstrated in a mouse mutant characterized by a single gene defect in all cells, including those in the CNS, leading to their death. The particular mouse modeled the lysosomal storage disease mucopolysaccharidosis type VII (MPS VII) caused by a deletion mutation of the β-glucuronidase *(GUSB)* gene. This incurable inheritable condition is characterized by neurodegeneration in mice and by progressive mental retardation in humans.[19] Although the particular disease was rare, it served as model for neurological diseases whose etiology stemmed from a genetically based loss of function. GUSB-secreting NSCs were implanted into the cerebral ventricles of newborn MPS VII mice, allowing the cells access to the subventricular zone (SVZ), a germinal zone from which the cells were disseminated throughout the brain (creating "chimeric forebrains"). These enzyme-producing cells, now in residence as normal cerebral constituents, not only metabolized lysosomal storage normally for themselves but also cross-corrected mutant cells throughout the brains of recipient mice (Fig. 68–1). Employing a similar strategy, retrovirally transduced NSCs implanted into the brains of fetal and neonatal mice (particularly into periventricular regions) have successfully mediated brainwide expression of other enzymes—for example, β-hexosaminidase, a deficiency of which leads to the pathological accumulation of GM_2 ganglioside.[20]

Findings such as these have helped to establish the paradigm of using NSCs for the transfer of other factors of therapeutic or developmental interest into and throughout the CNS. Although NSCs express baseline amounts of particular enzymes and neuroprotective factors, NSCs can be genetically modified to enhance their production of these molecules or to produce additional molecules that might enhance their therapeutic potential. For example, NSC have been used to deliver NT-3 within the hemisectioned rat spinal cord,[24,25] to express NGF and BDNF within the septum and basal ganglia,[26–28] to provide tyrosine hydroxylase to the parkinsonian striatum,[29] and to express myelin basic protein (MBP) throughout the dysmyelinated cerebrum.[14] In one illustrative set of experiments, NSCs that overexpressed NGF were transplanted into the striatum of a rat lesioned with quinolinic acid, a toxin used to emulate some of the neuronal loss see in Huntington's disease.[30] Delivery of NGF by the engrafted NSCs appeared to reduce the size of the lesion and to promote sparing of host striatal neurons. When implanted into the septum of aging rats, NGF-overexpressing NSCs appeared to blunt the typical cognitive decline by preventing age-related atrophy of forebrain cholinergic neurons. Well integrated into the host tissue, the engrafted NSCs continued to produce NGF until 9 months after grafting.

That NSCs appear to have a strong affinity for sites of pathology and will migrate extensive distances (even from the opposite cerebral hemisphere) to home in on them makes the NSC unique and valuable as a gene delivery vehicle. For example, a type of pathology particularly elusive to gene therapeutic interventions has been the brain tumor, especially the glioma. Gliomas are so exceptionally migratory and infiltrative that they elude even the most effective surgical, radiation, or gene therapeutic strategy. However, the ability of transgene-expressing NSCs to "track down" and deliver therapeutic gene products directly to these widely dispersed and invasive neoplastic cells makes them a potentially valuable adjunct in the treatment of these aggressive tumors.[21]

Although this therapeutic approach—exploiting the normal biological behavior of NSCs for transplantation-based gene therapy—is being extended to animal models of many neurological disorders, it is important to recognize that each pathophysiological process, each animal model, and each therapeutic molecule must be assessed and optimized individually.

Cell Replacement Using Neural Stem Cells

It is postulated that NSCs persist within the CNS long beyond cerebrogenesis to maintain homeostasis following perturbations in the CNS. Presumably the mechanisms that allow the endogenous NSC to perform this function are preserved when the cells are isolated from the CNS, expanded in culture, and reimplanted into the damaged CNS. Indeed, it appears that when NSCs are so implanted, they respond by shifting their pattern of differentiation toward replenishing the missing cell type.

The study that first demonstrated this phenomenon was performed on a model of experimentally induced apoptosis of selectively targeted pyramidal neurons in the adult mammalian neocortex.[13] When transplanted into this circumscribed, neuron-depleted region, 15% of the NSCs altered the differentiation path they would otherwise have pursued in the intact adult, nonneurogenic mammalian neocortex (i.e., to become glia); instead, they differentiated specifically into pyramidal neurons, partially replacing that lost neuronal population (Fig. 68–3). Of these, a subpopulation spontaneously sent axonal projections to their proper targets in the contralateral cortex. Outside the borders of this small region of selective neuronal death, the NSCs yielded only glia. Thus, neurodegeneration appeared to create a milieu that recapitulated embryonic development cues (e.g., for cortical neurogenesis), and the NSCs were sufficiently sensitive to detect and respond to this micromolecular alteration—possibly to therapeutic advantage.

Apoptosis is implicated in a growing number of both neurodegenerative and normal developmental processes. Whether this differentiation shift occurs only in response to signals associated with apoptosis or in response other types of cell death as well remains to be determined. Most neurological diseases are characterized by a mixture of neuropathological processes, making dissection of the key stimuli complex. For example, we have observed that following an ischemic insult, NSCs will robustly repopulate infarcted regions of the postdevelopmental cortex and differentiate into cortical

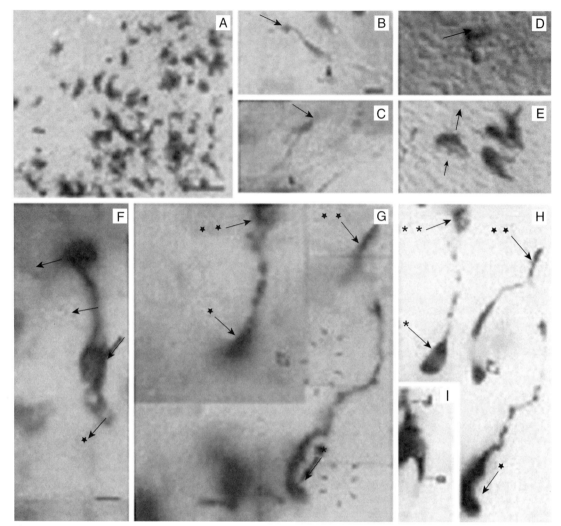

Figure 68-3. *Multipotent NSCs acquire neuronal morphology in regions of adult neocortex subjected to targeted apoptotic neuronal degeneration.* They differentiate into only glia or remain undifferentiated in intact control cortex. (A) Engrafted X-Gal[+] glia at low magnification 6 weeks following transplantation at 12 weeks; (B–E) higher magnification. (B and C) Donor-derived cells with astroglial features: Small, ovoid cell bodies (arrows) with few, short processes often extending as perivascular end-feet (arrowheads). (D) Small soma of a donor-derived presumptive glial cell (arrow) compared with a much larger (≈30 μm), unlabeled, host pyramidal neuron (small arrows). (E) Donor-derived cells with oligodendroglial features (arrow): Multiprocessed, ensheathing neuronal processes (short arrows). (F–I) A total of 15 ± 7% of engrafted cells in regions of neurodegeneration developed neuronal morphology, resembling pyramidal neurons within layer II/III 6 weeks following transplantation at 12 weeks. (F and G) Donor-derived cells with neuronal morphology (large arrows): Large somata (20–30 μm diameter) comparable to residual host pyramidal neurons (small arrows in panel G outline two host neurons, visualized under DIC, each with the characteristic large nucleus and prominent nucleolus of a pyramidal neuron), 300–600 μm presumptive apical dendrites positioned between host (small arrows) and donor (large arrows) neurons of similar morphology and size, and presumptive axons. (F) The dark object at the upper end of the presumptive dendrite is another X-Gal[+] cell out of the plane of focus. (H) DCM image of panel G, collapsing multiple planes of focus. The cell has the characteristic large nucleus of a pyramidal neuron. All but the terminal dendrite of the soma of the cell is out of the plane of focus in panel G. Cells and neurons are indicated to cross-reference views of the same field in panels G and H. (I) Two overlapping donor-derived pyramidal neurons in different focal planes show a characteristic large nucleus, prominent nucleolus, and axon of the overlying cell and a prominent dendrite of the underlying cell, imaged through multiple focal planes of this thick section under DCM. The identification of the previously mentioned cells was supported by immunocytochemical and ultrastructural analysis under electron microscopy. In addition, one could determine that donor-derived neurons received synaptic input from the host and were myelinated by host oligodendrocytes, further supporting their incorporation into the host cytoarchitecture (a: axon; d: dendrite; cells: *, **, ** and open arrow; and *: neurons). Bars = 25 μm. Adapted from Snyder *et al.*[13] (Please see CD-ROM for color version of this figure.)

neurons in these regions.[31] However, even hypoxic–ischemic cerebral injury—the quintessential example of necrotic and excitotoxic injury—is characterized by an apoptotic phase. An added level of complexity may be the tempo at which apoptotic signals are elaborated—an acute burst may be more instructive than a more languid burst.

Studies are ongoing to identify the key molecules that direct NSC fate during and following various kinds of neural injury. Intriguingly, we are starting to learn that cytokines released during an inflammatory reaction—those emanating from microphages and microglia as well as from parenchymal damage (e.g., SDF1-α)—play a pivotal role in "beckoning" NSCs. Coincidentally, we are starting to recognize that many processes regarded as neurodegenerative—including amyotrophic lateral sclerosis (ALS), Alzheimer's disease, tumors, and stroke—are characterized by a prominent inflammatory signature. Although each is different in its etiology, region of involvement, and course, inflammation may be their common denominator from the "viewpoint" of the NSC.

"Global" Cell Replacement Using Neural Stem Cells

The targeted-apoptosis model described in the previous section exemplifies a circumscribed type of neural cell loss. However, the pathologic lesions of many neurological disorders are often widely—even globally—dispersed throughout the brain. Such conditions include the neurodegenerative disorders of childhood (e.g., inborn errors of metabolism, storage diseases, leukodystrophies, and neuronal ceroid lipofuscinoses) and hypoxic–ischemic encephalopathy as well as some adult CNS diseases (e.g., multiple sclerosis, Alzheimer's disease, and ALS). Treatment for these disorders requires widespread replacement of genes, cells, or both as well as the regeneration, protection, or both of broad networks of neural circuitry. The ability of inherently migratory NSCs to integrate into germinal zones from which they can be "launched" and the inclination of NSCs to travel long distances to home in on pathologic regions makes these cells ideally—and perhaps uniquely—suited for this task.

Mouse mutants characterized by CNS-wide white matter disease provided the first models for testing the hypothesis that NSCs might be useful against neuropathologies requiring widespread neural cell replacement. The oligodendrocytes—the myelin-producing cells—of the dysmyelinated *shiverer (shi)* mouse are dysfunctional because they lack MBP, a molecule essential for effective myelination. Therapy, therefore, requires widespread replacement with MBP-expressing oligodendrocytes. NSCs transplanted at birth (employing the intracerebroventricular implantation technique described previously for the diffuse engraftment of enzyme-expressing NSCs to treat global metabolic lesions[14]) resulted in engraftment throughout the *shi* brain with repletion of significant amounts of MBP. Of the many donor cells that differentiated into oligodendrocytes, a subgroup myelinated ~40% of host neuronal processes. In some recipient animals, the symptomatic tremor decreased (Fig. 68–4). Therefore,

"global" cell replacement was shown to be feasible for some pathological conditions if cells with stem-like features are employed. This approach has been extended to other myelin-impaired animal models, such as the experimental allergic encephalomyelitis mouse model[32,33] of multiple sclerosis as well as rodent mutant models of Palezeus-Merzbacher,[34] Krabbe,[35] and Canavan leukodystrophies. Recently, it was demonstrated that neural progenitor–stem cells of human origin have a similar remyelinating capacity in the *shi* mouse brain. Viewed more parochially, the ability of NSCs to remyelinate is of significant importance because impaired myelination plays such an important role in many genetic (e.g., leukodystrophies and inborn metabolic errors) and acquired (e.g., traumatic, infectious, asphyxial, ischemic, and inflammatory) neurodegenerative processes. However, viewed more broadly, the ability of the NSC to replace this particular type of neural cell throughout the brain bodes well for its ability to replace other classes of neural cell across the broad terrains often demanded by other categories of complex neurodegenerative diseases.

Neural Stem Cells Display an Inherent Mechanism for Rescuing Dysfunctional Neurons

The examples cited previously highlight that an abnormal environment can direct the behavior of a grafted NSC. However, they leave the impression that the exogenous NSC alone fills gaps. The situation is more complex and richer. We are beginning to learn that the NSC and the injured host engage in a dynamic series of ongoing reciprocal interactions, each instructing the other. Under instruction from exogenous NSCs, the injured host nervous system also contributes to its own repair. These important stem cell phenomena were first illustrated in a few examples:

The effect of NSCs in directly rescuing endangered host neurons was first evinced in a series of experiments in aged rodents in which the nigrostriatal system was impaired (Fig. 68–5). Parkinson's disease is a degenerative disorder characterized by a loss of midbrain dopamine (DA) neurons with a subsequent reduction in striatal DA. The disease, in addition to incapacitating thousands of patients, has long served as a model for testing neural cell replacement strategies. Transplantation therapy for this CNS disorder has a long history (for a review, see Isacson *et al.*[36]). It was the neural disease first treated clinically by neural transplantation, using primary tissue from human fetal ventral mesencephalon to replace DA-expressing cells.[37,38] Indeed, in this disease, the limitations of fetal tissue grafts in not only rodent and primate models of Parkinson's disease[39] but also in clinical trials[37,38] were first recognized. These limitations include, on one hand, short graft survival and limited integration of the grafts and, on the other hand, the possibility of unregulated DA production in improper regions leading adversely to dyskinesias. Given the storied role of Parkinson's disease in the development of cellular therapies, it is appropriate that a model of this

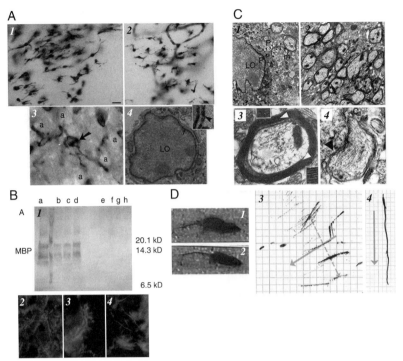

Figure 68–4. *"Global" cell replacement is feasible using NSC transplantation: evidence from the dysmyelinated* shi *mouse brain.* (A) NSCs engraft extensively throughout the *shi* dysmyelinated brain, including within white tracts, and differentiate into oligodendrocytes. *LacZ*-expressing, βgal-producing NSCs were transplanted into newborn *shi* mutants and analyzed systematically at intervals between 2 and 8 weeks following engraftment. Coronal sections through the *shi* brain at adulthood demonstrated widely disseminated integration of Xgal+ donor-derived cells throughout the neuraxis, similar to the pattern seen in Fig. 68–1A in the MPS VII mutant mouse. *(1 and 2)* Donor-derived Xgal+ cells (higher magnification) in sections through the corpus callosum possessed characteristic oligodendroglial features (small, round, or polygonal cell bodies with multiple fine processes oriented toward the neural fiber tracts). *(3)* Close-up of a donor-derived anti-β immunoreactive oligodendrocyte (arrow) extending multiple processes toward and beginning to enwrap large, adjacent axonal bundles (a) viewed on end in a section through the corpus callosum. That cells such as those in panel A *1–3* and in panel B *2-4* were oligodendroglia was confirmed by the electron micrograph in panel A *4* and in panel C, demonstrating their defining ultrastructural features. A donor-derived Xgal+ oligodendrocyte (LO) can be distinguished by the electron dense Xgal precipitate typically localized to the nuclear membrane (arrow), ER (arrowhead), and other cytoplasmic organelles. The ER is magnified in the inset to demonstrate the unique crystalline nature of individual precipitate particles. (B) MBP expression in mature transplanted and control brains. *(1)* Western analysis for MBP in whole-brain lysates. The brains of three transplanted *shi* mutants (lanes 2–4) expressed MBP at levels close to those of an age-matched unaffected mouse (lane 1, positive control) and significantly greater than the amounts seen in untransplanted (lanes 7–8, negative control) or unengrafted (lanes 5–6, negative control) age-matched *shi* mutants. (Identical total protein amounts were loaded in each lane.) *(2–4)* Immunocytochemical analysis for MBP. *(2)* The brain of a mature unaffected mouse was immunoreactive to an antibody to MBP (revealed with a Texas red-conjugated secondary antibody). *(3 and 4)* Age-matched engrafted brains from *shi* mice similarly showed immunoreactivity. Because untransplanted *shi* brains lack MBP, MBP immunoreactivity has classically been a marker for normal donor-derived oligodendrocytes in transplant paradigms. (C) NSC-derived "replacement" oligodendrocytes are capable of myelination of *shi* axons. In regions of MBP-expressing NSC engraftment, *shi* neuronal processes became enwrapped by thick, better-compacted myelin. *(1)* Two weeks after transplant, a donor-derived, labeled oligodendrocyte (LO), recognized by extensive Xgal precipitate (p) in the nuclear membrane, cytoplasmic organelles, and processes, was extending processes (arrowheads) to host neurites and was beginning to ensheathe them with myelin (m). *(2)* If engrafted *shi* regions *(1)* were followed to 4 weeks, the myelin began to appear healthier, thicker, and better-compacted (arrows) than that in age-matched untransplanted control mutants. *(3)* By 6 weeks after transplant, these matured into even thicker wraps; ~40% of host axons were ensheathed by myelin (white arrowheads; MDLs are evident) that was dramatically thicker and better-compacted than that of *shi* myelin (*4*, black arrowhead) from an unengrafted region of an otherwise successfully engrafted *shi* brain). (D) Functional and behavioral assessment of transplanted *shi* mutants and controls. The *shi* mutation is characterized by the onset of tremor and a "shivering gait" by postnatal week 2 or 3. The degree of motor dysfunction in animals was gauged in two ways: by blindly scoring periods of standardized, videotaped cage behavior of experimental and control animals and by measuring the amplitude of tail displacement along the body's rostral–caudal axis (an objective, quantifiable index of tremor). Video freeze-frames of (1) unengrafted and (2) successfully engrafted *shi* mice. (1) The whole body tremor and ataxic movement observed in the unengrafted symptomatic animal causes the frame to blur, a contrast with (1) the well-focused frame of the asymptomatic transplanted *shi* mouse. Of transplanted mutants, 60% evinced nearly normal-appearing behavior (2) and attained scores similar to normal controls. (3 and 4) Whole body tremor was mirrored by the amplitude of tail displacement (dotted gray arrow), measured perpendicularly from a line drawn in the direction of the animal's movement. Measurements were made by permitting a mouse, whose tail had been dipped in India ink, to move freely in a straight line on a sheet of graph paper. (3) Large degrees of tremor cause the tail to make widely divergent ink marks from the midline, representing the body's axis (solid gray arrow). (4) Absence of tremor allows the tail to make long, straight, uninterrupted ink lines on the paper congruent with the body's axis. The distance between points of maximal tail displacement from the axis was measured and averaged for transplanted and untransplanted *shi* mutants and for unaffected controls (dotted gray arrow). Panel 3 shows data from a poorly engrafted mutant that did not improve with respect to tremor, whereas panel 4 reveals lack of tail displacement in a successfully engrafted asymptomatic mutant. Overall, 64% of transplanted *shi* mice examined displayed at least a 50% decrement in the degree of tremor or "shiver." Several showed no displacement. Modified from Yandava *et al.*[14] (Please see CD-ROM for color version of this figure.)

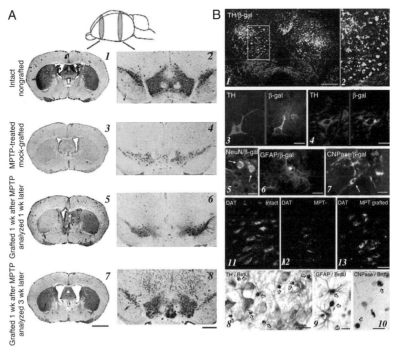

Figure 68–5. *NSCs possess an inherent mechanism for rescuing dysfunctional neurons: evidence from the effects of NSCs in the restoration of mesencephalic dopaminergic function.* (A) TH expression in mesencephalon and striatum of aged mice following MPTP lesioning and unilateral NSC engraftment into the substantia nigra–ventral tegmental area (SN–VTA). A model that emulates the slow dysfunction of aging dopaminergic neurons in SN was generated by giving aged mice repeated high doses of MPTP. Schematic indicates the levels of the analyzed transverse sections along the rostrocaudal axis of the mouse brain. Coronal sections are through the striatum in the left column and through the SN–VTA area in the right column. Immunodetection of TH (black cells) shows the normal distribution of DA-producing TH⁺ neurons in (2) coronal sections in the intact SN–VTA and (1) their projections to the striatum. Within one week, MPTP treatment caused extensive and permanent bilateral loss of TH immunoreactivity in both (3) the mesostriatal nuclei and (4) the striatum. Shown in this example, and matching the time point in 7 and 8, is the situation in a mock-grafted animal 4 weeks after MPTP treatment. Unilateral (right side) stereotactic injection of NSCs into the nigra is associated, within 1 week after grafting, with substantial recovery of TH synthesis within (6) the ipsilateral DA nuclei and (5) their ipsilateral striatal projections. By 3 weeks after transplant, however, the asymmetric distribution of TH expression disappeared, producing TH immunoreactivity in (8) the midbrain and (7) striatum of both hemispheres that approached the immunoreactivity of (1 and 2) the intact controls and gave the appearance of mesostriatal restoration. Similar observations were made when NSCs were injected 4 weeks after MPTP treatment (not shown). Bars: 2 mm (left), 1 mm (right). Note the ectopically placed TH⁺ cells in panel 8. These are analyzed in greater detail with the entire SN in B. (B) Immunohistochemical analyses of TH, DAT, and BrdU⁺ cells in MPTP-treated and grafted mouse brains. The initial presumption was that the NSCs had replaced the dysfunctional TH neurons. However, examination of the reconstituted SN with dual βgal and TH ICC showed that (1 and 3) 90% of the TH⁺ cells in the SN were rescued, host-derived cells, and (4) only 10% were donor-derived cells. Most NSC-derived TH⁺ cells were just above the SN ectopically (blocked area in panel 1; enlarged in panel 2). These photomicrographs were taken from immunostained brain sections from aged mice exposed to MPTP, transplanted 1 week later with NSCs and sacrificed after 3 weeks. The following combinations of markers were evaluated: (1–4) TH with βgal, (5) NeuN with βgal, (6) GFAP with βgal, (7) CNPase with βgal, (8) TH with BrdU, (9) GFAP with BrdU, and (10) CNPase with BrdU. Anti-DAT-stained areas are revealed in the SN of (11) intact, (12) mock-grafted, and (13) NSC-grafted brains. Fluorescence filters for Alexa Fluor 488 and Texas red and a double-filter for both types of fluorochromes were used to show antibody binding. (3, 4, and 8–10) Single-filter exposures; (1, 2, and 5–7) double-filter exposures. (1) Low-power overview of the SN–VTA of both hemispheres. Most TH⁺ cells within the nigra are of host origin (~90%), a much smaller proportion (~10%) are donor derived (close-up in panel 4). Although a significant proportion of NSCs differentiated into TH⁺ neurons, many of these resided ectopically, dorsal to the SN (boxed area in panel 1 enlarged in panel 2; and a high-power view of the donor-derived cell that was also TH⁺ in panel 3), where the ratio of donor-to-host cells was inverted: ~90% donor derived compared with ~10% host derived. Note the near absence of a βgal-specific signal in the SN–VTA, whereas ectopically, many of the TH⁺ cells were double labeled and thus NSC derived. (5) NSC-derived non-TH neurons (NeuN⁺, arrow), (6) astrocytes (GFAP⁺), and (7) oligodendrocytes (CNPase⁺, arrow) were also seen, both within the mesencephalic nuclei and dorsal to them. (10) The DAT-specific signal suggests that the reconstituted mesencephalic nuclei in the NSC-grafted mice were functional DA neurons comparable to those seen (8) in intact nuclei but not (9) in MPTP-lesioned, sham-engrafted controls. This further suggests that the TH⁺ mesostriatal DA neurons affected by MPTP are functionally impaired. Note that (9) sham-grafted animals contain only punctate residual DAT staining within their dysfunctional fibers, whereas DAT staining (8) in normal and (10) in engrafted animals was normally and robustly distributed both within processes and throughout their cell bodies. (11–12) Any proliferative BrdU⁺ cells after MPTP insult, graft, or both were confined to glial cells, whereas (11) the TH⁺ neurons were BrdU⁻. This finding suggested that the reappearance of TH⁺ host cells was not the result of neurogenesis but rather the recovery of extant host TH⁺ neurons. Bars = 90 μm (1), 20 μm (3–5), 30 μm (6), 10 μm (7), 20 μm (8–10), 25 μm (11), 10 μm (12), and 20 μm (13). Modified from Ourednik et al.⁴⁰ (Please see CD-ROM for color version of this figure.)

disease should have also played a pivotal role in revealing a little suspected but powerful therapeutic action that NSCs may play in preserving degenerating host cells by some heretofore unheralded mechanisms that are nevertheless inherent to stem cell biology.

In the hope that NSCs might spontaneously differentiate into DA neurons when implanted into a DA-depleted region of the CNS, unmanipulated murine NSCs were implanted unilaterally into the substantia nigra of aged mice exposed systemically to high-dose 1-methyl-4-phenyl-1,2,3,6-tetrahydropyridine (MPTP), a neurotoxin that produces a persistent impairment of mesencephalic DA neurons and their striatal projections.[40] The NSCs not only migrated from their point of implantation and integrated extensively within both hemispheres but also were associated with a dramatic reconstitution of DA function throughout the mesostriatal system. Although there was spontaneous conversion of a subpopulation of donor NSCs into dopaminergic neurons in DA-depleted areas, contributing to nigral reconstitution, most (80–90%) dopaminergic neurons in the "reconstituted midbrain" were actually host cells that had been "rescued" by factors produced constitutively by the NSCs with which they were juxtaposed and that had not become neurons. These chaperone cells constitutively produce substantial amounts of neurosupportive agents. One such prominent molecule was GDNF, a factor known to be neuroprotective of ventrally located neurons (including DA neurons and spinal–ventral horn cells). A similar observation is beginning to emerge from the implantation of human NSCs into the MPTP-lesioned, subhuman primate model of Parkinson's disease.

A sense for the extent of the cross talk also became evident when examining rodent models of hypoxia–ischemia, a common cause of neurological disability in adults and children. Hypoxia–ischemia causes much of its damage from extensive loss of cerebral parenchyma and the cells and connections that reside there. When NSCs are implanted into these regions of extensive degeneration (particularly when transiently supported by biodegradable scaffolds), robust reciprocal interactions ensue spontaneously between the exogenous implant and the injured host brain substantially reconstitute parenchyma and anatomical connections as well as reduce parenchymal loss, secondary cell loss, inflammation, and scarring.[31] Similar results are observed in the hemiresected adult rodent spinal cord in which evidence of an up-regulated host neuronal regenerative response is noted, resulting in significant functional improvement.[41]

Indeed, the ability of engrafted NSCs to exert a protective and regenerative influence on degenerating host neural systems because of their intrinsic expression of trophic factors is being observed in an increasing number of conditions. For example, the implantation of murine and human NSCs into the spinal cords of the SOD1 transgenic mouse model of ALS, a disease characterized by virulent motor neuron degeneration, has been pivotal in protecting these ventral horn cells from death, preserving motor and respiratory function, blunting disease progression, and extending life. NSCs can similarly protect other neuron pools, promote motor axonal outgrowth following traumatic spinal cord injury,[18] preserve infarcted regions of cerebrum,[31] induce vascularization of reconstituted regions of cortical parenchyma,[42] and inhibit inflammation and scarring following traumatic or ischemic insult.[31,41]

Together, these observations suggest that exogenous NSCs may not only replenish inadequate pools of endogenous NSCs to compensate for missing neural cells but also reactivate or enhance endogenous regenerative and protective capacities. It also highlights a heretofore unanticipated mechanism by which NSCs may exert a therapeutic effect—to be added to their more traditional roles in direct cell replacement and gene therapy.

Neural Stem Cells as the Glue That Holds Multiple Therapies Together

Experimentally, one may eliminate a particular cell type, lesion a particular region of CNS, knock out a particular gene, or choose a mouse strain in which, by chance, certain mutations have spontaneously occurred. However, most human neurodegenerative diseases are not as "clean." They are quite complex. And complex diseases, such as those affecting the nervous system, will require complex and multifaceted solutions—including pharmacological, gene and molecular, cell replacement, tissue engineering, angiogenic, antiinflammatory, antiapoptotic, proregenerative, proneurite outgrowth-promoting therapies. The NSC, as a key player in a set of fundamental developmental mechanisms, may serve as the glue that holds many of these strategies together. How they may be intelligently, effectively, safely, and practically orchestrated in actual patients will require a good deal of careful investigation.

For example, as our sophistication about disease processes grow, we are beginning to learn that more than one neural cell type probably needs to be replaced in a disease. For example, in a disease like ALS, a disorder characterized by progressive motor neuron degeneration, we are beginning to learn that astrocyte replacement may be just as critical as motor neuron replacement. Conversely, in multiple sclerosis, a white matter disease characterized by oligodendrocyte degeneration, replacing neurons and their axonal connections may be critical for the restoration of function. These same caveats may apply to many diseases in which replacement of multiple cell types may be the key to neurological reconstitution and to damaged milieu reconstruction. Because of their ability to develop into multiple integral, cytoarchitectural components of many regions throughout the host brain, NSCs may be able to replace a range of missing or dysfunctional neural cell types within the same region. This is important in the likely situation in which return of function may require the reconstitution of the milieu of a given region (e.g., not just the neurons but also the chaperone cells—the glia and support cells) to nurture, detoxify, guide, and/or myelinate the neurons. As noted previously, the NSCs, especially in particular differentiation states, express certain genes of intrinsic interest (many neurotrophic factors, lysosomal enzymes, angiogenic factors, anti-inflammatory molecules, antioxidants, etc.), or they can be engineered *ex vivo* to do so.

The challenge remains, however, to coordinate these multifaceted therapies so that they work in concert synergistically and not at cross-purposes.

Summary

The ability of NSCs to migrate and integrate throughout the brain as well as to disseminate a foreign gene product is of great significance for the development of new therapies for neurodegenerative diseases in humans. Lethal, hereditary neurodegenerative diseases of childhood, such as the gangliosidoses, leukodystrophies, neuronal ceroid lipofuscinoses, and other storage diseases, result in lesions throughout the CNS. Diseases of adult onset (e.g., Alzheimer's disease) are also diffuse in their pathology. Even acquired diseases such as spinal cord injury, head trauma, and stroke are broader in their involvement than typically assumed. Such abnormalities may benefit from the multifaceted approach NSCs may enable. First, they may replace a range of cell types—not only neurons to reconstitute neural connections but also oligodendrocytes to elaborate myelin and astrocytes to serve trophic, guidance, protective, and detoxification functions. Second, NSCs may deliver exogenous genes that might restore normal metabolism, complement a factor deficiency, support the survival of a damaged host neuron, neutralize a hostile milieu, counteract a growth-inhibitory environment, promote neurite regrowth, and reform stable and functional contacts. As noted previously, many molecules are produced inherently by NSCs when they are in particular states of differentiation. The production of other molecules might require *ex vivo* genetic engineering. NSCs appear to have their greatest therapeutic effect when used in the early stages of a degenerative process or in the subacute phase following injury.

A major requirement for the better use of NSCs will be a better understanding of the pathophysiology of the diseases to be targeted—that is, knowing what aspects require repair and which cell type or types require replacement or rescue.

Another challenge will be determining how to exploit stem cell biology for chronic conditions—in other words, how the acute milieu can be recreated in the chronic environment such that NSCs behave therapeutically there as well.

Among the methodological hurdles will be to devise how, when, where, and with what frequency to deliver NSCs to adults with disseminated diseases in regions not fed by readily accessible germinal zones, for example, the spinal cord in which the central canal is no longer patent. Linked to this is the need for a better understanding of the methods for augmenting yet controlling the propagation and the phenotype specification of NSCs *in vitro* and *in vivo*.

Another question has come to dominate the stem cell field: What is the most effective way to obtain NSCs for therapy? Should they be obtained directly from regions of neuroectodermal origin, and if so, should that be from a fetal source? Can an adult source be equally effective? Should stable lines of NSCs be established that can be used for all patients, or

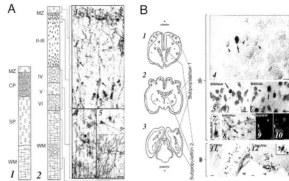

Figure 68–6. *Clonal human NSCs migrate from the VZ into the developing neocortex.* Schematics of the developing monkey neopallium (A) at the time of transplantation. *(1)* 12–13 wpc and *(2)* at the time of death (16–17 wpc). *(3–5)* Photomicrographs from selected locations spanning the neopallium. (Their location relative to the schematic is indicated by brackets.) *(3)* Injected into the left lateral ventricle and having integrated throughout the VZ, the human NSC–derived cells (d), identified by their BrdU immunoreactivity (black nuclei), migrated along the monkey's radial glial processes through the neopallial wall to reach their temporally appropriate destination in the nascent superficial layers II and III *(3)*, where they detached from the radial glia and took up residence as neurons. Arrows indicate climbing (donor- and host-derived) cells positioned along the processes of the vimentin-positive host radial glia. Some cells (inset) are still attached to these fibers and in the process of migration. *(4 and 5)* Immature, donor, human NSC–derived astrocytes intermixed with host-derived astrocytes in deeper cortical lamina, having differentiated as expected for that site and time. (B) Segregation of the fates of human NSCs and their progeny into two subpopulations in the brains of developing Old World monkeys. Schematics (left) and photomicrographs (right) illustrate the distribution and properties of clonal human NSC–derived cells. human NSCs (labeled with BrdU) dispersed throughout and integrated into the VZ. From there, clonally related human NSC–derived cells pursued one of two fates. Those donor cells that migrated outward from the VZ along radial glial fibers into the developing neocortex constituted one pool or subpopulation. *(4–12)* The differentiated phenotypes of cells in this subpopulation *(1)* (stars in the schematic), particularly in layers II and III. *(4)* An human NSC–derived BrdU+ cell (black nucleus, arrow)—likely a neuron according to its size, morphology, large nucleus, and location—is shown (under Nomarski optics) intermingled with the monkey's similar neurons (arrowheads) in neocortical layers II and III. The neuronal identity of such donor-derived cells is confirmed by immunocytochemical analysis. High-power photomicrographs of human donor-derived cells integrated into the monkey cortex double-stained with antibodies against BrdU and cell type-specific markers: *(5)* NeuN and *(6)* calbindin for neurons (arrows, donor-derived cells; arrowheads, host-derived cells). *(8)* CNPase for oligodendroglia (arrow). (BrdU+ is the black nucleus in the CNPase+ cell; the arrowhead indicates the long process emanating from the soma.) *(9, 10)* GFAP for astroglia antibody to BrdU revealed through fluorescein; *(9)* antibody to GFAP revealed through Texas red. The human origin of the cortical neurons is independently confirmed in panel 7, where the human-specific nuclear marker NuMA (black nucleus) is colocalized in the same cell with neurofilament immunoreactivity. Progeny from this same human NSC clone were allocated to a second cellular pool—subpopulation 2 (dots in the schematic; arrows in panels 9 and 10)—that remained mainly confined to the SVZ and stained only for an immature neural marker. (Vimentin colocalized with BrdU is easily seen in inset (arrows); the arrowhead indicates the host vimentin-positive cell.) Some members of subpopulation 2 were identified within the developing neocortex (dots) intermixed with differentiated cells. Panels 9 and 10 use immunofluorescence; the other immunostains use a DAB-based color reaction. Scale bars = 30 μm *(4-6)* and 20 μm *(7-12)*. (d: human NSC–derived cells, MZ: marginal zone, CP: cortical plate, SP: subplate, WM: white matter, and II–VI: cortical layers). Modified from Ourednik *et al.*[16] (Please see CD-ROM for color version of this figure.)

should NSCs be abstracted from each patient to be used as an autograft on a case-by-case basis? The degree to which the immune system presents a barrier to stem cell transplantation will likely determine the answers to this question and its sub-questions. If ES cells (from the inner cell mass of blastocysts) are directed to become NSCs *in vitro,* will such cells be equally as safe and effective?

The success in isolating stem-like cells from the CNS (the first "solid organ stem cells" discovered) and their therapeutic potential also gave rise to the search for and successful isolation of stem-like cells from other nonneural organ systems, including bone marrow mesenchyme, muscle, skin, retina, and liver, for the purposes of repairing those tissues. Whether such *nonneural* stem cells can yield *neural* stem cells—through metaplasia or transdifferentiation—remains unresolved and exceptionally controversial. Can NSCs be derived efficiently and effectively from nonneural organs with outcomes as good as from NSCs themselves?

A better understanding of fundamental NSC biology will be required before human NSCs can be transplanted efficaciously in true clinical settings. Nevertheless, progress in this regard is being made. Several NSC lines have been established from the human fetal telencephalon and spinal cord that seem to emulate many of the appealing properties of their rodent counterparts[7,15]: They differentiate *in vitro* and *in vivo* into neurons, astrocytes, and oligodendrocytes; they follow appropriate developmental programs and migrational pathways similar to endogenous precursors following engraftment into developing rodent and subhuman primate brain[16] (Fig. 68–6); they express foreign genes *in vivo* in a widely disseminated manner; and they can replace missing neural cell types when grafted into various mutant mice or rodent models of injury. The principal differences between human NSCs and mouse NSCs so far seem to be the length of the cell cycle (up to 4 days in the human) and the predilection of human NSCs to senesce (after ~100 cell divisions), obstacles that are being actively addressed. If human NSCs behave in lesioned subhuman primate brains with safe and effective engraftment and foreign gene expression as they seem to do in rodents, then human trials might be warranted for testing their value against certain genuine clinical neurodegenerative diseases. Through a careful and circumspect series of experiments and trials, we may learn whether we, indeed, have found within Nature's own toolbox a powerful and versatile therapeutic tool—one of the goals of experiments that started more than 15 years ago.

REFERENCES

1. Vescovi, A.L., and Snyder, E.Y. (1999). Establishment and properties of neural stem cell clones: plasticity *in vitro* and *in vivo*. *Brain Pathol.* **9,** 569–598.
2. Gage, F.H., (2000). Mammalian neural stem cells *Science* **287,** 1433–1438.
3. McKay, R. (1997). Stem cells in the central nervous system. *Science* **276,** 66–71.
4. D'Amour, K.A., and Gage, F.H. (2003). Genetic and functional differences between multipotent neural and pluripotent embryonic stem cells. *Proc. Natl. Acad. Sci. USA* **100**(Suppl. 1), 11,866–11,872.
5. Ivanova, N.B., Dimos, J.T., Schaniel, C., Hackney, J.A., Moore, K.A., and Lemischka, I.R. (2002). A stem cell molecular signature. *Science* **298,** 601–604.
6. Ramalho-Santos, M., Yoon, S., Matsuzaki, Y., Mulligan, R.C., and. Melton, D.A. (2002). "Stemness": transcriptional profiling of embryonic and adult stem cells. *Science* **298,** 597–600.
7. Villa, A., Snyder, E.Y., Vescovi, A., and Martinez-Serrano, A. (2000). Establishment and properties of a growth factor-dependent, perpetual neural stem cell line from the human CNS. *Exp. Neurol.* **161,** 67–84.
8. Kitchens, D.L., Snyder, E.Y., and Gottlieb, D.I. (1994). bFGF and EGF are mitogens for immortalized neural progenitors. *J. Neurobiol.* **25,** 797–807.
9. Ryder, E.F., Snyder, E.Y., Cepko, C.L. (1990). Establishment and characterization of multipotent neural cell lines using retrovirus vector-mediated oncogene transfer. *J. Neurobiol.* **21,** 356–375.
10. Renfranz, P.J., Cunningham, M.G., and McKay, R.D.G. (1991). Region-specific differentiation of the hippocampal stem cell line HiB5 upon implantation into the developing mammalian brain. *Cell* **66,** 713–719.
11. Snyder, E.Y., Deitcher, D.L., Walsh, C., Arnold-Aldea, S., Hartwieg, E.A., and Cepko, C.L. (1992). Multipotent neural cell lines can engraft and participate in development of mouse cerebellum. *Cell* **68,** 33–51.
12. Rosario, C.M., Yandava, B.D., Kosaras, B., Zurakowski, D., Sidman, R.L., and Snyder, E.Y. (1997). Differentiation of engrafted multipotent neural progenitors toward replacement of missing granule neurons in meander tail cerebellum may help determine the locus of mutant gene action. *Development* **124,** 4213–4224.
13. Snyder, E.Y., Yoon, C.H., Flax, J.D., and Macklis, J.D. (1997). Multipotent neural progenitors can differentiate toward replacement of neurons undergoing targeted apoptotic degeneration in adult mouse neocortex. *Proc. Natl. Acad. Sci. USA* **94,** 11,645–11,650.
14. Yandava, B.D., Billinghurst, L.L., and Snyder, E.Y. (1999). "Global" cell replacement is feasible via neural stem cell transplantation: evidence from the shiverer dysmyelinated mouse brain. *Proc. Natl. Acad. Sci. USA* **96,** 7029–7034.
15. Flax, J.D., Aurora, S., Yang, C., Simonin, C., Wills, A.M., Billinghurst, L.L., Jendoubi, M., Sidman, R.L., Wolfe, J.H., Kim, S.U., and Snyder, E.Y. (1998). Engraftable human neural stem cells respond to developmental cues, replace neurons, and express foreign genes. *Natl. Biotech.* **16,** 1033–1039.
16. Ourednik, V., Ourednik, J., Flax, J.D., Zawada, W.M., Hutt, C., Yang, C., Park, K.I., Kim, S.U., Sidman, R.L., Freed, C.R., and Snyder, E.Y. (2001). Segregation of human neural stem cells in the developing primate forebrain. *Science* **293,** 1820–1824.
17. Zlomanczuk, P., Mrugala, M., de la Iglesia, H.O., Ourednik, V., Quesenberry, P.J., Snyder, E.Y., and Schwartz, W.J. (2002). Transplanted clonal neural stem-like cells respond to remote photic stimulation following incorporation within the suprachiasmatic nucleus. *Exp. Neurol.* **174,** 162–168.
18. Lu, P., Jones, L.L., Snyder, E.Y., and Tuszynski, M.H. (2003). Neural stem cells constitutively secrete neurotrophic factors and promote extensive host axonal growth after spinal cord injury. *Exp. Neurol.* **181,** 115–129.
19. Snyder, E.Y., Taylor, R.M., and Wolfe, J.H. (1995). Neural progenitor cell engraftment corrects lysosomal storage throughout the MPS VII mouse brain. *Nature* **374,** 367–370.

20. Lacorazza, H.D., Flax, J.D., Snyder, E.Y., and Jendoubi, M. (1996). Expression of human β-hexosaminidase α-subunit gene (the gene defect of Tay-Sachs disease) in mouse brains upon engraftment of transduced progenitor cells. *Natl. Med.* **4**, 424–429.

21. Aboody, K.S., Brown, A., Rainov, N.G., Bower, K.A., Liu, S., Yang, W., Small, J.E., Herrlinger, U., Ourednik, V., Black, P.M., Breakefield, X.O., and Snyder, E.Y. (2000). Neural stem cells display extensive tropism for pathology in the adult brain: evidence from intracranial gliomas. *Proc. Natl. Acad. Sci. USA* **97**, 12,846–12,851

22. Akerud, P., Canals, J.M., Snyder E.Y., and Arenas, E. (2001). Neuroprotection through delivery of glial cell line-derived neurotrophic factor by neural stem cells in a mouse model of Parkinson's disease. *J. Neurosci.* **21**, 8108–8118.

23. Park, K.I., Ourednik, J., Ourednik, V., Taylor, R.M., Aboody, K.S., Auguste, K.I., Lachyankar, M.B., Redmond, D.E., and Snyder, E.Y. (2002). Global gene and cell replacement strategies via stem cells. *Gene Ther.* **9**, 613–614.

24. Liu, Y., Himes, B.T., Solwska, J., Moul, J., Chow, S.Y., Park, K.I., Tessler, A., Murray, M., Snyder, E.Y., and Fischer, I. (1999). Intraspinal delivery of neurotrophin-3 using neural stem cells genetically modified by recombinant retrovirus. *Exp. Neurol.* **158**, 9–26.

25. Himes, B.T., Liu, Y., Solowska, J.M., Snyder, E.Y., Fishere, I., and Tessler, A. (2001). Transplants of cells genetically modified to express neurotrophin-3 rescue axotomized Clarke's nucleus neurons after spinal cord hemisection in adults rats. *J. Neurosci. Res.* **65**, 549–564.

26. Martinez-Serrano, A., Fischer, W., and Bjorklund, A. (1995). Reversal of age-dependent cognitive impairments and cholinergic neuron atrophy by NGF-secreting neural progenitors grafted to the basal forebrain. *Neuron* **15**, 473–484.

27. Martinez-Serrrano, A., Lundber, C., Horellou, P., Fisher, W., Bentlage, C., Campbell, K., McKay, R.D.G., Mallet, J., and Bjorklund, A. (1995). CNS-derived neural progenitor cells for gene transfer of nerve growth factor to the adult rat brain: complete rescue of axotomized cholinergic neurons after implantation into the septum. *J. Neurosci.* **15**, 5668–5680.

28. Martinez-Serrano, A., and Bjorklund, A. (1996). Protection of the neostriatum against excitotoxic damage by neurotrophin producing genetically modified neural stem cells. *J. Neurosci.* **16**, 4604–4616.

29. Anton, R., Kordower, J.H., and Maidment, N.T. (1994). Neural-targeted gene therapy for rodent and primate hemiparkinsonism. *Exp. Neurol.* **127**, 207–218.

30. Kordower, J.H., Chen, E., Winkler, C., Fricker, R., Charles, V., Messing, A., Mufson, E.J., Wong, S.C., Rosenstein, J.M., Björklund, A., Emerich, D.F., Hammang, J., and Carpenter, M.K. (1997). Grafts of EGF-responsive neural stem cells derived form GFAP hNGF transgenic mice: trophic and tropic effects in a rodent model of Huntington's disease. *J. Comp. Neurol.* **387**, 96–113.

31. Park, K.I., Teng, Y.D., and Snyder, E.Y. (2002). The injured brain interacts reciprocally with neural stem cells supported by scaffolds to reconstitute lost tissue. *Natl. Biotechnol.* **20**, 1111–1117.

32. Ben-Hur, T., Einstein, O., Mizrachi-Kol, R., Ben-Menachem, O., Reinhartz, E., Karussis, D., and Abramsky, O. (2003). Transplanted multipotential neural precursor cells migrate into the inflamed white matter in response to experimental autoimmune encephalomyelitis. *Glia* **41**, 73–80.

33. Pluchino, S., Quattrini, A., Brambilla, E., Gritti, A., Salani, G., Dina, G., Galli, R., Del Carro, U., Amadio, S., Bergami, A., Furlan, R., Comi, G., Vescovi, A.L., and Martino, G. (2003). Injection of adult neurospheres induces recovery in a chronic model of multiple sclerosis. *Nature* **422**, 688–694.

34. Brustle, O., Jones, K.N., Learish, R.D., Karram, K., Choudhary, K., Wiestler, O.D., Duncan, I.D., and McKay, R.D. (1999). Embryonic stem cell-derived glial precursors: a source of myelinating transplants. *Science* **285**, 754–756.

35. Torchiana, E., Lulli, L., Cattaneo, E., Invernizzi, F., Orefice, R., Bertagnolio, B., Di Donato, S., and Finocchiaro, G. (1998). Retroviral-mediated transfer of the galactocerebrosidase gene in neural progenitor cells. *Neuroreport* **9**, 3823–3827.

36. Isacson, O., Bjorklund, L.M., and Schumacher, J.M. (2003). Toward full restoration of synaptic and terminal function of the dopaminergic system in Parkinson's disease by stem cells. *Ann. Neurol.* **53**, 135–146.

37. Lindvall, O., Brundin, P., Widner, H., Rehncrona, S., Gustavii, B., Frackowiak, R., Leenders, K.L., Sawle, G., Rothwell, J.C., Marsden, C.D., and Björklund, A. (1990) Grafts of fetal dopamine neurons survive and improve motor function in Parkinson's disease. *Science* **242**, 574–577.

38. Lindvall, O., Rehncrona, S., Brundin, P., Gustavvi, B., Astedt, B., Widner, H., Lindholm, T., Björklund, A., Leenders, K.L., and Rothwell, J.C. (1990). Neural transplantation in Parkinson's disease: the Swedish experiment. *Prog. Brain Res.* **82**, 729–734.

39. Mehta, V., Hong, M., Spears, J., and Mendez, I. (1998). Enhancement of graft survival and sensorimotor behavioral recovery in rats undergoing transplantation with dopaminergic cells exposed to glial cell line-derived neurotrophic factor. *J. Neurosurg.* **88**, 1088–1095.

40. Ourednik, J., Ourednik, V., Lynch, W.P., Schachner, M., and Snyder, E.Y. (2002). Neural stem cells display an inherent mechanism for rescuing dysfunctional neurons. *Natl. Biotechnol.* **20**, 1103–1110.

41. Teng, Y.D., Lavik, E.B., Qu, X., Ourednik, J., Zurakowski, D., Langer, R., and Snyder, E.Y. (2002). Functional recovery following traumatic spinal cord injury mediated by a unique polymer scaffold seeded with neural stem cells. *Proc. Natl. Acad. Sci. USA* **99**, 3024–3029.

42. Riess, P., Zhang, C., Saatman, K.E., Laurer, H.L., Longh, L.G., Raghupathi, R., Lenzlinger, P.M., Lifshitz, J., Boockvar, J., Neugebauer, E., Snyder, E.Y., and McIntosh, T.K. (2002). Transplanted neural stem cells survive, differentiate, and improve neurological motor function after experimental traumatic brain injury. *Neurosurgery* **51**, 1043–1052.

Spinal Cord Injury

John W. McDonald, Daniel Becker, and James Huettner

Spinal cord injury (SCI) is a major medical problem because there currently is no way to repair the central nervous system (CNS) and restore function. In this chapter, we focus on embryonic stem (ES) cells as an important research tool and potential therapy. We quickly review the epidemiology, functional anatomy, and pathophysiology of SCI and then describe spontaneous regeneration and limitations on repair. We also summarize features of spinal cord development that might guide restoration strategies. We then review studies that have used ES cells in spinal cord repair. We conclude that progress has been good, that knowledge is still too limited, and that harnessing the potential of ES cells will be important for solving the problem of SCI.

Problem

Nearly 12,000 people suffer a traumatic SCI every year, and about a quarter of a million Americans are living with this devastating condition.[1] There are also four to five times as many spinal cord injuries caused by medical conditions such as multiple sclerosis, a common disorder that destroys the myelin insulation on nerves in the cervical spinal cord. Other medical causes include ALS (Lou Gehrig's disease), polio and postpolio syndrome, HTLV-1, HIV-1, metabolic deficits such as vitamin B_{12} deficiency, as well as causes of myelopathy, such as stenosis and disc herniation.[2] The worldwide incidence of traumatic and nontraumatic SCI is greater per capita than in the United States.

The consequences of SCI depend on the level at which the cord is damaged. Generally, injuries in the neck produce tetraplegia, with loss of bowel and bladder function, whereas lesions in the thoracic or lumbar area may cause paraplegia, also with bowel and bladder dysfunction. In its severest form, SCI causes paralysis and loss of sensation throughout the body, inability to control bowel and bladder function, trouble controlling autonomic functions such as regulation of blood pressure, and inability to breathe or cough. The long-term disability from SCI results not only from the initial loss of function but also from the complications that accumulate. Up to 30% of individuals with SCI are hospitalized every year for complications[3] such as severe spasticity, infections (lung, skin, bowel, bone, and urinary tract), osteoporosis and

pathologic bone fractures, autonomic dysreflexia, and heterotropic ossification.[2,4] Another major long-term complication is muscle wasting. This results from disuse and from the absence of nerve impulses, which are critical for maintaining junctions between nerves and muscles.[5,6] Therefore, patients who maintain their body in the best condition for nervous system repair will benefit most from future therapeutic strategies.

Spinal Cord Organization

Unlike the brain, the spinal cord has its white matter (nerve axons) on the outside and gray matter (cell bodies) on the inside (Fig. 69–1). The gray matter houses neurons that project to the periphery at that level to control movement and receive sensory signals. The white matter carries axonal connections to and from the brain, and half of all those axons are myelinated. In general, the spinal cord has much less potential for regeneration than the peripheral nervous system. Moreover, most traumatic SCIs also injure the incoming and outgoing (or afferent and efferent) peripheral nerves at the injury level. In most SCIs, however, the caudal cord remains intact beginning several segments below the injury level. Circuitry in those segments can produce reflexes by activating a ventral motor neuron (MN) to produce muscle contraction when it receives a sensory stimulus from the periphery of the body (Fig. 69–1).

The distal spinal cord also contains groups of nerve cells that generate the patterns of activity needed for walking and running. Finally, central pattern generators that govern particular motor functions in the periphery are quite complex in nature and well controlled. Interested readers are referred to recent monographs on this subject.[7–9] Because the upper spinal cord plays only a limited role in controlling these pattern generators, people with injury to the cervical spine can walk or ride a stationary bicycle if their muscles are stimulated appropriately. The existence of additional pattern generators has also been predicted. For example, the phrenic nucleus, housed at C3 through C5 in the upper neck, appears to generate the pattern of movements needed for respiration. Unfortunately, this part of the spine is a common site of traumatic injury.

Injury

Traumatic injury occurs when broken fragments of bone and ligament impinge on the soft spinal cord, which is no wider than the thumb. The cord responds by swelling until

Handbook of Stem Cells
Volume 1

John W. McDonald, Daniel Becker, and James Huettner

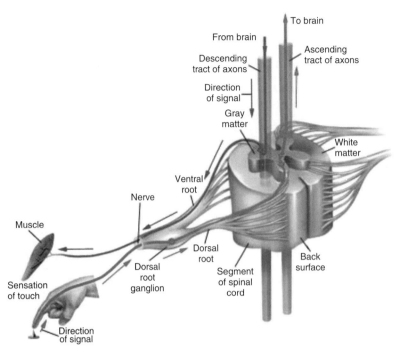

Figure 69-1. *Organization of the spinal cord.* A segment of cord reveals the butterfly-shaped gray matter at the core and a ring of white matter. The main components of the gray matter are neuronal cell bodies and glial cells and blood vessels. The outer white matter also contains astrocytes and blood vessels, but it consists mostly of axons and oligodendrocytes glial cells that wrap axons in white, insulated myelin. Axonal tracts that ascend in the cord convey sensory messages received from the body; the descending tracts carry motor commands to muscles. Reproduced with permission of Alexander and Turner Studio, FL, © 2002 Edmond Alexander. (Please see CD-ROM for color version of this figure.)

it encounters resistance from the bony canal of the spinal column. The swelling that compounds the initial injury reduces venous blood flow, causing a secondary venous infarct in the central part of the cord. This initiates a cascade of events that injures neighboring tissue. During this secondary phase, which occurs in the first 24 hours after the primary phase, cells die by excitotoxic necrosis as well as by apoptosis. This causes the initial injury site to rapidly enlarge into a hole in the middle of the spinal cord (Fig. 69–2). Because a donut-like rim of viable tissue usually remains at the level of injury, SCI affects preferentially gray matter.

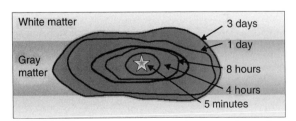

Figure 69-2. *Evolution of primary to secondary injury in the spinal cord.* Following the initial trauma, the injury rapidly enlarges as a consequence of secondary injury, particularly over the first 24 hours. (Please see CD-ROM for color version of this figure.)

A second wave of delayed cell death occurs during the weeks after a SCI.[10] It removes mostly oligodendrocytes, the myelinating cells, from adjacent white matter tracts. Since each oligodendrocyte myelinates 10 to 40 different axons, loss of one oligodendrocyte leads to exponential loss of myelin and therefore function. This progressive phase of secondary injury offers a good target for potential therapies such as neuroprotective stem cell transplantation.

The problem does not stop with the secondary wave of cell death, however. An injured, underactive nervous system may be unable to adequately replace cells, particularly glial cells that normally turn over. Therefore, individuals with SCI may experience a slow, progressive loss of neurological function over long periods in addition to complications from their initial injury. It is important to consider this potential for further loss of function when designing therapeutic regimens.

Spontaneous Regeneration

Not long ago, the adult nervous system was believed to have no capacity for repair or regeneration. A growing body of evidence indicates that the capacity for spontaneous regeneration may be much greater than previously perceived. Data obtained since the 1960s has demonstrated that new cells are

702

added to the nervous system continually; these cells include neurons in at least two brain regions, the hippocampus and olfactory bulb.[11,12] Moreover, glial cells are frequently born and are capable of regeneration.[13,14] Recent work has shown that severed or intact axons can sprout even long after injury.[15]

Nonetheless, our ability to maximize spontaneous regeneration is limited. The recent detection of endogenous stem cells within the spinal cord raises hope that such cells can be harnessed to repair the damaged spinal system. Although the birth of new neurons from these progenitors has never been demonstrated within the spinal cord,[16] new glial cells, including oligodendrocytes and astrocytes, are continually being added. In fact, injury stimulates cell birth. Our laboratory recently showed that nearly 2 million cells are born in the spinal cord each day, though most eventually die.[17] Collectively, these data suggest that cell turnover does occur in the nervous system, albeit much more slowly than in other organs of the body. Moreover, we recently showed that patterned neural activity can stimulate cell birth, which suggests that behavioral modification could be important for maximizing cord regeneration and functional recovery.[17]

Limitations and Approaches to Repair and Redefining Goals

Although some limited spontaneous regeneration is known to occur,[18,19] dramatic self-repair of the nervous system does not take place. A growing body of evidence suggests that factors in the nervous system actively inhibit regeneration. Such factors include inhibitory proteins in the cord, which guide regrowing connections, and scar tissue, which contains chondroitin sulfate and proteoglycans.[20] Reduced production of growth factors that stimulate regrowth also limits regeneration.

Fig. 69–3 and Fig. 69–15 outline the general strategies for repairing the damaged spinal cord. Note that a complete cure of nervous system injury is not practical or required. Partial repair translates into proportionally greater recovery of function. For example, only about 10% of the functional connections are required to support locomotion in cats,[21] and humans missing more than half the gray matter in the cervical spinal cord can still walk and run fairly normally.

One strategy for spinal cord repair is to transplant stem cells or other biomaterials to fill the cyst that forms at the eye

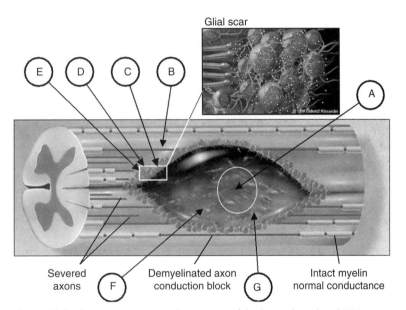

Figure 69–3. *Common strategies toward regeneration of the damaged spinal cord. (A) Prevention of progression of secondary injury: Necrotic and apoptotic cell death would be prevented by antiexcitotoxic drugs and antiapoptotic treatments. (B) Compensation for demyelination: Chemicals that prevent conduction block in demyelinated areas, and agents that encourage surviving oligodendrocytes to remyelinate axons, would be provided. Lost oligodendrocytes would be replenished. (C) Removal of inhibition: Agents that block the actions of natural inhibitors of regeneration or drugs that down-regulate expression of inhibitory proteins would be provided. (D) Promotion of axonal regeneration: Growth factors that promote regeneration (sprouting) of new axons would be provided. (E) Direction of axons to proper targets: Guidance molecules would be provided or their expression would be increased in host cells. (F) Creation of bridges: Bridges would be implanted into the cyst, which would provide directional scaffolding that encourages axon growth. (G) Replacement of lost cells: Cells capable of generation of all cell types (progenitor cells or ES cells) would be implanted. Substances that induce undifferentiated cells to replace dead cells would be provided. Also, transplanted cells to deliver regenerative molecules would be used. Reproduced with permission of Alexander and Turner Studio, FL, © 2002 Edmond Alexander. (Please see CD-ROM for color version of this figure.)*

of the injury. This cyst acts as a physical barrier to the growth of anatomically intact axons in the surrounding donut of white matter. The lost cells include segmental MNs, sensory neurons, oligodendrocytes, and astrocytes. Although it is possible for endogenous cells to give birth to new oligodendrocytes and astrocytes, this response is limited; moreover, it has not so far been possible to obtain new neurons in the spinal cord from endogenous cells.[16]

As well as filling in the cyst, it may be necessary to repair axons that no longer function properly because they have lost their myelin or have been inappropriately myelinated. Several approaches have been used to overcome this problem, which can manifest itself as a segmental conduction block. For example, potassium channels on dysfunctional axons can be blocked pharmacologically, and preexisting or transplanted oligodendrocytes and their progenitors can be encouraged to make new myelin.[22,23]

Another strategy is to remove or mask the effects of proteins in the glial scar around the cyst that actively inhibit the regrowth of new connections.[24] Antibodies that block the inhibitory effects of these proteins promote sprouting.[24] Alternatively, cells delivered to the cyst might be used to digest inhibitory proteins in the scar, or approaches might be taken to prevent the initial expression of the inhibitory proteins. Moreover, certain growth factors promote the self-repair of physically broken connections. These factors can be provided exogenously or by transplanting genetically altered cells that release them.[18,25,26]

It is important to understand the feasibility of various repair strategies and to redefine appropriate goals of repair. If we rank the preceding strategies in terms of likely success,[2] it becomes clear that it will be difficult to persuade axons to regrow across a lesion, extend down the spinal cord, and make connections with the appropriate target cells. Remyelination seems more feasible because it occurs continually at a steady rate in the damaged spinal cord. It is important to investigate all the possible strategies, however, because some will materialize sooner and some later. Most importantly, we must understand that multiple strategies delivered over time will be more important than the elusive magic bullet.

When defining appropriate goals for therapy, improving patients' quality of life must rank first. To this end, strategies that limit complications are important. Moreover, individuals with SCI often value small gains in function more highly than larger gains, such as walking. Thus, the top goal for most patients is recovery of bowel, bladder, or sexual function. Distant seconds include recovery of respiratory function for those whose respiration is impaired and use of a single hand for those without hand function.[2] Paradoxically, most animal models focus on recovery of the ability to walk. This is both the least appropriate goal and the most difficult to achieve.

Spinal Cord Development

To understand spinal cord regeneration, it is necessary to understand spinal cord development. In humans, oligodendrocytes are found in cultures of fetal spinal cord at 7 and 12 weeks of gestation.[27,28] Myelination begins at 10 to 11 weeks of gestation[29,30] and continues throughout the second year of life.[31,32] Signals derived from axons regulate the growth of progenitor cells and the survival of oligodendrocytes.[33] For example, Sonic hedgehog (Shh), a protein synthesized by notochord and floor plate cells, induces the differentiation of MNs in the ventral cord,[34] and Shh signaling induces oligodendrocyte precursors (OPs) to emerge in the embryonic spinal cord.[35] Platelet derived growth factor (PDGF) is a potent regulator of OP migration and proliferation, and insulin-like growth factor-1 acts on both neurons and oligodendrocytes. Other locally synthesized growth factors appear to control the balance between OP proliferation and OP differentiation.[36]

Many neuronal phenotypes arise from various progenitor pools during CNS development, but most of the pathways are poorly understood. One of the best described is the generation of spinal MNs,[37] which involves several steps. Through bone morphogenetic protein, fibroblast growth factor (FGF), and Wnt signaling, ectodermal cells obtain a rostral neural character.[38] In response to caudalizing signals, such as retinoic acid (RA), these progenitors acquire a spinal positional identity.[39] Through the ventralizing action of Shh, spinal progenitor cells gain their MN phenotype.[40]

These findings raise the question of whether ES cells can be shunted along specific pathways to produce specific neural cell populations for CNS repair. In fact, encouraging steps have already been taken. Early reports revealed the possibility of generating cells with MN characteristics from ES cells.[41] Later, Wichterle and colleagues[42] demonstrated that signaling factors operating along the rostrocaudal and dorsoventral axes of the neural tube to specify MN fate *in vivo* could be harnessed *in vitro* to direct the differentiation of mouse ES cells into functional MNs.

ES Cells

ES cells have unique features that are important for spinal cord repair. They represent every cell type in the body, are the earliest stem cells capable of replicating indefinitely without aging, and their DNA can be modified easily even in single cells. They also fulfill two criteria essential for nervous system repair: Transplantable cells should be cells that normally belong in the spinal cord, and transplantable cells should contain the recipient's own DNA to avoid the need for immunosuppression, which cannot be used in spinal cord patients because of the increased incidence of infections.

Several methods are available for obtaining ES cells. The most common is *in vitro* fertilization, which requires a fertilized egg and therefore produces cells that differ genetically from the host. A second strategy involves somatic nuclear transfer, which takes a nucleus from a somatic cell such as skin and transfers it to an enucleated fertilized egg[43] (Fig. 69–4A). The subsequent ES cells therefore contain only the genetic material of the recipient. Another possibility for women is parthenogenesis,[44] which tricks an egg into thinking it is fertilized, allowing it to begin duplicating its DNA (Fig. 69–4B). Although this process is unable to create a

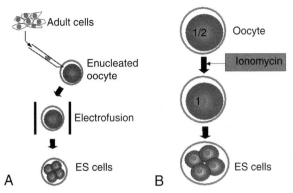

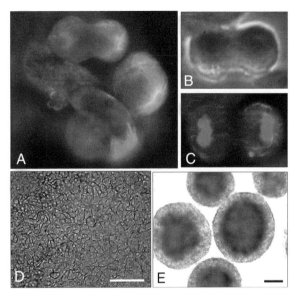

Figure 69-4. *ES cells can be made by* in vitro *fertilization and two additional methods. (A) Somatic nuclear transfer: Donor cells are placed under the zona pellucida into the perivitelline space of enucleated oocytes. The cell nucleus is introduced into the cytoplast by electrofusion, which also activates the oocyte. It can then be grown to the blastocyst stage to harvest the ES cells. (B) Parthenogenic activation: For activation, oocytes are briefly exposed to a calcium ionophore such as ionomycin. The resulting cell can mature for ES cell harvest. (Please see CD-ROM for color version of this figure.)*

Figure 69-5. *Undifferentiated mouse and human ES cells dividing in a culture dish. (A and C) Immunofluorescence images of mouse ES cells demonstrate anti-β-tubulin and anti-DNA (Hoechst). The phase image of (C) the identical field is shown in panel B. Panel D illustrates undifferentiated human ES cells. EBs derived from human ES cells are shown in panel E. Scale bar for panels D–E = 100 μm. (Please see CD-ROM for color version of this figure.)*

viable embryo (because factors derived from sperm are necessary for preimplantation), it can produce normal cells.

Many studies of spinal cord repair have involved differentiated cells. The earliest studies used peripheral nerve grafts to demonstrate that the nervous system has the capacity to regenerate but that the environment in the CNS is not permissive.[45] Substantial progress has been made with the transplantation of peripheral nervous system cells and non–nervous system cells, including genetically engineered fibroblasts, bone marrow cells, glial cells, neurons, and mixtures of glia and neurons.[26,46–49] In general, fetal sources of cells have been the most successful because derivatives of postnatal and adult cells are less able to withstand neural transplantation. One recent exception has been neural stem cells derived from the adult CNS.[50]

Another active area of investigation is transdifferentiation[51]: isolating cells from organs other than the nervous system and transforming them into neural progenitor cells. Although initial progress suggested that this strategy might work with many types of tissue, the problem of cell-to-cell fusion may have dampened enthusiasm for this approach.[52] Suffice to say that transdifferentiation has not yet produced cells suitable for transplantation, although clearly the potential exists.

ES Cells and the Neural Lineage

Several protocols are available for converting ES cells into neural lineage cells. However, protocols for mouse and human cells differ because the constraints of the human ES cell system have not yet been clearly defined (Fig. 69–5). Differentiating murine ES cells traditionally begins with floating spheres called embryoid bodies (EBs). These bodies are akin to the neural spheres of stem cells obtained from the

adult CNS. RA is a key induction agent for producing neural progenitors from mouse ES cells.[53] Neural cells resembling anatomically normal neurons, astrocytes, and oligodendrocytes from the CNS can be easily derived from mouse ES cells using these protocols (Fig. 69–6).

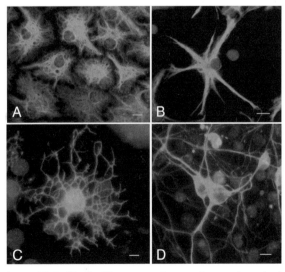

Figure 69-6. *ES cells differentiate into the principle types of neural cells. (A) Type one and (B) type II astrocytes (anti-GFAP), (C) oligodendrocytes (anti-O1), and (D) neurons (anti-β-tubulin). Scale bar = 10 μm. Reproduced with the permission of Becker et al.[76] (Please see CD-ROM for color version of this figure.)*

ES Cell Transplantation

Use of ES cells for neural transplantation is in its infancy, and only a limited amount of work has been completed with the spinal cord. These early studies have relied on transplantation during the embryonic,[42] postnatal,[54,55] and adult[54,56,57] period in the normal or injured spinal cord. Overall, they demonstrate that ES cells have a remarkable ability to integrate into the injured region of the cord and differentiate appropriately.

A recent study by Jessell and colleagues provides exceptional evidence that ES cells can participate in the normal development of spinal cord cells, including MNs.[42] It demonstrated that developmentally relevant signaling factors can induce mouse ES cells to differentiate into spinal progenitor cells and then MNs through the normal developmental pathway (Fig. 69–7). Thus, the signals that promote the differentiation of neural stem cells *in vivo* are effective when applied to ES cells. This group further demonstrated that MNs derived from ES cells can populate the embryonic spinal cord, extend axons, and form synapses with target muscles (Fig. 69–8). Therefore, they not only participate in normal development but also grow appropriately when transplanted into the embryonic spinal cord, targeting muscle. Thus, inductive signals in normal pathways of neurogenesis can direct ES cells to form specific classes of CNS neurons.

Brustle, Duncan, and McKay were the first to transplant ES cell–derived progenitors into the adult and embryonic spinal cord.[54] They demonstrated that ES cells transplanted into the brain and the spinal cord of normal adult animals can differentiate into oligodendrocytes that can myelinate axons. They generated OPs efficiently by supplementing cultures of ES cells with FGF and epidermal growth factor and later including PDGF. About 38% of the cells in the resulting cultures were oligodendrocytes. To investigate whether these oligodendrocytes could myelinate *in vivo*, cells grown in the presence of bFGF and PDGF were injected into the spinal cord of 1-week-old myelin-deficient rats, a model for a human myelin disorder. Two weeks after transplantation, numerous myelin sheaths were detected in six of the nine affected rats. The original 100,000 cells had migrated widely and made myelin with appropriate ultrastructure. Therefore, ES cell–derived glial precursors transplanted into the neonatal rat spinal cord migrated several millimeters and differentiated into myelinating oligodendrocytes and astrocytes.

This group also transplanted ES cell–derived precursors into the cerebral ventricles of developing rodents (embryonic day 17).[54] Three weeks later, proteolipid protein-positive myelin sheaths were evident in a variety of brain regions. The cells' exogenous origin was confirmed by *in situ* hybridization with a probe to mouse satellite DNA. Importantly, there was no observable evidence of abnormal cellular differentiation or tumor formation.

In the same year, McDonald, Gottlieb, and Choi demonstrated for the first time that ES cells that had been induced to become neural cell precursors could be successfully transplanted into the injured spinal cord.[56] Examination of the spinal cord 9 days after 1 million precursor cells were

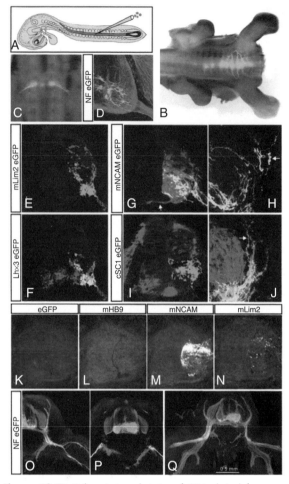

Figure 69–7. *Embryonic transplantation of MNs derived from mouse ES cells.* Integration of transplanted ES cell–derived MNs into the spinal cord *in vivo*. (A) Implantation of HBG3 ES cell–derived MN-enriched EBs into stage 15–17 chick spinal cord. (B) Bright-field–fluorescence image showing eGFP+ MNs in thoracic and lumbar spinal cord, assayed at stage 27 (ventral view). (C and D) Location of FACS, ES cell–derived, eGFP+ MNs in thoracic spinal cord, assayed at stage 27. (D) eGFP+ MNs are clustered in the ventral spinal cord. (E–J) Transverse sections through stage 27 chick spinal cord at rostral cervical levels after transplantation of MN-enriched EBs. (E) MNs are concentrated in the ventral spinal cord and are segregated from transplanted interneurons, labeled by a mouse-specific Lim2 antibody. (F) Many ES cell–derived MNs coexpress eGFP and Lhx3. (G) ES cell–derived MNs and (H) axons (arrow) are labeled by (I and J) rodent-specific anti-NCAM antibody, but do not express the chick MN marker protein SC1. (G and H) eGFP–, NCAM+ axons cross the floor plate but do not project out of the spinal cord (arrows). (K–N) Transverse sections of thoracic spinal cord at stage 27, after grafting EBs grown with RA (2 μM) and anti-Hh antibody (5E1, 30 μg/ml). No mouse-derived MNs were detected either (K) by eGFP or (L) by a mouse-specific anti-HB9 antibody. In contrast, many mouse-derived (M) NCAM+ and (N) Lim2+ interneurons are present. (O–Q) Transverse sections through stage 27 spinal cord at (O and P) thoracic and (Q) lumbar levels after grafting MN-enriched EBs. eGFP+ MNs are concentrated in the ventral spinal cord. Ectopic eGFP+ MNs are located within the lumen of the spinal cord. eGFP+ axons exit the spinal cord primarily through the ventral root and project along nerve branches that supply (O–Q) axial, (O and P) body wall, and (Q) dorsal and ventral limb muscles. The pathway of axons is detected by neurofilament (NF) expression. eGFP+ axons are not detected in motor nerves that project to sympathetic neuronal targets. Scale bar = .5 mm. Reproduced with the permission of Wichterle *et al.*[42] (Please see CD-ROM for color version of this figure.)

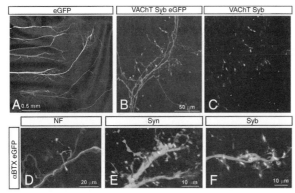

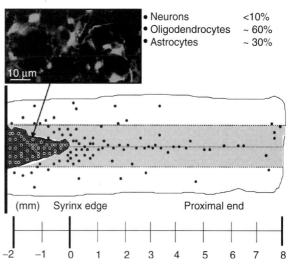

Figure 69-8. *Anatomic integration of MNs derived from transplanted mouse ES cells.* Synaptic differentiation of ES cell–derived MNs *in vivo*. (A) Whole-mount preparation of stage 35 chick embryonic rib cage. ES cell–derived eGFP+ motor axons contact intercostal muscles. (B and C) Coexpression of synaptobrevin (Syb) and vesicular ACh transporter (VAChT) in the terminals of eGFP+ motor axons at sites of nerve contact with muscle. The anti-Syb and VAChT antibodies recognize mouse but not chick proteins. (D) NF and eGFP expression in motor axons that supply intercostal muscles. eGFP+ axons lack NF expression. The terminals of eGFP+ axons coincide with clusters of ACh receptors, defined by α-bungarotoxin (αBTX) labeling. (E) Coincidence of synaptotagmin (Syn) expression in eGFP+ motor axon terminals and αBTX labeling. (F) Coincidence of Syb expression in eGFP+ motor axon terminals and αBTX labeling. Reproduced with the permission of Wichterle et al.[42] (Please see CD-ROM for color version of this figure.)

Figure 69-9. *In the contusion-injured spinal cord of the rat, ES cell–derived neural precursors survive, migrate, and differentiate following transplantation.* Schematic demonstrates the relative distribution of ES cell–derived cells 2 weeks after transplantation into the forming central cavity, which was done nine days after spinal contusion injury. The cavity is partially filled, and cells migrate long distances. Most distant cells are identified as oligodendrocytes, and astrocytes and neurons remain restricted to the site of transplantation. The inset shows GFP-expressing ES cell–derived neural cells. (Please see CD-ROM for color version of this figure.)

transplanted into a cyst caused by contusion injury showed that the cells had survived, grafted, migrated long distances, and differentiated into the three principle neural cell types: neurons, astrocytes, and oligodendrocytes (Figs. 69–9 and 69–10). This group also demonstrated that transplantation was associated with a significant and sizable improvement in function. Their study was the first demonstration that transplanted embryonic precursors can successfully repair the damaged adult nervous system, an important finding given that conditions in the damaged adult nervous system are much less favorable than those in the neonatal spinal cord. Subsequently, Liu and colleagues[57] demonstrated that stem cell-derived precursors transplanted into the injured adult nervous system can achieve substantial remyelination with appropriate anatomical characteristics (Fig. 69–11). Furthermore, they showed that ES cell–derived oligodendrocytes functioned normally, myelinating multiple axons in culture, just as they do in the normal nervous system (Fig. 69–12). Using patch clamp analysis, Huettner and McDonald later demonstrated that the physiologic characteristics of ES cell–derived oligodendrocytes are similar to those of oligodendrocytes taken from the adult spinal cord (Figs. 69–12C and 69–13). ES cell–derived oligodendrocytes represent the entire oligodendrocyte lineage, from early OPs to mature, myelinating oligodendrocytes.

In culture, ES cell–derived neurons rapidly differentiate and spontaneously create neural circuits with anatomical (Fig. 69–14) and physiological evidence of excitatory and inhibitory synapses.[58–60] Substantial neural differentiation is also evident *in vivo* in the model of contusion injury,[56] where

neurons show extensive axonal outgrowth with presumptive morphological evidence of synapse formation. Moreover, immunological evidence of cholinergic, serotonergic, GABAergic, glycinergic, and glutamatergic neurons has been obtained *in vitro* and *in vivo* (data not shown).

Implantation, survival, and migration of transplanted ES cell–derived precursors in the damaged spinal cord have

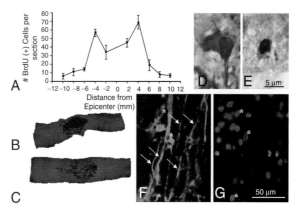

Figure 69-10. *BrdU-labeled ES cell-derived cells 2 weeks after transplantation.* Mean ± SEM BrdU-labeled nuclei per 1 mm segment in longitudinal sections. (A) Hoechst 33342-labeled sections 42 days after injury, transplanted with (B) vehicle or (C) ES cells 9 days after injury. (D) BrdU+ cell colabeled with GFAP. (E) BrdU-labeled cell colabeled with APC CC-1. (F) The mouse-specific marker EMA indicates processes (arrows) emanating from ES cells. (G) Corresponding nuclei are marked by asterisks. Modified from McDonald et al.,[56] with permission. (Please see CD-ROM for color version of this figure.)

been verified by using magnetic resonance imaging to track oligodendrocytes prelabeled with paramagnetic agents as well as real-time polymerase chain reaction. In both cases, migration up to 1 cm from the transplantation site was evident.[61,62]

After other groups demonstrated that multiple rounds of transplantation can deliver different types of stem cells to the CNS, our group systematically evaluated intravenous, intraventricular, intrathecal, and intraparenchymal transplantation of 4–/4+-staged embryo bodies derived from ES cell precursors. Although some cells were capable of entering the CNS along the intravenous route, they remained in blood vessels and showed only limited neural differentiation. Intracerebral ventricular administration led to some incorporation of transplanted ES cells into the CNS, but obstruction of the third and fourth ventricles led to hydrocephalus and discontinuation of this approach. We made a remarkable observation when we transplanted a large number of ES cell–derived neural precursors intrathecally into the lumbar spine.[63] Three to four months later, ES cells were observed in well-formed tissues surrounding the lumbar sacral nerve roots and extending down the sacral canal. Further evaluation clearly showed that the cells had differentiated into tissue that bore a remarkable resemblance of some components of the normal spinal cord. For example, there was extensive myelination, and cells resembling cholinergic MNs were present. Zones of the peripheral nervous system were also clearly demarcated from the CNS. These results were quite surprising because a characteristic feature of intraparenchymal transplantation into the spinal cord is abnormal macroorganization of cells. Thus, this was the first study to demonstrate that transplanted ES cells are able to organize themselves into CNS-like tissues. It will now be important to understand the constraints necessary for this degree of self-organization.

Novel Approaches to CNS Repair

Most neural transplantation studies, including those using ES cell precursors, have used cells to replace cells lost after injury. Given that we do not know which types of differentiated cells are required for repair, neural precursors may be ideal for this purpose because environmental clues can decide their developmental fate.[57,64,65] Moreover, ES cell–derived precursors can serve as bridges to support axonal regrowth.[46]

In an attempt to overcome the constraints of the injured nervous system, ES cells are often genetically altered so they will deliver growth molecules, such as NT3, after transplantation,[18,23,65] and they are particularly well suited to this task. McDonald and Silver recently adopted a novel approach to overcoming restraints by showing that early ES cell–derived progenitors can phagocytize key inhibitory molecules in glial scar tissue.[66] These cells therefore created an inhibitor-free bridge over which axons could rapidly sprout from the transplant into normal cord. By 9 days after transplantation, axons from the graft had grown up to 1 cm—a rate of more than 1 mm per day! This rate is similar to that seen in the normal embryo.[67]

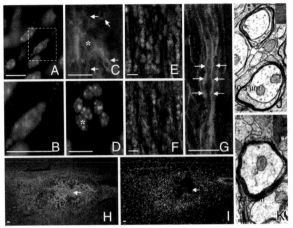

Figure 69–11. *Cells derived from ES oligospheres can migrate and myelinate axons when transplanted into dysmyelinated spinal cords of adult shiverer mice.* Such mice lack the gene for myelin basic protein (MBP). Transplanted cells were identified by Cell Tracker Orange (CTO), epifluorescence, or immunoreactivity for MBP. (A and B) CTO-labeled cells aligned with native intrafascicular oligodendrocytes in white matter. (C and D) An ES cell–derived (MBP+) oligodendrocyte (asterisk) with longitudinally oriented processes (white arrows) is shown. (C) Arrows mark probable myelination around an adjacent axon. (E) Little MBP immunoreactivity is seen in white matter in a longitudinal section of spinal cord from a mouse that received a sham transplantation. (F) A gradient of MBP immunoreactivity centers on the site of ES cell transplantation. (G) High magnification of intrafascicular oligodendrocyte nuclei and MBP immunoreactivity, two indications of axonal myelination (white arrows), in white matter from a mouse transplanted with ES cells. (H) The spatial distribution of MBP immunoreactivity 1 month after ES cell transplantation is shown at low magnification, with (I) corresponding Hoechst 33342 counterstaining. White arrows indicate the center of the transplant site. (J) Transmission EM shows four loose wraps of myelin, the maximal number of layers typically seen around axons in control animals (arrow), and (K) nine or more compact wraps around axons from the transplanted area (arrow). Shiverer mutant mice lack a functional *MBP* gene required to form mature compact myelin; therefore, the presence of mature compact myelin is a standard for transplant oligodendrocyte-associated myelin. Scale bars = 10 μm (A–I) and 0.3 μm (J and K). Reproduced with the permission of McDonald et al.,[56] (Please see CD-ROM for color version of this figure.)

Another novel approach is to use stem cell transplantation to limit the secondary injury that occurs after nervous system injury.[68] For example, we recently demonstrated that transplanting ES cells can limit the delayed death of neurons and oligodendrocytes. Since most transplantation studies are completed at the time of injury, it is possible that many of their results may be attributable to this neuroprotective role. It seems clear that even genetically unmodified ES cells release large quantities of growth factors.

Although replacing lost neurons is difficult, it might be possible to use neurons to create bridging circuits across the injury site. Descending axons could synapse onto ES cell–derived neurons that subsequently synapsed onto key pattern generators in the lower spinal cord. A more global delivery of neurotransmitters using synaptic or nonsynaptic mechanisms might enhance functions such as locomotion. Previous work by others has demonstrated that release of noradrenergic and serotonergic neurotransmitters can stimulate and enhance the

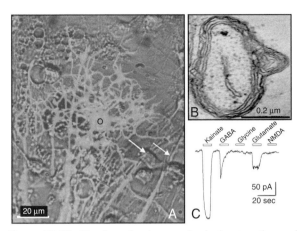

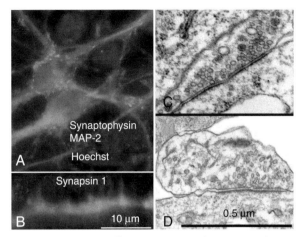

Figure 69-12. *ES cells produced mature oligodendrocytes with normal anatomical features of myelination and physiological response to neurotransmitters. Reproduced in adapted form with permission from Liu et al.[57] (Please see CD-ROM for color version of this figure.)*

Figure 69-14. *ES cells differentiate into neurons that spontaneously create neural circuits. (A and B) Presumptive presynaptic sites oppose dendrites. (C and D) Ultrastructural characteristics of synaptic profiles in vitro. (Please see CD-ROM for color version of this figure.)*

central pattern generator for locomotion.[69] More recent work indicates that release of the neurotrophins BDNF and NT3 can perform this function.[70]

Because ES cells are embryonic in nature, their progenitors may also be able to reprogram the adult CNS so that damage can be repaired.[71] ES cells are also unique in that they have the potential to replace cells derived from multiple

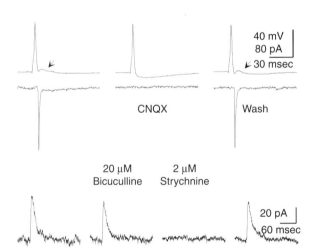

Figure 69-13. *Excitatory and inhibitory synaptic transmission among neurons derived in vitro from mouse ES cells. Action potentials were evoked in the presynaptic neuron by current injection. Excitatory (top) postsynaptic currents, blocked by superfusion with the selective glutamate receptor antagonist 6-cyano-7-nitroquinoxaline-2,3-dione (CNQX; 10 micromolar), were recorded under a voltage clamp. Arrows point to an autaptic excitatory synaptic potential also blocked by CNQX. Inhibitory (bottom) synaptic currents were evoked in a different ES cell pair and tested sequentially with the antagonists bicuculline and strychnine, which are selective for gamma-aminobutyric acid (GABA) and glycine receptors, respectively. For this cell pair, only the postsynaptic currents are shown. Transmission was blocked by strychnine, indicating glycine was the transmitter. Other presynaptic cells evoked bicuculline-sensitive synaptic currents, indicating transmission mediated by GABA (not shown).*

embryonic germ layers. In the CNS, it will be important to replace lost nonneural cells as well as neural cells to regain normal CNS function, such as neovascularization. The growing link between neovascularization and neurogenesis strengthens this approach. We recently found that ES cells in transplanted 4–/4+ EBs differentiate into both neural cells and vascular endothelial cells.[72]

In the embryo, stem cells differentiate into MNs and grow toward muscle. Using ES cell–derived MNs to replace lost MNs at injured segments will not enhance function because chronically denervated muscle is unable to reassemble functional neuromuscular junctions. However, transplantation might avoid the long-term muscle wasting that results from denervation. To maintain denervated muscle, for example, it might be possible to transplant ES cells into the distal nerve stump or directly into the muscle. Once in place, the transplanted cells could differentiate into MNs. If they were genetically altered, the MNs could be selectively removed once the repair was properly achieved.

Studies are beginning to combine stem cells, including ES cells, with biomaterials. The advent of nanotechnology should further enhance this approach.[73]

Finally, remyelination (Fig. 69–15) is one of the most pragmatic approaches to restoring function to the damaged spinal cord. Because many potentially functional connections remain in the outer donut of surviving tissue, appropriate remyelination could substantially improve function. One must consider, however, that dysmyelination rather than demyelination is the biggest problem in the damaged nervous system. Often, inappropriate myelination is more harmful than no myelination.

Toward Human Trials

Some of the animal studies described previously have prompted early human safety trials. Most have focused on

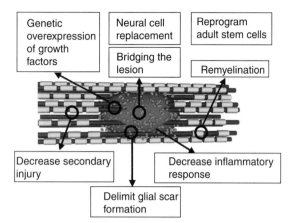

Figure 69–15. *Novel approaches to spinal cord repair using ES cells. Remyelination is one of the most pragmatic approaches to restoring function to the damaged spinal cord. ES cell–derived precursors can serve as bridges to support axonal regrowth. They can phagocytize key inhibitory molecules in glial scar tissue. These cells therefore created an inhibitor-free bridge over which axons could rapidly sprout from the transplant into normal cord. Newly generated neurons can be used to create bridging circuits across the injury site. ES cell transplantation can limit the secondary injury. To try to overcome the constraints of the injured nervous system, ES cells are often genetically altered so they will deliver growth molecules, such as NT3, after transplantation. Because ES cells are embryonic in nature, their progenitors may also be able to reprogram the adult CNS to optimize spontaneous host regeneration. Replacement of nonneural cells as well as neural cells will be important to regain normal CNS function, such as neovascularization. ES cells can have similar applications in the peripheral nervous system. (Please see CD-ROM for color version of this figure.)*

transplantation studies, however, the mechanisms underlying functional improvement remain unclear. Nevertheless, ES cells offer a novel approach to deciphering these mechanisms. For the first time, ES cell genetics is allowing investigators to track transplanted cells that have been engineered to express green fluorescent protein (GFP). This and other types of genetic modification permit one to track the integration and differentiation of ES cells, assess behavioral recovery, selectively remove the cells to see whether recovery wanes, and insert more cells to see if functional recovery occurs anew. This proof of principle will be required to identify mechanisms in neural repair.

Although it is impossible to predict the future of the field, it is clear that murine and human ES cells are tools that will revolutionize neurobiology and neural transplantation by providing the unprecedented ability to selectively deliver key regulatory factors. Also, ES cells promise to be one of the greatest therapies for chronic nervous system disorders. Only the future will reveal their full potential for treating human disease and disability, but it is possible to say with confidence that ES cells will have a major effect on repairing the human CNS within our lifetimes.

ACKNOWLEDGMENTS

We would like to thank the people in my laboratory who have contributed to this work over the years and also my collaborators: Jeff Bulte at the National Institutes of Health (NHI) and Dennis W. Choi, David I. Gottlieb, David Gutmann, Chung Hsu, Mark F. Jacquin, Gene Johnson, and Carl Lauryssen at Washington University in St. Louis. This team obtained a program project grant from the NIH (NS39577) to evaluate the potential of ES cells to repair SCI. We would also like to thank our animal technicians who express rodent bladders three times daily, 7 days a week, including holidays (Joan Bonnot, Joseph Galvez, Brandy Jones, and Amy Hansen) and our TC staff who passage ES cells every other day endlessly (Ashley Johnson, Laura Luecking, and Becky Purcell). This work was supported by NINDS and NIDCR grants NS39577, NS40520, NS45023, DE07734, and NS045023.

REFERENCES

1. National Spinal Cord Injury Database (2001). "Spinal Cord Injury: Facts and Figures, May 2001."
2. McDonald, J.W., and Sadowsky, C. (2002). Spinal-cord injury. *Lancet* **359,** 417–425.
3. McKinley, W.O., Jackson, A.B., Cardenas, D.D., and DeVivo, M.J. (1999). Long-term medical complications after traumatic spinal cord injury: a regional model systems analysis. *Arch. Phys. Med. Rehab.* **80,** 1402–1410.
4. Sjolund, B.H. (2002). Pain and rehabilitation after spinal cord injury: the case of sensory spasticity? *Brain Res. Brain Res. Rev.* **40,** 250–256.
5. Auld, D.S., and Robitaille, R. (2003). Perisynaptic Schwann cells at the neuromuscular junction: nerve- and activity-dependent contributions to synaptic efficacy, plasticity, and reinnervation. *Neuroscientist* **9,** 144–157.

Parkinson's disease, where unforeseen exaggeration of dystonia has limited advances in transplantation therapy.[74] Phase I human trials for repairing the spinal cord are also under way; they include transplantation of porcine-derived stem cells for the purpose of remyelination (see GenVec at http://www.genvec.com/) as well as allogeneic transplantation of olfactory ensheathing glia (Carlos Lima, Lisbon, Portugal). Although safety data are not yet available, it is important to note that such trials are paving the way for further uses of ES cells. With the recent advent of human ES cells, human transplantation appears more feasible, though somatic transplantation will be required to ensure a genetic match. Such manipulation of cells raises many regulatory concerns that must be addressed before clinical trials can move forward. The recent demonstration of *in vitro* oocyte generation from mouse ES cells raises the possibility that ethically acceptable procedures for human nuclear transfer may soon be available.[75]

Summary

Studies of neurotransplantation for repairing the damaged nervous system are making good progress. Early animal studies showed that mouse ES cells can replace neurons, astrocytes, and oligodendrocytes; instigate appropriate remyelination; and even improve locomotion. As is the case for all

6. Rossi, S.G., Dickerson, I.M., and Rotundo, R.L. (2003). Localization of the calcitonin gene-related peptide receptor complex at the vertebrate neuromuscular junction and its role in regulating acetylcholinesterase expression. *J. Biol. Chem.* **278,** 24,994–25,000.

7. Burke, R.E. (2001). The central pattern generator for locomotion in mammals. *Adv. Neurol.* **87,** 11–24.

8. Dietz, V. (1995). Central pattern generator. *Paraplegia* **33,** 739.

9. Barbeau, H., McCrea, D.A., O'Donovan, M.J., Rossignol, S., Grill, W.M., and Lemay, M.A. (1999). Tapping into spinal circuits to restore motor function. *Brain Res. Brain Res. Rev.* **30,** 27–51.

10. Crowe, M.J., Bresnahan, J.C., Shuman, S.L., Masters, J.N., and Beattie, M.S. (1997). Apoptosis and delayed degeneration after spinal cord injury in rats and monkeys. *Nat. Med.* **3,** 73–76.

11. Eriksson, P.S., Perfilieva, E., Bjork-Eriksson, T., Alborn, A.M., Nordborg, C., Peterson, D.A., and Gage, F.H. (1998). Neurogenesis in the adult human hippocampus. *Nat. Med.* **4,** 1313–1317.

12. Winner, B., Cooper-Kuhn, C.M., Aigner, R., Winkler, J., and Kuhn, H.G. (2002). Long-term survival and cell death of newly generated neurons in the adult rat olfactory bulb. *Eur. J. Neurosci.* **16,** 1681–1689.

13. Herndon, R.M., Price, D.L., and Weiner, L.P. (1977). Regeneration of oligodendroglia during recovery from demyelinating disease. *Science* **195,** 693–694.

14. Ludwin, S.K. (1984). Proliferation of mature oligodendrocytes after trauma to the central nervous system. *Nature* **308,** 274–275.

15. Weidner, N., Ner, A., Salimi, N., and Tuszynski, M.H. (2001). Spontaneous corticospinal axonal plasticity and functional recovery after adult central nervous system injury. *Proc. Natl. Acad. Sci. U. S. A.* **98,** 3513–3518.

16. Horner, P.J., Power, A.E., Kempermann, G., Kuhn, H.G., Palmer, T.D., Winkler, J., Thal, L.J., and Gage, F.H. (2000). Proliferation and differentiation of progenitor cells throughout the intact adult rat spinal cord. *J. Neurosci.* **20,** 2218–2228.

17. Becker, D., Grill, W.M., and McDonald, J.W. (2003). "Functional Electrical Stimulation Helps Replenish Neural Cells in the Adult CNS After Spinal Cord Injury." Paper presented at the 55th annual meeting of the American Academy of Neurology.

18. Tuszynski, M.H., Grill, R., Jones, L.L., McKay, H.M., and Blesch, A. (2002). Spontaneous and augmented growth of axons in the primate spinal cord: effects of local injury and nerve growth factor-secreting cell grafts. *J. Comp. Neurol.* **449,** 88–101.

19. Prewitt, C.M., Niesman, I.R., Kane, C.J., and Houle, J.D. (1997). Activated macrophage–microglial cells can promote the regeneration of sensory axons into the injured spinal cord. *Exp. Neurol.* **148,** 433–443.

20. Morgenstern, D.A., Asher, R.A., and Fawcett, J.W. (2002). Chondroitin sulphate proteoglycans in the CNS injury response. *Prog. Brain Res.* **137,** 313–332.

21. Blight, A.R. (1983). Cellular morphology of chronic spinal cord injury in the cat: analysis of myelinated axons by line sampling. *Neuroscience* **10,** 521–543.

22. Nashmi, R., and Fehlings, M.G. (2001). Mechanisms of axonal dysfunction after spinal cord injury: with an emphasis on the role of voltage-gated potassium channels. *Brain Res. Brain Res. Rev.* **38,** 165–191.

23. Novikova, L.N., Novikov, L.N., and Kellerth, J.O. (2002). Differential effects of neurotrophins on neuronal survival and axonal regeneration after spinal cord injury in adult rats. *J. Comp. Neurol.* **452,** 255–263.

24. Tatagiba, M., Brosamle, C., and Schwab, M.E. (1997). Regeneration of injured axons in the adult mammalian central nervous system. *Neurosurgery* **40,** 541–546.

25. Bregman, B.S., Coumans, J.V., Dai, H.N., Kuhn, P.L., Lynskey, J., McAtee, M., and Sandhu, F. (2002). Transplants and neurotrophic factors increase regeneration and recovery of function after spinal cord injury. *Prog. Brain Res.* **137,** 257–273.

26. Murray, M., Kim, D., Liu, Y., Tobias, C., Tessler, A., and Fischer, I. (2002). Transplantation of genetically modified cells contributes to repair and recovery from spinal injury. *Brain Res. Brain Res. Rev.* **40,** 292–300.

27. Dickson, J.G., Kesselring, J., Walsh, F.S., and Davison, A.N. (1985). Cellular distribution of 04 antigen and galactocerebroside in primary cultures of human fetal spinal cord. *Acta. Neuropathol. (Berl.)* **68,** 340–344.

28. Satoh, J., and Kim, S.U. (1994). Proliferation and differentiation of fetal human oligodendrocytes in culture. *J. Neurosci. Res.* **39,** 260–272.

29. Gamble, H.J. (1969). Electron microscope observations on the human fetal and embryonic spinal cord. *J. Anat.* **104,** 435–453.

30. Weidenheim, K.M., Kress, Y., Epshteyn, I., Rashbaum, W.K., and Lyman, W.D. (1992). Early myelination in the human fetal lumbosacral spinal cord: characterization by light and electron microscopy. *J. Neuropathol. Exp. Neurol.* **51,** 142–149.

31. Benes, F.M., Turtle, M., Khan, Y., and Farol, P. (1994). Myelination of a key relay zone in the hippocampal formation occurs in the human brain during childhood, adolescence, and adulthood. *Arch. Gen. Psychi.* **51,** 477–484.

32. Poduslo, S.E., and Jang, Y. (1984). Myelin development in infant brain. *Neurochem. Res.* **9,** 1615–1626.

33. Barres, B.A., and Raff, M.C. (1996). Axonal control of oligodendrocyte development. *In* "Glia Cell Development: Basic Principles and Clinical Relevance," (K.R. Jessen *et al.,* Eds.), pp. 71–83. Bios Scientific, Oxford.

34. Roelink, H., Porter, J.A., Chiang, C., Tanabe, Y., Chang, D.T., Beachy, P.A., and Jessell, T.M. (1995). Floor plate and motor neuron induction by different concentrations of the amino-terminal cleavage product of Sonic hedgehog autoproteolysis. *Cell* **81,** 445–455.

35. Hajihosseini, M., Tham, T.N., and Dubois-Dalcq, M. (1996). Origin of oligodendrocytes within the human spinal cord. *J. Neurosci.* **16,** 7981–7994.

36. Dubois-Dalcq, M., and Murray, K. (2000). Why are growth factors important in oligodendrocyte physiology? *Pathol. Biol. (Paris)* **48,** 80–86.

37. Jessell, T.M. (2000). Neuronal specification in the spinal cord: inductive signals and transcriptional codes. *Nat. Rev. Genet.* **1,** 20–29.

38. Munoz-Sanjuan, I., and Brivanlou, A.H. (2002). Neural induction, the default model, and embryonic stem cells. *Nat. Rev. Neurosci.* **3,** 271–280.

39. Durston, A.J., van der, W.J., Pijnappel, W.W., and Godsave, S.F. (1998). Retinoids and related signals in early development of the vertebrate central nervous system. *Curr. Top. Dev. Biol.* **40,** 111–175.

40. Briscoe, J., and Ericson, J. (2001). Specification of neuronal fates in the ventral neural tube. *Curr. Opin. Neurobiol.* **11,** 43–49.

41. Renoncourt, Y., Carroll, P., Filippi, P., Arce, V., and Alonso, S. (1998). Neurons derived *in vitro* from ES cells express homeoproteins characteristic of motoneurons and interneurons. *Mech. Dev.* **79,** 185–197.

42. Wichterle, H., Lieberam, I., Porter, J.A., and Jessell, T.M. (2002). Directed differentiation of embryonic stem cells into motor neurons. *Cell* **110,** 385–397.

43. Sotomaru, Y., Kato, Y., and Tsunoda, Y. (1999). Induction of pluripotency by injection of mouse trophectoderm cell nuclei into

blastocysts following transplantation into enucleated oocytes. *Theriogenology* **52**, 213–220.

44. Kaufman, M.H., Robertson, E.J., Handyside, A.H., and Evans, M.J. (1983). Establishment of pluripotential cell lines from haploid mouse embryos. *J. Embryol. Exp. Morphol.* **73**, 249–261.

45. Aguayo, A.J., David, S., and Bray, G.M. (1981). Influences of the glial environment on the elongation of axons after injury: transplantation studies in adult rodents. *J. Exp. Biol.* **95**, 231–240.

46. Bunge, M.B. (2002). Bridging the transected or contused adult rat spinal cord with Schwann cell and olfactory ensheathing glia transplants. *Prog. Brain Res.* **137**, 275–282.

47. Hains, B.C., Johnson, K.M., Eaton, M.J., Willis, W.D., and Hulsebosch, C.E. (2003). Serotonergic neural precursor cell grafts attenuate bilateral hyperexcitability of dorsal horn neurons after spinal hemisection in rat. *Neuroscience* **116**, 1097–1110.

48. Jiang, S., Wang, J., Khan, M.I., Middlemiss, P.J., Salgado-Ceballos, H., Werstiuk, E.S., Wickson, R., and Rathbone, M.P. (2003). Enteric glia promote regeneration of transected dorsal root axons into spinal cord of adult rats. *Exp. Neurol.* **181**, 79–83.

49. Akiyama, Y., Radtke, C., Honmou, O., and Kocsis, J.D. (2002). Remyelination of the spinal cord following intravenous delivery of bone marrow cells. *Glia* **39**, 229–236.

50. Cao, Q., Benton, R.L., and Whittemore, S.R. (2002). Stem cell repair of central nervous system injury. *J. Neurosci. Res.* **68**, 501–510.

51. Kennea, N.L., and Mehmet, H. (2002). Neural stem cells. *J. Pathol.* **197**, 536–550.

52. Liu, Y., and Rao, M.S. (2003). Transdifferentiation: fact or artifact. *J. Cell Biochem.* **88**, 29–40.

53. Gottlieb, D.I., and Huettner, J.E. (1999). An *in vitro* pathway from embryonic stem cells to neurons and glia. *Cells Tissue Organs* **165**, 165–172.

54. Brustle, O., Jones, K.N., Learish, R.D., Karram, K., Choudhary, K., Wiestler, O.D., Duncan, I.D., and McKay, R.D. (1999). Embryonic stem cell-derived glial precursors: a source of myelinating transplants. *Science* **285**, 754–756.

55. McKay, R. (1997). Stem cells in the central nervous system. *Science* **276**, 66–71.

56. McDonald, J.W., Liu, X.Z., Qu, Y., Liu, S., Mickey, S.K., Turetsky, D., Gottlieb, D.I., and Choi, D.W. (1999). Transplanted embryonic stem cells survive, differentiate, and promote recovery in injured rat spinal cord. *Nat. Med.* **5**, 1410–1412.

57. Liu, S., Qu, Y., Stewart, T.J., Howard, M.J., Chakrabortty, S., Holekamp, T.F., and McDonald, J.W. (2000). Embryonic stem cells differentiate into oligodendrocytes and myelinate in culture and after spinal cord transplantation. *Proc. Natl. Acad. Sci. U. S. A.* **97**, 6126–6131.

58. Strubing, C., Ahnert-Hilger, G., Shan, J., Wiedenmann, B., Hescheler, J., and Wobus, A.M. (1995). Differentiation of pluripotent embryonic stem cells into the neuronal lineage *in vitro* gives rise to mature inhibitory and excitatory neurons. *Mech. Dev.* **53**, 275–287.

59. Finley, M.F., Kulkarni, N., and Huettner, J.E. (1996). Synapse formation and establishment of neuronal polarity by P19 embryonic carcinoma cells and embryonic stem cells. *J. Neurosci.* **16**, 1056–1065.

60. Okabe, S., Forsberg-Nilsson, K., Spiro, A.C., Segal, M., and McKay, R.D. (1996). Development of neuronal precursor cells and functional postmitotic neurons from embryonic stem cells *in vitro. Mech. Dev.* **59**, 89–102.

61. Bulte, J.W., Douglas, T., Witwer, B., Zhang, S.C., Strable, E., Lewis, B.K., Zywicke, H., Miller, B., van Gelderen, P., Moskowitz, B.M., Duncan, I.D., and Frank, J.A. (2001). Magnetodendrimers allow endosomal magnetic labeling and *in vivo* tracking of stem cells. *Nat. Biotechnol.* **19**, 1141–1147.

62. Lu, J., Bulte, J.W., Liu, S., Schottler, F., Howard, M.J., Zywicke, H., van Gelderen, P., Douglas, T., Frank, J.A., and McDonald, J.W. (2003). "MR Imaging of Transplanted Labeled Embryonic Stem (ES) Cells in the Contusion Injured Spinal Cord." Paper presented at the 31st annual meeting of the Society for Neuroscience.

63. Ao, H., Qu, Y., and McDonald, J.W. (2003). Intrathecal ES cell transplantation: self-organization into CNS-like tissue with features resembling normal spinal cord. *Nat. Biotechnol.* Society for Neuroscience (abstract).

64. Cao, Q.L., Howard, R.M., Dennison, J.B., and Whittemore, S.R. (2002). Differentiation of engrafted neuronal-restricted precursor cells is inhibited in the traumatically injured spinal cord. *Exp. Neurol.* **177**, 349–359.

65. Murray, M., and Fischer, I. (2001). Transplantation and gene therapy: Combined approaches for repair of spinal cord injury. *Neuroscientist* **7**, 28–41.

66. Vadivelu, S., Stewart, T.J., Miller, J.H., Tom, V., Liu, S., Li, Q., Howard, M.J., Silver, J., and McDonald, J.W. (2003). "Embryonic Stem Cell Transplantation: Penetration of the Glial Scar and Robust Axonal Regeneration into White Matter in the Injured Adult Rat Spinal Cord." Paper to be presented at the 33rd annual meeting of the Society for Neuroscience.

67. Mouveroux, J.M., Verkijk, M., Lakke, E.A., and Marani, E. (2000). Intrinsic properties of the developing motor cortex in the rat: *In vitro* axons from the medial somatomotor cortex grow faster than axons from the lateral somatomotor cortex. *Brain Res. Dev. Brain Res.* **122**, 59–66.

68. Teng, Y.D., Lavik, E.B., Qu, X., Park, K.I., Ourednik, J., Zurakowski, D., Langer, R., and Snyder, E.Y. (2002). Functional recovery following traumatic spinal cord injury mediated by a unique polymer scaffold seeded with neural stem cells. *Proc. Natl. Acad. Sci. U. S. A.* **99**, 3024–3029.

69. Rossignol, S., Chau, C., Brustein, E., Giroux, N., Bouyer, L., Barbeau, H., and Reader, T.A. (1998). Pharmacological activation and modulation of the central pattern generator for locomotion in the cat. *Ann. NY Acad. Sci.* **860**, 346–359.

70. Ankeny, D.P., McTigue, D.M., Guan, Z., Yan, Q., Kinstler, O., Stokes, B.T., and Jakeman, L.B. (2001). Pegylated brain-derived neurotrophic factor shows improved distribution into the spinal cord and stimulates locomotor activity and morphological changes after injury. *Exp. Neurol.* **170**, 85–100.

71. Tada, M., Takahama, Y., Abe, K., Nakatsuji, N., and Tada, T. (2001). Nuclear reprogramming of somatic cells by *in vitro* hybridization with ES cells. *Curr. Biol.* **11**, 1553–1558.

72. McDonald, J.W. (Unpublished observations).

73. Lockman, P.R., Mumper, R.J., Khan, M.A., and Allen, D.D. (2002). Nanoparticle technology for drug delivery across the blood–brain barrier. *Drug Dev. Ind. Pharm.* **28**, 1–13.

74. Ma, Y., Feigin, A., Dhawan, V., Fukuda, M., Shi, Q., Greene, P., Breeze, R., Fahn, S., Freed, C., and Eidelberg, D. (2002). Dyskinesia after fetal cell transplantation for parkinsonism: a PET study. *Ann. Neurol.* **52**, 628–634.

75. Hubner, K., Fuhrmann, G., Christenson, L.K., Kehler, J., Reinbold, R., De La Fuente, R., Wood, J., Strauss, J.F., III, Boiani, M., and Scholer, H.R. (2003). Derivation of oocytes from mouse embryonic stem cells. *Science* **300**, 1251–1256.

76. Becker, D., Sadowsky, C.L., McDonald, J.W. (2003). Restoring function after spinal cord injury. *Neurologist.* **9**(1), 1–15.

Use of Embryonic Stem Cells to Treat Heart Disease

Joshua D. Dowell, Robert Zweigerdt, Michael Rubart, and Loren J. Field

Introduction

It is now well established that cardiomyocytes can be stably transplanted into normal or injured adult hearts. Recent studies have demonstrated that transplanted donor cells can form a functional syncytium with the host myocardium. It is also well established that embryonic stem (ES) cells can differentiate into functional cardiomyocytes *in vitro* and that these ES cell–derived cardiomyocytes form stable intracardiac grafts when transplanted into the myocardium. ES cells might thus be a suitable source of donor cardiomyocytes for cell transplantation therapies aimed at restoring lost myocardial mass in diseased hearts. In this chapter, a review of the literature describing factors that impact upon cardiomyogenic differentiation in ES cells is presented. In addition, studies wherein ES cell–derived cardiomyocytes were transplanted into recipient hearts are summarized. Finally, studies demonstrating the large-scale *in vitro* production of ES cell–derived cardiomyocytes suitable for cellular transplant are covered.

Cardiomyocyte Transplantation as a Paradigm for Treating Diseased Hearts

Cell transplantation has emerged as a potential therapeutic intervention to enhance angiogenesis, provide structural support, and perhaps even to restore lost myocardial mass in diseased hearts. Several donor cell types have been transplanted in efforts to attain these goals, including angioblasts and vascular precursors, bone marrow and mesenchymal stem cells, skeletal myoblasts, and fetal or ES cell–derived cardiomyocytes.[1,2] Clinical studies using skeletal myoblasts[3] or crude mononuclear hematopoietic stem cell preparations from either the bone marrow[4–6] or peripheral circulation[7] have been initiated. These studies collectively established that cell transplantation in injured hearts is relatively safe, although the presence of arrhythmias in patients receiving skeletal myoblast transplants has necessitated defibrillator implantation.[3] Although some degree of improvement in cardiac function has

been observed in these initial clinical studies, the underlying mechanism is not clear.[2]

Cardiomyocyte transplantation as a potential intervention to restore cardiac mass in diseased hearts was initially explored in the early 1990s. In these studies, single-cell suspensions generated by enzymatic digestion of fetal hearts were transplanted directly into the ventricle of histocompatibility-matched or immune-suppressed recipient animals. The transplanted cells were identified by virtue of reporter transgene activity[8] or alternatively by the expression of an endogenous gene product absent in the recipient myocardium.[9] The donor cells were stably engrafted into the recipient hearts, where they terminally differentiated and expressed many of the molecular and morphological attributes typical of normal adult cardiomyocytes. Ultrastructural analyses indicated that the transplanted donor cells formed intercalated disks with host cardiomyocytes comprised of fascia adherens, desmosomes, and gap junctions. Subsequent studies have demonstrated that donor cardiomyocytes could also stably engraft into injured hearts and that in some cases functional improvement could be obtained.[1]

Recent studies have demonstrated that transplanted cardiomyocytes formed a functional syncytium with the host myocardium.[10,11] In these experiments, fetal cardiomyocytes from transgenic mice expressing enhanced green fluorescent protein (eGFP) were transplanted into the ventricular septum of histocompatibility-matched nontransgenic recipient animals. A typical graft is shown in Fig. 70–1A. To demonstrate the formation of a functional syncytium, transplanted hearts were harvested and perfused on a Langendorff apparatus with rhod-2 (a calcium indicator dye that exhibits increased fluorescence with increased intracellular calcium content) and cytochalasin D (an excitation-contraction uncoupler).[11] The perfused hearts were then subjected to two-photon molecular excitation laser scanning microscopy under conditions that permitted simultaneous imaging of eGFP status (to distinguish the donor and host cardiomyocytes) and rhod-2 fluorescence (to monitor intracellular calcium transients). Examination of intracellular calcium transients in neighboring donor and host cardiomyocytes revealed that they occurred simultaneously and were indistinguishable (Fig. 70–1B and 70–1C). These data indicated that donor cells were able to directly participate in a functional syncytium with the host heart. Importantly, cardiomyocyte transplantation was not associated with any

Joshua D. Dowell, Robert Zweigerdt, Michael Rubart, and Loren J. Field

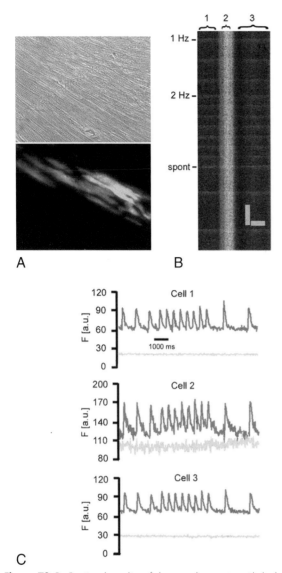

Figure 70–1. *Functional coupling of donor cardiomyocytes with the host myocardium. (A) Bright-field (top) and epifluorescence (bottom) image of an area of a mouse left ventricle containing eGFP-expressing donor cardiomyocytes and nonexpressing host cardiomyocytes. The heart was harvested 27 days after engraftment. (B) Simultaneous imaging of rhod-2 and eGFP fluorescence in a nontransgenic heart carrying an MHC–eGFP fetal cardiomyocyte graft. The image shows vertically stacked line scans that traverses three juxtaposed cardiomyocytes. Cells 1 and 3 are host cardiomyocytes, whereas cell 2 is an eGFP-expressing donor cardiomyocyte. The heart was paced using point stimulation at a remote site at the rates indicated. Spont indicates spontaneous [Ca2+]i transient. Scale bars = 20 microns horizontally, 1000 ms vertically. Time runs from top to the bottom. (C) Spatially integrated traces of the changes in rhod-2 (upper trace) and eGFP (lower trace) fluorescence for the three cardiomyocytes in panel B. The signal across the entire cell was averaged and plotted as a function of time. Note that both stimulated and spontaneous [Ca2+]i transients occur simultaneously in donor and host cardiomyocytes and exhibit similar kinetics. (Please see CD-ROM for color version of this figure.)*

anomalies in intracellular calcium handling in either the donor or the host cardiomyocytes.

Cardiomyogenic Differentiation of ES Cells *In Vitro*

The studies described above indicated that cardiomyocyte transplantation might be a useful mechanism to restore lost function in diseased hearts. Since clinical use of fetal donor cells is currently impractical, a surrogate source of donor cardiomyocytes would be required for clinical application. ES cells are multipotent cells derived from preimplantation embryos. ES cells can be amplified and maintained indefinitely in an undifferentiated state under appropriate conditions. For mouse ES cells, this entails culturing in the presence of leukemia inhibitory factor (LIF). Molecular analysis indicated that LIF enhanced the expression of Oct-4, a key transcription factor associated with maintenance of the multipotent state.[12] Growing mouse ES cells in suspension culture and in the absence of LIF resulted in the formation of multicellular aggregates known as embryoid bodies (EBs). Stochastic cell–cell interactions during EB formation mimicked normal developmental induction cues and resulted in the random differentiation of ecto-, endo- and mesodermal cell lineages.[13] Cardiomyogenic differentiation was frequently observed in differentiating EBs, and was easily recognized because of spontaneous contractile activity. ES cells with cardiomyogenic potential were also generated from rat,[14] rabbit,[15] monkey,[16] and human.[17–19]

Cardiomyocytes derived from ES cells have been fairly well characterized *in vitro* by many groups (Table 70–1). Molecular and electrophysiological analyses indicated that cells with characteristics of atrial, ventricular, and perhaps conduction system cardiomyocytes can be generated *in vitro*. The temporal pattern of terminal differentiation *in vitro* for ES cell-derived cardiomyocytes mirrored that of embryonic development.[20] Moreover, most gene expression qualitatively paralleled that seen during bona fide cardiac development. Although the preponderance of these studies were performed with mouse ES cells, preliminary assessment of cardiomyogenic induction in human ES cells revealed essentially similar results. When maintained under typical culture conditions, ES cell-derived cardiomyocytes did not acquire the gross morphologic attributes, or the quantitative levels of gene expression, characteristic of neonatal or adult cardiomyocytes.[20,21] However, since the introduction of ES cells into tetraploid blastocysts generated entirely ES cell–derived mice with normal hearts,[22] murine ES cells are clearly capable of bona fide cardiomyogenic differentiation when placed in the appropriate environment. Thus, the observed differentiated status of ES cell–derived cardiomyocytes *in vitro* likely reflects limitations in the cell culture conditions. It remains to be seen if the use of tissue bioengineering approaches that enhance fetal cardiomyocyte differentiation *in vitro*[23] will have a similar effect on ES cell–derived cardiomyocytes.

Cardiomyocytes have been reported to comprise from 0.5 to 5% of the cells in randomly differentiating ES cultures.[24,25]

TABLE 70–1
In Vitro Characterization of ES Cell–Derived Cardiomyocytes

Species	Comments	Citation
Mouse	Establishment of pluripotential cells in culture	56
Mouse	In vitro development mirrors embryonic development	13
Mouse	Cardiac myosin heavy chain (MHC) expression	57, 58
Mouse	Cholinoceptor and adrenoceptor expression	37
Mouse	In vitro differentiation system for cardiomyocytes	59
Mouse	Atrial, sinusoidal, and ventricular cell types represented	60
Mouse	Ventricular MLC-2 gene expression independent of heart tube formation	61
Mouse	Alteration in Ca^{2+} sensitivity during development similar in vivo	62
Mouse	Similar DNA synthesis levels to in vivo	63
Mouse	Similar transition in MHC isoforms	64
Mouse	Striated muscle actins are expressed in cardiomyocyte-like cells	65
Mouse	Cx expression, gap junction communication with Lucifer Yellow	66
Mouse	Similar cell morphology, sarcomere formation, cell–cell junctions as in vivo	67
Mouse	Relationships in channel expression during differentiation	68
Mouse	Role of ATP-dependent K^+ channels in cellular excitability	69
Mouse	Intermittent block of AP propagation with long-term electrical recordings	70
Mouse	NO fundamental in early-stage cardiomyocytes	71
Mouse	I_{CaL} insensitivity to β-adrenergic stimulation in early-stage cardiocytes	72
Mouse	Spontaneous contractile activity from intracellular $[Ca^{2+}]_i$ oscillations	73
Mouse	Ion channel expression similar to fetal in vivo	48
Mouse	Role of $I_{(to)}$ in electrical activity in early-stage cardiomyocytes	74
Mouse	Ca^{2+} sparks governed by Ca^{2+} load of the SR and/or density of RyRs	75
Mouse	Differentiation into at least three AP phenotypes promotes arrhythmogenecity	76
Rat	Establishment of pluripotential cells in culture	14
Rabbit	Establishment of pluripotential cells in culture	15
Monkey	Establishment of pluripotential cells in culture	16
Human	Establishment of pluripotential cells in culture	17–19
Human	Documentation of differentiation by RT-PCR	77
Human	Enrichment of cell types by specific growth factors	78
Human	Endoderm-like cell line induced cardiomyogenesis	20
Human	Morphological and ultrastructural analyses of cardiomyocytes	35
Human	Morphological and high-resolution activation mapping	34
Human	Multiple types of cardiac myocytes	36

Accordingly, considerable effort has been invested to enhance cardiomyogenic yield during in vitro differentiation. Toward that end, several growth factor and cell culture conditions have been identified that can be used to enhance cardiomyogenic induction in differentiating mouse and human ES cultures (Table 70–2). An alternative strategy to enhance cardiomyogenic yield in differentiating ES cultures would be to exploit genetic pathways that potentiate cardiomyocyte cell cycle activity. Many genes have been identified that either positively or negatively influenced cardiomyocyte cell

cycle activity.[26] Genetic modification of the ES cells, or development of small molecule agonists, antagonists, or both of the genetic pathways in question, could be exploited to enhance cardiomyogenic yield in differentiating ES cultures.

Transplantation of ES Cell–Derived Cardiomyocytes

Although the local tissue environment may have a minor influence on cell fate during differentiation, the ability to form

Joshua D. Dowell, Robert Zweigerdt, Michael Rubart, and Loren J. Field

TABLE 70–2
Interventions to Enhance ES Cell–Derived Cardiomyocyte Yield

Species	Intervention	Comments	Citations
Mouse	Genetic	Cardiomyocyte selection via cardiac-specific *G418* resistance gene	25
Mouse	Genetic	Lewis X structure enhances myocardial differentiation	79
Mouse	Exogenous	Acceleration of cardiomyocyte differentiation with RA	80
Mouse	Exogenous	Medium components enhance cardiogenic differentiation	81
Mouse	Electrical	DC field pulse increases the number of cardiomyocytes	82
Mouse	Exogenous	LIF modulates cardiogenesis in opposite manners	83
Mouse	Exogenous	H_2O_2 or menadione enhances cardiomyogenesis	84
Mouse	Exogenous	Parietal endoderm influences onset of cardiomyogenesis	85
Mouse	Genetic	Expression of mutant p193 and mutant p53 blocks E1A-induced apoptosis	86
Mouse	Genetic	Dominant-negative p53 rescues T-antigen lacking p53-binding domain	87
Mouse	Genetic	MLC-2v-eGFP ventricular cardiomyocyte selection	27
Mouse	Exogenous	TGF-β and BMP2 enhances cardiomyogenesis	88
Mouse	Genetic Exogenous	Large-scale production of cardiomyocytes with RA and G418 resistance	41
Human	Exogenous	5-Aza-2′-deoxycytidine, not DMSO or RA, enhances cardiomyogenesis	33
Human	Coculture	Coculture with visceral endoderm-like cells	21
Human	Exogenous	Ascorbic acid induces cardiac differentiation	89

multiple tissue lineages following transplantation is a hallmark of ES cells. Accordingly, the use of ES cells to treat heart disease would require *in vitro* differentiation and purification of donor cardiomyocytes prior to transplantation. Although cytokine- and growth factor-based approaches can enhance cardiomyogenic yield (Table 70–2), more rigorous methodologies would be required to generate cultures of sufficient purity for therapeutic transplantation. Importantly, elimination of multipotent cells would be absolutely required for clinical applications.

One approach to generate pure ES cell–derived cardiomyocyte cultures relied on genetic modification of the progenitor cells such that the resulting cardiomyocytes could be separated from nonmyocytes (Fig. 70–2). For example, undifferentiated ES cells carrying a transgene comprising the cardiac-restricted α-myosin heavy-chain promoter driving expression of a cDNA encoding aminoglycoside phosphotransferase were allowed to differentiate *in vitro*. After cardiomyogenic differentiation was apparent (by the appearance of spontaneous contractile activity), the cultures were treated with G418. Since the myosin heavy chain promoter was only active in cardiomyocytes, only those cells expressed aminoglycoside phosphotransferase and survived G418 treatment. Therefore, virtually all of the nonmyocytes were eliminated from the culture.[25] A similar approach was used to isolate cardiomyocytes by targeted expression of eGFP followed by fluorescence-activated cell sorting (FACS).[27] Klug *et al.*[25] transplanted cardiomyocytes purified by the G418 purification method described above into the hearts of adult mice. The ES cell–derived cardiomyocytes formed stable grafts in the host heart and were well aligned with host cardiomyocytes. Importantly, noncardiomyocyte outgrowths were not observed in this study, indicating that the purification method efficiently removed any residual multipotent cells from the differentiating ES cultures.

Other approaches have been used for ES cell–derived cardiomyocyte transplantation. For example, Xiao and colleagues performed a series of studies wherein mouse ES cell–derived cardiomyocytes isolated using microdissection from beating regions of attached EBs were transplanted into rats with myocardial infarcts.[28–30] Behfar and colleagues transplanted undifferentiated ES cells directly into myocardial infarcts. Interestingly, improved cardiac function was observed in all of these studies. However, given the extremely low content of ES cell–derived cardiomyocytes in the hearts after transplantation, and given the presence of noncardiomyocytes (presumably derived from the carryover of multipotent cells because of the purification methods employed), other indirect mechanism were likely to have contributed to the improved cardiac function in these studies. For example, cell transplantation could have resulted in enhanced angiogenesis with a concomitant rescue of at-risk myocardium.

716

Alternatively, the presence of exogenous cells might have strengthened the myocardial wall with a concomitant improvement in postmyocardial infarction remodeling. Both processes would result in an improvement in cardiac function without the ES cell–derived cardiomyocytes forming a functional syncytium with the host heart.[1]

Large-Scale Generation of ES Cell–Derived Cardiomyocytes

Successful clinical implementation of stem cell–derived cardiomyocyte transplantation would face several technical hurdles, of which the purity and safety of the stem cell–derived cardiomyocytes are among the most important. Additionally, from a commercial point of view, the ability to generate clinically relevant cell numbers through an economically viable bioprocess would be another fundamental prerequisite. In this context, it is interesting to make some projections of cell number requirements. Kajstura et al.[31] estimated that the left ventricle of the human heart contains about 6×10^9 cardiomyocytes. Consequently, cell transplantation therapies aimed at replacing tissues lost to myocardial infarction would require the successful seeding of as many as $5–10 \times 10^8$ donor cardiomyocytes per patient (assuming limited cardiomyocyte proliferation after transplantation). The robust generation of such large cardiomyocyte numbers would be only feasible in controlled bioreactors capable of high-density differentiation of ES cells in clinical scale.

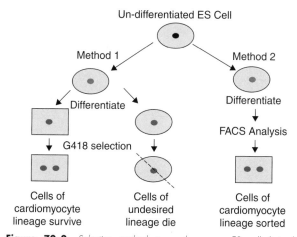

Figure 70–2. *Selection method to produce pure ES cell–derived cardiomyocyte cultures. Two methods to separate ES cell–derived cardiomyocytes from nonmyocytes by cardiac-specific expression of a transgene. In Method 1, undifferentiated ES cells carrying a transgene comprising the cardiac-restricted α-myosin heavy-chain promoter driving expression of aminoglycoside phosphotransferase were allowed to differentiate in vitro. Cultures were treated with G418 following cardiomyogenic differentiation to select for cardiomyocytes, since the transgene promoter was only active in cardiomyocytes. In Method 2, undifferentiated ES cells were transfected with a transgene comprising the ventricular-specific myosin light-chain-2v promoter driving expression of eGFP and allowed to differentiate in vitro. Following cardiomyogenic differentiation, FACS was used to isolate a cardiomyocyte-pure population. (Please see CD-ROM for color version of this figure.)*

Published studies have indicated that EB formation is an efficient strategy to induce cardiomyogenic differentiation in both mouse and human ES cells.[1,21,24,32–36] The main challenge to achieving large-scale generation of ES cell–derived cells is to establish conditions that would initially support the formation of numerous small EBs from undifferentiated ES cells and that upon subsequent culture would support the further growth of the resulting EBs in the absence of shear-induced damage. This goal would be particularly challenging because EB characteristics change continuously during the differentiation process: size, density, and robustness all change from the initial formation of EBs to the ultimate appearance of differentiated cells.

The hanging drop technique permitted the formation of EBs with highly uniform size and cell content.[37] Similarly, bulk EB induction on Petri dishes with or without semisolid media,[38,39] as well as culturing of ES cell suspensions on rotation devices,[40] have been used to affect controlled EB formation. Although these approaches were useful tools for bioprocess development (e.g., to test the effect of compounds on cell proliferation and differentiation and to optimize ES cell inoculation density), they were unsuitable for the large-scale production of differentiated cells.[38,40,41] Spinner flask cultures have been used in other systems to effect hydrodynamic control of cell aggregate formation. Large-scale cultures of neonatal hamster kidney[42,43] and neuronal stem cell aggregates[44–46] were produced with this approach. However, these studies focused on the expansion of cell aggregates and were not concerned with establishing conditions amenable to differentiation.

Wartenberg et al.[47] successfully used spinner cultures with a bulb-shaped impeller and inoculated with relatively high ES cell numbers to generate EBs. Although the diameter of the resulting EBs was 2–3 times larger than that of EBs generated by traditional protocols, efficient induction of microvessel-like structures and endothelial cells was observed. Spontaneous contractile activity indicative of cardiomyogenic induction was also noted in this experiment; however, cell proliferation kinetics were not presented. Despite these encouraging results, studies from our laboratory using spinner flasks with a paddle-type impeller resulted in the formation of large aggregates instead of homogeneous EBs, even though numerous conditions including various inoculation densities and various stirrer speeds were tested. The aggregates were essentially devoid of active cell proliferation and differentiation. Dang et al.[38] reported that fusion of EBs in the early stage of culture in spinner flasks was dependent at least in part on high levels of E-cadherin expression in undifferentiated ES cells and that E-cadherin was down-regulated upon further differentiation. Thus, by simply transferring Ebs that were pre-formed on Petri dishes for 3 days into spinner flasks, EB aggregation was avoided.[41] This technique has already been employed to efficiently form cardiomyocytes in "floating EBs."[48]

Although spinner flasks constituted an essential step for the transition from lab- to clinical-scale applications, the approach has numerous deficiencies, including the stringent limits on maximal cell density as well as the inability to adequately control oxygen concentration and pH levels. A single-step culture protocol to generate ES cell–derived cardiomyocytes in an actively aerated, fully controlled tank reactor was therefore developed.[40] A common two-liter tank reactor equipped with a blade impeller creating axial flow was used to determine the effects of agitation rates on resulting EB formation, cell yield, and differentiation toward cardiomyocytes. The cellular content of EBs was highly dependent upon the agitation rate (Fig. 70–3A). The average EB size for cultures maintained at 65 rpm was in agreement with that obtained with traditional approaches.[38] In terms of total yield, the maximal cell density was also obtained in cultures maintained at 65 rpm.

Using these culture parameters, additional experiments were performed to generate pure cardiomyocyte cultures.[40] Bioreactors were seeded with ES cells that carried the cardiac myosin heavy chain aminoglycoside phosphotransferase transgene described above. After 9 days of culture under conditions suitable for EB formation and differentiation and for cell expansion and differentiation, G418 was added to eliminate

the noncardiomyocytes. Cell density prior to the addition of G418 was approximately 7×10^6 cells/ml. The expected cell density dropped dramatically upon antibiotic addition and stabilized around 6×10^5 cells/ml. Immune cytochemical analysis revealed that more than 99% of the cells obtained from the antibiotic-treated bioreactor cultures expressed sarcomeric myosin (Fig. 70–3B and 70–3C), indicating that essentially pure cardiomyocyte cultures were generated. Overall, this correlated to a yield of more than 10^9 cardiomyocytes from a two-liter reaction.

Summary and Challenges for the Clinical Implementation of ES Cell–Derived Cardiomyocyte Transplantation

The data summarized above indicated that donor cardiomyocytes were stable following transplantation into normal or injured recipient hearts; furthermore, they were capable of forming a functional syncytium with the host myocardium. In addition, the data demonstrated that highly differentiated cardiomyocytes could be derived from ES cells and that these cells could be stably transplanted into recipient hearts. Growth factors and enrichment methods were described that enhanced cardiomyogenic differentiation and facilitated the generation of essentially pure cardiomyocyte cultures, respectively. Finally, conditions were established that permitted the generation of clinically relevant numbers of cardiomyocytes using bioreactor systems. Thus, the available data support the notion that transplantation of ES cell–derived cardiomyocytes for the treatment of heart disease might be both therapeutically useful and technically feasible. Nonetheless, several obstacles remain that must be overcome for clinical implementation.

A major limitation of current cardiomyocyte transplantation protocols is the relatively low levels of donor cell seeding in the host myocardium. Using fetal cardiomyocytes as donor cells, several groups have demonstrated that the preponderance of donor cardiomyocytes die following transplantation into the heart, with typically less than 5% of the cells successfully seeding the myocardium.[10,49,50] It is likely that interventions aimed at enhancing donor cell survival, posttransplantation proliferation, or both may be required to achieve high levels of de novo cardiomyocyte seeding. Toward that end, numerous cardiomyocyte prosurvival pathways have been identified.[51] Moreover, genes that affect cardiomyocyte proliferation during development, and in some cases result in cell cycle reentry in adult cardiomyocytes, have been identified.[26,52] Manipulation of these pathways in donor cells should greatly enhance seeding efficiencies. The genetic trackability of ES cells in vitro will likely facilitate this process.

Issues associated with the use of allogeneic donor cells constitute an additional potential hurdle for the widespread application of ES cell–derived cardiomyocyte transplantation. Although some degree of intervention is likely to be required, the evolution of comparably mild immune suppression protocols used for type 1 diabetic patients following cadaveric

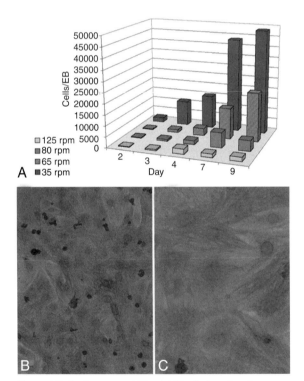

Figure 70–3. *Generation of EBs and ES cell–derived cardiomyocytes in bioreactors.* (A) Relationship between agitation rate, time in culture, and EB cellular content in a single-step culture protocol. (B and C) Low- and high-power images, respectively, of ES cell–derived cardiomyocytes generated in a bioreactor maintained at an agitation rate of 65 rpm. Cells from the bioreactor were enzymatically dispersed, plated onto chamber slides, and then processed for sarcomeric myosin immune reactivity (HPR-conjugated secondary antibody, signal indicates the presence of sarcomeric myosin). Virtually all cells present expressed sarcomeric myosin, although the level of expression per cell was variable under the culture conditions employed.

β-cell transplantation are quite encouraging.[53] Hope in this regard is bolstered by the observation that ES cell–derived cardiomyocytes did not appear to undergo acute rejection when transplanted into rat hearts with experimental infarctions.[28–30] Moreover, a novel system based on ablation of IL-15 responsive T-cells might ultimately be useful to induce tolerance to allogeneic ES cell–derived donor cells.[54] Finally, the potential use of nuclear transfer to generate autologous ES cells for the generation of donor cells could circumvent the need for chronic immune suppression, although this approach is not without ethical issues.[55]

In summary, the potential use of cellular transplantation for the treatment of heart disease is gaining greater acceptance. The notion of using stem cell–derived, and in particular ES cell–derived, donor cardiomyocytes for partial restoration of lost cardiac mass in diseased hearts has been validated in experimental animals. Additional research is required to determine if it is possible to seed sufficient numbers of donor cells to directly affect cardiac function and to develop viable strategies to prevent donor cell rejection. If these latter hurdles are overcome, cellular transplantation with ES cell–derived cardiomyocytes will emerge as a promising intervention for the treatment of heart disease.

ACKNOWLEDGMENTS

Loren J. Field thanks the NHLBI and Joshua D. Dowell thanks the AHA for support. We thank our many colleagues working in the field. We apologize in advance for any relevant views or studies that where inadvertently not included.

REFERENCES

1. Dowell, J.D., Rubart, M., Pasumarthi, K.B., Soonpaa, M.H., and Field, L.J. (2003). Myocyte and myogenic stem cell transplantation in the heart. *Cardiovasc. Res.* **58**, 336–350.

2. Hassink, R., Dowell, J., Brutel de la Rivière, A., Doevedans, P., and Field, L. (2003). Stem cell therapy for ischemic heart disease. *Trends Mol. Med.* **10**, 436–441.

3. Menasche, P., Hagege, A.A., Vilquin, J.T., Desnos, M., Abergel, E., Pouzet, B., Bel, A., Sarateanu, S., Scorsin, M., Schwartz, K., Bruneval, P., Benbunan, M., Marolleau, J.P., and Duboc, D. (2003). Autologous skeletal myoblast transplantation for severe postinfarction left ventricular dysfunction. *J. Am. Coll. Cardiol.* **41**, 1078–1083.

4. Perin, E.C., Dohmann, H.F., Borojevic, R., Silva, S.A., Sousa, A.L., Mesquita, C.T., Rossi, M.I., Carvalho, A.C., Dutra, H.S., Dohmann, H.J., Silva, G.V., Belem, L., Vivacqua, R., Rangel, F.O., Esporcatte, R., Geng, Y.J., Vaughn, W.K., Assad, J.A., Mesquita, E.T., and Willerson, J.T. (2003). Transendocardial, autologous bone marrow cell transplantation for severe, chronic ischemic heart failure. *Circulation* **107**, 2294–2302.

5. Strauer, B.E., Brehm, M., Zeus, T., Kostering, M., Hernandez, A., Sorg, R.V., Kogler, G., and Wernet, P. (2002). Repair of infarcted myocardium by autologous intracoronary mononuclear bone marrow cell transplantation in humans. *Circulation* **106**, 1913–1918.

6. Tse, H.F., Kwong, Y.L., Chan, J.K., Lo, G., Ho, C.L., and Lau, C.P. (2003). Angiogenesis in ischemic myocardium by intramyocardial autologous bone marrow mononuclear cell implantation. *Lancet* **361**, 47–49.

7. Assmus, B., Schachinger, V., Teupe, C., Britten, M., Lehmann, R., Dobert, N., Grunwald, F., Aicher, A., Urbich, C., Martin, H., Hoelzer, D., Dimmeler, S., and Zeiher, A.M. (2002). Transplantation of progenitor cells and regeneration enhancement in acute myocardial infarction (TOPCARE-AMI). *Circulation* **106**, 3009–3017.

8. Soonpaa, M.H., Koh, G.Y., Klug, M.G., and Field, L.J. (1994). Formation of nascent intercalated disks between grafted fetal cardiomyocytes and host myocardium. *Science* **264**, 98–101.

9. Koh, G.Y., Soonpaa, M.H., Klug, M.G., Pride, H.P., Cooper, B.J., Zipes, D.P., and Field, L.J. (1995). Stable fetal cardiomyocyte grafts in the hearts of dystrophic mice and dogs. *J. Clin. Invest.* **96**, 2034–2042.

10. Rubart, M., Pasumarthi, K.B., Nakajima, H., Soonpaa, M.H., Nakajima, H.O., and Field, L.J. (2003). Physiological coupling of donor and host cardiomyocytes after cellular transplantation. *Circ. Res.* **92**, 1217–1224.

11. Rubart, M., Wang, E., Dunn, K.W., and Field, L.J. (2003). Two-photon molecular excitation imaging of Ca^{2+} transients in Langendorff-perfused mouse hearts. *Am. J. Physiol. Cell Physiol.* **284**, C1654–C1668.

12. Niwa, H., Miyazaki, J., and Smith, A.G. (2000). Quantitative expression of Oct-3/4 defines differentiation, dedifferentiation, or self-renewal of ES cells. *Nat. Genet.* **24**, 372–376.

13. Doetschman, T.C., Eistetter, H., Katz, M., Schmidt, W., and Kemler, R. (1985). The *in vitro* development of blastocyst-derived embryonic stem cell lines: Formation of visceral yolk sac, blood islands, and myocardium. *J. Embryol. Exp. Morphol.* **87**, 27–45.

14. Iannaccone, P.M., Taborn, G.U., Garton, R.L., Caplice, M.D., and Brenin, D.R. (1994). Pluripotent embryonic stem cells from the rat are capable of producing chimeras. *Dev. Biol.* **163**, 288–292.

15. Moreadith, R.W., and Graves, K.H. (1992). Derivation of pluripotential embryonic stem cells from the rabbit. *Trans. Assoc. Am. Phys.* **105**, 197–203.

16. Thomson, J.A., Kalishman, J., Golos, T.G., Durning, M., Harris, C.P., Becker, R.A., and Hearn, J.P. (1995). Isolation of a primate embryonic stem cell line. *Proc. Natl. Acad. Sci. U. S. A.* **92**, 7844–7848.

17. Bongso, A., Fong, C.Y., Ng, S.C., and Ratnam, S. (1994). Isolation and culture of inner cell mass cells from human blastocysts. *Hum. Reprod.* **9**, 2110–2117.

18. Thomson, J.A., Itskovitz-Eldor, J., Shapiro, S.S., Waknitz, M.A., Swiergiel, J.J., Marshall, V.S., and Jones, J.M. (1998). Embryonic stem cell lines derived from human blastocysts. *Science* **282**, 1145–1147.

19. Reubinoff, B.E., Pera, M.F., Fong, C.Y., Trounson, A., and Bongso, A. (2000). Embryonic stem cell lines from human blastocysts: somatic differentiation *in vitro*. *Nat. Biotechnol.* **18**, 399–404.

20. Mummery, C., Ward, D., van den Brink, C.E., Bird, S.D., Doevendans, P.A., Opthof, T., Brutel de la Riviere, A., Tertoolen, L., van der Heyden, M., and Pera, M. (2002). Cardiomyocyte differentiation of mouse and human embryonic stem cells. *J. Anat.* **200**, 233–242.

21. Mummery, C., Ward-van Oostwaard, D., Doevendans, P., Spijker, R., van den Brink, S., Hassink, R., van der Heyden, M., Opthof, T., Pera, M., de la Riviere, A.B., Passier, R., and Tertoolen, L. (2003). Differentiation of human embryonic stem cells to

cardiomyocytes: role of coculture with visceral endoderm-like cells. *Circulation* **107**, 2733–2740.

22. Nagy, A., Rossant, J., Nagy, R., Abramow-Newerly, W., and Roder, J.C. (1993). Derivation of completely cell culture-derived mice from early passage embryonic stem cells. *Proc. Natl. Acad. Sci. U. S. A.* **90**, 8424–8428.

23. Eschenhagen, T., Fink, C., Remmers, U., Scholz, H., Wattchow, J., Weil, J., Zimmermann, W., Dohmen, H.H., Schafer, H., Bishopric, N., Wakatsuki, T., and Elson, E.L. (1997). Three-dimensional reconstitution of embryonic cardiomyocytes in a collagen matrix: a new heart muscle model system. *FASEB J.* **11**, 683–694.

24. Boheler, K.R., Czyz, J., Tweedie, D., Yang, H.T., Anisimov, S.V., and Wobus, A.M. (2002). Differentiation of pluripotent embryonic stem cells into cardiomyocytes. *Circ. Res.* **91**, 189–201.

25. Klug, M.G., Soonpaa, M.H., Koh, G.Y., and Field, L.J. (1996). Genetically selected cardiomyocytes from differentiating embryonic stem cells form stable intracardiac grafts. *J. Clin. Invest.* **98**, 216–224.

26. Pasumarthi, K.B., and Field, L.J. (2002). Cardiomyocyte cell cycle regulation. *Circ. Res.* **90**, 1044–1054.

27. Muller, M., Fleischmann, B.K., Selbert, S., Ji, G.J., Endl, E., Middeler, G., Muller, O.J., Schlenke, P., Frese, S., Wobus, A.M., Hescheler, J., Katus, H.A., and Franz, W.M. (2000). Selection of ventricular-like cardiomyocytes from ES cells *in vitro*. *FASEB J.* **14**, 2540–2548.

28. Min, J.Y., Yang, Y., Converso, K.L., Liu, L., Huang, Q., Morgan, J.P., and Xiao, Y.F. (2002). Transplantation of embryonic stem cells improves cardiac function in postinfarcted rats. *J. Appl. Physiol.* **92**, 288–296.

29. Min, J.Y., Yang, Y., Sullivan, M.F., Ke, Q., Converso, K.L., Chen, Y., Morgan, J.P., and Xiao, Y.F. (2003). Long-term improvement of cardiac function in rats after infarction by transplantation of embryonic stem cells. *J. Thorac. Cardiovasc. Surg.* **125**, 361–369.

30. Yang, Y., Min, J.Y., Rana, J.S., Ke, Q., Cai, J., Chen, Y., Morgan, J.P., and Xiao, Y.F. (2002). VEGF enhances functional improvement of postinfarcted hearts by transplantation of ES-differentiated cells. *J. Appl. Physiol.* **93**, 1140–1151.

31. Kajstura, J., Leri, A., Finato, N., Di Loreto, C., Beltrami, C.A., and Anversa, P. (1998). Myocyte proliferation in end-stage cardiac failure in humans. *Proc. Natl. Acad. Sci. U. S. A.* **95**, 8801–8805.

32. Sachinidis, A., Fleischmann, B.K., Kolossov, E., Wartenberg, M., Sauer, H., and Hescheler, J. (2003). Cardiac-specific differentiation of mouse embryonic stem cells. *Cardiovasc. Res.* **58**, 278–291.

33. Xu, C., Police, S., Rao, N., and Carpenter, M.K. (2002). Characterization and enrichment of cardiomyocytes derived from human embryonic stem cells. *Circ. Res.* **91**, 501–508.

34. Kehat, I., Gepstein, A., Spira, A., Itskovitz-Eldor, J., and Gepstein, L. (2002). High-resolution electrophysiological assessment of human embryonic stem cell-derived cardiomyocytes: a novel *in vitro* model for the study of conduction. *Circ. Res.* **91**, 659–661.

35. Kehat, I., Kenyagin-Karsenti, D., Snir, M., Segev, H., Amit, M., Gepstein, A., Livne, E., Binah, O., Itskovitz-Eldor, J., and Gepstein, L. (2001). Human embryonic stem cells can differentiate into myocytes with structural and functional properties of cardiomyocytes. *J. Clin. Invest.* **108**, 407–414.

36. He, J.Q., Ma, Y., Lee, Y., Thomson, J.A., and Kamp, T.J. (2003). Human embryonic stem cells develop into multiple types of cardiac myocytes: action potential characterization. *Circ. Res.* **93**, 32–39.

37. Wobus, A.M., Wallukat, G., and Hescheler, J. (1991). Pluripotent mouse embryonic stem cells are able to differentiate into cardiomyocytes expressing chronotropic responses to adrenergic and cholinergic agents and Ca^{2+} channel blockers. *Differentiation* **48**, 173–182.

38. Dang, S.M., Kyba, M., Perlingeiro, R., Daley, G.Q., and Zandstra, P.W. (2002). Efficiency of embryoid body formation and hematopoietic development from embryonic stem cells in different culture systems. *Biotechnol. Bioeng.* **78**, 442–453.

39. Keller, G., Kennedy, M., Papayannopoulou, T., and Wiles, M.V. (1993). Hematopoietic commitment during embryonic stem cell differentiation in culture. *Mol. Cell Biol.* **13**, 473–486.

40. Zweigerdt, R., Burg, M., Willbold, E., Abts, H., and Ruediger, M. (2003). Generation of confluent cardiomyocyte monolayers derived from embryonic stem cells in suspension. *Cytotherapy* **5**, 399–413.

41. Zandstra, P.W., Bauwens, C., Yin, T., Liu, Q., Schiller, H., Zweigerdt, R., Pasumarthi, K.B., and Field, L.J. (2003). Scalable production of embryonic stem cell-derived cardiomyocytes. *Tiss. Eng.* **9**, 767–778.

42. Moreira, J.L., Feliciano, A.S., Santana, P.C., Cruz, P.E., Aunins, J.G., and Carrondo, M.J. (1994). Repeated-batch cultures of baby hamster kidney cell aggregates in stirred vessels. *Cytotechnology* **15**, 337–349.

43. Moreira, J.L., Santana, P.C., Feliciano, A.S., Cruz, P.E., Racher, A.J., Griffiths, J.B., and Carrondo, M.J. (1995). Effect of viscosity upon hydrodynamically controlled natural aggregates of animal cells grown in stirred vessels. *Biotechnol. Prog.* **11**, 575–583.

44. Kallos, M.S., and Behie, L.A. (1999). Inoculation and growth conditions for high cell-density expansion of mammalian neural stem cells in suspension bioreactors. *Biotechnol. Bioeng.* **63**, 473–483.

45. Sen, A., Kallos, M.S., and Behie, L.A. (2002). Expansion of mammalian neural stem cells in bioreactors: effect of power input and medium viscosity. *Brain Res. Dev. Brain Res.* **134**, 103–113.

46. Kallos, M.S., Behie, L.A., and Vescovi, A.L. (1999). Extended serial passaging of mammalian neural stem cells in suspension bioreactors. *Biotechnol. Bioeng.* **65**, 589–599.

47. Wartenberg, M., Gunther, J., Hescheler, J., and Sauer, H. (1998). The embryoid body as a novel *in vitro* assay system for antiangiogenic agents. *Lab. Invest.* **78**, 1301–1314.

48. Doevendans, P.A., Kubalak, S.W., An, R.H., Becker, D.K., Chien, K.R., and Kass, R.S. (2000). Differentiation of cardiomyocytes in floating embryoid bodies is comparable to fetal cardiomyocytes. *J. Mol. Cell Cardiol.* **32**, 839–851.

49. Muller-Ehmsen, J., Whittaker, P., Kloner, R.A., Dow, J.S., Sakoda, T., Long, T.I., Laird, P.W., and Kedes, L. (2002). Survival and development of neonatal rat cardiomyocytes transplanted into adult myocardium. *J. Mol. Cell Cardiol.* **34**, 107–116.

50. Reinecke, H., Zhang, M., Bartosek, T., and Murry, C.E. (1999). Survival, integration, and differentiation of cardiomyocyte grafts: a study in normal and injured rat hearts. *Circulation* **100**, 193–202.

51. Kang, P.M., and Izumo, S. (2003). Apoptosis in heart: basic mechanisms and implications in cardiovascular diseases. *Trends Mol. Med.* **9**, 177–182.

52. Dowell, J.D., Field, L.J., and Pasumarthi, K.B. (2003). Cell cycle regulation to repair the infarcted myocardium. *Heart Fail. Rev.* **8**, 293–303.

53. Shapiro, A.M., Lakey, J.R., Ryan, E.A., Korbutt, G.S., Toth, E., Warnock, G.L., Kneteman, N.M., and Rajotte, R.V. (2000).

Islet transplantation in seven patients with type 1 diabetes mellitus using a glucocorticoid-free immunosuppressive regimen. *N. Engl. J. Med.* **343**, 230–238.

54. Strom, T.B., Field, L.J., and Ruediger, M. (2002). Allogeneic stem cells, clinical transplantation, and the origins of regenerative medicine. *Curr. Opin. Immunol.* **14**, 601–605.

55. Lanza, R.P., Cibelli, J.B., West, M.D., Dorff, E., Tauer, C., and Green, R.M. (2001). The ethical reasons for stem cell research. *Science* **292**, 1299.

56. Evans, M.J., and Kaufman, M.H. (1981). Establishment in culture of pluripotential cells from mouse embryos. *Nature* **292**, 154–156.

57. Robbins, J., Gulick, J., Sanchez, A., Howles, P., and Doetschman, T. (1990). Mouse embryonic stem cells express the cardiac, myosin heavy-chain genes during development *in vitro*. *J. Biol. Chem.* **265**, 11,905–11,909.

58. Sanchez, A., Jones, W.K., Gulick, J., Doetschman, T., and Robbins, J. (1991). Myosin heavy-chain gene expression in mouse embryoid bodies: an *in vitro* developmental study. *J. Biol. Chem.* **266**, 22,419–22,426.

59. Wobus, A.M., and Hescheler, J. (1992). Development of an *in vitro* cardiomyocytes cell model for embryotoxicological and pharmacological studies. *Altex.* **9**, 29–42.

60. Maltsev, V.A., Rohwedel, J., Hescheler, J., and Wobus, A.M. (1993). Embryonic stem cells differentiate *in vitro* into cardiomyocytes representing sinusoidal, atrial, and ventricular cell types. *Mech. Dev.* **44**, 41–50.

61. Miller-Hance, W.C., LaCorbiere, M., Fuller, S.J., Evans, S.M., Lyons, G., Schmidt, C., Robbins, J., and Chien, K.R. (1993). *In vitro* chamber specification during embryonic stem cell cardiogenesis: expression of the ventricular myosin light-chain-2 gene is independent of heart-tube formation. *J. Biol. Chem.* **268**, 25,244–25,252.

62. Metzger, J.M., Lin, W.I., and Samuelson, L.C. (1994). Transition in cardiac contractile sensitivity to calcium during the *in vitro* differentiation of mouse embryonic stem cells. *J. Cell Biol.* **126**, 701–711.

63. Klug, M.G., Soonpaa, M.H., and Field, L.J. (1995). DNA synthesis and multinucleation in embryonic stem cell-derived cardiomyocytes. *Am. J. Physiol.* **269**, H1913–H1921.

64. Metzger, J.M., Lin, W.I., Johnston, R.A., Westfall, M.V., and Samuelson, L.C. (1995). Myosin heavy-chain expression in contracting myocytes isolated during embryonic stem cell cardiogenesis. *Circ. Res.* **76**, 710–719.

65. Ng, W.A., Doetschman, T., Robbins, J., and Lessard, J.L. (1997). Muscle isoactin expression during *in vitro* differentiation of murine embryonic stem cells. *Pediatr. Res.* **41**, 285–292.

66. Oyamada, Y., Komatsu, K., Kimura, H., Mori, M., and Oyamada, M. (1996). Differential regulation of gap junction protein (connexin) genes during cardiomyocytic differentiation of mouse embryonic stem cells *in vitro*. *Exp. Cell Res.* **229**, 318–326.

67. Westfall, M.V., Pasyk, K.A., Yule, D.I., Samuelson, L.C., and Metzger, J.M. (1997). Ultrastructure and cell–cell coupling of cardiac myocytes differentiating in embryonic stem cell cultures. *Cell. Motil. Cytoskel.* **36**, 43–54.

68. Kolossov, E., Fleischmann, B.K., Liu, Q., Bloch, W., Viatchenko-Karpinski, S., Manzke, O., Ji, G.J., Bohlen, H., Addicks, K., and Hescheler, J. (1998). Functional characteristics of ES cell-derived cardiac precursor cells identified by tissue-specific expression of the green fluorescent protein. *J. Cell Biol.* **143**, 2045–2056.

69. Gryshchenko, O., Fischer, I.R., Dittrich, M., Viatchenko-Karpinski, S., Soest, J., Bohm-Pinger, M.M., Igelmund, P., Fleischmann, B.K., and Hescheler, J. (1999). Role of

70. Igelmund, P., Fleischmann, B.K., Fischer, I.R., Soest, J., Gryshchenko, O., Bohm-Pinger, M.M., Sauer, H., Liu, Q., and Hescheler, J. (1999). Action potential propagation failures in long-term recordings from embryonic stem cell-derived cardiomyocytes in tissue culture. *Pflugers Arch.* **437**, 669–679.

71. Ji, G.J., Fleischmann, B.K., Bloch, W., Feelisch, M., Andressen, C., Addicks, K., and Hescheler, J. (1999). Regulation of the L-type Ca^{2+} channel during cardiomyogenesis: switch from NO to adenylyl cyclase-mediated inhibition. *FASEB J.* **13**, 313–324.

72. Maltsev, V.A., Ji, G.J., Wobus, A.M., Fleischmann, B.K., and Hescheler, J. (1999). Establishment of β-adrenergic modulation of L-type Ca^{2+} current in the early stages of cardiomyocyte development. *Circ. Res.* **84**, 136–145.

73. Viatchenko-Karpinski, S., Fleischmann, B.K., Liu, Q., Sauer, H., Gryshchenko, O., Ji, G.J., and Hescheler, J. (1999). Intracellular Ca2+ oscillations drive spontaneous contractions in cardiomyocytes during early development. *Proc. Natl. Acad. Sci. U. S. A.* **96**, 8259–8264.

74. Gryschenko, O., Lu, Z.J., Fleischmann, B.K., and Hescheler, J. (2000). Outward currents in embryonic stem cell-derived cardiomyocytes. *Pflugers Arch.* **439**, 798–807.

75. Sauer, H., Theben, T., Hescheler, J., Lindner, M., Brandt, M.C., and Wartenberg, M. (2001). Characteristics of calcium sparks in cardiomyocytes derived from embryonic stem cells. *Am. J. Physiol. Heart Circ. Physiol.* **281**, H411–H421.

76. Zhang, Y.M., Hartzell, C., Narlow, M., and Dudley, S.C., Jr. (2002). Stem cell-derived cardiomyocytes demonstrate arrhythmic potential. *Circulation* **106**, 1294–1299.

77. Itskovitz-Eldor, J., Schuldiner, M., Karsenti, D., Eden, A., Yanuka, O., Amit, M., Soreq, H., and Benvenisty, N. (2000). Differentiation of human embryonic stem cells into embryoid bodies compromising the three embryonic germ layers. *Mol. Med.* **6**, 88–95.

78. Schuldiner, M., Yanuka, O., Itskovitz-Eldor, J., Melton, D.A., and Benvenisty, N. (2000). From the cover: effects of eight growth factors on the differentiation of cells derived from human embryonic stem cells. *Proc. Natl. Acad. Sci. U. S. A.* **97**, 11,307–11,312.

79. Sudou, A., Muramatsu, H., Kaname, T., Kadomatsu, K., and Muramatsu, T. (1997). Le(X) structure enhances myocardial differentiation from embryonic stem cells. *Cell Struct. Funct.* **22**, 247–251.

80. Wobus, A.M., Kaomei, G., Shan, J., Wellner, M.C., Rohwedel, J., Ji, G., Fleischmann, B., Katus, H.A., Hescheler, J., and Franz, W.M. (1997). Retinoic acid accelerates embryonic stem cell-derived cardiac differentiation and enhances development of ventricular cardiomyocytes. *J. Mol. Cell Cardiol.* **29**, 1525–1539.

81. Guan, K., Furst, D.O., and Wobus, A.M. (1999). Modulation of sarcomere organization during embryonic stem cell-derived cardiomyocyte differentiation. *Eur. J. Cell Biol.* **78**, 813–823.

82. Sauer, H., Rahimi, G., Hescheler, J., and Wartenberg, M. (1999). Effects of electrical fields on cardiomyocyte differentiation of embryonic stem cells. *J. Cell Biochem.* **75**, 710–723.

83. Bader, A., Al-Dubai, H., and Weitzer, G. (2000). Leukemia inhibitory factor modulates cardiogenesis in embryoid bodies in opposite fashions. *Circ. Res.* **86**, 787–794.

84. Sauer, H., Rahimi, G., Hescheler, J., and Wartenberg, M. (2000). Role of reactive oxygen species and phosphatidylinositol 3-kinase in cardiomyocyte differentiation of embryonic stem cells. *FEBS Lett.* **476**, 218–223.

85. Bader, A., Gruss, A., Hollrigl, A., Al-Dubai, H., Capetanaki, Y., and Weitzer, G. (2001). Paracrine promotion of cardiomyogenesis in embryoid bodies by LIF-modulated endoderm. *Differentiation* **68,** 31–43.

86. Pasumarthi, K.B., Tsai, S.C., and Field, L.J. (2001). Coexpression of mutant p53 and p193 renders embryonic stem cell-derived cardiomyocytes responsive to the growth-promoting activities of adenoviral E1A. *Circ. Res.* **88,** 1004–1011.

87. Huh, N.E., Pasumarthi, K.B., Soonpaa, M.H., Jing, S., Patton, B., and Field, L.J. (2001). Functional abrogation of p53 is required for T-Ag-induced proliferation in cardiomyocytes. *J. Mol. Cell Cardiol.* **33,** 1405–1419.

88. Behfar, A., Zingman, L.V., Hodgson, D.M., Rauzier, J.M., Kane, G.C., Terzic, A., and Puceat, M. (2002). Stem cell differentiation requires a paracrine pathway in the heart. *FASEB J.* **16,** 1558–1566.

89. Takahashi, T., Lord, B., Schulze, P.C., Fryer, R.M., Sarang, S.S., Gullans, S.R., and Lee, R.T. (2003). Ascorbic acid enhances differentiation of embryonic stem cells into cardiac myocytes. *Circulation* **107,** 1912–1916.

Insulin-Producing Cells Derived from Embryonic Stem Cells: A Potential Treatment for Diabetes

Gordon C. Weir, Alexandra Haagensen, and Susan Bonner-Weir

Importance of β-Cell Replacement Therapy

Although insulin was discovered more than 75 years ago, the complications of diabetes still produce devastating consequences. The link between high blood glucose levels and complications of retinopathy, nephropathy, and neuropathy is now established beyond doubt. An obvious path to prevention of complications is some form of β-cell replacement therapy in the form of transplantation. Since 1978, more than 12,000 pancreas transplants have been performed; now, more than 1000 are done yearly, although these require major surgery. It would be preferable to transplant only the pancreatic islet cells that comprise about 1% of the pancreas, but islet transplantation, lagging behind whole-organ transplants, were only done seriously in the late 1980s. Poor results were obtained throughout the 1990s, but the introduction of the Edmonton protocol in 2000 provided far better results, the improvement being caused by better islet preparations, transplantation of more islets, and improved immunosuppression.[1] Islets are introduced into the liver through the portal vein using transhepatic angiography. For most patients, more than one cadaver donor is usually required. By 2003, more than 100 patients worldwide had received transplants using Edmonton-like approaches, with similar results being obtained. However, over about 2 years, most patients slip back to mild diabetes, although their control is much easier and they are largely free of severe hypoglycemia.[2]

Limited Supplies of Insulin-producing Cells

In spite of this success, there is a major problem of an insufficient supply of insulin-producing cells, which is limited to heart-beating cadaver donors. In the United States, it would be a major challenge to obtain 3000 usable cadaver pancreases per year, yet the incidence of type 1 diabetes is about 30,000 cases per year, with more than 10 times as many people developing type 2 diabetes. Some encouraging results have come from using islets from a single cadaver pancreas for a recipient, but many patients are likely to need more than one donor pancreas, particularly if the recipient has a high insulin requirement. Currently, a great deal of attention is focused on finding a new source of insulin-producing cells that can be used for transplantation. The quest includes exploring the potential of embryonic and adult stem cells, transdifferentiation such as by directing acinar cells or hepatocytes to make insulin, altering cells with bioengineering, developing human cell lines, and using β-cells from other species as xenografts.

Promise of ES Cells

As a guide for exploiting the potential of human embryonic stem (ES) cells to make pancreatic β-cells, mouse ES cells should become an important model. With their potential to develop into virtually any cell type, they can be kept in an undifferentiated state being grown on feeder layers of irradiated mouse embryonic fibroblasts with leukemia inhibitory factor (LIF). To use human ES cells for clinical purposes, it will probably be necessary to grow them on something other than mouse cells, which might include gelatin or human fibroblasts. Once removed from feeder layers, ES cells develop embryoid bodies, expressing their pluripotency to develop the three germ lines: ectoderm, endoderm, and mesoderm (Fig. 71–1). Another potentially useful source of pluripotent cells is embryonic germ cells derived from primordial gonads.[3] There is also a report of pluripotent cells being derived from adult bone marrow cells.[4]

Directing Differentiation

ES cells can be directed toward different progeny by a variety of factors, including soluble growth and differentiation mediators, matrix materials, and cell–cell contacts. A good example of such directed differentiation by changing the environment is provided by studies showing the production of postmitotic neurons from mouse ES cells.[5, 6] These results were made possible by the five-stage differentiation process

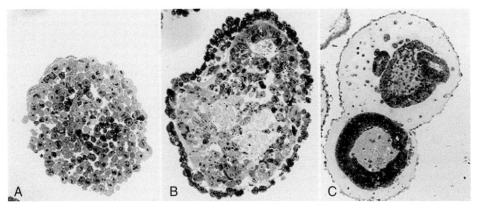

Figure 71-1. *Mouse embryoid bodies.* When LIF is removed, mouse ES cells form embryoid bodies that go on to differentiate into multiple tissues. (A) Embryoid bodies initially are loose aggregates of cells without much visible organization. (B) Embryoid bodies at 8 days start to show some organization with the visceral endoderm forming, separated from the rest by a thin layer of matrix. At such stages, microdomains are being formed, multiple cells are undergoing mitosis, and others undergo apoptosis. (C) Embryoid bodies after 22 days may be varied in their organization. Here, further elaboration of matrix under the visceral endoderm and tubular structures with columnar epithelium are evident. 1-um plastic sections, stained with toluidine blue.

of the McKay group, which has been successful at making neurons. The elements of this process include: stage 1: expansion of ES cells in the presence of LIF; stage 2: generation of embryoid bodies in suspension; stage 3: selection of nestin-positive cells using serum-free medium, ITSFn; stage 4: expansion of cells with growth factors such as basic fibroblast growth factor (bFGF); and stage 5: induction of differentiation. Future efforts are likely to focus on directing ES cells to an endodermal fate.

Genetic manipulations can also be used. Recently, the McKay group stably transfected mouse ES cells with a plasmid expressing the transcription factor nuclear receptor-related-1 (Nurr1) driven by cytomegalovirus (CMV).[7] This intervention led to the generation of postmitotic neurons producing dopamine, which produced symptomatic improvement in a mouse model of Parkinson's disease.

Another approach is called *trapping* with antibiotic selection. A cell-specific promoter linked with a gene for antibiotic resistance, aminoglycoside phosphotransferase, has been used to select remarkably pure cultures of cardiomyocytes.[8] The same approach was used by the group of Soria with the reported generation of insulin-producing cells.[9]

Key Factors Involved in Pancreatic and Islet Development

Knowledge of pancreatic and islet differentiation provides important clues for work with ES cells. The finding that Pdx-1 knockouts have virtually no pancreatic development identified a key early role for this transcription factor,[10,11] which is likely to be different than its role in maintaining β-cell differentiation at a later stage. Another key point is that Ngn3 is expressed in precursor cells committed to differentiating into islets.[12–14] Ngn3 expression, which is short-lived, is

thought to be induced by a combination of inhibition of Notch signaling and stimulation of signaling by molecules of the TGF-β family. Pax4 appears to play a key role in post-Ngn3 β-cell differentiation. Knockout of Pax4 leads to increased α-cell numbers but no β- or δ-cells.[15] Particularly noteworthy were data at the German Endocrine Society Meeting in February 2002 of Drs. Peter Gruss and Xunlei Zhou, in which mice were generated with Pax4 being driven by Pax6, known to be important at an earlier stage. At 6 weeks, these mice had four-fold the number of β-cell containing islets and extensive neogenesis. Other transcription factors important for β-cell development are β2/NeuroD,[16] Nkx2.2,[17] Nkx6.1,[18] and the recently discovered MafA.[19]

Papers Reporting Generation of Insulin-producing Cells from Mouse ES Cells

In the past 3 years, four papers have appeared describing the generation of insulin-producing cells from mouse ES cells. These papers have received a great deal of attention with concerns being raised about the identity and potential of the cells thought to contain insulin.

The first paper from Soria *et al.*[9] employed a trapping approach to obtain cells expressing the insulin gene. The insulin content was low, but the cells released insulin in response to glucose and, when transplanted, normalized glucose levels in diabetic mice. It has been difficult, even for the original authors, to generate additional clones of cells to confirm the data.[20]

The second paper by Lumelsky *et al.*[6] reported that functional insulin-producing cells could be derived from mouse ES cells using a variation of the McKay nestin selection protocol. This study has been criticized with the demonstration that the insulin staining can be an artifact of dying cells taking up insulin present in high concentrations in the media.[21] Despite this artifact, the Lumelsky paper showed the appearance of islet cell markers with reverse transcription–polymerase chain reaction (RT-PCR), including glucagon, GLUT2, and IAPP, as well as immunostaining for glucagon. Moreover, enhanced insulin secretion in response to glucose, tolbutamide, IBMX, and carbachol was found.

In a third paper, a different strategy was reported by Hori et al.[22] in which the phosphoinositide 3-kinase inhibitor (LY294002) was used to induce differentiation by inhibiting cell growth, a strategy previously used by others.[23] Using this inhibitor along with nicotinamide in stage 5 of the McKay method, insulin-producing cell clusters (IPCCs) were generated with 95–97% of the cells immunostained for insulin; only 2–3% were stained for glucagon, and no staining for somatostatin or pancreatic polypeptide was found. Unless something was wrong with the specificity of the staining as suggested by Rajagopal,[21] it appears that insulin-containing cells result from a remarkably efficient default or survival pathway. When LY294002 was not used, transplanted cells from stage 5 formed tumors that resembled teratomas, suggesting that undifferentiated cells capable of forming all three germ line derivatives were present.

These IPCCs contained a notable quantity of insulin, 5 ng/IPCC, but they are larger than typical rodent islets, being 300–400 μm in diameter compared to 150 μm for a typical rodent islet. It was suggested that the insulin content was about 10% of islets, but it is probably less. The volume of a sphere with a diameter of 300 μm is about eight times that of a sphere with a diameter of 150 μm. So, if the insulin content of a normal mouse islet is 40 ng, an islet of 300 μm should have about 320 ng. Therefore the 5 ng/320 ng is 1.5% rather than 10%. The actual insulin content per cell is probably higher because the center of a clump of cells that large should have an ischemic–necrotic center based upon what is known about oxygen diffusion and oxygen consumption of islets.[24] When transplanted, these IPCCs improved the survival of diabetic mice, had some effect upon blood glucose levels, and were able to increase plasma insulin levels. Other indications of success were that these IPCCs expressed a variety of β-cell markers by PCR and could be stained red with dithizone, which reacts with the zinc of β-cells.

Important questions remain about this study, in particular: (1) What happened to cells during the treatment with LY294002? The lack of acinar cells is not surprising because they are known to die rapidly in conventional tissue media.[25] (2) What will a more detailed in vitro evaluation of the IPCCs reveal? (3) What are the characteristics of these cells after transplantation? The paper does not provide enough information to know if these are real β-cells. We know that immature β-cells in rodents have undeveloped secretory machinery, but maturation occurs in only a few days. One might have expected β-cells derived from mouse ES cells to develop with the same timing.

In a fourth paper, Blyszczuk et al.[26] transduced mouse ES cells with Pax4 or Pdx1 expressed constitutively using a CMV promoter. Other important aspects in this study were the use of serum (20% fetal calf serum), the selection for nestin, and the generation of "spheroids" (aggregates of cells). Both transcription factors appeared to lead to the development of insulin-containing cells with Pax4 working somewhat better than Pdx1. Maximum insulin content with Pax4 was 455 ng/mg of protein, much less (0.5%) than normal β-cells (about 100 μg/mg of protein) and somewhat less than that reported by Hori et al.,[22] which was about 1.5% of normal. The transduced cells and wild-type cells subjected to the nestin selection protocol expressed insulin, GLUT2, and IAPP by RT-PCR. Insulin secretion was stimulated by a glucose concentration of 27.7 mM and by tolbutamide. Finally, when cells were transplanted under the kidney capsule and into the spleen, streptozocin-induced diabetes was prevented. Insulin staining of cells was shown in the grafts, but insulin content of the graft was not determined and no attempt was made to reverse the diabetes by surgical removal of the grafts.

Summary of Progress with Mouse ES Cells

Attempts to make β-cells from mouse ES cells have been in many ways frustrating, perhaps partly because too much has been expected too soon. In spite of the concerns about insulin staining having the potential to be artifactual, it appears, based upon published and unpublished data, that mouse ES cells can be directed to make some insulin-containing cells that express other gene characteristic of β-cells such as GLUT2 and IAPP. The problem is that no one has shown that these cells are truly similar to normal β-cells. Somehow, the differentiation seen in embryoid bodies and in later stages may only progress far enough to produce some kind of primitive cells that makes a small amount of insulin. Some cells in yolk sac, brain, and thymus have been reported produce small amounts of insulin,[27–29] so it would be interesting if these mouse ES cells derivatives had a similar primitive phenotype, as has been suggested by Edlund.[11]

Need for Rigorous Assessment of Insulin-producing Cells Derived from ES Cells

It is essential that future studies rigorously compare ES cell–derived cells with normal β-cells both in a culture and in a transplant graft. The cells should be assessed for insulin content; insulin secretory response to see if a normal glucose dose response curve is obtained; electron microscopy characterization of granules to see if dense core granules are present; characteristic staining for IAPP, C-peptide, GLUT2, and insulin; and finally gene expression profiles with a variety of techniques including gene arrays. Because the function and gene expression of β-cells in transplant grafts is a little different than when islets are studied in situ in the pancreas or ex vivo in culture, it will be necessary to perform elaborate studies of cells contained in a graft site, not only to compare them with transplanted normal β-cells but also to see if teratomas form.

Work with Human Precursor Cells

Several laboratories are intently working with human ES cells; there has been a published demonstration of immunostained insulin-containing cells in embryoid bodies.[30] This study also showed expression of various β-cells genes in the embryoid bodies using RT-PCR, including glucokinase, GLUT2, ngn-3, and PDX-1. Unfortunately, the insulin-staining cells were few in number and could not be further characterized. The possibility of using adult stem cells is also being pursued.[4,31–35]

Will Transplanted Insulin-producing Cells Derived from ES Cells Function Well Without Islet Non-β-Cells?

When developing strategies to transplant β-cells derived from ES cells, it is important to consider complexities of transplanting even normal islets. The pancreatic islet is a highly organized microorgan in which β-cells are typically found in the core and non–β-cells form a surrounding mantle.[36] This varies somewhat among species, but the non–β-cells nearly always are adjacent, remaining as clusters of cells separate from β-cells. The blood supply comes from arterioles that penetrate gaps in the islet mantle and then form a glomerular-like network of capillaries in the islet core. The capillaries leave an islet through the mantle to enter the acinar tissue to form the islet-acinar portal system.[37] The peptides produced by the different islet cells have the capacity to influence other islet cells; for example, glucagon can stimulate the secretion of insulin and somatostatin, somatostatin can inhibit glucagon and insulin secretion, and insulin can inhibit glucagon secretion.

In spite of this seeming potential, some of these interactions probably never take place *in vivo*. As fits with the known vascular pattern of islets, the upstream β-cells of the central core are probably protected from the potentially powerful effects of glucagon and somatostatin because blood and interstitial fluid flow from core to mantle[38] (Fig. 71–2). In contrast, the mantle cells, being downstream, are bathed in high concentrations of insulin, such that glucagon suppression by glucose appears to some extent indirectly mediated by local insulin secretion. Ingenious physiological experiments by Samols and Stagner indicate that these intraislet interactions are unidirectional, B to A to D (B–A–D), these referring to β-, α-, and δ-cells, respectively.[39] Additional data supporting this concept have recently been generated by Moens *et al.*[40] using a glucagon antagonist. Little is known about the potential interactions among pancreatic polypeptide (from PP cells) of the ventral lobe and the other islet cells. There is some evidence that glucagon-containing islets from the pancreatic dorsal lobe function better in transplants than islets isolated from the ventral lobe.[41] Such a benefit may be from the local effects of glucagon to promote insulin secretion and β-cell survival.

Little is known about the intraislet interrelationships of transplanted islets. It is clear that substantial remodeling of transplanted islets occurs[42] and that the vascular pattern of the new microvasculature does not faithfully recapitulate the preisolation pattern.[43–45] A key point is that the *in vivo* B–A–D relationship is disrupted when islets are isolated and may not be reestablished after transplantation, which could allow β-cells to be locally influenced by α-cells.

If some α-cells were upstream in a graft, the local glucagon secretion could potentiate insulin secretion, with a beneficial effect.[41, 46] On the other hand, it could lower the set point for glucose-stimulated insulin secretion by potentiating the stimulatory effect of normal concentrations of glucose and thus could cause hypoglycemia. We have seen a suggestion of an altered set point with islets contained in an immunobarrier device[47] and at times with fasted mice bearing syngeneic islet transplants.[48] Moreover, we have found that rats transplanted with islets in the liver become hypoglycemic with exercise.[49] Hypoglycemia has not been described with human transplants but could become an issue when it is possible to transplant a larger β-cell mass. There are, however, potential benefits from antiapoptotic effects of local glucagon upon β-cells. Two papers show that GLP-1 signaling, which is similar to that of glucagon, has an antiapoptotic influence on β-cells,[50,51] and this effect seems likely to be exerted through cAMP.

It is important to know if pure insulin-producing cells derived from ES cells will function appropriately when transplanted without non–β-cells. Based upon the B–A–D concept, our bias is that β-cells of the pancreas normally function well without seeing the secretory products from the mantle. The most valuable studies to date are those from Pipeleers and coworkers, who used flow cytometry to sort highly enriched populations of β-cells on the basis of endogenous fluorescence.

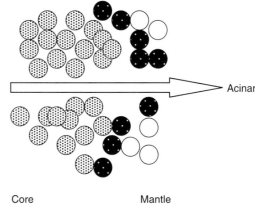

Figure 71–2. *Normal intraislet blood flow of pancreatic islets. Blood flows from the β-cell-rich core of islets to the mantle containing α- and δ-cells and then to the acinar cells, comprising the islet-acinar portal circulation. Therefore, islet mantle cells and acini should receive insulin via capillaries from upstream, but β-cells should not be exposed to islet glucagon or somatostatin via blood flow.*

When transplanted into the liver they did almost as well as intact islets.[52–55] These carefully done studies provide some assurance that ES cell–derived β-cells will function well when transplanted without islet non–β-cells, but there are still many questions. What will be the ideal site for the transplantation of such cells? An obvious site would be for the cells to be aggregated *in vitro* and then placed into the liver using the portal vein. Other candidate sites might include the peritoneal cavity, a subrenal capsular site, a subcutaneous pocket, or even the pancreas.

Should Islet Grafts Contain Stem–Precursor Cells for Optimal Function?

In the normal adult pancreas there is a slow turnover of β-cells, with apoptosis being countered by the birth of new β-cells from replication of preexisting β-cells and from neogenesis, which is the formation of new islets from precursor cells.[56]. It is not clear if current islet transplants contain islet or β-cell precursor cells. The presence of such cells should allow longer function of the graft. The question is important for projecting how cells derived from ES cells might function over time. At some point, it may be possible to transplant known numbers of precursor cells and fully differentiated cells. Perhaps the issue will not be important because useful cells obtained from ES cells may be available in unlimited numbers, which means that as the function of grafts declines through attrition of cells, more cells could be transplanted as needed.

What Immunological Barriers Will Be Faced by Transplanted Insulin-producing Cells Derived from ES Cells?

Cells transplanted into subjects with type 1 diabetes will face both allograft rejection and autoimmunity. Both could be controlled with immunosuppression, but the side effects of these drugs would limit the number of potential recipients.[2] Improvements in the tolerability of these and other drugs should occur with time, and eventually the goals of transplantation tolerance and safe control of autoimmunity should be realized. Many subjects with type 2 diabetes should also benefit from β-cell replacement therapy. They might be an easier population to target because autoimmunity would not be an issue. Selection of ES cells with a particular major histocompatibility complex match to make the insulin-producing cells may make it possible to limit or avoid allorejection. Another possibility would be to employ therapeutic cloning to obtain a perfect match.[57] Other possibilities for the future include genetic manipulation of the cells to allow them to elude both allorejection and autoimmunity.

Summary

For the purposes of making insulin-producing cells that are true β-cells, the potential of ES cells is tantalizing, especially considering the clinical need for cells that could solve the problem of diabetes. ES cells are capable of generating any specialized cell in the body, so they must have the capability to generate cells with a β-cell phenotype. There must be some combination of environment, coupled with growth and differentiation factors, that could make this happen. No simple default pathway has emerged to provide an easy route to this goal. Nonetheless, more work with ES cells aided by better insights into the mechanisms that govern the development of the endocrine pancreas should eventually point investigators in the right direction.

ACKNOWLEDGMENTS

The research that provides the background for this review has been supported by the National Institutes of Health (U19 DK61251), the Juvenile Diabetes Foundation Research Foundation, the Diabetes Research and Wellness Foundation, and an important group of private donors.

REFERENCES

1. Shapiro, A.M., Lakey, J.R., Ryan, E.A., Korbutt, G.S., Toth, E., Warnock, G.L., Kneteman, N.M., and Rajotte, R.V. (2000). Islet transplantation in seven patients with type 1 diabetes mellitus using a glucocorticoid-free immunosuppressive regimen. *N. Engl. J. Med.* **27,** 230–238.
2. Ryan, E.A., Lakey, J.R., Paty, B.W., Imes, S., Korbutt, G.S., Kneteman, N.M., Bigam, D., Rajotte, R.V., and Shapiro, A.M. (2002). Successful islet transplantation: continued insulin reserve provides long-term glycemic control. *Diabetes* **51,** 2148–2157.
3. Shamblott, M.J., Axelman, J., Littlefield, J.W., Blumenthal, P.D., Huggins, G.R., Cui, Y., Cheng, L., and Gearhart, J.D. (2001). Human embryonic germ cell derivatives express a broad range of developmentally distinct markers and proliferate extensively *in vitro. Proc. Natl. Acad. Sci. USA* **98,** 113–118.
4. Jiang, Y., Jahagirdar, B.N., Reinhardt, R.L., Schwartz, R.E., Keene, C.D., Ortiz-Gonzalez, X.R., Reyes, M., Lenvik, T., Lund, T., Blackstad, M., Du, J., Aldrich, S., Lisberg, A., Low, W.C., Largaespada, D.A., and Verfaillie, C.M. (2002). Pluripotency of mesenchymal stem cells derived from adult marrow. *Nature* **418,** 41–49.
5. Okabe, S., Forsberg-Nilsson, K., Spiro, A.C., Segal, M., and McKay, R.D. (1996). Development of neuronal precursor cells and functional postmitotic neurons from embryonic stem cells *in vitro. Mech. Dev.* **59,** 89–102.
6. Lumelsky, N., Blondel, O., Laeng, P., Velasco, I., Ravin, R., and McKay, R. (2001). Differentiation of embryonic stem cells to insulin-secreting structures similar to pancreatic islets. *Science* **292,** 1389–1393.
7. Kim, J.H., Auerbach, J.M., Rodriguez-Gomez, J.A., Velasco, I., Gavin, D., Lumelsky, N., Lee, S.H., Nguyen, J., Sanchez-Pernaute, R., Bankiewicz, K., and McKay, R. (2002). Dopamine neurons derived from embryonic stem cells function in an animal model of Parkinson's disease. *Nature* **418,** 50–56.
8. Klug, M.G., Soonpaa, M.H., Koh, G.Y., and Field, L.J. (1996). Genetically selected cardiomyocytes from differentiating embryonic stem cells form stable intracardiac grafts. *J. Clin. Invest.* **98,** 216–224.

9. Soria, B., Roche, E., Berna, G., Leon-Quinto, T., Reig, J.A., and Martin, F. (2000). Insulin-secreting cells derived from embryonic stem cells normalize glycemia in streptozotocin-induced diabetic mice. *Diabetes* **49**, 157–162.

10. Jonsson, J., Carlsson, L., Edlund, T., and Edlund, H. (1994). Insulin-promoter-factor 1 is required for pancreas development in mice. *Nature* **371**, 606–609.

11. Edlund, H. (1998). Transcribing pancreas. *Diabetes* **47**, 1817–1823.

12. Gradwohl, G., Dierich, A., LeMuer, M., and Guillemot, F. (2000). Neurogenin 3 is required for the development of the four endocrine cell lineages of the pancreas. *Proc. Natl. Acad. Sci. USA* **97**, 1607–1611.

13. Heremans, Y., Van De Casteele, M., in't Veld, P., Gradwohl, G., Serup, P., Madsen, O., Pipeleers, D., and Heimberg, H. (2002). Recapitulation of embryonic neuroendocrine differentiation in adult human pancreatic duct cells expressing neurogenin 3. *J. Cell Biol.* **159**, 303–312.

14. Gu, G., Dubauskaite, J., and Melton, D.A. (2002). Direct evidence for the pancreatic lineage: NGN3+ cells are islet progenitors and are distinct from duct progenitors. *Development* **129**, 2447–2457.

15. Sosapineda, B., Chowdhury, K., Torres, M., Oliver, G., Gruss, P. (1997). The *PAX4* gene is essential for differentiation of insulin-producing β-cells in the mammalian pancreas. *Nature* **386**, 399–402.

16. Naya, F.J., Huang, H.P., Qiu, Y., Mutoh, H., DeMayo, F.J., Leiter, A.B., and Tsai, M.J. (1997). Diabetes, defective pancreatic morphogenesis, and abnormal enteroendocrine differentiation in β2/neuroD-deficient mice. *Genes Dev.* **11**, 2323–2334.

17. Sussel, L., Kalamaras, J., Hartigan-O'Connor, D.J., Meneses, J.J., Pedersen, R.A., Rubenstein, J.L.R., and German, M.S. (1998). Mice lacking the homeodomain transcription factor Nkx2.2 have diabetes due to arrested differentiation of pancreatic β-cells. *Development* **125**, 2213–2221.

18. Mirmira, R.G., Watada, H., and German, M.S. (2000). β-Cell differentiation factor Nkx6.1 contains distinct DNA-binding interference and transcriptional repression domains. *J. Biol. Chem.* **275**, 14,743–14,751.

19. Olbrot, M., Rud, J., Moss, L.G., and Sharma, A. (2002). Identification of β-cell-specific insulin gene transcription factor RIPE3b1 as mammalian MafA. *Proc. Natl. Acad. Sci. USA* **99**, 6737–6742.

20. Soria, B., Skoudy, A., and Martin, F. (2001). From stem cells to β-cells: new strategies in cell therapy of diabetes mellitus. *Diabetologia* **44**, 407–415.

21. Rajagopal, J., Anderson, W.J., Kume, S., Martinez, O.I., and Melton, D.A. (2003). Insulin staining of ES cell progeny from insulin uptake. *Science* **299**, 363.

22. Hori, Y., Rulifson, I.C., Tsai, B.C., Heit, J.J., Cahoy, J.D., and Kim, S.K. (2002). Growth inhibitors promote differentiation of insulin-producing tissue from embryonic stem cells. *Proc. Natl. Acad. Sci. USA* **99**, 16,105–16,110.

23. Ptasznik, A., Beattie, G.M., Mally, M.I., Cirulli, V., Lopez, A., and Hayek, A. (1997). Phosphatidylinositol 3-kinase is a negative regulator of cellular differentiation. *J. Cell. Biol.* **137**, 1127–1136.

24. Dionne, K.E., Colton, C.K., and Yarmuch, M.L. (1993). Effect of hypoxia on insulin secretion by isolated rat and canine islets of Langerhans. *Diabetes* **42**, 12–21.

25. Korbutt, G.S., Elliott, J.F., Ao, Z., Smith, D.K., Warnock, G.L., and Rajotte, R.V. (1996). Large scale isolation, growth, and function of porcine neonatal islet cells. *J. Clin. Invest.* **97**, 2119–2129.

26. Blyszczuk, P., Czyz, J., Kania, G., Wagner, M., Roll, U., St-Onge, L., and Wobus, A.M. (2003). Expression of Pax4 in embryonic stem cells promotes differentiation of nestin-positive progenitor and insulin-producing cells. *Proc. Natl. Acad. Sci. USA* **100**, 998–1003.

27. Giddings, S.J., King, C.D., Harman, K.W., Flood, J.F., and Carnaghi, L.R. (1994). Allele specific inactivation of insulin 1 and 2, in the mouse yolk sac, indicates imprinting. *Natl. Genet.* **6**, 310–313.

28. Devaskar, S.U., Giddings, S.J., Rajakumar, P.A., Carnaghi, L.R., Menon, R.K., and Zahm, D.S. (1994). Insulin gene expression and insulin synthesis in mammalian neuronal cells. *J. Biol. Chem.* **269**, 8445–8454.

29. Hanahan, D. (1998). Peripheral antigen-expressing cells in thymic medulla: factors in self-tolerance and autoimmunity. *Curr. Opin. Immunol.* **10**, 656–662.

30. Assady, S., Maor, G., Amit, M., Itskovitz-Eldor, J., Skorecki, K.L., and Tzukerman, M. (2001). Insulin production by human embryonic stem cells. *Diabetes* **50**,1691–1697.

31. Bonner-Weir, S., Taneja, M., Weir, G.C., Tatarkiewicz, K., Song, K.H., Sharma, A., and O'Neil, J.J. (2000). *In vitro* cultivation of human islets from expanded ductal tissue. *Proc. Natl. Acad. Sci. USA* **97**, 7999–8004.

32. Beattie, G.M., Itkin-Ansari, P., Cirulli, V., Leibowitz, G., Lopez, A.D., Bossie, S., Mally, M.I., Levine, F., and Hayek, A. (1999). Sustained proliferation of PDX-1+ cells derived from human islets. *Diabetes* **48**, 1013–1019.

33. Zulewski, H., Abraham, E.J., Gerlach, M.J., Daniel, P.B., Moritz, W., Muller, B., Vallejo, M., Thomas, M.K., and Habener, J.F. (2001). Multipotential nestin-positive stem cells isolated from adult pancreatic islets differentiate *ex vivo* into pancreatic endocrine, exocrine, and hepatic phenotypes. *Diabetes* **50**, 521–533.

34. Storms, R.W., Goodell, M.A., Fisher, A., Mulligan, R.C., and Smith, C. (2000). Hoechst dye efflux reveals a novel CD7(+)CD34(−) lymphoid progenitor in human umbilical cord blood. *Blood* **96**, 2125–2133.

35. Ramiya, V.K., Marraist, M., Arfors, K.E., Schatz, D.A., Peck, A.B., and Cornelius, J.C. (2000). Reversal of insulin-dependent diabetes using islets generated *in vitro* from pancreatic stem cells. *Natl. Med.* **6**, 278–282.

36. Bonner-Weir, S. (1989). Pancreatic islets: Morphology, organization, and physiological implications. *In* "Insulin Secretion," (B. Draznin *et al.*, eds.), pp. 1–11. Alan R. Liss, New York.

37. Bonner-Weir, S., and Orci, L. (1982). New perspectives on the microvasculature of the islets of Langerhans in the rat. *Diabetes* **31**, 883–939.

38. Weir, G.C., and Bonner-Weir, S. (1990). Islets of Langerhans: the puzzle of intraislet interactions and their relevance to diabetes. *J. Clin. Invest.* **85**, 983–987.

39. Stagner, J.I., and Samols, E. (1992). The vascular order of islet cellular perfusion in the human pancreas. *Diabetes* **41**, 93–97.

40. Moens, K., Berger, V., Ahn, J.M., Van Schravendijk, C., Hruby, V.J., Pipeleers, D., and Schuit, F. (2002). Assessment of the role of interstitial glucagon in the acute glucose secretory responsiveness of *in situ* pancreatic β-cells. *Diabetes* **51**, 669–675.

41. Trimble, E.R., Halban, P.A., Wolheim, C.B., and Renold, A.E. (1982). Functional differences between rat islets of ventral and dorsal pancreatic origin. *J. Clin. Invest.* **69**, 405–413.

42. Davalli, A.M., Scaglia, L., Zangen, D.H., Hollister, J., Bonner-Weir, S., and Weir, G.C. (1996). Vulnerability of islets in the immediate posttransplantation period. *Diabetes* **45**, 1161–1167.

43. Menger, M.D., Jaeger, S., Walter, P., Feifel, G., Hammersen, F., and Messmer, K. (1989). Angiogenesis and hemodynamics of

microvasculature of transplanted islets of Langerhans. *Diabetes* **38** (Suppl. 1), 199–201.

44. Menger, M.D., Vajkoczy, P., Beger, C., and Messmer, K. (1994). Orientation of microvascular blood flow in pancreatic islet isografts. *J. Clin. Invest.* **93**, 2280–2285.

45. Carlsson, P.O., Palm, F., and Mattsson, G. (2002). Low revascularization of experimentally transplanted human pancreatic islets. *J. Clin. Endocrinol. Metab.* **87**, 5418–5423.

46. Schuit, F.C., and Pipeleers, D.G. (1985). Regulation of adenosine 3′,5′-monophosphate levels in the pancreatic β-cell. *Endocrinol.* **117**, 834–840.

47. Suzuki, K., Bonner-Weir, S., Trivedi, N., Yoon, K.H., Hollister-Lock, J., Colton, C.K., and Weir, G.C. (1998). Function and survival of macroencapsulated syngeneic islets transplanted into streptozocin-diabetic mice. *Transplantation* **66**, 21–28.

48. (Unpublished).

49. Omer *et al.* (In preparation).

50. Li, Y., Hansotia, T., Yusta, B., Ris, F., Halban, P.A., and Drucker, D.J. (2003). Glucagon-like peptide-1 receptor signaling modulates β-cell apoptosis. *J. Biol. Chem.* **278**, 471–478.

51. Farilla, L., Hui, H., Bertolotto, C., Kang, E., Bulotta, A., Di Mario, U., and Perfetti, R. (2002). Glucagon-like peptide-1 promotes islet cell growth and inhibits apoptosis in Zucker diabetic rats. *Endocrinology* **143**, 4397–4408.

52. Pipeleers, D., Pipeleers-Marichal, M., Markholst, H., Hoorens, A., and Kloppel, G. (1991). Transplantation of purified islet cells in diabetic BB rats. *Diabetologia* **34**, 390–396.

53. Pipeleers, D.G., Pipeleers-Marichal, M., Hannaert, J.C., Berghmans, M., In't Veld, P.A., Rozing, J., Van de Winkel, M., and Gepts, W. (1991). Transplantation of purified islet cells in diabetic rats: I. Standardization of islet cell grafts. *Diabetes* **40**, 908–919.

54. Pipeleers, D.G., Pipeleers-Marichal, M., Vanbrabandt, B., and Duys, S. (1991). Transplantation of purified islet cells in diabetic rats: II. Immunogenicity of allografted islet β-cells. *Diabetes* **40**, 920–930.

55. Pipeleers-Marichal, M., Ling, Z.D., Teng, H., and Pipeleers, D.G. (1991). Transplantation of purified islet cells in diabetic rats: III. Immunosuppressive effect of cyclosporin. *Diabetes* **40**, 931–938.

56. Bonner-Weir, S. (2000). Islet growth and development in the adult. *J. Mol. Endocrinol.* **24**, 1–6.

57. Lanza, R.P., Chung, H.Y., Yoo, J.J., Wettstein, P.J., Blackwell, C., Borson, N., Hofmeister, E., Schuch, G., Soker, S., Moraes, C.T., West, M.D., and Atala, A. (2002). Generation of histocompatible tissues using nuclear transplantation. *Natl. Biotechnol.* **20**, 689–696.

Burns and Skin Ulcers

Edward Upjohn, George Varigos, and Pritinder Kaur

Introduction

Burns and skin ulcers are major causes of morbidity and, in the case of burns, mortality in both the developed and developing world. Epidermal cells have been used in the therapy of these conditions for decades in the form of autologous skin grafts. For the last 20 years, advanced cell culture techniques have permitted the development of methods to identify and even isolate viable skin stem cells that could potentially be used in the treatment of these two conditions. These advances provide a strong foundation for building more advanced and exciting therapies based on stem cells to treat these challenging conditions.

The epidermis of the skin is a constantly renewing stratified squamous epithelium. It consists mostly of keratinocytes but also of Langerhans cells, melanocytes, and Merkel cells resting on a supporting dermis that contains the nerve and vascular networks, which nourish the epidermis. The dermis is also the location of epidermal appendages, fibroblasts, mast cells, macrophages, and lymphocytes. Epidermal stem cells are responsible for the ability of the epidermis to replace itself both in normal circumstances and in traumatic skin loss such as from burns and skin ulceration.

Burns and Skin Ulcers: The Problem

As with many medical conditions, it is difficult to quantify the burden and impact of these two conditions in a meaningful and tangible way. A study estimating the lifetime costs for injuries in the United States in 1985 rated fire and burns as the fourth largest cause of lifetime economic loss at $3.8 billion. Only motor vehicles, firearms, and poisonings were responsible for greater losses.[1] Burns are also an important cause of injury in the developing world, where more traditional methods of lighting and cooking, such as oil lamps and open fires, are still commonplace. Skin ulcers may be caused by several pathological processes, including infection, trauma, diabetes, and venous ulcer disease. Chronic venous ulceration is a common cause of skin ulcers, with an estimated prevalence of 1–1.3%.[2] Skin ulcers are also difficult and expensive

to manage because of their slow rates of healing and the requirement for expensive and labor intensive dressing regimes. A cost of care analysis by the Visiting Nurse Association in Boston[3] found the average cost per month in 1992 of an unhealed ulcer to be $1927.89. Diabetic foot ulcers, like venous ulcers, often have a chronic course. In one study, the cost estimates for foot ulcer care over a 2-year period in a population of type 1 and type 2 diabetics who developed an ulcer was $27,987.[4] These figures, especially when extrapolated to include lost productivity, are almost beyond comprehension. What is easily comprehended, however, is the personal cost and burden born by patients suffering from burns or skin ulcers.

Epidermal Stem Cells

The epidermis of the skin is a multilayered, continuously self-renewing tissue replaced every 30–60 days in human skin. *In vivo* cell turnover studies in mice have shown that all proliferative activity is restricted to the basal layer, which generates the mature functional suprabasal keratinocytes.[5–8] Thus, epidermal stem cells reside within the basal layer and are characterized by their capacity for self-maintenance and self-renewal.[9,10] In addition to producing more stem cells, the stem cells generate transient amplifying cells that divide three to five times before producing terminally differentiated keratinocytes *in vivo*. The ability to identify slowly cycling stem cells *in situ*, visualized as ^{3}H-Tdr or bromodeoxyuridine (BrdU) label-retaining cells, has permitted their localization at specific niches including the deep rete ridges of the interfollicular epidermis and the bulge region of hair follicles[11] (Fig. 72–1). The identification of epidermal stem cells *ex vivo* is a more controversial subject because there is no unequivocal assay for these cells *in vitro*.

Heterogeneity in the growth capacity of keratinocytes was first reported by Barrandon and Green[12] in 1987; they used clonal analysis to retrospectively identify cells capable of generating large colonies of cells exhibiting limited differentiation in culture, termed holoclones. These investigators proposed that holoclones were derived from stem cells because of their greater proliferative capacity. Importantly, this work did not provide a means to prospectively isolate keratinocyte stem cells (KSCs). Subsequent work from Watt and colleagues established that cell surface markers, specifically β1 integrin, could be used to distinguish basal keratinocytes with high (β1 bright) or low (β1 dim) proliferative capacity measured in terms of short-term colony-forming efficiency.[13,14] Despite the

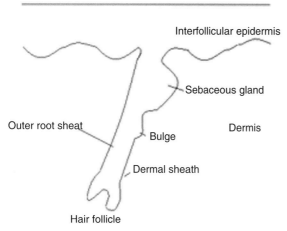

Figure 72–1. *Epidermis, dermis, and other structures.*

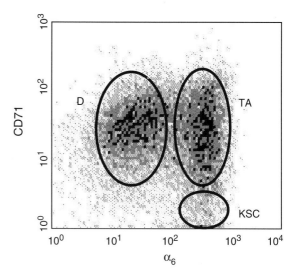

Figure 72–2. This FACS plot of primary human, neonatal, foreskin keratinocytes—labeled with antibodies to the cell surface marker α_6 integrin (FITC) and the transferrin receptor (CD71-PE)—reveals phenotypically discrete subpopulations of cells corresponding to stem cells (KSC) with the phenotype $\alpha_6^{bri}CD71^{dim}$, transit amplifying (TA) cells with $\alpha_6^{bri}CD71^{bri}$, and early differentiating (ED) cells with α_6^{dim}.

initial conclusion that $\beta 1$ integrin was a marker of KSCs, subsequent work from many laboratories has shown that although most basal cells are integrin bright, only a small subpopulation of these exhibit quiescence as defined by their ability to retain a ^{3}H-Tdr or BrdU label.[15–17] Work from our laboratory has further established that ^{3}H-Tdr label–retaining cells can be purified from integrin-bright keratinocytes on the basis of a second cell surface marker–that is, CD71, or the transferrin receptor. Thus, epidermal cells exhibiting the phenotype $\alpha_6^{bri}CD71^{dim}$ represent the stem cell population of both human neonatal and adult murine epidermis.[18] This fraction is enriched for label-retaining cells that are small (~9 μm) with a blast-like morphology, display a high nuclear-to-cytoplasmic ratio, and exhibit the greatest long-term proliferative capacity to regenerate keratinocytes *in vitro* and comprise about 5% of total basal cells (Fig. 72–2). Moreover, we have demonstrated that the progeny of KSCs can be distinguished by their cell surface phenotype: Transit amplifying (TA) cells exhibit high levels of CD71 ($\alpha_6^{bri}CD71^{bri}$), are enriched for actively cycling cells defined as pulse-labeled cells in murine epidermis, and exhibit intermediate keratinocyte cell regeneration capacity; and early differentiating (ED) cells are identifiable as α_6^{dim} cells exhibiting the poorest long-term proliferative capacity and expressing keratin 10 and involucrin—both markers of keratinocyte differentiation[16,18] (Fig. 72–2). Importantly, this work permits the prospective isolation of KSCs and their immediate progeny by fluorescence-activated cell sorting (FACS) so that the contribution of distinct classes of epidermal progenitors to tissue regeneration during homeostasis or in wound healing can be directly assessed. This work is an important prerequisite to the development of therapeutic strategies using KSCs for skin conditions, including gene therapy. The identification of growth factors that recruit KSCs to proliferate and regenerate tissue will be important to the development of techniques for rapid *ex vivo* expansion that facilitate earlier transplantation for burns victims.

Stem Cells in Burns and Skin Ulcers: Current Use

BURNS

Autografts

Epidermal cells have been used in the treatment of burns since the introduction of the split skin graft by Thiersh in the late 1800s.[19] Skin grafting to cover defects caused by burns or skin ulceration is limited by the area of skin that may be harvested on any one occasion. Full-thickness grafts (including all of the epidermis and dermis) provide good cosmetic results but require a primary closure of the donor site, limiting the area that may be grafted. To overcome this, the use of split skin grafts was developed, whereby epidermis and underlying dermis is shaved from the donor site to provide a graft. The donor site then reepithelializes from hair follicles, a process that is easily seen with the unaided eye and that takes 2 to 3 weeks, after which the donor site can be reharvested. It is thought that stem cells of the hair follicle are responsible for healing both the donor site and the grafted area. Experimental evidence in favor of this notion was recently provided by elegant experiments performed by Barrandon and colleagues, who demonstrated that microdissected hair follicle bulges (enriched for stem cells) from transgenic mice expressing the β-galactosidase gene could regenerate interfollicular epidermal tissue, as well as entire hair follicles,[20] when transplanted.

The limitations of skin grafting techniques are the area that can be covered by them and the many weeks it may take to cover a large area of burn with autologous split skin. Burns of

80–90% are survivable in the short term with resuscitation, but if coverage of the wounds is delayed because of a lack of grafts, then a high morbidity and mortality is the result.

In the mid-1970s, Rheinwald and Green[21] developed a technique for serial cultivation of epidermal cells, producing a 1000- to 10,000-fold area of graftable epidermis than the initial biopsy (Fig. 72–3 and Fig. 72–4). These epidermal sheets can then be grafted onto clean wound beds, but they are sensitive to loss by bacterial infection and blistering. In full-thickness burns where the dermis has been lost, the cultured epidermal autograft may be placed directly onto muscle or fascia (Fig. 72–5). These cultured epidermal autografts form a permanent covering, suggesting that the stem cells initially cultured and then transplanted have been maintained as stem cells and therefore retain their crucial role in epidermal maintenance. Histological examination of cultured epithelium reveals the structural similarity to normal epithelium *in vivo* (Fig. 72–6). Culturing epidermis is a time- and labor-intensive exercise estimated to cost between $600 to $13,000 per 1% of the body surface area covered[22] (depending on the proportion of the grafts that successfully take).

BURNS

Allografts

The development of allografts has been driven by the lack of available donor sites for split skin grafting in patients with massive burns and by the time taken to grow cultured autologous skin from these patients. Burn therapy requires coverage of the burnt areas to prevent secondary sepsis and other complications. An alternative to split skin grafts is needed that is immediately available, plentiful, effective, and affordable. Cadaveric skin is such an alternative; it is a true allograft and is always eventually rejected by the recipient. As mentioned earlier, skin that lacks a dermis is less able to resist trauma and is prone to contraction, resulting in a poor functional and cosmetic outcome. Alloderm (Lifecell, Branchburg, NJ) is a processed human dermis from which the epidermal and

Figure 72–4. *Secondary cultures of the epithelium in an incubator.* Reproduced with the permission of Joanne Paddle-Ledinek. (Please see CD-ROM for color version of this figure.)

dermal cells have been removed, leaving only the connective tissue matrix. Alloderm can then be applied to burns, and cultured autograft may be placed on top of it. Integra (Integra LifeSciences, Plainsboro, NJ) is another dermal substitute developed through the coprecipitation and lyophilization of bovine collagen, chondroitin-6-sulfate, and an artificial epidermal layer of synthetic, polysiloxane polymer. One to two weeks after application, the artificial epidermis is removed, and an ultrathin epidermal autograft (.003–.005 inches thick) is placed on the burn area.[23]

All currently available examples of artificial dermis lack a vascular plexus for the nourishment of the epidermis and require host vasculogenesis into the dermis graft to supply nourishment to the grafted epidermis. Efforts have therefore been focused on encouraging the process of vasculogenesis by genetic engineering of grafts to produce growth factors and cytokines vital to this process (see later sections of this chapter).

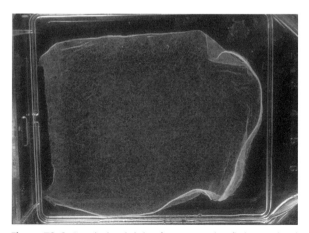

Figure 72–3. *Detached epithelial graft in a tissue culture flask.* Reproduced with the permission of Joanne Paddle-Ledinek. (Please see CD-ROM for color version of this figure.)

Figure 72–5. *Application of cultured autograft epidermis to a burn patient.* Reproduced with the permission of Joanne Paddle-Ledinek. (Please see CD-ROM for color version of this figure.)

Edward Upjohn, George Varigos, and Pritinder Kaur

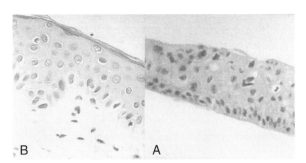

Figure 72-6. (A) Side-by-side histological comparison of cultured epidermis and (B) epidermis *in vivo*. Reproduced with the permission of Joanne Paddle-Ledinek. (Please see CD-ROM for color version of this figure.)

SKIN ULCERS

Therapy for skin ulcers is based on treating the precipitating and perpetuating factors. This includes antibiotic use for infective ulcers, rigorous pressure care for decubitus ulcers, and compression stockings for venous ulcers (for examples of skin ulcers, see Fig. 72–7 and Fig. 72–8). The use of occlusive dressing techniques has greatly expanded in recent decades, and these form the foundation for the treatment of many ulcers. In spite of advances like occlusive dressings, ulcer healing often takes months if not years to achieve. In burns therapy, the impetus behind the use of stem cells or cultured epidermal autografts is the need to cover large areas quickly. In ulcer therapy, the time constraints are not as severe, and for definitive closure, split skin grafts remain the gold standard. Cultured skin has been used in the treatment of skin ulcers—in particular, in the use of cultured allografts as a "living dressing." Cultured, autologous outer root sheath cells used in the treatment of chronic decubitus ulcers have been found to produce an *edging effect*, the contraction of the chronic wounds edges in response to the graft, believed to be caused by a release of growth factors, cytokines, and hormones from the outer root sheath cells.[24] Apligraf (Organogenesis, Canton, MA) is a cultured, bilayered living skin equivalent derived from neonatal foreskin keratinocytes, fibroblasts, and bovine type I collagen. It is indicated for the treatment of venous ulcers and neuropathic diabetic foot ulcers. Chronic wounds (e.g., those with dormant edges) reepithelialize when exposed to living allograft material. This edge effect, like that seen with outer root sheath cells, is most probably caused by the presence of stimulatory factors. Chronic wounds heal better after repeated application of skin grafts, suggesting that growth factors in the grafts are responsible. Bioengineered tissues such as Apligraf probably act as biologic systems for delivering growth factors to wounds.[25]

Future Developments

GENE THERAPY APPROACHES IN WOUND HEALING

Epidermal cells can be genetically modified both *in vivo* and *ex vivo* by both viral and nonviral methods (e.g., recombinant retro and adenovirus infection, liposomes, plasmid injection, and particle bombardment).[26] Initially, gene therapy of epidermal cells was pursued to correct inherited genetic defects, but it is now used to treat wound healing by using genetically engineered keratinocytes as a source of cytokines and growth factors. Fluid from chronic wounds has been found to be inhibitory to cell proliferation and contain degradation products that inhibit keratinocyte migration.[27] The beneficial effect that allografts have on wound healing is thought to be at least partly because of the production of cytokines and growth factors, although the allografts are eventually rejected by the host. Cultured autografts engineered to produce these cytokines and growth factors in supranormal quantities may expedite wound healing. Epidermal cells can be engineered to express a gene either permanently or transiently. These genes could encode growth factors or cytokines, as mentioned earlier, or they may antagonize some of the inhibitory factors found in chronic wounds.

The vascularization of cultured skin autografts is often delayed when compared to split skin grafting and may be a

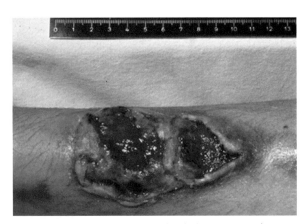

Figure 72-7. *Leg ulcer.* Reproduced with the permission of George Varigos. (Please see CD-ROM for color version of this figure.)

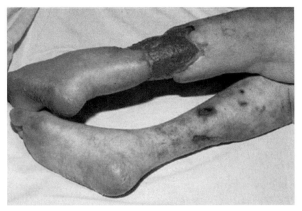

Figure 72-8. *Circumferential leg ulcer healing by granulation.* Reproduced with the permission of George Varigos. (Please see CD-ROM for color version of this figure.)

734

contributing factor to the failure of the cultured autograft to take. Cultured skin has been genetically modified *in vitro* to produce vascular endothelial growth factor (VEGF). These modified, cultured skin substitutes have been shown to secrete elevated levels of VEGF and to have decreased time to vascularization when grafted onto athymic mice.[28]

TISSUE ENGINEERING

Tissue engineering of skin is an active area of research and development. Efforts to develop temporary skin substitutes began in the early 1960s. The skin is one of the first organs to have been successfully generated *ex vivo,* and there are several tissue-engineered skin equivalents available today. In bioengineered skin, the epidermal component is either cultured allograft or cultured autograft. The keratinocyte sheets are then combined with the dermal component. The dermal component may be acellular, or it may contain allogeneic or autogenic fibroblasts or other cells. The optimum skin equivalent would be readily available, could be stored or frozen and ready for use, would be inexpensive to make, would have excellent take, and would give good cosmetic results. Such an ideal skin equivalent does not exist. Split skin grafts fulfill many of these requirements, but unfortunately, they are often not available in a sufficient amount. Currently, the culturing of autografts requires at least 3 weeks, is labor intensive, and is not available in many developing parts of the world. It would be a great advance if the technique could be made faster and easier to perform. Given our recent ability to use FACS methodology to separate KSC versus TA populations from the epidermis, we have been testing the hypothesis that the stem cell–enriched keratinocytes may provide faster and reliable skin regeneration in *in vitro* and *in vivo* transplantation model systems. Our recent studies indicate that both epidermal stem cells and TA cells can regenerate epithelial tissue in the short term fairly rapidly and that dermal cells, and specific components of the basement membrane (i.e., laminins), are critical regulators of this tissue-regenerative capacity.[29] Current studies in our laboratory are aimed at understanding how to recruit greater numbers of epidermal stem cells to proliferate *in vitro* as well as identifying factors capable of promoting stem cell expansion and renewal *ex vivo*. These studies will be important to the development of cellular therapies using epidermal stem cells as vehicles.

Summary

Investigators of epidermal stem cells have the advantage of easy access to their cells of interest. Keratinocytes are also relatively easy to culture and engineer into their normal "organ form" (i.e., sheets of epidermis). As stated earlier, there is an established role for epidermal stem cells in the therapy of human diseases and injuries. The concept of epidermal stem cells and their application to health care could form a conceptual framework for the education of the general public about stem cells and could help to demystify what is commonly perceived to be a complicated science. Epidermal stem cells are excellent targets for gene therapy seeking to correct genetic deficiencies permanently. This could form the basis of new therapies for previously untreatable genodermatoses (such as epidermolysis bullosa) as well as for burns and skin ulcers.

Epidermal appendages like hair, sweat glands, and sebaceous glands are often destroyed by burns, and their replacement with bioengineered equivalents is still to be achieved. The ability to develop a hair-bearing skin replacement, for example, would address many of the cosmetic problems caused by burns to the face and scalp.

The stem cells of the dermis have yet to be definitively identified and localized within the skin; this can be attributed to the complex cellular heterogeneity of this tissue. Tissue engineering of a replacement dermis to graft onto burns or other defects lacking a dermis would clearly benefit from the incorporation of dermal stem cells. Given that the dermis provides growth factors regulating epidermal growth and morphogenesis, as well as "hair inductive" capacity, further elucidation of its molecular, cellular, and functional components is essential to the development of cellular therapies.

Risk of viral transmission remains a concern with allografts, but they can be frozen, thawed, and used when needed. This is very convenient and contributes to their lifesaving potential. Tissue engineering with bovine or other sources of collagen must be carefully managed to reduce the risk of transmission of prion and other diseases to humans. For these reasons, research into cultured autografts will continue, with the goal being a cultured skin equivalent made from epidermal and dermal stem cells, tissue engineered to provide rapid wound coverage with excellent take. The great advances made in the last quarter of a century have saved many lives, in the case of burns, and made lives worth living again, in the case of skin ulcers. Our expanding understanding of stem cells and their manipulation will build on these advances to enable even better treatment of these conditions in the future.

ACKNOWLEDGMENTS

We wish to thank Joanne Paddle-Ledinek and Heather Cleland.

REFERENCES

1. Centers for Disease Control and Prevention (1989). Cost of injury—United States: a report to Congress. *MMWR* **38,** 743–746.
2. Callam, M.J., Ruckley, C.V., Harper, D.R., and Dale, J.J. (1985). Chronic ulceration of the leg: extent of the problem and provision of care. *BMJ* **290,** 1855–1856.
3. Hume, M. (1992). Venous ulcers, the vascular surgeon, and the Medicare budget. *J. Vasc. Surg.* **16,** 671–673.
4. Ramsey, S.D., Newton, K., Blough, D., McCulloch, D.K., Sandhu, N., Reiber, G.E., Wagner, E.H. (1999). Incidence, outcomes, and cost of foot ulcers in patients with diabetes. *Diabetes Care* **22,** 382–387.
5. Morris, R.J., Fischer, S.M., and Slaga, T.J. (1985). Evidence that the centrally and peripherally located cells in the murine epidermal proliferative unit are two distinct populations. *J. Invest. Dermatol.* **84,** 277–281.

6. MacKenzie, I.C., and Bickenbach, J.R. (1985). Localization of label-retaining cells in mouse epithelia. *Cell Tissue Res.* **242**, 551–556.

7. Potten, C.S. (1986). Cell cycles in cell hierarchies. *Int. J. Radiat. Biol.* **49**, 257–278.

8. Bickenbach, J.R., McCutecheon, J., and MacKenzie, I.C. (1986). Rate of loss of tritiated thymidine label in basal cells in mouse epithelial tissue. *Cell Tissue Kinet.* **19**, 325–333.

9. Lajtha, L.G. (1979). Stem cell concepts. *Differentiation* **14**, 23–34.

10. Pellegrini, G., Bondanza, S., Guerra, L., and De Luca, M. (1998). Cultivation of human keratinocyte stem cells: current and future clinical implications. *Med. Biol. Eng. Comp.* **36**, 778–790.

11. Miller, S.J., Lavker, R.M., and Sun, T.T. (1993). Keratinocyte stem cells of cornea, skin, and hair follicle: common and distinguishing features. *Semin. Dev. Biol.* **4**, 217–240.

12. Barrandon, Y., and Green, H. (1987). Three clonal types of keratinocyte with different capacities for multiplication. *Proc. Natl. Acad. Sci. USA* **84**, 2302–2306.

13. Jones, P.H., and Watt, F.M. (1993). Separation of human epidermal stem cells from transit amplifying cells on the basis of difference in integrin function and expression. *Cell* **73**, 713–724.

14. Jones, P.H., Harper, S., and Watt, F.M. (1995). Stem cell patterning and fate in human epidermis. *Cell* **80**, 83–93.

15. Bickenbach, J.R., and Chism, E. (1998). Selection and extended growth of murine epidermal stem cells in culture. *Exp. Cell Res.* **244**, 184–195.

16. Tani, H., Morris, R.J., and Kaur, P. (2000). Enrichment for murine keratinocyte stem cells based on cell surface phenotype. *Proc. Natl. Acad. Sci. USA* **97**, 10,960–10,965.

17. Albert, M.R., Foster, R.A., and Vogel, J.C. (2001). Murine epidermal label-retaining cells isolated by flow cytometry do not express the stem cell markers CD34, Sca-1, or Flk-1. *J. Invest. Dermatol.* **117**, 943–948.

18. Li, A., Simmons, P.J., and Kaur, P. (1998). Identification and isolation of candidate human keratinocyte stem cells based on cell surface phenotype. *Proc. Natl. Acad. Sci. USA* **95**, 3902–3907.

19. Limová, M., and Grekin, R.C. (1990). Synthetic membranes and cultured keratinocyte grafts. *J. Am. Acad. Dermatol.* **23**, 713–719.

20. Oshima, H., Rochat, A., Kedzia, C., Kobayashi, K., and Barrandon, Y. (2001). Morphogenesis and renewal of hair follicles from adult multipotent stem cells. *Cell* **104**, 233–245.

21. Rheinwald, J.G., and Green, H. (1975). Serial cultivation of strains of human epidermal keratinocytes: The formation of keratinizing colonies from single cells. *Cell* **6**, 331–344.

22. Pellegrini, G., Ranno, R., Stracuzzi, G., Bondanza, S., Guerra, L., Zambruno, G., Micali, G., De Luca, M. (1999). The control of epidermal stem cells (holoclones) in the treatment of massive full-thickness burns with autologous keratinocytes cultured in fibrin. *Transplantation* **68**, 868–879.

23. Stern, R., McPherson, M., and Longaker, M.T. (1990). Histologic study of artificial skin used in the treatment of full-thickness thermal injury. *J. Burn Care Rehab.* **11**, 7–13.

24. Jeschke, M.G., Richter, W., and Ruf, S.G. (2001). Cultured autologous outer root sheath cells: a new therapeutic alternative for chronic decubitus ulcers. *Plastic Reconst. Surg.* **107**, 1803–1806.

25. Eaglstein, W., and Falanga, V. (1998). Tissue engineering and the development of Apligraf, a human skin equivalent. *Cutis* **62**, 1–8.

26. Eming, S., Davidson, J., and Krieg, T. (2001). Gene transfer strategies in tissue repair. *In* "The Skin and Gene Therapy," (U. Hengge *et al.*, eds.), pp. 117–137. Springer, Berlin.

27. Grinnell, F., Ho, C.H., Wysocki, A. (1992). Degradation of fibronectin and vitronectin in chronic wound fluid: analysis by cell blotting, immunoblotting, and cell adhesion assays. *J. Invest. Dermatol.* **98**, 410–416.

28. Supp, D., Supp, A., Bell, S., and Boyce, S. (2000). Enhanced vascularization of cultured skin substitutes genetically modified to overexpress vascular endothelial growth factor. *J. Invest. Dermatol.* **114**, 5–13.

29. Li, A., Pouliot, N., Redvers, R., and Kaur, P. (2004). Extensive tissue regenerative capacity of neonatal human keratinocyte stem cells and their progeny. *J. Clin. Invest.* **113**, 390–400.

736

Embryonic Stem Cells in Tissue Engineering

Shulamit Levenberg, Ali Khademhosseini, and Robert Langer

Tissue engineering is an interdisciplinary science that involves the use of biological sciences and engineering to develop tissues that restore, maintain, or enhance tissue function. However, to realize the dream of creating off-the-shelf organs for transplantation, a renewable source of cells is required. Embryonic stem (ES) cells have the potential to provide such a source of cells for tissue engineering applications because of their ability to differentiate to all somatic cells and their unlimited proliferative capability. However, to use ES cells in tissue engineering, several challenges must be addressed regarding methods to direct ES cell differentiation, overcome host immune rejection, prevent tumor formation, scale-up the production process, and better control scaffold properties. This chapter introduces tissue engineering approaches and the role of ES cells in various tissue engineering applications.

Introduction

Traditionally, approaches to restore tissue function have involved organ donation. However, despite attempts to encourage organ donations,[1,2] there is a shortage of transplantable human tissues such as bone marrow, hearts, kidneys, livers, and pancreases. Currently, more than 74,000 patients in the United States are awaiting organ transplantation, and only 21,000 people receive transplants annually.[3]

Tissue engineering–based therapies may provide a possible solution to alleviate the current shortage of organ donors. In tissue engineering, biological and engineering principles are combined to produce cell-based substitutes with or without the use of materials. One of the major obstacles in engineering tissue constructs for clinical use is the limit in available human cells. Stem cells isolated from adults or developing embryos are a current source for cells for tissue engineering. The derivation of human embryonic stem (hES) cells in 1998[4,5] has generated great interest in their potential application in tissue engineering. This is because of the ability of ES cells to grow in culture and to generate differentiated cells of all adult tissues. However, despite their therapeutic potential, both adult and ES cells present several challenges

associated with their clinical application. For example, although adult stem cells can be directly isolated from the patient and are therefore immunologically compatible with the patient, they are typically hard to isolate and grow in culture. In contrast, ES cells can be easily grown in culture and differentiated to a variety of cell types, but ES-derived cells may be rejected by the patient, and undifferentiated ES cells may form tumors.

The goal of this chapter is to analyze the potential of ES cells in tissue engineering. The chapter explains the importance of ES cells as a source of cells for tissue engineering by using examples from current research in the field. Furthermore, the chapter explains some fundamental principles and seminal work in tissue engineering.

Tissue Engineering Principles and Perspectives

Tissue engineering is an interdisciplinary field that applies the principles of engineering and life sciences to developing biological substitutes, typically composed of biological and synthetic components, that restore, maintain, or improve tissue function.[6,7] Tissue-engineered products would provide a life-long therapy and would greatly reduce the hospitalization and health care costs associated with drug therapy, simultaneously enhancing the patients' quality of life.

In general, there are three main approaches to tissue engineering[7]:

1. To use isolated cells or cell substitutes as cellular replacement parts
2. To use acellular materials capable of inducing tissue regeneration
3. To use a combination of cells and materials (typically in the form of scaffolds)

Although host stem cells could be involved in all of these approaches, ES cells can be directly involved in the first and third approaches.

ISOLATED CELLS OR CELL SUBSTITUTES AS CELLULAR REPLACEMENT PARTS

Isolated cells have been used as a substitute for cell replacement parts for many years. The first application of stem cells as a cellular replacement therapy is associated with bone marrow transplantation or blood transfusion studies in which donor hematopoietic stem cells repopulated the host's blood cells.[8] Other stem cells have demonstrated their potential in various diseases. For example bone marrow–derived cells have been shown to (1) generate endothelial progenitor cells used to induce neovascularization of ischemic tissues[9–12]; (2) regenerate myocardium[13]; (3) give rise to bone, cartilage, and muscle cells[14]; and (4) migrate into the brain to produce neurons.[15,16] In addition, myoblasts isolated from skeletal muscle that upon injection into the heart restored heart muscle function[17,18] and neural stem cells that resulted in the treatment of Parkinson's disease[19–21] are examples of other potential adult stem cell–based therapies. Tissue engineering products based on cells have been developed in the form of skin substitutes through the use of allogeneic cells (from companies such as Organogenesis and Advanced Tissue Sciences). In addition, the injection of mesenchymal stem cells is under way for cartilage and bone regeneration.[22]

ES cells provide an alternative source for cellular substitutes. *In vitro* ES cells have been shown to generate cells of hematopoietic,[23–25] endothelial,[26] cardiac,[27–29] neural,[30–33] osteogenic,[34] hepatic,[35] and pancreatic[36,37] tissues. Although ES cells provide a versatile source of cells for the generation of many cell types, so far only a few experiments have demonstrated the use of ES cells to replace functional loss of particular tissues. One such example is the creation of dopamine-producing cells in animal models of Parkinson's disease.[38,39] These ES cell–derived, highly enriched populations of midbrain neural stem cells generated neurons that showed electrophysiological and behavioral properties similar to neurons. Although functional properties of neurons derived from hES cells still need to be investigated, it has been shown that hES cell–derived neural precursors can be incorporated into various regions of the mouse brain and differentiate into neurons and astrocytes.[32] Also, hES cells differentiated to neural precursors were shown to migrate within the host brain and differentiate in a region-specific manner.[31] ES cells were also tested for future use in the heart. It was shown that mouse ES cell–derived cardiomyocytes were morphologically similar to neighboring host cardiomyocytes.[29,40–44] In addition, mouse ES cells transfected with an insulin promoter (driving expression of the *neo* gene, a marker for antibiotic resistance) have been shown to generate insulin-producing cells that can restore glucose levels in animals.[45] Although these functional data were obtained using genetically modified ES cells, insulin production from ES cells[36,37] suggests that these cells may potentially be used for the treatment of diabetes.

ES cells have also been shown to produce functional vascular tissue. Early endothelial progenitor cells isolated from differentiating mouse ES cells were shown to generate three blood vessel cell components: hematopoietic, endothelial, and smooth muscle cells.[46] Once injected into chick embryos, these endothelial progenitors differentiated into endothelial and mural cells and contributed to the vascular development. We have shown that hES cells can differentiate into endothelial cells and have isolated these cells using platelet endothelial cell adhesion molecule-1 (PECAM-1) antibodies. *In vivo*, when transplanted into immunodeficient mice, the cells appeared to form microvessels.[47]

USING COMBINATIONS OF CELLS AND MATERIALS

Tissue engineering approaches that use cells and scaffolds can be divided into two categories: open and closed systems.[48] These systems are distinguished based on the exposure of the cells to the immune system upon implantation.

Open Systems

In open tissue engineering systems, cells are immobilized within a highly porous, three-dimensional scaffold. The scaffold could consist of synthetic or natural materials or composites of both.[7,49–51] Ideally, this scaffold provides the cells with a suitable growth environment, optimum oxygen and nutrients transport properties, good mechanical integrity, and a suitable degradation rate. The use of scaffolds provides three-dimensional environments and brings the cells close so that it provides the cells with sufficient time to enable self-assembly and the formation of various components associated with the tissue microenvironment. Ideally, the material is degraded as cells deposits their extracellular matrix molecules. The materials used for tissue engineering are either synthetic biodegradable materials—such as poly(lactic acid),[52,53] poly(glycolic acid),[54] poly(lactic–glycolic)acid (PLGA),[53] poly(propylene fumarate),[53a] and polyarylates—or natural materials such as hydroxyapatite,[55–58] calcium carbonate,[58a] collagen,[59] and alginate.[60] Natural materials are typically more favorable to cell adherence, but the properties of synthetic materials—such as degradation rate, mechanical properties, structure, and porosity—can be better controlled.[7]

Open tissue engineering systems have been successfully used to create several biological substitutes, such as bone,[61,62] cartilage,[63–65] blood vessels,[66,67] cardiac,[68] smooth muscle,[69] pancreatic,[70] liver,[71] tooth,[72] retina,[73] and skin[74,75] tissues. Several tissue-engineered products are under clinical trials for FDA approval. Engineered skin or wound dressing and cartilage are two of the most advanced areas with regards to clinical potential.[1] For example, a skin substitute that consists of living human dermis cells in a natural scaffold consisting of type I collagen has already received FDA approval to be used for a diabetic foot ulcer.[76] In addition, tissue engineered cartilage and bone are also in clinical stages, and bladder and urologic tissue are being tested in various stages of research.[77]

Despite the ability of stem cells to differentiate to cells with phenotypic and morphological structure of desired cell types, there have been few scaffold-based tissue engineering studies that use ES cells. For adult stem cells, scaffolds have been used with mesenchymal stem cells,[78–82] neural stem cells,[83] and oval cells.[84] One such example is the transplantation of neural stem cells onto a polymer scaffold subsequently implanted into the infarction cavities of mouse brains injured by hypoxia–ischemia. These stem cells generated an intricate meshwork of many neurites and integrated with the host.[83] We have seeded neural stem cells onto specialized scaffolds,[85,86] have demonstrated spinal cord regeneration, and have improved hind-leg function of adult rats from a hemisection injury model.[87] Also, mesenchymal stem cells have been differentiated on polyethylene glycol or PLGA scaffolds and have been shown to generate cartilage or bone depending on the medium conditions.[88]

ES cells may be differentiated in culture; desired cell types may be selected and subsequently seeded onto scaffolds. We have used this technique to study the behavior of ES cell–derived endothelial cells in tissue engineering constructs.[47] Human ES cell–derived endothelial progenitors seeded onto highly porous PLLA/PLGA biodegradable polymer scaffolds formed blood vessels that appeared to merge with the host vasculature when implanted into immunodeficient mice (Fig. 73–1).

There may be other approaches to using ES cells or their progeny with scaffold-based tissue engineering systems. For example, it may be possible to directly differentiate ES cells on scaffolds in culture. Finally, it may be possible to differentiate genetically engineered ES cells seeded onto scaffolds *in vivo* (Fig. 73–2).

Coercing cells to form tissues while differentiating is an important issue that has not been explored greatly. This may be achieved by seeding ES cells directly onto the scaffolds followed by inducing their differentiation *in situ*.[88a] Porous, biodegradable polymer scaffolds can be used to support the ES cells, and they are a promising system for allowing the formation of complex three-dimensional tissues during differentiation. The scaffold provides physical cues for cell orientation and spreading, and pores provide space for remodeling of tissue structures. These scaffolds should ideally provide the cells with cues to guide their differentiation into desired cell types. The possible advantages of this system could involve the assembly of the cells as they differentiate. This differentiation pattern may mimic the developmental differentiation of the cells much more closely and therefore may induce differentiation into desired tissue. Ultimately, *in vitro* differentiated constructs can potentially directly be used for transplantation.

An approach that has not been considered as an alternative to *in vitro* differentiation of ES cells is to use the adult body's

microenvironment to induce the differentiation of ES cells. *In vivo* differentiation of ES cells is not yet a feasible option because of the tumorigenic nature of ES cells as well as the heterogeneous cell population that results from their nondirected differentiation. However, it may be possible to use a cell's apoptotic response mechanism to induce selective pressure for the desired cells *in vivo*. Thus, genetically modified ES cells that undergo apoptosis upon differentiation into undesirable cell types could be used to direct the differentiation of these cells, and similar approaches could be adopted to control the proliferative behavior of these cells.

Closed Systems

One of the main difficulties associated with open tissue engineering systems is the potential immunological issues associated with the implanted cells. Closed systems aim to overcome this difficulty by immobilizing cells within polymeric matrices that provide a barrier for the immunological components of the host. For example, cells can be immobilized within semipermeable membranes that are permeable to nutrients and oxygen and can provide a barrier to immune cells, antibodies, and other components of the immune system.[48,89] Furthermore, the implants can be either implanted into the patient or used as extracortical devices. Closed tissue engineering systems have been used particularly for the treatment of diabetes,[90–92] liver failure,[93–95] and Parkinson's disease.[96–99] This system may prove to be particularly useful in conjunction with ES cells, since the immobilization of ES cells within a closed system may overcome the immunological barrier that faces ES cell–based therapies. For example, ES cell–derived β-cells can response to insulin, or domain-producing neurons can be used in clinics without the fear of rejection. In addition, closed systems protect the host against potentially tumorigenic cells as it limits the cells within the polymeric barrier. Currently, engineering and biological limitations such as material biocompatibility, molecular weight cutoff, and the immune system's reaction to shed antigens by the transplanted cells are some of the challenges that prevent these systems from widespread clinical applications.

Limitations and Hurdles of Using ES Cells in Tissue Engineering

Despite significant progress in the field of tissue engineering, there are several challenges limiting the use of ES cells in tissue engineering. These challenges range from understanding stem cell biology to questions concerning controlling stem cell fate, solving engineering challenges on scale-up, and answering business questions related to feasibility and pricing.

DIRECTING THE DIFFERENTIATION OF ES CELLS

Perhaps the biggest challenge in using ES cells in clinical applications is the lack of knowledge in directing their differentiation ability. All studies that have shown the generation of specific cell types have not shown a uniform differentiation into a particular cell type. This may be attributed to the intrinsic property of ES cells to differentiate stochastically in

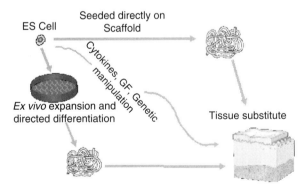

Figure 73–1. *Approaches for Using ES Cells for Scaffold-Based Tissue Engineering Applications.* ES cells can be used in tissue engineering constructs in a variety of methods. ES cells can be expanded in culture and then seeded directly onto scaffolds, where they are allowed to differentiate. Alternatively, stem cells can be directed to differentiate into various tissues and enriched for desired cells prior to the seeding of the cells onto scaffolds.

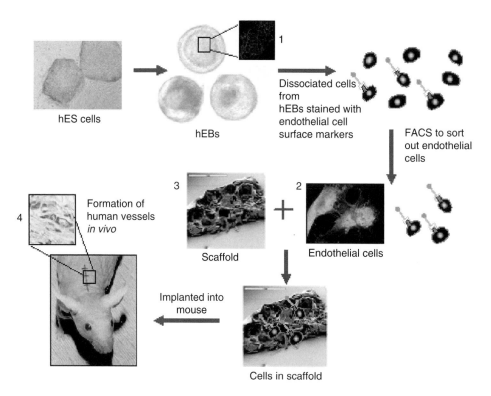

Figure 73-2. *Embryonic Endothelial Cells on Scaffolds In Vivo.* (A) Confocal image of vessel network formation within a 13-day-old human embryoid body (hEB), stained with PECAM-1 antibodies. The hES cells were induced to form EBs in which differentiation into endothelial cells and the formation of vessel-like network were observed. Embryonic endothelial cells were isolated from hEBs by staining dissociated EB cells with endothelial surface marker and sorting out positive cells using flow cytometry (FACS). (B) Isolated embryonic endothelial cells grown in culture stained with PECAM-1 and VWF antibodies. The isolated endothelial cells were seeded (C) on polymer scaffolds and implanted into immunodeficient mice. (C) Scanning electron microscopy of PLLA–PLGA scaffolds. (D) Immunoperoxidase staining of 7-day implants with anti-human PECAM-1 antibodies showing vessels lined with human endothelial cells. The embryonic endothelial cells appeared to form vessels *in vivo.*

absence of proper temporal and spatial signals from the surrounding microenvironment.

Techniques can be used to increase the ratio of cells that give rise to the desired lineages, including genetic and microenvironmental manipulations. Genetic techniques can be categorized into positive or negative regulators. The positive regulators include the constitutive or controlled expression of transcription factors that have been shown to derive the differentiation into particular tissues. For example, the overexpression of the Nurr transcription factor has been shown to increase the frequency of ES cells that differentiate into functional neural cells.[39] Alternatively, the negative regulators could be incorporated to induce the apoptosis of cells that differentiate to varying pathways. For example, neomycin selection and suicide genes activated by certain transcription factors can be used.[100] Clearly, these techniques will benefit from further understanding of inner workings of transient cells and knowledge of the differentiation pathways and lineages. Further analysis into stem cell and progenitor hierarchy through high-throughput analysis of microarray or proteomics data should accelerate this process.[101–103]

Another important criterion is the functionality of ES cell–derived cells as a source of tissues. The importance of rigorous testing has become clear in studies in which nestin-positive, putative pancreatic cells stained positive for insulin using antibodies because of cellular uptake from the surrounding medium.[104] Thus the incorporation of protein and functional tests should accompany the morphological and phenotypic analysis often used in ES cell literature to characterize differentiated cells.

ISOLATING THE DESIRED CELL TYPES FOR THERAPY

One of the main problems with ES cell–based therapies is finding suitable techniques to isolate desired cells from the heterogeneous population. One approach is to allow random differentiation of ES cells followed by isolation using a cell surface marker. We have used this method for the isolation of ES cell–derived endothelial cells using the PECAM-1 receptor.[47] Also, ES cell–derived hematopoietic progenitors have been isolated in a similar manner using the CD34 marker.[25] Another potential method is through reporter gene knockin modifications. These modifications have already been used on

ES cells to allow the labeling of cells at various stages of differentiation.[105,106] The use of other techniques, such as magnetic separation or neomycin selection, must be further examined for selecting various ES cell–derived progeny.

SCALE-UP OF ES CELLS IN TISSUE ENGINEERING

Although laboratory-scale ES cell cultures have been shown to produce differentiated progeny for both rodent[107] and human[108] ES cells, it is generally acceptable that these culturing methods are not feasible for the large-scale production of ES cells for therapeutic applications. The production of a sufficient quantity of differentiated cells from ES cells is an important challenge in realizing the clinical potential of ES cells. The large-scale production of ES cells will likely be specific to the type of tissue being generated and must remain reproducible, sterile, and economically feasible. Furthermore, this scale-up process must maintain appropriate control over bioprocess conditions—such as mechanical stimuli, medium conditions, and physicochemical parameters (such as temperature, oxygen, pH, and carbon dioxide levels)—as well as growth factor and cytokine concentrations.

ES cell differentiation protocols have generally used two-dimensional cultures, embryoid bodies (EBs), or both. Although each techniques provides specific advantages, the differentiation of ES cells in EBs produces a wider spectrum of cell types.[109] This has been attributed to the EBs' ability to better mimic the temporal pattern of cell differentiation as seen in the embryo. However, in some applications, the combined use of EBs and adherent cultures has resulted in better cell yields. For example, to induce ES cells to differentiate to cardiomyocytes, an EB formation in suspension cultures followed by a differentiation in adhesion cultures has been shown to optimize the percentage of cells that generate cardiomyocytes.[110,111] Similarly, the production of hepatocytes has been shown to be induced first by culturing the cell in EBs then by culturing on two-dimensional cultures.[35]

The formation of EBs in labs has been generally performed using techniques that have not been ideal for large-scale production. For example, many studies have used the "hanging drop protocol,"[112] in which ES cells are placed within a hanging drop and allowed to form an aggregate that can then be differentiated. Other techniques have formed EBs by placing the cells on nonadherent tissue culture dishes, which once more limit the quantity of cells produced. A technique that may allow the scale-up of the EB cultures is the use of suspension cultures using spinner flasks.[113] Such cultures have been shown to enhance the supply of oxygen and nutrients to the cells within the EB by exposing the surface of the cell aggregate to a continuous supply of fresh medium.[113,114]

To prevent the difficulties associated with EB heterogeneity, EBs have been immobilized in alginate microbeads. The microencapsulation of cells within these microbeads resulted in the differentiation of cells into cardiomyocytes and smooth muscle cells.[109] In addition, ES cells may be adhered to beads with desired extracellular matrices and differentiated. This approach also enhances the transportation of medium and

oxygen to the cells, in comparison to two-dimensional cultures, and provides additional mechanical stimuli, which may be an improved alternative to two-dimensional culture systems.

To enhance the supply of medium to tissue-engineered scaffolds or EBs, methods other than passive diffusion maybe required, such as the use of perfusion systems in which the medium is flown through the scaffold. Perfusion bioreactors have already been developed for a variety of tissue engineering applications, such as cartilage and cardiac.[115,116] For example, perfusion through scaffolds has been generated in rotating wall vessels[117–121] or by pumping medium directly through the scaffolds[116] to grow chondrocytes for cartilage generation.

It is a known that mechanical forces affect the differentiation and functional properties of many cell types;[67,117,118,122] thus, ES cell–based cultures that aim to direct the differentiation of ES cells require proper mechanical stimuli for the tissue. Our understanding of the effects of mechanical stimuli on ES cell differentiation is still primitive, but tissue engineering systems have been developed that incorporate the effects of mechanical forces. For example, functional autologous arteries have been cultured using pulsatile perfusion bioreactors.[67] Thus, the use of mechanical stimuli may further enhance the ability of these cells to respond to exogenous signals. Other environmental factors that maybe required include the use of electrical signals and spatially regulated signals to induce the differentiation and allow maturation of the desired tissues. Hopefully, with time such techniques will become particularly important in allowing scaled-up ES cell–based tissue engineering applications. The development of bioreactors that control the spatial and temporal signaling that induces ES cell differentiation requires a collaborative effort between engineers and biologists and is currently in the early stages.

TISSUE ENGINEERING LIMITATIONS

Synthetic scaffolds that support tissue growth by serving as the extracellular matrix for the cells do not represent the natural extracellular matrix associated with each cell type and tissue. ES cells and their progeny during development reside in a dynamic environment; thus, synthetic or natural substrates that aim to mimic the developing embryo must present similar signaling and structural elements. Several approaches are under development that may yield useful for scaffolds in which ES cells are seeded. For example, the use of "smart" scaffolds that release particular factors[123] and /or control the temporal expression of various molecules released from the polymer could be used to induce the differentiation of ES cells within the scaffolds.[124] For example, by dual delivery of vascular endothelial growth factor-165 and platelet-derived growth factor-BB—each with distinct kinetics—from a single, structural polymer scaffold, it has been shown that a mature vascular network can be formed.[124] An alternative approach to modifying the surface exposed to the cells is to immobilize desired ligands onto the scaffold. For example, RGD peptides, the adherent domain of fibronectin, can be incorporated into polymers to provide anchorage for adherent cells.[125]

Another difficulty with the current materials is their lack of control over the spatial organization within the scaffold. To create tissues that resemble the natural structure of biological tissues, the spatial patterning of cells must be recapitulated. For ES cells differentiated in scaffolds, this modeling and structure may be directly obtained as cells differentiate. The spatial arrangement of cells grown in EBs is typically organized with cells of particular tissues appearing in clusters. For example, blood precursors occur in the form of blood islands similar to their normal appearance in embryonic development. In the system in which ES cell–derived cells are plated onto scaffolds, spatial rearrangement can occur through direct patterning or cell "reorganization." In the direct cell-patterning system, cells can be seeded into the scaffold at particular regions within the scaffold. For example, the direct attachment of two cell types on different sides of the scaffold has been used to generate cells of the bladder.[126] Cell-patterning techniques, as have been developed using soft lithography for controlled coculture of hepatocytes and fibroblasts, could also be adapted for tissue engineering scaffolds to allow more controlled and complex cell patterning.[127–129]

Summary

ES cells have generated a great deal of interest as a source of cells for tissue engineering. However, several challenges exist in making ES cell–based therapy a reality. These include directing the differentiation of ES cells (using controlled microenvironments or genetic engineering), ensuring their safety and efficacy *in vivo*, ensuring the cells are immunologically compatible with the patient and will not form tumors, improving protocols for isolating desired cell types from heterogeneous populations, and enhancing current tissue engineering methods. Further research is required to control and direct the differentiation of ES cells. With the development of methods to generate tissues of various organs, this may lead to realizing the ultimate goal of tissue engineering. We are getting close to a day when ES cells can be manipulated in culture to produce fully differentiated cells that can be used to create and repair specific organs. Clearly, significant challenges remain, and the ability to overcome these difficulties does not lie within any scientific discipline but rather involves an interdisciplinary approach. Innovative approaches to solving these challenges could lead to improved quality of life for a variety of patients who could benefit from tissue engineering approaches.

REFERENCES

1. Niklason, L.E., and Langer, R. (2001). Prospects for organ and tissue replacement. *JAMA* **285,** 573–576.
2. Platt, J.L. (1998). New directions for organ transplantation. *Nature* **392,** 11–17.
3. Petit-Zeman, S. (2001). Regenerative medicine. *Nat. Biotechnol.* **19,** 201–206.
4. Shamblott, M.J., Axelman, J., Wang, S., Bugg, E.M., Littlefield, J.W., Donovan, P.J., Blumenthal, P.D., Huggins, G.R., and Gearhart, J.D. (1998). Derivation of pluripotent stem cells from cultured human primordial germ cells. *Proc. Natl. Acad. Sci. USA* **95,** 13,726–13,731.
5. Thomson, J.A., Itskovitz-Eldor, J., Shapiro, S.S., Waknitz, M.A., Swiergiel, J.J., Marshall, V.S., and Jones, J.M. (1998). Embryonic stem cell lines derived from human blastocysts. *Science* **282,** 1145–1147.
6. Nerem, R.M. (1991). Cellular engineering. *Ann. Biomed. Eng.* **19,** 529–545.
7. Langer, R., and Vacanti, J.P. (1993). Tissue engineering. *Science* **260,** 920–926.
8. Till, J.E., and McCulloch, E.A. (1980). Hemopoietic stem cell differentiation. *Biochim. Biophys. Acta.* **605,** 431–459.
9. Walter, D.H., and Dimmeler, S. (2002). Endothelial progenitor cells: regulation and contribution to adult neovascularization. *Herz.* **27,** 579–588.
10. Edelberg, J.M., Tang, L., Hattori, K., Lyden, D., and Rafii, S. (2002). Young adult bone marrow-derived endothelial precursor cells restore aging-impaired cardiac angiogenic function. *Circ. Res.* **90,** E89–E93.
11. Luttun, A., Carmeliet, G., and Carmeliet, P. (2002). Vascular progenitors: from biology to treatment. *Trends Cardiovasc. Med.* **12,** 88–96.
12. Kocher, A.A., Schuster, M.D., Szabolcs, M.J., Takuma, S., Burkhoff, D., Wang, J., Homma, S., Edwards, N.M., and Itescu, S. (2001). Neovascularization of ischemic myocardium by human bone marrow-derived angioblasts prevents cardiomyocyte apoptosis, reduces remodeling and improves cardiac function. *Natl. Med.* **7,** 430–436.
13. Orlic, D., Kajstura, J., Chimenti, S., Jakoniuk, I., Anderson, S.M., Li, B., Pickel, J., McKay, R., Nadal-Ginard, B., Bodine, D.M., Leri, A., and Anversa, P. (2001). Bone marrow cells regenerate infarcted myocardium. *Nature* **410,** 701–705.
14. Pittenger, M.F., Mackay, A.M., Beck, S.C., Jaiswal, R.K., Douglas, R., Mosca, J.D., Moorman, M.A., Simonetti, D.W., Craig, S., and Marshak, D.R. (1999). Multilineage potential of adult human mesenchymal stem cells. *Science* **284,** 143–147.
15. Brazelton, T.R., Rossi, F.M., Keshet, G.I., and Blau, H.M. (2000). From marrow to brain: expression of neuronal phenotypes in adult mice. *Science* **290,** 1775–1779.
16. Mezey, E., Chandross, K.J., Harta, G., Maki, R.A., and McKercher, S.R. (2000). Turning blood into brain: Cells bearing neuronal antigens generated *in vivo* from bone marrow. *Science* **290,** 1779–1782.
17. Taylor, D.A., Atkins, B.Z., Hungspreugs, P., Jones, T.R., Reedy, M.C., Hutcheson, K.A., Glower, D.D., and Kraus, W.E. (1998). Regenerating functional myocardium: improved performance after skeletal myoblast transplantation. *Natl. Med.* **4,** 929–933.
18. Dorfman, J., Duong, M., Zibaitis, A., Pelletier, M.P., Shum-Tim, D., Li, C., and Chiu, R.C. (1998). Myocardial tissue engineering with autologous myoblast implantation. *J. Thorac. Cardiovasc. Surg.* **116,** 744–751.
19. Storch, A., and Schwarz, J. (2002). Neural stem cells and Parkinson's disease. *J. Neurol.* **249** (Suppl. 3), III/30–32.
20. Okano, H., Yoshizaki, T., Shimazaki, T., and Sawamoto, K. (2002). Isolation and transplantation of dopaminergic neurons and neural stem cells. *Parkinsonism Relat. Disord.* **9,** 23–28.
21. Fricker, J. (1999). Human neural stem cells on trial for Parkinson's disease. *Mol. Med. Today* **5,** 144.
22. Bruder, S.P., Jaiswal, N., Ricalton, N.S., Mosca, J.D., Kraus, K.H., and Kadiyala, S. (1998). Mesenchymal stem cells in osteobiology and applied bone regeneration. *Clin. Orthop.* **355** (Suppl.), S247–S256.

23. Palacios, R., Golunski, E., and Samaridis, J. (1995). *In vitro* generation of hematopoietic stem cells from an embryonic stem cell line. *Proc. Natl. Acad. Sci. USA* **92,** 7530–7534.

24. Bigas, A., Martin, D.I., and Bernstein, I.D. (1995). Generation of hematopoietic colony-forming cells from embryonic stem cells: synergy between a soluble factor from NIH-3T3 cells and hematopoietic growth factors. *Blood* **85,** 3127–3133.

25. Kaufman, D.S., Hanson, E.T., Lewis, R.L., Auerbach, R., and Thomson, J.A. (2001). Hematopoietic colony-forming cells derived from human embryonic stem cells. *Proc. Natl. Acad. Sci. USA* **98,** 10,716–10,721.

26. Hirashima, M., Kataoka, H., Nishikawa, S., and Matsuyoshi, N. (1999). Maturation of embryonic stem cells into endothelial cells in an *in vitro* model of vasculogenesis. *Blood* **93,** 1253–1263.

27. Rohwedel, J., Maltsev, V., Bober, E., Arnold, H.H., Hescheler, J., and Wobus, A.M. (1994). Muscle cell differentiation of embryonic stem cells reflects myogenesis *in vivo:* developmentally regulated expression of myogenic determination genes and functional expression of ionic currents. *Dev. Biol.* **164,** 87–101.

28. Fleischmann, M., Bloch, W., Kolossov, E., Andressen, C., Muller, M., Brem, G., Hescheler, J., Addicks, K., and Fleischmann, B.K. (1998). Cardiac specific expression of the green fluorescent protein during early murine embryonic development. *FEBS Lett.* **440,** 370–376.

29. Kehat, I., Kenyagin-Karsenti, D., Snir, M., Segev, H., Amit, M., Gepstein, A., Livne, E., Binah, O., Itskovitz-Eldor, J., and Gepstein, L. (2001). Human embryonic stem cells can differentiate into myocytes with structural and functional properties of cardiomyocytes. *J. Clin. Invest.* **108,** 407–414.

30. Schuldiner, M., Eiges, R., Eden, A., Yanuka, O., Itskovitz-Eldor, J., Goldstein, R.S., and Benvenisty, N. (2001). Induced neuronal differentiation of human embryonic stem cells. *Brain Res.* **913,** 201–205.

31. Reubinoff, B.E., Itsykson, P., Turetsky, T., Pera, M.F., Reinhartz, E., Itzik, A., and Ben-Hur, T. (2001). Neural progenitors from human embryonic stem cells. *Natl. Biotechnol.* **19,** 1134–1140.

32. Zhang, S.C., Wernig, M., Duncan, I.D., Brustle, O., and Thomson, J.A. (2001). *In vitro* differentiation of transplantable neural precursors from human embryonic stem cells. *Natl. Biotechnol.* **19,** 1129–1133.

33. Brustle, O., Jones, K.N., Learish, R.D., Karram, K., Choudhary, K., Wiestler, O.D., Duncan, I.D., and McKay, R.D. (1999). Embryonic stem cell-derived glial precursors: a source of myelinating transplants. *Science* **285,** 754–756.

34. Buttery, L.D., Bourne, S., Xynos, J.D., Wood, H., Hughes, F.J., Hughes, S.P., Episkopou, V., and Polak, J.M. (2001). Differentiation of osteoblasts and *in vitro* bone formation from murine embryonic stem cells. *Tissue Eng.* **7,** 89–99.

35. Hamazaki, T., Iiboshi, Y., Oka, M., Papst, P.J., Meacham, A.M., Zon, L.I., and Terada, N. (2001). Hepatic maturation in differentiating embryonic stem cells *in vitro*. *FEBS Lett.* **497,** 15–19.

36. Lumelsky, N., Blondel, O., Laeng, P., Velasco, I., Ravin, R., and McKay, R. (2001). Differentiation of embryonic stem cells to insulin-secreting structures similar to pancreatic islets. *Science* **292,** 1389–1394.

37. Assady, S., Maor, G., Amit, M., Itskovitz-Eldor, J., Skorecki, K.L., and Tzukerman, M. (2001). Insulin production by human embryonic stem cells. *Diabetes* **50,** 1691–1697.

38. Bjorklund, L.M., Sanchez-Pernaute, R., Chung, S., Andersson, T., Chen, I.Y., McNaught, K.S., Brownell, A.L., Jenkins, B.G., Wahlestedt, C., Kim, K.S., and Isacson, O. (2002). Embryonic stem cells develop into functional dopaminergic neurons after transplantation in a Parkinson's rat model. *Proc. Natl. Acad. Sci. USA* **99,** 2344–2349.

39. Kim, J.H., Auerbach, J.M., Rodriguez-Gomez, J.A., Velasco, I., Gavin, D., Lumelsky, N., Lee, S.H., Nguyen, J., Sanchez-Pernaute, R., Bankiewicz, K., and McKay, R. (2002). Dopamine neurons derived from embryonic stem cells function in an animal model of Parkinson's disease. *Nature* **418,** 50–56.

40. Yang, Y., Min, J.Y., Rana, J.S., Ke, Q., Cai, J., Chen, Y., Morgan, J.P., and Xiao, Y.F. (2002). VEGF enhances functional improvement of postinfarcted hearts by transplantation of ESC-differentiated cells. *J. Appl. Physiol.* **93,** 1140–1151.

41. Klug, M.G., Soonpaa, M.H., Koh, G.Y., and Field, L.J. (1996). Genetically selected cardiomyocytes from differentiating embronic stem cells form stable intracardiac grafts. *J. Clin. Invest.* **98,** 216–224.

42. Min, J.Y., Yang, Y., Converso, K.L., Liu, L., Huang, Q., Morgan, J.P., and Xiao, Y.F. (2002). Transplantation of embryonic stem cells improves cardiac function in postinfarcted rats. *J. Appl. Physiol.* **92,** 288–296.

43. Mummery, C., Ward-van Oostwaard, D., Doevendans, P., Spijker, R., van den Brink, S., Hassink, R., van der Heyden, M., Opthof, T., Pera, M., de la Riviere, A.B., Passier, R., and Tertoolen, L. (2003). Differentiation of human embryonic stem cells to cardiomyocytes: Role of coculture with visceral endoderm-like cells. *Circulation* **107,** 2733–2740.

44. Kehat, I., Gepstein, A., Spira, A., Itskovitz-Eldor, J., and Gepstein, L. (2002). High-resolution electrophysiological assessment of human embryonic stem cell-derived cardiomyocytes: a novel *in vitro* model for the study of conduction. *Circ. Res.* **91,** 659–661.

45. Soria, B., Roche, E., Berna, G., Leon-Quinto, T., Reig, J.A., and Martin, F. (2000). Insulin-secreting cells derived from embryonic stem cells normalize glycemia in streptozotocin-induced diabetic mice. *Diabetes* **49,** 157–162.

46. Yamashita, J., Itoh, H., Hirashima, M., Ogawa, M., Nishikawa, S., Yurugi, T., Naito, M., and Nakao, K. (2000). Flk1-positive cells derived from embryonic stem cells serve as vascular progenitors. *Nature* **408,** 92–96.

47. Levenberg, S., Golub, J.S., Amit, M., Itskovitz-Eldor, J., and Langer, R. (2002). Endothelial cells derived from human embryonic stem cells. *Proc. Natl. Acad. Sci. USA* **99,** 4391–4396.

48. Uludag, H., De Vos, P., and Tresco, P.A. (2000). Technology of mammalian cell encapsulation. *Adv. Drug Deliv. Rev.* **42,** 29–64.

49. Vacanti, J.P., and Langer, R. (1999). Tissue engineering: the design and fabrication of living replacement devices for surgical reconstruction and transplantation. *Lancet.* **354** (Suppl. 1), SI32–SI34.

50. Lanza, R.P., Langer, R.S., and Chick, W.L. (1997). "Principles of tissues engineering." Academic Press/R.G. Landes, San Diego, Austin.

51. Langer, R.S., and Vacanti, J.P. (1999). Tissue engineering: the challenges ahead. *Sci. Am.* **280,** 86–89.

52. Laurencin, C.T., Attawia, M.A., Elgendy, H.E., and Herbert, K.M. (1996). Tissue-engineered bone regeneration using degradable polymers: the formation of mineralized matrices. *Bone* **19,** 93S–99S.

53. Mooney, D.J., Baldwin, D.F., Suh, N.P., Vacanti, J.P., and Langer, R. (1996). Novel approach to fabricate porous sponges of poly (D, L-lactic-co-glycolic acid) without the use of organic solvents. *Biomaterials* **17,** 1417–1422.

53a. He, S., Yaszemski, M.J., Yasko, A.W., Engel, P.S., and Mikos, A.G. (2000). Injectable biodegradable polymer composites based on poly(propylene furmate) crosslinked with poly(ethylene glycol)-dimethacrylate. *Biomaterials* **21,** 2389–2394.

54. Mooney, D.J., Mazzoni, C.L., Breuer, C., McNamara, K., Hern, D., Vacanti, J.P., and Langer, R. (1996). Stabilized polyglycolic acid fibre-based tubes for tissue engineering. *Biomaterials* **17,** 115–124.

55. Friedman, C.D., and Costantino, P.D. (1998). Hydroxyapatite cement, a smart biomaterial for craniofacial skeletal tissue engineering. *Surg. Technol. Int.* **7,** 421–423.

56. Pelissier, P., Villars, F., Mathoulin-Pelissier, S., Bareille, R., Lafage-Proust, M.H., and Vilamitjana-Amedee, J. (2003). Influences of vascularization and osteogenic cells on heterotopic bone formation within a madreporic ceramic in rats. *Plast. Reconstr. Surg.* **111,** 1932–1941.

57. Li, S.H., De Wijn, J.R., Layrolle, P., and de Groot, K. (2002). Synthesis of macroporous hydroxyapatite scaffolds for bone tissue engineering. *J. Biomed. Mater. Res.* **61,** 109–120.

58. LeGeros, R.Z. (2002). Properties of osteoconductive biomaterials: calcium phosphates. *Clin. Orthop.* **395,** 81–98.

58a Kreklau, B., Sittinger, M., Mensing, M.B., Voigt, C., Berger, G., Burmester, G.R., Rahmanzadeh, R., and Gross, U. (1999). Tissue engineering of biphasic joint cartilage transplants. Biomaterials **20,** 1743–1749.

59. Chevallay, B., and Herbage, D. (2000). Collagen-based biomaterials as 3D scaffold for cell cultures: applications for tissue engineering and gene therapy. *Med. Biol. Eng. Comput.* **38,** 211–218.

60. Rowley, J.A., Madlambayan, G., and Mooney, D.J. (1999). Alginate hydrogels as synthetic extracellular matrix materials. *Biomaterials* **20,** 45–53.

61. Ohgushi, H., Miyake, J., and Tateishi, T. (2003). Mesenchymal stem cells and bioceramics: strategies to regenerate the skeleton. *Novartis. Found. Symp.* **249,** 118–127; discussion 127–132, 170–174, and 239–241.

62. Cancedda, R., Mastrogiacomo, M., Bianchi, G., Derubeis, A., Muraglia, A., and Quarto, R. (2003). Bone marrow stromal cells and their use in regenerating bone. *Novartis. Found. Symp.* **249,** 133–143; discussion 143–147, 170–174, and 239–241.

63. Sherwood, J.K., Riley, S.L., Palazzolo, R., Brown, S.C., Monkhouse, D.C., Coates, M., Griffith, L.G., Landeen, L.K., and Ratcliffe, A. (2002). A three-dimensional osteochondral composite scaffold for articular cartilage repair. *Biomaterials* **23,** 4739–4751.

64. Baek, C.H., Lee, J.C., Jung, Y.G., Ko, Y.J., Yoon, J.J., and Park, T.G. (2002). Tissue-engineered cartilage on biodegradable macroporous scaffolds: cell shape and phenotypic expression. *Laryngoscope* **112,** 1050–1055.

65. Rahman, M.S., and Tsuchiya, T. (2001). Enhancement of chondrogenic differentiation of human articular chondrocytes by biodegradable polymers. *Tissue Eng.* **7,** 781–790.

66. Niklason, L.E., and Langer, R.S. (1997). Advances in tissue engineering of blood vessels and other tissues. *Transplant. Immunol.* **5,** 303–306.

67. Niklason, L.E., Gao, J., Abbott, W.M., Hirschi, K.K., Houser, S., Marini, R., and Langer, R. (1999). Functional arteries grown *in vitro. Science* **284,** 489–493.

68. Shinoka, T., Shum-Tim, D., Ma, P.X., Tanel, R.E., Isogai, N., Langer, R., Vacanti, J.P., and Mayer, J.E., Jr. (1998). Creation of viable pulmonary artery autografts through tissue engineering. *J. Thorac. Cardiovasc. Surg.* **115,** 536–545; discussion 545–546.

69. Kim, B.S., Nikolovski, J., Bonadio, J., Smiley, E., and Mooney, D.J. (1999). Engineered smooth muscle tissues: regulating cell phenotype with the scaffold. *Exp. Cell Res.* **251,** 318–328.

70. Cui, W., Kim, D.H., Imamura, M., Hyon, S.H., and Inoue, K. (2001). Tissue-engineered pancreatic islets: culturing rat islets in the chitosan sponge. *Cell Transplant.* **10,** 499–502.

71. Hasirci, V., Berthiaume, F., Bondre, S.P., Gresser, J.D., Trantolo, D.J., Toner, M., and Wise, D.L. (2001). Expression of liver-specific functions by rat hepatocytes seeded in treated poly(lactic-co-glycolic) acid biodegradable foams. *Tissue Eng.* **7,** 385–394.

72. Young, C.S., Terada, S., Vacanti, J.P., Honda, M., Bartlett, J.D., and Yelick, P.C. (2002). Tissue engineering of complex tooth structures on biodegradable polymer scaffolds. *J. Dent. Res.* **81,** 695–700.

73. Lu, L., Yaszemski, M.J., and Mikos, A.G. (2001). Retinal pigment epithelium engineering using synthetic biodegradable polymers. *Biomaterials* **22,** 3345–3355.

74. Badiavas, E.V., Paquette, D., Carson, P., and Falanga, V. (2002). Human chronic wounds treated with bioengineered skin: histologic evidence of host-graft interactions. *J. Am. Acad. Dermatol.* **46,** 524–530.

75. Herson, M.R., Mathor, M.B., Altran, S., Capelozzi, V.L., and Ferreira, M.C. (2001). *In vitro* construction of a potential skin substitute through direct human keratinocyte plating onto decellularized glycerol-preserved allodermis. *Artif. Organs* **25,** 901–906.

76. Griffith, L.G., and Naughton, G. (2002). Tissue engineering—current challenges and expanding opportunities. *Science* **295,** 1009–1014.

77. Oberpenning, F., Meng, J., Yoo, J.J., and Atala, A. (1999). *De novo* reconstitution of a functional mammalian urinary bladder by tissue engineering. *Natl. Biotechnol.* **17,** 149–155.

78. Weber, M., Steinert, A., Jork, A., Dimmler, A., Thurmer, F., Schutze, N., Hendrich, C., and Zimmerman, U. (2002). Formation of cartilage matrix proteins by BMP-transfected murine mesenchymal stem cells encapsulated in a novel class of alginates. *Biomaterials* **23,** 2003–2013.

79. Boo, J.S., Yamada, Y., Okazaki, Y., Hibino, Y., Okada, K., Hata, K., Yoshikawa, T., Sugiura, Y., and Ueda, M. (2002). Tissue-engineered bone using mesenchymal stem cells and a biodegradable scaffold. *J. Craniofac. Surg.* **13,** 231–239; discussion 240–243.

80. Howard, D., Partridge, K., Yang, X., Clarke, N.M., Okubo, Y., Bessho, K., Howdle, S.M., Shakesheff, K.M., and Oreffo, R.O. (2002). Immunoselection and adenoviral genetic modulation of human osteoprogenitors: *in vivo* bone formation on PLA scaffold. *Biochem. Biophys. Res. Commun.* **299,** 208–215.

81. Yamada, Y., Boo, J.S., Ozawa, R., Nagasaka, T., Okazaki, Y., Hata, K., and Ueda, M. (2003). Bone regeneration following injection of mesenchymal stem cells and fibrin glue with a biodegradable scaffold. *J. Craniomaxillofac. Surg.* **31,** 27–33.

82. Bensaid, W., Triffitt, J.T., Blanchat, C., Oudina, K., Sedel, L., and Petite, H. (2003). A biodegradable fibrin scaffold for mesenchymal stem cell transplantation. *Biomaterials* **24,** 2497–2502.

83. Park, K.I., Teng, Y.D., and Snyder, E.Y. (2002). The injured brain interacts reciprocally with neural stem cells supported by scaffolds to reconstitute lost tissue. *Natl. Biotechnol.* **20,** 1111–1117.

84. Suh, H., Song, M.J., and Park, Y.N. (2003). Behavior of isolated rat oval cells in porous collagen scaffold. *Tissue Eng.* **9,** 411–420.

85. Lavik, E.B., Hrkach, J.S., Lotan, N., Nazarov, R., and Langer, R. (2001). A simple synthetic route to the formation of a block copolymer of poly(lactic-co-glycolic acid) and polylysine for the fabrication of functionalized, degradable structures for biomedical applications. *J. Biomed. Mater. Res.* **58,** 291–294.

86. Lavik, E., Teng, Y.D., Snyder, E., and Langer, R. (2002). Seeding neural stem cells on scaffolds of PGA, PLA, and their copolymers. *Methods Mol. Biol.* **198,** 89–97.

87. Teng, Y.D., Lavik, E.B., Qu, X., Park, K.I., Ourednik, J., Zurakowski, D., Langer, R., and Snyder, E.Y. (2002). Functional recovery following traumatic spinal cord injury mediated by a unique polymer scaffold seeded with neural stem cells. *Proc. Natl. Acad. Sci. USA* **99,** 3024–3029.

88. Martin, I., Shastri, V.P., Padera, R.F., Yang, J., Mackay, A.J., Langer, R., Vunjak-Novakovic, G., and Freed, L.E. (2001). Selective differentiation of mammalian bone marrow stromal cells cultured on three-dimensional polymer foams. *J. Biomed. Mater. Res.* **55**, 229–235.

88a Levenberg, S., Huang, N.F., Lavik, E., Rogers, A.B., Itskovitz–Eldor, J., and Langer, R. (2003). Differentiation of human embryonic stem cells on three-dimensional polymer scaffolds. *Proc. Natl. Acad. Sci. U. S. A.* **100**, 12741–12746.

89. Lim, F., and Sun, A.M. (1980). Microencapsulated islets as a bioartificial endocrine pancreas. *Science* **210**, 908–910.

90. Sefton, M.V., May, M.H., Lahooti, S., and Babensee, J.E. (2000). Making microencapsulation work: conformal coating, immobilization gels, and *in vivo* performance. *J. Control Release* **65**, 173–186.

91. Zekorn, T., Siebers, U., Horcher, A., Schnettler, R., Zimmermann, U., Bretzel, R.G., and Federlin, K. (1992). Alginate coating of islets of Langerhans: *in vitro* studies on a new method for microencapsulation for immunoisolated transplantation. *Acta. Diabetol.* **29**, 41–45.

92. Chicheportiche, D., and Reach, G. (1988). *In vitro* kinetics of insulin release by microencapsulated rat islets: effect of the size of the microcapsules. *Diabetologia* **31**, 54–57.

93. Uludag, H., and Sefton, M.V. (1993). Microencapsulated human hepatoma (HepG2) cells: *in vitro* growth and protein release. *J. Biomed. Mater. Res.* **27**, 1213–1224.

94. Wang, L., Sun, J., Li, L., Harbour, C., Mears, D., Koutalistras, N., and Sheil, A.G. (2000). Factors affecting hepatocyte viability and CYPIA1 activity during encapsulation. *Artif. Cells Blood Substit. Immobil. Biotechnol.* **28**, 215–227.

95. Chandy, T., Mooradian, D.L., and Rao, G.H. (1999). Evaluation of modified alginate-chitosan-polyethylene glycol microcapsules for cell encapsulation. *Artif. Organs* **23**, 894–903.

96. Wang, Y., Wang, S.D., Lin, S.Z., Chiou, A.L., Chen, L.K., Chen, J.F., and Zhou, F.C. (1997). Transplantation of microencapsulated PC12 cells provides long-term improvement of dopaminergic functions. *Chin. J. Physiol.* **40**, 121–129.

97. Aebischer, P., Wahlberg, L., Tresco, P.A., and Winn, S.R. (1991). Macroencapsulation of dopamine-secreting cells by coextrusion with an organic polymer solution. *Biomaterials* **12**, 50–56.

98. Esposito, E., Cortesi, R., and Nastruzzi, C. (1996). Gelatin microspheres: influence of preparation parameters and thermal treatment on chemico-physical and biopharmaceutical properties. *Biomaterials* **17**, 2009–2020.

99. Vallbacka, J.J., Nobrega, J.N., and Sefton, M.V. (2001). Tissue engineering as a platform for controlled release of therapeutic agents: implantation of microencapsulated dopamine producing cells in the brains of rats. *J. Control Release* **72**, 93–100.

100. Soria, B., Roche, E., Berna, G., Leon-Quinto, T., Reig, J.A., and Martin, F. (2000). Insulin-secreting cells derived from embryonic stem cells normalize glycemia in streptozotocin-induced diabetic mice. *Diabetes* **49**, 157–162.

101. Ramalho-Santos, M., Yoon, S., Matsuzaki, Y., Mulligan, R.C., and Melton, D.A. (2002). "Stemness": transcriptional profiling of embryonic and adult stem cells. *Science* **298**, 597–600.

102. Ivanova, N.B., Dimos, J.T., Schaniel, C., Hackney, J.A., Moore, K.A., and Lemischka, I.R. (2002). A stem cell molecular signature. *Science* **298**, 601–604.

103. Phillips, R.L., Ernst, R.E., Brunk, B., Ivanova, N., Mahan, M.A., Deanehan, J.K., Moore, K.A., Overton, G.C., and Lemischka, I.R. (2000). The genetic program of hematopoietic stem cells. *Science* **288**, 1635–1640.

104. Rajagopal, J., Anderson, W.J., Kume, S., Martinez, O.I., and Melton, D.A. (2003). Insulin staining of ES cell progeny from insulin uptake. *Science* **299**, 363.

105. Eiges, R., Schuldiner, M., Drukker, M., Yanuka, O., Itskovitz-Eldor, J., and Benvenisty, N. (2001). Establishment of human embryonic stem cell-transfected clones carrying a marker for undifferentiated cells. *Curr. Biol.* **11**, 514–518.

106. Zwaka, T.P., and Thomson, J.A. (2003). Homologous recombination in human embryonic stem cells. *Natl. Biotechnol.* **21**, 319–321.

107. Chen, Y., Li, X., Eswarakumar, V.P., Seger, R., and Lonai, P. (2000). Fibroblast growth factor (FGF) signaling through PI 3-kinase and Akt/PKB is required for embryoid body differentiation. *Oncogene* **19**, 3750–3756.

108. Itskovitz-Eldor, J., Schuldiner, M., Karsenti, D., Eden, A., Yanuka, O., Amit, M., Soreq, H., and Benvenisty, N. (2000). Differentiation of human embryonic stem cells into embryoid bodies compromising the three embryonic germ layers. *Mol. Med.* **6**, 88–95.

109. Magyar, J.P., Nemir, M., Ehler, E., Suter, N., Perriard, J.C., and Eppenberger, H.M. (2001). Mass production of embryoid bodies in microbeads. *Ann. NY Acad. Sci.* **944**, 135–143.

110. Guan, K., Furst, D.O., and Wobus, A.M. (1999). Modulation of sarcomere organization during embryonic stem cell-derived cardiomyocyte differentiation. *Eur. J. Cell Biol.* **78**, 813–823.

111. Klinz, F., Bloch, W., Addicks, K., and Hescheler, J. (1999). Inhibition of phosphatidylinositol-3-kinase blocks development of functional embryonic cardiomyocytes. *Exp. Cell Res.* **247**, 79–83.

112. Maltsev, V.A., Ji, G.J., Wobus, A.M., Fleischmann, B.K., and Hescheler, J. (1999). Establishment of β-adrenergic modulation of L-type Ca2+ current in the early stages of cardiomyocyte development. *Circ. Res.* **84**, 136–145.

113. Dang, S.M., Kyba, M., Perlingeiro, R., Daley, G.Q., and Zandstra, P.W. (2002). Efficiency of embryoid body formation and hematopoietic development from embryonic stem cells in different culture systems. *Biotechnol. Bioeng.* **78**, 442–453.

114. Wartenberg, M., Gunther, J., Hescheler, J., and Sauer, H. (1998). The embryoid body as a novel *in vitro* assay system for antiangiogenic agents. *Lab Invest.* **78**, 1301–1314.

115. Carrier, R.L., Rupnick, M., Langer, R., Schoen, F.J., Freed, L.E., and Vunjak-Novakovic, G. (2002). Perfusion improves tissue architecture of engineered cardiac muscle. *Tissue Eng.* **8**, 175–188.

116. Davisson, T., Sah, R.L., and Ratcliffe, A. (2002). Perfusion increases cell content and matrix synthesis in chondrocyte three-dimensional cultures. *Tissue Eng.* **8**, 807–816.

117. Vunjak-Novakovic, G., Martin, I., Obradovic, B., Treppo, S., Grodzinsky, A.J., Langer, R., and Freed, L.E. (1999). Bioreactor cultivation conditions modulate the composition and mechanical properties of tissue-engineered cartilage. *J. Orthop. Res.* **17**, 130–138.

118. Martin, I., Obradovic, B., Treppo, S., Grodzinsky, A.J., Langer, R., Freed, L.E., and Vunjak-Novakovic, G. (2000). Modulation of the mechanical properties of tissue-engineered cartilage. *Biorheology* **37**, 141–147.

119. Botchwey, E.A., Pollack, S.R., Levine, E.M., and Laurencin, C.T. (2001). Bone tissue engineering in a rotating bioreactor using a microcarrier matrix system. *J. Biomed. Mater. Res.* **55**, 242–253.

120. Margolis, L., Hatfill, S., Chuaqui, R., Vocke, C., Emmert-Buck, M., Linehan, W.M., and Duray, P.H. (1999). Long term organ culture of human prostate tissue in a NASA-designed rotating wall bioreactor. *J. Urol.* **161**, 290–297.

121. Freed, L.E., Langer, R., Martin, I., Pellis, N.R., and Vunjak-Novakovic, G. (1997). Tissue engineering of cartilage in space. *Proc. Natl. Acad. Sci. USA* **94,** 13,885–13,890.

122. Li, C., and Xu, Q. (2000). Mechanical stress-initiated signal transductions in vascular smooth muscle cells. *Cell Signal* **12,** 435–445.

123. Murphy, W.L., Peters, M.C., Kohn, D.H., and Mooney, D.J. (2000). Sustained release of vascular endothelial growth factor from mineralized poly(lactide-co-glycolide) scaffolds for tissue engineering. *Biomaterials* **21,** 2521–2527.

124. Richardson, T.P., Peters, M.C., Ennett, A.B., and Mooney, D.J. (2001). Polymeric system for dual growth factor delivery. *Natl. Biotechnol.* **19,** 1029–1034.

125. Cook, A.D., Hrkach, J.S., Gao, N.N., Johnson, I.M., Pajvani, U.B., Cannizzaro, S.M., and Langer, R. (1997). Characterization and development of RGD-peptide-modified poly(lactic acid-co-lysine) as an interactive, resorbable biomaterial. *J. Biomed. Mater. Res.* **35,** 513–523.

126. Lanza, R.P., Cibelli, J.B., Blackwell, C., Cristofalo, V.J., Francis, M.K., Baerlocher, G.M., Mak, J., Schertzer, M., Chavez, E.A., Sawyer, N., Lansdorp, P.M., and West, M.D. (2000). Extension of cell life span and telomere length in animals cloned from senescent somatic cells. *Science* **288,** 665–669.

127. Bhatia, S.N., Yarmush, M.L., and Toner, M. (1997). Controlling cell interactions by micropatterning in cocultures: hepatocytes and 3T3 fibroblasts. *J. Biomed. Mater. Res.* **34,** 189–199.

128. Bhatia, S.N., Balis, U.J., Yarmush, M.L., and Toner, M. (1998). Probing heterotypic cell interactions: Hepatocyte function in microfabricated cocultures. *J. Biomater. Sci. Polym. Ed.* **9,** 1137–1160.

129. Bhatia, S.N., Balis, U.J., Yarmush, M.L., and Toner, M. (1998). Microfabrication of hepatocytes–fibroblast cocultures: role of homotypic cell interactions. *Biotechnol. Prog.* **14,** 378–387.

Immortal Cells, Moral Selves

Laurie Zoloth

Introduction

Genetic research, in its determination to seek the fundamental answers to human biology, has dominated scientific debate for the last 50 years, since Watson, Crick, Wilkins, and Franklin first caught glimpses of nuclear DNA.[1] Thus, human embryonic stem cell research—research that fully uses the insights and essential framework of genomics but seeks to understand far more about how cells signal, repress, and express the proteins that shape them—emerged as a part of the larger series of intellectual and social debates about molecular biology, human genetics, and medicine.[2,3] The debate about the meaning, telos, and nature of the work thus takes place on several levels of discourse simultaneously, signifying and symbolizing a great deal more than the mechanics of method, as do all great debates in science. Turning points in human understanding, such as those of Copernicus, Galileo, Newton, and Darwin, are always multilayered, for they lay claim to the largest subjects of knowledge—the central subjects of the whole of moral philosophy—about the nature of life itself and our place in it as humans. Claiming to deconstruct and define such questions have been problems firmly understood to be in the domain of ethics and religion, for the science of essential biology remained frustratingly speculative. As each piece of the puzzle of humanness, being, and behavior is set in place by biology, however, it threatens the theological and philosophical power of the classic disciplines to name and define the mystery of the whole. The struggle over the authority to name the nature, means, and ends of scientific knowledge is an old one in which, until the late 20th century, the hard sciences steadily gained ground. Many core issues and definitions were first contested and then largely ceded to biology by the late 19th century. The revolution on molecular biology accelerated the process as new frontiers were continually explored. However, the current ethical and moral debates on human stem cells mark both a new centrality of ethical reflection and a collective sense of caution about how we cross these new frontiers. Stem cell research challenges us: How should we become witnesses and interpreters of the transformation and of the use of the earliest stages of the human embryo? What are the boundaries of this journey?

At this stage, and despite the modern deference of ethics and religion to science in modernity, stem cell researchers have been confronted with the most serious religious and ethical challenge to science since the debate around nuclear fission. In the largely secular pluralistic world of the academic science community, one is led to ask: Why do religious and philosophical arguments so dominate the debate on stem cells? What is the warrant for listening to such ethical arguments in biology? Should science be a matter of politics or ethics at all? In this chapter, I give an account of how this came to be the case, summarize the leading arguments held by different sides in the debate, and describe the policy options engendered by the different moral appeals.

Tasks of Bioethics

First, it is the essential work of the field of ethics to delineate, reflect upon, consider comparatively, and then justify different moral appeals, asking questions about the nature, goal, and meaning of the moral activity. Finally, the field of ethics asks: What of many possible acts is the right act, and what makes it so? As a field, ethics is of particular use when several competing moral appeals seem justifiable.

In stem cell research, in a global scientific world, and in the 21st century, much of what had been previously agreed upon, even the very ability to find facts, is a subject for debate.[4,5] We share a deeply divided pluralistic society, a new sort of science, and a true moral uncertainty about both the limits of nature and the nature of limits. Religions have become central to the debate because they offer one consistent set of moral rules that, within the perimeters of each community, have at least a common ground.

Ethics reflects on our choices for moral action when we are decidedly not on such common ground, on issues at the margins of the grounds, and on areas of contention. Ethics as a field is largely a series of border negotiations. Furthermore, the debate about stem cells takes place at the junction of several social discourses: policy, science, and ethics. No one field can claim perfect rhetorical authority. In the past, debates about such things as moral status, as in the great debates about slavery or just war, was mediated by the dominate church and by the state with political or, finally, with military means. But in a society in which churches and states do not have hegemony, the debate is far more complex; it assumes a new character—a free-standing debate about the ethics of each act.

Ethical Debates at the Uncertain Borders

Our lack of ontic certainty reflects several new social doubts. We are collectively uncertain about the roles of religion and disparate worldviews in public life. There is a wide understanding that the U.S. Constitution prohibits the establishment of any state religion but a willingness to embrace good arguments that emerge from faith traditions. However, some worry that these should not be any more or less privileged than arguments that emerge from tradition of philosophy, such as those from Kant or Aristotle. What should the role be for the widely used term "moral repugnance" if an act is strongly repellent in one religious community but not in another?

We are confronted with scientific uncertainty as well, including ongoing debates about what stem cells are and what they might do. Are adult cells able to be reprogrammed and kept immortal? (And to what ends might that eventually lead?) Are embryonic cells somehow cached in the body? What is the mechanism in cell biology that differentiates the cell—how does "stemness" work? Embryology is still not fully understood, nor is the immune cascade response or other problems in histocompatibility, so important if medical researchers are to confront the problem of using the cells for tissue transplantation. In addition, there is not full agreement on the role of the cell as a signaling system.

We are confronted with uncertainty in our national—and any international—science policy. Who should make and then monitor such a policy? What is the scope of its power, and what is the right approach for a normative policy?

Policy statements conflict with the deliberations of each new commission, national organization, and science board.

The National Bioethics Advisory Committee, appointed by President Bill Clinton to advise him of bioethical issues, in 1999 supported the use of human embryonic stem cells in research and the limited use of embryos to produce them. The National Institutes of Health (NIH) crafted a compromise in late 2000 to allow the use of stem cells but not their derivation, a policy taken "under advisement" by President Clinton. After the election of George W. Bush, yet another new policy was proposed. President Bush's attention was turned fully to the debate in his first months in office, and it was the subject of his first public national address August 9, 2001. The American Association for the Advancement of Science (AAAS) and the Hastings Center had offered reports in 1999.

The National Academy of Sciences[6] issues reports on stem cells. When it was suggested that human "cloning" or somatic cell nuclear transfer (NT) would be a reasonable way to address issues of tissue incompatibility and a useful initial step in research on differentiation, reports on NT from the California Cloning Commission[7] in 2001 also took up the issue of stem cells.

Such uncertainty lead to a congressional debate, after which the House of Representatives passed a bill in August 2001 (265-162) that banned and criminalized research on the making of tissue or products from human embryonic stem cells as well as the use and the import of any products from that tissue. The Senate considered a complementary bill, the Brownback Bill, in June 2002 but did not come to a final resolution. In August 2003, they faced widespread opposition to such a bill from 70 Nobel laureates, the AAAS, scholars in religion and ethics, and more than 100 deans of medical schools.

Not only is the context of policy in flux, but the public is uncertain about its role and voice in the debate. We are an American polity with disagreement about the role and reach of the state; we are a polity rocked by debates about family and reproduction. We are a polity with complex and competing structures for apprehending illness, aging, and death; a polity with competing moral understandings of the nature of a good act; and a polity in debate about life's beginnings. Health care since the AIDS epidemic has been shaped largely by patient advocacy and consumer groups, a new force in the debate. Should patient advocacy matter? What role should activists play in promoting research, and should such advocacy groups have, as many argue, a larger role in the debate because they bear the costs of disease most directly and vividly?[a] How do we construct and defend our arguments in civic discourse (such as in public protests and in Senate hearings)? What is the role of the state as a mediator when citizens disagree seriously and are ready to go to extreme measures to defend their positions? Such defenses are as fierce in these debates about the moral status of the embryo as in earlier American civic debates about the Civil War, civil rights, and *Roe v Wade*.

Making the debate about the ethics of research on human embryonic stem cells ever more intense and divisive is the suggestion that NT as a technique should be allowed as a part of the research, thus wedding two of the most volatile issues in medical research—how we should regard the human embryo in its earliest stages, and how we should limit our capacity to create human replication. This debate was already strained by the explosion in advanced reproduction technology.

Research about the creation of life is not, to be sure, the only new biomedical and bioethical frontier in genetics. There has been an explosion of genetic knowledge about the etiology of disease, aging, and thus the new field of regenerative medicine, including its efficacy and its appropriateness. Safety concerns haunt all new research, and the past decade was further shaken by dramatic defeats in human gene transfer, confusing the public about what claims of research could be trusted. Even the tantalizing premise of tissue engineering and hopes for tissue transplantation; a cure for degeneration diseases; a genetic disease behind autoimmune diseases; an understanding of embryologic development; teratology; and an understanding of cellular reprogramming, growth, and death still seemed largely theoretical.

There were several serious problems in application. How to make histocompatible tissues for recipients would create several new ethical dilemmas. For example, if banks of stem

---

[a]*The case that advocacy groups have a larger role in the debate was made by an activist from the Christopher Reeves Foundation at the first meeting, to be held annually, in June 2003 of the International Society of Stem Cell Research in Washington, DC.*

cells from many different DNA sources were created, how would donors be recruited fairly? If a universal cell could be created, what was the assurance that genetic alteration would be stable or well tolerated? If chimerism–partial toleration was used to introduce new tissue into a recipient's body, as it is in adult tissue transplants and whole organ transplants, how would the side effects be addressed? If NT—cloning—was used, how would (nefarious) scientists be kept from trying to create humans, as fringe group scientists kept threatening to do throughout the debate?[8]

The polity erupted in controversy that became politicized—yet in unusual ways, with opponents and supporters from all points of the traditional political spectrum. The American Heart Association (AHA) rescinded its initial support of stem cells after Catholic donors expressed concern and withdrew support for AHA funding in this research. Prominent leaders on the left, such as ecologist William McKibben and William Kuchinic, opposed the research; former first lady Nancy Reagan, Sen. Orrin Hatch, Sen. Arlen Specter, and others traditionally of conservative leanings came out in public support. Like political leaders, religious groups differed in their approach. For Islam, Jewish, and liberal Protestant scholars, the research was either permissible or mandated as a positive act of healing, and the embryo was understood as lacking full moral status as a person. For many Roman Catholic and evangelical Protestants, the moral status of the embryo as fully ensouled at the moment of conception rendered acts of research on it sinful violations, and its destruction in research was regarded as the murder of a human being. Genetic research had already queried matters about the boundaries of life and our warrant and providence, and stem cell manipulation was seen merely as an extension of this hubris. For many, the controversy was the first time since the discovery of recombinant DNA technology that research was seriously questioned and its future course at stake. Many raised the argument of the outsider: Because of the separation between church and state, the faith communities and other dissonant groups felt it was reasonable to stand as outsiders to the debate and held this outsider status as a unique perspective. But others laid claim to the privilege of the insider. Patient advocates asked that their status be seen as more central, as the people most affected; scientists called for the debate to be located primarily within the academic scientific community or to be led by those with the most expertise in the actual science at issue.

Question of Limits

"There may be valuable scientific knowledge which it is morally impossible to obtain...."

Paul Ramsey, 1970

When the Christian moral theologian Paul Ramsey made the arguments for limits on our knowledge, he was partly concerned about genetic research, asking scientific researcher to first ask ethical questions: What is the proper object of our desire? What can one trust? In this, he was assuming that science is embedded in communities of responsibility.

Science's implications bear upon us all; hence, we all participate in them and have a right and responsibility to comment on them. In response to such early contentions in clinical research and clinical medicine, bioethics committees and a bioethics forum began to emerge as alternate venues for moral debate. For example, after the family of Karen Ann Quinlan went to court to gain permission to withdraw her from a ventilator that was keeping her alive, the NY State Commission on Issues at the End of Life was established to debate and set the policy to regulate such matters. When the mapping of the human genome was proposed, funding was set aside to allow ethics discourse and research to continue mapping the ethical, social, and legal issues raised by the science (ELSI Projects). Ethics and the attendant question of limits have been a potent force in the debate since Ramsey first raised the question.

Forbidden Knowledge

In several critical ways, research on human embryonic stem cells recapitulates old arguments about our faith in science, progress, and technology. Science in general, and genetics in particular, lays claim to topics that are controversial by their very nature—not only because they are new to our established normative narratives, causing some to claim that we are "moving rapidly toward a posthuman future," (Francis Fukuyama, Our Post Human Future, 2003) but also because they deconstruct the narrative of creation. In some ways, research raises fears about forbidden and new knowledge; in other ways, it potentiates fears about violations of "mother nature," an argument engaged by both fundamentalists and environmentalists. The forbidden nature or the speed of research is part of a larger debate about modernity, its pace, and its uses. This debate is waged around many other new areas of knowledge: anesthesia, vaccination, and electricity, among others.

Furthermore, new knowledge is threatening to an established order and to the nature of order (and the order of nature) envisioned as reflected in the nuclear family. Many have been adamant in their opposition to research on embryos or research in molecular genetics because they have felt it destabilizes families and natural reproduction. Hence, Kass has argued against stem cells because it may cause "moral harms" to the family unit.

This idea of a lost, beneficent, and essential primitive order, in which nature is seen as morally normative, is a familiar one in philosophy and in political life. In philosophy, Nietzsche and Heidegger both argued that modernity, science, and the social contract of the modern state distanced, as Heidegger states, "man in his essence" (a more authentic man) from a creature he was forced to be in a technological word. Heidegger called for "a more primal knowledge" as a basis for their ethics. In many religions, the same period that has witnessed fierce opposition to science has seen the rise of fundamentalism, the questioning of evolution, and the rejection of facticity. In politics, a fear of the future has often replaced an earlier optimism about the future. And in all of these arguments, a return to the past, or an imagined purer past, is both attractive and redemptive. It is against this strong cultural yearning that the first research on human embryonic stem cells was cast. This is partly why the reaction to this last in a series of experiments has catalyzed such attention toward the question of the essential morality of such research.

Four Sets of Questions About the Ethics of Research

In regarding the answers to the questions of what is the right act and what makes it so, ethicists have classically turned to four types of problems:

1. What are the origins of the materials used in research (issues of moral status)?
2. What is the process by which the materials are obtained and manipulated?
3. What is the telos, or end of the work?
4. What is the social context into which the work enters and exists?

Ethicists begin with two classic taxonomic tasks, or two types of questions that sort and define the problem: that of definitions and that of norms, or rules of action, on which policy and legal issues emerge.

Epistemic questions (how do we even know what we think we know?) always bedevil philosophy, and they abound in stem cell research, where the science is new and subtle. What counts as a truth claim? What language can we agree on when we define things? How do we define life, suffering, or goodness? Who is "we," and does our community include such being as embryos, "children yet to be born," or "the patients of the future"?

Normative questions also mark the debate: Whose truth claim wins out when many compete? How do we regulate research? How do we enforce regulations? How could we control the process and outcomes? What is the role of the state in science policy? In the science marketplace?

ORIGINS

What Is the Moral Status of the Blastocyst?
This question has dominated the controversy about any research on embryos and, in particular, about stem cell research. First, what is the essential nature of these cells? And second, what are our duties toward the blastocyst? If the cells are fully ensouled humans (like newborns), one needs to regard them as such, and one's duties to the cells are morally equivalent to duties toward any other dependent, vulnerable human. If they are regarded as tissue of worth (like hearts one can transplant), one has duties such as respect, care, and prudence to consider. If they are regarded as tissue like any other body tissue or like tissue to be discarded (like placentas), then one's duties are largely those of attention to the symbolic dignity of anything human.

When Does Life Begin?
Human eggs are alive (in that they are not inanimate objects and in that they are cells with the ability to divide). All eggs

are potentially fertilizable. Hogan as noted that when "life begins" is a complex question—think of a blastocyst as origami paper, she argues, that needs a genetic signal to be folded correctly.[9] This signal is one in a cascade of biological events and could be one mark of human life. Conversely, one could point to other moments within the activity called "fertilization" in 19th-century terms—that is, the many moments in which the one-cell being differentiates and individuates. Moral status is contended ground and can be defined relative to many factors, including when biological individuality is established, when a certain level of organization is achieved in the blastocyst, and standard temporality (ranging from 1 second to 40 days of maturity). One could define moral status by analyzing intent—by the reason for the creation and the existence of the embryo (intended to become a baby or intended to be used for research), by the physical location of the embryo (in the womb or in a test tube), by the potentiality of the embryo, by the likelihood that is it destined for destruction, or as some have suggested, by determining the rates of loss in the human reproduction of all embryos (close to 90%). Since moral status has been important in political, religious, and legal systems for centuries,[b,10] and since a pregnancy is not perceptible to the external world of the polity for months, most textual traditions rooted in antiquity assume an ancient tradition of an "unformed fetus." Such a term is found in the writings of Aristotle, in both the Hebrew Scripture and the subsequent Talmudic discourse, in the Sharia, in Islamic legal commentaries that interpret the Koran, in Augustine, and in Thomas Aquinas. The Vatican held the interpretation that an embryo had a null to limited moral status until 40 days into the pregnancy; for Muslims, it was until the bones had "knit," and for the Aristotelian tradition, it was until the menstrual blood had "congealed." In Canon law (the Catholic legal authority), this idea held until 1917, when, following the new science that could observe eggs and sperm, the idea of a homunculus at the head of a sperm being implanted like a seed into a woman was dispelled. Most theologians until the late 19th century had an idea that pregnancy was not an established and protected fact until this time; they ruled on cases and wrote as if this were indeed the case. Recent debates may tend to obscure this history, but the idea of personhood beginning at "the moment of conception" is a relatively new idea that grounds the primacy of fetal rights over maternal ones. It is an idea that has changed dramatically from earlier perceptions.

Linguistic and Narrative Uncertainty
The central concern about moral status, however, has led many to think of the ethical issue of stem cells as one synonymous with abortion. This has lead to the use of similar language in both debates: women's rights, babies, fetuses, reproduction, and choice vs life. It is not the only linguistic uncertainty. Several people have raised the issues of whether an artificially created or a very early blastocyst is properly called an embryo

---

[b]For matters of compensation in the loss of a pregnancy, for issues of when and under what circumstances a community mourns for the loss of a pregnancy, etc., see Feldman.[10]

and whether this term, when improperly used, merely confuses the public. The use of the term *cloning* is a further confusion, since the goal of human or animal cloning is to produce offspring, but the goal of cloning for research is to create genetically identical duplicates (of cells or regions of DNA). In this case, the goal of cloning is to make many exact copies of cells to study how very early development occurs. Narrative uncertainty has also been introduced into the discourse. By this I would argue that there has been a break in the standing cultural story of the nuclear family, the miracle of birth through loving sexual intercourse. Significant changes in the essential and primal narrative of human reproduction have raised the following questions: What is a family now? What does it mean to make embryos with a series of unions of parts from variable sources? What if the narrative has alternate possible endings? The traditional narrative of human reproduction—one man, one woman, a meaningful Adamic cleaving leading to progeny that carry the story forward—is at the heart of many faith traditions. Indeed, it is through this human story that Western traditions and several of the traditions of Eastern and indigenous religions[c] create a core narrative about the meaning, nature, and goal of being human.

Our understanding of ourselves as a part of this narrative, as children and then parents, strengthens the meaning of many theological constructs: natural law theory, the begotten creation of children, the pronatalist imperative, and the obligations and relationships in families and communities. However, since the early 1970s, the idea of the natural process of sexual reproduction has been disrupted by emerging scientific technology, which has created many possible origins for any human embryo: It may be fabricated by mixing eggs and sperm or by injecting an egg with a selected sperm. The course of development may be altered as well: Sperm may be "spun" and separated by weight to select for gender; the egg may be altered with extra mitochondrial DNA; embryos may be deselected by genetic trait; or the embryo may be implanted in a surrogate, the egg obtained from another woman, and the resulting child given to a third family, which may itself be constituted in a variety of genders and permutations. All of these disruptions in the core narrative elicited considerable alarm initially, and at each stage, social discourse has emerged as new possibilities are discovered. In many societies, the narrative has been reimagined and retold to account for these new variants. Regenerative medicine offers not only another set of beginnings for the narrative of reproduction but also other possible telos for the embryo. Now, a blastocyst fabricated in an *in vitro* fertilization (IVF) clinic faces at least four fates: It might be transferred to a human womb, where it might implant successfully, grow, and be born into childhood; it might be transferred but not develop; it might be frozen indefinitely; or it might be discarded. Alternately, the embryo might be destroyed in a lab in the process of being used to make stem cells—and some (such as Lebacqz and Peters) argue that this allows the DNA of that cell immortal replication.

Once our society allowed the first four outcomes, the last, in the lab, can be understood as yet another alternate ending or an alternative goal. For many, such a deconstructed narrative, with the possibility of origins other than monogamous union and ends other than reproduction, elicits a sense of moral repugnance, the ultimate horror of a scientific, desacralized world. But for others, this revised narrative elicits a curiosity and awe at the new possibilities for human understanding and at the possibility of altering other key aspects of what had been understood as moral fixities—the nature and scope of human suffering, the "natural" span of a human life, and the capacity for human reach.[d,11]

PROCESS: HUMAN-SUBJECT ISSUES

How Can Cells Be Obtained and Created Justly?

Ethical questions have emerged not only about the moral status and origins of the tissue but also about the "harvesting" of the gametes needed to fabricate the blastocyst. All eggs come from a particular woman, all sperm from a particular man. How are these obtained justly and safely from human subjects—and does this change if the women and men whose gametes are at stake are voluntarily (even desperately) trying to achieve a pregnancy and in so doing create "excess" embryos they do not choose to use? Dresser and others[12] have raised concerns that women might be exploited or manipulated into using their bodies to make money and be placed at undue risk if they are hormonally stimulated to produce eggs. Holland raises concerns about the reduction of women to the value of their reproductive capacity.

Others have raised epistemic issues in the process. What does it mean to "make" embryos with a series of unions of parts from variable sources? Will such disaggregating of the pieces of the person lead us toward a world of commodified, exchangeable selves—a sort of warehouse supply store that would cheapen unique human lives? Would disabled persons be seen as poor products and be discarded as some have claimed? What are we to make of the practice—already in place—of advertising for gametes from women of privilege social or intellectual status and competing for the "best eggs?" Since some marketplace relations have, in the past, understood human bodies as at least potential commodities, what protections might be instituted to protect human subjects from the pressures of the market?

"No Truth But the Thing Itself"

A second problem in the process of the design of all biological research is that one cannot make an abstract model of the problem, as one can in other sciences. Unlike physics or chemistry, the model is the actual human event. Hence, even making models creates the problems one needs to tentatively explore. Even a proof-of-principle experiment requires a blastocyst.

A third problem is the slippery-slope issue, or the "trigger" problem. It is argued that making and perfecting a small part

---

[c]Variants include heroic or divine-human conceptions, but all are based on sexual union, gestation, and birth.

[d]I wrote the first drafts of this paper and delivered the speech on which it is based prior to reading the seminal work by Shattuck on this central idea.[11]

of the technology that can be used for cloning or genetic engineering, which may in itself be only an incremental shift in knowledge, can allow a desensitized and facile acceptance to the next (troubling) step of the science. Here, the concern is that setting up a project that allows the "harvesting" of gametes, cloning, and so on would set the stage for cloning for reproductive purpose, genetic engineering for "designer" babies, or other such scenarios.

A final problem is a structural one. In the past, the public understood research on embryos as instrumental toward the goal of reproduction (hence the support of IVF research). Here, the process is geared toward a more abstract telos; hence, the charge arises that embryos are only being made to be destroyed. If the embryos used are created for reproductive purposes, then for many, their destruction in research is an event that occurs along the inevitable trajectory toward destruction and is a different ethical question than that raised by embryos newly created for research. Yet it is precisely this sort of experimental use that promises to yield an important understanding of early stages of cell signaling, cell programming, and genetic control mechanizes in both normal and disease states.

TELOS: CREATING A MORAL POLICY

How Do We Construct a World in Which Humans Flourish?

Thinking about the ends of the research on human stem cells has initiated a discussion on the nature of the ends and the goals of health care itself and has lead to a critical split in how we considered aging, human frailty, and illness. Kass, Meilander, Fukayama, and others[13–15] have raised serious concerns that if the goal of this research is to eliminate illness or human suffering, it is a flawed goal and it is a tragic error to pursue it. Kass has spoken of the character-building engagement of a life lived well as one ages, of lessons learned through the suffering and subjection of the creaturely body, and of the virtues enhanced with the acceptance of even serious disability. What will happen, ask these critics, to our sense of compassion if its objects—vulnerable, frail, and elderly—are enhanced to robust, cheerful perfection? Yet others, such as Stock, Silver, and Caplan, disagree,[16,17] arguing for a world progressively liberated from such limitations. Others have raised issues of unintended consequences—unknown and unknowable chaos that may result if this research is pursued. Clearly, since we are witnessing only the earliest stages of research that although interesting is still largely theoretical, the civic discourse will have to attend to and welcome such concerns and attend to the immediate issues of how investigators need to act now to structure such attention should such choices ever confront us.

CONTEXTUAL FRAMING OF THE ISSUES

Can Just Research Be Conducted in a World of Injustice?

The context of all research is that health care is an unfinished project of social justice. In America, the uninsured with minimal access to basic health care continue to vex political policy.

International issues of distributive justice render the problem of access to new research and the therapies that will emerge from such research as a central ethical concern. Moreover, as noted previously, stem cell research is placed in the context of the abortion debate, and the unsettled and volatile nature of the discourse about embryos is based in the unfinished debate about abortion. Like slavery, such a debate is about religion, moral status, civil rights, and civil duties, but it is also about health care funding and services. The debate about abortion has defined and has been thematic of American politics since 1973; hence, there was no *public* funding in the first debates about fetal tissue, and most of the first research projects were privatized, funded by independent capital. This created labs that by federal mandate could not be located in any building or institution that used federal funds, leading to new concerns about secrecy, profits, etc. The need to separate controversial research from research that could be supported by a polity and their tax revenues lead to a further separation than some critics are now comfortable with—hence the call for more federal oversight.

The second contextual problem is that stem cell research takes place against a background of four decades of unease about all things genetic. From genetic manipulation and the creation of genetically modified foods to issues of genetic testing and privacy, Americans, and to a larger extent Europeans, have been vocally mistrustful of the motives and aims of research genetics. This has risen to a level of concern that has been taken, literally, to the public square and linked with globalization and colonization. Protestors of international banking policy routinely appear in butterfly costumes, alluding to a report (never replicated) that genetically modified organisms corn negatively affects butterfly reproduction.

Furthermore, there is unease about human-subject research, as research errors have occurred at major medical centers such as the University of Pennsylvania, John Hopkins University, and Duke University. Further mistrust is created about the ability of the marketplace to self-regulate, as by the case of Enron. That several of these scandals in research (gene therapy) and in the market (Martha Stewart) are linked to genetics heightens the context of anxiety.

Finally, many have raised the issue of the context of the marketplace and the increasing involvement—through patenting, technology transfer, and licensing agreements—of biotechnology in the life of the academic science lab, an issue that Derek Bok and others query actively.

Normative Issues: Three "Bright Lines" Have Long Limited Research

Social concerns have thus driven the ethical debate, and ethicists have responded with recourse to the traditional sanctions suggested by bioethics' first principles: autonomy, beneficence or nonmalfeasance, and justice, with bioethics deep affection for autonomy as a premier principle. Hence, policies have been developed with strong privacy and informed consent requirements, and reproductive medicine has long operated with private, parental desire as both the main driver and the main funding source. Ethical boundaries were established in the 1970s to limit technologies seen then as remote. These three "bright lines" were a reluctance to sanction possible intervention in human-inheritable genetic material, a ban on the fabrication of human embryos for research alone, and a ban on cloning (NT) for any purpose. Human embryonic stem cell inquiry challenges each of these norms, and even a close examination of several IVF methodologies reveals that here, too, such "bright lines" have long been crossed. Normative oversight (civil committees, state, federal, or scientific) has been called for by nearly every deliberative body that has considered the issues of the regulation of stem cell research. But in so doing, six types of policy problems will have to be decided: How will differences in strongly held religious and moral stances be expressed and defended? How will the freedom of the scientific pursuit be limited? What of the power of the ends expressed by patient advocacy groups? What will happen to violators? Who will fund such oversight? And who will be chosen to be on such committees?

Summary

ARGUMENTS FOR PROCEEDING: ETHICAL RESEARCH ON HUMAN STEM CELLS CAN BE DONE

Let me summarize the central arguments for actively supporting, funding, and pursuing research in stem cells.

Teleological, Consequential, and Largely Utilitarian Arguments

Research on stem cells has a nearly unlimited potential for good ends. Various diseases that affect millions worldwide have as their case the disadvantages of cell growth or cell death; thus, understanding how cells grow, how they are genetically regulated, and how they develop both normally and abnormally will be key to therapy. It is this vision of future therapies and this attention to human suffering that ought to lie at the core of the medical endeavor. A correlative research end will be met by research on embryonic development. Stem cell cultures will allow an ability to test toxicity–pharmaceuticals in early embryos and in human tissues, a task that is dubious in animal models and ethically unacceptable in human pregnancies. A final, related, telos-based argument is that such research is of itself a good end, for it allows the ability to study the process of genetic diseases at cellular level, using the full power of recent genomic advances in understanding causality. Others note that the funding of open research is a valid goal, and they are eager to embrace a fully open telos as a principle of science policy.

Many diseases that affect millions worldwide would be cured—not merely treated—by the use of tissue transplants. Cardiac diseases, cardiovascular diseases, degeneration, or trauma to the spinal or central nervous system are obvious first candidates. That such tissue transplants have shown promise in early testing in animal models drives this argument into a central location in the debate.

Equivalency Arguments

Stem cell research is very much like other research on embryos that is already being done in universities and medical centers all over the country—IVF research in which many eggs are tested, injected with sperm, given growth factors to stimulate growth, and used as tools in teaching physicians their craft as infertility specialists. All such embryo experiments are approved by an institutional research board if the work, and the embryos created therein, are destroyed at 14 days of life, just prior to the development of an individuated primitive streak. Linked to this argument is the larger one that much of early IVF research (some would say all) is a vast experiment, and that many embryos are created with the clear understanding that few would survive. The protocols for IVF originally called for the implantation of up to eight embryos in the womb in the hopes that not all would die, thus building embryonic waste directly into the research and currant clinical practice. If more than three embryos do implant, the couple is routinely offered "embryo reduction," meaning targeted and selective abortion of the "excess" embryos, in the name of saving or enhancing the lives of the remaining sibling twins.

A variant of this is based on a naturalistic premise, which permits research on blastocysts since so many are simply nonviable in the natural course of things. Thus, embryonic loss is like the loss that occurs in nature, and many of the blastocysts would be lost in any case.

Deontological (Duty-Based) Arguments

In many religions, and in secular medicine's premise, there is a duty to heal. Obligations are correlative with rights. In this argument, the limited moral status of the *in vitro* blastocyst determines duties to it, and the relatively larger (some say unlimited) duties to the ill and vulnerable may be primary ones. We have a duty to heal, and this is expressed in legal and social policy. To turn from the possibility of healing would be an abrogation of an essential duty. Furthermore, justice concerns may mandate this research, because unlike whole organ transplants, tissue transplants and pharmecueticalized stem cell tissues many be made scaleable, universal, and affordable, thus allowing a widely applicable use for these transplants. Serious issues of histocompatibility may in theory block this path for now, but the duty to justice would mandate a fully expressed research effort in this direction.

Making the claim for duty can be religiously motivated or can come from sources such as the determinates of biology (that we need to protect kin, that we are dependent as neonates and need protection, and that primates have a long period of parenting until adulthood). Other sources include our shared aspirational duties to improve our situation of suffering, as is argued in Christianity; a divine command, as is posited by Judaism; our "experiences," as argued in American pragmatism; and our ability to be social beings making social contracts, as Locke and Jefferson suggest.

What are such duties? In other work, I have suggested six:[18]

1. *Duties to make justice:* Judged by social contracts that attend to healing the most vulnerable in our society and to making therapies accessible to all.

2. *Duties to discern and judge:* Assessed by our ability to be coherent moral actors, to set limits, and to see differences in moral status and ability.

3. *Duties to heal the ill, save lives if we can, and care for the dying if we cannot:* Enacted by the inherent duty of medicine that we must extrapolate to societies, in which no self can be exempted.

4. *Duties to guardianship:* Enacted by attention to a world unfinished and in need of protease inhibitors, vaccines, yeasted bread, eyeglasses, etc. This duty of rational discourse grounds a thoughtful civil debate.

5. *Duties to be readers of text:* Meaning that interpretation and analysis of the phenomenological world is suggested by the very way knowledge is structure—imperfect, mutable, and unrevealed.

6. *Duties toward solidarity:* Taken from European debates on genetic issues, this term means that we have a duty to social cohesion. Activities that merely instrumentally use one another (exploitative relationships with gamete donors, etc.) are a violation of this duty.

Arguments from Legal and Historical Precedents

Here, one can turn to the example of times when a severely divided country moved ahead on a issue of policy despite the deeply held moral opposition of many—Mennonites who opposed World War II and Quakers who opposed the war in Vietnam offer examples of how democracies must act for the majority and how the minority view must continue to be expressed, even if such dissent carries the risk of civil disobedience. America, from the time of Thoreau, has understood democracy as a serious matter of dissent as well as assent.

Arguments That Are Political in Nature

Here, the arguments are as follows: If research is not funded publicly, this could drive it into private and unconsidered spheres or could limit the goods of the research to particular sectors, specific groups, or the needs of the market (one thinks of Viagra instead of pediatric dieses, for example.)

ARGUMENTS FOR STOPPING: STEM CELL RESEARCH IS IMMORAL AND ILL-CONSIDERED

The arguments against stem cell research, whether they favor banning it for a time or banning it permanently, are summarized in the next sections.

Deontological Objections

First, stem cell research is murder of nascent humans and is deontologically forbidden. In the report from the President's Council on Bioethics, the majority argued for a moratorium on such research, with strong opposition from a significant portion of the commission. The members opposed to stem cell research argued largely deontologically, stating that the moral status of a cloned embryo is nascent human life and is thus a member of our shared humanity. As such, they argued, Americans had a special obligation to protect vulnerable members of our social contract, the most vulnerable being entities such as a blastocyst.

Furthermore, to use an embryo would be an exploitative use of human life as a tool, a serious moral wrong in addition to the moral wrong of killing. Such violations of essential duties to care thus create serious moral harm to society—coarsening our ideas of family union and exposing our culture to the uncertainties of asexual reproduction. It also was argued that it was a misunderstanding of our duty to heal to think that suffering can be cured or alleviated, especially with the sacrifice of life. Here is employed the caution that there is no moral obligation to treat all disease—and it is a moral error to think we can do so—and the complementary idea that our ability to suffer and to feel compassion for the suffering stranger is at the base of our shared humanity. The fulcrum of this sort of deontological argument rests on the view of suffering, frailty, and limitation as central to our human creatureliness and our human nature.

Teleological Vein

It is argued that such research will engender a terrifying, "posthuman" set of consequences—since we face a lack of moral consensus about the family and reproduction, allowing research on this volatile and contentious issue will create political chaos. Others fear that it *will not work* and hopes for cures will be cruelly dashed, that it *will work* and be unsafe and dangerous, or that it *will work* and give parents powerful, morally repugnant choices such as the elimination of all imperfect children, creating "designer babies" that may be, in this argument, very skillful and very beautiful but cruel and soulless. Such choices are disturbing and, as Kass, Hurlbut, and Dressor argue, "inherently, essentially morally repugnant." ("The yuck factor" is the term used by Callahan and others to describe this phenomena.)

Slippery-Slope Arguments

These are key to the opposition to stem cell research—a series of classic arguments that maintains that although the particular act may be marginally permissible, the road to which it leads will be a dark and downward descent. Powerful historical precedents in the form of American and German eugenics, as have been soundly exposed, document a slope of precisely this sort in which technology was used to marginalize and eliminate the ill, the disabled, and the socially different in the years prior to the elimination of the Jews of Europe.[19–21] Manipulation of embryos or cloning could lead down the slope to the possibility that governments will determine which sort of life is a good one, that cloning people will lead to two classes of human, or that human–animal chimeric monsters will be created.

Concerns of Justice, Especially Feminist and Environmentalist Ones

It is feared that stem cell research may exploit women for their eggs, that women may be coerced, that huge "embryo farms" will be needed to make enough stem cell cultures, or that human tissue will be merely another scarce commodity to which the poor contribute but do not have access.[12] Some raise the fear that Americans already spend too much on research such as this, especially on research for the privileged elderly, and not enough on preventive health care clinics for the poor;

others fear that profit-driven private pharmaceutical companies or illegal offshore laboratories will have too much control over the processes and the products of the research. Some raise the fear that such a violation of natural limits and borders is too closely akin to the errors made in the use of nature in the 19th century, and that human ecology, or a human "gene pool," may be disrupted by stem cell research. In this argument (partly deontological and partly teleological), nature is seen as normative, morally stable, and instructive.

Regulatory Concerns

These are concerns that scientists cannot be trusted to self-regulate, since a proportion of the research community believes that nature is flawed and in need of their ministrations. This can too easily segue into the research community "playing God with creation," a fear raised about all genetic research. The fear that the technology will be impossible to regulate is behind the policy of absolute bans.

FROM ETHICS TO POLICY IN HUMAN STEM CELL RESEARCH: EIGHT POLICY OPTIONS

Stem cell research is global in character,[e] with 8 of 12 sources and most lines named in the Bush administration's August 9, 2003, compromise plan for the use of stem cells in research outside of the United States. In each place, core ideas about informed consent vary, core cultural and social meanings of IVF differ, and core notions of the polity and process of oversight vary. Therefore, how can one speak of coherent, reflective public policy to adjudicate between the powerful arguments that I noted previously?

Leroy Walters has suggested six options; I would argue that eight choices of policy have already been employed globally.

Ban Outright All Research Involving Stem Cells

Considering this option are France, Germany, Ireland, Norway, Switzerland, Poland, and Brazil; 10 states in the United States (North and South Dakota, Michigan, Minnesota, Massachusetts, Pennsylvania, Maine, Rhode Island, Louisiana, Florida); and 2 states in Australia.

Permit Use Only of Cells from "Excess" Embryos Derived by Others from IVF Clinics

This was the option suggested by the NIH under President Clinton in 1999 and 2000, by Sen. Bill Frist in July 2001 (with a limit on number), and by President Bush in 2003 (with a limit on time of derivation).

[e]Sources for the cell lines in the Bush compromise: National Center for Biological Sciences, Bangalore, India (3 lines); Monash University, Melbourne, Australia (6 lines); National University of Singapore (6 lines); ES Cell International (6 lines); Reliance Life Sciences, Mumbai, India (7 lines); Technion-Israel Institute of Technology, Haifa, Israel (4 lines); Göteborg University, Göteborg, Sweden (19 lines); BresaGen, Athens, GA (and Adelaide, South Australia) (4 lines); Wisconsin Alumni Research Foundation, Madison, WI (5 lines); CyThera, San Diego, CA (9 lines); University of California, San Francisco, CA (2 lines); Geron, San Mateo, CA (2 lines).

Permit Derivation from "Excess" IVF Embryos by Stem Cell Researchers

This was suggested by President Clinton's National Bioethics Advisory Committee in September 1999; by the European Union Group on Ethics on Science and the New Technology in November 2000; by the Advisory Group to Canadian Institutes of Health Research in March 2001; by Deutsche Forschungsgemeinschaft in May 2001; in France by two national advisory groups in January and June 2001; by Japan's Expert Panel on Bioethics in August 2001; by the Australian House of Representatives' Committee on Constitutional and Legal Affairs in September 2001; by the Bioethics Advisory Board for the Howard Hughes Medical Institute; by Canada, Italy, Spain, and the Netherlands; and by 2 states in Australia and 40 states in the US.

Permit Derivation and Use from Embryos Created Just for This Research

This is the policy of the United Kingdom, China, Sweden, Belgium, Israel, Virginia, California, and The Jones Institute.

Permit Nonreproductive Cloning to Create Embryos for Research and Use

This is an option allowed by the United Kingdom, China, Belgium, Saudi Arabia, and Israel; by the California Cloning Commission; by the Bioethics Advisory Board of the National Academy of Science and Humanities (Sept. 9, 2001); and by the U.S. National Academy of Sciences Task Force Report (Sept. 11, 2001).

Permit a Separation Compromise

This tack would allow different populations or jurisdictions to do different things. In the United States, this is understood as a possible model for many controversial policies, often as a transitional policy ("the laboratory of the states") until consensus can be held federally (as in civil rights laws).

Allow All Ideas Uncovered in Research to Be Fully Explored

This would include the use of animal eggs, human DNA, the creation of chimeras, and parthenogenesis, a policy followed by China.

Create a Limited Year, or a Limited Technique, Moratorium

The President's Council on Bioethics has recommended such a policy, and the term varies. The point of a moratorium on various parts or all of the processes from use to application would be to have a more open debate in the political arena so that all views could be fully aired. It should be noted that all of the other seven options also call for such a robust debate.

POINTS OF CONVERGENCE: WHAT CAN BE AGREED ON?

Hence, we have deeply held beliefs and widely divergent policies. Can we agree on any point or convergence? I will argue that we can and present a few beginning candidates.

First, science is a kind of free speech, but free science is for public good; hence, it must be honest, freely open, and regulated in some way by the very public sphere in which it aspires to be considered. Second, science must be just, with its social goods available to all without discrimination. It must never coerce or exploit human subjects. Third, science must be prudent and safe, taking care to protect the environment even as it alters it. Fourth, *medical* research must aim at beneficence toward patients, whose futures and interests must be protected. Fifth, disability, aging, and illness must not be dishonored. Finally, although each human person has core human rights, such rights suggest correlative duties that must be fulfilled.

POINTS OF DIVERGENCE: WHAT CANNOT BE AGREED ON?

There are four matters that I would argue we will not come to agreement on, and we must find ways of negotiating our serious differences, which are ultimately serious religious matters. We must come to understand that we will likely not agree on the moral status of fetuses and embryos. Nor will we agree on the definition of a family. We will not agree on the meaning and content of what is "repugnant" in science. We will not agree on the place of suffering in our theo–social world view.

Conclusion and Recommendations: Creating a Civic Witness

Bioethics can be faulted if, after raising a chapter of questions, concerns, and inquiries, it does not offer a thoughtful recommendation of a way forward. How can we now apply ethics? How do we go beyond a call for justice or a call for deepening the public debate? Here are some specific recommendations. First, I would argue for the development of a range of civic responses to science research beyond the "red light–green light" approach. Research can be (rarely, I think) prohibited when it is abusive, deadly, or coercive (as has been done in certain human-subject research); permitted and regulated closely by citizenship oversight; or permitted with institutional oversight. Finally, research should be encouraged, funded, and socially rewarded. Each project needs our assessment, rather than just the projects that are given special scrutiny in the press. Many, such as Alta Charo, have noted that this largely is already our practice through the International Review Boards for Human Subject Research (IRB), Institutional Animal Care and Use Committees (IACUC), and NIH review process, especially in genetic research, but the mechanisms clearly need to be more fully explained to the American public so that they can be assured of research transparency. This will mean that the public will have to come to understand, without panic or hype, that all great research is inherently risky, given to failure and error, and may not yield success suddenly or ever. (That is why it is called "research.") Patience will have to be taught as a duty if public oversight is to be wise. Public accountability is a model for the Recombinant DNA Advisory Committee—a process begun with researchers at Asilomar, querying their own direction, and used to regulate genetic intervention. That such a

limited regulatory model is in place, as opposed to the broader model used in the United Kingdom, is a result of different regulatory etiologies. In the United States, regulation emerged after more than 15 years of debate after *Roe v Wade,* the unregulated growth of IVF industry (1979–1994), the commission of the Human Embryo Research Report, the rejection of findings, and the move to regulation at the state level.

But in the United Kingdom, IVF was debated in the government-sponsored Warnock Report, which recommended the Human Fertilization and Embryology Authority (HFEA) that has been in place since 1991 (issuing both public and private licenses and providing oversight to all uses of all embryos, from IVF clinics to stem cells).

A public oversight committee built along these lines would be a strong contribution to the resolution of the controversy. It will require public members and full, open, public debate; it will need to publish reports on the construction of standards, the conduct of human clinical trials, and the setting up of local IRB and Data Safety Monitoring Boards (DSMBs). It will have to foster a wide educational campaign, as does the HFEA, and provide oversight of all IVF procedures, use of eggs, and research protocols. It will have to decide if ongoing research will be supported and which will need more careful review. It should enforce the global ban on all cloning for reproduction.

DEVELOPMENT OF A THEORY OF VIRTUE FOR RESEARCH

Beyond such a committee, as in Britain, I would argue for making the question of moral agency in research a central one. That a serious debate about research asks a great deal from us is a good thing, and it is a development that researchers should not fear but should welcome. The question in the foreground is the moral status of the persons involved and of the witnessing public: What does this research make of us? Thinking about the moral relationships between researchers and donors is central. How does this work shape us as a society? Since many of the objections warn of the problem of complicity, one must ask: How does one avoid such evil? How does the gravitas of research itself sug-gest answers? When is civil disobedience and moral dissent rightly used?

NOTES TOWARD A RECOMMENDATION

If the British oversight model is employed, and if we make serious efforts to create a virtue ethics for basic research and to articulate it clearly, I would argue that is reasonable to support stem cell research. I would argue that this is a morally defensible gesture, one that may hold extraordinary promise for a shared human future. I would further argue that we may use early human embryos in research before 14 days—not frivolously, but where important new scientific knowledge can be gained; where new therapies may be able to be developed; and where, if use judiciously, well-designed research has the informed consent of the genetic providers and full and transparent public oversight.

The creativity and the tenacity of the biologist community have created an explosion in science knowledge. This calls us to respond with creative and tenacious ethical discourse.

ACKNOWLEDGMENTS

I wish to thank Leroy Walters, for work on policy options and international research. I thank Brigid Hogan, Leonard Zon, Doug Melton, Tom Okarma, John Gearheart, Ted Friedman, Larry Goldstein, Ron McKey, Jamie Thompson, David Anderson, and Irv Weissman for explanations of the scientific basis of the problems.

REFERENCES

1. Watson, J. (2003). "DNA." —Press.
2. Shamblott, G. *et al.* (1998). Derivation of pluripotent stem cells from cultured human primordial germ cells. *Proc. Natl. Acad. Sci. U. S. A.* **95,** 13,726–13,731.
3. Thomson, J. *et al.* (1998). Embryonic stem cell lines derived from human blastocysts. *Science* **282,** 1145–1147.
4. Callahan, D. (1995). The puzzle of profound respect. *Hasting Cent. Rep.* **25,** 39–40.
5. Brock, D. (1987). Truth or consequences: The role of philosophers in policy making. *Ethics* **97,** 789.
6. National Academy of Sciences. (2001). Report on human embryonic stem cells.
7. California Cloning Commission. (2002). Report on human embryonic stem cells.
8. The Raelians (2002). *NY Times* **Dec. 23,** A.
9. Hogan (October 2001). Talks at Vanderbilt University.
10. Feldman, D. Abortion and Birth Control in Jewish Law. *In* Feldman, D.M. (1968). "Birth Control in Jewish Law: Martial Relations, Contraception, and Abortion as set Forth in the Classic Texts of Jewish Law." New York University Press, New York.
11. Shattuck, R. (1996). "Forbidden Knowledge." Harcourt Brace, San Diego.
12. Dresser, R. (2002). *In* "Report of the President's Council on Bioethics."
13. President's Council on Bioethics (July 2003).
14. Kass, L. (2003).
15. Fukayama, F. (2003).
16. Stock, G.
17. Silver, L.
18. Zoloth, L. (2003). Freedoms, duties, and limits: The ethics of stem cell research. *In* "God and the Human Embryo," pp. 141–151. Georgetown University Press, Washington, DC.
19. Kevles
20. Duster
21. Lombardo

Ethical Considerations

Ronald M. Green

Human embryonic stem (hES) cell research is ethically controversial because it entails the destruction of human embryos. Here, I consider and discuss a series of key ethical questions associated with this research. These include whether it is morally permissible to destroy a human embryo and whether we should clone human embryos for therapeutic cloning research. I conclude by stating my own position—that hES cell and therapeutic cloning research are both acceptable—and I offer some guidelines for the actual conduct of this research.

There is consensus in the scientific community that hES cell research holds great promise for developing new treatments for a variety of serious and currently untreatable disease conditions.[1,2] However, because hES cell research requires the manipulation and destruction of human embryos, it has also been a focus of ethical controversy and opposition. In the course of these debates, several challenging ethical questions have been raised. Scientist, clinicians, or patients involved in hES cell research or therapies must formulate their answers to these questions. Society, too, must address them to determine the extent to which hES cell research may require oversight and regulation. Here, I present these questions and examine some of the leading answers that have been proposed to them.

Is It Morally Permissible to Destroy a Human Embryo?

Human ES cell lines are made by chemically and physically disaggregating an early, blastocyst-stage embryo and removing its inner cell mass. At this stage, the embryo is composed of approximately 200 cells, including an outer layer of differentiated placental material and the undifferentiated (totipotent or pluripotent) cells of the inner cell mass. The embryo inevitably dies as a result of this procedure. Hence the question: Can we intentionally kill a developing human being at this stage to expand scientific knowledge and potentially provide medical benefit to others?

At one end of the spectrum are those who believe that, in moral terms, human life begins at conception. For those holding this view, the early embryo is morally no different from a child or adult human being. It cannot be used in research that is not to its benefit, and it cannot be used without its consent.[3,4] Furthermore, proxy consent by parents in such cases is inadmissible since it is an accepted rule of pediatric research that parents may not volunteer a child for studies that are not potentially beneficial and that risk the child's life.[5] Many Roman Catholics, evangelical Protestants, and some Orthodox Jews take the position that life (morally) begins at conception, and they oppose hES cell research.

At the other end of the spectrum are those who believe that the embryo is not yet fully a human being in a moral sense. They hold a *developmental* or *gradualist* view of life's beginning.[6–10] They do not deny that the early embryo is alive and has the biological potential to become a person. Nevertheless, they believe that other features are needed for the full and equal protections we normally accord children and adults and that these features only develop gradually across the full term of gestation. These features include such things as bodily form and the ability to feel or think. The early embryo, they maintain, does not have these features or abilities. They note as well that the very early embryo lacks human individuality, since it can still undergo twinning at this early stage, and two separate embryos with distinct genomes can still fuse to become a single individual.[11] The very high mortality rate of such embryos (most never implant) also reduces the force of the argument from potentiality.[12,13] Those who hold this view do not agree on the classes of research that warrant the destruction of embryos, but most support some form of hES cell research. Their reasoning is that although the early embryo may merit some respect as a nascent form of human life,[14] the lives and health of children and adults outweigh whatever claim it possesses.

Each individual faced with involvement in hES cell research must arrive at his or her own answer to this first question. Legislators and others must also wrestle with these issues. Because American law (and the laws of most other nations) does not regard the early embryo as a person meriting the legal protections afforded to children and adults, it is hard to see how one can justify legal or regulatory prohibitions on privately financed hES cell research or clinical applications. Such prohibitions would interfere with individual liberty on grounds inconsistent with the lesser view of the embryo shown elsewhere in the law. However, because publicly funded research rests on more narrowly political considerations, including the way that a majority chooses to spend public funds, it may be expected that public support for hES cell research will depend on how a majority of citizens answer this first question.

Should We Postpone hES Cell Research?

Some who oppose the destruction of human embryos maintain that hES cell research should be deferred at least until science provides a better view of the likely benefits of adult stem cell research. They maintain that such research is as promising as hES cell research,[15] and they argue that the moral acceptability of this alternative justifies any delay in the availability of therapies. Others add that scientific uncertainty and the ethically controversial nature of this research warrant a moratorium on hES cell studies in both the private and the public sectors.[16] Scientific studies in this area continue to be equivocal, sometimes supporting and sometimes contradicting claims to the plasticity, the ability to immortalize, and the usefulness of adult stem cells.[17] This raises the question of whether it is justified to delay the development of therapies and cures for children and adults to protect embryos and respect the sensitivities of those opposed to embryo research. Many people feel that such a delay is not warranted and that it is scientifically and morally preferable to keep open multiple pathways to stem cell therapies. In the words of the National Research Council, "The application of stem cell research to therapies for human disease will require much more knowledge about the biological properties of all types of stem cells."[1]

Can We Benefit from Others' Destruction of Embryos?

It might seem that a negative answer to the first question ends discussion. If the embryo is morally as human as you and me, what could justify the use of cells derived from its deliberate destruction for other people's benefit? However, research or therapy has many steps, not all of which involve the destruction of embryos. This raises the question of whether downstream researchers, clinicians, or patients may *use* the stem cell lines that others have derived. Ethically, this is a question of whether we can ever benefit from deeds with which we disagree morally or regard as morally wrong.[18,19]

This question arises partly because most embryos used to produce stem cell lines are left over from infertility procedures. Couples using *in vitro* fertilization (IVF) routinely create more embryos than can safely be implanted. There are hundreds of thousands of these embryos in cryogenic freezers around the country and around the world.[20] Since few frozen embryos are made available for adoption,[21] most of these supernumerary embryos will be destroyed. In 1996, British law mandated the destruction of 3,600 such embryos.[22] This destruction continues regardless of whether some embryos are diverted to hES cell research.

Why is it morally wrong to benefit from others' wrongdoing? One answer is that by doing so, we encourage similar deeds in the future. This explains why we are morally and legally prohibited from receiving stolen goods or why it may

be wrong to benefit from research produced by scientists who choose to ignore human-subject constraints.[19] However, it seems less objectionable to benefit from others' wrongdoing when their deeds are independently undertaken, when our choices are not connected to theirs, and when these choices do not encourage the wrongful deeds. For example, few people would object to using the organs from a teenage victim of a gang killing to save the life of another dying child. The use of such organs benefits one young person and does not encourage teen violence. Similar logic might apply to stem cell research: using spare embryos remaining from infertility procedures. A downstream researcher, clinician, or patient may abhor the deeds that led to the existence of an hES cell line, including the creation and destruction of excess human embryos in infertility medicine. But nothing that a recipient of an hES cell line chooses to do is likely to alter, prevent, or discourage this continuing creation or destruction of human embryos or to make the existing lines go away. Those who use such embryos also know that if they refuse to use an hES cell line, they forego great therapeutic benefit. A researcher will fail to develop a lifesaving or health-restoring therapy. A clinician's decision may threaten a patient's life. People in this position will struggle with the question of whether it is worthwhile to uphold a moral ideal when doing so has no practical effect and when it risks injury to others.

Religious views on the question of whether one may ever benefit from others' wrongdoing are diverse. The Roman Catholic moral tradition, with its staunch opposition to complicity with wrongdoing, presents different answers, including some that permit one to derive benefit in particular cases.[19,23,24] This suggests that some researchers, clinicians, or patients who morally oppose the destruction of human embryos may nevertheless conscientiously conclude that they can *use* hES cell lines derived from embryos otherwise slated for destruction.

It is noteworthy that in his August 2001 address to the nation, President George W. Bush adopted a conservative version of the position that allows one to benefit from acts one morally opposes. Stating his belief that it is morally wrong to kill a human embryo, the president nevertheless permitted the use of existing stem cell lines on the grounds that the deaths of these embryos had already occurred.[25] Presumably, the president believed that it would not encourage further destruction of embryos to permit this use. The president did not go so far as to permit the use of lines derived from embryos slated for destruction. However, it is possible that if existing lines prove inadequate, as some scientists fear,[26] many people would support a slightly more expansive version of this willingness to benefit from what one regards as objectionable deeds. The reasoning here would be that such embryos are unavoidably slated for destruction, and their use will not, by itself, encourage the creation or destruction of other embryos.

Can We Create an Embryo to Destroy It?

A fourth question takes us into even more controversial territory. Is it ever morally permissible to deliberately create an embryo to produce a stem cell line? This was done in the summer of 2002 at the Jones Institute in Norfolk, VA.[26] Those in favor of this research defend it on several grounds. First, they say that in the future, if we seek to develop stem cell lines with special properties and perhaps closer genetic matches to tissue recipients, it will be necessary to produce stem cell lines to order using donor sperm and eggs. Second, they argue that it is *ethically* better to use an hES cell line created from embryos that have been produced just for this purpose, with the full and informed consent of their donor progenitors, than to use cell lines from embryos originally created for a different, reproductive purpose.

Those who believe the early embryo is our moral equal oppose the deliberate creation of embryos for research or clinical use. They are joined by some that do not share this view of the embryo's status but who believe that it is morally repellant to deliberately create a potential human being only to destroy it.[27] Such people argue that this research opens the way to the "instrumentalization" of all human life and the use of children or adult human beings as commodities. Some ask whether such research does not violate the Kantian principle that we should never use others as "a means only."[28]

On the other side of this debate are those who believe that the reduced moral status of the early embryo permits its creation and destruction for lifesaving research and therapies.[29,30] The proponents of this research direction ask why it is morally permissible to create supernumerary embryos in IVF procedures to help couples have children but morally wrong to do the same thing to save a child's life. They are not persuaded by the reply that the status of the embryo is affected by its progenitors' intent, such that it is permissible to create excess embryos for a "good" (reproductive) purpose but not for a "bad" (research) purpose. They point out that the embryo is the same entity. We do not ordinarily believe that a child's rights are dependent on its parents' intent or degree of concern.[31] They conclude that it is not parental intent that warrants the creation of excess of embryos in such cases but the embryos' lesser moral status and the likelihood of significant human benefit from their use. These same considerations, they believe, justify deliberately creating embryos for stem cell research.

Should We Clone Human Embryos?

A fifth question is whether we are willing to support human cloning for stem cell research. This question arises in connection to a specific stem cell technology known as "human therapeutic cloning." It involves the deliberate creation of an embryo by somatic cell nuclear transfer technology (cloning) to produce an immunologically compatible (isogenic) hES cell line.[32]

Immune rejection could occur if the embryo used to prepare a line of hES cells for transplant does not share the same genome as the recipient. This would be the case whether the cell line was created from a spare embryo or from one made to order. Therapeutic cloning offers a way around this problem. In the case of a diabetic child, the mother could donate

an egg whose nucleus would then be removed. A cell would be taken from the child's body and its nucleus inserted into the egg cytoplasm. With stimulation, the reconstructed cell would divide, just like a fertilized egg. If the resulting embryo were transferred back to a womb, it could go on to birth and become a new individual—a clone of the child. But in therapeutic cloning, the blastocyst would be dissected and an hES cell line prepared. Growth factors could be administered to induce the cells to become replacement pancreatic cells for the child. Because these cells contain the child's own DNA and even the same maternal mitochondrial DNA, they would not be subject to rejection. Recent research has shown that the small amount of alien RNA from the mitochondria of an egg other than the mother's might not provoke an immune rejection.[33]

Although this is a very promising technology, it raises a host of novel questions. One is whether the embryonic organism produced in this way should be regarded as a "human embryo" in the accepted sense of that term.[34] Those who believe that "life begins at conception" tend to answer this question affirmatively, even though cloned "embryos" are not the result of sexual fertilization.[35] They base their view on the biological similarities between cloned and sexually produced embryos and on the argument that both have the *potential* to become a human being. Nevertheless, the very high mortality rate of cloned embryos suggests significant biological differences from sexually produced embryos. Furthermore, if their status rests on their potential, this potential is more than significantly reduced; in an era of cloning, some degree of potentiality attaches to all bodily cells.

The promise of this technology rests on the ability to make stem cell lines "to order" for a specific patient. If you hold the view that the cloned organism is morally equivalent to a human embryo, therapeutic cloning research and therapies again raise the question of whether it is morally permissible to deliberately create an embryo to destroy it.

Another question often raised in this context is whether therapeutic cloning will create an enormous demand for human eggs. If it does, some believe this may create substantial problems of social justice, since collecting these eggs may involve hundreds or thousands of women, many of whom are likely to be poor women of color attracted by the financial rewards of egg donation.[36,37] Those who discount this problem offer several arguments. They point out that even if many eggs are needed for therapeutic cloning procedures, they are likely to be provided by relatives of patients. This reduces the magnitude of a market in oocytes. Others observe that therapeutic cloning is likely to be "transitional research."[38] As such, it may lead the way to direct somatic cell reprogramming, eliminating the need for eggs altogether.

Finally, there is a moral question specific to cloning itself. The more scientists are able to perfect therapeutic cloning, the more likely it is that they will sharpen the skills needed to accomplish reproductive cloning, which aims at the birth of a cloned child. There is a broad consensus in the scientific and bioethics communities that, at this time, the state of cloning technology poses serious health risks to any child born as a result of it.[39] There are also serious, unresolved questions about the psychological welfare of such children.[40] Finally, there is the possibility that embryos created for therapeutic cloning research might be diverted to reproductive cloning attempts. All these concerns raise the question: Do we really want to develop cloning technology for the production of isogenic stem cells if doing so hastens the advent of reproductive cloning.[24]

In 2001 and again in 2003, the U.S. House of Representatives answered "no" to this question and passed a bill by introduced by Rep. James Weldon that banned *both* reproductive and therapeutic cloning.[42,43] Similar bills have been introduced in the Senate.[44] Although the Senate initiatives have been stalled for some time, this may soon change. If a Senate bill passes, therapeutic cloning research and therapies will be outlawed in the United States. Similar prohibitions are either in effect or being considered for passage in continental Europe.[45] This would leave only a relatively small number of countries, including Great Britain, Israel, and China, in which such research would be allowed.[46]

Those who oppose these prohibitions believe that therapeutic and reproductive cloning research can be decoupled. They observe that strict regulations and governmental oversight, of the sort provided in Great Britain by the Human Fertilisation and Embryology Authority, make it unlikely that embryos produced for therapeutic cloning will be diverted to reproductive purposes. They also point out that several researchers or groups with minimal qualifications in cloning research have announced their intent to clone a child or have even tried to do so. Such attempts are likely to continue regardless of whether therapeutic cloning research is banned. As a result, a ban on therapeutic cloning will not protect children and will only have the negative effect of interrupting beneficial stem cell research.

What Ethical Guidelines Should Govern hES Cell and Therapeutic Cloning Research?

Mention of the need to prevent the diversion of cloned embryos to reproductive purposes raises the larger question of what guidelines should apply to the conduct of hES cell research and therapeutic cloning research. In August 2000, the U.S. National Institutes of Health released a series of guidelines for hES cell research that never went into effect because they were largely preempted by President Bush's decision to limit hES cell research to existing cell lines.[47] Guidelines have also been developed by the Chief Medical Officer's Expert Group in Great Britain[38] and by private ethics boards at the Geron Corporation[48] and Advanced Cell Technology in the United States.[49] The various recommendations share several features.

DONOR ISSUES

Because hES cell and therapeutic cloning research require a supply of human gametes or embryos, steps must be taken to elicit the informed consent of donors, to protect their privacy, and to minimize any risks to which they might be subject. Informed consent requires that donors fully understand the nature of the research being undertaken and that they explicitly consent to that research. For example, it is morally impermissible to elicit sperm, eggs, or embryos for the production of hES cell lines without informing donors that an immortalized, pluripotent cell line might result that could be widely used in research or therapeutic applications. If there are likely to be commercial benefits flowing from the research, donors must also be informed of this, and their rights (if any) in such benefits should be clearly specified. If the research involves therapeutic cloning, both egg and somatic cell donors must be informed that a cloned embryo and a cell line with the egg donor's mitochondrial genetic material and a somatic cell donor's nuclear DNA will result.

In conducting research, efforts should be made to preserve donor privacy by removing identifying information from gametes, embryos, and cell lines and keeping this information apart in a secure location. In view of the controversy surrounding much of this research, donors can be subjected to harassment or embarrassment if their association with the research is revealed without their consent.

Ovulation induction is an invasive medical procedure with known and undetermined risks.[50,51] Not only must egg donors be informed of these risks, but steps also must be taken to preserve the voluntary nature of their consent. This includes preventing them from being pressured into producing excess eggs or embryos for research in return for discounts on infertility services.[52] It also includes avoiding undue financial incentives. Although it is unreasonable to expect even altruistically motivated donors to undergo the inconvenience and risks of these procedures without some form of compensation, payment should not be so high as to lead a donor to ignore the risks involved. For Advanced Cell Technology's therapeutic cloning egg donor program, its Ethics Advisory Board set a payment level similar to that established for reproductive egg donors in the New England area. Payments were also prorated for the degree of participation in the program to allow donors to drop out at any time. Levels of stimulatory medications were maintained on the low side of current regimens, and payments were never attached to the number of eggs harvested. Additional protections ensured that donors had the educational level and backgrounds needed to appreciate the risks involved. A study monitor was employed to ensure that donors' consent was free and informed.

RESEARCH CONDUCT

Guidelines also apply to the actual conduct of research. These include the requirement that no embryo used in hES cell or therapeutic cloning research be allowed to develop beyond 14 days *in vitro*. This limit is based on the substantial changes that occur at gastrulation, which marks the beginning of individuation and organogenesis.[53] Also required is supervision and accountability of all staff and scientists involved in this research to prevent any diversion of gametes or embryos to reproductive purposes.

TRANSPLANTATION RESEARCH

If and when hES cell lines become available for research in transplant therapies, researchers and institutional review boards will have to address ethical questions raised by their use. For example, if such lines were cultured on mouse or other feeder layers, as almost all current lines are, there will be a safety question regarding the possible introduction of exogenous retroviruses or other pathogens into the human population. Basing their judgments on adequate preliminary animal studies, researchers and oversight bodies will have to assess the risks of rejection, including graft-versus-host disease. Issues surrounding the tumorigenicity of hES cells will also have to be resolved. Experience with fetal cell transplants for Parkinson's disease shows that cells can behave in unexpected ways when transplanted into the human body.[54] None of these problems are insurmountable, however, and their existence itself constitutes an argument for continued research in this area under careful ethical oversight.

Summary

Answering all of the questions I have identified would require an ethical treatise. However, by noting that I currently serve in a *pro bono* capacity as chairman of the Ethics Advisory Board of Advanced Cell Technology, I indicate my own answers to the most controversial of these questions. I would not have accepted this position if I did not believe that hES cell and therapeutic cloning research is both therapeutically important and ethically acceptable. In my view, the moral claims of the very early embryo do not outweigh those of children and adults that can be helped by hES cell and therapeutic cloning technologies. I also do not believe that therapeutic cloning research will lead to reproductive cloning, which we should take firm steps to forbid. I recognize that others may disagree with these conclusions. As our debates move forward, continuing dialogue about these questions and clearer scientific research results will bring us closer to a national consensus on these issues.

REFERENCES

1. National Research Council (2001). "Stem Cells and the Future of Regenerative Medicine." National Academy Press, Washington, DC.
2. Office of Science Policy (2001). "Stem Cells: Scientific Progress and Future Research Directions." National Institutes of Health, Bethesda, MD.
3. Pope John Paul II (2003). Address of John Paul II to the Members of the Pontifical Academy of Sciences, Monday, 10 November 2003. *Available at:* http://www.Vatican.va/holy_father/john_paul_ii/speeches/2003/November/documents/hf_jp-ii_spe_20031110_academy-sciences_en.html.
4. The Linacre Centre for Healthcare Ethics (2001). A theologian's brief on the place of the human embryo within the Christian tradition. *Available at:* http://www.lifeissues.net/writers/mis/mis_02christiantradition1.html#b1.
5. (2001). 45 CFR §46.401-409. *Available at:* http://ohrp.osophs.dhhs.gov/humansubjects/guidance/45cfr46.htm#subpartd.
6. Ford, N.M. (1988). "When Did I Begin?" Cambridge University Press, Cambridge.
7. Warren, M.A. (1997). "Moral Status: Obligations to Persons and Other Living Things." Oxford University Press, New York.
8. Green, R.M. (2001). "The Human Embryo Research Debates." Oxford University Press, New York.
9. McCormick, R.A. (1991). Who or what is the preembryo? *Kennedy Inst. Ethics J.* **1**, 1–15.
10. Shannon, T. (2001). From the micro to the macro. *In* "The Human Embryonic Stem Cell Debate," (S. Holland *et al.,* eds.), pp. 177–184. MIT Press, Cambridge, MA.
11. Strain, L., Dean, J.C.S., Hamilton, M.P.R., and Bonthron, D.T. (1998). A true hermaphrodite chimera resulting from embryo amalgamation after *in vitro* fertilization. *New Engl. J. Med.* **338**, 166–169.
12. Norwitz, E.R., Shust, D.J., and Fisher, S.J. (2001). Implantation and the survival of early pregnancy. *New Engl. J. Med.* **345**, 1400–1408.
13. Hardy, K., Spanos, S., Becker, D., Iannelli, P., Winston, R.M.L., and Stark, J. (2001). From cell death to embryo arrest: mathematical models of human preimplantation embryo development. *Proc. Natl. Acad. Sci. USA* **98:4**, 1655–1660.
14. Lebacqz, K. (2001). On the elusive nature of respect. *In* "The Human Embryonic Stem Cell Debate," (S. Holland *et al.,* eds.), pp. 149–162. MIT Press, Cambridge, MA.
15. Doerflinger, R. (1999). The ethics of funding embryonic stem cell research: a Catholic viewpoint. *Kennedy Inst. Ethics J.* **9**, 137–150.
16. President's Council on Bioethics (2002). "Human Cloning and Human Dignity: An Ethical Inquiry." President's Council on Bioethics, Washington, DC. *Available at:* http://www.bioethics. gov.
17. Pearson, H. (2002). Stem cells: articles of faith adulterated. *Nature* **420**, 734–735.
18. Kaveny, M.C. (2000). appropriation of evil: Cooperation's mirror image. *Theol. Stud.* **61**, 280–313.
19. Green, R.M. (2002). Benefiting from "evil": an incipient moral problem in human stem cell research. *Bioethics* **16:6**, 544–556.
20. Weiss, R. (2003). 400,000 human embryos frozen in U.S. Number at fertility clinics is far greater than previous estimates, survey finds. *Washington Post,* Thursday, May 8, 2003, A10.
21. Stolberg, S.G. (2001). Some see new route to adoption in clinics full of frozen embryos. *NY Times* **Feb. 25**, A1.
22. Ibrahim, Y.M. (1996). Ethical furor erupts in Britain: should embryos be destroyed? *NY Times* **Aug. 1 (late edition)**, A1.
23. Ashley, B.M., and O'Rourke, K.D. (1989). "Health Care Ethics: A Theological Analysis," 3rd Ed. Catholic Health Care Association of the United States, St. Louis, MO.
24. Miller, L.G. (1967). Scandal. *In* "New Catholic Encyclopedia," Vol. XII, pp. 1112–1113. McGraw Hill, New York.
25. Bush, G.W. (2001). President's statement on funding stem cell research. *NY Times* **Aug. 10 (late edition—final)**, A16.
26. Kolata, G. (2001). Researchers say embryos in labs are not available. *NY Times* **Aug. 26 (late edition—final)**, A1.
27. Annas, G., Caplan, A., and Elias S. (1996). The politics of human–embryo research—avoiding ethical gridlock. *New Engl. J. Med.* **334:20**, 1329–1332.
28. Green, R.M. (2001). What does it mean to use someone as "a means only": Rereading Kant. *Kennedy Inst. Ethics J.* **11:3**, 249–263.
29. National Institutes of Health. (1994) "Report of the Human Embryo Research Panel." National Institutes of Health, Bethesda, MD.

30. Davis, D.S. (1995). Embryos created for research purposes. *Kennedy Inst. Ethics J.* **5:4,** 343–354.

31. Parens, E. (2001). On the ethics and politics of embryonic stem cell research. *In* "The Human Embryonic Stem Cell Debate," (S. Holland *et al.,* eds.), pp. 37–50. MIT Press, Cambridge, MA.

32. Lanza, R.P., Caplan, A.L., Silver, L.M., Cibelli, J.B., West, M.D., and Green, R.M. (2000).The ethical validity of using nuclear transfer in human transplantation. *JAMA* **284:24,** 3175–3179.

33. Lanza, R.P., Chung, H.Y., Yoo, J.J., Wettstein, P.J., Blackwell, C., Borson, N., Hofmeister, E., Schuch, G., Soker, S., Moraes, C.T., West, M.D., and Atala, A. (2002). Generation of histocompatible tissues using nuclear transplantation. *Natl. Biotechnol.* **20,** 689–696.

34. Nature (2001). The meaning of life [editorial]. *Nature* **412: 6844,** 255.

35. Doerflinger, R.M. (2003). Testimony of Richard M. Doerflinger on behalf of the Committee for Pro-Life Activities, National Conference of Catholic Bishops, Testimony of Richard Doerflinger, January 14, 2003 before the Health and Human Development Committee of the Delaware House of Representatives concerning Senate Bill No. 55, "Cloning Prohibition and Research Protection Act." *Available at:* http://www.cloninginformation.org/congressional_testimony/doer-flinger_de.htm.

36. Dresser, R. (2001). Letter to the editor, *JAMA* **285:11,** 1439.

37. Holland, S. (2001). Beyond the embryo: A feminist appraisal of human embryonic stem cell research. *In* "The Human Embryonic Stem Cell Debate," (S. Holland *et al.,* eds.), pp. 73–86. MIT Press, Cambridge, MA.

38. Chief Medical Officer's Expert Group. (2000). "Stem Cell Research: Medical Progress with Responsibility." *Available at:* http://www.doh.gov.uk/cegc/stemcellreport.htm.

39. Jaenisch, R., and Wilmut, I. (2001). Don't clone humans! *Science* **291:5513,** 2552.

40. National Bioethics Advisory Commission (1997). "Cloning Human Beings." National Bioethics Advisory Commission, Rockville, MD.

41. Weiss, R. (1999). Stem cell discovery grows into a debate. *Wash. Post* **Oct. 9,** A1, A8–A9.

42. Stolberg, S.G. (2001). House backs ban on human cloning for any objective. *NY Times* **Aug. 1 (late edition—final),** A1.

43. Stolberg, S.G. (2003). House votes to ban all human cloning. *NY Times* **Feb. 28 (late edition—final),** A22.

44. New York Times. (2003). Cloning countdown [editorial]. *NY Times* **March 1 (late edition—final),** A18.

45. Osborn, A. (2003). MEPs vote against stem cell research. *Guardian* **April 11.** *Available at:* http://www.guardian.co.uk/international/story/0,3604,934363,00.html.

46. Israel Academy of Sciences and Humanities. (2001)."Report of the Bioethics Advisory Committee of the Israel Academy of Sciences and Humanities on the Use of Embryonic Stem Cells for Therapeutic Research." Israel Academy of Sciences and Humanities.

47. National Institutes of Health (2000). "Guidelines for Research Using Human Pluripotent Stem Cells (Effective August 25, 2000, 65 FR 51976) (Corrected November 21, 2000, 65 FR 69951)." National Institutes of Health, Bethesda, MD.

48. Geron Advisory Board. (1999). Research with human embryonic stem cells: Ethical considerations. *Hastings Cent. Rep.* **29:2,** 31–36.

49. Green, R.M., Olsen DeVries, K., Bernstein, J., Goodman, K.W., Kaufmann, R.W., Kiessling, A.A., Levin, S.R., Moss, S.L., and Tauer, C.A. (2002). Overseeing research on therapeutic cloning: a private ethics board responds to its critics. *Hastings Cent. Rep.* **32:3,** 27–33.

50. Rossing, M.A., Daling, J.R., Weiss, N.S., Moore, D.E., and Self, S.E. (1996). Ovarian tumors in a cohort of infertile women. *New Engl. J. Med.* **331:12,** 771–776.

51. Paulson, R.J. (1996). Fertility drugs and ovarian epithelial cancer: is there a link? *J. Assist. Reprod. Genet.* **13:10,** 751–756.

52. Cohen, C.B. (2001). Leaps and boundaries: Expanding oversight of human stem cell research. *In* "The Human Embryonic Stem Cell Debate," (S. Holland *et al.,* eds.), pp. 209–222. MIT Press, Cambridge, MA.

53. O'Rahilly, R., and Müller, F. (1992). "Human Embryology and Teratology." Wiley-Liss, New York.

54. Kolata, G. (2001). Parkinson's research is set back by failure of fetal cell implants. *NY Times* **March 8, (late edition—final),** A1.

Stem Cell Research: Religious Considerations

Margaret A. Farley

Scientific and technical advances continue to transform the ways we live, flourish, and die. In contemporary Western society, it is tempting to think of religion as either obstructionist or irrelevant in the face of these advances. Often when stunning new opportunities emerge for the treatment of disease and injury, religious groups (though not only religious groups) lead us into a quagmire of ethical problems. Yet religious traditions have endured largely because they help people to make sense of their lives. Major religious traditions become major because they offer some response to the large human questions of suffering and death, hope and transcendence, history and community, as well as the everyday issues of how we are to live together with some modicum of harmony and peace. Adherents to traditions of faith generally experience their shared beliefs and practices not as irrational but as part of the effort of reason to understand the actual and the possible in human life and all that is around it. Although religious sources of insight may reach beyond empirical data and logical reasoning, they need not ultimately do violence to either. As for moral discernment and deliberation, religious faith may at least shed light on questions it cannot answer on its own. A tradition is alive for believers only in so far as it can connect the faith of its past with the problems of its present and future.

Whether or not we are persuaded by religious voices in public debates about issues such as stem cell research, cloning, or genetic therapy, we cannot afford to dismiss these voices. Religious concerns are as much about meaning as about attitude, and any efforts to make human sense of newly discovered entities and processes should be welcome in the public forum as well as the private. In a pluralistic society, there will be varying worldviews—religious or secular, theological, philosophical, or scientific. Whether one finds the holy in a divine presence, the heights of human achievement, or the vast reaches of the cosmos, experiences of the sacred can transform our searches for meaning, medical progress, or justice. When we ask profound questions such as how humans ought to reproduce themselves, how extreme suffering can be alleviated, or whether the meaning of the human body changes when we exchange its parts, we can be helped by looking to the source and the substance of the attitudes, beliefs, and practices that animate people's lives. It can help

all of us to hear Jewish voices whose ultimate concerns are seeing the face of God as well as living by God's law; Muslim voices that speak of Divine Proximity and spiritual inwardness as well as moral guidance; Christian voices that deliberate about God's revelation through sacred texts but also through creation; Hindu voices that call for a "turning around" from obstacles to the divine; and Buddhist voices that challenge to achieve freedom through self-emptying.

Of course, when we look for guidance in the faith of believers, we do not find univocal voices—not from believers in general, and not from believers within particular traditions. Roman Catholics will often not agree with representatives of the United Church of Christ, many Jews will not agree with many Catholics about abortion, and so on. But the division within faith traditions today is often wider than between or among them. So, there is more than one view regarding stem cell research among Roman Catholics, more than one among the different strands of Judaism, and more than one among Muslims. Such disagreements do not make religious voices useless for societal and religious discernment, no more than disagreements among scientists render scientific research and the voices of scientists useless.

This chapter aims to review religious perspectives on stem cell research. It is not possible here to survey every religious or theological argument for and against stem cell research. What I offer is something of an overview; then I look at particular issues of concern articulated by representatives of some religious traditions.

Mapping the Terrain

SOURCES FOR STEM CELLS

The major disputed questions surrounding stem cell research are focused not on stem cells as such but on the sources from which stem cells are derived. Hence, debates rage regarding the moral status of human embryos and the permissibility of taking stem cells from already dead fetuses. Religious thinkers who consider the human embryo sacrosanct from its inception will consistently oppose the extraction of embryonic stem cells as a form of killing (of embryos). Those who do not appraise the value of an embryo as on a par with that of a human person are much more willing to favor embryo research in general, including the taking of stem cells for research. Still others who emphasize the ambiguity of the moral status of embryos are likely to weigh the advantages of embryo cell research over the possible violations of the embryo as an entity in itself. All religious traditions recognize an aborted fetus as a cadaver; hence, the derivation of stem cells from the gonadal ridge of dead fetuses may be as permissible as the harvesting of tissues or organs from any human cadavers. Nonetheless, representatives of traditions that prohibit abortion worry about complicity with and support of the moral evil of abortion when stem cells are derived from electively aborted fetuses.

Alternative sources for stem cells are championed by those who are opposed to embryo stem cell and fetal stem cell research. The least objectionable source often cited is stem cells taken from adult tissue (given that this does not ultimately harm the donors of the tissue). A compromise source (though still controversial) is embryonic stem cells that have already been harvested (i.e., the life of the original embryo has already been taken, and no new moral agency is involved in the killing of more embryos). Problems with both of these sources continue, however. Research on adult stem cells is less advanced than research on embryonic cells (and scientists argue that it is better to proceed on all fronts rather than on only one); moreover, the still undetermined (undifferentiated) nature of early embryonic cells is believed to be more readily suitable for the goals of research. Not surprisingly, the proposed use of existing embryonic cell lines encounters the same objections of complicity with evil that are involved in the use of fetal cells.

There are other issues that complicate moral assessments of the sources of stem cells and the aims of stem cell research. For example, almost all religious thinkers argue that some form of respect is due to embryos, even if it is not the same form of respect required for human persons. Yet there is lack of clarity about what respect can mean when it is aligned with the killing of the respected object.[1] It is not difficult to get minimal consensus on prohibitions against buying and selling human embryos or on safeguards of informed consent from the donors of embryos for research. For many religious believers, it makes a difference that these embryos are "spare" embryos, left over from *in vitro* fertilization procedures and destined to be discarded if they are not used in research. From other religious perspectives, however, this fact in itself does not lift the prohibition against killing them.

QUESTIONS OF JUSTICE

Quite another kind of ethical issue is raised by people from almost all religious traditions. This is the issue of justice.[2] Who will be expected to be the primary donors of embryos or aborted fetuses? Will gender, race, and class discrimination characterize the whole process of research on stem cells? And will the primary goals of research be skewed toward profit rather than toward healing? Who will gain from the predicted marvelous therapeutic advances achieved through stem cell research—the wealthy but not the poor? The powerful but not the marginalized? What will be the overall results for respect for human persons if human embryos and stem cells are commodified, wholly instrumentalized, and in some ways trivialized?

All of these are questions for secular philosophical, scientific, and medical ethics as well as for religious ethics. When they are identified by religious and theological thinkers, however,

they are always lodged in the larger questions with which religious traditions are concerned, and they almost always appeal to sacred texts and faith-community traditions, teachings, and practices, as well as to secular sources and forms of moral reasoning. To understand the importance of positions taken by faith traditions and individual religious thinkers, it is necessary at least to identify some of these deeper questions.

RELIGIOUS BELIEFS AND ETHICAL QUESTIONS

If we are to appreciate the significance of religious considerations in ethical debates about stem cell research, it is not enough to take notice of the current polls designed to report on the positions of cobelievers in various faith traditions and denominations. Such polls are not unimportant, since they may signal how strong the beliefs are of self-identified members of different traditions and communities. They can also tell us how divided cobelievers may be on the politics of stem cell research. It will be difficult to adjudicate controversies, however, without some effort to interpret beliefs on a particular issue, like stem cell research, in the light of the broader and more foundational beliefs that characterize a tradition.

Anchoring religious concerns for the moral status of the human embryo, the nature of moral evil and immoral complicity, and the questions of distributive justice are beliefs about the nature and destiny of human life, the meaning of bodily existence, the interaction between divine and human in the progress and healing of creation, the importance of consequences in moral reasoning along with the importance of religious laws and ontologically based norms, the basic equality of all people before God, and so forth. Even when there is no direct line between the most profound belief of a person and the answer to a particular moral question, such a belief makes a difference for moral discernment and conviction. There are no world religions today that oppose all human intervention in "nature," yet all religions recognize some limitations on what humans may do—either to themselves or to other created beings. All consider humility before concrete reality an important antidote to arrogance or pride (and in the wake of ecological disasters, all now take account of the risks of some interventions made only for the sake of the flourishing of some human generations). No religions favor illness over health or death over life, yet each has a perspective in which health may not be an absolute value and even death may be welcomed. In the present context of stem cell research, there is no religious tradition that does not take seriously the beneficial results promised by such research.

Hence, positions of religious believers regarding stem cell research tend to be highly complex. Each tradition needs to be understood in its complexity and its diversity. This chapter cannot track all of this, but it can try to show how some beliefs are coherent, whether or not they can be agreed upon by others in the same tradition or across faiths and cultures.

Particular Traditions: An Overview

A beginning understanding of positions taken by religious scholars and representatives of mainline traditions is, fortunately, available to some extent in the testimony and writings that have appeared in relation to the public debate on stem cell research. We have here, of course, just the proverbial tip of the iceberg. Nonetheless, these documents and essays point us to both the concrete moral positions being debated and the larger rationales behind them. In brief summaries, then, I survey some of these positions and rationales. Following this, I focus on specific arguments taken by representatives of the Roman Catholic tradition. I do this not to privilege this tradition but because its articulation of arguments is more prolific than most, it claims to be trying to be persuasive in a secular public sphere, its central positions are representative of strands of other religious as well as philosophical traditions, and it offers an ongoing critical conversation on both sides of the stem cell debate.

HINDUISM AND BUDDHISM

Representatives of the Hindu and Buddhist traditions have not been major players in the contemporary debate about stem cell research, at least not in the United States. There are historical reasons for this, no doubt, including that neither is as yet a majority religion in the West. Yet there is much in both of these traditions that may, for their adherents, be relevant to issues of stem cell research. Given the complexity of the traditions, it remains for their scholars and representatives to render accessible to outsiders the foundational beliefs and moral concerns that may shed light on such issues. Briefly, however, some elements in these faith traditions can be noted.

Both Hinduism and Buddhism incorporate beliefs in reincarnation. This complicates issues of what can be done with human embryos. According to some Hindu traditions, human life begins prior to conception; the "soul" may be present even in sperm, or it may be in some other life form before and after its human existence. Human incarnation, however, offers a unique opportunity to influence the future of an individual. Great caution must be taken whenever actions are considered that may destroy this opportunity. On the other hand, for Hindus, a belief in reincarnation is also tied to motivation to be compassionate toward others. Good actions that will change the course of suffering for oneself and others are exhorted not only so that one can advance morally (and thereby improve one's karma) but also because other people are worthy of beneficent deeds. Although the forms of compassion include nonviolence, there is in Hinduism also a broad tradition of sacrifice, wherein one human life can be taken for the sake of a higher cause. It is not impossible that these convictions provide a rationale for embryonic stem cell research.

For Buddhists, a goal of self-transcendence involves a process of self-forgetting. This undergirds a requirement for compassion, one of the Four-fold Holy Truths of Buddhism. In Mahayana Buddhism, the ideal is the Bodhisattva, one who achieves self-emptying but then returns to help those in need. Again, here is a possible rationale for embryonic stem cell research. Moreover, some Buddhists believe that a soul has some choice as to where it will be incarnated. It has even been suggested that souls will not elect to be embedded in "spare"

embryos that will only be destroyed. Hence, early embryos may not ever have the potential to become a human person and can therefore be used for some other purpose.

Whether or not such considerations are of overall significance in decisions to pursue embryonic or fetal stem cell research remains to be seen. At the very least, it can be said that they represent large concerns for the value of human life—whether at its inception or in response to later injury and illness.

ISLAM

Like other world religions, there are many schools of thought among Muslims. There are also multiple sources for moral guidance, including the Qur'an and its commentaries, *hadith* (a second source of moral indicators supplementary to the Qur'an), Muslim philosophies that range from a form of ontological realism to a version of divine command theory, Sharia (formulations of Islamic law), and centuries of juridical literature. Testifying before the U.S. National Bioethics Advisory Commission in 1999, the Islamic scholar Abdulaziz Sachedina attempted to provide some general insights from the tradition, taking into account the diverse interpretations of major Sunni and Shi'i schools of legal thought.[3] His analysis of various texts led him to infer guidelines for stem cell research from the rulings of the Sharia on fetal viability and the moral status of the embryo.

Islamic traditions have given serious attention to the moral status of the "fetus and its development to a particular point when it attains human personhood with full moral and legal status."[3] The early embryo has been variously valued in different eras, depending on the information available from science. Throughout the history of legal rulings in this regard, however, a developmental view of the fetus—according to a divine plan—has been sustained. This suggests that the moral status of personhood is not achieved at the earliest stages of embryonic life but only after sufficient biological development has taken place—the kind of development that includes a recognizable human anatomy and the possibility of "voluntary" movement. Most Sunni and some Shi'ite scholars therefore distinguish two stages in pregnancy. The first stage, "pre-ensoulment," is human biological life but not yet human personal life. It is only after the fourth month (120 days, or the time of quickening) that the "biological person" becomes a "moral person."[3] This is to say that at this stage of development, the fetus achieves the status of a moral and legal person. In the first stage, the biological entity is to be respected, yet abortion is allowed for grave reasons. In the second stage, killing the fetus is homicide.[4] The conclusion to be drawn from this is that there may be room for early embryonic stem cell extraction without violating divinely given laws or the embryo itself. In Islam, therefore, there are elements of the tradition that affirm embryonic stem cell research, though reasons can also be adduced against it.

JUDAISM

In the 21st century, Orthodox, Conservative, and Reform Jews take different positions on many issues of applied ethics.[a] These views are not easily specified when it comes to stem cell research. What is possible here is to present the opinions of some Jewish scholars, with the caution that not all views are represented. In the context of debates about stem cells, Reform Judaism may be the clearest supporter of this research even when it entails the derivation of stem cells from human embryos or from aborted fetuses. Jewish law does not give legal status to the fertilized ovum outside a mother's womb. When the embryo is inside a uterus, it has legal status but not that of a human person. In general, however, this strand of Judaism favors the use only of so-called spare embryos, those that will be otherwise discarded.

Rabbi Elliott Dorff has identified theological assumptions useful for understanding a Jewish response to stem cell research.[5,6] These include the following: moral discernment (of what God wants of God's people) must be based on both Jewish theology and Jewish law; all human beings are created in the image of God and are to be valued as such; human bodies belong to God and are only on loan to the individuals who have them; and human agency is important in responses to human illness, so that both "natural" and "artificial" means are acceptable in overcoming disease. Indeed, there is a duty to develop and use any therapies that can help in the care of the human body; yet because humans are not, like God, omniscient, humility and caution are essential, especially when human science and technology press to the edges of human knowledge.

There are grounds in Jewish law and theology for permitting the derivation of stem cells both from aborted fetuses and from human embryos. Just as abortion (though generally forbidden) can be justified for serious reasons, so can the use of fetuses for important research. A fetus *in utero* is considered not as a human person but as the "thigh of its mother."[6–8] One is not allowed to amputate a part of one's body (in this case, one's thigh) except for good reasons (e.g., to remove a gangrenous limb, save the life of a mother or remove other serious risk, and perhaps to remove a genetically malformed or diseased fetus). When an abortion is thus justified, the abortus may be used as a source of stem cells.

Embryos can also be legitimate sources for stem cells extracted for purposes of research. During the first 40 days of gestation, *in utero* embryos (and fetuses) are only like "water."[6] They are "nonsouled," with only a liminal status. Although abortion during this time is permitted only for good reasons, the situation is different when embryos are not in the womb. Here, there is no potential for embryos to develop into human persons; hence, they may be discarded, frozen, or used for promising research. Both Rabbi Dorff and Jewish scholar Laurie Zoloth argue that the duty to care for human bodies, the duty to heal, may strengthen not just permission to, but an ethical duty to pursue research on stem cells.[6,7]

The Jewish tradition places all of these considerations in a wider context of responsibilities to community, fairness in distribution of benefits and burdens, and caution about the connections of stem cell research to invidious programs of eugenics. Ethical norms that safeguard the common good as well as the good of individuals provide boundaries for the development and future uses of stem cell research; they focus it, perhaps obligate it, but do not forbid it.

CHRISTIANITY

The diversity and pluralism to be expected in Christian responses to stem cell research mirrors to some extent the historical institutional divisions within Christianity. From the early schisms between East and West, to the great Reformations in the West and the subsequent proliferations of Protestant denominations, to the Anglican and Roman Catholic church traditions, to the rise of new forms of Pentecostalism in the world's South, Christians have diversified in their beliefs and in their moral convictions and practices. There remains some important commonality in basic doctrines, largely expressed in creeds, and these are not irrelevant to issues of stem cell research. Examples include belief in divine revelation, particularly through sacred scripture; reconciliation made possible between humans and God through Jesus Christ; affirmation of the goodness of creation despite the damage sustained as the result of moral evil or sin; acceptance of the importance of human agency (in practice if not always in theology); a call to unconditional love of God and love and service of neighbor; a basic view of human equality; and the obligation to promote justice. Theological anthropologies vary importantly in terms of understandings of freedom and grace, virtue and sin. Strands of Christian moral theologies diverge when it comes to the basis and force of moral norms—depending primarily on either God's command or God's will manifest in creation itself, and holding to absolute moral norms or only *prima facie* norms relativized according to circumstances, consequences, or priorities among aims. Law and gospel are important to each Christian tradition, though the emphasis on one or the other may vary.

Articulating an Eastern Orthodox view of embryonic stem cell research, Demetrios Demopulos begins with concern for the alleviation of suffering.[9] "Medical arts" are to be encouraged, with the proviso that they be practiced as gifts from God ordered to divine purposes. Created in the image and likeness of God, people are destined for participation in the life of God—hence the telos of the human person is referred to as *theosis* or "deification." People are authentic in so far as they struggle to grow into this life; they remain "potential" persons until this is achieved. But even zygotes are potential persons in this sense; that is, they, too, are in a developmental process that ends in deification. Hence, human life is sacred from the beginning and, at every step along the way, entitled to protection and the opportunity to seek its destiny. "Even though not yet a person, an embryo should not be used for or sacrificed in experimentation."[9] Correlatively, practices of *in vitro* fertilization that yield "surplus" embryos that will be discarded cannot be condoned.

Though the development of alternative techniques and sources is preferable, Demopulos[9] allows the use of already harvested embryonic stem cells for research. "Wishing that something had not been done will not undo it." The compromise position, then, of continuing research on available cell lines is accepted so long as the research does not violate other norms of justice (by maximizing profits rather than the health of people, fostering trivial medical procedures for cosmetic purposes alone, or contributing to a questionable agenda for eugenics). The use of cadaver fetal cells is also acceptable if the abortion that provides them is spontaneous. But human life—potential human personal life—from zygote to a life beyond this world, remains sacred; what ultimately ends in God ought to be inviolable among humans.

Among the Protestant denominations in the United States, some support and some oppose embryonic stem cell research. Many churches do not yet have an official policy on this issue, though representatives indicate a kind of majority view. Southern Baptists are as a group generally opposed to this research, though there is some openness to the compromise position of using already harvested cells. Some leaders among United Methodists, without an official church position, nonetheless asked President George W. Bush to oppose federal funding for embryonic stem cell research. Presbyterians in General Assembly articulated their support of research on cells extracted from embryos that would otherwise be discarded and affirmed the use of federal funds to make this possible. Acknowledging the significance of concepts like "potential personhood" and the need to "respect" embryos, they nonetheless determined that whatever form this respect takes, it ought not to have priority over alleviating the suffering of actual people. Members of the United Church of Christ tend to approve embryonic stem cell research as long as it is motivated by a clear and attainable healing benefit.

Ethicists from a variety of Protestant backgrounds (though seldom speaking for their denominations) also vary in their approaches to stem cell research. Ted Peters[10] of the Pacific Lutheran School of Theology comes down on the side of supporting embryonic cell research because he believes that, on balance, concern for the human dignity not of embryos but of future real persons is more compelling. Ronald Cole-Turner[11] agrees with others in the United Church of Christ by approving the extraction of stem cells from embryos, but he sets conditions for research in terms of justice issues. Gene Outka[12] and Gilbert Meilaender,[13] both Lutherans, share certain theological and philosophical convictions about the irreducible value of the early embryo. Both want to affirm the continuity of human life between an early embryo and an actualized full person. This means that both will consider the taking of the life of an embryo as a violation of the prohibition against killing. Both also want to distinguish the question of embryo stem cell extraction from the question of abortion (in a variety of ways, but primarily because in the former there is no direct conflict between a woman and a fetus).

Outka, however, finally approves of the use of some embryos for the derivation of stem cells. He does so by introducing two conditions that can exempt one from the absolute force of the prohibition.[b,12] The first and most distinctive is the *nothing is lost* condition. That is, it is possible to relativize the prohibition against killing when those who are to be killed will die anyway. This is precisely the condition that characterizes the situation of spare (or excess) embryos (from *in vitro* fertilization procedures) destined to be discarded. The second condition is that other lives will be saved through this act of killing. Given the ultimate therapeutic aims of stem cell research, this condition is also present. It is the *nothing is lost* condition (or principle) that in the end allows Outka to continue to affirm the status of the embryo as an end and not a means only, yet to allow the taking of its life for purposes of research. It becomes, then, the basis of ethical acceptance of the derivation of stem cells from some human embryos and therefore a carefully circumscribed but nonetheless positive approval of embryonic stem cell research.

Meilaender, on the other hand, remains firm (though cautious and reluctant) in the conviction that embryonic stem cell research ought not to go forward or better, that it is not morally justifiable to use human embryos as the source for stem cells. Referencing three other Protestant theologians (Karl Barth, John Howard Yoder, and Stanley Hauerwas), Meilaender poses three arguments:

1. People should be considered people not on the basis of potentiality or actuality, not on the basis of capacities, but simply as members of the human community. To think inclusively about the human species should lead us to honor the dignity of even the weakest of living human being—the embryo—and thereby to "appreciate the mystery of the human person and the mystery of our own individuality."[13]
2. Immediately to opt for embryonic stem cell research is to prevent us from finding better solutions to the medical problems this research is designed to address. Given the ethical compromises involved in following this "handy" route, it would be better to "deny ourselves" this remedy and look to ones that do not denigrate the dignity of people however and wherever they live.
3. The church should bear witness to its beliefs by refusing to make sophistic distinctions such as those between funding embryonic stem cell research and funding the "procurement" of these cells. Meilaender is skeptical that only excess embryos or available cell lines will be used.

Along with evangelical Protestants, Roman Catholic voices have been prominent in the debates surrounding embryonic stem cell research. The position most frequently articulated in the public forum is that of opposition to the derivation of stem cells from embryos. This is the position of the Catholic hierarchy, promulgated through both Vatican and national Episcopal channels. It is a position ably supported theologically by spokespersons such as Richard Doerflinger.[14] Yet it is not the only position espoused by Roman Catholic ethicists and moral theologians or by all Roman Catholics.

_____

[b]Outka[12] indicates that his first awareness of the "nothing is lost" principle came from Paul Ramsey.

The alternate position is basically the "14 day" position, or the theory that an embryo in the first 14 days, prior to implantation in the uterus, is not yet even a "potential person" and hence need not be protected in the same way as human persons (or even in the same way as fetuses, considered potential persons after implantation). Neither of these positions goes the route of declaring absolutely that the early embryo is a person or the route of approving the exploitation of fetuses *in utero* in later stages of development. Since the debate between these two positions reflects similar philosophical and theological debates in other religious traditions and in the public forum (see, for example, Warnock[15]), it is worth looking at it in closer detail.

Roman Catholic Contributions and the 14-Day Theory

Before turning to the technicalities of the 14-day theory, it should be noted that Roman Catholics (including the official leaders of the church) tend to worry, like people in other traditions, about issues of justice, ecology, and the well-being of the whole Earth. Apart from the moral status of the embryo, Catholic concerns are focused on questions of equity in the shared lives of people across the world. For all the pressures to go forward with embryonic and fetal-tissue stem cell research, there is little assurance anywhere that the benefits of this research will be shared in the human community among the poor as well as the wealthy, across racial and gender lines, and in countries of the world's South as well as North. Moreover, as the research goes forward (for it surely will), some safeguards will need to be in place to keep the goals of the research focused on the healing of human persons rather than on the commodification of human bodies, their tissues, and their cells. And the specter of human genetic engineering for enhancement purposes (and not only for the treatment of diseases and injuries) is never far from the horizon. The other side of tremendous positive advances of modern technology is not to be ignored, not even if our present anxieties lead us desperately to seek means to lift the burdens of one generation or one group of people.

It is important to take preliminary note, also, of the shared community of discourse among Roman Catholic scholars, church leaders, and people. No matter how divided they may be among themselves—regarding the moral status of the early embryo or other particular moral questions—common moral convictions are nonetheless expressed in common language. As I have said elsewhere, the Catholic tradition is undivided in its affirmation of the goodness of creation, the role of human persons as agents in cooperation with ongoing divine creative activity, the importance of not only the individual but also the community, and the responsibilities of people to promote the health and well-being of one another.[16,17] At the same time, Catholics can disagree profoundly; a key example of disagreement is the debate about the status of the embryo and the moral evil or goodness of extracting stem cells from it in a way that leads to its demise.

The reason the debate within the Catholic community regarding stem cell research incorporates opposition over something like the 14-day theory is that the Roman Catholic moral tradition has consistently embraced a form of moral realism. At the heart of this tradition is the conviction that creation is itself revelatory. Embedded in an ultimately intelligible (though only partially so to humans) created reality is the possibility of perceiving and discerning moral claims of respect in response to every entity, especially human persons. This is what is at stake in the Catholic tradition of natural law. Though there are historical aberrations and contradictions in this long tradition, for the most part, natural law has not meant that morality can simply and fully be "read off" of nature, not even with the help of the special revelation of the Bible (though this is a help). What natural law theory does is tell people where to look—that is, to the concrete reality of the world around, to the basic needs and possibilities of human persons, and to the world as a whole. "Looking" involves discerning, deliberating, structuring insights, interpreting meanings, and taking account not only of what is similar among entities but also of what is particular in their histories, contexts, and relationships.

Roman Catholic thinkers engaged in discernment about human embryonic stem cell research tend, therefore, to "look" to the reality of stem cells and their sources—that is, human embryos and aborted fetuses, as well as adult tissues. All answers are not solely in the Bible, official church teachings, or individual experiences of the sacred. Discernment incorporates all of these sources of insight, but it also requires the knowledge available from the sciences, philosophy, and whatever other secular disciplines provide some access to the reality being studied. The ongoing intensity of the debate about the status of embryos bears witness that not all inquiries can be settled by one discipline or one interpreter or within one epistemological perspective.

The argument against procuring stem cells from human embryos is primarily that it entails the death of the embryos. No one disputes this fact, but disagreement rages as to whether this death can be justified. Those who oppose its justification argue that for each human person there is a biological and ontological continuum from the single-cell stage to birth, to whatever one has of childhood and adult life, and then to death.[18] Since a new and complete genetic code is present after fertilization, there is already a unique individual human, potential in an important sense but concretely and really (inherently) already directed to full actualization. The zygote itself, as a living organism, is both the "builder and the building...it is self-organizing."[19] The moral status of the early embryo is, therefore, that of a human person: It does not achieve this status by degrees or at some arbitrary point in development; nor is this status simply bestowed upon it by social recognition or convention.

But if the embryo has the status of a human person, then killing it in order to treat the illnesses of other people cannot—from a Catholic point of view—be justified. No human person, not even an inchoate one like an embryo, can be reduced to a pure means in relation to other ends. "Creating embryos for research purposes [or using embryos that will otherwise be discarded] is wrong because it treats this distinct human being, with his or her own inherent moral worth, as nothing more than a disposable instrument for someone else's benefit."[14] Those who oppose the extraction of stem cells from embryos on the grounds that it involves the destruction of a human person are not unsympathetic to the suffering that may be alleviated ultimately through research on stem cells. Part of the argument against the use of embryo sources for stem cells rests on the identification of alternative sources (particularly adult cells).[14]

On the other side of this debate are Catholic moral theologians who do not consider the human embryo in its earliest stages (prior to the primitive streak or to implantation) to be a human person, potential or actual. They hold the same meaning for "potency" as their opponents—that is, the Aristotelian and Thomistic meaning, signifying not an extrinsic or "sheer possibility" but rather an intrinsic principle already as such actual within a being, directing it to individualized species-specific development (even though the being may not yet be fully actualized developmentally). These moral theologians argue, then, precisely *against* the view that the early embryo has this inherent potency to become a person. Their argument harks back to a centuries-old Catholic position that a certain degree of biological development is necessary for the human spirit (or soul) to be embodied.[20] The conceptus, in other words, must have a baseline organization before it can embody a human person; it must embody the potentiality as well as the actuality that will lead to the formation of a human person. Although previous theories of embryological development were grounded in minimal (and to a great extent, erroneous) scientific evidence, proponents of embryonic stem cell research find in contemporary embryology insights that tend to support this developmental theory rather than defeat it.

Australian Catholic moral theologian Norman M. Ford has presented perhaps the most detailed argument in support of the view that an early embryo is not a potential human person.[c,21–26] The plausibility of "delayed personhood" is based on scientific evidence that suggests that the embryo prior to implantation is not yet a self-organizing organism. Fertilization itself does not take place in a "moment," as is sometimes rhetorically claimed; it comes about through a process that takes approximately 24 hours, finally issuing in the one-celled zygote. When the zygote then divides, there comes to be not a definitive, singular organism but a collection of cells, each with a complete genetic code. In other words, the first two cells, even if they interact, appear to be distinct cells—"not a two-cell ontological individual."[21] The same is true as division continues to 4, 8, and 16 cells, each with its own life cycle and nutrients for sustaining its life. Cells multiply and differentiate as they are gradually specified in their potential. Some cells form membranes that will finally enclose an organized individual entity approximately 14 days after fertilization. It is only then that a unified being can be said to be "self-organizing." Until this time, cells are *totipotential* in that they can become any part of what may ultimately

be a human being or even a human being as a whole.[23] "The totipotency of the early embryo does not imply that a human individual is formed before a definitive human individual is formed with heterogeneous parts. ...."[21]

The genotype of the zygote does not have a built-in blueprint for development as if it were a miniature person. Only with the formation of a single primitive streak (after implantation) does the totipotency of the embryo become a potency to develop into one human person. Ford concludes that "if this argument is accepted, fertilization is not the beginning of the development *of* the human individual but the beginning of the formative process and development *into* one (or more human individuals)."[22] Many who find this argument plausible tend to express it more simply (though with less illumination): Since at its early stages an embryo can twin and recombine, there is not here an individualized human entity with the inherent settled potential to become a human person. Critics of the position respond that *if* an embryo does *not* twin or recombine, then it may be supposed that an individual already exists. Ford's analysis goes farther than this, however, suggesting that the very undifferentiation of cells prior to implantation disallows the identification of individuality, whether or not there is twinning and recombining.

In addition to the argument from lack of individuation, some theologians have noted that the high rate of spontaneous early embryo loss undermines the credibility of the claim that human individuals begin at fertilization. In unassisted human reproduction, the development and loss of early embryos is estimated to be as high as 50–80%. From a Catholic theological point of view, it seems unbelievable that more than half of the individual human persons created by God should populate heaven without ever having seen the light of day in this world. This is a speculative observation, however, and it is generally not used today by those who favor embryonic stem cell research.

There are, then, two opposing cases articulated within the Roman Catholic tradition. This need not leave Catholics (or others) with a kind of "draw." Rather, it opens and sustains one significant conversation that takes account of scientific discoveries as well as of a larger set of theological and ethical insights. Moral theologians and ethicists attempt to provide reasons for their views that will be open to the scrutiny of all. Both sides claim a certain amount of epistemic humility, since there are only degrees of certainty available regarding the ontological status of the early embryo. Indeed, even official church documents acknowledge that there is no definitive answer to the question of when human individual life begins. In 1974, the "Declaration on Procured Abortion" stated in a footnote that "This declaration expressly leaves open the question of the moment when the spiritual soul is infused. There is not a unanimous tradition on this point and authors are as yet in disagreement."[27] In 1987, an instruction on "The Gift of Life" admitted that its authors were "aware of the current debates concerning the beginning of human life, concerning the individuality of the human being and concerning the identity of the human person.[28] And Pope John Paul II made no decision on the question of delayed ensoulment (or "hominization") in his 1995 encyclical letter, "Evangelium Vitae."

---

[c]It should be noted that although Ford argues well for a developmental view of the embryo,[21] he asserts that he does not disagree with the official Catholic position of protecting embryos from the start.

Uncertainty is dealt with in different ways by those who oppose and those who support embryonic stem cell research. Those who oppose it argue that "it suffices that this presence [in the embryo] of the soul be probable (and one can never prove the contrary) in order that the taking of life involve accepting the risk of killing a man [sic], not only waiting for, but already in possession of his soul."[27] And again, "what is at stake is so important that, from the standpoint of moral obligation, the mere probability that a person is involved would suffice to justify an absolutely clear prohibition of an intervention aimed at killing the human embryo."[29] In other words, probability (if not certitude) warrants the safer course. Hence, the embryo from fertilization on is to be *treated as* a human person, with the kind of unconditional respect due to all members of the human community.

For those who conclude that embryonic stem cell research can be permitted, uncertainty works the other way. First, the probability of an early embryo actually representing an individualized human being is much lower than is argued by opponents of embryonic stem cell research. Although there is not absolute certitude to be gained at this point from scientific evidence, the weight of the evidence *against* an individualized human being (incarnated in an embryo prior to implantation) is greater and more persuasive than any evidence for it. Moreover, the low level of uncertainty (for those who hold this position), when placed in relation to the prospect of great benefits for human healing (and some assurance that these benefits are not promised unrealistically), makes it possible—without yielding to a full-blown utilitarianism—to justify using early embryos as sources for stem cells for research. To *prohibit* all such research on the basis of a low probability of fact, or on a theological stipulation of moral status in the face of questionable accuracy of appraisal, seems itself not ethically justifiable.

Neither side in this debate wants to sacrifice the tradition's commitments to respect the dignity inherent in human life, promote human well-being, and honor the sacred in created realities. When a move forward is advocated for embryonic stem cell research, it need not soften the tradition's concerns to oppose the commercialization of human life and to promote distributive justice in the provision of medical care. The ongoing Roman Catholic conversation on all of these matters can be of assistance to others in a pluralistic society as long as it remains open to wider dialogue and respectful of all dialogue partners while retaining its own integrity. This is probably a lesson for all religious and secular traditions.

REFERENCES

1. Meyer, M.J. (2001). Respecting what we destroy: reflections on human embryo research. *Hastings Cent. Rep.* **31**, 16–28.
2. Holland, S. (2001). Beyond the embryo: A feminist appraisal of the embryonic stem cell debate. *In* "The Human Embryonic Stem Cell: Science, Ethics, and Public Policy," (S. Holland *et al.*, eds.), pp. 73–86. MIT Press, Cambridge, MA.
3. Sachedina, A. (2000). Testimony of Abdulaziz Sachedina. *In* "Ethical Issues in Human Stem Research," Vol. III, pp. G1–G6. National Bioethics Advisory Commission, Rockville, MD.
4. Hoffman, V.J. (1995). Islamic perspectives on the human body: Legal, social, and spiritual considerations. *In* "Embodiment, Morality, and Medicine," (M. Farley *et al.*, eds.), p. 37. Kluwer Academic Publishers, Boston.
5. Dorff, E. (2000). Testimony of Rabbi Elliott N. Dorff. *In*, "Ethical Issues in Human Stem Cell Research," Vol. III, pp. C1–C5. National Bioethics Advisory Commission, Rockville, MD.
6. Dorff, E. (2001). Stem cell research: a Jewish perspective. *In* "The Human Embryonic Stem Cell Debate," (S. Holland *et al.*, eds.), pp. 89–94. MIT Press, Cambridge, MA.
7. Zoloth, L. (2001). The ethics of the eighth day: Jewish bioethics and research on human embryonic stem cells. *In* "The Human Embryonic Stem Cell Debate," (S. Holland *et al.*, eds.), pp. 95–112. MIT Press, Cambridge, MA.
8. Tendler, M.D. (2000). Testimony of Rabbi Moshe David Tendler. *In* "Ethical Issues in Human Stem Cell Research," Vol. III, pp. H1–H5. National Bioethics Advisory Commission, Rockville, MD.
9. Demopulos, D. (2000). Testimony of Father Demetrios Demopulos. *In* "Ethical Issues in Human Stem Cell Research," Vol. III, pp. B1–84. National Bioethics Advisory Commission, Rockville, MD.
10. Peters, T. (2001). Embryonic stem cells and the theology of dignity. *In* "The Human Embryonic Stem Cell Debate," (S. Holland *et al.*, eds.), pp. 127–140. MIT Press, Cambridge, MA.
11. Cole-Turner, R. (2000). Testimony of Ronald Cole-Turner. *In* "Ethical Issues in Human Stem Cell Research," pp. A1–A4. National Bioethics Advisory Commission, Rockville, MD.
12. Outka, G. (2002). The ethics of human stem cell research. *Kennedy Inst. Ethics J.* **12**, 175–213.
13. Meilaender, G. (2001). Some Protestant reflections. *In* "The Human Embryonic Stem Cell Debate," (S. Holland *et al.*, eds.), pp. 141–148. MIT Press, Cambridge, MA.
14. Doerflinger, R. (1999). Destructive stem cell research on human embryos. *Origins* **28**, 771.
15. Warnock, M. (1984). "A Question of Life: The Warnock Report on Human Fertilization and Embryology." Basil Blackwell, Oxford.
16. Farley, M. (2000). Testimony of Margaret A. Farley. *In* "Ethical Issues in Human Stem Cell Research," Vol. III, pp. D1–D5. National Bioethics Advisory Commission, Rockville, MD.
17. Farley, M. (2001). Roman Catholic views on research involving human embryonic stem cells. *In* "The Human Embryonic Stem Cell Debate," (S. Holland *et al.*, eds.), pp. 113–118. MIT Press, Cambridge, MA.
18. Pellegrino, E. (2000). Testimony of Edmund D. Pellegrino. *In* "Ethical Issues in Human Stem Cell Research," pp. F1–F5. National Bioethics Advisory Commission, Rockville, MD.
19. Ashley, B., and Moraczewski, A. (2001). Cloning, Aquinas, and the embryonic person. *Nat. Catholic Bioethics Quart.* **1**, 193.
20. Donceel, J. (1970). Immediate and delayed hominization. *Theol. Stud.* **31**, 76–105.
21. Ford, N. (2002). "The Prenatal Person: Ethics from Conception to Birth." Blackwell Publishing, Oxford.
22. Ford, N. (2001). The human embryo as person in Catholic teaching. *Nat. Catholic Bioethics Quart.* **1**, 155–160.
23. Ford, N. (2001). Are all cells derived from an embryo themselves embryos? *In* "Pluripotent Stem Cells: Therapeutic Perspectives and Ethical Issues," (B. Dodet *et al.*, eds.), pp. 81–87. John Libbey Eurotest, Paris.
24. Ford, N. (1988). "When Did I Begin? Conception of the Human Individual in History, Philosophy, and Science." Cambridge University Press, New York.

25. Shannon, T., and Walter, A. (1990). Reflections on the moral status of the preembryo. *Theol. Stud.* **51,** 603–626.

26. McCormick, R. (1994). Who or what is the preembryo? *In* "Corrective Vision: Explorations in Moral Theology," pp. 176–188. Sheed & Ward, Kansas City, MO.

27. Congregation for the Doctrine of the Faith (1974). "Declaration on Procured Abortion (Acta Apostolicae Sedis)." **19.**

28. Congregation for the Doctrine of the Faith (1987). "The Gift of Life (Donum Vitae)." **1.**

29. John Paul II. (1995). "The Gospel of Life (Evangelium Vitae)." (Encyclical letter.) **60.**

Human Embryonic Stem Cells: Regulatory Considerations

Donald W. Fink

The shear scope and magnitude of information contained in the chapters of this definitive handbook on the topic of human embryonic stem (hES) cells details the relentless scientific advances being made with respect to derivation, expansion, and characterization of these pluripotent cell populations. This, in turn, continues to foster expectations that an array of promising novel cellular therapies will one day be developed from hES cells. It is envisioned that cellular biologic therapies derived from rigorously controlled differentiation of hES cells will be effective treatments for a multiplicity of medical conditions that necessitate replacement, restoration, repair, or regeneration of damaged or diseased tissues and organ systems for which there are current unmet medical needs. Beyond the promise of direct therapeutic efficacy achieved through seeding and repopulating of areas ravaged by trauma and disease, derivatives of undifferentiated hES cell cultures are being considered as vehicles that may be engineered for delivering functional genes and gene products to target sites where degenerative damage and disease is the consequence of genetic anomalies. Moreover, there is growing recognition that tissue-specific differentiation of hES cell cultures could generate important new *in vitro* model systems for investigating the underlying biologic basis of disease and for providing critical testing paradigms to screen potential lead candidate pharmaceuticals for toxicologic safety and putative therapeutic efficacy. The scientific underpinnings that will ultimately support initiation of clinical safety trials in humans involving cellular therapies derived from hES cells are being reinforced at a steady if not remarkable pace. Predictably, the era of irrational exuberance that characterized the nascent beginnings of this area of scientific inquiry has drawn to a close. It has been supplanted by a reasoned pragmatism that recognizes considerable hard work remains to be accomplished before concluding that it is reasonably safe to administer to patients products derived from hES cells for the purpose of investigating potential therapeutic efficacy. Continuationof ongoing science-based efforts to analyze and critically assess issues pertaining to hES cell safety is of vital importance to achieving the ultimate goal of producing novel cellular therapies that are both safe and effective. The challenge of drawing on all available scientific evidence to assess and gauge the relative safety of biologics produced from hES cells is the responsibility of the Center for Biologics Evaluation and Research (CBER) within the Food and Drug Administration (FDA). The explicit mission of CBER is to ensure the safety, purity, potency, and efficacy of new biologic therapies through a review process that is founded squarely on scientific principles thus making available to the public innovative new treatments in as timely a manner as is feasible.[1]

This chapter describes fundamentals of the approach that will be used by CBER to evaluate investigational new cellular therapies derived from hES cells. The focus is on issues related to preparation of an investigational cellular therapy destined for transplantation into patients to treat an expanding spectrum of disease indications.

Fundamental Principles Underlying the Center for Biologics Evaluation and Research's Approach to Assessing Human Embryonic Stem Cell Therapy Safety

Cellular therapies derived from populations of hES cells represent examples of complex, dynamic, phenotypically plastic biologic entities. Once transplanted in patients, cellular preparations obtained through differentiation of hES cells will interact intimately with and be influenced by the physiologic milieu of the recipient. Before producing a candidate cellular therapy, cultures of hES cells are maintained under specified conditions that favor retention of their undifferentiated, self-renewing properties. Preparation of a clinical grade cell population hinges on carefully controlled modification of the cell culture conditions to promote acquisition of differentiated biologic properties characteristic of the intended phenotypes that undifferentiated cultures of hES cells have the intrinsic capacity to assume. Theoretically, the target population of cells intended for transplantation may be isolated before completion of the differentiation process. In these circumstances it is anticipated that additional fine-tuning will occur following transplantation of partially differentiated hES cell populations in response to signals and instructional cues

Handbook of Stem Cells
Volume 1

received from the physiologic microenvironment of the recipient. It is these inherent capabilities of hES cells, namely their propensity for self-renewal and pluripotential phenotypic differentiation, that contribute simultaneously to their touted therapeutic promise and the challenge of performing a reliable, prospective safety assessment.

Reliable judgments regarding the safety of novel therapeutic candidates derived from hES cell cultures are dependent on formulation of a comprehensive strategy. The review approach, in turn, is built on sound scientific principles governed by regulatory requirements crafted to ensure that the level of risk exposure for patients enrolled in an investigative clinical study is acceptable with respect to any anticipated benefit. As a precedent for hES cells, issues influencing formulation of CBER's approach to evaluating the safety of stem cell therapies have been described in the National Institutes of Health report on stem cells.[2] The schematic diagram depicted in Fig. 77–1 coalesces and summarizes elements that must receive consideration to complete an adequate safety assessment of cellular therapies derived from hES cells. This framework constitutes the basis for the discussion of critical review elements that follows. One should not be misled by the linear, sequential depiction of the information. Instead, it is more appropriate to envision an interwoven web that incorporates each facet of the review process so as to enfold their objective, namely ensuring the safety of cellular therapies derived from hES cells. This image better projects the all-encompassing nature of the review process. Each component of the comprehensive review is interconnected and interrelated. Beginning with the evaluation and selection of eligible egg and sperm donors, every step involved in producing a hES-based cellular therapy intended for clinical testing is subjected to careful scrutiny. Derivation, expansion, manipulation, and characterization of cell lines established from hES cells are among the items included in this thorough assessment. In conjunction with the analysis of processes, procedures, and analytical tests used to generate a hES cellular therapy, equivalent emphasis is placed on preclinical testing conducted in appropriate animal models. Animal testing of "clinical grade" cellular preparations is performed for the expressed purposes of detecting potential toxicities, providing evidence indicative of possible efficacious outcomes, and determining cell doses that will be explored in human clinical safety studies. A key feature of the review approach not to be overlooked is the principle of linkage, or traceability. For those situations when an unanticipated adverse event occurs during the course of an investigative clinical trial, linkage affords investigators and study reviewers alike the opportunity to trace back from the patient through the cellular preparation process all the way to the initial acquisition of biologic materials used to generate the founder hES cells. Linkage makes it possible to establish with specificity where significant problems contributing causally to an untoward clinical event may have occurred during the process of preparing a cellular therapy derived from hES cells.

Sharply divided opinion exists among investigators as to the feasibility of initiating pilot clinical studies that involve cell therapy candidates produced from populations of undifferentiated hES cells. Some maintain it is reasonable to expect that within a relatively short period of time, perhaps as few as 5 years, that transplantation of hES-based cell therapies will be used clinically to replace dead or dying cells within organs such as the failing or myocardial infarct–damaged heart, diabetic pancreas, injured spinal cord, and diseased brain or that genetically transduced stem cells will be generated for the efficient, targeted delivery of therapeutic genes. Others argue that there simply is insufficient information pertaining to the basic biology of hES cells to justify initiation of clinical trials in the near-term citing concerns about the ability to reliably control cellular differentiation and fate specification; largely inadequate characterization of unique cell populations derived from hES cells with respect to identification; the difficulty demonstrating functional integration of cells after transplantation; and an incomplete understanding of biologic phenomena such as commitment, plasticity, and cell–cell fusion.[3,4] Regardless of one's position with respect to the issue of readiness, submission of an application to the FDA requesting permission to conduct a clinical study involving a novel cellular therapy derived from hES cells will require that CBER perform an evaluation of the proposal and reach a determination regarding safety based on all pertinent, available scientific information.

To consolidate a previously fractured approach to regulatory oversight of human cellular and tissue-based therapies, CBER has developed a framework intended to provide a unified paradigm for evaluation of cell- and tissue-based treatments including stem cells regardless of their source (embryonic, fetal, or adult).[5] This initiative was undertaken to provide a tiered regulatory review structure that is risk-based with respect to the public health. The specific aims of CBER's systematic approach are to (1) prevent the unintended transmission of infectious disease, (2) guard against improper handling or processing that might contaminate or damage cells or tissues intended for therapeutic use, and (3) ensure demonstration of clinical safety and effectiveness. Elements of CBER's approach to the evaluation of tissue- and cell-based therapies are coalesced under the programmatic umbrella of the Tissue Action Plan formulated to promote the timely development of policies, rules, and guidance necessary to ensure full implementation of the unified, tiered approach for evaluating the safety of these biologic entities.[6]

Evaluation of novel hES-based cellular therapies will be conducted in a manner consistent with the principles outlined in the framework of the tiered, risk-based approach. Moreover, CBER's regulatory review efforts in the arena of cellular treatments composed of differentiated hES cells are predicated on previous extensive experience obtained from evaluating the safety of hematopoietic stem cell (HSC) preparations being investigated in the context of numerous clinical trials. Investigative studies that involve transplantation of HSCs have been underway for a considerable number of years. Lymphohematopoietic reconstitution of the blood and immune systems is a crucial component of therapeutic procedures

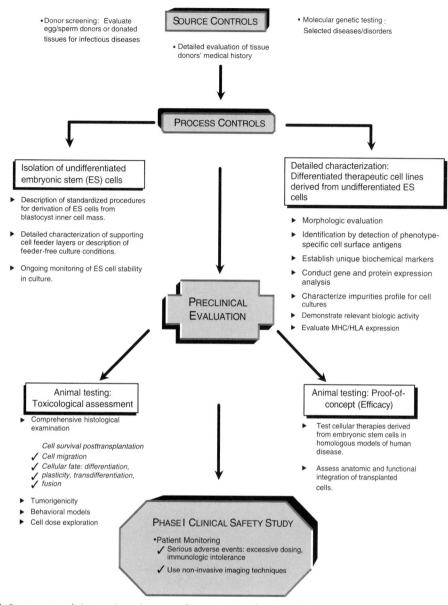

Figure 77-1. Representation of elements deemed necessary for ensuring the safety of novel human embryonic stem cell–derived cellular therapies.

designed to treat hematologic malignancies such as leukemia and lymphoma. Transplantation of HSCs resident in the bone marrow or isolated from circulating peripheral blood or umbilical cord blood is used to counter the destruction of specialized marrow cells responsible for hematopoiesis that results from high-intensity chemotherapeutic and total body irradiation preparative regimens used to combat hematologic malignancies and various solid tumors. As an extension of experience gained using stem cell transplantation to elicit hematopoietic reconstitution, current ongoing clinical studies explore the utility of coupling HSC transplantation with lower intensity chemotherapy conditioning regimens as a means to treat autoimmune diseases such as multiple

sclerosis, lupus, and rheumatoid arthritis that are persistent, refractory to standard medical interventions, and associated with significant morbidities. In addition, mesenchymal stem cell transplantation is being explored as a possible treatment for a variety of indications including metastatic cancer, high-risk hematologic malignancies, correction of genetic defects, and regeneration of bone. Corneal surface reconstruction achieved through the use of limbal epithelial stem cells represents still another example of a clinical investigation involving stem cells. In their collective, the accumulated experience gained through safety assessment of stem cell treatments in the context of these investigative clinical studies serves to shape and direct the approach CBER plans on using in the evaluation of biologic cellular therapies derived from hES cells.

Critical Elements for Developing a Safe Human Embryonic Stem Cell–based Cell Therapy

As represented schematically in Fig. 77–1, CBER's current approach for assessing the safety of a novel cellular therapy derived from hES cells is multidimensional and comprehensive. It encompasses, in its totality, acquisition of the starting biologic materials obtained from consented donors, isolation of undifferentiated hES cells, generation of differentiated cell lines from undifferentiated precursor cells, and preclinical toxicologic and proof-of-concept testing in appropriate animal models. At its core, ensuring safety of an hES-based biologic cellular therapy is all about establishing and maintaining complete and absolute control over every facet involved in the process of producing a clinical-grade cell preparation. Only in this manner is the degree of safety maximized and consistency from one cell preparation to the next ensured.

CONTROLLING SOURCE MATERIALS IS THE FIRST STEP IN SAFETY ASSURANCE

Demonstrating an acceptable safety profile for a novel hES-based cell therapy before commencing an investigative clinical study is initiated at a primordial stage, namely, qualification of the donor-derived egg and sperm used to generate embryos from which embryonic stem cells are to be isolated. Acceptance of donor tissues as suitable source material depends principally on screening and testing of donors for human infectious diseases including, at a minimum, human immunodeficiency virus types 1 and 2, hepatitis B virus, hepatitis C virus, *Treponema pallidum* (syphilis), human T-lymphotropic virus types I and II, and cytomegalovirus.[7] In addition, donor medical history evaluations and molecular genetic testing for selected diseases and disorders are under consideration within CBER as assessments of potential importance with respect to the qualification of donor tissue used in the production of a hES-based biologic.

Determining Donor Eligibility

Preventing the introduction, transmission, and spread of communicable diseases is one of FDA's principal public health obligations. Biologic therapies composed of cells obtained from the differentiation of hES cells pose a potential risk for transmitting communicable disease from donor to recipient because of their nature as derivatives of the human body. Recognizing the possibility for transmission of certain diseases through the implantation, transplantation, infusion, or transfer of cells and tissues derived from infected egg and sperm donors, it is essential appropriate measures are taken that guard against the use of cells or tissues obtained from these donors. To achieve this goal, screening and testing for relevant infectious and communicable diseases is performed. This screening serves to determine the eligibility of volunteer

donors to provide egg and sperm reproductive cells used for *in vitro* fertilization and subsequent isolation of embryonic stem cells from the inner cell mass of any viable, qualified blastocysts. In circumstances in which freshly derived blastocysts are designated to serve as the starting source material for generation of hES cells, the donors themselves may be screened for high-risk behaviors and tested serologically for evidence of infectious disease using FDA-licensed test kits. When cryopreserved fertilized embryos serve as source material and the original tissue donors are no longer available for communicable disease testing, cultures of self-renewing, undifferentiated embryonic stem cells, themselves, may be assessed directly for evidence of infectious disease once cell populations have expanded to numbers that are sufficient to support sampling. When possible, it is encouraged that collection and archiving of additional donor blood samples occur to provide for retrospective, *post hoc* testing. Archiving of donor-derived blood samples will permit screening for additional disease markers as new information and diagnostic techniques become available, thus providing an added measure of safety assurance with respect to a particular hES cell line.

Roles for Donor Medical Histories and Molecular Genetic Testing

The intended clinical use for a hES cell–derived cellular therapy provides sufficient rationale for proposing evaluation of tissue donor medical histories and targeted genetic testing as measures for establishing donor source material acceptability. Specifically, information obtained from these assessments could serve to establish whether a preparation of hES cells represents the best-qualified source material for generating a cellular therapy in the context of a particular disease setting. As a hypothetical example, hES cells isolated from a blastocyst for which either the egg or sperm donor has a family medical history blemished by evidence of serious cardiovascular disease may not represent the best choice for derivation of myocardial cells intended to repair damaged heart tissue. In a similar fashion, the use of genetic testing could, in theory, detect mutations in specific targets such as the gene that encodes α-synuclein. Evidence from genetic studies has identified two specific mutations in α-synuclein that cause familial Parkinson's disease with autosomal dominant inheritance.[8,9] Detection of such genetic anomalies in a population of hES cells could negate their use in generating neuronal progenitor cells for treating a number of neurodegenerative conditions, including Parkinson's disease. Admittedly, at this point a relatively small number of genes are known to be directly responsible for causing disease in a monogenetic fashion or to operate as suspected contributors to aberrant physiologic function. Undoubtedly this number will grow, perhaps substantially, because of advances in techniques for identifying, isolating, and analyzing genes, coupled with an increasing abundance of information certain to become available as one outcome of the human genome sequencing projects. In addition, it is expected that a great deal more will be learned as to how multiple gene products, each contributing incrementally to an overall outcome, will predispose individuals to development of certain diseases. Ultimately, with continued accumulation of genetic information it will become impossible and thus impractical to screen every donor or preparation of hES cells for the entire panoply of disease-associated genes. In this context, screening would be conducted only for targeted genes that are relevant to a specific clinical indication.

CONTROLLING PROCESSES USED TO ISOLATE AND DIFFERENTIATE HUMAN EMBRYONIC STEM CELLS ENHANCES SAFETY

Demonstrating rigorous control of standardized practices and procedures used during isolation, derivation, and maintenance of cultured hES cells ensures the integrity, uniformity, and reliability of candidate hES cell–derived therapies generated from hES cells. The initial stage of producing a hES cell therapy may be separated conveniently into two processes: (1) isolation of hES cells from the inner cell mast of the blastocyst and (2) induction of differentiation to push undifferentiated hES cells toward desired phenotypic lineages. Each process involves culturing of cells for some specified time period to obtain numbers sufficient for generating a master cell storage bank and to permit testing in a clinical transplantation study. Formulated liquid media supplemented with cytokines, growth factors, and chemical reagents that promote cellular replication and govern differentiation are critical to procedures developed for culturing hES cells and derivative differentiated cell lines. Because hES cells represent a complex, dynamic biologic entity, failure to standardize procedures for expansion and maintenance of cultured hES cells could result in unintended alterations of their intrinsic properties. As examples, density of the initial cell seeding, the frequency with which culture medium is replenished, the quality of the reagents used to supplement the culture media, and the degree of confluency cell cultures are permitted to achieve before subdividing could all have an impact on characteristics of cultured hES cells. Inadvertent changes in concentrations of supplemental growth factors and chemical substances added to the media, even simply switching from one supplier to another, may significantly alter properties of cultured hES cells, among them their intrinsic growth rate, expression of defining phenotypic markers, and differentiation potential. When available, use of clinical grade reagents, recombinant human materials, and FDA-licensed products is preferred. It is expected that variances in hES cell properties resulting from the use of nonstandardized culture practices will affect their stereotypic behavior and biologic effectiveness following transplantation into the recipient.

Isolation of Undifferentiated Human Embryonic Stem Cell Populations

Standardization of procedures used to acquire egg and sperm from eligible volunteer donors, perform *in vitro* fertilization, and isolate cleavage-stage embryos is crucial to the generation of quality, undifferentiated hES cell cultures. When cryopreserved embryos serve as the starting source material for deriving self-renewing hES cell cultures it is essential that critical information be documented and records maintained regarding the reagents and procedures used to perform embryo cryopreservation. This is the case particularly when more than one infertility clinic is providing cryopreserved embryos as source material for hES cell derivation. Differences in the concentration and type of cryoprotectant used, rate of initial cell freeze down, and routine length of cryopreservation storage may result in variability that precludes consistency from preparation to preparation. Perhaps the most significant issue with respect to use of frozen fertilized embryos is specification of prospective criteria used to ascertain the acceptability of a thawed, cryopreserved embryo as source material for generating hES cell cultures.

Establishing Cultures of Undifferentiated Human Embryonic Stem Cells. Historically, undifferentiated hES cells teased from the inner cell mass of cleavage-stage embryos by mechanical or enzymatic means have been propagated on layers of irradiated, nonreplicating feeder cells frequently composed of fibroblasts obtained from fetal mice. This is due to the fact that simply adding growth factors and cytokines to the culture media is insufficient to maintain hES cells in an undifferentiated form, and, thus, the presence of feeder cells is required. Moreover, it is not uncommon that medium used to sustain self-renewing hES cell cultures is supplemented with bovine-sourced serum. It has been suggested on several occasions from various sources that hES cells cultured under either of these conditions would be automatically disqualified from consideration for use in creating a clinical grade cellular preparation that could be tested in humans. It must be emphasized that statements to this effect, from a regulatory perspective, are categorically inaccurate.

SUPPLEMENTING CULTURE MEDIA WITH BOVINE SERUM As a consequence of spongiform encephalopathy (BSE) outbreaks in cattle herds, particularly those maintained in the United Kingdom, there is a measure of justifiable apprehension regarding inclusion of bovine serum as a media supplement for culturing hES cells designated for eventual clinical use. Consumption of beef contaminated with the infectious, BSE-causing, proteinaceous prion agent responsible for causing BSE has led to limited emergence of new variant Creutzfeldt-Jakob disease in humans. This disease results in the relentless destruction of brain tissue and is invariably fatal. Unquestionably, transplanting neural progenitor cells derived by a process of limited neuronal differentiation using cultures of hES cells contaminated with BSE infectious agent into the nervous system of a patient with neurologic disease represents an act that is both irresponsible and devastating. There exists a hierarchy of several options to safeguard against inadvertent transmission of BSE to patients through transplantation of contaminated hES cell–derived therapies. First, cultures of hES cells may be maintained in medium supplemented with bovine serum if it is demonstrated that the reagent is produced from cows reared for the entirety of their lives in herds maintained in countries certified to be free of BSE. A second alternative is to replace bovine serum with clinical grade serum sourced from humans. In this case, testing of the serum donors or final pooled serum product for infectious human diseases is critical. The third option is development of a chemically defined, serum-free medium thus obviating altogether risks associated with serum supplementation. Obviously CBER encourages vigorous efforts in this latter category, however, completely eliminating serum from culture media is not a mandatory regulatory requirement.

THE USE OF NON-HUMAN FEEDER CELL LAYERS AND XENOTRANS-PLANTATION The act of transplanting patients with cellular therapies composed of, or derived from, hES cells maintained originally on a feeder layer of murine fetal fibroblasts constitutes, by definition, xenotransplantation. As defined in the Public Health Service (PHS) guideline on this topic, xenotransplantation is any procedure that involves the transplantation, implantation, or infusion into human recipients of either (a) live cells, tissues, or organs from a nonhuman animal source, or (b) human body fluids, cells, tissues, or organs that have had *ex vivo* contact with live nonhuman animal cells, tissues, or body organs.[10] Clearly part (b) of this definition applies to hES cells cultured atop feeder layers composed of nonhuman cells. The PHS guideline on infectious disease issues in xenotransplantation was jointly developed by five components within the Department of Health and Human Services (DHHS)—the Centers for Disease Control and Prevention, FDA, Health Resources and Services Administration, National Institutes of Health, all parts of the PHS, plus the DHHS Office of the Assistant Secretary for Planning and Evaluation. This PHS document serves as a foundation for the Xenotransplantation Action Plan, which details the FDA's comprehensive approach to regulating xenotransplantation therapies.[11] The stated purpose of the action plan is to address potential public health safety issues associated with xenotransplantation including the possible infection of recipients with both recognized and unrecognized infectious agents that could result in subsequent transmission to their close contacts and to the population at large. Consistent with its stated purpose, the FDA action plan provides guidance for the development of safe xenotransplantation therapies. Statements suggesting that culture methods for hES cells must be devised so as to exclude contact with potentially contaminating mouse or other nonhuman cells to permit use of hES cells and their derivatives in an investigative clinical study are not only misleading but they are inaccurate.[12] Presently, FDA oversees a number of xenogeneic investigational therapies being evaluated in safety and efficacy clinical trials. These include hepatocytes, fetal neuronal cells, and pancreatic islet cells, all of porcine origin, for treating a variety of indications such as hepatic failure, Parkinson's disease, Huntington's disease, epilepsy, refractory pain associated with spinal cord injury, and type I diabetes mellitus. To ensure an adequate measure of safety for clinical studies involving xenotransplantation, additional requirements are overlaid atop those associated with the development of investigational human cellular therapies. Admittedly the challenge of complying with these added measures is not a trivial matter.

For clinical development of cell therapies derived from hES cells that have been cultured on murine fetal fibroblast feeder layers at any point during the derivation process, information about the nonhuman feeder cells will need to be provided. As an example, to investigate a stem cell product derived from an hES cell line propagated on murine feeder cell layers it will be necessary to demonstrate that the primary hES cell line is free from not only human infectious agents but murine infectious agents as well.[13] Given the capability of current technology, this testing should not pose undue burden. In contrast to therapies that involve the transplantation, implantation, or infusion of nonhuman cells, for hES cell–based therapies it will not be necessary to provide complete animal husbandry information for mice from which the mouse feeder layers were derived. If expansion of an hES cell line is conducted over a prolonged period of time with continued direct contact with the murine feeder cell layers, additional information may be requested demonstrating that the mouse colonies from which such murine feeder layers are obtained are maintained appropriately to ensure safety. This could include further details about the animal colonies from which the mice are obtained indicating whether or not they are specific pathogen-free. If the mice used to produce feeder cell layers are from pathogen-free colonies, information that describes what infectious agent testing is performed on the animal colony as a whole and on the individual mice that serve as source animals for generating feeder cells is valuable. In situations when primary cell banks of murine feeder cells are generated and stored, additional details about the banking procedure, the passage numbers of the cultures used, and testing conducted to verify their purity, phenotype, and viral adventitious agent profile are expected.

Arguably efforts to develop culture conditions for hES cells that do not rely on the use mouse feeder cells are motivated by the increased level of testing called for in the xenotransplantation guidelines. Several reports published recently represent potentially groundbreaking advances with respect to the challenging technical issue posed by stringent culture conditions required to support successful expansion and maintenance of undifferentiated hES cells. The first report details development of a feeder-free culture environment in which hES cells are propagated on an extracellular matrix in media preconditioned by cultures of murine embryonic fibroblast cells.[14] From CBER's perspective, treating patients with a hES cell therapy composed of cells cultured under these conditions would not constitute xenotransplantation because intimate, direct contact between the hES cells and nonhuman murine cells is avoided. Importantly, the investigators report that the hES cells maintained in feeder-free culture retained genotypic and phenotypic properties characteristic of undifferentiated embryonic stem cells. It should be noted, however, that the hES cells used to establish the culture conditions described in this study were originally derived on murine embryonic fibroblast feeder layers and then migrated to the feeder-free culture system. Consequently, because of their initial contact with a nonhuman feeder layer, transplantation of these hES cells or their derivatives would still be considered xenotransplantation.

The contributors of two other reports adopted a different strategy to avoid use of conditioned media obtained from cultures of nonhuman feeder cells and poorly characterized extracellular substrates such as Matrigel, which is composed of solubilized basement membrane extracted from a mouse sarcoma. These investigators describe the successful prolonged culture of undifferentiated hES cells on feeder layers composed of human fetal and adult fibroblasts[15] and adult human marrow stromal cells.[16] Significantly, the first of these two reports describes the generation of a nascent hES cell line in conditions completely free of animal-derived feeder layers. By definition, transplanting a cellular therapy derived from a culture of hES cells created under these conditions would not be considered xenotransplantation. In the case of the marrow stromal feeder layer there may be a second, unanticipated advantage beyond successful expansion of undifferentiated hES cells. Based on the observation that marrow stromal cells appear able to down-regulate host allogeneic immune responses, it is conceivable that the presence of human marrow stromal feeder cells derived from the recipient may help to induce immune tolerance thus reducing the risk for immune rejection of hES-derived cells received from an unrelated, genotypically disparate donor. As is the case for donors providing egg and sperm used to establish a hES cell line, it is necessary to screen and test human fibroblast and marrow cell donors, or the acquired populations of cells, for a panel of human infectious diseases to prevent inadvertent disease transmission.

Human Embryonic Stem Cell Line Stability. During early phases of development, it is likely that there will be a limited number of banked hES cell lines that serve as source material for generating novel investigational cellular therapies. This is due to the complexities and technical challenges affiliated with derivation of hES cell lines from the inner cell mass of the blastocyst. Accordingly, one key to the feasibility of this strategic approach involving reliance on a limited number of hES cell banks is the periodic, prospectively scheduled assessment of founder hES cell stability. Monitoring stability provides a means for ensuring consistency with respect to the repeated generation of a specific cellular therapy from a single source of well-characterized HES cells. Stability assessments are based on a panel of analytic tests and evaluations comparable to those used to perform initial characterization of a particular hES cell line. It is expected that stability testing programs for hES cell lines will include but not be limited to (1) demonstration of pluripotency, namely the capacity for hES cells to differentiate into tissues representative of all three germ layers; (2) an assessment of genetic stability involving karyotypic chromosomal analysis; (3) monitoring the rate of proliferation; (4) measuring telomerase activity; (5) inspection of morphology; and (6) expression of molecular markers such as the transcription factor Oct-4, membrane alkaline phosphatase, and the stage-specific embryonic antigen-4 that serve to uniquely identify undifferentiated hES cells. In addition, monitoring expression of molecular markers not expected to be present in populations of cultured hES cells serves as a barometer of their undifferentiated status.

Characterization of Differentiated Human Embryonic Stem Cell Lines

Among their many distinguishingly unique features, hES cells are defined by their capacity for continuous self-renewal and ability to differentiate into the complete spectrum of tissue types found throughout the body. With respect to their use in investigative clinical studies, at present, most counsel against developing cellular therapies that are composed principally of undifferentiated hES cells. This position is staked out, in part, because of the unmitigated risk posed by unregulated cellular proliferation that could occur following transplantation. Buttressing this position is an incomplete understanding of mechanisms that govern the processes of fate specification, differentiation, and plasticity. To effect an increased measure of control over these biologic complexities, it is envisioned that hES cells will be subject to specified *in vitro* culture conditions that prompt differentiation of the hES cells along phenotypic lineages targeted for treating a selected disease or medical condition. Critical to the development of differentiated hES cells as cellular therapies destined for clinical investigation is detailed characterization of differentiated cell populations intended for transplantation. Identity of unique cell lines derived from undifferentiated hES cells is established through robust testing. The specific analytical tests used and their results should be of sufficient rigor and accuracy so as to permit unambiguous identification of a specific cellular preparation. Validating identity. testing for undifferentiated, partially differentiated, or fully differentiated stem cell populations poses considerable challenges.

Based on intricate biologic properties that include the potential to differentiate along multiple phenotypic lineages giving rise to a variety of cell types, characterization of tissue-specific stem cell lines derived from undifferentiated hES cells requires a constellation of orthogonal assessments as is illustrated in Fig. 77–1. A representative panel of parameters judged to be useful in establishing identity includes (1) cell morphology (visual microscopic inspection of cells to assess their appearance, electron microscopy to detect characteristic structural elements); (2) detection of unique, phenotype-specific cell surface antigens (as is currently the case for use of the CD34, CD133, CD14, and CD56 surface antigens to isolate and enrich for select cell populations from apheresis blood collections); (3) assessment of exclusive biochemical markers including tissue-specific enzymatic activity (e.g., enzymes involved in the production of neurotransmitters selective for distinct neuronal populations); and (4) evaluation of tissue-specific gene and protein expression patterns. Continued development and standardization of DNA microarray (permitting the simultaneous screening for many genes) and proteomics (protein profiling) coupled with laser microcapture dissection technologies will significantly enhance the effectiveness and precision of stem cell characterization. Although a recommended panel of test parameters has been presented for performing detailed characterization of differentiated hES cell populations, it should not be construed, by any means, that this indicates the list is either definitive or all encompassing. As information and experience are accumulated, the composition of the list will be reevaluated and modified as is appropriate, consistent with advances occurring in the areas of basic science and clinical research.

Self-evident is the fact that regardless of the extent of differentiation achieved *in vitro,* cell preparations derived from hES cells will not be homogeneous with respect to cellular phenotypes expressed. Optimally, rigorous and quantitative identification of all cell types within a heterogeneous population of differentiating human stem cells serves as the means to establish both the characteristic phenotypic composition and impurities profile for a given cellular preparation. In turn, this permits an assessment as to the extent to which the cell phenotype profile predicts efficacy of a stem cell therapy following transplantation. Counterintuitive to the notion of purity, it is not necessarily the case that homogeneously pure populations composed of a single cell type will be more efficacious as a cell-replacement therapy than cell preparations composed of multiple phenotypes. For example, it is conceivable that the reason *in vitro* differentiation of cultured neural stem cells isolated from brain tissue results in formation of all the cell types found within the nervous system (namely, neurons, astrocytes, and oligodendrocytes) is the requirement for coincidental expression of each distinct phenotype to ensure maximal survival and optimal functional capability of all the cells in the culture. Elucidating the neighborhood effect of cells with different phenotypes interacting with one another within populations of differentiating stem cells constitutes an area of active basic research.

In addition to serving as an indicator of identity, the phenotypic impurities profile of a differentiated hES cell preparation is also useful for detecting changes that have occurred either as a consequence of inadvertent and undocumented errors made during the preparation of the cells or as a function of their intrinsic biologic volatility. Deviations in the impurities profile that fall outside what is expected because of normal biologic variability for a differentiated cell line derived from hES cells using standardized procedures could serve as a harbinger that significant, and possibly deleterious, changes have occurred. Such anomalies might reflect genetic instability driven by the culture conditions used to promote expansion and trigger differentiation of progenitor cell populations.

In addition to developing procedures and specifications for identity testing of cellular preparations derived from hES cells along with establishing an impurities profiles, it is essential to demonstrate that investigational human stem cell therapies possess a relevant biologic activity before initiating a clinical study. Relying on various types of bioassays to assess biologic activity provides a semiquantitative measure of the potency possessed by a cellular preparation. More importantly, the bioassay or potency test provides assurance that cells destined for transplantation are not inert biologically. Glucose-dependent secretion of insulin from pancreatic islet–like cells, demonstration of glycogen storage by cells intended for the regeneration of liver tissue, evidence of synchronous contraction in populations of stem cell–derived cardiomyocytes to be used to repair damaged heart muscle, and depolarization-evoked

release of neurotransmitter from putative neuronal cell populations represent examples of bioassays that are based on specific, characteristic biologic activities. Alternatively, it is appropriate to consider the use of surrogate markers that predict the eventual acquisition of an intended biologic activity in circumstances when populations of stem cells are to be transplanted before acquiring fully differentiated functionality. In these cases it is expected that incompletely differentiated cells resident within the preparation will continue to differentiate functionally following transplantation. For instance, quantifying the number of tyrosine hydroxylase–expressing neural progenitors present in a mixed population of cells intended to supply dopaminergic neurons for treating Parkinson's disease represents an acceptable approach for anticipating acquisition of a targeted biologic activity after transplantation.

Histocompatibility constitutes an additional safety issue meriting consideration with respect to the characterization of cell lines established following differentiation of hES cells. Initial reports suggested that hES cells derived from the inner cell mass of blastocyst-stage embryos do not express immune-recognition proteins raising the possibility that hES cells might be immuno-privileged and, therefore, unrecognized by the immune system of the recipient. This led investigators to the hope that transplanted tissue derived from hES cells would be immunologically silent and thus remain undetected by the recipient's immune surveillance system. In a more recent report, low level expression of major histocompatibility complex (MHC) class I proteins on the surface of hES cells is described, thus providing evidence that it might not be the case that hES cells are or remain immunologically inert.[17,18] MHC-I proteins are involved in tissue rejection mediated by cytotoxic T lymphocytes. In addition to the detection of low levels of MHC-I proteins on the surface of hES cells, moderate increases in their expression are noted in conjunction with *in vitro* or *in vivo* differentiation. At this point it is uncertain whether the level of MHC-I expressed in hES cells is sufficient to elicit a vigorous, let alone even a tepid immunologic rejection response; however, it does appear that characterization of MHC profiles for stem cell therapies derived from hES cells is warranted.

PRECLINICAL EVALUATION SUPPORTS SAFETY ASSESSMENT: PROOF-OF-CONCEPT AND TOXICITY TESTING IN ANIMAL MODELS

Preclinical testing of cellular therapies derived from hES cells in appropriate animal models is a linchpin of the safety assessment process depicted in the schematic diagram presented in Fig. 77–1. Two critical objectives govern preclinical testing: appraisal of toxicity and demonstration that the candidate therapy is capable of doing what it is projected to (proof-of-concept). With respect to the core biology of hES cells, namely a propensity for continuous self-renewal and broad differentiation potential, it is crucial that experimental animals are inspected carefully following transplantation of cell preparations derived from hES cells for evidence of unregulated growth and genesis of inappropriate cell types.

Toxicologic Assessment

Completing a comprehensive histologic examination following transplantation of cellular preparations derived from hES cells into immunosuppressed animals is fundamental to fulfilling requirements for an adequate preclinical toxicologic safety study. Important issues pertaining to the fate of stem cells posttransplantation are addressed in these types of preclinical analyses. Included are assessment of acute and long-term cell survival, the extent and pattern of cell migration, evidence for differentiation and plasticity, indication of hyperplastic growth or tumorigenicity, and anatomical and functional integration. The extent of valid safety information extracted from investigations conducted in animal models will be a direct function of the experimental design and technical limitations associated with the specific test methodologies used to identify and track transplanted populations of stem cells. Recently, investigators have reported successful monitoring of stem cell migration *in vivo* following transplantation in an experimental rat stroke model using high-resolution *in vivo* magnetic resonance imaging.[19] Continued advancements in noninvasive imaging technologies such as magnetic resonance imaging and positron emission tomography will allow cell fate monitoring to be carried out in real time with reasonable resolution and without having to expend excessively large numbers of animals. Monitoring the posttransplantation disposition of these cell therapies in preclinical animal models provides considerable challenges; however, the information gleaned will be vitally important to improving overall safety assessments for these as yet untested therapies.

The significance of evaluating the survival index for transplanted human stem cell preparations is intuitively obvious, however, there are subtleties to be considered. Without question, cell survival in the immediate period post transplantation is crucial, but the persistence of viable cells over time may assume a greater importance particularly when considering the fact that stem cell therapies are expected to elicit enduring, long-term clinical benefit. At issue is the length of time preclinical studies need to be carried out in appropriate animal models to gain a meaningful estimate of cell survival potential posttransplantation. Quantifying the proportion of cells that remain viable over a prolonged time frame provides a glimpse as to the robustness and durability of transplanted stem cells. Capturing this key piece of information requires longitudinal preclinical studies of sufficient duration. Not to be overlooked in the analysis is identification of the persistent cellular phenotypes and a determination as to whether or not they continue to contribute to the overall biologic activity of the transplant.

In addition to the recognized importance of evaluating post-transplantation survival of cell preparations derived from hES cells, it is also incumbent to assess the propensity for stem cells to migrate and home to specific tissue and organ targets. Experimental observations suggest that signals emitted by damaged or diseased tissues and organs serve as powerful attractants for elements of transplanted stem cell populations that share comparable developmental phenotypes with the target tissues. It is possible to envision how cellular

migration could be considered a favorable attribute of hES cell derivatives posttransplant, particularly with respect to their potential efficacy as tissue-specific delivery systems of gene products. The flip side of the same coin is that unintended, potentially adverse consequences could occur as an outcome of "misdirected" or reckless migration to adjacent even distant tissues. Migration of transplanted human stem cells to a non-target site and subsequent differentiation into a tissue type that is inappropriate for that specific anatomic location could prove to be problematic.

Precise assessment of the post-transplantation phenotypic fate for cellular therapies offers, perhaps, the single greatest test from a technical and conceptual perspective. A recent review on the topic of stem cell plasticity serves to capture the breadth of possibilities that might occur following transplantation of human stem cell preparations. Once situated within the physiologic microenvironments of the recipient, transplanted stem cells will be faced with several cell fate decisions including self-renewal versus induction of differentiation.[20] The prospect of determining with rigor in a preclinical animal model whether final phenotypic expression of transplanted stem cells is the result of activating an intrinsic differentiation program or occurs as a consequence of either transdifferentiation[21] or spontaneous cell–cell fusion[22] further complicates the picture. Although still a matter of contention, recent published reports from two independent laboratories provide compelling evidence that cell fusion and not transdifferentiation underlies the regeneration of liver following infusion of bonemarrow–derived stem cells.[23,24] Testing was conducted at the level of cytogenetic analysis revealing diploid to diploid and diploid to tetraploid karyotypes indicative of fusion between donor and host cells. It remains to be determined whether differentiated cell preparations derived from hES cells will behave in a similar fashion following transplantation.

Arguably, tumorigenicity or hyperplastic, unregulated cellular proliferation represents the single most important safety issue with respect to toxicologic preclinical animal testing of cellular therapies composed of or derived from hES cells. Concern as to the ramifications of dysregulated cellular replication following transplantation arises from one of the fundamental characteristics of true stem cells, namely their capacity to effect expansion through self-renewing proliferation. For hES cells, concern is heightened because of their pluripotential character and proclivity for generating teratomas when injected in sufficient numbers into immunodeficient strains of mice. This property, alone, serves as a persuasive argument against clinical testing of cellular therapies composed exclusively of unmodified, undifferentiated HES cells. Published findings from a preclinical animal study involving transplantation of embryonic stem cells in a Parkinson rat model reinforce the stance that the proliferative potential of undifferentiated hES cells makes their use as a cellular transplant therapy prohibitive. Results from the study did demonstrate that transplanted embryonic stem cells develop spontaneously into desired dopamine-producing neurons capable of supporting behavioral recovery in this model of neurodegenerative disease; however, teratoma-like structures in a significant proportion of the animals (25%) were noted after injecting what were considered to be low cell doses of embryonic stem cells.[25] A critical question is at what point during the differentiation of hES cells do risks attributable to tumorigenic potential and hyperplasia become insignificant, if ever? Successful identification of the precise stage in the differentiation process when the risk for tumor formation becomes negligible will depend on whether or not cellular differentiation proceeds in unidirectional manner or is reversible. Because of inherent inefficiencies in the biologic process of differentiation, it is unlikely that phenotypic maturation induced in cultures of undifferentiated hES cell cultures will be total and complete. Accordingly, it is essential that analytical techniques are developed permitting careful evaluation of cell preparations derived from hES cells to determine the number of residual undifferentiated hES cells and partially differentiated intermediates that are present. Careful preclinical toxicologic studies of appropriate duration that involve transplantation of undifferentiated or partially differentiated hES cells into immunocompromised animals must be carried out before initiating clinical trials to resolve the issue of unregulated growth potential and its relationship to the process of cell differentiation.

A further issue appropriately addressed during the preclinical animal testing phase is assertion of effective control over dose-related effects observed following transplantation of cell preparations composed of hES cell derivatives. Unlike standard pharmaceuticals or recombinant therapeutic proteins, once delivered, cell dose level is not readily amenable to adjustment nor is a cellular therapy easily retrieved. Furthermore, it is extremely difficult to predict with accuracy what cell dose-dependent events will be elicited after transplanting hES cell–derived cellular preparations. Each of the items mentioned previously that pertain to cellular fate posttransplantation, namely, survival, migration, and plasticity, will have an impact on dose-related effects. The importance of conducting carefully designed preclinical studies using well-characterized cellular preparations to explore issues related to cell dosing is underscored by published results from a clinical trial involving transplantation of minimally characterized fetal neuronal tissue fragments to treat severe Parkinson's disease.[26] Profound untoward effects on muscle tone and motor function were observed in approximately 15% of the patients receiving transplants. The presumed cause for these events is an "overdose" effect resulting from the survival of too many dopamine-producing neurons, although there are other plausible explanations. Developing strategies for effectively controlling cell dose levels after stem cell transplantation is paramount because this will improve the safety profile for hES cell–derived therapies. Potential solutions include ongoing efforts to introduce genetic switches into populations of hES cells that are capable of regulating cellular proliferation and that may be turned on or off using extrinsic means after the cells have been transplanted.

Demonstrating Proof-of-concept

Investigations performed using animal transplant models of human disease constitute an essential component of the assessment paradigm used for judging the safety of cellular therapies derived from hES cells. Results from these proof-of-concept investigations serve to substantiate a rationale for conducting a proposed clinical trial with an investigational hES cell–derived therapy. The ideal animal model will recapitulate with fidelity most if not all of the features of human disease. Granted it is recognized that animal models, in general, are imperfect because most human maladies and medical conditions do not occur spontaneously in animals. Chemical, surgical, and immunologic methods are used to damage neural tissue; induce diabetes; simulate myocardial infarction, stroke, and hypertension; or compromise organ function. In selected situations when focal monogenetic lesions are known to cause disease, creation of transgenic animal models in which the culpable gene is either eliminated or overexpressed results in the generation of animal disease models that are often more faithful in their recapitulation of human disease-specific pathologies.

It is neither essential nor required to demonstrate that a novel investigational stem cell therapy is curative in an animal model of human disease. The principal aim of studies performed in animal disease models is to obtain results that provide a reasonable level of assurance regarding the biologic activity of a novel therapy. Transplantation of functional neuronal cells or neural progenitors derived from cultures of hES cells should demonstrate activity in animal models that mimic human neurodegenerative diseases or neurologic disorders such as Parkinson's disease, Huntington's disease, Alzheimer's disease, amyotrophic lateral sclerosis, spinal cord injury, and stroke. Evidence for an improvement in liver function occurring after transplantation of hepatocyte precursors derived from hES cells in an animal model of hepatic failure serves to establish rationale. Normalization of blood insulin concentrations and amelioration of diabetic disease symptoms achieved following transplantation of pancreatic islet progenitors carried out in an animal model of diabetes represents still another concrete example of the type of outcomes observed in preclinical studies that serve to legitimize proof-of-concept arguments. In all cases, immunosuppression will serve a pivotal role because of the extreme immunologic incompatibility between humans and the species of animal used to generate the disease model. The impact of immunosuppressive regimens on the biologic properties of a cellular transplant will need to be considered. Importantly, demonstrating a corrective effect resulting from transplantation of an investigational hES cell therapy into an animal construct of human disease provides circumstantial evidence for anatomical and functional integration of transplanted cells within the host physiology that may be corroborated on histopathologic examination.

Summary

In this chapter a framework has been described that constitutes the FDA's approach to assessing the safety of novel cellular therapies derived from hES cells. It appears that in the not-to-distant future this paradigm could be put to the test in light of the relentless pace at which information is being accumulated as a consequence of ongoing basic research focused on hES cells. Primary responsibility for evaluating the safety of investigational new treatments composed of hES cell derivatives is assigned to FDA's CBER. Armed with a comprehensive approach developed for the regulation of tissue and cellular therapies, staffed by scientific reviewers with expertise in cell and developmental biology, and endowed with a wealth of experience in the evaluation of submissions involving administration of stem cell preparations to patients, the FDA is well positioned to successfully meet its obligation for ensuring that investigative human clinical trials are conducted in as safe a manner as is reasonably achievable. With respect to experimental treatments derived from hES cells, safety assurance is fundamentally about demonstrating control over every facet of the cell therapy preparation process beginning with the acquisition of source donor materials and carried forward through derivation of an hES cell line, its characterization, and ultimately the implementation of adequate and appropriate preclinical testing. Although the focus of the information presented in this chapter is intentionally circumspect, concentrating primarily on preparation of the putative hES cell therapy, this should not be misconstrued to suggest that the role of clinical testing with respect to establishing safety and efficacy is of less importance. Each element is equally critical to the successful regulation of cutting-edge investigative biologic therapies. Considering the pace at which new information about the biology of hES cells is being amassed, it is best to consider the regulatory approach described here as a work-in-progress. Although constructed on a concrete foundation of solid science-based principles, the evaluative strategy used to ensure the safety of biologic therapies is not to be viewed as permanently fixed or immutable. Rigorous but flexible are more suitable adjectives. To be credible and effective, any approach taken for assessing the safety of hES cell–based therapies must consider the dynamic complexity of their biology. Operating within the jurisdiction of its constitutionally mandated legal authority the FDA will meet its obligation to ensure the safety of nascent cellular therapies derived from hES cells by relying on an approach that encourages iterative and collaborative interactions with the innovators and which is updated based on the best available science.

REFERENCES

1. See www.fda.gov/cber/inside/mission.htm (accessed April 2003).
2. Assessing Human Stem Cell Safety. (July 2001). Available from www.nih.gov/news/stemcell/scireport.htm (accessed 2003).
3. Holden, C., and Vogel, G. (2002). Plasticity: time for reappraisal? *Science* **296**, 2126–2129.
4. Wurmser, A., and Gage, F. (2002). Cell fusion causes confusion. *Nature* **416**, 485–486.
5. Proposed Approach to Regulation of Cellular and Tissue-based Products. (February 28, 1997). Available from www.fda.gov/cber/gdlns/CELLTISSUE.pdf (accessed 2003).
6. Tissue Action Plan. (March 1998). Available from www.fda.gov/cber/tissue/tissue.htm (last updated: 04-10-03).
7. Suitability determination for donors of human cellular and tissue-base products. (1999). USPHS, *Federal Register* **64**, 189, 52696–52723.
8. Polymeropoulos, M.H., Lavedan, D., Leroy, E., Ide, S.E., Dehejia, A., Dutra, A., Pike, B., Root, H., Rubenstein, J., Boyer, R., Stenroos, E.S., Chandrasekharappa, S., Athanassiadou, A., Papapetropoulos, T., Johnson, W.G., Lazzarini, A.M., Duvoisin, R.C., Di Iorio, G., Golbe, L.I., and Nussbaum, R.L. (1997). Mutation in the α-synuclein gene identified in families with Parkinson's disease. *Science* **276**, 2045–2047.
9. Krüger, R., Kuhn, W., Müller, T., Woitalla, D., Graeber, M., Kösel, S., Przuntek, H., Epplen, J.T., Schöls, L., and Riess, O. (1998). Ala30Pro mutation in the gene encoding alpha-synuclein in Parkinson's disease. *Nat. Genet.* **18**, 106–108.
10. PHS Guideline on Infectious Disease Issues in Xenotransplantation. (January 19, 2001). Available from www.fda.gov/cber/gdlns/xenophs0101.pdf (accessed April 2003).
11. Xenotransplantation Action Plan: FDA Approach to the Regulation of Xenotransplantation. Available from www.fda.gov/cber/xap/xap.htm (accessed April 2003).
12. Holden, C. (2002). Versatile cells against intractable diseases. *Science* **297**, 500–502.
13. Guidance for Industry: Source Animal, Product, Preclinical, and Clinical Issues Concerning the Use of Xenotransplantation Products in Humans. Available from www.fda.gov/cber/gdlns/clinxeno.pdf (accessed April 3, 2003).
14. Xu, C., Inokuma, M.S., Denham, J., Golds, K., Kundu, P., Gold, J.D., and Carpenter, M. K. (2001). Feeder-free growth of undifferentiated human embryonic stem cells. *Nat. Biotechol.* **19**, 971–974.
15. Richards, M., Fong, C-Y., Chan, W-K., Wong, P-C., and Bongso, A. (2002). Human feeders support prolonged undifferentiated growth of human inner cell masses and embryonic stem cells. *Nat, Biotechnol.* **20**, 933–936.
16. Cheng, L., Hammond, Hl, Ye, Z., Zhan, X., and Dravid, G. (2003). Human adult marrow cells support prolonged expansion of human embryonic stem cells in culture. *Stem Cells* **21**, 131–142.
17. Vogel, G. (2002). Stem cells not so stealthy after all. *Science* **297**, 175–176.
18. Drukker, M., Katz, G., Urbach, A., Schuldiner, M., Markel, G., Itskovitz-Eldor, J., Reubinoff, B., Mandelboim, O., and Benvenisty, N. (2002). Characterization of the expression of MHC proteins in human embryonic stem cells. *Proc. Natl. Acad. Sci. U. S. A.* **99**, 9864–9869.
19. Hoen, M., Küstermann, E., Blunk, J., Wiedermann, D., Trapp, T., Wecker, S., Föcking, M., Arnold, H., Hescheler, J., Fleischmann, B., Schwindt, W., and Bührle, C. (2002). Monitoring of implanted stem cell migration *in vivo*: a highly resolved *in vivo* magnetic resonance imaging investigation of experimental stroke in rat. *Proc. Natl. Acad. Sci. U. S. A.* **99**, 16267–16272.
20. Lemischka, I. (2002). A few thoughts about the plasticity of stem cells. *Exp. Hematol.* **30**, 848–852.
21. Yang, L., Li, S., Hatch, H., Ahrens, K., Cornelius, J.G., Petersen, B.E., and Peck, A.B. (2002). *In vitro* trans-differentiation of adult hepatic stem cells into pancreatic endocrine hormone-producing cells. *Proc. Natl. Acad. Sci. U. S. A.* **99**, 8078–8083.
22. Ying, Q-L., Nichols, J., Evans, E.P., and Smith, A.G. (2002). Changing potency by spontaneous fusion. *Nature* **416**, 545–547.
23. Wang, X., Willenbring, H., Akkari, Y., Torimaru, Y., Foster, M., Al-Dhalimy, M., Lagasse, E., Finegold, M., Olson, S., and

Grompe, M. (2003). Cell fusion is the principal source of bone-marrow-derived hepatocytes. *Nature* **422,** 897–901.

24. Vassilopoulos, G., Wang, R., and Russell, D. (2003). Transplanted bone marrow regenerates liver by cell fusion. *Nature* **422,** 901–904.

25. Björklund, L.M., Sánchez-Pernaute, R., Chung, S., Andersson, T., Chen, I.Y.C., McNaught, K.St.P., Brownwell, A-L., Jenkins, B.G., Wahlestedt, C., Kim, K-S., and Isacson, O. (2002).

Embryonic stem cells develop into functional dopaminergic neurons after transplantation in a Parkinson rat model. *Proc. Natl. Acad. Sci. U. S. A.* **99,** 2344–2349.

26. Freed, C.R., Greene, P.E., Breeze, R.E., Tsai, W-Y., DuMouchel, W., Kao, R., Dillon, S., Winfield, H., Culver, S., Trojanowski, J.Q., Eidelberg, D., and Fahn, S. (2001). Transplantation of embryonic dopamine neurons for severe Parkinson's disease. *N. Engl. J. Med.* **344,** 710–719.

Commercial Development
of Stem Cell Technology

Michael J. Lysaght and Anne L. Hazlehurst

Just under 30 biotechnology startup firms in 11 countries are pursuing commercial development of stem cell technology and therapeutic cloning. These firms employ 950–1000 scientists and support staff and spend just under $200 million on research and development each year. The field has the look and feel of a high-tech cottage industry, with close to half the startups employing less than 15 full-time equivalents (FTEs). Funding is mostly from venture capitalists and private investors. Participants are geographically disperse with about 40% of the activity outside the United States. Focus is slightly weighted toward adult stem cells as compared with embryonic stem cells. Taken as a whole, both the structure and scope of private sector activity in stem cells seems appropriate to the promise and development time-frames of this important new technology.

Introduction

In the past 5 years, stem cells have emerged from condign obscurity to remarkable levels of prominence in both the scientific literature and lay consciousness. Reports in peer-reviewed journals are prominently covered as front page news in the *New York Times* and are summarized on nightly national network news. *Time, Newsweek, Business week, The Atlantic Monthly,* and many of their peer journals have all carried in-depth cover stories on stem cells. C-Span broadcasts the full 2-day National Academy of Sciences Workshop on the topic. Stem cells can fairly be said to have provided many scientists with their "15 minutes of fame."

Why all the attention, all of sudden? First, of course, was Dolly and the paradigmatic revelation that a fully differentiated adult cell could be reprogrammed back to totipotent stem cell status.[1] So far, the technologies for cloning and stem cell biology are inseparable: it is not yet possible to create a clone without first creating a stem cell by nuclear transfer. Furthermore, advances in the understanding of basic stem cell biology have potential relevance to therapeutic or reproductive cloning. Not long after Wilmut's announcement of Dolly

Handbook of Stem Cells
Volume 1

came the techniques for isolating and culturing human embryonic stem cells and the capability to begin teasing the cultured cells down defined lineage pathways.[2,3] Working largely with murine models, other investigators demonstrated that embryonic stem cells could be converted into tissue with functional utility in animal models of diabetes and Parkinson's disease.[4,5] Other groups pursued adult stem cells, demonstrating a hitherto unsuspected capacity for transdifferentiation.[6–8] However, concerns about separation, identification, proliferation, and cell fusion leave the plasticity of adult stem cells somewhat ambiguous. More controversial but certainly attention-getting were the reports of the cloning of an early stage human embryo by nuclear transfer[9] and the claim that parthenogenesis may eventually compete with nuclear transfer as a technique for cloning adult mammals.[10] This dramatic progress was well summarized in a recent editorial in *Nature* by C. DeWitt[11]

> Stem Cells are truly remarkable. They bridge the gulf between the fertilized egg that is our origin and the architecture that we become. They supply the cells that construct our bodies and, as we age, replenish worn out, damaged, and diseased tissues. They renew themselves, resisting the powerful pull toward differentiation that overcomes more prosaic cells. Scientists now face the formidable task of… bringing stem cell therapies to the clinic.

The potential therapeutic applications of stem cells span virtually every facet of regenerative medicine. Scientists have hailed them as the key to future cures for neurodegenerative diseases, diabetes, heart failure, and countless other disorders. With such strong claims come large expectations, and consequently, stem cells have a long way to go in living up to their reputation. The time and resources required to validate the clinical importance of the technology will not be insignificant but are justified by the potential therapeutic importance of this technology.

The Study

Stem cell science and technologies are being pursued by the National Institutes of Health (NIH) and other government research agencies and in the private sector. Our study concerns the latter and is intended to quantify and discuss current commercial involvement in the development of stem cell technology: How many scientists and support staff are involved? How many firms? With what sorts of financing?

And what patterns of activity and organization? Consideration of the impact of regulatory mechanisms and the status of clinical studies will help shed light on the complex issues facing the industry. No attempt is made to pick eventual winners and losers among the various companies or even to review and assess the validity of the underlying science. The analysis in this chapter is a revised and updated version of an earlier survey appearing in the journal *Tissue Engineering*.[12] Data presented here are correct and valid as of December 31, 2002. However, the field is evolving rapidly, and, thus, this report is best regarded as a snapshot of a single point in time.

To be eligible for inclusion in this study, firms needed to be significantly vested in stem cell technology. Typical focus areas included embryonic or adult stem cells, nuclear transfer and therapeutic cloning, banking of cord blood, and development or sale of enabling equipment and supplies. All firms identified by the NIH as custodians of "approved" stem cell lines were included. Not-for-profit organizations were excluded, as were firms involved in reproductive cloning of pets and livestock animals. Conventional bone marrow transplantation did not qualify. Firms that were peripherally or incidentally involved in stem cells were not included.

A list of qualifying firms was compiled from general awareness of the field, from keyword Web searches, from companies whose scientists presented at relevant technical or investor conferences (PTEI, Society for Regenerative Medicine, Techvest), and from the trade literature.[13] Once compiled, the list was circulated to and vetted by individuals knowledgeable in the field. The compilation is believed to be reasonably complete, although some smaller and newer firms will inevitably be missed in a field growing as rapidly as this.

A profile on each firm was then developed, including principle technical focus; date of founding; number of employees; source of funding; and, where appropriate, the fraction of the firm's efforts that were dedicated to stem cells.

For public firms, this information was available from annual reports and Securities and Exchange Commission (SEC) filings. For private firms, the information was obtained from the firm's Web site or by contacting the chief executive officer (CEO) or chief financial officer (CFO). Firms conducting operations in more than one country were asked for a breakdown of employees by geographic region. In a few cases, only a range of the number of FTEs was available; here, the midvalue of the range is reported. Wherever possible, information was double-checked against information available from proprietary databases.[13,14]

Private firms were generally unwilling to disclose their annual spending rate. Accordingly, where not directly available, this number was estimated from a lumped sum correlation of $200,000 in total annual company expenditure per employee per year. This correlation had been validated in earlier surveys of the tissue engineering field.[15,16]

Capital value for public companies was calculated as the product of the number of shares times individual share value, as of December 31, 2002. Number of shares were obtained from company financial statements and share values from

on-line listings. Share values denominated in foreign currencies were converted to dollars at the exchange rates prevailing on December 31, 2002. For firms involved in activities other than stem cells, the capital value was prorated according to the estimated fraction of the firm's activity devoted to stem cells. This implicitly assumes that all of a firm's activities contribute equally to its capital value.

A Snapshot of the Field

At the close of 2002, private sector research and development in stem cells was conducted by just under 1000 scientists and support staff in 31 firms, operating in 11 countries. Aggregate spending was $194 million. Four of the 29 firms are public, the remaining are private. Capital value of the public companies, prorated for their involvement in stem cells, is $98.7 million.

A list of the firms, their location, Web site, and a thumbnail sketch of each of the firm's activities is given in Table 78–1. Twelve firms employ fewer than 15 FTEs and spend a combined ~$22 million per year; 10 firms have between 15 and 35 FTEs and spend in aggregate ~$50 million per year; and 8 have more than 35 employees and spend an aggregate of ~$122 million per year (Table 78–2). Approximately 37% of the firms use embryonic stem cells and 57% rely on adult stem cells. Thirteen percent of the firms provide cell banking services (Fig. 78–1). The United States constitutes about half of the global resources devoted to stem cells (Fig. 78–2). Firms serving as repositories for approved human stem cell lines, that is, those that can be used in federally funded U.S. research, can be found in Table 78–3. Table 78–4 summarizes the total and prorated capital value, as of the close of 2002, for the 4 (of 31) firms that are public.

Perspectives

The 1000 FTEs and their associated costs are a substantial commitment but the net involvement of the private sector is nevertheless quite modest. Aggregate stem cell activity in the private sector is three times smaller than the total funds devoted to tissue engineering research and development in 2002. It is approximately the size of the staff that a pharmaceutical company would deploy for a single drug for each of the 12 years required to bring a lead compound to markets. It represents less than 1.5% of the annual research budget of Pfizer, a single drug company.

The size distribution of the individual firms in Table 78–2 is also telling. Companies with less than 15 employees, (just under half of all stem cell companies) are really just getting started. By the time a firm has 15–35 employees it can conduct discovery-level science and highly productive firms of this size can certainly affect a field and create increments in shareholder value through intellectual property. However, the actual discovery, definition, development, and regulatory management of a product is extremely labor intensive. It would be highly unusual for a company to be

TABLE 78-1
Stem Cell Firms (as of December 31, 2002)

Company	Web Address	FTEs	Cell Type	Description
Advanced Cell Technology Worcester, MA	www.advancedcell.com	12	ESC	Therapeutic cloning
Befutur Technologies Case Postale, Switzerland	www.befutur.com	12	Both	Tissue regeneration
BresaGen, Inc. Adelaide, Aus/Athens, GA	www.bresagen.com.au	35 (60)	ESC	Neuronal SCs for Parkinson's disease
Cardion Ag Erkath, Germany/Boston, MA	www.cardion-ag.de	14 (50)	ESC	Pancreatic islet cells for diabetes
Celgene Warren, NJ	www.celgene.com	90	Adult	Human SCs from the placenta for cell therapy and banking
CyThera, Inc. San Diego, CA	www.cytheraco.com	12	ESC	Tissue/organ repair, diabetes
Develogen Gottingen, Germany	www.develogen.com	60 (114)	?	Differentiation pathways–diabetes
ES Cell International Melbourne, Australia	www.escellinternational.com	40	ESC	Tissue/organ regeneration
Gamida Cell, Ltd Israel	www.gamida.com	28	Adult	Hematopoietic stem cell therapy, regenerative medicine
Genzyme Biosurgery Cambridge, MA	www.genzymebiosurgery.com	22	Adult	Expansion and transplantation of myoblasts for heart function
Geron Menlo Park, CA	www.geron.com	50 (142)	Both	Therapeutic cloning, drug discovery, xenotransplantation
Infigen Deforest, WI	www.infigen.com	10 (35)	N/A	Cloning, xenotransplantation
Ixion Biotechnology Alachua, Fl	www.ixion-biotech.com	6 (18)	Adult	Islet cell production for diabetes
Kaleidos Pharma Seattle, WA	www.kaleidospharma.com	6	Adult	Tissue/organ regeneration
Kourion Therapeutics Duesseldorf, Germany	www.kouriontx.com	19	Adult	Neural, cardiac, osteogenic, chondrogenic therapy
Maria Biotech Company, Ltd Soeul, Korea	www.mariabiotech.co.kr	22	ESC	Heart disease, diabetes, banking
NeuralStem Biopharmaceuticals Gaithersburg, MD	www.neuralstem.com	21	Adult	Neurodegenerative disease/damage–neural SCs
NeuroNova Stockholm, Sweden	www.neuronova.com	20	Adult	Neurologic disease/damage–neural SCs
Neuronyx Malvern, PA	www.neurononyx.com	42	Adult	CNS disorders, bone marrow SCs
Osiris Baltimore, MD	www.osiristx.com	80	Adult	Tissue/organ regeneration—hMSCs
Primegen Santa Ana, CA	www.primegenbiotech.com	20	?	SC therapy to counter aging
Reliance Life Sciences Bombay, India	—	25	ESC	Tissue/organ regeneration; banking
Reneuron Surrey, UK	www.reneuron.com	25	Adult	Neurologic disease/damage; drug discovery
SCS KK Kobe, Japan	—	3	ESC	SC therapy; gene and drug discovery
Stem Cell Sciences (SCS) Melbourne, Australia	www.stemcellsciences.com.au	13	ESC	Neurologic disease/damage; gene and drug discovery
Stem Cell, Inc. Palo Alto, CA	www.stemcellsinc.com	33	Adult	Tissue/organ regeneration; drug discovery; gene therapy

Continued

TABLE 78-1
Stem Cell Firms (as of December 31, 2002)—cont'd

Company	Web Address	FTEs	Cell Type	Description
StemCell Technologies Vancouver, Canada	www.stemcell.com	110	N/A	SC isolation, proliferation, differentiation
Stemron Gaithersburg, MD	www.stemron.com	6	Adult	Tissue/organ regeneration
StemSource Inc. Thousand Oaks, CA	www.stemsource.com	10	Adult	Banking, SCs from fat
ViaCell Boston, MA	www.viacellinc.com	138 (160)	Adult	Cord blood SC therapy; banking
VistaGen, Inc. Burlingame, CA	www.vistagen-inc.com	6	Both	Drug development; CNS, cardiovascular, cancer

CNS, central nervous system; ESC, embryonic stem cell; FTEs, full-time equivalents; hMSC, human mesenchymal stem cell; SC, stem cell.

TABLE 78-2
Stem Cell Companies Listed by Size (as of December 31, 2002)

	Number of FTEs	Estimated Spending (Million/yr)
Firms with <15 FTEs ACT, Befutur Technologies, Cardion, Cythera, Infigen,* Ixion,* Kaleidos Pharma, SCS KK, Stem Cell Sciences, Stemron, StemSource, Inc., Vistagen, Inc.	110	$22
Firms with 15–35 FTEs Bresagen,* Gamida Cell, Kourion, Maria Biotech, NeuralStem, NeuroNova, Primegen, Reliance, Reneuron, Stem Cells Inc.	248	$50
Firms with more than 35 FTEs Celgene,, Develogen, ES Cell International, Geron,, Neuronyx, Osiris, StemCell Technologies, ViaCell	610	$122

FTE refers to full-time equivalent supporting stem cell technology. Firms indicated with an asterisk have additional employees working in other areas.

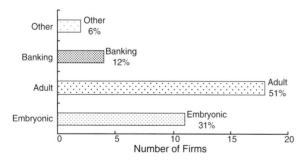

Figure 78-1. Principle activity of private sector, stem cell firms. The adult stem cell is the largest segment of this field but activity is well diversified across other areas of activity. Some companies have multiple activities and were included in more than one category.

successful at these latter activities with fewer than 100–150 employees.

There is only a weak correlation between company size and company age. Such a pattern is unusual for biotech startups that usually grow linearly for their first several years. For example, most tissue engineering startups were found to add about five employees per year for each of their first 5 years.[15] The different behavior of stem cell companies may result from funding limitations, or it may just be that the industry is in early stages with many firms not yet far enough along to prudently and profitably spend at a more rapid rate.

Given their size and resources, most stem cell firms are developing technology rather than products. The rationale is that such technology will have realizable value as the field grows and matures. Companies are also investing is "squatter sovereignty" with the intention of developing infrastructure, experience and, trade skills that will allow them to participate in, or even dominate, a potentially explosive area of future biomedicine. Although high risk, these business models appear sound. In the absence of defined products a "small is beautiful" approach to stem cell startups may be appropriate.

Location of Private Sector Stem Cell FTEs

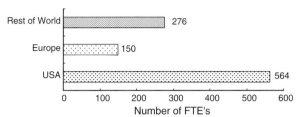

Figure 78-2. Location of full-time equivalents (FTEs) by geographic area. About half the commercial activity in this field is taking place in the United States. Europe is the least represented sector.

The established success of hematopoietic cell transplants makes these therapy formats a logical area for establishing the credibility of stem cell therapies. In addition, in the first FDA-sanctioned trials of stem cell therapy for nonhematopoietic tissue regeneration, Genzyme Biosurgery is co-sponsoring an investigation into the use of myoblasts (muscle stem cells) to improve heart function in patients who have suffered a myocardial infarction. The trial, which will take place primarily at European hospitals, represents a joint effort between government funded research from the Hopital European Georges Pompidos in France and the privately funded, U.S.-based Genzyme Biosurgery.

Funding, Market Value, and Regulatory Issues

Most of the stem cell startups are private and thus funded by capital from angels, venture groups, and mezzanine financiers. Four are public, that is, listed on National Association of Securities Dealers Automated Quotation System (NASDAQ) or an equivalent national exchange (Table 78–3). Three went public as stem cell firms (BresaGen, Geron, Renouron) and one (Stem Cell Inc.) raised funds under a different persona and subsequently moved its activities wholly into stem cells. Given the current condition of the stock market, not too much can be read into the current capital value of public stem cell companies. The soundest conclusion is that the market appears to be lumping these companies together with other biotech startups and that stem cell firms trade neither at a premium or discount over early-stage biotech startups. The constant calliope of publicity about stem cells has not lead to a rash of IPOs, which is probably a good thing. More disturbing is the lack of corporate partnerships or other flow of resources from big pharma or big med-devices into stem cells. This source of revenue has been critical to the success of biotechnology in the past and will likely prove necessary for stem cells in the future.

Stem cell firms are highly diversified in both their technology approaches and geographical bases. There is a tilt toward focus on adult cells as compared with embryonic cells, at least in the number of firms working on each (see Fig. 78–1). This is move away from the almost 50–50 split between the two in

A few firms do have defined products; others are selling services such as neonatal stem cell banking, and still others make and sell the specialized equipment needed for nuclear transfer. Although most activity is centered in pure-play technology-development, a select number of firms appear to be moving products into clinical trials. An Israeli company, Gamida Cell, Ltd., has entered Phase I FDA clinical trials with StemEx, a stem and progenitor cell proliferation technology designed to enhance immune reconstitution in patients undergoing intensive chemotherapy. The product is likely to compete with Osiris' human mesenchymal stem cells (hMSCs) transplant support system that is currently in FDA Phase II clinical trials.

TABLE 78–3

Firms Serving as Custodians for National Institutes of Health (NIH)-approved Embryonic Stem Cell Lines

Company	Number of Approved Cell Lines
Bresagen, Inc.	4
CyThera, Inc.	9
ES Cell International	9
Geron	7
Maria Biotech Ltd	3
Reliance Life Sciences	7

TABLE 78–4

Capital Value of Public Firms

	Shares Outstanding (Millions)	Share Price Where Listed	Share Price U.S. Dollars	Capital Value U.S. Dollars (Millions)	Prorated Capital Value (Millions of Dollars)
BresaGen (35%)	46	Aus$0.44	$0.26	$11.8	$5.9
Geron (100%)	24	US $3.60	$3.60	$88	$88
Reneuron (100%)	39	£0.08	$0.13	$5.0	$5.0
Stem Cells Inc. (100%)	24	$1.09	$1.09	$26.4	$26.4

Data is for December 31, 2002.

Conversion rates: 0.58 Australian Dollar = 1 U.S. Dollar; 1.60 Pounds = 1 U.S. Dollar.

In column 1, number in parenthesis represents fraction of company activities committed to stem cells. The prorated capital value is the total value times this fraction (see text).

mid-2002[12] and may reflect the ethical controversies over the use of embryonic cells. The dependence of future research and clinical applications on regulatory laws causes the broad geographic base of the industry to be very telling. Some countries are distinctly more hospitable to embryonic stem cells and therapeutic cloning than others. Among those countries that have thus far established policies, the United Kingdom, Sweden, Israel, and Japan are the most permissive, whereas Germany and the United States are the most constraining. In December of 2002, Australia's senate passed a bill allowing the use of previously created frozen embryos for embryonic cell harvesting, a legislative decision that is expected to promote the expansion of the country's demonstrated interest in stem cell technology. Meanwhile, the U.S. House of Representatives has voted to ban therapeutic cloning altogether in a decision mirroring one made in 2001. The Senate is believed likely to table or defeat the bill, as it did in 2001, but the U.S. government's continued examination of the issue is predictive of future regulatory battles and ethical disputes related to therapeutic cloning. As of yet, private sector firms in the United States seem relatively undeterred by potential legislative constraints. However, capital and scientists are likely to gravitate toward the region or environment where they can best flourish. Hence, the existence of a geographically dispersed industry ensures that restrictive legislation in one region will not stop the science from advancing.

The private sector is just one of many sources of stem cell research and development. Government agencies both perform work in their own laboratories and fund research in universities and research institutes. Foundations and non-for-profit laboratories also support stem cell research. No summary data on public sector spending on stem cells seems to be available. Based on the number and impact of publications in the peer-reviewed literature, it would appear that publicly supported stem cell research equals or exceeds that of the private sector. This pattern differs from that in classical tissue engineering, where support has always come almost entirely from the private sector.[15,16] Because the public and private sectors have different goals, different priorities, different time frames, and different constraints, a balance between the two seems very sensible. Furthermore, several companies such as BresaGen, Maria Biotech, and NeuroNova maintain working collaborations with government-funded research that is being conducted at nearby universities and research institutes. Such partnerships reflect a pooling of resources that may not occur between companies vying for future market share in a particular area. The field of genomics represents a good example of how a combination of critical mass research in both the public and private can accelerate development.

Conclusion

Private sector activity in stem cells has emerged as a small, clearly identifiable, high-tech cottage industry. If past history of biotech startups is a guide, these firms are attended by zeal, focus, high-energy, excitement, enthusiasm, and instability. Their relatively small size is likely an advantage at the current stage of development. If, and when, the field of stem cells achieves a clinically important role in 21st century health care, the commitment and belief of these early pioneers will be amply rewarded.

REFERENCES

1. Campbell, K.H., McWhir, J., Ritchie, W.A., and Wilmut, I. (1996). Sheep cloned by nuclear transfer from a cultured cell line. *Nature* **380,** 64–66.

2. Thomson, J.A., Itskovitz-Eldor, J., Shapiro, S.S., Waknitz, M.A., Swoergoe, K.K., Marshall, V.V., and Jones, J.M. (1998). Embryonic stem cell lines derived from human blastocysts. *Science* **282,** 1145–1147.

3. Shamblott, M.J., Axelman, J., Wang, S., Bugg, E.M., Littlefield, J.W., Donovan, P.J., Blumenthal, P.D., Huggins, G.R., and Gearhart, J.D. (1998). Derivation of pluripotent stem cells from cultured human primordial germ cells. *Proc. Natl. Acad. Sci. U. S .A.* **95,** 13,726–13,731.

4. Lumelsky, N., Blondel, O., Laeng, P., Velasco, I., Ravin, R., and McKay, R. (2001). Differentiation of embryonic stem cells to insulin-secreting structures similar to pancreatic islets. *Science* **292,** 1389–1394.

5. Kim, J.H., Auerbach, J.M., Rodriguez, G., Jose, A., Velasco, A., Gavin, D., Lumelsky, N., Lee, S.N., Nguyen, J., Sanchez-Pernuate, R., Bankiewicz, K., and McKay, R. (2002). Dopamine neurons derived from embryonic stem cells function in an animal model of Parkinson's disease. *Nature* **418,** 50–66.

6. Zuk, P.A., Zhu, M., Mizuno, H., Huang, J., Futrell, J.W., Katz, A.J., Benhaim, P., Lorenz, H.P., and Hedrick, M.H. (2001). Multilineage cells from human adipose tissue: implications for cell-based therapies. *Tissue Eng.* 211–228.

7. Jiang, B., Jahagirdar, R., Reinhardt, L., Schwartz, R.E., Keene, C.D., Ortiz-Gonzalez, X.R., Reyes, M., Lenvik, T., Lund, T., Blackstad, M., Du, J., Aldrich, S., Lisberg, A., Low, W.C., Largaespada, D.A., and Verfaillie, C.M. (June 2002). Pluripotency of mesenchymal stem cells derived from adult marrow. *Nature* (advance online publication) DOI: **10**.1038.

8. Orlic, D., Kajstura, J., Chimenti, S., Jakoniuk, I., Anderson, S.M., Li, B., Pickel, J., and Mckay, R. (2001). Bone marrow cells regenerate infracted myocardium *Nature* **410,** 701–705.

9. Cibelli, J.B., Lanza, R.P., West, M.D., and Ezzell, C. (2002). The first cloned embryo. *Sci. Am.* **286,** 44–51.

10. Cibelli, J.B., Grant, K.A., Chapman, K.B., Cunniff, K., Worst, T., Green, J.L., Walker, S.J., Gutin, P.H., Vilner, L., Tabar, V., Dominko, T., Kane, J., Wettstein, P.J., Lanza, R.P., Studer, L., Vrana-Kent, E., and West, M.D. (2002). Parthenogenetic stem cells in nonhuman primates. *Science* **195,** 819.

11. DeWitt, N. (2001). Stem cells. *Nature* **414,** 87.

12. Lysaght, M.J., and Hazlehurst, A. (2003). Private sector support of stem cell technology and therapeutic cloning. *Tissue Eng.* **9** (in press).

13. "Stem Cell Research News." Data Trends Publication Inc., Leesburg VA. Available at http://www.stemcellresearchnews.com (accessed).

14. VentureOne, San Francisco, CA. Available at http://www.venturesource.com (accessed).

15. Lysaght, M.J., Nguy, N., and Sullivan, K. (1998). An economic survey of the emerging tissue engineering industry. *Tissue Eng.* **4,** 231.

16. Lysaght, M.J., and Reyes, J. (2001). The growth of tissue engineering. *Tissue Eng.* **7,** 485–493.

Proprietary Considerations

Rebecca S. Eisenberg and Arti K. Rai

On August 9, 2001, U.S. President George W. Bush announced a compromise position on federal funding for human embryonic stem (HES) cell research, seeking a middle ground between the outright ban favored by the Right-to-Life movement and the active pursuit of stem cell research proposed by some scientists and disease advocacy groups. Henceforth, U.S. funds could be used for research with HES cell lines that had already been created as of that date but not to derive new cell lines nor to perform research with cell lines created after that date.[1]

For the next month, until the events of September 11, 2001 eclipsed all other stories, the terms of access to HES cell lines made front-page news in major newspapers across the United States.[2–6] Within this brief window, an unprecedented level of public attention focused on a problem that has been a growing challenge to the biomedical research community for years: how to get beyond a proliferation of proprietary claims and streamline access to research tools for use in biomedical research. However, while other material transfer agreements (MTAs) and patent licenses had typically languished for months on the desks of overburdened technology transfer professionals in research institutions and private firms, negotiations over the terms of access to HES cell lines proceeded briskly under the bright glare of media attention.

The National Institutes of Health (NIH), sponsor of past research on primate embryonic stem (PES) cells and prospective sponsor of HES cell research within the constraints announced by the President, took the lead in negotiating on behalf of the Public Health Service for terms that would apply to all government-sponsored researchers. On the other side were representatives of the technology transfer affiliate of the University of Wisconsin (Wisconsin Alumni Research Foundation [WARF]), the holder of a handful of qualifying cell lines and the owner of broad patents on HES cells. While reporters eagerly awaited updates, the NIH and WARF worked out the details of a memorandum of understanding (MOU) that would permit streamlined access to HES cells by academic researchers for "upstream" research, while allowing WARF to retain control over "downstream" commercial uses of the technology. Other owners of approved HES cell lines subsequently entered into agreements on similar terms.

The supply of HES cell lines that meet the President's criteria has been disappointing. In his announcement, President Bush indicated that the Department of Health and Human Services had identified 64 HES cell lines that met the stated criteria; as of this writing, it appears that fewer than a dozen viable cell lines qualify.[7] Nonetheless, the MOU negotiated by the NIH and WARF, which sets up a zone of relatively free access to HES cell lines for use in noncommercial research, is something of a triumph for the academic research community. This outcome is all the more remarkable because WARF had previously given exclusive commercial rights to a broad patent covering all HES cells to a private research sponsor Geron Corporation.

Notably, the federal government held its own trump card in the negotiations. Before Geron came on the scene, the NIH had sponsored research at Wisconsin that generated an even broader, "parent" patent covering all PES cells. Under the Bayh-Dole Act of 1980, Wisconsin owned this patent. Nonetheless, the government retained certain rights, including a retained license to use the invention for government purposes[8] and "march-in rights" to compel the granting of licenses to applicants on reasonable terms if necessary to achieve practical application of the invention.[9] Although the NIH has not formally invoked these rights in this context, the recitals at the beginning of the MOU state that "the Government has certain use and other rights to the intellectual property comprising the Wisconsin Patent Rights granted by law and regulation," and the prospect that the NIH could invoke these rights if negotiations reached an impasse clearly strengthened the bargaining position of the NIH.

The field of HES cell research is idiosyncratic in many respects. The cautious posture of public sponsors toward funding HES cell research has left this emerging field unusually dependent on private funding for support of early-stage, upstream research, aggravating the usual difficulties in negotiating terms of exchange for research tools. On the other hand, the strong interest of the Bush administration in legitimating the President's compromise position on HES cell research presumably enhanced its motivation to overcome remaining obstacles to research progress, and the extraordinary level of media attention may have constrained unreasonable bargaining behavior on all sides. For all these reasons, it is hardly a representative case study. Nonetheless, its media salience makes it a relatively accessible case study, and, to the extent that the result has been a diminution in proprietary obstacles to noncommercial research, it might even be an exemplary one.

Rebecca S. Eisenberg and Arti K. Rai

Of particular relevance to current debates over reform of the Bayh-Dole Act, this episode shows that the rarely invoked rights of government research sponsors over patents held by grantees are not merely a vestige of excess caution from an earlier era. These retained rights can give government agencies the leverage they need to promote the utilization and dissemination of technologies that might otherwise get stuck in a gridlock of proprietary claims.

The General Problem of Proprietary Research Tools

Universities have been struggling for decades about terms of exchange for materials and other inputs into biomedical research that might yield commercially valuable results. In an earlier era, academic norms of free exchange had pressured university scientists to put research results and the biologic data and materials supporting the research results into the public domain. In the late 1970s, as biomedical research started to show commercial potential, these free exchange norms came under increasing pressure.

Proprietary pressures intensified with the 1980 passage of the Bayh-Dole Act. The central goal of the Bayh-Dole Act, which encourages universities to patent the results of publicly sponsored research, is to facilitate commercial development of discoveries arising from such research.[a] The guiding philosophy behind this legislation—that patents and protection from competition are generally necessary to induce commercial investment in developing new technologies—is in tension with the free dissemination norm. Early dissemination before filing a patent application may make an invention unpatentable.[b] Even after a patent application is on file, the logic of technology transfer tends to encourage exclusive licensing, because a nonexclusive license can not provide the hedge against competition that the Bayh-Dole Act envisions as necessary for commercialization.

Although the philosophy of patenting and exclusive licensing to achieve commercial development has some merit, it does not apply uniformly to all university inventions. The problem lies in distinguishing inventions that are best developed through exclusive rights from those that will be more effectively disseminated and used on a nonexclusive basis. Exclusive rights are necessary for commercializing certain types of inventions, such as promising drug candidates that have high development costs. In contrast, many inventions arising in university research can be promptly disseminated for use by other researchers without substantial additional investment. Exclusive licensing is particularly problematic when, as is increasingly common, a university has a broad patent on a research tool that enables many subsequent paths of investigation. In these cases, exclusive licensing threatens creative development, because the holder of the exclusive right is unlikely to foresee all the follow-on paths. Moreover, subsequent research using these tools is likely to generate additional patents that will provide commercial exclusivity in any emerging downstream products that require substantial private investment.

Exclusive licensing is not only encouraged by the Bayh-Dole Act but university technology transfer officers often see it as most promising of the available options. According to a recent estimate by the Association of University Technology Managers (AUTM), about half of university licenses are exclusive, and 90% of licenses to start-ups are exclusive. Although nonexclusive licensing of broadly enabling research can be lucrative for universities, it may be difficult for university technology transfer officers to foresee these revenues at the time that they initially attempt to market the technology. In the case of an early-stage invention about which little is known, they may mistakenly believe that only one firm is interested and grant an exclusive license, only to determine later that it might have been profitable to license the invention nonexclusively to multiple firms.

Indeed, in the post–Bayh-Dole era, pressure to assert aggressive proprietary claims extends to all upstream research materials, whether or not they are patented. Universities and private firms try to leverage their control over these upstream materials into a percentage of profits from subsequent commercial products. For example, if a university is providing materials such as cell lines to a firm that might develop a commercial product, it may seek reach-through royalties on future product sales. Many firms resist this approach, which they believe overvalues mere research tools relative to the overall work of product development. Most products can trace their provenance to a great many different research materials, and, as more of these materials become subject to reach-through royalties, the prior obligations encumbering a commercial product could mount quickly.

A related strategy that is more common for extracting value from transfers to academic researchers and others who are unlikely to develop a commercial product is for the provider to seek reach-through rights to future intellectual property of the user, such as an option to license future discoveries. Universities view reach-through rights as an undue restriction of their control over the licensing of future discoveries. Moreover, if a university signs enough of these agreements, it can soon find itself committed to inconsistent obligations to assign future license rights or options on the same inventions to multiple institutions. Consequently, just as firms bargain hard to avoid reach-through royalty obligations, universities bargain hard to avoid reach-through license obligations. The net result can be

[a]*The Bayh-Dole Act states that its purpose is "to use the patent system to promote the utilization of inventions arising from federally funded research or development . . . " (35 U.S.C. Section 200 [emphasis added]).*

[b]*Under U.S. law, an invention may not be patented if it has been known or used by others or described in a printed publication more than a year before the filing date of a patent application (35 U.S.C. § 102(b)). Other patent systems do not provide this 1-year grace period, leaving inventions unpatentable as soon as they are released to the public.*

restricted access to research materials, even among academic researchers.[c]

Conflicts over patents and MTAs had been a source of growing concern in the biomedical research community and among policy analysts for years before the summer of 2001.[11–13] However, the issue did not catapult into the consciousness of the general public until August 2001, when the controversy over access to HES cell lines captured newspaper headlines.

The Specific Problem of Proprietary Human Embryonic Stem Cells

Research on HES cell lines presented two special circumstances that aggravated the usual problems with terms of exchange for research tools. First, prohibitions on the use of U.S. government funding for HES cell research forced universities—specifically the University of Wisconsin—to turn to private sponsors at an early stage, compromising its control over the relevant patents long before specific commercial applications came into view. Second, the Bush compromise itself, which limits future use of federal funds to research with existing HES cell lines, greatly enhanced the bargaining power of the institutions that had already developed the approved cell lines.

Both of these circumstances arose because of the ethical controversy surrounding HES cell research. Such research is ethically controversial because extracting HES cells requires destroying a fertilized human egg. Since 1995, Congress has put language in its appropriations bills prohibiting the NIH from funding research in which human embryos are created or destroyed. Despite these prohibitions, the U.S. federal government has, from the outset, been the primary sponsor of embryonic stem cell research using nonhuman tissue. In the 1990s, the NIH funded pioneering work by Dr. James Thomson and his colleagues at the University of Wisconsin that succeeded in deriving embryonic stem cells from rhesus monkeys and macaques. Consistent with the broad discretion to patent enjoyed by grantee institutions under the Bayh-Dole Act,[14] WARF sought to patent this advance and ultimately obtained a very broad patent.[15] Indeed, although the Wisconsin researchers had not, at the time of application, done work on humans, the patent application, which was granted in 1998, covered *all* PES cell lines.

To actually work with HES cells, however, the Wisconsin researchers had to look beyond federal funding. Dr. Thomson and his colleagues, therefore, set up a separate laboratory to work on HES cells and secured private funding from Geron

Corporation, a small biotechnology company based in Menlo Park, California.[16] In November 1998, the Wisconsin researchers succeeded in isolating HES cells, and WARF filed a second, subsidiary patent application with claims specifically drawn to HES cells. A broad patent based on this application, which covers all HES cell line, not just the particular cell lines derived with Geron funds, was issued on March 13, 2001.[17] The HES cell patent relies on precisely the same scientific disclosure as the prior patent that covers PES cells and is, therefore, merely a subset of this initial patent.

When the NIH sponsors research, universities enjoy considerable latitude to deploy the resulting patent rights as they wish, subject to the right of the sponsor to intervene if the resulting inventions are not being used. In contrast, when private companies sponsor research, they usually demand at least an option to acquire an exclusive license to the resulting patents. Operating within these constraints, WARF initially granted Geron exclusive rights to develop therapeutic and diagnostic products based on six important differentiated cell types derived from HES cells—heart, bone, nerve, pancreatic, blood, and cartilage cells. Following widespread media attention to this exclusivity, as well as to litigation,[18,19] the parties agreed to narrow Geron's exclusive license to products involving nerve, heart, and pancreatic cells. Wisconsin retained the right to distribute HES cell lines for research purposes, but Geron's exclusive commercial license constrains the terms of these research licenses.

The Bush administration introduced another important constraint by setting limits on which cell lines NIH-funded researchers could use. This restriction greatly increased the bargaining power of the holders of cell lines on the approved list, inasmuch as researchers who did not like the terms offered by approved cell line holders could not avoid these terms by simply making their own new cell lines. In particular, the bargaining power of WARF was enhanced. The Bush compromise ensured that even if the WARF patents were invalidated—or simply ignored, an illegal practice in which academic scientists nonetheless often indulge[d]—NIH-funded researchers would still be bound by WARF's restrictions on its tangible cell lines.

The National Institutes of Health's Role

As of August, 2001, the prospects for research access to HES cell lines did not look promising. Indeed, even today, most U.S. researchers remain extremely frustrated with their limited access to HES cell lines. Nonetheless, although the present situation is a far cry from the scientific community's normative ideal of free access, the NIH has played a constructive role by intervening aggressively on behalf of its grantees to set terms of access to the approved HES cell lines. Thus far, the NIH has signed MOUs with six institutions that hold cell lines meeting the administration's ethical criteria: WiCell Research

---

[c]*In a recent article reporting the results of a survey of academic geneticists, Eric Campbell and his colleagues[10] found that almost half of all academic geneticists had been denied access to additional data or materials regarding published research by their academic colleagues. Campbell and his colleagues specifically point to the complexity and restrictiveness of MTAs as a factor that inhibits sharing.*

[d]*Some university scientists assume that their research is exempt from infringement liability, but the courts disagree.[20]*

Institute (WiCell), a subsidiary of the WARF; ES Cell International, a private firm in Australia; BresaGen, a private firm in Athens, Georgia; the University of California at San Francisco (UCSF); Mizmedi Hospital, affiliated with Seoul National University; and Technion-Israel Institute of Technology.

The most important MOU negotiated by the NIH is with WiCell, the WARF subsidiary that holds both patent rights and tangible property rights in HES cells. Because the NIH had sponsored the research at Wisconsin that generated the broad parent patent that covers all PES cells (including HES cells) and because the patent that is specifically drawn to HES cells is merely a subsidiary derived from the same disclosure, the NIH retained certain rights under the Bayh-Dole Act to see to it that the technology covered by these patents was brought into practical application. Concerned that some grantees (or their licensees) might use patent rights in government-sponsored inventions to suppress new technologies, and thereby thwart the goal of widespread dissemination and use, Congress built certain safeguards into the Bayh-Dole Act. Although these safeguards are procedurally burdensome and hence rarely, if ever, formally exercised,[21] they nonetheless have the potential to play an important role. The first of these safeguards, which played no role in the case of HES cells, must be invoked by the funding agency in advance in the terms of a funding grant. At that time, the agency can declare the existence of "exceptional circumstances" in which the goals of the Bayh-Dole Act would be better promoted by withholding title to inventions from the grantee.[22,23] More significant to the HES cell story are the rights retained by the agency sponsor even when the grantee holds title to the invention. (Indeed, as noted earlier, these rights were explicitly acknowledged in the recitals at the beginning of the NIH–WiCell MOU.) Under the so-called march-in provisions, the agency may mandate compulsory licensing if it determines that the patentee or its licensee is not taking steps to achieve "practical application of the subject invention"[24] or that such licensing is necessary "to alleviate public health or safety needs or requirements for public use."[25] Moreover, the sponsor retains a government license to use the invention itself and to authorize others to use it on its behalf.[26] Soon after the information regarding Geron's exclusive licensing position in the HES cell arena became public, policy analysts began to study the possibility of exercising these retained rights.[16] This scrutiny intensified between the August 9, 2001 date of the Bush announcement and the conclusion of the MOU with WiCell on September 5, 2001.

The NIH–WiCell MOU addresses two different types of rights held by Wisconsin: tangible property rights in the actual cell lines that were derived at Wisconsin and patent rights that cover not only the Wisconsin cell lines but all the other cell lines on the approved list. As for the tangible property rights, the agreement provides for the transfer of the Wisconsin cell lines to NIH-funded investigators under the terms of a "Simple Letter Agreement" to be signed by the scientist and a representative of the university. Under that agreement WiCell retains ownership of the cells, along with progeny and derivatives. The material is made available for teaching or noncommercial research purposes only. The term *noncommercial research purposes* specifically excludes privately sponsored research under terms that give the sponsor a right to the results of the sponsored research, whether "actual" or "contingent." This could be a very significant exclusion, because it is common for sponsored research agreements to give the sponsor at least an option to acquire a license to future inventions. *Commercial research,* which is broadly defined to include any research done for the benefit of a sponsor, requires a separate written agreement to be negotiated with WiCell. Researchers may not distribute the material to anyone else without WiCell's consent. They must also pay a "transmittal fee" to reimburse WiCell for its costs; according to the MOU, the fee is "not expected to exceed $5,000."

As for the patent rights, the MOU provides that these are to be made available without cost for use in the NIH biomedical research program, including use of cell lines derived by other institutions that are within the scope of the Wisconsin patent rights. WiCell grants suppliers of these third-party materials—that is, other institutions that have developed cell lines falling within the broad scope of the Wisconsin patents—a "limited, revocable, non-commercial, research license…to provide such Third Party Materials to [NIH-funded] research programs provided that such Suppliers make such third party materials available on terms no more onerous than those contained in this Agreement." Specifically, suppliers of third-party materials cannot receive rights to the results of the research using their materials, and the patent license is only good for teaching or noncommercial research purposes. In effect, WiCell is promising not to enforce its patent rights against other institutions that make HES cell lines available to NIH-funded investigators, so long as those institutions do not try to insert provisions into their own MTAs that are more onerous than the provisions that WiCell is using. In other words, WiCell is willing to do its part to create freedom to operate within a noncommercial research and teaching zone so long as everyone plays by the same rules. The MOU with WiCell also acknowledges that users of the Wisconsin patent rights might make patentable discoveries in the course of research covered by the agreement and claims no rights under these potential patents for WiCell.

On first examination, WiCell appears to be offering an even-handed truce among all the holders of qualifying cell lines. WiCell will permit the use of its materials and patent rights for noncommercial purposes without reach-through rights if everyone else does the same. However, it is important to bear in mind that WiCell holds a very broad patent that is likely by its very terms to dominate many future commercial developments. Specifically, to the extent that commercialization requires continuing use of *any* HES cells (no matter how derived), the WiCell patents will cover the use. This dominant patent position makes it relatively easy for WiCell to be reasonable at the upstream stage, knowing that it can always assert its patent rights later at the point of commercialization. In effect, WiCell's broad patent claims give them enforceable reach-through rights without the need to claim such rights as a matter of contract.

Contrast the position of WiCell with that of other providers of cell lines who do not have such patent rights. Without contractual reach-through rights negotiated at the time they transfer the materials, these providers might have nothing left to bargain with when research using their cell lines yields a discovery that can be developed commercially using other HES cell lines. Thus, the MOU's seemingly even-handed approach might in fact favor WiCell over other cell line providers who have weaker patent positions. However, whatever the commercial implications for other cell providers, from the perspective of academic researchers, the MOU is quite attractive. Given that many or even most of these academic research projects will not yield commercially valuable results, the MOU has significantly reduced the number of MTAs and patent license agreements that have to be negotiated before research may proceed. Moreover, for those research projects that do yield commercially valuable results, the institutions performing the research will be able to retain their own patent rights without reach-through obligations.

The WiCell MOU has formed a template for similar MOUs with other HES cell providers[27] and has also set the terms for patent license agreements between WiCell and these providers.[28] Once again, the result is quite favorable for NIH-sponsored HES cell researchers. In effect, NIH has used its bargaining power to consolidate and expand the relatively unrestricted zone for noncommercial research initially set up by the WiCell MOU to cover the use of cell lines from these other providers. Given that the WiCell MOU arguably puts other cell providers at something of a commercial disadvantage, however, one might wonder why these other providers have entered into the framework created by the MOU. The explanation is probably that they have little choice given WiCell's broad patents (and, relatedly, the retained power the NIH has over these patents). Given the scope of WiCell's patents, these institutions may not make, use, or sell HES cell lines within the United States without a license from WiCell. They may also feel that they ultimately stand to benefit from the advances in biologic understanding of stem cells that will come from their use in NIH-funded research. Although they might prefer to provide their cell lines to researchers under agreements that include reach-through rights, at least the NIH-brokered deal provides them with a royalty-free license.

Implications for Current Policy Debates: The Assault on Retained Rights

In negotiations over access to HES cell lines, the NIH never formally exercised its retained rights in the patents held by WiCell. Nonetheless, those retained rights were a significant source of leverage that enabled the NIH to negotiate on behalf of future grantees for relatively streamlined access to HES cell lines to use in noncommercial research. While preserving WiCell's and Geron's control over commercial applications of HES cells, the NIH was able to claim the authority it needed to get six institutions to agree to provide HES cell lines to NIH-funded investigators on reasonable terms, free of reach-through obligations that might cast a shadow over upstream research in universities.

The retained rights that proved so useful in facilitating access to HES cell lines are currently facing some political opposition. The Integrated Dual-Use Commercial Companies (IDCC), a coalition of large commercial firms with a mission to change federal laws and regulations for the benefit of firms that perform government research and development (R&D) contract work, has argued that many private firms refuse to develop technology for the government because of the risk of losing control over the resulting patents if the government should choose to exercise its retained rights.[29] IDCC has collaborated with the American Bar Association Research and Development and Intellectual Property Committee to draft legislation that would permit research sponsors to waive in advance their retained rights under the Bayh-Dole Act in negotiating the terms of contracts and grants to make government R&D work more attractive to private contractors.[30] They characterize this proposal as providing the government with flexibility so that it may gain access to state-of-the-art technologies.

More accurately, the proposal would permit the government to bargain away at the point of entering into a contract the flexibility that current law reserves to the government at a later stage. When it enters into an R&D contract or grant, the government is negotiating from a position of substantial ignorance. It can only guess what sorts of technologies will be developed under the contract, what patent rights will be obtained on those technologies, how those patent rights will be licensed, and how broadly and effectively the technologies will be disseminated and used. For this reason, the Bayh-Dole Act preserves for sponsoring agencies the right to review the performance of contractors in bringing their inventions to the point of practical application later on and to intervene if necessary, subject to procedural safeguards to protect the expectations of contractors and their licensees.

Although agencies have almost never exercised their retained rights in the 23 years since passage of the Bayh-Dole Act, it may well be that the specter of retained rights deters some private contractors from getting involved in government R&D work. It is virtually impossible to apply a unitary patent policy across the vast and varied terrain of federally funded R&D without leaving some people unhappy. However, as the HES cell case study shows, the retained rights of the government can be a valuable check on behavior that might otherwise frustrate the public interest in dissemination of inventions.

Conclusion

The ethical debate over the derivation and use of HES cells continues to impose serious constraints on the use of HES cells in publicly funded research. Within these constraints, however, the NIH has done an impressive job of ensuring that proprietary considerations—whether they arise from patent rights or from tangible property rights—do not hamper access to HES cell lines by noncommercial academic researchers.

The NIH's ability to strike a favorable deal for academic researchers depended critically on the fact that it had previously funded *some* research on embryonic stem cells and, therefore, retained some authority to oversee deployment of the resulting patents. The case of HES cells, therefore, underscores not only the importance of public funding but also the importance of the retained rights of the government under the patents obtained by grantees.

REFERENCES

1. The White House, Office of Press Secretary. (August 9, 2001). Fact sheet, embryonic stem cell research. Available at http://www.whitehouse.gov/news/releases/2001/08/20010809-1.html (accessed July 11, 2003).

2. Zitener, A., and Chen, E. (August 11, 2001). Stem cell decision doesn't quell debate; Science: Uncertain but resolved researchers gear up to start limited tests. Senate hearing planned. *Los Angeles Times* p. A1.

3. Stolberg, S.G. (August 11, 2001). The President's decision: The research; U.S. acts quickly to put stem cell policy in effect. *New York Times* p. A1.

4. Weiss, R. (August 11, 2001). A stem cell ethics rules is eased; Bush decision may add colonies for research. *Washington Post* p. A01.

5. Mishra R., and Shadid, A. (August 11, 2001). Stem cell grants could begin in Jan. Battles loom on ownership of embryo 'lines.' *Boston Globe* p. A1.

6. Ackerman, T., and Roth, B. (August 11, 2001). In stem cell debate, what comes next?; Some scientists dubious of Bush-approved plan. *Houston Chronicle* p. A1.

7. Letter to President Bush on Stem Cell Research from 11 House Republicans, May 15, 2003. Available at http://www.aaas.org/spp/cstc/issues/stemhsltr.htm (accessed July 7, 2003).

8. 35 U.S. Code § 202(c)(4).

9. 35 U.S. Code § 203(1).

10. Campbell, E.C., Clarridge, B.R., Gokhale, M., Birenbaum, L., Hilgartner, S., Holtzman, N.A., and Blumenthal, D. (2002). Data withholding in academic genetics: data from a national survey. *JAMA* **287,** 473–480.

11. Heller, M.A., and Eisenberg, R.S. (1998). Can patents deter innovation? The anticommons in biomedical research. *Science* **280,** 698–701.

12. Report of the NIH Working Group on Research Tools. Available at http://www.nih.gov/news/researchtools/index.htm (accessed May 13, 2004).

13. Rai, A.K. (1999). Regulating scientific research: intellectual property rights and the norms of science. *Nw. U. L. Rev.* **94,** 77–152.

14. Act of Dec. 12, 1980, Pub.L.No. 96-517, Section 6(a), 94 Stat. 3015, 3019-28 (1980) (codified as amended at 35 U.S.C. Sections 200-212 (1994)).

15. U.S. Patent No. 5,843,780 (issued December 1, 1998).

16. National Research Council and Institute of Medicine. (2001). "Stem Cells and the Future of Regenerative Medicine." p 33, National Academic Press.

17. U.S. Patent No. 6,200,806 (issued March 13, 2001).

18. Pollack, A. (Novermber 2, 2001). University foundation says Geron may lose stem cell rights. *New York Times* p. C12.

19. Abate, T. (January 10, 2002). Stem-cell suit accord could help research; Geron gives up some rights in deal with university. *San Francisco Chronicle* p. B1.

20. Madey v. Duke University, 307 F.3d 1351 (Oct. 3, 2002).

21. Rai, A.K., and Eisenberg, R.S. (2003). Bayh-Dole Reform and the progress of biomedicine. *Law Contemporary Prob.* **66,** 289–314.

22. 35 U.S.Code § 203(2)

23. 35 U.S.Code § 202(b)(4) (providing for review of exceptional circumstances determinations).

24. 35 U.S.Code §§ 203(1)(a),(b).

25. 35 U.S.Code §§ 203(1)(b)-(c).

26. 35 U.S. Code § 202(c)(4).

27. NIH Web site at http://www.grants.nih.gov/grants (accessed May 13, 2004).

28. WARF signs stem cell license agreements. (April 26, 2002). University of Wisconsin Web site http://www.news.wisc.edu/packages/stemcells/index.msql?get=7437 (accessed July 12, 2003).

29. Testimony of Stanley D. Fry, Eastman Kodak Co. before the Subcommittee on Tech. & Procurement Policy, House Committee on Government Reform (May 10, 2002) (LEXIS).

30. Patent Rights in Inventions Made Under Federal Funding Agreements. Available at http://www.abanet.org/contract/ederal/randcomm/Bayh-DoleActpro.pdf (accessed May 13, 2004).

It Is Not About Curiosity, It Is About Cures
Stem Cell Research: People Help Drive Progress

Mary Tyler Moore

Choosing Life

Ah, but a man's reach should exceed his grasp. Or what's a heaven for?

Robert Browning, "Adrea del Sarto"

Many of you know that I have had type 1 (juvenile) diabetes for more than 35 years. As a consequence, I struggle everyday, like millions of others, to do what happens naturally for people who do not have diabetes: achieve a balance between what I eat, the energy I expend, and the amount of insulin I inject. Although to most, metabolic balance is as automatic as breathing, to people with type 1 diabetes, like me, it requires constant vigilance, constant factoring and adjusting, frequent finger sticks to check blood sugars, and multiple daily insulin injections just to stay alive. Even with the greatest of care and closest of personal scrutiny, I find that I am often unable to achieve good balance—my sugars are dangerously low or frighteningly high. Yes, dangerous and frightening—because, frankly, serious lows can lead to seizures, coma, and death, and highs, over time, result in life-limiting and life-shortening complications like blindness, amputation, kidney failure, heart disease, and stroke. Diabetes is an all too personal time bomb that can go off today, tomorrow, next year, or 10 years from now—a time bomb affecting millions, like me, that must be defused.

This reality is made all too clear by the recent sudden death of a young friend, Danielle Alberti. Danielle was 31. She was an aspiring artist. Although rapidly losing her vision because of diabetic retinopathy, Danielle stuck to her dream of being a painter and was pursuing her career when she, like too many young adults with type 1 diabetes, developed kidney failure. People with diabetes-related kidney failure do not do well on dialysis, so kidney transplant was her only real option. With her doctor's guidance, she and her mother decided to return home together to Australia where her chances for a transplant were greater. However, Danielle did not survive the flight. She died at 30,000 feet, seeking comfort in her mother's arms—her last words, "Mum, hold me."

Most of us share at least a piece of this experience—our loved ones, in times of pain or need, reaching out, looking to

us for comfort, for a way to stop their suffering. At that moment, we each would do anything in our power to change their reality, to take their pain from them. When given the choice or the power to effect change, we all would choose to protect the lives of those we love. This is the quest we join, together, when we contemplate the promise of stem cell research, debate its proper methods, and work toward making our hopes a reality—curing disease and disability through stem cell–derived therapies. We choose the idea of a better life and reach beyond our grasp to achieve it.

Size of the Promise

It is not unrealistic to say that [stem cell] research has the potential to revolutionize the practice of medicine and improve the quality and length of life.

Dr. Harold Varmus, Nobel Laureate and former director of National Institutes of Health (NIH)

Judgment does not only require choosing between the good and the bad. It often challenges us to balance more than one good or choose between the bad and the worse. Good judgment, therefore, demands that we make efforts to understand the relative impact of our choices, to come to an understanding of the greater good.

However, measuring the promise of stem cell research, for me, does not start with the recitation of the literally hundreds of millions of people who could benefit from the insights gained and therapies derived, it starts with understanding its potential for you and me, our parents and children, our friends and families, neighbors, and co-workers.

For people with type 1 diabetes, we look first to stem cell research as a means to help us replace the insulin-producing cells of the pancreas that are destroyed by our disease. However, it also may provide insights into the genetic basis for diabetes, including the differences between type 1 diabetes, which is an autoimmune disease like lupus and multiple sclerosis, and the more common, obesity-related, type 2 diabetes. It may also provide solutions to the devastating complications of diabetes: blindness, kidney failure, amputation, and cardiovascular disease. For people with Parkinson's disease, stem cell research holds the promise of replacing destroyed specialized brain cells and thereby freeing patients from the prison of disease-induced rigidity. For spinal injury

Handbook of Stem Cells
Volume 1

patients, it offers the potential for regeneration of neural tissue, which would reconnect the pathways of sensation and motor control and allow them to walk again, or talk again, or hug their child again. For people with heart failure, stem cell research may mean sleeping through the night without struggling for breath, dancing with a spouse, working in the garden, or sustaining one's job and independence. For the person with macular degeneration it might offer sight. Stem cell research offers hope for people with a great diversity of illnesses, for people of all ages and genders and all backgrounds. It offers hope for each of us, and that hope is not measured by numbers, it is very personal.

Personal Promises Fuel Progress

Never, never, never give up.

Sir Winston Churchill

I have had the privilege of serving as the International Chairman of the Juvenile Diabetes Research Foundation (JDRF) (www.jdrf.org) since the mid 1980s (Fig. 80–1). JDRF was founded in 1970 by the parents of children with type 1 diabetes. They were not satisfied with the only option offered to their children by health professionals—a lifetime of insulin injections just to stay alive, and the constant fear of the life-stealing complications they would face in the future. Insulin was not a cure, they knew it, and they wanted someone to do something about it.

Figure 80–1. Juvenile Diabetes Research Foundation (JDRF) founding moms, Lee Ducat and Carol Lurie.

So they challenged the established professional associations to do something, to think anew, and to invest in more research (especially type 1 diabetes research). They were brushed aside but not bowed. They may have been "just moms and dads," but they had a purpose that was highly personal. Each of them had promised their child, their loved one, that they would do all they could to find a cure. They intended to keep that promise, and they have. In the years since its founding, JDRF has grown to be the largest charitable contributor to diabetes research in the world, providing nearly $800 million in direct funding since 1975, including well over $400 million in the last 5 years alone. However, the impact of this "people-driven" effort to find a cure has been far greater than just the dollars that they have raised for research. JDRF families (supported by an extraordinary professional staff, many of whom have a direct connection to diabetes) have been key leaders in public advocacy that has resulted in the following:

1. The Diabetes Research and Education Act (mid-1970s) that established The National Institute of Diabetes Digestive and Kidney Diseases at the National Institutes of Health (NIH) and called for substantive increases in funding of diabetes research. At the time the NIH was only investing $18 million per year in diabetes research, it now spends more than $800 million per year.
2. Congressional earmarks for research into the genetics of diabetes and diabetes-related kidney disease (1980s).
3. The lifting of the ban on fetal tissue research in 1993, which President Clinton did "for Sam" a young man with type 1 diabetes.
4. The doubling of the NIH budget in 5 years. Between 1998 and 2003 the budget increased from approximately $13 billion per year to more than $26 billion per year.
5. The establishment of the congressionally mandated Diabetes Research Working Group that reports to Congress periodically on progress in diabetes research, on research needs and opportunities for the future, and on adequacy of funding (1998).
6. The Special Diabetes Initiative (1998–2008) that will, by fiscal year 2008, have provided more than $1 billion in supplemental funding for special initiatives in type 1 diabetes research (on top of usual NIH appropriations) and will provide an equal dollar amount (more than $1 billion) to fund special initiatives in diabetes care and education for Native Americans with diabetes.

JDRF was also a founder of the Coalition for the Advancement of Medical Research (CAMR) (www.stemcellfunding.org), which is a coalition of nearly 80 diverse health- and research-related organizations committed to sustaining federal funding of stem cell research. Working through CAMR and independently, JDRF volunteers and staff played a crucial role in convincing the George W. Bush administration and congressional leadership not to support a total ban on embryonic stem cell research in the United States (Fig. 80-2).

The experience of the JDRF along with the HIV and AIDS community, the women's health movement, the Parkinson's

Figure 80–2. Mary Tyler Moore (with Michael J. Fox) testifying before Congress in support of federal funding of stem cell research. (Photo courtesy of Larry Lettera/Camera 1.)

Action Network, and other grass roots organizations proves that in their quests to find a cure for their children and loved ones for whatever pains them, in their personal wars against disease, moms and dads, partners and spouses, and people who care will never give up. In fact, people personally affected by illness are the natural and necessary leaders of any global cure movement. They understand the urgency and are uniquely willing do anything required to ensure that their loved ones are freed of the burden of disease as soon as possible. For them, "failure is not an option," because their very survival is at stake.

Even when the day goes well, Amy says she and her husband John are still on duty all night. "Diabetes doesn't sleep … so neither do we. We keep a parent's vigil every four hours, no matter how tired we are from the day's battle. Imagine being adrift on a boundless ocean. You are tired of swimming, of trying to keep afloat, but to give yourself up to sleep would mean certain death." she says. "Sufferers of diabetes—and their parents—are adrift. They cannot rest from their vigilance, even in the dead of night. To relax completely, to give in to the peace of an eight-hour sleep that healthy people take for granted would invite seizures, unconsciousness, blindness, kidney failure, or heart disease."

Hope Versus Hype

I am not discouraged, because every wrong attempt discarded is another step forward.

Thomas A. Edison

What we know about any area of health or science is as much the "wisdom" accumulated through countless errors as it is the outcome of our research "successes." Furthermore, progress is often gained as much through the accidental collision of an unexpected finding and a willing mind as it is through the careful and detailed application of all that is "known."

What, then, drives the hope versus hype discussions regarding stem cell research? Do we know enough to project possibilities? Yes. Do we know enough to make assertions of a particular outcome by a date certain? No. Should this diminish our commitment to pushing the field forward to prove its potential? Certainly not. Too much is at stake for us to delay or to apply unreasonable constraints because we are worried we might be wrong or might be overestimating the potential. What if we are underestimating it?

Just like with any endeavor at the frontier of new worlds, there is risk in taking the next steps. However, we cannot shrink from these risks. Rather, we must—with proper deliberation and due consideration of the risks—chart our course, prepare ourselves for dealing with the unexpected, and move forward.

Giving Life

If you save one life, you save the world.

The Talmud

I understand that embryonic stem cell research raises concerns among people of good will, each trying to do what is right based on their very personal religious and moral beliefs. I have not shied from that personal soul searching nor has JDRF in its policy making nor should anyone. I have found comfort in my heartfelt view that human stem cell research is truly life affirming. It is a direct outcome of a young family

---

FRIENDS IN NEED AND DEED

LISA, 12 YEARS OLD

El Paso, Texas

Lisa has had type 1 diabetes since she was 5 years old. "It makes me sad to watch my parents cry when they tell people about my diabetes," she says. "I feel really sad when I think about the stuff that can happen if a cure isn't found soon. I don't want to go blind and never again see the faces of the people I love or the really pretty sunsets in El Paso. I don't want my legs amputated because I love to dance. I don't want to die early and have heart and kidney disease. I want a cure before any of these terrible complications can happen."

NICHOLAS, 4 YEARS OLD

Boca Raton, Florida

Nicholas was diagnosed with type 1 diabetes when he was 20 months old. Most nights, his mother, Rose Marie, must intervene in some way to keep Nicholas' blood sugar in the normal range. "As I hold him in the middle of the night, trying to coax him awake so I can feed him, I realize just how delicately his life hangs in the balance," Rose Marie says. "I rededicate myself to doing everything within my power to find a cure for this disease which robs my son, and millions of others like him, of a healthy, carefree childhood, and which carries the constant threat of danger—like a thief in the night lurking to strike."

ASHLEY, 10 YEARS OLD

Medina, Washington

Ashley was diagnosed with type 1 diabetes at the age of 7, right after a ballet rehearsal for a performance with the Pacific Northwest Ballet. She is passionate about a cure. "I want to find a cure for diabetes so no other children or families have to experience what my family goes through EVERY day. I want to find a cure so that I don't have the terrible headaches I get from the insulin ... and so I don't go low anymore; it feels so bad and it makes it hard to think in school. I want to find a cure so I can be a good mother some day."

KYLIE, 12 YEARS OLD

Ogden, Utah

Now 12, Kylie was diagnosed with type 1 diabetes at age 8. "Over Christmas vacation last year, I had a friend in my fifth grade class who died," she says. "He had diabetes just like me. During the middle of the night he went into insulin shock and never woke up." Kylie fears the same thing could happen to her. "I would love to have a guarantee that the rest of my life will be long and normal, but I know that there is a lot of work still to be done before they can find a cure."

BRENNAN, 6 YEARS OLD, AND TANNER, 8 YEARS OLD

Round Rock, Texas

Brennan, 6, was diagnosed with type 1 diabetes at the age of 2, just 7 months before his older brother Tanner was diagnosed. "Each day is filled with adversity and challenge," mom Amy says. "Will the disease win today? Will Brennan succumb to too-low blood sugar levels and lose consciousness? Will Tanner have his first seizure?"

COREY, 11 YEARS OLD

Secaucus, New Jersey

Corey, has had type 1 diabetes since the age of 5. Sitting at home and complaining about diabetes, he says, won't change things or get your voice heard or get us closer to a cure. Since the age of 7, he has spoken at schools and fundraisers to tell his story of what it is like to be very young and have to live with diabetes. "I've found that while millions have this disease, many people don't have a clue about what it really means to live with it each day," he says. He talks about the adjustments and fears that diabetes has brought to him and his family, adding that "it has not made me afraid to do what I want to do in life, but I know it *will* make things harder." At the moment of his sixth grade graduation, Corey says, "I want to leave a legacy to help ... other children as they strive to live a normal life and hope they'll never forget that we will find a cure."

EMILY, 15 YEARS OLD

Houston, Texas

Diagnosed with type 1 diabetes 9 years ago, Emily says each day is a battle. At first the finger pricks and shots were the most difficult thing that Emily had to handle, but now she has bigger fears. "Now the hardest part is facing the reality that there is no cure, and that my life could be determined by this awful disease." Emily is a straight A student and plays on her school's field hockey team. Her goal is to one day be an orthopedic surgeon—and to help find a cure for diabetes. "I and many others will not be able to rest until we find a cure," she says.

"A cure for diabetes will not just happen; it must be pursued, researched, and fought for."

Each of these courageous children, supported by their families, were delegates to the JDRF's 2003 Children's Congress where they met their elected leaders and advocated for a cure for themselves and all children (and adults) like them with type 1 diabetes (Fig. 80–3).

Excerpted, with permission, from the JDRF 2003 Children's Congress Yearbook.

making a choice, without coercion or compensation, to donate a fertilized egg not used for *in vitro* fertilization, for research. An egg that otherwise would have been discarded or frozen forever. Because of the great potential of stem cell research, donating unused fertilized eggs is much like the life-giving choice a mother, whose child has died tragically in an automobile accident, makes when donating her child's organs to save another mother's child. It is the true pinnacle of charity to give so totally, so freely of oneself, to give life to another. Public support for stem cell research is an extension of this affirmation of life and is the best way to ensure that it is undertaken with the highest of ethical standards.

People Drive Progress

I know of no safe depository of the ultimate powers of the society but the people themselves; and if we think them not enlightened enough to exercise their control with a wholesome discretion, the remedy is not to take it from them, but to inform their discretion by education.

Thomas Jefferson

In science, politics, even religion, the public often cedes decisions, important decisions, to an "expertocracy" or to dogma. Perhaps this is out of respect, humility, fear, or unfamiliarity—even out of a presumption of incapacity. It is, however, a well-informed public that is most capable of making decisions in its own interest and that, uniquely, has the power to effect change. It is, therefore, a true test of leadership to cede discretion back to people and bring comfort to public decision making through careful and objective expert counsel, access to a broad base of information, and support for taking specific actions to achieve goals.

This approach has defined the JDRF success. From its inception, the JDRF has been unique in the way that it conducts its review of research grants and how it decides what research is funded. Scientific experts (peer reviewers) are joined by people personally affected by diabetes (lay reviewers) in the discussion of all proposed research. Scientific merit is established in these peer/lay collaborative review sessions. Then the lay reviewers meet separately to discuss which of the meritorious grants are most responsive to the needs of people with diabetes—that is, which are most likely to have the greatest impact on finding a cure or reducing the burden of diabetes and its complications. It is the people personally affected by diabetes who make the final decisions of what to fund and what not to fund. The decisions of this lay review group are made in the context of cure goals and research priorities established by the JDRF Board, which is itself predominantly made up of people personally affected by diabetes. These goals and priorities were derived by the Board

Figure 80–3. Mary Tyler Moore at the Juvenile Diabetes Research Foundation's (JDRF's) Children's Congress of 2001. Joined on stage by Larry King, Tony Bennett, John McDonough, George Nethercutt, R-WA, Alan Silvestri, and child delegates from 50 states. (Photo courtesy of Larry Lettera/Camera 1.)

via a process of knowledge mapping, which was conducted by JDRF volunteers, staff, and expert advisors. Knowledge mapping identifies the current state of science along the many potential paths to a cure, where obstacles remain, and where there is the greatest opportunity for JDRF investment to make a difference.

The experience at JDRF infers that decisions regarding embryonic stem cell research are best made in the open, with the full engagement of the public and with particular attention to presentation of the broadest breadth of available information and opinion. We can be confident that the powers of society (in overseeing the conduct of science) can be safely ceded to the discretion of a well-informed populace.

Better Health For All

William Bradford, speaking in 1630 of the founding of the Plymouth Bay Colony, said that all great and honorable actions are accompanied with great difficulties, and both must be enterprised and overcome with answerable courage. If ... our progress teaches us anything, it is that man, in his quest for knowledge and progress, is determined and cannot be deterred.

President John F. Kennedy, speech at Rice University
September 12, 1962

People like me who struggle daily with disease or disability, and the people who love us, recognize the difficulties of scientific advancement, accept the challenges, and everyday answer with courage—if not for our own sake, for our children and our children's children. We do it not because we are curious, but because we are dedicated to finding cures. New therapies derived from embryonic stem cell research, conducted with public support by scientists from all areas of the globe, and made available to all who might benefit, are part of our broader vision of better health for all.

ACKNOWLEDGMENT

I'd like to thank my husband, Dr. S. Robert Levine, MD, for his invaluable help in putting this chapter together.

Patient Advocacy

Christopher Reeve

When I became a patient advocate in 1995, I thought that the major obstacles to achieving a cure for spinal cord injury would be a lack of funding and a shortage of scientists willing to dedicate their careers to an orphan condition. Those turned out not to be the problems. The budget of the National Institutes of Health (NIH) actually doubled. In 1998 the NIH research budget was $12 billion, and by fiscal year 2003 it had grown to just over $27.2 billion. Today researchers all over the world believe that effective therapies for Parkinson's disease, Alzheimer's disease, diabetes, heart disease, spinal cord injuries, and a wide variety of other afflictions can be achieved. Instead, the main obstacle is the controversy over embryonic stem (ES) cells and therapeutic cloning. The NIH has not been allowed to fund ES cell research using excess embryos from *in vitro* fertilization (IVF) clinics. The House banned therapeutic cloning for the second time in as many years, and the Senate remains gridlocked on the issue. The frustration of investigators all over the country became front-page news in the April 22, 2003 issue of *The Washington Post*:

> A series of important advances have boosted the potential of human embryonic stem cells to treat heart disease, spinal cord injuries and other ailments, but researchers say they are unable to take advantage of the new techniques under a two-year-old administration policy that requires federally supported scientists to use older colonies of stem cells. Now pressure is building from scientists, patient advocates and members of Congress to loosen the embryo-protecting restrictions imposed by President Bush.

The article goes on to say that the White House "has no intention of changing its position."

It appears that elected officials and average citizens have learned to fear "human cloning," and are failing or unwilling to appreciate the distinction between reproductive and therapeutic cloning. It is likely that somatic cell nuclear transplantation, the proper terminology for therapeutic cloning, will become standard medical procedure in the future. Perhaps there will be more progress when the public becomes aware of the advances at home and major breakthroughs overseas. However, while we wait, hundreds of thousands will have to endure prolonged suffering. An untold number will die.

Having lived with a spinal cord injury for nearly 9 years, I still have to emerge every morning from dreams in which I am completely healthy and adjust to the reality of paralysis. In the weeks and months after my injury that transition was often very difficult. After a few years it became less so, because I believed that the scientists were progressing well, that more funding would become available, and that the light at the end of the tunnel would continue to shine brighter every day. I never imagined that a heated political debate over the insertion of a patient's DNA into an unfertilized egg to derive genetically matched stem cells would have such an effect on me. Now instead of waking up just to rediscover that I am paralyzed, I wake up shocked by the realization that I may remain paralyzed for a very long time, if not forever.

Once that moment passes, I begin my day. Rationality and hope return. I am able to focus on what might be accomplished. Perhaps through education we can change people's minds, or even reverse the positions of powerful opponents.

The first task is to dispel misinformation. For example, the idea has been put forward that adult stem cells are better than ES cells because they have the same therapeutic potential without the controversy. However, adult tissue stem cells appear to have a much more restricted path for development, limiting their usefulness in therapies for diseases. Eighty Nobel Laureates sent a letter to President Bush stating that "it is premature to conclude that adult stem cells have the same potential as embryonic stem cells." The Department of Health and Human Services released a report, "Stem Cells: Scientific Progress and Future Research Directions" in June 2001. The report confirms the incredible potential of ES cells. It also stresses that there is limited evidence that adult stem cells can generate mature, fully functional cells or that the cells have restored lost function *in vivo*. As stated in Chapter 5 of the Committee on the Biological and Biomedical Applications of Stem Cell Research, Board on Life Sciences, National Research Council, Board on Neuroscience and Behavioral Health, Institute of Medicine of *Stem Cells and the Future of Regenerative Medicine* published by the National Academy of Sciences in 2002:

> A substantial obstacle to the success of transplantation of any cells, including stem cells and their derivatives, is the immune-mediated rejection of foreign tissue by the recipient's body. In current stem cell transplantation procedures with bone marrow and blood, success hinges on obtaining a close match between donor and recipient tissues and on the use of immunosuppressive drugs, which often have severe and potentially life-threatening side effects. To ensure that stem cell-based therapies can be broadly applicable for many conditions and people, new means of overcoming the problem of tissue rejection must be found.

Although ethically controversial, the somatic cell nuclear transfer technique promises to have that advantage.

It is extremely disturbing that the George W. Bush Administration prefers the opinions of social and religious conservatives instead of scientists on this issue. Those of us who hoped for a fair debate leading to governmental approval of therapeutic cloning were especially disheartened by a media opportunity that took place at the White House on April 10, 2002. The President urged the Senate to pass the Brownback Bill, S.1899, which would ban all forms of cloning. He stated the following:

> I believe all human cloning is wrong, and both forms of cloning ought to be banned, for the following reasons. First, anything other than a total ban on human cloning would be unethical. Research cloning would contradict the most fundamental principle of medical ethics, that no human life should be exploited or extinguished for the benefit of another.

At the President's side, in full dress uniform, was former New York City police officer Stephen McDonald, still confined to a wheelchair 16 years after suffering a gunshot wound that left him paralyzed from the shoulders down. Officer McDonald is a devout Catholic. After the press conference he told the media that his accident was "God's will" and echoed the Pope's position on the sanctity of human life.

Stephen McDonald does not represent most Americans living with paralysis. He was there purely as a prop for the Administration. In light of the fact that the Council on Bioethics that the President had appointed to advise him had not yet issued its opinion, the President's press conference was an inappropriate attempt to tip the balance of the debate.

I was one of many patient advocates who were greatly relieved to find an op-ed piece in the *New York Times* on April 25 by Michael Gazzaniga, Ph.D., Director of the Center for Cognitive Neuroscience at Dartmouth College. A fellow of the American Association for the Advancement of Science and the American Neurological Association, he is also one of the distinguished members of the President's advisory panel. He wrote:

> It was a surprise when, on April 10, the President announced his decision to ban cloning of all kinds. His opinions appeared fully formed even though our panel has yet to prepare a final report.... Some religious groups and ethicists argue that the moment of transfer of cellular material is an initiation of life and establishes a moral equivalency between a developing group of cells and a human being. This point of view is problematic when

viewed with modern biological knowledge. We wouldn't consider this clump of cells even equivalent to an embryo formed in normal human reproduction. And we now know that in normal reproduction as many as 50 percent to 80 percent of all fertilized eggs spontaneously abort and are simply expelled from the woman's body. It is hard to believe that under any religious belief system people would grieve and hold funerals for these natural events. Yet, if these unfortunate zygotes are considered human beings, then logically people should.... The biological clump of cells produced in biomedical cloning is the size of the dot on this i. It has no nervous system and is not sentient in any way. It has no trajectory to becoming a human being; it will never be implanted in a women's uterus. What it probably does have is the potential for the cure of diseases affecting millions of people. When I joined the panel, officially named the President's Council on Bioethics, I was confident that a sensible and a sensitive policy might evolve from what was sure to be a cacophony of voices of scientists and philosophers representing a spectrum of opinions, beliefs and intellectual backgrounds. I only hope that in the end the president hears his council's full debate.

Moral and ethical questions have always attended the birth of new ideas and new technologies. However, the questions and concerns surrounding the use of stem cells have remained unresolved in this country for too long. It is painful to contemplate what might have been achieved if the nation had rallied behind the scientists who isolated human ES cells for the first time in 1998. Now we can only hope that the federal government will not impose a ban or that other states will follow California and New Jersey and pass enabling legislation on their own. We can hope that Sweden, the United Kingdom, Israel, China, Singapore, and other countries that have decided in favor of government funded research using stem cells derived from any source will succeed in filling the void created by American public policy.

Will the United States surrender its preeminence in science by effectively killing stem cell research, the future of medicine, in its infancy? Before we make that unthinkable mistake we should remember Robert F. Kennedy, who said:

> The future does not belong to those who are content with today, apathetic toward common problems and their fellow man alike, timid and fearful in the face of bold projects and new ideas. Rather, it will belong to those who can blend passion, reason and courage in a personal commitment to the great enterprises and ideals of American society.

Index

Page numbers followed by "t" denote tables; those followed by "f" denote figures.

Formation and migration of neural crest cells

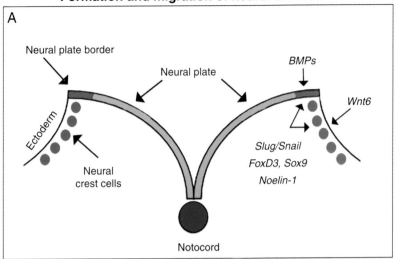

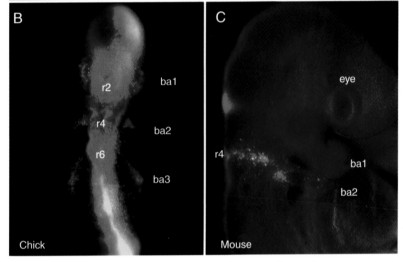

Color Plate 1. *Neural crest cell formation and migration.* (A) Neural crest cells are generated at the neural plate border, the junction between the neural plate and surface ectoderm. Both the surface ectoderm through Wnt6 and the neural plate through BMPs can induce neural crest cell formation. It remains to be determined whether Wnt and BMP signaling act during neural crest induction synergistically or independently to generate individual lineages within the neural crest. During their formation, neural crest cells express the transcriptional repressors Snail/Slug, which regulate the epithelial to mesenchymal transition and delamination of neural crest cells from the neural tube. Numerous genes, including Foxd3, Sox9, and Noelin-1, are also expressed in either the premigratory or the migratory neural crest cells. Cranial neural crest cells in (B) chick and (C) mouse embryos migrate ventrolaterally in discrete, segregated streams from specific rhombomeres (r) in the neural tube into the adjacent branchial arches (ba). (See Fig. 19–1, Volumes 1 and 2.)

Neural crest derivatives

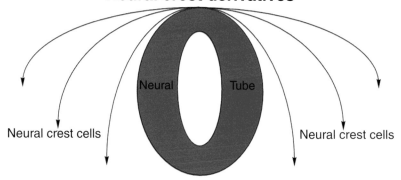

Cell type and tissue contributions

Sensory neurons
Cholinergic neurons
Adrenergic neurons
Rohon-Beard cells
Schwann cells
Glial cells
Chromaffin cells
Parafollicular cells
Calcitonin producing cells
Melanocytes
Chondroblasts, chondrocytes
Osteoblasts, osteocytes
Odontoblasts
Fibroblasts
Cardiac mesenchyme
Striated myoblasts

Spinal ganglia
Thyroid gland
Ultimobranchial body
Adrenal gland
Teeth
Dentine
Connective tissue
Adipose tissue
Smooth muscles
Cardiac septa
Dermis
Cornea
Endothelia
Adipocytes
Mesenchymal cells
Smooth myoblasts

Color Plate 2. *Neural crest cell derivatives.* Neural crest cells are a multipotent population derived from the dorsal edge of the neural tube that migrates extensively and generates an array of distinct cell fates specific for their axial origins. The primary difference between cranial and trunk neural crest cells is the ability of cranial neural crest cells to produce hard mesenchymal tissues such as bone, cartilage, and the odontoblasts of the teeth. Stem cells are a self-renewing pluripotent cell population, and hence, neural crest cells exhibit many of the hallmarks of a stem cell population. (See Fig. 19–2, Volumes 1 and 2.)

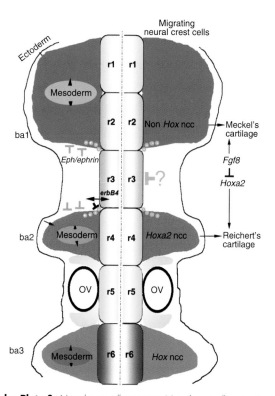

Color Plate 3. *Neural crest cell patterning.* Neural crest cells patterning is achieved through a combination of the information acquired in the neural tube during their formation and the influence of the environmental tissues they contact during their migration and differentiation. Interestingly, neural crest cells, mesoderm, ectoderm, and endoderm derived from the same axial level contribute to the formation of the same branchial arch (ba) in a conserved pattern. The mesoderm forms the myogenic cores of the branchial arches, which are enveloped by neural crest cells and are then surrounded by the surface ectoderm and endoderm. The cranial mesoderm is involved in maintaining the anterior–posterior character of migrating neural crest cells. The endoderm and ectoderm, respectively, influence neural crest cell differentiation into skeletogenic and tooth derivatives. It is important to note that Hox genes are not expressed in the first branchial arch, where Meckel's cartilage is one of the primary derivatives. In contrast, the second arch, which generates Reichert's cartilage, does express Hox genes; Hoxa2 in particular is the primary determinant of second arch fate. In experiments in which Hoxa2 is suppressed in the first arch either by null mutation or by ectopic sources of Fgf8, such as the isthmus, the second arch identity is transformed into that of a first arch. Conversely, when Hoxa2 is overexpressed in the first arch, its identity is transformed into that of a second arch. Therefore, it is crucial to keep Hox-expressing neural crest cells segregated from non–Hox-expressing neural crest cells. This is achieved through Erbb4 signaling from the neural tube with Eph and ephrin signaling as well as yet unidentified signals, which restrict the lateral migration of neural crest cells from rhombomeres (r) 3 and 5. (See Fig. 19–3, Volumes 1 and 2.)

Osteoclasts　　　　　Osteoblasts　　　　　Endothelial cells

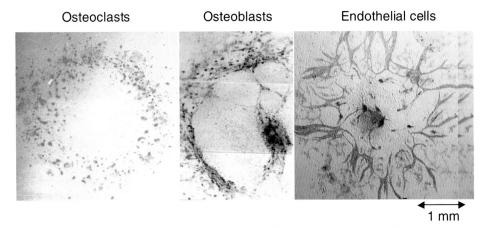

1 mm

Color Plate 4. *Osteoclasts, osteoblasts, and endothelial cells in ES cell colonies.* Staining of TRAP for osteoclasts (left), alkaline phosphatase (ALP) for osteoblasts (center), and staining with anti-CD31 antibody for endothelial cells (right) were performed on days 10–11 in the one-step culture. (See Fig. 27–2, Volume 1.)

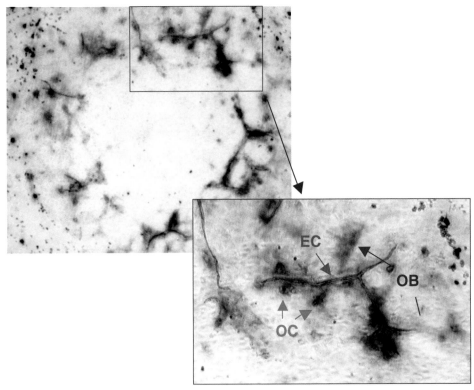

Color Plate 5. Triple staining of TRAP (red), ALP (blue), and anti-CD31 (yellow) of an ES cell colony on day 11 in the one-step culture on ST2 stromal cells (OC, osteoclasts; OB, putative osteoblasts; and EC, endothelial cells). (See Fig. 27–3, Volume 1.)

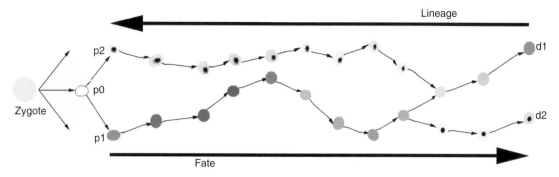

Color Plate 6. *Relationship between cell lineage and cell fate.* (See Fig. 57–1, Volume 1.)

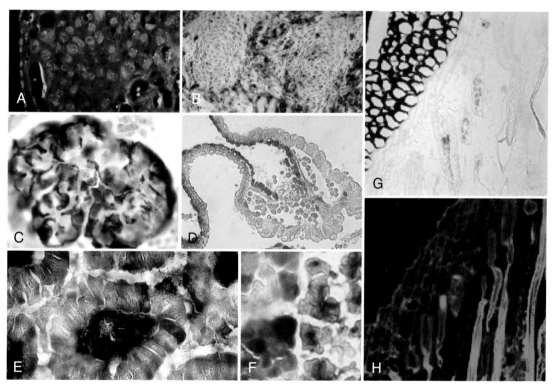

Color Plate 7. *Lineage marking at the cellular level.* (A) DNA *in situ* hybridization in trophoblast cells transgenic to the multicopy globin gene insertion.[26] (B) Chimeric tissue where one of the components is N-myc oncogene deficient and LacZ tagged with the Rosa-26 gene trap. (C) Immunohistochemical staining for podocyte-specific expression of green fluorescent protein (GFP). (D) LacZ staining of a chimeric yolk sac in which one of the components is expressing the reporter from the vascular endothelial growth factor locus.[30] (E and F) LacZ and human alkaline phosphatase double staining on mosaic intestine and pancreas.[41] (G and H) LacZ staining and GFP visualization of an adjacent section of skin of a Z/EG, K14-Cre recombinase double transgenic animal.[56] Part C provided by S. Quaggin. (See Fig. 57–2, Volume 1.)

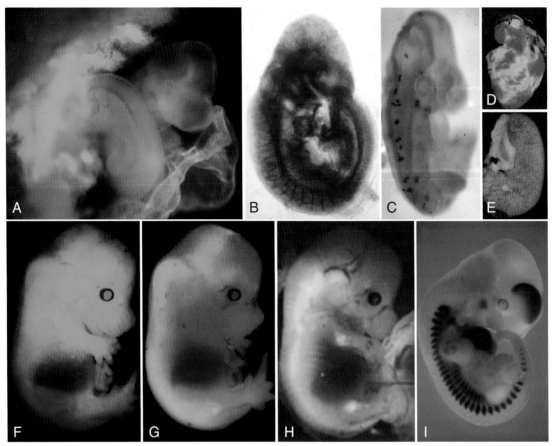

Color Plate 8. *Whole mount embryos and organs with lineage-marked cells.* (A) ES cell-derived embryo in the uterus. The trophoblast of the placenta and the yolk sac endoderm is GFP transgenic tetraploid embryo-derived. (B) Whole mount LacZ stained embryo in which the *lacZ* gene is inserted into the flk-1, endothelial cell specifically expressed receptor kinase.[70] (C) Z/AP and Cre recombinase double transgenic embryo with sporadic human placental alkaline phosphatase activation.[41] (D) Heart of the chimeric embryo between Cyan Fluorescent Protein expressor ES cells and GFP transgenic embryo.[36] Z/EG and Cre recombinase double transgenic embryos with (E) GFP podocyte-specific,[71] (F) complete, (G) differentiated neuron-specific, and (H) chondrocyte-specific activation. (I) LacZ-stained embryo derived from a Mef-2c gene trap ES cell line. Part H provided by J. Haigh, and part I provided by K. Vintersten and B. Stanford. (See Fig. 57–3, Volume 1.)